Features and Benefits

Merrill Algebra 2 with Trigonometry
Applications and Connections

1. **NCTM Standards** As the correlation on pages T20–T21 shows, strict attention was paid to the *NCTM Standards* in developing this program.

2. **Applications and Connections** Because the ability to grasp concepts and skills is greatly enhanced when they are tied to applications and connections, most lessons open with an application or a connection. This is strengthened by including *Applications* and/or *Connections* examples in every lesson. See pages 174–175. Every set of exercises also includes *Applications* and/or *Connections*. See pages 176–177.

3. **Problem Solving** Each Problem-Solving Strategy lesson relates a strategy to a real-world situation. See page 29. Problem solving is a focus of many lessons, not just strategy lessons. See pages 24–26.

4. **Critical Thinking** The ongoing attention to problem solving will help to improve the students' critical thinking and decision making. Critical thinking is specifically attended to in every set of exercises. See page 171.

5. **Technology** The role of the *scientific calculator* as a problem-solving tool is stressed, as it is integrated in lessons and in the exercises throughout the textbook. See page 20.

   Seventeen optional lessons on the graphing calculator are also included. The first one is on page 22. Key stroking for both the Casio and TI-81 is shown in each lesson.

   The *computer* as an aid in problem solving is addressed in various ways. See pages 91, 291, and 486.

6. **Mixed Review** To help students maintain prior-taught skills and concepts, a *Mixed Review* is included in every set of exercises. Students are able to find the necessary help because each problem is referenced to the related lessons. See page 291.

7. **Projects** The *Extended Projects* appendix offers ways for your students to work together on intriguing long-term projects. See page A1.

8. **Portfolios/Journals** The *Portfolio* suggestion asks students to select items from their work that represent different aspects of their mathematical knowledge. See page 143.

   The *Journal* entry gives students the opportunity to keep a log of their thoughts and ideas about the mathematics they are studying. See page 95.

9. **Teacher Support** The unique *Teacher's Wraparound Edition* includes all the elements that comprise a complete lesson plan for each lesson. See pages 409–415.

10. **Teacher's Classroom Resources** This package contains an extensive set of supplementary materials that are designed to meet the complete spectrum of student needs and interests. See pages 12–15 in the brochure that follows.

Today's Algebra Students Need More Than the Basics. They Need Applications and Connections!

Glencoe realizes that to help today's high school students be successful, algebra programs must show them how to integrate basic mathematical principles with their everyday lives. *Merrill Algebra 1* and *Merrill Algebra 2 with Trigonometry* do just that...by offering a perfect blend of content, applications, and connections.

When algebra concepts are introduced with applications and connections, your students will realize algebra's relevance to their lives. And once they see the practical applications of algebra, they remain interested, stay motivated, and want to learn all they can about this important mathematical topic.

The **Student Edition** is designed to motivate and excite your students about the study of algebra. It contains a vast array of lesson features, challenging activities, and thought-provoking applications that correlate with the four main NCTM Standards:
• Problem Solving
• Communication
• Reasoning
• Connections

The **Teacher's Wraparound Edition** organizes each lesson into six easy-to-follow steps: Introducing, Teaching, Evaluating, Reteaching, Applying, and Extending the Lesson. Right at your fingertips, you have a variety of classroom-proven teaching strategies and activities that help you create the most stimulating environment for learning.

The **Teacher's Classroom Resources** are filled with valuable teaching materials that support and enrich the content of every lesson.

Merrill Algebra Answers the Question, "When Am I Ever Going to Use This?"

With *Merrill Algebra 1* and *Merrill Algebra 2 with Trigonometry*, your students will come to understand the reasons for learning algebra. The content consistently applies and connects algebra principles to other areas of mathematics, other disciplines, and real-life applications, giving your students a greater appreciation for the relevance of algebra to their future lives and careers.

A stimulating **Chapter Opener** introduces your students to every chapter. *Algebra 1* chapters begin with real-world applications; *Algebra 2* with useful career information. These features engage and motivate your students to investigate the upcoming content.

Algebra 1

CHAPTER OBJECTIVES

In this chapter, you will:
* Find exact and approximate values for square roots.
* Simplify radical expressions.
* Solve radical equations.
* Solve problems that can be represented by radical equations.
* Solve problems by using tables.

CHAPTER 12 Radical Expressions

APPLICATION IN NATURE

The shell of a chambered nautilus is one of the many examples of mathematics occurring in nature's designs. This shell takes on its spiral shape because of the nautilus's growth pattern and the formation of small chambers of increasing size to accommodate this growth. The growth pattern of the shell's can be studied by looking at the size and shape of the spiral.

One method for studying the spiral is to use a set of right triangles winding around a point to represent the shape of the spiral. These right triangles are drawn so that the sides used to represent the spiral all have the same length, one unit, as shown in the figure below. Notice that each triangle has the same apex (top point). The longest side of each right triangle, called the hypotenuse, is also one of the shorter sides of the next triangle in the set. This design is called a "spiral of square roots" because of the relationship between the lengths of the sides of the right triangles.

Have you ever noticed that Mother Nature is a very skilled designer? Just look around and you can find many examples of mathematics in nature's designs.

The shell of the chambered nautilus is just one example of naturally occurring spirals. The next time you see a daisy, a sunflower, or a pineapple, see if you can find the spirals that are a part of their design.

ALGEBRA IN ACTION

Look at the triangle with sides 1, $\sqrt{1}$, and $\sqrt{2}$ in the figure at the left. Notice that $1^2 + (\sqrt{1})^2 = (\sqrt{2})^2$ since $(\sqrt{1})^2 = 1$ and $(\sqrt{2})^2 = 2$. Similarly, in the next few triangles, $1^2 + (\sqrt{2})^2 = (\sqrt{3})^2$, $1^2 + (\sqrt{3})^2 = (\sqrt{4})^2$, and $1^2 + (\sqrt{4})^2 = (\sqrt{5})^2$. This relationship between the measures of the sides of the right triangles is the basis for the Pythagorean Theorem. If you continue in this manner, what will be the measure of the side labeled ? in the figure?

473

CHAPTER 3 Systems of Equations and Inequalities

CHAPTER OBJECTIVES

In this chapter, you will:
* Solve systems of equations in two or three variables.
* Solve systems of inequalities.
* Use linear programming to find maximum and minimum values of functions.
* Graph linear equations in space.

CAREERS IN MARKET RESEARCH

Can you work accurately with detail? Are you patient and persistent? Can you work objectively and systematically to discovery solutions to problems no one has ever solved before? If so, perhaps you could be a successful market research analyst.

These days no company can afford to provide products or services to the public without first making sure exactly what the public wants. The early steps of any product development rely on market research. A market researcher first designs a survey—that is, decides what questions to ask the public.

Say a fast-food restaurant is being planned for a shopping mall. The researcher will need to ask lots of questions. What kinds of foods will mall shoppers buy—hot things or cold things, full meals or just snacks? Should the new restaurant have real ice cream or frozen yogurt? Which issues rank highest with mall shoppers: nutrition, taste, or speed?

The market research analyst heads a team that asks many, many mall shoppers all these questions and more. Then the team analyzes the data. They may need to perform a second or even a third survey, if results indicate that important questions were omitted. Finally, they present their findings both orally and in writing, with visual aids such as charts and graphs. From their work, businesses can know more surely than ever before what the marketplace wants.

The breakeven point is the level of sales where the revenue from the sales equals the cost of manufacturing those products. Can you list some of the costs of manufacturing a product or providing a service?

Cost and Revenue of Sales

Breakeven point

Total revenue
Total costs
Profits
Losses
Total variable costs
Fixed costs

Dollars

Units of production

102

MORE ABOUT MARKET RESEARCH

Degree Required:
* Bachelor's Degree in Marketing

Related Math Subjects:
* Statistics
* Calculus
* Applied Math

Some market research analysts like:
* working with people
* lots of travel
* the variety and challenge of their work
* good salaries

Some market research analyst dislike:
* working long hours, including evenings and weekends
* working under high pressure
* the competitive nature of this field

For more information on the various careers available in the field of Market Research, write to:
Marketing Research Association
111 East Wacker Drive
Chicago, Illinois 60601

Algebra

103

Applications

Most lessons begin with **Applications** that are visually supported by stimulating photographs and graphics. Clearly labeled application problems are integrated into every exercise set to reinforce how algebra is used in our society.

FYIs are "fast facts," entertaining tidbits, and fascinating math-related trivia.

8-7 Rational Expressions with Unlike Denominators

Objective

After studying this lesson, you should be able to:
- add or subtract rational expressions with unlike denominators.

Application

FYI···

The longest-running musical to date is *The Fantasticks*. So far, there have been over 12,000 performances.

Judith Paulsen, the choreographer of a big Broadway musical, has requested that the producer of the show hire enough dancers so that they can be arranged in groups of 4, 6, or 9 with no one sitting out. What is the least number of dancers that can be hired?

If the choreographer wanted to arrange the dancers in groups of 6, then the producer should hire a number of dancers that is a multiple of 6. But since she wants to arrange the dancers in groups of 4, 6, or 9, the producer must be concerned with multiples of all three numbers. The least number of dancers is given by the **least common multiple (LCM)** of the three numbers. The least common multiple is the smallest number that is a common multiple of two or more numbers.

The multiples of 4, 6, and 9 can be found by multiplying 4, 6, and 9 by each whole number.

You can find the LCM by making an organized list

multiples of 4: $4 \cdot 0, 4 \cdot 1, 4 \cdot 2, 4 \cdot 3, 4 \cdot 4, \ldots, 4 \cdot 9, \ldots$
       0,   4,   8, 12, 16,   36, . . .

multiples of 6: $6 \cdot 0, 6 \cdot 1, 6 \cdot 2, 6 \cdot 3, 6 \cdot 4, 6 \cdot 5, 6 \cdot 6, \ldots$
       0,   6, 12, 18, 24, 30, 36, . . .

multiples of 9: $9 \cdot 0, 9 \cdot 1, 9 \cdot 2, 9 \cdot 3, 9 \cdot 4, 9 \cdot 5, \ldots$
       0,   9, 18, 27, 36, 45, . . .

Compare these multiples. Aside from 0, the least number that is common to all three sets of multiples is 36. Thus, the LCM of 4, 6, and 9 is 36, and the producer should hire 36 dancers.

You can also use prime factorization to find the LCM

1. Find the prime factorization of each number.
    $4 = 2 \cdot 2$
    $6 = 2 \cdot 3$
    $9 = 3 \cdot 3$

LESSON 8-7 RATIONAL EXPRESSIONS WITH UNLIKE DENOMINATORS 329

FYI···

The longest-running musical to date is *The Fantasticks*. So far, there have been over 12,000 performances.

Connections

Throughout the text, you'll find a variety of **Connections**—examples and problems designed to give your students a more thorough understanding of how algebra is related to other areas of mathematics.

"This standard emphasizes the importance of...modeling connections between problem-solving situations that may arise in the real world or in disciplines other than mathematics; and mathematical connections between two equivalent representations..."
—*NCTM Standards*

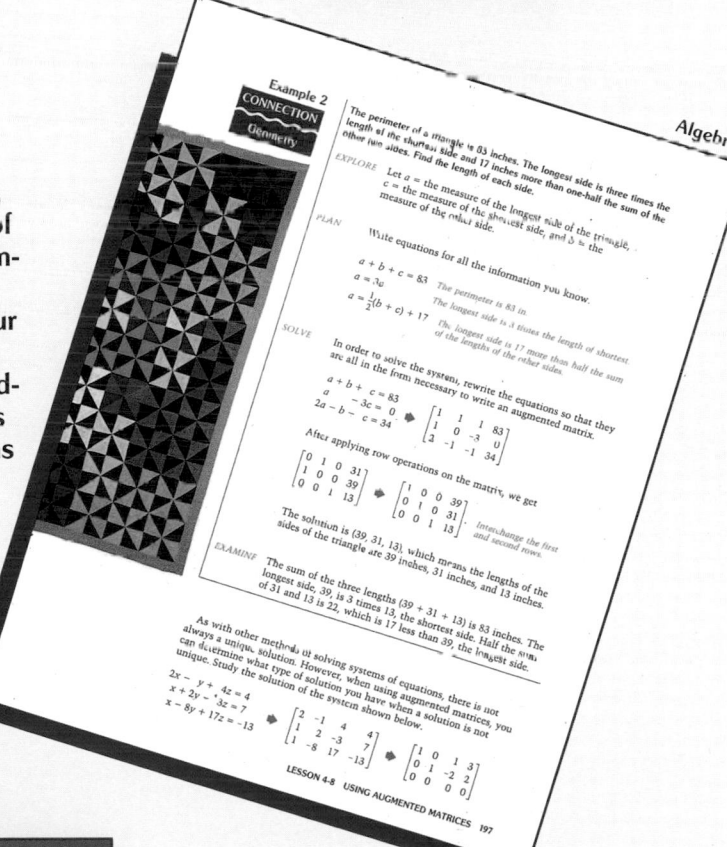

Example 2

CONNECTION
Geometry

The perimeter of a triangle is 83 inches. The longest side is three times the length of the shortest side and 17 inches more than one-half the sum of the other two sides. Find the length of each side.

EXPLORE Let a = the measure of the longest side of the triangle,
c = the measure of the shortest side, and b = the measure of the other side.

PLAN Write equations for all the information you know.

$a + b + c = 83$ *The perimeter is 83 in.*
$a = 3a$ *The longest side is 3 times the length of shortest*
$a = \frac{1}{2}(b + c) + 17$ *The longest side is 17 more than half the sum of the lengths of the other sides.*

SOLVE In order to solve the system, rewrite the equations so that they are all in the form necessary to write an augmented matrix.

$a + b + c = 83$
$a - 3c = 0$
$2a - b - c = 34$

$\begin{bmatrix} 1 & 1 & 1 & 83 \\ 1 & 0 & -3 & 0 \\ 2 & -1 & -1 & 34 \end{bmatrix}$

After applying row operations on the matrix, we get

$\begin{bmatrix} 0 & 1 & 0 & 31 \\ 1 & 0 & 0 & 39 \\ 0 & 0 & 1 & 13 \end{bmatrix} \Rightarrow \begin{bmatrix} 1 & 0 & 0 & 39 \\ 0 & 1 & 0 & 31 \\ 0 & 0 & 1 & 13 \end{bmatrix}$ *Interchange the first and second rows.*

The solution is (39, 31, 13), which means the lengths of the sides of the triangle are 39 inches, 31 inches, and 13 inches.

EXAMINE The sum of the three lengths (39 + 31 + 13) is 83 inches. The longest side, 39, is 3 times 13, the shortest side. Half the sum of 31 and 13 is 22, which is 17 less than 39, the longest side.

As with other methods of solving systems of equations, there is not always a unique solution. However, when using augmented matrices, you can determine what type of solution you have when a solution is not unique. Study the solution of the system shown below.

$2x - y + 4z = 4$
$x + 2y - 3z = 7$
$x - 8y + 17z = -13$

$\begin{bmatrix} 2 & -1 & 4 & 4 \\ 1 & 2 & -3 & 7 \\ 1 & -8 & 17 & -13 \end{bmatrix} \Rightarrow \begin{bmatrix} 1 & 0 & 1 & 3 \\ 0 & 1 & -2 & 2 \\ 0 & 0 & 0 & 0 \end{bmatrix}$

LESSON 4-8 USING AUGMENTED MATRICES 197

∼ HISTORY CONNECTION ∼

René Descartes

René Descartes (1596–1650) was one of the greatest scientists of the seventeenth century. It was he who used two perpendicular number lines to identify points in a plane. This rectangular coordinate system is called the *Cartesian coordinate system*, in honor of Descartes. The connecting of algebra and geometry through graphing is called *analytic geometry*. Although Descartes is considered to be the founder of analytic geometry, he did not consider himself a mathematician. He is often called the "father of modern philosophy," his great love.

History Connections are only one of the many enjoyable connection features contained throughout the text. This particular feature highlights men and women from various cultures who have played an integral part in the development of mathematics.

5

Problem-Solving Lessons Engage Your Students in Critical Thinking and Decision Making.

Merrill Algebra 1 **and** *Merrill Algebra 2 with Trigonometry* **offer you a vast array of problem-solving lessons and activities that make it easy for your students to learn and apply various problem-solving strategies.**

Problem Solving

Each chapter contains numerous problem-solving activities, including a **Problem-Solving Strategy Lesson** that gives your students a deeper understanding of a particular algebra concept. The strategies are then applied and integrated throughout subsequent lessons.

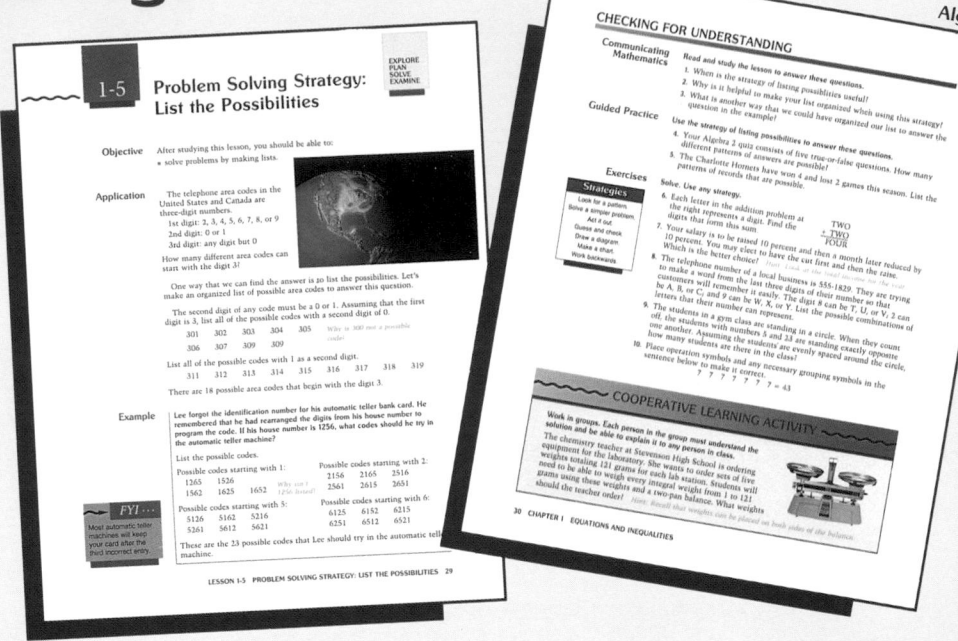

Algebra 1

Critical Thinking

Each lesson contains **Critical Thinking** problems that challenge your students to develop and apply higher-order thinking skills.

Critical Thinking

37. A butterfly lands on one of the six squares of the T-shaped figure shown and then randomly moves to an adjacent square. What is the probability that the butterfly ends up on the red square?

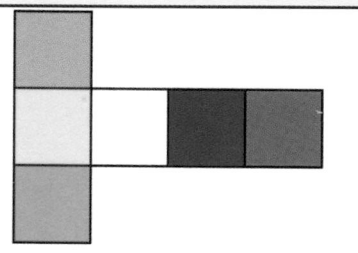

College Entrance Exam Preview

At the end of selected chapters, you will find a **College Entrance Exam Preview**, a two-page problem-solving review that gives your students the practice they need to do well on ACT and SAT examinations.

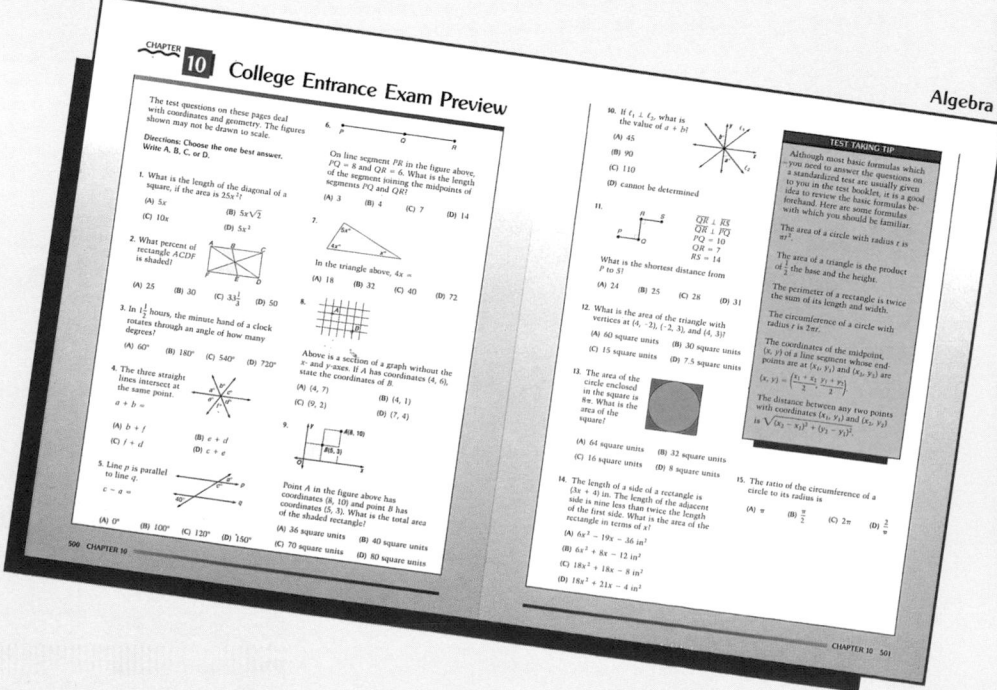

Algebra 2

6

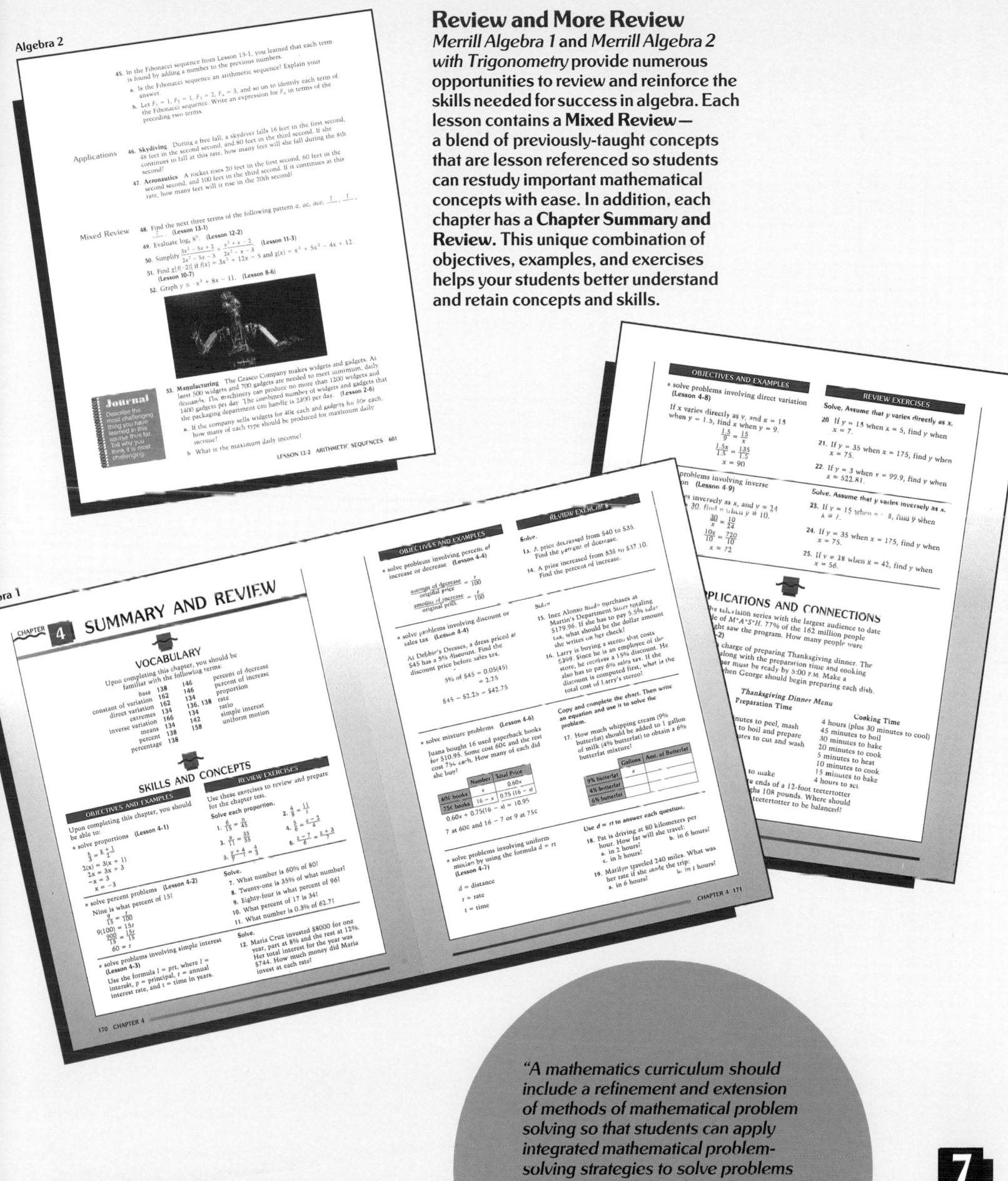

Review and More Review

Merrill Algebra 1 and *Merrill Algebra 2 with Trigonometry* provide numerous opportunities to review and reinforce the skills needed for success in algebra. Each lesson contains a **Mixed Review**— a blend of previously-taught concepts that are lesson referenced so students can restudy important mathematical concepts with ease. In addition, each chapter has a **Chapter Summary and Review.** This unique combination of objectives, examples, and exercises helps your students better understand and retain concepts and skills.

"A mathematics curriculum should include a refinement and extension of methods of mathematical problem solving so that students can apply integrated mathematical problem-solving strategies to solve problems from within and outside mathematics."
—NCTM Standards

Thought-Provoking Problems, Activities, and Frequent Use of Technology Teach Your Students How to Communicate Mathematicall

Glencoe realizes that for students to succeed in mathematics, they must be able to reflect upon and clarify their thinking about mathematical ideas and relationships. Our program offers numerous problems, activities, and features that develop and enhance your students' communication skills.

A **Cooperative Learning Activity** occurs in every chapter and provides multiple opportunities for discussion, questions, listening, and summarizing—all important techniques for successful communication in mathematics.

Communicating Mathematics	Read and study the lesson to complete the following.

Read and study the lesson to complete the following.

1. How do you undo addition? division?

2. Write an example of an equation requiring more than one operation to solve.

3. If n is an even integer, explain how to find the even integer just before it.

Communication
Every exercise set contains several **Communicating Mathematics** problems. These problems provide opportunities for your students to express mathematical concepts verbally, in writing, or through the use of pictures, symbols, models, tables, or graphs.

Algebra 2

Algebra 2

COOPERATIVE LEARNING ACTIVITY

Work in groups. Each person in the group must understand the solution and be able to explain it to any person in class.

Arrange nine coins as shown at the right with the center coin tails-up and the rest heads-up. A move consists of turning over the three coins in any row, column, or diagonal. In how many moves can you make all of the coins heads-up?

Algebra 2

PROJECT 3 **The Million-Dollar Challenge**

In 1856, the country of British Guiana issued a one-cent black-on-magenta

PROJECT 3 **Extending the Pythagorean Theorem**

The Pythagorean Theorem, discussed in Lesson 12-3, may be one of the most elegant, amazing, and useful results in all of mathematics. Mathematicians Gary Musser and William Burger have characterized the theorem as "perhaps the most spectacular result in geometry." Some mathematicians consider it a mark of honor to discover their own proofs of the theorem. In the classic 1907 book *The Pythagorean Proposition*, author Elisha Loomis gave more than 370 different proofs of the theorem, including one devised by President James Garfield. The theorem has wide applications and appears in nearly every branch of mathematics. What continues to intrigue and delight people who enjoy mathematics, even thousands of years after its discovery, is the utter simplicity of the Pythagorean relationship, combined with its far-reaching implications. No other relationship combines these two features so elegantly.

The Pythagorean Theorem states that in a right triangle, where a and b are the measures of the legs and c is the measure of the hypotenuse, then $c^2 = a^2 + b^2$.

What is not so well known, and what is likely to increase your appreciation for the Pythagorean relationship considerably, is that the theorem given above is only one of many closely related Pythagorean theorems. Consider a 6-8-10 right triangle with semicircles constructed on each side.

Notice that the radius of each semicircle is half the measure of that side of the triangle. By using the formula for the area of a circle ($A = \pi r^2$), we can determine the areas for the semicircles constructed on the legs. They are $\frac{1}{2}(\pi \cdot 3^2)$, $\frac{1}{2}(\pi \cdot 4^2)$, and $\frac{1}{2}(\pi \cdot 5^2)$ or 4.5π, 8π, and 12.5π. Notice that $4.5\pi + 8\pi = 12.5\pi$.

At least in this example, we have a *Pythagorean Theorem for Semicircles*:

In a right triangle, if A and B are the areas of semicircles constructed on the legs and C is the area of a semicircle constructed on the hypotenuse, then $C = A + B$.

Algebra 1

Polynomial Models

• The model is based on these three tiles.

x x^2

1

• Each tile shown above has an opposite.

• A zero-pair is formed by pairing one tile with its opposite.

1   x x^2

• You can remove or add zero-pairs without changing the value of the polynomial.

• *Like terms* are represented by tiles that are the same shape and size.

Algebra 2

Portfolio

Select an item from this chapter that you feel shows your best work and place it in your portfolio. Explain why you selected it.

A **Portfolio** suggestion appears in one of the last two lessons of each chapter. Students are asked to select items from their work that represent different aspects of their mathematical knowledge.

Projects
Both *Merrill Algebra 1* and *Merrill Algebra 2 with Trigonometry* include **Extended Projects**, located at the back of the book, which offer ways for your students to work together or fascinating long-term activities.

Algebra 1

Models and Manipulatives
At the back of *Merrill Algebra 1*, your students will find **Manipulative Activities** that help them bridge the gap from concrete models to the abstract algorithms the models represent.

Journal
Make up a number puzzle like the one at the beginning of the lesson. Be sure to try it out on another person to see if it works.

Two **Journal** entries appear in each chapter, giving students the opportunity to keep a log of their thoughts and ideas about the mathematics they are studying.

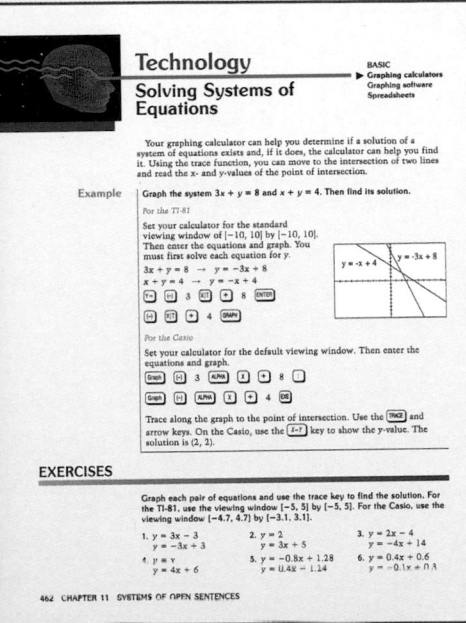

Merrill Algebra 2 with Trigonometry contains 17 **Graphing Calculator Explorations.** These lessons enable your students to use graphing calculators to explore mathematical concepts. They contain keystrokes for both TI-81 and Casio models.

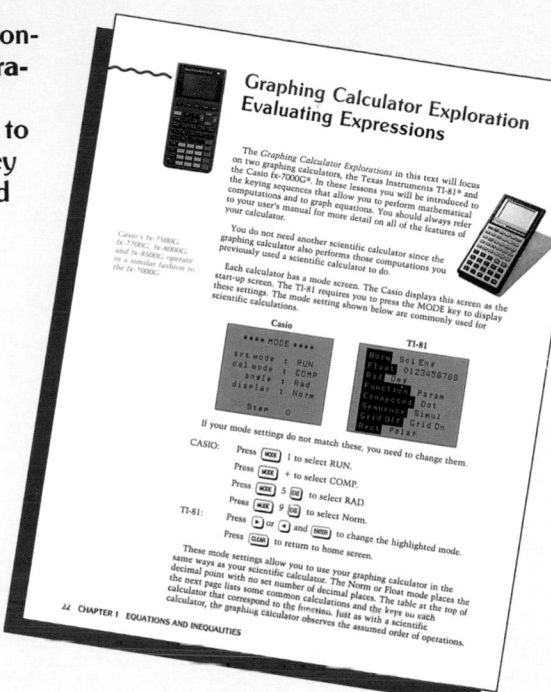

Technology

In addition to integrating the use of the scientific calculator, special high-interest **Technology** features introduce your students to spreadsheets, programming, graphing software, and graphing calculators. These features open their eyes to very powerful applications of mathematics.

Algebra 2

```
Computer    37. The BASIC program at the      1   PRINT "ENTER THE VALUE
                right generates the line of         OF N"
                coefficients in Pascal's triangle   5   INPUT Y
                for (a + b)^n. You must input the   10  FOR N = 0 TO Y
                value of n when running the         20  FOR R = 0 TO N
                program.                            30  LET C = 1
                                                    40  IF N < N - R + 1 THEN 80
                Use the program to express          50  FOR X = N TO N - R + 1
                each binomial in expanded               STEP - 1
                form.                               60  LET C = C*X/(N - X + 1)
                                                    70  NEXT X
                a. (a + b)^4    b. (a + b)^12       80  PRINT C;" ";
                c. (x - y)^6    d. (x - y)^10       90  NEXT R
                                                    100 PRINT
                                                    110 NEXT N
                                                    120 END
```

Computer exercises give your students experience solving algebraic problems using the BASIC language.

> "Technology is yet another avenue for mathematical communication, both in transmitting and receiving information."
> —NCTM Standards

Table of Contents

Merrill Algebra 1

1: An Introduction to Algebra
2: Rational Numbers
3: Equations
4: Applications of Rational Numbers
5: Inequalities
6: Polynomials
7: Factoring
8: Rational Expressions
9: Functions and Graphs
10: Graphing Linear Equations
11: Systems of Open Sentences
12: Radical Expressions
13: Quadratics
14: Statistics and Probability
15: Trigonometry
Manipulative Activities
Extended Projects

Merrill Algebra 2 with Trigonometry

1: Equations and Inequalities
2: Linear Relations and Functions
3: Systems of Equations and Inequalities
4: Matrices
5: Polynomials
6: Irrational and Complex Numbers
7: Quadratic Equations
8: Quadratic Relations and Functions
9: Conics
10: Polynomial Functions
11: Rational Polynomial Expressions
12: Exponential and Logarithmic Functions
13: Sequences and Series
14: Statistics
15: Probability
16: Trigonometric Functions
17: Trigonometric Graphs, Identities, and Equations
Extended Projects

The Teacher's Wraparound Edition Makes It Easy to Preview, Organize, Present, and Enhance the Content in Every Chapter.

Merrill Algebra 1 **and** *Merrill Algebra 2 with Trigonometry* **are the only algebra programs that offer you the advantages of a** Teacher's Wraparound Edition. **At your fingertips, you'll find a variety of unique teaching strategies that enable you to meet your instructional goals and to create the best and most captivating learning environment.**

Four Interleaf Pages precede each chapter. They provide a quick and easy reference for **Previewing, Organizing,** and **Enhancing** the chapter.

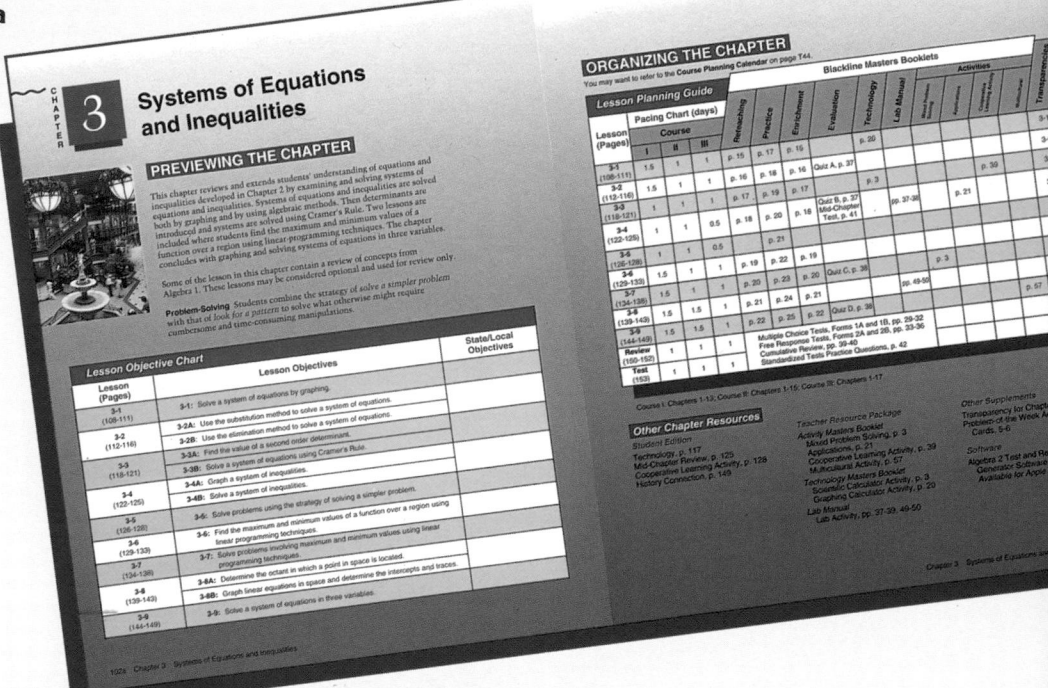

The Interleaf Pages contain an array of strategies and activities designed to strengthen your students' learning experiences. Some of the topics include:

- cooperative learning strategies
- lists of manipulatives used in the chapters
- technology highlights and suggestions
- critical-thinking strategies
- outside resources

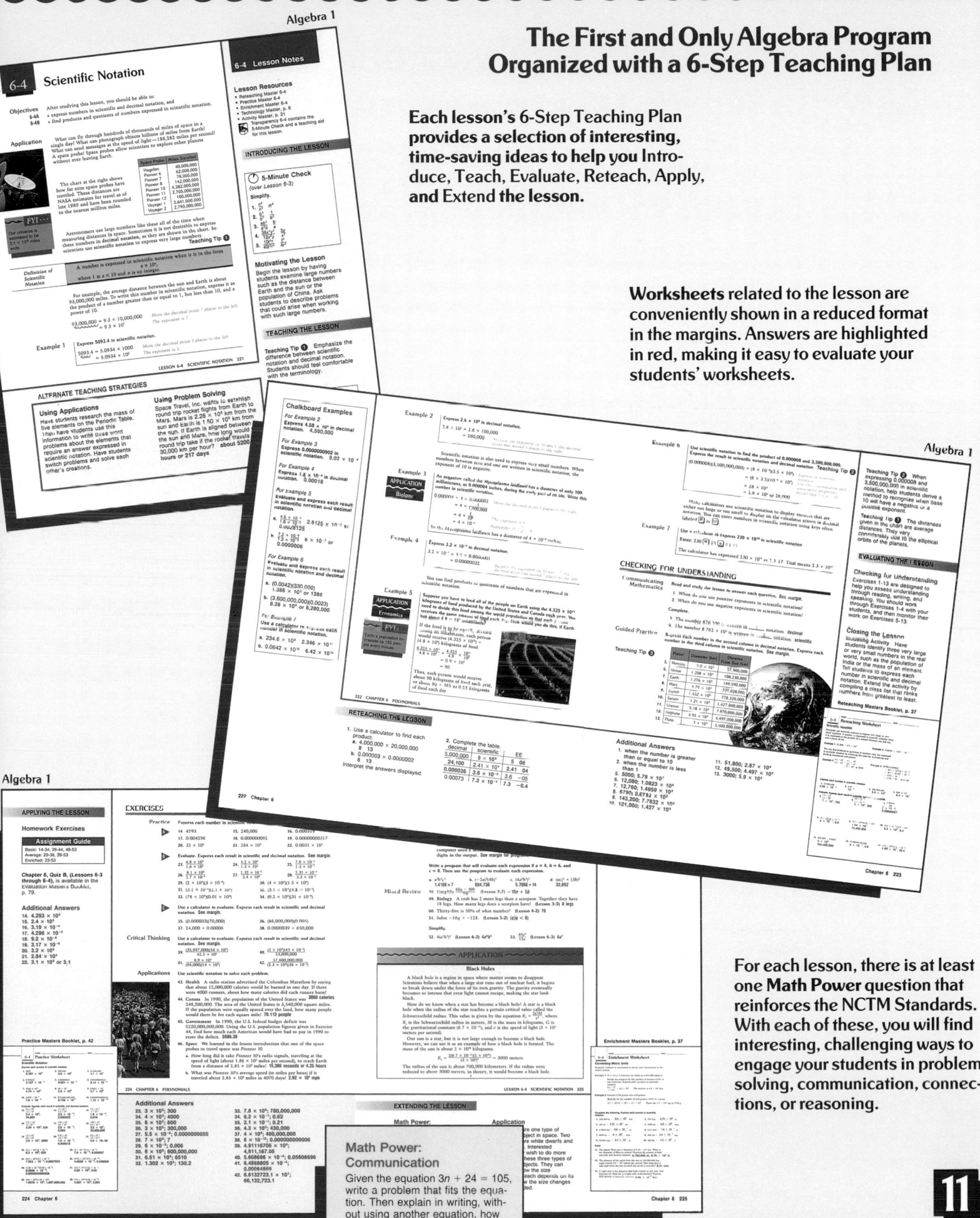

The First and Only Algebra Program Organized with a 6-Step Teaching Plan

Each lesson's 6-Step Teaching Plan provides a selection of interesting, time-saving ideas to help you Introduce, Teach, Evaluate, Reteach, Apply, and Extend the lesson.

Worksheets related to the lesson are conveniently shown in a reduced format in the margins. Answers are highlighted in red, making it easy to evaluate your students' worksheets.

For each lesson, there is at least one **Math Power** question that reinforces the NCTM Standards. With each of these, you will find interesting, challenging ways to engage your students in problem solving, communication, connections, or reasoning.

Math Power: Communication

Given the equation $3n + 24 = 105$, write a problem that fits the equation. Then explain in writing, without using another equation, how to solve the problem. Make sure to list the strategy and why it was chosen.

Count on *Merrill Algebra 1* and *Merrill Algebra 2 with Trigonometry* to Give You the Best, Most Comprehensive Teacher's Classroom Resources

No other algebra program can give you so many unique, stimulating, and thought-provoking support materials.

A wide selection of resources help you make your classroom the place where students widen their mathematical horizons.

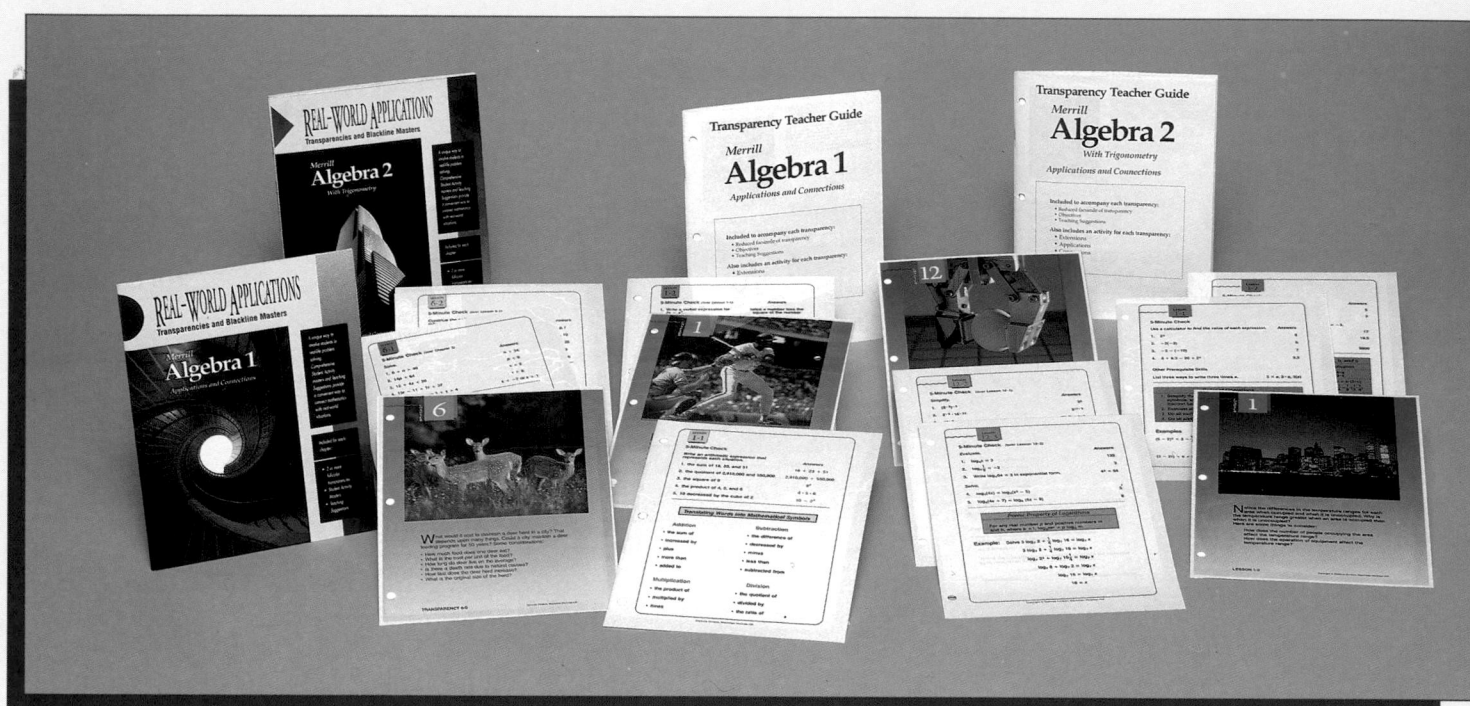

Transparencies

The **Teaching Transparencies** package for each text includes a full-color transparency for each lesson and each chapter opener. The package also contains captivating photographs, graphs, completely worked examples, and overlays, as well as a repeat of the 5-Minute Checks found in the Teacher's Wraparound Edition.

A Teacher's Guide with pictures of the transparencies, objectives, teaching suggestions, and extension activities is included for each transparency.

The **Real-World Applications: Transparencies and Blackline Masters** contain at least two transparencies for each chapter. Each transparency shows real-life photographs and current statistical information that students use to explore situations presented on an accompanying worksheet. Complete teaching suggestions and answers are also provided.

Applications

The **Activity Masters** booklet contains three interesting activities for each chapter to help your students get the most out of the lessons.

- **Application** activities that connect chapter content to common, everyday situations.
- **Mixed Problem-Solving** activities that provide your students with an assortment of verbal problems covering mathematical concepts from throughout the text.
- **Cooperative Learning Activities** that present problems or mini-projects requiring students to make observations, record data, survey, or make a decision while they develop important interpersonal skills.

Multicultural Activity Masters offer an activity for each chapter that relates mathematics to cultures or persons from various cultures.

Tech Prep Applications masters offer students the opportunity to see how algebra skills are applied in the workplace through real-life problem solving.

Problem-of-the-Week Cards give you a lively, diverting way to challenge your students to think mathematically.

Hands-On Activities

The **Algebra and Geometry Overhead Manipulative Resources** contain manipulatives, such as algebra titles, counters, spinners, and special transparencies that can be used with an overhead projector. A Teacher's Guide provides activities and teaching suggestions for demonstrating key topics in *Merrill Algebra 1*.

The **Lab Manual** includes 24 activities for both *Merrill Algebra 1* and *Merrill Algebra 2 with Trigonometry*. Each activity includes a full-page transparency master, a full-page student worksheet, and complete teaching instructions. **Easy-to-Make Manipulatives** are also included.

An Abundance of Additional Support Materials Offers Exciting Options for Instruction and Alternative Assessment.

Technology

Interactive Software (Macintosh), correlated to the Student Edition, allows students to explore and discover mathematical concepts.

Technology Masters contain calculator and computer activities to help your students practice using technological tools to develop algebraic skills and applications.

The **Teacher's Guide for Software Resources** describes many popular commercial software titles and how they can be used with *Merrill Algebra 1* and *Merrill Algebra 2 with Trigonometry*.

Assessment

Evaluation Masters provide a thorough representation of the chapter content through a variety of multiple-choice and free-response chapter tests, quizzes, a mid-chapter test, and cumulative reviews, as well as semester and final tests.

The **Test and Review Generator**, available in Apple, IBM, and Macintosh formats, provides a valuable resource for creating your own quizzes, tests, and worksheets.

The **Performance Assessment** booklet contains open-ended assessment items and a scoring rubric for each chapter.

The Glencoe Mathematics Professional Series includes teacher and student materials to enhance the learning environment:
- **Cooperative Learning in the Mathematics Classroom** describes how to implement cooperative learning groups successfully.
- **Alternative Assessment in the Mathematics Classroom** includes suggestions and ideas for projects, portfolios, questioning, and other assessment strategies.
- **Involving Parents and the Community in the Mathematics Classroom** presents suggestions on how parents and the community can be active participants in supporting mathematics instruction.
- **Graphing Calculators in the Mathematics Classroom** demonstrates how to use Texas Instruments and Casio graphing calculators to explore various topics in mathematics.
- **SAT/ACT Study Guide** helps students prepare for the SAT and ACT by providing test-taking tips and practice questions.

ting **Individual Needs**

ching Masters explore lesson pts using alternative methods, s modeling and graphing.

ice Masters provide additional ce for the concept exercise found h lesson.

hment Masters contain stimulat- tivities, including games and puz- o help extend and enrich the main in each lesson.

ish Resources give a Spanish ation of the English-language ary in the Student Edition. Key er objectives are also provided anish.

Plus

- **Teaching Algebra 1 in Two Years** gives day-by-day lesson plans for each year, review blackline masters of the content covered in the first year for use in the second year, hands-on activity masters, Semester Tests, and Final Tests.
- **Lesson Plans** for each lesson help you make the best use of time and learning materials.
- **The Solutions Manual** offers a complete solution for every problem in the Student Edition.

Give Your Students the Advantages of *Merrill Algebra*... Strong Algebra Content... Reinforced by Applications and Connections!

Merrill Algebra 1

Student Edition	0-02-824178-9
Teacher's Wraparound Edition	0-02-824179-7
Performance Assessment	0-02-824185-1
Reteaching Masters	0-02-824192-4
Practice Masters	0-02-824193-2
Practice Workbook	0-02-824194-0
Enrichment Masters	0-02-824195-9
Evaluation Masters	0-02-824196-7
Technology Masters	0-02-824197-5
Activity Masters	0-02-824183-5
Multicultural Activity Masters	0-02-824182-7
Lab Manual (Algebra 1 & 2)	0-02-824190-8
Lesson Plans	0-02-824188-6
Solutions Manual	0-02-824187-8
Teacher's Guide for Software Resources (Algebra 1 & 2)	0-02-824186-X
Overhead Manipulative Resources (Algebra 1)	0-02-824184-3
Test and Review Generator (Apple)	0-675-13124-3
Test and Review Generator (IBM)	0-675-13125-1
Test and Review Generator (Macintosh)	0-02-824094-4
Spanish Resources	0-02-824191-6
Transparency Package	0-675-13121-9
Teaching Algebra 1 in Two Years	0-02-824177-0
Interactive Software (Macintosh)	0-02-824181-19

Tech Prep Applications	0-02-824198-3
Real-World Applications: Transparencies and Blackline Masters	0-02-824201-7
Problem-of-the-Week Cards	0-675-13123-5

Merrill Algebra 2

Student Edition	0-02-824227-0
Teacher's Wraparound Edition	0-02-824228-9
Performance Assessment	0-02-824233-5
Reteaching Masters	0-02-824237-8
Practice Masters	0-02-824238-6
Enrichment Masters	0-02-824239-4
Evaluation Masters	0-02-824240-8
Technology Masters	0-02-824241-6
Activity Masters	0-02-824232-7
Multicultural Activity Masters	0-02-824231-9
Lesson Plans	0-02-824243-2
Solutions Manual	0-02-824242-4
Tech Prep Applications	0-02-824245-9
Test and Review Generator (Apple)	0-675-13132-4
Test and Review Generator (IBM)	0-675-13133-2
Test and Review Generator (Macintosh)	0-02-824095-2
Spanish Resources	0-02-824236-X
Transparency Package	0-675-13129-4
Real-World Applications: Transparencies and Blackline Masters	0-02-824246-7
Problem-of-the-Week Cards	0-675-13131-6
Interactive Software (Macintosh)	0-02-824230-0

Glencoe Mathematics Professional Series

Cooperative Learning in the Mathematics Classroom	0-02-824◼
Alternative Assessment in the Mathematics Classroom	0-02-824◼
Involving Parents and the Community in the Mathematics Classroom	0-02-824◼
Graphing Calculators in the Mathematics Classroom	0-02-824◼
SAT/ACT Study Guide	0-02-824◼

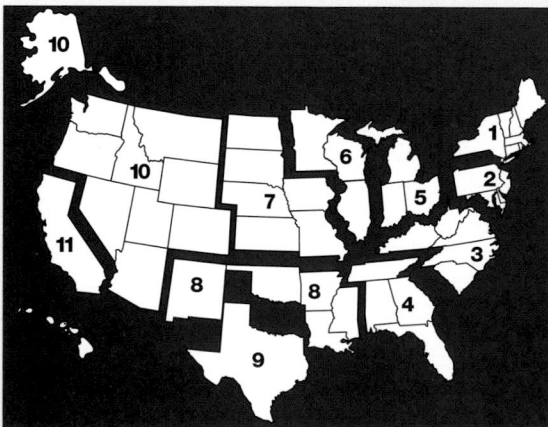

Merrill

Algebra 2

With Trigonometry

Applications and Connections

GLENCOE

McGraw-Hill

New York, New York
Columbus, Ohio
Mission Hills, California
Peoria, Illinois

Send all inquiries to:
Glencoe/McGraw-Hill
936 Eastwind Drive
Westerville, OH 43081

ISBN: 0-02-824227-0 (Student Edition)
ISBN: 0-02-824228-9 (Teacher Edition)

2   3   4   5   6   7   8   9   10   VH/LP   02   01   00   99   98   97   96   95

Alan G. Foster is chairperson of the mathematics department at Addison Trail High School, Addison, Illinois. He has taught mathematics courses at every level of the high school curriculum. Mr. Foster obtained his B.S. degree from Illinois State University and M.A. in mathematics from the University of Illinois. He is active in professional organizations at the local, state, and national levels. He is a past president of the Illinois Council of Teachers of Mathematics and a recipient of the Illinois Council of Teachers of Mathematics T.E. Rine Award for excellence in the teaching of mathematics. He also was a recipient of the 1987 Presidential Award for Excellence in the Teaching of Mathematics in the state of Illinois. Mr. Foster is a coauthor of *Merrill Geometry, Merrill Algebra Essentials,* and *Merrill Algebra 1.*

Leslie J. Winters is the Secondary Mathematics Specialist for the Los Angeles Unified School District. He has thirty years of classroom experience in teaching mathematics at every level from junior high school to college. Mr. Winters received bachelor's degrees in mathematics and secondary education from Pepperdine University and the University of Dayton, and master's degrees from the University of Southern California and Boston College. He is a past president of the California Mathematics Council-Southern Section and was a recipient of the 1983 Presidential Award for Excellence in the Teaching of Mathematics in the state of California. Mr. Winters is a coauthor of *Merrill Algebra Essentials* and *Merrill Algebra 1.*

Berchie W. Gordon is a Mathematics/Computer coordinator for the Northwest Local School District in Cincinnati, Ohio. Dr. Gordon has taught mathematics at every level from junior high school to college. She received her B.S. degree in Mathematics from Emory University in Atlanta, Georgia and M.A.T. in education from Northwestern University, Evanston, Illinois. She has done further study at the University of Illinois and the University of Cincinnati where she received her doctorate in curriculum and instruction. Dr. Gordon has developed and conducted numerous in-service workshops in mathematics and computer applications. She has served as a consultant for IBM. She has traveled nationally to make presentations on the graphing calculator to teacher groups.

James N. Rath has 30 years of classroom experience in teaching mathematics at every level of the high school curriculum. He is a mathematics teacher and former head of the mathematics department at Darien High School, Darien, Connecticut. Mr. Rath earned his B.A. degree in philosophy from the Catholic University of America and his M.Ed. and M.A. degrees in mathematics from Boston College. He is active in professional organizations at the local, state, and national levels. Mr. Rath is a coauthor of *Merrill Pre-Algebra, Merrill Algebra Essentials,* and *Merrill Algebra 1.*

Joan M. Gell is a mathematics teacher and department chairperson at Palos Verdes Peninsula High School in Palos Verdes Estates, California. Ms. Gell has taught mathematics at every level from junior high school to college. She received her B.S. degree in mathematics education from The State University of New York-Cortland, and M.A. degree in mathematics from Bowdoin College in Brunswick, Maine. Ms. Gell has developed and conducted in-service classes in mathematics and computer science and is past president of the California Mathematics Council. She serves as the chairperson of the 1992 MATHCOUNTS Problem Writing Committee. Ms. Gell was a finalist for the 1984 Presidential Award for Excellence in the Teaching of Mathematics in the state of California.

CONTRIBUTING AUTHOR

Lee E. Yunker
Mathematics Department Chairman
West Chicago Community High School
West Chicago, Illinois

CONSULTANTS

Donald W. Collins
Department of Mathematics and Informational
   Sciences
Sam Houston State University
Huntsville, Texas

Timothy D. Kanold
Mathematics/Science Division Chairman
Adlai Stevenson High School
Prairie View, Illinois

REVIEWERS

Pamela G. Adamson
Coordinator of Mathematics
Clayton County Schools
Morrow, Georgia

Trina Price
Mathematics Teacher
Carmel Junior High School
Carmel, Indiana

Ann Cumbie
Mathematics Teacher
Colen Cliff High School
Nashville, Tennessee

Peggy B. Stuart
Mathematics Teacher
Emmerich Manual High School
Indianapolis, Indiana

Susan Heicklen
Mathematics Department Chairperson
State College Area Senior High School South
State College, Pennsylvania

Darryl Beissler
Mathematics Teacher
Johnson High School
St. Paul, Minnesota

Patricia Stallings
Mathematics Department Chairperson
Farragut High School
Knoxville, Tennessee

Edward O'Reilly
Mathematics Teacher
Westerville North High School
Westerville, Ohio

Neal E. Anderson
Mathematics Department Chairperson
Irondale High School
New Brighton, Minnesota

We wish to acknowledge the contributions made to this text during the 1991–1992 school
year by Mr. Louis P. La Mastro and his AMP Algebra 2 class at North Bergen High School
in North Bergen, New Jersey.

Table of Contents

CHAPTER 1 Equations and Inequalities 6

1-1	Expressions and Formulas	8
1-2	Properties of the Real Numbers	13
1-3	Solving Equations	18
	Graphing Calculator Exploration: Evaluating Expressions	22
1-4	Applications of Equations	24
	Mid-Chapter Review	28
1-5	Problem-Solving Strategy: List the Possibilities	29
	Cooperative Learning Activity	30
1-6	Solving Absolute Value Equations	31
	History Connection: Mileva Einstein	35
1-7	Solving Inequalities	36
	Technology: Solving Equations and Inequalities	41
1-8	Solving Absolute Value Inequalities	42
	Chapter Summary and Review	46
	Chapter Test	49

CHAPTER 2 Linear Relations and Functions 50

2-1	Relations and Functions	52
	Graphing Calculator Exploration: Graphing Linear Equations	58
2-2	Linear Functions	60
2-3	Problem-Solving Strategy: Look for a Pattern	64
	Cooperative Learning Activity	65
2-4	Slopes and Intercepts	66
	Mid-Chapter Review	72
2-5	Writing Linear Equations	73
	History Connection: René Descartes	79
2-6	Scatter Plots and Predictions	80
	Graphing Calculator Exploration: Lines of Regression	85
2-7	Special Functions	87
	Technology: Median-Fit Lines	91
2-8	Graphing Linear Inequalities	92
	Chapter Summary and Review	96
	Chapter Test	99
	College Entrance Exam Preview	100

APPLICATIONS AND CONNECTIONS

APPLICATIONS

Banking	10
Chemistry	10
Construction	24
Travel	24
Manufacturing	25
Finance	32
Broadcasting	38
Recycling	43
Geology	53
Oceanography	61
Health	75
Commerce	81
Economics	88
	94

CONNECTIONS

Geometry	9, 15, 20, 26, 69
Statistics	82

Technology

Have you recently purchased something at a department store or grocery store? Do you have a library card? Are credit cards a part of your life or your parents' lives? If you answered yes to even one of these questions, perhaps you're already aware of the growing role technology plays in your everyday life.

The Technology pages in this text let you use technology to explore patterns, make conjectures, and discover mathematics. You will learn to use programs written in the BASIC computer language as well as computer software and spreadsheets. In the Graphing Calculator Explorations, you will investigate mathematical concepts using a graphing calculator.

Technology

MET: Solving Equations and Inequalities 41
Data Insights: Median-Fit Lines 91
BASIC: Solving Systems of Equations 117
BASIC: Cramer's Rule 194
MET: Factoring 235
MET: Solving Radical Equations 287
BASIC: Discriminants and Roots 332
BASIC: Quadratic Functions 365
MET: Conic Sections 431
Spreadsheets: Zeros of Polynomial Functions 486
MET: Rational Expressions 531
Spreadsheets: Compound Interest 579
Spreadsheets: Amortization 631
Data Insights: Statistical Graphs 663
BASIC: Coin Toss Simulation 725
BASIC: Solving Triangles 761
MET: Trigonometric Equations 828

MET (Mathematics Exploration Toolkit) was developed for IBM by Wicat Systems, Inc. Data Insights was developed by Sunburst Communications, Inc.

Graphing Calculator

Explorations 22, 58, 85, 104, 159, 201, 312, 350, 359, 425, 437, 457, 504, 551, 788, 801, 820

Keystrokes are provided for both Casio and Texas Instruments graphing calculators.

vi

CHAPTER 3

Systems of Equations and Inequalities

102

Graphing Calculator Exploration: Graphing Systems
of Equations 104
3-1 Graphing Systems of Equations 108
3-2 Solving Systems of Equations Algebraically 112
Technology: Solving Systems of Equations 117
3-3 Cramer's Rule 118
3-4 Graphing Systems of Inequalities 122
Mid-Chapter Review 125
3-5 Problem-Solving Strategy: Solve a Simpler Problem 126
Cooperative Learning Activity 128
3-6 Linear Programming 129
3-7 Applications of Linear Programming 134
3-8 Graphing Equations in Three Variables 139
3-9 Solving Systems of Equations in Three Variables 144
History Connection: Seki Kowa 149
Chapter Summary and Review 150
Chapter Test 153

CHAPTER 4

Matrices

154

4-1 Problem-Solving Strategy: Using Matrix Logic 156
Cooperative Learning Activity 158
Graphing Calculator Exploration: Matrices 159
4-2 An Introduction to Matrices 161
4-3 Matrices and Determinants 167
Challenge 172
4-4 Multiplication of Matrices 173
History Connection: Chinese Matrix 178
4-5 Identity and Inverse Matrices 179
Mid-Chapter Review 183
4-6 Using Inverse Matrices 184
4-7 Using Cramer's Rule 190
Technology: Cramer's Rule 194
4-8 Using Augmented Matrices 195
Language Connection 200
Graphing Calculator Exploration: Matrix Row Operations .. 201
Chapter Summary and Review 202
Chapter Test 205
College Entrance Exam Preview 206

APPLICATIONS AND CONNECTIONS

APPLICATIONS
Consumerism 109, 146
Business 131
Manufacturing 131
Education 134
Agriculture 135
Chemistry 174
Banking 187
.... 191

CONNECTIONS
Geometry 114, 120, 131,
140, 163, 169, 175, 197

CHAPTER 5 Polynomials 208

5-1	Monomials	210
5-2	Dividing Monomials	215
5-3	Problem-Solving Strategy: Draw a Diagram	220
	Cooperative Learning Activity	222
5-4	Polynomials	223
	Mid-Chapter Review	228
5-5	Factoring	229
	Biology Connection: Genetics and Population Predictions	234
	Technology: Factoring	235
5-6	Dividing Polynomials	236
	History Connection: Prehistoric Counting	240
5-7	Synthetic Division	241
	Chapter Summary and Review	246
	Chapter Test	249

CHAPTER 6 Irrational and Complex Numbers 250

6-1	Roots of Real Numbers	252
	Language Connection	257
6-2	Products and Quotients of Radicals	258
	Biology Connection	263
6-3	Computing with Radicals	264
6-4	Rational Exponents	269
	Mid-Chapter Review	274
6-5	Problem-Solving Strategy: Identify Subgoals	275
	Cooperative Learning Activity	276
6-6	Simplifying Expressions with Rational Exponents	277
6-7	Solving Equations Containing Radicals	281
	History Connection: Johann Kepler	286
	Technology: Solving Radical Equations	287
6-8	Pure Imaginary Numbers	288
6-9	Complex Numbers	292
	Technology Connection: Benoit Mendelbroit	296
6-10	Simplifying Expressions Containing Complex Numbers	297
	Chapter Summary and Review	302
	Chapter Test	305
	College Entrance Exam Preview	306

APPLICATIONS AND CONNECTIONS

APPLICATIONS

Astronomy	212
Chemistry	216
Horticulture	220
Health	237
Manufacturing	243, 255
Physics	261, 278
Sports	265
Music	271
Firefighting	283
Electronics	289, 298

CONNECTIONS

Geometry	221, 225, 229, 237, 293

CHAPTER 7 Quadratic Equations — 308

7-1	Problem-Solving Strategy: Guess-and-Check	310
	Cooperative Learning Activity	311
	Graphing Calculator Exploration: Quadratic Equations	312
7-2	Solving Quadratic Equations	316
7-3	Completing the Square	322
	Mid-Chapter Review	326
7-4	The Quadratic Formula and the Discriminant	327
	Technology: Discriminants and Roots	332
7-5	Sum and Product of Roots	333
	History Connection: Babylonians	338
7-6	Quadratic Techniques to Solve Polynomial Equations	339
	Chapter Summary and Review	344
	Chapter Test	347

CHAPTER 8 Quadratic Relations and Functions — 348

	Graphing Calculator Exploration: Families of Parabolas	350
8-1	Quadratic Functions	353
8-2	Problem-Solving Strategy: Make a Table	356
	Cooperative Learning Activity	358
	Graphing Calculator Exploration: Locating the Vertex of a Parabola	359
8-3	Graphing Quadratic Functions	360
8-4	Analyzing Graphs of Quadratic Functions	366
	Mid-Chapter Review	372
8-5	Applications of Quadratic Equations	373
8-6	Graphing Quadratic Inequalities	379
	History Connection: Hypatia	382
8-7	Solving Quadratic Inequalities	383
	Chapter Summary and Review	388
	Chapter Test	391
	College Entrance Exam Preview	392

APPLICATIONS AND CONNECTIONS

APPLICATIONS
Physics 319, 324, 384
Sports 335, 368
Entertainment 353
Business 356, 374

CONNECTIONS
Geometry 362, 380

Special Features

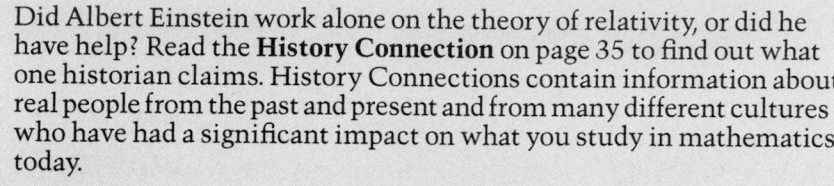

Did Albert Einstein work alone on the theory of relativity, or did he have help? Read the **History Connection** on page 35 to find out what one historian claims. History Connections contain information about real people from the past and present and from many different cultures who have had a significant impact on what you study in mathematics today.

When am I ever going to use this stuff? It may be sooner than you think. You'll find mathematics in most of the subjects you study in school. In the **Biology Connection** on page 578, you'll see how mathematics can be used to estimate wildlife population. The **Applications in Music** feature on page 641 shows how music and trigonometry are related.

History Connections

Mileva Einstein 35
René Descartes 79
Seki Kowa 149
Chinese Matrix 178
Prehistoric Counting 240
Johann Kepler 286
Babylonians 338
Hypatia 382
The Dogon of Mali 408
Carl Friedrich Gauss 456
Napier and Briggs 570
Games 688

Connections

Language 200, 257, 480
Biology 234, 263, 578
Fine Arts 515, 614
Technology 296

Applications

Architecture 422
Misleading Graphs 673
Music 741
Optics 745

CHAPTER 9 Conics 394

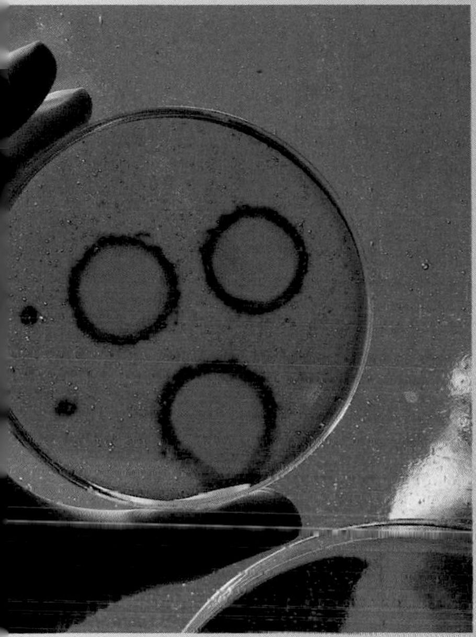

9-1	The Distance and Midpoint Formulas	396
9-2	Parabolas	400
9-3	Circles	405
	History Connection: The Dogon of Mali	408
9-4	Ellipses	409
	Mid-Chapter Review	415
9-5	Hyperbolas	416
	Applications in Architecture	422
9-6	Problem-Solving Strategy: Use a Model	423
	Cooperative Learning Activity	424
	Graphing Calculator Exploration: Conic Sections	425
9-7	Conic Sections	427
	Technology: Conic Sections	431
9-8	Graphing Quadratic Systems	432
	Graphing Calculator Exploration: Solving Quadratic Systems	437
9-9	Solving Quadratic Systems	439
	Chapter Summary and Review	444
	Chapter Test	447

CHAPTER 10 Polynomial Functions 448

10-1	Polynomial Functions	450
	History Connection: Carl Friedrich Gauss	456
	Graphing Calculator Exploration: Graphing Polynomial Equations	457
10-2	The Remainder and Factor Theorems	459
10-3	Problem-Solving Strategy: Combining Strategies	465
	Cooperative Learning Activity	467
10-4	Roots and Zeros	468
	Mid-Chapter Review	474
10-5	Rational Zero Theorem	475
	Language Connection	480
10-6	Graphing Polynomials and Approximating Zeros	481
	Technology: Zeros of Polynomial Functions	486
10-7	Composition of Functions	487
10-8	Inverse Functions and Relations	491
	Chapter Summary and Review	496
	Chapter Test	499
	College Entrance Exam Preview	500

APPLICATIONS AND CONNECTIONS

APPLICATIONS

Communication	402
Seismology	405
Aeronautics	410, 428, 433
Astronomy	418
Biology	452

CONNECTIONS

| Geometry | 397, 398, 477 |

11 Rational Polynomial Expressions 502

	Graphing Calculator Exploration: Graphing Rational Functions	504
11-1	Graphing Rational Functions	506
11-2	Direct, Inverse, and Joint Variation	510
	Fine Arts Connection	515
11-3	Multiplying and Dividing Rational Expressions	516
	Mid-Chapter Review	521
11-4	Adding and Subtracting Rational Expressions	522
11-5	Solving Rational Equations	527
	Technology: Rational Expressions	531
11-6	Problem-Solving Strategy: Organizing Data	532
	Cooperative Learning Activity	534
11-7	Applications of Rational Equations	535
	Chapter Summary and Review	540
	Chapter Test	543

12 Exponential and Logarithmic Functions 544

12-1	Real Exponents and Exponential Functions	546
	Graphing Calculator Exploration: Graphing Exponential and Logarithmic Functions	551
12-2	Logarithms and Logarithmic Functions	553
12-3	Properties of Logarithms	558
12-4	Common Logarithms	563
	Mid-Chapter Review	566
12-5	Natural Logarithms	567
	History Connection: Napier and Briggs	570
12-6	Problem-Solving Strategy: Using Estimation	571
	Cooperative Learning Activity	573
12-7	Exponential Equations	574
	Biology Connection	578
	Technology: Compound Interest	579
12-8	Applications of Logarithms	580
	Chapter Summary and Review	586
	Chapter Test	589
	College Entrance Exam Preview	590

APPLICATIONS AND CONNECTIONS

APPLICATIONS

Physics 512, 564, 568
Commerce 533
Biology 547
Communications 554
Chemistry 559, 581
Finance 568, 571, 574, 582
Aerospace 572
Business 581

CONNECTIONS

Geometry 512, 518, 571

CHAPTER 13 Sequences and Series 592

13-1	Problem-Solving Strategy: Look for a Pattern	594
	Cooperative Learning Activity	595
13-2	Arithmetic Sequences	596
13-3	Arithmetic Series	602
	Mid-Chapter Review	607
13-4	Geometric Sequences	608
	Fine Arts Connection	614
13-5	Geometric Series	615
13-6	Infinite Geometric Series	620
13-7	The Binomial Theorem	625
	Technology: Amortization	631
	Chapter Summary and Review	632
	Chapter Test	635

CHAPTER 14 Statistics 636

14-1	Problem-Solving Strategy: Make a Graph	638
	Cooperative Learning Activity	641
14-2	Line Plots and Stem-and-Leaf Plots	642
14-3	Central Tendency: Median, Mode, and Mean	648
14-4	Variation: Range, Interquartile Range, and Outliers	653
	Mid-Chapter Review	657
14-5	Box-and-Whisker Plots	658
	Challenge	662
	Technology: Statistical Graphs	663
14-6	Variation: Standard Deviation	664
14-7	The Normal Distribution	668
	Application: Misleading Graphs	673
	Chapter Summary and Review	674
	Chapter Test	677
	College Entrance Exam Preview	678

APPLICATIONS AND CONNECTIONS

APPLICATIONS

Flight	598
Design	604
Finance	610, 650
Physics	612, 622
Chemistry	616
Sports	639, 644, 655, 659
Education	639, 643, 650
Consumerism	643
Meteorology	644, 654
Business	649
Horticulture	664
Entertainment	665
Medicine	669
Health	670

CONNECTIONS

Probability	628

xiii

College Entrance Exam Preview

What should I do when I "grow up?" Will I go to college? If so, which one? What should I major in? These are questions that you must consider more and more as you approach your graduation from high school.

There are many things that you can do to prepare yourself for college. One of the things you will need to do before entering college is take the SAT (Scholastic Aptitude Test) or the ACT (American College Test). To help you practice for the mathematics portion of these tests and other similar tests, you can use the College Entrance Exam Previews given after every other chapter in this text. They are on pages 100-101, 206-207, 306-307, 392-393, 500-501, 590-591, 678-679, and 784-785.

CHAPTER 15 Probability 680

15-1	Problem-Solving Strategy: Using Models	682
	Cooperative Learning Activity	683
15-2	The Counting Principle	684
	History Connection: Games	688
15-3	Linear Permutations	689
15-4	Circular Permutations	694
15-5	Combinations	699
	Mid-Chapter Review	704
15-6	Probability	705
15-7	Multiplying Probabilities	710
15-8	Adding Probabilities	715
15-9	Simulation and Binomial Experiments	720
	Technology: Coin Toss Simulation	725
	Chapter Summary and Review	726
	Chapter Test	729

CHAPTER 16 Trigonometric Functions 730

16-1	Angles and the Unit Circle	732
	Challenge	736
16-2	Sine and Cosine Functions	737
	Applications in Music	741
16-3	Other Trigonometric Functions	742
	Applications in Optics	745
16-4	Inverse Trigonometric Functions	746
16-5	Finding Values for Trigonometric Functions	751
	Mid-Chapter Review	755
16-6	Solving Right Triangles	756
	Technology: Solving Triangles	761
16-7	Applications of Right Triangle	762
16-8	Law of Sines	767
16-9	Problem-Solving Strategy: Examine the Solution	771
	Cooperative Learning Activity	774
16-10	Law of Cosines	775
	Chapter Summary and Review	780
	Chapter Test	783
	College Entrance Exam Preview	784

APPLICATIONS AND CONNECTIONS

APPLICATIONS

Photography	690
Botany	700
Entertainment	711
Surveying	743
Architecture	747
Navigation	752, 763, 768
Physics	758
Forestry	762
Astronomy	763
Broadcasting	764
Engineering	773
Aviation	777

CONNECTIONS

Geometry	700, 734

17 Trigonometric Graphs, Identities, and Equations 786

Graphing Calculator Exploration:
    Graphing Trigonometric Functions 788
17-1 Graphs of Trigonometric Functions 790
17-2 Trigonometric Identities 797
Graphing Calculator Exploration:
    Verifying Trigonometric Identities 801
17-3 Verifying Trigonometric Identities 803
17-4 Problem-Solving Strategy: Working Backwards 807
Cooperative Learning Activity 809
17-5 Sum and Difference of Angles Formulas 810
Mid-Chapter Review 814
17-6 Double-Angle and Half-Angle Formulas 815
Graphing Calculator Exploration:
    Solving Trigonometric Equations 820
17-7 Solving Trigonometric Equations 822
Technology: Trigonometric Equations 828
17-8 Trigonometric Notation for Complex Numbers 829
Chapter Summary and Review 834
Chapter Test 837

APPLICATIONS

Physics 792, 804, 816
Firefighting 807
Geology 812
Optics 825

Appendix 838
Common Logarithm Tables 841
Values for Trigonometric Functions Tables ... 843
Glossary 848
Selected Answers 857
Index 900
Photo Credits 911

Extended Projects A1

Project 1: Predicting the Future A2
Project 2: Waste Not, Want Not A6
Project 3: The Million-Dollar Challenge A10
Project 4: Creating Order From Chaos A14

To The Teacher

The purpose of this 28-page *Teacher's Guide* is to provide an introduction to the format and philosophy of the ***Merrill Algebra Teacher's Wraparound Edition.*** It is also intended to relate some background information on several contemporary issues facing mathematics educators in the 1990s, such as the use of technology and alternative assessment strategies. Suggested time schedules for six-week and nine-week grading periods and clearly-defined instructional objectives are included to further make the learning of algebra smooth for both students and teachers.

Teacher's Guide Table of Contents

How to Use the Six-Step Teaching Plan in *Merrill Algebra* T18

Correlation of NCTM Standards to *Merrill Algebra* T20

Cooperative Learning. T22

Problem Solving in Algebra T24

Using Manipulatives in Your Algebra Classroom T25

Integrating Technology into Your Algebra Classroom T26

Using the Graphing Calculator. T28

Meeting Individual Needs T37

Alternate Assessment Strategies T38

Learning Objectives T40

Planning Your Algebra Course T44

How to Use the Six-Step Teaching Plan in Merrill Algebra

What do you search for when making a new textbook selection? You may search for a total program that is easy to teach. Your **Merrill Algebra Teacher's Wraparound Edition** delivers the collective teaching experience of its authors, consultants, and reviewers so that you will have the wealth of reliable information you search for. By furnishing you with an effective teaching model, this book saves you preparation time and energy. You, in turn, are free to spend that time and energy on your most important responsibility—your students.

As a professional, you will be pleased to find this program provides you with readily available activities to engage your students throughout the entire class period.

Each chapter begins with **Background Information** that gives

Connections and Applications provide you with real-world examples and exercises found in the chapter.

additional information about the career introduced in the Chapter Opener. A **Class Project** is also provided that is intended to be on-going throughout the chapter. The **Connections and Applications** chart provides you with a list of real-world examples and exercises found in the chapter.

Each lesson includes a comprehensive six-part teaching plan that, when utilized consistently, makes it easy for you to teach and easy for your students to learn.

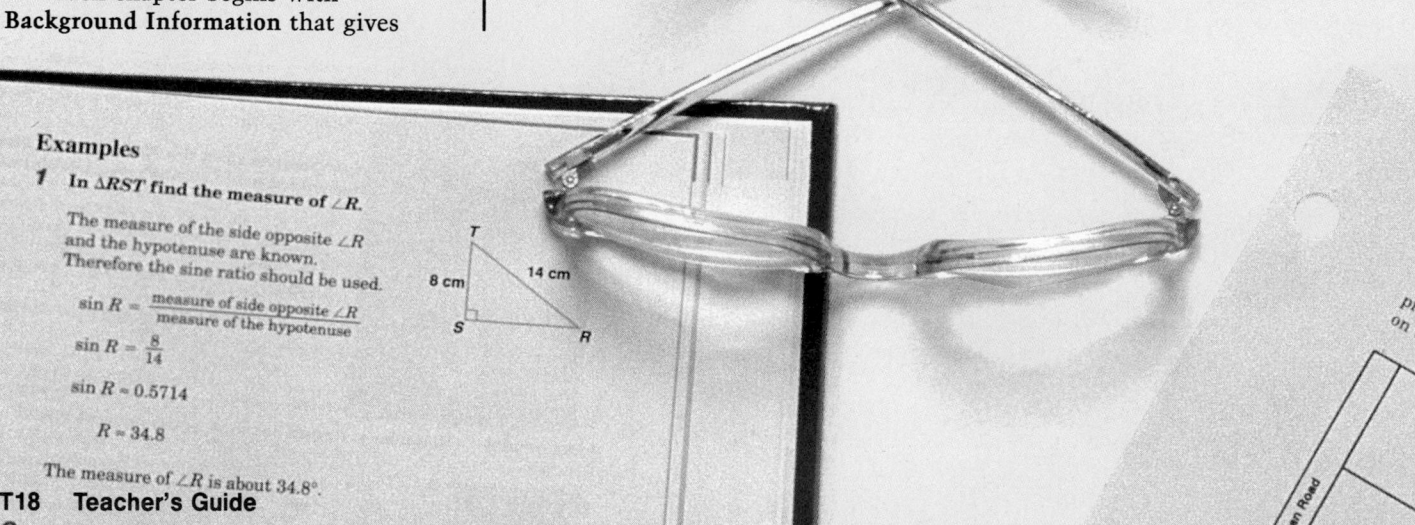

Examples

1 In $\triangle RST$ find the measure of $\angle R$.

The measure of the side opposite $\angle R$ and the hypotenuse are known. Therefore the sine ratio should be used.

$\sin R = \dfrac{\text{measure of side opposite } \angle R}{\text{measure of the hypotenuse}}$

$\sin R = \dfrac{8}{14}$

$\sin R \approx 0.5714$

$R \approx 34.8$

The measure of $\angle R$ is about 34.8°.

8 cm 14 cm

2 In $\triangle ABC$ find the...

1 INTRODUCING THE LESSON

INTRODUCING THE LESSON, or the anticipatory set as it is sometimes called, is the first step of the **Merrill Algebra** teaching plan.

INTRODUCING THE LESSON begins with two pre-lesson activities to engage your students. The **5-Minute Check** includes one to five questions from the previous lesson. This allows you to check retention of skills and concepts. **Motivating the Lesson** helps prepare students for learning the day's lesson by piquing their interest. It is intended to help focus the attention of the class so the lesson can begin.

The latter activity may also provide time for students to interact with you, thus enabling you to modify the lesson to fit what students already know. This activity usually can be completed within the first five minutes of class and should be a direct lead-in to the concepts that will be presented. By focusing your students, you will provide the structural framework for what is to come.

2 TEACHING THE LESSON

TEACHING THE LESSON, the second step of the teaching plan, is the heart of any lesson. The primary aim of the **Merrill Algebra** teaching plan is to give you the tools to accomplish the admittedly difficult task of enabling your students to learn algebraic concepts. Effective **Teaching Tips** as well as **Chalkboard Examples** are provided in this part of the teaching cycle.

ALTERNATE TEACHING STRATEGIES provides you various methods of teaching the content of the lesson. These strategies include Using Cooperative Groups, Using Manipulatives, Using Technology, and Using Critical Thinking, just to name a few.

With the materials presented in the TEACHING THE LESSON step of the six-part teaching plan, your efficiency and productivity as a teacher will increase. The TEACHING THE LESSON step brings together the major elements that form a sound teaching approach.

3 EVALUATING THE LESSON

As a teacher, you work hard at making the transfer of knowledge as efficient and productive as it can be. One finding of educational researchers is that teachers who closely guide their students during a lesson are more effective. This third step provides **Checking for Understanding** and **Error Analysis** to assist you in identifying and correcting common student errors. **Closing the Lesson** provides you with a quick way of determining if students have mastered the objectives of the lesson and gives students an opportunity for direct communication in written, spoken, or modeled form.

4 RETEACHING THE LESSON

No matter how thoroughly a subject is covered in the classroom, there usually will be students who do not understand the lesson the first time it is taught. A **RETEACHING THE LESSON** activity is provided for every lesson as a way to teach the same concepts or facts differently so they will be more amenable to students' individual learning styles.

Research shows that teachers who closely guide their students during a lesson are more effective.

5 APPLYING THE LESSON

A suggested **HOMEWORK ASSIGNMENT GUIDE** for three levels—Basic, Average, and Enriched—is provided for each lesson. In addition, **Teaching Tips** may be provided that give insight and hints into specific exercises.

6 EXTENDING THE LESSON

Every lesson has an **EXTENDING THE LESSON** activity that enriches and extends the concepts taught in the lesson.

As you review the Teacher's Wraparound Edition to **Merrill Algebra**, you will discover that you and your students are considered very important. With the enormous number of teaching tips and strategies provided by the **Teacher's Wraparound Edition**, you should be able to accomplish the goals of your curriculum with a minimum of time and effort. This is true whether you are teaching algebra for the first time, or whether you are a veteran teacher. The materials allow adaptability and flexibility so that student and curricular needs can be met. ■

How Merrill Algebra 2 Meets the NCTM Standards

Content that relates to specific NCTM standards are found on the following Student Edition pages:

STANDARD 1:

MATHEMATICS AS PROBLEM SOLVING
9, 10, 15, 20, 24, 25, 26, 29–32, 38, 43, 53, 57, 60–66, 69, 75, 78, 80–84, 87–90, 92, 94, 95, 98, 109, 114, 120, 126, 128, 131, 134, 135, 140, 146, 156–158, 163, 169, 174, 175, 187, 191, 197, 212, 216, 220–222, 225, 229, 237, 243, 255, 261, 265, 271, 275, 276, 278, 283, 289, 293, 298, 310, 311, 319, 324, 335, 350, 353, 356–358, 362, 368, 374, 380, 384, 397, 398, 400–402, 405, 410, 418, 423, 424, 428, 433, 452, 465–467, 474, 477, 512, 518, 532, 534, 547, 554, 559, 571, 572, 573, 574, 581, 582, 594, 595, 598, 604, 610, 612, 616, 622, 628, 638, 639, 641, 643, 644, 649, 650, 654, 655, 659, 664, 665, 669, 670, 682, 683, 690, 699, 700, 711, 734, 743, 747, 752, 758, 762–764, 768, 771, 773, 774, 777, 792, 804, 807, 809, 812, 816, 825

STANDARD 2:

MATHEMATICS AS COMMUNICATION
10, 16, 20, 26, 30, 33, 39, 44, 55, 62, 65, 70, 76, 82, 88, 94, 110, 114, 120, 127, 132, 136, 142, 147, 157, 164, 170, 175, 181, 188, 192, 198, 213, 218, 221, 225, 232, 238, 244, 255, 261, 266, 272, 276, 279, 284, 289, 294, 299, 311, 319, 324, 330, 336, 342, 354, 357, 364, 370, 375, 381, 385, 398, 402, 406, 413, 419, 423, 428, 434, 444, 454, 462, 466, 473, 478, 484, 489, 493, 508, 513, 519, 525, 529, 533, 537, 549, 556, 561, 565, 569, 572, 576, 582, 595, 599, 605, 612, 618, 623, 629, 640, 645, 651, 655, 660, 665, 670, 682, 686, 691, 697, 701, 707, 712, 717, 722, 734, 739, 743, 749, 753, 759, 764, 769, 773, 777, 795, 799, 805, 808, 813, 817, 825, 832

STANDARD 3:

MATHEMATICS AS REASONING
12, 17, 21, 27, 34, 40, 45, 57, 63–65, 71, 78, 84, 90, 95, 111, 115, 121, 125, 133, 138, 142, 148, 166, 171, 177, 182, 189, 193, 200, 214, 219, 227, 233, 239, 245, 256, 263, 267, 273, 280, 285, 290, 295, 300, 321, 325, 331, 337, 343, 355, 363, 371, 377, 381, 386, 399, 404, 407, 414, 421, 429, 435, 443, 456, 464, 474, 479, 485, 490, 495, 509, 514, 520, 526, 530, 539, 550, 557, 562, 566, 569, 577, 584, 600, 606, 613, 619, 624, 630, 640, 646, 652, 656, 667, 672, 688, 693, 698, 703, 709, 714, 718, 724, 735, 740, 744, 749, 754, 760, 766, 770, 778, 796, 800, 806, 813, 826, 833

STANDARD 4:

MATHEMATICAL CONNECTIONS
9, 10, 15, 20, 24, 25, 26, 32, 38, 43, 53, 61, 69, 75, 81, 82, 84, 88, 109, 114, 120, 131, 134, 135, 140, 146, 163, 169, 174, 175, 187, 191, 197, 212, 216, 220, 221, 225, 229, 237, 243, 255, 261, 265, 271, 278, 283, 289, 293, 298, 319, 324, 335, 353, 356, 362, 368, 374, 380, 384, 397, 398, 402, 405, 410, 418, 428, 433, 452, 477, 512, 518, 533, 547, 554, 559, 571, 572, 574, 581, 582, 598, 604, 610, 612, 616, 622, 628, 639, 643, 644, 649, 650, 654, 655, 659, 664, 665, 669, 670, 672, 676, 690, 700, 711, 734, 743, 747, 752, 758, 762, 763, 764, 768, 773, 777, 792, 804, 807, 812, 816, 825

STANDARD 5:

ALGEBRA
1, 4, 8, 21, 25–28, 32–45, 47, 48, 49, 54, 58–63, 66, 68, 69, 71–73, 80–87, 91–95, 104–112, 114, 120, 122–125, 129–138, 140–142, 150–152, 160, 162, 163–166, 173–203, 240, 281–286, 289, 290, 299, 312–321, 323, 329, 335, 338, 344, 350–352,

356–373, 379–386, 388–390, 400, 402–404, 431–438, 445, 451, 452, 459, 527–530, 533, 536, 542–552, 554, 574, 575, 576, 577, 578, 580–584, 638–645, 658–663, 668, 669, 672, 674, 675, 676, 680, 742, 820, 821–827, 842, 943

STANDARD 6:

FUNCTIONS
10, 24, 25, 32, 38, 43, 53–63, 66–79, 81, 88, 94, 96–98, 457–458

STANDARD 7:

GEOMETRY FROM A SYNTHETIC PERSPECTIVE
9, 12, 20–21, 24, 26, 49, 51, 64, 68–71, 75–79, 97, 112, 128, 148, 169, 171–172, 199, 220, 223, 225, 227, 229, 237, 252, 255, 281, 285, 310, 316, 343, 354–355, 362, 376, 380–382, 397–399, 405–407, 422, 444, 468, 476, 478, 482, 512, 514, 518, 572–573, 639, 700, 732–740, 756–779, 782

STANDARD 8:

GEOMETRY FROM AN ALGEBRAIC PERSPECTIVE
9, 12, 15, 20–21, 24, 26, 27, 57, 63, 69, 72, 78, 112, 114, 115, 120, 131, 132, 140, 148, 163, 165, 166, 169, 171–172, 175, 176, 177, 182, 197, 199, 220, 221, 223, 225–226, 227, 228, 229, 237, 252, 255, 262, 263, 264, 276, 281, 285, 293, 310, 316, 338, 343, 354, 355, 362, 376, 380, 381, 396, 397, 404, 410, 468, 476, 477, 478, 479, 482, 484, 486, 512, 514, 518, 520, 534, 550, 571, 572, 573, 600, 607, 614, 667, 700, 702, 714, 734, 737, 738, 745, 748, 757, 765, 766, 767–769, 770, 775, 778, 829

STANDARD 9:

TRIGONOMETRY
732–745, 756–779, 786–828, 829–833

STANDARD 10:

STATISTICS
80–86, 90, 91, 125, 133, 276, 521, 530, 636–677, 693, 703, 741, 750, 754, 770, 779, 796, 806, 819, 827, 833

STANDARD 11:

PROBABILITY
79, 430, 534, 628, 680–729, 736, 833

STANDARD 12:

DISCRETE MATHEMATICS
12, 17, 21, 27, 34, 35, 40, 45, 63, 64, 79, 94, 111, 114–117, 120, 121, 125, 129–140, 142, 143, 148, 151, 156–158, 163, 166, 169, 171, 175, 177, 178, 182, 189, 193, 194, 197, 200, 214, 219, 220–222, 227, 233, 239, 245, 256, 263, 267, 273, 280, 285, 290, 291, 295, 300, 321, 325, 331, 332, 337, 343, 355–358, 363, 365, 371, 377, 378, 381, 386, 399, 404, 407, 414, 421, 423, 424, 429, 430, 435, 443, 456, 464, 474, 479, 485, 486, 490, 495, 509, 514, 520, 526, 530, 539, 550, 557, 562, 566, 569, 577, 579, 584, 600, 606, 613, 619, 624, 630, 631, 638–641, 672, 673, 682–729, 735, 736, 740, 744, 749, 754, 760, 761, 766, 770, 778, 796, 800, 813, 819, 826, 827, 833

STANDARD 13:

CONCEPTUAL UNDERPINNINGS OF CALCULUS
92–94, 360–382, 432–437, 481–486, 506–515, 551, 552

STANDARD 14:

MATHEMATICAL STRUCTURE
13–19, 47, 64, 77, 252–275, 263, 264, 292–301, 459–461, 469–477, 547–548, 625–630, 634, 668, 669, 831, 833

Cooperative Learning

"The best answer to the question, 'What is the most effective method of teaching?' is that it depends on the goal, the student, the content, and the teacher. But the next best answer is, 'Students teaching other students.' There is a wealth of evidence that peer teaching is extremely effective for a wide range of goals, content, and students of different levels and personalities."

Wilbert McKeachie, et al, 1986

Cooperative learning groups *learn* things together, not just do things together. Studies show that cooperative learning promotes more learning than competitive or individual learning experiences regardless of student age, subject matter, or learning activity. More difficult learning tasks, such as problem solving, critical thinking, and conceptual learning, come out far ahead when cooperative strategies are used. Studies also show that in classroom settings, adolescents learn more from each other about subject matter than from the teacher.

The basic elements of a cooperative learning group are as follows:

(1) Students must perceive that they "sink or swim together."

(2) Students are responsible for everyone else in the group, as well as themselves, in learning the assigned material.

(3) Students must see that they all have the same goal, that they need to divide up the tasks and share the responsibility equally, and that they will be given one evaluation or reward that will apply to all members of the group.

General guidelines and suggestions for implementing cooperative learning in your algebra classroom are provided on this page and the next. In addition, specific guidelines are provided in the teacher material that precedes each chapter. The **Teacher Resource Package**

More difficult learning tasks, such as problem solving and critical thinking, come out far ahead when cooperative strategies are used.

also contains a Cooperative Learning Activity in the Activities Booklet that can be used with each chapter.

Preparation and Social Skills

1. *Arrange your room.* Students in groups should face each other as they work together. It is helpful to number the tables so you can refer to groups by number, or have groups choose a name.

2. *Decide on the size of the group.* Groups work best when teams are composed of two to five students. The materials available might dictate the size of the group.

3. *Assign students to groups.* Each group should be mixed socially, racially, ethnically, sexually, and by learning abilities. Occasionally a student may insist on working alone. This student usually changes his or her mind when seeing that everyone else's grades are better, and the groups are having more fun.

4. *Prepare students for cooperation.* This is a critical step. Tell students about the rationale, procedures, and expected outcomes of this method of instruction. Students need to know that you are not forcing them to be friends, but asking them to work together as they will later on in life with people who come together for a specific purpose.

5. *Plan Teaching Materials.* Distributing materials can help you communicate that the activity is to be a group and not an individual activity. You can provide only one set of materials or one copy of the worksheet to the group. Group members will quickly realize that they need to work together if they are to be successful. You can vary this by providing each member with a worksheet but collect only one of them.

6. *Explain group tasks.* For most activities, each group will need someone to take notes, someone to summarize as the group progresses, and someone to make sure everyone is involved. Classes that have less experience using these methods may need these roles assigned to group members at the beginning of each activity. These jobs should be done by different students each time, so that one student does not feel burdened doing the same job all the time.

7. *Explain the day's lesson.* On the chalkboard or overhead, write the following headings:

■ *Form Groups:* List the number of students in each group.

■ *Topic of the Day:* general academic topic.

■ *Task:* title of activity. At this time, go over instructions and relate the work to previous learning.

■ *Goal:* Indicate whether students will all do individual work of which you will select one person's paper or product to grade, or whether they will produce only one product per group. Student signatures on all the work indicates that they will accept the collected work for their grade.

■ *Cooperative Skills:* List the specific group skills you will be checking. Start with one or two basic skills. The following skills start from basic and move to more advanced.

a. Use quiet voices.
b. Encourage each other to participate.
c. Use each other's names. Use eye contact.
d. Ask your teacher for help only after you have decided as a group that you all need help.
e. Stress that all student contributions are valuable.

After students have some experience working in cooperative groups, you can expect group members to exhibit some or all of the following higher level cooperative skills.

a. Express support and acceptance, both verbal and nonverbal, through eye contact, enthusiasm, and praise.
b. Ask for help or clarification about what is happening.
c. Suggest new ideas.
d. Use appropriate humor that stays on task.
e. Describe feelings using "I messages," such as, "I like the way you praised my idea."
f. Summarize and elaborate on what others have contributed.
g. Develop memory aids and analogies that are clever ways of remembering important points.
h. Criticize ideas, not people.
i. Go beyond the first answer to a question.

Teacher Responsibilities During Cooperative Group Work

1. *Monitor student behavior.* Use a formal observation sheet to count the number of times you observe the behavior expected on that particular assignment for each group. Start with a few behaviors at the beginning and move up to many different behaviors when you feel comfortable doing so. Share your observations with each group.

2. *Provide assistance with the task.* Clarify instructions, review concepts, or answer questions. You will find students who see you nearby will automatically start asking

questions. Your first response should be, "Have you asked everyone in the group?"

Your role will be supportive supervisor rather than direct supervisor; you will help a group that has gotten stuck and is experiencing a high level of frustration. You might do this by asking a few open-ended questions. In a conflict situation, you might ask the group to identify the reason for the difficulty and ask them to come up with some strategies for handling the conflict.

3. *Intervene to teach cooperative skills.* As you observe that some groups have more problems than others with cooperative skills, you may wish to intervene by asking the group to think about why they are not being effective and have them work toward a solution.

4. *Provide closure for the lesson.* Students should be asked to summarize what they have learned and be able to relate it to what they have previously studied. You may want to review the main points and ask students to give examples. You should also answer any final questions.

5. *Evaluate the group process.* In order for groups to be aware of their progress in learning to work together, they must be given time to evaluate or process how they are working together. Allow a few minutes at the end of the lesson for groups to decide if they achieved the criterion you set up. Have them rate themselves on a

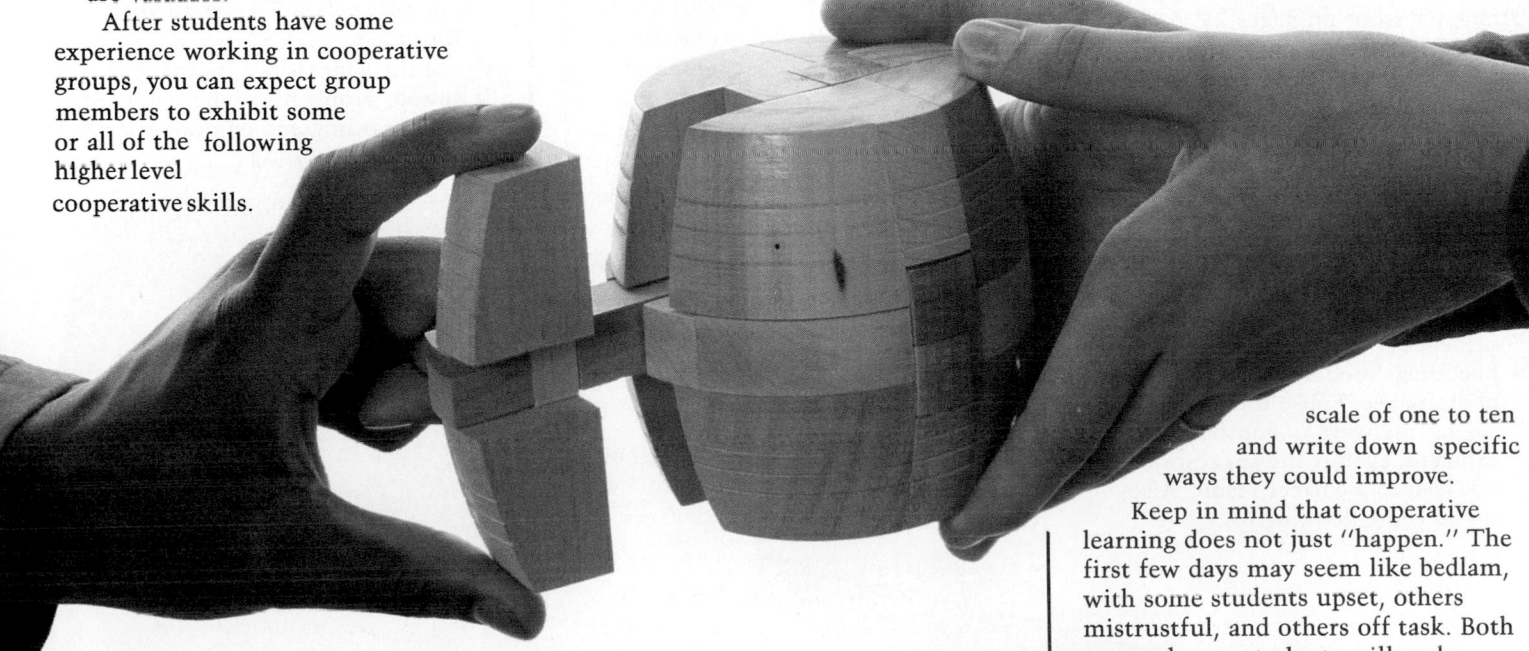

scale of one to ten and write down specific ways they could improve.

Keep in mind that cooperative learning does not just "happen." The first few days may seem like bedlam, with some students upset, others mistrustful, and others off task. Both you and your students will make mistakes. Be patient and keep at it. ■

Problem Solving in Algebra

One of the challenges of teaching mathematics is helping students learn to solve problems. Problem solving involves more than solving verbal problems—it also involves the ability to analyze a new problem and discover a way to solve it.

Algebra is a very useful tool for solving problems. Many verbal problems can be easily solved by translating the problem into an equation. This involves many skills which must be developed gradually—reading and exploring the problem, defining a variable, writing an equation, solving the equation, interpreting the result, and checking the solution.

Not all problems in real-life can be solved by using an equation. Sometimes there is no "clear-cut" method of solution. Thus, it is important for students to learn alternative strategies for solving problems. This text includes numerous *Problem-Solving Strategy* lessons that illustrate various strategies, such as guess-and-check (p. 310). Other strategies are introduced in *Problem-Solving Strategy* lessons on pages 29, 64, 126, 156, 220, 275, 356, 423, 465, 532, 571, 594, 638, 682, 771, and 807. The four-step problem-solving plan can be used to solve *any* type of problem, using *any* strategy.

It is important to create a classroom environment which encourages problem-solving abilities. The following suggestions should be helpful in building students' confidence in solving problems:

- Encourage students to try a variety of strategies. Praise them for suggesting ways to approach a problem, even if the suggestions do not lead to a correct result. Also, spend time "looking back" at

1. **EXPLORE** *the problem.* Read the problem and identify what is given and what is asked. Jot down important facts from the problem. Sometimes it is helpful to draw a chart or diagram. Think about how the facts are related.

If an equation will be used to solve the problem, choose a variable to represent one of the unspecified numbers in the problem. Read the problem again and use the variable in writing expressions for other unspecified numbers in the problem.

2. **PLAN** *the solution.* Many different strategies may be used. If an equation will be used to solve the problem, read the problem again. Decide how the unspecified numbers relate to other given information. Write an equation to represent the relationship.

3. **SOLVE** *the problem.* This involves doing the mathematics and interpreting the answer. If an equation was written, solve the equation and interpret the solution. State the answer to the verbal problem.

4. **EXAMINE** *the solution.* Check whether the answer makes sense with the conditions of the problem. If not, check your mathematics again. If the mathematics was correct, a mistake was made in "setting up" the problem. In that case, explore the problem again and try a different approach.

problems which were previously solved and discuss alternative ways to solve the problems.
- Assume that students will make mistakes when solving verbal problems. An evaluation system which gives partial credit for thoughtful attempts is recommended. For example, you could award 4 points for a correct solution, 3 points for a solution which has the right process but had a small mathematical error, 2 points for a thoughtful attempt with a mistake in "setting up" the solution, and 1 point for other meaningful attempts.
- Allow sufficient time for the class to explore problems. In some cases it is preferable to spend twice the time on half the problems. Although discussions may seem to move slowly, the extra time will give students more confidence.

- Throughout the year, emphasize the steps for solving problems. A chart listing the steps could be displayed on the bulletin board, along with a problem for students to solve in their spare time. Problems could be chosen from this text, or from other sources such as *The Mathematics Teacher.*

If the suggestions on this page are followed, problem solving will become more rewarding and enjoyable. ■

Using Manipulatives in Your Algebra Classroom

Most teachers agree that the use of manipulative materials helps students build a solid understanding of mathematical concepts and enhances students' achievement in mathematics. The universal anxiety today about achievement in mathematics should prompt educators in this field to heed results from recent studies which indicate that by using manipulative materials at every level, test scores are dramatically improved.

"Manipulative materials are the key to understanding operations and algorithms."[1] Because abstractions are an integral part of algebra and because students derive their abstract ideas primarily from their experience, it is imperative that they experiment with a variety of manipulative materials on the concrete level to develop an understanding of algebraic symbols and concepts.

The purpose of using manipulatives is to assist students in bridging the gap from the concrete to the abstract.

Many teachers find that demonstrations on an overhead projector ease students with little experience in hands-on learning into working with manipulatives. Simply observing such a demonstration, however, is not enough. Follow-up activities that involve the students in the act of physically manipulating such aids are essential if students are to experience the patterns and relations inherent in mathematics.

"The purpose of using manipulatives is to assist students in bridging the gap from their own concrete environment to the abstract level."[2] Affording students the opportunity for meaningful practice through modeling algorithms with manipulatives not only results in greater understanding of the concepts and skills in question but also provides a fun alternative to everyday, routine problem-solving exercises as well.

Merrill Algebra contains many opportunities for students to use manipulatives to discover and explore algebraic concepts. Students actually *do* mathematics and are encouraged to make conjectures based on their observations. The **Merrill Algebra Lab Manual** contains numerous activities that require the use of manipulatives, allowing students to make the connection from the concrete to the abstract.

To make sure that students understand what is expected of each activity, the teacher must discuss its goal and model how the manipulative is to be used to achieve it. Encouraging students to suggest ways in which manipulatives can be used helps them to relate concepts and to develop mathematical insights.

The important thing to keep in mind is that most students do not automatically abstract the concepts they explore with materials; they must be led to see how the concepts relate to traditional algorithms. Summarizing and recording group activity results helps to focus on such relationships and algebraic concepts. Used in this way, manipulative materials are a justifiable means to a desirable end.

No presentation advocating the use of manipulative materials in the algebra classroom would be totally complete without interjecting a note of caution. Despite the fact that manipulative materials are highly touted, and rightly so, they can, if used incorrectly, undo much of the good for which they are intended. Through careless or erroneous use of manipulatives, students might conclude that there are two distinct mathematical worlds—one of manipulatives and another of symbols—and that each has its own rules.

Teachers must, therefore, direct students to see the need for precise and exact connection between the symbols and the manipulatives; otherwise they cannot possibly develop proper mathematical understanding. The point that must be stressed repeatedly in teaching with manipulatives in the algebra classroom is that "symbols and manipulatives must always reflect the same concept."[3]

If mathematics educators sincerely want to challenge their students in the algebra classroom, perhaps they must first endorse the fact that the use of manipulative materials holds the promise of increasing students' understanding of and achievement in mathematics, and then translate that belief into classroom practice.

1. Beattie, Ian D., "Modeling Operations and Algorithms," *Arithmetic Teacher*, February 1986, p. 24.
2. Hynes, Michael C., "Selection Criteria," *Arithmetic Teacher*, February 1986, p. 11.
3. Bright, George W., "One Point of View: Using Manipulatives," *Arithmetic Teacher*, February 1986, p. 4.

Integrating Technology Into Your Algebra Classroom

"Students today can't prepare bark to calculate their problems. They depend upon their slates which are more expensive. What will they do when their slate is dropped and it breaks? They will be unable to write!"

Teachers' Conference, 1703

The above quote seems ridiculous today, but in 1703 it was not. Many people may ask, "Couldn't they see enough into the future to know that slates would be required?"; but as the old adage goes, hindsight is twenty-twenty. The difficulty lies in foreseeing the future.

The argument nowadays is in regard to computers and calculators; and while most people agree that technology should be used in the mathematics classroom, few are offering ideas on incorporation, testing, appropriate use, and other areas where teachers have questions. Some use this as an argument against using technology, but that is not the answer to the problem. Instead we must be able to recognize a good idea when we see one and adopt it for our classrooms.

Appropriate Use of Technology

There are many different ideas and definitions of "appropriate use of technology," and rightly so. Every class and every teacher is different. What is appropriate and works for one may not be appropriate or work for another. However, there are some classifications and generalizations that can be made for different grade levels. Keep in mind that many of your students are just learning the technology. You should refrain from getting "high-tech" with them. Give them opportunities for success early so that they can begin to feel comfortable with technology.

Have your students complete an easy calculation for their first encounter. For the students new to technology, this will give them a sense of accomplishment because they can see something they have done; for the more technologically experienced students, this will give them a sense of confidence because they already know what is being done.

At any level of teaching, try to get students to make generalizations about what they see or do with technology.

Using Technology in Your Classroom

Technology opens up many new ideas and opportunities. It is up to you to decide how to present and use technology in your classroom. Many of the standard teaching techniques are appropriate, such as using cooperative groups, or having students work in pairs, but there are also new ways of teaching that are appropriate when using technology in your classroom. For example, you can assign lab partners in each class. Each pair of students would then work together whenever technology is used. This can also be used if you have a limited supply of equipment.

Teaching Aids

There are many technological teaching aids as well as numerous products to assist in the teaching of technology. One of them is a projection panel for the overhead projector. This can be used in conjunction with a demonstration computer and can project the image from the computer onto a screen or wall.

Overhead projector calculators are also available for most models. They can serve the same purpose as a projection panel and demonstration computer.

Another teaching aid is a template of the computer or calculator keyboard that can be used on the overhead or put on the bulletin board

Technology teaches students in a way that piques their interest and leads to questions that show a desire to learn.

for easy reference. (Masters for the TI-34 and TI-81 calculators are provided on pages 9 and 10 in the *Merrill Algebra Lab Manual*.) This can help in conveying the location of keys, especially second function keys on graphing calculators.

Changes in the Classroom

There will be some changes in your classroom with the onset of technology. One will be your role. It most likely will change from leader to guide. Students will begin to do things on their own and it will be up to you to keep them headed in the right direction. Students will also begin to ask more questions, including more higher-order questions, than before.

You may not have all the answers, but the investigation can be enjoyable and enlightening for both you and your students.

Advantages of Technology

Probably the biggest advantage of technology is the amount of time it can save you. The ease of editing errors, the number of graphs and pictures that can be drawn in a short amount of time, the speed of calculating; all these and other time-saving advantages make technology a major plus for the mathematics classroom.

There are numerous other advantages. One is that students will have a deeper understanding of the

concepts being taught. As we develop toward a more pictorial society, students are becoming visual learners. Technology teaches them in a way that piques their interest and leads to questions that show a desire to learn.

Another advantage of technology is the cooperative efforts that develop among students. Since students will most likely need to work with others when they become members of the work force, it is best for them to learn to work with others while they are in school. With technology, you can teach your students to work cooperatively, which will benefit them in college and in their careers.

Technology Fears

Perhaps the biggest fear, and certainly one that is most often expressed, is that of the technology taking the place of the teacher. *This will never happen.* There is no way that a computer can do what a teacher does, and in particular, sense what a teacher can. For example, no computer can sense uncertainty of an answer in a student's tone of voice. Few students will be able to turn on a calculator or computer and teach themselves with it. They need teachers to explain the technology and to help make connections.

You can also see the evidence of needing the teacher when you relate the use of technology in education to its use in the business world. Computers have been in the mainstream of business for quite some time now, and there has not been a reduction in the number of persons needed. Yet a large number of business executives will tell you they would not want to do their job without the use of a computer. Many teachers who have incorporated technology into their classrooms are saying the same thing.

Computers and calculators are excellent tools for teaching mathematics concepts. Though there are still some who argue their use in the classroom, none can argue their educational advantage. Technology can teach students in ways that were never before possible. In the past, teachers could only dream of being able to do some of the things that they can now do with ease, thanks to technology. While incorporating technology into your mathematical classroom can be difficult at first, in the long run, it will definitely pay off for both you and your students. ■

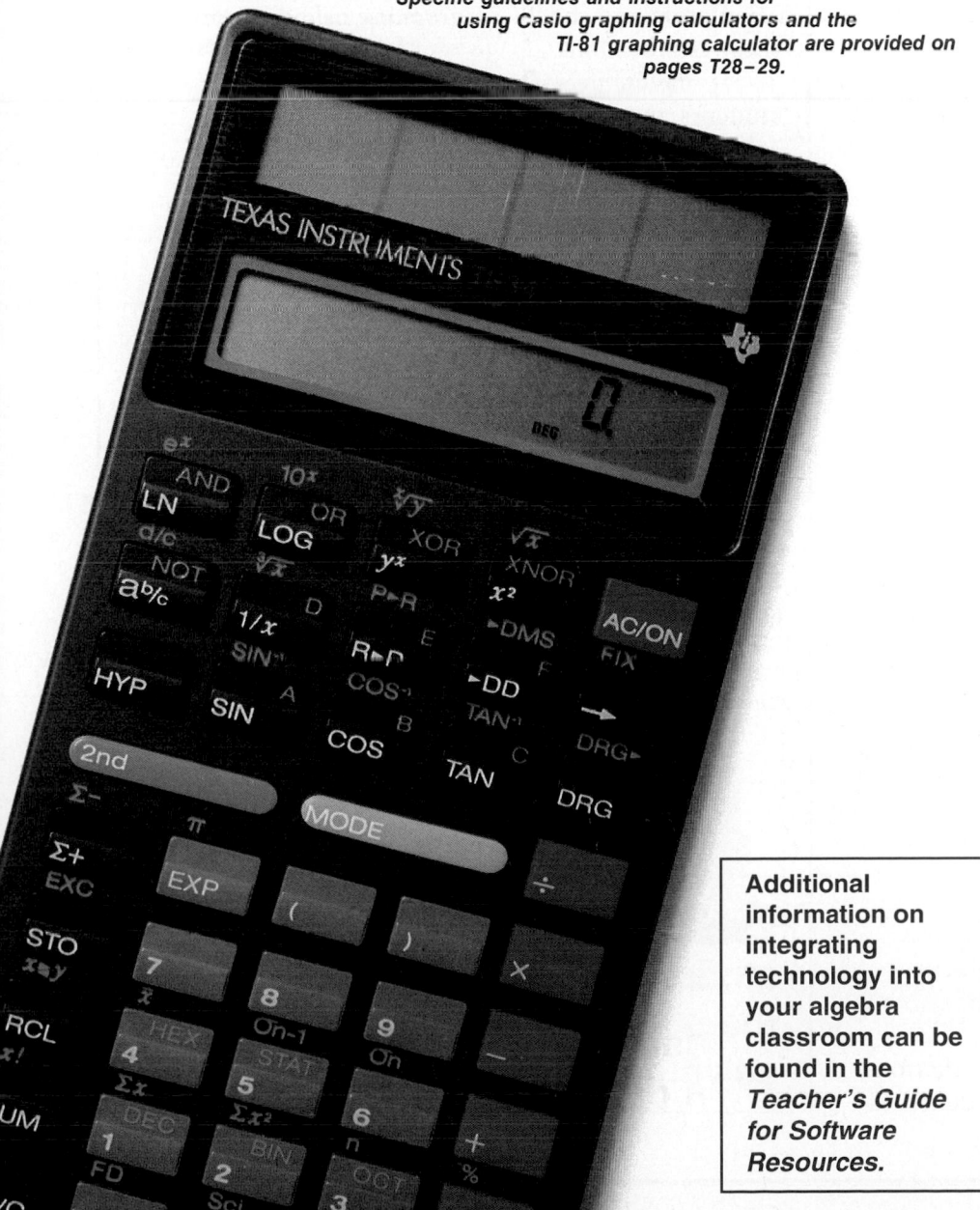

Specific guidelines and instructions for using Casio graphing calculators and the TI-81 graphing calculator are provided on pages T28–29.

Additional information on integrating technology into your algebra classroom can be found in the *Teacher's Guide for Software Resources.*

Using the Graphing Calculator

In the Beginning . . .

Today's technology offers teachers new and exciting opportunities to teach students in many different ways. It can add different dimensions to mathematics classrooms and can also help students gain a deeper understanding of the concepts being taught. The graphing calculator is one technological tool that can help you teach your students. And while learning to use the graphing calculator and getting started with it may be one of the most difficult problems to tackle, once this is accomplished, the only limits left are the limits of the calculator's capabilities.

In **Merrill Algebra 2,** there are seventeen Graphing Calculator Explorations. The chapters in which they occur and their titles are listed below.

Chapter 1:   Evaluating Expressions
Chapter 2:   Graphing Linear Equations
Chapter 2:   Lines of Regression
Chapter 3:   Graphing Systems of Equations
Chapter 4:   Matrices
Chapter 4:   Matrix Row Operations
Chapter 7:   Quadratic Equations
Chapter 8:   Families of Parabolas
Chapter 8:   Locating the Vertex of a Parabola
Chapter 9:   Conic Sections
Chapter 9:   Solving Quadratic Systems
Chapter 10:   Graphing Polynomial Equations
Chapter 11:   Graphing Rational Functions
Chapter 12:   Graphing Exponential and
              Logarithmic Functions
Chapter 17:   Graphing Trigonometric Functions
Chapter 17:   Verifying Trigonometric Identities
Chapter 17:   Solving Trigonometric Equations

Instruction is provided for both Casio graphing calculators and the TI-81 graphing calculator in these Explorations.

It may be necessary for you to give your students an introduction to the graphing calculator before you begin one of the Explorations since many may not have used a graphing calculator before. It may also be necessary for you to familiarize yourself with the graphing calculator before teaching the Explorations. The manuals for the calculators can help you get started. They can also be used as a guide or a reference, and they may clear up questions that you have along the way. The TI-81 manual has a section to help you get started and also has several examples throughout the manual that explain how the calculator can be used to teach certain concepts. You can also talk to other teachers who are using the calculator if you need help getting off the ground with the technology.

Using graphing calculators in your classroom can bring your students together and can help them learn to help each other solve problems.

Getting to Know Your Calculator

Both the Casio and the TI-81 graphing calculator have four "screens" in common; the text screen, the graphics screen, the range screen, and the mode screen. Each screen does something different. The *text screen* is the screen where you complete calculations, input programs, or input commands for the calculator to perform. When you press [AC] on the Casio and [CLEAR] (or in some situations [2nd] [QUIT]) on the TI-81, you are in the text screen.

The *graphics screen* is where the calculator graphs functions. Pressing the [G↔T] key on the Casio lets you alternate between graphics and text screens, while pressing the [GRAPH] key on the TI-81 will get you to the graphics screen.

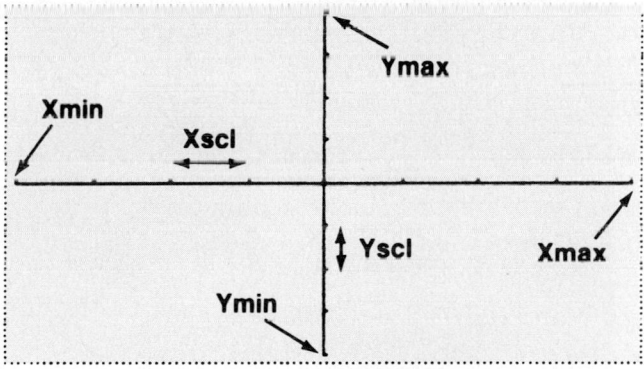

The *range screen* tells you the x- and y-endpoints and scale of the graphics screen. The TI-81 range screen also tells you the x-resolution, or how clearly your function(s) will be graphed. Pressing [RANGE] on either calculator will get you to the range screen.

And finally, the *mode screen* tells you at what mode settings your calculator is set. On the Casio, the mode screen can be seen when you turn the calculator on. It can also be accessed by pressing the [MDisp] key. To change the mode settings on the Casio, you can press the [MODE] key and the corresponding number for the mode setting you desire. The mode settings are listed under the screen of the calculator. On the TI-81, the mode screen is accessed by pressing the [MODE] key.

Casio

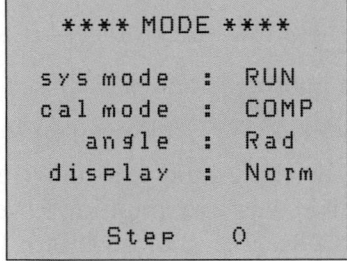

TI-81

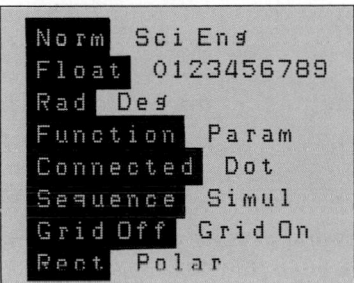

As you have realized, there is no "=" key on either the Casio graphing calculator or the TI-81 graphing calculator. Instead there is an [ENTER] key on the TI-81 and an [EXE] key on the Casio. This is because each key is more than just a key that completes all of the calculator's arithmetic calculations. It also completes other calculator operations, such as drawing a graph, moving to a new line of a program, selecting equations you want graphed, and so on. Both keys will perform the "=" function, but they will also do much more.

The insert ([INS]), delete ([DEL]), and arrow keys ([→], [←], [↑], [↓] on the Casio and [▶], [◀], [▲], [▼] on the TI-81) can be used for easy editing of inputed commands. On the Casio, the [→] and [←] arrow keys can be used to go directly to the point of error if you press one of them first when an error message appears. These are called the "replay" keys. The calculator will automatically return to the place where it found the error. You can also use the arrow keys to manually move to the place(s) where you want to insert into or delete from an equation or expression.

Both calculators have second function keys and alphabetical character keys. These can be found as [2nd] and [ALPHA] on the TI-81 and as [SHIFT] and [ALPHA] on the Casio. The second function keys ([2nd] or [SHIFT]) allow you to access the characters on the left-hand side above each key. The alphabetical key ([ALPHA]) allows you to access the letters on the right-hand side above each key.

The TI-81 has five graphing keys underneath the screen. These keys all deal with listing, graphing, and exploring functions. The [Y=] key allows you to list up to four functions that you want to graph. The [RANGE] key allows you to set your minimum and maximum values and your scale for the graphics screen. The [ZOOM] key allows you to look at smaller or larger sections of the function(s) you have graphed. The [TRACE] key does just what it says; it allows you to trace along any function on the graphics screen. Finally, the [GRAPH] key graphs the selected functions or returns you to the graphics screen.

Both calculators will let you know if you have done something that it does not understand by giving you an error message. The most common error messages are given when you have a math error or a syntax error. The Casio will list "Ma error" for a math error and "Syn error" for a syntax error and will write the error messages directly underneath the calculation. The TI-81 will write the kind of error on the top line of the error message. Perhaps the easiest way to get a math error on either calculator is to divide a number by zero. There are many other ways to get a math error, however. To see a syntax error, use the [(-)] key instead of the [−] key in an equation and then try to perform the calculation.

Error messages can be extremely frustrating, especially if they keep recurring and you cannot figure out what is wrong. There are some troubleshooting tips to help you find the problem when this situation occurs. First, check to see that your calculator is at the correct mode settings. If it is in write mode and not run mode or if you are in degrees instead of radians, your calculator will not do what you want it to do. Another tip is to use the replay keys on the Casio or the "Goto error" statement on the TI-81 and try to let the calculator do the troubleshooting for you. If you still cannot understand why the

calculator gave you an error statement, go through the problem step-by-step and try doing it as the calculator would. Make sure to use parentheses in necessary areas. And if all else fails, try rekeying parts of the problem or the entire problem and then reexecute. This may get rid of an invisible keystroke entry that you did not know was entered.

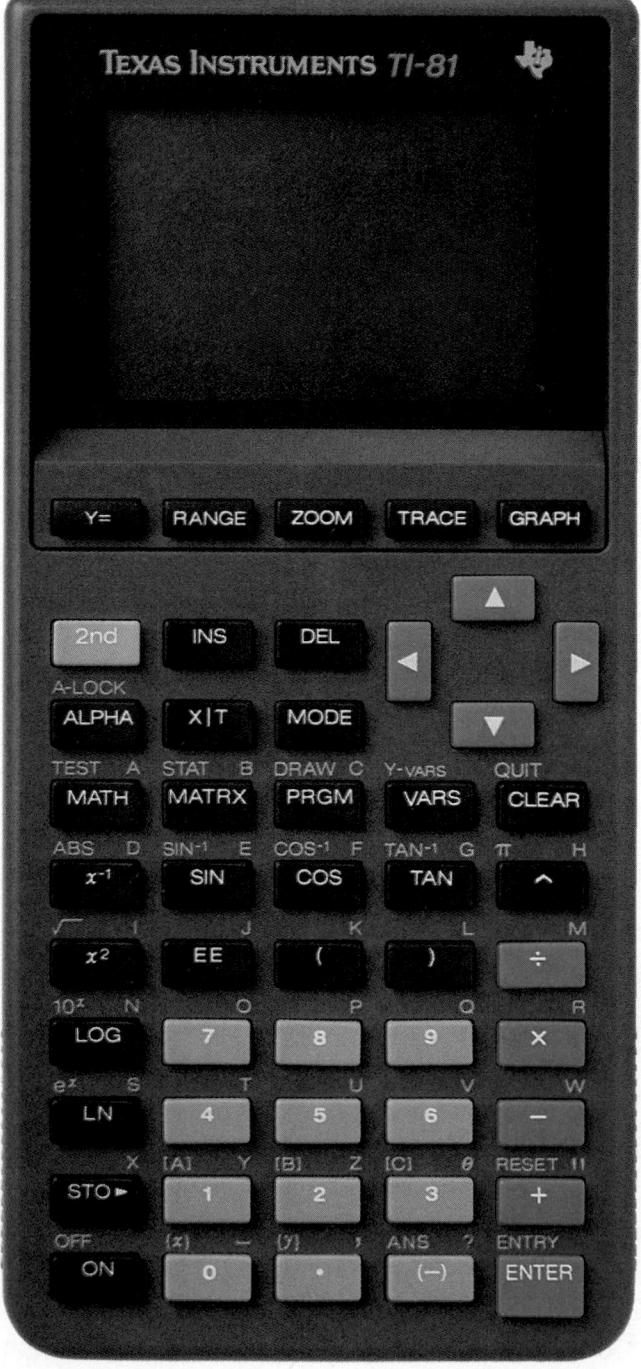

If you are graphing and having problems, check your range. Often an adjustment here will get rid of the problem. A blank screen often happens when you try to zoom or when the graph of the function is not in the range in which your calculator is set. Experimenting with different range values may be the solution here.

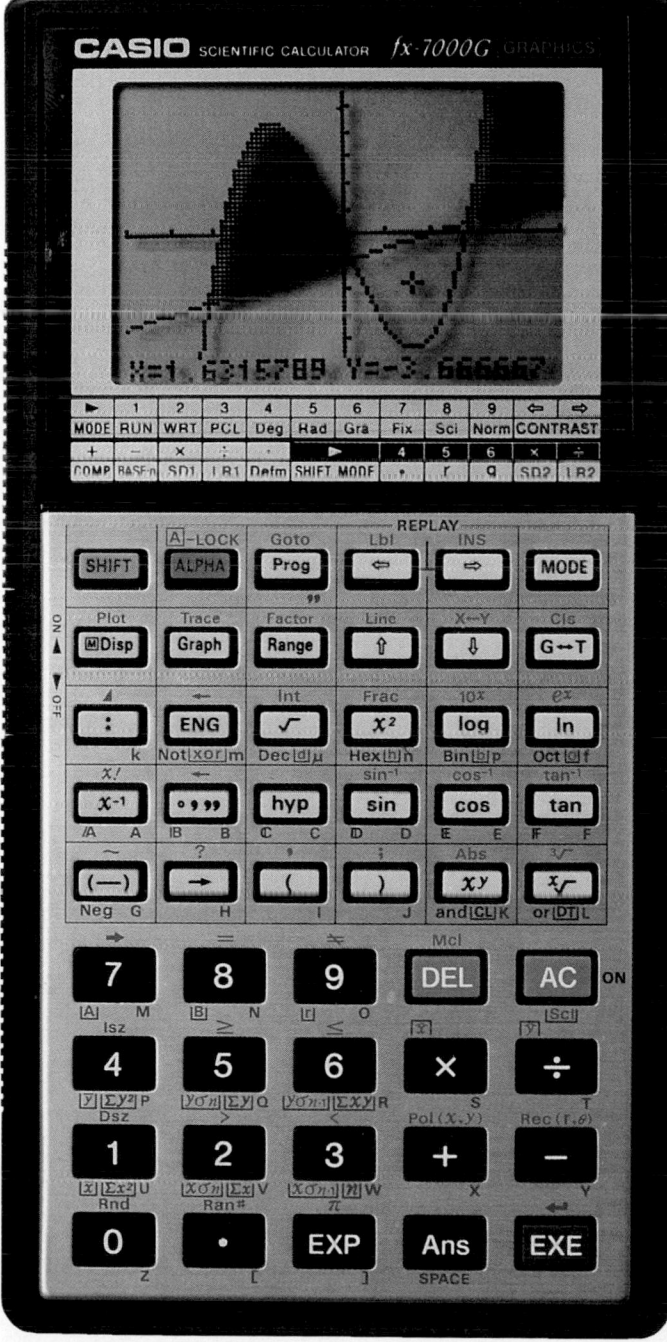

Teaching With the Graphing Calculator

Using the graphing calculator in your classroom will no doubt bring about some changes, if it hasn't done so for you already. There are some things that you can do to make teaching the use of the graphing calculator easier. For example, one of the most helpful teaching aids is an overhead transparency of the graphing calculator keyboard. If you are using the TI-81 graphing calculator, there is a picture of the calculator in the front of the TI-81 manual. You may want to make an enlarged copy of it and make a transparency of the keyboard from that. The *Merrill Algebra Lab Manual* (pages 9 and 10) also includes a master of both the TI-34 and the TI-81 calculator layout from which you can make a transparency. If you are using a Casio calculator, there is also a picture of it in the Casio manual.

Enlarging these pictures and making overlays of them will help you show your students where keys are if they are having trouble finding them or if you are explaining a lesson and need to demonstrate your keystrokes. You can also make a large poster of the calculator's keyboard and hang it in a visible location in the classroom. One of your students may like to do this for extra credit, or someone may just enjoy doing it.

Some of you may have begun teaching with a Casio graphing calculator and are now using TI-81 graphing calculators or a different type of Casio graphing calculator. If this is the case, you will notice that some things are different on each calculator. For example, the exponent key on the Casio is x^y, while on the TI-81 it is the $\wedge$ key.

Graphing calculators can often pique your students' curiosity about mathematics topics. You may begin to hear, "Why did it do that?" or "What's happening?" instead of "What's the answer?" or "I don't understand."

The locations of the arrow keys and trace key on the Casio *fx-7500G* are different from those of the Casio *fx-7000G*. While this may be confusing at first, it will probably not take too long for you to adjust to the new calculator. Finding new key locations or learning all of the new things the calculator can do may be the most difficult things you will have to deal with.

Using new or different calculators can also pose some difficulties if some of your students are still using the other ones. It will help if you know the keystrokes for both calculators so that you can translate one calculator's sequence into the other calculator's sequence. If this is not the case, then you can work with your student(s) to figure out a solution. Try to keep in mind that a solution is not impossible and even though the technology is not the same, the mathematical ideas and concepts that you convey to all your students will be.

The concept of "scale" will probably be one of the most difficult concepts for some of your students to understand and yet is one of the most important when working with graphs. You may want to use pictures and visuals to explain the concept. Ask your students if the range of [−10, 10] by [−10, 10] with a scale of 1 is different from [−20, 20] by [−20, 20] with a scale of 2. Look at each screen on a graphing calculator. Point out that even though the screens may look the same, they are actually extremely different. Try to get your students to get in the habit of checking their range and scale when they are looking at a graph and trying to interpret the information it gives them. Checking range and scale is also an important troubleshooting technique when problems occur.

Along these same lines, zoom in and zoom out are important problem-solving techniques for your students to learn, and there is a technique to

using them. There are a number of ways to zoom in and out. For example, you can manually change your range. In the problem $f(x) = x^3 - 3x^2 + 7$, you can approximate the zero of the function by initially graphing the function in the default viewing window of [−10, 10] by [−10, 10] with a scale of 1 along each axis and then changing this range to [−2, −1] by [−1, 1] with an x-scale of 0.1 and a y-scale of 0.2. You can then repeat this process as often as you like until you reach the desired accuracy, or until you reach the limits of the precision of the calculator.

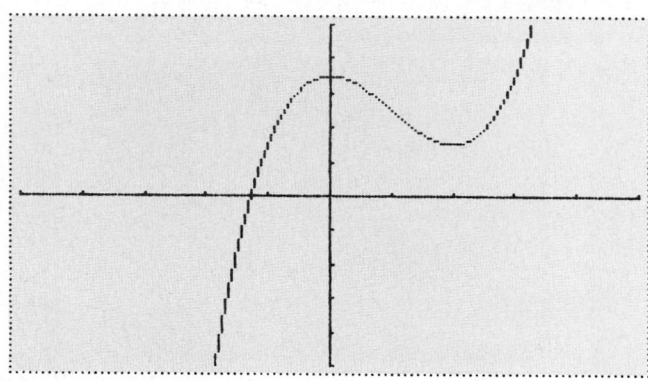

Another way to zoom is to use the ZOOM key on the TI-81. You have the option of zooming in by using a box, zooming in or out by setting factors, or by tracing along the function and zooming in or out at that point. Using the zoom box can be fun for your students because they create the box around the area they want to see. It is also a good way to solve certain problems, like finding the vertex of a parabola. Many times, zooming-in at a point will make it difficult to keep the shape of the function you are graphing. The more you zoom in, the more the function will look like a line as shown below.

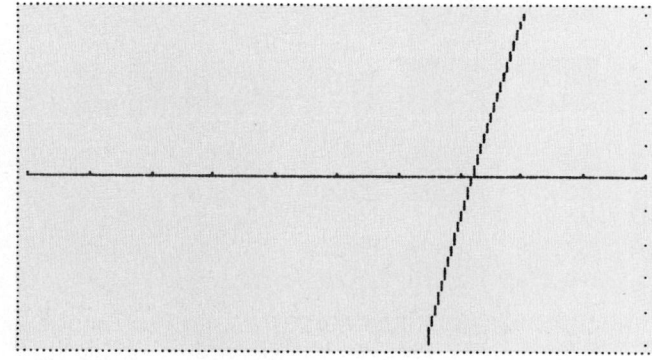

The graphing calculator allows you to look at many new areas of mathematics that until now were restricted at this level because of difficulty.

Teaching your students to know when and how to use a graphing calculator to solve problems will help your students become better problem solvers, and in the end this is what we really want them to become.

Using the zoom box can help you keep the correct shape, even at very small range values. For finding the vertex of a parabola, you can make square boxes around the vertex and the parabolic shape remains. If you make thin rectangles around the vertex, the function will look like a line very quickly. Your students will need to experiment with this to understand. It may help them if you point out that the box they create will be the next screen of the calculator.

Zooming in or out on a point by factors can be done on both the TI-81 and the Casio. On the TI-81, you use [ZOOM] 4 to set your factors and then zoom in or out. You cannot set your factors for a value less than one. If you try, the calculator will give you an error message. Zooming by a factor of one actually does not zoom at all. It merely redraws the graph in the same viewing window. On the Casio, you can use the [TRACE] key to move to a point on the graph and then press [SHIFT] [X] to zoom in at that point or [SHIFT] [÷] to zoom

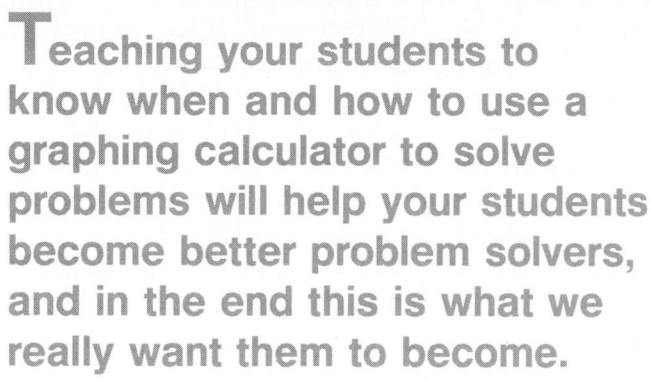

out at that point. The [Factor] key can be also be used here. Inserting " [Factor] (a value) [:] " before the command to graph a function will make the calculator zoom in or out. If the value is greater than one, the calculator will zoom in, and if the value is less than one, the calculator will zoom out.

Why Use It?

The graphing calculator offers you much more flexibility than before. Some people may not understand that it is okay to solve problems with a calculator and that most of the time the calculator does not "find the answer" for you but merely helps you to find appropriate solutions to problems. If you do not understand how to interpret the information the calculator provides, it will be of no use to you. For example, if you look at the graph of a line and ask what the slope of the graph is, some students may tell you they do not know how to find it. Still others will look at 2.718281828 . . . and not recognize it at the decimal approximation of e. It is still up to you as the teacher to make connections with the technology and to teach with it. The calculator simply saves time and effort and allows you to go deeper into mathematical concepts with your students than you could in the past.

It is also difficult for some people to understand that solving problems graphically is not cheating. It may seem like it is since it is so much easier than solving problems algebraically. However, they forget that we have been solving linear functions algebraically for years, and we have been using graphs of linear equations to help explain the algebra of linear functions. Why not do the same with quadratics, cubics, fourth-degree polynomials, and so on? With the graphing calculator, now we can. We can look at the "too hard to draw by hand" functions which in the past have been too tedious, too time-consuming, and too difficult to draw. Now with graphing calculators, we can solve problems graphically and use these pictorial representations to help us understand the algebraic representations. Both are important. Both should be addressed and related to each other in a mathematics classroom.

It may be difficult at times to know when to "say when" with the graphing calculator. For most practical purposes, accuracy of solutions to two or three decimal places is often sufficient,

and we can spend too much time finding solutions that are "too technical" if we are not specific with our students as to what we want from them. Your students may find it fun, however, to try to push the machine as far as it can go a few times, and then try to go beyond that point. If necessary, the graphing calculator can find solutions to problems with ten-digit accuracy. Knowing the limits of the machine will help your students understand what they can and cannot expect of it. Trying to get them to understand these limits, to understand what the calculator is doing, and what it is telling them is very important.

It may be difficult for each of your students to have their own graphing calculator. If this is a problem, you can have your students work in pairs like lab partners. Even if each of your students has his or her own graphing calculator, there are times when you may want to have them work together anyway. This can often lead to students answering other students' questions and solving problems on their own. You can also have them work in small groups on some of the graphing calculator lessons. If some students are having difficulty with the material, those students who understand it can help explain the concepts in this situation.

This may change your role in the classroom. You may realize that instead of being an instructor to your students you become a guide for your students. Graphing calculators can often pique your students' curiosity about mathematics topics, and they will begin to experiment themselves. You may begin to hear, "Why did it do that?" or "What's happening?" instead of "What's the answer?" or "I don't understand." Your students will actually begin to retain the mathematical content more since they explored and investigated the concepts for themselves.

As was mentioned, some of your students will begin to "take off" with the calculator and try to explore almost everything that it can do. Some may become interested in looking at the programming aspect of the calculator, which you can use to your advantage. For example, you can have some of the students write a program that you could use in one of your classes, like looking at prime factorization. The manual that accompanies the graphing calculator can help get them started, and they may be able write several useful programs for you to use in your classes.

The graphing calculator allows you to look at many new areas of mathematics that until now were restricted at this level because of difficulty. While it may take time to feel comfortable with using graphing calculators in your classroom, and you may be just beginning to learn how to use them, it is important to keep trying and to keep learning. Teaching your students to know when and how to use a graphing calculator to solve problems will help your students become better problem solvers, and in the end this is what we really want them to become. ■

For more information on using graphing calculators, see Glencoe's *Graphing Calculator Instruction Guide*, 1994.

Notes and Ideas on Using the Graphing Calculator

Meeting Individual Needs

"We cannot afford to have the majority of our population mathematically illiterate: Equity has become an economic necessity."

NCTM Standards (1989, p. 4)

Multicultural Perspective

There is no doubt that the United States is a multicultural society. Changing demographics, and changing economic and social orders are having a tremendous impact on the schools in this country. But, the term *multicultural* represents more than just *many cultures*. There is a multicultural basis to all knowledge, even mathematics.

From the ancient Egyptians, who used the "Pythagorean" theorem fifteen hundred years *before* Pythagoras, to the ancient Chinese, who calculated the value of π to ten places twelve hundred years *before* the Europeans, mathematics as we know it today has been shaped by many cultures. Even the term *algebra* was contributed by an Arabian mathematician, Al-Khowarizmi.

What is the role of the mathematics educator in all this? Students should have the opportunity to learn about persons from all cultures who have contributed to the development of mathematics. In addition, students should learn about persons from all cultures who have been successful in their respective careers. To this end, the *Merrill Algebra Activities Masters Booklet* contains one multicultural worksheet for each chapter.

As educators, we also must prepare all students for the new jobs of the future that will require mathematical literacy. The mathematics teacher must be in the vanguard of those who demand that *all* students be given the opportunity to study the more advanced forms of mathematics. It is our responsibility as educators to make every effort to prepare the students of today to participate in the complex world of tomorrow.

Limited English Proficiency Needs

One of the greatest factors contributing to the under-achievement in mathematics education for the language-minority student is his or her failure to understand the language of instruction. There are, however, strategies which the mathematics teacher can employ to help overcome the obstacles that beset language-minority students.

Ideally, these students would be afforded the opportunity of having new concepts and skills reinforced by discussing them in their native tongue. It may be that a bilingual teacher could meet this need, or perhaps a tutor proficient in the language could be procured to provide such service.

If the student is proficient in his or her native language, perhaps materials written in that language could be provided to supplement classroom instruction.

If the student is not especially literate in his or her own language, perhaps an oral approach using pictorial materials and/or manipulative devices would be feasible.

When a student does not respond to the prescribed expectations of the school, the teacher needs to substitute developmentally equivalent tasks to shape development. If, for example, the student does not participate in classroom discussion, the wise teacher will observe his or her verbal interaction with other students in informal, less structured environments.

Because students coming from diverse cultural backgrounds lack common educational experiences, the teacher soon recognizes that the only way to establish a basis for communication is to begin instruction with content that is familiar to one and all.

"The challenge is to find personally interesting and culturally relevant ways of creating new contexts for children, contexts in which the mastery of school skills can be meaningful and rewarding."[1]

By integrating the development of language in such new contexts, we may be able to open the door to the challenging and exciting world of mathematics for the language-minority student. ∎

1. Bowman, Barbara T., "Educating Language-Minority Children: Challenges and Opportunities," *Phi Delta Kappan*, October 1989, p. 120.

Alternative Assessment Strategies

Most students would agree that the test is often seen as the bottom line of educational enterprises. Most of them would also agree that the present tests used to determine a student's accomplishment often fall short of the goal of measuring a student's true understanding of the concepts being taught.

Most evaluation materials today include multiple-choice or true/false questions or questions that require objective one-word answers. These types of questions act as a mechanical means of evaluation that focuses on a student's ability to reiterate memorized and practiced definitions and procedures for solving each type of problem. This often does not accurately reflect the student's true capabilities and understanding.

"Mathematics teachers are participating in a major restructuring of the goals and practices of mathematics education. It is essential that assessment strategies be found that can adequately reflect this new conception of the subject."[1]

The purpose of assessment is to identify areas of weakness and strengths for individual students, to assign grades, to gather data for teachers to plan their course of instruction, and to evaluate the current course of instruction. The National Council of Teachers of Mathematics in its *Curriculum and Evaluation Standards for School Mathematics* (1989) suggests that different types of evaluation materials be used in making assessment. These evaluations are an ongoing process and are used to augment formal assessment, such as the traditional chapter test.

How Do I Begin?

Glencoe has provided many opportunities for you as a teacher to expand the avenues of assessment for your students. These are included in the *Student Edition, Teacher's Wraparound Edition,* and *Teacher's Classroom Resources.*

Some of the following suggestions may help you implement alternative forms of assessment in your classroom.

Open-ended Questions are perhaps the easiest way to employ a new evaluation strategy. In an assessment of this nature, students are forced to think for themselves and to express mathematical ideas in language that corresponds with their mathematical development.

- The *Communicating Mathematics* questions in each lesson ask students to interpret what they have read in the lesson.

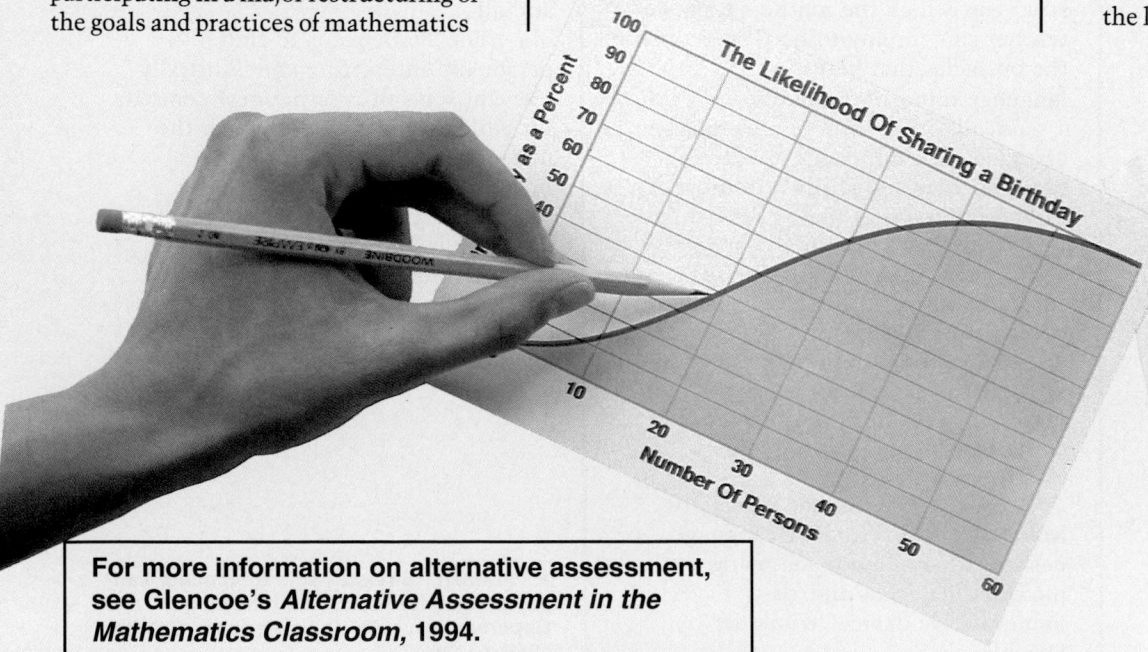

For more information on alternative assessment, see Glencoe's *Alternative Assessment in the Mathematics Classroom,* 1994.

> ## "Assessment must be more than testing; it must be a continuous, dynamic, and often informal process."
>
> *—NCTM Standards*

- Verbal questions in the *Exercises* often ask student to explain their answers rather than just giving a numerical response.
- *Critical Thinking* questions ask students to develop and apply higher order thinking skills.

Remember that when using open-ended questions, there may not be *one* correct answer, but rather an array of answers and explanations that are acceptable.

Classroom Observations are

another way of documenting student achievement. While observing your students at work, you often form quite accurate opinions concerning your students' capabilities.

- *Alternate Teaching Strategies* in the Teacher's Wraparound Edition suggests activities for use in observing students work.
- The *Cooperative Learning Activities* in the *Activity Masters* in the Teacher's Classroom Resources provide another opportunity for

watching students work together and for evaluating their understanding of the task at hand.

Performance Assessment is used to determine what students know and what they can do when presented with an authentic problem-solving situation.

- The *Performance Assessment* booklet in the Teacher's Classroom Resources contains student assessment items for each chapter, as well as scoring rubrics.

Questioning is an excellent tool for assessing the comprehension of students. Dialogue between you and your students is most beneficial in identifying comprehension errors and the use of process skills.

- *Guided Practice* questions in each lesson allow you to evaluate students' understanding before assigning homework.
- *Closing the Lesson* in the Teacher's Wraparound Edition asks students to summarize the lesson by using speech and writing.

Self-Evaluation permits students to monitor their own progress.

- The *Mid-Chapter Review* in the Student Edition gives students an opportunity to check their skills thus far in each chapter.
- The unique *Chapter Summary and Review* in the Student Edition allows students to review and practice concepts before a formal evaluation is

presented. The use of cooperative group instruction with this review not only provides students the opportunity to reinforce skills, but allows you to observe the strengths and weaknesses of students in an informal setting.

Portfolios are student collections of their work that are representative of their growth as a learner. A *Portfolio Suggestion* appears in one of the last lessons in each chapter.

Journal Entries allow students to express what they are learning. These may involve many different forms of expression such as graphs, drawings, models, and other explanations. Two *Journal Entry* features appear in each chapter.

Other Resources

In addition to the resources provided with the *Merrill Algebra 2 with Trigonometry* program, Glencoe publishes a *Mathematics Professional Series.* One of the booklets in this series, *Alternative Assessment in the Mathematics Classroom,* contains further information and activities to help you implement other types of evaluation strategies. ■

1. Clarke, David J., Doug M. Clarke, and Charles J. Lovitt, "Changes in Mathematics Teaching Call for Assessment Alternatives,: *Teaching and Learning Mathematics In the 1990s,* (1990 NCTM Yearbook, Reston, VA: NCTM, 1990), p. 118

Learning Objectives

1   Equations and Inequalities

1-1A: Use the order of operations to evaluate expressions.
1-1B: Use formulas.
1-2A: Determine if a number belongs to the set of natural numbers, integers, rational numbers, irrational numbers, or real numbers.
1-2B: Use the properties of real numbers to simplify expressions.
1-3: Solve equations using the properties of equality.
1-4A: Translate word expressions into mathematical expressions.
1-4B: Translate word sentences into equations.
1-4C: Use equations to solve problems.
1-5: Solve problems by making lists.
1-6: Solve equations containing absolute value.
1-7A: Use the properties of inequalities.
1-7B: Solve an inequality and graph the solution set.
1-7C: Use inequalities to solve problems.
1-8A: Identify and solve compound sentences using *and* and *or*.
1-8B: Solve absolute value inequalities.

2   Linear Relations and Functions

2-1A: Graph a relation, state its domain and range, and determine if the relation is a function.
2-1B: Find the values of functions for given elements of the domain.
2-2A: Identify equations that are linear and graph them.
2-2B: Write linear equations in standard form.
2-3: Solve a problem by identifying the pattern and using it to find the missing information.
2-4A: Determine the slope and intercepts of a line.
2-4B: Use the slope and intercepts to graph a line.
2-4C: Determine if two lines are parallel, perpendicular, or neither.
2-5A: Write the slope-intercept form of an equation given the slope and a point, or two points.
2-5B: Write the standard form of an equation given the slope and a point or two points.

2-5C: Write the equation of a line that is parallel or perpendicular to the graph of a given equation.
2-6A: Draw a scatter plot and find the prediction equation.
2-6B: Solve problems using prediction equations.
2-7: Identify and graph special functions (direct variation, constant, identify, absolute value, and greatest integer).
2-8A: Draw graphs of inequalities in two variables.
2-8B: Write an inequality to solve problems.

3   Systems of Equations and Inequalities

3-1: Solve a system of equations by graphing.
3-2A: Use the substitution method to solve a system of equations.
3-2B: Use the elimination method to solve a system of equations.
3-3A: Find the value of a second order determinant.
3-3B: Solve a system of equations using Cramer's Rule.
3-4A: Graph a system of inequalities.
3-4B: Solve a system of inequalities.
3-5: Solve problems using the strategy of solving a simpler problem.
3-6: Find the maximum and minimum values of a function over a region using linear programming techniques.
3-7: Solve problems involving maximum and minimum values using linear programming techniques.
3-8A: Determine the octant in which a point in space is located.
3-8B: Graph linear equations in space and determine the intercepts and traces.
3-9: Solve a system of equations in three variables.

4   Matrices

4-1: Solve problems using matrix logic.
4-2A: Create a matrix and name it using its dimensions.

4-2B: Perform scalar multiplication on a matrix.
4-2C: Add matrices.
4-2D: Find unknown values in equal matrices.
4-3A: Evaluate the determinant of a 3 x 3 matrix.
4-3B: Find the area of a triangle given the coordinates of its vertices.
4-4: Multiply two matrices and interpret the results.
4-5A: Write the identity matrix for any matrix.
4-5B: Find the inverse matrix of a 2 x 2 matrix.
4-6: Write a system of linear equations as a matrix and use the inverse to solve the system.
4-7: Use Cramer's Rule to solve a system of linear equations in three variables.
4-8: Solve a system of equations using an augmented matrix.

5 Polynomials

5-1A: Multiply monomials and powers of monomials.
5-1B: Represent numbers in scientific notation.
5-2A: Divide monomials.
5-2B: Divide expressions written in scientific notation.
5-3: Solve problems by using a diagram.
5-4A: Add polynomials.
5-4B: Subtract polynomials.
5-4C: Multiply polynomials.
5-5: Factor polynomials.
5-6: Divide polynomials using factoring and long division.
5-7: Divide polynomials using synthetic division.

6 Roots

6-1A: Simplify radicals having various indices.
6-1B: Use a calculator to estimate roots of numbers.
6-2A: Simplify radical expressions using multiplication and division.
6-2B: Rationalize the denominator of a fraction containing a radical expression.
6-3: Add, subtract, multiply, and divide radical expressions.
6-4A: Write expressions with rational exponents in simplest radical form and vice versa.
6-4B: Evaluate expressions in either exponential or radical form.
6-5: Solve problems by identifying and achieving subgoals.
6-6: Simplify expressions containing rational exponents.
6-7: Solve equations containing radicals.
6-8A: Simplify radicals containing negative radicands.
6-8B: Multiply pure imaginary numbers.
6-8C: Solve quadratic equations that have pure imaginary solutions.
6-9: Add, subtract, and multiply complex numbers.
6-10: Simplify rational expressions containing complex numbers in the denominator.

7 Quadratic Equations

7-1: Solve problems using the guess-and-check strategy.
7-2A: Solve quadratic equations by graphing.
7-2B: Solve quadratic equations by factoring.
7-3: Solve quadratic equations by completing the square.
7-4A: Solve quadratic equations using the quadratic formula.
7-4B: Use the discriminant to determine the nature of the roots of a quadratic equation.
7-5A: Find the sum and product of the roots of a quadratic equation.
7-5B: Find all possible integral roots of a quadratic equation.
7-5C: Find a quadratic equation to fit a given condition.
7-6A: Solve third and fourth degree equations that contain a quadratic factor.
7-6B: Solve other nonquadratic equations that can be written in quadratic form.

8 Quadratic Relations and Functions

8-1A: Write functions in quadratic form.
8-1B: Identify the quadratic term, the linear term, and the constant term of a quadratic function.
8-2: Solve problems by using tables.
8-3: Graph quadratic equations of the form $y = (x - h)^2 + k$, and identify the vertex and the equations of the axis of symmetry of a parabola.
8-4A: Graph equations of the form $y = a(x - h)^2 + k$, and identify the vertex, the equation of the axis of symmetry, and the direction of the opening.
8-4B: Determine the equation of a parabola from given information about the graph.
8-5: Solve problems using quadratic equations.
8-6: Graph quadratic inequalities.
8-7: Solve quadratic inequalities in one variable.

9 Conics

9-1A: Find the distance between two points in the coordinate plane.
9-1B: Find the midpoint of a line segment in the coordinate plane.
9-2A: Write equations of parabolas.
9-2B: Graph parabolas from given information.
9-3A: Write equations of circles.
9-3B: Draw a circle having certain properties.
9-4A: Write equations of ellipses.
9-4B: Draw an ellipse having certain properties.
9-5A: Write equations of hyperbolas.

9-5B: Draw hyperbolas.

9-6: Use a simulation to help solve problems.

9-7A: Write the equation of a conic section in standard form.

9-7B: Identify a conic section from its equation.

9-8: Graph systems of quadratic equations and identify the solution sets.

9-9A: Solve systems of equations algebraically.

9-9B: Solve systems of inequalities involving quadratics graphically.

10   Polynomial Functions

10-1A: Evaluate polynomial functions.

10-1B: Identify general shapes of the graphs of polynomial functions.

10-2: Find factors of polynomials using the Factor Theorem and synthetic division.

10-3: Solve problems by using more than one strategy.

10-4: Find the number of positive real zeros, negative real zeros, and complex zeros for a polynomial function.

10-5A: Identify all possible rational zeros of a polynomial function using the Rational Zero Theorem.

10-5B: Find zeros of polynomial functions.

10-6A: Approximate the real zeros of polynomial functions.

10-6B: Graph polynomial functions to find significant points.

10-7: Find the composition of functions.

10-8A: Determine the inverse of a function or relation.

10-8B: Graph a function and its inverse.

11   Rational Polynomial Expressions

11-1: Locate the asymptotes and sketch the graph of a rational function.

11-2: Solve problems involving direct, inverse, and joint variation.

11-3A: Simplify rational expressions.

11-3B: Simplify complex fractions.

11-4A: Find the least common denominator of two or more algebraic expressions.

11-4B: Add and subtract rational expressions.

11-5: Solve rational equations.

11-6: Solve problems by organizing data.

11-7: Use rational expressions to solve problems.

12   Exponential and Logarithmic Functions

12-1: Simplify expressions and solve equations involving real exponents.

12-2A: Write exponential equations in logarithmic form and vice versa.

12-2B: Evaluate logarithmic expressions.

12-2C: Solve equations involving logarithmic functions.

12-3: Solve equations or simplify and evaluate expressions using properties of logarithms.

12-4A: Identify the characteristic and the mantissa of a logarithm.

12-4B: Find common logarithms and antilogarithms.

12-5: Find natural logarithms of numbers.

12-6: Solve problems using estimation.

12-7: Solve equations with variable exponents using logarithms.

12-8: Use logarithms to solve problems.

13   Sequences and Series

13-1: Find the next number in a sequence.

13-2A: Find the nth term of an arithmetic sequence.

13-2B: Find the position of a given term in an arithmetic sequence.

13-2C: Find arithmetic means.

13-3A: Find sums of arithmetic series and find specific terms in the series.

13-3B: Use sigma notation to express the sum.

13-4A: Find the nth term of a geometric sequence.

13-4B: Find the position of a given term in a geometric sequence.

13-4C: Find geometric means.

13-5A: Find sums of geometric series, and find specific terms in the series.

13-5B: Use sigma notation to express the sum.

13-6: Find the sum of an infinite geometric series.

13-7A: Expand powers of binomials using Pascal's triangle and the Binomial Theorem.

13-7B: Find specific terms of the binomial expansion.

14   Statistics

14-1: Solve problems by organizing data and making graphs.

14-2A: Represent data using line plots and stem-and-leaf plots.

14-2B: Read and interpret data from line plots and stem-and-leaf plots.

14-3A: Find the median, mode, and mean of sets of data.

14-3B: Use the median, mode, and mean to interpret data.

14-4A: Find the range and interquartile range for a set of data.

14-4B: Determine if any values in a set of data are outliers.

14-5: Represent data using box-and-whisker plots.

14-6: Find the standard deviation for a set of data.

14-7: Solve problems involving normally distributed data.

15 Probability

15-1: Solve problems by using models.
15-2: Solve problems using the Basic Counting Principle.
15-3: Solve problems involving permutations.
15-4: Solve problems involving circular permutations.
15-5: Solve problems involving combinations.
15-6: Find the probability of an event and determine the odds of success or failure.
15-7: Find the probability of two or more independent or dependent events.
15-8: Find the probability of mutually exclusive events or inclusive events.
15-9A: Use simulation to solve various probability problems.
15-9B: Use binomial experiments to find probabilities.

16 Trigonometric Functions

16-1A: Change radian measure to degree measure and vice versa.
16-1B: Identify coterminal angles.
16-2A: Find the least possible angle that is coterminal to a given angle.
16-2B: Find the values of expressions involving sine and cosine.
16-3: Find the values of other trigonometric functions.
16-4: Find the values of expressions involving trigonometric functions.
16-5: Use a calculator to find values of trigonometric functions.
16-6A: Use right triangles to find trigonometric values.
16-6B: Solve problems involving right triangles using right triangle trigonometry.

16-7: Solve word problems using right triangle trigonometry.
16-8: Solve triangles and problems using the Law of Sines.
16-9: Determine, from a given set of information, the number of possible solutions and solve the triangle if solutions do exist.
16-10: Solve triangles and problems using the Law of Cosines.

17 Trigonometric Identities and Equations

17-1A: Graph trigonometric functions.
17-1B: Find the amplitude and period for variations of the sine and cosine functions.
17-2: Use trigonometric identities to simplify and/or evaluate expressions.
17-3: Verify trigonometric identities using various methods.
17-4: Solve problems using the strategy of working backwards.
17-5A: Find values of sine and cosine involving sum and difference formulas.
17-5B: Verify identities using the sum and difference formulas.
17-6A: Find values of sine and cosine involving half- and double-angles.
17-6B: Verify identities using half- and double-angle formulas.
17-7: Solve trigonometric equations.
17-8A: Convert numbers in the rectangular form to polar form and vice versa.
17-8B: Multiply complex numbers in polar form.
17-8C: Apply DeMoivre's Theorem.

Planning Your Algebra Course

The charts below give suggested time schedules for three types of courses: I, II, and III, and for two types of grading periods: 9-week and 6-week.

Course I covers Chapters 1–13. It allows for extra time for longer sessions and for reteaching and review. Course II covers Chapters 1–15. Generally, one day is allotted for each lesson, the Chapter Review, and the Chapter Test. Course III covers Chapter 1–17. This course is intended for students who master concepts quickly and retain skills well.

COURSE PLANNING CALENDAR
6-Week Grading Periods

Grading Period	TYPE OF COURSE					
	I		**II**		**III**	
	Chapter	Days	Chapter	Days	Chapter	Days
1	1 2	12 13	1 2 3 (Lessons 3-1 to 3-6)	11 11 6	1 2 3	9 10 10
2	3 4	14 14	3 (Lesson 3-7 to end) 4 5	6 12 10	4 5 6 (Lessons 6-1 to 6-4)	10 9 5
3	5 6	12 15	6 7 8 (Lessons 8-1 to 8-5)	13 9 6	6 (Lesson 6-5 to end) 7 8	7 8 8
4	7 8 9 (Lessons 9-1 to 9-6)	11 11 8	8 (Lesson 8-6 to end) 9 10	4 12 12	9 10 11	10 10 9
5	9 (Lesson 9-7 to end) 10 11	6 13 11	11 12 13 (Lessons 13-1 to 13-5)	10 11 5	12 13 14 15 (Lesson 15-1 to 15-3)	9 9 9 3
6	12 13	13 12	13 (Lesson 13-6 to end) 14 15	5 10 12	15 (Lesson 15-4 to end) 16 17	8 12 10
Total Days		165		165		165

COURSE PLANNING CALENDAR
9-Week Grading Periods

Grading Period	TYPE OF COURSE					
	I		**II**		**III**	
	Chapter	Days	Chapter	Days	Chapter	Days
1	1 2 3	12 13 14	1 2 3 4 (Lessons 4-1 to 4-4)	11 11 12 5	1 2 3 4	9 10 10 10
2	4 5 6	14 12 15	4 (Lesson 4-5 to end) 5 6 7	7 10 13 9	5 6 7 8 9 (Lessons 9-1 to 9-5)	9 12 8 8 5
3	7 8 9 10 (Lessons 10-1 to 10-4)	11 11 14 6	8 9 10 11	10 12 12 10	9 (Lesson 9-6 to end) 10 11 12 13	5 10 9 9 9
4	10 (Lesson 10-5 to end) 11 12 13	7 11 13 12	12 13 14 15	11 10 10 12	14 15 16 17	9 11 12 10
Total Days		165		165		165

Although most school years consist of 180 days, this planning guide is based on 165 days per year. This time frame will allow for special events that may occur during the school day causing classes to be shortened or omitted and also for cancellation of school due to weather conditions.

SYMBOLS

a^n	the nth power of a		!	factorial
$|a|$	the absolute value of a		$f \circ g$	composition function f of g
$-a$	additive inverse of a or the opposite of a		$>$	is greater than
Cos^{-1}	Arccosine		$<$	is less than
$C(n, r)$	combinations of n elements taken r at a time		$\geq$	is greater than or equal to
$a + b\boldsymbol{i}$	complex number		$\leq$	is less than or equal to
$\circ$	degrees		$\log_b x$	the logarithm to the base b of x
det	determinant			
e	base of natural logarithms		$P(n, r)$	permutations of n things taken r at a time
$\in$	is an element of			
$\emptyset$	empty set		$\pm$	positive or negative
$=$	equals or is equal to		$\{\ \}$	set
$\neq$	does not equal		$\sqrt{\ }$	the principal square root of
$\approx$	approximately equal to			
$f(x)$	f of x or the value of f at x		$\sqrt[n]{\ }$	the nth root of
f^{-1}	inverse function of f		Σ	(sigma) summation symbol

INSIDE YOUR BOOK

Understanding the Lesson

Each chapter is organized into lessons to make learning manageable. The basic plan of the lesson is easy to follow, beginning with a relevant application, followed by the development of the mathematical concept with plenty of examples, and ending with various types of exercises for you to complete.

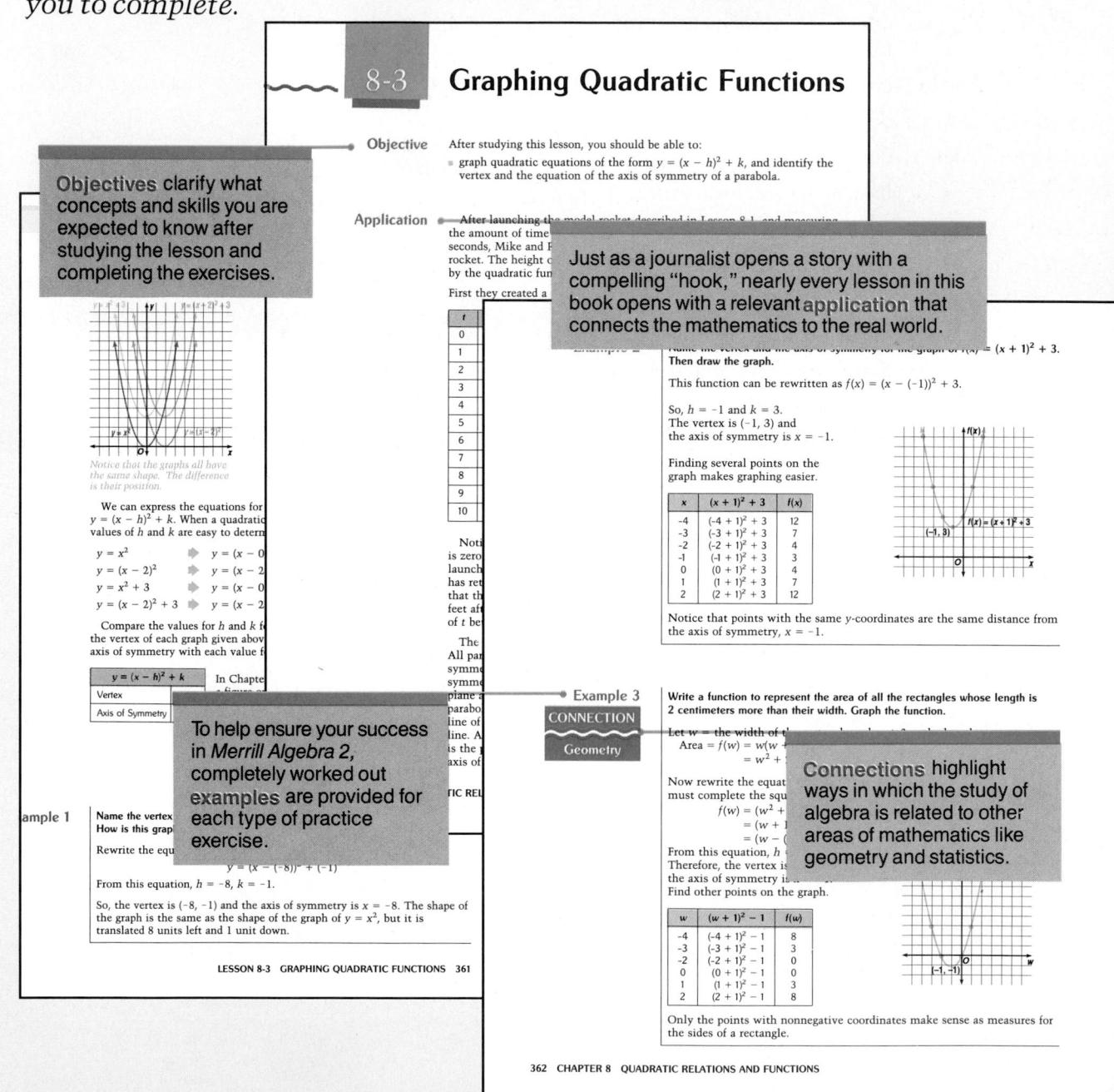

Objectives clarify what concepts and skills you are expected to know after studying the lesson and completing the exercises.

Just as a journalist opens a story with a compelling "hook," nearly every lesson in this book opens with a relevant application that connects the mathematics to the real world.

To help ensure your success in *Merrill Algebra 2*, completely worked out examples are provided for each type of practice exercise.

Connections highlight ways in which the study of algebra is related to other areas of mathematics like geometry and statistics.

8-3 Graphing Quadratic Functions

Objective

After studying this lesson, you should be able to:
- graph quadratic equations of the form $y = (x - h)^2 + k$, and identify the vertex and the equation of the axis of symmetry of a parabola.

Application

After launching the model rocket described in Lesson 8-1 and measuring the amount of time... seconds, Mike and... rocket. The height of... by the quadratic fun...

First they created a...

t	
0	
1	
2	
3	
4	
5	
6	
7	
8	
9	
10	

Notice that the graphs all have the same shape. The difference is their position.

We can express the equations for $y = (x - h)^2 + k$. When a quadratic... values of h and k are easy to determ...

$y = x^2$ ➡ $y = (x - 0$
$y = (x - 2)^2$ ➡ $y = (x - 2$
$y = x^2 + 3$ ➡ $y = (x - 0$
$y = (x - 2)^2 + 3$ ➡ $y = (x - 2$

Compare the values for h and k f... the vertex of each graph given abov... axis of symmetry with each value f...

$y = (x - h)^2 + k$
Vertex
Axis of Symmetry

ample 1 | Name the vertex... How is this grap...

Rewrite the equ...

$$y = (x - (-8))^2 + (-1)$$

From this equation, $h = -8$, $k = -1$.

So, the vertex is $(-8, -1)$ and the axis of symmetry is $x = -8$. The shape of the graph is the same as the shape of the graph of $y = x^2$, but it is translated 8 units left and 1 unit down.

LESSON 8-3 GRAPHING QUADRATIC FUNCTIONS 361

Name the vertex and the axis of symmetry for the graph of $f(x) = (x + 1)^2 + 3$. Then draw the graph.

This function can be rewritten as $f(x) = (x - (-1))^2 + 3$.

So, $h = -1$ and $k = 3$.
The vertex is $(-1, 3)$ and the axis of symmetry is $x = -1$.

Finding several points on the graph makes graphing easier.

x	$(x + 1)^2 + 3$	$f(x)$
-4	$(-4 + 1)^2 + 3$	12
-3	$(-3 + 1)^2 + 3$	7
-2	$(-2 + 1)^2 + 3$	4
-1	$(-1 + 1)^2 + 3$	3
0	$(0 + 1)^2 + 3$	4
1	$(1 + 1)^2 + 3$	7
2	$(2 + 1)^2 + 3$	12

Notice that points with the same y-coordinates are the same distance from the axis of symmetry, $x = -1$.

Example 3

CONNECTION

Geometry

Write a function to represent the area of all the rectangles whose length is 2 centimeters more than their width. Graph the function.

Let w = the width of...
Area $= f(w) = w(w + ...$
$= w^2 + ...$

Now rewrite the equat... must complete the squ...
$f(w) = (w^2 + ...$
$= (w + ...$
$= (w - ($
From this equation, h...
Therefore, the vertex is...
the axis of symmetry is...
Find other points on the graph.

w	$(w + 1)^2 - 1$	$f(w)$
-4	$(-4 + 1)^2 - 1$	8
-3	$(-3 + 1)^2 - 1$	3
-2	$(-2 + 1)^2 - 1$	0
0	$(0 + 1)^2 - 1$	0
1	$(1 + 1)^2 - 1$	3
2	$(2 + 1)^2 - 1$	8

Only the points with nonnegative coordinates make sense as measures for the sides of a rectangle.

362 CHAPTER 8 QUADRATIC RELATIONS AND FUNCTIONS

CHECKING FOR UNDERSTANDING

Communicating Mathematics

Read and study the lesson to answer these questions.

1. Did the model rocket described in the beginning of the lesson reach its maximum height 5 seconds after launch? Justify the answer.
2. The graph of a quadratic function is a ___?___. It is symmetric about a line called the ___?___.
3. Write a quadratic function whose graph has a vertex in the third quadrant.
4. Compare the graphs of the functions $f(x) = (x - 2)^2 + 2$ and $f(x) = (x + 2)^2 + 2$.
5. Write the equation of the function whose graph is shown at the right.

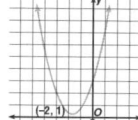

$(-2, 1)$

Guided Practice

Name the vertex and the axis of symmetry for the graph of each equation.

6. $f(x) = x^2$ 7. $g(x) = (x - 4)^2$ 8. $f(x) = (x + 6)^2$

9. $h(x) = x^2 + 3$ 10. $f(x) - x^2$ 9   11. $y = (x - 6)^2 + 4$

12. $y = (x + 10)^2 - 7$ 13. $y = \left(x - \frac{1}{5}\right)^2 + 1$ 14. $f(x) = (x + 1.5)^2 - 3.2$

Write the equation of the quadratic function for each graph.

15.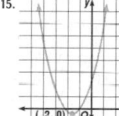

$(-2, 0)$

16.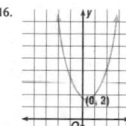

$(0, 2)$

Write each equation in the form $f(x) = (x - h)^2 + k$. Then name the vertex and the axis of symmetry for the graph of each function.

Graph each equation.

27. $y = (x - 5)^2$ 28. $y = (x + 7)^2$

29. $f(x) = x^2 + 6$ 30. $g(x) = x^2 - 4$

31. $y = (x - 3)^2 + 5$ 32. $f(x) = (x - 8)^2 + 3$

33. $g(x) = (x + 2)^2 - 3$ 34. $y = (x + 4)^2 + 1$

35. $f(x) = (x - 1)^2 - 4$ 36. $y = (x + 11)^2 - 1$

37. $y = x^2 + 6x + 2$ 38. $f(x) = x^2 + 10x + 27$

39. $g(x) = x^2 - 2x + 7$ 40. $y = x^2 + 3x$

41. $h(x) = x^2 - 5x$ 42. $f(x) = x^2 - x - 3$

TIC FUNCTIONS 363

Critical Thinking

Complete the following table for parabolas with equations of the form $y = (x - h)^2 + k$.

	Axis of Symmetry	Contains the Point	Vertex	Equation of the Parabola
43.	$x = 0$	$(2, -1)$		
44.	$x = -2$	$(-5, 9)$		
45.	$x = -3$	$(1, 18)$		
46.	$x = 1$	$(-1, -2)$		

Applications

47. **Physics** An arrow is shot upward with an initial velocity of 80 feet per second. The [...] the time since the arro[...]
   a. Draw the graph of th[...] arrow to the time.
   b. How long after the a[...] height? What is that [...]

48. **Sports** Shawn hit a fo[...] the ball over the level o[...] $- 16t^2$, where t is the t[...]
   a. Draw the graph of th[...] level of the bat to th[...]
   b. If the catcher is going to attempt to catch the ball, how long does she have to get ready?
   c. Where is the ball when the height found by the function is zero?

Mixed Review

49. Identify the quadratic term, the linear term, and the constant term of the function $f(x) = 4x^2 - 8x$ [...]
50. Find a quadratic equation hav[...]
51. Simplify $\sqrt[3]{2}(3\sqrt[3]{4} + 2\sqrt[3]{32})$.
52. Find the degree of the polynom[...] **(Lesson 5-4)**
53. Determine the slope of the lin[...] $(-3, 9)$. **(Lesson 2-4)**

364 CHAPTER 8 QUADRATIC RELATIONS AND FUNCTIONS

Getting into the Chapter

The list of **chapter objectives** lets you know what you can expect to learn in the chapter.

Detailed information about each career is given as well as an address where you may write to obtain even more information about the career.

CHAPTER 12

Exponential and Logarithmic Functions

CHAPTER OBJECTIVES

In this chapter, you will:
- Solve equations involving logarithmic and exponential functions.
- Find common and natural logarithms of numbers.
- Solve problems using estimation.
- Use logarithms to solve problems.

CAREERS IN SYSTEMS ANALYSIS

The world depends on computers today, depends on them far more than anyone have believed possible even thirty years ago. Research, business, government, education, sports, entertainment—almost every compa every field now has a computer system to he function and grow. Thus it follows that the

If the ant is $\frac{3}{8}$ inch long, estimate the s microchip.

544

You will be introduced to many different **careers** that are available to you after graduation from college.

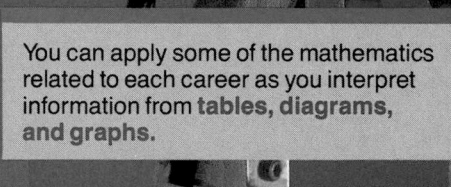

You can apply some of the mathematics related to each career as you interpret information from **tables, diagrams, and graphs.**

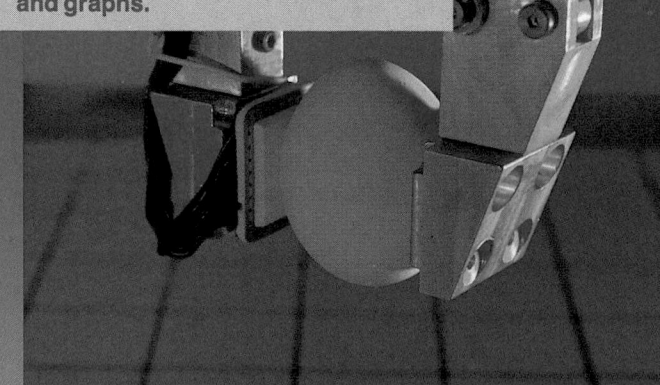

MORE ABOUT SYSTEMS ANALYSIS

Degree Required
Bachelor's degree in Computer Science

Some systems analysts like:
- challenge and variety in their work
- good employment opportunities
- good salaries
- interaction with people in solving problems

Related Math Subjects:
Advanced Algebra
Geometry
Statistics/Probability

Some systems analysts dislike:
- the need to update their knowledge with advances in technology
- working overtime to meet deadlines
- frustrating problems in computer programming

For more information on the various careers available in the field of Systems Analysis, write to:

Association of the Institute for Certification of Computer Professionals
2200 East Devon Avenue
Suite 268
Des Plaines, IL 60018

545

Wrapping Up the Chapter

VOCABULARY

Upon completing this chapter you should be
familiar with the following terms:

Complex Conjugates Theorem	471	451	polynomial function
composition of functions	487	450	polynomial in one va...
depressed polynomial	461	475	Rational Zero Theore...
Descartes' rule of signs	471	483	relative maximum
Factor Theorem	461	483	relative minimum
Fundamental Theorem of Algebra	469	459	Remainder Theorem
Integral Zero Theorem	475	469	root of polynomial equation
inverse function	491	460	synthetic substitution
inverse relation	493	469	zero of polynomial function
Location Principle	482		

Each Chapter Summary and Review opens with a listing of vocabulary words that were introduced in the chapter. You can use these to check your understanding of the chapter.

...IEW EXERCISES

...on, state the number of
...os, negative real zeros, and

$- x^3 + 5x^2 + 3x - 9$
$+ 5x - 1$
$- x^2 - x - 1$
$x^3 - 7x + 1$

...n changes, there are 2
...ros.

$+ 8x + 12$

...gn changes, there are
...zeros.

SKILLS AND CONCEPTS

OBJECTIVES AND EXAMPLES

Upon completing this chapter, yo...
be able to
■ evaluate polynomial functions.
(Lesson 10-1)

Find $p(a + 1)$ if $p(x) = 5x - x^2$

$p(a + 1) = 5(a + 1) - (a + 1)^2$
$3(a + 1)^3$
$= 5a + 5 - (a^2 + 2a$
$+ 3(a^3 + 3a^2 + 3a +$
$= 3a^3 + 8a^2 + 12a +$

■ find factors of polynomials usin...
Factor Theorem and synthetic
division. (Lesson 10-2)

The second part of the Chapter Summary and Review helps you review the important skills and concepts you developed in the chapter. You can use the objectives and examples provided in the left column to help you complete the exercises in the right column.

REVIEW EXERC...

OBJECTIVES AND ...

determine the inverse of...
relation. (Lesson 10-8)

Two functions are invers...
both of the compositions are the identity
function. If one function contains the
element (a, b), then the other contains
(b, a).

$g(x) = \frac{}{3}$ $g(x) = \frac{}{2}$

...nal zeros for each function.

$- 13x^2 + 17x + 12$
$5x^3 + 15x^2 + 19x + 8$
$3x^2 - 10x + 24$
$28x + 15$

...est tenth the real
...hen use the
...l. the function.

$1x + 3$

...s, f and g, find

18. $f(x) = x^2 + 2$
    $g(x) = x - 3$

$(3, 2)$ and $g =$
..., express $f \circ g$ and $g \circ f$,
of ordered pairs.

The Applications and Connections problems help you connect the material to the world beyond your textbook.

APPLICATIONS AND CONNECTIONS

22. **Investments** Four years ago, Mr. and
Mrs. Moon bought an apartment
building for $200,000. Two years ago,
they bought an office building for
$500,000. They bought an ocean-front
beach house for $100,000 last
year. (Lesson 10-2)

 a. Assuming that the investments have
 appreciated at a rate of $x\%$ per year,
 write a polynomial function to
 represent the current worth of their
 investments.

 b. Find the total worth of their
 investments if they appreciated at a
 rate of 12% per year.

24. **Manufacturing** The DrinKone
Company makes paper cups that are
cone shaped. The volume of a cone is
about 7.07 cubic inches. The diameter
of the top of the cone is equal to the
height of the cone. Determine the
dimensions of the cone. (Lesson 10-5)
*Hint: The formula for the volume of a cone
is $V = \frac{1}{3}\pi r^2 h$*

25. **Geometry** The volume of a
rectangular solid is 2475 cubic units.
The length of the box is three units
more than twice the width of the box.
The height is two units less than the
width. Find the dimensions of the
box. (Lesson 10-4)

23. **Education** Craig, Vanessa, Devin, and
Anita attend Harding High School.
Each will be attending a different
school next year. They will attend the
DeVry Institute of Technology, Judson
College, The Juilliard School, and Case
Western Reserve. The student
attending DeVry will study electronics
and the student attending Juilliard will
study the cello. The student attending
Judson has not chosen a major and the
student attending Case Western
Reserve will study chemical
engineering. Neither Devin nor Anita
can play an instrument. Vanessa will
study electronics next year, but Anita
has not yet decided what to study.
Who will be attending which
school? (Lesson 10-3)

26. **Business** The CD Menagerie adds a
100% markup to the wholesale price of
compact discs before placing them in the
store for sale. If a CD is on sale for 20% off
and the customer pays $12 for it, what is its
wholesale price? (Lesson 10-7)

Equations and Inequalities

PREVIEWING THE CHAPTER

This chapter basically provides a well-developed review of the essential algebraic skills and concepts presented in Algebra 1, thereby providing a firm foundation on which students will construct a series of successful learning experiences throughout the year. After discussions on evaluating expressions and the properties of real numbers, the procedures for solving linear equations are reviewed and extended to solving inequalities. The number line is used as a mathematical model to review absolute value, and equations involving absolute values are solved. The chapter ends with work on solving compound sentences and inequalities involving absolute values.

Problem Solving Strategy Students learn to list the possibilities as an effective strategy for solving many non-routine problems.

Lesson Objective Chart

Lesson (Pages)	Lesson Objectives	State/Local Objectives
1-1 (8-12)	**1-1A:** Use the order of operations to evaluate expressions.	
	1-1B: Use formulas.	
1-2 (13-17)	**1-2A:** Determine if a number belongs to the set of natural numbers, integers, rational numbers, irrational numbers, or real numbers.	
	1-2B: Use the properties of real numbers to simplify expressions.	
1-3 (18-21)	**1-3:** Solve equations using the properties of equality.	
1-4 (24-28)	**1-4A:** Translate word expressions into mathematical expressions.	
	1-4B: Translate word sentences into equations.	
	1-4C: Use equations to solve problems.	
1-5 (29-30)	**1-5:** Solve problems by making lists.	
1-6 (31-35)	**1-6:** Solve equations containing absolute value.	
1-7 (36-40)	**1-7A:** Use the properties of inequalities.	
	1-7B: Solve an inequality and graph the solution set.	
	1-7C: Use inequalities to solve problems.	
1-8 (42-45)	**1-8A:** Identify and solve compound sentences using *and* and *or*.	
	1-8B: Solve absolute value inequalities.	

ORGANIZING THE CHAPTER

You may want to refer to the **Course Planning Calendar** on page T44.

Lesson (Pages)	Course I	Course II	Course III	Reteaching	Practice	Enrichment	Evaluation	Technology	Lab Manual	Mixed Problem Solving	Applications	Cooperative Learning Activity	Multicultural	Transparencies
1-1 (8-12)	1.5	1.5	1	p. 1	p. 1	p. 1								1-1
1-2 (13-17)	1.5	1.5	1	p. 2	p. 2	p. 2	Quiz A, p. 9	p. 1					p. 1	1-2
1-3 (18-21)	1	1	0.5	p. 3	p. 3	p. 3			pp. 33-34					1-3
1-4 (24-28)	1.5	1	1	p. 4	p. 4	p. 4	Quiz B, p. 9 Mid-Chapter Test, p. 13							1-4
1-5 (29-30)	1	1	0.5		p. 5					p. 1				1-5
1-6 (31-35)	1	1	1	p. 5	p. 6	p. 5	Quiz C, p. 10							1-6
1-7 (36-40)	1.5	1	1	p. 6	p. 7	p. 6		p. 18			p. 19			1-7
1-8 (42-45)	1	1	1	p. 7	p. 8	p. 7	Quiz D, p. 10					p. 37		1-8
Review (46-48)	1	1	1	Multiple Choice Tests, Forms 1A and 1B, pp. 1-4 Free Response Tests, Forms 2A and 2B, pp. 5-8										
Test (49)	1	1	1	Cumulative Review, pp. 11-12 Standardized Test Practice Questions, p. 14										

Course II: Chapters 1-13; Course II: Chapters 1-15; Course III: Chapters 1-17

Other Chapter Resources

Student Edition
Chapter Opener, pp. 6-7
Journal Entries, pp. 21, 35
Graphing Calculator Exploration, pp. 22-23
Mid-Chapter Review, p. 28
Cooperative Learning Activity, p. 30
History Connection, p. 35
Technology, p. 41
Portfolio Suggestion, p. 45
Extended Project 1, pp. A2-A5

Teacher's Classroom Resources
Transparency 1-0
Real-World Applications Transparencies, 1, 2
Performance Assessment Booklet, pp. 1-2
Problem-of-the-Week Activity Cards, 1, 2
Tech Prep Applications Booklet, pp. 1-2
Lesson Plans, pp. 1-8

Other Supplements
Glencoe Mathematics Professional Series

Software
Test and Review Generator Software (Apple, IBM, and Macintosh)
Interactive Software (Macintosh)
Teacher's Guide for Software Resources

ENHANCING THE CHAPTER

Cooperative Learning

An Overview
For successful cooperative-learning experiences, research (Johnson and Johnson) indicates that the teacher's responsibilities include:

1. Deciding on the size of the groups.
2. Assigning students to the groups.
3. Arranging the room.
4. Describing the subject-matter and cooperative-skills objectives.
5. Planning teaching materials to promote group interdependence.
6. Assigning roles to students in the group.
7. Explaining the specific task to be performed.
8. Describing the student's responsibilities to the group.
9. Establishing individual accountability.
10. Explaining the criteria for success.
11. Specifying desired student behaviors.
12. Monitoring students' behavior.
13. Providing task assistance.
14. Intervening to teach cooperative-learning skills.
15. Providing closure to the lesson.
16. Evaluating the quality of students' learning.
17. Assessing how well the group functioned.

Technology

The Technology Feature after Lesson 1-8 employs the *Mathematical Exploration Toolkit* (MET). MET is a powerful calculator, symbolic manipulator, and graphing utility for IBM and IBM compatible microcomputers. Students will need some help getting started with the MET program. HELP screens are available at any point in the program by pressing the F1 key. Features using MET will appear from time to time in this text. These features can serve to introduce students to MET's commands and capabilities.

MET offers an authoring language within the Defer Sequence mode. No previous programming experience is required. Defer Sequences can be used as classroom demonstrations or students' laboratory modules. Consult the MET manual to learn how to create Defer Sequences or to use those provided with the software package.

Critical Thinking

The development of critical thinking skills is crucial for any real understanding of the concepts presented in this course. Although there are numerous exercises so labeled throughout the text, you should look for additional opportunities to ask questions that encourage students to classify and compare, identify and extend patterns, make and test predictions, make generalizations and draw conclusions, make conjectures and draw inferences, clarify by giving specific examples, look for more than one solution, look for more than one way to arrive at a solution, justify a solution, and relate a situation to other situations.

Cooperative Learning, p. 37

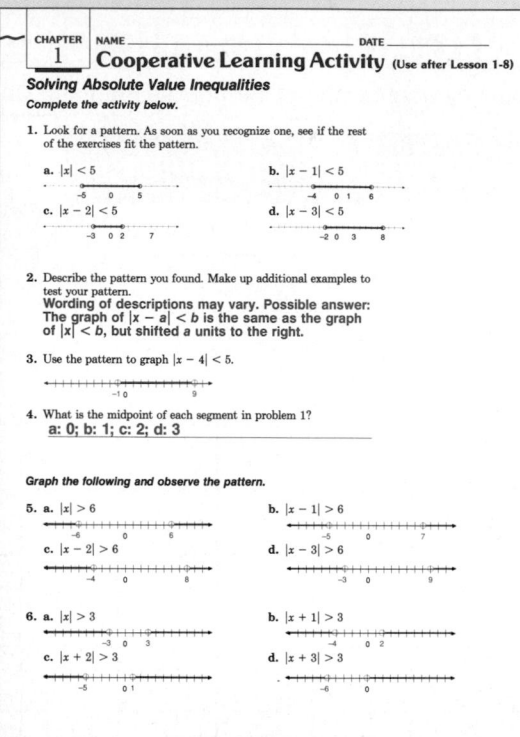

Technology, p. 1

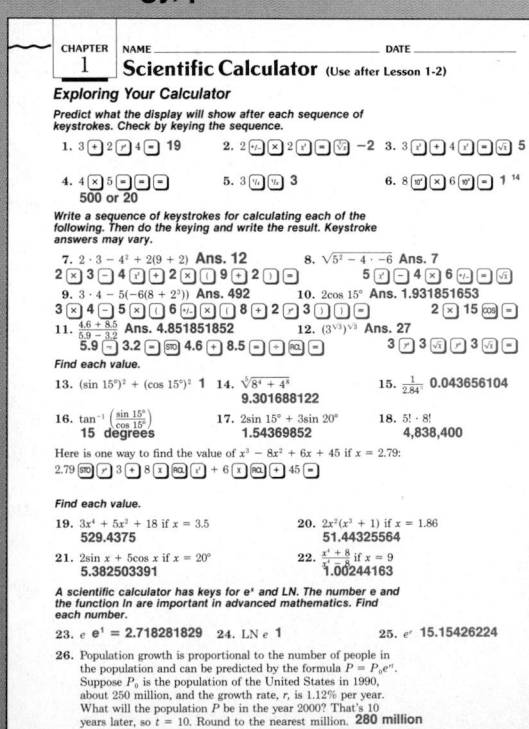

Problem of the Week Activity

The card shown below is one of two available for this chapter. It can be used as a class or small group activity.

Activity Card

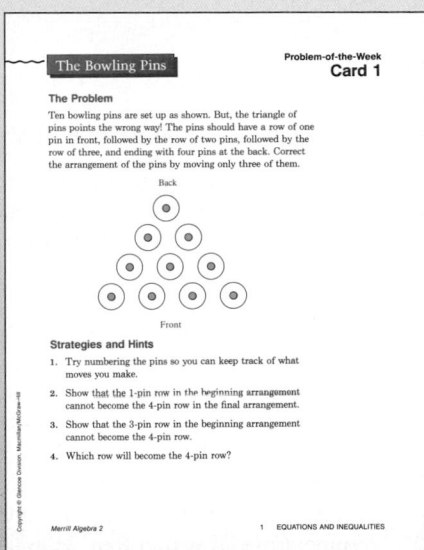

Manipulatives and Models

The following materials may be used as models or manipulatives in Chapter 1.

- rectangular prism (Lesson 1-1)
- cylinder (Lesson 1-1)
- square pyramid (Lesson 1-1)
- balance scale (Lesson 1-3)
- counters (Lesson 1-5)

Outside Resources

Books/Periodicals

Career Associates. *Career Choices - Mathematics.* Walker and Company, 1985.

National Council of Teachers of Mathematics. *Curriculum and Evaluation Standards for School Mathematics.* Reston, Va.: National Council of Teachers of Mathematics, 1989.

National Research Council. *Everybody Counts: A Report to the Nation on the Future of Mathematics Education.* Washington, D.C.: National Academy Press, 1989.

Films/Videotapes/Videodiscs

Computers: The Truth of the Matter, and *Computers: The Friendly Invasion,* Walt Disney Co. Educational Productions, 101 N. Brand Blvd., Glendale, CA 91203

Software

IBM Algebra Series, EduQuest, 4111 Northside Pkwy. NW, P.O. Box 2150, Atlanta, GA 30327-3015

Algebra Plus Volume One, Stone & Associates Software Publishing and Marketing, Inc., 7910 Ivanhoe Ave., La Jolla, CA 92037

Mathematics Exploration Toolkit, IBM, 4111 Northside Pkwy. NW, P.O. Box 2150, Atlanta, GA 30327-3015

Multicultural

Multicultural Activity, p. 1

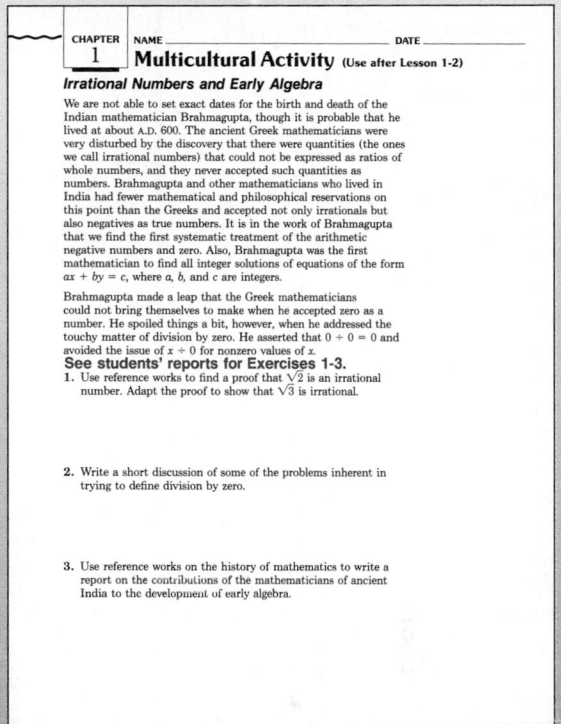

Lab Manual

Lab Activity, pp. 33-34

Background Information

Energy engineers use math to calculate heat loss and heat gain in buildings, energy usage, and building design efficiency. They generate graphs and control schedules, and design the electronic network for controlling electrical and mechanical equipment automatically. In addition to math, students should consider studying physics, chemistry, computer science, and some drafting. The projected demand for energy engineers in the 1990s looks good. They are also needed by electrical utility companies and in alternative energy areas such as solar and geothermal.

Equations and Inequalities

CHAPTER OBJECTIVES

In this chapter, you will:
- Use the properties of real numbers to simplify expressions.
- Solve equations using properties of equality.
- Solve inequalities and graph their solution sets.
- Solve absolute value equations and inequalities.

Notice the differences between the temperatures of occupied and unoccupied areas? Explain why you think the changes are greater in some areas than in others.

BUILDING TEMPERATURE RANGES								
	50	55	60	65	70	75	80	85
Classrooms								
Cafeteria								
Gymnasium								
Corridors								
Industrial								
Home Ec.								
Offices								
Auditorium								
Media Center								

Unoccupied ▬▬▬   Occupied ▬▬▬

6

CAREERS IN ENERGY ENGINEERING

A new generation of intelligent buildings are being "born"—and if you choose the career of energy engineer, you might be the obstetrician for one of them.

These buildings can sense and then adjust to changes in their environment very much like living beings can. Their brains are computer systems, managing the buildings' communications, security, and energy needs. For example, one new building in Boston, Massachusetts, has no fuel-burning furnaces at all, yet it maintains a comfortable indoor temperature all winter long. How? The computer-controlled energy management system circulates the heated air from sunny window sills and the heat generated by people and office machines—including lights and coffee makers.

Now, suppose one of these intelligent buildings develops a maintenance problem—maybe the air-conditioning compressors stop working early one Sunday morning in August. Though no one is in the building to notice the rising temperature and to telephone for repairs an energy engineer miles away has already noticed the system's overload on his or her monitor. Even though the Service Center for a dozen or more of these intelligent buildings may be hundreds of miles away from each building, the engineers on watch there can easily diagnose and correct the problem. It's a job with responsibility, will it one day be your job?

Chapter Project

Materials: Blueprints, graph paper, pencil and paper

Obtain blueprints of your school building from the maintenance department. Have students work in cooperative groups to draw a building floor plan to scale from the blueprints. Then have each group record on its floor plan the temperatures at which its members believe the thermostat in each area of the school *should* be set for heating (and air conditioning, if available) for occupied and unoccupied hours during weekdays, weekends, and vacations.

Have each group presents its floor plan, graphs, and findings to the class. Invite the maintenance supervisor to discuss methods being used for temperature control in the school.

Have each group generate a graph similar to the one in the chapter opener for each of these periods. Finally have each group check and compare their projected settings with the actual thermostat setting in each area of the building.

Connections and Applications

Lesson	Connections (C) and Applications (A)		Examples	Exercises
1-1	C:	Geometry	4	43-46, 50-51
	A:	Banking	5	39-42, 48
		Chemistry	6	
		Construction		49
1-2	C:	Statistics	3	
	A:	Business	3	
		Accounting		57
		Banking		61
1-3	C:	Geometry	8	
	A:	Banking		34
		Transporta-tion		35
1-4	C:	Geometry	4	
	A:	Construction	1	
		Travel	3	
		Entertain-ment		29
		Photography		30
1-6	A:	Manufactur-ing	5	43
		Cartography		42
1-7	A:	Finance	4	
		Manufactur-ing		47,48
1-8	A:	Broadcasting	5	
		Transporta-tion		48,49
		Manufactur-ing		50,51

MORE ABOUT ENERGY ENGINEERING

Degree Required:
- Bachelor's Degree in Electrical Engineering

Some energy engineers like:
- solving problems
- working in a new field that gives them opportunities to experiment and be creative
- the challenge in finding ways to conserve energy
- the variety and challenge of their work

Related Math Subjects:
- Geometry
- Trigonometry
- Advanced Algebra
- Calculus

Some energy engineers dislike:
- having to try to keep up with an ever-changing field
- working long hours to finish a project
- having to meet deadlines
- working against skeptical opinions

For more information on the various careers available in the field of Energy Engineering, write to:
Association of Energy Engineers
4025 Pleasantdale Road
Suite 420
Atlanta, GA 30340

7

Lesson Resources

Reteaching Master 1-1
Practice Master 1-1
Enrichment Master 1-1

 Transparency 1-1 contains the 5-Minute Check and a teaching aid for this lesson.

INTRODUCING THE LESSON

 5-Minute Check

Use a calculator to find the value of each expression.

1. 2^3 **8**
2. $-2(-3)$ **6**
3. $-3 - (-10)$ **7**
4. $6 + 8.3 - 20 \div 2^2$ **9.3**

Other Prerequisite Skills

List three ways to write three times *a*.

$3 \times a, \quad 3 \cdot a, \quad 3(a)$

Motivating the Lesson

You invest $2000 for 2 years. What is the simple interest rate if the interest is $500? What is the formula for simple interest?
12.5%; *prt* = *I*

TEACHING THE LESSON

Teaching Tip ❶ Ask students how they should key in the equation on a non-scientific calculator. Explain that you must key the numbers by grouping them. For example, $4 + 3.7 \times 3$ should be keyed in as $3.7 \times 3 + 4$.

Objectives

After studying this lesson, you should be able to:

1-1A ▪ use the order of operations to evaluate expressions, and

1-1B ▪ use formulas.

Application

To determine the efficiency of the insulation in a school building, an energy engineer needed to evaluate the expression $4 + 3.7(3)$. Her calculator gave a result of 23.1. Use your calculator to evaluate the expression. Is your result the same? **Teaching Tip ❶**

ENTER: 4 [+] 3.7 [×] 3

If you used a scientific calculator, it probably multiplied 3.7 by 3 and then added 4, giving an answer of 15.1. If you used a non-scientific calculator, as the engineer did, it probably added 4 and 3.7 before multiplying by 3. This can be very confusing. Do you add first or multiply first? A numerical expression should have exactly one value. In order to find that value, you must follow the established rules for the **order of operations.**

Order of Operations

1. **Simplify the expressions inside grouping symbols, such as parentheses, brackets, and fraction bars.**
2. **Evaluate all powers.**
3. **Do all multiplications and divisions from left to right.**
4. **Do all additions and subtractions from left to right.**

Using these rules, the value of $4 + 3.7(3)$ is 15.1.

Example 1

Find the value of $5 + 8^2 \div 4 \cdot 3$.

$$5 + 8^2 \div 4 \cdot 3 = 5 + 64 \div 4 \cdot 3 \qquad \textit{Evaluate all powers.}$$
$$= 5 + 16 \cdot 3$$
$$= 5 + 48 \qquad \textit{Do all multiplications and divisions left to right.}$$
$$= 53 \qquad \textit{Do all additions and subtractions left to right.}$$

The value is 53.

8 CHAPTER 1 EQUATIONS AND INEQUALITIES

ALTERNATE TEACHING STRATEGIES

Using Cooperative Groups

Have students work in groups. Give them models of a rectangular prism, cylinder, and a square pyramid. Have them measure the dimensions and use formulas to find the volume and surface area for each figure. Have them increase each measurement by 2 and recalculate the volume and surface area.

Using Discussion

In using order of operations we find that we always get the same answer. This is called the unique answer. Discuss what *unique* means. When using grouping symbols we always use them in pairs.

Grouping symbols can be used to change or clarify the order of operations. Frequently used grouping symbols are parentheses, ( ), and brackets, [ ]. When calculating the value of an expression, you should begin with the operation in the innermost set of grouping symbols.

Example 2

Find the value of $[(4 + 8)^2 \div 9] \cdot 5$.

$$
\begin{aligned}
[(4 + 8)^2 \div 9] \cdot 5 &= [(12)^2 \div 9] \cdot 5 \quad & \textit{First add 4 and 8.} \\
&= [144 \div 9] \cdot 5 \quad & \textit{Then find } 12^2. \\
&= [16] \cdot 5 \quad & \textit{Now divide 144 by 9.} \\
&= 80 \quad & \textit{Multiply 16 by 5.}
\end{aligned}
$$

The value is 80.

Algebraic expressions contain at least one variable. You can evaluate an algebraic expression by replacing each variable with a value and then applying the rules for the order of operations.

Example 3

Evaluate $4x^2 + 3xy$ if $x = -3$ and $y = 5$.

$$
\begin{aligned}
4x^2 + 3xy &= 4(-3)^2 + 3(-3)(5) \quad & \textit{Replace x by -3 and y by 5.} \\
&= 4(9) + 3(-3)(5) \quad & \textit{Find } (-3)^2. \\
&= 36 + (-45) \quad & \textit{Multiply left to right.} \\
&= -9 \quad & \textit{Add.}
\end{aligned}
$$

The value is -9.

A **formula** is a mathematical sentence that expresses the relationship between certain quantities. If you know a value for every variable in the formula except one, you can find the value for that remaining variable.

Example 4

CONNECTION
Geometry

The volume of a sphere is calculated by using the formula $V = \frac{4}{3}\pi r^3$. In the formula, r represents the measure of the radius. Use a calculator to find the volume of a sphere with a radius of 7.6 centimeters. Use the π key on your calculator.

$$
\begin{aligned}
V &= \frac{4}{3}\pi r^3 \\
&= \frac{4}{3}\pi (7.6)^3
\end{aligned}
$$

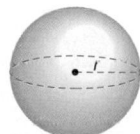

ENTER: 4 [÷] 3 [×] [π] [×] 7.6 [y^x] 3 [=] 8.78   **Teaching Tip ❷**
The display is rounded to the nearest hundredth.

The volume of the sphere is approximately 1838.78 cubic centimeters.

LESSON 1-1 EXPRESSIONS AND FORMULAS   9

EVALUATING THE LESSON

Checking for Understanding

Exercises 1–16 are designed to help you assess understanding through reading, writing, and speaking. You should work through Exercises 1–3 with your students, and then monitor their work on Exercises 4–16.

Error Analysis

Students sometimes misinterpret the fraction bar to mean only division, as in $\frac{10-4}{2}$. They may focus on the operations and want to divide before subtracting. $\frac{10-4}{2}$ means $(10 - 4) \div 2$, not $10 - 4 \div 2$. The fraction bar is a sign of division *and* a symbol of inclusion.

Reteaching Masters Booklet, p. 1

You are about to buy a new car. The sales associate offers you a simple interest loan to finance it. Simple interest is calculated using the formula $I = prt$. In the formula, p represents the principal in dollars, r represents the annual interest rate, and t represents the time in years. Find the amount of interest you would pay for a two-year loan if the principal is $6000 and the rate is 12%.

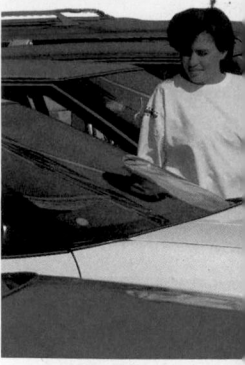

$$I = prt$$
$$= 6000(0.12)(2) \qquad 12\% = 0.12$$
$$= 1440$$

The interest on $6000 at 12% for 2 years is $1440.

The boiling point of the metal zinc is 787.1° on the Fahrenheit scale. Change the temperature to its equivalent on the Celsius scale.

The relationship between Celsius temperature, C, and Fahrenheit temperature, F, is given by $C = \frac{5(F - 32)}{9}$.

Find C if $F = 787.1$.

$$C = \frac{5(F - 32)}{9} \qquad \textit{Write the formula.}$$
$$= \frac{5(787.1 - 32)}{9} \qquad \textit{Replace F by 787.1.}$$
$$= 419.5$$

The Celsius temperature is 419.5°.

CHECKING FOR UNDERSTANDING

Communicating Mathematics

1. Subtract 4 from 15.

2. A sample answer is to add length and width and double the sum.

Guided Practice

Read and study the lesson to answer these questions.

1. When you evaluate $(15 - 4)^3 \div 3$, which operation is performed first?
2. Tell how you would find the perimeter of a rectangle.
3. Where would you insert grouping symbols so that the value of $7 \cdot 4 + 2 \cdot 8$ is 240? **$(7 \cdot 4 + 2) \cdot 8$**

Find the value of each expression.

4. $7 - 8 \div 2$ **3**
5. $9 - 4(3)$ **−3**
6. $4(7 + 3)$ **40**
7. $9(4 + 2)$ **54**
8. $5 - 4 \div 2$ **3**
9. $7 - (3 + 2)$ **2**

Find the value of each expression if $a = 2$, $b = -3$, and $c = 4$.

10. $a + b - c$ **−5**
11. $a + 2b - c$ **−8**
12. $a(b + c)$ **2**

RETEACHING THE LESSON

Write each series of instructions as a single algebraic phrase. Use x to represent the number at the start of each set of instructions.

1. Multiply by 6.
   Add 8.
   Divide by 2.

   $(6x + 8) \div 2$ or $\frac{6x + 8}{2}$

2. Add 8.
   Multiply by 6.
   Divide by 2.

   $\frac{(x + 8)6}{2}$

Find the value of C in each formula if the value of F is 98.6.

13. $C = \dfrac{5F - 160}{9}$ **37**

14. $F = \dfrac{9}{5}C + 32$ **37**

15. A rectangle has length $(y + 5)$ cm and width $(y - 5)$ cm. Write a formula to represent its area.
$A = (y + 5)(y - 5)$ cm^2

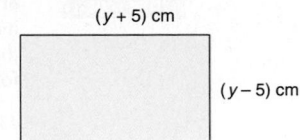

16. A triangle has height $(a + 2)$ ft and base $(a + 6)$ ft. Write a formula to represent its area.
$A = 0.5(a + 6)(a + 2)$ ft^2

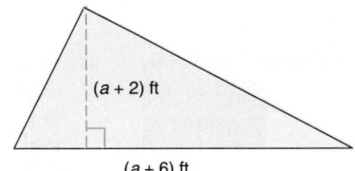

EXERCISES

Practice

Evaluate each expression.

17. $3(2^2 + 3)$ **21**

18. $2(3 + 8) - 3$ **19**

19. $(6 + 5)4 - 3$ **41**

20. $5 + 3^2 - 16 + 4$ **2**

21. $(5 + 3) - 16 \div 4$ **4**

22. $12 \mid 18 \div 6 + 7$ **22**

23. $4 + 8(4) \div 2 - 10$ **10**

24. $[19 - (8 - 1)] \div 3$ **4**

25. $3 + [8 \div (9 - 2(4))]$ **11**

26. $[(-8 + 3) \times 4 - 2] \div 6$

26. $-\dfrac{11}{3}$, **-3.667**

27. $15 \div 3 \times 5 + 1$ **26**

28. $3 + (21 \div 7) \times 8 \div 4$ **9**

29. $0.2(0.5 \mid 2.2) \div 6$ **0.09**

30. $\dfrac{1}{3} - \dfrac{13(77 \cdot 11)}{9}$ **-9**

Evaluate each expression if $a = 3$, $b = 7$, $c = -2$, $d = 0.5$, and $e = 0.3$.

31. $\dfrac{3ab}{cd}$ **-63**

32. $\dfrac{5a+3c}{3b}$ $\dfrac{3}{7}$, **0.429**

33. $(5a + 3d)^2 - e^2$ **272.16**

34. $(3b - 21d)^2$ $\dfrac{441}{4}$, **110.25**

35. $a(b - 7)^3$ **0**

36. $(a + c)^2 - de$ **0.85**

37. $\dfrac{4a - 6d}{2b + c}$ **0.75**

38. $c \mid de^2$ **-1.955**

Find the simple interest, I, given each of the values for the principal, rate, and time.

39. $p = \$2500$, $r = 7.37\%$, $t = 4$ years **\$737**

40. $p = \$5280$, $r = 8.2\%$, $t = 30$ months **\$1082.40**

41. $p = \$65,283.21$, $r = 9.32\%$, $t = 78$ months **\$39,548.57**

42. $p = \$20,005$, $r = 7.9\%$, $t = 2$ years, 3 months **\$3555.89**

LESSON 1-1 EXPRESSIONS AND FORMULAS **11**

C

The formula for the area of a trapezoid is $A = \frac{h}{2}(b_1 + b_2)$. A represents the measure of the area, h represents the measure of the altitude, and b_1 and b_2 represent the measures of the bases. Find the measure of the area of each trapezoid given the following values. **43–45. See margin.**

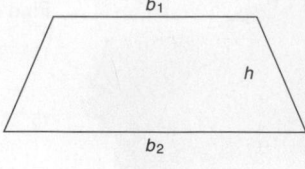

43. $h = 8$, $b_1 = 8.6$, and $b_2 = 14.8$ 44. $b_1 = 4$, $b_2 = 11$, and $h = 7$

45. $h = 9$, $b_2 = 7\frac{2}{3}$, and $b_1 = 4\frac{1}{6}$ 46. $h = 12$, $b_2 = 9.7$, and $b_1 = 6.2$ **95.4**

Critical Thinking

47. Create a formula that will determine the total surface area of this rectangular prism. What is the surface area if $a = 4$? if $a = 6.2$? $S = 22a^2 + 24a$; **448 sq. units; 994.48 sq. units**

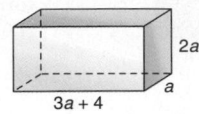

Applications

48. **Banking** Mary invests $7500 in a certificate of deposit at the Lombard Bank. The simple interest rate is 7.2%. How much interest will she have earned at the end of three years? **$1620**

49. **Construction** A contractor plans to paint the floor and the outside wall of a circular parking garage. The radius of the floor is 300 feet. The height of the wall is 20 feet. If one gallon of paint will cover 425 square feet, how many gallons of paint will it take to complete the job? *Hint: Draw a picture to help solve this problem.* **754 gallons**
Teaching Tip ➌

Computer

The BASIC computer language follows the same order of operations as algebra. However, parentheses and brackets do not indicate multiplication in BASIC. The symbol * must be used to multiply. This program finds the areas of three trapezoids. READ and DATA statements are used to assign values for the height and bases. **Teaching Tip ➍**

```
10   PRINT "H","B1","B2","A"
20   READ H, B1, B2
30   IF H = 0 THEN 90
40   DATA 8, 12, 20, 7, 4, 11
50   DATA 4.8, 5.6, 6.4, 0, 0, 0
60   LET A = H/2 *(B1 + B2)
70   PRINT H, B1, B2, A
80   GOTO 20
90   END
```

50. Write and run a program to find the area of each triangle. The formula for the area of a triangle is $A = \frac{1}{2}bh$ where b is the measure of the base (in cm) and h is the measure of the height (in cm).

    a. $b = 6.7$, $h = 13.8$ **46.23 cm²**   b. $b = 127.2$, $h = 82.6$ **5253.36 cm²**

51. Write and run a program to find the area of each parallelogram. The formula for the area of a parallelogram is $A = bh$ where b is the measure of the base (in ft) and h is the measure of the height (in ft).

    a. $b = 7.1$, $h = 3.5$ **24.85 ft²**   b. $b = 97.2$, $h = 26.9$ **2614.68 ft²**

12   CHAPTER 1   EQUATIONS AND INEQUALITIES

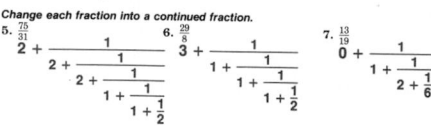

1-1 Enrichment Worksheet

NAME _____ DATE _____

Continued Fractions

The fraction below is an example of a continued fraction. Note that each fraction in the continued fraction has a numerator of 1.

$$2 + \cfrac{1}{3 + \cfrac{1}{4 + \cfrac{1}{5}}}$$

Example 1:
Evaluate the continued fraction above. Start at the bottom and work your way up.

Step 1: $4 + \frac{1}{5} = \frac{20}{5} + \frac{1}{5} = \frac{21}{5}$

Step 2: $\frac{1}{\frac{21}{5}} = \frac{5}{21}$

Step 3: $3 + \frac{5}{21} = \frac{63}{21} + \frac{5}{21} = \frac{68}{21}$

Step 4: $\frac{1}{\frac{68}{21}} = \frac{21}{68}$

Step 5: $2 + \frac{21}{68} = 2\frac{21}{68}$

Example 2:
Change $\frac{25}{11}$ into a continued fraction. Follow the steps.

Step 1: $\frac{25}{11} = \frac{22}{11} + \frac{3}{11} = 2 + \frac{3}{11}$

Step 2: $\frac{3}{11} = \frac{1}{\frac{11}{3}}$

Step 3: $\frac{11}{3} = \frac{9}{3} + \frac{2}{3} = 3 + \frac{2}{3}$

Step 4: $\frac{2}{3} = \frac{1}{\frac{3}{2}}$

Step 5: $\frac{3}{2} = \frac{2}{2} + \frac{1}{2} = 1 + \frac{1}{2}$
Stop, because the numerator is 1.

Thus, $\frac{25}{11}$ can be written as $2 + \cfrac{1}{3 + \cfrac{1}{1 + \frac{1}{2}}}$

Evaluate each continued fraction.

1. $1 + \cfrac{1}{1 + \cfrac{1}{2 + \cfrac{1}{2 + \frac{1}{3}}}}$ $1\frac{17}{24}$

2. $0 + \cfrac{1}{6 + \cfrac{1}{4 + \frac{1}{2}}}$ $\frac{9}{56}$

3. $2 + \cfrac{1}{4 + \cfrac{1}{6 + \cfrac{1}{8 + \frac{1}{10}}}}$ $2\frac{496}{2065}$

4. $5 + \cfrac{1}{7 + \cfrac{1}{9 + \frac{1}{11}}}$ $5\frac{100}{711}$

Change each fraction into a continued fraction.

5. $\frac{75}{31}$ $2 + \cfrac{1}{2 + \cfrac{1}{2 + \cfrac{1}{1 + \frac{1}{2}}}}$

6. $\frac{29}{8}$ $3 + \cfrac{1}{1 + \cfrac{1}{1 + \cfrac{1}{1 + \frac{1}{2}}}}$

7. $\frac{13}{19}$ $0 + \cfrac{1}{1 + \cfrac{1}{2 + \frac{1}{6}}}$

EXTENDING THE LESSON

Math Power: Connections

Suppose you invest $5000 at 8% simple interest. How many years will it take to accumulate $10,000? Reinvest the interest each year.
10 years

Discuss what formula you would use. Can you write a procedure to solve this equation?

Additional Answers

43. 93.6
44. 52.5
45. $53\frac{1}{4}$

Objectives

1-2A
1-2B

After studying this lesson, you should be able to:

- determine the sets of numbers to which a number belongs, and
- use the properties of real numbers to simplify expressions.

All the numbers that we use in everyday life are **real numbers.** Each re number corresponds to exactly one point on the number line, and every point on the number line represents exactly one real number.

FYI ...

When the Greek society of mathematicians, the Pythagoreans, discovered irrational numbers, they tried to keep their discovery a secret. According to legend, one of their members was drowned for telling the secret to outsiders.

Every real number can be classified as either **rational** or **irrational.** A rational number can be expressed as a ratio $\frac{m}{n}$, where m and n are intege and n is not zero. The decimal form of a rational number is either a terminating or repeating decimal. Some examples of rational numbers a $\frac{2}{3}$, $1.\overline{23}$, 5.8, -7, and 0. Any real number that is not rational is irrational. $\sqrt{2}$, π, and $\sqrt{7}$ are irrational numbers.   **Teaching Tip ❶**

The sets of natural numbers, $\{1, 2, 3, 4, 5, ...\}$, whole numbers, $\{0, 1, 2, 3, 4, ...\}$, and integers, $\{..., -2, -1, 0, 1, 2, ...\}$ are all subsets of the rational numbers.

The Venn diagram at the right shows the relationships between all of these sets of numbers.

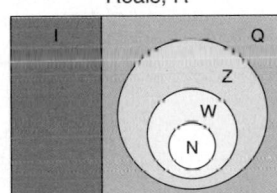

Reals, R

R = reals   Q = rationals
I = irrationals   Z = integers
W = wholes   N = naturals

Example 1

Name the sets of numbers to which each number belongs.

a. $\sqrt{6}$

    irrationals (I)
    reals (R)

b. $\frac{3}{8}$

    rationals (Q)
    reals (R)

c. -9

    integers (Z)
    rationals (Q)
    reals (R)

LESSON 1-2 PROPERTIES OF REAL NUMBERS 13

ALTERNATE TEACHING STRATEGIES

Using Modeling

Give students a rectangular piece of paper that measures 11 centimeters by 5 centimeters. Ask them to use the rectangle to illustrate the distributive property. For example, you can find the area of the rectangle in two different ways.

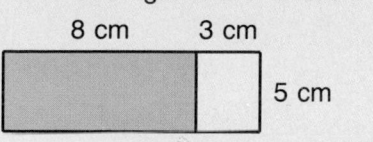

Method 1: Multiply the length by width.
$$A = 5(8 + 3)$$
$$= 5(11)$$

Method 2: Add the areas of the smaller rectangles.
$$A = 5(8) + 5(3)$$
$$= 40 + 15$$
$$= 55$$

Lesson Resources

Reteaching Master 1-2
Practice Master 1-2
Enrichment Master 1-2
Technology Master, p. 1
Multicultural Activity Master, p. 1

 Transparency 1-2 contains the 5-Minute Check and a teaching aid for this lesson.

INTRODUCING THE LESSON

5-Minute Check

(over Lesson 1-1)
Evaluate each expression.

1. $3^2 - 2(4 - 2)$ **5**
2. $[(8 + 3) \times 3 - 12] \div 7$ **3**

Evaluate each expression if $a = 0.5$, $b = 6$, and $c = -3$.

3. $ac - bc + a$ **17**
4. $a(b + c) + ab^2$ **19.5**
5. Find the interest I if $I = prt$ and $p = 2500$, $r = 8\%$, and $t = 3$. **$600**

Motivating the Lesson

Give examples of irrational numbers. Have students determine whether addition, subtraction, multiplication, and division of two irrational numbers always results in an irrational number.

If not, give a counterexample.

TEACHING THE LESSON

Teaching Tip ❶ Any number that is not a perfect square has an irrational square root.

Teaching Tip ❷   Point out to the students that a number and its reciprocal have the same sign.

Example 2

Evaluate each expression. Then name the sets of numbers to which each value belongs.

a. $\sqrt{9}$

$\sqrt{9} = 3$

natural numbers (N),
whole numbers (W), integers (Z),
rationals (Q), reals (R)

b. $6 \div 10$

$6 \div 10 = 0.6$ or $\frac{3}{5}$

rationals (Q),
reals (R)

Operations with real numbers have several important properties. One of the basic properties of addition and multiplication is **commutativity.** The order in which two real numbers are added or multiplied does not change their sum or their product.

$$5 + 9 = 9 + 5 \qquad\qquad 12 \cdot 4 = 4 \cdot 12$$
$$14 = 14 \qquad\qquad 48 = 48$$

Another basic property of addition and multiplication is **associativity.** The way three or more real numbers are grouped, or associated, does not change their sum or product.

$$(7 + 6) + 9 = 7 + (6 + 9) \qquad (10 \cdot 5) \cdot 2 = 10 \cdot (5 \cdot 2)$$
$$13 + 9 = 7 + 15 \qquad\qquad 50 \cdot 2 = 10 \cdot 10$$
$$22 = 22 \qquad\qquad 100 = 100$$

The sum of any real number and 0 is the original number. So, for real numbers, the **additive identity** is 0.

$$6.7 + 0 = 6.7 \qquad\qquad 0 + \sqrt{3} = \sqrt{3}$$

Each real number has a unique **additive inverse** or **opposite.** The sum of a number and its opposite is 0.

$$8 + (-8) = 0 \qquad\qquad -\frac{1}{3} + \frac{1}{3} = 0$$

The **multiplicative identity** for real numbers is 1, since the product of any real number and 1 is the original number.

$$\frac{5}{8} \cdot 1 = \frac{5}{8} \qquad\qquad (1)(3.9) = 3.9$$

Each real number, except 0, has a unique **multiplicative inverse** or **reciprocal.** The product of a real number and its reciprocal is 1.

Teaching Tip ❷

$$\frac{1}{8}(8) = 1 \qquad\qquad (-0.2)(-5) = 1$$

Why does zero not have a reciprocal?

The chart below summarizes the properties of real numbers for addition and multiplication.

For any real numbers a, b, and c		
	Addition	Multiplication
Commutative	$a + b = b + a$	$a \cdot b = b \cdot a$
Associative	$(a + b) + c = a + (b + c)$	$(a \cdot b) \cdot c = a \cdot (b \cdot c)$
Identity	$a + 0 = a = 0 + a$	$a \cdot 1 = a = 1 \cdot a$
Inverse	$a + (\text{-}a) = 0 = (\text{-}a) + a$	If a is *not* zero, then $a \cdot \dfrac{1}{a} = 1 = \dfrac{1}{a} \cdot a.$

-a *is read "the opposite of a."*

Chalkboard Examples

For Example 3
John makes $5 an hour mowing lawns. He worked 2 hours one day and 3.5 hours the next day. How much did he earn for both days? **$27.50**

For Example 4
Simplify $2(2x - 3y) - 8(x + 4y)$.
$-4x - 38y$

Example 3

CONNECTION

Statistics

A fast-food restaurant offered a special on their Biggie Burger to entice customers at lunch time. The 99¢ special ran Monday through Friday. The number of Biggie Burgers sold each day are recorded in the table below. What was the average amount received from the sale of Biggie Burgers during each day?

M	T	W	T	F
246	303	182	341	378

An average is calculated by dividing the total amount by the number of items. In this case, it would be the total dollar amount divided by the number of days, 5.

There are two ways to find the total dollar amount.

(1) $T = 0.99(246 + 303 + 182 + 341 + 378)$
$T = 243.54 + 299.97 + 180.18 + 337.59$
$\quad + 374.22$ or 1435.50

(2) $T = 0.99(246 + 303 + 182 + 341 + 378)$
$T = 0.99(1450)$ or 1435.50

Now find the average by dividing the total by 5.
$1435.50 \div 5 = 287.10$

The average daily revenue received from Biggie Burgers was $287.10.

This is an application of a property that involves both addition and multiplication. It is called the distributive property.

Distributive Property

For all real numbers a, b, and c,
$a(b + c) = ab + ac$ and $(b + c)a = ba + ca.$

LESSON 1-2 PROPERTIES OF REAL NUMBERS 15

RETEACHING THE LESSON

$2, 5.2, \text{-}3, -0.6, \dfrac{9}{17}, 0, \sqrt{5}, -\dfrac{7}{5}, \pi,$
$\dfrac{\sqrt{7}}{2}, \dfrac{\pi}{3}, 0.4, 0.\overline{28}, \sqrt{9}$

Which of the numbers above are:

a. natural numbers **2**
b. whole numbers **2, 0**
c. integers **2, -3, 0, $\sqrt{9}$**
d. rational numbers **$2, 5.2, \text{-}3, -0.6, \dfrac{9}{17}, 0, -\dfrac{7}{5}, 0.4, 0.\overline{28}, \sqrt{9}$**
e. irrational numbers **$\sqrt{5}, \pi, \dfrac{\sqrt{7}}{2}, \dfrac{\pi}{3}$**
f. real numbers **all**

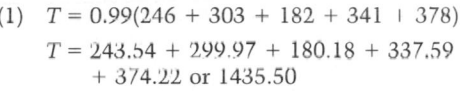

Checking for Understanding
Exercises 1–22 are designed to help you assess understanding through reading, writing, and speaking. You should work through Exercises 1–5 with your students, and then monitor their work on Exercises 6–22.

Closing the Lesson
Modeling Activity Have students draw the Venn diagram that describes the relationship of the number systems.

APPLYING THE LESSON

Homework Exercises

Assignment Guide
Basic: 23–45, 54–61
Average: 27–49, 54–61
Enriched: 31–61

Chapter 1, Quiz A, (Lessons 1-1 through 1-2), is available in the Evaluation Masters Booklet, p. 9.

Practice Masters Booklet, p. 2

> **Example 4**
> Simplify $5(3m - 7n) + 3(4m + n)$.
> $5(3m - 7n) + 3(4m + n)$
> $= 5(3m) - 5(7n) + 3(4m) + 3(n)$ *Use the distributive property.*
> $= 15m - 35n + 12m + 3n$ *Multiply.*
> $= 27m - 32n$ *Combine like terms.*

CHECKING FOR UNDERSTANDING

Communicating Mathematics

3–5. See margin.

Read and study the lesson to answer these questions.
1. What property is used to simplify $3y(4y + 2z)$? **distributive property**
2. Explain why there is no commutative property for subtraction and division. **$a - b \neq b - a$ and $a \div b \neq b \div a$**
3. Draw a geometric model to show how 4×3 is similar to 3×4.
4. List five irrational numbers. **Answers may vary. See margin for samples.**
5. List five rational numbers. **Answers may vary. See margin for samples.**

Guided Practice

Name the sets of numbers to which each number belongs.
6. -8 **Z, Q, R**   7. $\frac{4}{3}$ **Q, R**   8. -2.6 **Q, R**   9. π **I, R**
10. $-\frac{7}{2}$ **Q, R**   11. 10 **N, W, Z, Q, R** 12. $\sqrt{10}$ **I, R**   13. 5.11 **Q, R**
14. 0 **W, Z, Q, R**   15. $-\frac{12}{3}$ **Z, Q, R**   16. -1.0 **Z, Q, R**   17. $\sqrt{16}$ **N, W, Z, Q, R**

State the property illustrated in each equation.
18. $8 + (6 + 4) = (8 + 6) + 4$ **associative +**
19. $7(5) = 5(7)$ **commutative x**
20. $a(3 - 2) = a \cdot 3 - a \cdot 2$ **distributive**
21. $8 + (1 + 6) = 8 + (6 + 1)$ **commutative +**
22. $3 + (-3) = 0$ **additive inverse**

EXERCISES

For calculator use, fractional and irrational answers are also expressed in decimal form, rounded to the nearest thousandth.

Practice

Evaluate each expression. Then name the sets of numbers to which each value belongs. 23–30. See margin for sets of numbers.

23. $8 - 7$ **1**   24. $7 - 8$ **-1**   25. $-54 \div 6$ **-9**   26. $68 \div 100$ **0.68**
27. -2.4×10 **-24**   28. $3.9 + 2.6$ **6.5**   29. $6 \div 2^2$ **$\frac{3}{2}$, 1.5**   30. $\sqrt{36+5}$ **$\sqrt{41}$, 6.403**

Determine whether each statement is *true* or *false*. If *false*, give an example of a number that shows the statement is false.

31. Every whole number is an integer. **true**
32. Every integer is a whole number. **false; -1**

16   CHAPTER 1   EQUATIONS AND INEQUALITIES

Additional Answers
3.
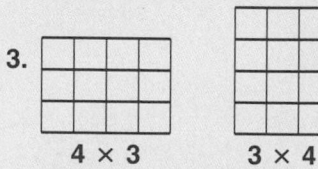
4×3 3×4
Both have area of 12.

23. N, W, Z, Q, R
24. Z, Q, R
25. Z, Q, R
26. Q, R
27. Z, Q, R
28. Q, R
29. Q, R
30. I, R

4. Sample answers are π, $\sqrt{2}$, 1.121231234 . . . , $\sqrt{7}$, 0.10010001 . . .
5. Sample answers are 0.111 . . . , 0, -6, $\frac{2}{7}$, and -0.3434 . . .

Determine whether each statement is *true* or *false*. If *false*, give an example of a number that shows the statement is false.

33. Every rational number is an integer. **false; $\frac{3}{2}$, 1.5**

34. Every real number is irrational. **false; $\frac{3}{2}$, 1.5**

35. Every irrational number is a real number. **true**

36. Every integer is a rational number. **true**

37. Every real number is either a rational number or an irrational number. **true**

State the property illustrated in each equation. **38–45. See margin.**

38. $(4 + 11) \cdot 6 = 4(6) + 11(6)$

39. $(a + b) + [-(a + b)] = 0$

40. $11 + a = a + 11$

41. $(3 + 9) + 14 = 14 + (3 + 9)$

42. $3 + (a + b) = (a + b) + 3$

43. $3\left(\frac{1}{3}\right) = 1$

44. $(4 + 9a)2b = 2b(4 + 9a)$

45. $a + b + 0 = a + b$

Simplify each expression. **46–53. See margin.**

46. $3(5a + 6b) + 8(2a - b)$

47. $3a + 5b + 7a - 3b$

48. $2(7c - 5d) - 3(d + 2c)$

49. $\frac{1}{4}(12 + 20a) + \frac{3}{4}(12 + 20a)$

50. $\frac{1}{2}(17 - 4x) - \frac{3}{4}(6 - 16x)$

51. $\frac{2}{3}\left(\frac{1}{2}a + 3b\right) + \frac{1}{2}\left(\frac{2}{3}a + b\right)$

52. $\frac{3}{4}(2x - 5y) + \frac{1}{2}\left(\frac{2}{3}x + 4y\right)$

53. $7(0.2m + 0.3n) + 5(0.6m - n)$

Critical Thinking

Use the definitions of the properties of real numbers to answer these questions.

54. If $a + b = a$, what is the value of b? **0**

55. If $ab = 1$, what is the value of b? What is b called? **$\frac{1}{a}$; multiplicative inverse of a**

56. If $ab = a$, what is the value of b? **1**

Applications

57. **Accounting** A number is divisible by 9 if the sum of its digits is divisible by 9. This fact is used by accountants to check figures in double entry books. If the totals of the credit and debit columns do not match, and the difference between the totals is divisible by 9, then the error was probably made when two digits were reversed in one of the entries. Tell if the errors in the following might have come from reversing the digits of an entry. **Teaching Tip ❸** **yes**

    a. credit = \$638, debit = \$577 **no**   b. credit = \$1050, debit = \$1095

    c. Why does this check work? *Hint: What is the difference between a number and the number whose digits are reversed?* **The difference of two such numbers is always divisible by 9.**

Mixed Review

Evaluate each expression. (Lesson 1-1)

58. $3 + (3 - 3)^3 - 3$ **0**

59. $-8 \div [20 \div (16 - 11)]$ **-2**

60. Find the value of $12a^2 + bc$ if $a = 3$, $b = 7$, and $c = -2$. (Lesson 1-1) **94**

61. **Banking** Find the interest earned in 6 years on a savings account containing \$20,000 if the interest rate is 14.5%. (Lesson 1-1) **\$17,400**

LESSON 1-2   PROPERTIES OF REAL NUMBERS   17

EXTENDING THE LESSON

Math Power: Reasoning

Below is a proof that $2.\overline{9} = 3$. Does this statement contradict the statement "each real number corresponds to exactly one point on the number line?" Let $n = 2.\overline{9}$.

$$10n = 29.\overline{9}$$
$$-n = 2.\overline{9}$$

$$9n = 27$$
$$n = 3$$

Lesson Resources

Reteaching Master 1-3
Practice Master 1-3
Enrichment Master 1-3
Lab Manual, pp. 33–34

 Transparency 1-3 contains the 5-Minute Check and a teaching aid for this lesson.

INTRODUCING THE LESSON

 5-Minute Check

(over Lesson 1-2)

1. Evaluate $\sqrt{25}$. To which sets of numbers does it belong?
   N, W, Z, Q, R
   Which property is illustrated?

2. $a + (4 + c) = (a + 4) + c$
   associative of addition

3. $3(4 + 0.2) = 3(4) + 3(0.2)$
   distributive

4. Simplify $(2c)(3d) + c + 5cd + 3c^2$ $\mathbf{11cd + c + 3c^2}$

Motivating the Lesson

In banking, a formula for simple interest accumulating over t years is $A = p + prt$. If you know A, amount in account, r, rate of interest, and t, time in years, explain how you could find p, the amount invested.

TEACHING THE LESSON

Teaching Tip ❶ Solution to introductory problem

Let s = the number of 25¢ stamps
   $3s$ = the number of 29¢ stamps

$0.25s + 0.29(3s) = 22.40$

Janet bought twenty 25¢ stamps and sixty 29¢ stamps.

Objective
1-3

After studying this lesson, you should be able to:
- solve equations using the properties of equality.

Application

 FYI…

In 1775, Benjamin Franklin was appointed the first Postmaster General by the Second Continental Congress.

Janet Graves needed to buy some stamps for her graduation announcements. She bought some 25-cent stamps and three times as many 29-cent stamps. She paid a total of $22.40. How many of each type of stamp did she buy? **20 – 25¢ stamps, 60 – 29¢ stamps**
Teaching Tip ❶

This problem can be solved by writing and then solving an open sentence. Sentences with variables to be replaced, such as $3x - 7 = 21$ and $3x + 4 > 9$, are called **open sentences.** When you solve an open sentence, you find replacements for the variables that will make the sentence true. Each of these replacements is called a **solution** of the open sentence.

An **equation** states that two mathematical expressions are equal. Solving an equation is like solving an open sentence. You find the values that you can put in place of the variables so that the equation is true.

Real numbers have certain properties that we can use when we solve equations or open sentences. Some of those properties are listed below.

Reflexive Property of Equality	For any real number a, $a = a$.
Symmetric Property of Equality	For all real numbers a and b, if $a = b$, then $b = a$.
Transitive Property of Equality	For all real numbers a, b, and c, if $a = b$ and $b = c$, then $a = c$.

Teaching Tip ❷

Example 1

Name the property of equality illustrated in each statement.

a. If $36 \cdot 2 = 72$, then $72 = 36 \cdot 2$.   a. symmetric property

b. $21.4 = 21.4$ b. reflexive property

c. If $8 = 6 + 2$ and $6 + 2 = 5 + 3$, then $8 = 5 + 3$.   c. transitive property

Some equations can be solved by making a substitution. The substitution property allows you to replace an expression with another equivalent expression.

ALTERNATE TEACHING STRATEGIES

Mini-Math Lab

Divide students into groups giving each group a balance scale. Have students use different weights to illustrate how to solve equations. The students should write down the combinations of weights used.

Example 2

Solve $y = 8(0.3) + 1.2$.

$y = 8(0.3) + 1.2$
$y = 2.4 + 1.2$ *Substitute 2.4 for 8(0.3).*
$y = 3.6$ The solution is 3.6.

Sometimes an equation can be solved by adding or subtracting the same number on each side.

Example 3

Solve $x + 28.3 = 56.0$.

$x + 28.3 = 56.0$ **Check:**
$x + 28.3 + (-28.3) = 56.0 + (-28.3)$ $x + 28.3 = 56.0$
$x = 27.7$ $27.7 + 28.3 \stackrel{?}{=} 56.0$
The solution is 27.7. $56.0 = 56.0 \checkmark$
This equation could also be solved by subtracting 28.3 from each side.

Addition and Subtraction Properties of Equality	For any real numbers a, b, and c, if $a = b$, then $a + c = b + c$ and $a - c = b - c$.

Some equations may be solved by multiplying or dividing each side by the same number.

Example 4

Solve $8x = 48$.

$8x = 48$
$\frac{1}{8} \cdot 8x = \frac{1}{8} \cdot 48$ *Multiply each side by $\frac{1}{8}$, the reciprocal of 8.*   **Check:** $8x = 48$
$x = 6$ The solution is 6. $8(6) \stackrel{?}{=} 48$
$48 = 48 \checkmark$
This equation could also be solved by dividing each side by 8.

Example 5

Solve $-\frac{2}{3}k = 14$.

$-\frac{2}{3}k = 14$
$-\frac{3}{2}\left(-\frac{2}{3}\right)k = \left(-\frac{3}{2}\right)(14)$ *Multiply each side by $-\frac{3}{2}$, the reciprocal of $-\frac{2}{3}$.*   **Check:** $\frac{2}{3}k = 14$
$k = -21$ The solution is -21. $-\frac{2}{3}(-21) \stackrel{?}{=} 14$
$14 = 14 \checkmark$

Multiplication and Division Properties of Equality	For any real numbers a, b, and c, if $a = b$, then $a \cdot c = b \cdot c$ and, if c is not zero, $\frac{a}{c} = \frac{b}{c}$.

Teaching Tip ❸

LESSON 1-3 SOLVING EQUATIONS   19

RETEACHING THE LESSON

Decide if each relation is reflexive, symmetric, or transitive. Use N for no, or Y for yes in the chart.

Relation	R	S	T
factor of	Y	N	Y
parallel	N	Y	Y
perpendicular	N	Y	N
congruent	Y	Y	Y
is less than	N	N	Y

Chalkboard Examples

For Example 1
Name the property of equality illustrated in each statement.

a. $x + 9 = 6 + 9$
$6 + 9 = 15$ **transitive**
$x + 9 = 15$
b. $28 = 6y + 4$
$6y + 4 = 28$ **symmetric**
c. $r + (6 + 9) = 32$
$r + 15 = 32$ **substitution**

For Example 2
Solve $5(1.3 - 0.7) = x$. $3 = x$

For Example 3
Solve $y - 25 = 13.4$. $y = 38.4$

For Example 4
Solve $9y = 63$. $y = 7$

For Example 5
Solve $30 = -\left(\frac{4t}{7}\right)$. $t = -\left(\frac{105}{2}\right)$

Reteaching Masters Booklet, p. 3

In order to solve some equations, it may be necessary to apply more than one property. The following examples illustrate the use of several properties in solving equations.

Example 6

Solve $0.75(8a + 20) - 2(a - 1) = 3$.

$$0.75(8a + 20) - 2(a - 1) = 3$$

$6a + 15 - 2a + 2 = 3$ *Distributive and substitution properties*

$4a + 17 = 3$ *Commutative, distributive, and substitution properties*

$4a = -14$ *Subtraction and substitution properties*

$a = -3.5$ *Division and substitution properties*

The solution is -3.5. *Check this result.*

Example 7

Use a calculator to solve $68x + 373 = 802$.

$68x + 373 = 802$ *Rewrite the equation to isolate the variable, x.*

$x = \dfrac{802 - 373}{68}$

ENTER: 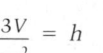 802 $-$ 373 $)$ $\div$ 68 $=$ `6.30882353`

The solution is approximately 6.309.

Example 8

CONNECTION
Geometry

The formula for the volume of a right circular cone is $V = \dfrac{1}{3}\pi r^2 h$, where r represents the radius of the circular base, and the height is represented by h. Solve the formula for h.

$$V = \frac{1}{3}\pi r^2 h$$

$3 \cdot V = 3 \cdot \dfrac{1}{3}\pi r^2 h$ *Multiply each side by 3.*

$\dfrac{3V}{\pi r^2} = \dfrac{\pi r^2 h}{\pi r^2}$ *Divide each side by πr^2.*

$\dfrac{3V}{\pi r^2} = h$ *This form of the formula could be used to find the height of a cone if its volume and radius are known.*

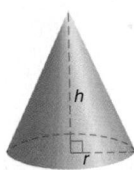

CHECKING FOR UNDERSTANDING

Communicating Mathematics

Read and study the lesson to answer these questions.

1. Describe in your own words the meaning of the transitive property of equality. **See students' work.**

2. Is the following an example of the transitive property of equality? Juanita has $37.62. Juanita has as much money as Earl. Earl has $37.62. **yes**

3. Explain how using a balance scale is similar to adding or subtracting a number from each side of an equation. **See students' work.**

Guided Practice

State the property illustrated in each statement. **4–9. See margin.**

4. If $x + 3 = 7$, then $x = 4$.

5. $(4 + 7) + 8 = (4 + 7) + 8$

6. If $6 + 5 = 11$, then $11 = 6 + 5$.

7. If $3x = 10$, then $3x + 6 = 10 + 6$.

8. If $3x = 5y$ and $5y = 10z$, then $3x = 10z$.

9. If $5x = 10$, then $15x = 30$.

Solve each equation.

10. $\frac{1}{3}q = 872$ **2616**

11. $7x + 2 = 23$ **3**

12. $2x + 7 = 8x - 11$ **3**

EXERCISES

Practice

Solve each equation.

13. $\frac{3}{8} - \frac{1}{4}x = \frac{1}{16}$ $\frac{5}{4}$

14. $1.2x + 3.7 = 13.3$ **8**

15. $4.5 - 3.9m = 20.1$ **-4**

16. $1.1x - 0.09 = 2.22$ **2.1**

17. $9 = 16d + 51$ **-2.625**

18. $5t + 4 = 2t + 13$ **3**

19. $2y - 8 = 14 - 9y$ **2**

20. $3x + 5 = 9x + 2$ **0.5**

21. $3x - 4 = 7x - 11$ **1.75**

22. $\frac{3}{4}s - \frac{1}{2} = \frac{1}{4}s + 5$ **11**

23. $\frac{2}{3} - \frac{3}{5}x = \frac{2}{5}x + \frac{4}{3}$ **-0.667**

24. $8 - x = 5x + 32$ **-4**

25. $3 = -3(y + 5)$ **-6**

26. $5(3x + 5) = 4x - 8$ **-3**

27. $2x - 4(x + 2) = -2x - 8$ **all reals**

28. $285 - 38x = 2033$ **-46**

29. $2(6 - 7k) = 2k - 4$ **1**

30. $8x - 3 = 5(2x + 1)$ **-4**

Critical Thinking

31. Write an equation that will have no solution. Explain why there is no solution. **Answers may vary. A sample answer is $x = x + 1$.**

32. Write an equation that will have an infinite number of solutions. Explain why. **Answers may vary. A sample answer is $4x - 2 = -2(1 - 2x)$.**

Applications

33. **Banking** The formula, $A = p + prt$, gives the amount, A, in an account when p dollars are invested at a rate of simple interest, r, for t years. Solve this formula for t. $t = \frac{A - p}{pr}$

34. **Transportation** The director of the Department of Transportation wants to know if the pile of salt for use on the icy roads is too tall to cover with their tarpaulin. The salt is in a pile that is shaped like a right circular cone. The formula for the volume of a right circular cone is $v = \frac{1}{3}\pi r^2 h$. The radius, r, of the circular base of the pile is 2.5 meters. The volume of the cone, V, is 40 cubic meters. If the tarpaulin can cover a cone up to 7 meters tall, can it cover the pile? **Teaching Tip ④**

Mixed Review

34. Yes, the pile is only 6.11 meters tall.

35. Evaluate $\sqrt{9 \div 3}$ and tell the sets of numbers to which the value belongs. **(Lesson 1-2)** $\sqrt{3}$; **I, R**

36. State the property illustrated by $11(3a + 2b) = 11(2b + 3a)$. **(Lesson 1-2) commutative +**

37. Evaluate $8a - 3bc$ if $a = 0.3$, $b = 7$, and $c = -2$. **(Lesson 1-1) 44.4**

EXTENDING THE LESSON

Math Power: Reasoning

Solve the equation.

$5(3x - 2) + 2(1 - x) =$
$3(7 + 3x) - 4(6 - x)$
no solution

Explain the steps taken to solve the equation.

Enrichment Masters Booklet, p. 3

INTRODUCING THE LESSON

Objective: Evaluate expressions using a graphing calculator.

Motivating the Lesson

Give students five minutes to play with the calculator. Have them write down three questions that they have in that five-minute time period. Then work on answering some of the simpler questions.

TEACHING THE LESSON

Teaching Tip ❶ The mode screen on the Casio fx-7000G appears when you turn on the calculator. It can also be accessed by pressing the [MDisp] key.

Teaching Tip ❷ The selected settings will be highlighted in black on the screen.

Teaching Tip ❸ All mode settings are listed under the screen on the Casio.

Graphing Calculator Exploration
Evaluating Expressions

The *Graphing Calculator Explorations* in this text will focus on two graphing calculators, the Texas Instruments TI-81® and the Casio fx-7000G®. In these lessons you will be introduced to the keying sequences that allow you to perform mathematical computations and to graph equations. You should always refer to your user's manual for more detail on all of the features of your calculator.

You do not need another scientific calculator since the graphing calculator also performs those computations you previously used a scientific calculator to do.

Casio's fx-7500G, fx-7700G, fx-8000G, and fx-8500G operate in a similar fashion to the fx-7000G.

Each calculator has a mode screen. The Casio displays this screen as the start-up screen. The TI-81 requires you to press the MODE key to display these settings. The mode setting shown below are commonly used for scientific calculations. **Teaching Tip ❶**

Casio	TI-81

Teaching Tip ❷

```
**** MODE ****

sys mode  :  RUN
cal mode  :  COMP
   angle  :  Rad
 display  :  Norm

   Step    0
```

```
Norm  Sci Eng
Float  0123456789
Rad  Deg
Function  Param
Connected  Dot
Sequence  Simul
Grid Off  Grid On
Rect  Polar
```

If your mode settings do not match these, you need to change them.

Teaching Tip ❸ CASIO: Press [MODE] 1 to select RUN.

Press [MODE] + to select COMP.

Press [MODE] 5 [EXE] to select RAD.

Press [MODE] 9 [EXE] to select Norm.

TI-81:   Press [▶] or [◀] and [ENTER] to change the highlighted mode.

Press [CLEAR] to return to home screen.

These mode settings allow you to use your graphing calculator in the same ways as your scientific calculator. The Norm or Float mode places the decimal point with no set number of decimal places. The table at the top of the next page lists some common calculations and the keys on each calculator that correspond to the function. Just as with a scientific calculator, the graphing calculator observes the assumed order of operations.

RETEACHING THE LESSON

If students are having problems with parentheses or order of operations, start with simple problems and work up to more difficult ones. Have them state each step in solving an expression. This can give you an insight into possible errors.

Mathematical Operation	Casio	TI-81
Evaluates the expression, acting as an = key.	Press [EXE]	Press [ENTER]
Clears the screen.	Press [AC]	Press [CLEAR]
To evaluate 3^7.	Press 3 [x^y] 7 [EXE]	Press 3 [^] 7 [ENTER]
To use a function listed above the regular calculator key.	Press [SHIFT] to get the function shown in orange.	Press [2nd] to get the function shown in blue.
Parentheses used as grouping, or in multiplication, such as 3(6) and (3)6.	Press [(] and [)] to group operations. Will evaluate 3(6), but not (3)6.	Press [(] and [)] to group operations. Will evaluate both 3(6) and (3)6.
Making a number negative. *This not the same as the minus key.*	Press the [(-)] key and enter the number.	Press the [(-)] key and enter the number.

Note that the procedure for entering a negative number is different from that used with a scientific calculator.

In each example in the *Graphing Calculator Explorations,* we will show both the Casio and TI-81 keystrokes.

Example

Evaluate $[(-5 + 13)^3 \div 6]3$.

Casio

ENTER: [(] [(] [(-)] 5 [+] 13 [)] [x^y] 3 [÷] 6 [)] [×] 3 [EXE] **256**

TI-81

ENTER: [(] [(] [(-)] 5 [+] 13 [)] [^] 3 [÷] 6 [)] 3 [ENTER] **256**

You may note that there are differences in the ways each calculator displays some operations. For example, the Casio displays $5 \div 2$ as $5 \div 2$, while the TI-81 displays $5 \div 2$ as 5/2. The Casio also displays the multiplication symbol as it appears on the key, while on the TI-81 it appears as a *.

EXERCISES

Use your graphing calculator to evaluate each expression.

1. $2\left[\dfrac{5 + \dfrac{4(3 + 7)}{5}}{4}\right] + 13$ **19.5**

2. $(42 \times 5)^3 + \dfrac{89}{12}$ **9261007.4167**

3. $(6.23 \times 10^{-7})(4.23 \times 10^3)$
   0.00263529

4. 543.2^4 **8.706408599E10**
   or 8.706408599E+10

GRAPHING CALCULATOR EXPLORATION 23

Lesson Resources

Reteaching Masters 1-4
Practice Master 1-4
Enrichment Master 1-4

 Transparency 1-4 contains the 5-Minute Check and a teaching aid for this lesson.

INTRODUCING THE LESSON

 5-Minute Check

(over Lesson 1-3)

State the property illustrated in each statement.

1. If $n = 8 + 1$ then $n = 9$.
   substitution
2. If $10 + 2 = 12$ then
   $(10 + 2) - 1 = 12 - 1$
   subtraction

Solve each equation.

3. $12f - 4 = 7 + f$ $f = 1$
4. $8(2n + 3) = 12$ $n = -\frac{3}{4}$
5. $6y + 1 = 3\left(2y - \frac{1}{3}\right)$
   no solution

Motivating the Lesson

Have a student pick a number. Have the student increase the number by 10. Next, find half of the new number. Decrease the number by five. Finally, double the result. What number did they get? Have several students try the sequence. Have students explain what happens.

1-4 Applications of Equations

Objectives

After studying this lesson, you should be able to:

1-4A ■ translate word expressions into mathematical expressions,
1-4B ■ translate word sentences into equations, and
1-4C ■ use equations to solve problems.

The language of algebra provides a powerful way to translate word expressions into algebraic or mathematical expressions. Variables are used to represent numbers that are not known. Any letter can be used as a variable.

Verbal Expression	Algebraic Expression
a number increased by 5	$x + 5$
twice the cube of *a number*	$2n^3$
the square of *a number* decreased by the cube of the *same number*	$x^2 - x^3$
three times the sum of *a number* and 7	$3(b + 7)$

Equations can be used to represent verbal mathematical sentences.

Verbal Sentence	Equation
Eight is equal to five plus three.	$8 = 5 + 3$
A number decreased by 7 is -3.	$y - 7 = -3$
A number divided by 3 is equal to $\frac{3}{4}$.	$\frac{x}{3} = \frac{3}{4}$

Example 1

APPLICATION

Construction

The Conte family is planning to put a railing around the deck in their backyard. The deck is in two pieces, a square and an equilateral triangle, which share a common side. They will buy 75 feet of railing to go around the outside of the deck. If the lumberyard will custom cut pieces of railing, how long should they have the pieces cut so that there is one piece for each side of the deck?

EXPLORE First, explore the problems and choose a variable to represent the unknown number. The problem asks us to find the length of each side.

Let s = the length of each side.

PLAN Now let's plan the solution. Write an equation that represents the relationship in the problem The diagram at the right may be helpful. The perimeter is five times the length of a side, so $5s = 75$.

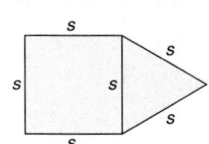

ALTERNATE TEACHING STRATEGIES

Using Critical Thinking

Given the equation $4 = 5 + x$, express the equation in words three different ways. Use a problem or a verbal sentence.

Do the same for each equation.
1. $x = 2(4)$
2. $15 = 2(x + 3)$

SOLVE Next, solve the equation.

$5s = 75$
$s = 15$ The length of a side is 15 feet.

EXAMINE Check your solution against the words of the problem and the diagram we drew. Since there are five equal sides that make up the perimeter of the deck, and $5 \times 15 = 75$, the solution is correct.

The four steps for solving problems that we just used are summarized below. **Teaching Tip ❶**

Problem-Solving Plan	1. **Explore the problem.** 2. **Plan the solution.** 3. **Solve the problem.** 4. **Examine the solution.**

Example 2

A number increased by 17 is 41. Find the number.

EXPLORE Let n stand for the number.

PLAN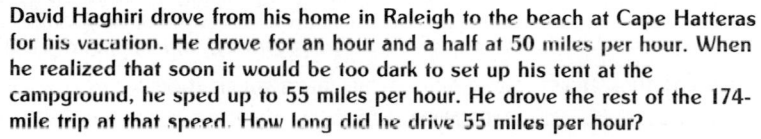

A number increased by 17 is 41.
  n $+$ $17 = 41$

SOLVE $n + 17 = 41$
$n = 24$ The number is 24.

EXAMINE Does 24 increased by 17 equal 41? $24 + 17 \stackrel{?}{=} 41$
$41 = 41$ ✓

Teaching Tip ❷

Example 3

David Haghiri drove from his home in Raleigh to the beach at Cape Hatteras for his vacation. He drove for an hour and a half at 50 miles per hour. When he realized that soon it would be too dark to set up his tent at the campground, he sped up to 55 miles per hour. He drove the rest of the 174-mile trip at that speed. How long did he drive 55 miles per hour?

EXPLORE Let t stand for the length of time he drove at 55 miles per hour.

PLAN total distance = distance at 50 mph + distance at 55 mph
         174   =   50(1.5)   +   55 · t

SOLVE $174 = 50(1.5) + 55 \cdot t$
$174 = 75 + 55t$
$99 = 55t$
$1.8 = t$ David drove 1.8 hours, or 1 hour 48 minutes, at 55 mph.

EXAMINE If David drives for 1.5 hours $1.5(50) + 1.8(55) \stackrel{?}{=} 174$
at 50 mph and for 1.8 hours at $75 + 99 \stackrel{?}{=} 174$
55 mph, will he travel 174 miles? $174 = 174$ ✓

FYI...

The city of Raleigh, North Carolina, is named for Sir Walter Raleigh. He established the first English settlement in North America on Roanoke Island in the 1580s.

LESSON 1-4 APPLICATIONS OF EQUATIONS 25

TEACHING THE LESSON

Teaching Tip ❶ Explain that in examining solutions the students should read the problem again rather than checking the equation. An incorrect equation can be solved but it will not answer the problem.

Teaching Tip ❷ Remind the students the formula for distance is rate times time.

Chalkboard Examples

For Example 1
Mrs. Campbell wants to put up new cabinets in her kitchen. She needs 1.5 feet for each cabinet and she has 10.5 feet of wall to put the cabinets on. How many cabinets can she put up?
7 cabinets

For Example 2
The product of three and a number is 10.5. Find the number.
n = the number $3n = 10.5$
$n = 3.5$

For Example 3
Alan Yoshio bought 5 pounds of peanuts for $2.50 per pound. He also bought cashews for $6.00 per pound. If Alan spent $30.50, how many pounds of cashews did he buy? p = pounds of cashews
$30.50 = 5(2.50) + p(6.00)$
$p = 3$

Chalkboard Example

For Example 4

The perimeter of a parallelogram is 52 cm. What is the length of the longer side if the shorter side measures 10 cm? ℓ = measure of the longer side

$2(10) + 2(\ell) = 52$

$20 + 2\ell = 52$

$\ell = 16$ cm.

EVALUATING THE LESSON

Check for Understanding

Exercises 1–14 are designed to help you assess understanding through reading, writing, and speaking. You should work through Exercises 1–3 with your students, and then monitor their work on Exercises 4–14.

Reteaching Masters Booklet, p. 4

Example 4

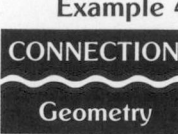
CONNECTION
Geometry

The perimeter of an isosceles triangle is 106 cm. The length of the base is 35 cm. What is the length of one of the equal sides?

EXPLORE   Draw a diagram and let n represent the length of one of the equal sides.

Sides of equal length are said to be congruent.

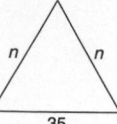

PLAN   The perimeter equals the sum of the lengths of the sides. So we can write the following equation.

$$n + n + 35 = 106$$

SOLVE $n + n + 35 = 106$

  $2n + 35 = 106$

  $2n = 71$

  $n = 35.5$ The length of one side is 35.5 cm.

EXAMINE   If one of the two equal sides has length 35.5 cm, then the perimeter is $35.5 + 35.5 + 35 = 106$ cm. The answer is correct.

CHECKING FOR UNDERSTANDING

Communicating Mathematics

Read and study the lesson to answer these questions.

1. Explain the difference between these word expressions: *the sum of twice a number and 2* and *twice the sum of a number and 2.*

2. Write an equation to find the length of a side of a regular octagon if its perimeter is 3000 centimeters. **$8s = 3000$**

3. Write an algebraic expression to represent the sum of 3 times a number and twice the sum of the number and 3. **$3n + 2(n + 3)$**

1. The first represents $2n + 2$, the second represents $2(n + 2)$.

Guided Practice

Choose a variable and write an algebraic expression to represent each verbal expression.

4. twice the sum of a number and 7 **$2(n + 7)$**

5. five times a number decreased by 4 **$5x - 4$**

6. the sum of twice a number and 7 **$2n + 7$**

7. three decreased by twice a number **$3 - 2n$**

8. twelve decreased by the square of a number **$12 - x^2$**

9. the product of the square of a number and six **$6x^2$**

10. one-fifth the sum of four and a number **$\frac{1}{5}(4 + x)$**

11. four times the sum of eight and a number **$4(8 + x)$**

12. eight times the sum of a number and its square **$8(x + x^2)$**

13. the sum of 8 and four times a number **$8 + 4n$**

14. the square of the sum of a number and 11 **$(x + 11)^2$**

RETEACHING THE LESSON

Write an equation and solve each problem.

1. If 60 is decreased by 3 times a number, the result is 24. Find the number.   **12**

2. The length of a rectangle is 3 inches less than twice the width. If the perimeter is 72 inches, find the dimensions of the rectangle.   **13 in. by 23 in.**

EXERCISES

Practice

A

Write an equation and solve each problem. Be sure to identify the variable.

15. You have $32 to spend on supplies for your science fair project. If you buy two plants for experiments, you will have $18 left for other supplies. How much is each plant? **$7**

16. Ida and Ron make doughnuts for the Homestyle Bakery. The order for Tuesday is two trays of glazed doughnuts and one tray of cinnamon rolls. If each tray contains 3 dozen items, how many pastries do they need to prepare? **108 items**

17. If you subtract 89 from a number, the result is 29. Find the number. **118**

18. The dealer's asking price for a new car is $9750. Maria Blackmunn offered to pay $7800. Maria's price is what percent of the dealer's price? **80%**

B

19. Darian's dad is 28 years older than Darian. The sum of their ages is 64. How old is Darian? **18 years old**

20. The sum of two consecutive odd integers is 124. What are the integers? **61, 63**

21. Mrs. Gampp was 24 years old when Brittany was born. In three years the sum of their ages will be 68 years. How old is each now? **Mrs. Gampp, 43; Brittany, 19**

22. Julie's scores on four English tests were 78%, 98%, 67%, and 90%. What must she score on the fifth test so that her average will be 85%? **92%**

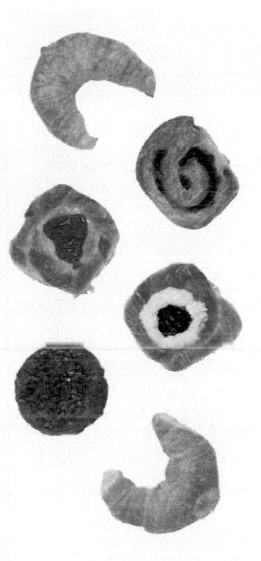

23. Don Owens bought a microwave oven for $60 more than half its original price. He paid $274 for the oven. What was the original price? **$428**

24. The Wilderness Club's treasurer, Eagan, bought some supplies for the fall rafting trip. He bought some raisins for 99¢ per pound and twice as many pounds of peanuts for $1.29 per pound. If the total bill was $24.99, how many pounds of peanuts did he buy? **14 lb**

25. Tickets to *A Midsummer Night's Dream* cost $10.50 for adults and $7.50 for students. Reba McGowen ordered $192 worth of tickets for a field trip for her English class. She ordered five times as many student tickets as adult tickets. How many of each did she order? **4 adult; 20 student**

26. The Forest Park High School Drama Club sold 320 adult tickets and 153 student tickets for their last performance. Adult tickets were 75¢ more than student tickets. If total receipts were $949.50, what was the price of each ticket? **$1.50 student, $2.25 adult**

C

CONNECTION
Geometry

27. Michael Werthan is on his way home to Fort Wayne for a family reunion. It is a 360 mile trip. He drives 65 mph for 3 hours. When the speed limit changes, he slows down to 55 mph for the rest of the trip. How long does Michael drive at 55 mph? **3 hours**

28. The width of a rectangular window frame is 12 inches less than its length. If you add 30 inches to both the length and the width, you double the perimeter. Find the length and the width of the original rectangle. **36 inches, 24 inches**

Critical Thinking

29. Write a verbal expression to represent the algebraic expression: $2y(y + 4) + 2(y + 6)$. **The sum of twice a number times the sum of the number and 4 and twice the sum of the number and 6**

LESSON 1-4 APPLICATIONS OF EQUATIONS 27

Error Analysis

Students may check their answers to verbal problems by substituting into their equation. The check requires that all conditions in the original problem have been met and should not assume the student's equation is correct. To help students complete checks to verbal problems, give students a set of verbal problems with a proposed answer to each problem. Students are to determine if the proposed answers are correct without solving the problem.

Assignment Guide

Basic: 15–26, 29–30, 32–35
Average: 17–35
Enriched: 19–35
All: Mid-Chapter Review, 1–16

Practice Masters Booklet, p. 4

1-4 **Practice Worksheet**

NAME _____ DATE _____

Applications of Equations

Write an equation and solve each problem. Be sure to identify the variable.

1. Fourteen less than twice some number is 154. Find the number. **84**

2. Craig is 24 years younger than his father. In 10 years, Craig's father will be three times as old as Craig will be. Find their ages now. **Craig: 2 years old; father: 26 years old**

3. The length of a rectangle is 9 centimeters more than half the width. Find the length if the perimeter is 60 centimeters. **16 cm**

4. It takes Kay 20 minutes to drive to work traveling 45 mph. Two minutes after she left home this morning, her husband, Dan, started out with her briefcase, which she had forgotten. If Dan arrived at Kay's office just as she did, how fast did he drive? **50 mph**

5. In an evening, a sporting goods store sold twice as many T-shirts as shorts. T-shirts are $9 each, and shorts are $14 each. The total amount of money taken in for both items was $256. Find the number of each that was sold. **8 shorts, 16 T-shirts**

Closing the Lesson

Writing Activity Have students make up their own problems. Then have them give it to a neighbor to solve. Have those who solve the problems analyze the word problem to see if they are solvable.

APPLYING THE LESSON

Homework Exercises

See assignment guide on page 27.

Chapter 1, Quiz B, (Lessons 1-3 through 1-4), is available in the Evaluation Masters Booklet, p. 9.

Enrichment Masters Booklet, p. 4

NAME _____ DATE _____

1-4 Enrichment Worksheet

Reading Mathematics

The following paragraph is an example of something you might have read in a first-year algebra textbook. The sentences in the paragraph are numbered.

01 The standard form of a linear equation is $Ax + By = C$, where A, B, and C are real numbers and the coefficients A and B are not both zero.

02 The graph of a linear equation is a straight line, so it is sometimes convenient to write a linear equation in the form $y = mx + b$, where m is the slope of the line and b is the y-intercept.

03 The slope is often defined informally as "rise over run."

04 The y-intercept is the value of b in the ordered pair $(0, b)$ and, as the figure shows, tells where the graph crosses the y-axis.

05 When discussing two different linear equations, you might write them as $A_1x + B_1y = C_1$ and $A_2x + B_2y = C_2$.

Use the paragraph to answer these questions.

1. In sentence 01, which letters stand for variables? Which stand for constants?
x and y are variables; A, B, and C are constants.
2. Use sentence 01. What form would a linear equation take if B were equal to zero?
$Ax = C$
3. Write three examples of the type of equation described in sentence 02.
Answers will vary.
4. What sections of the algebra textbook might help you find explanations for the terms "rise" and "run" used in sentence 03?
glossary, index, chapter summary and review
5. Sentence 04 refers to a drawing. Describe the drawing.
a line in the coordinate plane that crosses the y-axis at a point labeled $(0, b)$
6. In sentence 05, let $A_1 = B_1 = C_1 = 1$. Write two linear equations so that the coefficients of the second are double those of the first. **Answers will vary for C_2; possible answer: $x + y = 1$ and $2x + 2y = 1$**

Applications

31. add 6 inches to the length and 3 inches to the width

Mixed Review

30. **Entertainment** The Wheaton Theater sold 379 tickets on Tuesday for the movie *Home Alone 2*. On Wednesday, 532 tickets were sold. The total income for the two days was $5238.25. What was the price of each ticket? **$5.75**

31. **Photography** The perimeter of a rectangular photograph is 24 inches. The photographer wants to enlarge the photograph so that the perimeter is 42 inches. She will add twice as much to the length as to the width. How much should she add to the length and the width?

State the property illustrated in each equation.

32. $6 + a = 6 + a$ (**Lesson 1-3**) **reflexive property of equality**

33. $9 + (2 + 10) = 9 + 12$ (**Lesson 1-3**) **substitution property**

34. Simplify the expression $3(2x + 2) - 2(x - 1)$. (**Lesson 1-2**) **$4x + 8$**

35. Find the value of the expression $\frac{3a + 4c}{b}$, if $a = -3$, $b = 2$, and $c = 0.5$. (**Lesson 1-1**). **-3.5**

MID-CHAPTER REVIEW

Evaluate each expression. (**Lesson 1-1**)

1. $(6 + 3)5 - 6$ **39**
2. $4 + (3 + 6)9 - 2$ **83**

Evaluate each expression if $a = 6$, $b = -2$, and $c = 0.5$. (**Lesson 1-1**)

3. $ab - cb + a$ **-5**
4. $(ab)a + cb + abc$ **-79**

5. Given the formula for simple interest, $I = prt$, find the value of p when $I = \$23.45$, $r = 8\%$, and $t = 3$ years. **97.71**

Name the sets of numbers to which each number belongs. (**Lesson 1-2**)

6. 13π **I, R**
7. $12 \div 7$ **Q, R**
8. 67 **N, W, Z, Q, R**

State the property illustrated in each equation. (**Lesson 1-2**)

9. $3(4 - 2) = 3(4) - 3(2)$ **distributive**
10. $(3 + 4) + 5 = 3 + (4 + 5)$ **associative**

Solve each equation. (**Lesson 1-3**)

11. $1.2x + 3.7 = 34.6$ **25.75**
12. $2x - (3x - 6) + 4x = 3x + 45$ **no solution**

Write an algebraic expression to represent each verbal expression. (**Lesson 1-4**)

13. the sum of three times a number and nine **$3n + 9$**
14. the square of the sum of a number and 2 **$(n + 2)^2$**

Write an equation and solve each problem. Be sure to identify the variable. (**Lesson 1-4**)

15. A number increased by 45 is 213. What is the number? **168**
16. The sum of three times a number and 7 is 46. What is the number? **13**

EXTENDING THE LESSON

Math Power: Problem Solving

Carla DeLeon is traveling to Pittsburgh, which is 311 miles away. She drives at a fixed rate of speed for the first 2 hours. She increases her speed by 7 miles per hour for the next 3 hours. What are the rates of speed for each part of Carla's trip? **58 mph; 65 mph**

Mid-Chapter Review

The Mid-Chapter Review provides students with a brief review of the concepts and skills in Lessons 1–1 through 1–4. Lesson numbers are given at the end of problems or instruction lines so students may review concepts not yet mastered.

Problem Solving Strategy: List the Possibilities

EXPLORE
PLAN
SOLVE
EXAMINE

Objective
1-5

After studying this lesson, you should be able to:
■ solve problems by making lists.

Application

The telephone area codes in the United States and Canada are three-digit numbers.

1st digit: 2, 3, 4, 5, 6, 7, 8, or 9
2nd digit: 0 or 1
3rd digit: any digit but 0

How many different area codes can start with the digit 3?

One way that we can find the answer is to list the possibilities. Let's make an organized list of possible area codes to answer this question.

The second digit of any code must be a 0 or 1. Assuming that the first digit is 3, list all of the possible codes with a second digit of 0.

301	302	303	304	305	*Why is 300 not a possible*
306	307	308	309		*code?*

List all of the possible codes with 1 as a second digit.

311   312   313   314   315   316   317   318   319

There are 18 possible area codes that begin with the digit 3.

Example

Lee forgot the identification number for his automatic teller bank card. He remembered that he had rearranged the digits from his house number to program the code. If his house number is 1256, what codes should he try in the automatic teller machine?

List the possible codes.

Possible codes starting with 1:			Possible codes starting with 2:		
1265	1526		2156	2165	2516
1562	1625	1652	2561	2615	2651

Why isn't 1256 listed?

Possible codes starting with 5:			Possible codes starting with 6:		
5126	5162	5216	6125	6152	6215
5261	5612	5621	6251	6512	6521

These are the 23 possible codes that Lee should try in the automatic teller machine. **Teaching Tip** ❶

RETEACHING THE LESSON

At Pete's Pizza there are three possible toppings: pepperoni, mushrooms, and onions. List all 8 different types of pizza that can be made at Pete's Pizza. Use initials of toppings to abbreviate answers. For example, MP is a mushroom-pepperoni pizza.

1-5 Lesson Notes

Lesson Resources

Practice Master 1-5
Activity Master, p. 1

Transparency 1-5 contains the 5-Minute check and a teaching aid for this lesson.

INTRODUCING THE LESSON

⏱ 5-Minute Check

(over Lesson 1-4)

1. Choose a variable and write an expression.
   three times the sum of a number and its square
   $3(x + x^2)$

2. Write an equation and solve the problem.
   If you add 23 to a number, the result is 64. Find the number. $n + 23 = 64$ **41**

Motivating the Lesson

List all of the possible combinations for the combining of the first four letters of the alphabet.   **24**

TEACHING THE LESSON

Teaching Tip ❶   Remind students that if this really did happen he could not try all of these cases. Most machines only give you three chances.

Chalkboard Example

For the Example
Jason is a teller for Happy Valley Bank. He received three receipts for deposits and noticed that they did not add up to the total amount deposited into the customer's account. He thinks some of the numbers were transposed when they were added on the calculator. If all three deposits were two digits, how many combinations must he try to check his theory?   **7**

EVALUATING THE LESSON

Checking for Understanding

Exercises 1–5 are designed to help you assess understanding through reading, writing, and speaking. You should work through Exercises 1–3 with your students, and then monitor their work on Exercises 4–5.

Closing the Lesson

Modeling Activity Give students counters in five colors. Have the students model the combinations with one of the colors staying in the first place. Can they conjecture how many cases there will be from this one case?

APPLYING THE LESSON

Homework Exercises

Assignment Guide

Basic: 6–10
Average: 6–10
Enriched: 6–10

Practice Masters Booklet, p. 5

Communicating Mathematics

Read and study the lesson to answer these questions. 1–2. **See Solutions Manual.**

1. When is the strategy of listing possiblities useful?

2. Why is it helpful to make your list organized when using this strategy?

3. What is another way that we could have organized our list to answer the question in the example? **Answers may vary.**

Guided Practice

Use the strategy of listing possibilities to answer these questions.

4. Your Algebra 2 quiz consists of five true-or-false questions. How many different patterns of answers are possible? **32 patterns**

5. The Charlotte Hornets have won 4 and lost 2 games this season. List the patterns of records that are possible. **See margin.**

Exercises

Strategies
Look for a pattern.
Solve a simpler problem.
Act it out.
Guess and check.
Draw a diagram.
Make a chart.
Work backwards.

7. Over time, taking the raise first is best.

Solve. Use any strategy.

6. Each letter in the addition problem at the right represents a digit. Find the digits that form this sum.

$$\begin{array}{r} \text{TWO} \\ + \text{ TWO} \\ \hline \text{FOUR} \end{array}$$

Sample answer:
$$\begin{array}{r} 765 \\ +765 \\ \hline 1530 \end{array}$$

7. Your salary is to be raised 10 percent and then a month later reduced by 10 percent. You may elect to have the cut first and then the raise. Which is the better choice? *Hint: Look at the total income for the year.*

8. The telephone number of a local business is 555-1829. They are trying to make a word from the last three digits of their number so that customers will remember it easily. The digit 8 can be T, U, or V; 2 can be A, B, or C; and 9 can be W, X, or Y. List the possible combinations of letters that their number can represent. **See margin.**

9. The students in a gym class are standing in a circle. When they count off, the students with numbers 5 and 23 are standing exactly opposite one another. Assuming the students are evenly spaced around the circle, how many students are there in the class? **36 students**

10. Place operation symbols and any necessary grouping symbols in the sentence below to make it correct.
$$7\ 7\ 7\ 7\ 7\ 7\ 7 = 43$$

Sample answer: $7 \times 7 - 7 + 7 \div 7 \times 7 \div 7 = 43$

COOPERATIVE LEARNING ACTIVITY

Work in groups. Each person in the group must understand the solution and be able to explain it to any person in class.

The chemistry teacher at Stevenson High School is ordering equipment for the laboratory. She wants to order sets of five weights totaling 121 grams for each lab station. Students will need to be able to weigh every integral weight from 1 to 121 grams using these weights and a two-pan balance. What weights should the teacher order? *Hint: Recall that weights can be placed on both sides of the balance.*

1, 3, 9, 27, and 81 grams
30 CHAPTER 1 EQUATIONS AND INEQUALITIES

EXTENDING THE LESSON

Math Power: Communication

Given the equation $3n + 24 = 105$, write a problem that fits the equation. Then explain in writing, without using another equation, how to solve the problem. Make sure to list the strategy and why it was chosen.

Additional Answers

5. WWWWLL, WWWLLW,
   WLWLWW, WWWLWL,
   WWLWLW, LWWLWW,
   WWLWWL, WLWWLW,
   WLLWWW, WLWWWL,
   LWWWLW, LWLWWW,
   LWWWWL, WWLLWW,
   LLWWWW

8. TAW, TAX, TAY, TBW, TBX,
   TBY, TCW, TCX, TCY, UAW,
   UAX, UAY, UBW, UBX, UBY,
   UCW, UCX, UCY, VAW, VAX,
   VAY, VBW, VBX, VBY, VCW,
   VCX, VCY

Solving Absolute Value Equations

Objective
1-6

After studying this lesson, you should be able to:

■ solve equations containing absolute value.

Application

Suppose you and your friend, Terry, each live on the same street as your school, but on opposite sides of the school. You each live 5 miles from the school. What can you say about your trips to school each day? Do you each travel the same direction? Do you travel the same distance?

Consider placing both houses and the school on a number line with the school at the origin. Your house is located at 5, and Terry's is located at −5.

Certainly −5 and 5 are quite different, but they do have something in common. They are the same distance from 0 on the number line. This means that you and Terry travel the same distance, but in different directions, when you go to school.

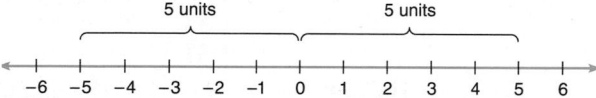

We say that −5 and 5 have the same **absolute value.** The absolute value of a number is the number of units it is from 0 on the number line. We use the symbol $|x|$ to represent the absolute value of a number x.

The absolute value of −5 is 5.

$$|-5| = 5$$

The absolute value of 5 is 5.

$$|5| = 5$$

We can also define absolute value in the following way.

Teaching Tip ❶

Absolute Value

> **For any real number a:**
> If $a \geq 0$, then $|a| = a$.
> If $a < 0$, then $|a| = -a$.

The symbol ≥ means "is greater than or equal to."

Example 1

Find the absolute value of 8 and the absolute value of −12.

$$|8| = 8 \qquad |-12| = -(-12) \text{ or } 12$$

Example 2

Find the absolute value of $x - 9$.

Let's make a list of the possible cases.
If x is 9 or greater, then $x - 9 \geq 0$. So, $|x - 9| = x - 9$.
If x is less than 9, then $x - 9 < 0$. So, $|x - 9| = -(x - 9)$ or $9 - x$.

LESSON 1-6 SOLVING ABSOLUTE VALUE EQUATIONS **31**

ALTERNATE TEACHING STRATEGIES

Using Critical Thinking

Have students solve the equation $4 - |x + 12| = 3$. How do they deal with the second step where $-|x + 12| = -1$? Explain to them that this expression is saying to take the opposite of the absolute value. Why does it have a solution?

Example 3

Evaluate $|2x - 4| + 1.2$ if $x = ^-3$.
$$\begin{aligned}
|2x - 4| + 1.2 &= |2(^-3) - 4| + 1.2 \\
&= |^-6 - 4| + 1.2 \\
&= |^-10| + 1.2 \\
&= 10 + 1.2 \\
&= 11.2 \qquad \text{The value is 11.2.}
\end{aligned}$$

Some equations contain absolute value expressions. The definition of absolute value is used in solving the equations. When more than one solution occurs, they are often written as a set, $\{a, b\}$.

Example 4

Solve $|x - 7| = 12$. Check each solution.
$$|x - 7| = 12$$

If $x - 7$ is positive or zero → $x - 7 = 12$ or $x - 7 = ^-12$ ← *If $x - 7$ is negative*
$$x = 19 \quad \text{or} \quad x = ^-5$$

Check: $|x - 7| = 12$
$|19 - 7| \overset{?}{=} 12$ or $|^-5 - 7| \overset{?}{=} 12$
$|12| \overset{?}{=} 12$ $|^-12| \overset{?}{=} 12$
$12 = 12$ ✓ $12 = 12$ ✓

The solutions are 19 and $^-5$. The solution set is $\{19, ^-5\}$.

Example 5

APPLICATION

Manufacturing

FYI ...

Each American eats an average of 62 pounds of sugar in one year.

A machine that fills boxes of sugar is to fill the boxes with 16 ounces of sugar. After the boxes are filled, another machine weighs the boxes. If the box is more than 0.2 ounces above or below the desired weight, the box is rejected. What is the weight of the heaviest and the lightest box that the machine will let pass?

Let w = the weight of the box. $|w - 16| = 0.2$
$w - 16 = 0.2$ or $w - 16 = ^-0.2$
$w = 16.2$ or $w = 15.8$

The heaviest box allowed to pass is 16.2 ounces. The lightest box allowed to pass is 15.8 ounces.

An absolute value equation may have no solution. For example, $|x| = ^-4$ is never true. Since the absolute value of a number is always positive or zero, there is no replacement for x that will make that sentence true. The solution set has no members. It is called the **empty set** and is symbolized by $\{\ \}$ or $\emptyset$.

Example 6

Solve $|3x + 7| + 4 = 0$.
$$|3x + 7| + 4 = 0$$
$$|3x + 7| = ^-4 \qquad \text{This sentence is \textit{never} true, so the equation}$$
has *no solution*. The solution set is $\emptyset$.

It is important to check your answers when solving absolute value equations. Even if the correct procedure for solving the equations is used, the answers may not be actual solutions to the original equation.

Example 7

Solve $|x - 8| = 3x - 4$.

$$|x - 8| = 3x - 4$$

$x - 8 = 3x - 4$ or $x - 8 = -(3x - 4)$
$-8 = 2x - 4$ $\qquad\qquad$ $x - 8 = -3x + 4$
$-4 = 2x$ $\qquad\qquad\quad$ $4x = 12$
$-2 = x$ $\qquad\qquad\qquad$ $x = 3$

Check: $\qquad\qquad\qquad |x - 8| = 3x - 4$

$|(-2) - 8| \stackrel{?}{=} 3(-2) - 4$ or $|(3) - 8| \stackrel{?}{=} 3(3) - 4$
$|-2 - 8| \stackrel{?}{=} -6 - 4$ $\qquad\qquad$ $|3 - 8| \stackrel{?}{=} 9 - 4$
$10 = -10$ *no* $\qquad\qquad\qquad$ $5 = 5$ $\checkmark$

The only solution is 3.

Teaching Tip ❷

Example 8

Use a calculator to evaluate $9|2y - 4.25|$ when $y = 1.5$.

First evaluate $2y - 4.25$.

ENTER: 2 [×] 1.5 [−] 4.25 [=] -1.25

Since an absolute value cannot be negative, change the sign of the number in the display before multiplying by 9.

ENTER: [+/−] [×] 9 [=] 11.25 The value is 11.25.

CHECKING FOR UNDERSTANDING

Communicating Mathematics

1. To be a solution, the absolute value of the expression would have to be -2, but absolute value cannot be negative.

Read and study the lesson to answer these questions.

1. Explain why the equation $|2x - 3| + 4 = 2$ has no solution.

2. Explain why there is no solution for the equation in Example 6. **$|3x + 7|$ must be non-negative, so it can never be equal to -4.**

3. The second part of the definition of absolute value is "If $a < 0$, then $|a| = -a$." To some people $-a$ may appear to represent a negative number. How would you explain that it always represents a positive number? **a is a negative number, so $-a$ is a positive number.**

4. Is $-x < x$ always true, sometimes true, or never true? Explain your answer. **Sometimes true. If $x < 0$ then $-x > x$. If $x > 0$, then $-x < x$. If $x = 0$, then $-x = x$.**

LESSON 1-6 SOLVING ABSOLUTE VALUE EQUATIONS 33

RETEACHING THE LESSON

Solve each equation.

1. $|x - 4| = 3$ **7, 1**
2. $|x + 5| = 3$ **-2, -8**
3. $|6 - x| = 10$ **-4, 16**
4. $|2x - 5| = 7$ **6, -1**
5. $|x - 7| = -4$ **∅**
6. $-3|x + 2| = -12$ **2, -6**

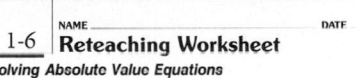
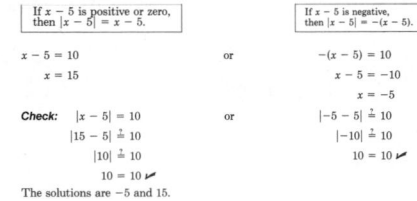

Error Analysis

Solving $|x - 3| = -4$ by applying the definition of absolute value yields $x - 3 = -4$ or $-(x - 3) = -4$

$x = -1$ or $x = 7$

Realizing that an absolute value can never be negative would have helped, but why didn't applying the definition of absolute value work? The overlooked subtlety is that $|x - 3| = x - 3$ only for $x - 3 \geq 0$ or $x \geq 3$. The solution set is $\{x | x \geq 3 \text{ and } x = -1\} \cup \{x | x < 3 \text{ and } x = 7\}$ or $\emptyset \cup \emptyset$, or $\emptyset$.

Closing the Lesson

Writing Activity   Write an explanation as to why $|x - 8| = 3x - 4$ has no solution when $x = -2$. Then write an absolute value problem of your own that has no solution.

Guided Practice

Evaluate each expression if $x = -4$.

5. $|4x|$ **16**

6. $|-2x|$ **8**

7. $-|3x - 4|$ **−16**

8. $|-2x - 5|$ **3**

9. $7 - |3x + 10|$ **5**

10. $2|x + 4| + |2x|$ **8**

Determine which numbers in the set $\{-2, -1, 0, 1, 2\}$ are solutions for each equation.

11. $|-x| = 2$ **2, −2**

12. $|x - 2| = 1$ **1**

13. $|x| = -x$ **−2, −1, 0**

14. $|x| = x$ **0, 1, 2**

15. $-x = |x - 2|$ **no solution**

16. $|x| = |x - 4|$ **2**

EXERCISES

Practice   Solve each equation.

A
17. $|x + 6| = 19$ **13, −25**

18. $|x + 11| = 42$ **31, −53**

19. $|x - 4| = 11$ **15, −7**

20. $|x - 3| = 17$ **20, −14**

21. $3|x + 6| = 36$ **6, −18**

22. $8|x - 3| = 88$ **14, −8**

23. $5|x + 4| = 45$ **5, −13**

24. $11|x - 9| = 121$ **20, −2**

B
25. $|2x + 9| = 30$ **10.5, −19.5**

26. $|2x - 37| = 15$ **26, 11**

27. $|2x + 7| = 0$ $-\frac{7}{2}$

28. $|4x - 3| = -27$ **no solution**

29. $3|3x + 2| = 51$ **5,** $-\frac{19}{3}$

30. $8|4x - 3| = 64$ $\frac{11}{4}, -\frac{5}{4}$

31. $-6|2x - 14| = -42$ **3.5, 10.5**

32. $4|6x - 1| = 29$ $\frac{11}{8}, -\frac{25}{24}$

33. $7|3x + 5| = 35$ **0,** $-\frac{10}{3}$

34. $|2a + 7| = a - 4$ **no solution**

C
35. $|x - 3| = 2x$ **1**

36. $3|x + 6| = 9x - 6$ **4**

37. $|7 + 3a| = 11 - a$ **1, −9**

38. $|3t - 5| = 2t$ **1, 5**

39. $|x - 3| + 7 = 2$ **no solution**

40. $5|3x - 4| = x + 1$ $\frac{3}{2}, \frac{19}{16}$

Critical Thinking
41. Solve $|x + 2| = |2x - 4|$ and explain your method of solution. **6,** $\frac{2}{3}$**; See students' work.**

Applications
42. **Cartography**   Columbus is between Cincinnati and Cleveland, and all three cities are located on Interstate 71. Cleveland is 140 miles from Columbus, and Cincinnati is 108 miles from Columbus. Draw a diagram of the situation and find the distance from Cleveland to Cincinnati. **See students' work; 248 miles**

43. **Manufacturing**   Mary Lou's Fudge Factory sells fudge in one pound tins. Each tin is weighed before it is packaged for shipping. If a tin weighs 0.05 pounds more or less than one pound, it is not shipped. What are the largest and smallest amounts of fudge that are allowable? **1.05 and 0.95 pounds**

34   CHAPTER 1   EQUATIONS AND INEQUALITIES

EXTENDING THE LESSON

Math Power: Reasoning

Solve $|3x| - |x + 1| = 5$. Show how you would set up the equations to be solved. Do you come up with some solutions that don't work?   **3, −2**

Computer Teaching Tip ❸

44. This program finds approximate solutions of the equation $|x^2 - 2| = 0$. Two values for x are entered, and two values for $|x^2 - 2|$ are printed as y-values. When one y-value is negative and the other is positive, a solution exists between the two x-values. Next, enter x-values between the previous two and check again for y-values with different signs.

```
10  DEFFNF(X) = ABS(X^2-2)
15  PRINT "ENTER 2 VALUES."
20  INPUT X1,X2
30  PRINT "X","Y"
40  PRINT X1,FNF(X1)
50  PRINT X2,FNF(X2)
60  PRINT "TRY AGAIN?(Y/N)";
70  GET A$
80  IF A$ = "Y" THEN 15
90  END
```

Journal

Tell how making a drawing might help you write the equation to solve a problem.

Continue this process until a y-value is obtained that is as close to zero as desired. The corresponding x-value is the approximate solution. For $|x^2 - 2| = 0$, the approximate solutions are 1.4 and -1.4 to the nearest tenth. Use the program above to approximate to the nearest tenth the number of solutions indicated for each equation. You will need to change line 10 of the program for each equation. All solutions are between -10 and 10. **See margin.**

a. $x^2 - 2 - 4 = 0$; 2 solutions
b. $x^3 - 3x = 0$; 3 solutions
c. $|3x - 2| - 4 = 0$; 2 solutions
d. $5x^3 + 3x^2 - 25x - 15 = 0$; 3 solutions

Mixed Review

46. E, A, AH;
E, AH, A;
A, E, AH;
A, AH, E;
AH, E, A;
AH, A, E

45. Lisa forgot the 3-digit address of her aunt's house, but remembered that the digits are 1, 3, and 9. What are all of the possible addresses? **(Lesson 1–5)** 139, 193, 319, 391, 913, 931

Teaching Tip ❹

46. What are all the possible arrangements of a class schedule containing English, Algebra 2, and American History? **(Lesson 1-5)**

47. Write an algebraic expression to represent the sum of a number and its square. **(Lesson 1-4)** $x + x^2$

48. Evaluate $\sqrt{16} + \sqrt{9}$ and tell the sets of numbers to which the solution belongs. **(Lesson 1-2)** 7; N, W, Z, Q, R

HISTORY CONNECTION

Mileva Einstein

In 1905, Albert Einstein published three papers that changed the world of science forever. His theory of relativity, quantum theory of light, and proof of the existence of the atom made him the symbol of genius. However, in recent years it has come to light that Einstein may have had some help with these discoveries . . . from his wife. Mileva Maric Einstein was a brilliant physicist, who attended the Swiss Federal Institute of Technology. In a biography of Mrs. Einstein, Abram Joffe claims to have seen the original manuscript for a paper on relativity that was signed Einstein-Maric. Maybe Albert Einstein wasn't a "solitary" genius after all.

History Connection

The History Connection features introduce students to persons or cultures who were involved in the development of mathematics. You may want students to further research the Einsteins or to research the theory of relativity.

Additional Answers

44a. $-2.4, 2.4$
44b. $-1.7, 0, 1.7$
44c. $-0.7, 2$
44d. $-2.2, -0.6, 2.2$

APPLYING THE LESSON

Homework Exercises

Assignment Guide

Basic: 17–34, 41–42, 45–48
Average: 20–37, 44–48
Enriched: 23–48

Chapter 1, Quiz C, (Lessons 1-5 through 1-6), is available in the Evaluation Masters Booklet, p. 10.

Teaching Tip ❸ You may want to show students the bisection method. Once two x-values yield y-values of different signs, use, as the next two x-values, one previous x-value and the value halfway between. If the new y-values do not have different signs, use the other previous x-value and the midpoint value.

Teaching Tip ❹ Make sure the students remember to be organized when they list the sets. This helps to ensure the inclusion of all the cases.

Enrichment Masters Booklet, p. 5

NAME _____ DATE _____

1-6 Enrichment Worksheet

Venn Diagrams

Relationships among sets can be shown using Venn diagrams. Study the diagrams below. The circles represent sets A and B, which are subsets of set S.

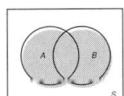 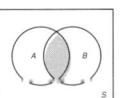 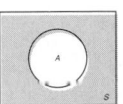

The union of A and B consists of all elements in *either* A or B.
The intersection of A and B consists of all elements in *both* A and B.
The complement of A consists of all elements *not* in A.

You can combine the operations of union, intersection, and finding the complement.

Example: Shade the region $(A \cap B)'$.

$(A \cap B)'$ means the complement of the intersection of A and B.
First find the intersection of A and B.
Then find its complement.

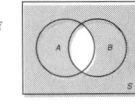

Draw a Venn diagram and shade the region indicated. **See students' diagrams.**

1. $A' \cap B$
2. $A' \cup B$
3. $A' \cap B'$
4. $A' \cup B'$
5. $(A \cup B)'$
6. $A \cap B'$

Draw a Venn diagram with three overlapping circles. Then shade the region indicated. **See students' diagrams.**

7. $(A \cup B) \cup C'$
8. $(A \cup B)' \cap C'$
9. $A \cup (B \cup C)$
10. $(A \cup B) \cup C$

11. Is the union operation associative? **yes**
12. Is the intersection operation associative? **yes**

Lesson Resources

Reteaching Master 1-7
Practice Master 1-7
Enrichment Master 1-7
Technology Master, p. 18
Activity Master, p. 19

Transparency 1-7 contains the
5-Minute Check and a teaching aid
for this lesson.

INTRODUCING THE LESSON

 5-Minute Check

(over Lesson 1-6)

1. Evaluate $|4x + 1|$ if $x = -2$.
   7

Solve each equation.

2. $|x + 10| = 12$ **2, -22**
3. $4|x - 9| = 44$ **-2, 20**
4. $2|2x + 1| = -10$
   no solution
5. $5|x - 2| = 2x + 11$ **7, $-\frac{1}{7}$**

Motivating the Lesson

Here are two inequalities.

$$-5 < -4 \qquad 8 > 5$$

Is each inequality still true if you:

1. add 2 to each side?
2. add -2 to each side?
3. multiply each side by 2?
4. multiply each side by -2?

1-7 Solving Inequalities

Objectives

After studying this lesson, you should be able to:

1-7A ▪ solve an inequality and graph the solution set, and

1-7B ▪ use inequalities to solve problems.

Application

José and Kyle are soccer players on the Union High School team. If you compare their scoring for the season, only one of the following statements will be true.

José scored fewer goals than Kyle.
José scored the same number of goals as Kyle.
José scored more goals than Kyle.

Let j represent the number of goals José scored and k represent the number of goals Kyle scored. You can compare the scoring using an inequality or an equation.

$$j < k \qquad\qquad j = k \qquad\qquad j > k$$

This is an illustration of the trichotomy property.

Trichotomy Property	For any two real numbers, a and b, exactly one of the following statements is true. $a < b \qquad a = b \qquad a > b$

Adding the same number to each side of an inequality does not change the truth of the inequality.

Addition and Subtraction Properties for Inequalities	For any real numbers, a, b, and c: 1. If $a > b$, then $a + c > b + c$ and $a - c > b - c$. 2. If $a < b$, then $a + c < b + c$ and $a - c < b - c$.

These properties can be used to solve an inequality. The solution set of an inequality can be graphed on a number line.

36 CHAPTER 1 EQUATIONS AND INEQUALITIES

ALTERNATE TEACHING STRATEGIES

Using Charts

Multiply the inequality by the set listed. Make a chart of the results.

$$-2 < 5$$
$$\{2, 1, 0, -1, -2\}$$

Write the results as a series of inequalities.

What do you notice about the results?

Using Computers

Write a flow chart showing how to solve inequalities. Make one flow chart for addition and one flow chart for multiplication. Remember to include the decision box.

Example 1

Solve $8x + 5 < 7x - 3$. Graph the solution set.

$$8x + 5 < 7x - 3$$
$$-7x + 8x + 5 < -7x + 7x - 3 \quad \textit{Add -7x to each side.}$$
$$x + 5 < -3$$
$$x + 5 + (-5) < -3 + (-5) \quad \textit{Add -5 to each side.}$$
$$x < -8$$

A circle means this point is not included.

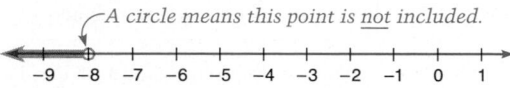

Any real number less than -8 is a solution.

To check, substitute -8 for x in $8x + 5 < 7x - 3$. The two sides should be equal. Then substitute a number less than -8. The inequality should be true. **Teaching Tip ❶**

You know that $15 > -6$ is a true inequality. What happens if you multiply the numbers on each side by a positive number or a negative number? Is it still true?

Try 7.	*Try $-\frac{1}{3}$.*
$15 > -6$	$15 > -6$
$7(15) \overset{?}{>} 7(-6)$	$-\frac{1}{3}(15) \overset{?}{>} -\frac{1}{3}(-6)$
$105 > -42 \quad True$	$-5 > 2 \quad False$

Multiply the inequality by other positive numbers. Do you think that the inequality will always remain true?

If you reverse the inequality, the statement is true.

$$-5 < 2 \quad True$$

Try other negative numbers as multipliers.

This suggests that when you multiply each side of an inequality by a negative number, the order of the inequality must be reversed.

These examples suggest the following properties.

Multiplication and Division Properties for Inequalities

For any real numbers a, b, and c:

1. If c is positive and $a < b$, then $ac < bc$ and $\dfrac{a}{c} < \dfrac{b}{c}$.

2. If c is positive and $a > b$, then $ac > bc$ and $\dfrac{a}{c} > \dfrac{b}{c}$.

3. If c is negative and $a < b$, then $ac > bc$ and $\dfrac{a}{c} > \dfrac{b}{c}$.

4. If c is negative and $a > b$, then $ac < bc$ and $\dfrac{a}{c} < \dfrac{b}{c}$.

Examples 2 and 3 show how to use these properties when solving inequalities.

Teaching Tip ❶ To check inequalities, first check the boundary point for the variable and see if the two sides are equivalent. To make sure the direction of the inequality is correct, check a point on each side of the boundary point.

Chalkboard Example

For Example 1
Solve $y + 6 > 3$. $\quad y > -3$

Reteaching Masters Booklet, p. 6

Example 2 Solve $-0.5y < 6$. Graph the solution set.

$$-0.5y < 6$$
$$(-2)(-0.5y) > (-2)(6)$$ *Reverse the inequality sign because each side is multiplied by a negative.*
$$y > -12$$

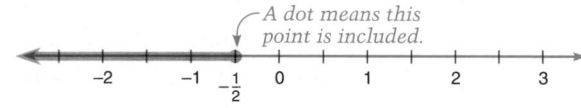

Any real number greater than -12 is a solution.

The solutions in Example 2 can be written using set-builder notation. This solution set can be written as $\{y|y > -12\}$. This is read as *the set of all numbers y such that y is greater than -12.*

Example 3 Solve $-x \geq \frac{x + 4}{7}$. Graph the solution set.

$$-x \geq \frac{x + 4}{7}$$
$$-7x \geq x + 4$$ *Multiply each side by 7.*
$$-8x \geq 4$$ *Add $-x$ to each side.*
$$x \leq -\frac{1}{2}$$ *Divide each side by -8, reversing the inequality sign.*

A dot means this point is included.

The solution set is $\left\{x|x \leq -\frac{1}{2}\right\}$.

Inequalities can be used to solve many verbal problems. You solve problems with inequalities the same way that you solve problems with equations.
Teaching Tip ❷

Example 4

APPLICATION

Finance

Judy Kildow received a $10,000 inheritance that she wishes to invest. She wants to earn at least $780 in interest this year so she can buy a stereo system with her earnings. She will invest some of the money in bonds that earn about 6% interest annually and the rest in stock that she expects to earn 9% interest annually. What is the minimum she should invest in the stock? *The phrase at least 780 means greater than or equal to 780.*

EXPLORE Let n = the amount invested in stocks.
Then $10,000 - n$ = amount invested in bonds.

PLAN (rate)(amount) + (rate)(amount) $\geq$ minimum desired
$(0.09)(n)$ $(0.06)(10,000 - n) \geq$ 780

SOLVE $0.09n + 600 - 0.06n \geq 780$
$0.03n \geq 180$
$n \geq 6000$

Judy must invest at least $6000 in stock.

RETEACHING THE LESSON

Solve each inequality. Graph the solution set. **See students' graphs.**

1. $3 - 2x < 9$ $x > -3$
2. $4x + 7 \geq 3(x + 2)$ $x \geq -1$
3. $3x > 4x$ $x < 0$
4. $2x > x + 1 + x$ $\varnothing$
5. $3(x + 2) < 3x + 8$ **all reals**
6. $4x + 3 \leq -33$ $x \leq -9$

EXAMINE Find the amount of interest she will earn from investing $6000
in stocks and $4000 in bonds. Is the total at least $780?

6% of $4000 = $240
9% of $6000 = $540
          $780 total √

Check an amount more than $6000 in stocks. Be sure the total is greater than $780.

CHECKING FOR UNDERSTANDING

Communicating Mathematics

1. Reverse the order of the inequality.

Read and study the lesson to answer these questions.

1. Explain in your own words what you must do if you are going to multiply each side of an inequality by a negative number.

2. Translate *twice the sum of a number and 3 is less than 6* into algebraic symbols. $2(x + 3) < 6$

3. Translate *eighteen is at least 3 three times the product of 5 and a number* into algebraic symbols. $18 \geq 3(5x)$

4. The graph below is a graph of the solution set of an inequality. What is the solution set? $\{x | x > -2\}$

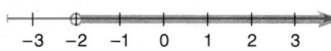

Guided Practice Graph the solution set of each inequality. **5–10. See margin.**

5. $x \leq 0$ 6. $x > -3$ 7. $x > 4.5$

8. $0.75x < 4$ 9. $-3x > 6$ 10. $x < -7.5$

EXERCISES

Practice Solve each inequality. Graph the solution set. **For graphs, see Solutions Manual.**

A

11. $6x + 4 > 34$ $\{x | x > 5\}$ 12. $8 - 3x < 44$ $\{x | x > -12\}$

13. $6s - 7 < 29$ $\{s | s < 6\}$ 14. $5r + 8 > 24$ $\{r | r > 3.2\}$

15. $15 - 5t \geq 55$ $\{t | t \leq -8\}$ 16. $x - 5 < 0.1$ $\{x | x < 5.1\}$

17. $11 - 5y < -77$ $\{y | y > 17.6\}$ 18. $28 - 6y < 23$

                                                                        $\left\{y | y > \frac{5}{6}\right\}$

Solve each inequality.

B

19. $3(4x + 7) < 21$ $\{x | x < 0\}$ 20. $5(2x - 7) > 10$ $\{x | x > 4.5\}$

21. $5(3z - 3) \leq 60$ $\{z | z \leq 5\}$ 22. $-49 > 7(2x + 3)$ $\{x | x < -5\}$

23. $7x - 5 > 3x + 4$ $\{x | x > 2.25\}$ 24. $40 \leq -6(5r - 7)$

25. $7 - 2x \geq 0$ $\{x | x \leq 3.5\}$ 26. $2(r - 4) + 5 \geq 9$ $\{r | r \geq 6\}$

27. $2(3m + 4) - 2 \leq 3(1 + 3m)$ 28. $2(m - 5) - 3(2m - 5) < 5m + 1$

29. $7 + 3y > 2(y + 3) - 2(-1 - y)$ 30. $3b - 2(b - 5) < 2(b + 4)$

31. $0.01x - 4.23 \geq 0$ $\{x | x \geq 423\}$ 32. $0.75x - 0.5 < 0$ $\{x | x < 0.\overline{6}\}$

24. $\left\{r | r \leq \frac{1}{15}\right\}$

27. $\{m | m \geq 1\}$

28. $\left\{m | m > \frac{4}{9}\right\}$

29. $\{y | y < -1\}$

30. $\{b | b > 2\}$

LESSON 1-7 SOLVING INEQUALITIES 39

Additional Answers

5.
-6 -5 -4 -3 -2 -1 0 1 2 3

6.
-5 -4 -3 -2 -1 0 1 2 3 4

7.
-2 -1 0 1 2 3 4 5 6 7

8.
-2 -1 0 1 2 3 4 5 6 7

9.
-6 -5 -4 -3 -2 -1 0 1 2 3

10.
-9 -8 -7 -6 -5 -4 -3 -2 -1 0

Closing the Lesson

Writing Activity Have students explain in writing why the Division Properties for Inequalities do not have restrictions about dividing by zero. Further have the students explain why the property works.

APPLYING THE LESSON

Homework Exercises

See assignment guide on page 39.

Teaching Tip **❸** Remember to use the four-step plan. When planning the strategies write down possible options for each problem.

Enrichment Masters Booklet, p. 6

$513\frac{2}{3}$ miles

Solve each inequality.

33. $2.55x - 4.25 \leq 0$ $\{x | x \leq 1.\overline{6}\}$

34. $\frac{4x + 2}{5} \geq -0.04$ $\{x | x \geq -0.55\}$

35. $\frac{2x + 3}{5} \leq 0.03$ $\{x | x \leq -1.425\}$

36. $20\left(\frac{1}{5} - \frac{w}{4}\right) \geq -2w$ $\{w | w \leq \frac{4}{3}\}$

37. $\frac{3x - 3}{5} < \frac{6(x - 1)}{10}$ **no solution**

38. $\frac{x + 8}{4} - 1 > \frac{x}{3}$ $\{x | x < 12\}$

Solve each problem. Teaching Tip ❸

39. Rhonda has $110.37 in her checking account. The bank does not charge for checks if $50 or more is in the account. What is the greatest amount for which she can write a check and not be charged? **$60.37**

40. The Oklahoma City Municipal Parking Garage charges $1.50 for the first hour and $0.50 for each additional hour or part of an hour. For how many hours can you park your car if you only have $4.50 in cash? **7 hours**

41. The Indiana Pacers play 84 games this season. At midseason, they have won 30 games. If they must win at least 60% of all of their games to play in the tournament, how many more games must they win? **20 games**

42. Karl Weekley invested part of $8000 in stock that lost 2%. He invested the rest at 8% annually. If his gain for the year was at least $400, what was the most he could have invested in stock? **$2400**

43. You are enrolled in an algebra course where five tests will be given in the first quarter. You need 450 points to get an A. Your scores on the first four tests were 89, 87, 95, and 98. What is the minimum score that you can earn on the last test and still get an A for the quarter? **81**

44. Reliable Rentables rents a car for $12.95 per day plus 15¢ per mile. Your company has limited you to $90 a day for car rental. What is the maximum number of miles that you can drive each day?

45. Jerome and Nicola Rugola left an estate that is estimated to be worth at most $300,000. Their will stated that one-fourth of the estate be given to their church and the remainder be divided equally among their four children. What are the maximum amounts to be paid to the church and to each child? **$75,000; $56,250**

Critical Thinking

46. Find the set of all numbers that satisfies $3x - 2 \geq 0$ and $5x - 1 \leq 0$. **∅**

$9.999 \leq d \leq 10.001$

Applications

47. **Manufacturing** A company manufactures auto parts. The diameter of a piston cannot vary more than 0.001 cm. Write an inequality to represent the diameter of a piston if its diameter is supposed to be 10 cm.

48. **Manufacturing** A factory can make a table in 30 minutes and a chair in 12 minutes. They produce dining sets with a table and 4 chairs. What is the maximum number of sets that can be produced in an 8-hour shift? **6 sets**

Mixed Review

49. Evaluate $|7(-3) + 10|$. **(Lesson 1-6) 11**

50. Solve $3|2x - 5| = -1$. **(Lesson 1-6) no solution**

51. Solve $3 - 2x = 18$. **(Lesson 1-3)** $-\frac{15}{2}$

52. Simplify $7x + 8y + 9y - x(7 - 2)$. **(Lesson 1-2) $2x + 17y$**

53. Simplify $\sqrt{9} \div \sqrt{4}$. **(Lesson 1-1)** $\frac{3}{2}$

EXTENDING THE LESSON

Math Power: Problem Solving

Jim plans to make an antifreeze solution by mixing some 30% antifreeze with some 90% antifreeze. How much 30% solution can he use to make 50 quarts of a solution that is at least 60% antifreeze and at most 75% antifreeze?

12.5 < x < 25

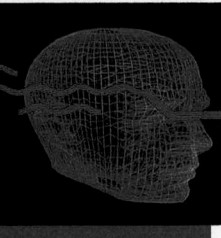

Technology

Solving Equations and Inequalities

BASIC
Spreadsheets
► Software

Using Technology
Objective This optional page shows how graphing software can be used to perform mathematical computations and to enhance and extend mathematical concepts.

Teaching Suggestions
Point out to students that there are many effective ways to solve an open sentence. The order of the steps may vary. Encourage students to use only the CALC commands shown and record the steps used. The command SOLVEFOR will solve equations automatically but will not provide the practice intended. SOLVEFOR will not solve equations automatically. You may wish to follow up this lesson by having students use SOLVEFOR and the command SSTEPS which reveals the steps used by the computer to solve equations. Have students compare the steps they chose to those chosen by the computer.

The *Mathematical Exploration Toolkit (MET)*, produced by IBM, can help you review the steps for solving equations and inequalities. Since the computer will perform all calculations and simplifying steps, you can concentrate on deciding which steps to choose. You will use these CALC commands. The abbreviations in the second column can also be used instead of typing the entire command.

ADD	add	MULTIPLY	mul
SUBTRACT	sub	DIVIDE	div
SIMPLIFY	simp		

Example 1 Solve $6x - 5 = 3x + 7$.

ENTER: $6x - 5 = 3x + 7$
  sub $3x$
  simp
  add 5
  simp
  div 3
  simp

$$6x - 5 = 3x + 7$$
$$6x - 5 - 3x = 3x + 7 - 3x$$
$$3x - 5 = 7$$
$$5 + (3x - 5) = 7 + 5$$
$$3x = 12$$
$$\frac{3x}{3} = \frac{12}{3}$$
$$x = 4$$

Example 2 Solve $x(x - 1) > 3x - (4x - 5)$.

ENTER: $2(x - 1) > 3x - (4x - 5)$
  simp
  add x
  simp
  add 2
  simp
  mult 1/3
  simp

$$2(x - 1) > 3x - (4x - 5)$$
$$2x - 2 > -x + 5$$
$$x + (2x - 2) > x + (-x + 5)$$
$$3x - 2 > 5$$
$$2 + (3x - 2) > 2 + 5$$
$$3x > 7$$
$$\frac{1}{3} \cdot (3x) > \frac{1}{3} \cdot (7)$$
$$x > \frac{7}{3}$$

EXERCISES

Use CALC to solve each equation or inequality. Record your steps and solution.

$x = \frac{2}{3}$ **1.** $2 - 5x = -8x + 4$ **2.** $\frac{x}{4} - \frac{x}{6} + \frac{1}{3}x = 4$ **3.** $\frac{2}{5}x + 1 < -7$
  $x < -20$

4. $2x - 3(1 - 6x) = 3(2x + 1) - 8$ $x = -\frac{1}{7}$

5. $1 - [2 - (3x - 1)] > 4x - 2(6 + 2x)$ $x > -\frac{10}{3}$

TECHNOLOGY 41

INTRODUCING THE LESSON

 5-Minute Check

(over Lesson 1-7)

Solve each inequality.

1. $3x + 7 > 43$ $\{x|x > 12\}$
2. $3(3w + 1) \geq 48$ $\{w|w \geq 5\}$
3. $7 + 3y > 2(y + 3) - 2(-1 - y)$ $\{y|y < -1\}$

Solve.

4. Tom makes $4.50 an hour. He worked 12 hours one week. If at least one third of his pay is taken out in taxes, what is the most amount of money he will take home? **$36**

Other Prerequisite Skills

What are the properties for equality? **see p. 19, Lesson 1-3**

Motivating the Lesson

Have students work in cooperative groups of four and write an inequality. Collect the problems and randomly return the problems to the groups. Have each student solve the problem for their group. The group should then discuss the solutions. Choose a student from each group to explain their problem and the solution.

1-8 Solving Compound Sentences and Absolute Value Inequalities

Objectives

After studying this lesson, you should be able to:

1-8A ■ solve compound sentences using *and* and *or*, and

1-8B ■ solve an inequality involving absolute value and graph its solution.

Application

April calculated her state income tax using the table at the left. Her tax is $29.00. According to the table, this means her taxable income is at least $3925, but less than $3950.

If Ohio taxable income (Line 5) is:		
At least:	But less than:	The tax is:
$ 3,800	$ 3,825	$ 28
3,825	3,850	29
3,850	3,875	29
3,875	3,900	29
3,900	3,925	29
3,925	3,950	29
3,950	3,975	29
3,975	4,000	30
$ 4,000		
4,000	4,025	30

Let I stand for April's taxable income. The two inequalities, $I \geq 3925$ and $I < 3950$, describe her taxable income. A sentence like this is called a **compound sentence.** A compound sentence containing *and* is true only if both parts of it are true.

Another way of writing $I \geq 3925$ and $I < 3950$ is $3925 \leq I < 3950$. The sentence is read "I is greater than or equal to 3925 and is less than 3950." To solve a compound sentence, you must solve each part of the sentence. **Teaching Tip ❶**

Example 1

Solve $7 < 4x + 3 < 19$.

Write the compound sentence using the word *and*. Then solve each part.

$7 < 4x + 3$	and	$4x + 3 < 19$	
$4 < 4x$	and	$4x < 16$	The solution set is
$1 < x$	and	$x < 4$	$\{x|1 < x < 4\}$.

Another way to solve this inequality is to solve both parts at the same time by adding -3 to each part of the sentence and then dividing each part by 4.

$$7 < 4x + 3 < 19$$
$$4 < 4x < 16$$
$$1 < x < 4$$

A compound sentence containing *or* is true if at least one part of it is true.

Example 2

Solve $3x + 1 < 7$ or $7 < 2x - 9$.

Solve each part separately.

$3x + 1 < 7$	or	$7 < 2x - 9$	
$3x < 6$	or	$16 < 2x$	
$x < 2$	or	$8 < x$	The solution set is $\{x|x < 2$ or $x > 8\}$.

There is no short way to write a sentence containing "or."

ALTERNATE TEACHING STRATEGIES

Using Discussion

What are two approaches to solving $|2x - 5| > 9$?

a. $2x - 5 > 9$ or $-(2x - 5) > 9$
b. $2x - 5 > 9$ or $2x - 5 < -9$

Why are they both valid?

Have the students make up their own simple example and explain the two approaches.

The absolute value of a number is its distance from 0 on the number line. We can use this idea to solve inequalities involving absolute value.

Teaching Tip ❷

Example 3

Solve $|x| < 6$.

$|x| < 6$ means that the distance between x and 0 is less than 6 units. To make $|x| < 6$ true, you must substitute values for x that are less than 6 units from 0.

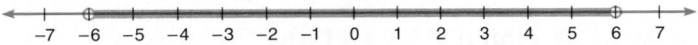

All of the numbers between -6 and 6 are less than 6 units from zero. The solution set is $\{x | -6 < x < 6\}$.

Example 4

Solve $|2x - 7| \geq 11$. Graph the solution set.

This inequality says that $2x - 7$ is more than or equal to 11 units from 0.

$$
\begin{array}{ccc}
2x - 7 \geq 11 & \text{or} & 2x - 7 \leq -11 \\
2x \geq 18 & \text{or} & 2x \leq -4 \\
x \geq 9 & \text{or} & x \leq -2
\end{array}
$$

The solution set is $\{x | x \leq -2 \text{ or } x \geq 9\}$.

Example 5

APPLICATION
Broadcasting

The radio station in Winchester sends out signals for a radius of 100 miles. The Theesville radio station sends out signals for a radius of 60 miles. You are driving from Winchester to Theesville, a distance of 200 miles. Write an inequality that represents your location while you can listen to one of the radio stations on your car radio.

EXPLORE   Let d = the distance you have traveled from Winchester.

PLAN   The station from Winchester can be heard up to 100 miles away, so you can listen to that station for the first 100 miles of the trip. The station in Theesville can be heard up to 60 miles away, so you can listen to it when you get to within 60 miles of Theesville. Write a compound inequality that describes the situation. *Remember that the distance, d, is measured from Winchester.*

SOLVE   Listening to   Listening to
           Winchester station   or   Theesville station

           $d \leq 100$ or $d \geq (200 - 60)$
                                      $d \geq 140$

           The solution set is $\{d \leq 100 \text{ or } d \geq 140\}$.

EXAMINE   You draw a diagram of the situation to check this solution.

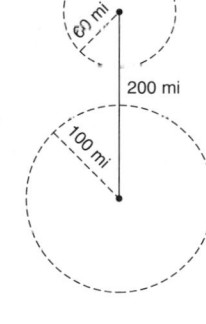

LESSON 1-8 SOLVING COMPOUND SENTENCES AND ABSOLUTE VALUE INEQUALITIES 43

RETEACHING THE LESSON

Solve each open sentence. Graph each solution set. **See students' graphs.**

1. $-5 < 0.5x + 1 \leq 4$ $\{x | -12 < x \leq 6\}$
2. $3 + x < 1$ or $x - 2 > -1$ $\{x | x < -2 \text{ or } x > 1\}$
3. $|x + 5| > 4$ $\{x | x < -9 \text{ or } x > -1\}$
4. $|x - 3| \leq 5$ $\{x | -2 \leq x \leq 8\}$
5. $|4 - 3x| < 1$ $\{x | 1 < x < \frac{5}{3}\}$
6. $|6 - x| \geq 4$ $\{x | x \leq 2 \text{ or } x \geq 10\}$

TEACHING THE LESSON

Teaching Tip ❶   This may also be read "3925 is less than or equal to l is less than 3950."

Teaching Tip ❷   You may want to use either of the following approaches to inequalities.
$|2x - 5| > 9$ means that
A) $2x - 5 > 9$ or $-(2x - 9) > 9$
B) $2x - 5 > 9$ or $2x - 5 < -9$

Chalkboard Examples

For Example 1
Solve $8 \leq m + 6 \leq 14$.
        $\{m | 2 \leq m \leq 8\}$

For Example 2
Solve $-3 \leq 2y + 9$ or $18 > 4y - 10$.
The solution set is all real numbers.

Reteaching Masters Booklet, p. 7

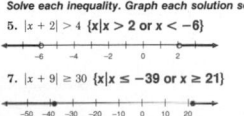

NAME _____ DATE _____
1-8 **Reteaching Worksheet**
Solving Compound Sentences and Absolute Value Inequalities

The absolute value of a number represents its distance from zero on the number line. You can often use this idea to solve absolute value inequalities.

Example: Solve $|x - 3| \leq 2$. Graph the solution set.
$|x - 3| \leq 2$ means that $x - 3$ is no more than 2 units from 0 on the number line.

$$
\begin{array}{ccc}
x - 3 \geq -2 & \text{and} & x - 3 \leq 2 \\
x \geq 1 & \text{and} & x \leq 5
\end{array}
$$

The solution set is $\{x | 1 \leq x \leq 5\}$.

Solve each compound sentence.

1. $3y - 2 < -6$ or $2y + 4 \geq 6$
   $\{y | y < -\frac{4}{3} \text{ or } y \geq 1\}$
2. $p + 7 > -2$ or $p - 4 < 8$
   all reals
3. $1 < z - 4 < 9$
   $\{z | 5 < z < 13\}$
4. $6a \leq 8 + 2a$ or $10 - 2a > 4$
   $\{a | a < 3\}$

Solve each inequality. Graph each solution set.

5. $|x + 2| > 4$ $\{x | x > 2 \text{ or } x < -6\}$
6. $|4x| + 1 > 27$ $\{x | x < -\frac{13}{2} \text{ or } x > \frac{13}{2}\}$
7. $|x + 9| \geq 30$ $\{x | x \leq -39 \text{ or } x \geq 21\}$
8. $|5x + 2| < 28$ $\{x | -6 < x < \frac{26}{5}\}$

Solve each problem.

9. The Vikings play 36 games this year. At midseason, they had won 16 games. How many of the remaining games must they win in order to win at least 80% of *all* their games?
   at least 13 games
10. The city parking lot charges $2.50 for the first hour and $0.25 for each additional hour. If the most you can pay is $6.50, how long can you park your car?
    at most 17 hours

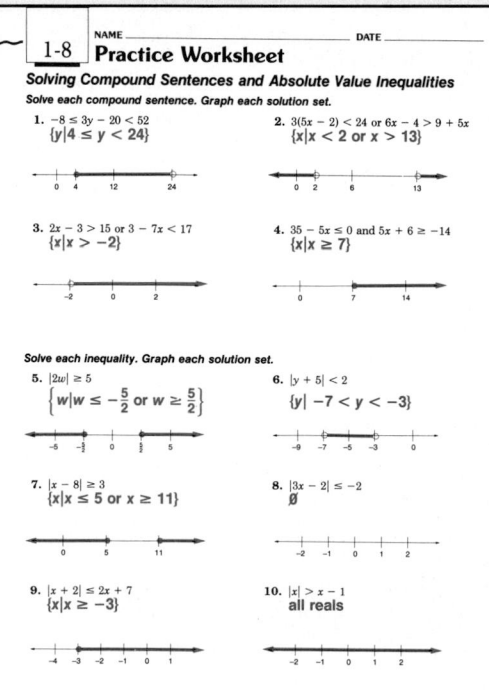

Some absolute value inequalities have no solution. For example, $|4x - 3| < -6$ is never true. Since the absolute value of a number is never negative, there is no replacement for x that will make this sentence true. So, the solution set to this inequality is the empty set.

Other absolute value inequalities are always true. One such inequality is $|x + 5| > -10$. The solution set of this inequality is all real numbers. Can you see why? *Think of the definition of absolute value.*

CHECK FOR UNDERSTANDING

Communicating Mathematics

Read and study the lesson to answer these questions. 1–4. See margin.

1. Explain why $|x + 2| \geq -4$ has all real numbers as its solution set.
2. Explain why $|x - 5| < 0$ has no solution.
3. Explain the meaning of a compound sentence containing the word *and*.
4. Explain the meaning of a compound sentence containing the word *or*.

Guided Practice

State an absolute value inequality for each of the following. Then graph each inequality. **See Solutions Manual for graphs.**

5. all numbers less than 7 and greater than –7 $|x| < 7$
6. all numbers between –3 and 3 $|x| < 3$
7. all numbers greater than 11 or less than –11 $|x| > 11$ $|x| \leq 5$
8. all numbers less than or equal to 5, and greater than or equal to –5

Teaching Tip

State an absolute value inequality for each of the following graphs.

9. $|x| < 6$ (graph: –6 0 6)

10. $|x| > 3$ (graph: –3 0 3)

11. $|x| \leq 9$ (graph: –9 0 9)

12. $|x| \geq 7$ (graph: –7 0 7)

13. $|x| \leq 6$ (graph: –6 0 6)

14. $|x| < 3$ (graph: –3 0 3)

EXERCISES

Practice

See Solutions Manual for graphs.
Solve each inequality. Graph each solution set.

A

15. $|x + 2| > 3$ $\{x|x < -5 \text{ or } x > 1\}$
16. $2 < x + 4 < 11$ $\{x|-2 < x < 7\}$
17. $|x| < 9$ $\{x|-9 < x < 9\}$
18. $-2 \leq x - 10 \leq 6$ $\{x|8 \leq x \leq 16\}$
19. $|2x| < 6$ $\{x|-3 < x < 3\}$
20. $1 < x - 2 < 7$ $\{x|3 < x < 9\}$

B

21. $|7x| \geq 21$ $\{x|x \leq -3 \text{ or } x \geq 3\}$
22. $|x - 9| > 5$ $\{x|x < 4 \text{ or } x > 14\}$
23. $|x| > 5$ $\{x|x < -5 \text{ or } x > 5\}$
24. $x - 4 < 1 \text{ or } x + 2 > 1$ all reals
25. $|2x| \geq 28$ $\{x|x \leq -14 \text{ or } x \geq 14\}$
26. $|2x| \geq -64$ all reals
27. $|5x| < -25$ $\varnothing$
28. $|x + 3| > 17$ $\{x|x < -20 \text{ or } x > 14\}$
29. $4 < 2x - 2 < 10$ $\{x|3 < x < 6\}$
30. $|x - 6| \leq -12$ $\varnothing$
31. $|x - 15| < 45$ $\{x|-30 < x < 60\}$
32. $x + 6 \geq -1 \text{ or } x - 2 \leq 4$ all reals

Additional Answers

1. Because the absolute value of $x + 2$ is ≥ 0 and zero is greater than –4.
2. The absolute value of an expression is always non-negative.
3. A compound sentence containing *and* is true only if both parts of it are true.
4. A compound sentence containing *or* is true if at least one part of it is true.

36. $\{x|x < 3\}$

38. $\left\{x \Big| x < -4 \text{ or } x > -\frac{10}{3}\right\}$

40. $\{x|-7 \le x \le -5\}$

33. $|2x - 9| \le 27$ $\{x|-9 \le x \le 18\}$

34. $|3x + 12| > 42$ $\{x|x < -18 \text{ or } x > 10\}$

35. $-1 < 3x + 2 < 14$ $\{x|-1 < x < 4\}$

36. $5x < 9 + 2x$ or $9 - 2x > 11$

37. $|5x - 7| < 81$ $\{x|-14.8 < x < 17.6\}$

38. $|3x + 11| > 1$

39. $|2x - 5| \le 9$ $\{x|-2 \le x \le 7\}$

40. $-4 \le 4x + 24 \le 4$

▶ **41.** $4 + |2x| > 0$ **all reals**

42. $|3x| + 3 \le 0$ ∅

43. $|x| \le x$ $\{x|x \ge 0\}$

44. $|x| > x$ $\{x|x < 0\}$

45. $2x - 1 < -5$ or $3x + 2 \ge 5$
$\{x|x < -2 \text{ or } x \ge 1\}$

46. $|x + 2| - x \ge 0$ **all reals**

Critical Thinking

47. Solve $|x + 1| + |x - 1| \le 2$. $\{x|-1 \le x \le 1\}$

Applications

48. Transportation   On some of the interstate highways, the maximum speed a car may drive is 65 miles per hour. A semi-truck may not drive more than 55 miles per hour. The minimum speed for all vehicles is 45 miles per hour.

a. Write an inequality to represent the allowable speed for a car on an interstate highway. $45 \le s \le 65$

b. Write an inequality to represent the speed at which a semi-truck may travel on an interstate highway. $45 \le s \le 55$

49. Manufacturing   A manufacturer of boat motors has specifications for parts with given tolerance limits. If a part is to be 3.2 inches wide with a tolerance of 0.01 inches, this means that it must be at least 3.19 inches wide or at most 3.21 inches wide. This tolerance limit can be expressed by the absolute value inequality, $|w - 3.2| \le 0.01$, where w represents the width of the part.

a. Find the maximum and minimum acceptable dimensions of a part that is supposed to be 7.32 centimeters long with a tolerance of 0.002 centimeter. **maximum = 7.322 cm; minimum = 7.318 cm**

b. Find the tolerance if a part must satisfy the inequality $5.18 \le w \le 5.24$. **tolerance = 0.03 cm**

Mixed Review

50. If you were to compare your height to the height of your best friend, you could make one of three comparative statements. What are those statements? **(Lesson 1-7) See margin.**

51. One number is twice another. Twice the lesser number increased by the greater number is at least 85. Find the least possible value for the lesser number. **(Lesson 1-7) 21.25**

52. Use a calculator to evaluate $48|7k - 30|$ if $k = 14$. **(Lesson 1-6) 3264**

53. Transportation   San Francisco and Los Angeles are 470 miles apart by train. An express train leaves Los Angeles for San Francisco at 5:00 P.M., the same time a passenger train leaves San Francisco for Los Angeles. The express train travels 10 miles per hour faster than the passenger train. The two trains pass each other at 7:30 P.M. How fast is each train traveling? **(Lesson 1-4) passenger train, 89 mph; express train, 99 mph**

54. What property is illustrated by $(11a + 3b) + 0 = (11a + 3b)$? **(Lesson 1-2) additive identity**

55. Banking   Find the annual simple interest rate on an account containing $5000 if the interest accumulated in 3 years is $1200. **(Lesson 1-1) 8%**

Portfolio

A portfolio is representative samples of your work, collected over a period of time. Begin your portfolio by selecting an item that shows something new you learned in this chapter.

EXTENDING THE LESSON

Math Power: Reasoning

Solve $|x - 6| + |x + 6| \le |3x|$. What do you need to do first? Explain why you need to have different choices.
$\{x|x \ge 4 \text{ or } x \le -4\}$

Additional Answer

50. My best friend is taller than I am; My best friend and I are the same height; My best friend is shorter than I am.

Closing the Lesson

Writing Activity   Explain the difference between *and* and *or* in inequalities. Use examples in your paragraph.

APPLYING THE LESSON

Homework Exercises

Assignment Guide

Basic: 15–40, 47–48, 50–55
Average: 18–43, 47–55
Enriched: 21–55

Chapter 1, Quiz D, (Lessons 1-7 through 1-8), is available in the Evaluation Masters Booklet, p. 10.

Teaching Tip ❸   Remind the students that the open circle means the point is not included and the closed circle means the point is included.

Enrichment Masters Booklet, p. 7

1-8 Enrichment Worksheet

NAME _____ DATE _____

Conjunctions and Disjunctions

An absolute value inequality may be solved as a compound sentence.

Example: Solve $|2x| < 10$.
  $|2x| < 10$ means $2x < 10$ and $2x > -10$.
  Solve each inequality. $x < 5$ and $x > -5$.
  Every solution for $|2x| < 10$ is a replacement for x that makes both $x < 5$ and $x > -5$ true.

A compound sentence that combines two statements by the word *and* is a *conjunction.*

Example: Solve $|3x - 7| \ge 11$.
  $|3x - 7| \ge 11$ means $3x - 7 \ge 11$ or $3x - 7 \le -11$.
  Solve each inequality. $3x \ge 18$ or $3x \le -4$
   $x \ge 6$ or $x \le -\frac{4}{3}$

Every solution for the inequality is a replacement for x that makes either $x \ge 6$ or $x \le -\frac{4}{3}$ true.

A compound sentence that combines two statements by the word *or* is a *disjunction.*

Solve each inequality. Then write whether the solution is a conjunction or disjunction.

1. $|4x| > 24$
   $x > 6$ or $x < -6$; disjunction

2. $|x - 7| \le 8$
   $x \le 15$ and $x \ge -1$; conjunction

3. $|2x + 5| < 1$
   $x < -2$ and $x > -3$; conjunction

4. $|x - 1| \ge 1$
   $x \ge 2$ or $x \le 0$; disjunction

5. $|3x - 1| \le x$
   $x \le \frac{1}{2}$ and $x \ge \frac{1}{4}$; conjunction

6. $7 - |2x| > 5$
   $x < 1$ and $x > -1$; conjunction

7. $\left|\frac{x}{5} + 1\right| \ge 7$
   $x \ge 12$ or $x \le -16$; disjunction

8. $\left|\frac{x - 4}{3}\right| < 4$
   $x < 16$ and $x > -8$; conjunction

9. $|8 - x| > 2$
   $x < 6$ or $x > 10$; disjunction

10. $|5 - 2x| \le 3$
    $x \ge 1$ and $x \le 4$; conjunction

CHAPTER **1** # SUMMARY AND REVIEW

VOCABULARY

Upon completing this chapter, you should be familiar with the following terms:

absolute value	**31**	**13**	irrational numbers
absolute value inequality	**42**	**14**	multiplicative identity
additive identity	**14**	**14**	multiplicative inverse
additive inverse	**14**	**18**	open sentence
algebraic expressions	**9**	**8**	order of operations
associative property	**14**	**13**	rational numbers
commutative property	**14**	**13**	real numbers
compound sentence	**42**	**14**	reciprocal
empty set	**32**	**18**	solution
integers	**13**		

SKILLS AND CONCEPTS

OBJECTIVES AND EXAMPLES	REVIEW EXERCISES

Upon completing this chapter, you should be able to:

Use these exercises to review and prepare for the chapter test.

▪ use the order of operations to evaluate expressions   (**Lesson 1-1**)

$12 \div 3 + 3 \cdot 2^2$
$= 12 \div 3 + 3 \cdot 4$
$= 4 + 12$
$= 16$

Find the value of each expression.

1. $(3 + 7)^2 - 16 \div 2$ **2.** $3 + 7^2 - 16 \div 2$
92   **44**

Evaluate each expression if $a = -0.5$, $b = 4$, $c = 5$, **and** $d = -3$.

3. $\dfrac{4a + 3c}{3b}$ **13/12**   **4.** $\dfrac{3ab^2 - d^3}{a}$ **-6**

▪ use formulas   (**Lesson 1-1**)

The distance, d, in feet that an object falls in t seconds is found by the formula $d = 16t^2$. How far will an object fall in 10 seconds?

$d = 16t^2$
$d = 16(10)^2$ or 1600

The object will fall 1600 feet.

5. Physics   Sandbags are used to weigh down a hot air balloon. If a sandbag is dropped from a balloon, use the formula $d = 16t^2$ to determine how far it will fall in 20 seconds. **6400 feet**

OBJECTIVES AND EXAMPLES	REVIEW EXERCISES

classify numbers (Lesson 1-2)

Name the sets of numbers to which $\sqrt{2}$ belongs.

irrational numbers, real numbers

Name the sets of numbers to which each number belongs. (Use N, W, Z, Q, I, and R.)

6. -32.4 **Q, R**   7. $73 \div 5$ **Q, R**

8. -8.0 **Z, Q, R**   9. 34π **I, R**

---

use the properties of real numbers to simplify expressions (Lesson 1-2)

$0.2a(3.5 - 3.2b) - 4a(3.6 + 2b)$
$= 0.7a - 0.64ab - 14.4a - 8ab$
$= -13.7a - 8.64ab$

State the property illustrated in each equation.

10. $4 + (a + r) = (4 + a) + r$ **associative +**

11. $(j + k) + 0 = (j + k)$ **additive identity**

Simplify each expression.

12. $(8 + 49)7 + 3$ **402**

13. $7a + 2b - 5a - 6b$ **$2a - 4b$**

14. $3(a + 4b) - 2(4a + 2b)$ **$-5a + 8b$**

---

solve equations using the properties of equality (Lesson 1-3)

$2(a - 1) = 8a - 6$
$2a - 2 = 8a - 6$
$-6a = -4$
$a = \dfrac{2}{3}$

Solve each equation.

15. $15x + 25 = 2(x - 4)$ $-\dfrac{33}{13}$

16. $2(3x - 1) = 3(x + 2)$ $\dfrac{8}{3}$

17. $6 = \dfrac{3x - 6}{3}$ **8**

18. $\dfrac{3a + 3}{4} = \dfrac{5}{2}$ $\dfrac{7}{3}$

---

use equations to solve problems (Lesson 1-4)

Problem Solving Plan

1. Explore the problem.
2. Plan the solution.
3. Solve the problem.
4. Examine the solution.

Write an equation and solve each problem. Be sure to identify the variable.

19. **Geometry** The width of a rectangular rug is four feet more than one-third of its length. The perimeter is 64 feet. What are the length and the width?
length 21 ft, width 11 ft

---

solve equations containing absolute value (Lesson 1-6)

$|q - 3| = 2$
$q - 3 = 2$ or $q - 3 = -2$
$q = 5$ $q = 1$

Solve each equation.

20. $|2x - 36| = 14$ **11, 25**

21. $|q - 3| + 7 = 2$ **no solution**

22. $8|2b - 3| = 64$ **-2.5, 5.5**

NAME _____ DATE _____

Cumulative Review (Chapter 1)

Find the value of each expression.

1. $4 \cdot 6 \div 3 + 12$ 1. **20**

2. $19 - [(6 + 24) - 7 \cdot 2^1]$ 2. **17**

3. Evaluate $\frac{3a + 3c}{4b}$ if $a = 3$, $b = 2$, and $c = 5$.   3. **3**

4. Use the formula $F = \frac{9}{5}C + 32$ to find the value of F if $C = 25$.   4. **77**

State the property illustrated in each equation.

5. $3(6 + 7) = 3(6) + 3(7)$ 5. **distributive**

6. $3 + 6 = 6 + 3$ 6. **comm. of ×**

7. Put a check in the box if the number belongs to that set.   7. **See students' work.**

	N	W	Z	Q	I	R
N-natural numbers						
W-whole numbers -6						
Z-integers						
Q-rational numbers 13						
I-irrational numbers						
R-real numbers $\sqrt{3}$						

8. Simplify $\frac{1}{4}(16x - 12) + \frac{1}{3}(9x + 3)$.   8. **7x − 2**

Solve each open sentence.

9. $12x - 51 = 3(x + 7)$ 9. **8**

10. $\frac{3}{5} + \frac{1}{3}y = \frac{1}{3}$ 10. **$-\frac{4}{5}$**

11. $3|2x - 5| = 15$ 11. **0, 5**

12. $3x + 7 > 5x + 1$ 12. **{x|x < 3}**

13. $4(t - 5) > 5 - t$ 13. **{t|t > 5}**

14. $|2y - 1| + 4 = 13$ 14. **−4, 5**

15. $-5(m - 5) = 3(10 - 2m) + 10m$ 15. **$\frac{5}{9}$**

NAME _____ DATE _____

Cumulative Review (Chapter 1)—continued

16. Write an algebraic expression to represent the following verbal expression. The square of a number increased by the cube of the same number.   16. **$n^2 + n^3$**

17. Write an equation to solve the following problem. Forty-seven decreased by three times the number is 36. Find the number. *You do not need to solve the equation.*   17. **47 − 3t = 36**

18. The sum of three consecutive odd integers is 177. Find the integers.   18. **57, 59, 61**

19. The Cincinnati Reds play 162 games in a season. So far they have won 57 games. How many more games must they win in order to win at least 65% of all games for the season?   19. **49**

20. A team has won 2 games and lost 3. How many patterns of records are possible?   20. **10**

Solve each compound sentence.

21. $-10 < 3x - 9 < 22$ 21. **$\{x|-\frac{1}{3} < x < \frac{31}{3}\}$**

22. $3x + 5 \le -10$ or $12 - x < 20$ 22. **all reals**

Graph the solution set of each inequality.

23. $|x + 3| \ge 4$ 23. **See students' graphs.**

24. $|4x + 1| < 9$ 24. **See students' graphs.**

25. $3x + 7 > 5x + 1$ 25. **See students' graphs.**

■ solve an inequality and graph its solution set (**Lesson 1-7**)

$$3 - 4x \le 6x - 5$$
$$-10x \le -8$$
$$x \ge \frac{4}{5}$$

Solve each inequality. Graph the solution set.

23. $9(x + 2) < 72$ **{x|x < 6}**

24. $3(3x + 2) > 7x - 2$ **{x|x > −4}**

25. $8(2x - 1) > 11x + 31$ **$\{x|x > \frac{39}{5}\}$**
For graphs, see margin.

■ solve compound sentences using *and* or *or* (**Lesson 1-8**)

$$-2 \le x - 4 < 3$$
$$-2 \le x - 4 \text{ and } x - 4 < 3$$
$$2 \le 4 \quad \text{and} \quad x < 7 \quad \text{So, } 2 \le x < 7$$

Solve each compound sentence.

26. $-1 < 3(y - 2) \le 9$ **$\{y|\frac{5}{3} < y \le 5\}$**

27. $4x - 10 < -10$ or $6x + 4 \ge 10$
    {x|x < 0 or x ≥ 1}

■ solve absolute value inequalities (**Lesson 1-8**)

$$|3x + 7| \ge 26$$
$$3x + 7 \ge 26 \text{ or } 3x + 7 \le -26$$
$$3x \ge 19 \text{ or } \qquad 3 \le -33$$
$$x \ge \frac{19}{3} \text{ or } \qquad x \le -11$$

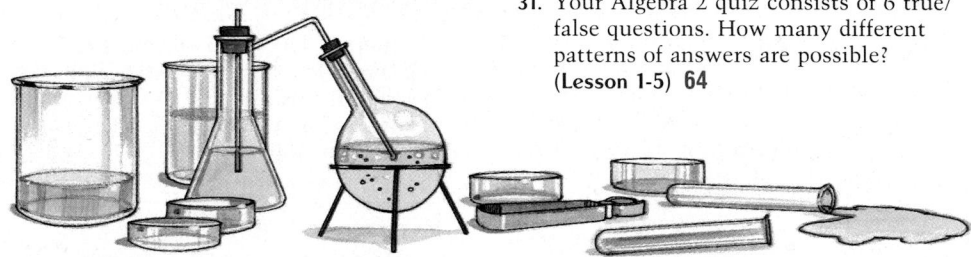

Solve each inequality. Graph the solution set.

28. $|2x + 6| \le 4$ **{x|−5 ≤ x ≤ −1}**

29. $7 + |9 - 5x| > 1$ **all reals**

30. $|4x| + 3 \le 0$ **∅**
For graphs, see margin.

APPLICATIONS AND CONNECTIONS

31. Your Algebra 2 quiz consists of 6 true/false questions. How many different patterns of answers are possible? (**Lesson 1-5**) **64**

32. **Chemistry** How much pure ammonia will a chemist need to add to 10 gallons of a 50% solution to obtain a solution that is at least 80% ammonia? (**Lesson 1-7**) **15 gallons**

33. **Consumerism** Where Tertius lives, gasoline is selling for between $1.40 and $1.60 per gallon. If he has $8.40 to spend on gas, how many gallons can he buy? (**Lesson 1-8**) **from 5.25 to 6 gal**

Additional Answers

23.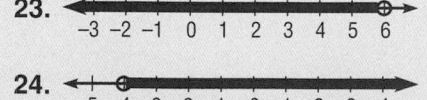

24.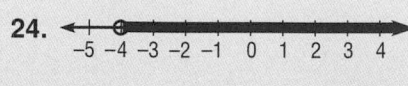

25.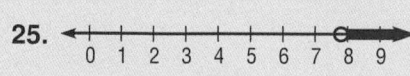

28.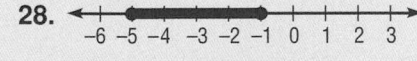

29.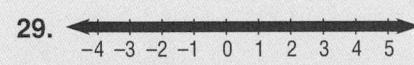

30.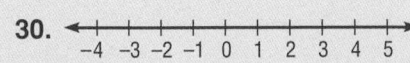

State the property illustrated in each equation or statement.

1. $(7 \cdot s) \cdot t = 7 \cdot (s \cdot t)$ **associative ×**

2. $(7 \cdot s) \cdot t = t \cdot (7 \cdot s)$ **commutative ×**

3. $\left(3 \cdot \frac{1}{3}\right) \cdot 7 = \left(3 \cdot \frac{1}{3}\right) \cdot 7$ **reflexive =**

4. $(6 - 2)a - 3b = 4a - 3b$ **substitution =**

5. If $(r + s)t = rt + st$,
then $rt + st = (r + s)t$. **symmetric =**

6. If $5(3) + 7 = 15 + 7$ and $15 + 7 = 22$,
then $5(3) + 7 = 22$. **transitive =**

Find the value of each expression.

7. $[2 + 3^3 - 4] \div 2$ **12.5**

8. $(2 + 3)^3 - 4 \div 2$ **123**

9. $(4^5 - 4^2) + 4^3$ **1072**

10. $[5(17 - 2) \div 3] - 2^4$ **9**

Evaluate each expression if $a = -9$, $b = \frac{2}{3}$, $c = 8$, and $d = -6$.

11. $\dfrac{db + 4c}{a} - \dfrac{28}{9}$

12. $\dfrac{a}{b^2} + c$ **-12.25**

13. $2b(4a + a^2)$ **60**

14. $\dfrac{4a + 3c}{3b}$ **-6**

Name the sets of numbers to which each number belongs. Use N, W, Z, Q, I, and R.

15. $\sqrt{17}$ **I, R**

16. 0.86 **Q, R**

17. $-10 \div 2$ **Z, Q, R**

18. $\sqrt{64}$ **N, W, Z, Q, R**

Solve each equation.

19. $2x - 7 - (x - 5) = 0$ **2**

20. $5t - 3 = -2t + 10$ **$\frac{13}{7}$**

21. $5r + 7 = 5r - 9$ **no solution**

22. $5m - (5 + 4m) - (3 + m) - 8$ **all reals**

23. $|8w + 2| + 2 = 0$ **no solution**

24. $|4y - 5| + 4 = 7y + 8$ **$\frac{1}{11}$**

Solve each inequality. Graph each solution set. **25–30. For graphs, see Solutions Manual.**

25. $4 > b + 1$ **$\{b|b < 3\}$**

26. $3q + 7 \geq 13$ **$\{q|q \geq 2\}$**

27. $5(3x - 5) + x < 2(4x - 1) + 1$ **$\{x|x < 3\}$**

28. $-12 < 7s - 5 < 9$ **$\{s|-1 < s \leq 2\}$**

29. $|9y - 4| + 8 > 4$ **all reals**

30. $|5 + k| \leq 8$ **$\{k|-13 \leq k \leq 3\}$**

31. **Statistics** To receive a B in his English class, Dale must earn at least 400 points on five tests. He scored 87, 89, 76, and 77 on his first four tests. What must he score on the last test to receive a B in the class? **71**

32. **Sports** Kathy's softball team has won 3 games and lost 2. How many patterns of records are possible? **10**

33. **Geometry** The formula $A = \dfrac{180(n - 2)}{n}$ relates the measure of an interior angle, A, of a regular polygon to the number of sides, n. If an interior angle of a regular polygon measures 150 degrees, find the number of sides. **12 sides**

Bonus

Find the set of all numbers x satisfying the given conditions.

$3x - 2 \geq 0$ and $5x - 1 \leq 0$ **∅**

Using the Chapter Test

This page may be used as a test or as a review. In addition, two multiple-choice tests and two free-response tests are provided in the Evaluation Masters Booklet. Chapter 1 Test, Form 1A is shown below.

Evaluation Masters Booklet, pp. 1–2

NAME _____ DATE _____

Chapter 1 Test, Form 1A

Write the letter for the correct answer in the blank at the right of each problem.

1. Find the value of $4 + 5[14 - (8 + 3)]$.
   A. 27   B. 19   C. 49   D. -46   1. __B__

2. Evaluate $(a - y)^2 + 2y^3$ if $a = 2$ and $y = -3$.
   A. -29   B. 43   C. 79   D. -8   2. __A__

3. The formula for the surface area of a sphere is $A = 4\pi r^2$, where r is the length of the radius. Find the surface area of a sphere with a radius of 14 inches. Use $\frac{22}{7}$ for π.
   A. 7248 sq ft   B. 7744 sq ft   C. 2464 sq ft   D. 704 sq ft   3. __C__

4. Name *all* the sets of numbers to which -28 belongs.
   A. integers   B. integers, reals
   C. integers, rationals   D. integers, rationals, reals   4. __D__

5. State the property illustrated in the following equation.
   $5n + (3t + 8n) = (5n + 3t) + 8n$
   A. associative property of addition
   B. inverse property of addition
   C. distributive property
   D. commutative property of addition   5. __A__

6. Simplify $\frac{1}{3}(6x + 1) - 4(3x - 2)$.
   A. $-10x + 8\frac{1}{3}$ B. $-9x + 8\frac{1}{3}$ C. $25 - 30x$ D. $-9x - 7\frac{2}{3}$ 6. __A__

Solve each open sentence.

7. $23 = 5 - \frac{2}{3}m$
   A. -42   B. -29.5   C. -27   D. 42   7. __C__

8. $18 = 3|4x - 10|$
   A. 4, -1   B. 1, 4   C. 4, 4   D. 4   8. __B__

9. $5(2x - 6) = 7x - 3$
   A. -9   B. 9   C. 11   D. ∅   9. __B__

10. $|x - 3| + 10 = 2$
    A. -5   B. -5, 11   C. 11   D. ∅   10. __D__

11. $0.38 > \frac{2x - 7}{5}$
    A. $\{x|x < 4.45\}$ B. $\{x|x < 90.5\}$
    C. $\{x|x < 13\}$ D. $\{x|x < 3.69\}$ 11. __A__

NAME _____ DATE _____

Chapter 1 Test, Form 1A (continued)

Solve.

12. $|2w - 3| \leq 7$.
    A. $\{x|x \leq 5\}$ B. $\{x| -5 \leq x \leq 5\}$
    C. $\{x| -2 \leq x \leq 5\}$ D. {real numbers}   12. __C__

13. Write an algebraic expression to represent the following verbal expression: the sum of eight times a number and nine.
    A. $8 + 9n$ B. $8(9 + n)$ C. $n(8 + 9)$ D. $8n + 9$ 13. __D__

14. Write an equation to solve the following problem: A number decreased by 14 is 225. What is the number?
    A. $n - 14 = 225$ B. $n + 14 = 225$ C. $14 - n = 225$ D. $n + 225 = 14$ 14. __A__

15. Jamie is 4 years younger than her brother. Five years from now, the sum of their ages will be 32. Find Jamie's present age.
    A. 9   B. 10   C. 13   D. 14   15. __A__

16. A coin is flipped three times in a row. If H stands for heads and T stands for tails, which list shows all possible outcomes?
    A. HHH, TTT, THT, HTH   B. HHH, HHT, TTT, HTH, THT
    C. HHH, HHT, HTH, HTT, TTT, TTH
    D. HHH, HHT, HTH, HTT, THH, THT, TTH, TTT   16. __D__

17. Sarah has $328.17 in her checking account. The bank does not charge for checks if there is a balance of $250 or more in the account. What is the greatest check Sarah can write without paying a check charge?
    A. $78.16   B. $78.17   C. $78.18   D. $250   17. __B__

Solve each compound sentence.

18. $5x - 4 \geq 26$ or $29 - 3x > 2$
    A. $\{x|6 \leq x < 9\}$ B. $\{x|x \leq 6$ or $x > 9\}$
    C. {real numbers}   D. $\{x|x \neq 9\}$ 18. __C__

19. $-18 \leq 5n + 7 < 2$
    A. $\{n|n \leq -1\}$ B. $\{n|n \neq -1\}$
    C. {real numbers}   D. $\{n|n < -1$ and $n \geq -5\}$ 19. __D__

20. Graph the solution set for $-2.3 < 4 + 0.9y$. Choose the correct graph.
    A.   B.   C.   D.   20. __A__

Bonus

Solve $|x| - x > 0$.
    A. $\{x|x < 0\}$ B. {all reals}   C. $\{0\}$ D. $\{x|x > 0\}$ Bonus __A__

A **Test and Review Generator** is provided in Apple, IBM and Macintosh versions. You may use this software to create your own tests or worksheets, based on the needs of your students.

The **Performance Assessment Booklet** provides an alternate assessment for evaluating student progress. An asessment for this chapter can be found on pages 1–2.

2 Linear Relations and Functions

PREVIEWING THE CHAPTER

This chapter makes the mathematical connection between an algebraic representation of a linear function and a geometric representation of the same function. Students begin by graphing relations and identifying those that are functions. Next, they graph linear equations from a table of ordered pairs, identify the slope and intercepts, and use these to group other linear equations. Then students write various linear equations including those for a line parallel or perpendicular to the graph of a given equation. They conclude their study by graphing linear inequalities.

Some of the lessons in this chapter contain a review of concepts from Algebra 1. These lessons may be considered as optional and used for review only.

Problem Solving Strategy   Students learn to solve problems by identifying a pattern and using the pattern to find missing data.

Lesson Objective Chart

Lesson (Pages)	Lesson Objectives	State/Local Objectives
2-1 (52-57)	**2-1A:** Graph a relation, state its domain and range, and determine if the relation is a function.	
	2-1B: Find the values of functions for given elements of the domain.	
2-2 (60-63)	**2-2A:** Identify equations that are linear and graph them.	
	2-2B: Write linear equations in standard form.	
2-3 (64-65)	**2-3:** Solve a problem by identifying the pattern and using it to find the missing information.	
2-4 (66-72)	**2-4A:** Determine the slope and intercepts of a line.	
	2-4B: Use the slope and intercepts to graph a line.	
	2-4C: Determine if two lines are parallel, perpendicular, or neither.	
2-5 (73-79)	**2-5A:** Write the slope-intercept form of an equation given the slope and a point, or two points.	
	2-5B: Write the standard form of an equation given the slope and a point, or two points.	
	2-5C: Write the equation of a line that is parallel or perpendicular to the graph of a given equation.	
2-6 (80-84)	**2-6A:** Draw a scatter plot and find the prediction equation.	
	2-6B: Solve problems using prediction equations.	
2-7 (87-90)	**2-7:** Identify and graph special functions (direct variation, constant, identity, absolute value, and greatest integer).	
2-8 (92-95)	**2-8A:** Draw graphs of inequalities in two variables.	
	2-8B: Write an inequality to solve problems.	

ORGANIZING THE CHAPTER

You may want to refer to the **Course Planning Calendar** on page T44.

Lesson Planning Guide				Blackline Masters Booklets						Activities				
Lesson (Pages)	**Pacing Chart (days)** Course			Reteaching	Practice	Enrichment	Evaluation	Technology	Lab Manual	Mixed Problem Solving	Applications	Cooperative Learning Activity	Multicultural	Transparencies
	I	**II**	**III**											
2-1 (52-57)	1.5	1.5	1	p. 8	p. 9	p. 8			pp. 35-36					2-1
2-2 (60-63)	1	1	1	p. 9	p. 10	p. 9	Quiz A, p. 23	p. 19						2-2
2-3 (64-65)	1	0.5	0.5		p. 11					p. 2				2-3
2-4 (66-72)	2	1.5	1.5	p. 10	p. 12	p. 10	Quiz B, p. 23 Mid-Chapter Test, p. 27	p. 2						2-4
2-5 (73-79)	1.5	1.5	1	p. 11	p. 13	p. 11					p. 20			2-5
2-6 (80-84)	1.5	1	1	p. 12	p. 14	p. 12	Quiz C, p. 24							2-6
2-7 (87-90)	1.5	1	1	p. 13	p. 15	p. 13						p. 38	p. 2	2-7
2-8 (92-95)	1	1	1	p. 14	p. 16	p. 14	Quiz D, p. 24							2-8
Review (96-98)	1	1	1	Multiple Choice Tests, Forms 1A and 1B, pp. 15-18 Free Response Tests, Forms 2A and 2B, pp. 19-22 Cumulative Review, pp. 25-26 Standardized Test Practice Questions, p. 28										
Test (99)	1	1	1											

Course 1: Chapters 1-13; Course II: Chapters 1-15; Course III: Chapters 1-17

Other Chapter Resources

Student Edition

Chapter Opener, pp. 50-51
Graphing Calculator Exploration, pp. 58-59
Cooperative Learning Activity, p. 65
Mid-Chapter Review, p. 72
History Connection, p. 79
Journal Entries, pp. 84, 90
Graphing Calculator Exploration, pp. 85-86
Technology, p. 91
Portfolio Suggestion, p. 95
College Entrance Exam Preview, pp. 100-101
Extended Project 1, pp. A2-A5

Teacher's Classroom Resources

Transparency 2-0
Real-World Applications Transparencies, 3, 4, 5
Performance Assessment Booklet, pp. 3-4
Problem-of-the-Week Activity Cards, 3, 4
Tech Prep Applications Booklet, pp. 3-4
Lesson Plans, pp. 9-16

Other Supplements

Glencoe Mathematics Professional Series

Software

Test and Review Generator Software (Apple, IBM, and Macintosh)
Interactive Software (Macintosh)
Teacher's Guide for Software Resources

ENHANCING THE CHAPTER

Cooperative Learning

Arranging the Room

Providing a physical environment conducive to cooperative-learning activities is important if success is to be achieved when using this learning technique. How the room is arranged should indicate to students what is expected of them as well as make it easy for both you and the groups to accomplish the defined goals. Since you will want to monitor the groups, they should be arranged in a way that permits you to pass among them, unobtrusively if possible, and also placed apart far enough so that the groups do not interfere with each other's learning. The students in each group must be able to see all of the pertinent materials, to see and converse with one another without disturbing students in other groups, and to exchange ideas and materials with other members of the group in a convenient manner. Among the best arrangements is one where the group members sit in a circle, although any arrangement that permits each group member to have eye contact with and easy access to all other members of the group also would be satisfactory.

Technology

The Technology Feature after Lesson 2-7 employs the *Data Insights* software from Sunburst. This package is a student-oriented utility for data analysis. The feature focuses on comparing two linearly-related measures by means of a scatter plot and median-fit line. The program is menu-driven. HELP screens are available at any point in the program. *Data Insights* supports printing the data, statistics, and graph. Encourage students to print out their results. Remind them to save their data on a data disk for editing and reference. The program provides for creating data disks.

Many statistical utilities are available for microcomputers. Most will compute regression lines and scatter plots. Regression lines can be used by students to interpolate and extrapolate. However at this time, students do not have the background to understand the least squares method by which they are obtained.

Critical Thinking

Identifying and extending patterns is not only a useful strategy for solving problems but a strategy that is valuable for discovering and mastering new mathematical content. Students should be encouraged to examine patterns, make conjectures about general algebraic properties based on their observations, and verify their conjectures with numerical substitutions. The lesson on scatter plots and prediction equations, for example, can be used as an opportunity for further explorations. Have students suggest possible pairs, such as arm length and shoe size or height and hand span, where data can be collected and plotted, a prediction equation proposed and drawn, and the results confirmed or rejected by collecting additional data.

Cooperative Learning, p. 38

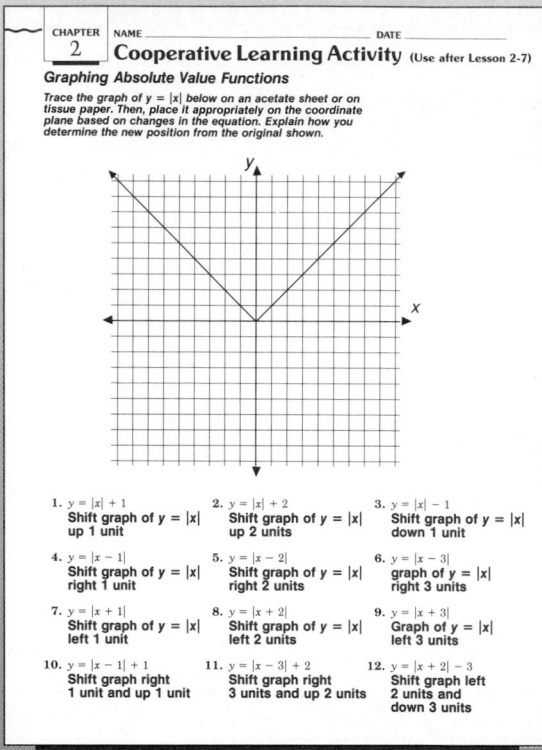

Technology, p. 19

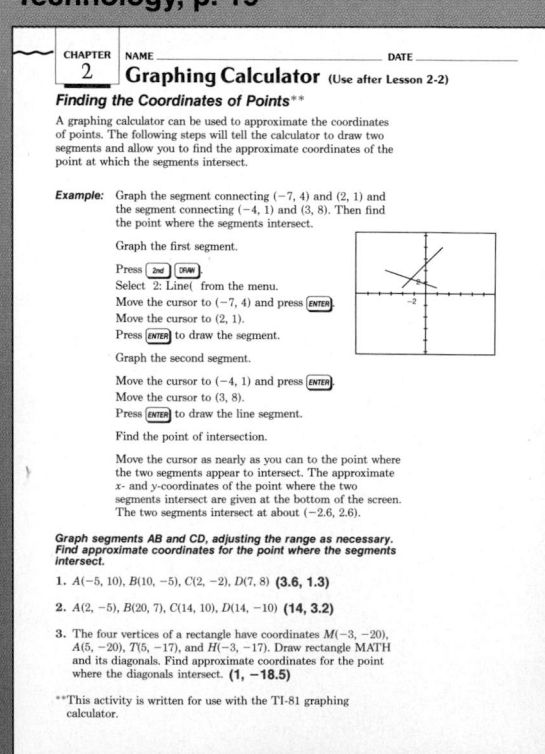

Problem of the Week Activity

The card shown below is one of two available for this chapter. It can
be used as a class or small group activity.

Activity Card

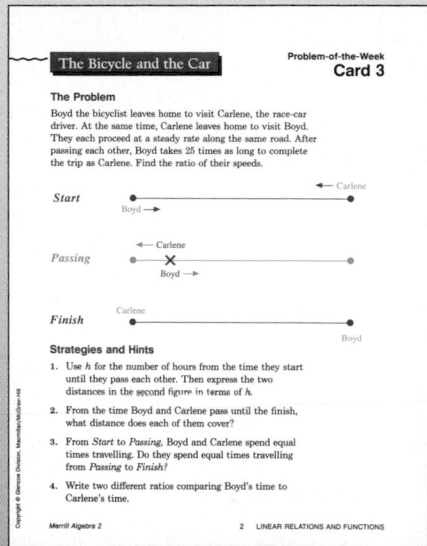

Manipulatives and Models

The following materials may be used as models or manipulatives in
Chapter 2.

phone bill (Lesson 2-7)
colored pencils (Lesson 2-8)
graphing calculator (pages 58-59, 85-86)

Outside Resources

Books/Periodicals

Bakst, Aaron. *Mathematical Puzzles and Pastimes*. Van Nostrand
Reinhold Company, 1965.

Stewart, B.M. *Theory of Numbers*. Macmillan, 1964.

Films/Videotapes/Videodiscs

*For All Practical Purposes: Introduction to Contemporary Mathematics I,
Management Science,* Consortium for Mathematics and Its Applications
(COMAP), Suite 210, 57 Bedford St., Lexington, MA 02173-4496

Software

Algebra and *Algebraic Proposer*, TrueBASIC, Inc., 12 Commerce Ave.,
West Lebanon, NH 03766

Data Insights, WINGS for Learning/Sunburst Commuications,
1600 Green Hills Rd., P.O. Box 660002, Scotts Valley, CA 95067-0002

Multicultural

Multicultural Activity, p. 2

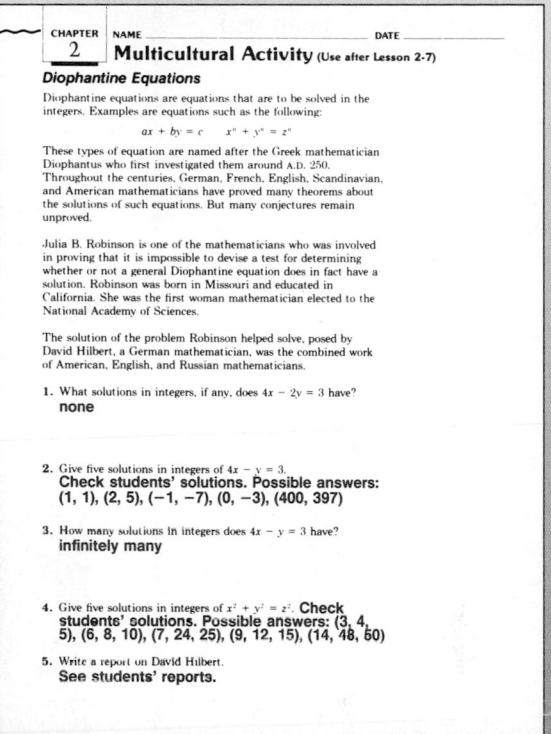

Lab Manual

Lab Activity, pp. 35-36

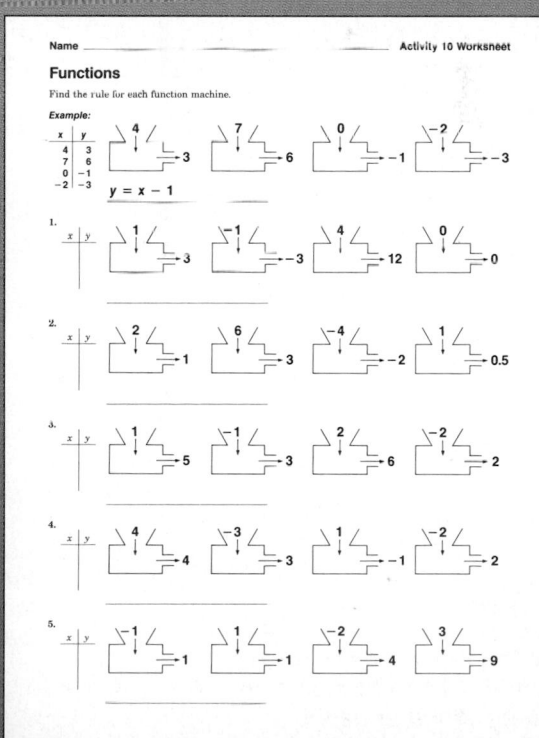

Using the Chapter Opener

Transparency 2–0 is available in the Transparency Package. It provides a full-color visual and motivational activity that you can use to engage students in the mathematical content of the chapter.

Background Information

Oceanographers use a wide range of math including collecting and analyzing data on waves, tides, and currents; plant and animal life; and chemical composition and reactions of the sea. They study and make graphs, maps, charts, tables, and reports. Oceanographers regularly use computers and hi-tech devices such as special cameras, sounding devices, and other exploration equipment. The demand for oceanographers is expected to grow 14% to 24% through the 1990s, with competition likely. Beginning oceanographers should expect to perform in the capacity of assistants and technicians.

Linear Relations and Functions

CHAPTER OBJECTIVES

In this chapter, you will:
- Identify different types of relations and functions.
- Graph relations and functions on the coordinate plane.
- Graph inequalities on the coordinate plane.
- Solve applications of equations and inequalities.

Can you see a pattern in the points plotted on this graph? Explain why you think the graph takes this shape.

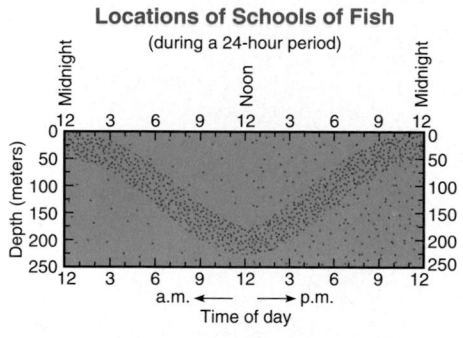

Locations of Schools of Fish
(during a 24-hour period)

50

CAREERS IN OCEANOGRAPHY

Are you constantly being nagged by relatives and friends to choose a career? Just tell them you've chosen oceanography. It will keep them quiet, and only you will know that the "career" you've named includes dozens of different careers from which you will still be able to choose.

Are you good at physics and math? Then physical oceanography might suit you. You'd study tides, currents, temperatures, water densities, sound propagation through water, and water's optical transparency.

Are chemistry and math your strong points? Try chemical oceanography. You'll examine many of the elements that make up seawater, their distribution, and their influence on marine life.

Do biology and math attract your interest? Biological oceanographers study marine animal and plant populations.

Earth's oceans are the biggest unexplored territories we have left. From studying the biology, chemistry, and physics of oceans, we may find new foods, new sources of energy, new clean water to drink, new sources of mineral ores, new medicines, and other unexpected gifts. The ocean is like a new continent, full of vast riches. Will you find some of these riches?

Chapter Project

Materials: pencil and paper (optional: aquarium and related equipment)

As a short-term project, obtain and have students review one or more of the many excellent video tapes and books from the series *The Ocean World of Jacques Cousteau*. For a longer-term project that could help maintain student interest in both math and science on an on-going basis, have students plan and set up an aquarium of local species of fish, plants, and other aquatic animals. (If an aquarium is not practical, the remainder can be completed as a separate research project.)

Have students work in cooperative groups to conduct research on local specimens, temperature requirements, chemical composition of water, feeding cycles, and breeding habits.

Lesson	Connections (C) and Applications (A)	Examples	Exercises
2-1	C: Geometry	2	36-37
	A: Recycling		
	Education		43
	Aviation		44
2-2	A: Geology	3	
	Finance		39
	Consumer		40
	Awareness		
2-4	C: Geometry	5	44
	A: Demo-		46
	graphics		
	Travel		47
2-5	A: Ocean-	3	43
	ography		
	Science		44
	Nature		45
	Studies		
	Economics		46
2-6	A: Health	1	
	Agriculture		13
	Personal		14
	Finance		
2-7	A: Sports		42
	Business		43
2-8	A: Commerce	2	
	Economics	3	
	Manufactur-		38
	ing		

MORE ABOUT OCEANOGRAPHY

Degree Required:

Bachelor's Degree in Oceanography, Marine Biology, or Geology

Some oceanographers like:

- knowing that their work may benefit others
- working outdoors, research
- variety in their work
- good salaries

Related Math Subjects:

- Geometry
- Advanced Algebra
- Trigonometry

Some oceanographers dislike:

- bad weather conditions at sea
- sometimes working long, irregular hours
- being separated from their families
- the physical demands of ocean exploration

For more information on the various careers available in the field of Oceanography, write to:

National Ocean Industries Association
1050 17th Street NW, Suite 700
Washington, D.C. 20036

51

Lesson Resources

Reteaching Master 2-1
Practice Master 2-1
Enrichment Master 2-1
Lab Manual, pp. 35–36

 Transparency 2-1 contains the 5-Minute Check and a teaching aid for this lesson.

INTRODUCING THE LESSON

5-Minute Check

(over Chapter 1)

1. Evaluate $2(3^2 + 8) + 3 \div \frac{1}{3}$.
   43
2. What property is illustrated?
   a. $b(4 + 1) = b \cdot 4 + b \cdot 1$
      distributive
   b. $6 + (2 + 3) = 6 + (3 + 2)$
      commutative,
Solve each equation.

3. $6(x + 2) = 2x + 4$ $x = -2$
4. $|2x + 3| = 5$ $x = 1, -4$
5. Solve the inequality
   $7r + .6 \le .11$. $\{r|r \le -.07\}$

Motivating the Lesson

Have the students generate a list of items that can be recycled. Find the costs that a recycling plant would pay for these items. Show students a graph of these items and their costs.

Objectives After studying this lesson, you should be able to:

2-1A ■ graph a relation, state its domain and range, and determine if the relation is a function, and

2-1B ■ find the values of functions for given elements of the domain.

Application

The number of pounds of waste recycled in recent years in the United States can be shown using **ordered pairs.** The first number of the ordered pair is the year, and the second number is the number of pounds recycled for every 10 people.

Year	1965	1970	1975	1980	1985	1990
Pounds Recycled	17	21	23	32	35	37
Ordered Pair	(1965, 17)	(1970, 21)	(1975, 23)	(1980, 32)	(1985, 35)	(1990, 37)

You can **graph** these ordered pairs by creating a **coordinate system** with two axes. The horizontal axis represents the years and the vertical axis represents the pounds of waste. Each point represents the ordered pairs shown in the chart above.

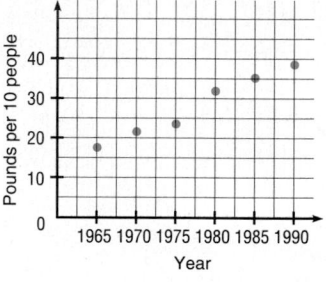

Recycled Waste in the U.S.

FYI...

In the United States, only about one-tenth of garbage is recycled.

Remember that each point in the coordinate plane can be named by exactly one ordered pair, and that every ordered pair names exactly one point in the coordinate plane.

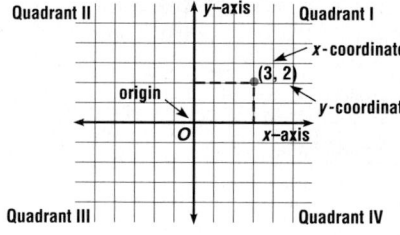

The points on the two axes do not lie in any quadrant.

When graphing real-world data, you usually use positive numbers. However, to graph the real numbers you must use the **Cartesian coordinate plane,** which is composed of the **x-axis** and the **y-axis** meeting at the **origin** (0, 0) and dividing the plane into four **quadrants.** The ordered pairs graphed on this plane can be represented by (x, y).

52   CHAPTER 2   LINEAR RELATIONS AND FUNCTIONS

ALTERNATE TEACHING STRATEGIES

Using Cooperative Groups

Have students divide into groups of four. Have one member of each group make up a relation. The other members of the group should make a mapping of some of the elements and determine if the relation is a function. The other members should also list the domain and the range.

Using Questioning

Ask students the following questions.

1. What is a relation?   **a set of ordered pairs**
2. What is the first member of the ordered pair called?   **domain**
3. What is the second member of the ordered pair called?   **range**

A set of ordered pairs forms a **relation.** The set of first members of the ordered pairs is called the **domain** of the relation. The set of second members of the ordered pairs is called the **range** of the relation. A **mapping** shows how each member of the domain is paired with a member in the range.

{(3, 2), (2, 7), (5, 8)}   {(8, −4), (−3, 9), (1, 2), (8, 5)}

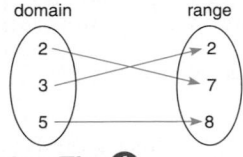   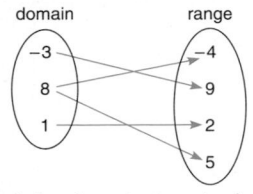

Teaching Tip ❶

A **function** is a relation in which each element of the domain is paired with *exactly one* element of the range. The first relation shown above is a function. In the second relation, you see that 8 in the domain is paired with both −4 and 5. This relation is not a function.

Example 1

Assume that each square on a graph represents 1 unit unless otherwise labeled.

Graph the relation {(8, 1), (4, −2), (1, 1), (−3, 2), (−6, 8)}. State the domain and the range of the relation. Is the relation a function?

Graph the ordered pairs on a coordinate plane.

The domain is {8, 4, 1, −3, −6}.
The range is {−2, 1, 2, 8}.

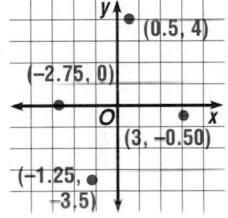

Each member of the domain is paired with exactly one member of the range, so this relation is a function.

Example 2

A recycling center received aluminum cans of varying weights which were sent to a smelter to be melted down for use in other aluminum products. The records for one week in June are shown below. Graph this information and determine if it represents a function.

Day	Number of Cans	Pounds of Aluminum
M	75,000	3000
T	80,000	3150
W	70,000	2850
Th	75,000	3050
F	85,000	3400

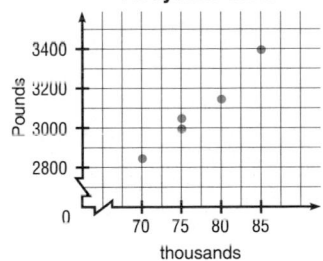

Since 75,000 in the domain is mapped to two members of the range, 3000 and 3050, the relation is not a function.

LESSON 2-1 RELATIONS AND FUNCTIONS 53

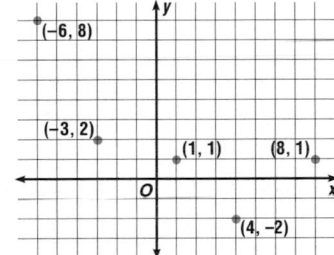
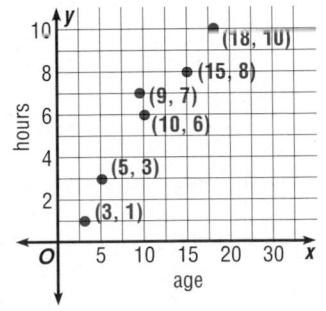

Teaching Tip ❷ Some functions are undefined for certain values. For example, $y = \frac{1}{x}$ is not defined when x is 0.

Example 3

Is the set of ordered pairs that satisfy $y^2 = 4x$ a function?

Prepare a table to find ordered pairs that satisfy the equation. In this case, it is easier to select values for y and then find the corresponding value of x.

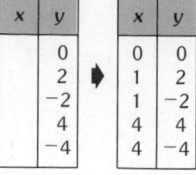

Now graph these ordered pairs.

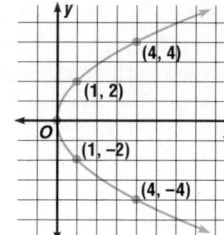

Since x can be any real number, there are an infinite number of ordered pairs that can be graphed. If all of them were graphed, they would take on the shape of a curve, called a *parabola*.

You can see from the graph that there can be two y values for almost all of the x values on the graph. This set of ordered pairs is *not* a function.

Look at the graph in Example 3. Suppose you drew a vertical line that intersects the graph. How many times would the line intersect the graph? If you can draw a vertical line anywhere so that it intersects the graph of the relation in more than one point, then the relation is not a function. This is often called the **vertical line test for a function.**   **Teaching Tip ❷**

Letters other than f can be used to represent a function. For example, the equation $y = 4x + 3$ can also be written as $g(x) = 4x + 3$.

Equations that represent functions are often written in a special way. The equation $y = 2x + 1$ can be written as $f(x) = 2x + 1$. The symbol $f(x)$ is read "f of x." Suppose you want to find the value in the range that corresponds to the element 3 in the domain. This is written as $f(3)$ and read "f of 3." The value of $f(3)$ is found by substituting 3 for x in the equation. Therefore, $f(3) = 2(3) + 1$ or 7.

Example 4

Find the value of $f(15)$ if $f(x) = 100x - 5x^2$.

$$f(x) = 100x - 5x^2$$
$$f(15) = 100(15) - 5(15)^2 \qquad \textit{Substitute 15 for x.}$$
$$= 1500 - 5(225) \qquad \textit{15}^2 = 225$$
$$= 375$$

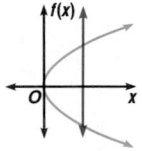

Therefore, $f(15) = 375$.

54   CHAPTER 2   LINEAR RELATIONS AND FUNCTIONS

RETEACHING THE LESSON

Complete the chart for relations A and B at the right.

relation	A 2→3 5→6 7→5	B {(1,4), (2,6), (3,7), (3,9)}
a. domain	2,5,7	1,2,3
b. range	3,5,6	4,6,7,9
c. Is it a function?	yes	no
d. Why or why not?	Each x is paired with one y.	3 is paired with two range elements.

Example 5

Use your calculator to find $f(1.6)$ if $f(x) = 3x^3 - 4x^2$.

ENTER: 3 $\boxed{x}$ 1.6 $\boxed{y^x}$ 3 $\boxed{-}$ 4 $\boxed{x}$ 1.6 $\boxed{x^2}$ 2.048

Therefore, $f(1.6) = 2.048$.

Example 6

Find $g(a + 2)$ if $g(x) = x^2 - 7$.

$$g(x) = x^2 - 7$$
$$g(a + 2) = (a + 2)^2 - 7 \qquad \text{Substitute } (a + 2) \text{ for } x.$$
$$= a^2 + 4a + 4 - 7 \qquad (a + b)^2 = a^2 + 2ab + b^2$$
$$= a^2 + 4a - 3 \qquad \text{Combine like terms.}$$

Therefore, $g(a + 2) = a^2 + 4a - 3$.

CHECKING FOR UNDERSTANDING

Communicating Mathematics

Read and study the lesson to answer each question   1–5. See margin.

1. What is the domain and range of the recycling relation shown on page 52?

2. Tell the difference between a relation and a function.

3. A *counterexample* is an example that shows that a given statement is not true. Sam says every straight line is a function. Find a counterexample for this statement.

4. If $f(x) = 2x - 1$, explain how to find $f(7)$.

5. Draw a Cartesian coordinate plane. Name the seven possible locations on the plane where a point might be graphed. Then graph a point in each of these locations.

Guided Practice

Tell in which quadrant the graph of (x, y) will lie for each situation.

6. x is positive and y is negative   **quadrant IV**

7. x is negative and y is negative   **quadrant III**

8. x is negative and y is positive   **quadrant II**

9. x is 0 and y is positive.   **no quadrant, y-axis**

State whether each mapping is a function, or simply a relation.

10.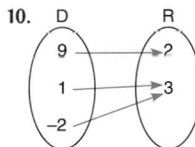
function

11.
relation

12.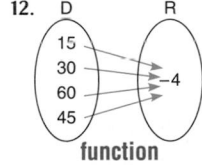
function

Additional Answers

1. D = {1965, 1970, 1975, 1980, 1985, 1990}, R = {17, 21, 23, 32, 35, 37}

2. A relation is any set of ordered pairs. A function is a relation in which no member of the domain is paired with more than one member of the range.

3. any vertical line where $x = a$

4. Substitute 7 for x and evaluate the expression.

5.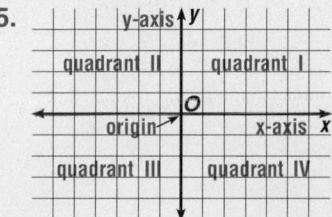

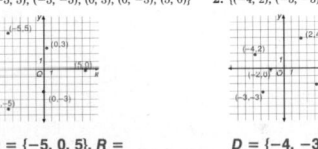

Homework Exercises

Assignment Guide

Basic: 18–37, 42–50
Average: 21–38, 42–50
Enriched: 24–50

Graph each set of ordered pairs on the same coordinate plane. State the domain and range of each relation. Is the relation a function?

13–16. See margin.

13. {(4, 3), (8, -2), (-10, 4), (4, 8)}

14. {(-3, -3), (-2, -2), (2, 2), (4, 4)}

15. {-3, 3), (-2, 2), (2, -2), (-3, -4)}

16. {(-3, 3), (-2, 3), (2, 3), (4, 3)}

17. Find $f(4)$ if $f(x) = x^2 - 3x$. **4**

EXERCISES

Practice Graph each set of ordered pairs on the same coordinate plane. State the domain and range of each relation. Is the relation a function?

18. {(3, 9), (2, 4), (1, 1), (0, 0), (-1, 1), (-2, 4), (-3, 9)} **18–20. See margin.**

19. {(0, -15), (5, -20), (0, -1), (12, 12)}

20. $\left\{\left(-2, \frac{1}{2}\right), \left(-1, 1\frac{1}{2}\right), \left(0, \frac{3}{4}\right), \left(1\frac{1}{2}, -2\right)\right\}$

Find each value if $g(x) = \dfrac{7}{x - 2}$.

21. $g(12)$ $\dfrac{7}{10}$

22. $g(5.5)$ **2**

23. $g(-5)$ **-1**

24. $g(0)$ $-\dfrac{7}{2}$

25. $g(2)$ **undefined**

26. $g(u + 2)$ $\dfrac{7}{u}$

Use the vertical line test to determine if each relation is a function.

27.

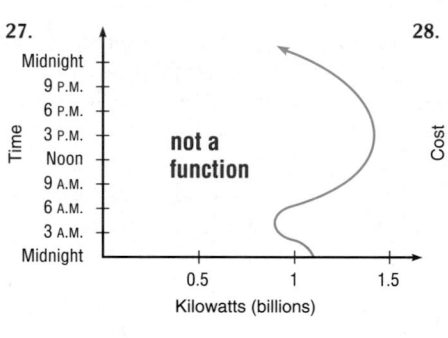

not a function

28.

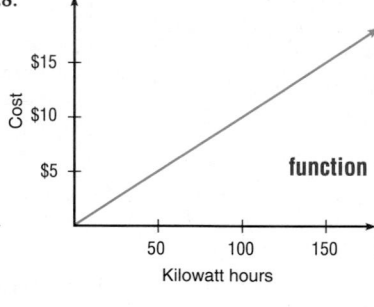

function

29.

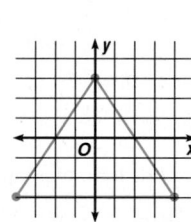

not a function

30.

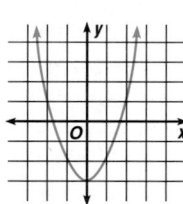

function

31.

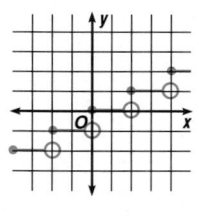

function

Use your calculator to find each value if $j(x) = x^4 - 3x + 1$.

32. $j(5)$ **611**

33. $j(-7)$ **2423**

34. $j(0.25)$ **0.25390625**

35. $j\left(\dfrac{-12}{5}\right)$ **41.3776**

Additional Answers

For graphs of 13–16 and 18–20, see Solutions Manual.

13. D = {4, 8, -10},
    R = {3, 4, 8, -2}; no

14. D = {-3, -2, 2, 4},
    R = {-2, -3, 2, 4}; yes

15. D = {-3, -2, 2},
    R = {-2, -4, 2, 3}; no

16. D = {-3, -2, 2, 4},
    R = {3}; yes

18. D = {-3, -2, -1, 0, 1, 2, 3},
    R = {0, 1, 4, 9}; yes

19. D = {0, 5, 12},
    R = {-20, -15, -1, 12}; no

20. D = $\left\{-2, -1, 0, 1\frac{1}{2}\right\}$,
    R = $\left\{-2, \frac{1}{2}, \frac{3}{4}, 1\frac{1}{2}\right\}$; yes

---

Practice Masters Booklet, p. 9

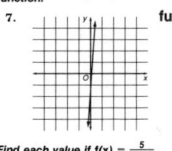 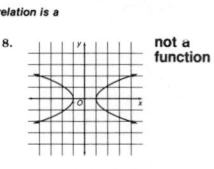
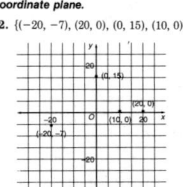

Three vertices of a rectangle are given. Graph them and find the coordinates of the fourth vertex. **For graphs, see Solutions Manual.**

36. (3, 1), (3, -3), (-5, -3) **(-5, 1)**   **37.** (-3, 4), (5, 4), (5, -3) **(-3, -3)**

▷ Find each value if $h(x) = \dfrac{x^2 + 5x - 6}{x + 3}$.

38. $h(3)$ **39.** $h(-2)$ **40.** $h\left(\dfrac{1}{2}\right)$ **41.** $h(a - 1)$

3   **-12** $-\dfrac{13}{14}$ $\dfrac{a^2 + 3a - 10}{a + 2}$

Critical Thinking

42. When a fraction contains a variable in the denominator, there are some values of the variable for which the fraction is undefined. Find the domain of $f(x) = \dfrac{14}{x^2 - 4}$. **all reals except 2 and -2**

Applications

43. Education Jacob is saving for college. To anticipate the money he may need for tuition, he collected information on the average tuition for public colleges for the years 1986 to 1990. Make a graph of this information. Do the points form a straight line? **no**   **Teaching Tip ❸**

Year	1986	1987	1988	1989	1990
Cost per Year	$3963	$4190	$4242	$4736	$4960

44. Aviation The air pressure in the cabin of a fighter jet decreases as the plane ascends. Graph the data below. Project what you think the air pressure would be at 60,000 feet. **Answers will vary. about 0.5 lb/in²**

Altitude (ft)	10,000	20,000	30,000	40,000	50,000
Air Pressure (lb/in²)	10.2	6.4	4.3	2.7	1.6

Mixed Review

Solve each inequality. **(Lesson 1-8)**

45. $4x + 3 < -9$ or $7 < 2x - 11$ **46.** $|y + 1| < 7$
{x|x < -3 or x > 9}   **{y|-8 < y < 6}**

47. The number of posters (x) the Art Club can produce in a week can be expressed by the sentence $3x + 7 < 43$. Solve this inequality to find out the maximum number of posters they can produce. **(Lesson 1-7)**
11 posters

48. Name the sets of numbers to which $\sqrt{36}$ belongs. **(Lesson 1-2)**
N, W, Z, Q, R

Find the value of each expression. **(Lesson 1-1)**

49. $(-4.8)^2 - 144 + 36$ **50.** $[-2 + (-18)]^3 - (\sqrt{10000})(16 + 2)$
-84.96   **-9800**

LESSON 2-1 RELATIONS AND FUNCTIONS   57

EXTENDING THE LESSON

Math Power: Connections

The coordinates of three vertices of a parallelogram are (2,2), (3,-1), and (0,-2). Find the coordinates of the fourth vertex. Can there be more than one point? **(-1,1), (5,3), or (1,-5); yes**

Teaching Tip ❸ Have students define the domain and the range.

Enrichment Masters Booklet, p. 8

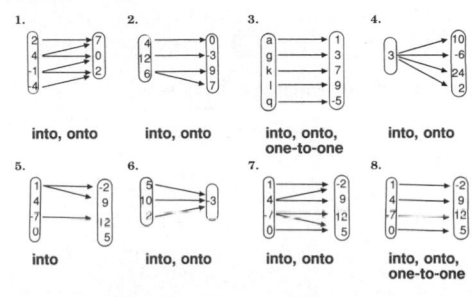

Objective: Graph linear equations on a graphing calculator.

Motivating the Lesson

If you have an overhead graphing calculator or a demonstration computer, use it to draw the graph of $y = 2x + 1$ in the range [-10, 10] by [-10, 10] and then in the range [-5, 5] by [-10, 10]. Ask students if they are pictures of the same graph. Why or why not? Why do they look different? They are graphs of the same line. The scale makes them look different.

Teaching Tip ① The standard viewing rectangle is *not* the default viewing rectangle for the Casio. The default viewing rectangle is [-4.7, 4.7] by [-3.1, 3.1] and can be obtained by keying [SHIFT] [MCL] [EXE] while in the Range screen.

Teaching Tip ② The lower the resolution, the longer it will take for the TI-81 to graph the function. This is because the calculator does not have to calculate as many points with a high resolution since it plots fewer points. It will not be as clear as a low resolution graph.

Teaching Tip ③ Use the range key to make sure your calculator is set at the standard viewing window.

Teaching Tip ④ The "x" is the alpha function of [+] key.

Graphing Calculator Exploration: Graphing Linear Equations

The graphing calculator is a powerful tool for studying graphs of a wide variety of functions. Let's take a look at some linear functions and their graphs. **Teaching Tip ①**

The **viewing window** for a graph is that portion of the coordinate grid displayed on the **graphics screen** of the calculator; that is, the portion of the domain and range for the x and y variables shown on the screen. The viewing window can be written as [left, right] by [bottom, top]. So [-10, 10] by [-10, 10] denotes the domain values $-10 \leq x \leq 10$ and the range values $-10 \leq y \leq 10$. This viewing window is called the **standard viewing window**. In order to set the viewing window on both the Casio fx-7000G and the TI-81, press the [RANGE] key. The following **range screen** display settings are for the standard viewing window. If your calculator is not already set for the standard viewing window, use these values to set it now. You can easily set the TI-81 viewing window to the standard window by pressing [ZOOM] 6.

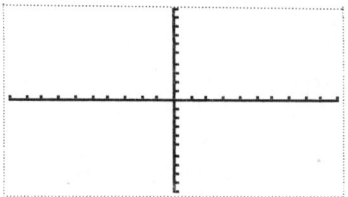

The standard viewing window
is [-10, 10] by [-10, 10].

Casio

```
Range
Xmin: -10
Xmax: 10
scl: 1
Ymin: -10
Ymax: 10
scl: 1
```

TI-81

```
RANGE
Xmin = -10
Xmax = 10
Xscl = 1
Ymin = -10
Ymax = 10
Yscl = 1
Xres = 1
```

Teaching Tip ② The **Xscl, Yscl,** and **scl** values set the frequency of the tick marks along each of the axes. For example, Xscl = 1 means that there will be a tick mark for every one unit along the x-axis. The **Xres** for the TI-81 establishes the quality of the resolution on the graphics screen. The Xres value can be set between 1 and 8, with 1 being the best resolution.

The key sequences for graphing with the Casio and the TI-81 are slightly different. The example below demonstrates how to graph a linear equation on each calculator.

Example 1

Teaching Tip ③

Teaching Tip ④

Graph $y = 3x + 5$ using the standard viewing window.

First, make sure that your calculator is set for the standard viewing window. Then enter the appropriate key sequence.

Casio [GRAPH] 3 [ALPHA] [X] [+] 5 [EXE]

TI-81 [Y=] 3 [X|T] [+] 5 [GRAPH]

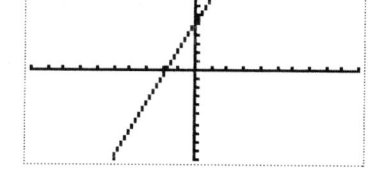

58 CHAPTER 2 LINEAR RELATIONS AND FUNCTIONS

Have the students graph equations that have the same slope in the same viewing window. You can use the colon (:) key on the Casio to graph two functions and you can select two functions to be graphed on the TI-81. Also graph functions that are perpendicular.

Once you have plotted a graph on the graphics screen of the Casio, it remains on the screen until it is cleared by pressing [SHIFT] [Cls] [EXE] or until the range values are changed. The TI-81 will automatically clear the graphics screen when a new equation is entered.

A graph that appears in the viewing window of the graphics screen is said to be a **complete graph** if all of the important characteristics of the graph are displayed. For a linear equation, this would include the points where the graph crosses the axes.

Example 2

Graph $y = -x + 20$.

Use the standard viewing window.

Casio [GRAPH] [(-)] [ALPHA] [X] [+] 20 [EXE]

TI-81 [Y=] [(-)] [X|T] [+] 20 [GRAPH]

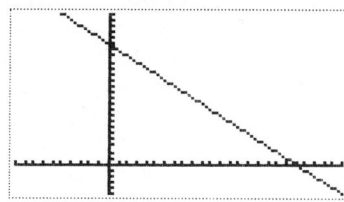

None of the graph is shown when you graph this equation in the standard viewing window, so we must change the range values to view a complete graph. There are several viewing windows that will allow us to view the complete graph. Change your viewing window to $[-10, 25]$ by $[-5, 25]$ with scale factors of 1 for each scale. Now graph by pressing [EXE] on the Casio or [GRAPH] on the TI-81.

EXERCISES

Use your graphing calculator to graph each equation. State the range values that you used to view a complete graph for each equation. **See margin.**

1. $y = 6x + 7$
2. $y = -5x - 6$
3. $y = -3x + 12$
4. $y = -7x + 22$
5. $y = 5x - 35$
6. $y = -8x + 32$
7. $y = 0.1x - 1$
8. $y = 12x$
9. $y = 0.5x + 12$
10. $y = 0.01x$
11. $y = x - 55$
12. $y = 100x - 126$

GRAPHIC CALCULATOR EXPLORATION: GRAPHING LINEAR EQUATIONS   59

Additional Answers

Answers may vary. Sample answers are given.
1. $[-10, 10]$ by $[-10, 10]$
2. $[-10, 10]$ by $[-10, 10]$
3. $[-10, 10]$ by $[-10, 20]$
4. $[-10, 10]$ by $[-10, 25]$
5. $[-10, 10]$ by $[-40, 10]$
6. $[-10, 10]$ by $[-10, 40]$
7. $[-2, 15]$ by $[-10, 10]$
8. $[-10, 10]$ by $[-10, 10]$
9. $[-30, 5]$ by $[-5, 15]$
10. $[-10, 10]$ by $[-0.5, 0.5]$
11. $[0, 60]$ by $[-60, 0]$
12. $[-2, 2]$ by $[-150, 10]$

Teaching Tip ⑥ You can switch between the graph and text screens. To do this on the Casio, use the [G↔T] key. On the TI-81, use [2nd] [QUIT] to go to the text screen from the graphics screen, and use the [GRAPH] key to see the graphics screen from the text screen.

More Examples

Graph each function on a graphing calculator.

1. $y = 5$
2. $y = 7x + 4$
3. $y = -4x - 11$
4. $y = 1000x + 500$
5. $y = .007x - .04$

EVALUATING THE LESSON

Closing the Lesson

Modeling Activity Give students ten linear equations and have them guess a starting viewing window. Then graph the equations to check their viewing windows.

APPLYING THE LESSON

Homework Exercises

Assignment Guide

All: 1–12

EXTENDING THE LESSON

Math Power: Problem Solving

Have students use the Trace function to solve linear equations. Use zoom In to find a solution that is accurate to two decimal places. Then do the same thing algebraically by setting the expression in x equal to zero and solving for x. Explain that both methods achieve the same result.

Lesson Resources

Reteaching Master 2-2
Practice Master 2-2
Enrichment Master 2-2
Technology Master, p. 19

 Transparency 2-2 contains the 5-Minute Check and a teaching aid for this lesson.

INTRODUCING THE LESSON

 5-Minute Check

(over Lesson 2-1)

1. State the domain and range of {(4, 4), (1, 1), (3, 3)}. Is it a function?   **D = {1, 3, 4}, R = {1, 3, 4}; yes**

2. In what quadrants can the point (*a, a*) lie?   **I and III**

3. Find $f(-3)$ if $f(x) = x^2 + 3x + 2$.   **2**

4. Graph {(1970, 80), (1975, 82), (1980, 80), (1985, 90), (1990, 95)}. Is it a function?   **yes**

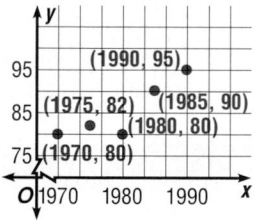

5. Draw the graph of a line that is not a function.

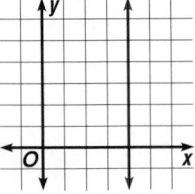

Objectives

2-2A

2-2B

After studying this lesson, you should be able to:
- identify equations that are linear and graph them, and
- write linear equations in standard form.

Application

The employees at the Speedy Repair Shop use a table like the one below to compute their customers' bills.

Labor Hours	$\frac{1}{2}$	$\frac{3}{4}$	1	$1\frac{1}{4}$	$1\frac{1}{2}$	$1\frac{3}{4}$	2
Charge	$29	$33.50	$38	$42.50	$47	$51.50	$56

Usually x is the independent variable and y is the dependent variable. The value of y depends on the value of x.

The **open sentence** that describes this relationship is $y = 18x + 20$, where x represents the number of hours and y represents the charge to the customer. When this information is graphed, the points lie in a line. This graph is a relation and a function.

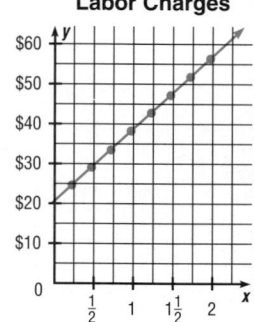

Labor Charges

The independent variable is graphed on the horizontal axis and the dependent variable is graphed on the vertical axis.

Suppose we connect the points with a line. The line would contain an infinite number of points, all of which satisfy the equation $y = 18x + 20$. An equation whose graph is a line is called a **linear equation.**

When variables other than x and y are used, assume that the letter coming first in the alphabet represents the domain or horizontal coordinate.

Linear equations may contain one or two variables with no variable having an exponent other than 1.

Linear equations $4x + 3y = 7$ $y = 8$ $5m - n = 1$

$y = 7 + 2x$ $x = -7$

NOT linear equations $3x + y^2 = y$ $\frac{1}{x} + y = 4$ *Remember $\frac{1}{x} = x^{-1}$.*

Teaching Tip ❶

Every equation can be written in many forms. For example, $5m - n = 1$ could also be written as $5m = n + 1$ and $n = 5m - 1$. Any linear equation can be written in **standard form.**

Standard Form of a Linear Equation	**The standard form of a linear equation is** $Ax + By = C,$ **where A, B, and C are real numbers and** **A and B are not both zero.**

Usually A, B, and C are given as integers whose greatest common factor is 1.

60   CHAPTER 2   LINEAR RELATIONS AND FUNCTIONS

ALTERNATE TEACHING STRATEGIES

Using Critical Thinking

An equation with a power of *x* other than 1 is not linear. Explain why this is true. Use graphs of several cases to explain.

Using Charts

Have students make charts of the solutions of the equation. Note that a chart of values helps organize the information. Students can use these charts to graph the equations and determine whether they are linear functions.

Example 1

Write the equation $x = \frac{3}{4}y - 1$ in standard form.

$$x = \frac{3}{4}y - 1$$
$$4x = 3y - 4 \qquad \textit{Multiply each side by 4 to eliminate the fraction.}$$
$$4x - 3y = -4 \qquad \textit{Add } -3y \textit{ to each side.}$$

To graph a linear equation it is often helpful to make a table of ordered pairs that satisfy the equation. Since any line can be defined by only two points, only two ordered pairs are needed. Finding a third ordered pair is a good idea to check the accuracy of the first two. **Teaching Tip ②**

Example 2

Graph $3y = -2x - 6$.

First solve the equation for y.

$$3y = -2x - 6$$
$$y = -\frac{2}{3}x - 2 \qquad \textit{Divide each side by 3.}$$

Find three ordered pairs that satisfy the equation. Then graph the ordered pairs and connect the points with a line.

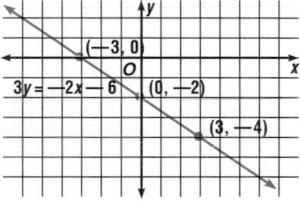

x	-3	0	3
y	0	-2	-4

Example 3

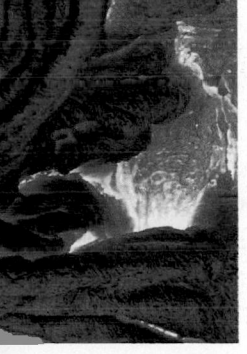

APPLICATION

Geology

Geothermal energy is generated wherever water comes into contact with heated underground rocks. This heat turns the water into steam that can be used to make electricity. The underground temperature of rocks varies with their depth below the surface. The deeper the rocks are, the hotter they are. The temperature t in degrees Celsius is estimated by the equation $t = 35d + 20$, where d is the depth in kilometers. Complete the table and graph the linear equation. What would be the temperature of the rocks at a depth of 3 km?

Depth (d) in km	Temperature (t) in °C
0	20
0.5	37.5
1	55
1.5	72.5
2	90

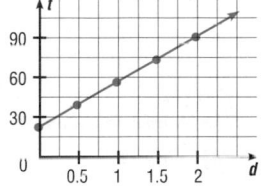

By substituting 3 for d in the equation, $t = 35(3) + 20$ or 125°C.

RETEACHING THE LESSON

Write each linear equation in standard form.

1. $y = 4 - x$ $x + y = 4$
2. $6 - y = -2x$ $2x - y = -6$
3. $5 + 2y = 3x$ $-3x + 2y = -5$
        or
        $3x - 2y = 5$

Solve for y.

4. $8 + 2y = 6y$ $y = 3x - 4$
5. $x + 3y = 12$ $y = \frac{-x}{3} + 4$

Motivating the Lesson

Discuss hourly wages. Have students who work explain their pay system. If no one works, use the hourly wage of $5.00. Generate a table of values and graph them. Discuss the type of graph formed.

TEACHING THE LESSON

Teaching Tip ①   These equations are not linear because they contain variables that are not to the first power.

Teaching Tip ②   Point out that students may want to use 0 as one x-value, along with one negative and one positive value.

Chalkboard Example

For Example 1
Write the equation $y = x + 3$ in standard form. $-x + y = 3$

Reteaching Masters Booklet, p. 9

2-2 **Reteaching Worksheet**

NAME _____ DATE _____

Linear Functions

An equation whose graph is a straight line is called a **linear equation**. Any linear equation can be written in **standard form**.

The standard form of a linear equation is $Ax + By = C$, where A, B, and C are real numbers, and A and B are not both zero.

To graph a linear equation, it is helpful to make a table of ordered pairs that satisfy the equation. These ordered pairs can then be graphed and connected with a straight line.

Example. Write the equation $x = \frac{1}{4}y - 9$ in standard form.

$$x = \frac{1}{4}y - 9$$
$$4x = y - 9 \quad \text{Multiply each side by 4 to eliminate the fraction.}$$
$$4x - y = -9 \quad \text{Add } -y \text{ to each side.}$$

Write each equation in standard form.

1. $x = \frac{2}{7} + y$ $x - y = \frac{2}{7}$
2. $y = \frac{7}{12}x + 1$ $-7x + 12y = 12$
3. $y = 3x - 5$ $3x - y = 5$
4. $x = 10$ $x + 0y = 10$
5. $y = 5x$ $-5x + y = 0$
6. $5x = 5 + 2x + y$ $3x - y = 5$
7. $y - 6 = 0$ $0x + y = 6$
8. $y = -7x + 2$ $7x + y = 2$
9. $4s + 3r = 12$ in standard form

Complete the table. Then graph the equation.

10. $y = 6x + 2$

x	-2	-1	0	1	2
y					

11. $x - y = -7$

x	-4	-2	0	1	2
y					

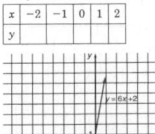
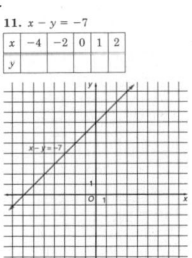

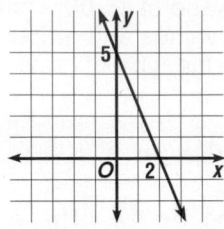
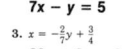
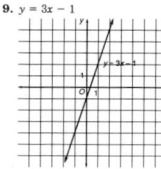 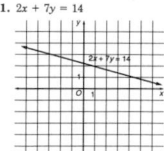
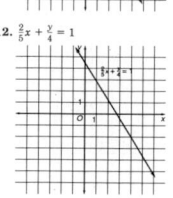
Any function whose ordered pairs satisfy a linear equation is called a **linear function**.

Definition of Linear Function	A function is linear if it can be defined by $f(x) = mx + b$, where m and b are real numbers.

In the definition of a linear function, m or b may be zero. If $m = 0$, then $f(x) = b$. The graph is a horizontal line. This function is called a **constant function**. If $f(x) = 0$, the function is called the *zero function*.

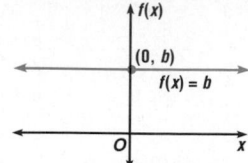

Example 4

Tell whether each function is a linear function.

a. $f(x) = x^4 + 18$

This cannot be written in the form $f(x) = mx + b$, since x has a power of 4. Thus, $f(x)$ is not a linear function.

b. $g(x) = 4 - x$

This can be written in the form $f(x) = mx + b$, where $m = -1$ and $b = 4$. Thus, $g(x)$ is a linear function.

CHECKING FOR UNDERSTANDING

Communicating Mathematics

Read and study the lesson to answer each question.

1. An equation whose graph is a line is called a ___?___. **linear equation**

2. standard

2. An equation in the form $Ax + By = C$ is said to be in ___?___ form.

3. Write the equation $3x + 5y = -2$ in two other forms. **See margin.**

4. How many points are on any line? Choose the best answer. **d**
   a. 2   b. 4   c. 100   d. an infinite number

Guided Practice

State whether each equation is a linear equation. If it is not a linear equation, explain why.

5. $x^2 + y^2 = 7$ 6. $x + y = 4$ **yes**   7. $x - 2y = 5$ **yes**
5. no; contains exponent greater than 1

State whether each function is a linear function. If it is not a linear function, explain why.

8. $f(x) = x^2 + 3$ 9. $g(x) = 7$ **yes**   10. $h(x) = 1.2 - 3.7x$
8. no; contains exponent greater than 1   **yes**

EXERCISES

Practice

Write each equation in standard form.

11. $y = 3x - 2$
    $3x - y = 2$

12. $y = -5x + 1$
    $5x + y = 1$

13. $x = 10$
    $x = 10$

14. $y = \frac{5}{8}x + 1$
    $5x - 8y = -8$

15. $x = \frac{1}{3}y - 4$
    $3x - y = -12$

16. $y = 14x$
    $14x - y = 0$

Additional Answer

3. $y = -\frac{3}{5}x - \frac{2}{5}$, $x = -\frac{5}{3}y - \frac{2}{3}$

17. $y = 4.5 - 2x$

18. $b = \dfrac{7 - 5a}{3}$

23. $r = \dfrac{144 - 9t}{8}$

17. Solve $4x + 2y = 9$ for y.

18. Solve $5a + 3b = 7$ for b.

19. Graph $y = x$. **See margin.**

20. Graph $y = 5x - 4$. **See margin.**

 Solve each equation for the specified variable.

21. $-5m - 3 = n$, for m $m = \dfrac{n + 3}{-5}$

22. $x - y = 3$, for y $y = x - 3$

23. $\dfrac{3}{4}t + \dfrac{2}{3}r = 12$, for r

24. $2a = 3b - 4$, for b $b = \dfrac{2a + 4}{3}$

Graph each equation. **25–36. See Solutions Manual.**

25. $b = 2a - 3$

26. $x - y = 4$

27. $2a + 3b = 6$

28. $5 = 5x$

29. $x + y = 7$

30. $4x + 3y = 12$

31. $f(x) = 2x + 1$

32. $3y + 7 = 12$

33. $f(x) = 3x - 1$

34. $\dfrac{1}{3}x + \dfrac{1}{2}y = 1$

35. $\dfrac{x}{4} - \dfrac{y}{3} = 2$

36. $\dfrac{x}{3} + \dfrac{y}{2} = \dfrac{15}{2}$

37. $S = 150 + 0.30 (n - 50)$, where n = number of magazines, and $n > 50$

Critical Thinking

37. Emilio earns a salary of $150 per week for selling computer game magazines by phone. He receives an extra 30¢ for each magazine over 50 that he sells. Write the equation that represents his total salary for any week.

38. The graph of a vertical line has the form $x = c$, where c is any number. Is this linear equation a linear function? Why or why not? **no, because the same x-value is paired with an infinite number of y-values**

Applications

39. Finance Frontier Auto Shop has a standard $12 shop charge for every job it takes. In addition, the mechanic working on the job charges $20 per hour. The equation that represents the total charge for a job is $c = 12 + 20t$. Find the total charge for a repair requiring 4.5 hours labor. **$102**

40. Consumer Awareness Monique's Fine Fashions allows its customers to charge their purchases on a delayed payment plan. When the customer receives a bill from Monique's, there is a $5 charge for using the delayed payment plan plus 2% interest on the purchase. Calculate the bill for a purchase of $110. **$117.20**

41. It is not a function because one of the x-values is paired with two different y-values.

Mixed Review

41 Graph $\{(3, 4), (4, 5), (-5, -2), (-6, 4), (3, -5)\}$. Is this a function? Explain your answer. **(Lesson 2-1)**

42. Find the value of $f(-3)$ if $f(x) = x^2 - 3x - 9$. **(Lesson 2-1)** **9**

43. There are four points on a line that are labeled with the letters M, A, T, and H. How many different ways can these points be labeled? **(Lesson 1-5)** **24 ways**

Solve. **(Lesson 1-4)**

44. Geometry The perimeter of a square is 42 inches. Find the length of one side of the square. **10.5 inches**

45. Zoology The population of gorillas at the zoo was decreased by moving 5 of them to a neighboring city's zoo. Write an expression to represent the original number of gorillas at the zoo if there are p gorillas there now. **$p + 5$**

EXTENDING THE LESSON

Math Power: Communication

Do you think $y = |x|$ is a linear function? Why or why not? **No, the graph isn't a straight line. The equation can't be written in the form $Ax + By = C$.**

Additional Answers

19–20.

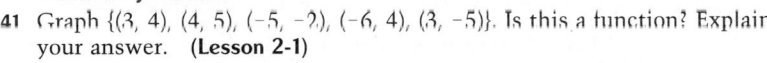

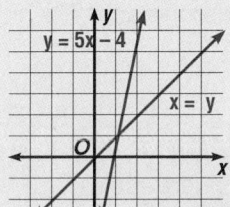

2-2 Enrichment Worksheet

NAME _____ DATE _____

Greatest Common Factor

Suppose we are given a linear equation $ax + by = c$ where a, b, c are nonzero integers, and we want to know if there exist *integers* x and y that satisfy the equation. We could try guessing a few times, but this process would be time consuming for an equation such as $588x + 432y = 72$. By using the Euclidean Algorithm, we can determine not only if such integers x and y exist, but also find them. The following example shows how this algorithm works.

Example: Find integers x and y that satisfy $588x + 432y = 72$.

Divide the greater of the two coefficients by the lesser to get a quotient and remainder. Then, repeat the process by dividing the divisor by the remainder until you get a remainder of 0. The process can be written as follows.

$588 = 432(1) + 156$	(1)
$432 = 156(2) + 120$	(2)
$156 = 120(1) + 36$	(3)
$120 = 36(3) + 12$	(4)
$36 = 12(3)$	

The last nonzero remainder is the GCF of the two coefficients. If the constant term 72 is divisible by the GCF, then integers x and y do exist that satisfy the equation. To find x and y, work backwards in the following manner.

$72 = 6 \cdot 12$
$\quad = 6 \cdot [120 - 36(3)]$ substitute for 12 using (4)
$\quad = 6(120) - 18(36)$
$\quad = 6(120) - 18[156 - 120(1)]$ substitute for 36 using (3)
$\quad = -18(156) + 24(120)$
$\quad = -18(156) + 24[432 - 156(2)]$ substitute for 120 using (2)
$\quad = 24(432) - 66(156)$
$\quad = 24(432) - 66[588 - 432(1)]$ substitute for 156 using (1)
$\quad = 588(-66) + 432(90)$

Thus, $x = -66$ and $y = 90$.

Find integers x and y, if they exist, that satisfy the following equations.

1. $27x + 65y = 3$
$x = -36$ and $y = 15$

2. $45x + 144y = 36$
$x = -12$ and $y = 4$

3. $90x + 117y = 10$
no integral solutions exist

4. $123x + 36y = 15$
$x = 25$ and $y = -85$

5. $1032x + 1001y = 1$
$x = -226$ and $y = 233$

6. $3125x + 3087y = 1$
$x = -1381$ and $y = 1398$

Problem-Solving Strategy: Look for a Pattern

EXPLORE
PLAN
SOLVE
EXAMINE

Lesson Resources

Practice Master 2-3
Activity Master, p. 2

 Transparency 2-3 contains the 5-Minute Check and a teaching aid for this lesson.

INTRODUCING THE LESSON

5-Minute Check

(over Lesson 2-2)

1. State whether $x^2 = 9$ is a linear function. **no**

Write each equation in standard form.

2. $y = 2x - 6$ **$2x - y = 6$**

3. $x = \frac{3}{5} + \frac{y}{4}$ **$20x - 5y = 12$**

4. Solve $3x + 2y = 8$ for y.
   $y = \left(-\frac{3}{2}\right)x + 4$

Motivating the Lesson

Have five students come to the front of the class. Determine how many handshakes there would be in all if each person shook the hand of everyone else. Have the class make a chart together that would illustrate the pattern.

TEACHING THE LESSON

Teaching Tip ❶ Note to students that charts help to organize and to see what pattern exists, if any.

Teaching Tip ❷ Have students draw the 7-sided figure to prove that Darlene was right.

Chalkboard Example

For the Example
Look for a pattern to find the next number.
1, 4, 7, 10, 13, □ **16**

Objective 2-3

After studying this lesson you should be able to:
■ Solve a problem by identifying the pattern and using it to find the missing information.

Connection

In geometry class, Darlene was daydreaming. She began doodling on paper, drawing various shapes, and connecting the points to draw the diagonals. As she continued to draw, she wondered if there was a way to find how many diagonals there were in any figure. She made a chart to record her findings. **Teaching Tip ❶**

These figures are convex polygons. Diagonals of convex polygons lie inside the figure.

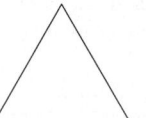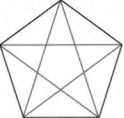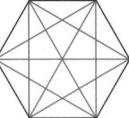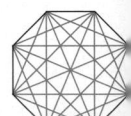

Number of Sides	3	4	5	6	7	8
Number of Diagonals	0	2	5	9	?	20

+2 +3 +4 +? +?

Notice that a pattern seems to be developing. Darlene didn't want to take time to draw a polygon with 7 sides. She looked at the pattern and said that a 7-sided figure must have 14 diagonals. Was she right? **Teaching Tip ❷**

Example

Look for a pattern to find the next number in (1, 2, 4, 8, 16, 32, □).

There is more than one way to interpret this pattern.

Strategies
Look for a pattern.
Solve a simpler problem.
Act it out.
Guess and check.
Draw a diagram.
Make a chart.
Work backwards.

Method 1: Look for an operation from one number to the next.

1 2 4 8 16 32 □
  ×2 ×2 ×2 ×2 ×2 ×2   The next number is 2×32 or 64.

Method 2: Look for an expression that describes each term.

1 2 4 8 16 32 □
2^0 2^1 2^2 2^3 2^4 2^5 2^6 The next number is 2^6 or 64.

64 CHAPTER 2 LINEAR RELATIONS AND FUNCTIONS

RETEACHING THE LESSON

1. Find the next number in each group.
   a. 2, 5, 8, 11, ___ **14**
   b. 18, 6, 2, $\frac{2}{3}$, ___ **$\frac{2}{9}$**

2. How many squares are on a chessboard? Hint: There are squares of different sizes: $1 \times 1, 2 \times 2, \ldots, 8 \times 8$. **204**

CHECKING FOR UNDERSTANDING

Communicating Mathematics

Read and study the lesson to answer each question.

1. What is a diagonal? **a segment that connects two nonconsecutive vertices of a polygon**

2. How many diagonals does a 12-sided polygon have? **54**

3. What are the next 3 numbers after 64 in the Example? **128, 256, 512**

Guided Practice

Find the next number in each group of numbers.

4. 6, 10, 15, 21, 28, __?__ **36**

5. 1, 4, 9, 16, 25, __?__ **36**

EXERCISES

Solve. Use any strategy.

6. Find the total number of triangles in Figure A. **27**

7. Find the total number of squares in Figure B. **30**

8. Place a piece of paper over the figure at the right. Can you trace it without lifting your pencil or tracing over any line you have already drawn? **yes**
Intersecting a line is permitted.

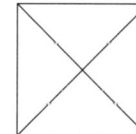

9. If you had one bill from each type of bill from the game of Monopoly®, how much play money would you have? **$686**

10. How many aluminum cans does it take to build a pyramid 120 cm tall? Each can is 12 cm tall. The base of the pyramid is a single row of cans and each can in the rows above it rests on two cans below it, and so on. **55 cans**

COOPERATIVE LEARNING ACTIVITY

Work in groups. Each person in the group must understand the solution and be able to explain it to any person in class.

At Dunbar High School, there are 500 students and 500 lockers, numbered 1 through 500. Suppose the first student opens each locker. Then the second student closes every second locker. The third student changes the state of every third locker (that is, closes the ones that were open and opens the ones that were closed). The fourth student changes the state of every fourth locker. This process continues until the 500th student changes the state of the 500th locker. Which lockers are open? **lockers whose numbers are perfect squares (1, 4, 9, 16, 25, and so on)**

LESSON 2-3   PROBLEM-SOLVING STRATEGY: LOOK FOR A PATTERN   65

EXTENDING THE LESSON

Math Power: Reasoning

Can you trace the figure below without lifting your pencil or tracing over any line? **yes**

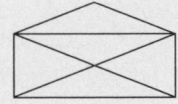

Cooperative Learning Activity

Have students solve a simpler problem. Have them open and close 30 lockers. Make a conjecture based on the smaller number of lockers.

EVALUATING THE LESSON

Checking for Understanding

Exercises 1–5 are designed to help you assess understanding through reading, writing, and speaking. You should work through Exercises 1–3 with your students, and then monitor their work on Exercises 4–5.

Closing the Lesson

Speaking Activity   Have students explain why charts are helpful to see patterns. Can they name other areas where patterns are found?

APPLYING THE LESSON

Homework Exercises

Assignment Guide
Basic: 6–10
Average: 6–10
Enriched: 6–10

Practice Masters Booklet, p. 11

2-3   **Practice Worksheet**

NAME _____   DATE _____

Problem Solving Strategy: Look for a Pattern

Solve. Look for a pattern.

1. How many shaded triangles will there be in the tenth figure? **55**

  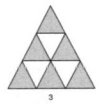 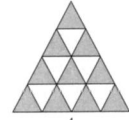

2. How many shaded squares will there be in the tenth figure? **45**

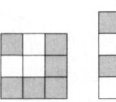 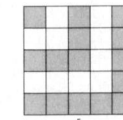

Solve. Use any strategy.

3. Can you trace the figure at the right without lifting your pencil or tracing over any line you have already drawn? **no**

4. A pyramid of aluminum cans is built against a wall so that there are two cans in the top row, four cans in the second row, six cans in the third row, and so on. How many rows are there if the pyramid contains 1190 cans? **34**

Lesson Resources

Reteaching Master 2-4
Practice Master 2-4
Enrichment Master 2-4
Technology Master, p. 2

 Transparency 2-4 contains the 5-Minute Check and a teaching aid for this lesson.

INTRODUCING THE LESSON

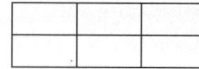 **5-Minute Check**

(over Lesson 2-3)

Find the next number in each group of numbers.

1. 1, 3, 0, 4, −1, 5 **−2**
2. 1, 1, 2, 6, 24 **120**
3. How many rectangles are in the figure? **31**

Other Prerequisite Skills

4. What is the definition of a polygon? **a many-sided figure. "Poly" means many and "gon" means sides.**

Motivating the Lesson

Have students bring in pictures of objects that slant such as ladders, stairs, mountains, and roads. Measure the base and the height of the figures. Divide the vertical distance by the horizontal distance. Discuss the value of the slope.

TEACHING THE LESSON

Teaching Tip ❶ When discussing the slope formula, emphasize that any two points may be used to compute the slope. It is important to be consistent as to where you put the values from the first point and the values from the second point.

Objectives

After studying this lesson, you should be able to:

2-4A ▪ determine the slope and intercepts of a line,
2-4B ▪ use the slope and intercepts to graph a linear equation, and
2-4C ▪ determine if two lines are parallel, perpendicular, or neither.

Application

Caryn and Brad used a long board and bricks to build a ramp for their radio-controlled model car. At every 24 inches, they placed bricks to create an incline of 4 more inches. The steepness, or **slope,** of the ramp is the ratio of the vertical change to the horizontal change.

$$\text{slope} = \frac{\text{change in the vertical units}}{\text{change in the horizontal units}}$$

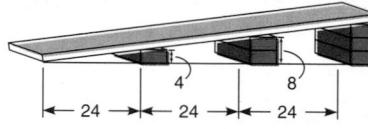

The slope of the car ramp is $\frac{4}{24}$ or $\frac{1}{6}$.

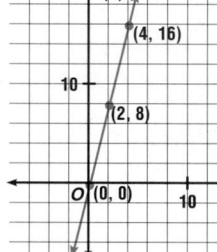

Slope is also defined for the graphs of linear functions. In the graph of $f(x) = 4x$ shown at the left, *look for a pattern* in the relationship of the change in the y-coordinates to the change in the x-coordinates of the points on the graph.

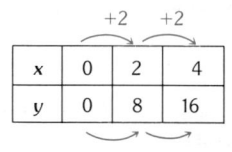

x	0	2	4
y	0	8	16

The pattern for x-coordinates is a difference of 2.

The pattern for y-coordinates is a difference of 8.

The y-coordinates increase 8 units for each 2-unit increase in the x-coordinates. The slope of the line whose equation is $f(x) = 4x$ is $\frac{8}{2}$ or 4. The vertical change is the difference between the y-coordinates of any two points on the graph. The horizontal change is the difference between the corresponding x-coordinates. You can use the following formula to find the slope of a line if you know the coordinates of two points on the line.

Definition of Slope

The slope *m* of a line passing through points (x_1, y_1) and (x_2, y_2) is given by $m = \frac{y_2 - y_1}{x_2 - x_1}$. **Teaching Tip ❶**

66 CHAPTER 2 LINEAR RELATIONS AND FUNCTIONS

ALTERNATE TEACHING STRATEGIES

Using Models

Use a geoboard as a model for the coordinate plane. Let the peg in the lower left-hand corner represent the origin. Have students make as many line segments with different nonnegative slopes as possible. An example of a line segment that has a slope of $\frac{6}{5}$ is shown in the figure.

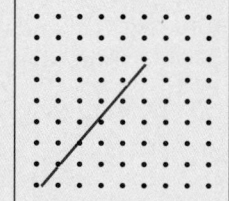

Example 1

Determine the slope of the line that passes through points (1, −3) and (0, −5). Then graph the line.

$$m = \frac{y_2 - y_1}{x_2 - x_1}$$

$$= \frac{-5 - (-3)}{0 - 1} \qquad (x_1, y_1) = (1, -3)$$
$$(x_2, y_2) = (0, -5)$$

$$= \frac{-2}{-1} \text{ or } 2 \qquad \textit{The slope of the line is 2.}$$

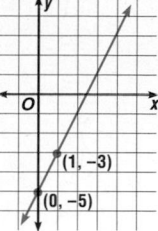

Graph the two points and draw the line. Use the slope to check your graph by selecting any point on the line and then go up 2 and right 1. This point should also be on the line.

Example 2

Graph the line passing through the point (−4, −1) with a slope of $\frac{-2}{3}$. Describe the manner in which the line rises or falls.

First graph the ordered pair (−4, −1). Since the slope of the line is $\frac{-2}{3}$, the vertical change is −2 and the horizontal change is 3. From (−4, −1) move 2 units down and 3 units to the right. This point is (−1, −3).

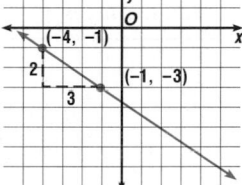

Connect the points to draw the line.

Notice that the line falls to the right.

Teaching Tip ❷

The slope of a line tells the direction in which it rises or falls. In Example 2, the slope is negative and the line falls to the right. The graphs below show the three other possibilities for a linear graph.

If the line is horizontal, then the slope is zero.	If the line rises to the right, then the slope is positive.	If the line is vertical, then the slope is *undefined*.
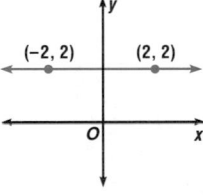 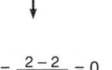	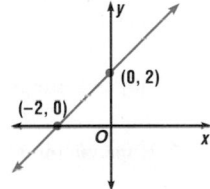	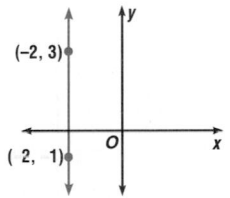
$m = \frac{2-2}{2-(-2)} = 0$	$m = \frac{0-2}{-2-0} = 1$	$m = \frac{3-(-1)}{-2-(-2)} = \frac{4}{0}$

Teaching Tip ❷ A vertical line is also said to have no slope. Students sometimes confuse no slope with zero slope, although they do not have the same meaning.

Chalkboard Examples

For Example 1
Determine the slope of the line passing through each pair of points.

a. (−2, 3) and (−4, 4) $-\frac{1}{2}$
b. (7, 5) and (−3, 5)   **0**
c. (5, 7) and (5, −3)   **undefined**

For Example 2
Graph the line passing through the point (4, 5) with a slope of 3.

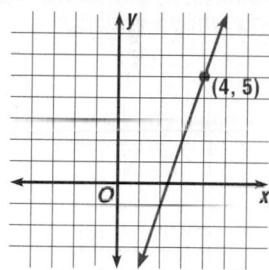

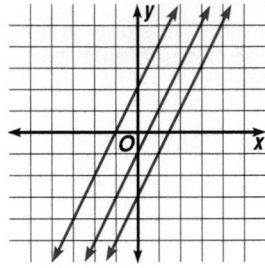
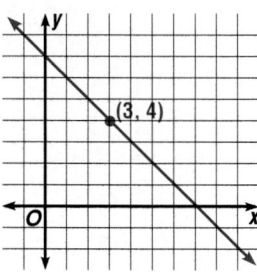
Example 3

Graph $f(x) = 3x + 2$, $g(x) = 3x$, and $h(x) = 3x - 5$ on the same coordinate plane. Find the slope of each line and describe what you notice about the graphs.

Find ordered pairs to satisfy each function. Connect the ordered pairs to draw each line.

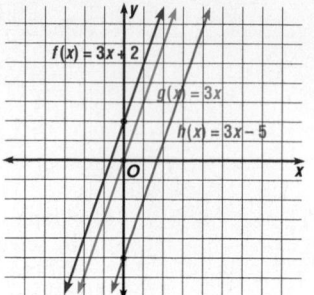

The slope of each line is 3. The lines appear to be parallel.

Equations whose graphs have similar characteristics are often called families of equations.

In Example 3, you saw that lines that have the same slope are parallel.

Definition of Parallel Lines	In a plane, lines with the same slope are parallel. All vertical lines are parallel and all horizontal lines are parallel.

If you know the slope of one line, you can use it to graph a line through a given point, parallel to that line.

Example 4

Graph the line that goes through the point (0, 3) and is parallel to the line whose equation is $6y - 10x = 30$.

Graph the equation $6y - 10x = 30$. Find the slope of the line. The slope of the line is $\frac{5}{3}$.

Now use the slope $\frac{5}{3}$ and the point (0, 3) to graph the line parallel to the graph of $6y - 10x = 30$.

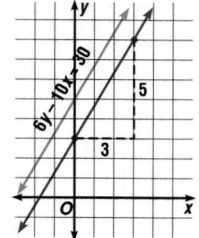

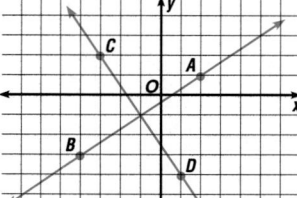

The figure at the left shows the graphs of two lines that are perpendicular. We found that parallel lines have the same slope. Is there a special relationship between the slopes of two perpendicular lines?

$$\text{slope of line } AB = \frac{1 - (-3)}{2 - (-4)} = \frac{4}{6} = \frac{2}{3}$$

$$\text{slope of line } CD = \frac{2 - (-4)}{-3 - 1} = \frac{6}{-4} = -\frac{3}{2}$$

The slopes are negative reciprocals of each other. That is, when you multiply the slopes of two perpendicular lines, the product is always -1.

Definition of Perpendicular Lines	**In a plane, two nonvertical lines are perpendicular if and only if the product of their slopes is –1. Any vertical line is perpendicular to any horizontal line.**

Another way to state the definition is to say that the slopes of perpendicular lines are negative reciprocals of each other.

Example 5

CONNECTION

Geometry

The consecutive sides of a rectangle are perpendicular. In rectangle WXYZ, the coordinates of point X are (2, 0) and the coordinates of point Y are (5, 1). Find the slope of the line containing side $\overline{YZ}$ of the rectangle.

In rectangle WXYZ, side $\overline{XY}$ is perpendicular to side $\overline{YZ}$. First find the slope of side $\overline{XY}$.

slope of $\overline{XY} = \dfrac{1 - 0}{5 - 2} = \dfrac{1}{3}$

Let m = slope of $\overline{YZ}$. Since the product of the slopes must be –1, you can use this equation.

$m\left(\dfrac{1}{3}\right) = -1$

$m = -1\left(\dfrac{3}{1}\right)$ or –3

The slope of the line containing $\overline{YZ}$ is –3.

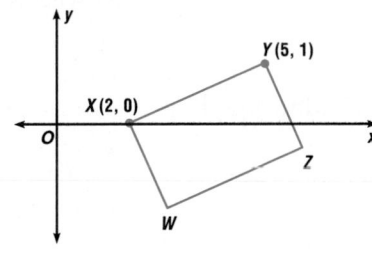

Knowing where a graph crosses each axis often provides a quick way to graph an equation. The point where a graph crosses the y-axis is called the **y-intercept**. Likewise, the point where it crosses the x-axis is called the **x-intercept**. These two points can be found without graphing the equation.

Example 6

Without graphing, find the y-intercept and the x-intercept of the graph of 3x + 5y = 30.

Since all points on the y-axis have an x-coordinate of 0, you can find the y-intercept by substituting 0 for x in the equation.

$3x + 5y = 30$

$3(0) + 5y = 30$ *Substitute 0 for x.*

$5y = 30$

$y = 6$ The y-intercept is 6.   *The ordered pair for the y-intercept is (0, 6).*

To graph 3x + 5y = 30, place a point at 6 on the y-axis and another point at 10 on the x-axis. Then connect the points to draw the line.

Likewise, to find the x-intercept, you substitute 0 for y, since all points on the x-axis have 0 as a y-coordinate.

$3x + 5(0) = 30$

$3x = 30$

$x = 10$ The x-intercept is 10.   *The ordered pair for the x-intercept is (10, 0).*

LESSON 2-4 SLOPES AND INTERCEPTS   69

EVALUATING THE LESSON

Checking for Understanding
Exercises 1–14 are designed to help you assess understanding through reading, writing, and speaking. You should work through Exercises 1–7 with your students, and then monitor their work on Exercises 8–14.

Error Analysis
Students sometimes invert the slope. They divide the difference of the *x*-coordinates by the difference of *y*-coordinates. Also, students sometimes subtract the *x*- and *y*-coordinates in opposite directions. Remind students the slope is a ratio of the change in *y* to the change in *x*.

Additional Answers
1. **Answers will vary. Check students' responses.**
2. **Slope of vertical lines = undefined**
   Slope of horizontal lines = 0
   Slope of nonvertical, nonhorizontal lines = all real numbers except 0
3. **In a plane, lines with the same slope are parallel.**

Reteaching Masters Booklet, p. 10

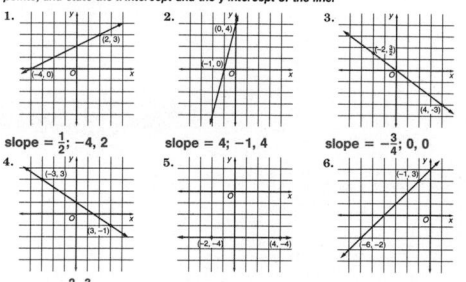

CHECKING FOR UNDERSTANDING

Communicating Mathematics   Read and study the lesson to answer each question. **1–7. See margin.**

1. Explain in your own words how to find the slope of a line.
2. Describe the slopes of vertical lines, horizontal lines, and other nonvertical, nonhorizontal lines.
3. What is the geometric definition of parallel lines?
4. What is the geometric definition of perpendicular lines?
5. Use a dictionary to find other definitions of slope.
6. What is the relationship between the slopes of two perpendicular lines?
7. What is true of the slopes of two parallel lines?

Guided Practice   State the *y*-intercept, *x*-intercept, and slope of each line.

8. $-2, -3, \dfrac{-2}{3}$
9. $2, -2, 1$
10. none, -5, undefined
11. 2, none, 0
12. $-4, 2, 2$
13. $2, 3, \dfrac{-2}{3}$

8.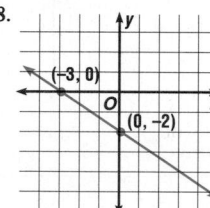
9.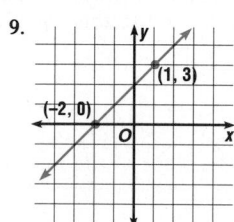
10.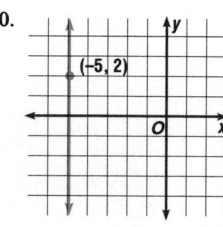

11.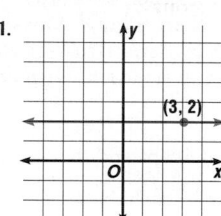
12.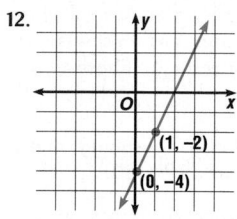
13.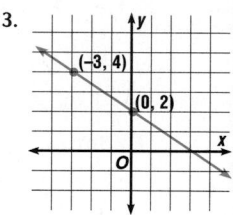

14. Suppose all the graphs shown above were placed on one coordinate plane. Which graphs, if any, would be parallel? Which graphs, if any, would be perpendicular? **parallel: 8 and 13, perpendicular: 10 and 11**

EXERCISES

Practice   Determine the slope of the line passing through each pair of points.

 A

15. $(8, -4)$ and $(6, 1)$ $-\dfrac{5}{2}$
16. $(5, 7)$ and $(4, -6)$ **13**
17. $(-5, -4)$ and $(5, 2)$ $\dfrac{3}{5}$
18. $(1, 8)$ and $(7, 8)$ **0**
19. $(2.5, 3)$ and $(1, -9)$ **8**
20. $(b, 2)$ and $(b, -2)$ **undefined**

RETEACHING THE LESSON

Determine the slope of the line passing through each pair of points.

a. $(1, 2)$ and $(3, 8)$ **3**
b. $(3, -4)$ and $(-1, -2)$ $\dfrac{-1}{2}$
c. $(2, -2)$ and $(-3, 13)$ **−3**

Additional Answers
4. **In a plane, two nonvertical lines are perpendicular if and only if the product of their slopes is −1.**
5. **Answers will vary. Check students' responses.**
6. **They are negative reciprocals of each other.**
7. **They are equal.**

Determine whether the graph of each equation rises to the right, falls to the right, is horizontal, or is vertical.

21. $x + y = 3$ **falls**   22. $2x + 12 = 0$ **vertical**   23. $2x - y = 6$ **rises**

24. $2x + 3y + 32 = 0$ 25. $2x - 3y = 0$ **rises**   26. $2y + 7 = 3.5(4)$
    falls   **horizontal**

 Find the *y*-intercept and the *x*-intercept of the graph of each equation.

27. $y = 6x + 9$ 28. $y = -3x - 5$ 29. $y = -2$
    y: 9, x: $-\frac{3}{2}$ **y: -5, x: $-\frac{5}{3}$**   **y: -2, x: none**
30. $x = 8$ 31. $y + 6 = 5x$ 32. $3x = y$
    y: none, x: 8   **y: -6, x: $\frac{6}{5}$**   **y: 0, x: 0**
33. $f(x) = x - 2$ 34. $g(x) = 4x - 1$ 35. $5x + 3y = 15$
    y: -2, x: 2   **y: -1, x: $\frac{1}{4}$**   **y: 5, x: 3**

36–44. See Solutions Manual.

36. Graph a line that passes through (0, 0) and has slope 3.

37. Graph a line that passes through (−1, 1) and is parallel to a line whose slope is $\frac{1}{4}$.

38. Graph a line that passes through (−4, 1) and is perpendicular to a line whose slope is $\frac{-5}{3}$.

39. Graph a line that passes through (2, 2) and is perpendicular to the graph of $y - 2$.

40. Graph a line that passes through the origin and is parallel to the graph of $x + y = 12$.

 41. Graph a line that passes through (−3, −1) and has an undefined slope.

42. One line has a slope of 0 and another line has an undefined slope, but they both pass through (1, 1). Graph the lines.

43. Graph the line that is perpendicular to the graph of $3x - 2y = 24$ at its *x*-intercept.

44. The graphs of $2y + x = 6$ and $y = 2x + 3$ contain two sides of a rectangle. If one vertex of the rectangle has coordinates (8, 4), draw the rectangle. **Teaching Tip ❸**

Critical Thinking

45. Graph this family of equations on the same coordinate plane: $y = x$, $y = 2x$, $y = 5x$, $y = \frac{1}{2}x$, and $y = \frac{1}{5}x$. Study the graphs and make a conjecture about how the slope of the line affects how steeply it slants. **The greater the absolute value of the slope, the steeper the line is.**

Closing the Lesson
Writing Activity   Have students write an equation and find the slope and intercepts of its graph. Have them write the equation in slope-intercept form. Also have them write an equation whose graph is parallel to the original line. Repeat for a perpendicular line.

APPLYING THE LESSON

Homework Exercises

Assignment Guide

Basic: 15–35, 45–51
Average: 18–39, 45–51
Enriched: 21–51
All: Mid-Chapter Review, 1–10

Chapter 2, Quiz B, (Lessons 2-3 through 2-4), is available in the Evaluation Masters Booklet, p. 23.

Teaching Tip ❸   Remind students that the sides of a rectangle are perpendicular and parallel.

Practice Masters Booklet, p. 12

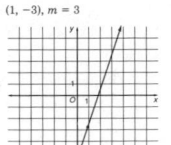
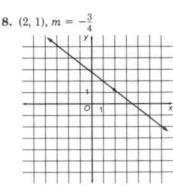

2-4 **Practice Worksheet**

Slopes and Intercepts

Determine the slope of the line passing through each pair of points.

1. (3, −8) and (−5, 2) $-\frac{5}{4}$ 2. (−10, −3) and (7, 2) $\frac{5}{17}$

3. (−7, −6) and (3, −6) **0**   4. (8, 2) and (8, −1) **undefined**

Find the y-intercept and the x-intercept of the graph of each equation.

5. $y = 7x + 5$ **x: $-\frac{5}{7}$, y: 5**   6. $y = -9x + 15$ **x: $\frac{5}{3}$, y: 15**

Graph a line that passes through the given point and has the given slope.

7. (1, −3), $m = 3$ 8. (2, 1), $m = -\frac{3}{4}$

State whether the graphs of the following equations are parallel, perpendicular, or neither.

9. $2x + 3y = 4$ 10. $\frac{1}{2}x + 2y = 1$ 11. $6x - 9y = 4$ 12. $y - 7 = 0$
   $3x + 2y = 6$ $4x - y = 3$ $\frac{2}{3}x - y = 11$ $3x = 5$
   neither   **perpendicular**   **parallel**   **perpendicular**

Find an equation of the line that passes through the given point and is perpendicular to the line with the given equation.

13. (3, 2); $y = 3x - 1$ **$y = -\frac{1}{3}x + 3$**   14. (−4, 2); $y = 2x + 3$ **$y = -\frac{1}{2}x$**

Find an equation of the line that passes through the given point and is parallel to the line with the given equation.

15. (4, 1); $y = 2x - 5$ **$y = 2x - 7$**   16. (−10, 3); $y = \frac{3}{5}x + 4$ **$y = \frac{3}{5}x + 9$**

Additional Answers

1b.

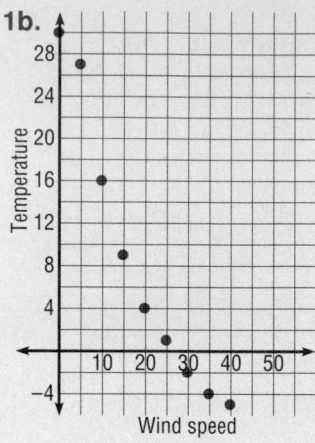

7.

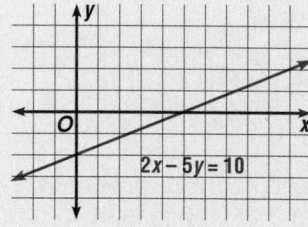

Enrichment Masters Booklet, p. 10

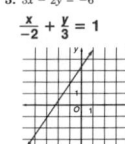 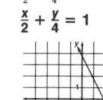 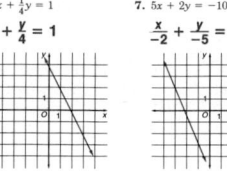

Applications

46. Demographics The population of Ashville, North Carolina was 172,000 in 1988. In three years the population grew to 183,000. If x represents the year and y represents the population, find the rate of increase (slope) for the growth of Ashville. $\frac{11,000}{3}$ **or about 3667 people per year**

47. Travel At 10:00 A.M., Eric traveled 195 miles across the plains states on his way to California. At 2:00 P.M., he had traveled 455 miles. Use slope to calculate his rate of travel. **65 mph**

Mixed Review

48. Find the next number in the set {100, 95, 85, 70, _?_}. **(Lesson 2-3) 50**

49. A board is 12 feet long. It is to be cut into pieces 2 feet long. How many cuts are needed? **(Lesson 2-3) 5**

50. Solve $|x - 6| = 3x + 4$. **(Lesson 1-6)** $\frac{1}{2}$

51. What property is illustrated by $3(x - 4) = 3x - 12$? **(Lesson 1-2) distributive prop**

MID-CHAPTER REVIEW

1. **Meteorology** When the temperature is 30°F, the speed of the wind makes the temperature feel colder. This is called the windchill factor. The chart below shows how the wind effects your perception of how cold it is when the temperature is 30°. **(Lesson 2-1)**

Wind Speed (mph)	0	5	10	15	20	25	30	35	40
Windchill Factor (°F)	30	27	16	9	4	1	−2	−4	−5

   a. State the domain and range of the relation. **D = {0, 5, 10, 15, 20, 25, 30, 35, 40}**
   b. Graph the relation. Is it a function? **See margin. R = {30, 27, 16, 9, 4, 1, −2, −4, −5}**

2. Find $g(7)$, if $g(x) = \frac{x^2 - 2x + 3}{x - 5}$. **(Lesson 2-1) 19**

Solve for the indicated variable. (Lesson 2-2)

3. $2x + 4y = 7$, for y 4. $\frac{3}{2}t + \frac{4}{7}s = 12$, for s 5. $3a + 2b - 4c = 24$, for c
$y = \frac{7 - 2x}{4}$ $s = 21 - \frac{21}{8}t$ $c = \frac{3}{4}a + \frac{1}{2}b - 6$

6. Determine if $g(x) = x(2 - x)$ is a linear function. **(Lesson 2-2) no**

7. Graph $2x - 5y = 10$. **(Lesson 2-2) See margin.**

8. **Geometry** In the ordered pairs below, the first coordinate is the number of sides in a regular polygon, and the second coordinate is the degree measure of the angle at each vertex. Find the pattern to complete the last ordered pair. **(Lesson 2-3)**

   $(3, 60), (4, 90), (5, 108), (6, 120), \left(7, 128\frac{4}{7}\right), (8, \square)$ **135**

Graph each equation. Find the slope, the x-intercept, and the y-intercept. (Lesson 2-4)

9. $2x - 3y = 6$ $m = \frac{2}{3}$, **x: 3, y: −2**   10. $2x + 3y = 9$ $m = \frac{-2}{3}$, **x: 4.5, y: 3**

EXTENDING THE LESSON

Math Power: Reasoning

Find q in terms of a, b, and p if the line passing through (a, b) and (p, q) has slope $\frac{ap}{b}$. $\frac{ap^2 - a^2p + b^2}{b}$

Mid-Chapter Review

The Mid-Chapter Review provides students with a brief review of the concepts and skills in Lessons 2-1 through 2-4. Lesson numbers are given at the end of problems or instruction lines so students may review concepts not yet mastered.

2-5 Writing Linear Equations

Objectives After studying this lesson, you should be able to:

2-5A ▪ write the slope-intercept form of an equation given the slope and a point, or two points,

2-5B ▪ write the standard form of an equation given the slope and a point, or two points, and

2-5C ▪ write an equation of a line that is parallel or perpendicular to the graph of a given equation.

In Lesson 2–2 you learned if a function can be written in the form $y = mx + b$, then it is a linear function. But what numbers do m and b represent?

Look at the graph below. The line passes through points $A(0, b)$ and $C(x, y)$. Notice that b is the y-intercept of $\overleftrightarrow{AC}$. Suppose you need to find the slope of $\overleftrightarrow{AC}$.

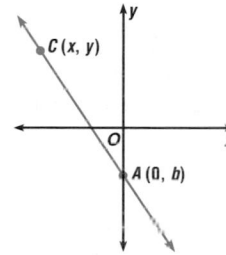

$$m = \frac{y - b}{x - 0}$$

$$m = \frac{y - b}{x}$$

Now solve the equation for y.

$$m = \frac{y - b}{x}$$

$mx = y - b$ *Multiply each side by x.*

$mx + b = y$ *Add b to each side.*

or $y = mx + b$ *Symmetric property of equality*

You may recognize this as the form of a linear function. When an equation is written in the form $y = mx + b$, it is in **slope-intercept form**.

Teaching Tip ❶

Slope-Intercept Form of a Linear Equation	The slope-intercept form of the equation of a line is $y = mx + b$, where m is the slope and b is the y-intercept.

If you are given the slope and the y-intercept of a line, you can find an equation of the line by substituting the values of m and b into the slope-intercept form of the equation. Then the equation can be written in standard form. For example, if you know that the slope of a line is $\frac{2}{3}$ and the y-intercept is 6, an equation of the line is $y = \frac{2}{3}x + 6$, or, in standard form, $2x - 3y = -18$.

LESSON 2-5   WRITING LINEAR EQUATIONS   73

ALTERNATE TEACHING STRATEGIES

Using Discussion
Derive the point-slope form of a linear equation, given point (x_1, y_1) and slope m. Thus,

$$m = \frac{y - y_1}{x - x_1}, \text{ or } m(x - x_1) = y - y_1.$$

Discuss why this is true for any point.

Using Critical Thinking
In studying this lesson, students should be able to answer the following questions.
1. What is the equation of a line that has no y-intercept?   **$x = k$, where k is not zero.**
2. What is the equation of a line that has no x-intercept?   **$y = b$, where b is not zero.**
3. Can a line have no intercepts?   **no**

Lesson Resources
Reteaching Master 2-5
Practice Master 2-5
Enrichment Master 2-5
Activity Master, p. 20

Transparency 2-5 contains the 5-Minute Check and a teaching aid for this lesson.

INTRODUCING THE LESSON

 5-Minute Check
(over Lesson 2-4)

1. State the y-intercept, x-intercept, and slope of the line in the graph below.

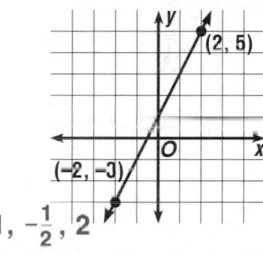

$1, -\frac{1}{2}, 2$

2. Determine the slope of the line that passes through points $(2.3, 9.5)$ and $(3.8, 20)$.   **7**
3. Find the y-intercept and the x-intercept of the graph of the equation $2x - 3y = 0$.   **0, 0**
4. Describe the slope of the graph of the equation $y - 3x = 2$.   **rises to right**
5. Graph a line that passes through $(2, 2)$ and whose slope is 2.

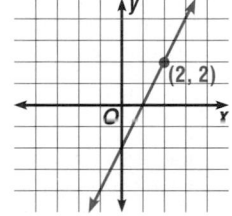

Example 1

Motivating the Lesson

Have students find the monthly rate for a car phone and the cost per minute of use. Write an equation that represents the cost per month for the phone. Is this a linear function? Find the slope.

TEACHING THE LESSON

Teaching Tip ❶   You may wish to derive the point-slope form of the equation in a plane.
$$m(x - x_1) = y - y_1$$

Teaching Tip ❷   Remind students of the relationships of the slopes of parallel lines and perpendicular lines.

Chalkboard Examples

For Example 1
Find the slope-intercept form of the equation of the line that has a slope of 2 and passes through $(-1, 3)$.   **$y = 2x + 5$**

For Example 2
Find the standard form of the equation that passes through $(2, 3)$ and $(1, 5)$.   **$2x + y = 7$**

Example 1

Find the slope-intercept form of the equation of the line that has a slope of $\frac{3}{4}$ and passes through $(8, 2)$.

You know the slope and the x and y values of one point on the graph. Substitute for m, x, and y in the slope-intercept form.

$$y = mx + b$$
$$2 = \left(\frac{3}{4}\right)(8) + b$$
$$2 = 6 + b$$
$$-4 = b \quad \text{The } y\text{-intercept is } -4.$$

The equation in slope-intercept form is $y = \frac{3}{4}x - 4$.

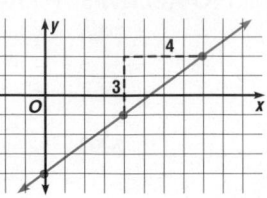

Remember that the standard form of the equation of a line is $Ax + By = C$. Suppose we write this general equation in slope-intercept form.

$$Ax + By = C$$
$$By = -Ax + C \qquad \textit{Subtract Ax from each side.}$$
$$y = -\frac{A}{B}x + \frac{C}{B} \qquad \textit{Divide each side by B.}$$

The slope is $-\frac{A}{B}$ and the y-intercept is $\frac{C}{B}$, for $B \neq 0$.

This can be used to write an equation in standard form when you are given the information you usually use to find the slope-intercept form.

Example 2

Find the standard form of the equation that passes through $(-2, 5)$ and $(3, 1)$.

First use the two given points to find the slope of the line.

$$m = \frac{1 - 5}{3 - (-2)} \text{ or } \frac{-4}{5}$$

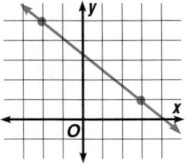

If the slope is $\frac{-4}{5}$ or $-\left(\frac{4}{5}\right)$, then $-\frac{A}{B} = -\left(\frac{4}{5}\right)$.
Thus, $A = 4$ and $B = 5$.

Substitute these values into the standard form. The resulting equation is $4x + 5y = C$. Since one of the points on the line is $(3, 1)$, you can substitute these values into the equation to find C.

$$Ax + By = C \qquad \textit{Standard form of a linear equation}$$
$$4x + 5y = C \qquad \textit{Substitute values for A and B.}$$
$$4(3) + 5(1) = C \qquad \textit{Substitute values for x and y.}$$
$$12 + 5 = C$$
$$17 = C$$

The standard form of the equation is $4x + 5y = 17$.

Example 3

APPLICATION

Oceanography

The atmospheric pressure at sea level is 14.7 pounds per square inch. As divers go deeper into the ocean the pressure increases. Use the chart below to write an equation in slope-intercept form that approximates this relationship. Then find the pressure at 30,000 feet below sea level.

Depth (in feet)	Pressure (lb/in²)
(Sea level) 0	14.7
600	269
1200	536
3000	1338
7200	3208
18,000	8019

Let x represent the ocean depth and y represent the pressure.

Use your calculator and a pair of points to find the slope of the line.

$$m = \frac{269 - 536}{600 - 1200} = 0.445$$

You may want to use another pair of points to confirm your slope.

$$m = \frac{3208 - 1338}{7200 - 3000} = 0.445238095$$

The slope of the line is approximately 0.445. The y-intercept corresponds to an ocean depth of 0 (at sea level). So the y-intercept is 14.7. An equation that approximates the pressure at certain ocean depths is

$$y = 0.445x + 14.7.$$ *The equation that is derived may differ based on the set of points used to determine the slope.*

Use your calculator again to find the approximate pressure at 30,000 feet below sea level.

ENTER: 0.445 $\boxed{\times}$ 30000 $\boxed{+}$ 14.7 $\boxed{=}$ $\mathit{13364.7}$

The result is 13,364.7 pounds per square inch.

The slope-intercept form can also be used to find the equations of lines that are parallel or perpendicular. **Teaching Tip ❷**

Example 4

Write an equation of the line that passes through (4, 6) and is parallel to the line whose equation is $y = \frac{2}{3}x + 5$.

Parallel lines have the same slope, so the slope of both lines is $\frac{2}{3}$. Use the slope-intercept form and the point (4, 6) to find the equation.

$y = mx + b$

$6 = \left(\frac{2}{3}\right)(4) + b$ *Substitute $\frac{2}{3}$ for m, 4 for x, and 6 for y.*

$6 = \frac{8}{3} + b$

$\frac{10}{3} - b$ *Subtract $\frac{8}{3}$ from each side.*

The y-intercept is $\frac{10}{3}$.

An equation of the line is $y = \frac{2}{3}x + \frac{10}{3}$.   *The standard form is $2x - 3y = -10$.*

LESSON 2-5   WRITING LINEAR EQUATIONS   75

Chalkboard Example

For Example 5

Write an equation in standard form for a line that passes through (3, 2) and is perpendicular to the line whose equation is $y = 2x + 5$. $x + 2y = 7$.

EVALUATING THE LESSON

Checking for Understanding

Exercises 1–12 are designed to help you assess understanding through reading, writing, and speaking. You should work through Exercises 1–5 with your students, and then monitor their work on Exercises 6–12.

Error Analysis

Students sometimes confuse zero slope with undefined slope. A line with a slope of 0 is a horizontal line. It neither rises nor falls from left to right and, thus, its slope is between negative and positive. Zero is between negative and positive. A vertical line does not go from left to right, so its slope is not positive, negative, nor zero. The slope of a vertical line is undefined.

Closing the Lesson

Writing Activity   Have the class divide into groups of four. Have each group research an application for linear equations and write a problem. Have groups exchange problems with other groups and solve them, making sure there is an equation and a slope stated.

Example 5   Write an equation in standard form for the line that passes through (4, 6) and is perpendicular to the line whose equation is $y = \frac{2}{3}x + 5$.

The slope of the given line is $\frac{2}{3}$. Since the product of this slope and the slope of the perpendicular line is -1, the slope of the perpendicular line is $-\frac{3}{2}$. You can use the slope $-\frac{3}{2}$ and the point (4, 6) to write the equation in standard form.

Use a graphing calculator to verify that the equations in Examples 4 and 5 are correct.

$Ax + By = C$	*Standard form of linear equation*
$3x + 2y = C$	$m = -\frac{A}{B} = -\left(-\frac{3}{2}\right)$ or $\frac{3}{2}$, $A = 3$ and $B = 2$
$3(4) + 2(6) = C$	*Substitute 4 for x and 6 for y.*
$12 + 12 = C$	
$24 = C$	

The standard form of the equation is $3x + 2y = 24$.

CHECKING FOR UNDERSTANDING

Communicating Mathematics

Read and study the lesson to answer each question.

1. What is the slope-intercept form of an equation and what does each variable mean? **See margin.**

2. On which axes are the variables graphed? **x on horizontal, y on vertical**

3. Explain how to write an equation of a line if you know two points on the line. **See margin.**

4. The slope of a line is $\frac{1}{2}$. What is the slope of a line parallel to this line? What is the slope of a line perpendicular to this line? **parallel: $\frac{1}{2}$, perpendicular: −2**

5. What is the slope of the line whose equation is $cx - dy = k$? $\frac{c}{d}$

Guided Practice

6. What is the slope and y-intercept of the graph of $y = -3x - 4$? **$m = -3, b = -4$**

7. Write $y = -3x - 4$ in standard form. **$3x + y = -4$**

The slope and y-intercept of a line are given. Write the slope-intercept form of the equation for each line described.

8. $m = 5, b = 6$ **$y = 5x + 6$**
9. $m = 2.5, b = 0$ **$y = 2.5x$**

10. $m = -\frac{1}{4}, b = -9$ **$y = -\frac{1}{4}x - 9$**
11. $m = 0, b = 0$ **$y = 0$**

12. Write an equation of a line that passes through (0, 5) and is parallel to the graph of $y = 4x + 12$. **$y = 4x + 5$**

Additional Answers

1. $y = mx + b$
   m is the slope.
   b is the y-intercept.

3. Find the slope; this is the same as $-\frac{A}{B}$. Use A and B to substitute the values into the standard form $Ax + By = C$. Substitute the value for one of the points in place of x and y to find C. Now you know A, B, and C and can put these into the form $Ax + By = C$.

EXERCISES

Practice

State the slope and y-intercept of the graph of each equation. **See margin.**

13. $y = -\frac{3}{4}x - 3$ **14.** $y = \frac{1}{3}x$ **15.** $-y = 0.2x + 6$

16. $6y = 3x - 12$ **17.** $-5y = 3x - 30$ **18.** $y = cx + t$

19. The slope of $\overleftrightarrow{CD}$ is $\frac{3}{2}$. Line FG is perpendicular to $\overleftrightarrow{CD}$ and has a y-intercept of 4. Write the equation of $\overleftrightarrow{FG}$.
2x + 3y = 12

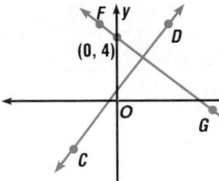

Find the slope-intercept form of each equation.

20. $2x - 5y = 10$ $y = \frac{2}{5}x - 2$ **21.** $3x - y = 6$ $y = 3x - 6$

22. $2x - 2y = 4$ $y = x - 2$ **23.** $2x = 11$ **no slope-intercept form**

Write an equation for the line that satisfies each of the given conditions in slope-intercept form and in standard form.

24. slope $= \frac{1}{2}$, passes through $(6, 4)$ $y = \frac{1}{2}x + 1, x - 2y = -2$

25. slope $= -\frac{4}{5}$, passes through $(2, -3)$ $y = -\frac{4}{5}x - \frac{7}{5}, 4x + 5y = -7$

26. slope $= 5$, passes through the origin **$y = 5x, 5x - y = 0$**

27. passes through $(6, 1)$ and $(8, -4)$ $y = -\frac{5}{2}x + 16, 5x + 2y = 32$

28. passes through $(6, 1)$ and $(6, 7)$ **no slope-intercept form, $x = 6$**

29. passes through $(4, 6)$ and $(0, 0)$ $y = \frac{3}{2}x, 3x - 2y = 0$

30. x-intercept $= -3$, y-intercept $= 6$ **$y = 2x + 6, 2x - y = -6$**

31. x-intercept $= -\frac{1}{3}$, y-intercept $= -\frac{1}{4}$ $y = \frac{3}{4}x - \frac{1}{4}, 3x - 4y = 1$

32. x-intercept $= 0$, y-intercept $= 2$ **no slope-intercept form, $x = 0$**

33. passes through $(-1, -1)$ and $(8, -1)$ $y = -1, y = -1$

34. Write an equation of a line that passes through $(4, 2)$ and is parallel to the line whose equation is $y = 2x - 4$. **$y = 2x - 6$**

35. Write an equation of a line that passes through $(-2, 0)$ and is perpendicular to the line whose equation is $y = -3x + 7$. $y = \frac{1}{3}x + \frac{2}{3}$

36. Write an equation of a line that passes through $(-3, -1)$ and is parallel to the line that passes through $(3, 3)$ and $(0, 6)$. **$y = -x - 4$**

37. Write an equation of a line that passes through $(6, -5)$ and is perpendicular to the line whose equation is $3x - \frac{1}{5}y = 3$.

$y = -\frac{1}{15}x - \frac{23}{5}, x + 15y = -69$

LESSON 2-5 WRITING LINEAR EQUATIONS 77

Homework Exercises

Reteaching Masters Booklet, p. 11

Additional Answers

13. $m = -\frac{3}{4}, y: -3$

14. $m = \frac{1}{3}, y: 0$

15. $m = -0.2, y: -6$

16. $m = \frac{1}{2}, y: -2$

17. $m = -\frac{3}{5}, y: 6$

18. $m = c, y: t$

Find the value of k in each equation if the given ordered pair is a solution of the equation.

38. $5x + ky = 8$, $(3, -1)$ **7**

39. $4x - ky = 7$, $(4, 3)$ **3**

40. $3x + 8y = k$, $(0, 0.5)$ **4**

41. $kx + 3y = 11$, $(7, 2)$ $\frac{5}{7}$

Critical Thinking

CONNECTION

Geometry

Applications

42. Three vertices of a parallelogram are $(10, 3)$, $(-1, 2)$, and $(1, -1)$. Find the coordinates of the fourth vertex. **(12, 0) or (8, 6) or (-10, -2)**

43. Oceanography The Mariana Trench is the deepest point in any of the oceans. It is located in the western Pacific Ocean north of Australia. The deepest point in the trench is 35,840 feet below sea level. Find the approximate pressure at this point. **15,963.5 lb/in²** **Teaching Tip ➌**

44. Science Crickets vary the number of chirps they produce with the temperature. If you count the number of chirps in a minute, you can tell the temperature. The chart below records the number of chirps in a minute and the approximate temperature. Write an equation to describe this linear relationship. Then calculate the temperature when the number of chirps is 130. $t = \frac{1}{5}n + 6$, **32C**

Chirps	50	60	70
Temperature	16°C	18°C	20°C

45. Nature Studies A nature preserve worker calculates there are 6000 deer in Sharon Woods Park. She also estimates that 75 more deer die than are born each year. How many deer will be in the park in x years?
$d = 6000 - 75x$

46. Economics The Serves-You-Best Rental Car Company has two rental offers. The first offer gives the renter a compact car that costs 25¢ a mile to drive plus an initial fee of $20. The second offer gives the renter a luxury car that costs 25¢ a mile plus an initial fee of $35.

a. Write an equation to represent each offer. $y = 0.25x + 20$ $y = 0.25x + 35$

b. What is the relationship between the graphs of these offers? **parallel**

c. If both cars are driven 750 miles, what is the cost difference between renting the compact car and the luxury car? **$15**

Practice Masters Booklet, p. 13

47. The BASIC program at the right finds the slope and y-intercept of the line passing through two given points. Use the program to find the slope and y-intercept of the line passing through each pair of points. Then write the equation of the line.

```
10   PRINT "ENTER THE
     COORDINATES"
20   PRINT "OF TWO POINTS"
30   INPUT X1,Y1,X2,Y2
35   PRINT
40   IF X1 = X2 THEN 100
50   LET M = (Y2 - Y1)/(X2 - X1)
60   PRINT "SLOPE = ";M
70   LET B = Y1 - M * X1
80   PRINT "Y-INTERCEPT = ";B
90   GO TO 120
100  PRINT "UNDEFINED SLOPE"
110  PRINT "NO Y-INTERCEPT"
120  END
```

a. $(-1, 4)$, $(2, -2)$

b. $(-2, 3)$, $(1, 7)$

c. $(2, 2)$, $(-1, -2)$

d. $(-1, -4)$, $(3, -2)$

47a–d. See margin.

48. $\frac{2}{3}$

Mixed Review

48. Find the slope of the line passing through $(5, 4)$ and $(2, 2)$. **(Lesson 2-4)**

49. Find the x-intercept and the y-intercept of the graph of $3x - 2y = 12$. **(Lesson 2-4, x: 4, y: -6**

50. Find the value of $f(-2)$, if $f(x) = x^2 - 4$. **(Lesson 2-1) 0**

51. Solve $3x - 5 > -26$. **(Lesson 1-7) $\{x | x > -7\}$**

52. Probability You have a red button, a green button, a blue button, and a white button. These buttons are to be sewn in a row as decoration on a pocket of a shirt. In how many ways can these four buttons be arranged in that row? **(Lesson 1-5) 24 ways**

Rene Descartes (1596–1650) was a French mathematician and philosopher. He is credited with the invention of a branch of mathematics called analytic geometry. Analytic geometry combines the following from algebra and geometry.

1. the coordinate plane

2. the correspondence of ordered pairs of numbers to points in the coordinate plane

3. graphs of functions like $f(x) = 2x + 1$

Descartes, in 1637, became the first mathematician to put the three ideas together.

Sometimes, ordered pairs are referred to as Cartesian coordinates. The word Cartesian is taken from the name Descartes.

LESSON 2-5   WRITING LINEAR EQUATIONS   79

EXTENDING THE LESSON

Math Power: Problem Solving

Give the equation $k = \frac{1}{4}m + 10$ to the students. Have them write a problem to fit the equation. State the slope, x-intercept, and y-intercept.

History Connection

History features introduce students to people who were involved in the development of mathematics. You may want students to further research Descartes to find out what other things he did for mathematics.

Teaching Tip ④ Point out that the coordinates of the two points are entered without using parentheses. Remind students that computers express fractional values as in decimal form. Encourage them to graph the points and lines. Ask students if it is possible for the slopes of two of the three lines to be equal but not equal to the slope of the third line.

Additional Answers

47a. $m = -2$, y: 2, $y = -2x + 2$

47b. $m = \frac{4}{3}$, y: $5\frac{2}{3}$, $y = \frac{4}{3}x + 5\frac{2}{3}$

47c. $m = \frac{4}{3}$, y: $-\frac{2}{3}$, $y = \frac{4}{3}x - \frac{2}{3}$

47d. $m = \frac{1}{2}$, y: $-3\frac{1}{2}$, $y = \frac{1}{2}x - 3\frac{1}{2}$

Enrichment Masters Booklet, p. 11

NAME _____   DATE _____

2-5 Enrichment Worksheet

Finding Equations for Non-Linear Functions

You can often find an equation for a non-linear function by looking for a pattern in a chart that shows values of the variables.

Example: Write an equation describing the relationship between the variables in the chart.

x	-3	-2	-1	0	1	2	3
y	2	1	0	1	2	3	4

Notice that the function is not linear. The values of y are positive. As x goes from -3 to 3, the values of y decrease steadily then increase steadily. This suggests a function similar to $y = |x|$. Clearly $y = |x|$ does not quite work, but a little adjustment shows that $y = |x + 1|$ does. Why is the equation *not* $y = |x| + 1$?
The y values would be 4, 3, 2, 1, 2, 3, 4.

Write an equation describing the relationship between the variables in each table.

1.
x	-3	-2	-1	0	1	2	3
y	4	3	2	1	0	1	2
$y = |x - 1|$

2.
x	-3	-2	-1	0	1	2	3
y	6	4	2	0	2	4	6
$y = |2x|$

3.
x	-3	-2	-1	0	1	2	3
y	8	5	2	1	4	7	10
$y = |3x + 1|$

Solve each of the following.

4. Rob's charges for mowing a lawn are directly proportional to the number of hours he works. He charged Mr. Wilson \$13.75 for 2.5 hours work. Write an equation for Rob's charges C as a function of the number of hours h that he works. **$C = 5.5h$**

5. A cube-shaped box with no top has a surface area of S square units. Write an equation for the length E of an edge as a function of S. **$E = \sqrt{\frac{S}{5}}$**

Lesson Resources
Reteaching Master 2-6
Practice Master 2-6
Enrichment Master 2-6

Transparency 2-6 contains the
5-Minute Check and a teaching aid
for this lesson.

INTRODUCING THE LESSON

 5-Minute Check

(over Lesson 2-5)

1. State the slope and y-intercept of the graph of the equation $y = \frac{2}{5}x + 1$. $\frac{2}{5}; 1$

2. Find the slope-intercept form of the equation $4x + 8y = 11$.
$y = -\frac{1}{2}x + \frac{11}{8}$

3. Find the slope-intercept form of the equation of the line that has a slope of $\frac{2}{3}$ and passes through $(6, -2)$. $y = \frac{2}{3}x - 6$

Other Prerequisite Skills

4. How can you tell if two lines are parallel or perpendicular? **Parallel lines have the same slope; perpendicular lines have slopes whose product is -1.**

Motivating the Lesson

Have students give their height in inches and their shoe size. Record these on a chart. Then graph them using height as the independent variable and the shoe size as a dependent variable. Is the relationship between the height and the shoe size a linear function? Can you predict anything from the graph?

2-6 Scatter Plots and Prediction Equations

Objectives

After studying this lesson, you should be able to:

2-6A ▪ draw a scatter plot and find a prediction equation, and

2-6B ▪ solve problems using prediction equations.

When data is collected in real-life situations, the relation determined by the variables usually does not form a straight line. However, the graph may *approximate* a linear relationship. When this is the case, a **best-fit line** can be drawn and a **prediction equation** can be determined. A prediction equation can be determined by employing a process similar to that used to determine an equation of a line when you know two points.

The best-fit line does not necessarily contain any points from the data.

Application

The Zimco Bottling Company is promoting a continuing education program for its employees. The personnel director, Ms. Dirr, would like to be able to predict an employee's salary if she knows the number of years the employee attended college. From the current personnel files, Ms. Dirr randomly selected the files of ten employees. She recorded each employee's salary and the corresponding number of years of college for the employee.

Years of College	3	2	4	6	2.5	7.5	7	1	5.5	4
Salary (in $1000)	15	20	22	47	19	18	32	10	30	28

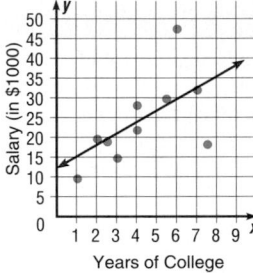

To determine the relationship between the number of years of college and the salary, Ms. Dirr graphed the data points to obtain a **scatter plot**. She found that the points did not lie in a straight line, but clustered in a linear pattern. She drew a line suggested by this pattern of points.

Teaching Tip ❶

She then selected the points $(2.5, 19)$ and $(7, 32)$ on that line to determine the equation of the line. To find the equation of this line, she first used the slope formula and the two points.

$$m = \frac{32 - 19}{7 - 2.5} = \frac{13}{4.5} \text{ or about } 2.9$$

Let s represent an employee's annual salary. Let c represent the number of years of college education. Use one of the points and the slope to find the prediction equation.

$s = 2.9c + b$	*$y = mx + b$, where $s = y$, $m = 2.9$, and $c = x$*
$32 = 2.9(7) + b$	*Point $(7, 32)$ is used for the values of c and s.*
$11.7 = b$	A prediction equation is $s = 2.9c + 11.7$.

ALTERNATE TEACHING STRATEGIES

Mini-Math Lab

Have students follow the stock market for a week. Plot the units sold versus the cost for a particular stock. Is there a relationship? If there is a relationship, have students write the equation.

By using her prediction equation, Ms. Dirr can encourage the employees with little college education to go back to school. For example, she can predict that with five years of college education, their salary might be $26,200.

Teaching Tip ❶ When drawing the line try to center it within the points.

Teaching Tip ❷ Have students draw three best-fit lines for Example 1. Have them make a prediction based on their lines.

Example 1

APPLICATION
Health

The table below shows the heights and the corresponding ideal weights of adult women. Find a prediction equation for this relationship.

Height (inches)	60	62	64	66	68	70	72
Weight (pounds)	105	111	123	130	139	149	158

First graph the data. Draw a line that appears most representative of the data. Use two points, (62, 111) and (66, 130), from that line to find the slope.

$$m = \frac{130 - 111}{66 - 62} = \frac{19}{4} \text{ or about } 4.8$$

Now use the slope and one of the points in the slope-intercept form to find the value of b.

$$y = mx + b \qquad x = 62,$$
$$111 = 4.8(62) + b \qquad y = 111,$$
$$-186.6 = b \qquad m = 4.8$$

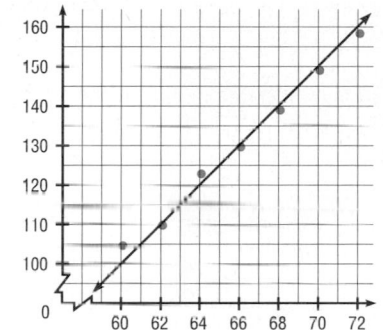

Let h be the independent variable and represent the height. Let w be the dependent variable and represent the corresponding weight. Using the slope and intercept values, we obtain the prediction equation $w = 4.8h - 186.6$.

FYI...

The tallest woman ever recorded was Zeng Jinlian (pronounced San Chung Lin). She was 8 ft $1\frac{1}{4}$ in. tall when she died in 1982.

Chalkboard Example

For Example 1
Each of seven executives oversees a varied number of salespersons. Below is a chart with the number of salespersons and total sales for one month for each executive.

number of salespersons	sales
12	250
33	699
17	350
22	460
24	501
8	162
19	398

Find the prediction equation for this relationship. **$y = 21.3x - 5.6$**

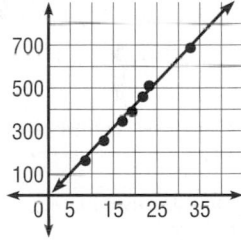

The Technology feature on page 91 presents one of these software programs for scatter plots.

The procedure for determining a prediction equation is dependent upon your judgement. You decide where to draw the best-fit line. You decide which two points on the line are used to find the slope and intercept. Your prediction equation may be different from someone else's. The prediction equation is used when a rough estimate is sufficient. For better analysis of the data, statisticians normally use other, more precise procedures, often relying on computers and high-level programming. **Teaching Tip ❷**

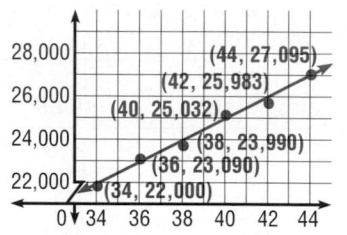
Example 2

CONNECTION

Statistics

Typing speed is dependent on experience, so the first number in the ordered pair is the number of weeks of experience.

Draw a scatter plot and find two prediction equations to show how typing speed and experience are related. Predict the typing speed of a student who has 11 weeks of experience.

Experience (weeks)	4	7	8	1	6	3	5	2	9	6	7	10
Typing Speed (wpm)	33	45	46	20	40	30	38	22	52	44	42	55

The pattern of dots suggests a possible line that passes through (5, 36) and (8, 49).

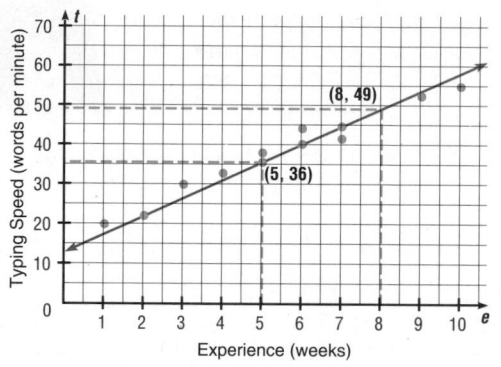

$$\text{slope} = \frac{49 - 36}{8 - 5}$$

$$= \frac{13}{3} \text{ or about } 4.3$$

Let e stand for experience. Let t stand for typing speed.

$$y = mx + b$$
$$t = 4.3e + b$$
$$36 = 4.3(5) + b$$
$$14.5 = b$$

One prediction equation is $t = 4.3e + 14.5$.

Another line can be suggested by using points (2, 22) and (9, 52). Using these points results in a prediction equation of $t = 4.3e + 13.4$.

If a student had 11 weeks experience, the first equation would predict that the student could type approximately 62 words per minute. For the second equation, the prediction would be 61 words per minute. Thus, either prediction equation produces a good estimate.

CHECKING FOR UNDERSTANDING

Communicating Mathematics

Read and study the lesson to answer each question.

1. What is the purpose of a prediction equation? **to provide an equation that can be used for predictions when only an estimate is needed**

2. What do you call the graphs of data that form a cluster of dots? **scatter plot**

3. In Example 2, why is the weight the dependent variable? **because weight might be affected by height, but weight does not determine height**

82   CHAPTER 2   LINEAR RELATIONS AND FUNCTIONS

RETEACHING THE LESSON

Have students work in groups of three. Use the average SAT math and verbal scores in a recent year for seniors in each of the 50 states.

1. Make a scatter plot of average SAT math score (y) versus the average SAT verbal score (x).

2. Draw a line suggested by the data.

3. Pick two points on the line and find the slope.

4. Find the y-intercept.

5. Write a prediction equation.

6. Predict the math score in any state given its verbal score.

Guided Practice

In a study of the relationship between the number of times (t) a plant is watered per month and the height (h) of the plant in centimeters, the prediction equation is $h = 0.5t + 0.5$. Predict the height for each number of waterings.

4. 2 **1.5 cm**

5. 5 **3.0 cm**

6. 12 **6.5 cm**

7. According to a certain prediction equation, if Luther's Soap spends $20,000 on advertising, sales will be $10,000,000. If Luther's Soap spends $50,000 on advertising, sales will be $22,000,000. Let A be advertising expenditures and S be sales revenues.
   a. Find the slope of the prediction equation. **400**
   b. Find the y-intercept of the prediction equation. **2,000,000**
   c. Find the prediction equation. **$S = 400A + 2,000,000$**
   d. Predict the sales if $10,000 is spent on advertising. **$6,000,000**
   e. Predict the amount of money spent on advertising if $16,000,000 of sales revenue was generated. **$35,000**

EXERCISES

Practice

8. The distance measured around your head is related to your height. According to the prediction equation, a person 72 in. tall has a head measurement of about 24 in., and a person 60 in. tall has a head measurement of about 20 in. Let h be the height of an individual and m be that person's head measurement.
   a. Find the slope of the prediction equation. **3**
   b. Use the value of the slope to complete the following statement: As the person's height (increases/decreases), the head size (increases/decreases) **increases, increases**
   c. Find the y-intercept of the prediction equation. **0** Write a prediction equation. **$h = 3m$**
   d. Predict the head size if a person is 66 in. tall. **22 in.**
   e. Predict the head size if a person is 76 in. tall. **$25\frac{1}{3}$ in.**
   f. Predict the height of an individual whose head size is 18 in. **54 in.**

9. The table below shows the years of experience for eight encyclopedia sales representatives and the amount of sales during a given period of time.

Amount of Sales	$9000	$6000	$4000	$3000	$3000	$5000	$8000	$2000
Years of Experience	6	5	3	1	4	3	6	2

   a. Draw a scatter plot to show how the years of experience and the amount of sales are related. **See margin.**
   b. Write a prediction equation from this data. **$y = 1333x$**
   c. Predict the amount of sales for a representative with 8 years of experience. **$10,664**

EVALUATING THE LESSON

Checking for Understanding
Exercises 1–7 are designed to help you assess understanding through reading, writing, and speaking. You should work through Exercises 1–3 with your students, and then monitor their work on exercises 4–7.

Closing the Lesson
Writing Activity Have students write an explanation as to why best-fit lines are helpful and why they may not be reliable.

APPLYING THE LESSON

Homework Exercises

Assignment Guide
BASIC: 9, 9, 13, 16–19
Average: 9–19
Enriched: 9–19

Chapter 2, Quiz C, (Lessons 2-5 through 2-6), is available in the Evaluation Masters Booklet, p. 24.

Practice Masters Booklet, p. 14

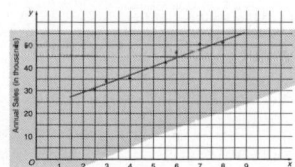

2-6 Practice Worksheet

NAME _____ DATE _____

Scatter Plots and Prediction Equations

According to a certain linear prediction equation, a person 25 years old needs 2400 calories of food intake a day. A person 30 years old needs 2300 calories. Let x stand for age in years and y stand for calories.

1. Find the slope of the prediction equation. **−20**

2. Find the y-intercept of the prediction equation. What does it measure? **2900; the calories needed by a newborn**

3. Find the prediction equation. **$y = −20x + 2900$**

4. Predict the caloric needs of a person who is 34 years old. **2220 calories**

The Cody Company ran a study on its sales force and learned that the average number of years of experience for each sales team was in direct relation to annual sales volume. Use the data below to answer the following.

Annual Sales (in thousands)	46	35	51	42	33	50	30
Average Years of Experience	6	4	8	5.5	3	7	2.5

5. Draw a scatter diagram to show how years of experience per sales team and annual sales are related.

6. Find a prediction equation to show how years of experience and annual sales are related. **Typical answer: $y = 3.6x + 22.2$**

Additional Answer

9a.

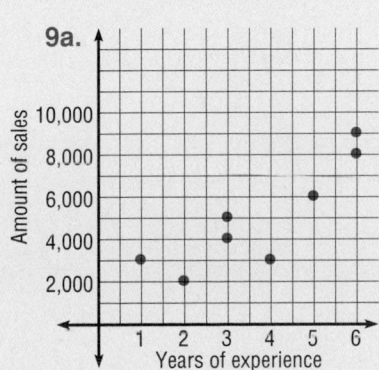

13a.

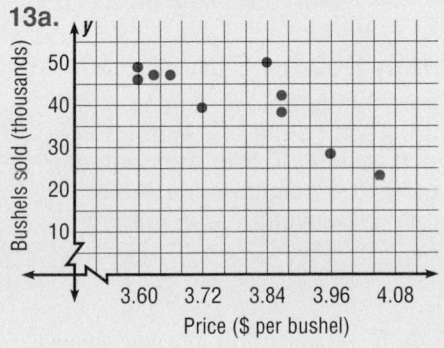

Teaching Tip ❸ Remind students that their prediction equation may differ from the prediction equations of other students.

Additional Answers

10d. They are very similar and when graphed almost define the same line.

11. Answers will vary. Students could make a table showing the x-coordinates and y-coordinates for the data. Add a column to the table for the y-coordinates that result using the x values from the data and the prediction equation. If the two sets of y-coordinates vary greatly, the prediction equation is probably not a good one.

12. No, eventually there is a maximum speed one can obtain regardless of how much experience they have. The graph would climb and then level off at that point.

Enrichment Masters Booklet, p. 12

Journal

Write a few sentences to tell how a scatter plot might be used to determine a trend in marketing.

d. Predict the amount of sales for a representative with no experience. **$0**

e. Predict the year of experience for a representative who sells $7300 of encyclopedias. **about 5.5 years**

C▶10. The table below shows the ideal weight for a man for a given height.

Height (inches)	66	68	70	72	74	76	78
Weight (pounds)	143	153	164	171	183	198	206

a. Use the information from the chart above to write a prediction equation for the relationship between a man's height and his ideal weight. $y = 5x - 187$

b. Predict the weight of a man who is 71 inches tall. **168 lb**

c. Predict the height of a man who weighs 190 pounds. **75.4 in.**

d. Write a paragraph to compare and contrast the prediction equation for women in Example 1 with your prediction equation for men. **See margin.**

Critical Thinking

11. Describe how you could test your prediction equation to see if it is an accurate representation of the data in a scatter plot. **See margin.**

12. Refer to Example 2. Is the prediction equation true for all values of t? Why or why not? **See margin.**

Teaching Tip ❸   13a–c. **Answers will vary.**

Applications

13. Agriculture Farmers will sometimes hold their crops from market until the price goes up to a level they think is satisfactory. The table below records the price per bushel and how many thousand bushels of wheat were sold at that price during a 10-day selling period in Iowa.

Price ($ per bushel)	3.84	3.66	3.87	3.96	3.60	4.05	3.63	3.60	3.72	3.87
Bushels Sold (thousands)	50	47	38	28	49	23	47	46	39	42

a. Draw a scatter plot and find a prediction equation for the data.

b. If next week, the market price of wheat is $3.90/bushel, how many bushels of wheat can you predict will be sold? **31,500 bushels.**

c. Estimate what the price of wheat was when 25,500 bushels were sold. **$4.02**
    a. $y = -50x + 226.5$

14. Personal Finance Sonia works at a clothing store. She earns $8 an hour plus 40¢ for every item over 20 that she sells. She works 30 hours a week. How much money will she make if she sells c items?
    $p = 240 + 0.40(c - 20)$ if $(c > 20)$ $p = \$240$ if $c \le 20$

Mixed Review

15. Write an equation in standard form of a line that passes through $(5, 1)$ and $(8, -2)$. **(Lesson 2-5)** $y + x = 6$

16. What is the slope of a line perpendicular to the line that passes through $(0, 0)$ and $(-4, -2)$? **(Lesson 2-5)**   **-2**
                                                                      See margin.

17. Graph $y - 3x = 2$ using the slope and y-intercept. **(Lesson 2-4)**

18. Evaluate $|30x - 20| + 72$ if $x = -2$. **(Lesson 1-6)**   **152**

19. Simplify $3(x + 2y) - 4(3x - 2y)$. **(Lesson 1-2)**   **$-9x + 14y$**

EXTENDING THE LESSON

Math Power: Connections

Draw 6 different rectangles. Measure each height and width. Find each perimeter. Plot the perimeter versus the height. Is there a relationship between these numbers?

Additional Answer

17.

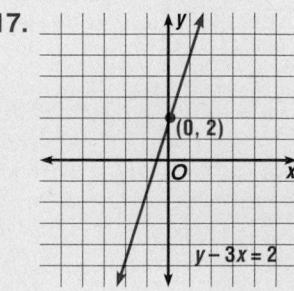

Graphing Calculator Exploration: Lines of Regression

You can use your graphing calculator to draw scatter plots and a line that best fits the points in the scatter plot. This line is called a **regression line.** Once you have drawn the regression line, you can use the tracing function on the graphing calculator to make predictions about the data.

Example 1

Draw a scatter plot and a regression line for the data about the orbits of ten asteroids that is given in the following table.

Asteroid	Ceres	Pallas	Juno	Vesta	Astraea	Hebe	Iris	Flora	Metis	Hygeia
Mean Distance from Sun (millions of miles)	257.0	257.4	247.8	219.3	239.3	225.2	221.4	204.4	221.7	222.6
Orbital Period (in years)	4.60	4.61	4.36	3.63	4.14	3.78	3.68	3.27	3.69	5.59

First, set the range parameters. The values of the data suggest that we use the viewing window [200, 260] by [3, 6] with a scale factor of 10 for the x-axis and 0.5 for the y-axis. *Can you see why this window was chosen?*

Next, set your calculator in the proper statistical mode and clear the statistical memories and the graphics screen.

Teaching Tip ❶   **Teaching Tip ❷**

Casio ENTER: [SHIFT] [Cls] [EXE] [SHIFT] [MODE] [÷] [SHIFT] [SCL] [EXE]

TI-81 ENTER: [2nd] [STAT] [◄] 2 [ENTER] [2nd] [STAT] [◄] [ENTER]

Teaching Tip ❸   **Teaching Tip ❹**

Now enter your data. **Teaching Tip ❺**

Casio ENTER: 257.0 [SHIFT] [,] 4.60 [DT] . . . 222.6 [SHIFT] [,] 5.59 [DT]

TI-81 ENTER: 257.0 [ENTER] 4.60 [ENTER] . . . 222.6 [ENTER] 5.59 [ENTER]

Now draw the scatter plot and the regression line.

Casio ENTER: [GRAPH] [SHIFT] [LINE] 1 [EXE]   *Draws the regression line.*

TI-81 ENTER: [2nd] [STAT] [►] 2 [ENTER]   *Draws the scatter plot.*

[2nd] [STAT] 2 [ENTER]   *Calculates the coefficients of the regression line.*

Teaching Tip ❻

[Y=] [VARS] [►] [►] 4 [ENTER]   *Writes the equation of the regression line.*

[GRAPH]   *Graphs the regression line.*

[2nd] [STAT] [►] 2 [ENTER]   *Restores the scatter plot.*

GRAPHING CALCULATOR EXPLORATION: LINES OF REGRESSION 85

Teaching Tip **6** The *a* is the *y*-intercept and the *b* is the slope in the regression equation $y = a + bx$. The *r* is the correlation coefficient and represents the "goodness of fit" of the regression line.

Teaching Tip **7** If you want to find a value for the regression line that is outside of the viewing window, use TRACE and the ▶ on the TI-81. On the Casio, you will have to change the range values to include the location where you want to look.

More Examples

1. Draw a scatter plot and regression line for the data below.

x	12	13	14	15	16	17
y	2.1	4.6	5.8	7.1	8.9	10

See students' work.
2. Use the tracing function on the regression line found in problem 1 above to predict the value at 22. **17.92381**

EVALUATING THE LESSON

Closing the Lesson

Speaking Activity Have students work through Exercise 1 and explain what they are doing at each step. Make sure they do not just say what keys they press but what is happening when they press the keys.

APPLYING THE LESSON

Homework Exercises

Assignment Guide
All: 1–3

Example 2 Use the tracing function on the regression line found in Example 1 to predict the orbital period of an asteroid that is an average of 236.0 million miles from the sun.

First activate the tracing function.

Casio ENTER: [SHIFT] [TRACE]

TI-81 ENTER: [TRACE] **Teaching Tip 7**

Now use the arrow keys to find the *x*-coordinate value that best approximates 236.0. Then find the corresponding *y*-value to determine the orbital period. The TI-81 will display the *x*- and *y*-coordinates simultaneously. To find the *y*-coordinate on the Casio, find the *x*-coordinate value closest to 236.0 and then press the [x-y] key to display the corresponding *y*-coordinate value. Based on this regression line, an asteroid that is an average of 236.0 million miles from the sun would have an orbital period of about 4.22 years.

EXERCISES

Use your graphing calculator to draw a scatter plot and a regression line for the data in the following tables. See students' graphs.

1.
x	0.1	2	3	4	5
y	1	0.2	−1	−1.5	−2

2.
x	−2	−1	0.5	1	2.5
y	−2	1	−1	2	0.5

3. The following table shows the number of thousands of men and women who graduated from college in the years 1981–1988.

Year	1981	1982	1983	1984	1985	1986	1987	1988
Men	470	473	479	482	483	486	481	472
Women	465	480	490	492	497	502	510	517

a. Use a graphing calculator to draw a scatter plot and regression line to show how the year is related to the number of thousands of men who graduated from college in the years 1981 to 1988. **See students' graphs.**
b. Use the tracing function to predict the number of men who will graduate from college in 2000. **about 492 thousand**

c. Use a graphing calculator to draw a scatter plot and regression line to show how the year is related to the number of thousands of women who graduated from college in the years 1981 to 1988. **See students' graphs.**
d. Use the tracing function to predict the number of women who will graduate from college in 2000. **about 596 thousand**

EXTENDING THE LESSON

Math Power: Reasoning

Use the data in Example 1 except change the orbital period of Hygeia to 3.59. Then calculate the coefficients of the regression line and the correlation coefficient, *r* (it should change from .512868328 to .9961588598). What does the drastic change in *r* mean? **That one piece of data that is "way off" can affect the validity of your data and the goodness of fit can be greatly influenced by a bad or incorrect piece of data.** What would happen if there were 100 pieces of data and one piece was "way off"? 1000 pieces? Discuss how more data can increase validity.

Objective
2-7

After studying this lesson, you should be able to:
- identify and graph special functions (direct variation, constant, identity, absolute value, and greatest integer).

Application

During a thunderstorm, Kelly recorded how long it was between seeing the lightning and hearing the thunder. The distance d in kilometers between Kelly and the lightning can be estimated by $d = \frac{1}{3}s$, where s is the number of seconds between seeing the lightning and hearing the thunder.

Time (sec)	2	4	6	8	12
Distance (km)	0.6	1.3	2.0	2.6	4

From the equation written in slope-intercept form, you find that the slope is $\frac{1}{3}$ and the y-intercept is 0. Whenever a linear function in the form $y = mx + b$, has $b = 0$ and $m \neq 0$, the function is called a **direct variation**. In this situation, the distance varies directly as the number of seconds. In other words, if you hear the thunder soon after you see the lightning, you are fairly close to the lightning. On the other hand, if you don't hear the thunder for a long time after you see the lightning, then the lightning is far away.

There are other special cases of linear functions. Two of these, the **constant function** and the **identity function**, are shown below.

constant function
$m = 0$

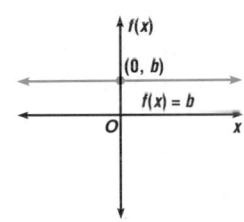

identity function
$m = 1, b = 0$

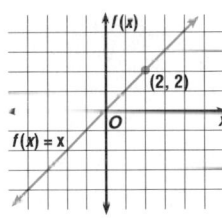

absolute value function

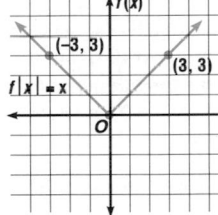

Several other functions are closely related to linear functions. An **absolute value function** is one example. Consider $f(x) = |x|$ or $y = |x|$. Look for a pattern when studying the values in the chart.

x	−3	−2	−1	0	1	2	3
y	3	2	1	0	1	2	3

You see that when x is positive or zero, the absolute value function looks like the graph of $y = x$. When x is negative, the absolute value function looks like the graph of $y = -x$.

LESSON 2-7 SPECIAL FUNCTIONS 87

Lesson Resources
Reteaching Master 2-7
Practice Master 2-7
Enrichment Master 2-7
Activity Master, p. 38
Multicultural Activity Master, p. 2

Transparency 2-7 contains the 5-Minute Check and a teaching aid for this lesson.

INTRODUCING THE LESSON

5-Minute Check
(over Lesson 2-6)
A certain prediction equation says that if the average temperature outside is 22° F then the cost of fuel for a household is $50 for the month. If the temperature averages 15° F, then the average cost for fuel is $64.

1. Find the slope of the prediction equation. −2

2. Find the y-intercept of the prediction equation. 94

3. Find the prediction equation. $f = -2t + 94$

4. Predict the cost for fuel if the temperature averages 11° F for the month. $72

Motivating the Lesson
Have students find the speeds for the last 10 winners of the Indianapolis 500. Have students determine the time it took to drive the race (excluding time for pit stops). Discuss the relationship between rate, time and distance.

ALTERNATE TEACHING STRATEGIES

Using Problem Solving
Write a problem for a direct variation situation involving the workplace. Explain how you know it is a direct variation. Write the equation for the situation.

Using Logical Reasoning
Tell what type of function is described. The domain is the number of local telephone calls made per month. The range is the cost for the local calls.
1. A phone company charges a basic monthly fee, plus a fixed amount for each local call. **linear**
2. A phone company charges a fixed amount per month no matter how many calls are made. **constant**

Chalkboard Examples

For Example 1

Graph $f(x) = |x + 2|$ and $f(x) = |x| + 2$ on the same plane.

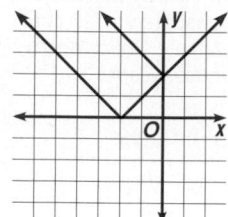

For Example 2

The price of aluminum given by a recycling center is based on its weight. If the aluminum weighs more than 0 pounds but less than or equal to 1 pound, there is no payment. If the aluminum weighs more than 1 pound but less than or equal to 2 pounds, the price is $2.00. For each additional pound, the price of aluminum increases $1.00. Graph the function that describes this relationship.

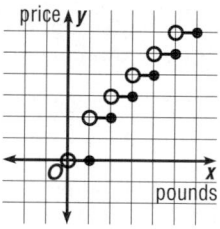

Reteaching Masters Booklet, p. 13

2-7 | **Reteaching Worksheet**

NAME _____ DATE _____

Special Functions

Some linear functions have special names and special graphs.

Function	Written as	Graph
constant	$y = b$ or $f(x) = b$	horizontal line
identity	$y = x$ or $f(x) = x$	passes through origin; forms congruent angles with axes
direct variation	$y = mx$ or $f(x) = mx$ where $m \neq 0$	passes through origin
absolute value	$y = |x|$ or $f(x) = |x|$	mirror image
greatest integer	$f(x) = [x]$	one-unit horizontal segments (right endpoints missing) arranged like steps

Identify each type of function. Graph each function.

1. $f(x) = 2[x]$

greatest integer function

2. $f(x) = 2$

constant

3. $f(x) = |2x + 1|$

absolute value

4. $f(x) = x$

identity

5. $r(x) = |2x|$

absolute value

6. $f(x) = [x - \frac{1}{2}]$

greatest integer function

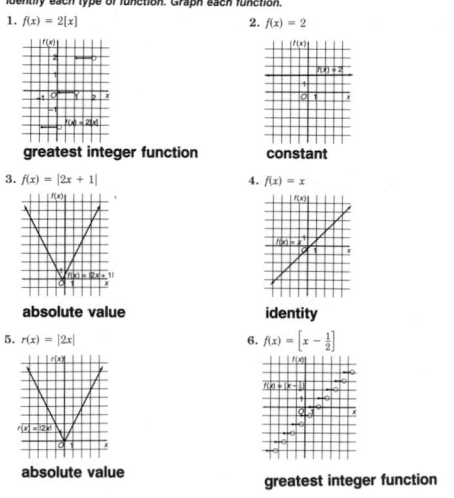

Example 1

Graph $f(x) = |x| + 3$ and $g(x) = |x + 3|$ on the same coordinate plane. Determine the similarities and differences in the two graphs.

Find several ordered pairs that satisfy each function.

x	$|x| + 3$
0	3
-1	4
1	4
-2	5
2	5

x	$|x + 3|$
0	3
1	4
-1	2
2	5
-2	1
-3	0

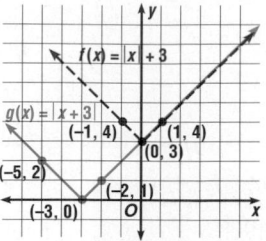

Graph the points and connect them. Both graphs have the same shape and form congruent angles, but have their vertices at different points.

Step functions like the ones shown below are also related to linear functions. The open circle means that the point is not included in that part of the graph.

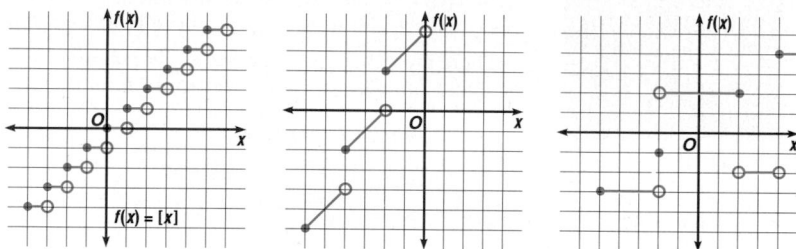

One type of step function is the **greatest integer function.** The symbol $[x]$ means the greatest integer not greater than x. For example, $[6.2]$ is 6 and $[-1.8]$ is -2, because $-1 > -1.8$. The greatest integer function is given by $f(x) = [x]$. Its graph is the first step function shown above.

Teaching Tip ❶

Example 2

APPLICATION

Commerce

The Speedy-Fast Parcel Service charges for delivering packages by the weight of the package. If the package weighs less than 1 pound, the cost of delivery is $2. If the package weighs at least 1 pound but less than 2 pounds, the cost is $3.50. For each additional pound the cost of delivery increases $1.50. Graph the function that describes this relationship.

This is an example of an application of the greatest integer function. The equation that describes this function is $f(x) = 1.50[x] + 2$.

88   CHAPTER 2   LINEAR RELATIONS AND FUNCTIONS

Identify each function as C for constant, D for direct variation, A for absolute value, G for greatest integer or I for identity. Then graph each function.

1.–3.

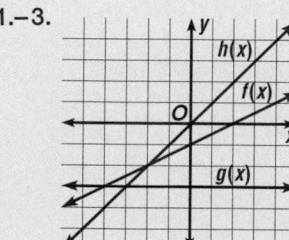

1. $f(x) = 0.5x$ **D**
2. $g(x) = -3$ **C**
3. $h(x) = x$ **I**
4. $j(x) = [x + 2]$ **G**
5. $k(x) = 1 - |x - 2|$ **A**

Make a table of values to help you draw the graph.

x	[x]	f(x)
0.1	0	2.00
0.5	0	2.00
0.7	0	2.00
1.0	1	3.50
1.4	1	3.50
1.9	1	3.50
2.4	2	5.00
2.7	2	5.00
3.1	3	6.50
3.7	3	6.50

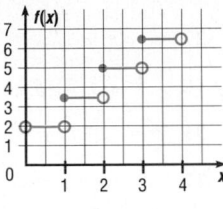

CHECKING FOR UNDERSTANDING

Communicating Mathematics

3. Both form congruent angles but $y = |x - 5|$ has its vertex at (5, 0) instead of (0, 0) as in $y = |x|$.

Read and study the lesson to answer each question.

1. How far away would the lightning be if there was 5 seconds between seeing the lightning and hearing the thunder? **about 1.67 km**

2. Which of the following is an example of a constant function? **a and c**
   a. $f(x) = 4$ b. $x = 6$ c. $y = -3$

3. Discuss what the difference would be in the graphs of $y = |x|$ and $y = |x - 5|$.

4. What is the greatest integer function?

5. The value of [4.1] is 4, but the value of [−4.1] is −5. Why? **[−4.1] = −5 instead of −4 because −4 > −4.1**

Guided Practice

4. The function that identifies the greatest integer not greater than the given number.

Identify each function as C for constant, D for direct variation, A for absolute value, or G for greatest integer function.

6. $f(x) = |3x - 2|$ **A**   7. $f(x) = [-x]$ **G**   8. $g(x) = 3x$ **D**

9. $f(x) = \left|x - \frac{2}{3}\right|$ **A**   10. $m(x) = \frac{2}{3}$ **C**   11. $f(x) = -\frac{1}{2}x$ **D**

12. If $g(x) = [x - 4]$, find $g(3)$. **−1**

EXERCISES

Practice

A

Identify each type of function.

13. $p(x) = x$ **identity**   14. $h(x) = -7$ **constant**   15. $g(x) = [2x + 1]$ **greatest integer function**

If $h(x) = [2x + 1]$, find each value.

16. $h(2)$ **5**   17. $h(-3)$ **−5**   18. $h(1.4)$ **3**   19. $h\left(\frac{2}{3}\right)$ **2**   20. $h\left(-\frac{9}{7}\right)$ **−2**

B

Graph each function. **See Solutions Manual.**

21. $f(x) = x + 2$ 22. $f(x) = |x + 2|$ 23. $f(x) = [x + 2]$

24. $g(x) = |x| + 2$ 25. $g(x) = [x] + 2$ 26. $g(x) = 2|x|$

LESSON 2-7 SPECIAL FUNCTIONS 89

Answers to Reteaching the Lesson

4.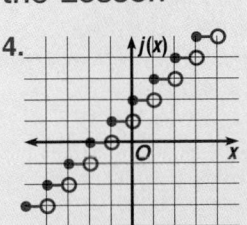

5.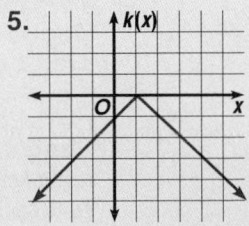

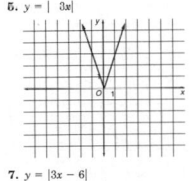 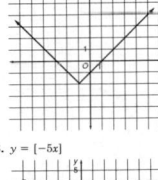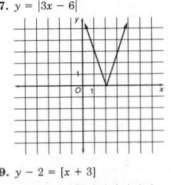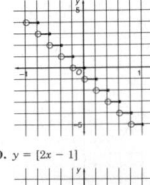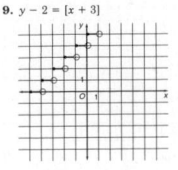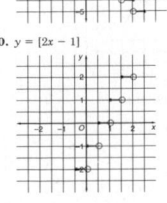

Closing the Lesson

Speaking Activity Have students explain the absolute value function. How can it translate up and down the *y*-axis? How can it translate left and right on the *x*-axis?

APPLYING THE LESSON

Homework Exercises

See assignment guide on page 89.

Additional Answers

Answers for Exercises 27–36 compare the second graph to the first.

27. same graph translated 4 units right
28. same graph translated 8 units down
29. same graph translated 1 unit down
30. 2[x] steps 2 units vertically at intervals of 1 unit. [2x] steps 1 unit vertically at intervals of $\frac{1}{2}$ unit.
31. identical
32. identical
33. same shape graph reflected over x-axis
34. −3[x] steps 3 units vertically at intervals of 1 unit. [−3x] steps 1 unit vertically at intervals of $\frac{1}{3}$ unit.

Enrichment Masters Booklet, p. 13

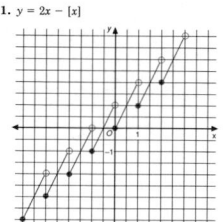 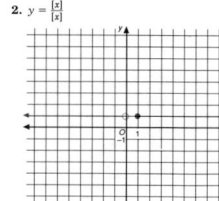
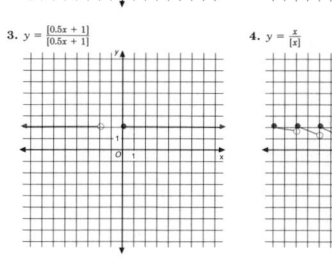 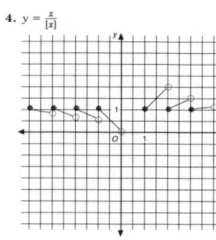

For graphs, see Solutions Manual.

Graph each pair of equations on the same coordinate plane. Discuss the similarities and differences in the two graphs. 27–36. **See margin.**

Journal

Describe something new you learned in this lesson. Be sure to give examples.

27. $y = |x + 2|$, $y = |x - 2|$
28. $y = |x| + 4$, $y = |x| - 4$
29. $y = |x + 2|$, $y = |x + 2| - 1$
30. $y = 2[x]$, $y = [2x]$
31. $y = [x + 5]$, $y = [x] + 5$
32. $y = |3x|$, $y = 3|x|$
33. $y = -2|4x|$, $y = 4|-2x|$
34. $y = -3[x]$, $y = [-3x]$

35. Compare and contrast the graphs of $y = |ax|$ and $y = a|x|$.

36. Compare and contrast the graphs of $y = |x + b|$ and $y = |x| + b$.

Graph each equation. **See Solutions Manual.**

37. $y = [|x|]$
38. $y = |[x]|$
39. $y = x - [x]$
40. $y = x + |x|$

Critical Thinking

41. Draw a graph that represents how all rational numbers from 0 to 10 are rounded to the nearest whole number. What kind of function is this? Explain your answer. **See margin.**

$y = 12.79t$, constant function

Applications

42. **Sports** In the 1988 Winter Olympics, Bonnie Blair set a world record for women's speed skating by skating approximately 12.79 meters per second in the 500 meter race. If she could maintain that speed, what would be the equation that represents how far she could travel for a given time? What type of function does the equation represent?

43. **Business** The Fix-It Auto Repair Shop has a sign in the Service Department that states that the labor costs are $35 per hour or any fraction thereof. What type of function does this relationship represent? **step function**

Mixed Review

44. **Answers will vary. Sample answers are given.**

44a. For graph, see Solutions Manual.
$y = -400x + 18,125$

44. **Statistics** A developer surveyed families in a suburb of Raleigh, North Carolina, to find out each household's monthly income and what percentage of that income was spent on housing. The table below shows the data from eight families. **(Lesson 2-6)**

Average Monthly Income	$870	$1430	$1920	$2460	$2850	$3240	$3790	$4510
Percentage Spent on Housing	44	39	40	35	43	38	37	33

a. Graph a scatter plot and find a prediction equation for this data.
b. Predict the percentage of income spent on housing for a family with an average monthly income of $3000. **about 37.8%**
c. Predict the income for a family who spends 41% of their money for housing. **about $1725**

45. Find the slope and *y*-intercept of the graph of $3x - 4y = -10$. **(Lesson 2-4)** $m = \frac{3}{4}$, $b = \frac{5}{2}$

46. Evaluate $\frac{3a^2 + 2b}{c^2}$, if $a = 1$, $b = 2$, and $c = 3$. **(Lesson 1-1)** $\frac{7}{9}$

90   CHAPTER 2   LINEAR RELATIONS AND FUNCTIONS

EXTENDING THE LESSON

Math Power: Reasoning

Use the greatest integer function to write a function that rounds any number to the nearest integer.
$f(x) = [x + 0.5]$

Additional Answers

35. If $a \geq 0$, the two graphs are the same. If $a < 0$, the graphs are reflected images over the x-axis.

36. $y = |x + b|$ is the graph of $y = |x|$ translated b units along x-axis. $y = |x| + b$ translates $y = |x|$ b units vertically.

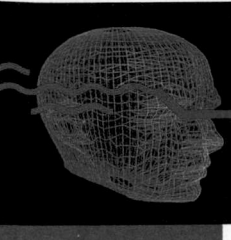

Technology
Median-Fit Lines

BASIC
▶ Software
Spreadsheets

In Lesson 2–6, you learned to graph scatter plots and find the prediction equation that can describe the linear pattern for a group of ordered pairs. A software product from Sunburst, Inc., called *Data Insights*, enables you to graph data. Then the program will draw a line suggested by the points, if one exists. *Data Insights* describes this line as the **median-fit line.**

The data below is a list of years and the millions of students in elementary and secondary schools in the United States. The graph done by *Data Insights* shows the graphed data and median-fit line. Notice that *Data Insights* labels your axes and gives you the equation of the median-fit line. It will also title the graph.

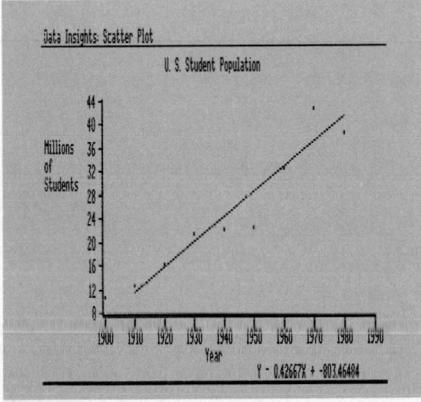

Year	Millions of Students
1900	10.6
1910	12.6
1920	16.2
1930	21.3
1940	22.0
1950	22.3
1960	32.5
1970	42.5
1980	38.2
1990	38.0

In the median-fit line equation, or prediction equation, $Y = 0.42333X + -796.93359$, the X is the year and the Y is the number of students (in millions).

EXERCISES

1. Use the median-fit line given above and your calculator to estimate the number of students in each year.

   a. 1922   b. 1955   c. 1978   d. 1991   e. 2005
   16.7 million   30.7 million   40.4 million   45.9 million   51.8 million

2. Use *Data Insights* to enter the data below for the fuel efficiency for city driving of various 1990 cars. What is the median-fit line equation?
   HP = horsepower, MPG = miles per gallon

Buick Regal	135 HP	19 MPH	Chevrolet Camaro	245 HP	16 MPG
Dodge Colt	75 HP	27 MPG	Ford Probe	145 HP	21 MPG
Geo Prizm	102 HP	25 MPG	Honda Accord	125 HP	22 MPG
Mercury Sable	140 HP	18 MPG	Pontiac Bonneville	165 HP	18 MPG
Toyota Corolla	102 HP	25 MPG			

   $Y = -0.12963X + 37.84569$

Using Technology
Objective   This optional page shows how graphing software can be used to perform mathematical computations and to enhance and extend mathematical concepts.

Teaching Suggestions
The manual accompanying *Data Insights* explains how median-fit lines are computed. You may wish to share this method with the students. Emphasize that interpolated and extrapolated results are estimates. In particular, extrapolation can produce implausible results. For example, the median-fit line equation for Exercise 2 will estimate the fuel efficiency of a 300 hp engine to be negative! You may wish to have students collect data and to use *Data Insights* for analysis. The following body measurements usually exhibit a linear relationship.
- height/weight (separate for males and females)
- waist circumference/weight
- height/elbow-hand length
- height/knee-to-floor length

Additional Answers, p. 90

41.

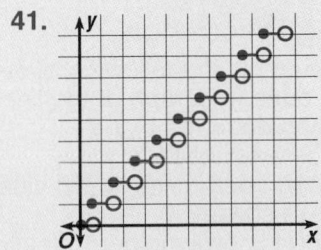

Lesson Resources

Reteaching Master 2-8
Practice Master 2-8
Enrichment Master 2-8

 Transparency 2-8 contains the 5-Minute Check and a teaching aid for this lesson.

INTRODUCING THE LESSON

 5-Minute Check

(over Lesson 2-7)
Identify each type of function.

1. $y = |2x|$ **absolute value**
2. $g(x) = [2x]$ **greatest integer**
3. $f(x) = 2x$ **direct variation**
4. Graph $f(x) = |x - 1|$.

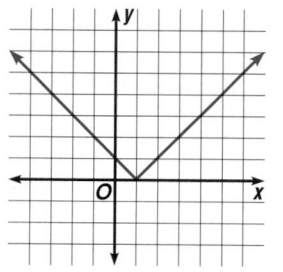

Motivating the Lesson

Have students graph an equation such as $y = -2x + 4$. Select a point above the line. What relationship does it have to the equation? Select a point below the line. How does this point relate to the points on the line?

2-8 Graphing Linear Inequalities

Objectives

2-8A
2-8B

After studying this lesson, you should be able to:
- draw graphs of inequalities in two variables, and
- write an inequality to solve problems.

Application

Mr. Harris wants to rent a car for a business trip. Reasonable Car Rental advertises that their daily rental rate is $30 plus $0.25 a mile. Mr. Harris would like to compare this rate with the rates offered by other car rental agencies.

First he determines the equation containing the points that represent the relationship between the number of miles driven (d) and the total cost of the rental (r).

The initial cost of the car is $30. Since this is the point where no miles are driven, it would be the y-intercept of the graph. The slope would be the rate of change in the total cost. In this case, the rate is $0.25 per mile. Since $0.25 = \frac{1}{4}$, the slope is $\frac{1}{4}$. Thus, an equation of the line is $r = \frac{1}{4}d + 30$.

The graph of $r = \frac{1}{4}d + 30$ separates the coordinate plane into two regions. The line is called the *boundary* of the regions. To graph an inequality, first you graph the boundary and then determine which region to shade.

Miles Driven	Total Cost
0	$30
40	$40
100	$55
200	$110

The graph of $r > \frac{1}{4}d + 30$ contains points that are located *above* the boundary. In that region, the value of the dependent variable r is greater than the value of $\frac{1}{4}d + 30$. This graph represents car rental costs that are greater than those offered by Reasonable Car Rental. For example, Executive Rental charges $70 for a car rental with 100 miles. The point (100, 70) lies above the boundary.

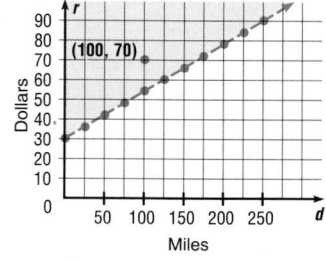

FYI ...

About 344 trillion miles are traveled in cars each year by people on business-related trips.

The graph of $r < \frac{1}{4}d + 30$ contains points that are located *below* the boundary. In that region, the value of r is less than the value of $\frac{1}{4}d + 30$. This graph represents car rental costs that are less than those offered by Reasonable Car Rental. For example, Econo-Rental charges $40 for a car rental with 100 miles. The point (100, 40) lies below the boundary.

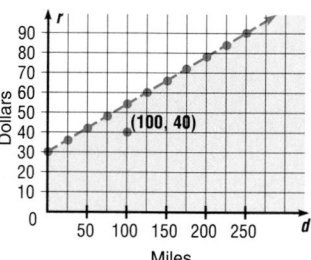

TEACHING THE LESSON

Teaching Tip ❶ You may want students to test two points, one on each side of the boundary, when determining which region should be shaded.

Teaching Tip ❷ Remind students what happens to absolute value graphs when a quantity is subtracted.

ALTERNATE TEACHING STRATEGIES

Using Connections

Have students plot a rectangle on the coordinate system. Then have them make up a set of inequalities to shade in the area of the rectangle. Try it with other figures such as a square and a triangle.

Using Discussion

Ask students the following questions. What does the graph of the linear equation do to the plane? What is a boundary? How can I determine which side of the graph to shade? How do I know whether to make the graph of the equation a dashed line or a solid line?

When graphing an inequality, the boundary you draw may be solid or dashed. If the inequality uses the symbol $\le$ or $\ge$, which include equality, the boundary will be solid. Otherwise, it will be dashed. After graphing the boundary, you must determine which region is to be shaded. Test a point on one side of the line. If the ordered pair satisfies the inequality, that region contains solutions to the inequality. If the ordered pair does not satisfy the inequality, the other region is the solution. **Teaching Tip ❶**

Example 1

Graph $2y - 5x \le 8$.

The boundary will be the graph of $2y - 5x = 8$. Let's use intercepts to graph the boundary more easily.

x-intercept	y-intercept
$2(0) - 5x = 8$	$2y - 5(0) = 8$
$-5x = 8$	$2y = 8$
$x = -\dfrac{8}{5}$	$y = 4$

Draw a solid line connecting the two intercepts. This is the boundary.

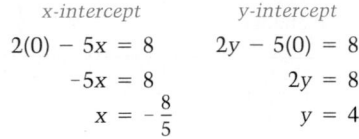

The boundary is included.

Now test a point.

Try (2, 0). 　　$2y - 5x \le 8$
　　　　　　　$2(0) - 5(2) \le 8$
　　　　　　　　　$-10 \le 8$ 　*true*

The region that contains (2, 0) should be shaded.

Example 2

Graph $y > |x| - 1$. **Teaching Tip ❷**

The absolute value has two conditions to consider.

$$y > |x| - 1$$

when $x < 0$ 　　　　when $x > 0$

$y > -x - 1$ 　and 　$y > x - 1$

Graph each inequality for the specified values of x. The lines will be dashed.

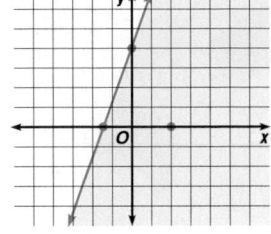

Test (0, 0): 　$y > |x| - 1$
　　　　　　$0 > |0| - 1$
　　　　　　$0 > -1$ 　*true*

Note that the boundary is not included.

The shaded region should include (0, 0).

Inequalities can sometimes be used to analyze a situation and determine the trends in business and profitability.

LESSON 2-8　GRAPHING LINEAR INEQUALITIES　93

RETEACHING THE LESSON

Have students graph the equation $x = y$. Then have them identify which part of the graph represents each of the following.

1. $x < y$ 　points above the line
2. $x = y$ 　the line itself
3. $x \ge y$ 　points below the line and the line

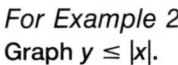
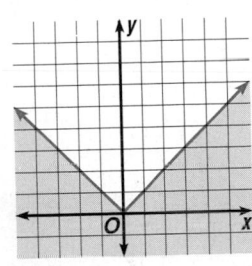
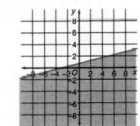
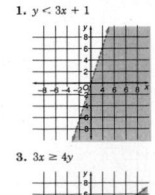
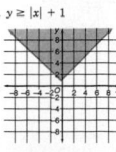
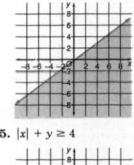
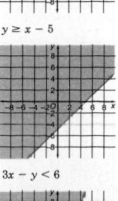
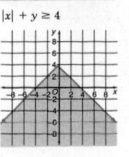

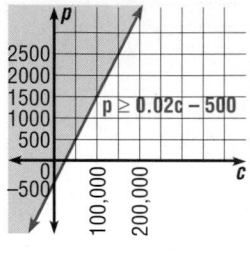
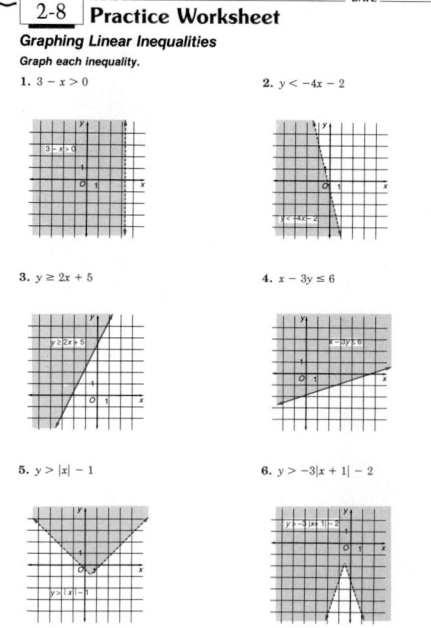
Example 3

APPLICATION

Economics

The No-Drip Sponge Company must produce a certain number of sponges each day to keep the assembly line staff busy. If production falls, then layoffs may be possible. The equation that describes this relationship is $s > 50e + 25$, where e is the number of employees and s is the number of sponges. Graph this inequality.

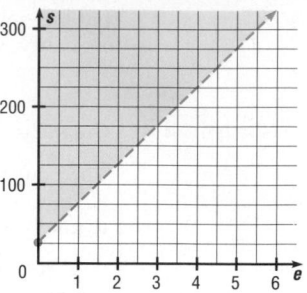

Graph the equation $s = 50e + 25$.

Select a point, such as $(2, 50)$, and substitute it into the inequality.

$s > 50e + 25$
$50 > 50(2) + 25$
$50 > 125$ *false*

The region that does not contain $(2, 50)$ should be shaded.

Any ordered pair that lies in the shaded portion represents an acceptable production rate in relation to the number of employees.

CHECKING FOR UNDERSTANDING

Communicating Mathematics

Read and study the lesson to answer each question. **1–5. See margin.**

1. What is the purpose of the boundary? How do you find it?

2. Suppose Mr. Harris found a rental rate that had points that were the same as those of the boundary. Explain what kind of deal this is.

3. Why is $(0, 0)$ a convenient point to use to test a solution for an inequality?

4. How do you decide if a boundary should be solid or dashed?

5. Explain why $(0, 2)$ satisfies $y \geq -8x + 2$.

Guided Practice

State which points, $(0, 0)$, $(2, -3)$, or $(-1, 2)$, satisfy each inequality.

6. $x + 2y < 7$ 7. $3x + 2y \leq 0$ 8. $4x + 2y \geq 7$ 9. $y > 0$
   $(0, 0)$, $(2, -3)$, $(-1, 2)$ $(0, 0)$, $(2, -3)$ **none** $(-1, 2)$

Graph each inequality. **For graphs, see Solutions Manual.**

10. $y < 3$ 11. $x > -1$ 12. $x - y \geq 0$

EXERCISES

Practice

A

Graph each inequality. **For graphs, see Solutions Manual.**

13. $y + 1 < 5$ 14. $x - 3 < -5$ 15. $y > 5x - 3$

16. $x - 7 \leq y$ 17. $y \geq -3x + 1$ 18. $y - 3 < 2x$

94   CHAPTER 2   LINEAR RELATIONS AND FUNCTIONS

19. Graph all the points on the coordinate plane to the right of $x = 4$. Write an inequality to describe these points. **$x > 4$**

B

Graph each inequality. 20–37. For graphs, see Solutions Manual.

20. $y > \frac{1}{3}x + 7$ **21.** $y \geq \frac{1}{2}x - 3$ **22.** $2 \geq x - 2y$

23. $-2x + 5 \leq 3y$ **24.** $y \geq |x|$ **25.** $|x| - 3 \leq y$

26. $|x| + y \geq 3$ **27.** $y + |x| < 2$ **28.** $y \geq |3x|$

29. Describe the graph of $|y| < x$ in your own words.

30. Graph all second quadrant points bounded by the lines $x = -2$, $x = -5$, and $y = 3$.

31. Graph all points in the first quadrant bounded by the two axes and the line $x + 2y = 4$.

32. Graph all points in the fourth quadrant bounded by the two axes and the lines $3x - y = 4$ and $x - y = 5$.

C

Draw a graph of each inequality.

33. $|x| \leq |y|$ **34.** $|x| - |y| = 1$

35. $|x| + |y| \geq 1$ **36.** $|x + y| > 1$

Critical Thinking

37. Draw the graph of a region where $2 \leq x \leq 8$ and $0 \leq y \leq 5$, excluding the region where $4 \leq x \leq 6$ and $2 \leq y \leq 3$.   **Teaching Tip ❸**

Application

38. Manufacturing The Hoosier Auto Company has a daily production quota of \$100,000 worth of cars per day. They produce two types of cars. Their compact model (C) is valued at \$10,000 and their luxury car (L) is valued at \$20,000. The equation $10,000C + 20,000L = 100,000$ describes the production quota. Make a graph of the quota equation. **For graphs, see Solutions Manual.**
  a. On January 14, the factory produced 5 compacts and 2 luxury cars. Was the company above, below, or on target with their quota? Write equation or inequality that contains this point. **below,**
   $10,000C + 20,000L < 100,000$
  b. On February 15, the factory produced 6 compacts and 2 luxury cars. Write the equation or inequality that contains this point.
   $10,000C + 20,000L = 100,000$
  c. On March 9, the factory produced 9 compacts and 1 luxury car. Write the equation or inequality that contains this point.
   $10,000C + 20,000L > 100,000$

Mixed Review

39. Graph $y = 2|x| + 7$.   **(Lesson 2-7)**   **See Solutions Manual.**

40. Graph $y = |x| - 4$.   **(Lesson 2-7)**   **See Solutions Manual.**

41. Find the value of $h(a - 3)$ if $h(x) = x^2 + 5$.   **(Lesson 2-1)**   **$a^2 - 6a + 14$**

42. See Solutions Manual for graph.

42. Solve $|4x + 2| \geq -10$. Graph the solution.   **(Lesson 1-8)**   **All reals**

43. How many 3-digit numbers are possible to complete the license plate number CNH-☐☐☐?   **(Lesson 1-5)**   **1000**

LESSON 2-8   GRAPHING LINEAR INEQUALITIES   95

EXTENDING THE LESSON

Math Power: Reasoning

Graph all points bounded by the graphs of $y = |2x|$ and $|y| = x + 2$.

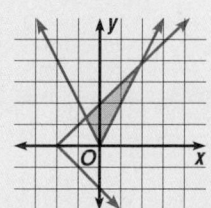

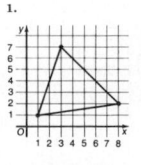

The Chapter Summary and Review begins with an alphabetical listing of the new terms that were presented in the chapter. Have students define each term and provide an example of it, if appropriate.

The Skills and Concepts presented in the chapter are reviewed using a side-by-side format. Encourage students to refer to the Objectives and Examples on the left as they complete the Review Exercises on the right.

The Chapter Summary and Review ends with exercises that review Applications and Connections.

Additional Answers

1.

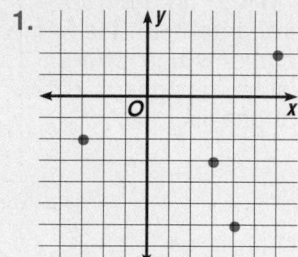

The domain is {–3, 4, 3, 6}.
The range is {–2, –6, –3, 2}.
It is a function.

2.

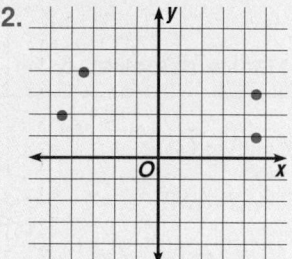

The domain is {4.5, –4.5, –3.5}.
The range is {1, 2, 3, 4}.
It is not a function.

3.

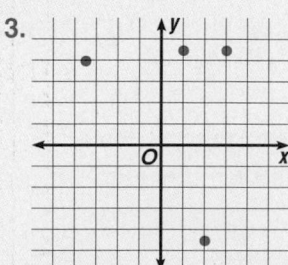

The domain is {1, 2, 3, –3.5}.
The range is {4.5, –4.5, 4}.
It is a function.

CHAPTER **2** SUMMARY AND REVIEW

VOCABULARY

Upon completing this chapter, you should be familiar with the following terms:

absolute value function	87	53	range
constant function	62	53	relation
direct variation	87	80	scatter plot
domain	53	66	slope
function	53	73	slope-intercept form
greatest integer function	88	60	standard form
identity function	87	88	step functions
linear equation	60	54	vertical line test
linear function	62	69	x-intercept
prediction equation	80	69	y-intercept

SKILLS AND CONCEPTS

OBJECTIVES AND EXAMPLES	REVIEW EXERCISES
Upon completing this chapter, you should be able to:	Use these exercises to review and prepare for the chapter test.

- graph a relation, state its domain and range, and determine if the relation is a function (**Lesson 2-1**)

  A function is a relation in which each element of the domain is paired with exactly one element of the range.

Graph each relation. Then state its domain and range. Is the relation a function? See margin.

1. {(–3, –2), (4, –6), (3, –3), (6, 2)}
2. {(4.5, 1), (–4.5, 2), (4.5, 3), (–3.5, 4)}
3. {(1, 4.5), (2, –4.5), (3, 4.5), (–3.5, 4)}

- find the values of functions for given elements of the domain (**Lesson 2-1**)

  If $f(x) = x^2 - 2$, find $f(2)$.
  $f(2) = 2^2 - 2$ or 2

Find the value of each function. –29

4. If $f(x) = 2x^3 + 4x^2 + 4x + 1$, find $f(-3)$.
5. If $f(x) = 3x^2 - 2x - 1$, find $f(2a)$.
   $12a^2 - 4a - 1$

- identify equations that are linear and graph them (**Lesson 2-2**)

  $3x + y^2 = 1$ is not a linear equation.
  $3x + y = 1$ is a linear equation.

  Find ordered pairs and graph them.

Determine if each equation is a linear equation. If it is, graph it.

6. $x^2 + y^2 = 4$ **no**   7. $y = 5$ **yes**
8. $y = 2x^2 - 1$ **no**   9. $4y = x + 8$ **yes**
For graphs, see Solutions Manual.

OBJECTIVES AND EXAMPLES	REVIEW EXERCISES

■ determine the slope of a line (**Lesson 2-4**)

Determine the slope of the line that passes through $(-4, 2)$ and $(4, 0)$.

$$m = \frac{0 - 2}{4 - (-4)}$$
$$= \frac{-1}{4}$$

Determine the slope of the line passing through each pair of points.

10. $(5, 1)$ and $(3, 7)$ -3
11. $(-3, 2)$ and $(5, -1)$ $\frac{-3}{8}$
12. $(2, -1)$ and $(-7, -5)$ $\frac{4}{9}$

■ use the slope and intercept to graph a line and determine if two lines are parallel, perpendicular, or neither   (**Lesson 2-4**)

The slope of parallel lines are the same. The product of the slope of perpendicular lines is -1.

Graph each equation. Then determine if the lines are parallel, perpendicular, or neither. See margin.

13. $x + 4y = 8$ and $4x - y = -2$
14. $2x - 4y = 8$ and $2x - y = 4$
15. $2y = -4x - 5$ and $2x + y = 10$

■ Write the slope-intercept form and the standard form of an equation given the slope and a point, or two points (**Lesson 2-5**)

The slope-intercept form of the line that has a slope of $\frac{2}{3}$ and a y-intercept of 3 is $y = \frac{2}{3}x + 3$. The standard form of this equation is $-2x + 3y = 9$.

Write the slope-intercept form and the standard form of an equation for each graph described. 16. $y = 5x - 7$, $5x - y = 7$
17. $3x + y = -1$, $y = -3x - 1$
16. slope of 5 and y-intercept of -7
17. slope of -3 and passes through $(1, -4)$
18. passes through $(-3, 0)$ and $(1, -4)$ $y = -x - 3$
19. x-intercept = 2 and y-intercept -5 $x + y = -3$
    $y = \frac{5}{2}x + 5$, $5x - 2y = -10$

■ write the equation of a line that is parallel or perpendicular to the graph of a given equation   (**Lesson 2-5**)

The equation of a line parallel to $y = 2x - 2$ is $y = 2x + 1$.

The equation of a line perpendicular to $y = 2x - 2$ is $y = -\frac{1}{2}x + 1$.

Write the slope intercept form and the standard form of an equation for each graph described. $y = 3x - 2$; $3x - y = 2$
20. passes through $(2, 4)$ and is parallel to the line whose equation is $y = 3x - 5$
21. passes through $(-1, -1)$ and is perpendicular to the line whose equation is $2y + 3x = 10$ $2x - 3y = 1$ $y = \frac{2}{3}x - \frac{1}{3}$;

■ draw a scatter plot and find the prediction equation   (**Lesson 2-6**)

Draw a scatter plot and draw a line suggested by the pattern of dots. Then select two points on the line and determine the equation of the line. Use this equation to predict.

22. $w = \frac{19}{20}h - 95$
24. **about 193 centimeters**

On the average, a person 180 centimeters tall weighs about 76 kilograms. A person who is 160 centimeters tall weighs about 57 kilograms. Let h represent the height and w represent the weight.

22. Find the prediction equation.
23. Predict the weight of a person who is 174 centimeters tall. **70.3 kilograms**
24. Predict the height of a person who weighs 88 kilograms.

Additional Answers

13.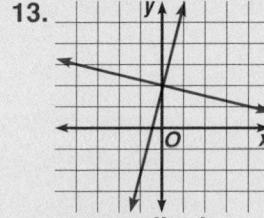
perpendicular

14.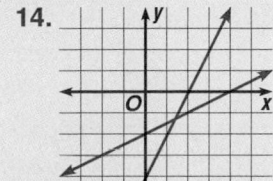
neither

15.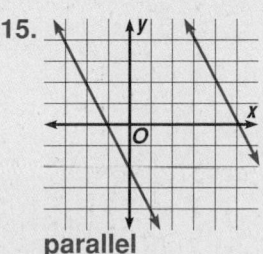
parallel

Alternate Review Strategy

To provide a brief in-class review, you may wish to read the following questions to the class and require a verbal or written response.

1. Find the value of $f(x) = 4x^2 + x + 10$ for $x = -5$.   **105**

2. Graph the linear equation $y = 5x + 2$.

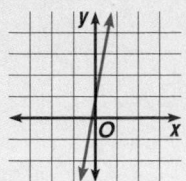

3. Find the slope of the line passing through $(1, 2)$ and $(4, 2)$. $m = 0$

4. Determine if the lines $x - y = 4$ and $2x + y = 4$ are parallel, perpendicular, or neither.   **neither**

5. Find an equation in slope-intercept form for the line with slope 3 and y-intercept -1. $y = 3x - 1$

6. A person 150 centimeters tall weighs about 60 kilograms. Another person 165 centimeters tall weighs about 66 kilograms. Let h represent height and w represent the weight. Find a prediction equation. $w = \frac{2}{5}h$

7. Predict the weight of a person 130 centimeters tall.   **52 kilograms**

8. Graph $f(x) = |x| + 4$.

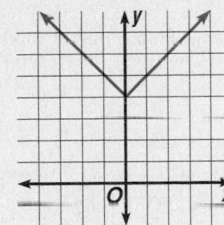

9. Find the next number: 1, 4, 10, 22, . . .   **46**

The Cumulative Review shown below can be used to review skills and concepts presented thus far in the text. Standardized Test Practice Questions are also provided in the Evaluation Masters Booklet.

Evaluation Masters Booklet, pp. 25–26

OBJECTIVES AND EXAMPLES

- identify and graph special functions to include direct variation, constant, identity, absolute value, and greatest integer **(Lesson 2-7)**

  Make a table of values to help you draw the graph.

- draw graphs of inequalities in two variables **(Lesson 2-8)**

  Replace the inequality symbol with an equals sign to find the equation for the boundary line. Graph the boundary line, using a solid line for $\le$ or $\ge$, or a dashed line for $<$ or $>$. Test a point to determine which region to shade.

REVIEW EXERCISES

Graph each function.

25. $f(x) = |x + 4|$ 26. $f(x) = 0.5|x|$

27. $f(x) = [x] - 1$ 28. $g(x) = 2[x]$

For graphs, see Solutions Manual.

Graph each inequality.

29. $y - 3 > -2x$ 30. $2x - 5y \ge 4$

31. $3x + 4y < 9$ 32. $y \le |x| + 5$

For graphs, see Solutions Manual.

~~~ APPLICATIONS AND CONNECTIONS ~~~

33. **Postal Services** The cost of mailing a package is determined by its weight. The overnight cost (c) for mailing a package is $10 plus 15¢ an ounce. Write an equation to describe this relationship. Is this a linear function? **(Lesson 2-2)**
$c = 10 + 0.15x$; **yes**

35. **Personal Finance** As an employee of the Yogurt Delight, Maria receives a salary of $5.50 an hour less $10 a week for cleaning her uniforms. Write an equation to describe her weekly salary and then find her salary for 32 hours of work. **(Lesson 2-5)** $s = 5.5h - 10$, **$166**

34. Beginning at the letter S and moving only up, down, right, or left, how many different paths can you find to spell the word SLOPE? **(Lesson 2-3)** **60**

```
            E
          E P E
        E P O P E
      E P O L O P E
    E P O L S L O P E
      E P O L O P E
        E P O P E
          E P E
            E
```

Graph each relation. State the range and domain. Is the relation a function?

1. $\{(-8, 1), (-4, 8), (3, 0), (8, 8), (3, -5)\}$ **D = {-8, -4, 3, 8} R = {1, 8, 0, -5}, no**

2.

Year	1988	1989	1990	1991	1992
Expenses	4000	4200	4000	4300	4100

**D = {1988, . . . , 1992}
R = {4000, 4200, 4300, 4100} yes**

Use the vertical line test to determine if each relation is a function.

3. 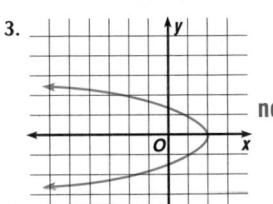 **no**

4. 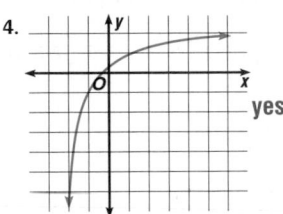 **yes**

5. 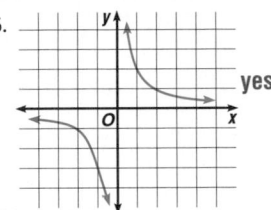 **yes**

6. Given $f(x) = 3x^2 - 5x - 4$, find $f(4)$. Then find $f(c + 2)$. **24, $3c^2 + 7c - 2$**

Graph each sentence. See Solutions Manual.

7. $y = \dfrac{8}{7}x$

8. $y = -7$

9. $x = 6$

10. $y = -3x + 4$

11. $5x - 2y = 12$

12. $2x + 3y > 9$

13. $2x + 6y \geq 18$

14. $f(x) = |x - 2|$

15. $y = 2[x] - 1$

16–20. See margin.

Write the slope-intercept form and standard form of an equation for each graph described.

16. slope = $\dfrac{1}{3}$, y-intercept = -7

17. slope = 4, passes through $(-3, 3)$

18. x-intercept = 6, y-intercept = -6

19. passes through $(0, 7)$ and $(5, 2)$

20. passes through $(7, 7)$ and is parallel to a line whose equation is $2x + 3y = 6$

The table below shows the age in years and the systolic blood pressure for a group of ten people tested at a hospital.

Age	50	35	24	34	55	48	26	30	41	37
Blood Pressure	135	128	108	119	146	140	104	122	132	121

21. Draw a scatter plot to show how age and systolic blood pressure are related. **See Solutions Manual.**

22. Find a prediction equation to show how age and systolic blood pressure are related.

23. Predict the systolic blood pressure of a person who is 45 years old. **136**

24. Predict the age of a person who has a systolic blood pressure of 120. **33 years old**

25. Find the next number in the pattern 2, 5, 9, 14, 20, $\underline{\ ?\ }$. **27**

22. $y = \dfrac{4}{3}x + 76$

Bonus Olivia earns $275 per week at a shoe store. She also gets an additional 40¢ for each pair of shoes over 60 that she sells. How much will she earn if she sells p pairs of shoes?

$d = 275 + 0.40(p - 60)$ if $p > 60$; $d = 275$ if $p \leq 60$

Additional Answers

16. $y = \dfrac{x}{3} - 7$
    $x - 3y = 21$

17. $y = 4x + 15$
    $4x - y = -15$

18. $y = -x - 6$
    $x + y = -6$

19. $y = -x + 7$
    $x + y = 7$

20. $y = -\dfrac{2}{3}x + \dfrac{35}{3}$
    $2x + 3y = 35$

Using the Chapter Test

This page may be used as a test or as a review. In addition, two multiple-choice tests and two free-response tests are provided in the Evaluation Masters Booklet. Chapter 2 Test, Form 1A is shown below.

Evaluation Masters Booklet, pp. 15–16

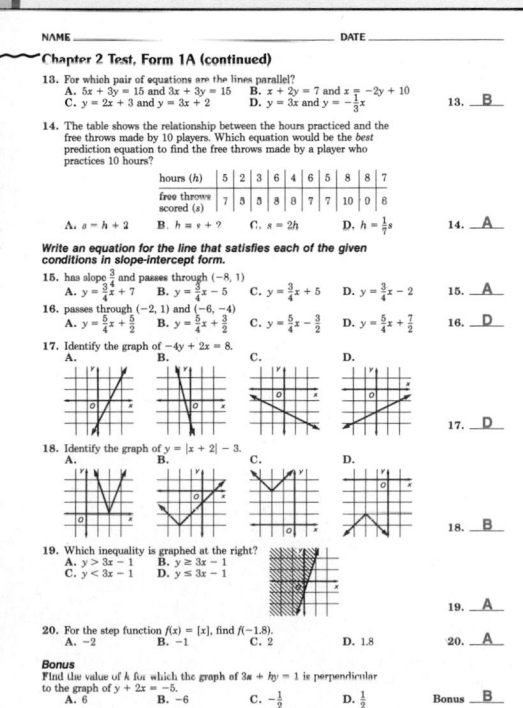

A **Test and Review Generator** is provided in Apple, IBM, and Macintosh versions. You may use this software to create your own tests or worksheets, based on the needs of your students.

The **Performance Assessment Booklet** provides an alternate asssessment for evaluating student progress. An assessment for this chapter can be found on pages 3–4.

The questions on these pages may be used to help students prepare for college entrance exams such as the SAT test. These questions require careful analysis and a thorough understanding of the concepts.

These pages can be used as an overnight assignment.

After students have completed the pages, discuss how each problem can be solved, or provide copies of the solutions from the *Merrill Algebra 2 Solutions Manual*.

CHAPTER **2**

College Entrance Exam Preview

The test questions on these pages deal with a variety of concepts from arithmetic to algebra.

Directions: Choose the one best answer. Write A, B, C or D.

1.
B

A   B   C   D   E

Figure is not drawn to scale.

Suppose numbers $\frac{5}{6}$, 1, $\frac{1}{3}$, $\frac{3}{2}$, and $\frac{6}{5}$ are arranged from least to greatest on the number line above, with each number corresponding to a letter. If the greatest number corresponds to E, which corresponds to $\frac{5}{6}$?

(A) A (B) B (C) C (D) D

2. If $8x + 10y$ represents the perimeter of a
A rectangle, and $x + 3y$ represents it width, the length is

(A) $3x + 2y$ (B) $7x + 7y$

(C) $6x + 4y$ (D) $3.5x + 3.5y$

3. In the series 2, 6, 11, 17, 24, ___, ___,
C ___ , the eighth term is

(A) 41   (B) 45   (C) 51   (D) 62

4. If 9 less than the product of a number
A and -4 is greater than 7, which of the following could be that number?

(A) -5 (B) -3 (C) 4   (D) 5

5. The value of $(4 + 3)\, 2^2 - 5$ is
C (A) -7 (B) 11   (C) 23   (D) 291

6. Which of the following is not
D equivalent to $-\frac{6}{8}$?

(A) $\frac{-3}{4}$ (B) $\frac{3}{-4}$

(C) $-\frac{-12}{-16}$ (D) $-\frac{6}{-8}$

7. Which of the following is the least?
C (A) $\frac{1}{2}$ (B) $\frac{7}{13}$ (C) $\frac{4}{9}$ (D) $\frac{8}{15}$

8. If the radius of a circle is tripled, then
C the area is multiplied by

(A) 3   (B) 6   (C) 9   (D) 27

9. A point on the graph of $x + 3y = 13$ is
B (A) $(4, 4)$ (B) $(-5, 6)$

(C) $(-2, 3)$ (D) $(4, -3)$

10. Which represents an irrational number?
C (A) $\frac{-2}{3}$ (B) $\sqrt{4}$ (C) π (D) 0

11. For what values of y will $2y - 4$ be
D equal to $2y + 6$?

(A) all negative values

(B) 0

(C) all positive values

(D) no value

12. The average of 7, 5, 9, 3, and 2x is x.
D What is the value of x?

   (A) 2.4   (B) 4

   (C) 6   (D) 8

13. If a number is increased by 5 and the
A result is multiplied by 8, the product is
   168. What is the original number?

   (A) 16   (B) 42

   (C) 26   (D) 128

14. The radius of a wheel is 4 cm. How
C many revolutions will it make if it is
   rolled a distance of 400π cm?

   (A) 25π   (B) 25

   (C) 50   (D) 100π

15. Which of the following is the difference
A of two consecutive prime numbers less
   than 40?

   (A) 1   (B) 5

   (C) 8   (D) 11

16. How many integers between 199 and
D 301 are divisible by 4 or 10?

   (A) 26   (B) 31

   (C) 35   (D) 37

17. A patient must be given medication
B every 7 hours starting at 7:00 A.M.
   Monday. On what day will the patient
   first receive medication at 6 P.M.?

   (A) Monday   (B) Tuesday

   (C) Wednesday   (D) Friday

18. Which of the following is not always
B true?

   (A) $a + b = b + a$

   (B) $a - b = b - a$

   (C) $a - b = a + (-b)$

   (D) $a - b = (-b) + a$

TEST TAKING TIP

Most standardized tests have a time limit, so you must budget your time carefully. Some questions will be much easier than others. If you cannot answer a question within a few minutes, go on to the next one. If there is still time left when you get to the end of the test, go back to the ones that you skipped.

19. The value of $|a| > a$ if
B

   (A) $a > 0$ (B) $a < 0$

   (C) $a = 0$ (D) $a \neq 0$

20. Which of the following is true if
D $|x + 3| > 5$?

   (A) $-8 < x < 2$ (B) $x > 2$

   (C) $x < -8$ (D) none of these

21. Evaluate $\dfrac{\frac{1}{a} + \frac{1}{b}}{ab}$ if $a = 3$ and $b = 5$.
B

   (A) $\dfrac{1}{120}$ (B) $\dfrac{8}{225}$

   (C) 8   (D) $18\frac{1}{8}$

22. When a certain number is divided by 3
C there is no remainder. If when the
   number is divided by 6 there is a
   remainder, the remainder must be

   (A) 1   (B) 2

   (C) 3   (D) 4

23. A point off the graph $2x - y < 5$ is
D

   (A) $(-2, 11)$ (B) $(1, 7)$

   (C) $(2, 6)$ (D) $(3, -11)$

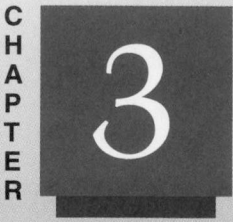

Systems of Equations and Inequalities

PREVIEWING THE CHAPTER

This chapter reviews and extends students' understanding of equations and inequalities developed in Chapter 2 by examining and solving systems of equations and inequalities. Systems of equations and inequalities are solved both by graphing and by using algebraic methods. Then determinants are introduced and systems are solved using Cramer's Rule. Two lessons are included where students find the maximum and minimum values of a function over a region using linear-programming techniques. The chapter concludes with graphing and solving systems of equations in three variables.

Some of the lesson in this chapter contain a review of concepts from Algebra 1. These lessons may be considered optional and used for review only.

Problem-Solving Students combine the strategy of *solve a simpler problem* with that of *look for a pattern* to solve what otherwise might require cumbersome and time-consuming manipulations.

Lesson Objective Chart

Lesson (Pages)	Lesson Objectives	State/Local Objectives
3-1 (108-111)	**3-1:** Solve a system of equations by graphing.	
3-2 (112-116)	**3-2A:** Use the substitution method to solve a system of equations.	
	3-2B: Use the elimination method to solve a system of equations.	
3-3 (118-121)	**3-3A:** Find the value of a second order determinant.	
	3-3B: Solve a system of equations using Cramer's Rule.	
3-4 (122-125)	**3-4A:** Graph a system of inequalities.	
	3-4B: Solve a system of inequalities.	
3-5 (126-128)	**3-5:** Solve problems using the strategy of solving a simpler problem.	
3-6 (129-133)	**3-6:** Find the maximum and minimum values of a function over a region using linear programming techniques.	
3-7 (134-138)	**3-7:** Solve problems involving maximum and minimum values using linear programming techniques.	
3-8 (139-143)	**3-8A:** Determine the octant in which a point in space is located.	
	3-8B: Graph linear equations in space and determine the intercepts and traces.	
3-9 (144-149)	**3-9:** Solve a system of equations in three variables.	

ORGANIZING THE CHAPTER

You may want to refer to the **Course Planning Calendar** on page T44.

Lesson (Pages)	Pacing Chart (days) Course I	II	III	Reteaching	Practice	Enrichment	Evaluation	Technology	Lab Manual	Activities Mixed Problem Solving	Applications	Cooperative Learning Activity	Multicultural	Transparencies
3-1 (108-111)	1.5	1	1	p. 15	p. 17	p. 15		p. 20						3-1
3-2 (112-116)	1.5	1	1	p. 16	p. 18	p. 16	Quiz A, p. 37					p. 39		3-2
3-3 (118-121)	1	1	1	p. 17	p. 19	p. 17		p. 3						3-3
3-4 (122-125)	1	1	0.5	p. 18	p. 20	p. 18	Quiz B, p. 37 Mid-Chapter Test, p. 41		pp. 37-38					3-4
3-5 (126-128)	1	1	0.5		p. 21									3-5
3-6 (129-133)	1.5	1	1	p. 19	p. 22	p. 19					p. 21			3-6
3-7 (134-138)	1.5	1	1	p. 20	p. 23	p. 20	Quiz C, p. 38			p. 3			p. 3	3-7
3-8 (139-143)	1.5	1.5	1	p. 21	p. 24	p. 21			pp. 49-50					3-8
3-9 (144-149)	1.5	1.5	1	p. 22	p. 25	p. 22	Quiz D, p. 38							3-9
Review (150-152)	1	1	1	Multiple Choice Tests, Forms 1A and 1B, pp. 29-32 Free Response Tests, Forms 2A and 2B, pp. 33-36										
Test (153)	1	1	1	Cumulative Review, pp. 39-40 Standardized Tests Practice Questions, p. 42										

Blackline Masters Booklets header spans Reteaching through Transparencies columns. *Lesson Planning Guide* / *Pacing Chart (days)* / *Course* apply to the first four columns.

Course I: Chapters 1-13; Course II: Chapters 1-15; Course III: Chapters 1-17

Other Chapter Resources

Student Edition

Chapter Opener, pp. 102-103
Graphing Calculator Exploration, pp. 104-107
Journal Entries, pp. 111, 138
Technology, p. 117
Mid-Chapter Review, p. 125
Cooperative Learning Activity, p. 128
Portfolio Suggestion, p. 143
History Connection, p. 149
Extended Project 1, pp. A2-A5

Teacher's Classroom Resources

Transparency 3-0
Real-World Applications Transparencies, 6, 7
Performance Assessment Booklet, pp. 5-6
Problem-of-the-Week Activity Cards, 5, 6
Tech Prep Applications Booklet, pp. 5-6
Lesson Plans, pp. 17-25

Other Supplements

Glencoe Mathematics Professional Series

Software

Test and Review Generator Software (Apple, IBM, and Macintosh)
Interactive Software (Macintosh)
Teacher's Guide for Software Resources

ENHANCING THE CHAPTER

Cooperative Learning

Describing the Objectives

Before students engage in any cooperative-learning activity, it is important that you specify two types of objectives and make sure that both are clearly understood by all members of the groups. The first objective is the algebraic or content objective. For this you clearly describe the mathematical task or experiment that is to be completed. The second objective describes the cooperative-learning skills that will be emphasized during the activity. Examples of these skills include: stay with the group; use quiet voices; communicate support; encourage every-member participation; expand on other member's answers or explanations; criticize ideas, not people; and so on. Usually no more than one or two of these skills should be stressed per session while maintaining other skills that were introduced and emphasized earlier.

Technology

The Technology Feature after Lesson 3-2 uses a BASIC program to find the equations of the lines through a given point and parallel to or perpendicular to a given line. Challenge students to describe other givens that determine a unique line and then to write a program that finds the equation of that line.

Critical Thinking

Be alert for opportunities to provide students with critical-thinking activities by modifying some of the more routine problems provided in the textbook to pose open-ended problems.

Textbook example: Mr. and Mrs. Leshin have more than ten children. The sum of the squares of the number of boys and the number of girls in the family equals 100. How many children do Mr. and Mrs. Leshin have?

Modified example: After you solve the original problem, change the data in the second sentence to create another problem that has a different solution.

The modified example provokes students to consider alternatives, to analyze the situation, and to relate it to the mathematics they know.

Cooperative Learning, p. 39

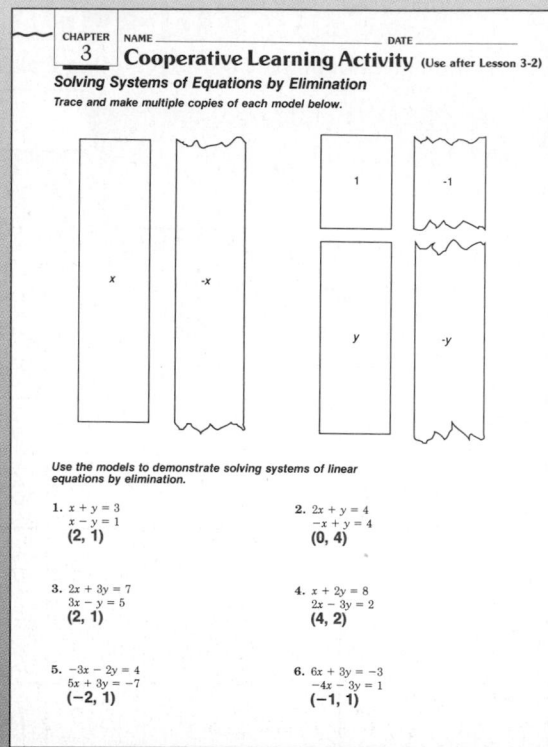

Technology, p. 3

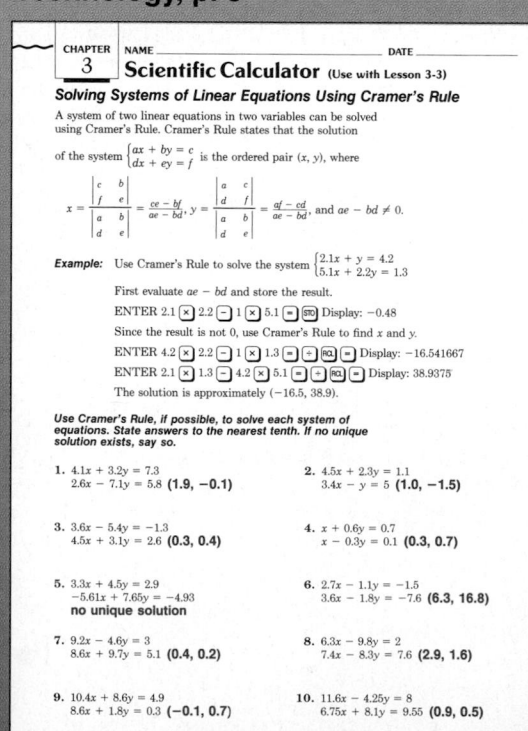

Problem of the Week Activity

The card shown below is one of two available for this chapter. It can be used as a class or small group activity.

Activity Card

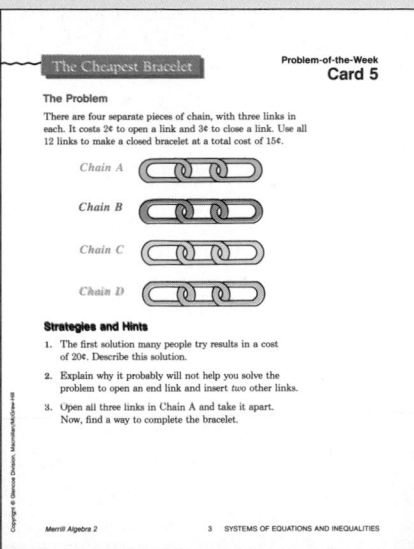

The Cheapest Bracelet

Problem-of-the-Week
Card 5

The Problem

There are four separate pieces of chain, with three links in each. It costs 2¢ to open a link and 3¢ to close a link. Use all 12 links to make a closed bracelet at a total cost of 15¢.

Chain A

Chain B

Chain C

Chain D

Strategies and Hints

1. The first solution many people try results in a cost of 20¢. Describe this solution.

2. Explain why it probably will not help you solve the problem to open an end link and insert two other links.

3. Open all three links in Chain A and take it apart. Now, find a way to complete the bracelet.

Manipulatives and Models

The following materials may be used as models or manipulatives in Chapter 3.
- graphing calculator (all Lessons)
- coins (Lesson 3-5)
- balance scale (Lesson 3-5)
- rulers (Lesson 3-8)
- box (Lesson 3-8)

Outside Resources

Books/Periodicals

Dudeney, Henry Ernest. *536 Puzzles & Curious Problems.* Charles Scribner's Sons, 1967.

Beckenbach, E.F., and R. Bellman. *An Introduction to Inequalities.* Mathematical Association of America, 1975.

Films/Videotapes/Videodiscs

For All Practical Purposes: Introduction to Contemporary Mathematics III, Social Choice, Consortium for Mathematics and Its Applications (COMAP), Suite 210, 57 Bedford St., Lexington, MA 02173-4496

Software

Algebra Concepts, Ventura Educational Systems, 3440 Brokenhill St., Newbury Park, CA 91320

Green Globs and Graphing Equations, WINGS for Learning/Sunburst Communications, 1600 Greens Hills Rd., P.O. Box 660002, Scotts Valley, CA 95067-0002

Algebra Arcade, Wadsworth School Group, 10 Davis Drive, Belmont, CA 94002-3098

Multicultural

Multicultural Activity, p. 3

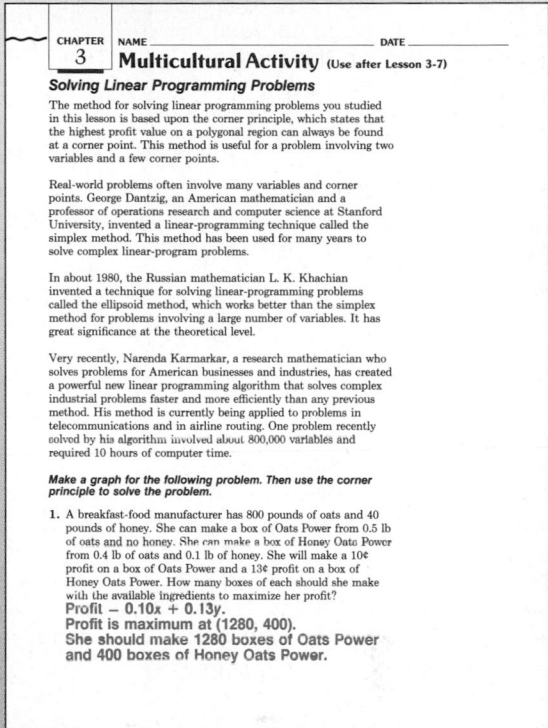

CHAPTER 3

Multicultural Activity (Use after Lesson 3-7)

Solving Linear Programming Problems

The method for solving linear programming problems you studied in this lesson is based upon the corner principle, which states that the highest profit value on a polygonal region can always be found at a corner point. This method is useful for a problem involving two variables and a few corner points.

Real-world problems often involve many variables and corner points. George Dantzig, an American mathematician and a professor of operations research and computer science at Stanford University, invented a linear-programming technique called the simplex method. This method has been used for many years to solve complex linear-program problems.

In about 1980, the Russian mathematician L. K. Khachian invented a technique for solving linear-programming problems called the ellipsoid method, which works better than the simplex method for problems involving a large number of variables. It has great significance at the theoretical level.

Very recently, Narenda Karmarkar, a research mathematician who solves problems for American businesses and industries, has created a powerful new linear programming algorithm that solves complex industrial problems faster and more efficiently than any previous method. His method is currently being applied to problems in telecommunications and in airline routing. One problem recently solved by his algorithm involved about 800,000 variables and required 10 hours of computer time.

Make a graph for the following problem. Then use the corner principle to solve the problem.

1. A breakfast-food manufacturer has 800 pounds of oats and 40 pounds of honey. She can make a box of Oats Power from 0.5 lb of oats and no honey. She can make a box of Honey Oats Power from 0.4 lb of oats and 0.1 lb of honey. She will make a 10¢ profit on a box of Oats Power and a 13¢ profit on a box of Honey Oats Power. How many boxes of each should she make with the available ingredients to maximize her profit?
Profit = 0.10x + 0.13y.
Profit is maximum at (1280, 400).
She should make 1280 boxes of Oats Power and 400 boxes of Honey Oats Power.

Lab Manual

Lab Activity, pp. 37-38

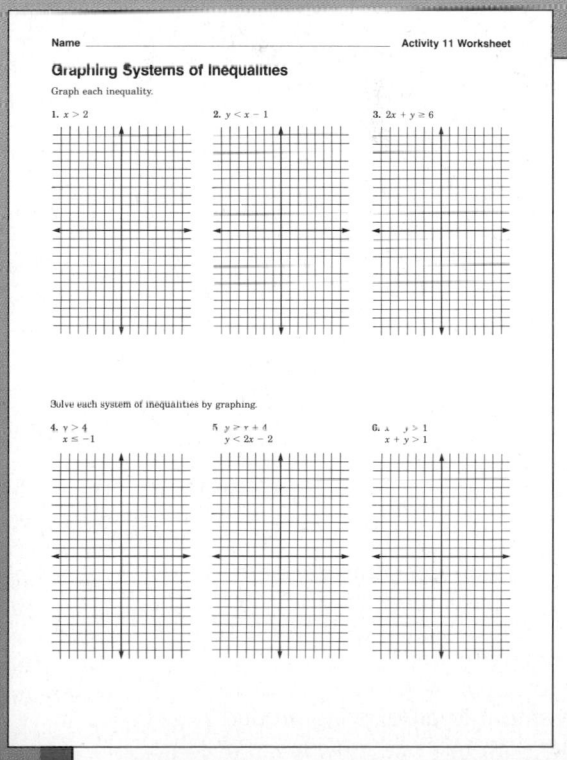

Name

Activity 11 Worksheet

Graphing Systems of Inequalities

Graph each inequality.

1. $x > 2$ 2. $y < x - 1$ 3. $2x + y \geq 6$

Solve each system of inequalities by graphing.

4. $y > 4$
   $x \leq -1$

5. $y \geq x + 4$
   $y < 2x - 2$

6. $x - y > 1$
   $x + y > 1$

Using the Chapter Opener

Transparency 3–0 is available in the Transparency Package. It provides a full-color visual and motivational activity that you can use to engage students in the mathematical content of the chapter.

Background Information

Marketing research executives use math extensively in collecting, analyzing, and interpreting data to find the appeal of products or services, arrange sales and distribution policies, and study the effectiveness of company advertising. They choose statistical samples of the population and design questionnaires or conduct interviews to find who uses their products or services and why. The project demand for marketing research executives is expected to grow by 35% or more through the 1990s as demand for new products stimulates marketing activity.

CHAPTER 3

Systems of Equations and Inequalities

CHAPTER OBJECTIVES

In this chapter, you will:

- Solve systems of equations in two or three variables.
- Solve systems of inequalities.
- Use linear programming to find maximum and minimum values of functions.
- Graph linear equations in space.

The breakeven point is the level of sales where the revenue from the sales equals the cost of manufacturing those products. Can you list some of the costs of manufacturing a product or providing a service?

Cost and Revenue of Sales

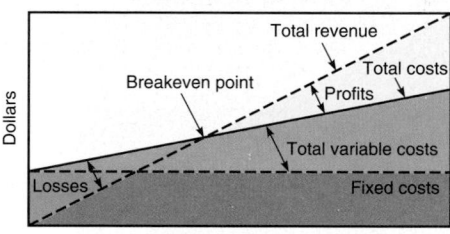

CAREERS IN MARKET RESEARCH

Can you work accurately with detail? Are you patient and persistent? Can you work objectively and systematically to discovery solutions to problems no one has ever solved before? If so, perhaps you could be a successful market research analyst.

These days no company can afford to provide products or services to the public without first making sure exactly what the public wants. So the early steps of any product development rely on market research. A market researcher first designs a survey—that is, decides what questions to ask the public.

Say a fast-food restaurant is being planned for a shopping mall. The researcher will need to ask lots of questions. *What kinds of foods will mall shoppers buy—hot things or cold things, full meals or just snacks? Should the new restaurant have real ice cream or frozen yogurt? Which issues rank highest with mall shoppers: nutrition, taste, or speed?*

The market research analyst heads a team that asks many, many mall shoppers all these questions and more. Then the team analyzes the data. They may need to perform a second or even a third survey, if results indicate that important questions were omitted. Finally, they present their findings both orally and in writing, with visual aids such as charts and graphs. From their work, businesses can know more surely than ever before what the marketplace wants.

102

Chapter Project

Materials: graph paper, pencil and paper

Organize students into cooperative groups of marketing research executives. Assign each the task of coming up with an idea for a new product or service or an improvement to an existing product or service.

Have each group select a representative sample of the population for which advertising for the product or service will be directed.
Have each group prepare a questionnaire and use it to interview the selected number of individuals in its sample.

Then, tabulate and graph the results of the survey and design an advertising campaign that reflects the results. Finally, have each group prepare a brief report outlining suggested approaches to advertising the new product or service.

MORE ABOUT MARKET RESEARCH

Degree Required:

- Bachelor's Degree in Marketing

Some market research analysts like:

- working with people
- lots of travel
- the variety and challenge of their work
- good salaries

Related Math Subjects:

- Statistics
- Calculus
- Applied Math

Some market research analyst dislike:

- working long hours, including evenings and weekends
- working under high pressure
- the competitive nature of this field

For more information on the various careers available in the field of Market Research, write to:

Marketing Research Association
111 East Wacker Drive
Chicago, Illinois 60601

103

Connections and Applications

Lesson	Connections (C) and Applications (A)	Examples	Exercises
3-1	A: Consumerism Business Consumer Awareness	3	29 30
3-2	C: Geometry A: Photography Construction	3	37 38
3-3	C: Geometry A: Consumer Awareness Banking	3	41 42
3-4	A: Business Design Sports	5	34 35
3-6	A: Business Agriculture Community Service	1	31 32
3-7	A: Manufacturing Education Business Retail Veterinary Medicine	1 2	17-19, 23 20-21 12-14 15 16 24-25
3-8	C: Geometry A: Manufacturing	3	31-33
3-9	A: Consumerism Surveying Consumer Awareness Banking	1	32 33 34

Objective: Graph and solve systems of equations on a graphing calculator.

Motivating the Lesson

Ask students what is meant by "systems of equations." Have several students try to define what they think a system of equations would be if they do not know. How many equations does a system have? After you have explained what a system of equations is, have each student write a system of equations.

Teaching Tip ❶ A system can have none, one, or an infinite number of solutions.

Teaching Tip ❷ If there are other equations entered in your calculator, clear them or turn them off (i.e. if the "=" is black, use the arrow keys to move to the "=" and press ENTER).

Teaching Tip ❸ The ▼ and ▲ keys on the TI-81 will let you alternate between functions. The ▶ and ◀ keys will move you along a function. On the Casio, only the ⇥ and ⇤ keys will move you along the last function graphed.

Graphing Calculator Exploration: Graphing Systems of Equations

Teaching Tip ❶

You can use a graphing calculator to graph and solve systems of equations, since several equations can be graphed on the screen at the same time. If the system of equations has a solution, it is located where the graphs intersect. The coordinates of this intersection point, (x, y), can be determined by using the trace function.

Graph the system of equations $y = -5.01x + 3.12$ and $y = 3.78x - 2.56$ on the standard viewing window.

Casio

ENTER: [GRAPH] [(-)] 5.01 [ALPHA] [X] [+] 3.12 [:] [GRAPH] 3.78 [ALPHA] [X] [-] 2.56 [EXE]

TI-81   **Teaching Tip ❷**

ENTER: [Y=] [(-)] 5.01 [XIT] [+] 3.12 [ENTER] 3.78 [XIT] [-] 2.56 [GRAPH]

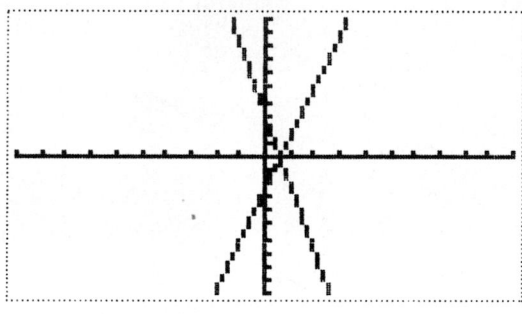

Now use the trace function to determine the coordinates of the intersection point.

Casio   *TI-81*

ENTER: [SHIFT] [TRACE]   ENTER: [TRACE]

Teaching Tip ❸

The trace function on the Casio accesses the last function graphed, while the TI-81 allows you to access any of the functions by pressing the up or down arrow keys. Use the arrow keys to move the cursor along one of the functions to the intersection point and determine the coordinates of the point.

104   CHAPTER 3   SYSTEMS OF EQUATIONS AND INEQUALITIES

Using Discussion

Have students graph the system of equations used as an example in the text. Ask them if they think the system has a solution and, if it does, where they think the solution is. Does it have more than one solution? Graph other systems and ask them if they have a solution, and if so, how many. Try to get students to make guesses or conjectures about the material.

Using Connections

After you have gone through the example and solved the system graphically, solve the system algebraically. Show students that they will get the same solution if they solve the equation either way, but they can solve it to a different degree of accuracy graphically.

Teaching Tip ❹

The "zoom-in" feature of the calculator is very useful for determining the coordinates of the intersection point with greater accuracy. Begin by setting the cursor on the intersection point and observing the coordinates of this point. Then zoom-in and place the cursor on the intersection point again. Any digits that are unchanged since the last trace are accurate. Repeat this process of zooming-in and checking digits until you have the number of accurate digits that you desire.

To zoom-in on the Casio, return to the text screen and insert a factor command before the original function. This will reduce each range value by the factor entered.

Casio

ENTER: [G↔T] [⇒] [SHIFT] [INS] [SHIFT] [Factor] 10 [:] [EXE]

Once the lines have been replotted, trace to the intersection point again and check the coordinates. If you need to zoom-in again, simply press [G↔T] and [EXE] .

To zoom-in on the TI-81, use the [ZOOM] key and set the factors to 10. This will reduce the values in the range setting by a factor of 10.

TI-81

ENTER: [ZOOM] 4 10 [ENTER] 10 [ZOOM] 2 [ENTER]

Now, trace to the point of intersection again and check the coordinates. If you need to zoom-in again, press [ZOOM] 2 and [ENTER] .

This process determines that the x- and y-coordinates of the intersection point of the system $y = -5.01x + 3.12$ and $y = 3.78x - 2.56$ are (0.646188, -0.117406), accurate to six digits. You will need to zoom-in about six times to obtain this degree of accuracy.

Teaching Tip ❺

You can also graph systems of inequalities on a TI-81 graphing calculator. Prepare to graph by resetting the range values to the standard viewing window. Then clear any functions from the Y= list. Do this by pressing [Y=] and then using the arrow keys and the CLEAR key to select and clear all functions. Next, return to the home screen by pressing [2nd] and then [QUIT] .

Let's graph the system of inequalities $y \geq x + 3$ and $y \leq -2x - 1$.

Teaching Tip ❹ On the Casio, you will need to press [SHIFT] [TRACE] every time you want to trace. On the TI-81, you can move the blinking dot in the center of the screen to the intersection point and press [ZOOM] 2 [ENTER] (in which case you will need to use all four arrow keys) or you can press [TRACE] again and trace along a function (in which case you will only need to use the left and right arrow keys).

Teaching Tip ❺ The standard viewing window of [⁻10, 10] by [⁻10, 10] is easily accessed on the TI-81 by pressing [ZOOM] 6.

Teaching Tip ⑥ Enter the larger function or the "greater than" function first, and the smaller function or the "lesser than" function second.

Teaching Tip ⑦ "Shade" will appear on the text screen.

Teaching Tip ⑧ Use the standard viewing window.

More Examples

1. Solve the system of equations $y = 3.25x + 4.3$ and $y = -2.2x - 1.78$ by graphing. **$x = -1.115596$, $y = 0.674311$ accurate to six decimal places**

2. Graph the system of inequalities.
   $y \leq .25x + 3.31$
   $y \geq 3.41x - .19$

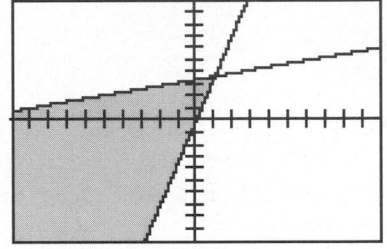

3. Graph the system of inequalities.
   $y \geq -3.33x - 4.44$
   $y \leq 2.22x + 1.11$

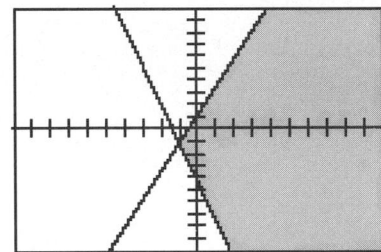

Teaching Tip ⑥ We will graph the system of inequalities with the **Shade** function. It graphs functions and shades above the first function entered and below the second function entered. The "greater than or equal to" symbol in $y \geq x + 3$, indicates that values on the line and above the line $y = x + 3$ will satisfy the inequality. Similarly, the "less than or equal to" in $y \leq -2x - 1$ indicates that values on the line and below the line $y = -2x - 1$ will satisfy the inequality. Therefore, the function $y = x + 3$ will be entered first and $y = -2x - 1$ will be entered second.

TI-81

Teaching Tip ⑦ ENTER: [2nd] [DRAW] 7 [X|T] [+] 3 [ALPHA] [,] [(-)] 2 [X|T] [−] 1 [)] [ENTER]

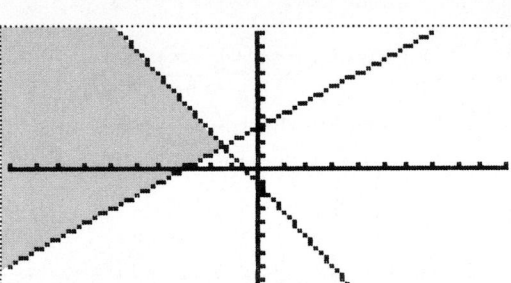

The shaded area indicates points which will satisfy the system of inequalities $y \geq x + 3$ and $y \leq -2x - 1$.

Before you graph another system of inequalities, you must clear the graphics screen.

TI-81

ENTER: [2nd] [DRAW] 1 [ENTER]   *Clears the graphics screen.*

Example | Graph the system of inequalities $\begin{cases} y < 0.5x - 2 \\ y > -4x + 1 \end{cases}$. **Teaching Tip ⑧**

Values below the line $y = 0.5x - 2$ will satisfy the inequality $y < 0.5x - 2$.

Values above the line $y = -4x + 1$ will satisfy the inequality $y > -4x + 1$.

So, we will enter the function $y = -4x + 1$ first and the function $y = 0.5x - 2$ second.

RETEACHING THE LESSON

Have students check their range values after each zoom to get an idea of what is happening with their viewing window. The graphs may look the same when you zoom in, but they are really looking at a smaller and smaller area of the graph.

ENTER: 2nd DRAW 7 (-) 4 X|T + 1 ALPHA , 0.5
X|T - 2) ENTER

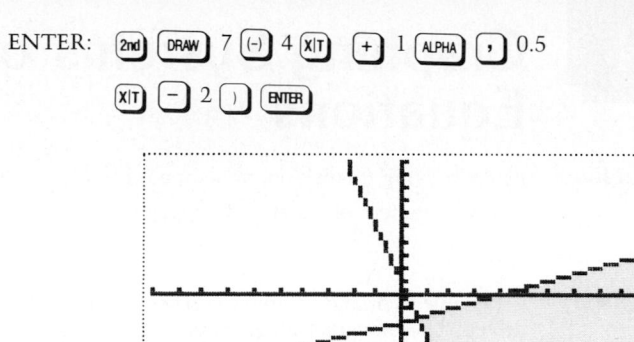

The points in the shaded area satisfy both $y < 0.5x - 2$ and $y > -4x + 1$.

Closing the Lesson
Writing Activity Have each student write a system of equations and, if you have TI-81 graphing calculators, a system of inequalities. Then have students exchange equations (and inequalities) and solve them on their graphing calculators.

Homework Exercises

EXERCISES

Use your graphing calculator to solve the following systems of equations by graphing. Determine the x- and y-coordinates accurate to six decimal places.

See margin.

1. $y = 1.236x - 1.0825$
$y = -0.7896x + 5.1783$

2. $y = 2.5x - 3$
$y = -1.8x + 2$

3. $2.1x + 3.2y = 4.3$
$1.4x - 1.8y = 1.6$

4. $3.12x + 4.68y = 5$
$-4.38x + 9.21y = 1.6$

5. $y = 8x + 1.27$
$y = -5x - 3.61$

6. $y = 2.345x + 1$
$y = 0.8765x - 3$

If you have a TI 81 graphing calculator, graph each system of inequalities and sketch the graph. **See Solutions Manual.**

7. $y \geq x$
$y \leq 3$

8. $y \geq 5x$
$y \leq 8x$

9. $y \leq 4x - 2$
$y \geq 0.5x$

10. $y \leq -0.1x - 5$
$y \geq 0.2x - 5$

11. $y \geq 5 - x$
$y \leq 0.8x - 7$

12. $y \geq 12 - 4x$
$y \leq -3x + 9$

13. $y \geq 3x + 0.5$
$y \leq -6x - 2.8$

14. $12x + 6y \geq 12$
$y \leq x$

GRAPHING CALCULATOR EXPLORATION: GRAPHING SYSTEMS OF EQUATIONS   107

Additional Answers
1. $x = 3.0908373$
   $y = 2.7377749$
2. $x = 1.1627807$
   $y = -0.093023$
3. $x = 1.5569007$
   $y = 0.3220339$
4. $x = 0.78324559$
   $y = 0.54621234$
5. $x = -0.3753846$
   $y = -1.7330769$
6. $x = -2.7238679$
   $y = -5.3874702$

Math Power: Reasoning

Why can't you graph $y \leq x + 2$ and $y \leq -x - 4$ on the TI-81? Remember that the calculator shades an area above one function and below another. If you wanted to graph the two equations above, you would have to graph below both lines and the calculator cannot do that.

Graphing Systems of Equations

Lesson Resources

Reteaching Master 3-1
Practice Master 3-1
Enrichment Master 3-1
Technology Master, p. 20

 Transparency 3-1 contains the 5-Minute Check and a teaching aid for this lesson.

INTRODUCING THE LESSON

 5-Minute Check

(over Chapter 2)

1. State the domain and range of {(3, 1), (4, 2), (3, 8), (2, −4)}. Is it a function?   D = {2, 3, 4}, R = {−4, 1, 2, 8}, no

2. Name the slope, *y*-intercept, and *x*-intercept of the graph of $2x - 4y = 10$.
   slope $= \frac{1}{2}$
   y-intercept $= -\frac{5}{2}$
   x-intercept $= 5$

3. Find the slope-intercept form and the standard form of the equation of the line that has a slope of 4 and passes through the point (4, 1).
   $4x - y = 15$
   $y = 4x - 15$

Motivating the Lesson

Using the graphing calculator, graph $x + y = 4$ and $x + y = -10$. Do these graphs intersect? Graph $x + y = 2$ and $3x + 4y = 7$. Do these graphs intersect? What does it mean to have common points?

TEACHING THE LESSON

Teaching Tip ❶   A solution of a system of equations with two variables will be one ordered pair or an infinite number of ordered pairs (lines that coincide), if it exists.

Objective

After studying this lesson, you should be able to:
- solve a system of equations by graphing.

Application

Reliable Rentables rents moving trucks for $40 a day plus 35¢ per mile driven. The Mover's Helper rents trucks for $36 a day plus 45¢ per mile driven. When is the total cost for a day's rental the same for both companies? When is it better to rent from Reliable Rentables?

Let d = the total cost of a day's rental.
Let m = the miles driven.

We can write the following equations.

$d = 40 + 0.35m$ *Total cost of renting from Reliable Rentables*
$d = 36 + 0.45m$ *Total cost of renting from The Mover's Helper*

FYI ...

The first recorded round-the-world drive by a truck took 2 years 245 days. The 114,300-mile route included 1500 miles driven off-road.

By graphing these two equations, we can see how the rental rates compare. Each point on a line has coordinates that satisfy the equation of the line. Since (40, 54) is on both lines, it satisfies both equations. So, if you rent a truck from either company and drive 40 miles, the price will be $54. It is better to rent from Reliable Rentables when you drive more than 50 miles.

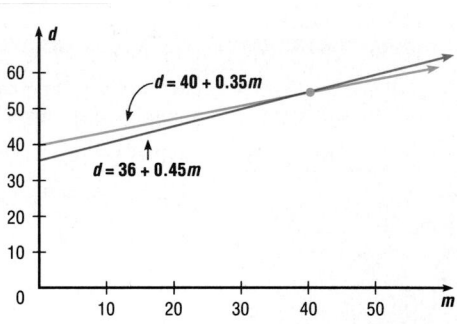

Together the equations $d = 40 + 0.35m$ and $d = 36 + 0.45m$ are called a **system of equations.** The **solution** of this system is (40, 54).

Example 1

Solve this system of equations by graphing: $\begin{cases} x + y = 4 \\ 2x + 3y = 9 \end{cases}$.

The slope-intercept form of $x + y = 4$ is $y = -x + 4$.

The slope-intercept form of $2x + 3y = 9$ is $y = -\frac{2}{3}x + 3$.

Since the two lines have different slopes, the graphs of the equations are intersecting lines. They intersect at (3, 1).

The solution of the system is (3, 1).

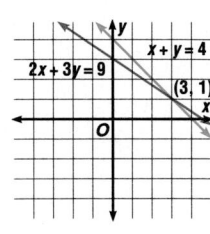

108   CHAPTER 3   SYSTEMS OF EQUATIONS AND INEQUALITIES

ALTERNATE TEACHING STRATEGIES

Using Calculators

Have students use graphing calculators to graph. Reading off the display find the points of intersection, if any. Describe the graphs of the lines and their solutions.

Using Critical Thinking

Discuss the following questions.
1. What is the relationship between the *x*- and *y*-intercepts of parallel lines and lines that coincide?
2. If two linear equations are in point-intercept form, how can you tell if a unique solution exists?

Example 2

Solve this system by graphing: $\begin{cases} 2y + 3x = 6 \\ 4y + 6x = 12 \end{cases}$.
Teaching Tip ❷

$y = -\frac{3}{2}x + 3$ is the slope-intercept form of $2y + 3x = 6$.

$y = -\frac{3}{2}x + 3$ is the slope-intercept form of $4y + 6x = 12$.

Since the lines have the same slope *and* y-intercept, their graphs are the same line. Any ordered pair on that line will satisfy both equations. So, there are *infinitely many* solutions to this system.

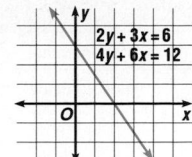

The solution set is $\{(x, y) \mid 2y + 3x = 6\}$.

A system of equations that has at least one solution is called a **consistent** system of equations. The systems in Examples 1 and 2 are consistent. If a system has exactly one solution, it is an **independent** system. The system is **dependent** if it has an infinite number of solutions. So, the system in Example 1 is consistent and independent, and the system in Example 2 is consistent and dependent.

Example 3

APPLICATION
Consumerism

Perry's Plumbing charges $35 for any service call plus an additional $40 an hour for labor. A service call from Rapid Repair Plumbing costs $45 plus an additional $40 an hour for labor. When is the total price for a service call the same for both companies? When is it better to use Perry's Plumbing?

Let h represent the hours of labor and p represent the total price of the repair.

Write and graph a system of equations.

$p = 40h + 35$ *Total price of service call from Perry's*

$p = 40h + 45$ *Total price of service call from Rapid Repair*

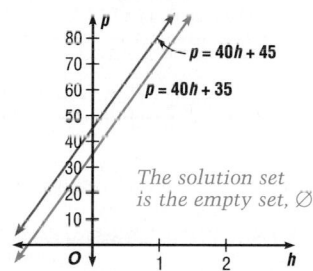

The solution set is the empty set, $\emptyset$.

These lines have the same slope but different y-intercepts. Their graphs are parallel lines. Since they never intersect, there are no solutions to this system. So, the total price of a service call from these two companies is never the same. It is always less expensive to use Perry's Plumbing.

A system with no solutions, like the one in Example 3, is called an **inconsistent** system. **Teaching Tip** ❸

LESSON 3-1 GRAPHING SYSTEMS OF EQUATIONS   109

RETEACHING THE LESSON

Graph the system of equations and state its solution.

1. $x + y = 4$ **(1, 3)**
    $2x + y = 5$

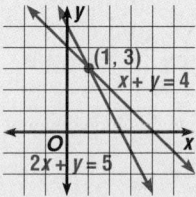

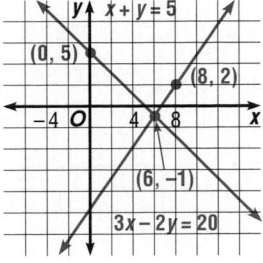
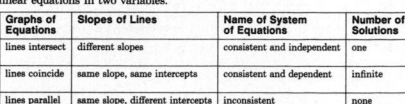

Chalkboard Examples

For Example 2

Solve the system by graphing.

$y = -3x + 5$
$9x + 3y = 15$

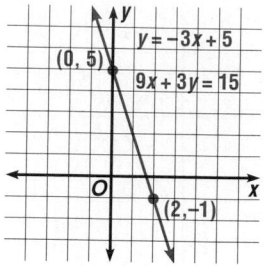

The solution set is
$\{(x,y) \mid y = -3x + 5\}$.

For Example 3

Barry's Carpet has carpet on sale for $12 per square yard. They charge an additional $20 for installation. Carpet Corner has carpet on sale for $24 for every two square yards. They charge an additional $30 for installation. When is it cheaper to buy from Barry's Carpet if you want carpet installed? **It is always cheaper to buy from Barry's Carpet.**

Practice Masters Booklet, p. 17

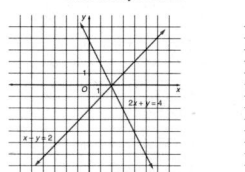 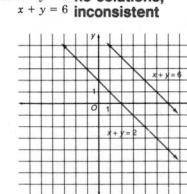
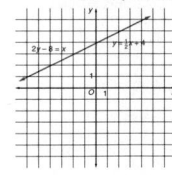 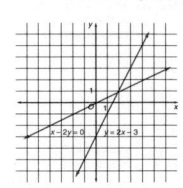
This chart summarizes the possibilities for the graphs of two linear equations in two variables.

Graphs of Equations	Slopes of Lines	Name of System of Equations	Number of Solutions
lines intersect	different slopes	consistent and independent	one
lines coincide	same slope, same intercepts	consistent and dependent	infinite
lines parallel	same slope, different intercepts	inconsistent	none

CHECKING FOR UNDERSTANDING

Communicating Mathematics

Read and study the lesson to answer these questions.

1. Does the graph at the right represent a system of equations that is *consistent and independent, consistent and dependent,* or *inconsistent?* **inconsistent**

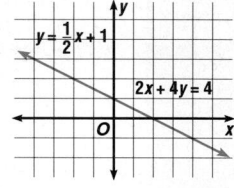

2. Describe the slope and *y*-intercepts of the lines whose graphs are shown in Exercise 1. **same slope, different *y*-intercepts**

3. Explain the difference between an independent and a dependent system of equations. **See margin.**

4. Write a system of equations that is inconsistent. **See margin.**

Guided Practice

State the number of solutions to each system of equations graphed below. State whether the system is *consistent and independent, consistent and dependent,* or *inconsistent.* If the system is consistent and independent, estimate the solution.

5. **consistent and independent,** $\left(\frac{11}{7}, \frac{1}{7}\right)$

6. **consistent and dependent**

5. $y = 2x - 3$
   $4x + 5y = 7$

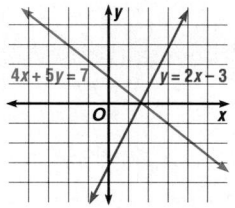

6. $y = -\frac{1}{2}x + 1$
   $2x + 4y = 4$

EXERCISES

Practice

Graph each system of equations and state its solution. Also, state whether the system is *consistent and independent, consistent and dependent,* or *inconsistent.* **See Solutions Manual for graphs.**

7. $x + y = 6$ **no solutions;**
   $3x + 3y = 3$ **inconsistent**

8. $x + 2y = 5$ $\{(x, y) \mid x + 2y = 5\}$;
   $3x - 15 = -6y$ **cons. and dep.**

9. $x + 1 = y$ **no solutions;**
   $2x - 2y = 8$ **inconsistent**

10. $2x + 4y = 8$ $\{(x, y) \mid x + 2y = 4\}$;
    $x + 2y = 4$ **cons. and dep.**

11. $y = -3x$ **(2, -6); cons.**
    $6y - x = -38$ **and ind.**

12. $x + 5y = 10$ **no solutions;**
    $x + 5y = 15$ **inconsistent**

110   CHAPTER 3   SYSTEMS OF EQUATIONS AND INEQUALITIES

Additional Answers

3. **Independent systems have exactly one solution. Dependent systems have infinitely many.**

4. **Answers may vary. A sample answer is $y = 3x + 2$ and $y = 3x + 7$.**

B

13. $x + y = 1$ **(-1, 2); cons.**
    $3x + 5y = 7$ **and ind.**

14. $\frac{1}{2}x + \frac{1}{3}y = 2$ **(2, 3); cons.**
    $x - y = -1$ **and ind.**

15. $3x - 8y = 4$ **no solutions;**
    $6x - 42 = 16y$ **inconsistent**

16. $\frac{3}{4}x - y = 0$ **(8, 6); cons.**
    $\frac{y}{3} + \frac{x}{2} = 6$ **and ind.**

17. $x + y = -6$ $\left(-\frac{4}{3}, -\frac{14}{3}\right)$**; cons.**
    $2x - y = 2$ **and ind.**

18. $2x + 3y = 5$ $\{(x, y)|2x + 3y = 5\}$
    $-6x - 9y = -15$ **cons. and dep.**

19. $3x + 6 = 7y$ **(5, 3); cons.**
    $x + 2y = 11$ **and ind.**

20. $y = \frac{x}{2}$ **no solutions;**
    $2y = x + 4$ **inconsistent**

21. $\frac{2}{3}x = \frac{5}{3}y$ $\{(x, y)|2x - 5y = 0\}$
    $2x - 5y = 0$ **cons. and dep.**

22. $-2x + 5y = -14$ **(-3, -4); cons.**
    $x - y = 1$ **and ind.**

C

23. $9x + 8y = 8$ **no solutions;**
    $\frac{3}{4}x + \frac{2}{3}y = 8$ **inconsistent**

24. $9x - 5 = 7y$ **cons. and**
    $4\frac{1}{2}x - 3\frac{1}{2}y = 2\frac{1}{2}$ **dep.**
    $\{(x, y)|9x - 5 = 7y\}$

Find a and b so that each of the following are true.

26. Answers may vary. Sample answer: $a = -6$, $b = 2$.

25. $ax + 5y = b$ and $6x + 10y = 16$ are consistent and dependent equations. **$a = 3$, $b = 8$**

26. The solution of the system $2x + 3y = 7$ and $ax + by = -10$ is (2, 1).

27. There is no solution to the system $5x - 4y = 12$ and $bx + ay = 3$.
    Answers may vary. A sample answer is $a = -4$, $b = 5$.

Critical Thinking

28. Mr. and Mrs. Leshin have more than ten children. The sum of the squares of the number of boys and the number of girls in the family equals 100. How many children do Mr. and Mrs. Leshin have? **14**

Applications

29. **Business** Mr. George bought 7 drums of two different cleaning fluids for his dry cleaning business. One of the fluids cost $30 a drum and the other was $20 a drum. The total price of the supplies was $160. How much of each fluid did Mr. George buy? Write a system of equations and solve by graphing. **2 of the $30 drums and 5 of the $20 drums**

30. **Consumer Awareness** Mrs. Katz is planning a family vacation. She bought 8 rolls of film and 2 camera batteries for $23.00. The next day, her daughter went back and bought 6 more rolls of film and 2 batteries for her camera. This bill was $18.00. What is the price of a roll of film and of a camera battery? Write a system of equations and solve by graphing. **film $2.50, battery $1.50**

Mixed Review

31. Name which points, (0, 0), (-1, -3), or (4, 0), satisfy $4x - |y| \le 12$. (**Lesson 2-8**) **(0, 0), (-1, -3)**

32. Draw a graph of the inequality $y > x + 4$. (**Lesson 2-8**) **See margin.**

33. Determine the slope of the line that passes through (2, 0) and (-3, 5). (**Lesson 2-4**) **-1**

34. State the domain and range of the relation $\{(9, 3), (2, -7), (1, 1)\}$. Is this relation a function? (**Lesson 2-1**) **D = {9, 2, 1}, R = {3, -7, 1}; yes**

35. Solve the inequality $3x + 7 > 43$. (**Lesson 1-7**) **$\{x|x > 12\}$**

Journal

Tell how you could use a graphing calculator to solve a system of linear equations.

EXTENDING THE LESSON

Math Power: Connections

(Refer to the comparison between Reliable Rentals and Mover's Helper in the lesson). Sam was to rent a truck to drive 50 miles. Rick's Movers charge $32 a day plus $0.55 per mile. Should he rent from Reliable Rentals, Mover's Helper, or Rick's Movers?

Additional Answers

32.
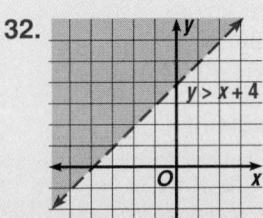

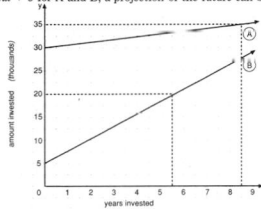

INTRODUCING THE LESSON

 5-Minute Check

(over Lesson 3–1)
Solve each system of equations by graphing. State whether the system is consistent and independent, consistent and dependent, or inconsistent.

1. $2x + 3y = 5$ **consistent**
   $3x - 4y = -1$ **and**
                    independent

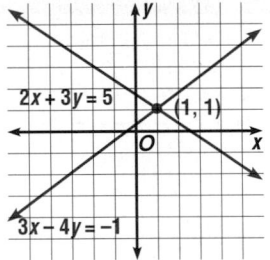

2. $x - y = 3$ **inconsistent**
   $x - y = 7$

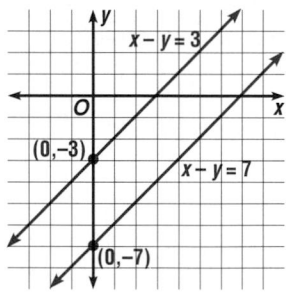

Motivating the Lesson

Solve the system of equations by graphing.
$x - y = 10$ **(11.8, 1.8)**
$x + y = 13.6$
What happens when you try to determine the solution? How could you solve the difficulty?

3-2 Solving Systems of Equations Algebraically

Objectives
3-2A
3-2B

After studying this lesson, you should be able to:
- use the substitution method to solve a system of equations, and
- use the elimination method to solve a system of equations.

Application

Liz bought 12 feet of oak framing material to make a frame for the painting she is planning to enter in the Community Art Fair. If the difference between the length and the width of the rectangular frame is to be 18 inches, what will the dimensions of the frame be?

Let ℓ represent the length and w represent the width.
$2\ell + 2w = 12$ *The perimeter of the frame will be 12 feet.*
$\ell - w = 1.5$ *18 inches is 1.5 feet.*

Let's try solving by graphing.

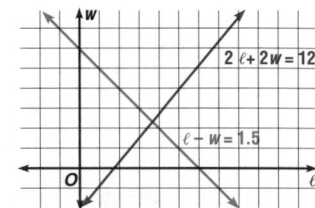

It is very difficult to determine an exact solution from the graph. However, we can use the graph to estimate the solution. The width is a little over 2 feet and the length is a little under 4 feet.

When the solution is a decimal or a fraction, it is usually easier to solve the system by using algebraic methods rather than by graphing. Two algebraic methods are **substitution** and **elimination.** Let's try using substitution to solve this problem.

First, solve one of the equations for one of the variables. Solving for ℓ in the second equation is a good choice.   *Why?*
$\ell = 1.5 + w$

Next, find w by substituting $1.5 + w$ for ℓ in the first equation.
$$2\ell + 2w = 12$$
$$2(1.5 + w) + 2w = 12$$ *Substitute $1.5 + w$ for ℓ.*
$$3 + 2w + 2w = 12$$ *The resulting equation now has only one variable, w.*
$$4w = 9$$
$$w = 2.25$$ *Solve for w.*

Now, find ℓ by substituting 2.25 for w in $2\ell + 2w = 12$.
$$2\ell + 2w = 12$$
$$2\ell + 2(2.25) = 12$$ *Substitute 2.25 for w.*
$$2\ell + 4.5 = 12$$
$$2\ell = 7.5$$
$$\ell = 3.75$$ *Solve for ℓ.*

Teaching Tip ❶

The length of the frame will be 3.75 feet and the width will be 2.25 feet. Our estimate from the graph was very close to the solution.

112   CHAPTER 3   SYSTEMS OF EQUATIONS AND INEQUALITIES

ALTERNATE TEACHING STRATEGIES

Using Models

Pieces of paper cut into different shapes can represent systems of equations. Use square pieces of paper to represent the coefficients of x and circular pieces of paper to represent the coefficients of y. First, write both equations in the form $Ax + By = C$. Then, if both terms have positive coefficients, place the squares and circles in a row next to each other on a piece of paper and write the constant term underneath them. If one term is negative, place the symbols for the positive coefficient in the top row and the symbols for the negative coefficient in the bottom row next to the constant term. The representations of the system of equations $\begin{array}{l} 3x - y = 1 \\ 3x + 2y = 16 \end{array}$ are shown at the right.

The second algebraic method is the elimination method. There are two approaches to using this method.

Example 1

Teaching Tip ❷

Use the elimination method to solve this system: $\begin{cases} x + 2y = -2 \\ 3x - 2y = 10 \end{cases}$.

Add the second equation to the first to eliminate y.

$$
\begin{array}{ll}
x + 2y = -2 & \text{The y-coefficients, 2 and -2, are additive inverses.} \\
\underline{3x - 2y = 10} & \text{Add.} \\
4x \quad\ = 8 & \text{The variable y is eliminated.} \\
\quad x = 2 & \text{Solve for x.}
\end{array}
$$

Now, find y by substituting 2 for x in either original equation.

First equation		*Second equation*
$x + 2y = -2$		$3x - 2y = 10$
$2 + 2y = -2$	*Substitute 2 for x.*	$3(2) - 2y = 10$
$2y = -4$		$-2y = 4$
$y = -2$	*Solve for y.*	$y = -2$

The solution is $(2, -2)$. **Check:** *First equation:* $2 + 2(-2) = -2$ ✓
Second equation: $3(2) - 2(-2) = 10$ ✓

Example 2

Use the elimination method to solve this system: $\begin{cases} 2x + 3y = 2 \\ 3x - 4y = -14 \end{cases}$.

This time, adding the two equations will not eliminate either of the variables. However, if we multiply the first equation by 4 and the second equation by 3, the variable y can be eliminated by addition.

Teaching Tip ❸

$2x + 3y = 2$ ➤ *Multiply by 4.* ➤ $8x + 12y = 8$
$3x - 4y = -14$ ➤ *Multiply by 3.* ➤ $9x - 12y = -42$

We could also solve the system by eliminating x first. Multiply the first equation by 3 and the second by -2.

$$
\begin{array}{l}
6x + 9y = 6 \\
\underline{-6x + 8y = 28} \\
17y = 34 \\
y = 2
\end{array}
$$

Now, add to eliminate y.

$$
\begin{array}{ll}
8x + 12y = 8 & \\
\underline{9x - 12y = -42} & \text{Add.} \\
17x \quad\ = -34 & \text{The variable y is eliminated.} \\
\quad x = -2 &
\end{array}
$$

Then solve for x.
$2x + 3(2) = 2$
$2x = -4$
$x = -2$

Find y by substituting -2 for x in $2x + 3y = 2$.

$$
\begin{array}{ll}
2(-2) + 3y = 2 & \text{Substitute -2 for x.} \\
-4 + 3y = 2 & \\
3y = 6 & \\
y = 2 & \text{Solve for y.}
\end{array}
$$

The solution is $(-2, 2)$.

TEACHING THE LESSON

Chalkboard Examples

For Example 1
Solve by elimination.

$x + 2y = 11$ $x = 5, y = 3$
$x - 2y = -1$

For Example 2
Solve by elimination.

$7x - 4y = 17$ $x = 3, y = 1$
$3x + 5y = 14$

Teaching Tip ❶ Point out that 2.25 could be substituted for w in either equation. Students should use whichever equation seems simpler. However, remind them they should substitute in the original form of the equation.

Teaching Tip ❷ Make sure that students understand that the substitution method is chosen when one of the equations can be easily solved for one of the variables. The elimination method is used more frequently.

Teaching Tip ❸ Discuss with students that there are other combinations of multipliers that can be used. For example, the first equation can be multiplied by 9 and the second equation by -6. You may want students to suggest other multipliers.

$3x - y = 1$ $3x + 2y = 16$ $2 + 2 + 2 = 6$

□ □ □   □ □ □ ○ ○   □ □ □
   ○ 1   16   ○ 1
                       5 + 1 = 6

$2 + 2 + 2 + 5 + 5 = 16$

□ □ □ ○ ○
  16 ◄

The solution to this system is $(2, 5)$. Use the representations of the equations to check the solution as shown at the right.

Chalkboard Example

For Example 3

Two sides of a square are parts of two lines whose equations are $2x - 5y = 19$ and $5x + 2y = 4$. Find the coordinates of the vertex of the square where the two sides meet. **(2, −3)**

EVALUATING THE LESSON

Checking for Understanding

Exercises 1−9 are designed to help you assess understanding through reading, writing, and speaking. You should work through Exercises 1−3 with your students, and then monitor their work on Exercises 4−9.

Error Analysis

Students might solve one of the equations for one variable and then substitute that expression into the same equation. When they do this, they will arrive at $0 = 0$ and incorrectly conclude that the solution set is infinite.

Reteaching Masters Booklet, p. 16

Example 3

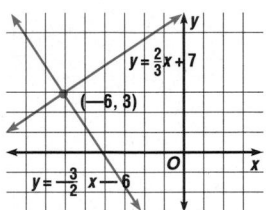
CONNECTION
Geometry

The sides of an angle are parts of two lines whose equations are $y = -\frac{3}{2}x - 6$ and $y = \frac{2}{3}x + 7$. Find the coordinates of the vertex of the angle.

Solve the system of equations.

$$y = -\frac{3}{2}x - 6$$
$$y = \frac{2}{3}x + 7$$

Substitute $\frac{2}{3}x + 7$ for y in the first equation.

$\frac{2}{3}x + 7 = -\frac{3}{2}x - 6$

$4x + 42 = -9x - 36$ *Multiply each side by 6 to eliminate fractions.*

$13x = -78$

$x = -6$

Substitute -6 for x in $y = -\frac{3}{2}x - 6$.

$y = -\frac{3}{2}(-6) - 6$

$y = 9 - 6$

$y = 3$

The coordinates of the vertex are $(-6, 3)$.   *The graph verifies the solution.*

CHECKING FOR UNDERSTANDING

Communicating Mathematics

Read and study the lesson to answer these questions.

1. Describe how we could have solved the framing problem using the elimination method. **See margin.**

2. Explain when you would use the substitution method to solve a system of equations. **See margin.**

3. Would you use the substitution or elimination method to solve this system of equations? Why?

   $3x + 5y = 12$
   $-3x + y = 34$

   elimination because x is easily eliminated by adding the two equations

Guided Practice

For each system, state the multipliers you would use to eliminate each variable by addition. Then solve each system of equations. **4−9. See margin.**

4. $x - y = 1$
   $3x - y = 3$ **(1, 0)**

5. $2x + 3y = 7$
   $3x - 4y = 2$ **(2, 1)**

6. $3x - 2y = 10$
   $4x + y = 6$ **(2, −2)**

7. $3x + 4y = 6$
   $2x + 5y = 11$ **(−2, 3)**

8. $2x + 4y = 6$
   $5x - 3y = 2$ **(1, 1)**

9. $x + 8y = 12$
   $3x - 7y = 5$ **(4, 1)**

114 CHAPTER 3 SYSTEMS OF EQUATIONS AND INEQUALITIES

RETEACHING THE LESSON

Solve each system of equations using the elimination method.

1. $x - 2y = 1$ **(5, 2)**
   $3x + 2y = 19$

2. $2x - y = 6$ **(4, 2)**
   $3x + 5y = 22$

Solve each system of equations using the substitution method.

3. $y = 5 - 2x$ **(3, −1)**
   $3x - 2y = 11$

4. $x - 2y = 1$ **(5, 2)**
   $3x + 2y = 19$ **See #1.**

Solve by either algebraic method.

5. $2x - 3y = 13$ **(2, −3)**
   $x - y = 5$

EXERCISES

Practice

Solve each system of equations using the substitution method. $\left(\frac{1}{3}, 2\right)$

10. $y = 3x$ **(-3, -9)**
$x + 21 = -2y$

11. $x + y = 2$ $\left(\frac{4}{3}, \frac{2}{3}\right)$
$x - 2y = 0$

12. $3x - 2y = -3$
$3x + y = 3$

13. $2r + s = 1$
$r - s = 8$ **(3, -5)**

14. $5s - 2t = 16$
$s + 3t = 10$ **(4, 2)**

15. $2.5x - y = 11$
$3.25x + y = 12$
(4, -1)

Solve each system of equations using the elimination method.

16. $m + n = 6$
$2m - n = 3$ **(3, 3)**

17. $3x - 6y = 15$
$-3x + 5y = -8$ **(-9, -7)**

18. $4s + t = 9$
$3s - 2t = 4$ **(2, 1)**

19. $4a + 3b = -2$
$5a + 7b = 17$ **(-5, 6)**

20. $4x - 6y = 12$
$x - 7y = 14$ **(0, -2)**

21. $8x + 3y = 4$
$4x - 9y = -5$
$\left(\frac{1}{4}, \frac{2}{3}\right)$

Teaching Tip ④ **Solve each system of equations. (Use either algebraic method.)**

22. $6x + 4y = 80$
$x - 7y = -2$ **(12, 2)**

23. $m + n = 6$
$m - n = 4.5$ **(5.25, 0.75)**

24. $3x + 2y = 8$ $\left(\frac{4}{5}, \frac{14}{5}\right)$
$y - x = 2$

25. $9x + y = 30$
$6x - 15 = y$ **(3, 3)**

26. $2x - y = 36$
$3x - \frac{1}{2}y = 26$ **(4, -28)**

27. $3y - 2x = 4$
$\frac{1}{6}(3y - 4x) = 1$
$\left(-1, \frac{2}{3}\right)$

28. $5a + 2b = -8$
$4a + 3b = 2$ **(-4, 6)**

29. $4x + 4y = -6$ $\left(\frac{21}{4}, -\frac{27}{4}\right)$
$5x + 3y = 6$

30. $a - b = 0$
$3a + 2b = -15$
(-3, -3)

31. $\frac{1}{4}x + y = \frac{7}{2}$
$2x - y = 4$ $\left(\frac{10}{3}, \frac{8}{3}\right)$

32. $\frac{s + 3t}{7} = 3$
$11s \quad t = \quad 7$ **(0, 7)**

33. $\frac{2x + y}{3} = 15$
$3x \quad y = 5$
(10, 25)

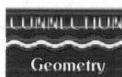
Geometry

34. Find the coordinates of the vertices of the triangle whose sides are contained in the lines whose equations are $x - y = 7$, $3x - 11y = -11$, and $x + y + 1 = 0$. **(11, 4), (3, -4), and $\left(-\frac{11}{7}, \frac{4}{7}\right)$**

CONNECTION
Geometry

35. Find the coordinates of the vertices of the parallelogram whose sides are contained in the lines whose equations are $2x + y = -12$, $2x - y = -8$, $2x - y - 4 = 0$, and $4x + 2y = 24$. **(-5, -2), (4, 4), (-2, -8), (1, 10)**

Critical Thinking

36. Solve the system $\begin{cases} \frac{1}{x} - \frac{1}{y} = \frac{5}{8} \\ \frac{3}{x} + \frac{2}{y} = -\frac{5}{8} \end{cases}$ *Hint: Let $m = \frac{1}{x}$ and $n = \frac{1}{y}$.* **(8, -2)**

Applications

37. **Photography** The perimeter of a rectangular picture is 86 inches. Twice the width exceeds the length by 2 inches. What are the dimensions of the picture? **15 inches by 28 inches**

38. **Construction** The steel braces for a new bridge are in the shape of a right triangle. The hypotenuse is 75 meters. The length of one leg is four times one-third of the length of the other leg. Find the lengths of the legs. **45 m and 60 m**

Teaching Tip ⑤

Additional Answers

1. **Answers may vary. A sample answer is multiply the second equation by 2 and add to eliminate *w*.**
2. **When you can easily solve one equation for a variable and substitute in to the other equation.**
Answers to Exercises 4-9 will vary. Typical answers are given.
4. **x: first by -3; y: first by -1**

5. **x: first by 3 and second by -2; y: first by 4 and second by 3**
6. **x: first by 4 and second by -3; y: second by 2**
7. **x: first by -2 and second by 3; y: first by -5 and second by 4**
8. **x: first by 5 and second by -2; y: first by 3 and second by 4**
9. **x: first by -3; y: first by 7 and second by 8**

Closing the Lesson

Speaking Activity Divide the class into groups of three. Give them a system of equations such as $2x + 3y - 8 = 0$ and $3x + 2y - 17 = 0$. Have each group solve the equation by the three methods studied so far. Discuss which method is better and why.

APPLYING THE LESSON

Homework Exercises

Assignment Guide

Basic: 10-21, 36-43
Average: 13-26, 36-43
Enriched: 22-43

Chapter 3, Quiz A, (Lessons 3-1 through 3-2), is available in the Evaluation Masters Booklet, p. 37.

Teaching Tip ④ Encourage students to decide which method, substitution or elimination, is easier to use for solving a given system.

Practice Masters Booklet, p. 18

3-2 Practice Worksheet

NAME _____ DATE _____

Solving Systems of Equations Algebraically

Solve each system of equations using the substitution method.

1. $2x + y = 4$
$3x + 2y = 1$ **(7, -10)**

2. $x - 9 = 3y$
$x + 2y = -1$ **(3, -2)**

3. $x + 3y = 8$
$\frac{1}{3}x + y = 9$ **no solutions**

4. $2x - 3y = 6$
$-\frac{2}{3}x + y = -2$ **{(x, y)|2x - 3y = 6}**

Solve each system of equations using the elimination method.

5. $2x + y = 1$
$3x - y = 14$ **(3, -5)**

6. $2x - y = -1$
$3x + 2y = 30$ **(4, 9)**

7. $6x + 3y = 6$
$8x + 5y = 12$ **(-1, 4)**

8. $\frac{3x - y}{2} = 5$
$\frac{4x - y}{4} = 4$ **(6, 8)**

Solve each system of equations. (Use either algebraic method.)

9. $8x + 3y + 5 = 0$
$10x + 6y + 13 = 0$ $\left(\frac{1}{2}, -3\right)$

10. $\frac{2x}{5} - \frac{3y}{4} = -2$
$\frac{x}{5} + \frac{y}{4} = 7$ **(10, 8)**

11. $\frac{x}{4} - \frac{y}{3} = 1$
$\frac{1}{3}x - \frac{4y}{9} = \frac{4}{3}$ **{(x, y)|$\frac{x}{4} - \frac{y}{3} = 1$}**

12. $4x - 2y = 5$
$2x = y - 1$ **no solutions**

Teaching Tip 5 You may want to review the Pythagorean Theorem before assigning Exercise 38.

Teaching Tip 6 Point out that some results may be decimals. For example, if the current ages are 6 and 15 and if the factor chosen is 13, the younger person was 0.75 years old, and the older was 9.75. Suggest that students convert the fractional parts to months or days.

Enrichment Masters Booklet, p. 16

Computer
Teaching Tip 6

39. If two people are different ages, was the older ever twice as old as the younger? The answer to any question of this type is yes. This BASIC program will find the year and ages at which one person's age was or will be any factor times a younger person's age. Let a_1 be the current age of the older person, a_2 be the age of the younger, and f be the factor. Let x_1 be the age at which the older person is f times x_2, the age of the younger person. The following equations are used to find the ages.

```
10   PRINT "ENTER CURRENT YEAR"
20   INPUT Y1
30   PRINT "ENTER AGES OF YOUNGER
     AND OLDER"
40   INPUT A1, A2
50   PRINT "ENTER FACTOR"
60   INPUT F
70   LET X2 = (A1-A2)(F-1)
80   LET X1 = X2 + A1 - A2
90   LET Y2 = Y1 - A1 + X1
100  PRINT "YEAR", "OLDER",
     "YOUNGER"
110  PRINT Y2, X1, X2
120  END
```

$x_1 = f \cdot x_2$ *The age of the older person is f times the younger person's.*
$x_1 - x_2 = a_1 - a_2$ *The difference in age is the same, then and now.*

Solve the system of equations by substitution.

$f \cdot x_2 - x_2 = a_1 - a_2$
$x_2(f - 1) = a_1 - a_2$ *Distributive property*
$x_2 = \dfrac{a_1 - a_2}{f - 1}$

Once x_2 is found, the formula $x_1 = x_2 + a_1 - a_2$ is used to solve for x_1.

a. Maggie is 12 years old and Dwayne is 16. How many years ago was Dwayne five times as old as Maggie? How old were they at that time? **11 years ago; 1 and 5**

b. Barry is 9 years old and Karen is 27. How old were they when Karen was ten times as old as Barry? How long ago was that? **2 and 20; 7 years ago**

c. Tiffany is 17 years old and her mother is 45. How old will they be when Tiffany's mother is twice as old as Tiffany? How many years from now will that be? **28 and 56; 11 years from now**

Mixed Review

Draw the graph of each system of equations and state its solution. (Lesson 3-1) **For graphs, see Solutions Manual.**

40. $2x + 3y = -16$
    $2y = 4x$ **(−2, −4)**

41. $3x + 4y = 8$
    $6y - 8x = 12$ **(0, 2)**

42. Find the slope-intercept form of the equation of the line that has slope −2 and passes through (3, 1). **(Lesson 2-5)** $y = -2x + 7$

43. Find a value of a for which the graph of $y = ax + 9$ is perpendicular to the graph of $x + 3y = 14$. **(Lesson 2-4) 3**

EXTENDING THE LESSON

Math Power: Reasoning

Solve the system of equations.

$\dfrac{1}{x} - \dfrac{1}{y} = \dfrac{5}{8}$

$\dfrac{3}{x} + \dfrac{2}{y} = \dfrac{5}{8}$

You may want to give the hint to substitute m for $\dfrac{1}{x}$ and n for $\dfrac{1}{y}$.

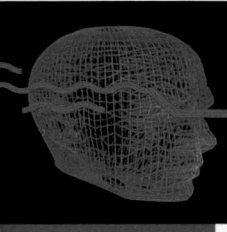

Technology

► BASIC
Spreadsheets
Software

Solving Systems of Equations

You have studied several ways to solve a system of equations. You can also use the BASIC program below to solve a system of two equations. It gives one of three outputs: the ordered pair solution, a message saying there are infinitely many solutions, or a message saying there is no solution. The ordered pair solution is the ordered pair that satisfies both equations. The second response tells you that the two equations are equivalent and there are an infinite number of solutions that satisfy both equations. The third response states that there are no ordered pairs that satisfy both equations.

The BASIC program requires you to first write each equation of the system in standard form. The first equation will be named $Ax + By = C$ and the second equation will be named $Dx + Ey = F$. The program will ask you to enter the values for A, B, and C and then for D, E, and F.

```
100  PRINT "ENTER A, B, AND C FOR THE EQUATION AX + BY = C."
110  INPUT A,B,C
120  PRINT "ENTER D, E, AND F FOR THE EQUATION DX + EY = F."
130  INPUT D,E,F
140  IF A*E = B*D GOTO 190
150  X = (C*E-F*B)/(A*E-B*D)
160  Y = (A*F-D*C)/(A*E-B*D)
170  PRINT "(";X;", ";Y;")"
180  GOTO 230
190  IF A*F=C*D GOTO 220
200  PRINT "THERE IS NO SOLUTION."
210  GOTO 230
220  PRINT "THERE ARE INFINITELY MANY SOLUTIONS."
230  END
```

To run the program, type RUN and then hit the enter key. Enter each value requested when a question mark appears.

EXERCISES

Use the BASIC program to determine what type of solution each system of equations has. If it has a unique solution, state it.

1. $x - 3y = 6$
$2x + 6y = 24$ **(9, 1)**

2. $3x - y = 1$
$-6x + 2y = -2$ **inf.**

3. $x - 5y = 2$
$-2x + 10y = 4$ $\varnothing$

4. $x + 4y = 2$
$-x + y = -7$ **(6, -1)**

5. $3x - 6y = 12$
$2x + 3y = 1$ **(2, -1)**

6. $9x + 3y = 9$
$3x + y = 3$ **inf.**

TECHNOLOGY   117

Using Technology

Objective   This optional page shows how the BASIC programming language can be used to perform mathematical computations and to enhance and extend mathematical concepts.

Teaching Suggestions

This BASIC program requires students to first write the equations in standard form. Have students work in pairs. Ask them to analyze their pairs of equations after they are written in standard form. Have them make a conjecture about the answer before running the program for each exercise.

Lesson Resources

Reteaching Master 3-3
Practice Master 3-3
Enrichment Master 3-3
Technology Master, p. 3

Transparency 3-3 contains the 5-Minute Check and a teaching aid for this lesson.

INTRODUCING THE LESSON

 5-Minute Check

(over Lesson 3–2)

Solve each system of equations by substitution.

1. $x - 4y = -12$
   $3x + 2y = 20$ **(4, 4)**
2. $x + 2y = 6$
   $2x + 4y = 15$ **no solution**

Solve each system of equations by elimination.

3. $2x + 5y = 9$
   $-2x + 8y = 4$ **(2, 1)**
4. $x + 2y = 7$
   $14 - 4y = 2x$
   $\{(x, y)|x + 2y = 7\}$

Solve the system of equations by using either substitution or elimination.

5. $3x - 5y = 17$
   $4x + 5y = 46$ **(9, 2)**

Motivating the Lesson

Solve the system of equations $6x + 2y = 4$ and $3x + y = 5$. The lines are parallel, so the system has no solution. Now multiply the coefficient of x in the first equation and the coefficient of y in the second equation and call this value m. Then multiply the coefficient of y in the first equation and the coefficient of x in the second equation and call this value n. Subtract n from m. What is this value? **0**

Objectives
3-3A
3-3B

After studying this lesson, you should be able to:
- find the value of a second order determinant, and
- solve a system of equations using Cramer's rule.

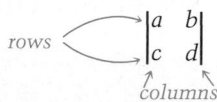 *FYI . . .*

The theory of determinants is attributed to a German, Gottfried Wilhelm Leibniz. His work expanded upon the earlier work of Japanese mathematician Seki Kōwa.

Another method for solving systems of equations is to use Cramer's rule. The rule gives us a quick way to find the solution to a system of two equations with two unknowns. Cramer's rule makes use of determinants.

A **determinant** is a square array of numbers or variables. Vertical bars are used to enclose the array and to signify a determinant. The determinant below has two rows and two columns and is called a **second order determinant.**

rows $\begin{vmatrix} a & b \\ c & d \end{vmatrix}$ *The quantities in a determinant are called elements.*

columns

We find the value of a second order determinant as follows.

Value of a Second Order Determinant	$\begin{vmatrix} a & b \\ c & d \end{vmatrix} = ad - bc$

Did you notice that the value of a second order determinant is found using products along the diagonals?

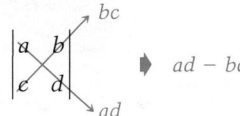

Example 1

Find the value of each determinant.

a. $\begin{vmatrix} 4 & 2 \\ 6 & 8 \end{vmatrix}$

$\begin{vmatrix} 4 & 2 \\ 6 & 8 \end{vmatrix} = 4 \cdot 8 - 2 \cdot 6$
$= 20$

b. $\begin{vmatrix} -2 & 0 \\ 7 & -6 \end{vmatrix}$

$\begin{vmatrix} -2 & 0 \\ 7 & -6 \end{vmatrix} = -2(-6) - 0(7)$
$= 12$

To discover how Cramer's rule uses determinants to solve a system of linear equations, let's consider the following system.

$ax + by = c$ *a, b, c, d, e, and f represent*
$dx + ey = f$ *constants, <u>not</u> variables.*

118 CHAPTER 3 SYSTEMS OF EQUATIONS AND INEQUALITIES

ALTERNATE TEACHING STRATEGIES

Using Cooperative Groups

Have students divide into groups of four. Then, have them evaluate a second order determinant with one row or column composed of zeros. Give an example of a second order determinant which has a value of zero. What can you say about the relationship between the elements when the determinant has value of zero?

Using Discussion

1. Why is it important to have the system of equations written in standard form in order to use Cramer's rule?
2. Why is it necessary to check to see if the denominator is zero when you use Cramer's rule?
3. Why should slopes be checked before solving the system of equations using Cramer's rule?

Solve for y using the elimination method.

$$\begin{array}{rl} adx + bdy &= cd \\ -adx - aey &= -af \\ \hline bdy - aey &= cd - af \\ (bd - ae)y &= cd - af \\ y &= \dfrac{cd - af}{bd - ae} \\ y &= \dfrac{af - cd}{ae - bd} \end{array}$$

Multiply the first equation by d.
Multiply the second equation by $-a$.
Add.
Factor.
Notice that $bd - ae$ cannot be zero.
Multiply numerator and denominator by -1.

Solving for x the same way, we find the following expression for x.

$$x = \frac{ce - bf}{ae - bd}$$

So, the solution to the system $\begin{cases} ax + by = c \\ dx + ey = f \end{cases}$ is $\left[\dfrac{ce - bf}{ae - bd}, \dfrac{af - cd}{ae - bd} \right]$.

Notice that the two fractions have the same denominator. It can be written as a determinant. The numerators can be written as determinants too.

$$ae - bd = \begin{vmatrix} a & b \\ d & e \end{vmatrix} \qquad ce - bf = \begin{vmatrix} c & b \\ f & e \end{vmatrix} \qquad af - cd = \begin{vmatrix} a & c \\ d & f \end{vmatrix}$$

So, we can find the solution to a system of two linear equations in two variables using determinants. This method is **Cramer's rule.**

Cramer's Rule

The solution to the system $\begin{cases} ax + by = c \\ dx + ey = f \end{cases}$ is (x, y),

where $x = \dfrac{\begin{vmatrix} c & b \\ f & e \end{vmatrix}}{\begin{vmatrix} a & b \\ d & e \end{vmatrix}}$, $y = \dfrac{\begin{vmatrix} a & c \\ d & f \end{vmatrix}}{\begin{vmatrix} a & b \\ d & e \end{vmatrix}}$, and $\begin{vmatrix} a & b \\ d & e \end{vmatrix} \neq 0$.

Teaching Tip ❶

Example 2

Use Cramer's rule to solve the system $\begin{cases} 3x + 4y = -7 \\ 2x + y = -3 \end{cases}$.

$$x = \frac{\begin{vmatrix} -7 & 4 \\ -3 & 1 \end{vmatrix}}{\begin{vmatrix} 3 & 4 \\ 2 & 1 \end{vmatrix}} \qquad y = \frac{\begin{vmatrix} 3 & -7 \\ 2 & -3 \end{vmatrix}}{\begin{vmatrix} 3 & 4 \\ 2 & 1 \end{vmatrix}}$$

$$= \frac{-7(1) - 4(-3)}{3(1) - 4(2)} \qquad = \frac{3(-3) - (-7)(2)}{3(1) - 4(2)}$$

$$= \frac{5}{-5} \qquad\qquad = \frac{5}{-5}$$

$$= -1 \qquad\qquad = -1$$

The solution is $(-1, -1)$. **Teaching Tip ❷**

RETEACHING THE LESSON

Find the value of each determinant.

1. $\begin{vmatrix} 4 & 5 \\ -11 & -1 \end{vmatrix}$ 51

2. $\begin{vmatrix} 7 & 5 \\ 2 & -1 \end{vmatrix}$ -17

3. $\begin{vmatrix} 7 & 4 \\ 2 & -11 \end{vmatrix}$ -85

4. $\begin{vmatrix} 5 & 15 \\ 2 & 6 \end{vmatrix}$ 0

Chalkboard Examples

For Example 1
Find the value of the determinant.
$\begin{vmatrix} 3 & 4 \\ 2 & 5 \end{vmatrix}$ **7**

For Example 2
Solve the system using Cramer's Rule.

$6x + 7y = -9$
$x - y = 5$ **$x = 2; y = -3$**

Teaching Tip ❶   Emphasize that in order to use Cramer's Rule, equations must be in standard form. Discuss why the condition $\begin{vmatrix} a & b \\ d & e \end{vmatrix} \neq 0$ is necessary.

If two lines do not intersect, then their slopes are equal.

$ax + by = c$ has slope $-\frac{a}{b}$.

$dx + ey = f$ has slope $-\frac{d}{e}$.

So, if $-\frac{a}{b} = -\frac{d}{e}$, the lines have the same slope, and therefore there is no unique solution.

$-\frac{a}{b} = -\frac{d}{e}$

$ae = bd$

$ae - bd = 0$ or $\begin{vmatrix} a & b \\ d & e \end{vmatrix} = 0$

Reteaching Masters Booklet, p. 17

NAME _____ **DATE** _____

3-3 Reteaching Worksheet

Cramer's Rule

A **determinant** is a square arrangement of numbers or variables enclosed between vertical lines.

To find the value of the determinant use the following:

$$\begin{vmatrix} a & b \\ c & d \end{vmatrix} = ad - bc$$

The solution to a system of two linear equations in two variables can be found using determinants. This method is known as **Cramer's Rule:**

If $\begin{vmatrix} a & b \\ d & e \end{vmatrix} \neq 0$, then the solution of $\begin{cases} ax + by = c \\ dx + ey = f \end{cases}$ is $x = \dfrac{\begin{vmatrix} c & b \\ f & e \end{vmatrix}}{\begin{vmatrix} a & b \\ d & e \end{vmatrix}}$, $y = \dfrac{\begin{vmatrix} a & c \\ d & f \end{vmatrix}}{\begin{vmatrix} a & b \\ d & e \end{vmatrix}}$.

Use Cramer's Rule to solve each system of equations.

1. $7x - 2y = 4$
   $3x + y = -6$ $\left(-\frac{8}{13}, -\frac{54}{13} \right)$

2. $2x - 5y = 18$
   $-x + 3y = -10$ **(4, −2)**

3. $3x - 2y = 15$
   $4x + y = 9$ **(3, −3)**

4. $5x + 4y = -1$
   $2x - y = 10$ **(3, −4)**

5. $-7x + 5y = 1$
   $x - 2y = 9$ $\left(-\frac{47}{9}, -\frac{64}{9} \right)$

6. $6x - 4y = 1$
   $-3x + 3y = 2$ $\left(\frac{11}{6}, \frac{5}{2} \right)$

7. $\frac{1}{2}x - \frac{7}{5}y = 8$
   $\frac{1}{3}x - y = 1$ **(198, 65)**

8. $5x + 6y = 7$
   $4x + 5y = -9$ **(89, −73)**

Example 3

CONNECTION

Geometry

Two sides of a parallelogram are contained in the lines whose equations are $3x + 2y = 8$ and $4x - 2y = 20$. Find the coordinates of a vertex of the parallelogram.

Solve this system of equations using Cramer's rule $\begin{cases} 3x + 2y = 8 \\ 4x - 2y = 20 \end{cases}$

$x = \dfrac{\begin{vmatrix} 8 & 2 \\ 20 & -2 \end{vmatrix}}{\begin{vmatrix} 3 & 2 \\ 4 & -2 \end{vmatrix}}$ $y = \dfrac{\begin{vmatrix} 3 & 8 \\ 4 & 20 \end{vmatrix}}{\begin{vmatrix} 3 & 2 \\ 4 & -2 \end{vmatrix}}$

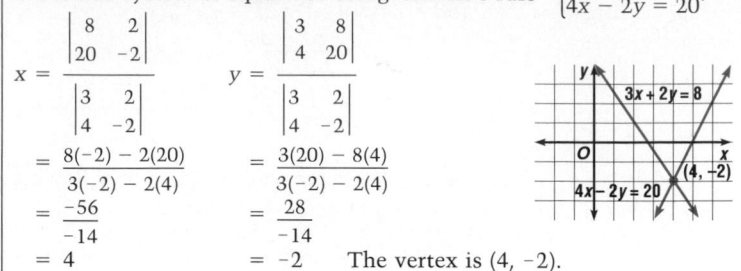

$= \dfrac{8(-2) - 2(20)}{3(-2) - 2(4)}$ $= \dfrac{3(20) - 8(4)}{3(-2) - 2(4)}$

$= \dfrac{-56}{-14}$ $= \dfrac{28}{-14}$

$= 4$ $= -2$ The vertex is (4, −2).

CHECKING FOR UNDERSTANDING

Communicating Mathematics

Read and study the lesson to answer these questions.

1. What would be the value of a determinant if both elements in a row or column are zero? **0**

2. Describe some possible situations where a determinant would have a value of zero when none of its elements are zero. **when $ad = bc$**

3. Given the system $\begin{cases} 345x + 678y = 0.8765 \\ 234x - 0.459y = 1836 \end{cases}$, which method, elimination or Cramer's rule, would be the best way to solve this system? Why? Would you use your calculator with either method? **See margin.**

Guided Practice

Find the value of each determinant.

4. $\begin{vmatrix} 6 & 1 \\ 4 & 3 \end{vmatrix}$ **14** 5. $\begin{vmatrix} 1 & 0 \\ 1 & 0 \end{vmatrix}$ **0** 6. $\begin{vmatrix} 7 & -3 \\ 0 & 1 \end{vmatrix}$ **7**

7. $\begin{vmatrix} 1 & 0 \\ 0 & 1 \end{vmatrix}$ **1** 8. $\begin{vmatrix} -5 & -2 \\ -3 & 11 \end{vmatrix}$ **−61** 9. $\begin{vmatrix} -8 & -7 \\ -4 & -6 \end{vmatrix}$ **20**

10. $\begin{vmatrix} 4 & 2 \\ 1 & -3 \end{vmatrix}$ **−14** 11. $\begin{vmatrix} 5 & -3 \\ -1 & -2 \end{vmatrix}$ **−13** 12. $\begin{vmatrix} 4 & -11 \\ 0 & -9 \end{vmatrix}$ **−36**

Write the determinants that you would use to solve each system using Cramer's rule. Then solve. **For determinants, see margin.**

13. $4x - y = 3$
$3x + 2y = 5$ **(1, 1)**

14. $4m + 2n = 8$
$6m - 3n = 0$ **(1, 2)**

15. $x - 2y = 8$
$3x - 5y = 21$ **(2, −3)**

16. $a - b = 0$
$4a + 10b = -6$ $\left(\dfrac{-3}{7}, \dfrac{-3}{7}\right)$

17. $s + t = 6$
$s - t = 2$ **(4, 2)**

18. $3x - 5y = -7$
$x + 2y = 16$ **(6, 5)**

Additional Answers

3. Cramer's Rule is best. Since there are fewer calculations, there is less chance of making an error. A calculator would be very helpful.

13. $x = \dfrac{\begin{vmatrix} 3 & -1 \\ 5 & 2 \end{vmatrix}}{\begin{vmatrix} 4 & -1 \\ 3 & 2 \end{vmatrix}}$, $y = \dfrac{\begin{vmatrix} 4 & 3 \\ 3 & 5 \end{vmatrix}}{\begin{vmatrix} 4 & -1 \\ 3 & 2 \end{vmatrix}}$

14. $m = \dfrac{\begin{vmatrix} 8 & 2 \\ 0 & -3 \end{vmatrix}}{\begin{vmatrix} 4 & 2 \\ 6 & -3 \end{vmatrix}}$, $n = \dfrac{\begin{vmatrix} 4 & 8 \\ 6 & 0 \end{vmatrix}}{\begin{vmatrix} 4 & 2 \\ 6 & -3 \end{vmatrix}}$

15. $x = \dfrac{\begin{vmatrix} 8 & -2 \\ 21 & -5 \end{vmatrix}}{\begin{vmatrix} 1 & -2 \\ 3 & -5 \end{vmatrix}}$, $y = \dfrac{\begin{vmatrix} 1 & 8 \\ 3 & 21 \end{vmatrix}}{\begin{vmatrix} 1 & -2 \\ 3 & -5 \end{vmatrix}}$

EXERCISES

Practice

Find the value of each determinant.

19. $\begin{vmatrix} -4 & 6 \\ -13 & 24 \end{vmatrix}$ **-18**
20. $\begin{vmatrix} -6 & 7 \\ -9 & 10 \end{vmatrix}$ **3**
21. $\begin{vmatrix} 2 & -5 \\ -1 & 11 \end{vmatrix}$ **17**

22. $\begin{vmatrix} -13 & -11 \\ 17 & -12 \end{vmatrix}$ **343**
23. $\begin{vmatrix} 0.9 & 0.12 \\ 89 & -23 \end{vmatrix}$ **-31.38**
24. $\begin{vmatrix} 0.007 & 0.873 \\ 0.063 & 7.857 \end{vmatrix}$ **0**

Use Cramer's rule to solve each system of equations.

25. $x - 4y = 1$
    $2x + 3y = 13$ **(5, 1)**
26. $s + t = 5$
    $3s - t = 3$ **(2, 3)**
27. $m - n = 4$
    $m + 2n = 1$ **(3, -1)**

28. $3x + 2y = 9$
    $2x - 3y = 19$ **(5, -3)**
29. $r + 11 = 8s$
    $8(r - s) = 3$ $\left(2, \frac{13}{8}\right)$
30. $2x - y = 7$
    $x + 3y = 7$ **(4, 1)**

31. $3x + 8 = -y$
    $4x - 2y = -14$ **(-3, 1)**
32. $5a + 4b = -1$
    $2a - b = 10$ **(3, -4)**
33. $3x - 7y = 2$
    $6x - 13y = 4$ $\left(\frac{2}{3}, 0\right)$

35. (0.75, 0.5)
36. (2, -3)

34. $6x + 5y = -7$
    $2x - 3y = 7$ $\left(\frac{1}{2}, -2\right)$
35. $0.2a = 0.3b$
    $0.4a - 0.2b = 0.2$
36. $3.5x + 4y = -5$
    $2(x - y) = 10$

37. $\frac{1}{6}x - \frac{1}{9}y = 0$
    $x + y = 15$ **(6, 9)**
38. $\frac{x}{2} - \frac{2y}{3} = 2\frac{1}{3}$
    $3x + 4y = -50$ **(-6, -8)**
39. $7y + 4x = 22$
    $8x - 2y = -5$
    $\left(\frac{9}{64}, \frac{49}{16}\right)$

Critical Thinking

40. Explain why Cramer's rule will not work if a system of equations is dependent or inconsistent. **The denominator will be zero, and division by zero is undefined.**

Applications

41. **Consumer Awareness** Handy Hal's Hardware Store sells packages of screws that contain two different sizes of screws. One package contains 5 half-inch screws and 12 quarter-inch screws. It sells for 56¢. A package of 8 half-inch screws and 15 quarter-inch screws sells for 77¢. How much does each type of screw cost? **half-inch, 4¢; quarter-inch, 3¢**

42. **Banking** Donna Bowers has a total of $4000 in her savings account and in a certificate of deposit. Her savings account earns 6.5% interest annually. The certificate of deposit pays 8% if the money is invested for one year. How much does she have in each investment if her interest earnings for the year will be $297.50? **$2500 in certificates of deposit $1500 in savings**

Teaching Tip ❸

Mixed Review

Solve each system of equations by using either the elimination or substitution method. (Lesson 3-2)

43. $2x + y = 0$
    $5x + 3y = 1$ **(-1, 2)**
44. $4a - 3b = -4$
    $3a - 2b = -4$ **(-4, -4)**

45. Find the slope of a line that is perpendicular to the line whose equation is $x = 4y + 7$. **(Lesson 3-1) -4**

46. State the domain and range of the relation $\{(9, 0), (3, 1), (12, 7), (1, -4), (12, 8), (-11, -3), (0, -6)\}$. Is this relation a function? **(Lesson 2-1)**

47. Solve the equation $|x - 8| = 9$. **(Lesson 1-6) 17, -1**

46. D = {-11, 0, 1, 3, 9, 12}, R = {-6, -4, -3, 0, 1, 7, 8}; no

EXTENDING THE LESSON

Math Power: Reasoning
Solve for x.
$$\begin{vmatrix} x^2 & 5 \\ x & 1 \end{vmatrix} = 36$$

Homework Exercises

Assignment Guide

Basic: 19–33, 40–41, 43–47
Average: 22–36, 40–47
Enriched: 25–47

Teaching Tip ❸ Remind students that the $4000 is divided between the two accounts.

Additional Answers

16. $a = \dfrac{\begin{vmatrix} 0 & -1 \\ -6 & 10 \end{vmatrix}}{\begin{vmatrix} 1 & -1 \\ 4 & 10 \end{vmatrix}}, b = \dfrac{\begin{vmatrix} 1 & 0 \\ 4 & -6 \end{vmatrix}}{\begin{vmatrix} 1 & -1 \\ 4 & 10 \end{vmatrix}}$

17. $s = \dfrac{\begin{vmatrix} 6 & 1 \\ 2 & -1 \end{vmatrix}}{\begin{vmatrix} 1 & 1 \\ 1 & -1 \end{vmatrix}}, t = \dfrac{\begin{vmatrix} 1 & 6 \\ 1 & 2 \end{vmatrix}}{\begin{vmatrix} 1 & 1 \\ 1 & -1 \end{vmatrix}}$

18. $x = \dfrac{\begin{vmatrix} -7 & -5 \\ 16 & 2 \end{vmatrix}}{\begin{vmatrix} 3 & -5 \\ 1 & 2 \end{vmatrix}}, y = \dfrac{\begin{vmatrix} 3 & -7 \\ 1 & 16 \end{vmatrix}}{\begin{vmatrix} 3 & -5 \\ 1 & 2 \end{vmatrix}}$

Enrichment Masters Booklet, p. 17

3-3 **Enrichment Worksheet**

NAME _____ DATE _____

Properties of Determinants

The following properties often help when evaluating determinants.

(1) If all the elements of a row (or column) are zero, the value of the determinant is zero.

$\begin{vmatrix} a & b \\ 0 & 0 \end{vmatrix} = 0 \quad (a \cdot 0) - (0 \cdot b) = 0$

(2) Multiplying all the elements of a row (or column) by a constant is equivalent to multiplying the value of the determinant by the constant.

$3\begin{vmatrix} 4 & -1 \\ 5 & 3 \end{vmatrix} = \begin{vmatrix} 12 & -3 \\ 5 & 3 \end{vmatrix} \quad \begin{matrix} 3[4(3) - 5(-1)] = \\ 3[12 + 5] = 51 \\ 12(3) - 5(-3) = 51 \end{matrix}$

(3) If two rows (or columns) have equal corresponding elements, the value of the determinant is zero.

$\begin{vmatrix} 5 & 5 \\ -3 & -3 \end{vmatrix} = 0 \quad 5(-3) - (-3)(5) = 0$

(4) The value of a determinant is unchanged if any multiple of a row (or column) is added to corresponding elements of another row (or column).

(Row 2 is added to row 1.) $\begin{vmatrix} 4 & -3 \\ 2 & 5 \end{vmatrix} = \begin{vmatrix} 6 & 2 \\ 2 & 5 \end{vmatrix}$

$\begin{matrix} 4(5) - 2(-3) = & 6(5) - 2(2) = \\ 20 + 6 = 26 & 30 - 4 = 26 \end{matrix}$

(5) If two rows (or columns) are interchanged, the sign of the determinant is changed.

$\begin{vmatrix} 4 & 5 \\ -3 & 8 \end{vmatrix} = -\begin{vmatrix} -3 & 8 \\ 4 & 5 \end{vmatrix}$

$\begin{matrix} 4(8) - (-3)(5) = & -[(-3)(5) - 4(8)] = \\ 32 + 15 = 47 & -[-15 - 32] = 47 \end{matrix}$

(6) The value of the determinant is unchanged if row 1 is interchanged with column 1, and row 2 is interchanged with column 2. The result is called the transpose.

$\begin{vmatrix} 5 & -7 \\ 3 & 4 \end{vmatrix} = \begin{vmatrix} 5 & 3 \\ -7 & 4 \end{vmatrix}$

$\begin{matrix} 5(4) - 3(-7) = & 5(4) - (-7)(3) = \\ 20 + 21 = 41 & 20 + 21 = 41 \end{matrix}$

Exercises 1-6

Verify each property above by evaluating the given determinants and give another example of the property. **Examples will vary.**

INTRODUCING THE LESSON

 5-Minute Check

(over Lesson 3–3)

1. Find the value of each second order determinant.

   a. $\begin{vmatrix} 3 & 4 \\ -2 & 9 \end{vmatrix}$ **35**

   b. $\begin{vmatrix} 5 & 2 \\ -2 & 5 \end{vmatrix}$ **29**

Solve each system using Cramer's Rule.

2. $-3x + 5y = 4$ $\left(\dfrac{12}{11}, \dfrac{16}{11} \right)$
   $-2x - 4y = -8$

3. $y = 3x + 5$
   $-6x + 2y = 6$ **no solution**

Other Prerequisite Skills

4. What is the difference between an inequality and an equation?
   An inequality contains the symbols > or <. It may also include the equality symbol (≥ or ≤).

Motivating the Lesson

In order to ride a roller coaster you must be at least 50 inches tall and at least six years of age. Explain how you would find all solutions to the situation. Graph each inequality on different graphs. Does this help in solving the situation?

TEACHING THE LESSON

Teaching Tip ❶   Remind students that the boundary is dashed if it is not included in the solution and it is solid if it is included in the solution.

3-4 Graphing Systems of Inequalities

Objectives
After studying this lesson, you should be able to:

3-4A   ■ graph a system of inequalities, and
3-4B   ■ solve a system of inequalities.

Application

Ben Yeo intends to major in market research at Oakdale College. He must graduate from high school with at least a 2.5 grade point average and earn a total score of at least 900 points on the Scholastic Aptitude Test (SAT) to be admitted to this program.

Teaching Tip ❶

This situation can be represented by a **system of inequalities.** To solve a system of inequalities, we must find the ordered pairs that satisfy both inequalities. One way of doing that is to graph both inequalities on the same coordinate plane. The intersection of the two graphs contains the ordered pairs in the solution set. If the graphs do not intersect, then the system has no solution. Let's try graphing the system described above.

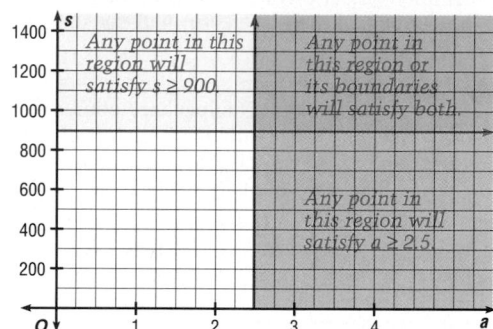

First, we need to write a system of inequalities to represent the situation.

Let a represent Ben's grade point average and s represent his SAT score.

$a \geq 2.5$ *Ben's average must be 2.5 or greater.*
$s \geq 900$ *His test score must be a 900 or greater.*

Graph the system. Any point in the intersection of the two graphs is a solution to the system. If Ben has a 2.75 grade point average and scores a 900 on the SAT, will he be admitted to Oakdale College?

Example 1

Solve this system of equations by graphing: $\begin{cases} y > 2x + 1 \\ y < 2x - 2 \end{cases}$.

Graph each inequality.

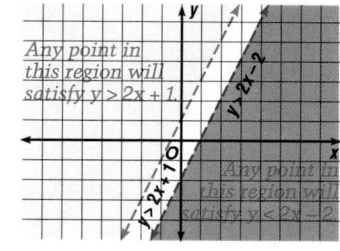

The graphs of the two inequalities have no points in common. So, no ordered pair will satisfy both inequalities. The solution set is the empty set, ∅.

The broken lines indicate that the boundaries are not part of the graphs.

ALTERNATE TEACHING STRATEGIES

Using Questioning

1. If you have a system of inequalities that involves three inequalities, how do you determine the solution once the graphs of the inequalities are drawn?
2. How do you know a system has no solution by looking at the graph?

Using Calculators

Use a graphing calculator to graph the system of inequalities $a \geq 2.5$ and $s \geq 900$.

1. How does the calculator illustrate the system?
2. How could you graph $|x| \geq 3$ using a calculator?

Example 2 | Solve this system of inequalities by graphing $\begin{cases} y \leq 3 \\ y > x \\ x \geq -2 \end{cases}$

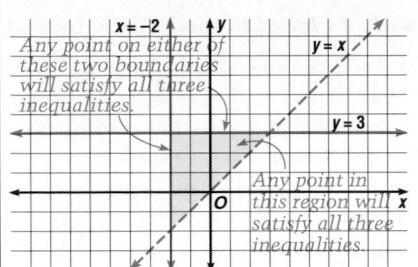

Any point on either of these two boundaries will satisfy all three inequalities.

Any point in this region will satisfy all three inequalities.

As you recall, an absolute value inequality can be restated as two inequalities using an *and* or an *or*. So, an absolute value inequality can be graphed like a system of inequalities.

Example 3 | Graph $|y| \leq 4$.

First, rewrite the inequality as two inequalities.
$y \geq -4$ and $y \leq 4$ *We could also write this as $-4 \leq y \leq 4$.*
Now graph.

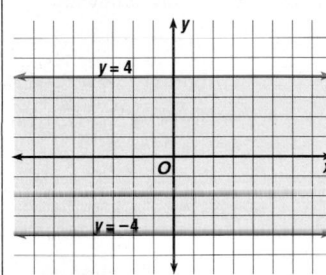

The "and" tells us that the solution set is the intersection of the two graphs. Both inequalities must be satisfied for an ordered pair to be a solution.

Example 4 | Graph $|x| > 3$.

This inequality can be rewritten as $x < -3$ or $x > 3$.

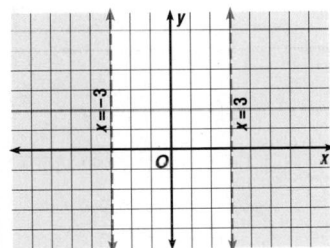

The "or" tells us that an ordered pair only has to satisfy one inequality or the other to be a solution. So, the solution is the union of the two graphs.

LESSON 3-4 GRAPHING SYSTEMS OF INEQUALITIES 123

RETEACHING THE LESSON

Solve this system by graphing.

$y > 3x - 2$
$x + y < 6$

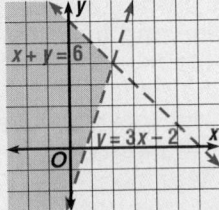

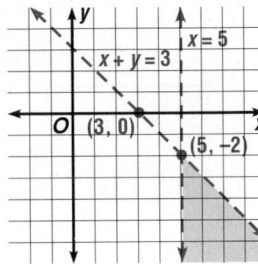
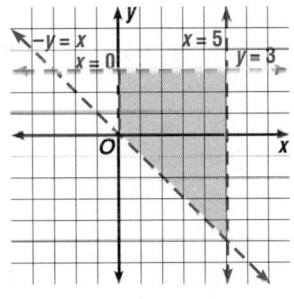

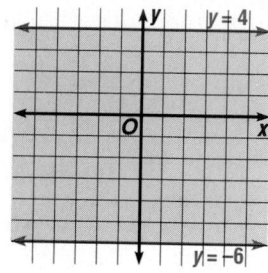
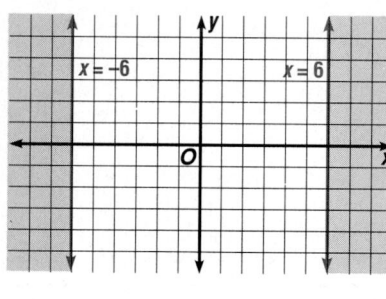 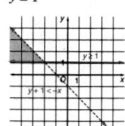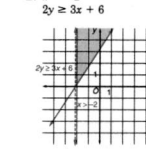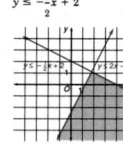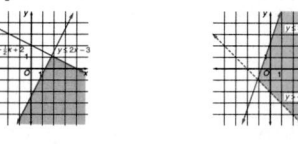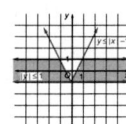
CHECKING FOR UNDERSTANDING

Communicating Mathematics

Read and study the lesson to answer these questions. 1–3. See margin.

1. How do you determine whether a point is a solution to a system of inequalities?

2. When you draw a graph of a linear inequality, how do you determine which side of the equation to shade?

3. Can you draw graphs of linear inequalities on a graphing calculator?

4. Name which points, (0, 0), (2, 5), (-1, 3), or (-2, -4), are solutions to the inequality graphed at the right.   (2, 5)

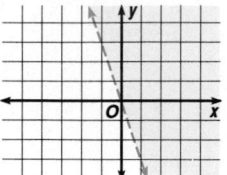

Guided Practice

Does the given point satisfy the system of inequalities?

5. $y < x - 2$; (0, 1)
   $y > -x$ **no**

6. $y < 2x + 4$; (0, 0)
   $y > 3x - 2$ **yes**

7. $y < 3$; (4, 4)
   $x \geq -1$ **no**

8. $x \leq 1$; (1, 1)
   $y > -2$ **yes**

Determine which, if any, of the ordered pairs (3, 1), (-3, -1), (2, 1), (1, 2), and (-1, -2) satisfy each of the following.

9. $|y| \leq 2$ (3, 1), (-3, -1), (2, 1), (1, 2)

10. $|x| > 3$ Ø

11. $|y| \leq 2x + 2$
    (3, 1), (2, 1), (1,2)   (-1, -2)

12. $y < 2x - 1$ Ø
    $y > 3x + 2$

13. $y \geq 3x - 7$
    $y \leq 2x + 4$ (2, 1), (1, 2), (-1, -2)

14. $|x| \geq 1$ (2, 1), (1, 2), (-1, -2)
    $|x| \leq 2$

EXERCISES

Practice

Solve each system by graphing. **See Solutions Manual for graphs.**

A

15. $x + y > 2$
    $y > 3$

16. $x \leq 1$
    $y > 3$

17. $y < -2$
    $y - x > 1$

18. $y \geq x - 3$
    $y \geq -x + 1$

19. $y - x \leq 3$
    $y \geq x + 2$

20. $y \geq 2x - 2$
    $y \leq -x + 2$

B

21. $y < -x - 3$
    $x > y - 2$

22. $x \geq 3 - y$
    $2x - 3y \leq 6$

23. $x + 2y \geq 7$
    $3x - 4y < 12$

24. $y > x + 2$
    $2y < x - 3$

25. $|x| > 5$
    $x + y < 6$

26. $|x + 2| < 3$
    $x + y \geq 1$

27. $x > 1$
    $y < -1$
    $y < x$

28. $y < 2$
    $y \geq 2x$
    $y \geq x + 1$

29. $x \geq -2$
    $2y \geq 3$
    $x - y \leq -5$

C

30. $y < 2x + 1$
    $y > 2x - 2$
    $3x + y > 8$

31. $x + y < 9$
    $x - y > 3$
    $y - x > 4$

32. $y > x + 3$
    $y < x - 4$
    $2y + 3x > 4$

Additional Answers

1. If it is a solution to all of the inequalities in the system.

2. Choose a point on one side of the line and test it. If it makes the inequality true, shade that side of the line. If it does not make the inequality true, then shade the other side of the line.

3. Answers may vary. The TI-81 graphing calculator can graph inequalities.

Critical Thinking

33. Write a system of three inequalities that will have no intersection. The system will have no solution. Then, explain how to change one of the inequalities so that a solution exists. **Answers may vary.**

Applications

34. **Design**   Joe is designing a new dart board. The center of the board is defined by the inequality $|x| + |y| \leq 2$. Draw the graph of this inequality to see what Joe's new dart board will look like.

35. **Sports**   In a baseball game, a ball that lands to the right of the right field baseline or to the left of the left field baseline is a foul ball. Think of placing a baseball diamond on a coordinate plane with home plate at the origin. Let first base be on the x-axis and third base be on the y-axis. Write a system of inequalities that will describe foul territory.
$y < 0$ or $x < 0$ 34. See Solutions Manual.

Mixed Review

Solve each system of equations using Cramer's rule.   **(Lesson 3-3)**

36. $2x + 3y - 8 = 0$
    $3x + 2y - 17 = 0$ **(7, -2)**

37. $6a + 7b = -10.15$
    $9.2a - 6b = 69.944$ **(4.27, -5.11)**

38. **Statistics**   The prediction equation in a study of the relationship between minutes spent studying, s, and test scores, t, is $t = 0.36s + 61.4$. Predict the score a student would receive if she spent 1 hour studying. **(Lesson 2-6) 83**

39. $x + 3y = -54$

39. Write the linear equation $y = -\frac{1}{3}x - 18$ in standard form.   **(Lesson 2-2)**

40. Write a mathematical expression for the verbal expression "the theater can hold no more than 400 people."   **(Lesson 1-8) $p \leq 400$**

MID-CHAPTER REVIEW

1. Solve this system of equations by graphing.   **(Lesson 3-1)**
    $3x + 2y = 8$
    $4x - 3y = 5$ **(2, 1)**

Solve each system of equations by substitution or elimination.   **(Lesson 3-2)**

2. $4x + y = 7$
   $2x - 3y = -7$ **(1, 3)**

3. $4r - 2s = 13$
   $2r + 2s = 7$ $\left(\dfrac{10}{3}, \dfrac{1}{6}\right)$

4. $x + y = 6$
   $-2x + y = -3$ **(3, 3)**

5. $6x - y = 20$
   $4x + y = 6$ $\left(\dfrac{13}{5}, -\dfrac{22}{5}\right)$

6. Find the value of the determinant $\begin{vmatrix} 3 & 4 \\ -7 & 2 \end{vmatrix}$.   **(Lesson 3-3) 34**

Solve each system using Cramer's rule.   **(Lesson 3-3)**

7. $5x - 2y = 13$
   $2x + 4y = 10$ **(3, 1)**

8. $2x - 3y = 7$
   $3x - y = 2$ $\left(-\dfrac{1}{7}, -\dfrac{17}{7}\right)$

Solve each system of inequalities by graphing.   **(Lesson 3-4) See Solutions Manual.**

9. $x + y \geq 3$
   $x - y \leq 1$

10. $x \geq -3$
    $2y \geq 4$
    $x - y \leq -5$

EXTENDING THE LESSON

Math Power: Reasoning

Graph the inequality $|x| + |y| \leq 2$. How many cases do you have to consider? What are the cases?

Mid-Chapter Review

The Mid-Chapter Review provides students with a brief review of the concepts and skills in Lessons 3–1 through 3–4. Lesson numbers are given at the end of problems or instruction lines so students may review concepts not yet mastered.

EVALUATING THE LESSON

Checking for Understanding

Exercises 1–14 are designed to help you assess understanding through reading, writing, and speaking. You should work through Exercises 1–4 with your students, and then monitor their work on Exercises 5–14.

Closing the Lesson

Writing Activity   Have students write an explanation for solving a system of inequalities. This explanation should be a step-by-step procedure.

APPLYING THE LESSON

Homework Exercises

Assignment Guide

Basic: 15–29, 33–34, 36–40
Average: 18–30, 33–40
Enriched: 21–40
All: Mid-Chapter Review 1–10

Chapter 3, Quiz B, (Lessons 3–3 through 3–4), is available in the Evaluation Masters Booklet, p. 37.

Enrichment Masters Booklet, p. 18

NAME _____   DATE _____

3-4   Enrichment Worksheet

Tracing Strategy

Try to trace over each of the figures below without tracing the same segment twice.

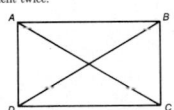
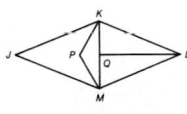

The figure at the left cannot be traced, but the one at the right can. The rule is that a figure is traceable if it has no more than two points where an odd number of segments meet. The figure at the left has three segments meeting at each of the four corners. However, the figure at the right has only two points, L and Q, where an odd number of segments meet.

Determine if each figure can be traced without tracing the same segment twice. If it can, then name the starting point and name the segments in the order they should be traced.

1. 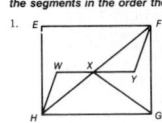   2.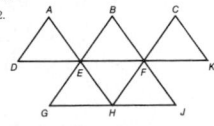

yes; X; $\overline{XY}$, $\overline{YF}$, $\overline{FX}$, $\overline{XG}$, $\overline{GF}$, $\overline{FE}$, $\overline{EH}$, $\overline{HX}$, $\overline{XW}$, $\overline{WH}$, $\overline{HG}$

yes; E; $\overline{ED}$, $\overline{DA}$, $\overline{AE}$, $\overline{EB}$, $\overline{BF}$, $\overline{FC}$, $\overline{CK}$, $\overline{KF}$, $\overline{FJ}$, $\overline{JH}$, $\overline{HF}$, $\overline{FE}$, $\overline{EH}$, $\overline{AG}$, $\overline{GE}$

3.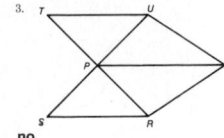

no

Lesson Resources

Practice Master 3-5

Transparency 3-5 contains the 5-Minute Check and a teaching aid for this lesson.

INTRODUCING THE LESSON

🕐 5-Minute Check

(over Lesson 3–4)

1. Does the point (2, 1) satisfy this system of inequalities?

$y < 2x + 1$ **no**
$y > 2x - 1$

Determine which, if any, of the ordered pairs (1, 1), (2, 2), (−1, −1) and (0, 0) satisfy each system.

2. $|x| > 1$ **(2, 2)**
$|y| < 3$

3. $y \le x + 4$ **(1, 1), (2, 2),**
$y \ge 2x - 3$ **(−1, −1), (0, 0)**

4. Solve this system by graphing.

$y \le 3x + 2$
$y > -5x - 7$

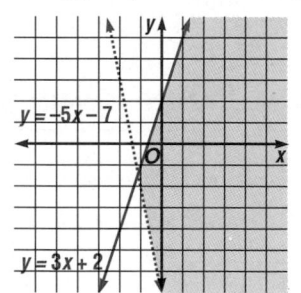

Motivating the Lesson

If there are 20 people in a room and everybody shakes hands once with everyone else, how many handshakes will there be? What strategies can be used to solve this problem?

3-5 Problem-Solving Strategy: Solve a Simpler Problem

Objective
3-5

After studying this lesson, you should be able to:
■ solve problems using the strategy of solving a simpler problem.

Application

Sandy is a marketing research executive for a soda company. The research team has arranged to perform a survey in 16 different local shopping malls. To insure that competing soda companies will not learn of the survey results, Sandy will arrange for telephone lines to be set up so that each of the survey stations has a direct line to each of the other stations. How many telephone lines does Sandy need to have installed?

Sometimes if a method for solution is not obvious, solving a problem directly can be difficult. In these cases, it may be helpful to set aside the original problems for a moment to solve one or more simpler, similar problems. After you have solved the simpler problems, you can use the concepts that were used to solve those on the original. Let's try using this strategy to find the number of telephone lines that Sandy will have to have installed.

Draw diagrams of lines required for different numbers of survey stations.

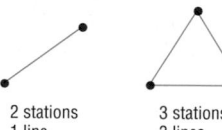 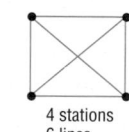 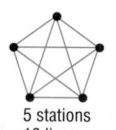 

| 2 stations | 3 stations | 4 stations | 5 stations | 6 stations |
| 1 line | 3 lines | 6 lines | 10 lines | 15 lines |

Teaching Tip ❶

Let's organize our results in a table and look for a pattern.

Number of stations	2	3	4	5	6	. . .	n
Number of lines	1	3	6	10	15	. . .	$\frac{n(n-1)}{2}$

Using the formula that we have discovered by solving simpler problems, we can see that Sandy will need to have $\frac{(16)(15)}{2}$ or 120 telephone lines installed.

126　CHAPTER 3　SYSTEMS OF EQUATIONS AND INEQUALITIES

ALTERNATE TEACHING STRATEGIES

Mini-Math Lab

If you have 6 coins that look alike but one of them weighs less, how can you determine the lighter coin in two weighings? Try weighing the coins on a balance scale. What other strategies can you use to solve this problem? Suggest using a chart, guess and check, and other strategies.

Example

Find the sum of the whole numbers 1 to 1000.

We could add all of those numbers directly, but even with a calculator that would be time consuming and tedious. Let's look at the sum of the whole numbers 1 to 10 to see if we can find a faster way.

$$S = 1 + 2 + 3 + \ldots + 10$$
$$\underline{S = 10 + 9 + 8 + \ldots + 1}$$
$$2S = 11 + 11 + 11 + \ldots + 11$$
$$2S = 10 \cdot 11$$
$$S = 5 \cdot 11 \text{ or } 55$$

Now, extend this concept to the original problem.

$$S = 1 + 2 + 3 + \ldots + 1000$$
$$\underline{S = 1000 + 999 + 998 + \ldots + 1}$$
$$2S = 1001 + 1001 + 1001 + \ldots + 1001$$
$$2S = 1000 \cdot 1001$$
$$S = 500 \cdot 1001 \text{ or } 500{,}500$$

The sum of the whole numbers from 1 to 1000 is 500,500.

CHECKING FOR UNDERSTANDING

Communicating Mathematics

1. When a method for solution of a difficult problem is not obvious.

Read and study the lesson to answer these questions.

1. When is the strategy of solving a simpler problem useful?

2. How many telephone lines would Sandy need to have installed if the number of survey stations was increased to 20? **190**

3. What is the sum of the whole numbers from 1 to 2000? **2,001,000**

Guided Practice

4. A team is eliminated from the All-City basketball tournament if they lose one game. If there are 30 teams playing in the tournament, how many games will need to be played to determine a champion? **29**

5. A sewer drain pipe is 750 inches long. A spider climbs up 100 inches during the day but falls back 80 inches during the night. If the spider starts at the bottom of the pipe, on what day will it get to the top? **34th**

EXERCISES

Use any strategy.

6. Find the digits X, Y, and Z that make the following equation true. Assume that XX and $YYZZ$ are two-digit and four-digit base-ten numbers. $(XX)^2 = YYZZ$ **$X = 8$, $Y = 7$, $Z = 4$** **Teaching Tip ❷**

7. A total of 3001 digits were used to print the page numbers on the Kettering High School Yearbook. How many pages are in the book? **1027 pages**

LESSON 3-5 PROBLEM-SOLVING STRATEGY: SOLVE A SIMPLER PROBLEM 127

Writing Activity Have students list strategies for solving equations and problems. Then have them explain in one or two sentences when they would use each strategy.

APPLYING THE LESSON

Homework Exercises

See assignment guide on page 127.

Practice Masters Booklet, p. 21

3-5 NAME _____ DATE _____
Practice Worksheet

Problem Solving Strategy: Solve a Simpler Problem
Use any strategy.

1. Thirty people are at a party. If each person shakes hands exactly once with every other person, how many handshakes will there be? **435 handshakes**

2. Runners in a marathon must wear a sign that contains their entry numbers. The signs are numbered consecutively, beginning with 1. A total of 432 contestants entered the marathon. If one felt-tip marker can write 35 digits, how many markers will be needed to complete all of the signs? **34 markers**

3. A snail is at the bottom of a well that is 24 feet deep. The snail can climb 2 inches each hour, but then falls back 1 inch. How many hours will it take the snail to crawl out of the well? **287 hours**

4. What is the sum of the first 5000 counting numbers? **12,502,500**

---

8. The mailing list for the Discovery Record Club has 50,000 names. Their clerk is trying to find one of the names to update the address. She is trying to locate the name by cutting the alphabetical list in half and keeping the half with the name. If she continues this procedure, how many times will she have to cut the list before she finds the name? **16 times**

9. Arrange twelve toothpicks as shown at the right. Form five squares by moving three toothpicks.

10. The community food pantry had a number of cans of vegetables to distribute. If they put ten cans in a bag, there would be one bag with only nine cans. If they put nine cans in a bag, there would be one bag with only eight. Bags of eight would leave one bag with only seven, and so on, down to bags of two that would leave one bag with only one can. What is the smallest possible number of cans that the food pantry could have? **2519**

11. Simplify the following expression.
    $(99 - 9)(99 - 19)(99 - 29) \cdots (99 - 199)$ **0**

12. If you could say one number in a second, about how long would it take you to count to one billion? **11,575 days or 31 years and 9 months**

13. Triskaidekaphobia is the fear of the number thirteen. Can there be a year with no "Friday the thirteenth?" What is the greatest number of "Friday the thirteenth"'s that can occur in one year? **no; 3**

14. A cube that is 3 inches on each edge is painted green on all six faces. If you were to cut the cube into 27 smaller cubes of 1 inch on each edge, how many of these cubes would have exactly three faces painted green? How many would have two faces painted? 1 face painted? 0 faces painted? **8, 12, 6, 1**

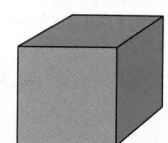

COOPERATIVE LEARNING ACTIVITY

Work in groups. Each person in the group must understand the solution and be able to explain it to any person in class.

How many distinct convex polygons can you find whose vertices are some, or all, of the ten points that are marked on this circle? **968**

Hint: Distinct polygons can have the same shape, but cannot have the same vertices.

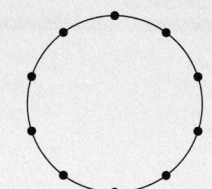

EXTENDING THE LESSON

Math Power: Problem Solving

You need 12 gallons of water. If you only have two buckets, one that holds 4 gallons and one that holds 9 gallons, how can you bring in 12 gallons of water?
Fill 4-gallon bucket twice and dump in 9-gallon bucket. Then fill 4-gallon bucket. You now have 12 gallons.

Cooperative Learning Activity

This activity provides students with an opportunity to *learn* things together, not just do things together. You may wish to refer to pages T6–T8 and page 6C for the various elements of cooperative groups and specific goals and strategies for using them.

3-6   Linear Programming

Objective
3-6
After studying this lesson, you should be able to:
- find the maximum and minimum values of a function over a region using linear programming techniques.

Application

The Northern Wisconsin Paper Mill can convert wood pulp to either notebook paper or newsprint. The mill can produce, at most, 200 units of paper a day. At least 10 units of notebook paper and 80 units of newsprint are required daily by regular customers. Write inequalities to show the possible daily production of the paper mill.

Let x represent the number of units of notebook paper produced.
Let y represent the number of units of newsprint produced.

Since the mill cannot produce negative units of paper, x and y must be nonnegative numbers.

$$x \geq 0 \text{ and } y \geq 0$$

The mill cannot produce more than 200 units of paper in a day.

$$x + y \leq 200$$

The plant must produce at least 10 units of notebook paper and 80 units of newsprint.

$$x \geq 10 \text{ and } y \geq 80$$

If we graph these inequalities, all of the points in their intersection are possible combinations of notebook paper and newsprint that the mill can produce. This area of intersection of the graphs is called the **feasible region** of production for the mill. The inequalities are called the **constraints.**

Let's graph the constraints.

$x \geq 0$
$y \geq 0$
$x \geq 10$
$y \geq 80$
$x + y \leq 200$

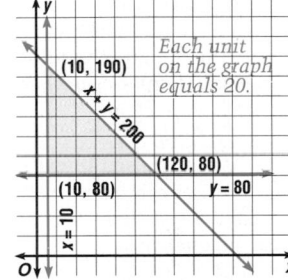

Each unit on the graph equals 20.

(10, 190)
$x + y = 200$
(120, 80)
(10, 80) $y = 80$
$x = 10$

The first two constraints indicate that the graph is in first quadrant, so we only need to graph the last three constraints.

Lesson Resources

Reteaching Master 3-6
Practice Master 3-6
Enrichment Master 3-6
Activity Master, p. 21

 Transparency 3-6 contains the 5-Minute Check and a teaching aid for this lesson.

INTRODUCING THE LESSON

5-Minute Check
(over Lesson 3–5)

1. A digital clock shows 1:23 as the time. How many times in one day will the clock show consecutive digits in ascending order like 1-2-3?   **10**

2. Alice is one of four children. Her grandparents had four children, each of whom had four children. Everyone is planning to get together for a reunion in the summer. If her grandparents are still living, all of their children are married, and all of the grandchildren are 10 years old or younger, how many people will be at the reunion?   **26**

Motivating the Lesson

Given a rectangle with vertices at (1, 2), (1, 6), (4, 6), and (4, 2), find a system of inequalities that would result in the shading of the area of the figure.
x > 1 and x < 4
y > 2 and y < 6

ALTERNATE TEACHING STRATEGIES

Using Charts

When solving linear programming problems, a chart of the vertices can be helpful. Have students make charts for Example 2. In setting up the chart, use columns for the ordered pairs, the equations, and the value. In doing this the maximum and minimum points can be easily read from the chart.

Using Logical Reasoning

When setting up the constraints, some of the constraints are not given but implied. It is necessary to define the possibilities of the values. Sometimes the values can only be positive because they are talking about production. Have students ask themselves if it makes sense for the values to be negative.

Teaching Tip ❶ Remind students that only integer values are considered because you are talking about production.

Teaching Tip ❷ Sometimes you do not need to check all the vertices of the maximum and minimum points.

Chalkboard Example

For Example 1

Brad's News Stand has room for 100 newspapers. In his town, there are two newspapers: *The Journal* and *The Globe.* Every day, Brad sells 20 *Journals* and 25 *Globes* to regular customers. If Brad makes 5¢ for every *Journal* sold and 10¢ for every *Globe* sold, how many *Globes* and *Journals* should he put on his stand to make the most money?
x + y ≤ 100   x = Journals
x ≥ 20   y = Globes
y ≥ 25
f(x, y) = 0.05x + 0.1 y
He should stock 20 Journals and 80 Globes.

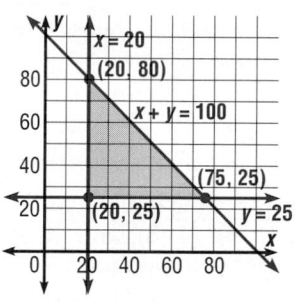

The shaded region is the feasible region. It contains all possible solutions.

If we choose any point within the region it should be a solution to each inequality. Let's try (30, 130). **Teaching Tip ❶**

Check: $30 \geq 0$
$130 \geq 0$
$30 \geq 10$
$130 \geq 80$
$30 + 130 \leq 200$ All are true.

Choose a point outside the region and test it in each inequality. Is it a solution to all of the inequalities?

The manager of the mill needs to decide how many units of each kind of paper the plant should produce. There are many options, as we have seen by graphing the constraints. Of course the company would like to make as much profit as possible. If the profit on a unit of notebook paper is $500 and the profit on a unit of newsprint is $350, how much should the manager have the mill produce?

The profit can be defined by the function: $f(x, y) = 500x + 350y$.

Mathematicians have shown that the maximum and minimum values of a function, $f(x, y)$, occur at the vertices of the feasible region. So, the points we need to try are (10, 80), (10, 190), and (120, 80). Let's make a chart to organize our results.

(x, y)	500x + 350y	profit($)
(10, 80)	500(10) + 350(80)	33,000
(10, 190)	500(10) + 350(190)	71,500
(120, 80)	500(120) + 350(80)	88,000

Teaching Tip ❷

Check some other values within the feasible region to convince yourself that we have found the maximum profit for the mill. According to our results, the manager should have the mill produce 120 units of notebook paper and 80 units of newsprint in order to maximize profit.

We have just used **linear programming.** This procedure is used to find the maximum or minimum value of a function subject to given conditions on the variables, called constraints. The constraints are usually expressed as linear inequalities.

Example 1

APPLICATION

Business

Jerry works no more than 20 hours a week during the school year. He is paid $10 an hour for tutoring geometry students and $7 an hour for delivering pizzas for Pizza King. He wants to spend at least 3 hours, but no more than 8 hours, a week tutoring. Find Jerry's maximum weekly earnings.

Let t represent the number of hours spent tutoring and d represent the number of hours spent delivering pizzas.

The constraints are:
$t + d \leq 20$
$3 \leq t \leq 8$
$d \geq 0$.

Graph the constraints.

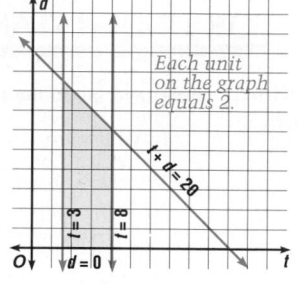

Each unit on the graph equals 2.

Jerry can work no less than zero hours at either job, so the graph is in the first quadrant.

The vertices of the region are (3, 0), (8, 0), (8, 12), and (3, 17). Now, find Jerry's earnings for each of these combinations to find his maximum weekly earnings. The function $f(t, d) = 10t + 7d$ defines Jerry's weekly earnings.

(t, d)	10t + 7d	earnings
(3, 0)	10(3) + 7(0)	30
(8, 0)	10(8) + 7(0)	80
(8, 12)	10(8) + 7(12)	164
(3, 17)	10(3) + 7(17)	149

Jerry can earn $164 a week if he tutors for 8 hours and delivers pizzas for 12 hours.

Example 2

CONNECTION

Geometry

Use your calculator to find the maximum and minimum values of $f(x, y) = 3x + 4y$ for the polygonal region determined by these inequalities. Identify the polygon.
$x \leq 6$ $y \leq 3$ $x - 3y \leq 9$ $3x + y \leq 6$

First we must find the vertices of the feasible region. Graph the inequalities.
The coordinates of the vertices are (1, 3), (6, 3), (2.7, -2.1), and (6, -1).
Now use your calculator to evaluate $f(x, y) = 3x + 4y$ for each vertex.

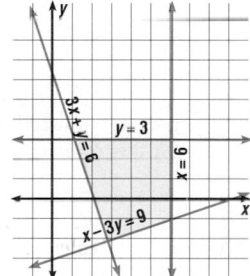

You may use a graphing calculator to find the vertices if one is available.

RETEACHING THE LESSON

A convex polygon has vertices $A(0, 2)$, $B(4, -1)$, $C(5, 1)$, and $D(3, 5)$. Find the maximum and minimum values of each function for the region determined by the polygon.

1. $f(x, y) = 2x + 5y$
   min. is 3 at B; max is 31 at D.
2. $g(x, y) = -3x + y$
   min. is -14 at C; max is 2 at A.

Chalkboard Example

For Example 2
Use a calculator to find the maximum and minimum values of $f(x, y) = 0.5x + y$ for the polygonal region determined by the following inequalities.

$x \geq 2$
$3y \leq 15$
$0.5x + 2y \geq 6$
$2x - 5y \leq 12$
Max. − (18.5, 5) = 14.25
Min. − (2, 2.5) = 3.5

Reteaching Masters Booklet, p. 19

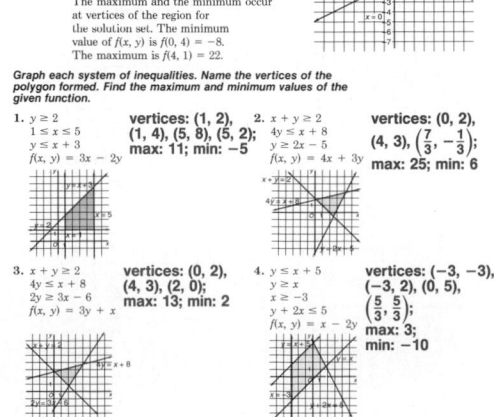

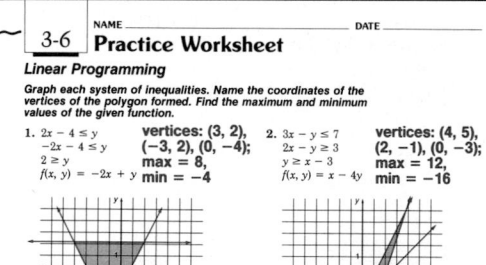

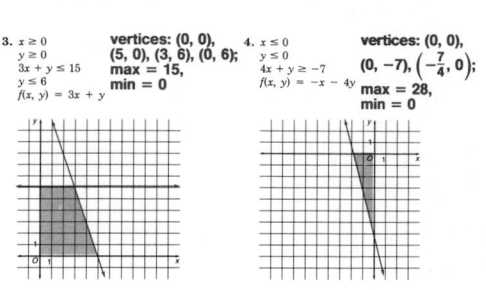

ENTER: 3 $\boxed{\times}$ 1 $\boxed{+}$ 4 $\boxed{\times}$ 3 $\boxed{=}$ 15
The other values are found in a similar manner.

The maximum value of $f(x, y) = 3x + 4y$ for this region is 30 at (6, 3) and the minimum value is –0.3 at (2.7, –2.1). The polygon is a quadrilateral.

CHECKING FOR UNDERSTANDING

Communicating Mathematics

Read and study the lesson to answer these questions. **1–3. See margin.**

1. In your own words, define linear programming.

2. Why was it important that the shaded region in Example 1 be in the first quadrant?

3. In a business like the one described in the introductory problem, is it always possible or desirable to obtain the maximum profit each day?

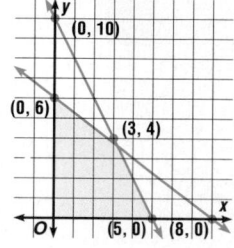

4. Name the points where a maximum or minimum value of a function could occur for the constraints graphed at the right. **(0, 0), (5, 0), (3, 4), (0, 6)**

Guided Practice

Given the function $f(x, y) = 3x + 2y$, find each value.

5. $f(4, 1)$ **14**   6. $f(3, 3)$ **15**   7. $f(-2, 1)$ **–4**   8. $f(6, 0)$ **18**

A polygonal region has vertices (0, 0), (4, 0), (5, 5), and (0, 8). Find the maximum and minimum values of each function over this region.

9. $f(x, y) = x + 3y$
   max: $f(0, 8) = 24$
   min: $f(0, 0) = 0$

10. $f(x, y) = -x - 3y$
    max: $f(0, 0) = 0$
    min: $f(0, 8) = -24$

11. $f(x, y) = 0.5x - 1.5y$
    max: $f(4, 0) = 2$
    min: $f(0, 8) = -12$

EXERCISES

Practice

Given the function $f(x, y) = 5x - 2y$, use a calculator to find each value.

12. $f(0, 0)$ **0**   13. $f(4, 1)$ **18**   14. $f(-2, -6)$ **2**

15. $f(5, 4)$ **17**   16. $f(3, 1.5)$ **12**   17. $f(-0.2, -1)$ **1**

Graph each system of inequalities. Name the coordinates of the vertices of the polygon formed. Find the maximum and minimum values of the given function for this region. **18–20. See margin. For graphs, see Solutions Manual.**

CONNECTION
Geometry

18. $y \geq 1$
    $x \leq 6$
    $y \leq 2x + 1$
    $f(x, y) = x + y$

19. $y \geq 2$
    $1 \leq x \leq 5$
    $y \leq x + 3$
    $f(x, y) = 3x - 2y$

20. $4y \leq x + 8$
    $x + y \geq 2$
    $y \geq 2x - 5$
    $f(x, y) = 4x + 3y$

132 CHAPTER 3 SYSTEMS OF EQUATIONS AND IRREGULARITIES

21–26. See margin. For graphs, see Solutions Manual.

21. $x + y \geq 2$
$2y \geq 3x - 6$
$4y \leq x + 8$
$f(x, y) = 3y + x$

22. $y \leq x + 6$
$y + 2x \geq 6$
$2 \leq x \leq 6$
$f(x, y) = -x + 3y$

23. $y \leq 2x + 1$
$1 \leq y \leq 3$
$y \leq -0.5x + 6$
$f(x, y) = 3x + y$

24. $y \leq 7$
$y \geq -x + 6$
$y \leq x + 4$
$x \leq 5$
$f(x, y) = 2x - 3y$

25. $y \geq x$
$y \leq x + 5$
$x \geq -3$
$y + 2x \leq 5$
$f(x, y) = x - 2y$

26. $0 \leq x \leq 5$
$y \geq 0$
$-x + y \leq 2$
$x + y \leq 6$
$f(x, y) = 5x - 3y$

 Use a calculator to find the maximum and minimum values of each function for the polygonal region determined by the given inequalities.

27. $y \leq 1$ **max: 0.4**
$y \geq -2$ **min: -20.32**
$5x \leq -2$
$1.2x - y \geq -2.9$
$f(x, y) = 4x + 2y$

28. $x \geq 0$ **max: 15**
$y \geq 0$ **min: -5**
$x + 2y \leq 6$
$2y - x \leq 2$
$x + y \leq 5$
$f(x, y) = 3x - 5y$

29. $x \leq 3$ **max: 56**
$y \leq 5$ **min: 12**
$x + y \geq 1$
$x \geq 0$
$y \geq 0$
$f(x, y) = 2x + 8y + 10$

Critical Thinking

30. Create a system of inequalities that determines a feasible region in the shape of a parallelogram. Two of the vertices must be on the x-axis and one must be on the y-axis. **Answers may vary. A sample answer is** $y \leq 4, y \geq 0, y - x \leq 4, y - x \geq -5$.

Applications

31. Agriculture A farmer has 20 days in which to plant corn and soybeans. The corn can be planted at a rate of 10 acres per day and the soybeans at a rate of 15 acres per day. The farm has 250 acres available for planting. If the profit on corn is $30 per acre, and the profit on soybeans is $25 per acre, how much of each should the farmer plant for maximum profit? **100 acres of corn, 150 acres of soybeans**

32. Community Service A theater where a drug abuse program is being presented seats 150 people. The proceeds will be donated to a local drug information center. Admission is $2.00 for adults and $1.00 for students. Every two adults must bring at least one student. How many adults and students should attend in order to raise the maximum amount of money? **100 adults and 50 students**

33–34. For graphs, see Solutions Manual.

Mixed Review

Solve each system of inequalities by graphing. **(Lesson 3-4)**

33. $x + y > 5$
$x - y \leq 3$ **(4, 1)**

34. $y > x + 1$
$y < x - 3$ **∅**

35. Graph the function $f(x) = |x - 3|$. **(Lesson 2-7)** **See Solutions Manual.**

36. State the x- and y-intercepts of the graph of the line with equation $3x - 12y = 24$. **(Lesson 2-4)** **(8, 0) and (0, -2)**

37. Statistics There will be four tests given in your Algebra 2 course this quarter. On the first three, you scored 87, 92, and 81. If you must have at least 350 points to earn an A, what must you score on the fourth test to earn an A? **(Lesson 1-7)** **90**

EXTENDING THE LESSON

Math Power: Reasoning

Is it possible to have more than one value that produces a maximum or minimum for a given function?

Yes, if the function represents a line that is a boundary of the polygonal region. If so, the coordinates of any point on that side of the polygon would produce the same maximum or minimum value.

APPLYING THE LESSON

Homework Exercises

Assignment Guide

Basic: 12–26, 30–31, 33–37
Average: 15–27, 30–37
Enriched: 18–37

Teaching Tip ❸ Define the inequalities for the situation. Make sure students remember that there are no negative days so the x- and y-axis are part of the constraints.

Additional Answers

27. vertices: (-4.08, -2), (-1.58, 1), (-0.4, 1), (-0.4, -2); max: f(-0.4, 1) = 0.4; min: f(-4.08, -2) = -20.32

28. vertices: (0, 0), (0, 1), (2, 2), (4, 1), (5, 0); max: f(5, 0) = 15; min: f(0, 1) = -5

29. vertices: (1, 0), (0, 1), (0, 5), (3, 0), (3, 5); max: f(3, 5) = 56; min: f(1, 0) = 12

Enrichment Masters Booklet, p. 19

NAME _____ DATE _____

3-6 Enrichment Worksheet

Truth Tables

In mathematics, the basic operations are addition, subtraction, multiplication, division, taking a root, and raising to a power. In logic, the basic operations are the following: not (~), and (∧), or (∨), implies (→).

If P and Q are statements, then $\sim P$ means not P; $\sim Q$ means not Q; $P \wedge Q$ means P and Q; $P \vee Q$ means P or Q; and $P \rightarrow Q$ means P implies Q. The operations are defined by truth tables. On the left below is the truth table for the statement $\sim P$. Notice that there are two possible conditions for P, true (T) or false (F). If P is true, $\sim P$ is false; if P is false, $\sim P$ is true. Also shown are the truth tables for $P \wedge Q$, $P \vee Q$, and $P \rightarrow Q$.

P	$\sim P$
T	F
F	T

P	Q	$P \wedge Q$
T	T	T
T	F	F
F	T	F
F	F	F

P	Q	$P \vee Q$
T	T	T
T	F	T
F	T	T
F	F	F

P	Q	$P \rightarrow Q$
T	T	T
T	F	F
F	T	T
F	F	T

You can use this information to find out under what conditions a complex statement is true.

Example: Under what conditions is $\sim P \vee Q$ true?

Create the truth table for the statement. Use the information from the truth table above for $P \vee Q$ to complete the last column.

P	Q	$\sim P$	$\sim P \vee Q$
T	T	F	T
T	F	F	F
F	T	T	T
F	F	T	T

When one statement is true and one is false, the conjunction is true.

The truth table indicates that $\sim P \vee Q$ is true in all cases except where P is true and Q is false.

Use truth tables to determine the conditions under which each statement is true.

1. $\sim P \vee \sim Q$ **all except where both P and Q are true**
2. $\sim P \rightarrow (P \rightarrow Q)$ **all**
3. $(P \vee Q) \vee (\sim P \wedge \sim Q)$ **all**
4. $(P \rightarrow Q) \vee (Q \rightarrow P)$ **all**
5. $(P \rightarrow Q) \wedge (Q \rightarrow P)$ **both P and Q are true; both P and Q are false**
6. $(\sim P \wedge \sim Q) \rightarrow \sim (P \vee Q)$ **all**

INTRODUCING THE LESSON

 5-Minute Check

(over Lesson 3–6)

Graph the system of inequalities. Find the maximum and minimum values of the given function.

1. $x \geq 0$ max: $f(5, 0) = 10$;
   $y \geq 0$ min: $f(0, 6) = -6$
   $x \leq 5$
   $y \leq 6$
   $x + y \leq 6$
   $f(x, y) = 2x - y$

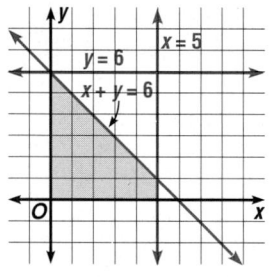

Motivating the Lesson

Have students find the maximum and minimum values of $f(x, y) = x + 2y$ for the system of inequalities graphed below.

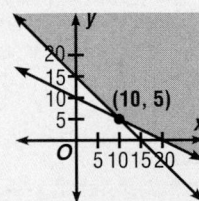

There is no maximum. Minimum is 20 at any point (x, y) on the segment between $(10, 5)$ and $(20, 0)$.

3-7 Applications of Linear Programming

Objective
3-7

After studying this lesson, you should be able to:
- solve problems involving maximum and minimum values using linear programming techniques.

Linear programming can be used to solve many types of problems. These problems have certain restrictions placed on the variables, and some function of the variables must be maximized or minimized. Listed below are the steps necessary to solve a problem using linear programming.

Linear Programming Procedure

1. **Define the variables.**
2. **Write a system of inequalities.**
3. **Graph the system of inequalities.**
4. **Find the coordinates of the vertices of the polygon formed.**
5. **Write an expression to be maximized or minimized.**
6. **Substitute values from the vertices into the expression.**
7. **Select the greatest or least result. Answer the problem.**

Example 1

APPLICATION

Manufacturing

TeeVee Inc. makes console and wide screen televisions. The equipment in the factory allows for making at most 450 console televisions and 200 wide screen televisions in one month. The chart below shows the cost of making each type of television and the profit. During the month of November, the company can spend $360,000 to make these televisions. To maximize profit, how many of each type should they make?

First define the variables.

Let c = the number of consoles.
Let w = the number of wide screens.

Television	Cost per Unit	Profit per Unit
Console	$600	$125
Wide screen	$900	$200

FYI ...

The longest pre-scheduled television program was the broadcast by GTV 9 of Melbourne, Australia covering the 1969 Apollo XI moon mission. It was 163 hours 18 minutes long.

Then write the inequalities.

$0 \leq c \leq 450$ *The number of consoles made is at most 450.*
$0 \leq w \leq 200$ *The number of wide screens is at most 200.*
$600c + 900w \leq 360,000$ *The cost of the consoles plus the cost of the wide screens cannot exceed $360,000.*

Now graph the system.

Any point in the shaded region or its boundaries will satisfy the conditions of the problem. The vertices of the polygon are $(0, 0)$, $(0, 200)$, $(300, 200)$, $(450, 100)$, and $(450, 0)$.

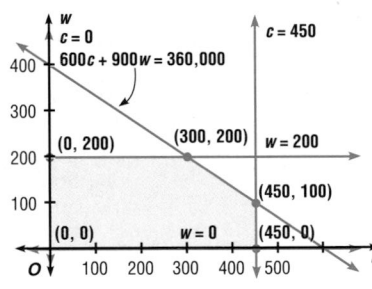

ALTERNATE TEACHING STRATEGIES

Using Communication

Have students tell what inequality they would use to express each statement.
1. The company can produce at least 12 gadgets in an hour. $g \geq 12$
2. More than 15 dyes are needed each day. $d > 15$
3. The number of widgets produced daily is greater than 40 but not more than 60. $40 < w \leq 60$

Using Questioning

Ask students these questions when solving a problem.
1. What are the possible values of the variables? Are they always positive or negative?
2. What are the inequalities defined by the problem?
3. What are the vertices of the polygonal region?

We need to maximize the profit. An expression for profit is as follows.

profit = profit on consoles + profit on wide screens
$P(c, w) =$ $125c$ + $200w$

Since the maximum or minimum value is always a vertex, substitute the values from the vertices into the expression.

(c, w)	$(0, 0)$	$(0, 200)$	$(300, 200)$	$(450, 100)$	$(450, 0)$
$125c + 200w$	$0	$40,000	$77,500	$76,250	$56,250

TeeVee Inc. will make the greatest profit by making 300 console televisions and 200 wide screen televisions. This produces a profit of $77,500.

Example 2

APPLICATION

Education

The Algebra 2 quiz consists of computation problems and graphing problems. Computation problems are worth 6 points each and graphing problems are worth 10 points each. You can answer a computation problem in 2 minutes and a graphing problem in 4 minutes. You have forty minutes to take the quiz and may choose no more than 12 problems to answer. Assuming you answer all the problems attempted correctly, how many of each type should you answer to get the highest score?

Let c = the number of computation problems.
Let g = the number of graphing problems.

You can write the following inequalities.
$c \geq 0$
$g \geq 0$
$2c + 4g \leq 40$ *You can spend no more than 40 minutes on the quiz.*
$c + g \leq 12$ *You can answer no more than 12 questions.*

Graph the system.

The vertices are $(0, 0)$, $(0, 10)$, $(4, 8)$, and $(12, 0)$.

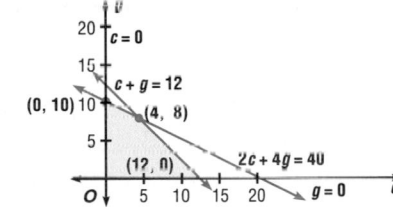

We want to maximize your score. Write the expression to maximize.

total score = computational score + graphing score
$S(c, g) =$ $6c$ + $10g$

Substitute the values of the vertices in the expression.

(c, g)	$(0, 0)$	$(0, 10)$	$(4, 8)$	$(12, 0)$
$S(c, g)$	0	100	104	72

You should answer 4 computation and 8 graphing problems. Your score will be 104 points, if you answer them all correctly.

Chalkboard Examples

For Example 1
A farmer has 25 days to plant cotton and soybeans. The cotton can be planted at a rate of 9 acres per day, and the soybeans at a rate of 12 acres per day. The farm has 275 acres available. If profit for cotton is $25 per acre and profit for soybeans is $18 per acre, how many of each should be planted to maximize profit?
c = number of acres of cotton
t = number of acres of soybeans
$f(c, t) = 25c + 18t$
$c \geq 0$
$t \geq 0$
$c + t \leq 275$
$\frac{c}{9} + \frac{t}{12} \leq 25$

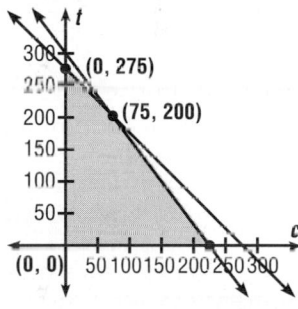

Plant 225 acres of cotton for a maximum profit of $5625.

For Example 2
Mary works selling cards over the telephone. She sells two types of cards: birthday cards and holiday cards. Mary makes $2 for each pack of birthday cards she sells and $2.50 for each pack of holiday cards she sells. She can work no more than 10 hours per week and it takes her an average of 15 minutes to sell one pack of birthday and an average of 20 minutes to sell one pack of holiday cards. If she can sell no more than 35 packs of cards, how many packs of each type of card should she sell to make the most money? **(solution on next page)**

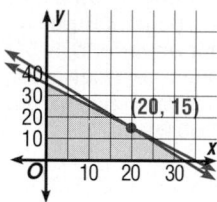
CHECKING FOR UNDERSTANDING

Communicating Mathematics

Read and study the lesson to answer these questions. 1–2. See margin.

1. Find the slope of the profit function in Example 1. Think of a line with that slope and move it up and down by changing the y-intercept. As this line moves, where does it touch the shaded region first? Where does it touch last? How do these points compare with the maximum and minimum values for the profit function?

2. Is it possible to have more than one value that produces a maximum or a minimum for a given function? Explain.

3. Can a function have no maximum value for a region? Explain. **Yes; if the region is not bounded, there may be no maximum.**

Guided Practice

Two raw materials are needed to make one of the products produced by Dartmouth Inc. The product must contain no more than 9 units of material A and at least 18 units of material B. The company can spend no more than $300 on materials for each piece produced. Material A costs $4 per unit and weighs 10 pounds per unit. Material B costs $12 per unit and weighs 20 pounds per unit. How much of each material should be used to maximize the weight of the product?

4. Write an expression to represent the weight. **$P(A, B) = 10A + 20B$**

5. Write an inequality to represent the amounts of materials A and B allowed. **$0 \leq A \leq 9; B \geq 18$**

6. Write an inequality to represent the cost of a product. **$4A + 12B \leq 300$**

7. Graph the system of inequalities. **See Solutions Manual.**

8. Name the vertices of the polygon. **(0, 18), (0, 25), (9, 22), (9, 18)**

9. $P(0, 18) = 360$
   $P(0, 25) = 500$
   $P(9, 22) = 530$
   $P(9, 18) = 450$

9. Evaluate the expression from Exercise 4 for each vertex.

10. To maximize weight, how much of each material should be used?
9 units of A, 22 units of B

11. What is the maximum weight? **530 pounds**

EXERCISES

Applications

12. **Business** The available parking area of a parking lot is 600 square meters. A car requires 6 square meters of space and a bus requires 30 square meters of space. The attendant can handle no more than 60 vehicles.

    a. Let c be the number of cars and let b be the number of buses. Write a system of inequalities to represent the amount of space available and the total number of vehicles allowed. **$6c + 30b \leq 600$; $c + b \leq 60$**

    12b. **50 cars, 10 buses; income of $200**

    b. If a car is charged $2.50 to park and a bus is charged $7.50, how many of each should the attendant accept to maximize income?

    c. The parking lot prices for special events are $4.00 for cars and $8.00 for buses. How many of each vehicle should the attendant accept during a special event? **50 cars, 10 buses; income of $280**

RETEACHING THE LESSON

Have students work in groups of 3 to solve the following problem.

A tailor has 16 yd^2 of cotton cloth, 11 yd^2 of silk, and 15 yd^2 of wool. A suit requires 2 yd^2 cotton, 1 yd^2 silk, and 1 yd^2 wool. A gown requires 1 yd^2 of cotton, 2 yd^2 silk, and 3 yd^2 wool. A suit sells for $30 and a gown sells for $50. Let

x = the number of suits and y = the number of gowns.

a. Find $f(x, y)$ to find total sales.
b. Express constraints in as a system of inequalities.
c. Graph the feasible region.
d. Check values of $f(x, y)$ at the vertices of the region.
e. How many of each garment should the tailor make to maximize his income?
7 suits, 2 gowns; $310

13. **Manufacturing** The Oklahoma City division of SuperSport Inc. produces footballs and basketballs. It takes 4 hours on machine A and 2 hours on machine B to make a football. Producing a basketball requires 6 hours on machine A, 6 hours on machine B, and 1 hour on machine C. Machine A is available 120 hours a week, machine B is available 72 hours a week, and machine C is available 10 hours per week. If the company makes $3 profit on each football and $2 profit on each basketball, how many of each should they make to maximize their profit? **30 footballs, 0 basketballs**

14. **Veterinary medicine** The table below shows the amounts of nutrient A and nutrient B in two types of dog food: X and Y.

Food Type	Amount of Ingredient A	Amount of Ingredient B
X	1 unit per pound	$\frac{1}{2}$ unit per pound
Y	$\frac{1}{3}$ unit per pound	1 unit per pound

The dogs in Ken's K-9 Kennel must get at least 40 pounds of food per day. The food may be a mixture of foods X and Y. The daily diet must include at least 20 units of nutrient A and at least 30 units of nutrient B. The dogs must not get more than 100 pounds of food per day.

a. Food X cost $0.80 per pound and food Y costs $0.40 per pound. What is the least possible cost per day for feeding the dogs? **$20**

b. If the price of food X is raised to $1.00 per pound, and the price of food Y stays the same, should Ken change the combination of foods he is using? **no**

15. **Retail** The sales associate at a paint store plans to mix as many gallons as possible of colors A and B. She has exactly 32 units of blue dye and 54 units of red dye. Each gallon of color A requires 4 units of blue dye and 1 unit of red dye. Each gallon of color B requires 1 unit of blue dye and 6 units of red dye.

a. Let a be the number of gallons of color A and let b be the number of gallons of color B. Write the inequalities. $a \geq 0, b \geq 0, 4a + b \leq 32, a + 6b \leq 54$

b. Find the maximum number of gallons, $a + b$, possible. **14 gallons** $(6a, 8b)$

16. **Manufacturing** Oaken Treasures makes two different kinds of chairs, rockers and swivels. Work on machines A and B is required to make both kinds. Machine A can be run no more than 20 hours a day. Machine B is limited to 15 hours a day. The following chart shows the amount of time on each machine that is required to make one chair. The profit made on each chair is also shown.

Chair	Operation A	Operation B	Profit
Rocker	2 h	3 h	$12
Swivel	4 h	1 h	$10

How many chairs of each kind should Oaken Treasures make each day to maximize their profit? **4 rockers, 3 swivels**

Practice Masters Booklet, p. 23

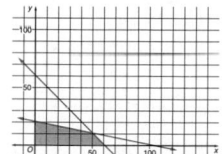

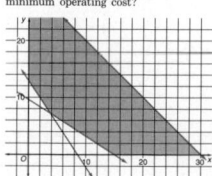

3-7 **Practice Worksheet**
Applications of Linear Programming
Solve.

1. The area of a parking lot is 600 square meters. A car requires 6 square meters. A bus requires 30 square meters. The attendant can handle only 60 vehicles. If a car is charged $2.50 and a bus $7.50, how many of each should be accepted to maximize income?

50 cars, 10 buses

2. The cost to run Machine 1 for an hour is $2. During that hour, Machine 1 produces 240 bolts and 100 nuts. The cost to run Machine 2 for an hour is $2.40. During that hour, Machine 2 produces 160 bolts and 160 nuts. With a combined running time of no more than 30 hours, how long should each machine run to produce an order of at least 2080 bolts and 1520 nuts at the minimum operating cost?

Machine 1: 4 hours
Machine 2: 7 hours

138 Chapter 3

Closing the Lesson

Writing Activity Have students write in detail an explanation of how to solve one of the problems in the exercises. Have them go through the questions that are asked in the Guided Practice.

APPLYING THE LESSON

Homework Exercises

See assignment guide on page 137.

Chapter 3, Quiz C, (Lessons 3–5 through 3–7), is available in the Evaluation Masters Booklet, p. 38.

Teaching Tip ❶ Review the characteristics of a regular hexagon.

Enrichment Masters Booklet, p. 20

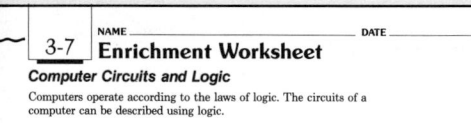

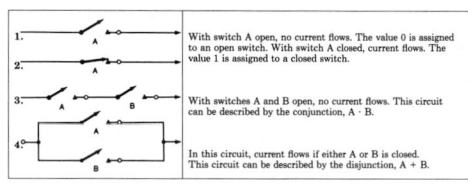

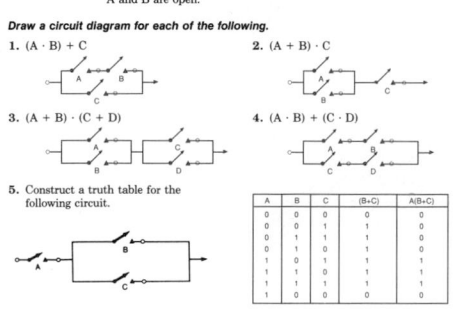

17. **Manufacturing** Stitches Inc. can make at most 30 jean jackets and 20 leather jackets in a week. It takes a worker 10 hours to make a jean jacket and 20 hours to make a leather jacket. The total number of hours worked by all of the employees can be no more than 500 hours per week.

    a. If the profit on a jean jacket is the same as the profit on a leather jacket, how many of each should be made to maximize profit? **30 jean jackets, 10 leather jackets**

    b. How many of each should be made if the profit on a leather jacket is three times the profit on a jean jacket? **10 jean jackets, 20 leather jackets**

18. **Education** Your semester test in English class consists of short answer and essay questions. Each short answer question is worth 5 points and each essay question is worth 15 points. You may choose up to 20 questions of any type to answer. It takes 2 minutes to answer each short answer question and 12 minutes to answer each essay question.

    a. You have one hour to complete the test. Assuming that you answer all of the questions that you attempt correctly, how many of each type should you answer to earn the highest score? **18 short answer, 2 essay for a score of 120**

    b. You have two hours to complete the test. Assuming that you answer all of the questions that you attempt correctly, how many of each type should you answer to earn the highest score? **12 short answer and 8 essay for a score of 180 points**

Critical Thinking

19. Create a system of inequalities for which the graph will be a regular hexagon, and its interior will be located in the first quadrant. **Answers may vary.** **Teaching Tip ❶**

Mixed Review

Graph each system of inequalities. Name the vertices of the polygon formed. Find the maximum and minimum values of the given function. (**Lesson 3-6**)

20. $x \geq 0$ **(0, 3), (0, 6)**
$y \geq 3$ **(2, 5), (1, 3)**
$y \geq 2x + 1$ **max: $f(1, 3) = -3$**
$y \leq -0.5x + 6$ **min: $f(0, 6) = -12$**
$f(x, y) = 3x - 2y$

21. $0 \leq x \leq 50$ **(0, 60), (0, 70),**
$0 \leq y \leq 70$ **(10, 70), (50, 30),**
$60 \leq x + y \leq 80$ **(50, 10)**
$f(x, y) = 4x + 3y$
max: $f(50, 30) = 290$
min: $f(0, 60) = 180$

Journal

Describe a situation in your life where you might use linear programming to solve a problem.

22. State whether $y = x^2 - 4$ is a linear equation. (**Lesson 2-2**) **no**

23. Solve $|a + 5| + 5 = 3$. (**Lesson 1-7**) **no solution**

24. State the property illustrated by $(6 + 4) = (6 + 4)$. (**Lesson 1-3**)
Reflexive property of equality

138 CHAPTER 3 SYSTEMS OF EQUATIONS AND INEQUALITIES

EXTENDING THE LESSON

Math Power: Problem Solving

Corporation A has a fixed cost of $4000 per week. It costs $10,000 to produce 500 units. The units are sold for $40 each. Write the equations for the cost and the sales. Find the break-even point. The break-even point is where the cost and sales are equal.
4,000 + 20x = c, 40x = s; 200 units

3-8 Graphing Equations in Three Variables

Objectives

After studying this lesson, you should be able to:

3-8A ▪ determine the octant in which a point in space is located, and

3-8B ▪ graph linear equations in space and determine the intercepts and traces.

Application

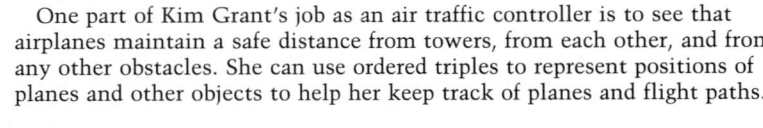

One part of Kim Grant's job as an air traffic controller is to see that airplanes maintain a safe distance from towers, from each other, and from any other obstacles. She can use ordered triples to represent positions of planes and other objects to help her keep track of planes and flight paths.

The equation $3x + 4y + z = 12$ is an open sentence in three variables, x, y, and z. You can write the solutions of open sentences in three variables as sets of **ordered triples.** For example, $(1, 2, 1)$ is a member of the solution set of this open sentence.

To draw the graph of an equation in three variables, it is necessary to add a third dimension to our coordinate system. The graph of an equation of the form $Ax + By + Cz = D$, where A, B, C, and D are real numbers, is a plane.

Equation of a Plane	If A, B, C, and D are real numbers, such that A, B and C are not all zero, then the graph of the equation $Ax + By + Cz = D$ is a plane.

When graphing in space, it is necessary to separate space into eight regions, called **octants.** Think of three coordinate planes intersecting at right angles as shown at the right. The octants are numbered as shown at the right. Any point lying in one of the coordinate planes is not in any octant.

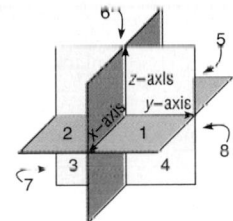

Example 1

Locate the point (3, 6, 1).

First, locate 3 on the positive x-axis, 6 on the positive y-axis, and 1 on the positive z-axis. Complete a "box" by drawing lines parallel to the axes through each intercept.

This point is in octant 1.

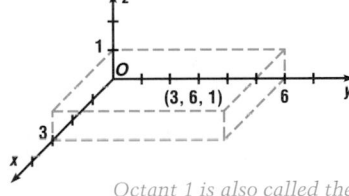

Octant 1 is also called the first octant.

LESSON 3-8   GRAPHING EQUATIONS IN THREE VARIABLES   139

ALTERNATE TEACHING STRATEGIES

Using Models

Have each student draw an x-axis and y-axis on a sheet of paper, with the positive x-axis pointing toward them and the positive y-axis pointing toward the right. Then have each student hold a pencil perpendicular to the sheet of paper at the origin. Explain that the pencil represents the positive z-axis. The three axes divide space into 8 octants. (There are 4 above the desktop and 4 below.) Then

have students tell the location of the octants described.

1. x pos., y pos., z pos. **right front, above**
2. x neg., y pos., z neg. **right back, below**
3. x neg., y neg., z pos. **left back, above**
4. x pos., y pos., z neg. **right front, below**

3-8 Lesson Notes

Lesson Resources

Reteaching Master 3-8
Practice Master 3-8
Enrichment Master 3-8
Lab Manual, pp. 49-50

Transparency 3-8 contains the 5-Minute Check and a teaching aid for this lesson.

INTRODUCING THE LESSON

5-Minute Check

(over Lesson 3–7)

1. The cost to run Machine A for an hour is $2.00. During that hour, Machine A produces 240 bolts and 100 nuts. The cost to run Machine B for an hour is $2.40. During that hour, Machine B produces 160 bolts and 160 nuts. Machine A and Machine B combined, can run no longer than 30 hours. How long should each machine run to produce an order of at least 2080 bolts and 1520 nuts at the minimum operating costs?

$A \geq 0$
$B \geq 0$
$A + B \leq 30$
$240A + 160B \geq 2080$
$100A + 160B \geq 1520$
$f(x, y) = 2.4x + 2y$
Machine A = $y = 4$ hours
Machine B = $x = 7$ hours

Motivating the Lesson

Discuss with students how they locate points on a plane. Ask them how they think points in space could be located. Have them use the classroom to explain their location theory. Ask students what occupations might require their employees to locate points in space on a graph.

Chalkboard Examples

For Example 1

Locate the point and state the octant in which the point lies.
(3, −2, 5)

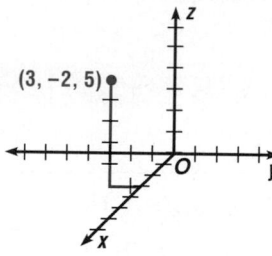

The point lies in octant 2.

For Example 2

Locate the point and state the octant in which the point lies.
(3, 2, −4)

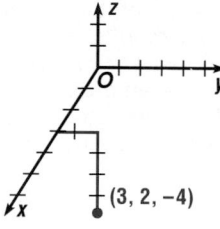

The point lies in octant 4.

For Example 3

Find the volume of the "box" formed when locating the point
(2, −6, −3).   2 × 6 × 3 = 36 cubic units

It is not necessary to show the entire "box" when you graph an ordered triple. The desired point will always be the corner farthest from the origin.

If one of the coordinates is zero, the sketch will be a rectangle instead of a box.

Example 2

Locate the point (−3, −5, 2).

First, locate −3 on the x-axis. Then draw a segment 5 units long in the negative direction, parallel to the y-axis. From that point, draw a segment 2 units long in the positive direction, parallel to the z-axis.

The point is in octant 6.

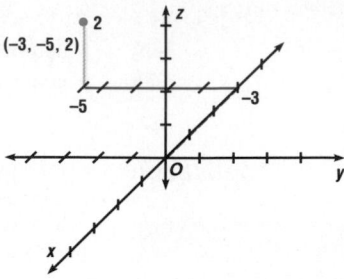

Example 3

CONNECTION

Geometry

Find the volume of the "box" formed when locating the point (3, 7, −1).

Let's graph the point.

The lengths of the sides of the "box" are 3 units, 7 units, and 1 unit.

The volume of the "box" is $3 \times 7 \times 1$ or 21 cubic units.

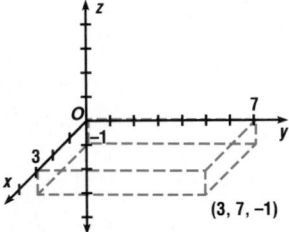

To graph a linear equation in three variables, first find the intercepts of the graph. Connect the intercepts on each axis. This forms a portion of a plane that lies in a single octant. Study the following example.

Example 4

Graph $2x + 4y + 3z = 12$.

To find the x-intercept, let $y = 0$ and $z = 0$.
$$2x = 12$$
$$x = 6$$
To find the y-intercept, let $x = 0$ and $z = 0$.
$$4y = 12$$
$$y = 3$$
To find the z-intercept, let $x = 0$ and $y = 0$.
$$3z = 12$$
$$z = 4$$
To indicate the plane, connect the intercepts. Remember, a plane extends indefinitely.

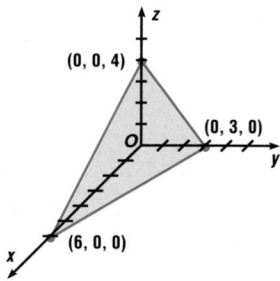

The portion in octant 1 is shown.

140 CHAPTER 3 SYSTEMS OF EQUATIONS AND INEQUALITIES

A **trace** is the intersection of a plane with one of the coordinate planes. The *xy*-trace is the line formed by the intersection of a plane with the *xy*-plane. All points in the *xy*-trace have a *z*-coordinate of zero, so we can find the equation of the *xy*-trace by letting $z = 0$ in the equation of the plane. We can find the equations for the other two traces in a similar manner.

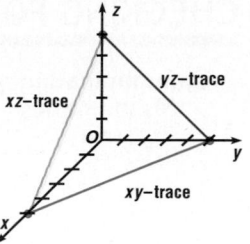

The portion of the plane in octant 1 is shown.

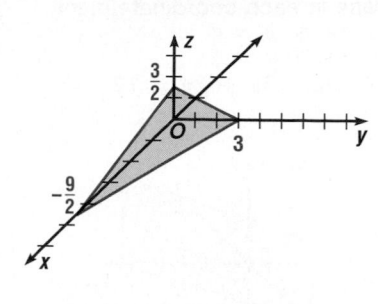
Example 5

Each intercept can be found by substituting 0s for two of the variables and solving for the third.

Graph $15x - 5y + 6z = 30$ and find the equation of the trace in each coordinate plane.

The *x*-, *y*-, and *z*-intercepts are 2, –6, and 5. To find the equation of the *xy*-trace, let $z = 0$.

$$15x - 5y = 30$$
$$3x - y = 6 \qquad \textit{Simplify.}$$

To find the equation of the *xz*-trace, let $y = 0$.

$$15x + 6z = 30$$
$$5x + 2z = 10 \qquad \textit{Simplify.}$$

To find the equation of the *yz*-trace, let $x = 0$.

$$-5y + 6z = 30$$

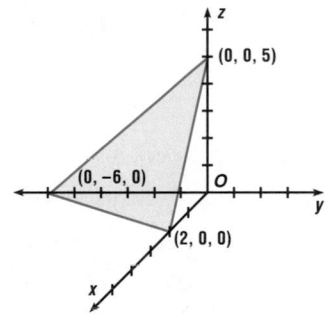

The portion of the plane in octant 2 is shown.

If you know the equations of two traces, you can write the equation of the plane containing the two traces.

Example 6

The equations of two traces of a plane are $-2x + 8y = -16$ and $2x + 4z = 16$. Find the equation of the plane.

First find the intercepts of the two traces.
The *xy*-trace is $-2x + 8y = -16$. So the *x*- and *y*-intercepts are 8 and –2.
The *xz*-trace is $2x + 4z = 16$. So the *x*- and *z*-intercepts are 8 and 4.

Now use the intercepts to write the equation of the plane.
The *x*-, *y*-, and *z*-intercepts of the plane are 8, –2, and 4 respectively. Use 8, the least common multiple of the absolute values of 8, –2, and 4, as the constant in the equation so that the coefficients in the equation will be integers. Divide 8 by each of the intercepts to obtain the coefficients.

$$\frac{8}{8} = 1 \qquad \frac{8}{-2} = -4 \qquad \frac{8}{4} = 2 \qquad \textbf{Teaching Tip ❶}$$

The equation of the plane is $x - 4y + 2z = 8$.

Check this result by finding the equations of the trace in each coordinate plane.

RETEACHING THE LESSON

Graph the equation. Find the *x*-, *y*-, and *z*-intercepts and the traces in the coordinate planes.

$x + 2y + 3z = 6$

x-intercept: 6; *y*-intercept: 3;

z-intercept: 2

xy-trace: $x + 2y = 6$

yz-trace: $2y + 3z = 6$

xz-trace: $x + 3z = 6$

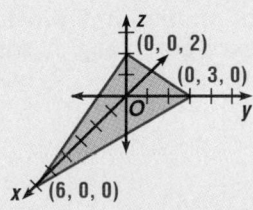

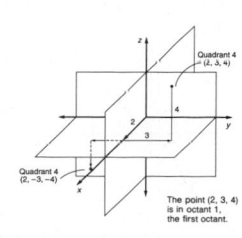

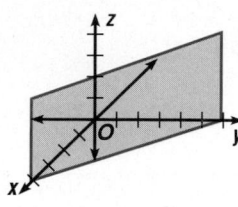
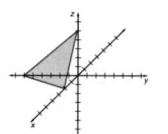 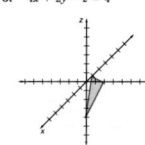
142   Chapter 3

CHECKING FOR UNDERSTANDING

Communicating Mathematics

Read and study the lesson to answer these questions. 1–2. See margin.

1. What is the difference between an equation whose graph is a plane and an equation whose graph is a line?

2. Write two ordered triples that satisfy the equation $3x + 4y + z = 12$.

3. Write the equation of the xy-trace of $3x + 4y + z = 12$. $3x + 4y = 12$

Guided Practice

In which octant does each point lie?

4. $(5, 2, 3)$ **1**   5. $(7, 5, -6)$ **4**   6. $(3, 0, 1)$ **none**   7. $(3, -7, 2)$ **2**

Find the x-, y-, and z-intercepts for each equation.

8. x:6, y:12, z:-12   8. $2x + y - z = 12$ 9. $20x - 4y + 10z = 20$
9. x:1, y:-5, z:2   10. $2x + y - 3z = 10$ 11. $3x + 5y + 2z = 30$
                   x: 5, y: 10; z:$\frac{-10}{3}$ x: 10, y: 6, z: 15

EXERCISES

Practice

Given the following conditions, name the octant in which the point (x, y, z) lies.

A

12. $x < 0, y = 4, z > 0$ **5**   13. $x > 0, y = 3, z < 0$ **4**

18. x:3, y:$\frac{3}{2}$, z:$\frac{9}{2}$

14. $x > 2, y > 1, z = 7$ **1**   15. $x < 0, y < 0, z < 0$ **7**

   $x + 2y = 3$
   $3x + 2z = 9$

16. $x > 3, y < -3, z = 3$ **2**   17. $x > 2, y < -1, z < -2$ **3**

   $6y + 2z = 9$

B

Graph each equation. Find the x-, y-, and z-intercepts and the traces in the coordinate planes. See Solutions Manual for graphs.

19. x:$\frac{5}{2}$, y:-10, z:5

18. $3x + 6y + 2z = 9$ 19. $4x - y + 2z = 10$

   $4x - y = 10$
   $2x + z = 5$

20. $3x - y = 3$ 21. $5y + 2z = 20$ *z*: none

   $-y + 2z = 10$

22. $3z - 2x = 5$ x: $\frac{-5}{2}$, y: none, z: $\frac{5}{3}$ 23. $5x - 8y = -12$ x: $\frac{-12}{5}$, y: $\frac{3}{2}$,

20. x:1, y:-3, z:none

   $2x = -5, 3z = 5, 3z - 2x = 5$ $5x = -12, 2y = 3,$
   $3x - y = 3$ $5x - 8y = -12$
   $x = 1, y = -3$

Write an equation of the plane given its x-, y-, and z-intercepts.

21. x:none, y:4, z:10

24. $2, -2, 5$ $5x - 5y + 2z = 10$ 25. $\frac{1}{2}, 3, -2$ $12x + 2y - 3z = 6$

   $y = 4, z = 10$
   $5y + 2z = 20$

C

Write an equation of the plane given two of its traces in the coordinate planes.

26. $5x + 3z = 15, y + z = 5$ 27. $x - 4y = 1, 8y + z = -2$

28. $3y - 4z = 6, y = 2$ $3y - 4z = 6$ 29. $x = -2, z = 5$ $5x - 2z = -10$

26. $5x + 3y + 3z = 15$ 27. $2x - 8y - z = 2$

Critical Thinking

30. Describe the equations of two parallel planes. Write an example of two equations whose graphs are parallel planes. **The coefficients of each variable are the same, but the constant term is different. Sample answer:** $x + y + z = 5$ and $x + y + z = 10$

142   CHAPTER 3   SYSTEMS OF EQUATIONS AND INEQUALITIES

Additional Answers

1. **An equation of a line has two variables and an equation of a plane has three.**

2. **Answers may vary. A sample answer is $(2, 1, 2)$ and $(1, 1, 5)$.**

Application

31. Manufacturing Conner's Corrugated Crates makes cardboard boxes for shipping goods. If a corner of their smallest box is placed at the origin of a coordinate system with 1-inch units on all three axes, the coordinates of the corner farthest from the origin are (12, 10, 10).

a. Find the volume of the box. **1200 cubic inches**

b. Find the amount of material needed to make the box. **680 square inches**

c. Conner's manager decided that this box would be much more useful if they double all of the dimensions. How does the volume of this new box compare to the original? **It is eight times greater.**

Computer

32. The BASIC program below finds the distance between two points in space. Line 70 uses the formula for distance.

$$d = \sqrt{(x_2 - x_1)^2 + (y_2 - y_1)^2 + (z_2 - z_1)^2}$$

Enter the coordinates (x_1, y_1, z_1), for the first point. Then enter the coordinates (x_2, y_2, z_2) for the second point.

```
10 PRINT "ENTER THE          50 PRINT "THE SECOND POINT"
   COORDINATES OF"           60 INPUT X2, Y2, Z2
20 PRINT "THE FIRST POINT."  70 LET D = SQR((X2-X1)^2 +
30 INPUT X1, Y1, Z1             (Y2-Y1)^2 + (Z2-Z1)^2)
40 PRINT "ENTER THE          80 PRINT "DISTANCE = ";D
   COORDINATES OF"           90 END
```

Portfolio

Select an item from this chapter that you feel shows your best work and place it in your portfolio. Explain why you selected it.

Use the BASIC program to find the distance between each pair of points to the nearest hundredth.

a. (3, 0, 0), (0, 4, 0) **5**

b. (0, 0, 0), (1, 2, 3) **3.74**

c. (5, 1, 3), (3, -2, 6) **4.69**

d. (-1, 7, 1), (-2, -1, -3) **9**

e. Use the program to find a set of four positive whole numbers that satisfy the equation $a^2 + b^2 + c^2 = d^2$. Use (0, 0, 0) as one point and (a, b, c) as the other point. *Hint: See Exercise 32b.* **Answers may vary. A sample answer is 4, 4, 2, 6.**

33a. $c \geq 0, r \geq 0, c + r \leq 275, \dfrac{c}{9} + \dfrac{r}{12} < 25$

Mixed Review

33. Agriculture A North Carolina farmer has 25 days to plant cotton and corn. The cotton can be planted at a rate of 9 acres per day and the corn at a rate of 12 acres per day. The farm has 275 acres available. The farmer estimates that the profit on an acre of cotton will be $25 and the profit on an acre of corn will be $18. **(Lesson 3-7)**

a. Let c represent the number of acres of cotton and let r represent the number of acres of corn. Write the inequalities.

b. How many acres of each crop should the farmer plant? **(Lesson 3-7)** **225 acres of cotton and 0 acres of corn for a profit of $5625**

34. Name which points, (0, 0), (1, -2), or (-3, 1), satisfy the inequality $x + 2y \leq 7$. **(Lesson 2-8)** **(0, 0), (1, -2), and (-3, 1)**

35. Find the next number in the group of numbers $\dfrac{1}{2}, \dfrac{2}{3}, 1, \dfrac{8}{5}, \dfrac{8}{3}, \dfrac{?}{}$. **(Lesson 2-3)** $\dfrac{32}{7}$

36. Solve $|m - 4| + 2 \geq 0$. **(Lesson 1-8)** **all reals**

EXTENDING THE LESSON

Math Power: Reasoning

Write the equation of the plane passing through (1, 1, 1), (4, -1, 2) and (0, 2, 0).
$x + 2y + z = 4$

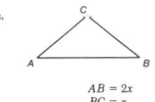

Lesson Resources

Reteaching Master 3-9
Practice Master 3-9
Enrichment Master 3-9

Transparency 3-9 contains the 5-Minute Check and a teaching aid for this lesson.

INTRODUCING THE LESSON

 5-Minute Check

(over Lesson 3–8)

1. Name the octant in which (2, −2, 2) lies.   **2**

2. Name the octant in which (−3, −2, −2) lies.   **7**

3. Write an equation of the plane with *x*-intercept 3, *y*-intercept −5, and *z*-intercept 2.
$10x − 6y + 15z = 30$.

4. Write the equation of a plane if two of its traces are $3x − y = 6$ and $2y + 3z = -12$.
$6x − 2y − 3z = 12$

Motivating the Lesson

A palindromic number reads the same from right-to-left as from left-to-right such as 6226. Find a palindromic number for which the sum of the digits is 26.   **989**

Objective
3-9

After studying this lesson, you should be able to:
■ solve a system of equations in three variables.

Application

Courtney has a total of 256 points on three algebra tests. His score on the first test exceeds his score on the second by 6 points. His total score before taking the third test was 164 points. What were Courtney's scores on the three tests?

Explore

Problems like this one can be solved by using a **system of equations in three variables.** Solving these systems is very similar to solving systems of equations in two variables. Let's try solving this problem.
Let f = Courtney's score on the first test.
Let s = Courtney's score on the second test.
Let t =. Courtney's score on the third test.

Plan

Write the system of equations from the information given.

$$f + s + t = 256$$ *The total of the scores is 256.*
$$f − s = 6$$ *The difference between the first and second is 6 points.*
$$f + s = 164$$ *The total before taking the third test is the sum of the first and second tests.*

Solve

Now solve. First use elimination on the last two equations to solve for f.

$$\begin{array}{r} f − s = 6 \\ \underline{f + s = 164} \\ 2f = 170 \\ f = 85 \end{array}$$ The first test score is 85.

Then substitute 85 for f in one of the original equations to solve for s.

$$\begin{array}{r} f + s = 164 \\ 85 + s = 164 \\ s = 79 \end{array}$$ The second test score is 79.

Next substitute 85 for f and 79 for s in $f + s + t = 256$.

$$\begin{array}{r} f + s + t = 256 \\ 85 + 79 + t = 256 \\ t = 92 \end{array}$$ The third test score is 92.

Courtney's test scores were 85, 79, and 92.

Examine

Now check your results against the original problem.
Is the total number of points on the three tests 256 points?
$$85 + 79 + 92 = 256 \checkmark$$
Is one test score 6 more than another test score? $79 + 6 = 85 \checkmark$
Do two of the tests total 164 points? $85 + 79 = 164 \checkmark$
Our answers are correct.

ALTERNATE TEACHING STRATEGIES

Using Discussion

How can you use Cramer's Rule to solve three variable equations? Show how to use with 3 × 3 determinants.

$$\begin{vmatrix} a & b & c \\ d & e & f \\ g & h & i \end{vmatrix} = aei + bfg + chd − gec − hfa − ibd$$

How would you use this to solve equations?

Using Problem Solving

Have students write a problem involving three variables. Have them explain what information is needed in order to solve an equation with variables.

You know that a system of two linear equations in two variables does not always have a solution that is a unique ordered pair. Similarly, a system of three linear equations in three variables does not always have a solution that is a unique ordered triple.

Recall that a system of two equations in two variables can have a unique solution, an infinite number of solutions, or no solution.

The graph of each equation in a system of three linear equations in three variables is a plane. Depending on the constraints involved, one of the following possibilities occurs.

<table>
<tr>
<td>The three planes intersect at one point. So the system has a unique solution.

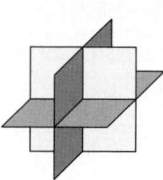</td>
<td>The three planes intersect in a line. There are an infinite number of solutions to the system.

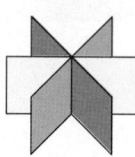</td>
</tr>
</table>

Each of the diagrams below shows three planes that have no points in common. These systems of equations have no solutions.

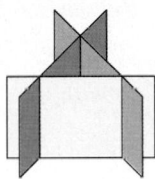 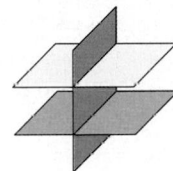 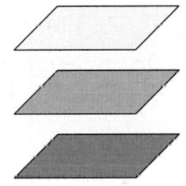

Example 1

Solve this system of equations: $\begin{cases} x + 2y + z = 9 \\ 3y - z = -1 \\ 3z = 12 \end{cases}$.

Solve the third equation, $3z = 12$.

$$3z = 12$$
$$z = 4$$

Substitute 4 for z in the second equation, $3y - z = -1$, to find y.

$$3y - (4) = -1$$
$$3y = 3$$
$$y = 1$$

Substitute 4 for z and 1 for y in the first equation, $x + 2y + z = 9$, to find x.

$$x + 2(1) + (4) = 9$$
$$x + 6 = 9$$
$$x = 3 \qquad \text{The solution is } (3, 1, 4).$$

Check: *First equation:* $\qquad (3) + 2(1) + (4) = 9$ ✓

Second equation: $\qquad 3(1) - 4 = -1$ ✓

Third equation: $\qquad 3(4) = 12$ ✓

Chalkboard Example

For Example 1
Solve this system of equations.

$x + 2y + z = 4$
$4y - 3z = 1$
$y + 5z = 6$
The solution is (1, 1, 1).

Teaching Tip ❶ You may want to reteach this example by eliminating f first, then solving a system of two equations in b and s.

Teaching Tip ❷ Stress that students check their solution in all three original equations.

Example 2

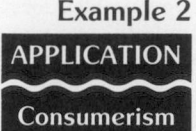
APPLICATION
Consumerism

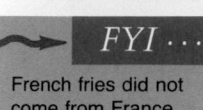
FYI ...

French fries did not come from France. They originated in Belgium and were first sold by street vendors in the 1800's.

Carmen, Jack, and Carol went to Bernie's Burgers to get food for their friends at school. Carmen spent $5.95 on two burgers, one order of french fries, and two sodas. Jack's order of 3 burgers, 3 orders of french fries, and 3 sodas totaled $10.41. Carol ordered 1 burger, 2 orders of french fries, and 2 sodas. Her bill was $5.35. How much is a burger, an order of french fries, and a soda?

Let b = the price of a burger, f = the price of an order of french fries, and s = the price of a soda.

Write a system of equations.

$2b + f + 2s = 5.95$ *Carmen's order*
$3b + 3f + 3s = 10.41$ *Jack's order*
$b + 2f + 2s = 5.35$ *Carol's order*

Teaching Tip ❶

Use elimination to make a system of two equations in two variables.

$2b + f + 2s = 5.95$ *Multiply by −1* $-2b - f - 2s = -5.95$

$b + 2f + 2s = 5.35$ *Multiply by 2* $\underline{2b + 4f + 4s = 10.70}$

              Add to eliminate b. $3f + 2s = 4.75$

$3b + 3f + 3s = 10.41$ *Multiply by −1* $-3b - 3f - 3s = -10.41$

$b + 2f + 2s = 5.35$ *Multiply by 3* $\underline{3b + 6f + 6s = 16.05}$

              Add to eliminate b. $3f + 3s = 5.64$

The result is two equations with the same two variables.

$3f + 2s = 4.75$
$3f + 3s = 5.64$

Use elimination to solve for s.

$3f + 2s = 4.75$ *Multiply by −1* $-3f - 2s = -4.75$
$3f + 3s = 5.64$ $\underline{3f + 3s = 5.64}$
                               $s = 0.89$

Now substitute 0.89 for s in one of the equations to find f.

$3f + 2(0.89) = 4.75$
$3f + 1.78 = 4.75$
$3f = 2.97$
$f = 0.99$

Now substitute 0.99 for f and 0.89 for s in one of the original equations.

$b + 2f + 2s = 5.35$ *Substituting the values for f and s*
$b + 2(0.99) + 2(0.89) = 5.35$ *in either of the other original*
$b + 3.76 = 5.35$ *equations would give the same*
$b = 1.59$ *result.*

A burger costs $1.59, an order of french fries costs $0.99, and a soda costs $0.89. **Teaching Tip ❷**

CHECKING FOR UNDERSTANDING

Communicating Mathematics

Read and study the lesson to answer these questions.

1. What other methods might we have used to solve the system of two equations in two variables in Example 2? **substitution or Cramer's rule**

2. Why is substitution the best method to use to solve the system in Example 1? **z is easy to find.**

3. Assume that a system of three equations in three variables has no solution. What might happen while you are trying to solve the system that would tell you that there is no solution? **Answers may vary.**

4. What might happen while you are trying to solve a system of equations that would tell you that there are infinitely many solutions? **Answers may vary.**

Guided Practice

For each system of equations an ordered triple is given. Determine whether it is a solution of the system.

5. $x + 2y + z = 0$ **yes**
$x - y + z = 0$
$2x + 3y - z = 0$; $(0, 0, 0)$

6. $x - 3y + 2z = 1$ **no**
$2x - y + 2z = 0$
$x + y + z = 6$; $(2, 2, 2)$

7. $4x + y - 2z = 0$ **no**
$x - 2y = 0$
$2x - y - z = 0$; $(3, 0, 6)$

8. $2x + y - z = 2$ **yes**
$3x + 2y + z = 5$
$x + y + z = 0$; $(8, -11, 3)$

9. $x - z = 1$ **yes**
$x + y + z = 3$
$z - y = 4$; $(3, -2, 2)$

10. $x + y = -6$ **no**
$x + z = -2$
$y + z = 2$; $(4, 2, 2)$

EXERCISES

Practice

Solve each system of equations.

A

11. $x - 2y + z = -9$
$2y + 3z = 16$
$2y = 4$ $(-9, 2, 4)$

12. $2a + b = 2$
$5a = 15$
$a + b + c = -1$ $(3, -4, 0)$

13. $x + y - z = -1$
$x + y + z = 3$
$3x - 2y - z = -4$ $(0, 1, 2)$

14. $b + c = 4$
$2a + 4b - c = -3$
$3b = -3$ $(3, -1, 5)$

LESSON 3-9 SOLVING SYSTEMS OF EQUATIONS IN THREE VARIABLES 147

RETEACHING THE LESSON

Solve each system of equations.

1. $2x - y + z = 3$
$x + 3y - 2z = 11$ $(3, 2, -1)$
$3x - 2y + 4z = 1$

2. $2x - y + 2z = -8$
$x + 2y - 3z = 9$ $(-1, 2, -2)$
$3x - y - 4z = 3$

Chapter 3, Quiz D, (Lessons 3–8 through 3–9), is available in the Evaluation Masters Booklet, p. 38.

Teaching Tip ❸ Remind students that drawing a figure and labeling it helps to solve a problem.

B

15. $r + s + t = 15$
$r + t = 12$
$s + t = 10$ **(5, 3, 7)**

16. $2x + y - 2z = 31$
$x - 2y - 3z = 23$
$x - 2y + z = 3$ **(10, 1, -5)**

17. $a + b + c = 0$
$2a + 2b + c = 5$
$2a + b - c = 2$ **(-8, 13, -5)**

18. $x + y + z = 4$
$x - y - z = -2$
$x - y + z = 0$ **(1, 2, 1)**

19. $r + s - 2t = 4$
$r - 3s - 4t = -2$
$2r + s + 2t = 0$ **(0, 2, -1)**

20. $2x + 3y + z = 28$
$3x + 4y - 2z = 24$
$x + y + z = 16$ **(10, 1, 5)**

21. $3x - 2y + 2z = -2$
$x - 3y + z = -2$
$2x - y + 4z = 7$ **(-2, 1, 3)**

22. $a + 8b + 2c = -24$
$3a + b + 7c = -3$
$4a - 3b + 6c = 9$ **(0, -3, 0)**

23. $x + y + z = -1$
$3x - 2y - 4z = 16$
$2x - y + z = 19$ **(4, -8, 3)**

24. $4x + 3y + 2z = 34$
$2x + 4y + 3z = 45$
$3x + 2y + 4z = 47$ **(1, 4, 9)**

C

25. $3a + b + 2c = 6$
$6a - 2b = 2$
$3a + b - 2c = 0$ $\left(\frac{2}{3}, 1, \frac{3}{2}\right)$

26. $x + y + z = 1$
$2x - y = 0$
$-3x + z = 0$ $\left(\frac{1}{6}, \frac{1}{3}, \frac{1}{2}\right)$

27. $2r + 3s + 4t = 3$
$5r - 9s + 6t = 1$
$\frac{1}{3}r - \frac{1}{2}s + \frac{2}{3}t = \frac{1}{6}$ $\left(\frac{1}{2}, \frac{1}{3}, \frac{1}{4}\right)$

28. $2x + y + z = 7$
$12x - 2y - 2z = 2$
$\frac{2x}{3} - y + \frac{z}{3} = -\frac{1}{3}$ **(1, 2, 3)**

29. Three numbers have a total of 6. The first number is twice the second, and the third is three times the second. What are the three numbers? **2, 1, 3**

30. The sum of three numbers is 20. The first number is the sum of the second and the third. The third number is three times the first. What are the three numbers? **10, -20, 30**

Critical Thinking

31. Since you know how to solve a system of three equations in three variables, use what you know to try to solve this system of four equations in four variables.
$w + x + y + z = 2$
$2w - x - y + 2z = 7$
$2w + 3x + 2y - z = -2$
$3w - 2x - y - 3z = -2$ **(1, 0, -1, 2)**

Applications

32. **Surveying** The perimeter of a triangular lot is 180 meters. The longest side is twice as long as the shortest side. The length of the remaining side is the average of the lengths of the longest and shortest sides. Find the lengths of the three sides. **80 m, 60 m, 40 m**

Teaching Tip ❸

Practice Masters Booklet, p. 25

33. **Consumer Awareness** Melissa works at Angela's Pizza. Her last three orders were 5 slices of pizza, 2 salads, and 2 sodas for $9.75; 3 slices of pizza, 2 salads, and 1 soda for $7.15; and 2 slices of pizza, 1 salad, and 1 soda for a total of $4.35. What are the individual prices for pizza, salad, and soda at Angela's? **pizza - $1.05, salad - $1.75, soda - $0.50**

34. **Banking** Pat Juarros has $5000 to invest in a certificate of deposit, stocks, or bonds. Since the investment is more risky, the estimated interest rate of the stocks is 1.5% more than that of the certificate of deposit. If she uses all of the money to buy a certificate of deposit, the interest earned in one year will be $400. The interest earned in one year on a $2000 certificate of deposit, $2000 worth of savings bonds, and $1000 in stocks would be $385. What are the interest rates of the three investments? **c.d. - 8%, bonds - 6.5%, stocks - 9.5%**

Mixed Review   Find the x-, y-, and z-intercepts for each equation.   (**Lesson 3-8**)

35. $-3x + 6y - 4z = 24$
$x = -8, y = 4, z = -6$

36. $9x + 6y - 3z = 36$
$x = 4, y = 6, z = -12$

37. Solve the following system of equations using the substitution method. (**Lesson 3-2**) $2x + 3y = -4$
$-3x + y = -5$ **(1, -2)**

38. The Forest Park Animal Clinic charges $35 for any office visit. In addition, the veterinarian charges $25 an hour after the first one-half hour. Write a linear equation to describe the cost of an office visit of t hours. Assume t is greater than one-half hour. (**Lesson 2-5**)
$c = 25(t - 0.5) + 35$

39. Find an equation of the line that passes through $(-3, 4)$ and is perpendicular to the line with equation $3y = 2x + 3$. (**Lesson 2-4**)
$y = -\frac{3}{2}x - \frac{1}{2}$

HISTORY CONNECTION

Who developed Cramer's rule? Most of us would answer "Cramer," since his name is attached to the rule. However, Chinese mathematicians had developed a system of determinants long before the Swiss mathematician Cramer published his rule in 1750. Further, it was a Japanese mathematician, **Seki Kowa,** who first applied the Chinese system of determinants to solving systems of equations. According to Japanese traditions, Seki make a pilgrimage to the ancient shrines at Nara to study the Chinese mathematical works preserved in the Buddhist temples there. He is said to have spent three years mastering the contents of those works. Seki's work with the application of determinants laid the foundation for all later work with determinants, including Cramer's.

EXTENDING THE LESSON

Math Power: Reasoning

The sum of four numbers is 22. The first number is twice the difference of the second and the fourth. The second number is 5 times the difference of the third and the fourth. The third number is twice the difference of the first and the fourth. What are the four numbers? **4, 5, 6, 7**

History Connection

The History Connection features introduce students to persons or cultures who were involved in the development of mathematics. You may want students to further research what other items we have today that were first introduced in China.

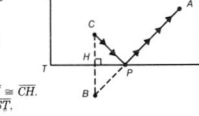

3-9 **Enrichment Worksheet**

Billiards

The figure at the right shows a billiard table. The object is to use a cue stick to strike the ball at point C so that the ball will hit the sides (or cushions) of the table at least once before hitting the ball located at point A. In playing the game, you need to locate point P.

Step 1 Find point B so that $\overline{BC} \perp \overline{ST}$ and $\overline{BH} \cong \overline{CH}$. B is called the reflected image of C in $\overline{ST}$.

Step 2 Draw $\overline{AB}$.

Step 3 AB intersects $\overline{ST}$ at the desired point P.

For each billiards problem, the cue ball at point C must strike the indicated cushion(s) and then strike the ball at point A. Draw and label the correct path for the cue ball using the process described above.

1. cushion $\overline{KR}$

2. cushion $\overline{RS}$

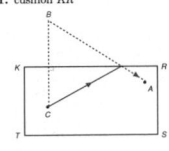

3. cushion $\overline{TS}$, then cushion $\overline{RS}$

4. cushion $\overline{KT}$, then cushion $\overline{RS}$

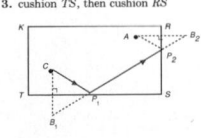

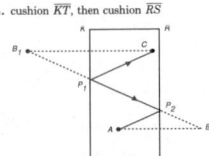

Using the Chapter Summary and Review

The Chapter Summary and Review begins with an alphabetical listing of the new terms that were presented in the chapter. Have students define each term and provide an example of it, if appropriate.

The Skills and Concepts presented in the chapter are reviewed using a side-by-side format. Encourage students to refer to the Objectives and Examples on the left as they complete the Review Exercises on the right.

The Chapter Summary and Review ends with exercises that review Applications and Connections.

Additional Answers

13.
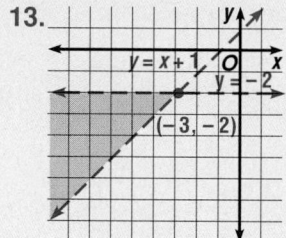

14.
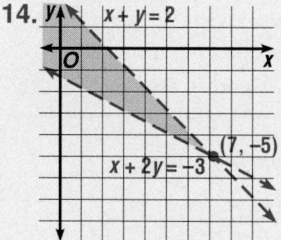

15.
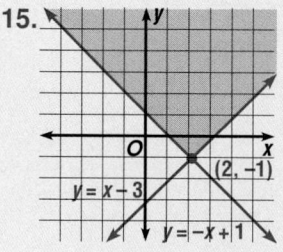

VOCABULARY

Upon completing this chapter, you should be familiar with the following terms:

consistent	109	130	linear programming
constraints	129	139	octants
Cramer's rule	119	139	ordered triple
dependent	109	118	second order determinant
determinant	118	108	solution of a system
elimination method	112	112	substitution method
equation of a plane	139	108	system of equations
feasible region	129	122	system of inequalities
inconsistent	109	141	trace
independent	109		

SKILLS AND CONCEPTS

OBJECTIVES AND EXAMPLES	REVIEW EXERCISES

Upon completing this chapter, you should be able to:

- solve a system of equations by graphing **(Lesson 3-1)**

  Graph each equation. The intersection of the graphs is the solution.

  $$4x - y = 10$$
  $$2x + 3y = 12$$

  The solution is (3, 2).

Use these exercises to review and prepare for the chapter test. **For graphs, see Solutions Manual.**

Graph each system of equations and state its solution. Also, state whether the system is *consistent and independent, consistent and dependent,* or *inconsistent.* **(0, –2), cons., ind.**

1. $y = 3x - 1$ **consistent,** $\{(x,y)|y = 3x - 1\};$
   $3x - y = 1$ **dependent**
2. $x - 2y = 4$
   $y = x - 2$

3. $2x - 3y = 7$ **(8, 3);**
   $x - y = 5$ **consistent, independent**
4. $x + y = 5$ **(3, 2);**
   $2x - y = 4$ **cons., ind.**

- solve a system of equations using the substitution or elimination method **(Lesson 3-2)**

  $$\begin{array}{ll} x + 3y = 2 & 1 + 3y = 2 \\ 2x - 3y = 1 & 3y = 1 \\ \hline \dfrac{3x}{3} = \dfrac{3}{3} & y = \dfrac{1}{3} \\ x = 1 \end{array}$$

Solve each system of equations using the elimination or substitution method.

5. $x + y = 8$ **(6.25, 1.75)**
   $x - y = 4.5$
6. $3x - 5y = -13$
   $4x + 3y = 2$ **(-1, 2)**

7. $2x + 3y = 8$ $\left(\dfrac{14}{5}, \dfrac{4}{5}\right)$
   $x - y = 2$
8. $\dfrac{1}{6}x - \dfrac{1}{9}y = 0$
   $\dfrac{1}{3}x + \dfrac{1}{3}y = 5$ **(6, 9)**

Additional Answer

16.
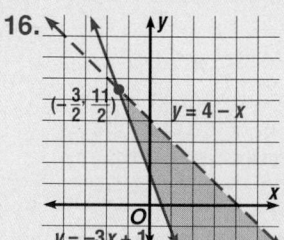

■ find the value of a second order determinant **(Lesson 3-3)**

$$\begin{vmatrix} -2 & 0 \\ 3 & 1 \end{vmatrix} = -2(1) - 0(3) = -2$$

Find the value of each determinant.

9. $\begin{vmatrix} 2 & 4 \\ 3 & 5 \end{vmatrix}$ **-2**   10. $\begin{vmatrix} 8 & -1 \\ 3 & -2 \end{vmatrix}$ **-13**

■ solve a system of equations using Cramer's rule **(Lesson 3-3)**

The solution to the system $\begin{cases} ax+by=c \\ dx+ey=f \end{cases}$ is (x, y), where

$$x = \frac{\begin{vmatrix} c & b \\ f & e \end{vmatrix}}{\begin{vmatrix} a & b \\ d & e \end{vmatrix}}, \quad y = \frac{\begin{vmatrix} a & c \\ d & f \end{vmatrix}}{\begin{vmatrix} a & b \\ d & e \end{vmatrix}}, \text{ and } \begin{vmatrix} a & b \\ d & e \end{vmatrix} \neq 0.$$

Use Cramer's rule to solve each system of equations.

11. $4x - 8y = 12$ **(7, 2)**   12. $x + 2y = 8$ **(-2, 5)**
    $3x + y = 23$ $-5x - 3y = -5$

■ solve a system of inequalities by graphing **(Lesson 3-4)**

$x + y < 1$

$y \geq x - 1$

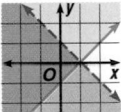

Solve each system by graphing. See margin.

13. $y < -2$ 14. $x + 2y > -3$
    $y > x + 1$ $x + y < 2$

15. $y \geq -x + 1$ 16. $y < 4 - x$
    $y \geq x - 3$ $y \geq -3x + 1$

■ find the maximum and minimum values of a function over a region using linear programming techniques **(Lesson 3-6)**

Graph the constraints. Then evaluate the function for each vertex to find the maximum and minimum values.

17. V: (0, 0), (0, 3), (2, 0) $\left(\frac{3}{2}, \frac{3}{2}\right)$;
    max: 12 at (0, 3), min: 0 at (0, 0)

18. V: (0, 0), (0, 6), (3, 6), (5, 4) (5, 0), max: 24 at (3, 6), min: 0 at (0, 0)

Graph each system of inequalities. Name the coordinates of the vertices of the polygon formed. Find the maximum and minimum values of the given function.

17. $x \geq 0$ 18. $0 \leq x \leq 5$
    $y \geq 0$ $0 < y \leq 6$
    $y \leq 3 - x$ $x + y \leq 9$
    $3x + y \leq 6$ $f(x, y) = 2x + 3y$
    $f(x, y) = 2x + 4y$

■ determine the octant in which a point in space is located **(Lesson 3-8)**

Octant	Signs of Coordinates
1	(+, +, +)
2	(+, -, +)
3	(+, -, -)
4	(+, +, -)
5	(-, +, +)
6	(-, -, +)
7	(-, -, -)
8	(-, +, -)

In which octant does each point lie?

19. (9, -3, 1) **2**   20. (-5, -2, -11) **7**

21. (0, 3, 0) **none**   22. (4, 2, -1) **4**

23. (2, 7, 10) **1**   24. (-9, -1, 9) **6**

25. (7, -4, -2) **3**   26. (-2, -1, 7) **6**

To provide a brief in-class review, you may wish to read the following questions to the class and require a verbal response.

1. Give an example of a system of equations that are inconsistent. **Answers will vary.**
2. State the multipliers you would use to eliminate each variable by addition.
   $2x + 3y = 5$ **Multiply by 3.**
   $3x + 2y = 5$ **Multiply by -2.**
3. What would you substitute into the second equation from the first, given the equations?
   $y = 2x$
   $x + 3y = 6$ $y = 2x$
4. Find the value of the determinant.
   $\begin{vmatrix} 2 & 3 \\ 2 & 5 \end{vmatrix}$ **4**
5. Solve the system of inequalities.
   $x < 4$
   $y < 3$
   $y < x$
   Tell three points that make the system true. **Answers will vary.**
6. Name the vertices of the polygon formed, given the system.
   $x \geq 0$
   $y \geq 0$ **(0, 0)**
   $x + y \leq 4$ **(0, 4), (4, 0)**
7. Find the x-, y-, and z-intercepts. $x + y + 2z = 4$
   x:4, y:4, z:2
8. Solve the system of equations.
   $x - y + z = 3$
   $2y - z = 1$
   $2y - x + 1 = 0$ **(3, 1, 1)**

Additional Answers

27.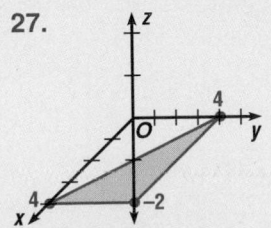

    xy-trace: x + y = 4
    xz-trace: x - 2z = 4
    yz-trace: y - 2z = 4

28.

    xy-trace: 5x - 2y = 6
    xz-trace: 5x + 3z = 6
    yz-trace: -2y + 3z = 6

The Cumulative Review shown below can be used to review skills and concepts presented thus far in the text. Standardized Test Practice Questions are also provided in the Evaluation Masters Booklet.

Evaluation Masters Booklet, pp. 39–40

NAME _____ DATE _____

Cumulative Review (Chapters 1-3)

1. Find the value of $8 + (3 + 2)^2 - 16$.   1. **17**

2. Name the set(s) of numbers to which $-\frac{12}{7}$ belongs.   2. **Q, R**

3. State the property shown in $1 \cdot 7 = 7$.   3. **multiplicative identity**

Solve.

4. $2(x - 3) = x + 3$.   4. **9**

5. $-6 < 3y \le 18$.   5. **$\{y|-2 < y \le 6\}$**

6. $3|x - 4| = 27$.   6. **−5, 13**

Solve and graph the solution set.

7. $3b - b \ge 5b - 15$ 7. **$\{b|b \le 5\}$**

8. $|2x + 5| + 7 \le 20$ 8. **$\{x|-9 \le x \le 4\}$**

9. Beth bought some 15¢ lollipops and the same number of 25¢ candy bars. If she spent $2.80, how many of each did she buy?   9. **7 of each**

10. Carlos has test scores of 86, 91, and 89 to date. To get an A he must average 92% per test. What must be the average of the last two test scores?   10. **97 or greater**

11. Given $f(x) = 3x^2 - 2x$, find the value of $f(5)$.   11. **65**

12. Find the slope, x-intercept, and y-intercept of $6x + 3y = 1$.   12. **$-2, \frac{1}{6}, \frac{1}{3}$**

13. State the domain and range of the relation. Then state if it is a function. $\{(-4, 6), (-2, 6), (0, 6), (-7, 6), (-9, 6)\}$ 13. **d: $\{-4, -2, 0, -7, -9\}$, y: $\{6\}$, function**

14. State whether the diagram is the graph of a function.   14. **yes**

15. Graph $y = \frac{2}{5}x - 1$.   15. **See students' graphs.**

NAME _____ DATE _____

Cumulative Review (Chapters 1-3)—continued

16. Write the equation of the line with slope $\frac{2}{3}$ that passes through the point (6, 9). Write the equation in standard form.   16. **$2x - 3y = -15$**

17. Find the standard form of the equation of the line that passes through (1, 3) and (−3, 7).   17. **$x + y = 4$**

18. Find an equation of the line through (2, −3) and parallel to the graph of $y = -4x + 3$. Write the equation in slope-intercept form.   18. **$y = -4x + 5$**

19. Find an equation of the line through (−6, 1) and perpendicular to the graph of $y = 3x - 2$. Write the equation in slope-intercept form.   19. **$y = -\frac{1}{3}x - 1$**

20. Graph $h(x) = |1 - x|$.   21. Graph $3y < 2x - 3$.   20. **See students' graphs.**   21. **See students' graphs.**

Solve each system of equations.

22. $x + y = 5$ $2x - y = 1$ 23. $7x + 3y = -1$ $2x - y = 9$ 22. **(2, 3)**   23. **(2, −5)**

Find the value of each determinant.

24. $\begin{vmatrix} 3 & 4 \\ 2 & 1 \end{vmatrix}$ 25. $\begin{vmatrix} 3 & -3 \\ 2 & 0 \end{vmatrix}$ 26. $\begin{vmatrix} 6 & 8 \\ 3 & 4 \end{vmatrix}$ 24. **−5**   25. **6**   26. **0**

Solve each system of inequalities by graphing.

27. $x + y < 1$ $x - y > 3$ 28. $x + y < 2$ $2x + 2y \ge 0$ 27. **See students' graphs.**   28. **See students' graphs.**

29. Graph the system of inequalities. Name the vertices of the polygon formed. $x \ge 0$ $y \ge 0$ $x + y \le 3$ 29. **See students' graphs. vertices: (0, 3), (3, 0), (0, 0)**

152 Chapter 3

- graph linear equations in space and determine the intercepts and traces   **(Lesson 3-8)**

To find the x-intercept, let $y = 0$ and $z = 0$. To find the y-intercept, let $x = 0$ and $z = 0$. To find the z-intercept, let $x = 0$ and $y = 0$. To find the equation of the xy-trace, let $z = 0$. To find the equation of the xz-trace, let $y = 0$. To find the equation of the yz-trace, let $x = 0$.

Graph each equation. Find the x-, y-, and z-intercepts and the traces in the coordinate planes. See margin p. 151 for graphs.

27. $x + y - 2z = 4$
28. $5x - 2y + 3z = 6$

27. $x = 4, y = 4, z = -2; x + y = 4, x - 2z = 4, y - 2z = 4$

28. $x = \frac{6}{5}, y = -3, z = 2; 5x - 2y = 6, 5x + 3z = 6, -2y + 3z = 6$

- solve a system of equations in three variables   **(Lesson 3-9)**

Use elimination to make a system of two equations in two variables. Then use elimination to solve the two equations. Substitute to find the value of the third variable.

Solve each system of equations.

29. $x + 2y - 3z = -3$ **(−4, 2, 1)**
$x + y + z = -1$
$2x + 4y + z = 1$

30. $a + b + 3c = 7$ **(1, −6, 4)**
$2a - 2b - 3c = 2$
$3a - b - 2c = 1$

~~~~~ APPLICATIONS AND CONNECTIONS ~~~~~

31. How many numbers from 10 to 1000 read the same forward or backward?   **(Lesson 3-5) 99**

32. **Manfacturing** Denim Duds makes denim jackets and jeans. Each garment must be cut from a pattern and sewn. There are 40 worker-hours per day available for cutting and 52 worker-hours per day for sewing. The chart below shows the number of hours for each operation needed to make both garments, as well as the profit on the garment.

Garment	Cutting Hours	Sewing Hours	Profit
jacket	1	4	$14
jeans	2	2	$8

How many of each garment should the company make to maximize profit? **(Lesson 3-7) 18 pair jeans, 4 jackets**

33. **Education** You may answer up to 30 questions on your final exam in history class. It consists of multiple-choice and essay questions. Two 48-minute class periods have been set aside for taking the test. It will take you 1 minute to answer each multiple-choice question and 12 minutes for each essay question. Correct answers on multiple-choice questions earn 5 points and correct essay questions earn 20 points. If you are confident that you will answer all of the questions you attempt correctly, how many of each type of question should you answer to receive the highest score? **(Lesson 3-7) 24 multiple-choice and 6 essay**

Additional Answers, Chapter Test

9.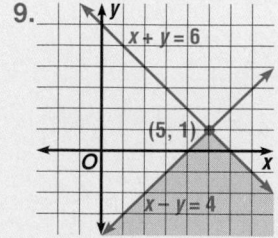

10.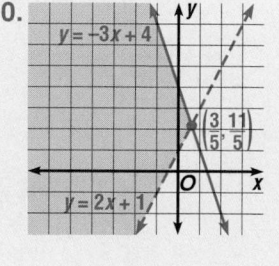

17.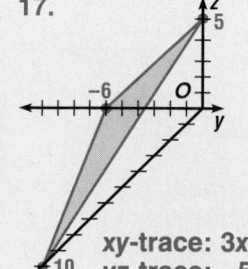

xy-trace: $3x + 5y = 30$
yz-trace: $-5y + 6z = 30$
xz-trace: $x + 2z = 10$

Graph each system of equations and state its solution. **For graphs, see Solutions Manual.**

1. $2x + y = 11$
   $x - y = 1$ **(4, 3)**

2. $x - 2y = -1$
   $2x + 3y = -16$ **(-5, -2)**

Solve each system of equations using the elimination or substitution method.

3. $2x + 3y = 5$
   $3x - 6y = -12$ $\left(-\dfrac{2}{7}, \dfrac{13}{7}\right)$

4. $2x + y - 5z = 4$
   $x + 3y + z = 5$
   $3x - y - 4z = -11$ **(-5, 4, -2)**

5. Find the value of $\begin{vmatrix} -3 & 1 \\ -2 & -4 \end{vmatrix}$. **14**

6. Find the value of $\begin{vmatrix} 6 & 5 \\ 0 & -9 \end{vmatrix}$. **-54**

Use Cramer's Rule to solve each system of equations.

7. $4x + 7y = -1$
   $2x + y = 7$ **(5, -3)**

8. $8x - 3y = -10$ $\left(\dfrac{1}{4}, 4\right)$
   $4x + y = 5$

9. Solve $\begin{cases} x + y \leq 6 \\ x - y \geq 4 \end{cases}$ by graphing. **9–10. margin.**

10. Solve $\begin{cases} y \leq -3x + 4 \\ y > 2x + 1 \end{cases}$ by graphing.

Graph each system of inequalities. Name the coordinates of the vertices of the polygon formed. Find the maximum and minimum values of the given function.

11. $x \geq 1$ **V: (1, 1), (1, 5), (5, 1);**
    $y \geq 1$ **max: 16 at (1, 5);**
    $x + y \leq 6$ **min: 4 at (1, 1)**
    $f(x, y) = x + 3y$

12. $-2 \leq x \leq 10$ **V: (-2, -2), (10, -2), (10, 1),**
    $y \geq -2$ **(-2, 5), (3, 15); max: 34 at**
    $2x + y \leq 21$ **(10, -2); min: -21 at (3, 15)**
    $y - 2x \leq 9$ $f(x, y) = 3x - 2y$

A toy manufacturer makes a \$3 profit on yo-yo's and a \$3 profit on tops. Department A requires 3 hours to make parts for 100 yo-yo's and 4 hours to make parts for 100 tops. Department B needs 5 hours to make parts for 100 yo-yo's and 2 hours to make parts for 100 tops. Department A has 450 hours available and department B has 400 hours available.

13. How many yo-yo's and tops should be made? **5000 yo-yo's and 7500 tops**

14. What is the maximum profit the company can make from these two products? **\$37,500**

15. In which octant does $(-9, -2, 7)$ lie? **6**

16. In which octant does $(3, -1, 8)$ lie? **2**

Graph each equation. Find the x-, y-, and z-intercepts and the traces in the coordinate planes.

17. $3x - 5y + 6z = 30$ **See margin for graph.**
    x: 10, y: -6, z: 5

18. $4x - 2y + 3z = 6$ **x: $\dfrac{3}{2}$, y: -3, z: 2**
    See margin for graph.

A new housing development has sixty lots available for building houses, where the builder can build colonial or ranch style houses. Sales experience has taughter her that should should plan to build at least three times as many ranch-style houses as colonial.

19. If she will make a profit of \$5000 on each colonial and \$4500 on each ranch, how many of each kind should she build? **15 colonial, 45 ranch**

20. Local regulations require that the builder use different materials than she planned, so her profit will be \$3500 on each colonial and \$4000 on each ranch. How many of each should she build? **0 colonial, 60 ranch**

Bonus Graph $|x| + |y| \leq 5$. **See Solutions Manual.**

Additional Answer

18.

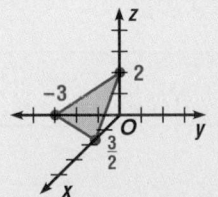

xy-trace: 2x − y = 3
yz-trace: −2y + 3z = 6
xz-trace: 4x + 3z = 6

Using the Chapter Test

This page may be used as a test or as a review. In addition, two multiple-choice tests and two free-response tests are provided in the Evaluation Masters Booklet. Chapter 3 Test, Form 1A is shown below.

Evaluation Masters Booklet, pp. 29–30

A **Test and Review Generator** is provided in Apple, IBM, and Macintosh versions. You may use this software to create your own tests or worksheets, based on the needs of your students.

The **Performance Assessment Booklet** provides an alternate asssessment for evaluating student progress. An assessment for this chapter can be found on pages 5–6.

NAME _____ DATE _____

Chapter 3 Test, Form 1A

Write the letter for the correct answer in the blank at the right of each problem.

1. What kind of system of equations is $2x - 3y = 5$
   $9y = 6x - 15$?
   A. consistent and independent
   B. consistent and dependent
   C. inconsistent
   D. inconsistent and dependent   1. **B**

2. Which expression can be substituted for y in the top equation of the system $\begin{matrix} 5x + 3y = 9 \\ 4x - y = 8 \end{matrix}$ to solve the system by substitution?
   A. $12x - 3y$ B. $-\frac{3}{5}x + 3$ C. $4x - 8$ D. $8 - 4x$ 2. **C**

3. You want to eliminate y by addition in the system: $\begin{matrix} 6x + 8y = 5 \\ 9x - 6y = 1 \end{matrix}$
   If you multiply both sides of the top equation by 3, by which number would you multiply both sides of the bottom equation?
   A. -2 B. 2   C. -4 D. 4   3. **D**

4. What does x equal in the solution $\begin{matrix} 4x - y = 4 \\ 6x - 5y = -1 \end{matrix}$
   of the system at the right?
   A. $\frac{3}{2}$ B. 2   C. $\frac{5}{2}$ D. $\frac{19}{4}$ 4. **A**

5. What is the value of $\begin{vmatrix} 11 & 8 \\ -12 & 6 \end{vmatrix}$?
   A. 162   B. -30 C. 30   D. -162 5. **A**

6. Which expression represents x in $\begin{matrix} 3x - 7 = 2y \\ 4x + 6y = 8 \end{matrix}$
   the system at the right?
   A. $\begin{vmatrix} 3 & 2 \\ 4 & 8 \end{vmatrix}$ B. $\begin{vmatrix} 7 & -2 \\ 8 & 5 \end{vmatrix}$ C. $\begin{vmatrix} 2 & -7 \\ 8 & 5 \end{vmatrix}$ D. $\begin{vmatrix} 3 & 7 \\ 4 & 8 \end{vmatrix}$ 6. **B**

7. What does y equal in the solution of $\begin{matrix} \frac{x}{2} + \frac{y}{3} = 1 \\ \frac{x}{4} + \frac{y}{9} = 1 \end{matrix}$
   the system at the right?
   A. $\frac{2}{11}$ B. $\frac{42}{19}$ C. $\frac{18}{11}$ D. $\frac{2}{19}$ 7. **C**

8. Which system of inequalities is graphed at the right?
   A. $y < x - 1$ and $y \geq -2x + 2$
   B. $y > x - 1$ and $y \leq -2x + 2$
   C. $y < x - 1$ and $y \leq -2x + 2$
   D. $y > x - 1$ and $y \geq -2x + 2$ 8. **B**

9. Given $0 \leq 2x - y + 2$, $x \geq 0$, $y \leq 4$, and $3y \geq 8x - 24$, find the maximum value of $f(x, y) = 2x - y$.
   A. 8   B. 6   C. -2 D. 10   9. **B**

NAME _____ DATE _____

Chapter 3 Test, Form 1A (continued)

10. A person is buying x units of vegetables and y units of meat. The minimum daily requirements are 6 units of protein and 10 units of vitamins. Use the table to determine which inequalities describe how to obtain the minimum daily requirements.

	Protein	Vitamins
1 unit of vegetables	2 units	5 units
1 unit of meat	4 units	3 units

   A. $2x + 5y \geq 6$ B. $2x + 5y \leq 6$ C. $2x + 4y \geq 6$ D. $2x + 4y \leq 6$
      $4x + 3y \geq 10$ $4x + 3y \leq 10$ $5x + 3y \geq 10$ $5x + 3y \leq 10$
      $x \geq 0$ $x \geq 0$ $x \geq 0$ $x \geq 0$
      $y \geq 0$ $y \geq 0$ $y \geq 0$ $y \geq 0$ 10. **C**

11. Find the value of w which makes $\begin{vmatrix} 8 & w \\ 6 & -7 \end{vmatrix} = 2w - 4$
    the sentence at the right true.
    A. 5   B. -5 C. 3   D. $\frac{3}{2}$ 11. **D**

12. What does y equal in the solution $\begin{matrix} 2x + 3y + z = 9 \\ x - 2y - z = 4 \\ x - 3y + 2z = -3 \end{matrix}$
    of the system at the right?
    A. $-\frac{9}{4}$ B. 2   C. 7   D. 1   12. **D**

13. What is the equation of the xy-trace of $3x - 6y - 9z = 15$?
    A. $x = 5$ B. $3x - 6y = 15$ C. $y = -\frac{5}{2}$ D. $-6y - 9z = 15$ 13. **B**

14. In which octant does $(-1, 4, 9)$ lie?
    A. 5   B. 2   C. 6   D. none of these   14. **A**

15. Which of the following planes does not have a z-intercept?
    A. $3x - 2z = 9$ B. $3x + 7y - 2z = 0$
    C. $y = 2z - 1$ D. $4x - 8y = 12$ 15. **D**

16. Which of the following is not a trace in the coordinate planes of the plane with equation $4x - 6y + 8z = 24$?
    A. $4x - 6y = 24$ B. $6y - 8z = -24$ C. $x - 2z = 24$ D. $z = \frac{3}{4}y + 3$ 16. **C**

17. What is the y-intercept of $2x - 10y + 15z = 30$?
    A. 15   B. -3 C. 3   D. 2   17. **B**

18. For which system is there no solution?
    A. $2x + y = 1$ B. $2x + y = 1$ C. $2x + y = 4$ D. $x - y = 8$
       $4x + 2y = 2$ $4x + 2y = 5$ $2x - y = 8$ $x + y = 16$ 18. **B**

19. How many multiples of 2 or 5 (or both) are there from 1 through 1000?
    A. 200   B. 500   C. 700   D. 600   19. **D**

20. Which point is not on the graph of $2x - y + z = 8$?
    A. $(0, 0, 8)$ B. $(0, -8, 0)$ C. $(4, 0, 0)$ D. $(0, 8, 0)$ 20. **D**

Bonus
What does x equal in the system at the right? $\begin{matrix} \frac{1}{x} + \frac{1}{y} = \frac{3}{4} \\ \frac{2}{x} + \frac{2}{y} = \frac{3}{2} \end{matrix}$
    A. 4   B. 2   C. $\frac{1}{2}$ D. $\frac{1}{4}$ Bonus **B**

CHAPTER 4

Matrices

PREVIEWING THE CHAPTER

The chapter introduces matrices by having students create a matrix, perform scalar multiplication on it, and then add matrices. Determinants are then related to matrices, and students discover numerous applications, making the connections between the content and real-life applications as well as with other areas of mathematics such as transformational geometry. Students then use matrices and Cramer's Rule to solve systems of equations in three variables. The chapter concludes with attention to solving a system of equations using an augmented matrix.

Problem-Solving Strategy   Students use *matrix logic* to organize known data in a table that enables them to eliminate possibilities and arrive at the only possible solution.

Lesson Objective Chart

Lesson (Pages)	Lesson Objectives	State/Local Objectives
4-1 (156-158)	**4-1:** Solve problems using matrix logic.	
4-2 (161-166)	**4-2A:** Create a matrix and name it using its dimensions.	
	4-2B: Perform scalar multiplication on a matrix.	
	4-2C: Add matrices.	
	4-2D: Find unknown values in equal matrices.	
4-3 (167-172)	**4-3A:** Evaluate the determinant of a 3 x 3 matrix.	
	4-3B: Find the area of a triangle given the coordinates of its vertices.	
4-4 (173-178)	**4-4:** Multiply two matrices and interpret the results.	
4-5 (179-183)	**4-5A:** Write the identity matrix for any matrix.	
	4-5B: Find the inverse matrix of a 2 x 2 matrix.	
4-6 (184-189)	**4-6:** Write a system of linear equations as a matrix and use the inverse to solve the system.	
4-7 (190-193)	**4-7:** Use Cramer's Rule to solve a system of linear equations in three variables.	
4-8 (195-200)	**4-8** Solve a system of equations using an augmented matrix.	

ORGANIZING THE CHAPTER

You may want to refer to the **Course Planning Calendar** on page T44.

Lesson (Pages)	Pacing Chart (days) Course I	II	III	Reteaching	Practice	Enrichment	Evaluation	Technology	Lab Manual	Mixed Problem Solving	Applications	Cooperative Learning Activity	Multicultural	Transparencies
4-1 (156-158)	1	1	0.5		p. 26					p. 4				4-1
4-2 (161-166)	2	1.5	1.5	p. 23	p. 27	p. 23	Quiz A, p. 51		pp. 51-52					4-2
4-3 (167-172)	1.5	1.5	1	p. 24	p. 28	p. 24		p. 21					p. 4	4-3
4-4 (173-178)	1.5	1.5	1	p. 25	p. 29	p. 25	Quiz B, p. 51 Mid-Chapter Test, p. 55				p. 22			4-4
4-5 (179-183)	1.5	1	1	p. 26	p. 30	p. 26		p. 4						4-5
4-6 (184-189)	2	1.5	1	p. 27	p. 31	p. 27	Quiz C, p. 52							4-6
4-7 (190-193)	1	1	1	p. 28	p. 32	p. 28						p. 40		4-7
4-8 (195-200)	1.5	1	1	p. 29	p. 33	p. 29	Quiz D, p. 52							4-8
Review (202-204)	1	1	1	Multiple Choice Tests, Forms 1A and 1B, pp. 43-46 Free Response Tests, Forms 2A and 2B, pp. 47-50										
Test (205)	1	1	1	Cumulative Review, pp. 53-54 Standardized Test Practice Questions, p. 56										

Course I: Chapters 1-13; Course II: Chapters 1-15; Course III: Chapters 1-17

Other Chapter Resources

Student Edition
Chapter Opener, pp. 154-155
Cooperative Learning Activity, p. 158
Graphing Calculator Exploration
    pp. 159-160
Challenge, p. 172
Journal Entries, pp. 177, 193
History Connection, p. 178
Mid-Chapter Review, p. 183
Technology, p. 194
Portfolio Suggestion, p. 200
Communicating Algebra, p. 200
Graphing Calculator Exploration,
    p. 201
College Extrance Exam Preview,
    pp. 206-207
Extended Project 1, pp. A2-A5

Teacher's Classroom Resources
Transparency 4-0
Real-World Applications
    Transparencies, 8, 9
Performance Assessment Booklet,
    pp. 7-8
Problem-of-the-Week Activity Cards, 7, 8
Tech Prep Applications Booklet, pp. 7-8
Lesson Plans, pp. 26-33

Other Supplements
Glencoe Mathematics
    Professional Series

Software
Test and Review Generator Software
    (Apple, IBM, and Macintosh)
Interactive Software (Macintosh)
Teacher's Guide for Software
    Resources

ENHANCING THE CHAPTER

Cooperative Learning

Deciding on the Size of Groups

Considerable research indicates that, for most schools, six is the maximum number of students to assign to a cooperative-learning group. A large group of this size provides more opportunities to have members with different cooperative-learning skills to be helpful to the whole group. It also can decrease the time required to do the assigned task since there are more members with more talents to do the work. However, because group skills must be learned by students, few may have the skills required for a group of this size. Therefore, if your students lack these skills, it is advisable to begin with groups of no more than two or three students each. A small group can be more effective in these cases because it takes less time for the members to get organized, and it provides more opportunity for each member to participate and to develop cooperative-learning skills.

Technology

The Technology Feature after Lesson 4-4 contains a BASIC program which uses Cramer's Rule to solve systems of three equations in three variables. Data is entered as an augmented matrix. The program reports the solution or that a unique solution does not exist.

You may wish to have students write programs that perform matrix operations. Remind them that matrices must have certain dimensions to be conformable under a particular operation. Encourage them to include checks within the program for such dimensions.

Critical Thinking

One technique that you may find useful to stimulate critical thinking and productive discussion is to challenge students with problems that have multiple methods of solution. Many of the problems that involve real-life applications of the content in this chapter can be used to utilize this technique. When students work independently or in small groups to solve these problems, assign the additional task that they must find at least two different ways to solve the problem. Although their initial focus will be on matrices, this added requirement will force them to think of other algebraic or geometric approaches. Have the methods discussed in class, focusing on the unique features of each method and the similarities and differences between them.

Cooperative Learning, p. 40

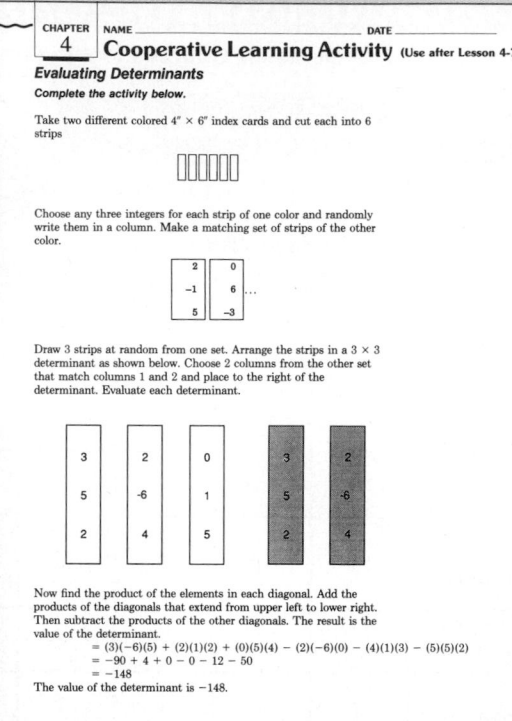

Technology, p. 21

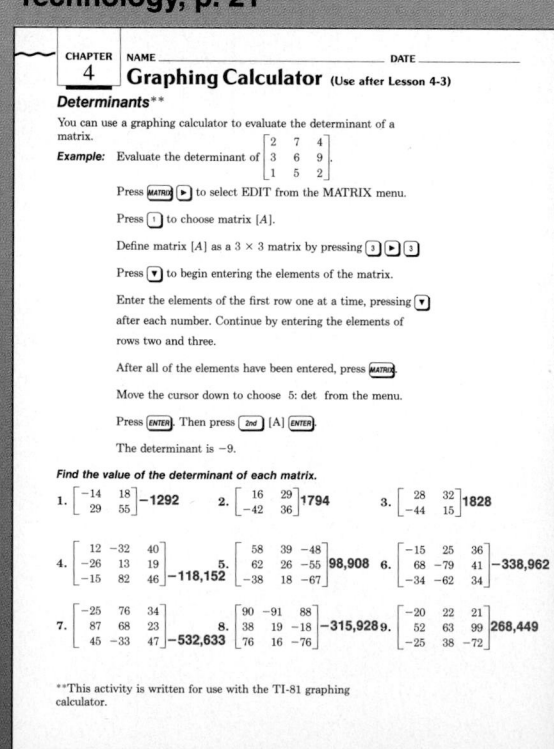

Problem of the Week Activity

The card shown below is one of two available for this chapter. It can be used as a class or small group activity.

Activity Card

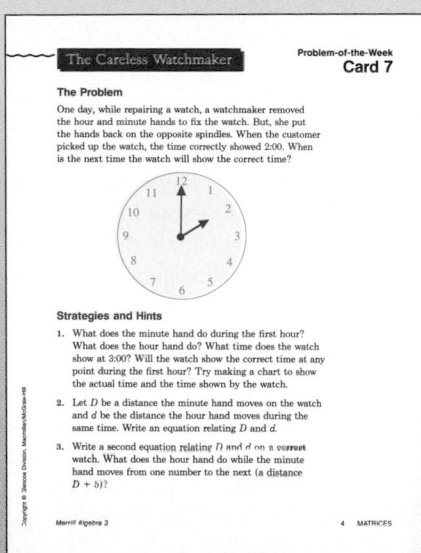

Manipulatives and Models

The following materials may be used as models or manipulatives in Chapter 4.

- graph paper (Lessons 4-2 and 4-4)
- poster board (Lesson 4-2)
- scientific calculator (Lesson 4-3)
- blue food coloring (Lesson 4-6)
- plastic cup (Lesson 4-6)
- cardboard, tagboard, or 3 x 5 index cards (Lesson 4-7)
- graphing calculator (pp. 159-160, 201)

Outside Resources

Books/Periodicals

Hunter, J.A.H., and Joseph S. Madachy. *Mathematical Diversions.* Dover Publications, Inc. 1975.

Fox, Linda, L. Brody, and Diane Tobin. *Women and the Mathematical Mystique.* John Hopkins University Press, 1980.

Films/Videotapes/Videodiscs

The Mechanical Universe. . .and Beyond, Part I, California Institute of Technology and the Southern California Consortium, Write to: The Mechanical Universe, California Institute of Technoloy, 1-70, Pasadena, CA 91125-0001

Software

Mathematics Exploration Toolkit, IBM, 4111 Northside Pkwy. NW, P.O. Box 2150, Atlanta, GA 30327-3015

Introduction to College Mathematics: Matrix, The Department of Mathematics and Computer Science, North Carolina School of Science and Mathematics, 1219 Broad St., Durham, NC 27705

Supplementary MathTools, William K. Bradford Publishing Company, 310 School St., Acton, MA 01720

Multicultural

Multicultural Activity, p. 4

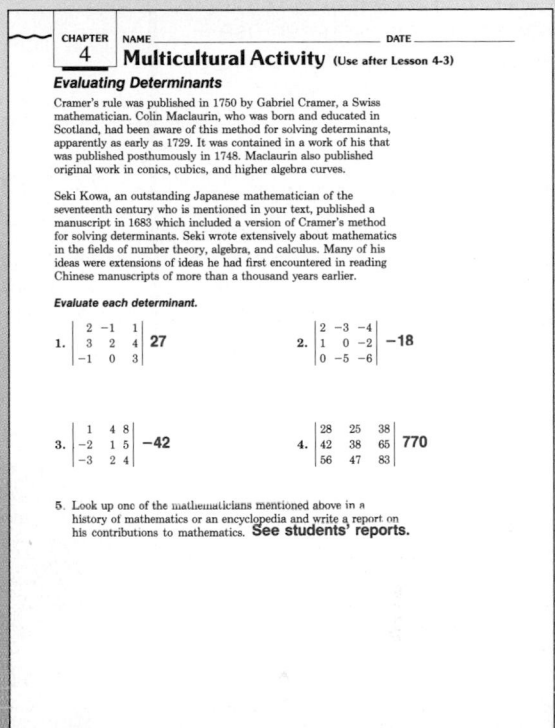

Lab Manual

Lab Activity, pp. 51-52

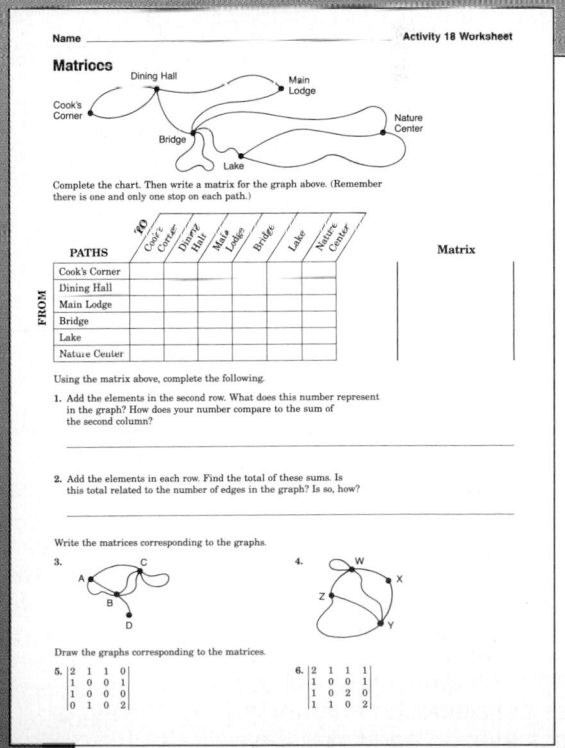

Transparency 4–0 is available in the Transparency Package. It provides a full-color visual and motivational activity that you can use to engage students in the mathematical content of the chapter.

Background Information

Technical designers combine artistic talent with math, especially in an area called anthropometrics, or the study of human body measurements. They must be able to account for precise human body measurements in the design of cars, tools, toys, and countless other manufactured products. Mathematics plays a significant role in developing specifications, sketching designs, making simulated models, and using computer assisted design (CAD). Demand for technical designers should grow 25% to 34% through the 1990s as a result of emphasis on quality and visual appeal.

C
H
A
P
T
E
R

4

Matrices

CHAPTER OBJECTIVES

In this chapter, you will:

- Create matrices to represent data and algebraic expressions.
- Perform operations with matrices.
- Use matrices to achieve transformations of geometric figures.
- Use matrices to solve systems of equations.

Study the graph. For the engineer what seems to be the most important thing to concentrate on when solving an engineering problem? Do you as a consumer have the same priority in a product?

How Design Engineers Solve Engineering Problems

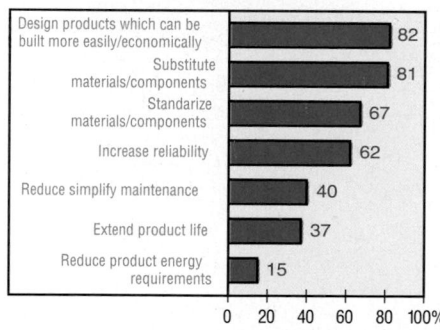

Design products which can be built more easily/economically	82
Substitute materials/components	81
Standarize materials/components	67
Increase reliability	62
Reduce simplify maintenance	40
Extend product life	37
Reduce product energy requirements	15

0   20   40   60   80   100%

154

CAREERS IN INDUSTRIAL DESIGN

When you buy a tool or product, of course, you are interested in how much it costs. But do you also care whether it works well and looks good? If you do, then you care about good design, and you just might make a good designer.

A designer needs creativity, a strong color sense, a visual imagination, a sense of proportion, a feel for balance, and—even in industrial design—a sensitivity to beauty. When a new car or a monorail transportation system is designed right, it is beautiful. Form fits function.

Most industrial designers, especially those in the aerospace, automative, and electronic industries, work on the computer. Computer-aided design (CAD) lets the operator insert, edit, and replace images on screen, long before a model is manufactured for testing.

When you're designing, you ask questions. *Who will use it? What will it do? What size should it be? What weight? What shape? What color? Of what materials? How can I make it maintenance-easy? How can I make it safe? How can I keep costs down? What are my design's competitors? How will my design be better?* Market research results need to be considered before you can answer many of these questions. Then you'll make sketches or computer images of several possible designs, which you'll offer to your product development team. It may take several tries to satisfy them. Last, you'll make a model, a sample, or detailed plans drawn to scale.

Chapter Project

Materials: paper, pencil, and graph paper

Organize students into cooperative groups of technical designers. Instruct each group to select and generate design ideas for a new or improved product. One that requires consideration of anthropometrics (human body measurements) would be especially appropriate. Assign each group the task of drawing two- and three-dimensional, free-hand sketches of the product from all four sides, and from the top and bottom. Then, have each group transfer the drawings onto graph paper, using a scale. While some members are creating graphic drawings of a group's product, have other members write detailed specifications. These should include all measurements and should describe in detail to a manufacturer how the product is to be made. If time permits, have each group build a scale model of the product. Finally, have each group present its product ideas, design sketches, and scale model to the class.

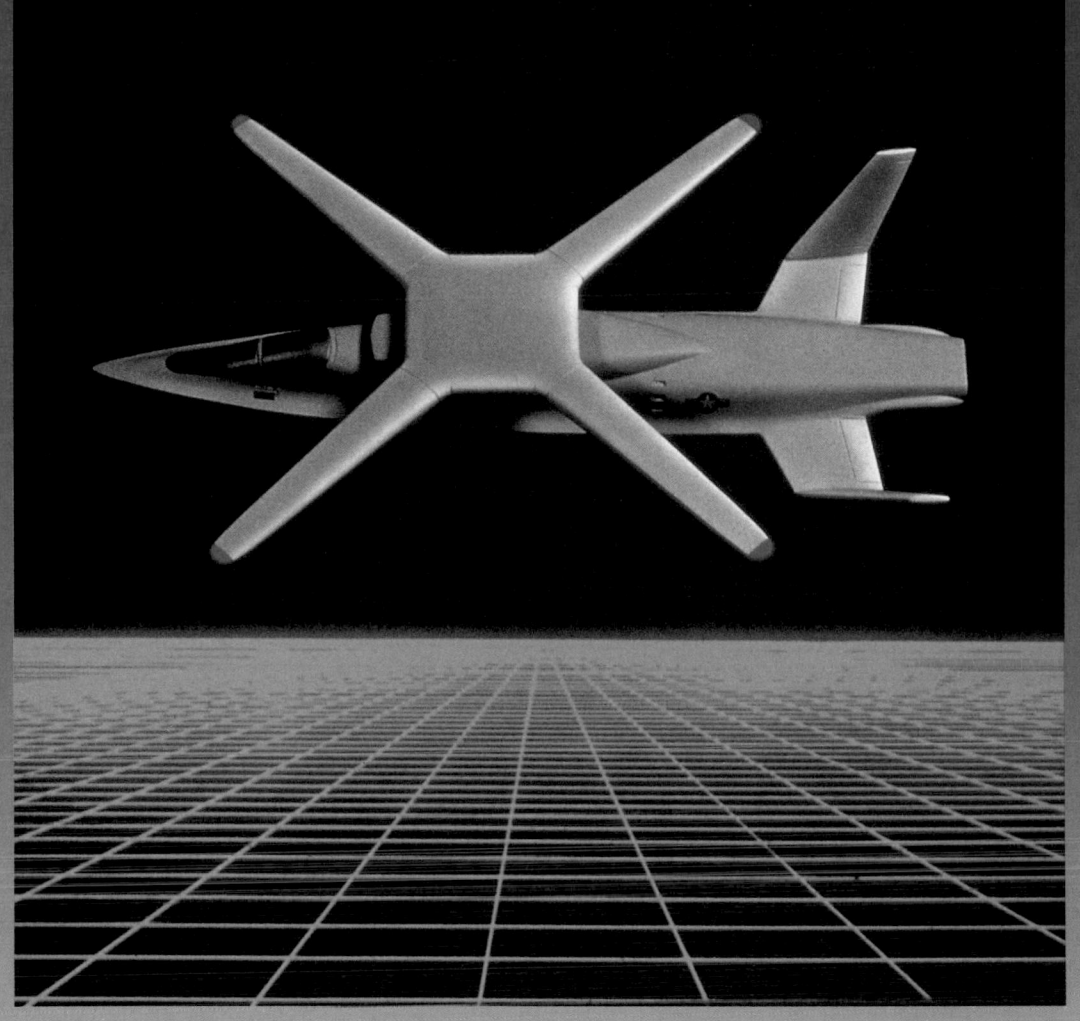

MORE ABOUT INDUSTRIAL DESIGN

Degree Required:
- Bachelor's Degree in Industrial Engineering

Some industrial designers like:
- pleasant working conditions
- good salaries
- opportunity to use their creative and artistic talents
- variety in their work

Related Math Subjects:
- Geometry
- Advanced Algebra
- Trigonometry
- Calculus

Some industrial designers dislike:
- having their ideas rejected
- working under pressure
- working overtime to meet deadlines

For more information on the various careers available in Industrial Design, write to:

Industrial Designers Society of America
1142 Walker Road, Suite E
Great Falls, VA 22066-1836

155

Lesson	Connections (C) and Applications (A)		Examples	Exercises
4-2	C:	Geometry	2, 3	20, 25-26, 31-32
	A:	Business		33
4-3	C:	Geometry	3	18, 24, 27
	A:	Metallurgy		30
		Horticulture		31
4-4	C:	Geometry	4	24-25, 30-32
	A:	Agriculture	3	
		Sports		34
		Coin Collecting		35
		Consumerism		41
4-5	C:	Geometry		21
	A:	Topology		22
4-6	A:	Chemistry	4	
		Landscaping		21
		Metallurgy		22
4-7	A:	Banking	2	
		Sports		22
		Retail		23
		Communica-tions		27
4-8	C:	Geometry	2	19
	A:	Auto-mechanics		22
		Restaurant Manage-ment		23

Lesson Resources

Practice Master 4-1
Activity Master, p. 4

   Transparency 4-1 contains the 5-Minute Check and a teaching aid for this lesson.

INTRODUCING THE LESSON

🕐 5-Minute Check

(over Chapter 3)
Solve each system of equations.

1. $4a + b = 4$
   $8a = 16$ $(2, -4, 0)$
   $a + b + c = -2$
2. $x + y - z = -1$
   $x + y + z = 7$ $(0, 3, 4)$
   $3x - 2y - z = -10$

Use Cramer's Rule to solve each system of equations.

3. $3a - 6b = 9$ $(7, 2)$
   $2a + b = 16$
4. $2a + b = 10$ $(6, -2)$
   $-4a - 3b = -18$

Motivating the Lesson

Have the students make a table for the following situation. Archie, Peggy, and Doug played each other in several games of tic-tac-toe. Archie played Peggy and won 4 of 7 games. He played Doug and won 6 of 9 games. Doug played Peggy and lost 5 of 8 games. Show the win-loss records.

TEACHING THE LESSON

Teaching Tip ❶ The first and fifth clues can help in eliminating Mary as Fred's date.

4-1 Problem-Solving Strategy: Using Matrix Logic

Objective
4-1

After studying this lesson, you will be able to:
- solve problems using matrix logic.

Many problems can be solved using a method sometimes referred to as **matrix logic.**

When you use matrix logic, you create a table, or **matrix,** that helps you organize all the information in the problem. By using the matrix, you can eliminate one possibility after another until you eventually arrive at a solution.

Example

> Fred, Ted, and Ed are taking Mary, Cari, and Terri to the homecoming dance. Use these clues to find out which couples will be attending the homecoming dance.
>
> 1. Mary is Ed's sister and lives on Fifth Avenue.
> 2. Ted drives a car to school each day.
> 3. Ed is taller than Terri's date.
> 4. Cari and her date ride their bicycles to school every day.
> 5. Fred's date lives on State Street.

First create a table that allows you to record all that you can learn from each clue. It should look something like the one below. You can then use an X to mark any square that is not a valid conclusion and a √ to mark any square that is a valid conclusion.

Look at the first clue. Since Mary is Ed's sister, she's not his date. Put an X in Mary's column beside Ed's name. Are there any other clues about Ed?

Teaching Tip ❶

Look at the third clue. Since Ed is taller than Terri's date, he's not Terri's date. Put an X in Terri's column next to Ed's name.

	Mary	Cari	Terri
Fred			
Ted			
Ed	X		X

ALTERNATE TEACHING STRATEGIES

Using Critical Thinking

Have students ask each other questions about each situation presented. They should ask first what is needed to be found and then what is known. In the logic problems they should ask what clues are given about an individual by looking at the relationships stated.

You can now deduce that Ed's date must be Cari. Put a √ in her column in Ed's row. You can also eliminate the other boys as Cari's date. Put X's in her column for their names.

Continue to evaluate each clue, making decisions, and recording your deductions until you can identify each couple. When you finish you should find that the couples are Ed and Cari, Ted and Mary, and Fred and Terri.

	Mary	Cari	Terri
Fred		X	
Ted		X	
Ed	X	✓	X

CHECKING FOR UNDERSTANDING

Communicating Mathematics

Read and study the lesson to answer these questions.

1. Why is this problem-solving strategy called matrix logic? **See margin.**

2. How do you keep track of the decisions you have made? **Use X for items you are eliminating and ✔ for conclusions.**

Guided Practice

Use matrix logic to solve this problem. **Teaching Tip ②**

3. Rae, Carol, and Dena are neighbors. Their hobbies are sculpturing, fixing cars, and gardening. Their occupations are doctor, teacher, and lawyer. Use these clues to find each person's hobby and occupation.

 ▪ The gardener and the teacher both graduated from the same college.

 ▪ Both the lawyer and Rae have poodles, as does the sculptor.

 ▪ The doctor bandaged the sculptor's broken thumb.

 ▪ Carol and the lawyer have lived next door to each other for five years.

 ▪ Dena beat both Carol and the gardener in tennis.

Carol is a teacher and does sculpture. Dena is a lawyer and fixes cars. Rae is a doctor and likes gardening.

EXERCISES

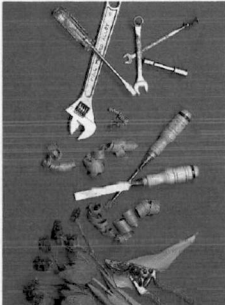

Strategies
Look for a pattern.
Solve a simpler problem.
Act it out.
Guess and check.
Draw a diagram.
Make a chart.
Work backwards.

Solve. Use any strategy.

4. Find a two-digit number such that the sum of its digits is 10 and 3 times the tens digit is twice the ones digit. **46**

5. How many capital letters, when folded, have halves that match exactly? Name them. **16: A, B, C, D, E, H, I, K, M, O, T, U, V, W, X, Y**

6. How many times is the hour display on a digital clock greater than the minute display in a 12-hour period? **78 times**

LESSON 4-1 PROBLEM-SOLVING STRATEGY: USING MATRIX LOGIC 157

RETEACHING THE LESSON

Use matrix logic to solve this puzzle. Bob, Cid, Fred, Mac and Sam live on different floors of an apartment house that has five floors.

1. Bob does not live on the top floor.

2. Cid does not live on the bottom floor.

3. Fred does not live on either the top or the bottom floor.

4. Mac lives on a higher floor than Cid.

5. Sam does not live on a floor adjacent to Fred's.

6. Fred does not live on a floor adjacent to Cid's.

On which floor does each live? answer from top to bottom: **Mac, Fred, Bob, Cid, and Sam**

Closing the Lesson

Writing Activity Have students make up their own logic problem. Have another student in the class evaluate whether it is possible for the problem to be solved.

APPLYING THE LESSON

Homework Exercises

See assignment guide on page 157.

---

7. Determine if each pattern can be folded to form a rectangular solid.

a. 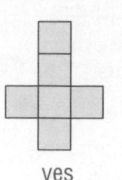 b. 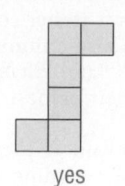 c. 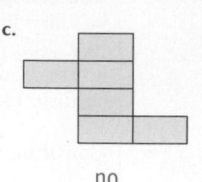 d.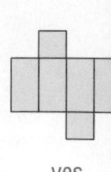

yes   yes   no   yes

Each figure can be viewed from two different perspectives. Describe the one you see first. What is the other perspective?

8.

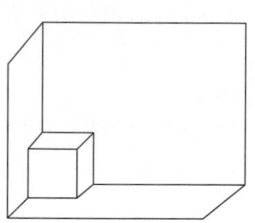

a small block sitting in a corner, a small block cut out of a large block

9.

rabbit, duck

10. Insert parentheses into the following expression to make the equation valid.

$$2 \cdot 1 + 2 \cdot 3 - 2 \div 2 - 1 = 12$$
$$\mathbf{2 \cdot (1 + 2 \cdot 3) - 2 \div (2 - 1) = 12}$$

∼∼∼∼∼ COOPERATIVE LEARNING ACTIVITY ∼∼∼∼∼

Work in groups. Each person in the group must understand the solution and be able to explain it to any person in class.

Five rock band members are named Bobbie, Bebe, Bruno, Bart, and Benito. Their last names are Cassady, Casto, Coffman, Crosby, and Cortez. Each band member has a different color trunk for their stage costumes. The colors are red, blue, black, white, and tan. Use the following clues to identify each band member by first and last name and which trunk each owns.

1. Bebe is not a Coffman and does not own a black trunk.
2. Bruno, Bart, and Crosby do not own a red trunk or a white trunk.
3. Of Bobbie and Bart, one is named Cassady and one owns a tan trunk.
4. The owner of the red trunk and Cortez are not named Bebe or Benito.
5. Either Casto or Coffman (who owns a white trunk) is named Bart.

Bobbie Cassady, red; Bebe Crosby, blue; Bruno Cortez, black; Bart Casto, tan; Benito Coffman, white

158   CHAPTER 4   MATRICES

EXTENDING THE LESSON

Math Power: Communication

Have students make up a problem about themselves and share it with their classmates.

Cooperative Learning Activity

This activity provides students with an opportunity to *learn* things together, not just do things together. You may wish to refer to pages T6–T8 and page 6C for the various elements of cooperative groups and specific goals and strategies for using them.

Graphing Calculator Exploration: Matrices

Teaching Tip ❶

The TI-81 graphing calculator is designed to handle most of the matrix operations and procedures introduced in this chapter. It will find determinants and inverses of matrices, as well as perform operations with matrices.

The [MATRX] key accesses the matrix operations menus. The first menu to appear is the MATRIX menu, which lists the matrix functions available. The EDIT menu allows you to define matrices. When the EDIT menu is accessed, the dimensions of the matrices A, B, and C are listed. A matrix dimension of 2 × 3 indicates a matrix has 2 rows and 3 columns. The TI-81 will accommodate a maximum of 6 rows and 6 columns in a matrix.

To enter a matrix into your calculator, choose the EDIT menu and select matrix [A]. Then enter the dimensions and elements of the matrix. As you enter the elements, notice the small graphics box to the right of the dimension definition that shows the size of the matrix and the current element position.

Define matrix $A = \begin{bmatrix} 3 & -1 \\ 4 & 2 \end{bmatrix}$ in your TI-81 graphing calculator.

ENTER: [MATRX] [▶] [ENTER] 2 [ENTER] 2 [ENTER]

Teaching Tip ❷

Enter the matrix dimensions. Enter the matrix elements.

3 [ENTER] [(-)] 1 [ENTER]

4 [ENTER] 2

Teaching Tip ❸

You can display the matrix by pressing [2nd] [QUIT] to return to the home screen, then [2nd] [A] [ENTER] to display the matrix.

The graphing calculator can find the determinant and the inverse of a matrix.

Example 1

Find the determinant and the inverse of the matrix A.

First find the determinant. *The determinant of A is denoted det A.*

ENTER: [MATRX] 5 [2nd] [A] [ENTER] | 0

Now find the inverse. *The inverse of A is denoted A^{-1}.*

ENTER: [2nd] [A] [x⁻¹] [ENTER] $\begin{bmatrix} .2 & .1 \\ -.4 & .3 \end{bmatrix}$

The determinant of matrix A is 10 and the inverse is $\begin{bmatrix} 0.2 & 0.1 \\ -0.4 & 0.3 \end{bmatrix}$.

INTRODUCING THE LESSON

Objective: Enter and manipulate matrices on the TI-81 graphing calculator.

Motivating the Lesson

Begin the lesson by writing the equations $3x - y = 0$ and $4x + 2y = 0$ on the chalkboard or overhead. How would the students solve these equations? They could do it graphically or algebraically. There are a number of ways to solve this algebraically, and one of them is using matrices.

TEACHING THE LESSON

Teaching Tip ❶   The concepts presented in this exploration make the arithmetic manipulations in the following lessons unnecessary. You may wish to present the use of the graphing calculator after you have presented the lessons containing these concepts.

Teaching Tip ❷   Enter the values of the matrix by rows. On the TI-81, "1, 2" means first row, second column.

Teaching Tip ❸   The [A] key is the second function of the 1 key.

RETEACHING THE LESSON

Have students work in groups and write their own matrices and manipulate them. Each student in each group must complete one matrix manipulation and explain it.

Teaching Tip ❹   The [B] key is the second function of the 2 key.

Teaching Tip ❺   You do not need to enter a "×" sign. The calculator knows that 2[A] is 2 × [A], or that AB is [A] × [B].

More Examples

Find the determinant and the inverse of the matrix
$A = \begin{bmatrix} 2 & -3 \\ -6 & 6 \end{bmatrix}$.

det $A = -6$

$A^{-1} = \begin{bmatrix} -1 & -0.5 \\ -1 & -0.3333333333 \end{bmatrix}$

or

$\begin{bmatrix} -1 & -0.5 \\ -1 & -\dfrac{1}{3} \end{bmatrix}$

EVALUATING THE LESSON

Closing the Lesson

Speaking Activity   Go around the room and have each student say a number between -20 and 20. Numbers can be repeated. Use these numbers as entries in a matrix. Make the matrix 5 × 6 if you have 30 students or 5 × 5 if you have 25 students, etc. Then have the students enter and manipulate the matrix on the TI-81 graphing calculator.

APPLYING THE LESSON

Homework Exercises

Assignment Guide

All: 1–18

You can also use the graphing calculator to perform operations on matrices.

Example 2   Enter matrix $B = \begin{bmatrix} 2 & 4 & 8 \\ -4 & -2 & 6 \end{bmatrix}$. Then find $2B$, AB, A^2, and $B + AB$.

Use the procedure shown on page 159 to enter matrix B.   *The dimension of the matrix is 2 × 3.*

Teaching Tip ❹

Find $2B$.

ENTER: 2 [2nd] [[B]] [ENTER] $\begin{bmatrix} 4 & 8 & 16 \\ -8 & -4 & 12 \end{bmatrix}$

Teaching Tip ❺

Then find AB.

ENTER: [2nd] [[A]] [2nd] [[B]] [ENTER] $\begin{bmatrix} 10 & 14 & 18 \\ 0 & 12 & 44 \end{bmatrix}$

Next find A^2.

ENTER: [2nd] [[A]] [x²] [ENTER] $\begin{bmatrix} 5 & -5 \\ 20 & 0 \end{bmatrix}$

Now find $B + AB$.

ENTER: [2nd] [[B]] [+] [2nd] [[A]] [2nd] [[B]] [ENTER] $\begin{bmatrix} 12 & 18 & 26 \\ -4 & 10 & 50 \end{bmatrix}$

Therefore, $2B = \begin{bmatrix} 4 & 8 & 16 \\ -8 & -4 & 12 \end{bmatrix}$, $AB = \begin{bmatrix} 10 & 14 & 18 \\ 0 & 12 & 44 \end{bmatrix}$, $A_2 = \begin{bmatrix} 5 & -5 \\ 20 & 0 \end{bmatrix}$,

and $B + AB = \begin{bmatrix} 12 & 18 & 26 \\ -4 & 10 & 50 \end{bmatrix}$.

EXERCISES

Enter the matrices into your graphing calculator in the appropriate locations. Then find each of the following. See Solutions Manual.

$A = \begin{bmatrix} 2 & 8 & 3 \\ 1 & 0 & -1 \\ 3 & 4 & 3 \end{bmatrix}$ $B = \begin{bmatrix} 5 & -2 & 6 \\ 4 & 7 & -1 \end{bmatrix}$ $C = \begin{bmatrix} 1 & -5 \\ 4 & -3 \\ 7 & -6 \end{bmatrix}$

1. $-C$
2. $5B$
3. det A
4. $-2C$
5. A^{-1}
6. CB
7. BC
8. det BC
9. BA
10. $CB - A$
11. det CB
12. $A + CB$
13. $(BC)^{-1}$
14. A^2
15. $(BC)^2$
16. $B + BA$
17. BAC
18. CBA

EXTENDING THE LESSON

Math Power: Problem Solving

What happens if you try to find det AB using the matrices A and B given in the lesson? The calculator will give you an error. Why do you get an error? Explain to students that you cannot find the determinant of a matrix that is not square, or has the same number of rows as columns.

4-2 An Introduction to Matrices

Objectives

After studying this lesson, you should be able to:

4-2A   ■ create a matrix and name it using its dimensions,

4-2B   ■ perform scalar multiplication on a matrix,

4-2C   ■ add matrices, and

4-2D   ■ find unknown values in equal matrices.

In Lesson 4-1, you learned that a **matrix** is a system of rows and columns. A matrix is a problem-solving tool that organizes numbers or data so that each position in the matrix has a purpose.

Connection

In algebra, a matrix is not expressed as a table, but as an array of values. Each value is called an **element** of the matrix. Suppose we want to write the coordinates of the vertices of $\triangle ABC$ as a matrix. Let row 1 be the x-coordinates and row 2 be the y-coordinates. Each column represents the coordinates of vertices A, B, and C.

3 columns

2 rows $\begin{bmatrix} 3 & -2 & 1 \\ 2 & 1 & -4 \end{bmatrix}$

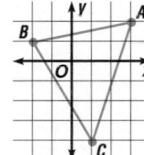

A matrix containing coordinates of a geometric figure is often called a coordinate matrix.

A matrix is usually named using an uppercase letter. We might call the matrix for $\triangle ABC$ matrix T to stand for triangle. A matrix can also be named by using the matrix **dimensions** with the letter name. The dimensions tell how many rows and columns there are in the matrix. The matrix above would be named $T_{2 \times 3}$, since it has two rows and 3 columns.

Teaching Tip ❶

Certain matrices have special names. A matrix that has only one row is called a *row matrix*, and a matrix that has only one column is called a *column matrix*. A matrix that has the same number of rows and columns is called a *square matrix*.

The plural of matrix is matrices.

Two matrices are considered equal if they have the same dimensions and each element of one matrix is equal to the corresponding element of the other matrix. This definition can be used to find values when elements of the matrices are algebraic expressions.

Definition of Equal Matrices	**Two matrices are equal *if and only if* they have the same dimensions and their corresponding elements are equal.**

ALTERNATE TEACHING STRATEGIES

Using Connections

Have one student draw a triangle on graph paper. Have another student find the vertices and draw a second triangle that is either a dilation or a translation. The paper should then be given back to the first student. The first student then determines whether the triangle is a dilation or a translation.

Lesson Resources

Reteaching Master 4-2
Practice Master 4-2
Enrichment Master 4-2
Lab Manual, pp. 51–52

 Transparency 4-2 contains the 5-Minute Check and a teaching aid for this lesson.

INTRODUCING THE LESSON

🕐 5-Minute Check

(over Lesson 4-1)

Joe, Bill, and Nick each have a hobby collecting something: coins, stamps, and baseball cards. Use these clues to find the hobby of each man.

a. Joe asked the coin collector if he knew the value of his coin collection.

b. The stamp collector and Nick went to college together.

c. Bill introduced Joe to Nick last week at a collector's meeting.

Joe–baseball cards
Bill–stamps
Nick–coins

Motivating the Lesson

Solve the system of equations.
$$x + y = 6$$
$$x - y = 4$$
Explain how you solved it.

TEACHING THE LESSON

Teaching Tip ❶   Students should be able to realize that $T_{2 \times 3}$ does not have the same dimensions as $T_{3 \times 2}$.

Example 1

Teaching Tip ❷

Solve for x and y.

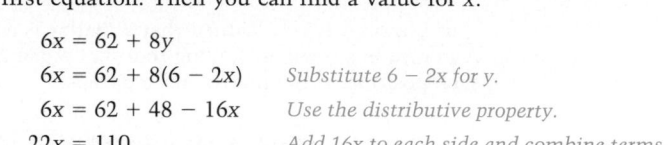

$$\begin{bmatrix} 6x \\ y \end{bmatrix} = \begin{bmatrix} 62 + 8y \\ 6 - 2x \end{bmatrix}$$

Since the matrices are equal, the corresponding elements are equal. When you write the sentences that show this equality, two linear equations are formed.

$$6x = 62 + 8y$$
$$y = 6 - 2x$$

The second equation gives you a value for y that can be substituted into the first equation. Then you can find a value for x.

$$6x = 62 + 8y$$
$$6x = 62 + 8(6 - 2x) \qquad \textit{Substitute } 6 - 2x \textit{ for y.}$$
$$6x = 62 + 48 - 16x \qquad \textit{Use the distributive property.}$$
$$22x = 110 \qquad \textit{Add 16x to each side and combine terms.}$$
$$x = 5 \qquad \textit{Divide by 22.}$$

To find a value for y, you can substitute 5 into either equation.

$$y = 6 - 2x$$
$$y = 6 - 2(5) \qquad \textit{Substitute 5 for x.}$$
$$y = -4$$

Check your solutions by substituting the values into the equation you *did not* use to find y.

Check: $6x = 62 + 8y$
$$6(5) \stackrel{?}{=} 62 + 8(-4) \qquad \textit{Substitute 5 for x and −4 for y.}$$
$$30 = 62 - 32 \text{ or } 30 \quad \checkmark$$

You can multiply any matrix by a constant. This is called **scalar multiplication.** When scalar multiplication is performed each element is multiplied by that constant, and a new matrix is formed. This is summarized by the following rule.

Scalar Multiplication of a Matrix	$k\begin{bmatrix} a & b & c \\ d & e & f \end{bmatrix} = \begin{bmatrix} ka & kb & kc \\ kd & ke & kf \end{bmatrix}$

If the perimeter of a figure triples, this does not mean its area triples.

Scalar multiplication of matrices can be used to find the coordinates of the vertices of a geometric figure when it is enlarged or reduced. This type of change is called a **dilation.** When the size of a figure changes, the measures of its sides change in the same proportion. For example, if a figure triples in perimeter, its sides triple in length.

Example 2

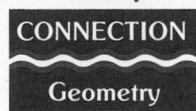

CONNECTION

Geometry

Enlarge △*ABC*, with vertices *A*(3, 2), *B*(−2, 1), and *C*(1, −4), so that its perimeter is twice the perimeter of the original figure.

Graph △*ABC*, then multiply the coordinate matrix by 2.

$$2\begin{bmatrix} 3 & -2 & 1 \\ 2 & 1 & -4 \end{bmatrix} = \begin{bmatrix} 6 & -4 & 2 \\ 4 & 2 & -8 \end{bmatrix}$$

The coordinates of the vertices of △*A'B'C'* are (6, 4), (−4, 2), and (2, −8). Graph △*A'B'C'*.

The two triangles are similar. The perimeter of △*A'B'C'* is twice the perimeter of △*ABC*.
You can measure to verify this result.

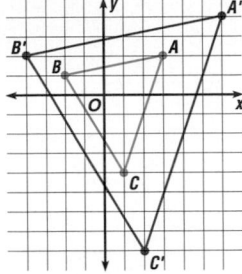

Matrices can also be added. In order to add two matrices, they must have the same dimensions.

Addition
of Matrices

> If *A* and *B* are two *m* × *n* matrices, then *A* + *B* is an *m* × *n* matrix where each element is the sum of the corresponding elements of *A* and *B*.
>
> $$\begin{bmatrix} a & b & c \\ d & e & f \\ g & h & i \end{bmatrix} + \begin{bmatrix} j & k & l \\ m & n & o \\ p & q & r \end{bmatrix} = \begin{bmatrix} a+j & b+k & c+l \\ d+m & e+n & f+o \\ g+p & h+q & i+r \end{bmatrix}$$

When a figure is moved from one location to another on the coordinate plane without changing its orientation, size, or shape, a **translation** occurs. You can use matrix addition to find the coordinates of the translated figure.

Example 3

CONNECTION

Geometry

Find the coordinates of the vertices of quadrilateral *QUAD* if the figure is moved 5 units to the right and 1 unit down.

Write the coordinates of quadrilateral *QUAD* in the form of a matrix.

$$\begin{bmatrix} -2 & 1 & 3 & -2 \\ -2 & -2 & 4 & 1 \end{bmatrix}$$

To translate the quadrilateral 5 units to the right means that each *x*-coordinate increases by 5. Translating the figure 1 unit down decreases each *y*-coordinate by 1.

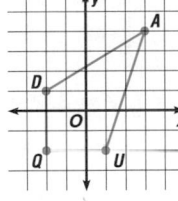

LESSON 4-2 AN INTRODUCTION TO MATRICES   163

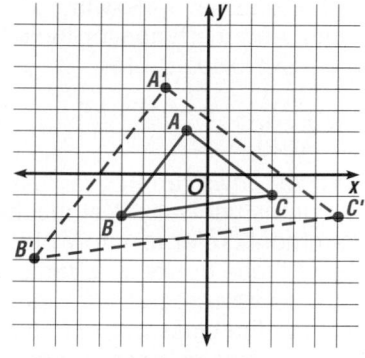
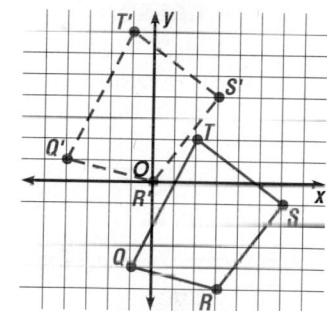

Checking for Understanding
Exercises 1–10 are designed to help you assess understanding through reading, writing, and speaking. You should work through Exercises 1–5 with your students, and then monitor their work on Exercises 6–10.

Error Analysis
In matrices, rows run horizontally and columns vertically. Yet teachers commonly refer to a row of desks as those desks in a vertical line (i.e. a line perpendicular to the front of the classroom). In theatres and stadiums rows run horizontally. For consistency and transfer, teachers could refer to a line of desks parallel to the sides of a room as a column.

Closing the Lesson
Speaking Activity Have students explain how to add and to use scalar multiplication.

Reteaching Masters Booklet, p. 23

4-2 NAME _____ DATE _____
Reteaching Worksheet
Reading Algebra

The ability to use definitions is extremely important in mathematics. Writing a clear, workable definition is not always easy. A good definition must meet several criteria: It must be clear enough and complete enough so that it is possible to be sure whether a particular thing is or is not an example of the kind of thing the definition seeks to describe. It must be possible to show that things of that kind actually *exist*. The definition must include everything you are seeking to describe, but nothing else.

Example: What is wrong with this proposed definition of the distance from a point P in a plane to a ray AB in the same plane?

"The real number d is the distance from the point P in the plane to the ray AB in the plane if and only if P is on the ray and $d = 0$ or d is not on the ray and d is the length of the segment PX such that X is on $\overline{AB}$ and $\overline{PX} \perp \overline{AB}$."

The definition overlooks the fact that for P not on $\overline{AB}$ the line through P perpendicular to *line* AB may not intersect the *ray* AB. Also, if P is on *line* AB but not on *ray* AB, how is the distance from P to AB to be determined?

State what is wrong with the following "definitions." The term being defined is in boldface.

1. A **matrix** is a group of numbers arranged in rows and columns. **Answers will vary. Possible answer: Does not state that all rows (columns) have the same number of elements. Hence, would allow arrangements such as $\begin{bmatrix} 3 & 0 & 5 & 9 \\ 2 & 4 \\ -6 & 7 & 3 \end{bmatrix}$ to be matrices.**

2. The **sum** of two matrices A and B is the matrix obtained by adding the element in the ith row and j^{th} column of matrix A to the element in the ith row of jth column of matrix B. **Answers will vary. Possible answer: Fails to specify that the dimensions of A and B must be the same.**

3. The **additive identity** matrix M results in the same matrix M. **Answers will vary. Possible answer: No such matrix exists.**

4. Tell how you could correct the flaws in each "definition" in exercises 1-3 to arrive at a workable definition. **See students' work. Students should be able to defend their revised definitions.**

The matrix, called a *translation matrix,* that increases each x-value by 5 and decreases each y-value by 1 is $\begin{bmatrix} 5 & 5 & 5 & 5 \\ -1 & -1 & -1 & -1 \end{bmatrix}$.

To find the coordinates of the translated quadrilateral $Q'U'A'D'$, add the two matrices.

$$\begin{bmatrix} -2 & 1 & 3 & -2 \\ -2 & -2 & 4 & 1 \end{bmatrix} + \begin{bmatrix} 5 & 5 & 5 & 5 \\ -1 & -1 & -1 & -1 \end{bmatrix} = \begin{bmatrix} 3 & 6 & 8 & 3 \\ -3 & -3 & 3 & 0 \end{bmatrix}$$

Now graph the coordinates of quadrilateral $Q'U'A'D'$ to check the accuracy of your coordinates. The two quadrilaterals have the same size and shape. Quadrilateral $Q'U'A'D'$ is $QUAD$ moved right 5 units and down 1 unit.

The two figures are congruent.

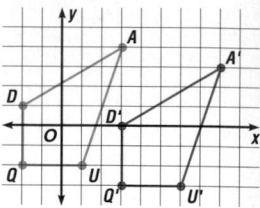

CHECKING FOR UNDERSTANDING

Communicating Mathematics

Read and study the lesson to answer each question.

1. What is a matrix? **an array of numbers in columns and rows**
2. Describe the matrix $A_{3\times2}$. **A matrix that has 3 rows and 2 columns.**
3. Under what conditions are two matrices equal? **See margin.**
4. Under what conditions can matrices be added? **See margin.**
5. Explain the difference between a dilation and a translation. **See margin.**

Guided Practice

Name each matrix using the dimensions. Then multiply the matrix by -2.

$A_{4\times3}$;

$\begin{bmatrix} -14 & 4 & 8 \\ 16 & -18 & -20 \\ -2 & -34 & -20 \\ -42 & 6 & -12 \end{bmatrix}$

6. $A = \begin{bmatrix} 7 & -2 & -4 \\ -8 & 9 & 10 \\ 1 & 17 & 10 \\ 21 & -3 & 6 \end{bmatrix}$

7. $V = [-7 \quad 5 \quad 26] \ V_{1\times3};$
$[14 \quad -10 \quad -52]$

Solve for the variables.

$x = 1, y = 3, z = 5$

8. $\begin{bmatrix} 2 & x \\ y & 5 \end{bmatrix} = \begin{bmatrix} 2 & 1 \\ 3 & z \end{bmatrix}$

$x = 2\frac{1}{2}, y = 1, z = 3$

9. $[2x \quad 3 \quad 3z] = [5 \quad 3y \quad 9]$

10. Translate $\triangle DEF$ with $D(7, -2)$, $E(4, 5)$, and $F(-3, 4)$ 5 units left and 1 unit up. Graph $\triangle DEF$ and $\triangle D'E'F'$. State the coordinates of the translated triangle. $D'(2, -1)$, $E'(-1, 6)$, $F'(-8, 5)$
For graphs, see Solutions Manual.

164   CHAPTER 4   MATRICES

RETEACHING THE LESSON

Use the class seating arrangement to form matrices with each student's desk as an element or cell. Make large cards to denote values of elements of several matrices. Some cards for matrix $A_{4\times3}$ might be $A_{2,3} = 7$ or $B_{3,1} = -4$. Form two matrices $A_{4\times3}$ and $B_{4\times3}$ using two arrangements of seats with 4 rows and 3 columns.

Have students deliver cards to each member (student) of the matrix. Here are some problems to consider.
1. Does $A = B$?
2. Find $A + B$.
3. Find $3A$.
4. If $B_{3,2} = 4x - 6$, find x.
Try different size matrices.

EXERCISES

Practice

Perform the indicated operations. Name the resulting matrix by its dimensions. Letter names will vary. See margin for resulting matrices.

11. $4\begin{bmatrix} 2 & -3 \\ 4 & 1 \\ 0 & 3 \end{bmatrix}$ $A_{3\times2}$ 12. $\begin{bmatrix} 3 & 7 \\ -2 & 1 \end{bmatrix} - \begin{bmatrix} 2 & -3 \\ 5 & -4 \end{bmatrix}$ $B_{2\times2}$ 13. $[4 \quad 1 \quad -3] + [6 \quad -5 \quad 8]$ $C_{1\times3}$

Solve for the variables.
$x = -6, y = 12, z = 5, w = 20$

16. $x = 1, y = 5,$
$z = 10$

17. $x = 5, y = 3,$
$z = 2$

14. $\begin{bmatrix} 2x & 3y \\ 40 & 50 \end{bmatrix} = \begin{bmatrix} -12 & 36 \\ 8z & 2.5w \end{bmatrix}$ 15. $\begin{bmatrix} 2x \\ y+1 \end{bmatrix} = \begin{bmatrix} y \\ 3 \end{bmatrix}$ $x = 1$ $y = 2$

16. $y\begin{bmatrix} 3 & -4 \\ 2 & x \end{bmatrix} = \begin{bmatrix} 15 & -20 \\ z & 5 \end{bmatrix}$ 17. $4\begin{bmatrix} x & y-1 \\ 3 & z \end{bmatrix} = \begin{bmatrix} 20 & 8 \\ 6z & x+y \end{bmatrix}$

18. $\begin{bmatrix} x^2 & 7 & 9 \\ 5 & 12 & 6 \end{bmatrix} = \begin{bmatrix} 25 & 7 & y \\ 5 & 2z & 6 \end{bmatrix}$ 19. $\begin{bmatrix} x+3y \\ 3x+y \end{bmatrix} = \begin{bmatrix} -13 \\ 1 \end{bmatrix}$ $x = 2$ $y = -5$

$x = \pm5, y = 9, z = 6$

CONNECTION Geometry

20. Translate $\triangle RST$ with $R(5, -2)$, $S(8, 4)$, and $T(-3, -1)$, so that R' is located at $(3, 4)$. Graph both triangles and state the coordinates of S' and T'. $S'(6, 10), T'(-5, 5)$ **For graph, see Solutions Manual.**

Perform the indicated operations. See margin.

21. $3\begin{bmatrix} 3 & -2 & 5 \\ 2 & 7 & -5 \end{bmatrix} + 2\begin{bmatrix} -1 & 3 & 4 \\ 2 & -3 & 0 \end{bmatrix}$ 22. $\frac{1}{2}\begin{bmatrix} 4 & 12 & 9 \\ 3 & 6 & 0 \end{bmatrix} - \frac{2}{3}\begin{bmatrix} 9 & 27 & 6 \\ 0 & 3 & 4 \end{bmatrix}$

23. $3\begin{bmatrix} 4 \\ 1 \\ 7 \end{bmatrix} + 2\begin{bmatrix} 3 \\ -2 \\ 6 \end{bmatrix} - 5\begin{bmatrix} -2 \\ 3 \\ 6 \end{bmatrix}$

24. $5\begin{bmatrix} -2 & 4 \\ 1 & -1 \\ 3 & 0 \end{bmatrix} - 2\begin{bmatrix} 5 & 3 \\ -3 & 2 \\ 8 & -9 \end{bmatrix} + \begin{bmatrix} 0 & -5 \\ 9 & -3 \\ -2 & 7 \end{bmatrix}$

CONNECTION Geometry

25. Quadrilateral $BURT$ has vertices with coordinates $B(6, 1)$, $U(3, 5)$, $R(-1, 4)$, and $T(-3, -5)$.

25a. $\begin{bmatrix} 4 & 4 & 4 & 4 \\ -2 & -2 & -2 & -2 \end{bmatrix}$

a. What translation matrix would you need to translate $BURT$ so that R' has coordinates $(3, 2)$?

b. Use the translation matrix to find the coordinates of B', T', and U'.

25b. $B'(10, -1), T'(1, -7), U'(7, 3)$

26. The vertex of the right angle of a right triangle is located at the origin with its other vertices at $(0, 12)$ and $(5, 0)$. Find the coordinates of the vertices of a similar triangle whose perimeter is four times that of the original triangle. $(0, 48), (20, 0), (0, 0)$

Additional Answers

3. The two matrices must have the same dimensions and corresponding elements are equal.
4. They must have the same dimensions.
5. A dilation changes the size but not the shape of a figure. A translation moves a figure, but does not change its orientation, size, or shape.

11. $\begin{bmatrix} 8 & -12 \\ 16 & 4 \\ 0 & 12 \end{bmatrix}$

12. $\begin{bmatrix} 1 & 10 \\ -7 & 5 \end{bmatrix}$

13. $[10 \quad -4 \quad 5]$

Homework Exercises

Assignment Guide

Basic: 11–26, 32–37
Average: 14–28, 32–37
Enriched: 16–37

Chapter 4, Quiz A, (Lessons 4-1 through 4-2), is available in the Evaluation Masters Booklet, p. 51.

Additional Answers

21. $\begin{bmatrix} 7 & 0 & 23 \\ 10 & 15 & -15 \end{bmatrix}$

22. $\begin{bmatrix} -4 & -12 & \frac{1}{2} \\ 1\frac{1}{2} & 1 & -2\frac{2}{3} \end{bmatrix}$

23. $\begin{bmatrix} 28 \\ -16 \\ 3 \end{bmatrix}$

24. $\begin{bmatrix} -20 & 9 \\ 20 & -12 \\ -3 & 25 \end{bmatrix}$

Practice Masters Booklet, p. 27

NAME _____ DATE _____

4-2 Practice Worksheet

An Introduction to Matrices

Solve for the variables.

1. $\begin{bmatrix} 3x & 4y \\ -48 & 49 \end{bmatrix} = \begin{bmatrix} 27 & -16 \\ -3w & 7z \end{bmatrix}$ $x = 9, y = -4, w = 16, z = 7$

2. $\begin{bmatrix} 3x \\ y+4 \end{bmatrix} = \begin{bmatrix} y+8 \\ 17 \end{bmatrix}$ $x = 7, y = 13$

3. $x\begin{bmatrix} 2 & -5 \\ 7 & y \end{bmatrix} = \begin{bmatrix} 8 & -20 \\ z & 24 \end{bmatrix}$ $x = 4, y = 6, z = 28$

4. $5\begin{bmatrix} x & y+2 \\ 6 & z \end{bmatrix} = \begin{bmatrix} 10 & 25 \\ 2z & 30x+5y \end{bmatrix}$ $x = 2, y = 3, z = 15$

5. $\begin{bmatrix} a^2 & -9 & 15 \\ 2 & 16 & 18 \end{bmatrix} = \begin{bmatrix} 36 & -9 & -5b \\ 2 & 2c & 18 \end{bmatrix}$ $a = 6$ or $-6, b = -3, c = 8$

6. $\begin{bmatrix} 2x+y \\ x-3y \end{bmatrix} = \begin{bmatrix} 23 \\ 15 \end{bmatrix}$ $x = 12, y = -1$

Perform the indicated operations.

7. $3\begin{bmatrix} 2 & 5 & -1 & 9 \\ 4 & 0 & 8 & -6 \end{bmatrix}$ $\begin{bmatrix} 6 & 15 & -3 & 27 \\ 12 & 0 & 24 & -18 \end{bmatrix}$

8. $\begin{bmatrix} 2 & -1 \\ 3 & 7 \\ 14 & -9 \end{bmatrix} + \begin{bmatrix} -6 & 9 \\ 7 & -11 \\ -8 & 17 \end{bmatrix}$ $\begin{bmatrix} -4 & 8 \\ 10 & -4 \\ 6 & 8 \end{bmatrix}$

9. $6\begin{bmatrix} 1 \\ -3 \\ 0 \end{bmatrix} + 5\begin{bmatrix} 2 \\ 7 \\ -8 \end{bmatrix} - 4\begin{bmatrix} -1 \\ 4 \\ 12 \end{bmatrix}$ $\begin{bmatrix} 19 \\ 5 \\ -76 \end{bmatrix}$

10. $6\begin{bmatrix} 2 & 3 \\ -1 & 4 \\ 8 & -6 \end{bmatrix} + 5\begin{bmatrix} 7 & -4 \\ 3 & 2 \\ 0 & -1 \end{bmatrix}$ $\begin{bmatrix} 47 & -2 \\ 9 & 34 \\ 48 & -41 \end{bmatrix}$

11. $7\begin{bmatrix} 2 & -1 & 8 \\ 4 & 7 & 9 \end{bmatrix} - 2\begin{bmatrix} -1 & 4 & -3 \\ 7 & 2 & -6 \end{bmatrix}$ $\begin{bmatrix} 16 & -15 & 62 \\ 14 & 45 & 75 \end{bmatrix}$

12. $4\begin{bmatrix} 3 & 8 & 12 \\ -16 & 20 \end{bmatrix} + \frac{2}{3}\begin{bmatrix} 27 & -9 \\ 54 & -18 \end{bmatrix}$ $\begin{bmatrix} 24 & 3 \\ 24 & 3 \end{bmatrix}$

32. triangle perimeter is half and triangle is rotated 180°

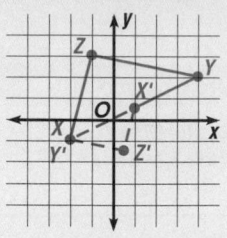

33a. $M = \begin{bmatrix} 120 & 97 & 64 & 75 \\ 80 & 59 & 36 & 60 \\ 72 & 84 & 29 & 48 \end{bmatrix}$

$T = \begin{bmatrix} 112 & 87 & 56 & 74 \\ 84 & 65 & 39 & 70 \\ 88 & 98 & 43 & 60 \end{bmatrix}$

$S = \begin{bmatrix} 232 & 184 & 120 & 149 \\ 164 & 124 & 75 & 130 \\ 160 & 182 & 72 & 108 \end{bmatrix}$

Enrichment Masters Booklet, p. 23

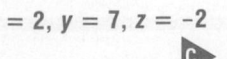

NAME _____ DATE _____

4-2 Enrichment Worksheet

Sundaram's Sieve

The properties and patterns of prime numbers have fascinated many mathematicians. In 1934, a young East Indian student named Sundaram constructed the following matrix.

4	7	10	13	16	19	22	25	. . .
7	12	17	22	27	32	37	42	. . .
10	17	24	31	38	45	52	59	. . .
13	22	31	40	49	58	67	76	. . .
16	27	38	49	60	71	82	93	. . .

A surprising property of this matrix is that it can be used to determine whether or not some numbers are prime.

Complete these problems to discover this property.

1. The first row and the first column are created by using an arithmetic sequence. What is the common difference used in the sequence?
3
2. Find the next four numbers in the first row.
28, 31, 34
3. What are the common differences used to create the sequences in rows 2, 3, 4, and 5?
5, 7, 9, 11
4. Write the next two rows of the matrix. Include eight numbers in each row. **row 6: 19, 32, 45, 58, 71, 84, 97, 110
row 7: 22, 37, 52, 67, 82, 97, 112, 127**
5. Choose any five numbers from the matrix. For each number, n, that you chose from the matrix, find $2n + 1$.
Answers will vary.
6. Write the factorization of each value of $2n + 1$ that you found in problem 5. **Answers will vary, but all numbers are composite.**
7. Use your results from problems 5 and 6 to complete this statement: If n occurs in the matrix, then $2n + 1$ **is not** (is/is not) a prime number.
8. Choose any five numbers that are not in the matrix. Find $2n + 1$ for each of these numbers. Show that each result is a prime number. **Answers will vary, but all numbers are prime.**
9. Complete this statement: If n does not occur in the matrix, then $2n + 1$ is **a prime number**

Solve for the variable.

$x = 2, y = 7, z = -2$

27. $\begin{bmatrix} x \\ 7z \\ 2y \end{bmatrix} - \begin{bmatrix} 4z \\ -3y \\ 3x \end{bmatrix} + \begin{bmatrix} -2y \\ 2x \\ -5z \end{bmatrix} = \begin{bmatrix} -4 \\ 11 \\ 18 \end{bmatrix}$

28. $\begin{bmatrix} r^2 - 24 & 17 \\ 7 & t^3 \end{bmatrix} = \begin{bmatrix} 1 & 2y + 3 \\ z^2 - 12 & 27 \end{bmatrix}$

28. $r = \pm 5, y = 7, t = 3, z = \pm\sqrt{19}$

29. $\begin{bmatrix} 5x - 7 & 11 \\ 5 & 23 \end{bmatrix} = \begin{bmatrix} 8 & 21 - m \\ r^3 - 3 & 4y + x \end{bmatrix}$

30. $\begin{bmatrix} 13 - 7y & a \\ 1 & 2b - 38 \end{bmatrix} = \begin{bmatrix} 5x & 2 - 6b \\ 2x + 3y & 5a \end{bmatrix}$

29. $x = 3, y = 5, m = 10, r = 2$ **30.** $x = 32, y = -21, a = -7, b = \frac{3}{2}$

CONNECTION
Geometry

31. Find the coordinates of quadrilateral $MNPQ$ that is congruent to quadrilateral $XYZW$ whose vertices have coordinates $X(5, -3)$, $Y(2, 7)$, $Z(-3, 3)$, and $W(-5, 1)$, if M is located at the origin. $M(0, 0), N(-3, 10), P(-8, 6), Q(-10, 4)$

Critical Thinking
CONNECTION
Geometry

32. The coordinate matrix for triangle XYZ is $\begin{bmatrix} -2 & 4 & -1 \\ -1 & 2 & 3 \end{bmatrix}$. Explain what happens to the triangle when the matrix is multiplied by $-\frac{1}{2}$. Make a drawing to justify your answer. **See margin.**

Applications

33. Business A local bakery keeps a log of each type of donut sold at three of their branch stores so that they can monitor their purchases of supplies without having extra inventory. Two days of sales are shown below.

Monday	jelly	glazed	plain	frosted
Big Donut	120	97	64	75
Cal's Donut	80	59	36	60
Donuts Inc.	72	84	29	48

Tuesday	jelly	glazed	plain	frosted
Big Donut	112	87	56	74
Cal's Donuts	84	65	39	70
Donuts Inc.	88	98	43	60

a. Write a matrix for each day's sales. Name each matrix. Then find the sum of the two days' sales expressed as a matrix. **See margin.**

b. Each type of donut takes approximately one-fourth cup of flour. If there are four cups of flour in a pound, how many pounds of flour were needed for these two days of baking? **106.25 pounds**

Mixed Review

34. Find an equation of the line that passes through $(-1, 2)$ and is parallel to the graph of $2x - 7y = 11$. **(Lesson 2-4)** $2x - 7y = -16$

35. If $f(x) = 2x^2 + 5x - 3$, find $f\left(\frac{2}{3}\right)$. **(Lesson 2-1)** $1\frac{2}{9}$

36. Solve $5a + 1 \le 8a - 3$. **(Lesson 1-7)** $\left\{a \mid a \ge \frac{4}{3}\right\}$

37. Solve $\frac{3}{4}(x - 5) = \frac{4}{5}(x + 4)$. **(Lesson 1-3)** -139

EXTENDING THE LESSON

Math Power: Problem Solving

Find the values x, y, z, and w for which this equation is true.

$3\begin{bmatrix} x & y \\ z & w \end{bmatrix} = \begin{bmatrix} 6 & 12 \\ 3 & 15 \end{bmatrix}$

$x = 2, y = 4$
$z = 1, w = 5$

Objectives

After studying this lesson, you should be able to:

4-3A ■ evaluate the determinant of a 3 × 3 matrix, and

4-3B ■ find the area of a triangle given the coordinates of its vertices.

Every square matrix has a **determinant.** The determinant has the same elements as the matrix, but they are enclosed between vertical bars instead of brackets. In Chapter 3 you learned a method for evaluating a 2 × 2 determinant.

The determinant of $\begin{bmatrix} 3 & -2 \\ 17 & 11 \end{bmatrix}$ is $\begin{vmatrix} 3 & -2 \\ 17 & 11 \end{vmatrix}$. To evaluate the determinant, use the rule for second-order determinants.

$$\begin{vmatrix} 3 & -2 \\ 17 & 11 \end{vmatrix} = 3(11) - (-2)(17) \qquad \textit{Remember that } \begin{vmatrix} a & b \\ c & d \end{vmatrix} = ad - bc.$$

$$= 33 - (-34) \text{ or } 67$$

Teaching Tip ❶

Determinants of 3 × 3 matrices are called third order determinants.

A method called **expansion by minors** can be used to evaluate the determinant of a 3 × 3 matrix. The **minor** of an element is the determinant formed when the row and column containing that element are deleted. For

the determinant $\begin{vmatrix} 1 & 3 & 7 \\ 4 & 8 & 2 \\ 9 & 5 & 6 \end{vmatrix}$, the minor of 5 is $\begin{vmatrix} 1 & 3 & 7 \\ 4 & 8 & 2 \\ 9 & 5 & 6 \end{vmatrix}$ or $\begin{vmatrix} 1 & 7 \\ 4 & 2 \end{vmatrix}$. The

minor of 1 is $\begin{vmatrix} 1 & 3 & 7 \\ 4 & 8 & 2 \\ 9 & 5 & 6 \end{vmatrix}$ or $\begin{vmatrix} 8 & 2 \\ 5 & 6 \end{vmatrix}$.

To use expansion by minors with third-order determinants, each member of one row is multiplied by its minor. The signs of the products alternate, beginning with the second product. The definition below shows an expansion using the elements in the first row of the determinant. However, any row can be used.

Expansion of a Third-Order Determinant

$$\begin{vmatrix} a & b & c \\ d & e & f \\ g & h & i \end{vmatrix} = a\begin{vmatrix} e & f \\ h & i \end{vmatrix} - b\begin{vmatrix} d & f \\ g & i \end{vmatrix} + c\begin{vmatrix} d & e \\ g & h \end{vmatrix}$$

LESSON 4-3 MATRICES AND DETERMINANTS 167

ALTERNATE TEACHING STRATEGIES

Using Calculators

Have students use calculators to find the value of determinants using the diagonal method. Students will find it easier to keep track of the values and signs by using the calculator. The values can be put into one equation.

$$\begin{vmatrix} a & b & c \\ d & e & f \\ g & h & i \end{vmatrix} = (aei + bfg + cdh) - (gec + dbi + ahf)$$

Lesson Resources

Reteaching Master 4-3
Practice Master 4-3
Enrichment Master 4-3
Technology Master, p. 21
Multicultural Activity Master, p. 4

 Transparency 4-3 contains the 5-Minute Check and a teaching aid for this lesson.

INTRODUCING THE LESSON

🕐 5-Minute Check

(over Lesson 4-2)

Name the matrix using the dimensions.

1. $M = \begin{bmatrix} 8 & 0 & 2 \\ 6 & 3 & -1 \end{bmatrix}$

2. $N = \begin{bmatrix} 6 & -3 & 4 \end{bmatrix}$
   1. $M_{2 \times 3}$ **2.** $N_{1 \times 3}$

3. Solve for the variables.
   $\begin{bmatrix} 1 & 3a \end{bmatrix} = \begin{bmatrix} 4b & 21 \end{bmatrix}$
   $a = 7 \quad b = \frac{1}{4}$

Perform the indicated operation.

4. $3\begin{bmatrix} 2 & 7 & -2 \\ 1 & -3 & 5 \end{bmatrix}$
   $\begin{bmatrix} 6 & 21 & -6 \\ 3 & -9 & 15 \end{bmatrix}$

5. $\begin{bmatrix} 4 & 3 \\ -1 & 6 \end{bmatrix} + \begin{bmatrix} -5 & 7 \\ 6 & -2 \end{bmatrix}$
   $\begin{bmatrix} -1 & 10 \\ 5 & 4 \end{bmatrix}$

6. Solve for the variables.
   $\begin{bmatrix} 5a - 2b \\ a + 6b \end{bmatrix} = \begin{bmatrix} 18 \\ 10 \end{bmatrix}$
   $a = 4$
   $b = 1$

Motivating the Lesson

Have students name some necessary conditions for

$$\begin{vmatrix} a & b \\ c & d \end{vmatrix} = 0$$

to be true. Remind them about determinants from Cramer's rule.

Teaching Tip ❶ The determinant of an $n \times n$ matrix is called the nth order determinant.

Teaching Tip ❷ The diagonal method does not work for fourth or higher order determinants.

Chalkboard Example

For Example 1
Evaluate the determinant of

$$\begin{bmatrix} 5 & -1 & 2 \\ 2 & -3 & 5 \\ 3 & 2 & -3 \end{bmatrix}$$ using expansion by minors.   0

Example 1

Evaluate the determinant of $\begin{bmatrix} 2 & 3 & 4 \\ 6 & 5 & 7 \\ 1 & 2 & 8 \end{bmatrix}$ using expansion by minors.

Decide which row of elements you will use for the expansion. Let's use the first row.

After entering this matrix in your TI-81 calculator, try this. Press MATRIX, select #5: det, press 2nd [A], ENTER. What is your answer?

$$\begin{vmatrix} 2 & 3 & 4 \\ 6 & 5 & 7 \\ 1 & 2 & 8 \end{vmatrix} = 2\begin{vmatrix} 5 & 7 \\ 2 & 8 \end{vmatrix} - 3\begin{vmatrix} 6 & 7 \\ 1 & 8 \end{vmatrix} + 4\begin{vmatrix} 6 & 5 \\ 1 & 2 \end{vmatrix}$$

The determinant of $\begin{bmatrix} 2 & 3 & 4 \\ 6 & 5 & 7 \\ 1 & 2 & 8 \end{bmatrix}$ is $\begin{vmatrix} 2 & 3 & 4 \\ 6 & 5 & 7 \\ 1 & 2 & 8 \end{vmatrix}$.

$$= 2(40 - 14) - 3(48 - 7) + 4(12 - 5)$$
$$= 52 - 123 + 28 \text{ or } -43$$

You can check your work by evaluating the determinant again using a different row of elements.

Teaching Tip ❷

Another method for evaluating a third-order determinant is using diagonals. In this method, you begin by repeating the first two columns on the right side of the determinant.

$$\begin{vmatrix} a & b & c \\ d & e & f \\ g & h & i \end{vmatrix} \blacktriangleright \begin{vmatrix} a & b & c \\ d & e & f \\ g & h & i \end{vmatrix}\begin{matrix} a & b \\ d & e \\ g & h \end{matrix}$$

Now draw a diagonal from each element in the top row diagonally downward. Find the product of the numbers on each diagonal.

$$\begin{vmatrix} a & b & c \\ d & e & f \\ g & h & i \end{vmatrix}\begin{matrix} a & b \\ d & e \\ g & h \end{matrix}$$

$aei \quad bfg \quad cdh$

Then draw a diagonal from each element in the bottom row diagonally upward. Find the product of the numbers on each diagonal.

$gec \quad hfa \quad idb$

$$\begin{vmatrix} a & b & c \\ d & e & f \\ g & h & i \end{vmatrix}\begin{matrix} a & b \\ d & e \\ g & h \end{matrix}$$

To find the value of the determinant, add the products in the first set of diagonals and then subtract the products from the second set of diagonals.

The value is $aei + bfg + cdh - gec - hfa - idb$.

Example 2

Evaluate $\begin{vmatrix} -1 & 4 & 0 \\ 3 & -2 & -5 \\ -3 & -1 & 2 \end{vmatrix}$ using diagonals.

First, rewrite the first two columns along side the determinant.

Next, find the values using the diagonals.

$\begin{vmatrix} -1 & 4 & 0 \\ 3 & -2 & -5 \\ -3 & -1 & 2 \end{vmatrix} \begin{matrix} -1 & 4 \\ 3 & -2 \\ -3 & -1 \end{matrix}$

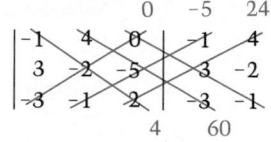

Now add the bottom products and subtract the top products.

$4 + 60 + 0 - 0 - (-5) - 24 = 45$

The value of the determinant is 45.

Determinants can be used to find the area of a triangle when you know the coordinates of the three vertices. The area of a triangle whose vertices have coordinates (a, b), (c, d) and (e, f) can be found by using the formula

$A = \dfrac{1}{2}\begin{vmatrix} a & b & 1 \\ c & d & 1 \\ e & f & 1 \end{vmatrix}$, and then finding $|A|$, since the area cannot be negative.

Example 3

CONNECTION

Geometry

Find the area of the triangle whose vertices have coordinates $(-4, -1)$, $(3, 2)$, and $(4, 6)$.

Assign values to a, b, c, d, e, and f and substitute them into the area formula and evaluate.

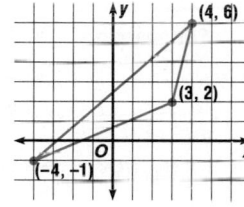

$A = \dfrac{1}{2}\begin{vmatrix} a & b & 1 \\ c & d & 1 \\ e & f & 1 \end{vmatrix}$ $a = -4, b = -1,$
$c = 3, d = 2,$
$e = 4, f = 6$

$= \dfrac{1}{2}\begin{vmatrix} -4 & -1 & 1 \\ 3 & 2 & 1 \\ 4 & 6 & 1 \end{vmatrix} = \dfrac{1}{2}[(-4)2 + (-1)4 + (3)6 - (-4)6 - (-1)3 - (2)4]$

$= \dfrac{1}{2}(-8 - 4 + 18 + 24 + 3 - 8)$

$= \dfrac{1}{2}(25)$ or $12\dfrac{1}{2}$ $\left|12\dfrac{1}{2}\right| = 12\dfrac{1}{2}$

The area of the triangle is $12\dfrac{1}{2}$ square units.

Checking for Understanding

Exercises 1–11 are designed to help you assess understanding through reading, writing, and speaking. You should work through Exercises 1–4 with your students, and then monitor their work on Exercises 5–11.

Error Analysis

Students sometimes miss the signs of the terms when expanding by minors. Common mistakes are to start with the wrong sign for the first term or to not alternate the signs. An easy rule to determine the sign of each term uses the sum of the indices (row # and column #). The sign of a term is positive if the sum of the indices is even and the sign of the term is negative if the sum of the indices is odd. For example, $A_{3,4}$ uses a negative sign while $A_{1,3}$ uses a positive sign.

Reteaching Masters Booklet, p. 24

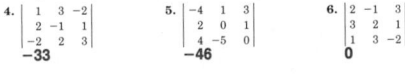

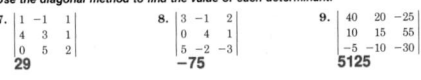

Sometimes one or more of the elements of a determinant may be unknown, but the value of the determinant is known. You can use expansion to find the values of the variable.

Example 4

Solve for n if $\begin{vmatrix} 4 & 3 & 6 \\ 2 & 2n & 7 \\ -4 & -3n & 3 \end{vmatrix} = -582$.

By expanding the determinant, you get this equation.

$$24n - 36n - 84 + 48n - 18 + 84n = -582$$
$$120n - 102 = -582 \quad \textit{Combine like terms.}$$
$$120n = -480 \quad \textit{Add 102 to each side.}$$
$$n = -4 \quad \textit{Divide each side by 120.}$$

The value of n is -4.

CHECKING FOR UNDERSTANDING

Communicating Mathematics

1. when it is a square matrix

See margin.

Read and study the lesson to answer each question.

1. Under what conditions does a matrix have a determinant?

2. Describe the steps in finding the minor of 6 in $\begin{vmatrix} 1 & 2 & 3 \\ 4 & 5 & 6 \\ 7 & 8 & 9 \end{vmatrix}$. **See margin.**

3. Name an application of geometry that may use determinants.

4. In Example 4, explain how you can check the solution.
   Substitute −4 for n and re-evaluate the determinant.

Guided Practice

Determine whether each matrix has a determinant. If it does, find the value of the determinant. **6. no determinant   7. no determinant**

5. $\begin{bmatrix} 2 & 5 \\ -3 & 8 \end{bmatrix}$ **31**   6. $\begin{bmatrix} 7 \\ -2 \end{bmatrix}$ 7. $\begin{bmatrix} 5 & 4 & -7 \\ 8 & 4 & 1 \end{bmatrix}$ 8. $\begin{bmatrix} 6 & 9 \\ 2 & 3 \end{bmatrix}$ **0**

Solve for x.

9. $\begin{vmatrix} 5 & x \\ 2x & 7 \end{vmatrix} = -63$ $x = \pm 7$ 10. $\begin{vmatrix} 3 & -2 & x \\ x & 1 & -5 \\ 2 & 0 & -1 \end{vmatrix} = 1$ $x = 4$

11. $A = \dfrac{1}{2}\begin{vmatrix} 4 & -5 & 1 \\ 3 & 8 & 1 \\ -2 & 3 & 1 \end{vmatrix}$

11. Write an expression for finding the area of a triangle whose vertices have coordinates (4, −5), (3, 8), and (−2, 3) using determinants.

RETEACHING THE LESSON

Find the value of the determinant of each matrix. Only square matrices have determinants.

1. $\begin{vmatrix} 3 & 5 \\ -1 & 4 \end{vmatrix}$ **17**   2. $\begin{vmatrix} 4 \\ 3 \end{vmatrix}$
   no determinant

3. $\begin{vmatrix} 4 & 2 \\ 6 & 3 \end{vmatrix}$ **0**   4. $\begin{vmatrix} 0 & -2 \\ -1 & 2 \end{vmatrix}$ **−2**

Additional Answers

2. Cross out the row containing 6. Cross out the column containing 6. The four remaining elements are the minor of 6.
3. Finding the area of a triangle.

EXERCISES

Writing Activity Have students write a system of equations involving three unknowns and then find the determinants of the matrices for Cramer's Rule.

Practice

Determine whether each matrix has a determinant. If it does, find the value of the determinant.

no determinant

 12. $\begin{bmatrix} 7 \\ 2 \\ 1 \\ -5 \end{bmatrix}$ **13.** $\begin{bmatrix} 9 & -3 \\ 17 & 4 \end{bmatrix}$ **14.** $\begin{bmatrix} -2 & 9 \\ 7 & -4 \\ -6 & 1 \end{bmatrix}$ **15.** $\begin{bmatrix} 4 & -6 & -9 & 3 \\ 0 & -4 & 2 & -8 \end{bmatrix}$

no determinant   **87**   **no determinant**

APPLYING THE LESSON

Homework Exercises

Solve for x.

16. $\begin{vmatrix} 5 & 7 \\ -2 & 2x \end{vmatrix} = 54$ $x = 4$ **17.** $\begin{vmatrix} x & 7 & 5 \\ 0 & 3 & 4 \\ 3 & 2 & -x \end{vmatrix} = 11$ $x = \dfrac{-14}{3}$ or 2

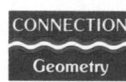

18. Find the area of a triangle whose vertices have coordinates (0, 0), (5, –6), and (3, 7). **26.5 units²**

Determine the value of the determinant of each matrix.

 19. $\begin{bmatrix} 6 & 4 \\ -3 & 2 \end{bmatrix}$ **24**   **20.** $\begin{bmatrix} 2 & -3 & 4 \\ -2 & 1 & 5 \\ 5 & 3 & -2 \end{bmatrix}$ **–141**   **21.** $\begin{bmatrix} 6 & 5 & -2 \\ -3 & 0 & 6 \\ 1 & 4 & 2 \end{bmatrix}$ **–60**

Solve for the variable.

22. $\begin{vmatrix} 5a & 3 \\ a & 5 \end{vmatrix} = 7$ $a = \dfrac{7}{22}$ **23.** $\begin{vmatrix} x^2 & x \\ 3 & 1 \end{vmatrix} = 4$ $x = 4$ or –1

24. Find the value of x so that the area of a triangle whose vertices have coordinates (6, 5), (8, 2), and (x, 11) is 30. **x = 22**

Solve for x.   **26.** $x = \dfrac{1}{2}$

25. $x = \dfrac{5}{3}$ or –4 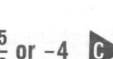 **25.** $\begin{vmatrix} x & 5 & 2 \\ -6 & 4 & 1 \\ 3 & 1 & x \end{vmatrix} = x^2 + 22x - 1$ **26.** $\begin{vmatrix} 2x & 4 & 1 \\ 2 & 3 & -1 \\ 0 & -2 & x \end{vmatrix} = 6x^2 - 10$

27. How can you convince someone that the formula for the area of a triangle could be used to show that three given points are collinear (lie on the same line)? **If the area = 0, the points are collinear.**

Critical Thinking

28. Find a third order matrix in which no element is 0, but the value of the determinant of the matrix is 0. **See margin.**

29. By multiplying only rows or columns of $\begin{vmatrix} 8 & 3 \\ -3 & 5 \end{vmatrix}$ by a constant, create a determinant whose value is six times the value of $\begin{vmatrix} 8 & 3 \\ -3 & 5 \end{vmatrix}$. **See margin.**

Additional Answers

28. Answers will vary. One matrix is
$\begin{bmatrix} 1 & 1 & 1 \\ 1 & 1 & 1 \\ 1 & 1 & 1 \end{bmatrix}.$

29. $\begin{bmatrix} 48 & 18 \\ -3 & 5 \end{bmatrix},$ $\begin{bmatrix} 8 & 3 \\ -18 & 30 \end{bmatrix},$ $\begin{bmatrix} 48 & 3 \\ -18 & 5 \end{bmatrix},$ **or** $\begin{bmatrix} 8 & 18 \\ -3 & 30 \end{bmatrix}$

Practice Masters Booklet, p. 28

Applications

30. **Metallurgy** Mary Sitzco has a blueprint of a metal plate in the shape of a quadrilateral having vertices with coordinates $(-5, 2)$, $(4, -1)$, $(3, 8)$, and $(-3, 7)$ that is to be used as part of a sculpture. She needs to know the area of the quadrilateral in order to calculate the amount of ore needed to make the metal plate.

    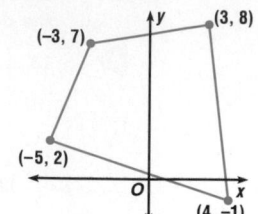

    a. Explain how she could use the area of triangles to find the area of this plate. **See margin.**

    b. Find the area of the plate. **53 units²**

31. **Horticulture** A rose garden is being planted as a border around two sides of a triangular shaped lawn in a city park. Two of the vertices of the triangular lawn have coordinates $(-2, 4)$ and $(3, -5)$. The gardener wishes to locate the third vertex so that the lawn's area is 25 square feet. Find the value of f if the coordinates of the third vertex are $(3, f)$. **5**

    Teaching Tip ❸

Mixed Review

32. Find $\begin{bmatrix} -3 & 14 & 12 \\ -2 & -1 & 7 \end{bmatrix} + \begin{bmatrix} 1 & -5 & 10 \\ 22 & 13 & -8 \end{bmatrix}$. **(Lesson 4-2)** $\begin{bmatrix} -2 & 9 & 22 \\ 20 & 12 & -1 \end{bmatrix}$

33. Find $4\begin{bmatrix} -7 & 5 & -11 \\ 2 & -4 & 9 \end{bmatrix}$. **(Lesson 4-2)** $\begin{bmatrix} -28 & 20 & -44 \\ 8 & -16 & 36 \end{bmatrix}$

34. Graph $15x + 10y + 6z = 30$. **(Lesson 3-8) See Solutions Manual.**

35. Sherri bought 24 cans of soda at the store. She bought r cans at \$0.19 per can and t cans at \$0.29 per can. Find r and t if she spent \$5.46 on soda. **(Lesson 1-4) 15, 9**

36. Find the standard form of the equation whose x-intercept is 6 and whose y-intercept is -5. **(Lesson 2-5)** $5x - 6y = 30$

CHALLENGE

In this lesson, you learned that one way to find the area of a triangle is to find half the value of the determinant containing the coordinates of the vertices of the triangle.

Use the figure at the right to help you write a convincing argument as to why the formula for the area of a triangle using determinants is valid.

See margin.

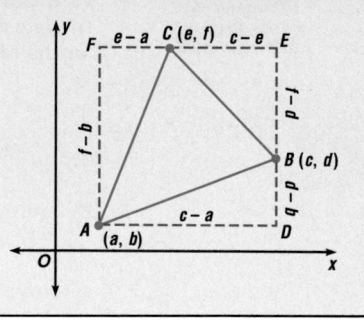

EXTENDING THE LESSON

Math Power: Reasoning

Find x if $(-1, 8)$, $(2, 5)$, and $(x, 3)$ are collinear. **4**

Additional Answer

30a. Draw a line to make the quadrilateral into two triangles. Then use the formula.

Objective
4-4

After studying this lesson, you should be able to:
- multiply two matrices and interpret the results.

Application

Mac McDonough owns three fruit farms on which he grows peaches, apricots, plums, and apples. When picked, the fruit is sorted into layered boxes in which they will be sold. The chart below shows the number of boxes for each type of fruit.

Location	Peaches	Apricots	Plums	Apples
Farm 1	165	217	430	290
Farm 2	243	190	235	175
Farm 3	74	150	198	0

Suppose he sells peaches for $26 a box, apricots for $18 a box, plums for $32 a box, and apples for $19 a box. The total income from this picking of fruit could be found by multiplying matrices. *The solution to this problem is shown in Example 3.*

Teaching Tip

You can multiply two matrices only if the number of columns in the first matrix is equal to the number of rows in the second matrix.

Multiplying Matrices

> The product of an $m \times n$ matrix, A, and an $n \times r$ matrix, B, is the $m \times r$ matrix AB. The element in the ith row and the jth column of AB is the sum of the products of the corresponding elements in the ith row of A and the jth column of B. Multiplication of matrices is *not* commutative.

The steps in Example 1 will illustrate how two matrices can be multiplied.

Example 1

If $A = \begin{bmatrix} 2 & -1 \\ 3 & 4 \end{bmatrix}$ and $B = \begin{bmatrix} 3 & -9 & 2 \\ 5 & 7 & -6 \end{bmatrix}$, find AB.

Matrix BA is not defined since B has 3 columns and A has 2 rows.

$$AB = \begin{bmatrix} 2(3) + (-1)(5) & 2(-9) + (-1)(7) & (2)(2) + (-1)(-6) \\ 3(3) + 4(5) & 3(-9) + 4(7) & (3)(2) + 4(-6) \end{bmatrix}$$

$$= \begin{bmatrix} 6 - 5 & -18 - 7 & 4 + 6 \\ 9 + 20 & -27 + 28 & 6 - 24 \end{bmatrix}$$

$$= \begin{bmatrix} 1 & -25 & 10 \\ 29 & 1 & -18 \end{bmatrix} \quad A_{2\times2} \cdot B_{2\times3} = (AB)_{2\times3}$$

LESSON 4-4 MULTIPLICATION OF MATRICES **173**

ALTERNATE TEACHING STRATEGIES

Using Cooperative Groups

Divide the class into groups. Have each group make three triangles and place them on a grid. Then have them rotate the figures clockwise 90°. Determine the matrix that would give the new coordinates for the rotation. Prove the matrix works by multiplying each triangle's coordinate with the new

matrix. $\begin{bmatrix} 0 & 1 \\ -1 & 0 \end{bmatrix}$

Lesson Resources

Reteaching Master 4-4
Practice Master 4-4
Enrichment Master 4-4
Activity Master, p. 22

 Transparency 4-4 contains the 5-Minute Check and a teaching aid for this lesson.

INTRODUCING THE LESSON

🕐 **5-Minute Check**

(over Lesson 4-3)

1. Determine whether the matrix has a determinant. If it does, find the value of the determinant.

   $\begin{bmatrix} 2 & 7 & -1 \\ 4 & 5 & 10 \end{bmatrix}$ **no determinant**

2. Evaluate $\begin{vmatrix} 1 & 3 & -2 \\ 2 & -1 & 4 \\ 4 & 3 & 5 \end{vmatrix}$ using expansion by minors.
   −19

3. Evaluate $\begin{vmatrix} -1 & 1 & 2 \\ 2 & 1 & 0 \\ 3 & 6 & -2 \end{vmatrix}$ using diagonals. **24**

4. Find the area of the triangle whose vertices are $A(6, 4)$, $B(-2, 3)$, and $C(2, -3)$ **26**

5. Solve for x if $\begin{vmatrix} 1 & -2 & -3 \\ 7 & 5 & 0 \\ x & 2x & 1 \end{vmatrix} = -35$ **2**

Motivating the Lesson

Two grocery stores have two kinds of fruits, apples and oranges. Saver's Mart has 45 apples and 55 oranges. Sam's Shoppe has 15 apples and 80 oranges. Make a matrix to show the relationship.

Chalkboard Examples

For Example 1

If $A = \begin{bmatrix} 3 & 2 \\ -1 & -2 \end{bmatrix}$

and $B = \begin{bmatrix} 5 & 1 & 2 \\ 4 & 3 & -1 \end{bmatrix}$,

find AB. $\begin{bmatrix} 23 & 9 & 4 \\ -13 & -7 & 0 \end{bmatrix}$

For Example 2

If $A = \begin{bmatrix} 7 \\ 2 \\ 1 \end{bmatrix}$

and $B = \begin{bmatrix} 3 & 4 & 1 \\ -2 & 7 & -5 \end{bmatrix}$,

find AB. **not defined**

For Example 3

On two days the student store sold the following amounts of pencils, erasers, and binders.

	Pencils	Erasers	Binders
Monday	48	7	9
Tuesday	54	10	6

If pencils sold for 20¢, erasers for 35¢, and binders for $2.85, set up matrices to find the total sales for each day.
Mon. = $37.70
Tues. = $31.40

Example 2  If $A = \begin{bmatrix} 6 & 8 & 10 \\ 2 & 3 & -5 \end{bmatrix}$ and $B = \begin{bmatrix} 2 & 5 & -3 \\ 3 & -6 & 2 \end{bmatrix}$, find AB.

A has 3 columns and B has 2 rows. In order to find AB, A must have the same number of columns as B has rows. Since this is not the case, AB is not defined.

Example 3 shows how matrix multiplication can be used to find the total income for Mr. McDonough's fruit farms.

Example 3

APPLICATION

Agriculture

Find the total income of the three fruit farms owned by Mr. McDonough.

The first matrix represents the numbers of boxes of each type of fruit for each farm. The second matrix will list the prices per box for each type of fruit.

$$A_{3 \times 4} \qquad \cdot \qquad B_{4 \times 1} = (AB)_{3 \times 1}$$

$$\begin{bmatrix} 165 & 217 & 430 & 290 \\ 243 & 190 & 235 & 175 \\ 74 & 150 & 198 & 0 \end{bmatrix} \cdot \begin{bmatrix} 26 \\ 18 \\ 32 \\ 19 \end{bmatrix} = \begin{bmatrix} 27,466 \\ 20,583 \\ 10,960 \end{bmatrix}$$

Farm 1 earned $27,466, Farm 2 earned $20,583, and Farm 3 earned $10,960. The total income is $59,009. *Verify the resulting totals.*

Another use of matrix multiplication is in transformational geometry. You have already learned to translate a figure and change the size of a figure using matrices. When you wish to move a figure by rotating it, you can use a **rotation matrix**.

The matrix $\begin{bmatrix} 0 & -1 \\ 1 & 0 \end{bmatrix}$ will rotate a figure on a coordinate plane 90° counterclockwise about the origin. In the figure at the right, segment AB is rotated 90° counterclockwise, using the origin as the point of rotation. The result is segment $A'B'$.

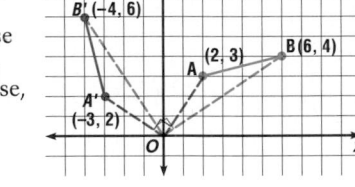

Segments AO and OA' form a 90° angle. Likewise, segments OB and OB' form a 90° angle.

Example 4

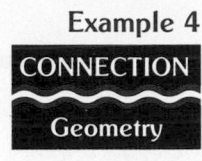

CONNECTION

Geometry

Teaching Tip ❷

Triangle *RST* has vertices with coordinates *R*(-1, -2), *S*(2, -4), and *T*(5, 3). Find the coordinates of the vertices of this triangle after it is rotated counterclockwise 90° about the origin.

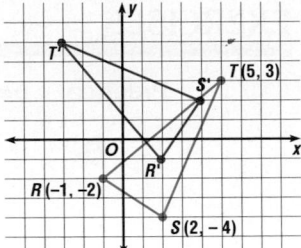

Let each column of a matrix represent an ordered pair of the triangle with the top row containing the *x*-values. Then multiply the coordinate matrix by the rotation matrix.

$$\begin{bmatrix} 0 & -1 \\ 1 & 0 \end{bmatrix} \cdot \begin{bmatrix} -1 & 2 & 5 \\ -2 & -4 & 3 \end{bmatrix} = \begin{bmatrix} 2 & 4 & -3 \\ -1 & 2 & 5 \end{bmatrix}$$

The coordinates of the vertices of the rotated triangle are *R'*(2, -1), *S'*(4, 2), and *T'*(-3, 5).

CHECKING FOR UNDERSTANDING

Communicating Mathematics

Read and study the lesson to answer each question.

1. Under what conditions can two matrices be multiplied? **See margin.**

2. How do the conditions for adding matrices differ from those for multiplying matrices? **See margin.**

3. Use the definition of matrix multiplication to find the dimension of matrix *M* if $M - A_{3\times2} \cdot B_{2\times4}$. **3 × 4**

See margin.

4. Describe in your own words the process of multiplying two matrices.

5. $\begin{bmatrix} 0 & -1 \\ 1 & 0 \end{bmatrix}$

5. What is the rotation matrix for a 90° counterclockwise rotation about the origin?

Guided Practice

Find the dimension of each matrix *M*.

6. $A_{3\times2} \cdot B_{2\times5} = M$ **3 × 5**

7. $C_{4\times4} \cdot D_{4\times2} = M$ **4 × 2**

Find each matrix *N*, if it exists.

not defined

8. $\begin{bmatrix} 5 & 5 & -18 \\ 36 & -20 & 30 \end{bmatrix}$

8. $N = \begin{bmatrix} 3 & -1 \\ 2 & 4 \end{bmatrix} \cdot \begin{bmatrix} 4 & 0 & -3 \\ 7 & -5 & 9 \end{bmatrix}$

9. $N = \begin{bmatrix} 4 & 0 & -3 \\ 7 & -5 & 9 \end{bmatrix} \cdot \begin{bmatrix} 3 & -1 \\ 2 & 4 \end{bmatrix}$

10. $\begin{bmatrix} 6 & 0 \\ 0 & 3 \end{bmatrix}$

10. $N = \begin{bmatrix} 2 & 3 & 4 \\ 1 & 0 & -1 \end{bmatrix} \cdot \begin{bmatrix} 1 & 2 \\ 0 & 0 \\ 1 & -1 \end{bmatrix}$

11. $N = \begin{bmatrix} 2 & -1 \\ 0 & 1 \end{bmatrix} \cdot \begin{bmatrix} 3 & 0 \\ 1 & 2 \end{bmatrix} \begin{bmatrix} 5 & -2 \\ 1 & 2 \end{bmatrix}$

Additional Answers

1. **The number of columns in the first matrix must equal the number of rows in the second.**

2. **In adding matrices, the two matrices must have the same dimensions. In multiplying, the dimensions are frequently different, but the matrices can be multiplied if the number of columns in the first matrix equals the number of rows in the second.**

4. **Answers will vary. One sample is**

$$\begin{bmatrix} a & b \\ c & d \end{bmatrix} \cdot \begin{bmatrix} e & f & g \\ h & i & j \end{bmatrix} =$$

$$\begin{bmatrix} (ae + bh) & (af + bi) & (ag + bj) \\ (ce + dh) & (cf + di) & (cg + dj) \end{bmatrix}$$

Closing the Lesson

Writing Activity Have students write a paragraph explaining why the multiplication of matrices is not commutative.

APPLYING THE LESSON

Homework Exercises

Assignment Guide

Basic: 12–25, 32–34, 37–41
Average: 16–28, 32–41
Enriched: 20–41

Chapter 4, Quiz B, (Lessons 4-3 through 4-4), is available in the Evaluation Masters Booklet, p. 51.

16. $\begin{bmatrix} 6 & 4 \\ 7 & 27 \end{bmatrix}$

17. $\begin{bmatrix} 15 & -8 & -10 \\ -7 & 23 & 16 \end{bmatrix}$

20. $\begin{bmatrix} -21 & 48 \\ -13 & 22 \end{bmatrix}$

22. $\begin{bmatrix} 0 & 64 & -40 \\ 9 & 11 & -11 \\ -3 & 39 & -23 \end{bmatrix}$

Reteaching Masters Booklet, p. 25

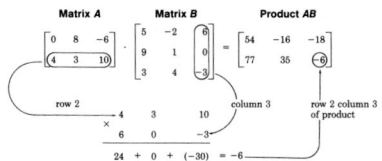

NAME _____ DATE _____

4-4 Reteaching Worksheet

Multiplication of Matrices

The product AB of two matrices is defined if and only if the number of columns in A equals the number of rows in B. For the product AB, the element in row i column j is found as follows: Use the ith row of A and the jth row of B. Multiply the corresponding elements and add the products.

Example:

Matrix A   Matrix B   Product AB

$\begin{bmatrix} 0 & 8 & -6 \\ 4 & 3 & 10 \end{bmatrix} \cdot \begin{bmatrix} 5 & -2 & 6 \\ 9 & 1 & 0 \\ 3 & 4 & -3 \end{bmatrix} = \begin{bmatrix} 54 & -16 & -18 \\ 77 & 35 & -6 \end{bmatrix}$

row 2 ⟶ 4   3   10
column 3   row 2 column 3 of product
× 6   0   -3
24 + 0 + (-30) = -6

Find each product.

1. $\begin{bmatrix} 4 & 1 \\ -2 & 3 \end{bmatrix} \cdot \begin{bmatrix} 3 & 0 \\ 0 & 3 \end{bmatrix}$ 2. $\begin{bmatrix} -1 & 0 \\ 3 & 7 \end{bmatrix} \cdot \begin{bmatrix} 3 & -1 \\ 2 & 4 \end{bmatrix}$ 3. $\begin{bmatrix} 3 & -1 \\ 2 & 4 \end{bmatrix} \cdot \begin{bmatrix} 3 & -1 \\ 2 & 4 \end{bmatrix}$

$\begin{bmatrix} 12 & 3 \\ -6 & 9 \end{bmatrix}$ $\begin{bmatrix} -3 & 1 \\ 23 & 25 \end{bmatrix}$ $\begin{bmatrix} 7 & -7 \\ 14 & 14 \end{bmatrix}$

Use matrices A, B, C, and D to evaluate each expression. Write "not defined" if the product does not exist.

$A = \begin{bmatrix} 3 & 4 \\ 5 & 6 \end{bmatrix}$ $B = \begin{bmatrix} -3 & -4 & -5 \\ -1 & -2 & -3 \end{bmatrix}$ $C = \begin{bmatrix} 6 & 8 & 10 \\ 10 & 4 & 2 \\ -3 & 0 & -5 \end{bmatrix}$ $D = \begin{bmatrix} 3 & 6 \\ 9 & 12 \end{bmatrix}$

4. AD 5. DB 6. BD

$\begin{bmatrix} 45 & 66 \\ 69 & 102 \end{bmatrix}$ $\begin{bmatrix} -15 & -24 & -33 \\ -39 & -60 & -81 \end{bmatrix}$ not defined

7. DA 8. BC 9. AB

$\begin{bmatrix} 39 & 48 \\ 87 & 108 \end{bmatrix}$ $\begin{bmatrix} -43 & -40 & -13 \\ -17 & -16 & 1 \end{bmatrix}$ $\begin{bmatrix} -13 & -20 & -27 \\ -21 & -32 & -43 \end{bmatrix}$

EXERCISES

Practice Determine the dimension of each matrix product.

 A

12. $M_{4\times2} \cdot N_{2\times3}$ **4 × 3**   13. $A_{1\times4} \cdot b_{4\times2}$ **1 × 2**

14. $A_{3\times4} \cdot B_{4\times1}$ **3 × 1**   15. $A_{3\times2} \cdot B_{3\times2}$ **not defined**

Perform the indicated operations.

16. $3\begin{bmatrix} 4 & -2 \\ 5 & 7 \end{bmatrix} + 2\begin{bmatrix} -3 & 5 \\ -4 & 3 \end{bmatrix}$ 17. $\begin{bmatrix} 3 & -1 \\ 2 & 5 \end{bmatrix} \cdot \begin{bmatrix} 4 & -1 & -2 \\ -3 & 5 & 4 \end{bmatrix}$

18. $\begin{bmatrix} 4 & 0 & -8 \\ 7 & -2 & 10 \end{bmatrix} \cdot \begin{bmatrix} -1 & 3 \\ 6 & 0 \end{bmatrix}$ **not possible to evaluate**   19. $\begin{bmatrix} 6 & 4 & 1 \end{bmatrix} \cdot \begin{bmatrix} 2 & 5 \\ -3 & 0 \\ -1 & 3 \end{bmatrix}$ **[-1 33]**

 B

20. $\begin{bmatrix} -6 & 3 \\ 4 & 7 \end{bmatrix} \cdot \begin{bmatrix} 2 & -5 \\ -3 & 6 \end{bmatrix}$ 21. $\begin{bmatrix} 2 & 7 \end{bmatrix} \cdot \begin{bmatrix} 5 \\ -4 \end{bmatrix}$ **[-18]**

22. $\begin{bmatrix} 0 & 8 \\ 3 & 1 \\ -1 & 5 \end{bmatrix} \cdot \begin{bmatrix} 3 & 1 & -2 \\ 0 & 8 & -5 \end{bmatrix}$ 23. $\begin{bmatrix} 3 & 4 \\ 1 & 0 \\ 2 & -5 \end{bmatrix} \cdot \begin{bmatrix} -2 & 4 & 5 \\ 3 & 0 & -1 \\ 1 & 0 & -1 \end{bmatrix}$ **not possible to evaluate**

CONNECTION **Geometry**

Find the new coordinates of the vertices of each polygon after the polygon is rotated 90° counterclockwise about the origin. **A'(-4, 3), B'(-5, 6), C'(0, 0)**

24. triangle ABC with vertices $A(3, 4)$, $B(6, 5)$, $C(0, 0)$

25. rectangle $DEFG$ with vertices $D(-1, -1)$, $E(-4, -1)$, $F(-4, -3)$, and $G(-1, -3)$ **D'(1, -1), E'(1, -4), F'(3, -4), G'(3, -1)**

 **C**

Use matrices A, B, C, and D to evaluate each expression. See margin.

$A = \begin{bmatrix} 3 & -1 \\ 2 & 4 \end{bmatrix}$ $B = \begin{bmatrix} 4 & 0 & -3 \\ 7 & -5 & 9 \end{bmatrix}$ $C = \begin{bmatrix} -6 & 4 \\ -2 & 8 \\ 3 & 0 \end{bmatrix}$ $D = \begin{bmatrix} -1 & 0 \\ 3 & 7 \end{bmatrix}$

26. $AB + B$ 27. $CB + B$ 28. $AD + CB$ 29. $AD + BC$

CONNECTION **Geometry**

30. Find the new coordinates of the vertices of square $MOBY$ with vertices $M(-2, -2)$, $O(2, -2)$, $B(2, 2)$, and $Y(-2, 2)$, when the square is rotated 90° counterclockwise about the origin. Graph the original square and its rotation $M'O'B'Y'$. Describe the result. **They are the same square in the same position. See margin for graph.**

Additional Answers

26. $\begin{bmatrix} 9 & 5 & -21 \\ 43 & -25 & 39 \end{bmatrix}$

27. **not defined**
28. **not defined**

29. $\begin{bmatrix} -39 & 9 \\ 5 & 16 \end{bmatrix}$

30.

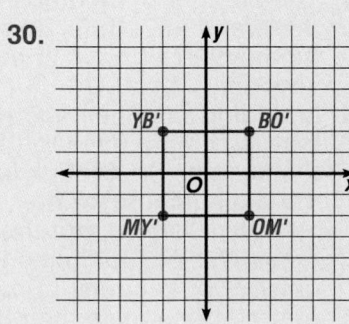

31. After a triangle was rotated 90° counterclockwise about the origin its vertices had coordinates (-3, -5), (-2, 7), and (1, 4). What were the coordinates of the triangle in its original position? **(-5, 3), (7, 2), (4, -1)**

32. The coordinates (a, b) become (-a, -b).

32. Find the new coordinates of quadrilateral *ROSE*, with vertices $R(-2, -1)$, $O(3, 0)$, $S(2, 2)$ and $E(-1, 2)$, if it is rotated 90° counterclockwise about the origin *twice*. Compare the new coordinates to the original ones. Make a conjecture about what effect this rotation has on any figure.

Teaching Tip ③

33. $\begin{bmatrix} 1 & 0 \\ 0 & 1 \end{bmatrix}$; $w = 1$, $y = 0$, $x = 0$, $z = 1$; the same matrix you began with

33. Find the values of w, x, y, and z to make the statement

$$\begin{bmatrix} 1 & 2 \\ 3 & 4 \end{bmatrix} \cdot \begin{bmatrix} w & y \\ x & z \end{bmatrix} = \begin{bmatrix} 1 & 2 \\ 3 & 4 \end{bmatrix} \text{ true. If the matrix containing } w, x, y, \text{ and } z$$

were multiplied by any other matrix containing two columns, what do you think the result would be?

Applications

34. Birmingham = 56
Chatsworth = 62
Monroe = 53

34. Sports In a three team track meet, the following numbers of first-, second-, and third-place finishes were recorded.

School	First Place	Second Place	Third Place
Birmingham	4	10	6
Chatsworth	7	6	9
Monroe	8	3	4

If 5 points are awarded for first, 3 for second, and 1 for third, use matrices to find the final scores for each school.

35. nickels $243.20
dimes $199.80
quarters $521.95
$964.95

35. Coin Collecting Jana Wyssman is a coin collector. She specializes in coins of the early 20th century. In her collection, she has 64 nickels, 37 dimes, and 73 quarters. Because these coins are collectors items they are worth more than face value. Each nickel is worth $3.80, each dime is worth $5.40, and each quarter is worth $7.15. Use matrices to find the total value of each group of coins and the value of Miss Wyssman's whole collection.

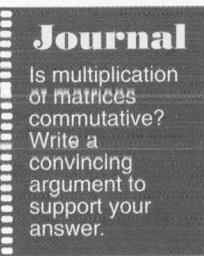    

Computer

Teaching Tip ④

36. The BASIC program at the top of the next page multiplies two matrices. First enter the dimensions of each matrix. Next, enter each row of the first matrix. Continue on to enter each row of the second matrix. The computer will print the product of the two matrices. Note that line 50 makes sure that the multiplication is possible.

Use this program to check your answers to Exercises 17–23.

LESSON 4-4 MULTIPLICATION OF MATRICES 177

RETEACHING THE LESSON

As in the Reteaching Activity for Lesson 4-2, use the class seating arrangement to form matrices with each student's desk as a cell. Fill two matrices $A_{2\times3}$ and $B_{3\times2}$ with values. For $AB = C$, write a blank 2×2 matrix on the chalkboard.

For each element of C (say C_{ij}) have students "walk out" the products of corresponding elements of A_{ix} and B_{xj} (x represents corresponding position number) to get the addends for C_{ij}. Write these values on the board. Point out how the elements "zipper together." Try matrices of different sizes.

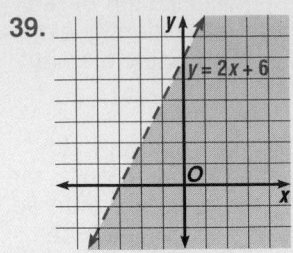
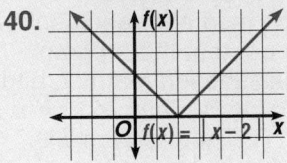
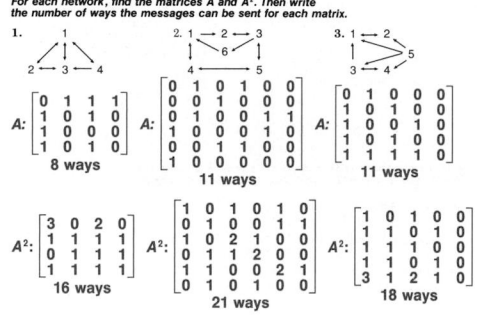
```
 10 PRINT "ENTER SIZE OF L."     180 FOR Q = 1 TO Z
 20 INPUT X,Y1                   190 FOR P = 1 TO X
 30 PRINT "ENTER SIZE OF R."     200 C(P,Q) = O
 40 INPUT Y2,Z                   210 FOR I = 1 TO Y1
 50 IF Y1 <> Y2 THEN 500         220 C(P,Q) = C(P,Q) + L(P,I)
 60 PRINT "ENTER MATRIX L."          * R(I,Q)
 70 FOR M = 1 TO X               230 NEXT I
 80 FOR N = 1 TO Y1              240 NEXT P : PRINT
 90 INPUT L(M,N)                 250 NEXT Q
100 NEXT N : PRINT               260 PRINT "L * R" : PRINT
110 NEXT M                       270 FOR M = 1 TO X
120 PRINT "ENTER MATRIX R."      280 FOR N = 1 TO Z
130 FOR M = 1 TO Y2              290 PRINT C(M,N);" ";
140 FOR N = 1 TO Z               300 NEXT N : PRINT
150 INPUT R(M,N)                 310 NEXT M
160 NEXT N : PRINT               320 END
170 NEXT M                       500 PRINT "TRY AGAIN."
                                 510 GOTO 10
```

Mixed Review

37. Evaluate $\begin{vmatrix} 2 & -3 & 1 \\ 3 & 5 & 2 \\ 1 & 0 & -3 \end{vmatrix}$. **(Lesson 4-3)** **−68**

38. Solve $\begin{cases} 2x - 3y = -9 \\ x + 7y = -13 \end{cases}$. **(Lesson 3-2)** **(−6, −1)**

39. Graph $y < 2x + 6$. **(Lesson 2-8)** **See margin.**

40. Graph $f(x) = |x - 2|$. **(Lesson 2-7)** **See margin.**

41. Consumerism Leon bought a 10-speed bicycle on sale for 75% of its
original price. The sale price was $41 less than the original price. Find
the original price and the sale price. **(Lesson 1-4)** **$164, $123**

HISTORY CONNECTION

The most influential mathematics book in China
was *Nine Chapters on the Mathematical Art,*
written about 250 B.C. This book contained many
problems that are solved using matrices. The
Chinese matrix was a large counting board that
resembled a checkerboard. We read our matrices a
row at a time from left to right. The Chinese
organized their data differently because they read
from top to bottom and from right to left.

EXTENDING THE LESSON

Math Power: Problem Solving

Apply the rotation matrix twice on
the triangle with vertices $(-2,5)$,
$(1,-3)$, and $(4,6)$. Discuss what
effect it has on the original vertices. Could you have done this
"double rotation" using one rotation? The double rotation has the
same effect as multiplying each
coordinate by -1.

History Connection

The History Connection features
introduce students to persons or
cultures who were involved in the
development of mathematics. You
may want students to further research the Chinese matrix or to
practice writing matrices in the
style of the Chinese.

Identity and Inverse Matrices

Objectives

4-5A
4-5B

After studying this lesson, you should be able to:

- write the identity matrix for any matrix, and
- find the inverse matrix of a 2 × 2 matrix.

There are certain properties of real numbers that are related to special matrices. Remember that 1 is the identity for multiplication because $1 \cdot a = a \cdot 1 = a$. The **identity matrix** is a square matrix that, when multiplied by another matrix, equals that same matrix.

With 2 × 2 matrices, $\begin{bmatrix} 1 & 0 \\ 0 & 1 \end{bmatrix}$ is the identity matrix because

$\begin{bmatrix} a & b \\ c & d \end{bmatrix} \cdot \begin{bmatrix} 1 & 0 \\ 0 & 1 \end{bmatrix} = \begin{bmatrix} a & b \\ c & d \end{bmatrix}$ and $\begin{bmatrix} 1 & 0 \\ 0 & 1 \end{bmatrix} \cdot \begin{bmatrix} a & b \\ c & d \end{bmatrix} = \begin{bmatrix} a & b \\ c & d \end{bmatrix}$. The identity

matrix is symbolized by I. In any identity matrix, the principal diagonal extends from upper left to lower right and consists only of 1's.

Identity Matrix
for Multiplication

> **The identity matrix I for multiplication is a square matrix with a 1 for every element of the principal diagonal and a 0 in all other positions.**

Example 1

Find I so that $\begin{bmatrix} 3 & 2 & -1 \\ -8 & 4 & 1 \end{bmatrix} I = \begin{bmatrix} 3 & 2 & -1 \\ -8 & 4 & 1 \end{bmatrix}$.

In order for you to multiply the matrices, remember that the number of columns of the first matrix must equal the number of rows in the second one.

The dimensions of the first matrix are 2 × 3. So I must have 3 rows. Since all identity matrices are square, it also has 3 columns. The principal diagonal contains 1's. Complete the matrix with 0's.

$\begin{bmatrix} 1 & & \\ & 1 & \\ & & 1 \end{bmatrix}$ ➡ $\begin{bmatrix} 1 & 0 & 0 \\ 0 & 1 & 0 \\ 0 & 0 & 1 \end{bmatrix}$ The 3 × 3 identity matrix is $\begin{bmatrix} 1 & 0 & 0 \\ 0 & 1 & 0 \\ 0 & 0 & 1 \end{bmatrix}$.

Teaching Tip ❶

Another property of real numbers is that any real number, except 0, has a multiplicative inverse. That is, $\frac{1}{a}$ is the multiplicative inverse of a because $a \cdot \frac{1}{a} = \frac{1}{a} \cdot a = 1$. Likewise, if matrix A has an **inverse** named A^{-1}, then $A \cdot A^{-1} = A^{-1} \cdot A = I$. The following example shows how the inverse of a 2 × 2 matrix can be found.

ALTERNATE TEACHING STRATEGIES

Using Discussion

Have the students discuss the inverses of real numbers. Why does zero not have an inverse? What restrictions must be made on matrices for inverses? Why do these restrictions have to be made?

Lesson Resources

Reteaching Master 4-5
Practice Master 4-5
Enrichment Master 4-5
Technology Master, p. 4

 Transparency 4-5 contains the 5-Minute Check and a teaching aid for this lesson.

INTRODUCING THE LESSON

🕐 5-Minute Check

(over Lesson 4-4)
Find each matrix *N*.

1. $N = \begin{bmatrix} 3 & 2 \\ -1 & 5 \end{bmatrix} \cdot \begin{bmatrix} 3 & -2 \\ 0 & 4 \end{bmatrix}$

$\begin{bmatrix} 9 & 2 \\ -3 & 22 \end{bmatrix}$

2. $N = \begin{bmatrix} 4 & 2 & -3 \end{bmatrix} \cdot \begin{bmatrix} 2 & -3 \\ 5 & 0 \\ -6 & 2 \end{bmatrix}$

$[36 \quad -18]$

3. Triangle *ABC* has vertices with coordinates *A*(−8, 0), *B*(2, −3), and *C*(5, 6). Find the coordinates of the vertices of the triangle after it is rotated counterclockwise 90° about the origin. *A′*(0,−8), *B′*(3,2), *C′*(−6,5)

Other Prerequisite Skills

Solve the system of equations.

4. $2x + 3y = 2$
   $3x − 4y = −14$ (−2, 2)

Motivating the Lesson

Define and discuss an identity element and an inverse element. What are the identity elements for real-number multiplication and addition? What are the inverse elements for real-number multiplication and addition?

Emphasize that an inverse matrix for matrix *A* is the multiplicative inverse of matrix *A*.

Chalkboard Examples

For Example 1

Find the identity matrix for each matrix.

a. $\begin{bmatrix} 5 & 1 & 2 \\ 4 & 3 & -1 \end{bmatrix}$ $\begin{bmatrix} 1 & 0 & 0 \\ 0 & 1 & 0 \\ 0 & 0 & 1 \end{bmatrix}$

b. $[6 \quad -2 \quad 5]$ $\begin{bmatrix} 1 & 0 & 0 \\ 0 & 1 & 0 \\ 0 & 0 & 1 \end{bmatrix}$

For Example 2

If $A = \begin{bmatrix} 5 & 3 \\ 2 & 1 \end{bmatrix}$, find A^{-1}.

$\begin{bmatrix} -1 & 3 \\ 2 & -5 \end{bmatrix}$

For Example 3

Find the inverse of $\begin{bmatrix} 2 & -5 \\ 0 & 7 \end{bmatrix}$.

$\frac{1}{14}\begin{bmatrix} 7 & 5 \\ 0 & 2 \end{bmatrix}$

Example 2

The TI-81 calculator can be used to find the inverse of a matrix. Enter your matrix as matrix A. Clear the screen. Then press 2nd [A] and x⁻¹.

If $A = \begin{bmatrix} 3 & 2 \\ 5 & 7 \end{bmatrix}$, find A^{-1} and check your result.

Let $A^{-1} = \begin{bmatrix} x & y \\ z & w \end{bmatrix}$. By the definition of an inverse, $A \cdot A^{-1}$ must equal I.

So, $\begin{bmatrix} 3 & 2 \\ 5 & 7 \end{bmatrix} \cdot \begin{bmatrix} x & y \\ z & w \end{bmatrix} = \begin{bmatrix} 1 & 0 \\ 0 & 1 \end{bmatrix}$.

Multiply the two matrices.

$\begin{bmatrix} 3 & 2 \\ 5 & 7 \end{bmatrix} \cdot \begin{bmatrix} x & y \\ z & w \end{bmatrix} = \begin{bmatrix} 3x + 2z & 3y + 2w \\ 5x + 7z & 5y + 7w \end{bmatrix}$

Thus, $\begin{bmatrix} 3x + 2z & 3y + 2w \\ 5x + 7z & 5y + 7w \end{bmatrix} = \begin{bmatrix} 1 & 0 \\ 0 & 1 \end{bmatrix}$.

When matrices are equal the corresponding elements are equal. So the following equations can be generated from the two equal matrices.

(1) $3x + 2z = 1$ (2) $3y + 2w = 0$ (3) $5x + 7z = 0$ (4) $5y + 7w = 1$

Use equations (1) and (3) to find values for *x* and *z*.

First solve for x.   Then substitute the x value into one of the equations to find z.

$\begin{array}{l} 3x + 2z = 1 \\ 5x + 7z = 0 \end{array}$ ➡ $\begin{array}{r} 21x + 14z = 7 \\ -10x - 14z = 0 \\ \hline 11x \qquad = 7 \\ x = \dfrac{7}{11} \end{array}$ $\quad \begin{array}{l} 3\left(\dfrac{7}{11}\right) + 2z = 1 \\[2mm] \dfrac{21}{11} + 2z = 1 \\[2mm] z = -\dfrac{5}{11} \end{array}$

Use equations (2) and (4) to find values for *y* and *w*.

First solve for y.   Then substitute the y value into one of the equations to find w.

$\begin{array}{l} 3y + 2w = 0 \\ 5y + 7w = 1 \end{array}$ ➡ $\begin{array}{r} 21y + 14w = 0 \\ -10y - 14w = -2 \\ \hline 11y \qquad = -2 \\ y = -\dfrac{2}{11} \end{array}$ $\quad \begin{array}{l} 3\left(-\dfrac{2}{11}\right) + 2w = 0 \\[2mm] -\dfrac{6}{11} + 2w = 0 \\[2mm] w = \dfrac{3}{11} \end{array}$

Thus $A^{-1} = \begin{bmatrix} \dfrac{7}{11} & -\dfrac{2}{11} \\[3mm] -\dfrac{5}{11} & \dfrac{3}{11} \end{bmatrix}$.

Check: $\begin{bmatrix} 3 & 2 \\ 5 & 7 \end{bmatrix} \cdot \begin{bmatrix} \dfrac{7}{11} & -\dfrac{2}{11} \\[3mm] -\dfrac{5}{11} & \dfrac{3}{11} \end{bmatrix} = \begin{bmatrix} \dfrac{21}{11} - \dfrac{10}{11} & -\dfrac{6}{11} + \dfrac{6}{11} \\[3mm] \dfrac{35}{11} - \dfrac{35}{11} & -\dfrac{10}{11} + \dfrac{21}{11} \end{bmatrix} = \begin{bmatrix} 1 & 0 \\ 0 & 1 \end{bmatrix} \checkmark$

The same method used in Example 2 can be used to develop the general form of the inverse of a 2×2 matrix.

The inverse of $\begin{bmatrix} a & b \\ c & d \end{bmatrix}$ is $\begin{bmatrix} \dfrac{d}{ad-bc} & \dfrac{-b}{ad-bc} \\ \dfrac{-c}{ad-bc} & \dfrac{a}{ad-bc} \end{bmatrix}$ or $\dfrac{1}{ad-bc} \begin{bmatrix} d & -b \\ -c & a \end{bmatrix}$.

Notice that $ad - bc$ is the value of the determinant of the matrix. Remember that $\dfrac{1}{ad-bc}$ is not defined when $ad - bc = 0$. Therefore, if the value of the determinant of a matrix is 0, the matrix cannot have an inverse.

**Inverse of a
2×2 Matrix**

Any matrix M, $\begin{bmatrix} a & b \\ c & d \end{bmatrix}$, will have an inverse M^{-1} *if and only if*
$\begin{vmatrix} a & b \\ c & d \end{vmatrix} \neq 0$. Then $M^{-1} = \dfrac{1}{ad-bc} \begin{bmatrix} d & -b \\ -c & a \end{bmatrix}$.

Teaching Tip ②

Example 3

If $A = \begin{bmatrix} -3 & 5 \\ 1 & -4 \end{bmatrix}$, find A^{-1} and check your result.

Compute the value of the determinant.

$\begin{vmatrix} -3 & 5 \\ 1 & -4 \end{vmatrix} = 12 - 5 = 7$

Since the determinant does not equal 0, A^{-1} exists.

$A^{-1} = \dfrac{1}{7} \begin{bmatrix} -4 & -5 \\ -1 & -3 \end{bmatrix} \quad \dfrac{1}{ad-bc} \begin{bmatrix} d & -b \\ -c & a \end{bmatrix}$

Check: $\dfrac{1}{7} \begin{bmatrix} -4 & -5 \\ -1 & -3 \end{bmatrix} \cdot \begin{bmatrix} -3 & 5 \\ 1 & -4 \end{bmatrix} = \dfrac{1}{7} \begin{bmatrix} 12-5 & -20+20 \\ 3-3 & -5+12 \end{bmatrix} = \begin{bmatrix} 1 & 0 \\ 0 & 1 \end{bmatrix} \checkmark$

CHECKING FOR UNDERSTANDING

**Communicating
Mathematics**

4. $\begin{bmatrix} 1 & 0 & 0 & 0 \\ 0 & 1 & 0 & 0 \\ 0 & 0 & 1 & 0 \\ 0 & 0 & 0 & 1 \end{bmatrix}$

Read and study the lesson to answer each question.

1. What is the result when matrix A is multiplied by the identity matrix? **matrix A**
2. What letter is used to represent the identity matrix? **I**
3. How would you represent the inverse of matrix Z? **Z^{-1}**
4. Write the 4×4 identity matrix.

RETEACHING THE LESSON

Evaluate.

1. $\begin{bmatrix} 3 & 2 \\ 4 & 3 \end{bmatrix} \cdot \begin{bmatrix} 3 & -2 \\ -4 & 3 \end{bmatrix} \quad \begin{bmatrix} 1 & 0 \\ 0 & 1 \end{bmatrix}$

2. $\begin{bmatrix} 2 & 3 \\ 1 & 4 \\ -5 & 6 \end{bmatrix} \cdot \begin{bmatrix} 1 & 0 \\ 0 & 1 \end{bmatrix} \quad \begin{bmatrix} 2 & 3 \\ 1 & 4 \\ -5 & 6 \end{bmatrix}$

Teaching Tip ② Make sure students notice the changes in the original matrix.

EVALUATING THE LESSON

Checking for Understanding
Exercises 1–9 are designed to help you assess understanding through reading, writing, and speaking. You should work through Exercises 1–4 with your students, and then monitor their work on Exercises 5–9.

Error Analysis
Students sometimes give the inverse of a matrix A as

$\begin{bmatrix} \dfrac{1}{a_{11}} & \dfrac{1}{a_{12}} & \cdots \\ \dfrac{1}{a_{21}} & & \\ \vdots & & \end{bmatrix}$

To dispel this notion have students verify that

$\begin{bmatrix} a & b \\ c & d \end{bmatrix} \begin{bmatrix} \dfrac{1}{a} & \dfrac{1}{b} \\ \dfrac{1}{c} & \dfrac{1}{d} \end{bmatrix} \neq I$.

Reteaching Masters Booklet, p. 26

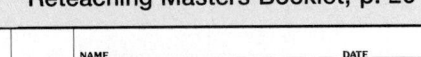

NAME _____ DATE _____

4-5 Reteaching Worksheet

Identity and Inverse Matrices

Apply the following definitions for identities and inverses of matrices.

Identity Matrix for Multiplication

Definition	Example
The identity matrix, I, for multiplication is a square matrix with a 1 for every element of the principal diagonal and a 0 for all other positions. The principal diagonal extends from upper left to lower right.	For 2×2 matrices, $\begin{bmatrix} 1 & 0 \\ 0 & 1 \end{bmatrix}$ is the identity matrix because $\begin{bmatrix} a & b \\ c & d \end{bmatrix}\begin{bmatrix} 1 & 0 \\ 0 & 1 \end{bmatrix} = \begin{bmatrix} a & b \\ c & d \end{bmatrix}$ and $\begin{bmatrix} 1 & 0 \\ 0 & 1 \end{bmatrix}\begin{bmatrix} a & b \\ c & d \end{bmatrix} = \begin{bmatrix} a & b \\ c & d \end{bmatrix}$

Inverse of a 2×2 Matrix

Definition	Example
If $M = \begin{bmatrix} a & b \\ c & d \end{bmatrix}$, then there is an inverse matrix, M^{-1}, if and only if $\begin{vmatrix} a & b \\ c & d \end{vmatrix} \neq 0$. Then $M^{-1} = \dfrac{1}{ad-bc}\begin{bmatrix} d & -b \\ -c & a \end{bmatrix}$	Find the inverse of $A = \begin{bmatrix} 4 & 3 \\ -2 & 8 \end{bmatrix}$, if it exists. 1. Compute the value of the determinant to make sure that the inverse exists. $\begin{vmatrix} 4 & 3 \\ -2 & 8 \end{vmatrix} = 32 - (-6) = 38$ 2. Since the determinant does not equal 0, A^{-1} exists and $A^{-1} = \dfrac{1}{38}\begin{bmatrix} 8 & -3 \\ 2 & 4 \end{bmatrix}$

Find the inverse of each matrix, if it exists.

1. $\begin{bmatrix} 24 & 12 \\ 8 & 4 \end{bmatrix}$
no inverse exists

2. $\begin{bmatrix} 26 & -8 \\ 4 & -9 \end{bmatrix}$
$\dfrac{1}{202}\begin{bmatrix} -9 & 8 \\ -4 & 26 \end{bmatrix}$

3. $\begin{bmatrix} 40 & -10 \\ -20 & 30 \end{bmatrix}$
$\dfrac{1}{1000}\begin{bmatrix} 30 & 10 \\ 20 & 40 \end{bmatrix}$

4. $\begin{bmatrix} -5 & -4 \\ 0 & 3 \end{bmatrix}$
$-\dfrac{1}{15}\begin{bmatrix} 3 & 4 \\ 0 & -5 \end{bmatrix}$

5. $\begin{bmatrix} 18 & 9 \\ 3 & 6 \end{bmatrix}$
$\dfrac{1}{81}\begin{bmatrix} 6 & -9 \\ -3 & 18 \end{bmatrix}$

6. $\begin{bmatrix} 3 & 6 \\ 4 & 8 \end{bmatrix}$
no inverse exists

7. $\begin{bmatrix} 1 & 0 \\ 0 & 1 \end{bmatrix} \begin{bmatrix} 1 & 0 \\ 0 & 1 \end{bmatrix}$

8. $\begin{bmatrix} -2 & 0 \\ 0 & -2 \end{bmatrix} \begin{bmatrix} -\frac{1}{2} & 0 \\ 0 & -\frac{1}{2} \end{bmatrix}$

9. $\begin{bmatrix} 1 & 1 \\ 0 & 1 \end{bmatrix} \begin{bmatrix} 1 & -1 \\ 0 & 1 \end{bmatrix}$

Closing the Lesson

Writing Activity Have students write an explanation as to how to find the inverse matrix for a third degree determinant.

APPLYING THE LESSON

Homework Exercises

Assignment Guide
Basic: 10–19, 21–26
Average: 12–26
Enriched: 13–26
All: Mid-Chapter Review, 1–9

Teaching Tip ❸ Remind students when the inverse of a matrix will not exist.

Practice Masters Booklet, p. 30

Guided Practice   Determine whether each matrix can have an inverse. If not, explain why.

5. $\begin{bmatrix} 8 & 5 \\ 3 & 3 \end{bmatrix}$ yes   6. $\begin{bmatrix} 3 & 6 \\ 2 & 4 \end{bmatrix}$ no, det = 0   7. $\begin{bmatrix} 6 & 6 \\ -6 & -6 \end{bmatrix}$ no, det = 0   8. $\begin{bmatrix} -6 & 8 \\ 2 & 1 \end{bmatrix}$ yes

9. Find the inverse of $\begin{bmatrix} 1 & 2 \\ 2 & 1 \end{bmatrix}$, if it exists. $-\frac{1}{3}\begin{bmatrix} 1 & -2 \\ -2 & 1 \end{bmatrix}$

EXERCISES

Practice   Find the inverse of each matrix, if it exists. **See margin.**

Teaching Tip ❸   **A**

10. $\begin{bmatrix} 4 & -3 \\ 3 & 8 \end{bmatrix}$ 11. $\begin{bmatrix} 2 & -5 \\ 6 & 1 \end{bmatrix}$ 12. $\begin{bmatrix} 2 & -4 \\ -1 & 2 \end{bmatrix}$

13. $\begin{bmatrix} 3 & 1 \\ -4 & 1 \end{bmatrix}$ 14. $\begin{bmatrix} 4 & 0 \\ 0 & 1 \end{bmatrix}$ 15. $\begin{bmatrix} 8 & 4 \\ -4 & -2 \end{bmatrix}$

Determine whether each statement is true or false.

16. true
17. true
18. true
19. false

B

16. $\begin{bmatrix} 0 & 1 \\ 1 & 1 \end{bmatrix} \cdot \begin{bmatrix} -1 & 1 \\ 1 & 0 \end{bmatrix} = I$ 17. $\begin{bmatrix} 2 & 1 & -4 \\ -3 & 6 & 5 \end{bmatrix} \cdot \begin{bmatrix} 1 & 0 & 0 \\ 0 & 1 & 0 \\ 0 & 0 & 1 \end{bmatrix} = \begin{bmatrix} 2 & 1 & -4 \\ -3 & 6 & 5 \end{bmatrix}$

18. $\begin{bmatrix} 1 & 5 \\ 1 & -2 \end{bmatrix} \cdot \begin{bmatrix} \frac{2}{7} & \frac{5}{7} \\ \frac{1}{7} & -\frac{1}{7} \end{bmatrix} = I$ 19. $\begin{bmatrix} \frac{1}{3} & -\frac{2}{3} \\ \frac{2}{3} & -\frac{1}{3} \end{bmatrix} \cdot \begin{bmatrix} 1 & 2 \\ 2 & 1 \end{bmatrix} = I$

C

20. Determine if $-\frac{1}{64}\begin{bmatrix} -20 & 8 & 4 \\ 16 & 0 & -16 \\ -10 & -12 & 2 \end{bmatrix}$ is the inverse of $\begin{bmatrix} 3 & 1 & 2 \\ -2 & 0 & 4 \\ 3 & 5 & 2 \end{bmatrix}$. **It is.**

Critical Thinking

CONNECTION
Geometry

21. Find the inverse of the rotation matrix given in Lesson 4-4. Then make a conjecture about what movement this describes on the coordinate plane. Make a drawing to verify your conclusion. **90° clockwise about the origin**

Applications

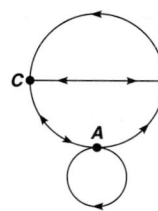

22. **Topology**   The figure at the left shows a directed network. The small arrows tell the direction you can travel on each pathway from point to point. These diagrams are used to plan airline routes. A matrix can be designed to represent this network. Each number in the matrix shows how many *direct* paths there are from one number to the next. For example, the 1 in the first row, second column states that there is one path from A to B. The last number in the second row states that there are 2 paths from B to C. Copy the matrix and complete it using the network diagram. **See margin.**

$$\begin{array}{c} \\ A \\ B \\ C \end{array} \begin{array}{ccc} A & B & C \\ \begin{bmatrix} 1 & 1 & ? \\ ? & ? & 2 \\ 1 & ? & 0 \end{bmatrix} \end{array}$$

Additional Answers

10. $\frac{1}{41}\begin{bmatrix} 8 & 3 \\ -3 & 4 \end{bmatrix}$

11. $\frac{1}{32}\begin{bmatrix} 1 & 5 \\ -6 & 2 \end{bmatrix}$

12. **No inverse exists.**

13. $\frac{1}{7}\begin{bmatrix} 1 & -1 \\ 4 & 3 \end{bmatrix}$

14. $\frac{1}{4}\begin{bmatrix} 1 & 0 \\ 0 & 4 \end{bmatrix}$

15. **No inverse exists.**

22. $\begin{array}{c} \\ A \\ B \\ C \end{array} \begin{array}{ccc} A & B & C \\ \begin{bmatrix} 1 & 1 & 1 \\ 0 & 0 & 2 \\ 1 & 1 & 0 \end{bmatrix} \end{array}$

23. $\begin{bmatrix} -5 & -2 & 15 & -15 \\ 21 & -6 & -63 & 27 \\ -11 & 18 & 33 & 23 \end{bmatrix}$

23. Find $\begin{bmatrix} -2 & 1 \\ 3 & -6 \\ 4 & 5 \end{bmatrix} \cdot \begin{bmatrix} 1 & 2 & -3 & 7 \\ -3 & 2 & 9 & -1 \end{bmatrix}$. **(Lesson 4-4) See margin.**

24. Graph $5x - 3y = 6$. **(Lesson 2-7) See margin.**

25. Find the slope, x-intercept, and y-intercept of the line whose equation is $9x - 2y = 4$. **(Lesson 2-4)** $\frac{9}{2}, \frac{4}{9}, -2$

26. How many different ways are there to arrange the letters, A, B, C, and D such that A is never the first letter? **(Lesson 1-5) 18 arrangements**

MID-CHAPTER REVIEW

1. Three women and their husbands were given a total of $5400. The women received $2400 in all. Sue had $200 more than Jane, and Liz had $200 more than Sue. Lou got half as much as his wife, Bob got the same as his wife, and Matt got twice as much as his wife. Who is married to whom? **(Lesson 4-1) Sue/Lou, Liz/Matt, Jane/Bob**

2. **Geometry** Use matrix addition to translate quadrilateral $MATH$ 4 units left and 3 units up if the vertices have coordinates $M(3, 5)$, $A(2, -6)$, $T(-3, -1)$, and $H(-7, 5)$. **(Lesson 4-2)** $M'(-1, 8)$, $A'(-2, -3)$, $T'(-7, 2)$, $H'(-11, 8)$

Perform the indicated operation. (Lesson 4-2) See margin.

3. $\begin{bmatrix} -2 & 1.5 \\ 3 & -0.25 \end{bmatrix} - \begin{bmatrix} -6 & 2 \\ 3 & 1.25 \end{bmatrix}$

4. $-4 \begin{bmatrix} -1 & -\frac{1}{4} \\ 0 & 2 \\ \frac{1}{2} & 4 \end{bmatrix}$

5. Evaluate the determinant of $\begin{bmatrix} -1 & 3 & 4 \\ 0 & 5 & 1 \\ 6 & -2 & 3 \end{bmatrix}$. **(Lesson 4-3) −119**

6. **Geometry** Use determinants to find the area of a triangle with vertices having coordinates $(0, 0)$, $(12, 0)$, and $(0, 5)$. **(Lesson 4-3) 30 square units**

Perform each operation. (Lesson 4-4) See margin.

7. $\begin{bmatrix} -2 & 3 \\ 1 & 10 \\ 0 & -6 \end{bmatrix} \cdot \begin{bmatrix} 9 & 3 \\ 1 & 4 \end{bmatrix}$

8. $\begin{bmatrix} 1 & 0 & 2 \\ 0 & 4 & 2 \\ 3 & 5 & 0 \end{bmatrix} \cdot \begin{bmatrix} 1 & 0 \\ 0 & 1 \end{bmatrix}$

9. Find the inverse of $\begin{bmatrix} -2 & 5 \\ 3 & 1 \end{bmatrix}$. **(Lesson 4-5)** $-\frac{1}{17} \begin{bmatrix} 1 & -5 \\ -3 & -2 \end{bmatrix}$

EXTENDING THE LESSON

Math Power: Reasoning

Find a 2 × 2 matrix, other than the identity matrix, that is its own inverse.

$\begin{bmatrix} 0 & 1 \\ 1 & 0 \end{bmatrix}$ $\begin{bmatrix} -2 & 1 \\ -3 & 2 \end{bmatrix}$ **are typical answers.**

Mid-Chapter Review

The Mid-Chapter Review provides students with a brief review of the concepts and skills in Lessons 4-1 through 4-5. Lesson numbers are given at the end of problems or instruction lines so students may review concepts not yet mastered.

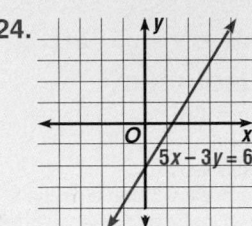

Lesson Resources

Reteaching Master 4-6
Practice Master 4-6
Enrichment Master 4-6

 Transparency 4-6 contains the 5-Minute Check and a teaching aid for this lesson.

INTRODUCING THE LESSON

 5-Minute Check

(over Lesson 4-5)
Find the identity matrix for each matrix.

1. $[4 \quad -7 \quad 12]$
$\begin{bmatrix} 1 & 0 & 0 \\ 0 & 1 & 0 \\ 0 & 0 & 1 \end{bmatrix}$

2. $\begin{bmatrix} 6 & 9 & 7 \\ 4 & 2 & -2 \\ -3 & 5 & 1 \end{bmatrix}$ $\begin{bmatrix} 1 & 0 & 0 \\ 0 & 1 & 0 \\ 0 & 0 & 1 \end{bmatrix}$

3. If $A = \begin{bmatrix} 43 & 12 \\ -7 & -2 \end{bmatrix}$, find A^{-1}.
$\frac{1}{-2}\begin{bmatrix} -2 & -12 \\ 7 & 43 \end{bmatrix}$

4. If $A = \begin{bmatrix} 2 & -1 \\ 3 & -2 \end{bmatrix}$, find A^{-1}.
$-1\begin{bmatrix} -2 & 1 \\ -3 & 2 \end{bmatrix}$

5. If $A = \begin{bmatrix} 1 & 1 \\ 0 & 1 \end{bmatrix}$, find A^{-1}.
$\begin{bmatrix} 1 & -1 \\ 0 & 1 \end{bmatrix}$

Motivating the Lesson

Review substitution and elimination as two ways of solving systems of equations. Discuss whether every matrix has an inverse.

Objective 4-6

After studying this lesson, you should be able to:
■ write a system of linear equations as a matrix and use the inverse to solve the system.

You have learned to solve systems of equations by several methods already. Matrices can be used to provide several other ways of solving systems of equations. In this lesson you will learn to solve a system of equations by using the inverses of matrices.

The matrices below represent three parts of a system of equations written in standard form. Matrix A is a matrix showing the coefficients of the variables in the two equations. Matrix B shows the variables in the system, and matrix C shows the constant terms.

Matrix A is called a coefficient matrix.

$$A = \begin{bmatrix} 5 & 3 \\ 7 & 5 \end{bmatrix} \quad B = \begin{bmatrix} x \\ y \end{bmatrix} \quad C = \begin{bmatrix} -5 \\ -11 \end{bmatrix}$$

When the first two matrices are multiplied and set equal to the third matrix, the result is a system of equations.

$$\begin{bmatrix} 5x + 3y \\ 7x + 5y \end{bmatrix} = \begin{bmatrix} -5 \\ -11 \end{bmatrix} \implies \begin{matrix} 5x + 3y = -5 \\ 7x + 5y = -11 \end{matrix} \quad A \cdot B = C$$

The equation $\begin{bmatrix} 5 & 3 \\ 7 & 5 \end{bmatrix} \cdot \begin{bmatrix} x \\ y \end{bmatrix} = \begin{bmatrix} -5 \\ -11 \end{bmatrix}$ is called a **matrix equation.**

This equation represents the system $\begin{cases} 5x + 3y = -5 \\ 7x + 5y = -11 \end{cases}$.

Example 1

Teaching Tip ❶

Write each system of equations as a matrix equation.

a. $6x + 5y = 8$
$3x - y = 7$

b. $2x + y - z = 9$
$x - 3y + 2z = 16$
$3x + 2y - z = 5$

The matrix equation is

$\begin{bmatrix} 6 & 5 \\ 3 & -1 \end{bmatrix} \cdot \begin{bmatrix} x \\ y \end{bmatrix} = \begin{bmatrix} 8 \\ 7 \end{bmatrix}$.

The matrix equation is

$\begin{bmatrix} 2 & 1 & -1 \\ 1 & -3 & 2 \\ 3 & 2 & -1 \end{bmatrix} \cdot \begin{bmatrix} x \\ y \\ z \end{bmatrix} = \begin{bmatrix} 9 \\ 16 \\ 5 \end{bmatrix}$.

184 CHAPTER 4 MATRICES

ALTERNATE TEACHING STRATEGIES

Using Computers

Have students make a flow chart for the solution of matrices involving inverses. Then have students write a program to solve matrix equations, using the steps on page 185 as a guide.

Mini-Math Lab

Have students make a solution of colored water. Put 1 ounce of blue food coloring into 7 ounces of water. Then pour 4 ounces of water into the solution. What is the percent of food coloring in the new solution? **about 8%**

Study the steps in solving this equation.

$$3w = 42$$
$$\left(\tfrac{1}{3}\right)3w = \left(\tfrac{1}{3}\right)42 \quad$$ *Multiply each side by the multiplicative __inverse__ of the coefficient.*
$$\phantom{\left(\tfrac{1}{3}\right)}(1)w = 14 \quad$$ *1 is the __identity__ element for multiplication.*
$$\phantom{\left(\tfrac{1}{3}\right)(1)}w = 14 \quad$$ *The solution is 14.*

You can use the same steps and a matrix equation to solve a system of equations.

- Write the matrix equation. **Teaching Tip ②**
- Multiply each side by the inverse of the coefficient matrix.
- The result will be the identity matrix multiplied by the variables.
- Interpret the solution.

Follow these steps in Examples 2 and 3.

Example 2

Use a matrix equation to solve $\begin{cases} 5x + 3y = -5 \\ 7x + 5y = -11 \end{cases}$.

The matrix equation is $\begin{bmatrix} 5 & 3 \\ 7 & 5 \end{bmatrix} \cdot \begin{bmatrix} x \\ y \end{bmatrix} = \begin{bmatrix} -5 \\ 11 \end{bmatrix}$.

Now find the inverse of the coefficient matrix $\begin{bmatrix} 5 & 3 \\ 7 & 5 \end{bmatrix}$ so you can complete the second step.

The inverse of $\begin{bmatrix} 5 & 3 \\ 7 & 5 \end{bmatrix}$ is $\dfrac{1}{25 - 21}\begin{bmatrix} 5 & -3 \\ -7 & 5 \end{bmatrix}$ or $\dfrac{1}{4}\begin{bmatrix} 5 & -3 \\ -7 & 5 \end{bmatrix}$.

Multiply each side of the matrix equation by the inverse matrix. Note the placement of the inverse when multiplying.

$$\tfrac{1}{4}\begin{bmatrix} 5 & 3 \\ 7 & 5 \end{bmatrix} \cdot \begin{bmatrix} 5 & 3 \\ 7 & 5 \end{bmatrix} \cdot \begin{bmatrix} x \\ y \end{bmatrix} = \tfrac{1}{4}\begin{bmatrix} 5 & -3 \\ -7 & 5 \end{bmatrix} \cdot \begin{bmatrix} -5 \\ -11 \end{bmatrix}$$

$$\begin{bmatrix} 1 & 0 \\ 0 & 1 \end{bmatrix} \cdot \begin{bmatrix} x \\ y \end{bmatrix} = \tfrac{1}{4}\begin{bmatrix} 8 \\ -20 \end{bmatrix} \qquad \tfrac{1}{4}\begin{bmatrix} 5 & 3 \\ -7 & 5 \end{bmatrix} \cdot \begin{bmatrix} 5 & 3 \\ 7 & 5 \end{bmatrix} = \begin{bmatrix} 1 & 0 \\ 0 & 1 \end{bmatrix}.$$

$$\begin{bmatrix} x \\ y \end{bmatrix} = \begin{bmatrix} 2 \\ -5 \end{bmatrix}$$

The solution is (2, -5).

The graph at the right confirms the solution.

How else could you check the solution?

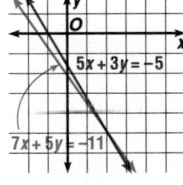

LESSON 4-6 USING INVERSE MATRICES 185

TEACHING THE LESSON

Teaching Tip ❶ Remind students that positioning of the matrices is important since multiplication of matrices is not commutative.

Teaching Tip ❷ Emphasize the necessity to multiply each side of the equation by the inverse matrix. Also note that the inverse matrix must be placed in the same location on each side.

Chalkboard Examples

For Example 1
Write each system of equations as a matrix equation.

a. $4a - 12b = 7$
   $a + 6b = 9$

$$\begin{bmatrix} 4 & -12 \\ 1 & 6 \end{bmatrix} \cdot \begin{bmatrix} a \\ b \end{bmatrix} = \begin{bmatrix} 7 \\ 9 \end{bmatrix}$$

b. $m - 2n + p = 14$
   $-3m - 3n + 5p = -22$
   $11m + 4n - 7p = 35$

$$\begin{bmatrix} 1 & -2 & 1 \\ -3 & -3 & 5 \\ 11 & 4 & -7 \end{bmatrix} \cdot \begin{bmatrix} m \\ n \\ p \end{bmatrix} = \begin{bmatrix} 14 \\ -22 \\ 35 \end{bmatrix}$$

For Example 2
Use a matrix equation to solve
$\begin{cases} 7x - 11y = 10 \\ 3x + 2y = 58 \end{cases}$. **(14, 8)**

Chalkboard Examples

For Example 3

Use a matrix equation to solve

$$\begin{cases} 8x - y + 2z = 7 \\ -5x + y - z = -2 \\ 4x - 2y + 4z = 2 \end{cases}$$

if the inverse of the coefficient matrix is

$$\frac{1}{12}\begin{bmatrix} 2 & 0 & -1 \\ 16 & 24 & -2 \\ 6 & 12 & 3 \end{bmatrix}.$$

$$\frac{1}{12}\begin{bmatrix} 12 \\ 60 \\ 24 \end{bmatrix} = \begin{bmatrix} 1 \\ 5 \\ 2 \end{bmatrix} = (1, 5, 2)$$

For Example 4

Dan bought 5 pieces of gum and 7 jawbreakers for 76 cents. Tom bought 7 pieces of gum and 4 jawbreakers for 60 cents. What was the cost of each piece of gum and each jawbreaker?

gum = 4 cents
jawbreaker = 8 cents

Example 3

Use a matrix equation to solve $\begin{cases} 3x - 2y + z = 0 \\ 2x + 3y = 12 \\ y + 4z = -18 \end{cases}$, if the inverse of the

coefficient matrix is $\dfrac{1}{54}\begin{bmatrix} 12 & 9 & -3 \\ -8 & 12 & 2 \\ 2 & -3 & 13 \end{bmatrix}$.

To help you write the coefficient matrix it may be helpful to write the system so that each equation contains all three variables with the proper coefficients.

$$3x - 2y + 1z = 0$$
$$2x + 3y + 0z = 12 \qquad \Rightarrow \qquad \begin{bmatrix} 3 & -2 & 1 \\ 2 & 3 & 0 \\ 0 & 1 & 4 \end{bmatrix}$$
$$0x + 1y + 4z = -18$$

Write the matrix equation. $\begin{bmatrix} 3 & -2 & 1 \\ 2 & 3 & 0 \\ 0 & 1 & 4 \end{bmatrix} \cdot \begin{bmatrix} x \\ y \\ z \end{bmatrix} = \begin{bmatrix} 0 \\ 12 \\ -18 \end{bmatrix}$

Multiply each side by the inverse and find a solution.

$$\frac{1}{54}\begin{bmatrix} 12 & 9 & -3 \\ -8 & 12 & 2 \\ 2 & -3 & 13 \end{bmatrix} \cdot \begin{bmatrix} 3 & -2 & 1 \\ 2 & 3 & 0 \\ 0 & 1 & 4 \end{bmatrix} \cdot \begin{bmatrix} x \\ y \\ z \end{bmatrix} = \frac{1}{54}\begin{bmatrix} 12 & 9 & -3 \\ -8 & 12 & 2 \\ 2 & -3 & 13 \end{bmatrix} \cdot \begin{bmatrix} 0 \\ 12 \\ -18 \end{bmatrix}$$

$$\begin{bmatrix} 1 & 0 & 0 \\ 0 & 1 & 0 \\ 0 & 0 & 1 \end{bmatrix} \cdot \begin{bmatrix} x \\ y \\ z \end{bmatrix} = \frac{1}{54}\begin{bmatrix} 162 \\ 108 \\ -270 \end{bmatrix}$$

Remember that the product of a matrix and its inverse is the identity matrix.

$$\begin{bmatrix} x \\ y \\ z \end{bmatrix} = \begin{bmatrix} 3 \\ 2 \\ -5 \end{bmatrix}$$

Check:

$3x - 2y + z = 0$	$2x + 3y = 12$	$y + 4z = -18$
$3(3) - 2(2) + (-5) \overset{?}{=} 0$	$2(3) + 3(2) \overset{?}{=} 12$	$2 + 4(-5) \overset{?}{=} -18$
$0 = 0 \checkmark$	$12 = 12 \checkmark$	$-18 = -18 \checkmark$

The solution is $(3, 2, -5)$.

You can use matrices to help you solve problems that involve systems of equations. Using matrices often simplifies the process of solving these systems.

Example 4

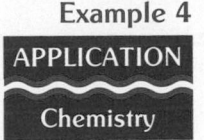

APPLICATION

Chemistry

FYI ···

Acetylsalicylic acid was first produced in 1899. It is better known as aspirin.

Giem Nguyen is a chemist who is preparing an acid solution to be used as a cleaner for machine parts. The machine shop needs several batches of 200 mL of solution at a 48% concentration. Giem only has 60% and 40% concentration solutions. The two solutions can be combined to make the 48% solution. How much of each solution should Giem use to make 200 mL of solution?

EXPLORE   Let a represent the amount of 60% solution and let b represent the amount of 40% solution.

$a + b = 200$ *The total of the two amounts must be 200 mL.*
Now write an equation that represents the proportions of each solution needed.

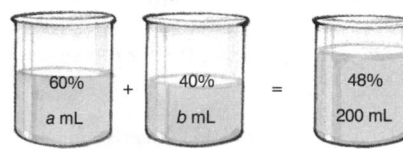

60% (a) + 40% (b) = 48% ($a + b$)   *Each part contributes to the total.*
$0.60a + 0.40b = 0.48a + 0.48b$ *Percents can be written in decimal form.*
$60a + 40b = 48a + 48b$ *Multiply by 100 to remove the decimals.*
$12a - 8b = 0$ *Write the equation in standard form.*

PLAN   Write a system of equations. Then write the system as a matrix equation.

$$\begin{cases} a + b = 200 \\ 12a - 8b = 0 \end{cases} \Rightarrow \begin{bmatrix} 1 & 1 \\ 12 & -8 \end{bmatrix} \cdot \begin{bmatrix} a \\ b \end{bmatrix} = \begin{bmatrix} 200 \\ 0 \end{bmatrix}$$

SOLVE   To solve the matrix equation, first find the inverse of the coefficient matrix.

$$\frac{1}{ad - bc}\begin{bmatrix} d & -b \\ -c & a \end{bmatrix} \Rightarrow -\frac{1}{20}\begin{bmatrix} -8 & -1 \\ -12 & 1 \end{bmatrix}$$

Now multiply each side of the matrix equation by the inverse and solve.

$$-\frac{1}{20}\begin{bmatrix} -8 & 1 \\ -12 & 1 \end{bmatrix} \cdot \begin{bmatrix} 1 & 1 \\ 12 & -8 \end{bmatrix} \cdot \begin{bmatrix} a \\ b \end{bmatrix} = -\frac{1}{20}\begin{bmatrix} -8 & -1 \\ 12 & 1 \end{bmatrix} \cdot \begin{bmatrix} 200 \\ 0 \end{bmatrix}$$

$$\begin{bmatrix} a \\ b \end{bmatrix} = \begin{bmatrix} 80 \\ 120 \end{bmatrix}$$

This means that 80 mL of the 60% solution is added to 120 mL of the 40% solution to make 200 mL of the 48% solution.

EXAMINE   A solution of 48% is closer in acidity to 40% than to 60%. It makes sense that there would be more 40% solution in the mixture than 60% solution. Also, the total amount is 200 mL.

RETEACHING THE LESSON

Follow the steps at the right to solve each system of equations by using matrices.

a. $3x - 2y = 12$
    $2x + y = -1$
b. $2x + 3y - z = 2$
    $x + 2y + z = 3$
    $-x - y + 3z = 1$

1. Write the matrix equation $AX = B$.
2. Find the inverse A^{-1} of the coefficient matrix A in the 2×2 system in part a.

$$A^{-1} = \frac{1}{7}\begin{bmatrix} 1 & 2 \\ -2 & 3 \end{bmatrix}$$

Reteaching Masters Booklet, p. 27

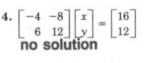

Checking for Understanding

Exercises 1–7 are designed to help you assess understanding through reading, writing, and speaking. You should work through Exercises 1–2 with your students, and then monitor their work on Exercises 3–7.

Closing the Lesson

Speaking Activity Have students divide into groups of four. Give them a system of equations to solve using matrices.

$x - y + z = 3$
$\quad 2y - z = 1$ **(3, 1, 1)**
$2y - x + 1 = 0$

Have one student from each group explain how they solved the system.

Practice Masters Booklet, p. 31

CHECKING FOR UNDERSTANDING

Communicating Mathematics

Read and study the lesson to answer each question.

1. What is the matrix equation for $\begin{cases} 2x - 3y = 8 \\ 7x - 3y = 5 \end{cases}$? **See margin.**

2. What is the product of the coefficient matrix and its inverse? *I*

Guided Practice

Write a matrix equation for each system. **See margin.**

3. $\begin{cases} 5a + 2b = -49 \\ 2a + 9b = 5 \end{cases}$

4. $\begin{cases} 2x - 3y + z = 29 \\ x + 4y + 2z = 3 \\ 3x + y - 2z = -3 \end{cases}$

Write each matrix equation as a system of linear equations. **See margin.**

5. $\begin{bmatrix} 5 & 1 \\ 2 & -3 \end{bmatrix} \cdot \begin{bmatrix} x \\ y \end{bmatrix} = \begin{bmatrix} 26 \\ 41 \end{bmatrix}$

6. $\begin{bmatrix} 2 & 1 & -1 \\ 1 & -4 & 3 \\ 6 & -2 & 5 \end{bmatrix} \cdot \begin{bmatrix} m \\ n \\ p \end{bmatrix} = \begin{bmatrix} -7 \\ 5 \\ 9 \end{bmatrix}$

7. Given that the inverse of the coefficient matrix is $\frac{1}{6}\begin{bmatrix} 3 & -1 \\ -9 & 5 \end{bmatrix}$, solve the matrix equation $\begin{bmatrix} 5 & 1 \\ 9 & 3 \end{bmatrix} \cdot \begin{bmatrix} x \\ y \end{bmatrix} = \begin{bmatrix} 1 \\ 1 \end{bmatrix}$. $\left(\frac{1}{3}, -\frac{2}{3}\right)$

EXERCISES

Practice

Write the system of linear equations represented by each matrix equation.

8. $\begin{bmatrix} 5 & 4 \\ 3 & -5 \end{bmatrix}\begin{bmatrix} x \\ y \end{bmatrix} = \begin{bmatrix} -3 \\ -24 \end{bmatrix}$

9. $\begin{bmatrix} 3 & 1 \\ 4 & -2 \end{bmatrix}\begin{bmatrix} x \\ y \end{bmatrix} = \begin{bmatrix} 13 \\ 24 \end{bmatrix}$

8. $5x + 4y = -3$
$3x - 5y = -24$

9. $3x + y = 13$
$4x - 2y = 24$

10. $\begin{bmatrix} 2 & 0 & 5 \\ 1 & 8 & 2 \\ 3 & -5 & 7 \end{bmatrix}\begin{bmatrix} x \\ y \\ z \end{bmatrix} = \begin{bmatrix} 1 \\ 2 \\ 3 \end{bmatrix}$

11. $\begin{bmatrix} 1 & -2 & 0 \\ 3 & 1 & 2 \\ 4 & -3 & 3 \end{bmatrix}\begin{bmatrix} x \\ y \\ z \end{bmatrix} = \begin{bmatrix} -8 \\ 9 \\ 1 \end{bmatrix}$

10. $2x + 5z = 1$
$x + 8y + 2z = 2$
$3x - 5y + 7z = 3$

Write a matrix equation for each system of linear equations. **See margin.**

12. $3x - y - 5$
$2x + 3y = 29$

13. $2x + 5y = 1$
$3x + 4y = 12$

14. $6a + 9b = 6$
$4a + 6b = 8$

11. $x - 2y = -8$
$3x + y + 2z = 9$
$4x - 3y + 3z = 1$

Use the given inverse matrix M^{-1} to solve each matrix equation.

15. $\begin{bmatrix} 4 & 8 \\ 2 & -3 \end{bmatrix} \cdot \begin{bmatrix} x \\ y \end{bmatrix} = \begin{bmatrix} 7 \\ 0 \end{bmatrix}$ $M^{-1} = -\frac{1}{28}\begin{bmatrix} -3 & -8 \\ -2 & 4 \end{bmatrix}$ $\left(\frac{3}{4}, \frac{1}{2}\right)$

Additional Answers

1. $\begin{bmatrix} 2 & -3 \\ 7 & -3 \end{bmatrix} \cdot \begin{bmatrix} x \\ y \end{bmatrix} = \begin{bmatrix} 8 \\ 5 \end{bmatrix}$

3. $\begin{bmatrix} 5 & 2 \\ 2 & 9 \end{bmatrix} \cdot \begin{bmatrix} a \\ b \end{bmatrix} = \begin{bmatrix} -49 \\ 5 \end{bmatrix}$

4. $\begin{bmatrix} 2 & -3 & 1 \\ 1 & 4 & 2 \\ 3 & 1 & -2 \end{bmatrix} \cdot \begin{bmatrix} x \\ y \\ z \end{bmatrix} = \begin{bmatrix} 29 \\ 3 \\ -3 \end{bmatrix}$

5. $5x + y = 26$
$2x - 3y = 41$

6. $2m + n - p = -7$
$m - 4n + 3p = 5$
$6m - 2n + 5p = 9$

12. $\begin{bmatrix} 3 & -1 \\ 2 & 3 \end{bmatrix} \cdot \begin{bmatrix} x \\ y \end{bmatrix} = \begin{bmatrix} 5 \\ 29 \end{bmatrix}$

16. $\begin{bmatrix} 3 & 1 & 1 \\ -6 & 5 & 3 \\ 9 & -2 & -1 \end{bmatrix} \cdot \begin{bmatrix} x \\ y \\ z \end{bmatrix} = \begin{bmatrix} -1 \\ -9 \\ 5 \end{bmatrix}$ $M^{-1} = -\frac{1}{9}\begin{bmatrix} 1 & -1 & -2 \\ 21 & -12 & -15 \\ -33 & 15 & 21 \end{bmatrix}$ $\left(\frac{2}{9}, -\frac{4}{3}, -\frac{1}{3}\right)$

17. $\begin{bmatrix} 1 & 2 & 2 \\ 2 & -1 & 1 \\ 3 & -2 & 3 \end{bmatrix} \cdot \begin{bmatrix} a \\ b \\ c \end{bmatrix} = \begin{bmatrix} 0 \\ -1 \\ -4 \end{bmatrix}$ $M^{-1} = -\frac{1}{9}\begin{bmatrix} -1 & -10 & 4 \\ -3 & -3 & 3 \\ -1 & 8 & -5 \end{bmatrix}$ $\left(\frac{2}{3}, 1, -\frac{4}{3}\right)$

Solve each system of equations by using a matrix equation.

 18. $6a + 2b = 11$ $\left(\frac{5}{3}, \frac{1}{2}\right)$
$3a - 8b = 1$

19. $4x + 3y = 5$ $\left(\frac{3}{4}, \frac{2}{3}\right)$
$8x - 9y = 0$

Critical Thinking

20. Rosalyn tried to use inverse matrices to solve a system of equations. However she found the determinant of the coefficient matrix to be 0. Can she still use this method? Why or why not? Describe the graph of such a system of equations. **See margin.**

Teaching Tip ❸

Applications

21. **Landscaping**   Two trucks have capacities of 10 tons and 12 tons. They made a total of 20 round trips to haul 226 tons of sand to the community park. How many round trips did each truck make? **7 trips for the 10-ton truck and 13 for the 12-ton truck**

22. **Metallurgy**   To make 20 kg of aluminum alloy with 70% aluminum, a metallurgist wants to use two metals with 55% and 80% aluminum content. How much of each metal should she use? **8 kg of 55% and 12 kg of 80%**

Mixed Review

23. Find the inverse of $\begin{bmatrix} 1 & 2 \\ -3 & 6 \end{bmatrix}$. **(Lesson 4-5)** $\frac{1}{18}\begin{bmatrix} 6 & -2 \\ 3 & 4 \end{bmatrix}$

24. Find M if $\begin{bmatrix} 3 & 6 & 1 \\ 2 & -1 & 0 \end{bmatrix} \cdot M = \begin{bmatrix} 3 & 6 & 1 \\ 2 & -1 & 0 \end{bmatrix}$. **(Lesson 4-5)** $\begin{bmatrix} 1 & 0 & 0 \\ 0 & 1 & 0 \\ 0 & 0 & 1 \end{bmatrix}$

25. Graph this system of inequalities and name the vertices of the polygon formed. Then find the maximum and minimum values of $f(x, y) = 4x - 3y$ for the region.   **(Lesson 3-6)**

$$x \le 5 \qquad y \ge -3x \qquad 2y \le x + 7 \qquad y \ge x - 4$$

(1, -3), (-1, 3), (5, 6), (5, 1); 17; -13; See Solutions Manual for graph.

26. Find the value of a for which the graph of $y = ax - 3$ is perpendicular to the graph of $-6x + 11y = 4$.   **(Lesson 2-4)** $-\frac{11}{6}$

27. Find the standard form of the equation that passes through $(4, -1)$ and $(-3, 2)$.   **(Lesson 2-5)** $3x + 7y = 5$

Solve each inequality.   **(Lesson 1-8)**

28. $5 < 2x - 9 < 11$
$\{x | 7 < x < 10\}$

29. $|9 - 3t| > 5$ $\left\{t | t < \frac{4}{3} \text{ or } t > \frac{14}{3}\right\}$

EXTENDING THE LESSON

Math Power: Reasoning

Find the matrix M if
$$\begin{bmatrix} 4 & 1 \\ -3 & 2 \end{bmatrix} M = \begin{bmatrix} 8 & -9 \\ 5 & 4 \end{bmatrix}$$

$$M = \begin{bmatrix} 1 & -2 \\ 4 & -1 \end{bmatrix}$$

Explain how you solved the problem.

Additional Answers

13. $\begin{bmatrix} 2 & 5 \\ 3 & 4 \end{bmatrix} \cdot \begin{bmatrix} x \\ y \end{bmatrix} = \begin{bmatrix} 1 \\ 12 \end{bmatrix}$

14. $\begin{bmatrix} 6 & 9 \\ 4 & 6 \end{bmatrix} \cdot \begin{bmatrix} a \\ b \end{bmatrix} = \begin{bmatrix} 6 \\ 8 \end{bmatrix}$

20. **No, because you can't find an inverse for a matrix whose determinant is 0. The graphs of the equations would be parallel lines, or the same line.**

APPLYING THE LESSON

Homework Exercises

Assignment Guide

Basic: 8–17, 20–21, 23–29
Average: 12–18, 20–29
Enriched: 12–29

Chapter 4, Quiz C, (Lessons 4-5 through 4-6), is available in the Evaluation Masters Booklet, p. 52.

Teaching Tip ❸   Make sure students write equations first. Then they can write matrices to solve the systems.

Enrichment Masters Booklet, p. 27

NAME _____   DATE _____

4-6   **Enrichment Worksheet**

Tessellations

A tessellation is an arrangement of polygons covering a plane without any gaps or overlapping. One example of a tessellation is a honeycomb. Three congruent regular hexagons meet at each vertex, and there is no wasted space between cells. This tessellation is called a regular tessellation since it is formed by congruent regular polygons.

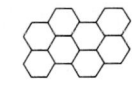

A **semi-regular tessellation** is a tessellation formed by two or more regular polygons such that the number of sides of the polygons meeting at each vertex is the same.

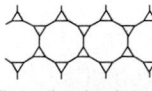   For example, the tessellation at the left has two regular dodecagons and one equilateral triangle meeting at each vertex. We can name this tessellation a 3-12-12 for the number of sides of each polygon that meet at one vertex.

Name each semi-regular tessellation shown according to the number of sides of the polygons that meet at each vertex.

1.   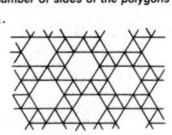   **3-3-3-3-6**

2.   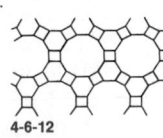   **4-6-12**

An equilateral triangle, two squares, and a regular hexagon can be used to surround a point in two different orders. Continue each pattern to see which is a semi-regular tessellation.

3. 3-4-4-6   **not semi-regular**

4. 3-4-6-4   **semi-regular**

On another sheet of paper, draw part of each design. Then determine if it is a semi-regular tessellation.

5. 3-3-4-12   **not semi-regular**
6. 3-4-3-12   **not semi-regular**
7. 4-8-8   **semi-regular**
8. 3-3-3-4-4   **semi-regular**

INTRODUCING THE LESSON

5-Minute Check

(over Lesson 4-6)

1. Write a matrix equation for the system
   $5a - 2b = 16$
   $-3a + b = -7.$

$$\begin{bmatrix} 5 & -2 \\ -3 & 1 \end{bmatrix} \cdot \begin{bmatrix} a \\ b \end{bmatrix} = \begin{bmatrix} 16 \\ -7 \end{bmatrix}$$

2. Write the matrix equation as a system of linear equations.

$$\begin{bmatrix} 6 & 3 & 5 \\ -2 & 1 & 7 \\ 1 & -4 & -2 \end{bmatrix} \cdot \begin{bmatrix} r \\ s \\ t \end{bmatrix} = \begin{bmatrix} -2 \\ 5 \\ 11 \end{bmatrix}$$

$6r + 3s + 5t = -2$
$-2r + s + 7t = 5$
$r - 4s - 2t = 11$

3. Solve the matrix equation.

$$\begin{bmatrix} 3 & -2 \\ 4 & 1 \end{bmatrix} \cdot \begin{bmatrix} x \\ y \end{bmatrix} = \begin{bmatrix} 10 \\ 17 \end{bmatrix} \quad (4, 1)$$

Other Prerequisite Skills

Use Cramer's Rule to solve the system of equations.

4. $x - 4y = 1$
   $2x + 3y = 13$ **(5, 1)**

Motivating the Lesson

Have students review Cramer's Rule for solving a system of equations. Discuss whether a determinant with a value of zero provides a solution to the system. What happens if the denominator is zero and the determinant in each numerator is not zero? The system has no solution.

4-7 Using Cramer's Rule

Objective 4-7

After studying this lesson, you should be able to:
- use Cramer's rule to solve a system of linear equations in three variables.

You have learned to solve a system of linear equations in three variables algebraically and by using inverse matrices. In Chapter 3, you learned to solve a system of linear equations in two variables by using Cramer's rule. Now you will learn to use Cramer's rule to solve a system of three equations in three variables.

Test for Unique Solutions

The system of equations $\begin{cases} a_1x + b_1y + c_1z = d_1 \\ a_2x + b_2y + c_2z = d_2 \\ a_3x + b_3y + c_3z = d_3 \end{cases}$ has a unique

solution *if and only if* $\begin{vmatrix} a_1 & b_1 & c_1 \\ a_2 & b_2 & c_2 \\ a_3 & b_3 & c_3 \end{vmatrix} \neq 0.$

To use Cramer's rule on a system of three equations in three variables you follow the same steps as with a system of two equations in two variables. The denominator is the determinant containing the coefficients. The numerators are the same determinant except that the coefficients of the variable for which you are finding a solution are replaced with the constant terms. Study this procedure in the following example.

Example 1

Determine whether the system $\begin{cases} a + 2b - c = -7 \\ 2a + 3b + 2c = -3 \\ a - 2b - 2c = 3 \end{cases}$ has a unique solution. If it **Teaching Tip ❶**

does, then solve the system using Cramer's rule.

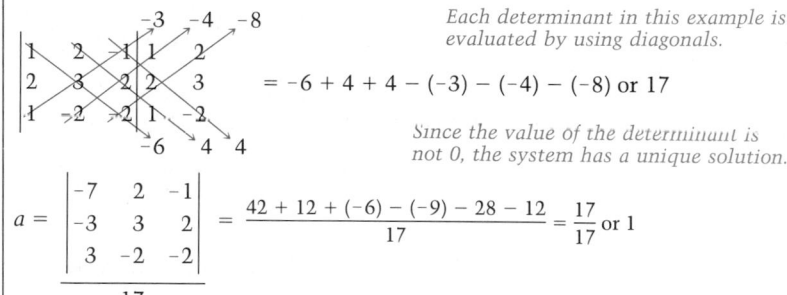

Each determinant in this example is evaluated by using diagonals.

$= -6 + 4 + 4 - (-3) - (-4) - (-8)$ or 17

Since the value of the determinant is not 0, the system has a unique solution.

$a = \begin{vmatrix} -7 & 2 & -1 \\ -3 & 3 & 2 \\ 3 & -2 & -2 \end{vmatrix} = \dfrac{42 + 12 + (-6) - (-9) - 28 - 12}{17} = \dfrac{17}{17}$ or 1

17

ALTERNATE TEACHING STRATEGIES

Using Models

Using cardboard, tagboard, or 3 × 5 cards, have students make models of the various intersections of planes in space. These will help to clarify the meaning of unique, non-unique, and no solution. A discussion relating a system of equations to each model will help the students to visualize what is meant by solving a system.

$$b = \frac{\begin{vmatrix} 1 & -7 & -1 \\ 2 & -3 & 2 \\ 1 & 3 & -2 \end{vmatrix}}{17}$$

$$c = \frac{\begin{vmatrix} 1 & 2 & -7 \\ 2 & 3 & -3 \\ 1 & -2 & 3 \end{vmatrix}}{17}$$

$$= \frac{6 + (-14) + (-6) - 3 - 6 - 28}{17}$$

$$= \frac{9 + (-6) + 28 - (-21) - 6 - 12}{17}$$

$$= \frac{-51}{17} \text{ or } -3$$

$$= \frac{34}{17} \text{ or } 2$$

The solution is (1, -3, 2).   *Check this solution.*

Example 2

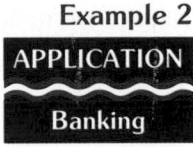

APPLICATION

Banking

Last year, Kathie Faught invested $48,000, some in stocks, some in bonds, and the remainder in a term account. She earned 4% on the stocks, 7% on the bonds, and 6% on the term account. For the year, she earned a total of $2860. She earned three times as much from the term account as she did from the stocks. How much did she invest in each?

EXPLORE   Let s represent the amount in stocks, b represent the amount in bonds, and t represent the amount in the term account.

PLAN   Write a system of equations.

$$s + b + t = 48000$$
$$0.04s + 0.07b + 0.06t = 2860$$
$$0.06t = 3(0.04s) \quad \text{or} \quad 0.12s - 0.06t = 0$$

SOLVE   Solve the system of equations. Use Cramer's rule.
Each determinant will be evaluated using diagonals.

Teaching Tip ❷

$$\begin{vmatrix} 1 & 1 & 1 \\ 0.04 & 0.07 & 0.06 \\ 0.12 & 0 & -0.06 \end{vmatrix} = -0.0042 + 0.0072 - (0.0084 - 0.0024)$$

$$= -0.003$$

Since the value of the determinant is not zero, the system has a unique solution.

$$s = \frac{\begin{vmatrix} 48000 & 1 & 1 \\ 2860 & 0.07 & 0.06 \\ 0 & 0 & 0.06 \end{vmatrix}}{-0.003}$$

$$t = \frac{\begin{vmatrix} 1 & 1 & 48000 \\ 0.04 & 0.07 & 2860 \\ 0.12 & 0 & 0 \end{vmatrix}}{-0.003}$$

$$= \frac{-201.6 - (-171.6)}{-0.003} \text{ or } 10,000$$

$$= \frac{343.2 - 403.2}{-0.003} \text{ or } 20,000$$

$$b = \frac{\begin{vmatrix} 1 & 48000 & 1 \\ 0.04 & 2860 & 0.06 \\ 0.12 & 0 & -0.06 \end{vmatrix}}{-0.003} = \frac{174 - 228}{-0.003} \text{ or } 18,000$$

Kathie invested $10,000 in stocks, $18,000 in bonds, and $20,000 in a term account.

RETEACHING THE LESSON

$$x - 3y - 2z = 9$$
$$3x + 2y + 6z = 20$$
$$4x - y + 3z = 25$$

1. Write the coefficient matrix for the system above.
2. Find its determinant D.   **-35**
3. Is there a unique solution for the system of equations above?   **yes**

Hint: What kind of value does D have if a unique solution exists?   **nonzero**

TEACHING THE LESSON

Teaching Tip ❶   Remind students that the same properties of Cramer's Rule for a system of equations in two variables apply here to get the numerators.

Teaching Tip ❷   Ask students why there are only four terms in the addition of the values for the determinant.

Chalkboard Example

For Example 1
Determine whether each system has a unique solution. If it does, then solve the system using Cramer's Rule.

a. $2x - y + z = -2$
   $x + 2y + 6z = 3$
   $3x - y + 2z = -1$
   (3, 6, -2)

b. $5x - y + 2z = 5$
   $2x - 3y + 5z = 1$
   $3x + 2y - 3z = 4$
   no unique solution exists

Reteaching Masters Booklet, p. 28

EVALUATING THE LESSON

Checking for Understanding

Exercises 1–8 are designed to help you assess understanding through reading, writing, and speaking. You should work through Exercises 1–3 with your students, and then monitor their work on Exercises 4–8.

Closing the Lesson

Writing Activity Have students write the three cases for using Cramer's Rule. They should write what happens and include a drawing.

Practice Masters Booklet, p. 32

192   Chapter 4

CHECKING FOR UNDERSTANDING

Communicating Mathematics

Read and study the lesson to answer each question.

1. Will Cramer's Rule apply for all systems of linear equations? Explain your answer. **No. It only works for systems with unique solutions.**

2. If the three linear equations represent three parallel planes, what would be the value of the coefficient determinant? **0**

3. What condition would have to exist for the value of the coefficient determinant to be a fraction? **At least one of the coefficients must be a fraction.**

Guided Practice

Write the coefficient determinant for each system of equations. **See margin.**

4. $3a = 5b + 6$
$a - b = 4$

5. $6t + u = 0$
$5t - 8u = -19$

6. $3x + 2y = 0$
$4x - z = 3$
$3z = -5x$

Name the determinants you would use to solve each system by Cramer's rule. Then solve each system using Cramer's rule. **See margin for determinants.**

7. $2x + 4y - z = -6$
$x - 2y + 3z = 2$
$x + 2y - 4z = -10$
$\left(-3, \frac{1}{2}, 2\right)$

8. $a - 2b + 3c = -4$
$2a - b + 4c = -1$
$2a + 3b + 5c = 1$
(4, 1, –2)

EXERCISES

Practice

Ⓐ

Determine whether each system of equations has a unique solution.

9. $2a + 4b - c = -6$
$a - 2b + 3c = 2$
$a + 2b - 4c = -10$
yes

10. $2x + 2z = 5$
$3y - 3z = -2$
$-3x - 2y = 11$
yes

11. $-r + 7s + 2t = 6$
$2r + s = -11$
$3r - 6s - 2t = -25$
no

Solve each system of equations using Cramer's Rule.

12. $4a + b + 3c = 1$
$2a + c = 3$
$4a - 6b = 8$
(5, 2, –7)

13. $2x - y + 3z = 5$
$3x + 2y - 5z = 4$
$x - 4y + 11z = 3$
no unique solution

14. $a + 2b - 3c = -13$
$2a - b + 3c = 23$
$3a + b - 3c = -8$
(3, 1, 6)

Ⓑ

15. $3x - y + 2z = 11$
$6x - 3y + z = -1$
$-3x - 2y + 2z = 11$
$\left(-\frac{1}{3}, 2, 7\right)$

16. $x + 9y - 2z = 2$
$-x - 3y + 4z = 1$
$2x + 3y - 6z = -5$
$\left(-5, \frac{2}{3}, -\frac{1}{2}\right)$

17. $x + 4y + 3z = 10$
$2x - 2y + z = 15$
$x + 2y - 3z = -1$
$\left(6, -\frac{1}{2}, 2\right)$

Additional Answers

4. $\begin{vmatrix} 3 & -5 \\ 1 & -1 \end{vmatrix}$

5. $\begin{vmatrix} 6 & 1 \\ 5 & -8 \end{vmatrix}$

6. $\begin{vmatrix} 3 & 2 & 0 \\ 4 & 0 & -1 \\ 5 & 0 & 3 \end{vmatrix}$

7. $x = \dfrac{\begin{vmatrix} -6 & 4 & -1 \\ 2 & -2 & 3 \\ -10 & 2 & -4 \end{vmatrix}}{\begin{vmatrix} 2 & 4 & -1 \\ 1 & -2 & 3 \\ 1 & 2 & -4 \end{vmatrix}}$ $y = \dfrac{\begin{vmatrix} 2 & -6 & -1 \\ 1 & 2 & 3 \\ 1 & -10 & -4 \end{vmatrix}}{\begin{vmatrix} 2 & 4 & -1 \\ 1 & -2 & 3 \\ 1 & 2 & -4 \end{vmatrix}}$ $z = \dfrac{\begin{vmatrix} 2 & 4 & -6 \\ 1 & -2 & 2 \\ 1 & 2 & -10 \end{vmatrix}}{\begin{vmatrix} 2 & 4 & -1 \\ 1 & -2 & 3 \\ 1 & 2 & -4 \end{vmatrix}}$

Write a system of equations for each problem. Do not solve the problem.

18. $p + n + d = 16$
$p + n - d = 0$
$p + 5n + 10d = 108$

18. Floyd has 16 coins in pennies, nickels, and dimes. The number of dimes is equal to the sum of the number of pennies and number of nickels. If the total value of the coins is $1.08, how many of each kind does he have?

19. At Burger Heaven, 2 cheeseburgers and 3 orders of fries cost $3.65. A cheeseburger and 2 milkshakes cost $2.47. A cheeseburger, 2 orders of fries, and a milkshake cost $3.01. What is the cost of each item?

Journal

Write a paragraph to tell what you like and dislike about using Cramer's rule to solve equations.

C ▶ 20. At Tapeland, T-60 blank tapes cost $3.19, T-90 blank tapes cost $3.89, and T-120 blank tapes cost $4.59. Carl bought 10 blank tapes for $40.30. If he bought twice as many T-90 tapes as T-120 tapes, how many of each tape did he buy?

19. $2c + 3f = 3.65$
$c + 2m = 2.47$
$c + 2f + m = 3.01$

20. $s + n + t = 10$
$3.19s + 3.89n + 4.59t = 40.30$
$n - 2t = 0$

Critical Thinking

21. Study the following problem and determine what effect using Cramer's Rule has when trying to solve it. Does the problem have a unique answer? If so, what is it?

Fred Chaves has $1.35 in nickels, dimes, and quarters. If he has the same amount of money in nickels as he has in dimes, how many of each does he have? **can't find 3 equations in 3 variables. It does have a unique answer: 6 nickels, 3 dimes, 3 quarters.**

Applications

22. **Sports** At the student-faculty basketball game, Mrs. Winters, Mrs. Gordon, and Mr. Gossell scored a total of 63 points for the faculty team before they collapsed from exhaustion. Mrs. Winters scored twice as many points as Mr. Gossell. Mrs. Gordon scored three points more than the sum of points scored by Mr. Gossell and Mrs. Winters. How many points did each person score? **Winters: 20, Gordon: 33, Gossell: 10**

23. **Retail** The Yogurt Shoppe sells cones in three sizes: small, 89¢; medium, $1.19; large, $1.39. One day, Kyla Martin sold 52 cones. She sold two more than twice as many mediums as larges. If she sold $58.98 in cones, how many of each size did she sell? **17 small, 24 medium, and 11 large**

Mixed Review

24. Describe $A_{2 \times 4}$. **(Lesson 4-1)** a matrix with 2 rows and 4 columns

25. Graph $y \geq |3x|$. **(Lesson 2-8)** See Solutions Manual.

26. Solve $\begin{cases} y > x \\ y < x - 3 \end{cases}$ by graphing. **(Lesson 3-4).** See Solutions Manual.

27. **Communications** A certain telephone call to a sports hotline costs $3.38 for the first three minutes and $0.96 for each minute thereafter. What is the cost of a 12-minute phone call? **(Lesson 1-4)** $12.02

LESSON 4-7 USING CRAMER'S RULE **193**

EXTENDING THE LESSON

Math Power: Reasoning

Find k such that this system of equations has no unique solution.
$kx + y + 5z = 2$
$-3x + 4y - 2z = -1$
$2x - y + z = 8$
$k = 13$

Homework Exercises

Assignment Guide

Basic: 9–19, 21–22, 24–27
Average: 12–27
Enriched: 12–27

Additional Answers

8.

$a = \dfrac{\begin{vmatrix} -4 & -2 & 3 \\ -1 & -1 & 4 \\ 1 & 3 & 5 \end{vmatrix}}{\begin{vmatrix} 1 & -2 & 3 \\ 2 & -1 & 4 \\ 2 & 3 & 5 \end{vmatrix}}$

$b = \dfrac{\begin{vmatrix} 1 & -4 & 3 \\ 2 & -1 & 4 \\ 2 & 1 & 5 \end{vmatrix}}{\begin{vmatrix} 1 & -2 & 3 \\ 2 & -1 & 4 \\ 2 & 3 & 5 \end{vmatrix}}$

$c = \dfrac{\begin{vmatrix} 1 & -2 & -4 \\ 2 & -1 & -1 \\ 2 & 3 & 1 \end{vmatrix}}{\begin{vmatrix} 1 & -2 & 3 \\ 2 & -1 & 4 \\ 2 & 3 & 5 \end{vmatrix}}$

Enrichment Masters Booklet, p. 28

4-7 **Enrichment Worksheet**

NAME _____ DATE _____

Properties of Matrices

Computing with matrices is different from computing with real numbers. Stated below are some properties of the real number system. Are these also true for matrices? In the problems on this page, you will investigate this question.

For all real numbers a and b, $ab = 0$ if and only if $a = 0$ or $b = 0$.

Multiplication is commutative. For all real numbers a and b, $ab = ba$.

Multiplication is associative. For all real numbers a, b, and c, $a(bc) = (ab)c$.

Use the matrices A, B, and C for the problems. Write whether each statement is true. Assume that a 2-by-2 matrix is the 0 matrix if and only if all of its elements are zero.

$A = \begin{bmatrix} 3 & 1 \\ 1 & 3 \end{bmatrix}$
$B = \begin{bmatrix} 1 & -3 \\ -1 & 3 \end{bmatrix}$
$C = \begin{bmatrix} 3 & 6 \\ 1 & 2 \end{bmatrix}$

1. $AB = 0$ **no**
$AB = \begin{bmatrix} 2 & -6 \\ -2 & 6 \end{bmatrix}$

2. $AC = 0$ **no**
$AC = \begin{bmatrix} 10 & 20 \\ 6 & 12 \end{bmatrix}$

3. $BC = 0$ **yes**
$BC = \begin{bmatrix} 0 & 0 \\ 0 & 0 \end{bmatrix}$

4. $AB = BA$ **no**
$BA = \begin{bmatrix} 0 & -8 \\ 0 & 8 \end{bmatrix}$
So, $AB \neq BA$.

5. $AC = CA$ **no**
$CA = \begin{bmatrix} 15 & 21 \\ 5 & 7 \end{bmatrix}$
So, $AC \neq CA$.

6. $BC = CB$ **no**
$CB = \begin{bmatrix} -3 & 9 \\ -1 & 3 \end{bmatrix}$
So, $BC \neq CB$.

7. $A(BC) = (AB)C$ **yes**
Both products equal
$\begin{bmatrix} 0 & 0 \\ 0 & 0 \end{bmatrix}$.

8. $B(CA) = (BC)A$ **yes**
Both products equal
$\begin{bmatrix} 0 & 0 \\ 0 & 0 \end{bmatrix}$.

9. $B(AC) = (BA)C$ **yes**
Both products equal
$\begin{bmatrix} -8 & -16 \\ 8 & 16 \end{bmatrix}$.

10. Write a statement summarizing your findings about the properties of matrix multiplication.
Based on these examples, matrix multiplication is associative, but not commutative. Two matrices may have a product of zero even if neither of the factors equals zero.

Teaching Suggestions

Be sure students understand how to modify the DATA line to enter the coefficients of each new system. Point out that the program employs expansion by minors in lines 150–180. Challenge students to modify the program so that it reports whether the system has no solutions or an infinite number of solutions. You may want to have students write programs to solve 2 × 2 or 4 × 4 systems. Point out that changes to the 3 × 3 program will be required in nearly every line.

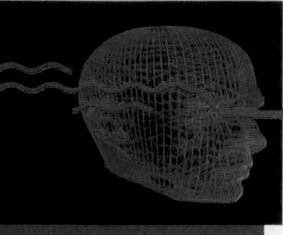

Technology
Cramer's Rule

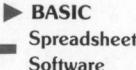

▶ **BASIC**
Spreadsheets
Software

The BASIC program below can be used to solve a system of equations in three variables.

```
5    DIM A[3,4], B[3,4]
10   FOR I=1 TO 3
20   FOR J=1 TO 4
30   READ A[I,J]
40   NEXT J
50   NEXT I
55   DATA 1,2,-1,-7,2,3,2,-3,1,-2,-2,3
60   FOR K=0 TO 3
70   FOR J=1 TO 3
80   FOR I=1 TO 3
90   IF J=K THEN 120
100  LET B[I,J]=A[I,J]
110  GOTO 130
120  LET B[I,J]=A[I,4]
130  NEXT I
140  NEXT J
150  LET M1=B[2,2]*B[3,3]-B[3,2]*B[2,3]
160  LET M2=B[2,1]*B[3,3]-B[3,1]*B[2,3]
170  LET M3=B[2,1]*B[3,2]-B[3,1]*B[2,2]
180  LET D[K]=B[1,1]*M1-B[1,2]*M2+B[1,3]*M3
190  NEXT K
200  IF D[0]=0 THEN 250
210  PRINT "X=";D[1];"/";D[0];"OR";D[1]/D[0]
220  PRINT "Y=";D[2];"/";D[0];"OR";D[2]/D[0]
230  PRINT "Z=";D[3];"/";D[0];"OR";D[3]/D[0]
240  GOTO 260
250  PRINT "NO UNIQUE SOLUTION"
260  END
```

Line 55 in the program shows the coefficients of the system as DATA:

$$x + 2y - z = -7$$
$$2x + 3y + 2z = -3$$
$$x - 2y - 2z = 3$$

In line 10–50, the computer interprets the data as an augmented matrix. In the program, $A(I, J)$ is the element in row I and column J of that matrix.

Lines 60–190 form a loop for evaluating four different 3 × 3 determinants. For each determinant, three columns of the augmented matrix are used. The four values are stored as $D(0)$, $D(1)$, $D(2)$, and $D(3)$.

Line 200 checks whether the system has a unique solution by looking at the value of the determinant $D(0)$. If $D(0) = 0$, then the computer will print "NO UNIQUE SOLUTION." Otherwise, a solution will be printed.

The output for this system of equations is:
```
X = 17/17 OR 1
Y = -51/17 OR -3
Z = 34/17 OR 2
```

EXERCISES

Change line 55 and run the program for each system of equations.

1. $2x + 3y + 4z = 4$
   $2x - 8z = -1$
   $4x - 6y + 4z = -1 \left(\frac{1}{2}, \frac{2}{3}, \frac{1}{4} \right)$

2. $5x - y + 2z = 5$
   $2x - 3y + 5z = 1$
   $3x + 2y - 3z = 4 \varnothing$

194 CHAPTER 4 MATRICES

4-8 Using Augmented Matrices

Objective
4-8

After studying this lesson, you should be able to:

■ solve a system of equations using an augmented matrix.

A system of equations may also be solved using a matrix called an **augmented matrix.** The augmented matrix of a system contains the coefficient matrix with an extra column containing the constant terms. Study how the system below can be written as an augmented matrix.

$$\begin{array}{r} x - 4y - 2z = 11 \\ 3x + 2y + z = 5 \\ 2x - 4y - 3z = 19 \end{array} \quad \blacktriangleright \quad \begin{bmatrix} 1 & -4 & -2 & 11 \\ 3 & 2 & 1 & 5 \\ 2 & -4 & -3 & 19 \end{bmatrix}$$

The system of equations can be solved by manipulating the rows of the matrix rather than the equations themselves. In this way, you perform the same operations that you would in working with the equations, but you do not have to bother writing the variables or worrying about the order in which the terms are written—the organization of the matrix keeps all of this in its proper place.

Teaching Tip ❶

Suppose you multiplied the first equation by -2. The result would be -2x + 8y + 4z = -22. The corresponding change in the matrix is that the first row becomes [-2 8 4 -22]. The result is the same as the result of multiplying the first row by -2. This is only one of the row operations you can perform in manipulating an augmented matrix. Here is a summary of the row operations on matrices you can use.

1. **Interchange any two rows.**
2. **Replace any row with a nonzero multiple of that row.**
3. **Replace any row with the sum of that row and a multiple of another row.**

The solution to the system of equations above is (3, 0.5, -5). That is, the three planes meet where x = 3, y = 0.5, and z = -5. Suppose we write these three equations in the form of an augmented matrix.

$$\begin{array}{r} x = 3 \\ y = 0.5 \\ z = -5 \end{array} \quad \blacktriangleright \quad \begin{bmatrix} 1 & 0 & 0 & 3 \\ 0 & 1 & 0 & 0.5 \\ 0 & 0 & 1 & -5 \end{bmatrix}$$

Notice that the first three columns form the 3 × 3 identity matrix. When doing row operations, your goal should be to find an augmented identity matrix.

LESSON 4-8 USING AUGMENTED MATRICES 195

ALTERNATE TEACHING STRATEGIES

Using Logical Reasoning
Ask students to explain what happens when zeros appear in the bottom row of the matrix.

$$\begin{bmatrix} 1 & 0 & 0 & 3 \\ 0 & 1 & 0 & 0.5 \\ 0 & 0 & 1 & -5 \end{bmatrix}$$

This means that the last variable equals -5.
Solve the system by substituting this value in the equations.

Lesson Resources
Reteaching Master 4-8
Practice Master 4-8
Enrichment Master 4-8

 Transparency 4-8 contains the 5-Minute Check and a teaching aid for this lesson.

INTRODUCING THE LESSON

🕐 5-Minute Check
(over Lesson 4-7)
Write the coefficient determinant for each system of equations.

1. $2a = 4c + 5$
   $3a - 2b + c = -7$
   $4b = 5c$

   $$\begin{vmatrix} 2 & 0 & -4 \\ 3 & -2 & 1 \\ 0 & 4 & -5 \end{vmatrix}$$

2. $2x + 5z = 11$
   $x + 3y - 2z = 20$
   $4z = -6y$

   $$\begin{vmatrix} 2 & 0 & 5 \\ 1 & 3 & -2 \\ 0 & 6 & 4 \end{vmatrix}$$

Solve each system using Cramer's rule.

3. $x + y + 2z = 3$
   $2x - 2y - 3z = 2$
   $3x - y - 2z = 1$

   (1, -6, 4)

4. $2x - y + 3z = 4$
   $3x + 2y + z = 9$ ∅
   $x + 3y - 2z = 3$

5. At Chester's Pizza, a drink, a salad, and 2 slices of pizza cost $4.12. A drink, 2 salads, and 3 slices of pizza cost $6.30. A salad, 2 drinks, and 4 slices of pizza cost $7.25. Find the cost of each item.
   slice = $1.19
   salad = $0.99
   drink = $0.75

Motivating the Lesson

Given a system of equations in three variables, what effect will the following operations have on the system?

1. interchange the equations **no effect**
2. replace any equation with a nonzero multiple of that equation **no effect**
3. replace any equation with the sum of that equation with a multiple of another equation **The system will have the same solution.**

TEACHING THE LESSON

Teaching Tip ❶ Point out that these row operations are suggested by the techniques used when solving a system of equations by the elimination method.

Teaching Tip ❷ Point out that this matrix now has all zeros in the "bottom triangle." The system could now be solved by setting $c = 2$ and substituting into the other equations.

Just as there is no one single order of steps to solve a system of equations, there is also no one single group of row operations that arrive at the correct solution. The order in which you solve a system may be different from the way your classmate solves it, but you may both be correct. Study Example 1 to see how the row operations are used.

Example 1

Use an augmented matrix to solve $\begin{cases} a + 2b + c = 0 \\ 2a + 5b + 4c = -1. \\ a - b - 9c = -5 \end{cases}$

Write the augmented matrix.

$\begin{bmatrix} 1 & 2 & 1 & 0 \\ 2 & 5 & 4 & -1 \\ 1 & -1 & -9 & -5 \end{bmatrix}$

The first element in row 1 is already 1.

Multiply row 1 by -1 and add to row 3.

$\begin{bmatrix} 1 & 2 & 1 & 0 \\ 2 & 5 & 4 & -1 \\ 0 & -3 & -10 & -5 \end{bmatrix}$

The first element in row 3 is now 0.

Multiply row 1 by -2 and add to row 2.

$\begin{bmatrix} 1 & 2 & 1 & 0 \\ 0 & 1 & 2 & -1 \\ 0 & -3 & -10 & -5 \end{bmatrix}$

The first element in row 2 is now 0, and the second element in row 2 is now 1.

Multiply row 2 by -2 and add to row 1.

$\begin{bmatrix} 1 & 0 & -3 & 2 \\ 0 & 1 & 2 & -1 \\ 0 & -3 & -10 & -5 \end{bmatrix}$

The second element in row 1 is now 0.

Multiply row 2 by 3 and add to row 3.

$\begin{bmatrix} 1 & 0 & -3 & 2 \\ 0 & 1 & 2 & -1 \\ 0 & 0 & -4 & -8 \end{bmatrix}$

The second element in row 3 is now 0. **Teaching Tip ❷**

Multiply row 3 by $-\frac{1}{4}$.

$\begin{bmatrix} 1 & 0 & -3 & 2 \\ 0 & 1 & 2 & -1 \\ 0 & 0 & 1 & 2 \end{bmatrix}$

The third element in row 3 is now 1.

Multiply row 3 by 3 and add to row 1.

$\begin{bmatrix} 1 & 0 & 0 & 8 \\ 0 & 1 & 2 & -1 \\ 0 & 0 & 1 & 2 \end{bmatrix}$

The third element in row 1 is now 0.

Multiply row 3 by -2 and add to row 2.

$\begin{bmatrix} 1 & 0 & 0 & 8 \\ 0 & 1 & 0 & -5 \\ 0 & 0 & 1 & 2 \end{bmatrix}$

This matrix contains an augmented identity matrix. Now you can read the solution.

The last augmented matrix represents $a = 8$, $b = -5$, and $c = 2$. Therefore, the solution is $(8, -5, 2)$.

The process of performing row operations to get the desired matrix is called **reducing a matrix.** The resulting matrix is called a **reduced matrix.**

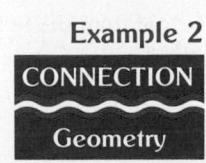

Example 2

CONNECTION

Geometry

The perimeter of a triangle is 83 inches. The longest side is three times the length of the shortest side and 17 inches more than one-half the sum of the other two sides. Find the length of each side.

EXPLORE Let a = the measure of the longest side of the triangle, c = the measure of the shortest side, and b = the measure of the other side.

PLAN Write equations for all the information you know.

$a + b + c = 83$ *The perimeter is 83 in.*

$a = 3c$ *The longest side is 3 times the length of shortest.*

$a = \frac{1}{2}(b + c) + 17$ *The longest side is 17 more than half the sum of the lengths of the other sides.*

SOLVE In order to solve the system, rewrite the equations so that they are all in the form necessary to write an augmented matrix.

$$\begin{array}{rl} a + b + c = 83 \\ a - 3c = 0 \\ 2a - b - c = 34 \end{array} \quad\Rightarrow\quad \begin{bmatrix} 1 & 1 & 1 & 83 \\ 1 & 0 & -3 & 0 \\ 2 & -1 & -1 & 34 \end{bmatrix}$$

After applying row operations on the matrix, we get

$$\begin{bmatrix} 0 & 1 & 0 & 31 \\ 1 & 0 & 0 & 39 \\ 0 & 0 & 1 & 13 \end{bmatrix} \quad\Rightarrow\quad \begin{bmatrix} 1 & 0 & 0 & 39 \\ 0 & 1 & 0 & 31 \\ 0 & 0 & 1 & 13 \end{bmatrix}. \quad \textit{Interchange the first and second rows.}$$

The solution is (39, 31, 13), which means the lengths of the sides of the triangle are 39 inches, 31 inches, and 13 inches.

EXAMINE The sum of the three lengths (39 + 31 + 13) is 83 inches. The longest side, 39, is 3 times 13, the shortest side. Half the sum of 31 and 13 is 22, which is 17 less than 39, the longest side.

As with other methods of solving systems of equations, there is not always a unique solution. However, when using augmented matrices, you can determine what type of solution you have when a solution is not unique. Study the solution of the system shown below.

$$\begin{array}{rl} 2x - y + 4z = 4 \\ x + 2y - 3z = 7 \\ x - 8y + 17z = -13 \end{array} \quad\Rightarrow\quad \begin{bmatrix} 2 & -1 & 4 & 4 \\ 1 & 2 & -3 & 7 \\ 1 & -8 & 17 & -13 \end{bmatrix} \quad\Rightarrow\quad \begin{bmatrix} 1 & 0 & 1 & 3 \\ 0 & 1 & -2 & 2 \\ 0 & 0 & 0 & 0 \end{bmatrix}$$

LESSON 4-8 USING AUGMENTED MATRICES 197

EVALUATING THE LESSON

Checking for Understanding

Exercises 1–8 are designed to help you assess understanding through reading, writing, and speaking. You should work through Exercises 1–4 with your students, and then monitor their work on Exercises 5–8.

Closing the Lesson

Writing Activity Have students write a paragraph explaining why there might be no solution for a system of equations.

Reteaching Masters Booklet, p. 29

198 Chapter 4

The row of zeros tells us that the last equation was derived from the first two so that this is a dependent system—there is no unique solution. However, a solution can be written. Let's write the two equations represented in the matrix. Then solve each equation for z.

$$x + z = 3 \qquad\qquad y - 2z = 2$$
$$x = 3 - z \qquad\qquad y = 2 + 2z$$

The solution would be the ordered triple $(3 - z, 2 + 2z, z)$. By choosing values for z you can find points on the line that is the solution to the system.

Let's look at the solution to another system of equations.

$$\begin{array}{l} x + 5y - 3z = 4 \\ 4x - 3y + 2z = 4 \\ 8x - 6y + 4z = 14 \end{array} \Rightarrow \begin{bmatrix} 1 & 5 & -3 & 4 \\ 4 & -3 & 2 & 4 \\ 8 & -6 & 4 & 14 \end{bmatrix} \Rightarrow \begin{bmatrix} 1 & 5 & -3 & 4 \\ 0 & -23 & 14 & -12 \\ 0 & 0 & 0 & 3 \end{bmatrix}$$

Notice the last row in the last matrix. This represents the equation $0 = 3$. This cannot be. Therefore the system is inconsistent and no solution exists.

Example 3

Describe the solution for the system of equations represented by each reduced augmented matrix.

a. $\begin{bmatrix} 1 & 0 & 7 \\ 0 & 2 & -6 \end{bmatrix}$

b. $\begin{bmatrix} 1 & 0 & 3 & 11 \\ 0 & 2 & 1 & 0 \\ 0 & 0 & 0 & 0 \end{bmatrix}$

c. $\begin{bmatrix} 2 & 0 & 0 & 3 \\ 0 & 0 & 0 & 6 \\ 0 & 5 & 0 & 6 \end{bmatrix}$

a. The solution is $(7, -3)$.

b. The solution is a line containing points $\left(11 - 3z, -\frac{1}{2}z, z\right)$.

c. There is no solution.

CHECKING FOR UNDERSTANDING

Communicating Mathematics

Read and study the lesson to answer each question.

1. **A matrix containing the coefficients of the variables along with a column containing the constant terms.**

1. What is an augmented matrix?

2. What does it mean when an augmented matrix has a row containing all zeros? **The system is dependent, and the solution is a line.**

3. What does it mean when an augmented matrix has a row that is all zeros except for the last element? **The system has no solution.**

4. What are the row operations that you can use with an augmented matrix? **See margin.**

198 CHAPTER 4 MATRICES

RETEACHING THE LESSON

Solve this 3×3 system of equations by elimination.
(1) $a + 2b + c = 0$
(2) $2a + 5b + 4c = -1$
(3) $a - b - 9c = -5$
Ask students what they would multiply the first equation by to eliminate the a terms from equations 2 and 3? **−2, −1**

Eliminate the a terms and rewrite the system. Ask students what they would multiply the second equation by to eliminate the b terms in equations 1 and 2? **−2, 3**

Eliminate the b terms and rewrite the system. Now have students identify the solutions. Compare this to using augmented matrices.

Guided Practice

5. Write a system of equations represented by $\begin{bmatrix} 1 & 0 & 3 & -2 \\ 3 & 9 & -2 & -5 \\ -4 & 1 & -7 & 3 \end{bmatrix}$.
See margin.

6. State the row operations you would use to change $\begin{bmatrix} 1 & 3 & 2 \\ 2 & 1 & 7 \end{bmatrix}$ to $\begin{bmatrix} 1 & 0 & \frac{19}{5} \\ 0 & 1 & -\frac{3}{5} \end{bmatrix}$. **Answers will vary.**

Write an augmented matrix for each system of equations. Then solve each system.

7. $5a - 3b = 7$
   $3a + 9b = -3$
   $\begin{bmatrix} 5 & -3 & 7 \\ 3 & 9 & -3 \end{bmatrix}$
   $\left(1, -\frac{2}{3}\right)$

8. $6x - 7z = 13$
   $8y + 2z = 14$
   $7x + z = 6$
   $\begin{bmatrix} 6 & 0 & -7 & 13 \\ 0 & 8 & 2 & 14 \\ 7 & 0 & 1 & 6 \end{bmatrix}$
   $(1, 2, -1)$

EXERCISES

Practice

9. State the row operations you would use to reduce $\begin{bmatrix} 2 & 4 & 3 \\ -2 & -3 & 1 \end{bmatrix}$.
   Answers will vary.

Write an augmented matrix for each system of equations. Then solve.

10. $4x + 3y = 10$
    $5x - y = 3$
    $(1, 2)$
    See margin for matrices.

11. $7m - 3n = 41$
    $2m + 5n = 0$
    $(5, -2)$

12. $3a - 5b + 2c = 22$
    $2a + 3b - c = -9$
    $4a + 3b + 3c = 1$
    $(1, -3, 2)$

Describe the solution for the system of equations represented by each reduced augmented matrix. **15. an equation in two variables**

13. $\begin{bmatrix} 1 & 0 & 3 \\ 0 & 1 & 5 \end{bmatrix}$
    unique

14. $\begin{bmatrix} 1 & 3 & 5 & -2 \\ 0 & 0 & 0 & 3 \\ 0 & 0 & 1 & 2.6 \end{bmatrix}$
    $\varnothing$

15. $\begin{bmatrix} 5 & 0 & 4 & 7 \\ 0 & 1 & -2 & 1 \\ 0 & 0 & 0 & 0 \end{bmatrix}$

Solve each system of equations using augmented matrices.

16. $6r + s = 9$
    $3r + 2s = 0$
    $(2, -3)$

17. $a + b + c = -2$
    $2a - 3b + c = -11$
    $-a + 2b - c = 8$
    $(-1, 2, -3)$

18. $2x + y + z = 0$
    $3x - 2y - 3z = -21$
    $4x + 5y + 3z = -2$
    $(-2, -3, 7)$

19. In triangle ABC, the measure of $\angle A$ is twice the measure of $\angle B$. The measure of $\angle C$ exceeds four times the measure of $\angle B$ by 12 degrees. Find the measure of each angle. **48°, 24°, 108°**

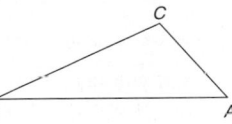

20. Solve $\begin{cases} 8m - 3n - 4p = 6 \\ 4m + 9n - 2p = -4 \\ 6m + 12n + 5p = -1 \end{cases}$ using augmented matrices. $\left(\frac{3}{4}, -\frac{2}{3}, \frac{1}{2}\right)$

Additional Answers

4. Interchange any two rows.
   Replace any row with a nonzero multiple of that row.
   Replace any row with the sum of that row and a multiple of another row.
5. Variables used may vary.
   $x + 3z = -2$
   $3x + 9y - 2z = -5$
   $-4x + y - 7z = 3$

10. $\begin{bmatrix} 4 & 3 & 10 \\ 5 & -1 & 3 \end{bmatrix}$

11. $\begin{bmatrix} 7 & -3 & 41 \\ 2 & 5 & 0 \end{bmatrix}$

12. $\begin{bmatrix} 3 & -5 & 2 & 22 \\ 2 & 3 & -1 & -9 \\ 4 & 3 & 3 & 1 \end{bmatrix}$

APPLYING THE LESSON

Homework Exercises

Assignment Guide

Basic: 9–19, 21–22, 24–28
Average: 11–28
Enriched: 13–28

Chapter 4, Quiz D, (Lessons 4-7 through 4-8), is available in the Evaluation Masters Booklet, p. 52.

Practice Masters Booklet, p. 33

4-8 **Practice Worksheet**
NAME_____ DATE_____
Using Augmented Matrices
Solve each system of equations using augmented matrices.

1. $5x + 9y = 19$
   $2x - y = -20$
   $(-7, 6)$

2. $2x + y - 3z = -3$
   $3x + 2y + 4z = 5$
   $-4x - y + 2z = 4$
   $(-1, 2, 1)$

3. $4x - 3y - z = -3$
   $5x + 2y + 2z = 7$
   $3x + 3y + z = 10$
   $(1, 3, -2)$

4. $x + 2z = 11$
   $2x + y = 4$
   $x + 3y + z = 1$
   $(3, -2, 4)$

5. $2x + y + z = 2$
   $-x - y + 2z = 7$
   $-3x + 2y + 3z = 7$
   $(0, -1, 3)$

6. $3x - 2y + 5z = -14$
   $x + 5y - 3z = 18$
   $-2x - 3y + 8z = -8$
   $(-2, 4, 0)$

7. $2x - y + z = 4$
   $x + y - z = 11$
   $4x - 2y + 2z = 5$
   $\varnothing$

8. $3x - 2y + 4z = 8$
   $x + y - 3z = 1$
   $6x - 4y + 8z = 16$
   $\left(\frac{2}{5}z + 2, \frac{13}{5}z - 1, z\right)$

Critical Thinking

21. You have learned what kind of solution a system has when one row of the reduced matrix contains all zeros. What kind of solution do you think you have when two rows of the three in the augmented matrix contain all zeros? Explain your answer.

Applications

22. **Automechanics** Ann Brauen is inventory manager for a local repair shop. If she orders 6 batteries, 5 cases of spark plugs, and 2 dozen pair of wiper blades, she will pay $830. If she orders 3 batteries, 7 cases of spark plugs, and 4 dozen pair of wiper blades, she will pay $820. If the batteries are $22 less than twice as expensive as a dozen wiper blades, what is the cost of each item on her order?

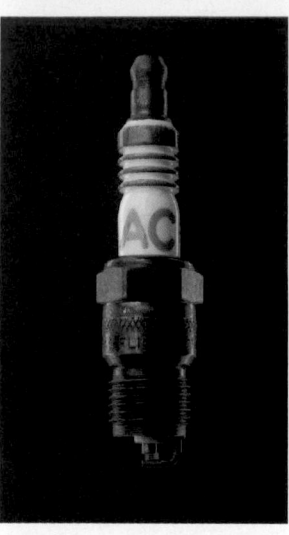

23. **Restaurant Management** There are several meals that can be purchased at Frank's Fried Chicken. A salad, 2 rolls, and 2 pieces of chicken costs $3.65. If you order a roll and 3 pieces of chicken, your meal costs $3.20. If a salad is 3 times as expensive as a roll, what is the cost of each item?

Mixed Review

24. Write the matrix equation for $\begin{cases} x + 5y + 2z = 10 \\ 3x - 3y + 2z = 2 \\ 2x + 4y - z = -15 \end{cases}$. **(Lesson 4-7)**

25. Evaluate $\begin{vmatrix} 4 & -2 \\ 3 & 7 \end{vmatrix}$. **(Lesson 4-3)**

26. Use Cramer's Rule to solve $\begin{cases} 9a - b = 1 \\ 3a + 2b = 12 \end{cases}$. **(Lesson 3-3)**

27. Solve $\begin{cases} x + 5y = 14 \\ -2x + 6y = 4 \end{cases}$ by graphing. **(Lesson 3-1)**

28. What property of real numbers is demonstrated by $x(a + b) = xa + xb$? **(Lesson 1-2)**

~~~~~~~~~~ LANGUAGE CONNECTION ~~~~~~~~~~

When you need to refer to a specific member of a matrix, a symbol is used to name each element of the matrix. The notation e_{34} denotes the element that is in the third row and fourth column.

What is the first element and last element in a matrix called $B_{m \times n}$?

EXTENDING THE LESSON

Math Power: Connections

The general form of the equation of a parabola is $y = ax^2 + bx + c$. Find the equation of a parabola that contains the points $(1, 9)$, $(4, 6)$, and $(6, 14)$.

Substitute each ordered pair into the equation and then solve the system of equations for a, b, and c. The equation is $y = x^2 - 6x + 14$.

Language Connection

Note that the order of the numbers in the subscript in an element name is just as important as the order of an ordered pair. $(1, 2)$ is the point over 1 and up 2. d_{12} is the element in the first row and second column. However, d_{21} is the element in the second row and first column.

Graphing Calculator Exploration: Matrix Row Operations

Teaching Tip ①

You can solve a system of linear equations by using the TI-81 calculator and the functions listed on its (MATRX) menu. Each of the functions is listed below with instructions on the keying procedure after that function has been selected from the (MATRX) menu. For convenience, suppose your augmented matrix has been entered as matrix (A).

RowSwap(**Interchanges two rows.**
- Enter the name of the matrix followed by a comma. *The comma is entered using the (ALPHA) key and the (·) key.*
- Enter one of the rows you want to interchange followed by a comma.
- Enter the other row you want to interchange followed by (1).

To interchange rows 2 and 3 in matrix A: RowSwap((A) (,) 2 (,) 3 (1) (ENTER)

Row+(**Adds two rows and stores the result in the last row you entered.**
- Enter the name of the matrix followed by a comma.
- Enter the row you want to add, followed by a comma.
- Enter the row you want it added to, followed by (1).

To add row 3 to row 1 in matrix A: Row +((A) (,) 3 (,) 1 (1) (ENTER)

*Row(**Does scalar multiplication on one row.**
- Enter the number you want to multiply by, followed by a comma.
- Enter the name of the matrix followed by a comma.
- Enter the row you want multiplied, followed by (1).

To multiply row 3 by −2 in matrix A: *Row(−2 (A) (,) (,) 3 (1) (ENTER)

*Row+(**Multiplies one row and adds the result to another.**
- Enter the number you want to multiply by, followed by a comma.
- Enter the name of the matrix followed by a comma.
- Enter the row you want multiplied, followed by a comma.
- Enter the row you want the result added to, followed by (1).

To multiply row 2 by $\frac{1}{2}$ and add it to row 3 in matrix A:

*Row+(0.5, (,) (A) (,) 2 (,) 3 (1) (ENTER)

To perform one operation after another in completely reducing a matrix, use (ANS) to be your matrix name so the operations will be done on the matrix you just finished.

To add row 2 of the matrix you just altered to row 1: Row+((ANS) (,) 2 (,) 1 (1) (ENTER)

Now use your TI-81 to check your answers in Lesson 4-8.

LESSON 4-8 USING AUGMENTED MATRICES 201

CHAPTER **4** # SUMMARY AND REVIEW

VOCABULARY

Upon completing this chapter you should be familiar with the following terms:

augmented matrix	195	179	identity matrix
coefficient matrix	184	179	inverse matrix
coordinate matrix	161	156	matrix
Cramer's rule	190	184	matrix equation
determinant	167	156	matrix logic
dilation	162	167	minor
dimension	161	174	rotation matrix
element	161	162	scalar multiplication
expansion by minors	167	163	translation

SKILLS AND CONCEPTS

OBJECTIVES AND EXAMPLES	REVIEW EXERCISES

Upon completing this chapter, you should be able to:

create a matrix and name it using its dimensions (**Lesson 4-2**)

$R = [5 \quad -3 \quad 9 \quad 7]$

The matrix above would be named $R_{1 \times 4}$.

Use these exercises to review and prepare for the chapter test.

Name each matrix using its dimensions.

1. $P = \begin{bmatrix} 3 & 2 & 1 \\ -5 & 6 & -3 \end{bmatrix}$ 2. $Q = \begin{bmatrix} 6 \\ -2 \\ 1 \end{bmatrix}$

$P_{2 \times 3}$ $Q_{3 \times 1}$

---

perform operations such as addition of matrices and scalar multiplication of a matrix (**Lesson 4-2**)

$2\begin{bmatrix} 18 & -6 \\ 9 & 21 \end{bmatrix} = \begin{bmatrix} 36 & -12 \\ 18 & 42 \end{bmatrix}$

Perform the indicated operations.

3. $3\begin{bmatrix} 8 & -3 & 2 \\ 4 & 1 & 7 \end{bmatrix}$ $\begin{bmatrix} 24 & -9 & 6 \\ 12 & 3 & 21 \end{bmatrix}$

4. $2\begin{bmatrix} 8 & -1 \\ 3 & 4 \end{bmatrix} - 3\begin{bmatrix} 1 & 6 \\ -2 & -3 \end{bmatrix}$ $\begin{bmatrix} 13 & -20 \\ 12 & 17 \end{bmatrix}$

---

find unknown values in equal matrices (**Lesson 4-2**)

To find x and y for $\begin{bmatrix} 2x \\ y \end{bmatrix} = \begin{bmatrix} 32 + 6y \\ 7 - x \end{bmatrix}$, solve the system $2x = 32 + 6y$ and $y = 7 - x$.

5. Find the values of x and y for which the equation is true. (**3, 8**)

$\begin{bmatrix} 7x \\ x + y \end{bmatrix} = \begin{bmatrix} 5 + 2y \\ 11 \end{bmatrix}$

OBJECTIVES AND EXAMPLES

- evaluate the determinant of a 3×3 matrix **(Lesson 4-3)**

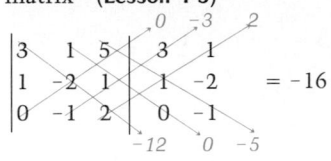

$$= -16$$

- multiply two matrices and interpret the results **(Lesson 4-4)**

The product of an $m \times n$ matrix, A, and an $n \times r$ matrix, B, is the $m \times r$ matrix AB. The element in the ith row and the jth column of AB is the sum of the products of the corresponding elements in the ith row of A and the jth column of B.

- write the identity matrix for any given matrix **(Lesson 4-5)**

The identity matrix is a square matrix which when multiplied by another matrix equals that same matrix.

- find the inverse matrix of a 2×2 matrix **(Lesson 4-5)**

Any matrix M, $\begin{bmatrix} a & b \\ c & d \end{bmatrix}$, will have an inverse M^{-1} if and only if $\begin{vmatrix} a & b \\ c & d \end{vmatrix} \neq 0$.

Then $M^{-1} = \dfrac{1}{ad - bc}\begin{bmatrix} d & -b \\ -c & a \end{bmatrix}$.

- write a system of linear equations as a matrix and use the inverse to solve the system **(Lesson 4-6)**
  - Multiply both sides by the inverse of the coefficient matrix.
  - The result will be the identity matrix multiplied by the variables.
  - Interpret the solution.

REVIEW EXERCISES

Evaluate each determinant.

6. $\begin{vmatrix} 5 & -1 & 2 \\ -6 & -7 & 3 \\ 7 & 0 & 4 \end{vmatrix}$ **-87**

7. $\begin{vmatrix} 2 & -3 & 1 \\ 0 & 7 & 8 \\ 2 & 1 & 3 \end{vmatrix}$ **-36**

Find each product.

8. $\begin{bmatrix} 2 & -3 \\ 6 & 4 \end{bmatrix} \cdot \begin{bmatrix} 1 & -3 & 4 \\ 3 & 1 & 1 \end{bmatrix}$ $\begin{bmatrix} -7 & -9 & 5 \\ 18 & -14 & 28 \end{bmatrix}$

9. $[5 \quad -2 \quad 3] \cdot \begin{bmatrix} 2 & 5 \\ -1 & 3 \\ 6 & 4 \end{bmatrix}$ **[30 31]**

10. $\begin{bmatrix} 4 \\ -1 \\ 3 \end{bmatrix} \cdot \begin{bmatrix} 1 & 0 & 0 \\ 0 & 1 & 0 \\ 0 & 0 & 1 \end{bmatrix}$ **not defined**

11. Write the 4×4 identity matrix.
    See margin.

12. Write the identity matrix, $I_{6 \times 6}$.
    See margin.

Find the inverse of each matrix.

13. $\begin{bmatrix} 8 & 6 \\ 9 & 7 \end{bmatrix}$ $\dfrac{1}{2}\begin{bmatrix} 7 & -6 \\ -9 & 8 \end{bmatrix}$

14. $\begin{bmatrix} 3 & 2 \\ 4 & -2 \end{bmatrix}$ $-\dfrac{1}{14}\begin{bmatrix} -2 & -2 \\ -4 & 3 \end{bmatrix}$

Solve each matrix equation.

15. $\begin{bmatrix} 3 & 2 \\ 1 & -2 \end{bmatrix} \cdot \begin{bmatrix} x \\ y \end{bmatrix} = \begin{bmatrix} 9 \\ 11 \end{bmatrix}$ **(5, -3)**

16. $\begin{bmatrix} 3 & 1 & 1 \\ 2 & 4 & 1 \\ 1 & 3 & 2 \end{bmatrix} \cdot \begin{bmatrix} a \\ b \\ c \end{bmatrix} = \begin{bmatrix} -2 \\ 4 \\ 12 \end{bmatrix}$ if the

inverse is $\dfrac{1}{14}\begin{bmatrix} 5 & 1 & -3 \\ -3 & 5 & -1 \\ 2 & -8 & 10 \end{bmatrix}$. **(-3, 1, 6)**

Additional Answers

11. $\begin{bmatrix} 1 & 0 & 0 & 0 \\ 0 & 1 & 0 & 0 \\ 0 & 0 & 1 & 0 \\ 0 & 0 & 0 & 1 \end{bmatrix}$

12. $\begin{bmatrix} 1 & 0 & 0 & 0 & 0 & 0 \\ 0 & 1 & 0 & 0 & 0 & 0 \\ 0 & 0 & 1 & 0 & 0 & 0 \\ 0 & 0 & 0 & 1 & 0 & 0 \\ 0 & 0 & 0 & 0 & 1 & 0 \\ 0 & 0 & 0 & 0 & 0 & 1 \end{bmatrix}$

Alternate Review Strategies

To provide a brief in-class review, you may wish to read the following questions to the class and require a verbal response.

1. Name the matrix using its dimension.
$$D = \begin{bmatrix} 1 & 2 & 5 \\ 0 & 3 & 7 \\ 2 & 5 & 8 \end{bmatrix} \quad \mathbf{D_{3 \times 3}}$$

2. Multiply the matrix by the scalar.
$$5\begin{bmatrix} 3 & 1 & 5 \\ -2 & 3 & -7 \end{bmatrix}$$
$$\begin{bmatrix} 15 & 5 & 25 \\ -10 & 15 & -35 \end{bmatrix}$$

3. Find the values of x and y for which the equation is true.
$$\begin{bmatrix} 3x \\ x+y \end{bmatrix} = \begin{bmatrix} 24 \\ 7 \end{bmatrix}$$
$$x = 8, y = -1$$

4. Evaluate the determinant.
$$\begin{vmatrix} 2 & 1 & 4 \\ 1 & -2 & 3 \\ 3 & -1 & 4 \end{vmatrix} \quad \mathbf{15}$$

5. Multiply.
$$[1 \quad 2 \quad 1]\begin{bmatrix} 4 \\ 2 \\ 1 \end{bmatrix} \quad \mathbf{[9]}$$

6. Find the inverse of the matrix.
$$\begin{bmatrix} 3 & -2 \\ 4 & 1 \end{bmatrix} \quad \dfrac{1}{11}\begin{bmatrix} 1 & 2 \\ -4 & 3 \end{bmatrix}$$

7. Solve the matrix equation.
$$\begin{bmatrix} 1 & 2 \\ 2 & 3 \end{bmatrix} \cdot \begin{bmatrix} x \\ y \end{bmatrix} = \begin{bmatrix} 2 \\ 4 \end{bmatrix}$$
$$x = 2$$
$$y = 0$$

8. Solve the system using Cramer's Rule.
$$x + y + 2z = 3$$
$$2x - 2y - 3z = 2 \quad \mathbf{(1, -6, 4)}$$
$$3x - y - 2z = 1$$

9. Solve using augmented matrices.
$$x + y = 1$$
$$2x - 3y = 17 \quad \mathbf{(4, -3)}$$

The Cumulative Review shown below can be used to review skills and concepts presented thus far in the text. Standardized Test Practice Questions are also provided in the Evaluation Masters Booklet.

Evaluation Masters Booklet, pp. 53–54

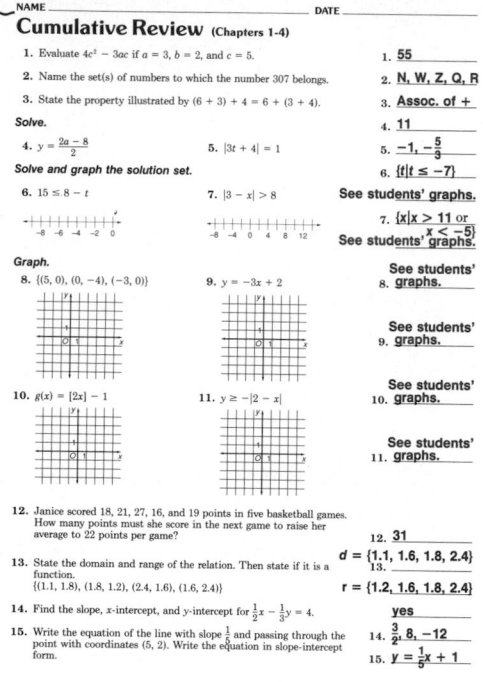
OBJECTIVES AND EXAMPLES	REVIEW EXERCISES

■ use Cramer's Rule to solve a system of linear equations in three variables **(Lesson 4-7)**

   ■ Determine if the system of equations has a unique solution.
   ■ If the system has a unique solution, then solve using Cramer's Rule.

Solve each system using Cramer's Rule.

17. $2a - b - 3c = -20$
   $4a + 2b + c = 6$
   $2a + b - c = -6$ $\left(-\frac{1}{2}, \mathbf{1}, \mathbf{6}\right)$

18. $2x - y + 3z = 1$
   $x - y + 4z = 0$ **(2, 6, 1)**
   $3x - 2y + z = -5$

■ solve a system of equations using an augmented matrix   **(Lesson 4-8)**

The solution represented by the reduced augmented matrix $\begin{bmatrix} 1 & 0 & 0 & 4 \\ 0 & 1 & 0 & 3 \\ 0 & 0 & 1 & \frac{7}{4} \end{bmatrix}$ is $\left(4, 3, \frac{7}{4}\right)$.

Solve using augmented matrices.

19. $x + 5y = 1$
   $2x - 3y = 15$ **(6, −1)**

20. $a - 2b + c = 6$
   $3a + 2b - c = 0$ $\left(\frac{3}{2}, -2, \frac{1}{2}\right)$
   $2a + b - 6c = -2$

∼∼∼∼ APPLICATIONS AND CONNECTIONS ∼∼∼∼

21. Use matrix logic to solve this problem. **(Lesson 4-1)** Alan, Bill, and Cathy each had different lunches. One had soup, one had a sandwich, and one had a salad. Alan did not have a sandwich. Bill did not have soup or a sandwich. What did each person have for lunch? **Alan: soup, Bill: salad, Cathy: sandwich**

Triangle ABC has vertices with coordinates A(5, −2), B(−3, 4), and C(−2, −3). Find the coordinates of the vertices of triangle A′B′C′ for each transformation. (Lesson 4-2)

22. Triangle $A'B'C'$ has a perimeter three times that of triangle ABC. **A′(15, −6), B′(−9, 12), C′(−6, −9)**

23. Triangle $A'B'C'$ is translated 4 units right and 1 unit down. **A′(9, −3), B′(1, 3), C′(2, −4)**

24. Find the area of a triangle with vertices $X(-2, 6)$, $Y(-3, -2)$, and $Z(3, 5)$. **(Lesson 4-3) 20.5 units²**

25. Triangle MPQ has vertices $M(5, 0)$, $P(-2, 6)$, and $Q(3, -4)$. Find the coordinates of the triangle after it is rotated 90° counterclockwise about the origin. **(Lesson 4-4) M′(0, 5), P′(−6, −2), Q′(4, 3)**

26. **Investment Planning** Maria Hernandez invested $29,000, part in stocks at 4% return, part in bonds at 6% return, and the remainder in a term account at 5.5% return. The amount she invested in stocks was equal to the total amount invested in bonds and term accounts together. If her total annual interest was $1414, how much money did she invest in each item? **(Lesson 4-7) stocks = $14,500, bonds = $7300, term acc = $7200**

State the dimensions of each matrix. Then evaluate the determinant of the matrix, if it exists.

1. $\begin{bmatrix} 2 & -3 & 1 \\ 3 & -1 & 2 \\ 1 & 2 & -3 \end{bmatrix}$ **3 × 3, -28**

2. $\begin{bmatrix} 7 & -10 & 1 & 4 \\ 6 & 8 & 5 & -1 \end{bmatrix}$ **2 × 4, no determinant**

3. $\begin{bmatrix} 1 & 3 & 1 \\ 2 & 1 & -5 \\ 3 & -1 & -4 \end{bmatrix}$ **3 × 3, -35**

Perform the indicated operations.

4. $\begin{bmatrix} 1 & 2 \\ -4 & 3 \\ 5 & 2 \end{bmatrix}\begin{bmatrix} 5 \\ 4 \end{bmatrix}$ $\begin{bmatrix} \mathbf{13} \\ \mathbf{-8} \\ \mathbf{33} \end{bmatrix}$

5. $\begin{bmatrix} 2 & -4 & 1 \\ 3 & 8 & -2 \end{bmatrix} - 2\begin{bmatrix} 1 & 2 & -4 \\ -2 & 3 & 7 \end{bmatrix}$ $\begin{bmatrix} \mathbf{0} & \mathbf{-8} & \mathbf{9} \\ \mathbf{7} & \mathbf{2} & \mathbf{-16} \end{bmatrix}$

6. Solve $\begin{bmatrix} x \\ 2y \end{bmatrix} - 3\begin{bmatrix} y+1 \\ 2x \end{bmatrix} = \begin{bmatrix} 5 \\ -16 \end{bmatrix}$. **(2, -2)**

7. Find the inverse of $\begin{bmatrix} 5 & -2 \\ 6 & 3 \end{bmatrix}$. $\frac{1}{27}\begin{bmatrix} \mathbf{3} & \mathbf{2} \\ \mathbf{-6} & \mathbf{5} \end{bmatrix}$

8. Determine whether the system $\begin{cases} r + s + t = 7 \\ 3r - 7s + 2t = 11 \\ -9r + 21s + 3t = -3 \end{cases}$ has a unique solution.

If it does, find it using Cramer's rule. **It does:** $\left(3, \frac{2}{3}, \frac{10}{3}\right)$

9. Solve $\begin{cases} x + 8y = -3 \\ 2x - 6y = -17 \end{cases}$ using a matrix equation. $\left(-7, \frac{1}{2}\right)$

Solve each system of equations using augmented matrices.

10. $6x - y = -15$
    $5x + 2y = -4$ **(-2, 3)**

11. $2x - 3y + z = 7$
    $3x - y + 2z = 1$
    $x + 2y - 3z = 14$ **(-2, -3, 2)**

For Exercises 12–14, use △ABC whose vertices have coordinates A(6, 3), B(1, 5), and C(-1, 4).

12. Translate triangle ABC so that the coordinates of B' are (3, 1). What are the coordinates of A' and C'?
A'(8, -1), C'(1, 0)

13. Find the coordinates of the vertices of a similar triangle whose perimeter is five times that of △ABC. **A'(30, 15), B'(5, 25), C'(-5, 20)**

14. Find the coordinates of the vertices of triangle ABC after it has been rotated counterclockwise 90° about the origin. **A'(-3, 6), B'(-5, 1), C'(-4, -1)**

Bonus
Find the coordinates of a similar triangle whose perimeter is half that of △ABC and has been rotated *clockwise* 90° about the origin. $\left(1\frac{1}{2}, -3\right), \left(2\frac{1}{2}, -\frac{1}{2}\right), \left(2, \frac{1}{2}\right)$

Using the Chapter Test

This page may be used as a test or as a review. In addition, two multiple-choice tests and two free-response tests are provided in the Evaluation Masters Booklet. Chapter 4 Test, Form 1A is shown below.

Evaluation Masters Booklet, pp. 43–44

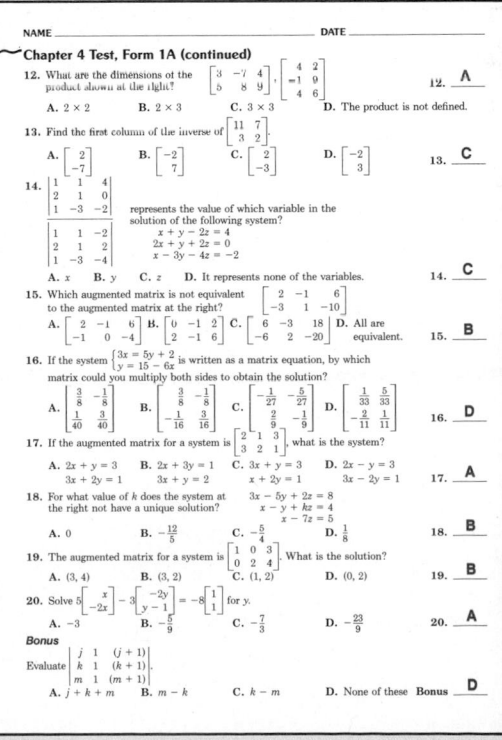

A **Test and Review Generator** is provided in Apple, IBM, and Macintosh versions. You may use this software to create your own tests or worksheets, based on the needs of your students.

The **Performance Assessment Booklet** provides an alternate assessment for evaluating student progress. An assessment for this chapter can be found on pages 7–8.

College Entrance Exam Preview

The test questions on these pages deal with ratios, proportions, and percents.

Directions: Choose the one best answer. Write A, B, C, or D.

1. 40% of 10 inches is how many sixths of
B 2 feet?

   (A) $\frac{1}{3}$ (B) 1

   (C) 2   (D) 4

2. For nonzero numbers, a, b, c, and d,
C $\frac{a}{b} = \frac{c}{d}$. Which of the following must be true?

   (A) $\frac{a}{b} = \frac{b}{c}$ (B) $\frac{a+b}{b} = \frac{c+b}{d}$

   (C) $\frac{d}{b} = \frac{c}{a}$ (D) $\frac{b}{c+d} = \frac{d}{a+b}$

3. Find the percent of increase if your
B salary increases from $250 a week to $300.

   (A) $16\frac{2}{3}\%$ (B) 20%

   (C) 22%   (D) 25%

4. If your grade was 90 and is now 75, find
A the percent of decrease.

   (A) $16\frac{2}{3}\%$ (B) 18%

   (C) 20%   (D) 22%

5. 9 is 6% of what number?

D (A) 100   (B) 120

   (C) 130   (D) 150

6. If $\frac{x}{y} = \frac{5}{6}$, then $18x =$

C (A) $\frac{5y}{3}$ (B) $90y$ (C) $15y$ (D) $\frac{5y}{6}$

7. The price of an item was reduced by
B 20% then later reduced by 5%. The two reductions were equivalent to the single reduction of

   (A) 15%   (B) 24%   (C) 25%   (D) 75%

8. Ten gallons of gas were added to a tank
A that had been $\frac{1}{4}$ full. If it is now $\frac{7}{8}$ full, how many gallons does the tank hold?

   (A) 16   (B) 18   (C) 20   (D) 24

9. The ratio of Jean's weight to Jim's
D weight is 3:4. If Jean gains 30 pounds and Jim does not gain any, the ratio will be 7:8. How much does Jim weigh?

   (A) 60   (B) 170   (C) 180   (D) 240

10. Last year Joe attended one-half the
D number of sporting events that Jan did. George attended one-third the number that Jan did. If George attended 8 sporting events, how many did Joe attend?

   (A) 1   (B) 4   (C) 8   (D) 12

11. If $\frac{1}{9} = \frac{x}{.45}$, what is the value of x?

A (A) 0.05   (B) 0.5   (C) 5   (D) 6

12. In a class of 54 students, 12 are honor
B students. What part of the class are not honor students?

(A) $\frac{21}{33}$ (B) $\frac{7}{9}$ (C) $\frac{2}{7}$ (D) $\frac{2}{9}$

13. 22% of 440 is 4.4% of

D (A) 96.8   (B) 425.92

(C) 220   (D) 2200

14. 75% of $10a$ is b. What percent of $2b$ is a?

B (A) $13\frac{1}{3}$ (B) $6\frac{2}{3}$ (C) $7\frac{1}{2}$ (D) 15

15. John spent $\frac{1}{4}$ of his money on a book
C and then $\frac{2}{5}$ of the remaining money for lunch. What fractional part of the original amount is left?

(A) $\frac{3}{20}$ (B) $\frac{3}{8}$ (C) $\frac{9}{20}$ (D) $\frac{4}{9}$

16. Write 0.4% as a fraction.

A (A) $\frac{1}{250}$ (B) $\frac{2}{125}$

(C) $\frac{1}{25}$ (D) $\frac{2}{5}$

17. $\frac{1}{2}$% of 500 is

D (A) 2500   (B) 250

(C) 25   (D) 2.5

18. If $3n = m$, then $\frac{2}{3}m =$

A (A) $2n$ (B) $\frac{3}{2}n$ (C) $\frac{2}{3}n$ (D) $\frac{1}{2}n$

TEST TAKING TIP

Guessing can improve your score if you make educated guesses. First, find out if there is a penalty for incorrect answers. If there is no penalty, a guess can only increase your score, or at the worst, leave your score the same. If there is a penalty, try to eliminate enough choices to make the probability of a correct guess greater than the penalty for an incorrect answer. That is, if there is a quarter point penalty for an incorrect response and you have a choice of three responses, the probability of making a correct guess is 1 out of 3 which is better than the penalty.

---

19. Ms. Kwan earns a salary of $300 per
C week plus a 6% commission on her sales. What must her sales be for the week if she earned $345?

(A) $5750   (B) $2070

(C) $750   (D) $207

20. The side of one square is 3 in. and the
D side of another square is $1\frac{1}{4}$ ft. The ratio of the areas of the two squares is

(A) 1:5   (B) 1:25

(C) 12:5   (D) 144:25

21. What is t% of 8?

A (A) $\frac{2t}{25}$ (B) $\frac{2}{25t}$ (C) $\frac{25t}{2}$ (D) $\frac{25}{2t}$

5 Polynomials

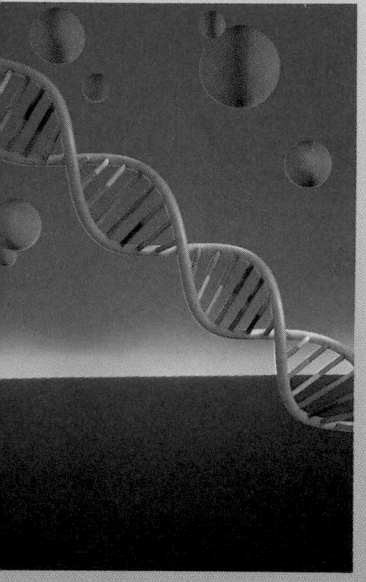

PREVIEWING THE CHAPTER

This chapter reviews and extends students' knowledge of operations on monomials and polynomials. The careful development utilizes geometric models throughout for clarification and to make the connection between algebra and another area of mathematics. The opening lessons increase the students' operational skills with monomials. Next, addition, subtraction, and multiplication of polynomials are addressed. Then students attend to various methods of factoring polynomials. The chapter concludes with methods for dividing polynomials including synthetic division.

Some of the lessons in this chapter contain a review of concepts from Algebra 1. These lessons may be considered optional and used for review only.

Problem-Solving Strategy Students use the strategy *draw a diagram* to help them organize and visualize the data presented in problems and write the equations that will enable them to find the solutions.

Lesson Objective Chart

Lesson (Pages)	Lesson Objectives	State/Local Objectives
5-1 (210-214)	5-1A: Multiply monomials and powers of monomials.	
	5-1B: Represent numbers in scientific notation.	
5-2 (215-219)	5-2A: Divide monomials.	
	5-2B: Divide expressions written in scientific notation.	
5-3 (220-222)	5-3: Solve problems by using a diagram.	
5-4 (223-228)	5-4A: Add polynomials.	
	5-4B: Subtract polynomials.	
	5-4C: Multiply polynomials.	
5-5 (229-234)	5-5: Factor polynomials.	
5-6 (236-240)	5-6: Divide polynomials using factoring and long division.	
5-7 (241-245)	5-7: Divide polynomials using synthetic division.	

ORGANIZING THE CHAPTER

You may want to refer to the **Course Planning Calendar** on page T44.

Lesson Planning Guide

Blackline Masters Booklets

Lesson (Pages)	Pacing Chart (days) Course I	II	III	Reteaching	Practice	Enrichment	Evaluation	Technology	Lab Manual	Mixed Problem Solving	Applications	Cooperative Learning Activity	Multicultural	Transparencies
5-1 (210-214)	1.5	1	1	p. 30	p. 34	p. 30							p. 5	5-1
5-2 (215-219)	1.5	1	1	p. 31	p. 35	p. 31	Quiz A, p. 65							5-2
5-3 (220-222)	1	1	0.5		p. 36			p. 22		p. 5				5-3
5-4 (223-228)	1.5	1.5	1.5	p. 32	p. 37	p. 32	Quiz B, p. 65 Mid-Chapter Test, p. 69	p. 5			p. 23			5-4
5-5 (229-234)	1.5	1.5	1	p. 33	p. 38	p. 33	Quiz C, p. 66		pp. 53-54			p. 41		5-5
5-6 (236-240)	1.5	1	1	p. 34	p. 39	p. 34								5-6
5-7 (241-245)	1.5	1	1	p. 35	p. 40	p. 35	Quiz D, p. 66							5-7
Review (246-248)	1	1	1	Multiple Choice Tests, Forms 1A and 1B, pp. 57-60 Free Response Tests, Forms 2A and 2B, pp. 61-64										
Test (249)	1	1	1	Cumulative Review, pp. 67-68 Standardized Test Practice Questions, p. 70										

Course I: Chapters 1-13; Course II: Chapters 1-15; Course III: Chapters 1-17

Other Chapter Resources

Student Edition

Chapter Opener, pp. 208-209
Journal Entries, pp. 214, 219
Cooperative Learning Activity, p. 222
Mid-Chapter Review, p. 228
Biology Connection, p. 234
Technology, p. 235
Portfolio Suggestion, p. 240
Extended Project 2, pp. A6-A9

Teacher's Classroom Resources

Transparency 5-0
Real-World Applications
    Transparencies, 10, 11
Performance Assessment Booklet,
    pp. 9-10
Problem-of-the-Week Activity Cards, 9, 10
Tech Prep Applications Booklet, pp. 9-10
Lesson Plans, pp. 34-40

Other Supplements

Glencoe Mathematics
    Professional Series

Software

Test and Review Generator Software
    (Apple, IBM, and Macintosh)
Interactive Software (Macintosh)
Teacher's Guide for Software
    Resources

ENHANCING THE CHAPTER

Cooperative Learning

Assigning Students to Groups

Research indicates that a heterogeneous group will allow for a more effective cooperative-learning situation than will a homogeneous group. Therefore, it is inadvisable to allow students to choose their own groups. A more desirable method would be to randomly assign students by having them count off and placing the 1s in one group, the 2s in another, and so on. A better method is to form groups so that each group has members of varying levels of ability. It is not necessary that students remain members of the same group for the entire year. In fact, it may be desirable if membership is changed periodically, giving students the opportunity and experience of working with most of their classmates at one time or another.

Technology

The Technology Feature after Lesson 5-5 employs the *Mathematical Exploration Toolkit* (MET). CALC can completely factor polynomials involving one variable and find common monomial factors of polynomials involving more than one variable. A command is available to display the steps used by the computer in finding the factors. Common monomial, linear, and quadratic factors are found. Integral powers and rational coefficients are supported.

Critical Thinking

When pondering Bloom's taxonomy of thinking processes—knowledge, comprehension, application, analysis, synthesis, and evaluation—people may assume that critical-thinking skills are utilized only at the levels of analysis, synthesis, and evaluation. This is not necessarily so. For example, when a student gives an answer to an exercise that calls only for knowledge or comprehension of content, before you say whether the answer is correct, ask the student to explain how the answer was arrived at and to justify it. Then ask others whether they agree with the explanation and justification. Using this procedure on a regular basis will signal students that it is they, not you, who are responsible for doing the thinking.

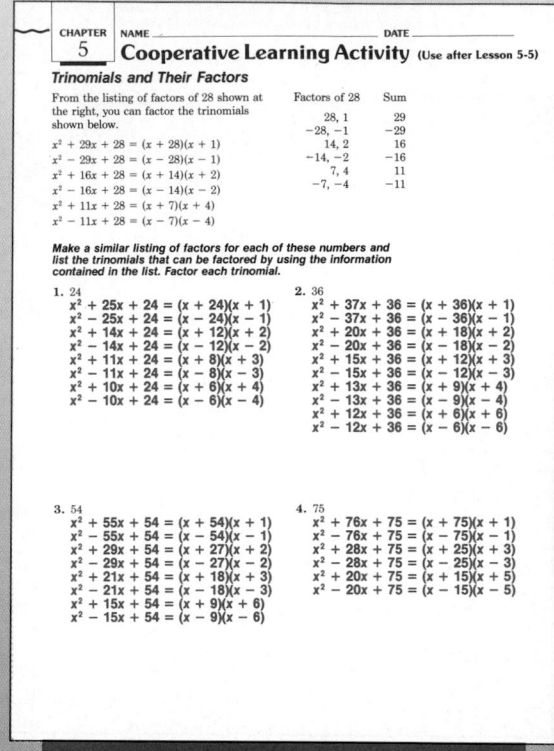

Cooperative Learning, p. 41

Technology, p. 5

Problem of the Week Activity

The card shown below is one of two available for this chapter. It can be used as a class or small group activity.

Activity Card

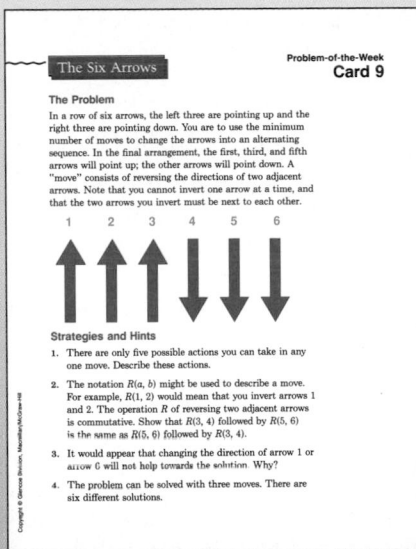

Multicultural

Multicultural Activity, p. 5

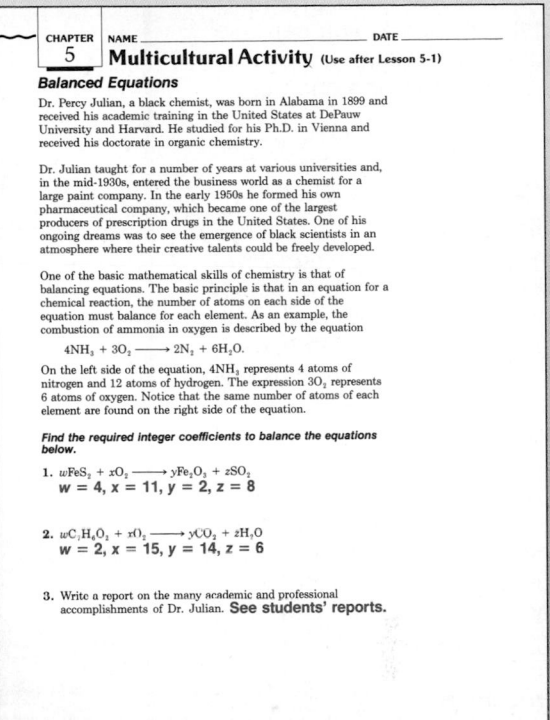

Manipulatives and Models

The following materials may be used as models or manipulatives in Chapter 5.

- graph paper (Lessons 5-3 and 5-4)
- algebra tiles (Lesson 5-4)

Lab Manual

Lab Activity, pp. 53-54

Outside Resources

Books/Periodicals

Kadesch, Robert, R. *Math Menagerie*. Harper & Row, Publishers, 1970.

Bell, E.T. *Men of Mathematics*. Simon & Schuster, 1986.

Films/Videotapes/Videodiscs

Polynomials, part of the Project Mathematics Series, The National Council of Teachers of Mathematics (NCTM), 1096 Association Dr., Reston, VA 22091-1593

Software

Alge-Blaster Plus, Davidson & Associates, 3135 Kashiwas St., Torrance, CA 90505

Algebra Series and *Mathematics Exploration Toolkit*, IBM, 4111 Northside Pkwy. NW, P.O. Box 2150, Atlanta, GA 30327-3015

MathTools for Algebra and *MathTools for Advanced Algebra*, William K. Bradford Publishing Company, 310 School St., Acton, MA 01720

Background Information
Genetic engineering has emerged as a result of the meshing of two disciplines: science and engineering. Working with DNA and protein sequence data makes it necessary for genetic engineers to operate at advanced levels of both math and science. The use of computers to implement complex equations is often required. Mathematical analysis of equations is essential. The current demand for genetic engineers is expected to increase by at least 20% to 25% during the 1990s, largely because of increasing applications of genetic research.

CHAPTER OBJECTIVES

In this chapter, you will:
- Multiply monomials.
- Represent numbers in scientific notation.
- Factor polynomials.
- Divide polynomials.

Punnett squares can predict the possible types of offspring from two parents with specific traits. If the parents were a pink flower and a red flower, what types of offspring might they produce?

Punnett Squares

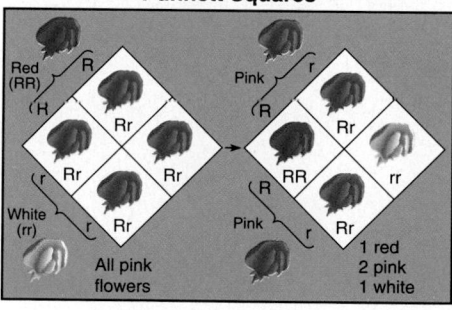

208

CAREERS IN GENETIC ENGINEERING

What qualities would you select if you were breeding the perfect melon?
- sweet, flavorful, firm flesh
- early ripening
- easy to see whether ripe or not

How about the perfect tomato?
- full of sun-ripened flavor
- meaty, yet juicy
- easy to grow, harvest, and ship

If you were designing a new strain of cauliflower, how about adding a naturally cheesy flavor? Why not design a broccoli that could be grown in fields irrigated with salt water, or maybe even not irrigated at all. Add resistance to frost and disease too, if you like. Genetic engineers are doing all these things and more right now.

If designer greens don't interest you, how about designer pharmaceuticals? Genetic engineers are now manufacturing insulin and hepatitis-B surface antigen safely and economically, and others are producing new hope for sufferers of AIDS and cystic fibrosis. Still in the planning stages are an artificial pancreas and liver.

A third trend is bioremediation. In this field, genetic engineers design and then produce organisms that eat toxic and hazardous waste.

Genetic engineering, or altering genetic characteristics for a specific purpose, is a young field that grows bigger each year. There may be a career in that field for you.

Chapter Project
Materials: pencil, paper, and library resources

Organize students into cooperative groups of biotechnology researchers. Explain that genetic engineering is but one specific area under a much broader field of study called biotechnology. Assign each group the task of selecting one of the following areas of biotechnology on which to conduct research at the school or local library.

- Molecular biology
- Microbiology
- Immunology
- Bioprocess engineering
- Bioanalytical chemistry/ biochemistry
- Recombinant DNA technology/ genetic engineering
- Biocomputation
- Environmental biotechnology
- Formulations chemistry

Instruct each group to prepare a report to present to the class on (1) the definiton and explanation of the area of biotechnology selected; (2) ongoing research, products, and services; (3) career opportunities; and (4) courses and programs at colleges and universities.

Connections and Applications

Lesson	Connections (C) and Applications (A)	Examples	Exercises
5-1	A: Astronomy Chemistry Sports	7	53 54 60
5-2	A: Chemistry Astronomy Communication	2	 62 63
5-3	C: Geometry A: Horticulture	2 1	
5-4	C: Geometry A: Business Consumer Awareness Manufacturing	7	16-17, 55-57, 68-69, 73 70 71 72
5-5	C: Geometry A: Manufacturing Interior Design	1	 56 57
5-6	C: Geometry A: Genetics Entertainment Manufacturing	5 6	 46 47, 51
5-7	A: Manufacturing Retail	4	33 34

MORE ABOUT GENETIC ENGINEERING

Degree Required:

- Bachelor's Degree in Molecular Biology or Chemistry

Some genetic engineers like:

- working on the cutting edge of technological research and new applications of science
- working in a field that requires creativity
- knowing that their work may benefit others

Related Math Subjects:

- Advanced Algebra
- Probability/Statistics
- Trigonometry
- Calculus

Some genetic engineers dislike:

- working long hours indoors
- having to work under pressure
- having to try to keep up with the new developments in the field
- having to meet deadlines

For more information on the various careers in the field of genetic engineering, write to:
Industrial Biotechnology Association
1625 K Street, N.W.
Suite 1100
Washington, D.C. 20006

209

Lesson Resources

Reteaching Master 5-1
Practice Master 5-1
Enrichment Master 5-1
Multicultural Activity Master, p. 5

 Transparency 5-1 contains the 5-Minute Check and a teaching aid for this lesson.

INTRODUCING THE LESSON

 5-Minute Check

(over Chapter 4)

1. Evaluate the determinant of
$$\begin{bmatrix} -1 & 4 & 0 \\ 3 & -2 & -5 \\ -3 & 1 & 2 \end{bmatrix} \quad 35$$

2. If $A = \begin{bmatrix} 3 & -1 \\ 2 & 4 \end{bmatrix}$ and

$B = \begin{bmatrix} 4 & 0 & -3 \\ 7 & -5 & 9 \end{bmatrix}$, find AB.

$AB = \begin{bmatrix} 5 & 5 & -18 \\ 36 & -20 & 30 \end{bmatrix}$

3. Find the inverse of $\begin{bmatrix} 2 & 6 \\ -5 & 1 \end{bmatrix}$.

$\frac{1}{32} \begin{bmatrix} 1 & -6 \\ 5 & 2 \end{bmatrix}$

4. Solve the system using Cramer's rule.
$2x - y + z = -2$
$x + 2y + 6z = 3$
$3x - y + 2z = -1$
$(3, 6, -2)$

5. Solve the system using the augmented matrix method.
$x + y + z = -2$
$2x - 3y + z = -11$
$-x + 2y - z = 8$
$(-1, 2, -3)$

Objectives

After studying this lesson, you should be able to:

5-1A ■ multiply monomials and powers of monomials, and

5-1B ■ represent numbers in scientific notation.

Application

Stephanie bought some of the supplies for the Wilderness Club's winter weekend getaway. She bought three bags of apples, 4 boxes of granola bars, and 2 packages of recyclable paper plates.

The quantities of items that Stephanie bought can be described using **monomials.** A monomial is an expression that is a number, a variable, or the product of a number and one or more variables. If a is the number of apples in a bag, $3a$ would be a monomial describing the number of apples that Stephanie bought. Some other monomials are -3, z, t^4, and $\frac{2}{3}ab^2$.

Expressions like $\frac{1}{x}$ and $\sqrt{x}$ are not monomials. Monomials cannot contain variables whose exponents can be written as a fraction or as a negative number.

Constants are monomials that contain no variables. The numerical factor of a monomial is the **coefficient** of the variable. For example, the coefficient of g in $-4g$ is -4. The **degree of a monomial** is the sum of the exponents of its variables. The degree of a nonzero constant is 0. The constant 0 has no degree.

This table summarizes some terms related to monomials.

Monomial	Coefficient	Variable(s)	Exponent(s)	Degree
s	1	s	1	1
$-7a^2$	-7	a	2	2
k^8	1	k	8	8
$\frac{2}{3}ab^2$	$\frac{2}{3}$	a and b	1, 2	3

Remember that $s = 1 \cdot s$.

If two monomials are the same, or differ only by their numerical coefficients, they are called **like terms.** For example, $5xy^2$ and $12xy^2$ are like terms, but $5x^2y$, $3x^3$, and $12xy^2$ are not.

Example 1

Simplify $4a^3b + 11a^3b - a^3b$.

$4a^3b + 11a^3b - a^3b = (4 + 11 - 1)a^3b$ *The three terms are like terms.*

$= 14a^3b$ **Teaching Tip ❶**

Motivating the Lesson

Ask questions about the size of the national debt and the population of the world. Use an almanac to find very large or small numbers and discuss ways they can be written.

ALTERNATE TEACHING STRATEGIES

Using Discussion

Ask students the following questions.

1. What is the greatest number that can be represented by using 3 threes? 3^{33}

2. What is the greatest number that can be represented by using 4 twos? 2^{222}

3. What is the least whole number that can be represented by at least one exponent and 4 twos? 222^2

Example 2
Simplify $(r^3s^2)(r^4s^4)$.

$(r^3s^2)(r^4s^4) = (r \cdot r \cdot r \cdot s \cdot s)(r \cdot r \cdot r \cdot r \cdot s \cdot s \cdot s \cdot s)$

$\qquad\qquad = r \cdot r \cdot r \cdot r \cdot r \cdot r \cdot r \cdot s \cdot s \cdot s \cdot s \cdot s \cdot s$ *7 factors of r and*

$\qquad\qquad = r^7 s^6$ *6 factors of s*

Example 2 suggests the following property.

| *Multiplying Powers* | **For any real number a, and positive integers m and n, $a^m \cdot a^n = a^{m+n}$.** |

Let's use this property to find how to raise a power to a power. Try this.

Example 3
Simplify $(d^3)^4$.

$(d^3)^4 = d^3 \cdot d^3 \cdot d^3 \cdot d^3$

$\qquad = d^{3 + 3 + 3 + 3}$ *Multiplying powers*

$\qquad = d^{12}$

This example suggests the following property.

| *Raising a Power to a Power* | **For any real number a, and positive integers m and n, $(a^m)^n = a^{mn}$.** |

Example 4
Simplify $(xy)^3$.

$(xy)^3 = (xy)(xy)(xy)$

$\qquad = x \cdot x \cdot x \cdot y \cdot y \cdot y$ *Commutative property*

$\qquad = x^3 y^3$

Example 4 demonstrates the following property.

| *Finding a Power of a Product* | **For any real numbers a, b, and positive integer m, $(ab)^m = a^m b^m$.** |

We can simplify many kinds of expressions using the properties of exponents and the commutative and associative properties.

LESSON 5-1 MONOMIALS 211

Teaching Tip ① Remind students that when adding and subtracting like terms, the coefficients are combined, but the exponents do not change.

Chalkboard Examples

For Example 1
Simplify.

a. $12x^5 + 2x^5 - 11x^5 + 2x^5$
  $5x^5$
b. $5a^2b^3 - 2a^2b^3 - 6a^2b^3$
  $-3a^2b^3$

For Example 2
Simplify.

a. $(ab^2c^3)(a^2bc)$ $a^3b^3c^4$
b. $(r^2s^4t^3)(rst^2)$ $r^3s^5t^5$

For Example 3
Simplify

a. $(2^2)^4$ $2^8 = 256$
b. $(x^2)^3$ x^6

For Example 4
Simplify.

a. $(3xy^2)^2$ $9x^2y^4$
b. $\left(\frac{1}{4}a\right)^2$ $\frac{1}{16}a^2$
c. $(-2r^2s)^3$ $-8r^6s^3$

For Example 5
Simplify.

a. $(2ab^2)(-1a^3b^3c)$ $-8a^4b^5c$
b. $(6x^2y^3)(xyz)$ $6x^3y^4z$

Teaching Tip ❷ If you multiply the numbers in scientific notation using pencil and paper, first group the integers and then group the powers of ten.

EVALUATING THE LESSON

Checking for Understanding

Exercises 1–24 are designed to help you assess understanding through reading, writing, and speaking. You should work through Exercises 1–3 with your students, and then monitor their work on Exercises 4–24.

Reteaching Masters Booklet, p. 30

Example 5

Simplify $(3a^3b)(-5a^2b^2)$.

$(3a^3b)(-5a^2b^2) = 3 \cdot (-5) \cdot a^3 \cdot a^2 \cdot b \cdot b^2$
$= -15 \cdot a^{3+2} \cdot b^{1+2}$
$= -15a^5b^3$

An important use of exponents is **scientific notation.** Very large numbers are often written in scientific notation. Study the following examples.

$246,000,000,000$

$= 2.46 \times 100,000,000,000$

$= 2.46 \times 10^{11}$ $10^{11} = 100,000,000,000$

$3,220,000$

$= 3.22 \times 1,000,000$

$= 3.22 \times 10^6$ $10^6 = 1,000,000$

Definition of Scientific Notation

A number is in scientific notation when it is in the form $a \times 10^n$, where $1 \le a < 10$ and n is an integer.

Example 6

Use a calculator to multiply 3.2×10^4 by 1.9×10^2. Express the solution in both scientific and decimal notation.

The exponential shift key may vary depending upon the calculator you are using.

Your calculator may display 3.2×10^4 as $3.2 + 4$.

ENTER: 3.2 [EXP] 4 [×] 1.9 [EXP] 2 [=]

The solution is 6.08×10^6 or $6,080,000$.   **Teaching Tip ❷**

Example 7

APPLICATION

Astronomy

When a solar flare occurs on the sun, it sends out light waves that travel through space at a speed of 1.08×10^9 km/h. If a satellite in space detects the flare 2 hours after its occurrence, how far is the satellite from the sun?

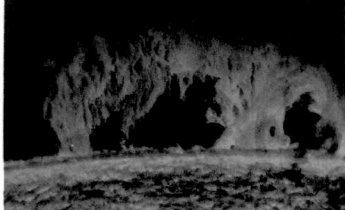

$rt = d$ *rate × time = distance*

$(1.08 \times 10^9)(2) = d$ *Substitute the given values into the formula for distance.*

$2.16 \times 10^9 = d$

The satellite is 2.16×10^9 or $2,160,000,000$ km from the Sun.

RETEACHING THE LESSON

Which of the following expressions are not monomials?

a. $3x^{-2}$

b. $5x^{0.5}$

c. $-6xy^2$

d. 6

e. $5x^2 + 4x$

f. $\frac{4}{x^3}$

g. $\frac{-x}{4}$

a, b, e, f

CHECKING FOR UNDERSTANDING

Communicating Mathematics

Read and study the lesson to answer these questions.

1. Are $4x^2$ and $(4x)^2$ equivalent? **No, $(4x)^2 = (4x)(4x)$ or $16x^2$.**

2. Is a negative number raised to the seventh power negative or positive? Explain. **See margin.**

3. In the problem in the introduction, suppose there are g granola bars in a box. Express the number of granola bars that Stephanie bought for the Wilderness Club's getaway as a monomial. **4g**

Guided Practice

State whether each expression is a monomial. If it is, name its coefficient and degree.

4. $3x$ **yes, 3, 1**
5. a^2 **yes, 1, 2**
6. $4rs + s$ **no**
7. $-5ab$ **yes, -5, 2**
8. $\frac{11xy}{7}$ **yes, $\frac{11}{7}$, 2**
9. $\sqrt{cd}$ **no**
10. $5x^3y^2z^4$ **yes, 5, 9**
11. 0 **yes, 0, none**
12. $\frac{3rs}{t}$ **no**

Express each of the following in scientific notation.

13. 810.4 **8.104×10^2**
14. 2100 **2.1×10^3**
15. $9,000,000,000$ **9×10^9**
16. $786,500,000$ **7.865×10^8**
17. $72,100,000$ **7.21×10^7**
18. $528,000$ **5.28×10^5**

Express each of the following in decimal notation.

19. 4.2×10^4 **42,000**
20. 2.541×10^2 **254.1**
21. 5.7×10^1 **57**
22. 4.27×10^1 **42.7**
23. 3.21×10^6 **3,210,000**
24. 7.2×10^4 **72,000**

EXERCISES

Practice

Simplify.

25. $3x + 2x + (-4x)$ **x**
26. $4d^3 - d^3 + 2d^3$ **$5d^3$**
27. $4ab^2 - 3ab^2$ **ab^2**
28. $3x^2 + 4 - 3x^2$ **4**
29. $y^5 \cdot y^7$ **y^{12}**
30. $b^4 \cdot b^3 \cdot b^2$ **b^9**
31. $8^6 \cdot 8^4 \cdot (8^2)^2$ **8^{14}**
32. $(y^5)^2$ **y^{10}**
33. $(3a)^4$ **$81a^4$**
34. $(x^2y^2)^2x^3y^3$ **x^7y^7**
35. $\left(-\frac{3}{4}x^2y^3\right)^2\left(\frac{8}{9}xy^4\right)$ **$\frac{1}{2}x^5y^{10}$**
36. $\left(\frac{3}{5}c^2f\right)\left(\frac{4}{3}cd\right)^2$ **$\frac{16}{15}c^4d^2f$**
37. $(-4a)(a^2)(-a^3) + 3a^2(a^4)$ **$7a^6$**
38. $2(rk)^4(5rt^2) - k(2rk)(2rt)^2$ **$2k^2r^3t^2$**
39. $(5a)(6a^2b)(3ab^3) + (4a^2)(3b^3)(2a^2b)$ **$114a^4b^4$**
40. $(5mn^2)(m^3n)(-3p^2) + (8np)(3mp)(m^3n^2)$ **$9m^4n^3p^2$**

Practice Masters Booklet, p. 34

Additional Answers

2. Negative; a negative number raised to an odd power is negative.

Error Analysis

Students often confuse $x^m \cdot x^n$ and $(x^m)^n$. To help end the confusion, compare and contrast terms.

$x^m \cdot x^n$	vs.	$(x^m)^n$
product of two powers with same base		power of a power
base written twice		base written once

Try values for m and n, for example, $m = 3$ and $n = 2$.

$x^3 \cdot x^2$	vs.	$(x^3)^2$
x^5		x^6

When in doubt, write it out.

Assignment Guide

Basic: 25–44, 51–53, 55–60
Average: 29–47, 51–60
Enriched: 33–60

5-1 **Practice Worksheet**

NAME _____ DATE _____

Monomials

Simplify.

1. $3n^2v^3 - n^2v^3 + 8v^3n^2$ **$10n^2v^3$**
2. $4r^6w^2 + 9r^2w^6 - r^6w^2$ **$3r^6w^2 + 9r^2w^6$**
3. $y^7 \cdot y^3 \cdot y^2$ **y^{12}**
4. $(n^6)^3$ **n^{18}**
5. $(2n)^4 + 2n^4$ **$18n^4$**
6. $(3r^7t^2)(-5rt^9)$ **$-15r^8t^{11}$**
7. $(4a^3c^2)^3(-3ac^4)^2$ **$576a^{11}c^{14}$**
8. $\left(\frac{3}{2}e^2f^4\right)^4\left(-\frac{4}{3}e^2f\right)^3\left(-\frac{1}{6}ef^5\right)$ **$2e^{24}f^{24}$**
9. $-5v^2(2r^3v^2)(rv^3) - (-r^2)(16r^2v^7)$ **$6r^4v^7$**
10. $(-n)^4(2xy^2n)^3 + (4xy^3n^2)^2(-3xn^3)$ **$-40x^3y^6n^7$**
11. $(3b^2)^4(-2b^3)^8$ **$20,736b^{32}$**
12. $(m^4n^5)^4(m^3n^2p^5)^6$ **$m^{34}n^{36}p^{30}$**
13. $(3x^2y)(2xy^4) + (4xy^2)(3x^2y^3)$ **$18x^3y^5$**
14. $(7v^3w^4)(2v^2w^6) + (3vw^5)(2v^4w^5)$ **$20v^5w^{10}$**

Evaluate. Express each answer in both scientific and decimal notation.

15. $(2.3 \times 10^4)^2$ **5.29×10^8; 529,000,000**
16. $(8.7 \times 10^3)^2$ **7.569×10^7; 75,690,000**
17. $(4.8 \times 10^2)(6.9 \times 10^4)$ **3.312×10^7; 33,120,000**
18. $(3.7 \times 10^9)(8.7 \times 10^2)$ **3.219×10^{12}; 3,219,000,000,000**
19. $(46,000)(0.025)$ **1.15×10^3; 1150**
20. $(54,000)(0.00073)$ **3.942×10^1; 39.42**

Evaluate. Express each answer in both scientific and decimal notation.

41. $(9.5 \times 10^3)^2$

42. $(7.2 \times 10^5)(8.1 \times 10^3)$

43. $(4.5 \times 10^3)(7.0 \times 10^2)$

44. $(2.5 \times 10^2)(1.1 \times 10^2)$

45. $(34{,}000)(0.0056)$

46. $(4{,}300)(0.02)$

47. $(3{,}000)(82{,}500)$

48. $(45{,}000)(0.0025)$

49. $(4.4 \times 10^5) - (3.2 \times 10^5)$

50. $1.2 \times 10^3 - 1.2 \times 10^2$

Critical Thinking

51. The number 64 is a square, a cube, and a sixth power since:
$$64 = 8^2 = 4^3 = 2^6.$$
Find the least integer greater than 1 that is a square, a cube, a sixth, and a ninth power. 2^{18}

52. Which is greater, 100^{10} or 10^{100}? Explain your answer. 10^{100} **is greater, since $100^{10} = (10^2)^{10} = 10^{20}$.**

Applications
Teaching Tip ❸

53. **Astronomy**   Moonlight takes 1.25 seconds to reach Earth. If the speed of light is 3.00×10^5 kilometers per second, how far from Earth is the moon? **3.75×10^5 kilometers**

54. **Chemistry**   The mole is a standard unit of measure in chemistry. One mole of any compound contains 6.02×10^{23} molecules. How many molecules are in 19.9 moles of ammonia? **1.20×10^{25} molecules**

Mixed Review

Solve each system of equations using the augmented matrix method. (**Lesson 4-8**)

55. $4x - y + z = 6$
$2x + y + 2z = 3$
$3x - 2y + z = 3$ **(2, 1, -1)**

56. $x + 3y - 2z = 9$
$-x + 5y + 2z = 31$
$2x - 9z = -32$ **(2, 5, 4)**

57. The sum of two numbers is 42. Their difference is 12. What are the two numbers? (**Lesson 3-2**) **27, 15**

58. Solve $3x + 4y = 16$ for y. (**Lesson 2-2**) $y = 4 - \dfrac{3}{4}x$

59. Solve $|x + 1| \le 3$. (**Lesson 1-8**) $\{x | -4 \le x \le 2\}$

60. **Sports**   It is possible to score 2, 3, 6, or 7 points in a football game. Assuming the game was not a forfeit, are there any total scores less than 50 points that are impossible to make? If so, name them. (**Lesson 1-5**)
yes; 1

Journal

Do some research to find some numbers written in scientific notation. Tell what each means and then write the numbers in order from least to greatest.

EXTENDING THE LESSON

Math Power:
Problem Solving

Solve $a^{4x} \cdot a^{10} = a^{9x}$ for x.   **2**

What properties did you use to solve the equation?

Additional Answers

41. 9.025×10^7; 90,250,000

42. 5.832×10^9; 5,832,000,000

43. 3.15×10^6; 3,150,000

44. 2.75×10^4; 27,500

45. 1.904×10^2; 190.4

46. 8.6×10^1; 86

47. 2.475×10^8; 247,500,000

48. 1.125×10^2; 112.5

49. 1.2×10^5; 120,000

50. 1.08×10^3; 1,080

Closing the Lesson

Writing Activity   Have students give examples for the properties stated in this section.

APPLYING THE LESSON

Homework Exercises

See assignment guide on page 213.

Teaching Tip ❸   Group the integers then multiply. Then group the powers of ten and multiply. The final answer will need to be converted to scientific notation.

Enrichment Masters Booklet, p. 30

NAME _____ DATE _____

5-1 Enrichment Worksheet

Square Tilings

Some rectangles can be divided up into squares of unequal size.

Solve these problems about the square tiling shown.

1. Start with the square immediately above the square labeled $x + 2y$. Write a binomial in the form $Ax \pm By$ for the length of a side of each square.
See diagram.

2. Write an expression for the length of the top side of the rectangle.
$15x - 7y$

3. Write an expression for the bottom side.
$6x + 9y$

4. Write an equation using the expressions you found for problems 2 and 3.
$15x - 7y = 6x + 9y$

5. Find the ratio of x to y for the equation in problem 4.
$9x = 16y$, so $\dfrac{x}{y} = \dfrac{16}{9}$.

For problems 6–12 refer to the diagram at the right.

6. Write a binomial for the length of a side of each square.
See diagram.

7. Write an expression for the left side.
$5x + 2y$

8. Write an expression for the right side.
$x + 2y$

9. Write an equation showing that the left and right sides have equal length.
$5x + 2y = x + 2y$

10. Solve the equation in problem 9 for x.
$x = 0$

11. What did you learn about the rectangle shown in the drawing?
The large rectangle is a square.

12. What must be the area of the small square? **0 (The "square" is actually a point.)**

5-2 Dividing Monomials

Objectives
After studying this lesson, you should be able to:
- **5-2A** ▪ divide monomials, and
- **5-2B** ▪ divide expressions written in scientific notation.

Application

The spaceprobe *Pioneer 10* was as far from Earth as the planet Pluto in April of 1983. It sent radio signals that traveled at the speed of light back to Earth. If Pluto is 4.58×10^9 km from Earth and the speed of light is 3.00×10^5 km per second, how long after *Pioneer 10* sent the signals did the Earth-based tracking stations receive them?

Problems like this one require division of powers. You know that when you multiply powers of the same base you add the exponents. Knowing this, it seems reasonable to expect to subtract exponents when you divide powers. Let's try a problem and see if this is true.

Example 1

Simplify $\frac{m^8}{m^3}$.

$$\frac{m^8}{m^3} = \frac{m \cdot m \cdot m \cdot m \cdot m \cdot \overset{1}{\cancel{m}} \cdot \overset{1}{\cancel{m}} \cdot \overset{1}{\cancel{m}}}{\underset{}{\cancel{m} \cdot \cancel{m} \cdot \cancel{m}}}$$

Remember m cannot equal 0.

$$= m \cdot m \cdot \overset{1}{\cancel{m}} \cdot \overset{1}{\cancel{m}} \cdot \overset{1}{\cancel{m}}$$

5 or (8 − 3) factors

$$= m^{8-3} \text{ or } m^5$$

This example suggests that it is true. To divide powers of the same base, you subtract exponents. This is stated more formally below.

Dividing Powers
Teaching Tip ❶

> For any real number a, except $a = 0$, and integers m and n,
> $$\frac{a^m}{a^n} = a^{m-n}.$$

Why is 0 not an acceptable value for a?

Let's use this property to do some investigation. Study the two ways of simplifying $\frac{n^3}{n^3}$ shown below.

$$\frac{n^3}{n^3} = \frac{n \cdot n \cdot n}{n \cdot n \cdot n} \qquad \frac{n^3}{n^3} = n^{3-3}$$
$$= 1 \qquad\qquad = n^0$$

Since $\frac{n^3}{n^3}$ cannot have two values, we can conclude that $n^0 = 1$, where n is not equal to zero. In general, any nonzero number raised to the zero power is equal to 1.

LESSON 5-2   DIVIDING MONOMIALS   215

ALTERNATE TEACHING STRATEGIES

Using Models

Pieces of paper cut into different shapes can be used to represent a quotient of monomials. Use square pieces of paper to represent x and circular pieces of paper to represent y. The representation for the quotient of monomials $\frac{(2xy)^5}{(x^2y)^2}$ is shown.

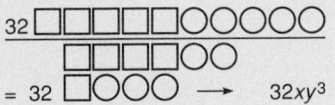

$$= 32 \;\square\bigcirc\bigcirc\bigcirc \;\longrightarrow\; 32xy^3$$

5-2 Lesson Notes

Lesson Resources
Reteaching Master 5-2
Practice Master 5-2
Enrichment Master 5-2

Transparency 5-2 contains the 5-Minute Check and a teaching aid for this lesson.

INTRODUCING THE LESSON

> 🕐 **5-Minute Check**
>
> *(over Lesson 5-1)*
> Simplify.
>
> 1. $7xyz^2 + 3xyz^2 - 12xyz^2 - 2xyz^2$
> 2. $(-3m^4n^3)^2$ $9m^8n^6$
> 3. $\left(\frac{1}{2}x^2\right)^3$ $\frac{1}{8}x^6$
> 4. $(5x^6y^4)(-3xy^5)$ $-15x^7y^9$
> 5. Multiply 1.8×10^3 by 42000 using scientific notation. 7.56×10^7

Motivating the Lesson

Have students write large numbers in scientific notation. Then give them some very small numbers. Ask them how they think they can write these numbers with exponents.

TEACHING THE LESSON

Teaching Tip ❶   Some mathematicians prefer to state this property separately for the different cases that may arise. If $m > n$, $\frac{a^m}{a^n} = a^{m-n}$. If $m < n$, $\frac{a^m}{a^n} = \frac{1}{a^{n-m}}$. This method results in all exponents being positive.

Chalkboard Examples

For Example 1
Simplify.

a. $\dfrac{x^{11}}{x^5}$ x^6

b. $\dfrac{r^3s^2}{r}$ r^2s^2

For Example 2
A chemist has performed an experiment that yields 1.2×10^{25} molecules of ethanol. There are 6.02×10^{23} molecules in a mole. How many moles of ethanol did the experiment yield?
$\approx\mathbf{0.199 \times 10^2}$ **or 19.9 moles**

For Example 3
Use your calculator to divide.

a. 4.8×10^{-5} by 1.6×10^{-2}
   $\mathbf{3 \times 10^{-3}}$ **or 0.003**

b. 9.25×10^5 by 2.5×10^{-3}
   $\mathbf{3.7 \times 10^8}$ **or 370,000,000**

For Example 4
Simplify.

a. $3^{-5} \cdot 3^2$ $\dfrac{1}{27}$

b. $\dfrac{(rs^2)^3(r^3s)^2}{r^2s^4t^{-2}}$ $r^7s^4t^2$

c. $\dfrac{(a^3b^3c^5)^2(ab^4c^2)}{b^{-3}(a^2cd)^2}$ $\dfrac{a^3b^{13}c^{10}}{d^2}$

d. $\dfrac{(2ab)^3(a^3c)^3}{4a^6b^5c^5}$ $\dfrac{2a^6}{b^2c^2}$

Why is 0^0 not defined? If we interpret 0^0 as 0^{m-m}, then it represents $\dfrac{0^m}{0^m}$. Since 0^m is 0, this implies division by zero. Division by zero is not defined, so 0^0 is also not defined.

Example 2

APPLICATION
Chemistry

A chemist has performed an experiment that yields 1.8×10^{24} molecules of ethanol. The mole is the standard unit of measure for the chemical quantity of a substance. There are 6.02×10^{23} molecules in a mole. How many moles of ethanol did the experiment yield?

Let n represent the number of moles of ethanol.

number of moles × number of molecules per mole = number of molecules

$$n(6.02 \times 10^{23}) = 1.8 \times 10^{24}$$

$$n = \frac{1.8 \times 10^{24}}{6.02 \times 10^{23}}$$

$$= \left(\frac{1.8}{6.02}\right) \times \left(\frac{10^{24}}{10^{23}}\right)$$

$$\approx 0.299 \times 10^1 \text{ or } 2.99$$

The experiment yielded about 2.99 moles of ethanol.

Let's do some more investigation with the properties of exponents. Study the two ways of simplifying $\dfrac{t^4}{t^8}$. Assume t is a nonzero real number.

Method 1

$$\frac{t^4}{t^8} = \frac{t \cdot t \cdot t \cdot t}{t \cdot t \cdot t \cdot t \cdot t \cdot t \cdot t \cdot t}$$

$$= \frac{1}{t \cdot t \cdot t \cdot t}$$

$$= \frac{1}{t^4}$$

Method 2

$$\frac{t^4}{t^8} = t^{4-8}$$

$$= t^{-4}$$

We can conclude that $\dfrac{1}{t^4} = t^{-4}$ since $\dfrac{t^4}{t^8}$ cannot have two values. Find the reciprocal of $\dfrac{t^4}{t^3}$ in two ways. What do you conclude?

Negative Exponents	For any real number a, except $a = 0$, and any integer n, $a^{-n} = \dfrac{1}{a^n}$ and $\dfrac{1}{a^{-n}} = a^n$.

You know how to write a very large number in scientific notation. We can also write very small numbers in scientific notation by using negative exponents. Study the following example.

$$0.0064 = 6.4 \times 0.001$$

$$= 6.4 \times \frac{1}{10^3}$$

$$= 6.4 \times 10^{-3}$$

$0.0064 = 6.4 \times 0.001$

$0.001 = \dfrac{1}{1000}$ or $\dfrac{1}{10^3}$

Example 3 | Use your calculator to divide 8.4×10^3 by 2.25×10^{-2}.

ENTER: 8.4 **EXP** 3 ÷ 2.25 **EXP** 2 **+/-** **=** ⅎ⊐ⅎⅎⅎⅎⅎⅎⅎⅎⅎ

The answer is 373333.3333 or $3.7\overline{3} \times 10^5$.

When you are asked to simplify an expression, write an equivalent form that uses only positive exponents and no parentheses. Each base should appear only once and all fractions should be in simplest form.

Example 4 | Simplify $\dfrac{(3rs)^2(s^3t)^2}{12s^2t^4}$.

$\dfrac{(3rs)^2(s^3t)^2}{12s^2t^4} = \dfrac{(9r^2s^2)(s^6t^2)}{12s^2t^4}$ *Multiplying powers property*

$= \dfrac{9r^2(s^2 \cdot s^6)t^2}{12s^2t^4}$ *Associative property*

$= \left(\dfrac{9}{12}\right)\left(\dfrac{r^2}{1}\right)\left(\dfrac{s^8}{s^2}\right)\left(\dfrac{t^2}{t^4}\right)$ *Group like terms.*

$= \dfrac{3}{4}r^2s^6t^{-2}$

$= \dfrac{3r^2s^6}{4t^2}$ **Teaching Tip ❷**

Example 5 | Simplify $\dfrac{8^{3n}}{8^{3n-2}}$.

$\dfrac{8^{3n}}{8^{3n-2}} = 8^{3n-(3n-2)}$ *Division of powers*

$= 8^{3n-3n+2}$

$= 8^2$ or 64

Example 6 | Simplify $\left(\dfrac{3}{4}\right)^{-3}$.

$\left(\dfrac{3}{4}\right)^{-3} = \left[\left(\dfrac{3}{4}\right)^{-1}\right]^3$ *Use the power property.*

$= \left(\dfrac{4}{3}\right)^3$ $\left(\dfrac{3}{4}\right)^{-1} = \dfrac{1}{\frac{3}{4}} = \dfrac{4}{3}$.

$= \dfrac{4}{3} \cdot \dfrac{4}{3} \cdot \dfrac{4}{3}$

$= \dfrac{4^3}{3^3}$ or $\dfrac{64}{27}$

Example 6 suggests the following properties.

Powers of Quotients	**For any nonzero real numbers a and b, and integer n,** $\left(\dfrac{a}{b}\right)^n = \dfrac{a^n}{b^n}$ and $\left(\dfrac{a}{b}\right)^{-n} = \left(\dfrac{b}{a}\right)^n$ or $\dfrac{b^n}{a^n}$.

RETEACHING THE LESSON

To help in developing rules for zero and negative exponents, consider the pattern below.

$2^4 = 16$ As the exponent of
$2^3 = 8$ 2 decreases by 1, the
$2^2 = 4$ value is cut in half.
$2^1 = 2$
$2^0 = ?$

What should 2^0 be to continue the pattern? Cut the previous value in half. 2^0 should be 1 to preserve the pattern. Likewise, what value could 2^{-1} have to continue the pattern? Cut previous value in half. $2^{-1} = \dfrac{1}{2}$. Continuing to decrease the exponent by 1 while halving the value suggests that

$2^{-2} = \dfrac{1}{4}$ or $\dfrac{1}{2^2}$

$2^{-3} = \dfrac{1}{8}$ or $\dfrac{1}{2^3}$.

Chalkboard Examples

For Example 5
Simplify.

a. $\dfrac{5^{(2n+4)}}{5^{(2n-2)}}$ 5^6

b. $\dfrac{3^{(4k+3)}}{3^{(4k+2)}}$ 3^1 or 3

For Example 6
Simplify.

a. $\left(\dfrac{2}{5}\right)^{-2}$ $\dfrac{25}{4}$

b. $\left(\dfrac{4}{n}\right)^{-3}$ $\dfrac{n^3}{4^3}$ or $\dfrac{n^3}{64}$

c. $\left(\dfrac{2x}{5y^3}\right)^{-2}$ $\dfrac{25y^6}{4x^2}$

Teaching Tip ❷   Remind students to use the order of operations. All expressions involving powers are evaluated before any other operation is performed.

Reteaching Masters Booklet, p. 31

Checking for Understanding

Exercises 1–16 are designed to help you assess understanding through reading, writing, and speaking. You should work through Exercises 1–4 with your students, and then monitor their work on Exercises 5–16.

Error Analysis

Students sometimes think that $(2x)^3 = 2x^3$ and that $-2^4 = 16$. Point out that $(2x)^3$ means three factors of $(2x)$, or $(2x)(2x)(2x)$ which equals $8x^3$, as the exponent 3 refers to both the 2 and the x in $(2x)^3$. -2^4 means $-(2^4)$. In order to write -2 to the fourth power, parentheses must be used, $(-2)^4$.

Closing the Lesson

Speaking Activity Have students tell you what the properties for negative powers are. Also have them explain how to find negative powers and what they mean.

Practice Masters Booklet, p. 35

Communicating Mathematics

Read and study the lesson to answer these questions. 1-4. See margin.

1. Explain in your own words why $0^0 \neq 1$.
2. Write 7^{-3} using a positive exponent.
3. Is $2(x^2y)^3$ in simplest form? Explain your answer.
4. Use the information given in the introductory problem to find the time it took for the Earth-based stations to receive the signals from *Pioneer 10*.

Guided Practice

Simplify. Assume no variable equals 0.

5. $\dfrac{x^5}{x^3}$ x^2

6. $\dfrac{n^4}{n^4}$ 1

7. $\dfrac{r^4}{r}$ r^3

8. $\dfrac{t^6}{t^8}$ $\dfrac{1}{t^2}$

9. $\dfrac{5y^{10}}{y^{13}}$ $\dfrac{5}{y^3}$

10. $\dfrac{1}{m^{-2}}$ m^2

11. $\dfrac{3^{-3}}{3^{-2}}$ $\dfrac{1}{3}$

12. $\left(\dfrac{1}{2}\right)^{-2}$ 4

13. $\left(\dfrac{2}{3}\right)^0$ 1

14. $\left(\dfrac{3}{b}\right)^6$ $\dfrac{729}{b^6}$

15. $\left(\dfrac{1}{10}\right)^{-4}$ $10{,}000$

16. $\left(\dfrac{k}{4}\right)^{-3}$ $\dfrac{64}{k^3}$

EXERCISES

Practice

Simplify. Assume no variable equals 0.

 A

17. $t^{-2}t^4$ t^2

18. $m^{-8}m^3$ $\dfrac{1}{m^5}$

19. $\dfrac{12x^8}{4x^3}$ $3x^5$

20. $\dfrac{an^6}{n^5}$ an

21. $\dfrac{-24s^8}{2s^5}$ $-12s^3$

22. $\dfrac{6mn^2}{3m}$ $2n^2$

23. $\dfrac{xy^7}{x^4}$ $\dfrac{y^7}{x^3}$

24. $\dfrac{48a^8}{12a^{11}}$ $\dfrac{4}{a^3}$

25. $\dfrac{4z^3}{28z^5}$ $\dfrac{1}{7z^2}$

B

26. $\dfrac{-15r^4}{30r^3}$ $-\dfrac{r}{2}$

27. $\dfrac{12b^4}{60b^6}$ $\dfrac{1}{5b^2}$

28. $\dfrac{2x^{-3}}{6(x^2)^2}$ $\dfrac{1}{3x^7}$

29. $\dfrac{16b^6c^5}{4b^4c^2}$ $4b^2c^3$

30. $\dfrac{8(k^{-2})^2}{4k^{-2}}$ $\dfrac{2}{k^2}$

31. $\dfrac{1}{x^0 + y^0}$ $\dfrac{1}{2}$

32. $\dfrac{-27w^3t^7}{-3w^3t^{12}}$ $\dfrac{9}{t^5}$

33. $\dfrac{-15r^5s^2}{5r^5s^{-4}}$ $-3s^6$

34. $\dfrac{8}{m^0 + n^0}$ 4

35. $\dfrac{-2c^3d^6}{24c^2d^2}$ $\dfrac{-cd^4}{12}$

36. $\dfrac{(3c^2)^2(-d^5)}{-45c^7d^3}$ $\dfrac{d^2}{5c^3}$

37. $\dfrac{20a^5b^9}{20ab^7}$ a^4b^2

C

38. $\dfrac{16s^6t^5}{(2s^2t)^2}$ $4s^2t^3$

39. $\dfrac{3^{xy+5}}{3^{xy}}$ 243

40. $\dfrac{s^{3x}}{s^{3x-2}}$ s^2

41. $\dfrac{5^{2x}}{5^{2x+2}}$ $\dfrac{1}{25}$

42. $(m^4n^5)^{-2}$ $\dfrac{1}{m^8n^{10}}$

43. $36a^3b^5(12a^2b^2)^{-1}$ $3ab^3$

44. $3^3x^3y^3(3x)^{-2}$ $3xy^3$

45. $\left(\dfrac{a}{b^{-1}}\right)^{-1}$ $\dfrac{1}{ab}$

46. $\left(\dfrac{x}{y^{-1}z^2}\right)^{-1}$ $\dfrac{z^2}{xy}$

47. $\left(\dfrac{1}{5}\right)^{-2} + \left(\dfrac{1}{4}\right)^{-1}$ 29

48. $\dfrac{-15m^5n^8(m^3n^2)}{45m^4n}$ $\dfrac{-m^4n^9}{3}$

49. $\dfrac{(-2t^3)^2(t^{-2})^{-1}}{(t^2)^{-3}}$ $4t^{14}$

50. $\dfrac{(4x^3y)(4^2x^{-1}y)}{4^3xy^2}$ x

51. $\left(\dfrac{-3y^4}{2y^2}\right)^{-2}$ $\dfrac{4}{9y^4}$

52. $\left(\dfrac{1}{2}\right)^{-2} + \left(\dfrac{1}{3}\right)^2$ $4\dfrac{1}{9}$

Additional Answers

1. 0^n for $n > 0 = 0$, 0^n for $n \leq 0$ is undefined. No factor of 0 can produce a 1.

2. $\dfrac{1}{7^3}$

3. No, it should not contain parentheses. $2x^6y^3$

4. 1.53×10^4 second s ≈ 4 hours 15 minutes

Evaluate. Express each answer in both scientific and decimal notation.

55. 6×10^0; 6

56. 4.93×10^0; 4.93

59. 2.1×10^6; 2,100,000

60. 3.1×10^7; 31,000,000

53. $\dfrac{8 \times 10^{-1}}{16 \times 10^{-2}}$ 5×10^0; 5

54. $\dfrac{15 \times 10^4}{6 \times 10^{-2}}$ 2.5×10^6; 2,500,000

55. $(4.5 \times 10^3)(7.5 \times 10^2)^{-1}$

56. $(6.9 \times 10^3)(1.4 \times 10^3)^{-1}$

57. $\dfrac{0.000000036}{0.00011}$ $3.2\overline{7} \times 10^{-4}$; 0.000327

58. $\dfrac{5,600,000,000}{60,000}$ $9.\overline{3} \times 10^4$; 93,333.$\overline{3}$

59. $\dfrac{(84,000,000)(0.00004)}{0.0016}$

60. $\dfrac{(93,000,000)(0.0005)}{0.0015}$

Critical Thinking

61. Express the quotient $\dfrac{x + x^2 + x^3 + x^4 + x^5 + x^6 + x^7}{x^{-3} + x^{-4} + x^{-5} + x^{-6} + x^{-7} + x^{-8} + x^{-9}}$ in simplest form. Assume that x is not equal to zero. *Hint: Simplify the denominator first.* x^{10}

Applications

62. Astronomy Earth has an average distance of 1.496×10^8 kilometers from the Sun. If light travels 3.00×10^5 kilometers per second, how long does it take sunlight to reach Earth? **$4.98\overline{6} \times 10^2$ seconds or about 8 minutes 19 seconds**

63. Communication Television signals travel at the speed of light. If the speed of light is 3.00×10^5 kilometers per second, how long would it take for signals broadcasting from a television station to reach a house 36 kilometers away?
1.2×10^{-4} or 0.00012 seconds

Mixed Review

64. 4.5×10^9; 4,500,000,000

65. 5.0625×10^{12}; 5,062,500,000,000

66. $\begin{bmatrix} -14 & -15 \\ 4 & 20 \end{bmatrix}$

Evaluate. Express each answer in both scientific and decimal notation. (Lesson 5-1)

64. $(5 \times 10^6)(9 \times 10^2)$

65. $(1.5 \times 10^3)^4$

66. If $A = \begin{bmatrix} 2 & -3 \\ 1 & 4 \end{bmatrix}$ and $B = \begin{bmatrix} 4 & 0 \\ 2 & 5 \end{bmatrix}$, evaluate AB. Write "not defined" if the product does not exist. (Lesson 4-4)

67. In which octant does the point $(5, -1, 9)$ lie? (Lesson 3-8) **2**

68. State the multipliers you would use to eliminate each of the variables from the system $\begin{cases} 3x + 4y = 7 \\ 4x - 3y = 1 \end{cases}$ by addition. (Lesson 3-2) **See margin.**

69. Write the equation $\frac{1}{4}x = 2y - 1$ in standard form. (Lesson 2-2)
$x - 8y = -4$

70. Evaluate $2|-3x| - 9$ if $x = 5$. (Lesson 1-6) **21**

EXTENDING THE LESSON

Math Power: Problem Solving

Acceleration, a, is the change in velocity, that is, the final velocity, V_f minus the initial velocity, V_i, divided by the interval of time in which the change occurs, t. It is measured in meters per second squared. The formula is:

$$a = \frac{V_f - V_i}{t}.$$

If an electron has an acceleration of $+4.0 \times 10^{11}$ m/s^2, an initial velocity of 0.5×10^5 m/s and final velocity of $+3.1 \times 10^5$ m/s, what was the time period needed for this acceleration?
6.5×10^{-7} s

Assignment Guide

Basic: 17–37, 61–70
Average: 22–44, 61–70
Enriched: 36–70

Chapter 5, Quiz A, (Lessons 5-1 through 5-2), is available in the Evaluation Masters Booklet, p. 65.

Additional Answer

68.
equation 1 × 3   equation 1 × 4
or
equation 2 × 4   equation 2 × -3

Enrichment Masters Booklet, p. 31

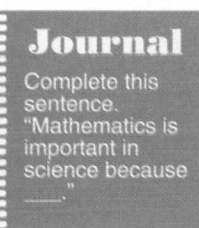

5-2 Enrichment Worksheet

Working with Exponents

The rules about powers and exponents are usually given with letters such as m, n, and k to represent exponents. For example, one rule states that $a^m \cdot a^n = a^{m+n}$.

In practice, such exponents are handled as algebraic expressions and the rules of algebra apply.

Example: Simplify $2a^2(a^{n+1} + a^{4n})$.

$2a^2(a^{n+1} + a^{4n}) = 2a^2 \cdot a^{n+1} + 2a^2 \cdot a^{4n}$ *Use the distributive law.*
$= 2a^{2+n+1} + 2a^{2+4n}$ *Recall $a^m \cdot a^n = a^{m+n}$.*
$= 2a^{n+3} + 2a^{2+4n}$ *Simplify the exponent $2 + n + 1$ as $n + 3$.*

It is important always to collect *like* terms only.

Example: Simplify $(a^n + b^m)^2$.

$(a^n + b^m)^2 = (a^n + b^m)(a^n + b^m)$

      F   O   I   L
$= a^n \cdot a^n + a^n \cdot b^m + a^n \cdot b^m + b^m \cdot b^m$ *The second and third terms are like terms.*
$= a^{2n} + 2a^n b^m + b^{2m}$

Simplify each expression by performing the indicated operations.

1. $2^3 2^m$ **2^{3+m}**
2. $(a^3)^n$ **a^{3n}**
3. $(4^n b^2)^k$ **$4^{kn} b^{2k}$**
4. $(x^3 a^j)^n$ **$x^{3n} a^{jn}$**
5. $(-ay^n)^3$ **$-a^3 y^{3n}$**
6. $(-b^k x)^2$ **$-b^{2k} x^2$**
7. $(c^2)^{hk}$ **c^{2hk}**
8. $(-2d^n)^5$ **$-32d^{5n}$**
9. $(a^2)(a^n b^2)$ **$a^{2+n} b^3$**
10. $(x^n y^m)(x^m y^n)$ **$x^{n+m} y^{n+m}$**
11. $\frac{a^n}{a^2}$ **a^{n-2}**
12. $\frac{12x^3}{4x^n}$ **$3x^{3-n}$**
13. $(ab^2 - a^2 b)(3a^n + 4b^n)$ **$3a^{n+1} b^2 + 4ab^{n+2} - 3a^{n+2} b - 4a^2 b^{n+1}$**
14. $ab^2(2a^2 b^{n-1} + 4ab^n + 6b^{n+1})$ **$2a^3 b^{n+1} + 4a^2 b^{n+2} + 6ab^{n+3}$**

Lesson Resources

Practice Master 5-3
Technology Master, p. 22
Activity Master, p. 5

Transparency 5-3 contains the
5-Minute Check and a teaching aid
for this lesson.

INTRODUCING THE LESSON

5-Minute Check

(over Lesson 5-2)
Simplify.

1. $\dfrac{x^3z^2}{xz}$ x^2z

2. $\dfrac{3(a^2b)^4}{(3ab)^3}$ $\dfrac{a^5b}{9}$

3. $\dfrac{(2x^2y^3z^4)^2(x^3y)}{8x^6y^2z^{12}}$ $\dfrac{xy^5}{2z^4}$

4. $24\,x^3y^2(-3xy)^{-2}$ $\dfrac{8x}{3}$

5. $\left(\dfrac{2x}{3z^2}\right)^{-4}$ $\dfrac{81z^8}{16x^4}$

Motivating the Lesson

Read the first example to students. Have them draw the picture they would use to solve it. Discuss the drawings and why the drawing would help them solve the problem.

TEACHING THE LESSON

Teaching Tip ❶   Remind students that the width of each rectangle is $\frac{1}{5}$ of its length, which is $\frac{1}{4}$ the perimeter of the square.

5-3 Problem-Solving Strategy: Draw a Diagram

**Objective
5-3**

After studying this lesson, you should be able to:
- solve problems by using a diagram.

Many times you write an equation to solve a math problem. Drawing a diagram of the situation described in a problem can be helpful. You can use the diagram to help you write an equation or devise another plan to solve the problem. You will draw diagrams to help you work problems with polynomials in the next lesson.

Example 1

The New Bern Garden Club has a square garden in the city park. The garden is divided into five rectangular flower beds that are as long as one side of the square. The perimeter of each rectangle is 60 meters. If the club were to build a fence around the entire garden, how much fencing would they need to buy?
Teaching Tip ❶

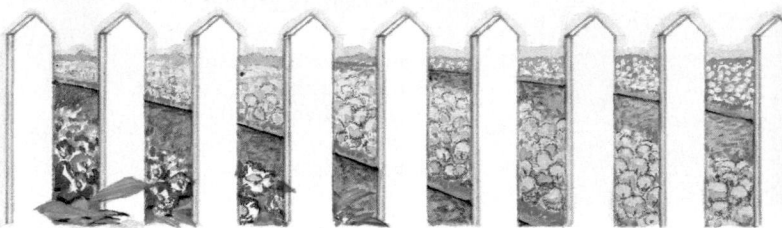

Draw a diagram of the garden to help find a solution.

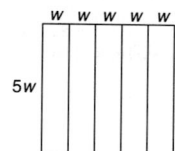

Let w represent the width of a rectangle. The length of a rectangle is 5w since the figure is a square.

Now, we can write an equation to represent the perimeter of one rectangle.

$$w + 5w + w + 5w = 60$$
$$12w = 60$$
$$w = 5 \qquad \text{The width of each rectangle is 5 meters.}$$

Each side of the square is $5w$ meters, so the perimeter of the square is $4(5w)$ or 100 meters. The club would need to buy 100 meters of fencing material to enclose the garden.

ALTERNATE TEACHING STRATEGIES

Using Manipulatives

Trace the figure for students. Have them make a square out of the pieces. Then have them explain their reasoning in completing this activity.

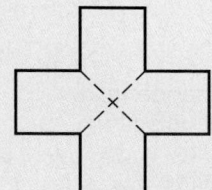

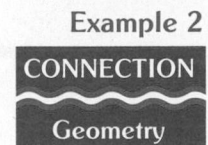

Example 2

CONNECTION

Geometry

Suppose that you have a square piece of paper on which you draw the largest possible circle. You cut the circle out and discard the leftover scraps of paper. Inside the circle you draw the largest possible square, cut it out, and discard the leftover scraps of paper. How much of the original square do you have left? **Teaching Tip ❷**

Draw a diagram. The shaded region represents the square of paper that is left after all of the scraps have been discarded. If we separate the remaining paper into four congruent triangles as shown by the dotted lines, we can see that one-half of each of the regions remains. So one-half of the original square is left.

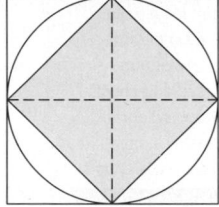

Chalkboard Examples

For Example 1
How much fencing would the Garden Club need to buy if the perimeter of each rectangular is 90 meters?   **150 meters**

For Example 2
If you make 4 slices across a pie, what is the greatest number of pieces that you could have?   **11**

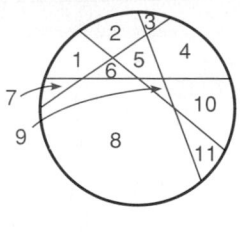

CHECKING FOR UNDERSTANDING

Communicating Mathematics

Read and study the lesson to answer these questions.

1. How much fencing would the Garden Club have had to buy if the rectangular flower beds had a perimeter of 42 meters? **70 meters**

2. What is the length of a diagonal of the remaining square of paper as described in Example 2? **the length of a side of the original square**

3. If you were to repeat the process described in Example 2 using the remaining square, how much of the original square would still remain? **one-fourth**

Teaching Tip ❷   Do the experiment using two pieces of paper the same size. Cut one as directed and keep one intact. Compare the cut one to the original.

EVALUATING THE LESSON

Guided Practice

Solve. Draw a diagram.

4. Lee and Susan can wallpaper a 25-square-foot wall in one hour. At that same rate, how long would it take them to wallpaper an area of 5 square feet? **12 minutes**

5. Six equilateral triangles are placed together to form a hexagon. The length of a side on one triangle is 2 inches. What is the diameter of the smallest circle that includes all six vertices of the hexagon? **4 inches**

6. Carole was traveling from Asheville to Indianapolis by bus. After half the trip, she fell asleep. When Carole awoke, she had half of the distance she traveled when asleep yet to go. For what fraction of the trip was Carole asleep? $\frac{1}{3}$

Checking for Understanding
Exercises 1–6 are designed to help you assess understanding through reading, writing, and speaking. You should work through Exercises 1–3 with your students, and then monitor their work on Exercises 4–6.

LESSON 5-3   PROBLEM-SOLVING STRATEGY: DRAW A DIAGRAM   221

RETEACHING THE LESSON

Use diagrams to help solve.
Ann's and Bo's houses are 4 miles apart. Clyde's house is 3 miles from Ann's and 2 miles from Bo's. Draw a diagram to show the location of Clyde's house.

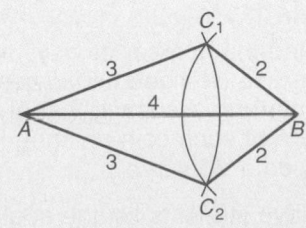

The two possible locations for Clyde's house are shown.

Closing the Lesson

Modeling Activity Model Exercise 15 using a scale drawing of the situation. Explain how seeing the situation helps to solve it.

APPLYING THE LESSON

Homework Exercises

Assignment Guide
Basic: 7–15
Average: 7–15
Enriched: 7–15

Teaching Tip ❸ Remind students that when adding three numbers of the same kind you can carry 1, 2, or 3. Also remind them that the only numbers that when added in threes do not involve carrying are 1, 2, and 3.

Additional Answer

11. Any line in the plane of the square that passes through the point of intersection of the diagonals of the square separates it into two congruent parts, so there are infinitely many ways.

Practice Masters Booklet, p. 36

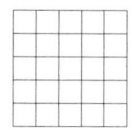
EXERCISES

Practice   Solve. Use any strategy.

Strategies
Look for a pattern.
Solve a simpler problem.
Act it out.
Guess and check.
Draw a diagram.
Make a chart.
Work backwards.

7. How many different acute angles can be traced using the rays in the figure at the right? **10**

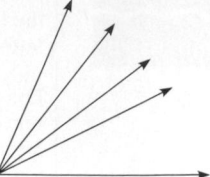

8. You scored 5 points for every correct answer on a math test. For each incorrect answer 2 points were deducted. The test consisted of 15 questions. If you attempted every problem and received a score of 61, how many questions did you answer correctly? **13**

9. Draw an array of dots as shown at the right. Without lifting your pencil, draw four straight lines to pass through all of the dots.

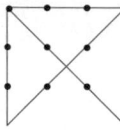

Teaching Tip ❸

10. Find the digit represented by each different letter in the problem at the right. $A = 1, B = 4, C = 8$

$$\begin{array}{r} ABC \\ ABC \\ + ABC \\ \hline BBB \end{array}$$

11. In how many ways can a straight line separate a square into two congruent regions? **See margin.**

12. A parallelogram has consecutive sides with lengths 9 m and 7 m. The measures of the diagonals are integers. How long are the diagonals? **14 m and 8 m**

13. Express 96 as the difference of two squares. There are four different possibilities. $10^2 − 2^2, 11^2 − 5^2, 14^2 − 10^2, 25^2 − 23^2$

14. An isosceles triangle has a base 10 cm long and two sides 13 cm long. A different triangle with two sides 13 cm long has the same area as the first triangle. What is the length of the base of that second triangle? **24 cm**

15. A square barn is 40 feet on each side. The tether for a horse is attached to one corner of the barn as shown at the right. If the rope is 25 feet long, how many square feet of land is the horse able to graze? **≈1473 square feet**

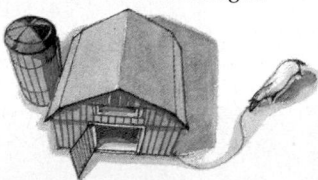

COOPERATIVE LEARNING ACTIVITY

Work in groups. Each person in the group must understand the solution and be able to explain it to any person in class.

$$m(n + 1) + n(m + 1)$$

Toothpicks are used to lay out a grid like the outlines of the squares on a checkerboard. The grid is m toothpicks long and n toothpicks wide. How many toothpicks are used?

EXTENDING THE LESSON

Math Power: Reasoning

Find the number of ways that $12 can be changed into dimes and quarters, assuming that at least one of each coin must be used.   **23 ways**

Have students list the strategies that they used to solve the problem. Discuss the different ways used.

Cooperative Learning Activity

This activity provides students with an opportunity to *learn* things together, not just do things together. You may wish to refer to pages T6–T8 and page 6C for the various elements of cooperative groups and specific goals and strategies for using them.

5-4 Polynomials

Objectives

After studying this lesson, you should be able to:

5-4A ■ add polynomials,
5-4B ■ subtract polynomials, and
5-4C ■ multiply polynomials.

Application

After their project on ecology, the earth science class began a recycling program at Woodfield High School. Tim decided to place a box to collect paper to be recycled next to the library copy machine. The piece of cardboard he chose to make the box was a $y \times y$ inch square. From each corner of the cardboard, he cut a square x inches on a side. Using the diagram, we can see that the area of the remaining cardboard is $y^2 - 4x^2$ square inches.

The expression $y^2 - 4x^2$ is a **polynomial.** A polynomial is a monomial or a sum of monomials. $4 + \frac{3}{x}$ is not a polynomial. Why?
Remember a difference can be written as a sum.

The monomials that make up a polynomial are called the **terms** of the polynomial. A polynomial with two unlike terms is called a **binomial** and one with three terms is a **trinomial.** The **degree of a polynomial** is the degree of the monomial with greatest degree.

Example 1

Find the degree of $8a^3 - 5a^2b^2 - 4ab^2 + b - 1$.

The terms of polynomials are usually arranged so that the powers of one of the variables are in descending order. In this case, the variable is a.

$$8a^3 - 5a^2b^2 - 4ab^2 + b - 1 = 8a^3 + (-5a^2b^2) + (-4ab^2) + b + (-1)$$

$8a^3$ has degree 3. $-5a^2b^2$ has degree 4. $-4ab^2$ has degree 3.
b has degree 1. -1 has degree 0.

The highest degree is 4. The degree of the polynomial is 4.

Example 2

Simplify $4x^2y - 2xy^3 + y + 6xy^3 - x^2y + 9y$.

$4x^2y - 2xy^3 + y + 6xy^3 - x^2y + 9y$
$= (4x^2y - x^2y) + (-2xy^3 + 6xy^3) + (y + 9y)$
$= (4 - 1)x^2y + (-2 + 6)xy^3 + (1 + 9)y$
$= 3x^2y + 4xy^3 + 10y$

LESSON 5-4   POLYNOMIALS   223

ALTERNATE TEACHING STRATEGIES

Using Logical Thinking

Have the students solve the following multiplication problems.

1. $(x + y)(x + y)$ $x^2 + 2xy + y^2$
2. $(x - y)(x - y)$ $x^2 - 2xy + y^2$
3. $(x + y)(x - y)$ $x^2 - y^2$

Have the students try to find other special products such as those in which the product is the sum or difference of two cubes.

INTRODUCING THE LESSON

 5-Minute Check

(over Lesson 5-3)

1. Kim and Beth can wallpaper a 30-square foot wall in an hour and 15 minutes. At the same rate, how long would it take them to wallpaper an area of 40 square feet?   **100 minutes or 1 hour 40 minutes**

2. Six equilateral triangles are placed together to form a hexagon. The length of a side of one triangle is 5 inches. What is the diameter of the smallest circle that includes all six vertices of the hexagon?   **10 inches**

Other Prerequisite Skills

Simplify using the distributive property.

3. $-4(2a - 3b)$ $-8a + 12b$
4. $(7x - 1)(-x)$ $-7x^2 + x$
5. $(-x + 5)(-3)$ $3x - 15$

Motivating the Lesson

A rectangular plot of a lawn is $x + y$ feet long and $2x + y$ feet wide. Find the area of the plot. Have students draw a figure modeling the lawn and label it. Have them explain how they would solve the problem.

Lesson Resources

Reteaching Master 5-4
Practice Master 5-4
Enrichment Master 5-4
Technology Master, p. 5
Activity Master, p. 23

Transparency 5-4 contains the 5-Minute Check and a teaching aid for this lesson.

TEACHING THE LESSON

Chalkboard Examples

For Example 1

Find the degree of the following polynomials.

a. $x^2 - 3x^3 + 2x$ **3**
b. $7xy^2 - 7x^2y + 8x^3y - 16xy^4$ **5**

For Example 2

Simplify.

$8a^2 - 3ab + 6b^3 + 4ab - 16a^2 - 2b^3$ $\mathbf{-8a^2 + ab + 4b^3}$

For Example 3

Simplify.

a. $(-4x^3 - 3x + 10x^2) - (8x^2 + 2x - x^3 - x^4)$ $\mathbf{x^4 - 3x^3 + 2x^2 - 5x}$
b. $(2x^2 - 3xy + 5y^2) - (4x^2 - 3xy - 2y^2)$ $\mathbf{-2x^2 + 7y^2}$

For Example 4

Find $-9a^2(3a - 7b^3)$.
$\mathbf{-27a^3 + 63a^2b^3}$

For Example 5

a. **Find $(x + 8)(x + 12)$.** $\mathbf{x^2 + 20x + 96}$
b. **Find $(x + 3)^2$.** $\mathbf{x^2 + 6x + 9}$

Teaching Tip 1 Caution students to carefully observe the sign of each term. Rewriting subtraction as adding the opposite may prove helpful.

We can simplify a polynomial using the distributive property, as we have just seen, or by adding or subtracting the coefficients of like terms. Study Example 3 to see how to simplify by adding or subtracting coefficients.

Example 3 **Simplify $(4s^2 + 7st - 2t^2) - (2s^2 + 8st - 5t^2)$.**

$$(4s^2 + 7st - 2t^2) - (2s^2 + 8st - 5t^2) = 4s^2 - 2s^2 + 7st - 8st - 2t^2 + 5t^2$$
$$= 2s^2 - st + 3t^2$$

The distributive property is also useful in multiplying monomials.

Example 4 **Find $5a(5ab^2 + 2a^2b^2 - 9b)$.**

$$5a(5ab^2 + 2a^2b^2 - 9b) = 5a \cdot 5ab^2 + 5a \cdot 2a^2b^2 - 5a \cdot 9b$$
$$= 25a^2b^2 + 10a^3b^2 - 45ab$$

Example 5 **Find $(x + 2)(x + 10)$.**

$$(x + 2)(x + 10) = (x + 2)x + (x + 2)10 \quad \textit{Distribute } x + 2.$$
$$= (x \cdot x) + (2 \cdot x) + (x \cdot 10) + (2 \cdot 10)$$
$$= x^2 + 2x + 10x + 20$$
$$= x^2 + 12x + 20$$

The **FOIL method** is an application of the distributive property that makes multiplying binomials faster. Take another look at Example 5 using the FOIL method.

$$(x + 2)(x + 10) = x \cdot x + x \cdot 10 + 2 \cdot x + 2 \cdot 10$$
$$= x^2 + 12x + 20$$

FOIL method of Multiplying Polynomials

The product of two binomials is the sum of the products of
F the *first* terms,
O the *outer* terms,
I the *inner* terms, and
L the *last* terms.

Example 6 **Use the FOIL method to find $(9a - 3)(a + 4)$.**

$$(9a - 3)(a + 4) = \overset{F}{9a \cdot a} + \overset{O}{9a \cdot 4} + \overset{I}{(-3) \cdot a} + \overset{L}{(-3) \cdot 4}$$
$$= 9a^2 + 36a - 3a - 12$$
$$= 9a^2 + 33a - 12$$

Teaching Tip 1

Example 7

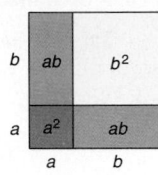

CONNECTION

Geometry

Show geometrically that $(a + b)^2 = a^2 + 2ab + b^2$.

Draw a diagram of a square that has sides of length $a + b$.

b	ab	b^2
a	a^2	ab
	a	b

The area of the square can be expressed by $(a + b)^2$ or by $a^2 + 2ab + b^2$.

We can also extend the distributive property to multiply polynomials with more than two terms.

Example 8

Find $(2x^2 + 10x - 4)(x - 12)$.   **Teaching Tip** ❷

$(2x^2 + 10x - 4)(x - 12)$

$= (2x^2 + 10x - 4)x - (2x^2 + 10x - 4)12$ *Distribute* $2x^2 + 10x - 4$.

$= 2x^2 \cdot x + 10x \cdot x - 4 \cdot x - 2x^2 \cdot 12 - 10x \cdot 12 + 4 \cdot 12$

$= 2x^3 + 10x^2 - 4x - 24x^2 - 120x + 48$

$= 2x^3 - 14x^2 - 124x + 48$

CHECKING FOR UNDERSTANDING

Communicating Mathematics

Read and study the lesson to answer these questions. **1, 3. See margin.**

1. Explain how the FOIL method and the distributive property are related.

2. Multiply $(2x + 3)$ by $(5x - 8)$ using the FOIL method. **$10x^2 - x - 24$**

3. Could you modify the FOIL method to find the product in Example 8? If so, how?

Guided Practice

Find the degree of each polynomial.

4. $4a^2 + 12ab$ **2**

5. $s^2 + 2s + 3$ **2**

6. $x^8 + 2x^7 - 3x^4 + 11x^3 + x - 9$ **8**

7. $3x^4y^2 - 5x^2y + 3$ **6**

8. $3r^5 - 3r^4 - 7r - 5$ **5**

9. $m^3 + 2mn^2 + 4n^3$ **3**

10. $5xy - 2x^2 - 3y^2$ **2**

11. $13xy^7 + 36x^3y^5 - 2x^4y^5 - xy$ **9**

Simplify.

12. $(4a + 2) + (2a + 6)$ **$6a + 8$**

13. $(5x + 6y) - (3x + 8y)$ **$2x - 2y$**

14. $(12n^2 - 4n + 8) - (4n^2 - 1)$
   $8n^2 - 4n + 9$

15. $3p(p^2 - 2p + 3)$ **$3p^3 - 6p^2 + 9p$**

Chalkboard Examples

For Example 6
Use the FOIL method to find each product.

a. $(4c - 5)(2c - 3)$
   $8c^2 - 22c + 15$
b. $(3y^2 - 2)(-2y + 1)$
   $-6y^3 + 3y^2 + 4y - 2$

For Example 7
Find the area of the figure.

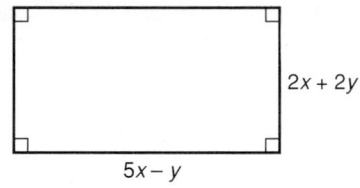

$2x + 2y$

$5x - y$

$10x^2 + 8xy - 2y^2$

For Example 8
Find $(3x + y)(4x + 5xy - 9y)$.
$12x^2 + 15x^2y - 23xy + 5xy^2 - 9y^2$

Teaching Tip ❷   You may want to show students the vertical form of multiplication as well as the horizontal form.

EVALUATING THE LESSON

Checking for Understanding
Exercises 1–15 are designed to help you assess understanding through reading, writing, and speaking. You should work through Exercises 1–3 with your students, and then monitor their work on Exercises 4–15.

EXERCISES

Practice Find the area of each triangle.

CONNECTION
Geometry

16.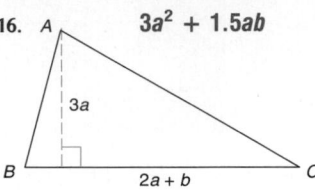
$3a^2 + 1.5ab$

17. $10y^2 + 6y$
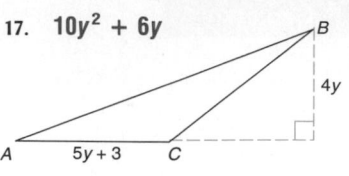

Simplify.

19. $-9a + 13b$
20. $-2m^2 + 8m + 1$
21. $4a^2 - 10d + 20$
22. $5y^2 - 2y + 3$
23. $r^2 - r + 6$
24. $7n^2 - 8nt + 4t^2$

18. $(9x + 4y) + (7x - 2y)$ **16x + 2y**
19. $(-3a + 5b) + (-6a + 8b)$
20. $(m^2 + 9m + 3) - (3m^2 + m + 2)$
21. $(3a^2 - 5d + 17) - (-a^2 + 5d - 3)$
22. $(3y^2 + 5y - 7) + (2y^2 - 7y + 10)$
23. $(8r^2 + 5r + 14) - (7r^2 + 6r + 8)$
24. $(10n^2 - 3nt + 4t^2) - (3n^2 + 5nt)$
25. $(-12y - 6y^2) + (-7y + 6y^2)$ **−19y**
26. $(x^3 - 3x^2y + 4xy^2 + y^3) - (7x^3 + x^2y - 9xy^2 + y^3)$
27. $4f(gf - bh)$ **4gf² − 4bfh**
28. $-5mn^2(-3m^2n + 6m^3n - 3m^4n^4)$

 B

26. $-6x^3 - 4x^2y + 13xy^2$
28. $15m^3n^3 - 30m^4n^3 + 15m^5n^6$
29. $\dfrac{1}{x^2} + \dfrac{1}{x^3} - \dfrac{3}{x^4}$
31. $12a^2 + 4ab + \dfrac{b}{4}$
32. $xy^3 + y + \dfrac{1}{x}$
36. $y^4 + y^3 + 5y^2 + 5y$
40. $6x^2 - xy - 15y^2$
42. $9y^3 + 18y^2 - y - 2$

29. $x^{-4}(x^2 + x - 3)$
30. $r^{-3}(r^5 - 2r^3 + r^{-1})$ $r^2 - 2 + \dfrac{1}{r^4}$
31. $4a^{-1}b^2(a^2b^{-1} + 3a^3b^{-2} + 4^{-2}ab^{-1})$
32. $y^2x^{-3}(yx^4 + y^{-1}x^3 + y^{-2}x^2)$
33. $(x + 7)(x + 2)$ **x² + 9x + 14**
34. $(a + 5)(a - 7)$ **a² − 2a − 35**
35. $(s^2 + 5)(s^2 - 4)$ **s⁴ + s² − 20**
36. $(y^2 + y)(y^2 + 5)$
37. $(2x + 7)(3x + 5)$ **6x² + 31x + 35**
38. $(3t - 8)(2t + 7)$ **6t² + 5t − 56**
39. $(w^2 - 5)(2w^2 + 3)$ **2w⁴ − 7w² − 15**
40. $(2x + 3y)(3x - 5y)$
41. $(6p - 5)(7p - 9)$ **42p² − 89p + 45**
42. $(9y^2 - 1)(y + 2)$

Find each product.

43. $(a - b)^2$ **a² − 2ab + b²**
44. $(a - b)(a + b)$ **a² − b²**
45. $(d + 3)^2$ **d² + 6d + 9**
46. $(r - 8)^2$ **r² − 16r + 64**
47. $(y - 2)^2$ **y² − 4y + 4**
48. $(y - 5)(y + 5)$ **y² − 25**
49. $(2p + q^3)^2$ **4p² + 4pq³ + q⁶**
50. $(x - 3y)^2$ **x² − 6xy + 9y²**
51. $(4m - 3n)^2$ **16m² − 24mn + 9n²**
52. $(5r - 2)^2$ **25r² − 20r + 4**
53. $(1 + 4r)^2$ **1 + 8r + 16r²**
54. $(x^3 - y)(x^3 + y)$ **x⁶ − y²**

Find the area of each figure.

CONNECTION
Geometry

55.
$3x + 6y$
$x + y$
$3x^2 + 9xy + 6y^2$

56. $a - 2b$
$a - 2b$
$a^2 - 4ab + 4b^2$

57.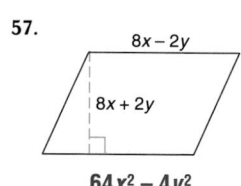
$8x - 2y$
$8x + 2y$
$64x^2 - 4y^2$

RETEACHING THE LESSON

Have students use algebraic tiles to model the multiplication of a polynomial by a monomial, $x(x + 2)$.

Consider a rectangle with a width of x and a length of $x + 2$. Use the edge of a $1 \times x$ tile to mark off the dimensions of the rectangle. Then complete the rectangle by filling it in with tiles.

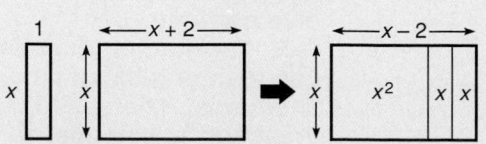

Now find the area of the large rectangle by adding the areas of the individual tiles. The area is $x^2 + 2x$.

60. $x^3 - xy^2 + xy^3 - y^4$

61. $3m^3 - 7m^2 - 24m + 16$

63. $b^3 + 2b^2 - 5b - 6$

64. $6x^3 - 7x^2 - 7x + 6$

65. $2a^3 - 7a^2 + 4a + 4$

Find each product.

58. $(a + b)(a^2 - ab + b^2)$ $\;a^3 + b^3$

60. $(x - y)(x^2 + xy + y^3)$

62. $r(r - 2)(r - 3)$ $\;r^3 - 5r^2 + 6r$

64. $(2x - 3)(x + 1)(3x - 2)$

66. $(a - b)(a^2 + ab + b^2)$ $\;a^3 - b^3$

$2x^3 - 9x^2 - 7x + 24$

59. $(2x - 3)(x^2 - 3x - 8)$

61. $(m - 4)(3m^2 + 5m - 4)$

63. $(b + 1)(b - 2)(b + 3)$

65. $(2a + 1)(a - 2)^2$

67. $(2k + 3)(k^2 - 7k + 21)$
$\;2k^3 - 11k^2 + 21k + 63$

68. Write two different polynomials that represent the area of the figure at the right.

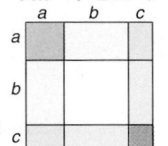

$(a + b + c)^2,\ a^2 + 2ab + b^2 + 2ac + 2bc + c^2$

Critical Thinking

69. Recall that the measure of an angle inscribed in a circle is half the measure of its intercepted arc. That is, $m\angle B = \frac{1}{2}m\widehat{ADC}$. Given a circle with inscribed quadrilateral $ABCD$ with the given arc measures, find the ratio of $m\angle A$ to $m\angle B$.

$\dfrac{10x + 14}{9x - 2}$

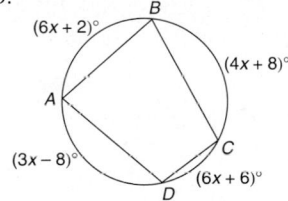

Applications

70. Business Dawn is writing a computer program to find the salaries of her employees after their annual raise. The percentage of increase is represented by p in the program. Marty's salary is \$23,450 now. Write a polynomial to represent Marty's salary in one year and one to represent Marty's salary after three years. Assume that the rate of increase will be the same for the next three years. $23,450(1 + p);\ 23,450(1 + p)^3$

71. Consumer Awareness The Ready Rentals Car Company rents cars for \$19.95 a day with 50 free miles. A charge of \$0.25 is assessed for each mile driven over 50 miles. Express the cost of renting a car for one day as a polynomial. Assume that you drive more than 50 miles.
$19.95 + 0.25(m - 50)$

Practice Masters Booklet, p. 37

Mixed Review

CONNECTION
Geometry

74. $\begin{bmatrix} \frac{1}{3} & 0 \\ \frac{1}{15} & \frac{1}{5} \end{bmatrix}$

72. Manufacturing The Marysville Metalworks cuts the largest possible circle from a 4-inch square of tin to make the top for a soup can. How much metal do they have for scrap after the circle is cut? **(Lesson 5-3)**
$16 - 4\pi$ or about 3.4 square inches

73. The length of rectangle $ABCD$ is twice its width. The perimeter is 48 meters. If W, X, Y, and Z are the midpoints of the sides of $ABCD$, find the area of parallelogram $WXYZ$. **(Lesson 5-3) 64 square meters**

74. Find the inverse for the matrix $\begin{bmatrix} 3 & 0 \\ -1 & 5 \end{bmatrix}$. **(Lesson 4-5)**

75. Use Cramer's Rule to solve the following system of equations. **(Lesson 3-3)**
$2x - 3y = 0$
$6x + 5y = 7$ $\left(\frac{3}{4}, \frac{1}{2}\right)$

76. Explain how the graphs of $y = [3x]$ and $y = 3[x]$ differ. **(Lesson 2-7)**
See margin.

77. Evaluate $\frac{3ab^2 - c^3}{a + c}$ if $a = 3$, $b = 7$, and $c = -2$. **(Lesson 1-1) 449**

MID-CHAPTER REVIEW

Simplify. (Lesson 5-1)

1. $5c^2 + 8d^2 - 10c^2$ **$8d^2 - 5c^2$**

2. $3d^3 - 4d^3 + d^3$ **0**

3. $(4x^2y)^2(3x^2y)$ **$48x^6y^3$**

4. $\left(\frac{1}{3}x^2y\right)^3\left(\frac{2}{3}xy\right)^2$ **$\frac{4}{243}x^8y^5$**

5. Evaluate $(32,000,000)(48,000)$. Express the answer in both scientific and decimal notation. **(Lesson 5-1) 1.536×10^{12}, 1,536,000,000,000**

Simplify. (Lesson 5-2)

6. $\frac{18b^4}{6b^2}$ **$3b^2$**

7. $\frac{20m^5n^4}{10mn^2}$ **$2m^4n^2$**

8. $\left(\frac{1}{4y}\right)^{-1}$ **$4y$**

9. $\frac{-3w^2t^3}{(4w^2)(6w^3t^4)}$ **$-\frac{1}{8w^3t}$**

Evaluate. Express each answer in both scientific and decimal notation. (Lesson 5-2)

10. $\frac{42 \times 10^5}{14 \times 10^{-2}}$ **3×10^7, 30,000,000**

11. $\frac{682,000}{480}$ **$1.4208\overline{3} \times 10^3$, $1420.8\overline{3}$**

12. If 2 miles of fence will enclose a square field of 160 acres, how large of a field will 4 miles of fence enclose? **(Lesson 5-3) 640 acres**

Simplify. (Lesson 5-4)

13. $(3x - 2y) - (4x + 7y)$ **$-x - 9y$**

14. $(4d^2 - 2d + 8) - (6d^2 - 7d + 2)$ **$-2d^2 + 5d + 6$**

15. $(3y - 8)(2y + 9)$ **$6y^2 + 11y - 72$**

16. $(x + 7)(x - 3)$ **$x^2 + 4x - 21$**

17. $(m + 2)^2$ **$m^2 + 4m + 4$**

18. $(2x - 3)^2$ **$4x^2 - 12x + 9$**

19. $(x + 2)(x - 3)^2$ **$x^3 - 4x^2 - 3x + 18$**

20. $(2y - 4)(y^2 + 2y - 7)$ **$2y^3 - 22y + 28$**

EXTENDING THE LESSON

Math Power: Communication

Find $(x^2 - y^2)(x^2 + y^2)$.
$x^4 - y^4$
Discuss how knowing this and other special products can help in multiplying polynomials using mental math.

Mid-Chapter Review

The Mid-Chapter Review provides students with a brief review of the concepts and skills in Lessons 5-1 through 5-4. Lesson numbers are given at the end of problems or instruction lines so students may review concepts not yet mastered.

5-5 Factoring

Objective
5-5

After studying this lesson, you should be able to:
- factor polynomials.

You know what it means to express a composite number as the product of its prime factors. We can also express a polynomial as the product of its prime factors. This way of expressing a polynomial is called its factored form. The first step in finding the factored form of a polynomial is to find the greatest common factor, or GCF, of the terms of the polynomial. Let's try factoring $12y^2 + 15y$.

First, write each term as the product of its prime factors.

$$12y^2 = 2 \cdot 2 \cdot 3 \cdot y \cdot y$$
$$15y = 3 \cdot 5 \cdot y$$

The greatest common factor of $12y^2$ and $15y$ is $3y$.

The distributive property states that $a(b + c) = ab + ac$. Factoring "undoes" the distribution. That is, $ab + ac = a(b + c)$.

$$12y^2 + 15y = (3y \cdot 4y) + (3y \cdot 5)$$
$$= 3y(4y + 5)$$

The factored form of $12y^2 + 15y$ is $3y(4y + 5)$.

A geometric way of interpreting factoring is to think of the area of a rectangle expressed as the product of the length and the width.

$3y$ | Area = $3y(4y + 5)$
or
$12y^2 + 15y$

$4y + 5$

Example 1

Factor $24a^2b - 18ab^2$. Draw the geometric representation of the expression.

$$24a^2b - 18ab^2 = (2 \cdot 2 \cdot 2 \cdot 3 \cdot a \cdot a \cdot b) - (2 \cdot 3 \cdot 3 \cdot a \cdot b \cdot b)$$
$$= (6ab \cdot 4a) - (6ab \cdot 3b) \qquad \text{6ab is the GCF.}$$
$$= 6ab(4a - 3b)$$

$6ab$ | Area = $6ab(4a - 3b)$
or
$24a^2b - 18ab^2$

$4a - 3b$

The rectangle is $6ab$ units wide and $(4a - 3b)$ units long.

Example 2

Factor $3s^2t + 4st^2 + st^3$.

$$3s^2t + 4st^2 + st^3 = (3 \cdot s \cdot s \cdot t) + (2 \cdot 2 \cdot s \cdot t \cdot t) + (s \cdot t \cdot t \cdot t)$$
$$= (st \cdot 3s) + (st \cdot 4t) + (st \cdot t^2) \qquad \text{st is the GCF.}$$
$$= st(3s + 4t + t^2)$$

LESSON 5-5 FACTORING **229**

Lesson Resources
Reteaching Master 5-5
Practice Master 5-5
Enrichment Master 5-5
Lab Manual, pp. 53–54
Activity Master, p. 41

 Transparency 5-5 contains the 5-Minute Check and a teaching aid for this lesson.

INTRODUCING THE LESSON

5-Minute Check
(over Lesson 5-4)

1. Find the degree of $6x^3y^2 - 12x^2y^3 - y^4 + 26$. **5**

Simplify.

2. $6x^2y + 3xy^4 + 7 + 5xy^4 - 9x^2y + 8y$ $-3x^2y + 8xy^4 + 8y + 7$
3. $(10a^3 - 6a^2b + 7ab^2 + b^3) - (5a^3 + 4a^2b - 3ab^2 - 1)$ $5a^3 - 10a^2b + 10ab^2 + b^3 + 1$

Use the FOIL method to find each product.

4. $(a - 4b)^2$ $a^2 - 8ab + 16b^2$
5. $(10r - 6s)(r + 2s)$ $10r^2 + 14rs - 12s^2$

Motivating the Lesson
Review with students how to find the greatest common factor. Have the students solve the following GCF problems.
1. 10 and 25   **5**
2. 16 and 32   **16**
3. $24ab$ and $18ab$ **6ab**
4. $3s^2t$, $4st^2$, st^3 **st**

ALTERNATE TEACHING STRATEGIES

Using Cooperative Groups
Have the students work in groups of four. Have them factor $3x^2 + 5x + 12x + 20$ three different ways. The students should be able to explain the steps they took in finding their solution. Which method would they choose to solve this problem?

Chalkboard Examples

For Example 1
Factor $16m^2n + 12mn^2$. Draw the geometric representation of the expression. $4mn(4m + 3n)$
The rectangle is $4mn$ units wide and $(4m + 3n)$ units long.

| $4mn$ | $A = 16m^2n + 12mn^2$ |

$4m + 3n$

For Example 2
Factor $2x^3yz^3 - 7xy^5z^2$.
$xyz^2(2x^2z - 7y^4)$

For Example 3
Factor $a^2x - b^2x + a^2y - b^2y$.
$(a^2 - b^2)(x + y)$

For Example 4
Factor.

a. $x^2 + 8x + 15$
   $(x + 5)(x + 3)$
b. $x^2 - 13x + 30$
   $(x - 3)(x - 10)$

Sometimes just factoring out the GCF does not result in a completely factored polynomial. In those cases, rearranging and grouping the terms may be helpful.

Example 3

Factor $a^2 - 2ab + a - 2b$.   **Teaching Tip ❶**

$$\begin{aligned}
a^2 - 2ab + a - 2b &= (a^2 - 2ab) + (a - 2b) \\
&= a(a - 2b) + 1(a - 2b) \\
&= (a - 2b)(a + 1)
\end{aligned}$$

Look at the terms in pairs.
Factor out the GCF of each.
$(a - 2b)$ is the GCF of the two new terms.

In the last lesson you learned how to multiply binomials using the FOIL method. Let's see if we can find a way that the process can be reversed to factor a trinomial into its binomial factors.

$$\begin{aligned}
(x + r)(x + s) &= x \cdot x + x \cdot s + r \cdot x + r \cdot s \\
&= x^2 + (r + s)x + rs
\end{aligned}$$

Look at the coefficient of the second term, $r + s$. It is the sum of the two constant terms in the original binomials. The constant term in the product is the product of the constants from the original binomials. Now that we know where this coefficient and constant come from, factoring a trinomial like this will be easy.

Example 4

Factor $x^2 - 2x - 35$.

We need to find two numbers whose product is -35 and whose sum is -2. List the pairs of factors of -35 and look for the pair that has a sum of -2. Make a table to organize our search.

Factors of -35	Sum of Factors
$-1, 35$	34
$1, -35$	-34
$-5, 7$	2
$5, -7$	-2

The two numbers are 5 and -7.   *Check this using the FOIL method.*
$x^2 - 2x - 35 = (x + 5)(x - 7)$

Example 5

Factor $x^2 - 49$.

We must find two factors of -49 that have a sum of 0. The only two that do are 7 and -7.

So, $x^2 - 49 = (x + 7)(x - 7)$.

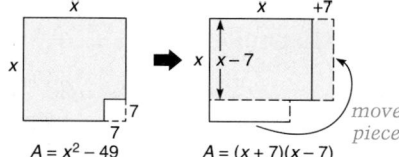

$A = x^2 - 49$ $A = (x + 7)(x - 7)$

move piece

230   CHAPTER 5   POLYNOMIALS

Did you notice that the two terms in the original polynomial are perfect squares? The geometric representation is a square with a square cut out. This is a special case called **the difference of two squares.** The difference of two squares is simple to factor.

Difference of Two Squares	**For real numbers a and b, $a^2 - b^2 = (a - b)(a + b)$.**

The method we have used on the last two examples works when the coefficient of x^2 is 1. Is there an easy way to factor trinomials when the coefficient of x^2 is not 1? Try using the FOIL method on two other binomials to see if you can find a rule.

$$\begin{aligned}(ax + b)(cx + d) &= ax \cdot cx + ax \cdot d + b \cdot cx + b \cdot d \\ &= acx^2 + (ad + bc)x + bd\end{aligned}$$

Notice that the product of the *coefficient* of x^2 and the *constant* term is *abcd.* The product of the two coefficients of the x term, *bc* and *ad,* is also *abcd.*

Example 6

Factor $2x^2 - 11x - 21$.

The product of the coefficient and the constant term is $2 \cdot -21$ or -42. So, the two coefficients of x must have a sum of -11 and a product of -42. They must be 3 and -14, since $3 + (-14) = -11$ and $3(-14) = -42$.
Check to see that this is the only pair that meets the criteria.

Now, rewrite the expression using $3x$ and $-14x$ in place of $-11x$ and factor by grouping.

$$\begin{aligned}2x^2 - 11x - 21 &= 2x^2 + (3x - 14x) - 21 && \textit{Substitute } (3x - 14x) \textit{ for } -11x. \\ &= (2x^2 + 3x) + (-14x - 21) && \textit{Group the terms.} \\ &= x(2x + 3) - 7(2x + 3) && \textit{Find the GCF of each group.} \\ &= (2x + 3)(x - 7) && \textit{Distributive property}\end{aligned}$$

Example 7

Factor $16r^2 - 24r + 9$.

$$\begin{aligned}16r^2 - 24r + 9 &= 16r^2 - 12r - 12r + 9 && \textit{-12 and -12 have a sum of -24 and a product of } 16 \cdot 9 \textit{ or 144.} \\ &= 4r(4r - 3) - 3(4r - 3) \\ &= (4r - 3)(4r - 3) \text{ or } (4r - 3)^2\end{aligned}$$

Example 7 shows one of the special cases that occur when factoring. It is a **perfect square trinomial,** which is a square of a binomial. The other special case is **the sum** or **difference of two cubes.** The methods for factoring these special cases are listed on the next page.

Chalkboard Examples

For Example 5
Factor.

a. $a^2 - 81$ $(a + 9)(a - 9)$
b. $16a^2 - 100b^2$ $(4a + 10b)(4a - 10b)$ or $4(2a + 5b)(2a - 5b)$

For Example 6
Factor.

a. $4x^2 + 7x + 3$ $(4x + 3)(x + 1)$
b. $6a^2 + 19a + 10$ $(3a + 2)(2a + 5)$

For Example 7
Factor.

a. $4a^2 - 12a + 9$ $(2a - 3)(2a - 3)$ or $(2a - 3)^2$
b. $16x^2 + 40x + 25$ $(4x + 5)(4x + 5)$ or $(4x + 5)^2$

Perfect Square Trinomials	**For any numbers a and b,** $a^2 + 2ab + b^2 = (a + b)^2$, and $a^2 - 2ab + b^2 = (a - b)^2$.
Sum or Difference of Two Cubes	**For any numbers a and b,** $a^3 + b^3 = (a + b)(a^2 - ab + b^2)$, and $a^3 - b^3 = (a - b)(a^2 + ab + b^2)$.

Teaching Tip ❷

Example 8

Factor $x^3 + 64$.

$$x^3 + 64 = x^3 + (4)^3$$
$$= (x + 4)(x^2 - x \cdot 4 + 4^2) \quad \text{\textit{Use the pattern}}$$
$$\qquad\qquad\qquad\qquad\qquad a^3 + b^3 = (a + b)(a^2 - ab + b^2).$$
$$= (x + 4)(x^2 - 4x + 16)$$

Use the following steps to factor a polynomial.

1. Find the greatest common factor of the terms and factor it out.
2. Check for special products.
   a. If there are *two terms*, look for a difference of two squares, difference of two cubes, or sum of two cubes.
   b. If there are *three terms*, look for a perfect square trinomial.
3. Try other factoring methods.
   a. If there are *three terms*, try the trinomial pattern.
   b. If there are *four or more terms*, try grouping.

Example 9

Factor $3x^3 + 6x^2 - 3x - 6$.

$$3x^3 + 6x^2 - 3x - 6 = 3(x^3 + 2x^2 - x - 2) \quad \text{\textit{3 is the GCF.}}$$
$$= 3[(x^3 + 2x^2) + (-x - 2)] \quad \text{\textit{Group the terms.}}$$
$$= 3[x^2(x + 2) - 1(x + 2)] \quad \text{\textit{Factor each group.}}$$
$$= 3(x + 2)(x^2 - 1) \quad \text{\textit{Factor out x + 2.}}$$
$$= 3(x + 2)(x + 1)(x - 1) \quad \text{\textit{$x^2 - 1$ is the difference of two squares.}}$$

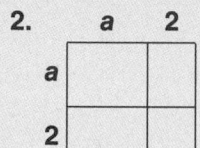
CHECKING FOR UNDERSTANDING

Communicating Mathematics

Read and study the lesson to answer these questions.

1. What polynomial is represented by the area of rectangle at the right? What is its factored form?
   $2x^2 + 7x + 3$; $(2x + 1)(x + 3)$

2x + 1
Area = $2x^2 + 7x + 3$

   (x + 3)

2. Draw a geometric representation of $(a + 2)^2$.
   See margin.

RETEACHING THE LESSON

Students may use the reverse of FOIL to factor trinomials.

Step given: $ax^2 + bx + c$	Example $6x^2 + x - 15$
1. Find ac	$(6)(-15)$ or -90
2. Find factors of ac that add or subtract (per sign of constant) to b	factors of -90 that subtract (constant sign is "$-$") to 1; -9 and 10
3. Rewrite middle term bx as a sum or difference of factors of ac found in step 2	$6x^2 + 1x - 15$ Rewrite $1x$ as $6x^2 + 10x - 9x - 15$
4. Factor by grouping.	$2x(3x + 5) - 3(3x + 5)$
5. Check by FOIL.	$(2x - 3)(3x + 5)$ $6x^2 + 10x - 9x - 15$

1, 4, 9, 16, 25, 36, 49, 64, 81, 100, 121, 144, 169, 196, 225, 256, 289, 324, 361, 400; 1, 8, 27, 64, 125, 216, 343, 512, 729, 1000

3. You know how to factor the difference of two squares and the sum or difference of two cubes, but to factor these you must recognize the squares and cubes. Use a calculator to help you make a list of the squares of the integers from 1 to 20 and the cubes of the integers from 1 to 10. Memorize the list so that you will be able to recognize special cases quickly.

4. Group the terms in Example 9 differently and factor. Did you get the same prime factorization? **See margin.**

Guided Practice

Factor.

6. $2(4a - b)$
9. $(r + 3)(r - 3)$
11. $(10 + m)(10 - m)$
12. $(y + 9z)(y - 9z)$
13. $(3y - 2)(y + 4k)$

5. $3s + 3t$ $3(s + t)$
6. $8a - 2b$
7. $ab + ac$ $a(b + c)$
8. $x^2 - x$ $x(x - 1)$
9. $r^2 - 9$
10. $x^2 - 25$ $(x + 5)(x - 5)$
11. $100 - m^2$
12. $y^2 - 81z^2$
13. $y(3y - 2) + 4k(3y - 2)$
14. $2x^2 + 6y + 8b$ $2(x^2 + 3y + 4b)$
15. $9p^2 - 3pq$ $3p(3p - q)$
16. $3m(m - 7) + k(m - 7)$ $(m - 7)(3m + k)$

EXERCISES

Practice

Factor. 17–52. See margin.

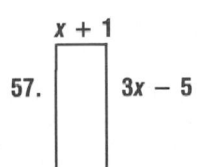

Teaching Tip ❸

A

17. $-15x^2 - 5x$
18. $s^2 - 6s + 8$
19. $2ab(c - d) + 10d(c - d)$
20. $a^2 + 5a + 6$
21. $y^2 + 6y + 9$
22. $a(y - b) - c(y - b)$
23. $r^2 + 16r + 64$
24. $x^2 + xy + 3x$
25. $3a^2 + 6a + 9y$

B

26. $a^4 + a^3b + a^2b^2$
27. $5x^2y - 10xy^2$
28. $49s^2 - 100$
29. $x^3 + 8$
30. $d^3 - 27$
31. $f^2 - 18f + 81$
32. $t^2 + 12t + 35$
33. $s^2 + 12s + 36$
34. $a^2 + 4ab + 4b^2$
35. $4x^2 - 9$
36. $3y^2 + 5y + 2$
37. $4s^2 - 20s + 21$
38. $3d^2 - 48$
39. $x^3 + 2x^2 - 35x$
40. $4s^2 - 20st + 4t^2$
41. $p^2 - 4bp + 4b^2$
42. $6d^2 + 33d - 63$
43. $f^3 - 1$

C

44. $x^4 - 13x^2 + 36$
45. $(x + y)^2 - \dfrac{1}{4}$
46. $2r^3 - 16s^3$
47. $m^2 - k^2 + 6k - 9$
48. $16y^4 - z^4$
49. $a + b + 3a^2 - 3b^2$
50. $a^3b^3 - 27$
51. $1 - 8m^6$
52. $4a^2 + 4ab - y^2 + b^2$

Critical Thinking

53. Factor $a^{2n} - 64$. $(a^n - 8)(a^n + 8)$
54. Factor $x^{3n} - y^{3n}$. $(x^n - y^n)(x^{2n} + x^n y^n + y^{2n})$
55. Find $\dfrac{3}{a + b}$ if $\left(\dfrac{3}{a + b}\right)^2 - \dfrac{6}{a + b} + 1 = 0$. **1**

Applications

56. **Manufacturing** A square boat cover is designed as shown at the right. Express the area of the blue region in factored form. $A = (x - y)(x + y)$

57. **Interior Design** A designer preparing to paint a wall found that its area is $3x^2 - 2x - 5$ square feet. Find the length and width of the rectangular wall. Draw and label a diagram to represent the wall. $(3x - 5)(x + 1)$

$x + 1$
57. $\quad$ $3x - 5$

Additional Answers

17. $-5x(3x + 1)$
18. $(s - 4)(s - 2)$
19. $2(ab + 5d)(c - d)$
20. $(a + 2)(a + 3)$
21. $(y + 3)^2$
22. $(a - c)(y - b)$
23. $(r + 8)^2$
24. $x(x + y + 3)$
25. $3(a^2 + 2a + 3y)$
26. $a^2(a^2 + ab + b^2)$
27. $5xy(x - 2y)$
28. $(7s - 10)(7s + 10)$
29. $(x + 2)(x^2 - 2x + 4)$

30. $(d - 3)(d^2 + 3d + 9)$
31. $(f - 9)^2$
32. $(t + 5)(t + 7)$
33. $(s + 6)^2$
34. $(a + 2b)^2$
35. $(2x - 3)(2x + 3)$
36. $(3y + 2)(y + 1)$
37. $(2s - 7)(2s - 3)$
38. $3(d - 4)(d + 4)$
39. $x(x + 7)(x - 5)$
40. $4(s^2 - 5st + t^2)$
41. $(p - 2b)^2$

EVALUATING THE LESSON

Checking for Understanding

Exercises 1–16 are designed to help you assess understanding through reading, writing, and speaking. You should work through Exercises 1–4 with your students, and then monitor their work on Exercises 5–16.

Closing the Lesson

Writing Activity Write a step-by-step method for solving the factorization of the polynomials in this lesson.

APPLYING THE LESSON

Homework Exercises

Assignment Guide

Basic: 17–43, 53–56, 58–64
Average: 22–48, 53–64
Enriched: 26–64

Chapter 5, Quiz C, (Lesson 5-5), is available in the Evaluation Masters Booklet, p. 66.

Teaching Tip ❸ Remind students to factor out the GCF first before factoring the polynomial.

Practice Masters Booklet, p. 38

Additional Answers

42. $3(2d - 3)(d + 7)$

43. $(f - 1)(f^2 + f + 1)$

44. $(x - 3)(x + 3)(x - 2)(x + 2)$

45. $\left(x + y - \frac{1}{2}\right)\left(x + y + \frac{1}{2}\right)$

46. $2(r - 2s)(r^2 + 2rs + 4s^2)$

47. $(m - k + 3)(m + k - 3)$

48. $(4y^2 + z^2)(2y - z)(2y + z)$

49. $(a + b)(1 + 3a - 3b)$

50. $(ab - 3)(a^2b^2 + 3ab + 9)$

51. $(1 - 2m^2)(1 + 2m^2 + 4m^4)$

52. $(2a + b + y)(2a + b - y)$

Enrichment Masters Booklet, p. 33

Mixed Review Use the FOIL method to find each product. (Lesson 5-4)

58. $(s + 3)^2$ $s^2 + 6s + 9$

59. $(2x + 4)(7x - 1)$ $14x^2 + 26x - 4$

60. State the system of equations represented by the matrix equation
$\begin{bmatrix} 3 & 0 \\ 1 & -2 \end{bmatrix}\begin{bmatrix} x \\ y \end{bmatrix} = \begin{bmatrix} 12 \\ 8 \end{bmatrix}$. (Lesson 4-7) $3x = 12; x - 2y = 8$

61. Find the dimension of matrix M if $A_{3\times3} \cdot B_{3\times5} = M$. (Lesson 4-2) $M_{3\times5}$

62. Given $f(x, y) = 1.2x - 0.8y$ use a calculator to find the value of $f(0.1, -0.3)$. (Lesson 3-6) 0.36

63. Is $\{(9, 0), (-1, 0), (0, 0), (0, 1), (11, -11)\}$ a function? (Lesson 2-1) no

64. Solve the equation $\frac{3}{4}t + 1 = 10$. (Lesson 1-3) $t = 12$

~~~~~~~~~~~ BIOLOGY CONNECTION ~~~~~~~~~~~

Genetics and Population Predictions

Reproductive cells contain pairs of chromosomes that contain the genetic code in the form of genes. When the chromosomes split and recombine with other chromosomes, pairs of genes are formed containing codes that may be pure dominant, pure recessive, or hybrid. The Punnett squares shown on page 208 demonstrate these combinations, called genotypes.

Suppose that p represents the ratio of dominant gene A in a population and q represents the ratio of recessive gene a in a population. The next generation is the result of $(p + q)^2$. This results in p^2 pure dominant genotypes (AA), q^2 pure recessive genotypes (aa), and $2pq$ hybrid genotypes (Aa). Since all members of the population must have at least one recessive gene or dominant gene present in their genotypes, $p + q = 1$.

Application In the population of a village, the recessive left-handedness gene (r) had a frequency of 1:4, and the dominant right-handedness gene (R) had a frequency of 3:4. In the next generation, what would you predict the population genotypes to be?

$p = \frac{3}{4}$, ratio of the dominant gene $\qquad$ $q = \frac{1}{4}$, ratio of the recessive gene

right-handed (pure)	right-handed (hybrid)	left-handed (pure)
$p^2 = \left(\frac{3}{4}\right)^2$ or $\frac{9}{16}$	$2pq = 2\left(\frac{3}{4}\right)\left(\frac{1}{4}\right)$ or $\frac{6}{16}$	$q^2 = \left(\frac{1}{4}\right)^2$ or $\frac{1}{16}$
9 out of 16 have RR.	6 out of 16 have Rr.	1 out of 16 have rr.

In the next generation, 15 of 16 would be expected to be right-handed.

EXTENDING THE LESSON

Math Power: Problem Solving

Factor completely $x^9 + 512$.
$(x + 2)(x^2 - 2x + 4)(x^6 - 8x^3 + 64)$

Remind students they could rewrite the original expression to read $(x^3)^3 + (8)^3$.

Biology Connection

Review the chapter opener with students. They should be familiar with Punnett Squares. Ask them why $(p + q)^2$ can be used to represent the next generation. If the frequency for the left-handedness was $\frac{1}{2}$, ask students what the frequency for right-handedness would be and why. $\frac{1}{2}$ because $p + q = 1$.

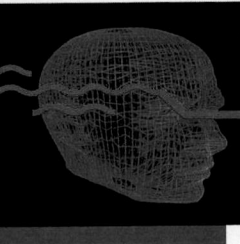

Technology

Factoring

The examples below show how to use the *Mathematical Exploration Toolkit (MET)* to factor polynomials. The computer can find common monomial factors, linear factors, and quadratic factors of polynomials in one variable. You will need the CALC commands listed below. Their shortened forms are shown in parentheses. To enter an exponent, you must use the ^ symbol. For example, x^2 is entered as x^2.

FACTOR (fac)   FSTEPS (fst)   SIMPLIFY (simp)

The FACTOR command will find only the common monomial factor in polynomials with more than one variable. In polynomials of only one variable, it will factor the expression completely. The FSTEPS command displays the steps used to perform the most recent FACTOR command.

Example 1 Factor $6x^3y^4 - 9xy^2 + 12xy$.

ENTER: 6x^3y^4−9xy^2+12xy
        fac

    6 x³ y⁴ - 9 x y² + 12 x y
    3 x y (2 x² y³ - 3 y + 4)

Example 2 Factor $2p(3q + 6) + 3pq(4p - 2)$.

ENTER: 2p(3q+6)+3pq(4p−2)
        simp
        fac

    2p (3q + 6) + 3pq (4p - 2)
    12 p²q + 12 p
    12 p (p q + 1)

Example 3 Factor $z^7 - 256z^3$.

ENTER: z^7−256z^3
        fac

    z⁷ - 256 z³
    z³ (z - 4) (z + 4) (z² + 16)

Suppose you use fst *after entering the polynomial.*

    z⁷ - 256 z³
    (z⁶ - 16 z³) · (z² + 16)
    (z⁴ - 4 z³) · (((z + 4) (z² + 16)))
    (z³) · ((z - 4) ((z + 4) (z² + 16))
    z³ (z - 4) (z + 4) (z² + 16)

EXERCISES

Use FACTOR and FSTEPS to factor each polynomial. Record each step.

1. $96a^3b^3 - 80a^2b + 112ab$

2. $15m(n^2 + 10m) - 20m^2$

3. $9x^4 - 144$

4. $x^9 + 1$ $(x + 1)(x^2 - x + 1)$
   $(x^6 - x^3 + 1)$

1. $16ab(6a^2b^2 - 5a + 7)$ 2. $5m(26m + 3n^2)$ 3. $9(x - 2)(x + 2)(x^2 + 4)$

TECHNOLOGY   235

Using Technology

Objective This optional page shows how software can be used to perform mathematical computations and to enhance and extend mathematical concepts.

Teaching Suggestions

The FACTOR command will not factor terms within a polynomial, but will only find factors common to all terms. Integral exponents and rational coefficients are supported. Encourage students to record the steps shown by FSTEPS. You may want to have them use SIMPLIFY to check factors. Challenge them to attempt to stump the computer by multiplying factors of their choice and entering the product into CALC.

The factoring steps used by the computer may be in a different order than is usually suggested. You may want students to use the GCFACTOR (gcf) command to factor out common monomials first. Then use FACTOR (fac) to force factoring of the polynomial. FSTEPS (fst) will display steps in the usual order.

Lesson Resources

Reteaching Master 5-6
Practice Master 5-6
Enrichment Master 5-6

 Transparency 5-6 contains the 5-Minute Check and a teaching aid for this lesson.

INTRODUCING THE LESSON

🕐 5-Minute Check

(over Lesson 5-5)

Factor.

1. $5x^2y - 20xy^2z + 35y^3z^2$
   $5y(x^2 - 4xyz + 7y^2z^2)$
2. $4a^2 - 9$ $(2a + 3)(2a - 3)$
3. $6y^3 + 13y^2 + 5y$
   $y(3y + 5)(2y + 1)$

Other Prerequisite Skills

Rewrite each polynomial in descending order, adding zero coefficients as needed.

4. $2x - 4 + 3x^3 - x^2$
   $3x^3 - x^2 + 2x - 4$
5. $x^5 - 10 - 2x^2$ $x^5 + 0x^4 +$
   $0x^3 - 2x^2 + 0x - 10$

Motivating the Lesson

Have students divide 11,106 by 9. Next, divide 1107 by 9. Then divide 111,105 by 9. Explain why the pattern is occuring. What would be the division of 111,111,102 and 9?

TEACHING THE LESSON

Teaching Tip ❶ Another approach is to factor the numerator and cancel.

Objective 5-6

After studying this lesson, you should be able to:
■ divide polynomials using factoring and long division.

Application

FYI ...

When a vaccine is given, a small amount of a virus is introduced to activate the natural immune system against the virus.

Yū Kamin is a genetic engineer working on a vaccine for influenza. The number of people in a small town who catch influenza during an epidemic is estimated to be $n = \dfrac{170t^2}{t^2 + 1}$, where n represents the number of people and t represents the number of weeks from the beginning of the epidemic. After one week of an epidemic, $\dfrac{170(1)^2}{(1)^2 + 1}$ or 85 people would have influenza.

Sometimes it is necessary to divide polynomials by monomials or by other polynomials to solve problems. The properties of exponents that you learned in Lesson 5-2 will be very helpful in this process.

Example 1

Divide $25a^4$ by $5a^2$.

$$25a^4 \div 5a^2 = \frac{25a^4}{5a^2} \qquad \text{\textit{A denominator cannot have a value of 0, so } } a \neq 0.$$

$$= \frac{25}{5} \cdot a^{4-2} \qquad \text{\textit{Quotient of powers property}}$$

$$= 5a^2$$

Example 2

Simplify $\dfrac{8x^2y^3 - 28x^3y^2}{4xy^2}$. **Teaching Tip ❶**

$$\frac{8x^2y^3 - 28x^3y^2}{4xy^2} = \frac{8x^2y^3}{4xy^2} - \frac{28x^3y^2}{4xy^2} \qquad x \neq 0, y \neq 0$$

$$= \frac{8}{4} \cdot x^{2-1}y^{3-2} - \frac{28}{4} \cdot x^{3-1}y^{2-2}$$

$$= 2xy - 7x^2 \qquad y^{2-2} = y^0 = 1$$

$$= x(2y - 7x)$$

We can use a process similar to long division to divide a polynomial by a polynomial. When doing the division, remember that you must have like terms to add and subtract.

236 CHAPTER 5 POLYNOMIALS

ALTERNATE TEACHING STRATEGIES

Using Communication

Ask students to explain why you cannot divide by zero. Review the properties studied in Lesson 5-2.

Have students determine the values of m that will make the denominator of $\dfrac{24m^2}{m^2 - 1}$ zero. **1, −1**

Example 3

Divide $9b^2 + 9b - 10$ by $3b - 2$.

$$
\begin{array}{r}
3b \\
3b - 2 \overline{)\, 9b^2 + 9b - 10} \\
\underline{9b^2 - 6b} \\
15b - 10
\end{array}
$$

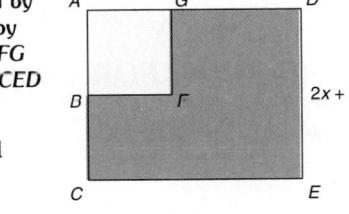

$$
\begin{array}{r}
3b + 5 \\
3b - 2 \overline{)\, 9b^2 + 9b - 10} \\
\underline{9b^2 - 6b} \\
15b - 10 \\
\underline{15b - 10} \\
0
\end{array}
$$

Example 4

Simplify $(5m^2 - 34m - 7)(m - 7)^{-1}$. $m \neq 7$

$(5m^2 - 34m - 7)(m - 7)^{-1} = \dfrac{5m^2 - 34m - 7}{m - 7}$

$\phantom{(5m^2 - 34m - 7)(m - 7)^{-1}} = \dfrac{(5m + 1)(m - 7)}{m - 7}$ *Factor the numerator.*

$\phantom{(5m^2 - 34m - 7)(m - 7)^{-1}} = 5m + 1$ *Simplify $\frac{m - 7}{m - 7}$.*

Example 5

CONNECTION

Geometry

The area of rectangle *ACED* is represented by $6x^2 + 38x + 56$. Its width is represented by $2x + 8$. Point *B* is the midpoint of *AC*. *ABFG* is a square. Find the length of rectangle *ACED* and the area of square *ABFG*.

Divide $6x^2 + 38x + 56$ by $2x + 8$ to find the length of the rectangle.

$$
\begin{array}{r}
3x + 7 \\
2x + 8 \overline{)\, 6x^2 + 38x + 56} \\
\underline{6x^2 + 24x} \\
14x + 56 \\
\underline{14x + 56} \\
0
\end{array}
$$

The length of rectangle *ACED* is $3x + 7$.

The length of one side of square *ABFG* is $\dfrac{2x + 8}{2}$ or $x + 4$. The area of the square is $(x + 4)^2$ or $x^2 + 8x + 16$.

Example 6

APPLICATION

Health

Simplify the formula for the number of people who catch influenza during an epidemic, $n = \dfrac{170t^2}{t^2 + 1}$, as given in the beginning of the lesson.

$n = \dfrac{170t^2}{t^2 + 1}$

$ = 170t^2 \div (t^2 + 1)$

$ = 170 - \dfrac{170}{t^2 + 1}$

$$
\begin{array}{r}
170 \\
t^2 + 1 \overline{)\, 170t^2 + 0t + 0} \\
\underline{170t^2 + 170} \\
-170
\end{array}
$$

What happens to the value of n as t becomes very great?

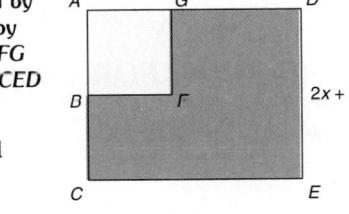
(arrow)

Chalkboard Examples

For Example 1

Divide $\dfrac{27a^2b^3c}{21ab^7} \cdot \dfrac{9ac}{7b^4}$

For Example 2

Simplify.

a. $\dfrac{3a^2b + 6a^3b^2 + 18ab}{3ab}$

$\quad a + 2a^2b + 6$

b. $\dfrac{12x^2y + 3x}{3x}$ $4xy + 1$

For Example 3

Divide $(x^2 - 5x - 24)$ by $(x + 3)$.

$x - 8$

For Example 4

Simplify $(h^2 - 11h + 28)(h - 4)^{-1}$.

$h - 7$

For Example 5

The area of rectangle *ABEF* is represented by $2x^2 + 20x + 50$. Its width is represented by $x + 5$. Find the area and the length of the sides of square *ACDF*. Points *E* and *B* are midpoints of $\overline{FD}$ and $\overline{AC}$, respectively.

area $= 4x^2 + 40x + 100$

length $= 2x + 10$

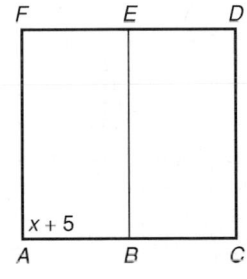

Teaching Tip ❷ Sometimes the divisors must be placed in decending order.

EVALUATING THE LESSON

Checking for Understanding

Exercises 1–14 are designed to help you assess understanding through reading, writing, and speaking. You should work through Exercises 1–4 with your students, and then monitor their work on Exercises 5–14.

Reteaching Masters Booklet, p. 34

As you know from long division with real numbers, the divisor is a factor of the dividend if the remainder upon division is zero. The example below uses this fact to prove that a binomial is a factor of the polynomial.

Example 7

Show that $4 - n$ is a factor of $n^3 - 6n^2 + 13n - 20$.

$$\begin{array}{r} -n^2 + 2n - 5 \\ -n + 4\overline{)n^3 - 6n^2 + 13n - 20} \\ \underline{n^3 - 4n^2} \\ -2n^2 + 13n \\ \underline{-2n^2 + 8n} \\ 5n - 20 \\ \underline{5n - 20} \\ 0 \end{array}$$

$4 - n = -n + 4$

The remainder is 0, so $4 - n$ is a factor of $n^3 - 6n^2 + 13n - 20$.

Teaching Tip ❷

CHECKING FOR UNDERSTANDING

Communicating Mathematics

Read and study the lesson to answer these questions.

1. About how many people will have influenza after 6 weeks of an epidemic? **about 165 people**

2. Why is $m \neq 7$ in Example 4? **See margin.**

3. What can you conclude about the dividend and divisor if the remainder is zero? **The divisor is a factor of the dividend.**

4. When is it easier for you to divide using factoring instead of the long division technique? **See margin.**

Guided Practice

Simplify.

5. $\dfrac{5ab^2 - 4ab + 7a^2b}{ab}$ $5b - 4 + 7a$

6. $\dfrac{x^3y^2 - x^2y + 2x}{-xy}$ $-x^2y + x - \dfrac{2}{y}$

7. $\dfrac{6r^2s^2 + 3rs^2 - 9r^2s}{3rs}$ $2rs + s - 3r$

8. $\dfrac{3(x - 7)^6}{(x - 7)^{10}}$ $\dfrac{3}{(x - 7)^4}$

9. $\dfrac{2(y^2 - 5)^3}{8(y^2 - 5)^5}$ $\dfrac{1}{4(y^2 - 5)^2}$

10. $\dfrac{2(t + 3)^4}{10(t + 3)^2}$ $\dfrac{(t + 3)^2}{5}$

11. $\dfrac{c^2 - c - 30}{c - 6}$ $c + 5$

12. $\dfrac{m^2 + 8m + 16}{m + 4}$ $m + 4$

13. $(w^2 - w^3)(w^2 - 1)^{-1}$ $-\dfrac{w^2}{w + 1}$

14. $(a^3 - b^3)(a - b)^{-2}$ $\dfrac{a^2 + ab + b^2}{a - b}$

RETEACHING THE LESSON

Use long division to find the missing factors.

a. $x^3 - 125 = (x - 5)(?)$
   $x^2 + 5x + 25$

b. $8x^3 + 27 = (2x + 3)(?)$
   $4x^2 - 6x + 9$

Divide $(4x^4 - 17x^3 + 17x^2 - x - 3)$ by $(x^2 - 3x)$. $4x^2 - 5x + 2 +$
$\dfrac{5x - 3}{x^2 - 3x}$

EXERCISES

15. $4q^2 + 3pq - 5p$ 16. $-6m^3n - 4m - 5n^2$ 17. $2k^2 - 3py + 4p^2y$

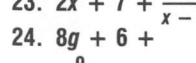

Practice

Simplify. 19–22. See margin. 18. $5r + \frac{23}{3}s + \frac{2s}{r}$

Teaching Tip ③

A

15. $\dfrac{12pq^3 + 9p^2q^2 - 15p^2q}{3pq}$ 16. $\dfrac{6m^4n^2 + 4m^2n + 5mn^3}{-mn}$

23. $2x + 7 + \dfrac{5}{x-3}$

24. $8g + 6 + \dfrac{9}{g-3}$

17. $\dfrac{28k^3py - 42kp^2y^2 + 56kp^3y^2}{14kpy}$ 18. $\dfrac{15r^2s + 23rs^2 + 6s^2}{3rs}$

19. $(a^2 - 5a - 84)(a+7)^{-1}$ **$a - 12$** 20. $(2r^2 + 5r - 3) \div (r + 3)$ **$2r - 1$**

21. $(n^2 - 12n - 45) \div (n + 3)$ **$n - 15$** 22. $(6y^2 + 7y - 3)(2y + 3)^{-1}$ **$3y - 1$**

B

23. $(2x^2 + x - 16) \div (x - 3)$ 24. $(8g^2 - 18g - 9)(g - 3)^{-1}$

25. $-s - 10 + \dfrac{44}{6-s}$

25. $(s^2 + 4s - 16) \div (6 - s)$ 26. $(8x^2 - 4x + 11)(x + 5)^{-1}$

26. $8x - 44 + \dfrac{231}{x+5}$

27. $2y^2 + 5y + 2$

27. $(6y^3 + 13y^2 + y - 2)(3y - 1)^{-1}$ 28. $(56c^2 - 113c + 59) \div (8c - 7)$

28. $7c - 8 + \dfrac{3}{8c-7}$

29. $(6x^3 + 5x^2 + 9) \div (2x + 3)$ 30. $(y^3 - 1) \div (y - 1)$ **$y^2 + y + 1$**

29. $3x^2 - 2x + 3$

31. $(r^3 - 9r^2 + 27r - 28) \div (r - 3)$ 32. $(m^3 - 7m + 3m^2 - 21)(m^2 - 7)^{-1}$ **$m + 3$**

31. $r^2 - 6r + 9 - \dfrac{1}{r-3}$

C

33. $2x^2 - 3x - 2$

33. $(6x^3 - 5x^2 - 12x - 4) \div (3x + 2)$ 34. $(x^2 + 4x - 4) \div (x + 2)$

34. $x + 2 - \dfrac{8}{x+2}$

35. $(2t^3 - 2t - 3) \div (t - 1)$ 36. $(v^4 + 4) \div (v^2 - 2v + 2)$ **$v^2 + 2v + 2$**

35. $2t^2 + 2t - \dfrac{3}{t-1}$

37. $(s^3 - 8) \div (s - 2)$ **$s^2 + 2s + 4$**

38. $(y^4 + 4y^3 + 10y^2 + 12y + 9) \div (y^2 + 2y + 3)$ **$y^2 + 2y + 3$**

39. $(x^4 - 4x^2 + 12x - 9) \div (x^2 + 2x - 3)$ **$x^2 - 2x + 3$**

40. Is $3y - 2$ a factor of $6y^3 - y^2 - 5y + 2$? **yes**

41. One factor of $a^3 - 2a^2 - a + 2$ is $a - 2$. Find the other factors. **$a + 1$, $a - 1$**

42. Find the remainder when dividing $x^2 + 3x + 5$ by $x - 2$. If $f(x) = x^2 + 3x + 5$, find $f(2)$. Compare the answers. **Both are 15.**

43. Find the value of k so that the remainder upon dividing $(x^2 + 8x + k)$ by $(x - 4)$ is zero. **-48**

44. Simplify $\left(\dfrac{y^2 + 2y - 15}{y^2 + 3y - 10}\right)\left(\dfrac{y^2 - 9}{y^2 - 9y + 14}\right)^{-1}$ **$\dfrac{y - 7}{y + 3}$**

Critical Thinking

45. Suppose that the quotient upon dividing one polynomial by another is $3x^2 - x + 32 - \dfrac{121}{x + 4}$. What is the dividend? **$3x^3 + 11x^2 + 28x + 7$**

Applications

46. **Entertainment** A magician asked a member of his audience to choose any number. He said "Multiply your number by 3. Add the sum of your number and 8 to that result. Now divide by the sum of your number and two." The magician announced the final answer without asking the original number. What was the final answer and how did he know what it was? **4; If x = your number, you can write an expression for this, $\dfrac{3x + (x + 8)}{(x + 2)}$, which equals 4.**

Additional Answers

2. If $m = 7$, then we are dividing by 0 and division by 0 is undefined.

4. when the numerator and denominator are both easily factorable and contain a common factor

---

Error Analysis

In long division of polynomials, students sometimes subtract the second or third terms of partial products incorrectly. For example:

$$\begin{array}{r} 6x - 8 \\ x - 3 \overline{)\, 6x^2 + 10x + 24} \\ \underline{6x^2 - 18x} \\ -8x \\ \underline{-8x + 24} \end{array}$$

Point out that the whole binomial $6x^2 - 18x$ is being subtracted, not just the $6x^2$. Subtracting $6x^2 - 18x$ means adding $-(6x^2 - 18x)$. Answer for the example is $6x + 28 + \dfrac{108}{x - 3}$.

Assignment Guide

Basic: 15–32, 45–53
Average: 19–38, 45–53
Enriched: 23–53

Teaching Tip ③ You may wish to have students write the excluded values first.

Practice Masters Booklet, p. 39

NAME _____ DATE _____

5-6 **Practice Worksheet**

Dividing Polynomials

Simplify.

1. $(30x^3y + 12x^2y^2 - 18x^2y) \div (-6x^2y)$
$5x - 2y + 3$

2. $(2x^2 + 3x - 4) \div (x - 2)$
$2x + 7 + \dfrac{10}{x - 2}$

3. $(4x^2 - 2x + 6)(2x - 3)^{-1}$
$2x + 2 + \dfrac{12}{2x - 3}$

4. $(x^4 - 3x^3 + 5x - 6) \div (x + 2)$
$x^3 - 5x^2 + 10x - 15 + \dfrac{24}{x + 2}$

5. $(6x^2 - x - 7) \div (3x + 1)$
$2x - 1 - \dfrac{6}{3x + 1}$

6. $(2x^3 + 4x - 6) \div (x + 3)$
$2x^2 - 6x + 22 - \dfrac{72}{x + 3}$

7. $(4x^3 - 8x^2 + 3x - 8) \div (2x - 1)$
$2x^2 - 3x - \dfrac{8}{2x - 1}$

8. $(x^4 - 2x^3 + 6x^2 - 8x + 10) \div (x + 2)$
$x^3 - 4x^2 + 14x - 36 + \dfrac{82}{x + 2}$

APPLYING THE LESSON

Homework Exercises

See assignment guide on page 239.

47. **Manufacturing**   A machinist who makes square metal pipes found a formula for the amount of metal she needed to make a pipe. She found that to make a pipe $8x$ inches long she needed $32x^2 + x$ square inches of metal. In figuring the area needed, the machinist allowed some fixed length of metal for overlap of the seam. If the width of the finished pipe will be x inches, how much did the machinist leave for the seam? **$\frac{1}{8}$ inch**

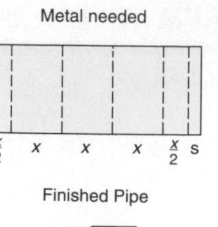

Metal needed

s = width of seam

$\frac{x}{2}$ x x x $\frac{x}{2}$ s

Finished Pipe

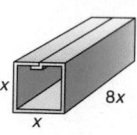

x $8x$

x

Mixed Review   Factor.   **(Lesson 5-5)**

48. $4a^2 - 16$ **$4(a - 2)(a + 2)$**   49. $d^2 - 11d - 26$ **$(d - 13)(d + 2)$**

50. Simplify $\frac{1}{2x^0 + y^0}$.   **(Lesson 5-2)** **$\frac{1}{3}$**

51. **Manufacturing**   Earthly Treasures Inc. makes wood chairs and tables. A chair requires 4 hours of cutting and 4 hours of assembly. A table requires 3 hours of cutting and 2 hours of assembly. Each week there are 40 hours of worker time available in the cutting department and 36 hours of worker time available in the assembly department. If the profits on chairs and tables are $28 and $22 respectively, how many of each item should the company produce for a maximum profit?   **(Lesson 3-7) 7 chairs, 4 tables**

52. Determine which numbers in $\{-2, -1, 0, 1, 2\}$ are solutions of $|x| + x = 0$.   **(Lesson 1-6)** **$-2, -1, 0$**

53. Name the sets of numbers to which $2.121221222 \ldots$ belongs.   **(Lesson 1-2) I, R**

HISTORY CONNECTION

What mathematical topics were there before algebra? Historians have relied on cave pictures from ancient civilizations to trace much of the development of our number system. Early man used his fingers to count, but found this inconvenient when numbers exceeded 10. Many caves in North America show piles of stones used as a counting tool. These piles often contain 5 or 10 stones which correspond to the numbers of fingers possible. The Maya Indians of South America had a number system based on 20, which indicates they also used their toes when counting.

EXTENDING THE LESSON

Math Power: Problem Solving

Simplify $(36x^2 - 84xy + 49y^2 - 16a^2 - 24ab - 9b^2) \div (-18xz + 21yz + 12az + 9bz)$.

$$\frac{6x - 7y + 4a + 3b}{-3z}$$

Remind students that partial factors may be helpful.

Synthetic Division

Objective
5-7

After studying this lesson, you should be able to:
- divide polynomials using synthetic division.

In Lesson 5-6, you learned to divide a polynomial by another polynomial using long division. A simpler process called **synthetic division** has been devised to divide a polynomial by a binomial. Study the example below to see how the process works.

Example 1

Divide $2x^3 - 7x^2 - 8x + 16$ by $x - 4$.

Write the terms of the polynomial so that the degrees of the terms are in descending order. Then write just the coefficients as shown at the right.

$$2x^3 - 7x^2 - 8x + 16$$

$$2 \quad -7 \quad -8 \quad 16$$

Write the constant, r, of the divisor $x - r$ to the left. In this case, $r = 4$.

$$4 \,\rfloor\, 2 \quad -7 \quad -8 \quad 16$$

Now bring the first coefficient down as shown.

$$4 \,\rfloor\, 2 \quad -7 \quad -8 \quad 16$$
$$\underline{}$$
$$2$$

Multiply the first coefficient by r and write the product under the second coefficient.

$$4 \,\rfloor\, 2 \quad -7 \quad -8 \quad 16$$
$$\underline{8}$$
$$2$$

Add the product and the second coefficient. $-7 + 8 = 1$. Write the sum as shown.

$$4 \,\rfloor\, 2 \quad -7 \quad -8 \quad 16$$
$$\underline{8}$$
$$2 \quad 1$$

Multiply the sum, 1, by r. Write the product under the next coefficient.

$$4 \,\rfloor\, 2 \quad -7 \quad -8 \quad 16$$
$$\underline{8 \quad 4}$$
$$2 \quad 1$$

Add. $8 + 4 = 4$. Write the sum as shown.

$$4 \,\rfloor\, 2 \quad -7 \quad -8 \quad 16$$
$$\underline{8 \quad 4}$$
$$2 \quad 1 \quad -4$$

Repeat the process. Multiply the sum, -4 by r and write the product under the next coefficient.

$$4 \,\rfloor\, 2 \quad -7 \quad -8 \quad 16$$
$$\underline{8 \quad 4 \quad -16}$$
$$2 \quad 1 \quad -4$$

Add. $16 + (-16) = 0$. The remainder is 0.

$$4 \,\rfloor\, 2 \quad -7 \quad -8 \quad 16$$
$$\underline{8 \quad 4 \quad -16}$$
$$2 \quad 1 \quad -4 \,\rfloor\, 0$$

Teaching Tip ❶

Writing the result is easy. The numbers along the bottom row are the coefficients of the powers of x in descending order. Start with the power that is one less than that of the dividend. The result of this division is $2x^2 + x - 4$.

Check this result. Does $(x - 4)(2x^2 + x - 4) = 2x^3 - 7x^2 - 8x + 16$?

LESSON 5-7   SYNTHETIC DIVISION   241

Lesson Resources

Reteaching Master 5-7
Practice Master 5-7
Enrichment Master 5-7

 Transparency 5-7 contains the 5-Minute Check and a teaching aid for this lesson.

INTRODUCING THE LESSON

> **⏱ 5-Minute Check**
>
> *(over Lesson 5-6)*
> Simplify.
>
> 1. $\dfrac{36m^4y^4 - 18m^3y}{6m^2y}$ $6m^2y^3 - 3m = 3m(2my^3 - 1)$
> 2. $(2x^2 - x - 15)(x - 3)^{-1}$ $2x + 5$
> 3. $(8y^2 + 8y + 3) \div (2y + 1)$ $4y + 2 + \dfrac{1}{2y + 1}$
> 4. $(x^3 + 4x - 4) \div (x + 2)$ $x^2 - 2x + 8 - \dfrac{20}{x + 2}$
> 5. Is $3y - 2$ a factor of $6y^3 - y^2 - 5y + 2$? **yes**

Motivating the Lesson

Write the expression $(2x^4 - 5x^3 + x^6 + 3 + 2x) \div (x + 4)$ in the descending order for the dividend and in the form $(x - r)$ for the divisor. Then divide by long division writing the steps taken at each level.

TEACHING THE LESSON

Teaching Tip ❶   Ask students to explain why the power of the variable is one less than that of the dividend.

ALTERNATE TEACHING STRATEGIES

Using Charts

Have the students make a chart to show the quotient of $3y^2 - 5y - 2$ divided by polynomials $x - 1$, $x - 2$, $x - 3$, $x + 1$, $x + 2$, and $x + 3$.

Do any of them have zeros for the remainder? What does that mean? Make other charts for other division problems and see if there are any generalizations you can make.

Teaching Tip ❷ Remind students that the divisor must be in the form $x - r$.

Let's compare the process of synthetic division to long division. We have used both methods to divide $3x^3 - 8x^2 + 5x - 1$ by $x - 2$. Study the results below.

$$\begin{array}{r|rrrr} 2 & 3 & -8 & 5 & -1 \\ & & 6 & -4 & 2 \\ \hline & 3 & -2 & 1 & | \ 1 \end{array}$$

$$\begin{array}{r} 3x^2 - 2x + 1 \\ x - 2 \,\overline{\smash{\big)}\, 3x^3 - 8x^2 + 5x - 1} \\ \underline{3x^3 - 6x^2} \\ -2x^2 + 5x \\ \underline{-2x^2 + 4x} \\ x - 1 \\ \underline{x - 2} \\ 1 \end{array}$$

Compare the numbers in the second row of the synthetic division with those that appear in the long division. Why do you think that in synthetic division you add these numbers that you would subtract when using long division? *Look at the divisors.*

Example 2 Use synthetic division to find $(5s^3 + s^2 - 7) \div (s + 1)$.

In synthetic division, every power of the variable must be represented in the dividend. So, $5s^3 + s^2 - 7$ must be written as $5s^3 + s^2 + 0s - 7$.

$$\begin{array}{r|rrrr} -1 & 5 & 1 & 0 & -7 \\ & & -5 & 4 & -4 \\ \hline & 5 & -4 & 4 & -11 \end{array}$$ The result is $5s^2 - 4s + 4 - \dfrac{11}{s + 1}$.

To check the result, multiply the divisor, $s + 1$, by the quotient, $5s^2 - 4s + 4$. Then add the remainder, -11.

$$\begin{aligned}
(s + 1)(5s^2 - 4s + 4) + (-11) &= s(5s^2 - 4s + 4) + (5s^2 - 4s + 4) + (-11) \\
&= 5s^3 - 4s^2 + 4s + 5s^2 - 4s + 4 - 11 \\
&= 5s^3 + s^2 - 7 \ \checkmark
\end{aligned}$$

It checks because this polynomial is the dividend. **Teaching Tip ❷**

Example 3 Use a calculator to divide $x^3 + 13x^2 - 12x - 8$ by $x + 2$.

ENTER: 2 [+/-] [×] 1 [=] [+] 13 [=] 11 $\begin{array}{r|rr} -2 & 1 & 13 \\ & & -2 \\ \hline & 1 & 11 \quad | \end{array}$

ENTER: [×] 2 [+/-] [=] [+] 12 [+/-] [=] -34 $\begin{array}{r|rrr} -2 & 1 & 13 & 12 \\ & & -2 & -22 \\ \hline & 1 & 11 & -34 \ | \end{array}$

ENTER: [×] 2 [+/-] [=] [+] 8 [+/-] [=] 60 $\begin{array}{r|rrrr} -2 & 1 & 13 & -12 & -8 \\ & & -2 & -22 & 68 \\ \hline & 1 & 11 & -34 & | \ 60 \end{array}$

The result is $x^2 + 11x - 34 + \dfrac{60}{x + 2}$.

So far we have used synthetic division on problems with divisors with leading coefficients of one. You can also use synthetic division when the divisor has a leading coefficient other than 1. Study the example below.

Example 4

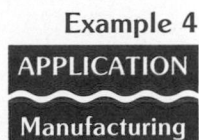

APPLICATION

Manufacturing

The Cookie Crate Co. makes cookie tins in several sizes. The largest tin they make is three inches longer than twice its width. It has a volume of $4w^3 + 8w^2 + 3w$ in³, where w represents the width of the tin. If the lid is made separately, how much metal is required to make this cookie tin?

We need to find the dimensions of the tin to be able to find the surface area. If w represents the width, then the length is $2w + 3$. We can divide the volume by both the width and the length to find the height.

$$\text{height} = \frac{4w^3 + 8w^2 + 3w}{w(2w + 3)} \text{ or } \frac{4w^2 + 8w + 3}{2w + 3}$$

Since synthetic division requires a divisor of the form $x - r$, we must get the divisor in this form before using synthetic division. We can do that by factoring the leading coefficient of the divisor from the divisor and the dividend. Let's rewrite the division and take another look.

$$\text{height} = \frac{2\left(2w^2 + 4w + \frac{3}{2}\right)}{2\left(w + \frac{3}{2}\right)} \text{ or } \frac{2x^2 + 4w + \frac{3}{2}}{w + \frac{3}{2}}$$

Factor 2 from both the divisor and the dividend. Then simplify the expression.

Now we can use synthetic division. since the leading coefficient of $w + \frac{3}{2}$ is 1.

The height is $2w + 1$.

$$
\begin{array}{c|ccc}
-\frac{3}{2} & 2 & 4 & \frac{3}{2} \\
& & -3 & -\frac{3}{2} \\
\hline
& 2 & 1 & 0
\end{array}
$$

If the lid for the cookie tin is to be made separately, we need to find the sum of the areas of the four sides and the bottom to know how much metal will be needed to make the tin. **Teaching Tip ❸**

Area of a long side $= (2w + 3)(2w + 1) = 4w^2 + 8w + 3$
Area of a short side $= w(2w + 1)$ $= 2w^2 + w$
Area of bottom $= w(2w + 3)$ $= 2w^2 + 3w$

Total area $= 2(4w^2 + 8w + 3) + 2(2w^2 + w) + 2w^2 + 3w$
$= 8w^2 + 16w + 6 + 4w^2 + 2w + 2w^2 + 3w$
$= 14w^2 + 21w + 6$

An area of $14w^2 + 21w + 6$ square inches of metal will be needed to make the cookie tin.

RETEACHING THE LESSON

Use long division process to solve $(3x^3 - 4x^2 - 3x - 2) \div (x - 3)$.

$3x^2 + 5x + 12 + \frac{34}{x - 3}$

Now use synthetic division to solve the same problem. Compare the methods. Both use descending order for the dividend. In synthetic division the coefficients are detached, subtraction is replaced by an equivalent addition and the lines of numbers are compacted. Since synthetic division is a method for dividing a polynomial by the binomial $x - c$ (c is a constant), how could synthetic division by $x + 3$ be done? Use $x - (^-3)$.

Teaching Tip ❸ Students could use the strategy of drawing a picture to see what is happening.

Example 5

Use synthetic division to find $(2x^3 - x^2 + 5x - 12) \div (2x - 3)$.

$$\frac{2x^3 - x^2 + 5x - 12}{2x - 3} = \frac{2\left(x^3 - \frac{1}{2}x^2 + \frac{5}{2}x - 6\right)}{2\left(x - \frac{3}{2}\right)} \text{ or } \frac{x^3 - \frac{1}{2}x^2 + \frac{5}{2}x - 6}{x - \frac{3}{2}}$$

Now, use synthetic division to divide
$x^3 - \frac{1}{2}x^2 + \frac{5}{2}x - 6$ by $x - \frac{3}{2}$.

$$\begin{array}{c|cccc} \frac{3}{2} & 1 & -\frac{1}{2} & \frac{5}{2} & -6 \\ & & \frac{3}{2} & \frac{3}{2} & 6 \\ \hline & 1 & 1 & 4 & 0 \end{array}$$

The result is $x^2 + x + 4$.
Check the solution.

CHECKING FOR UNDERSTANDING

Communicating Mathematics

Read and study the lesson to answer these questions.

1. Explain why 2 was factored out of both the divisor and the dividend in Example 5. **See margin.**

2. Why is it necessary to include terms with zero coefficients in the row of numbers for synthetic division? **See margin.**

3. In Example 4, suppose $w = 6.5$. How many square inches of metal are needed to make the box? What is its volume? **734 in²; 1456 in³**

Guided Practice

Use synthetic division to determine which of the following binomials are factors of $2x^2 - 7x - 4$.

4. $x - 4$ **yes**   5. $x + 1$ **no**   6. $2x - 1$ **no**

7. $x - 1$ **no**   8. $2x + 1$ **yes**   9. $2x - 3$ **no**

EXERCISES

10. $3y^2 + 11y + 1 + \frac{5}{y-3}$ 11. $2b^2 - b - 1 + \frac{4}{b+1}$ 12. $2c^2 + c + 5 + \frac{6}{c-2}$

Practice

Divide using synthetic division. 20–27. **See margin.**   14. $t^3 + t - 1$

13. $3x^2 + x + 3 + \frac{2}{x-1}$

Ⓐ
10. $(3y^3 + 2y^2 - 32y + 2) \div (y - 3)$
11. $(2b^3 + b^2 - 2b + 3) \div (b + 1)$
12. $(2c^3 - 3c^2 + 3c - 4) \div (c - 2)$
13. $(3x^3 - 2x^2 + 2x - 1) \div (x - 1)$
14. $(t^4 - 2t^3 + t^2 - 3t + 2) \div (t - 2)$
15. $(3r^4 - 6r^3 - 2r^2 + r - 6) \div (r + 1)$

15. $3r^3 - 9r^2 + 7r - 6$

Ⓑ
16. $(z^4 - 3z^3 - z^2 - 11z - 4) \div (z - 4)$
17. $(2b^3 - 11b^2 + 12b + 9) \div (b - 3)$

16. $z^3 + z^2 + 3z + 1$
17. $2b^2 - 5b - 3$
18. $6s^2 - s - 2$
19. $x^2 + 4x + 3$

18. $(6s^3 - 19s^2 + s + 6) \div (s - 3)$
19. $(x^3 + 2x^2 - 5x - 6) \div (x - 2)$
20. $(x^3 + 3x^2 - 7x + 1) \div (x - 1)$
21. $(n^4 - 8n^3 + 54n + 105) \div (n - 5)$
22. $(2x^4 - 5x^3 + 2x - 3) \div (x - 1)$
23. $(z^5 - 6z^3 + 4z^2 - 3) \div (z - 2)$
24. $(y^4 + 3y^3 + y - 1) \div (y + 3)$
25. $(4s^4 - 5s^2 + 2s + 3) \div (2s - 1)$

Ⓒ
26. $(2x^3 - 3x^2 - 8x + 4) \div (2x + 1)$
27. $(4x^4 - 5x^2 - 8x - 10) \div (2x - 3)$
28. $(6j^3 - 28j^2 + 19j + 3) \div (3j - 2)$
29. $(y^5 - 3y^2 - 20) \div (y - 2)$

$2j^2 - 8j + 1 + \frac{5}{3j-2}$ $y^4 + 2y^3 + 4y^2 + 5y + 10$

Additional Answers

1. Synthetic division assumes that the coefficient of x in the divisor is 1, so the 2 was factored out to make that coefficient 1.

2. If the zero coefficients were not included you would be combining unlike terms when the division is performed.

20. $x^2 + 4x - 3 - \frac{2}{x-1}$

21. $n^3 - 3n^2 - 15n - 21$

22. $2x^3 - 3x^2 - 3x - 1 - \frac{4}{x-1}$

23. $z^4 + 2z^3 - 2z^2 - \frac{3}{z-2}$

24. $y^3 + 1 - \frac{4}{y+3}$

25. $2s^3 + s^2 - 2s + \frac{3}{2s-1}$

26. $x^2 - 2x - 3 + \frac{7}{2x+1}$

27. $2x^3 + 3x^2 + 2x - 1 - \frac{13}{2x-3}$

30. Use synthetic division to find $(3y^3 - 5y - 2) \div (y - 2)$. If $f(y) = 3y^3 - 5y - 2$, find $f(2)$. Compare the remainder from the division to the value of $f(2)$. **Both are 12.**

31. Use synthetic division to find $(2x^4 - 3x^2 + 1) \div (x + 1)$. If $f(x) = 2x^4 - 3x^2 + 1$, find $f(-1)$. Compare the remainder from the division to the value of $f(-1)$. **Both are 0.**

Critical Thinking

32. Based on your answers to Exercises 30 and 31, how do you think $f(r)$ and the division of $f(r)$ by $x - r$ are related? $f(r) =$ **remainder of division.**

Applications

33. **Manufacturing** The volume of a small tin made by The Cookie Crate Co. is $6w^3 - 4w^2 - 16w$ in^3, where w represents the width of the tin. If the height of the tin is four inches more than three times the width, what is the length of the tin? $2w - 4$ **inches**

34. **Retail** The store *Bunches of Boxes and Bags* assembles boxes to package items for mailing. The store manager found that the volume of a box made from a piece of cardboard with a square of length x inches cut from each corner is $4x^3 - 168x^2 + 1728x$ in^3. If the piece of cardboard is 48 inches long, how wide is it? **36 inches**

Computer

Press RETURN after each coefficient.

This BASIC program uses synthetic division to compute the coefficients of the quotient and remainder from a polynomial divided by a linear binomial. Input the degree of the polynomial. Next input the constant R for the divisor $x - R$. Finally, input the coefficients of the polynomial.

```
10   INPUT "DEGREE OF POLYNOMIAL:      90   PRINT B(1); " ";
     "; N                             100  FOR X = 1 TO N-1
20   INPUT "CONSTANT R: "; R          110  B(X + 1) = A(X + 1) + R * B(X)
30   PRINT "ENTER COEFFICIENTS:"      120  PRINT B(X + 1); " ";
40   FOR X = 1 TO N + 1               130  NEXT X
50   INPUT A(X)                       140  PRINT
60   NEXT X                           150  PRINT "REMAINDER: "; A(N + 1) +
70   LET B(1) = A(1)                       R * B(N)
80   PRINT "COEFFICIENTS OF           160  END
     QUOTIENT ARE: "
```

Enter the program on a computer and use it to perform the following divisions.

Teaching Tip ❹

37. $2x^4 + x^3 - 7x^2 + 13x - 21 + \dfrac{24}{x + 1}$

35. $(x^4 + 2x^3 - 7x^2 + 2x - 8) \div (x - 3)$ $x^3 + 5x^2 + 8x + 26 + \dfrac{70}{x - 3}$

36. $(x^4 + 8x^3 + 22x^2 + 24x + 9) \div (x + 1)$ $x^3 + 7x^2 + 15x + 9$

37. $(2x^5 + 3x^4 - 6x^3 + 6x^2 - 8x + 3) \div (x + 1)$

38. $(x^5 - 3x^2 - 20) \div (x - 2)$ $x^4 + 2x^3 + 4x^2 + 5x + 10$

39. $(x^5 - 15x^3 - 10x^2 + 60x + 72) \div (x + 3)$
$x^4 - 3x^3 - 6x^2 + 8x + 36 - \dfrac{36}{x + 3}$

Mixed Review

41. $a^2 + 3a - 2 - \dfrac{1}{a + 4}$

Use long division to simplify each expression.   (Lesson 5-6)

40. $(x^2 - 7x + 6)(x - 1)^{-1}$ $x - 6$ **41.** $(a^3 + 7a^2 + 10a - 9)(a + 4)^{-1}$

42. Find the dimension of the matrix M if $A_{1 \times 9} \cdot M = B_{1 \times 1}$.   (Lesson 4-2)
9×1

43. Find the value of the determinant $\begin{vmatrix} 3 & -2 \\ 0 & 1 \end{vmatrix}$.   (Lesson 4-3) **3**

44. Write the equation $y = -11x + 2$ in standard form.   (Lesson 2-2)
$11x + y = 2$

EXTENDING THE LESSON

Math Power: Problem Solving

Use synthetic division to find the value of k so that the remainder is zero when $x^2 - 2x + (2k - 16)$ is divided by $x - k$. $k = 4$ **or** -4

Closing the Lesson

Writing Activity   Have students write a paragraph comparing long division and synthetic division for polynomials. They should include an example showing both ways and an explanation why they would choose one method over the other.

APPLYING THE LESSON

Homework Exercises

Assignment Guide

Basic: 10–25, 32–37, 40–44
Average: 13–28, 32–44
Enriched: 16–44

Chapter 5, Quiz D, (Lessons 5-6 through 5-7), is available in the Evaluation Masters Booklet, p. 66.

Teaching Tip ❹   Remind students to enter zeros for the coefficients of missing terms. Be sure they understand how to enter the problems. The program will work with polynomials having degrees less than ten. For higher degrees, a DIM statement is required.
5 DIM A(n), B(n)   The value of n must be one greater than the degree of the polynomial.

Enrichment Masters Booklet, p. 35

Using the Chapter Summary and Review

The Chapter Summary and Review begins with an alphabetical listing of the new terms that were presented in the chapter. Have students define each term and provide an example of it, if appropriate.

The Skills and Concepts presented in the chapter are reviewed using a side-by-side format. Encourage students to refer to the Objectives and Examples on the left as they complete the Review Exercises on the right.

The Chapter Summary and Review ends with exercises that review Applications and Connections.

VOCABULARY

Upon completing this chapter, you should be familiar with the following terms:

binomial	**223**	**210**	monomial
coefficient	**210**	**231**	perfect square trinomial
constant	**210**	**223**	polynomial
degree of monomial	**210**	**212**	scientific notation
degree of polynomial	**223**	**231**	sum of cubes
difference of cubes	**231**	**241**	synthetic division
difference of squares	**231**	**223**	term
FOIL	**224**	**223**	trinomial
like terms	**210**		

SKILLS AND CONCEPTS

OBJECTIVES AND EXAMPLES	REVIEW EXERCISES

Upon completing this chapter, you should be able to:

Use these exercises to review and prepare for the chapter test.

■ multiply monomials and powers of monomials   (**Lesson 5-1**)

$$(x^2y^2)^3(2x)^2 = (x^6y^6)(4x^2)$$
$$= 4x^8y^6$$

Simplify. 1. m 2. $2d^3$
5. $144x^4y^6$ 6. $-108x^8y^3$

1. $4m + 3m + (-6m)$ 2. $4d^3 - 7d^3 + 5d^3$

3. $y^8(y^5)$ y^{13} 4. $x^2(x^4)(x^5)$ x^{11}

5. $(3xy^2)^2(4xy)^2$ 6. $(-3x^2y)^3(2x)^2$

■ represent numbers in scientific notation   (**Lesson 5-1**)

$(9.1 \times 10^6)(2 \times 10^3)$
$= 1.82 \times 10^{10}$
$= 18,200,000,000$

7. 1.344×10^{15};
$1,344,000,000,000,000$

Evaluate. Express each answer in both scientific notation and decimal notation.

7. $(3.2 \times 10^5)(4.2 \times 10^9)$

8. $(4.7 \times 10^2)(11 \times 10^4)$ 5.17×10^7;
$51,700,000$

■ divide polynomials and simplify expressions containing negative and zero exponents   (**Lesson 5-2**)

$(mn^3)^{-3} = \dfrac{1}{m^3n^9}$

$\dfrac{36x^2y}{9xy^2} = \dfrac{4x}{y}$

$a^0 = 1$

Simplify.

9. $\dfrac{a^5}{a^3}$ a^2 10. $\dfrac{5y^{10}}{y^7}$ $5y^3$

11. $\dfrac{4^{-6}}{4^{-3}}$ $\dfrac{1}{64}$ 12. $\left(\dfrac{3}{4}\right)^0$ 1

13. $(a^3b^2)^{-2}$ $\dfrac{1}{a^6b^4}$ 14. $\dfrac{25m^2n^3}{5mn}$ $5mn^2$

OBJECTIVES AND EXAMPLES	REVIEW EXERCISES

■ divide expressions written in scientific notation (Lesson 5-2)

$$\frac{24 \times 10^{-2}}{8 \times 10^3} = 3 \times 10^{-5}$$
$$= 0.00003$$

Evaluate. Express each answer in both scientific and decimal notation.

15. $\frac{20 \times 10^5}{10 \times 10^{-2}}$ 2×10^7; 20,000,000

16. $\frac{(34,000,000)(24,000)}{6800}$ 1.2×10^8; 120,000,000

■ add, subtract, and multiply polynomials (Lesson 5-4)

$(3x + y) + (2x - 4y) = 5x - 3y$

$(x^2 - 4y^2) - (3x^2 - 2y^2)$
$= -2x^2 - 2y^2$

$(3a - b)(a + 2b) = 3a^2 + 6ab - ab - 2b^2$
$= 3a^2 + 5ab - 2b^2$

Simplify.   18. $10y^2 - y - 5$
    21. $n^3 - n^2 - 5n + 2$

17. $(9x + 2y) - (7x - 3y)$ $2x + 5y$

18. $(4y^2 + 2y - 7) + (6y^2 - 3y + 2)$

19. $(m - 2)(m + 5)$ $m^2 + 3m - 10$

20. $(2y + 7)(3y - 9)$ $6y^2 + 3y - 63$

21. $(n + 2)(n^2 - 3n + 1)$

22. $(r + 4)(r - 1)^2$ $r^3 + 2r^2 - 7r + 4$

■ factor polynomials (Lesson 5-5)

$ab - 2a + b - 2 = a(b - 2) + 1(b - 2)$
$= (a + 1)(b - 2)$

$3a^2 - 48 = 3(a^2 - 16)$
$= 3(a - 4)(a + 4)$

$2x^2 - 5x - 3 = (x - 3)(2x + 1)$

Factor.

23. $5a + 5b$
    $5(a + b)$
24. $-14x^2 - 7x$
    $-7x(2x + 1)$
25. $s^2 + 7s + 6$
    $(s + 1)(s + 6)$
26. $a(y + 2) - b(y + 2)$
    $(a - b)(y + 2)$
27. $b^3 - 64$
    $(b - 4)(b^2 + 4b + 16)$
28. $8a^3 + 27$
    $(2a + 3)(4a^2 - 6a + 9)$
29. $x^2 + 6x + 9$
    $(x + 3)^2$
30. $4x^2 - 81$
    $(2x - 9)(2x + 9)$
31. $2y^3 - 98y$
    $2y(y - 7)(y + 7)$
32. $y^{2n} - 81$
    $(y^n - 9)(y^n + 9)$

■ divide polynomials using factoring and long division (Lesson 5-6)

$(x^2 + 2) \div (x - 1)$

$$\begin{array}{r} x + 1 \\ x - 1\overline{)x^2 + 0x + 2} \\ \underline{x^2 - x} \\ x + 2 \\ \underline{x - 1} \\ 3 \end{array}$$

$x + 1 + \dfrac{3}{x - 1}$

Use division to simplify each expression.

33. $(6y^2 + 16y + 8) \div (y + 2)$ $6y + 4$

34. $(x^3 - 2x^2 + 5) \div (x - 3)$

35. $(8s^2 - 2) \div (2s + 1)$ $4s - 2$

36. $(2d^4 + 2d^3 - 9d^2 - 3d + 9) \div (2d^2 - 3)$
    $d^2 + d - 3$

34. $x^2 + x + 3 + \dfrac{14}{x - 3}$

Alternate Review Strategy

To provide a brief in-class review, you may wish to read the following questions to the class and require a verbal response.

1. Simplify $3x^2 + 5x + 6x^2 - 3$. $9x^2 + 5x - 3$
2. Evaluate (1.2×10^4) (5.2×10^3). 6.24×10^7
3. Simplify $\frac{125c^2d^5}{5cd}$. $25cd^4$
4. Evaluate $\frac{25 \times 10^7}{5 \times 10^3}$. 5×10^4
5. Simplify $(4x - 7y) - (2x + 9y)$. $2x - 16y$
6. Simplify $(7c + 2)(2c - 5)$. $14c^2 - 31c - 10$
7. Factor $24a + 18b$. $6(4a + 3b)$
8. Factor $16n^4 - 1$. $(4n^2 + 1)(2n - 1)(2n + 1)$
9. Solve $(x^2 + 8x + 12) \div (x + 2)$ using long division. $x + 6$
10. Solve $(x^3 - 9x^2 + 27x - 28) \div (x - 3)$ using synthetic division. $x^2 - 6x + 9 - \frac{1}{x - 3}$

The Cumulative Review shown below can be used to review skills and concepts presented thus far in the text. Standardized Test Practice Questions are also provided in the Evaluation Masters Booklet.

Evaluation Masters Booklet, pp. 67–68

■ divide polynomials using synthetic division   (Lesson 5-7)

$(3c^3 + 4c^2 - 2c - 1) \div (c + 2)$

$$\begin{array}{r|rrrr} -2 & 3 & 4 & -2 & -1 \\ & & -6 & 4 & -4 \\ \hline & 3 & -2 & 2 & -5 \end{array}$$

$3c^2 - 2c + 2 - \dfrac{5}{c + 2}$

Divide using synthetic division.

37. $(x^3 - 4x^2 + 3x - 7) \div (x - 4)$

38. $(n^4 - 16) \div (n + 2)$ **$n^3 - 2n^2 + 4n - 8$**

39. $(6y^3 + 11y^2 + y - 1) \div (2y + 3)$

40. $(10a^4 - 11a^3 + a^2 - 3a + 1) \div (2a - 1)$
    $5a^3 - 3a^2 - a - 2 - \dfrac{1}{2a - 1}$

37. **$x^2 + 3 + \dfrac{5}{x - 4}$**   39. **$3y^2 + y - 1 + \dfrac{2}{2y + 3}$**

～ APPLICATIONS AND CONNECTIONS ～

41. **Astronomy**   A light year is the distance that light travels in one year. If light travels 186,000 miles per second, how many miles are in a light year? Express the answer in both scientific and decimal notation. Assume a 365-day year. **(Lesson 5-1)**
    5.865696×10^{12} or 5,865,696,000,000 miles

42. **Physics**   Newton's law of gravitation can be used to compute the mass of Earth in grams. His formula applied is:
    $$908 = \frac{6.67 \times 10^{-8} \times M}{(6.37 \times 10^8)^2}.$$
    If M represents mass, what is the mass of Earth in grams? Express the answer in both scientific and decimal notation. **(Lesson 5-2)** **about 5.5238×10^{27} g, 5,523,800,000,000,000,000,000,000,000 g**

43. **Travel**   Troy was traveling from Atlanta to Memphis by train. His lunch arrived after one-third of the trip was over. When he finished lunch, he had half the distance traveled before lunch yet to go. Draw a diagram to find the fraction of the trip Troy traveled while he was eating lunch. **(Lesson 5-3)** **one-half**

44. **Retail**   The Bargain Barn gets a new shipment of merchandise each Monday. When the new shipment comes in, every item in the store is marked down 10%. If the original price of an item is p, what will its price be after 3 weeks in the store? **(Lesson 5-4)** **$(0.9)^3 p$ or $0.729p$**

45. **Interior Design**   The amount of carpeting needed for the Leshin's living room is $2x^2 + x - 6$ square yards. They plan to place a new baseboard around the room after the carpeting is installed. The wood for the baseboard is sold according to the length needed. How much wood should they buy for the baseboard?   **(Lesson 5-5)** **$6x - 2$ yards**

Simplify.

1. $4y + 7y - 14y$ **$-3y$**

2. $9a^2 + 4a^2 - 2a^2$ **$11a^2$**

3. $x^4y^3(x^8)$ **$x^{12}y^3$**

4. $(4y)^3(2y)^2$ **$256y^5$**

5. $\dfrac{n^4}{n^4}$ **1**

6. $\dfrac{y^2(3x)^3}{4x^{-2}}$ **$\dfrac{27}{4}x^5y^2$**

7. $\left(\dfrac{4s}{3t}\right)^0$ **1**

8. $\dfrac{13^{-6}}{13^{-9}}$ **13^3 or 2197**

9. $\dfrac{r^2s^{-3}}{s^{-2}t^4}$ **$\dfrac{r^2}{st^4}$**

Evaluate. Express each answer in both scientific and decimal notation.

10. $(7.82 \times 10^3)(934 \times 10^2)$
7.30388×10^8; 730,388,000

11. $\dfrac{84,000,000 \times 0.0013}{0.021}$ **5.2×10^6; 5,200,000**

12. The Carpet Experts installation team can install carpet in a room that is 10 ft by 10 ft in 1 hour. Draw a diagram and find how long it would take them to do a walk-in closet that is 5 ft by 5 ft. **15 minutes**

Simplify.

13. $(3x + 2) - (7x - 6)$ **$-4x + 8$**

14. $(m + 2)(m - 8)$ **$m^2 - 6m - 16$**

15. $(4n - 9)(5n + 2)$ **$20n^2 - 37n - 18$**

16. $(s + 2)(s + 1)^2$ **$s^3 + 4s^2 + 5s + 2$**

17. $(t - 1)(t^2 - 2t - 6)$ **$t^3 - 3t^2 - 4t + 6$**

18. $(r - 8)(r + 8)$ **$r^2 - 64$**

Factor.

19. $3ab - 9b^2$ **$3b(a - 3b)$**

20. $y^2 - 7y + 6$ **$(y - 1)(y - 6)$**

21. $f^2 + 16f + 64$ **$(f + 8)^2$**

22. $w^2 - 144$ **$(w - 12)(w + 12)$**

23. $y^3 - 125$ **$(y - 5)(y^2 + 5y + 25)$**

24. $8x^3 + 1$ **$(2x + 1)(4x^2 - 2x + 1)$**

25. $x^{2n} - 49$ **$(x^n - 7)(x^n + 7)$**

26. $ay + 2a - by - 2b$ **$(a - b)(y + 2)$**

Use division to simplify each expression.

27. $\dfrac{5(w + 1)^6}{(w + 1)^3}$ **$5(w + 1)^3$**

28. $\dfrac{4r^2st + 12rst^2 - 10rt}{2rt}$ **$2rs + 6st - 5$**

29. $(16s^3 - 8s^2 - 40s + 15) \div (2s^2 - 5)$ **$8s - 4 - \dfrac{5}{2s^2 - 5}$**

30. $(x^4 - x^3 + x^2 - 2x - 2) \div (x^2 + 2)$ **$x^2 - x - 1$**

Divide using synthetic division.

31. $(2x^3 + x^2 + 4x - 7) \div (x - 1)$ **$2x^2 + 3x + 7$**

32. $(m^3 - 2m^2 - 17m + 30) \div (m + 4)$ **$m^2 - 6m + 7 + \dfrac{2}{m + 4}$**

33. **Manufacturing** The Owen Container Corporation makes cardboard boxes to sell to manufacturers for transporting products to retail stores. One of their boxes has dimensions $2y$ by $3y$ by $4y$. Write a polynomial to represent the minimum area of cardboard needed to make this closed box if all lengths are in centimeters. **$52y^2$ cm^2**

Bonus
Simplify $(36x^2 - 84xy + 49y^2 - 16a^2 - 24ab - 9b^2) \div (-18xz + 21yz + 12az + 9bz)$. $\dfrac{6x - 7y + 4a + 3b}{-3z}$

Using the Chapter Test

This page may be used as a test or as a review. In addition, two multiple-choice tests and two free-response tests are provided in the Evaluation Masters Booklet. Chapter 5 Test, Form 1A is shown below.

Evaluation Masters Booklet, pp. 57–58

NAME _____ DATE _____

Chapter 5 Test, Form 1A

Write the letter for the correct answer in the blank at the right of each problem.

1. Simplify: $\dfrac{12m^4t^{-3}}{15m^3t^{-2}}$
   A. $\dfrac{4m^4t^3}{5}$ B. $-\dfrac{3m^4}{t^3}$ C. $\dfrac{4m^4}{5t}$ D. $\dfrac{m^4t^3}{3}$ 1. __C__

2. Simplify: $(7m - 8)^2$
   A. $49m^2 + 64$ B. $49m^2 - 64$
   C. $49m^2 - 112m + 64$ D. $49m^2 - 30m + 64$ 2. __C__

3. Simplify: $(3w^3)(-m)^4$
   A. $3m^4w^5$ B. $-3m^4w^5$ C. $-12m^4w^5$ D. $3w^5 + m^4$ 3. __A__

4. Simplify: $(x + 3)(x^2 + 5x - 4)$
   A. $x^2 + 8x^2 + 11x - 12$ B. $x^3 + 5x - 12$
   C. $x^3 + 8x^2 + 4x - 12$ D. $x^3 + 8x^2 - 11x - 12$ 4. __A__

5. Simplify: $\dfrac{a^2(r^{-3}s)^{-2}}{a^3r^3s^3}$
   A. $\dfrac{1}{a^3r^3s^3}$ B. $\dfrac{r^3}{a^3s}$ C. $\dfrac{r^3}{a^3s}$ D. $\dfrac{a^3s}{r^3}$ 5. __B__

6. Express 86,400,000 in scientific notation.
   A. 864×10^{-5} B. 864×10^5
   C. 8.64×10^{-7} D. 8.64×10^7 6. __D__

7. Express 5.83×10^{-8} in decimal notation.
   A. 0.00000583   B. 58,300,000
   C. 0.0000000583   D. 583,000,000   7. __C__

8. Divide $\dfrac{4 \times 10^{-2}}{16 \times 10^{-3}}$. Express the answer in scientific notation.
   A. 0.25×10^2 B. 2.5×10^1
   C. 2.5×10^3 D. 2.5×10^{-3} 8. __B__

9. Simplify: $(3a^3 - 7a^2 + a) - (6a^3 - 4a^2 - 8)$.
   A. $-3a^6 - 3a^4 + a + 8$ B. $-3a^3 - 11a^4 + a - 8$
   C. $-3a^6 - 11a^4 + a - 8$ D. $-3a^3 - 3a^2 + a + 8$ 9. __D__

10. Rich was traveling by plane from New York to San Francisco. After one third of the trip, the movie started. When the movie was over, the amount of the trip left was one third of the trip completed during the movie. What fraction of the trip did the movie take?
    A. $\dfrac{1}{2}$ B. $\dfrac{1}{3}$ C. $\dfrac{2}{3}$ D. $\dfrac{1}{4}$ 10. __A__

A **Test and Review Generator** is provided in Apple, IBM, and Macintosh versions. You may use this software to create your own tests or worksheets, based on the needs of your students.

The **Performance Assessment Booklet** provides an alternate assessment for evaluating student progress. An assessment for this chapter can be found on pages 9–10.

NAME _____ DATE _____

Chapter 5 Test, Form 1A (continued)

11. Simplify: $(6y^2 + 3y - 1) + (2y^2 + y - 4)$
    A. $8y^2 + 4y - 5$ B. $8y^4 + 4y - 5$
    C. $8y^2 + 3y - 5$ D. $8y^2 + 3y - 5$ 11. __A__

Factor each polynomial completely.

12. $y^3 - 64$
    A. $(y - 4)^3$ B. $(y - 4)(y^2 + 4y + 16)$
    C. $(y - 4)(y + 4)^2$ D. $(y - 8)(y^2 + 16y + 64)$ 12. __B__

13. $4n^2 - 36$
    A. $(2n - 6)(2n + 6)$ B. $(4n - 6)(4n + 6)$
    C. $4(n - 6)(n + 6)$ D. $4(n - 3)(n + 3)$ 13. __D__

14. $21x^2 + 29x - 10$
    A. $(3x - 2)(7x - 5)$ B. $(3x + 5)(7x - 2)$
    C. $(3x + 2)(7x + 5)$ D. $(3x - 5)(7x + 2)$ 14. __B__

15. $5y - 21x + 3xy - 36$
    A. $(y - 7)(3x + 5)$ B. $y(5 + 3x) + 7(-3x - 5)$
    C. $y(5 + 3x) - 7(3x - 5)$ D. not factorable   15. __A__

16. One factor of $x^3 + 4x^2 - 11x - 30$ is $x + 2$. What are the other factors?
    A. $x - 5, x + 3$ B. $x - 3, x + 5$
    C. $x - 6, x + 5$ D. $x - 5, x + 6$ 16. __B__

17. Divide using long division: $(4 - 7x^2 + 13x + x^4 + x^3) \div (x^2 + 4x + 1)$
    A. $x^2 - 3x - 4 + \dfrac{32x + 8}{x^2 + 4x + 1}$ B. $x^2 + 3x - 18 + \dfrac{62x + 22}{x^2 + 4x + 1}$
    C. $x^2 - 3x + 4$ D. $x^2 - 3x + 4 - \dfrac{8}{x^2 + 4x + 1}$ 17. __C__

18. Divide: $(24x^4y^2 + 12x^3y^3 - 6x^2y^4) \div (3x^2y)$
    A. $8x^2y + 4xy^2 - 2y^3$ B. $8x^2y^2 + 4xy^3 - 2y^4$
    C. $21x^2y + 9xy - 4y^2$ D. $8x^2y + 4xy^2 - 2y^3$ 18. __D__

19. To find $(4a^3 + 3a^2 - 2a + 1) \div (a - 2)$ by using synthetic division, which is the correct first line of the process?
    A. $2\rfloor\ 4\ \ 3\ -2\ \ 1$ B. $-2\rfloor\ 4\ \ 3\ -2\ \ 1$
    C. $2\rfloor\ 4\ \ 0\ \ 3\ -2\ \ 1$ D. $-2\rfloor\ 4\ \ 0\ \ 3\ -2\ \ 1$ 19. __C__

20. Divide using synthetic division: $(2x^3 + 6x^2 + 5x - 6) \div (x + 2)$
    A. $2x^2 + 2x - 4x + 13 - \dfrac{32}{x + 2}$ B. $2x^2 + 2x + x - 8$
    C. $2x^2 + 2x + x - \dfrac{8}{x + 2}$ D. $2x^3 + 2x^2 + x - \dfrac{8}{x + 2}$ 20. __A__

Bonus
Find the value of k so $(x^3 - 2x^2 + kx + 6) \div (x + 2)$ has remainder 8.
    A. -9 B. 9 C. 0 D. None of these   Bonus __A__

Irrational and Complex Numbers

PREVIEWING THE CHAPTER

This chapter develops basic concepts and skills related to working with radicals. Students learn to simplify radicals with various indices and to add, subtract, multiply, and divide radicals. After making the connection between fractional exponents and radicals, students simplify expressions with fractional exponents. Real-life applications help students recognize the importance of learning how to solve equations containing radicals. Then complex numbers and operations on complex numbers are addressed, and students simplify expressions containing complex numbers.

Problem-Solving Strategy Students learn to solve multi-step problems by breaking them into subgoals to be achieved in order to find the solution.

Lesson Objective Chart

Lesson (Pages)	Lesson Objectives	State/Local Objectives
6-1 (252-257)	**6-1A:** Simplify radicals having various indices.	
	6-1B: Use a calculator to estimate roots of numbers.	
6-2 (258-263)	**6-2A:** Simplify radical expressions using multiplication and division.	
	6-2B: Rationalize the denominator of a fraction containing a radical expression.	
6-3 (264-268)	**6-3:** Add, subtract, multiply, and divide radical expressions.	
6-4 (269-274)	**6-4A:** Write expressions with rational exponents in simplest radical form and vice versa.	
	6-4B: Evaluate expressions in either exponential or radical form.	
6-5 (275-276)	**6-5:** Solve problems by identifying and achieving subgoals.	
6-6 (277-280)	**6-6:** Simplify expressions containing rational exponents.	
6-7 (281-286)	**6-7:** Solve equations containing radicals.	
6-8 (288-291)	**6-8A:** Simplify radicals containing negative radicands.	
	6-8B: Multiply pure imaginary numbers.	
	6-8C: Solve quadratic equations that have pure imaginary solutions.	
6-9 (292-296)	**6-9:** Add, subtract, and multiply complex numbers.	
6-10 (297-301)	**6-10:** Simplify rational expressions containing complex numbers in the denominator.	

ORGANIZING THE CHAPTER

You may want to refer to the **Course Planning Calendar** on page T44.

Lesson Planning Guide / Blackline Masters Booklets

Lesson (Pages)	Pacing Chart (days) Course I	II	III	Reteaching	Practice	Enrichment	Evaluation	Technology	Lab Manual	Mixed Problem Solving	Applications	Cooperative Learning Activity	Multicultural	Transparencies
6-1 (252-257)	1.5	1.5	1	p. 36	p. 41	p. 36			pp. 55-56					6-1
6-2 (258-263)	1.5	1.5	1	p. 37	p. 42	p. 37		p. 6						6-2
6-3 (264-268)	1	1	1	p. 38	p. 43	p. 38	Quiz A, p. 79							6-3
6-4 (269-274)	2	1.5	1.5	p. 39	p. 44	p. 39								6-4
6-5 (275-276)	1	0.5	0.5		p. 45		Quiz B, p. 79 Mid-Chapter Test, p. 83				p. 24			6-5
6-6 (277-280)	1	1	1	p. 40	p. 46	p. 40								6-6
6-7 (281-286)	1.5	1	1	p. 41	p. 47	p. 41	Quiz C, p. 80			p. 6				6-7
6-8 (288-291)	1	1	1	p. 42	p. 48	p. 42								6-8
6-9 (292-296)	1	1	1	p. 43	p. 49	p. 43		p. 23				p. 42	p. 6	6-9
6-10 (297-301)	1.5	1	1	p. 44	p. 50	p. 44	Quiz D, p. 80							6-10
Review (302-304)	1	1	1	Multiple Choice Tests, Forms 1A and 1B, pp. 71-74 Free Response Tests, Forms 2A and 2B, pp. 75-78										
Test (305)	1	1	1	Cumulative Review, pp. 81-82 Standardized Test Practice Questions, p. 84										

Course I: Chapters 1-13; Course II: Chapters 1-15; Course III: Chapters 1-17

Other Chapter Resources

Student Edition

Chapter Opener, pp. 250-251
Language Connection, p. 257
Biology Connection, p. 263
Journal Entries, pp. 274, 279
Mid-Chapter Review, p. 274
Cooperative Learning Activity, p. 276
History Connection, p. 286
Technology, p. 287
Portfolio Suggestion, p. 295
Technology Connection, p. 296
College Entrance Exam Preview, pp. 306-307
Extended Project 2, pp. A6-A9

Teacher's Classroom Resources

Transparency 6-0
Real-World Applications Transparencies, 12, 13
Performance Assessment Booklet, pp. 11-12
Problem-of-the-Week Activity Cards, 11, 12, 13
Tech Prep Applications Booklet, pp. 11-12
Lesson Plans, pp. 41-50

Other Supplements

Glencoe Mathematics Professional Series

Software

Test and Review Generator Software (Apple, IBM, and Macintosh)
Interactive Software (Macintosh)
Teacher's Guide for Software Resources

ENHANCING THE CHAPTER

Cooperative Learning

Specifying Desired Student Behavior

To make sure that students exhibit the group skills required for a successful cooperative-learning experience, you should clearly define the expected behaviors at the outset. Initially, skills will include the more obvious, such as "stay with your group," "use quiet voices," and "take turns when speaking." As groups begin to operate more effectively, add other expected behaviors, such as "criticize ideas, not people," "encourage everyone to participate," "use names and look at other members when speaking," "paraphrase statements made by others," "ask for elaboration," "probe by asking in-depth questions," "check to make sure every member understands and can explain the material," and so on. Research indicates that it is more effective if you define and focus on only one or two of these skills in each session.

Technology

The Technology Feature after Lesson 6-7 shows how to use the *Mathematical Exploration Toolkit* (MET) to solve equations involving square roots. The CALC command SOLVEFOR will automatically solve some radical equations, but others must first be simplified. Students will need to choose operations to change the form of the equations. As when solving radical equations by hand, all solutions must be checked. MET provides a way to test solutions in the original equation. MET can be used to solve for only real number solutions or to solve for real and complex number solutions. You may want to extend this feature later in the chapter to find complex number solutions to radical equations. Consult the MET manual for instructions to enter complex number mode.

Critical Thinking

Students who correctly answer the practice exercises, for the most part, are demonstrating only their knowledge and comprehension of the content presented in the lesson. They are not necessarily exhibiting any ability to utilize the higher-level thinking skills that would be required in real life where conditions do not always remain stable. One way to help accustom students to sudden or unexpected changes in the rules that often occur in real life is to ask What-if questions. For example, after students demonstrate their ability to simplify an expression by rationalizing the denominator, say, "What if we want to rationalize the numerator? Now what is the solution?" (Such rationalizations are sometimes required in calculus.)

Cooperative Learning, p. 42

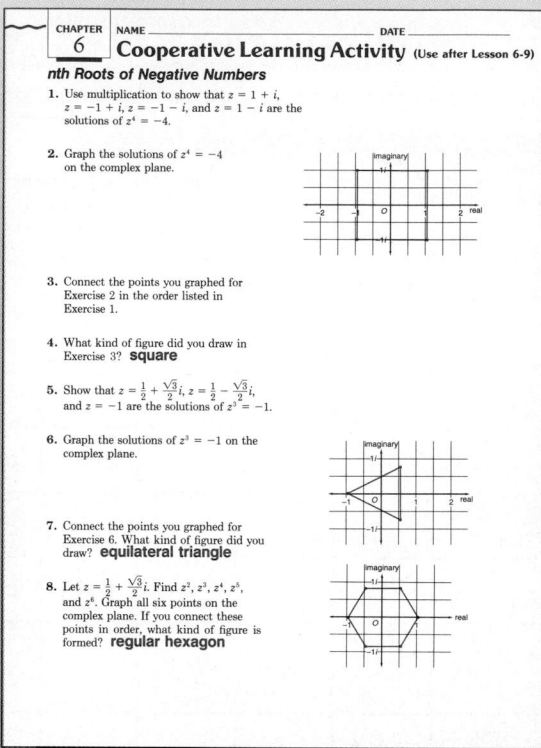

Technology, p. 23

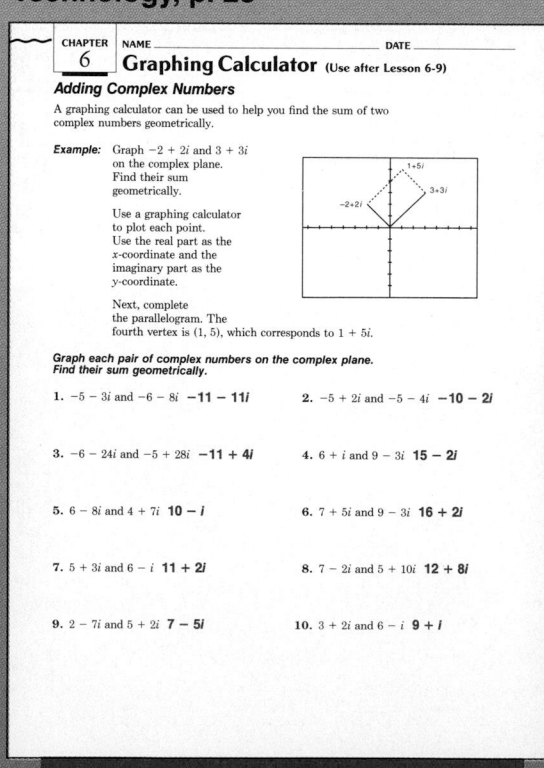

e card shown below is one of three available for this chapter. It can
used as a class or small group activity.

ivity Card

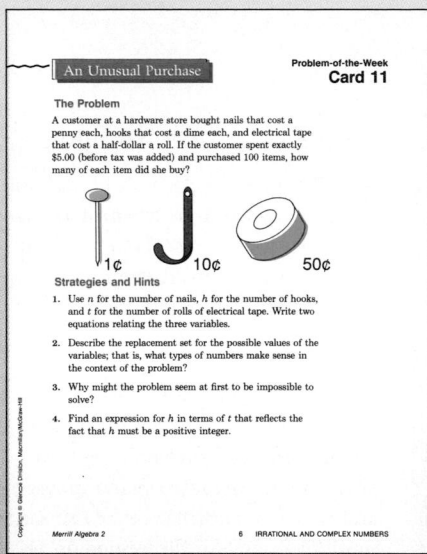

Multicultural Activity, p. 6

CHAPTER 6 NAME _____ DATE _____

Multicultural Activity (Use after Lesson 6-9)

Fractals

Dr. Benoit Mandelbrot was born in Poland in 1924; he was educated in France and now works as a research fellow for IBM in the United States. He is best known for his work with fractals. Fractals can be informally defined as figures that have the property of self-similarity. Such figures are usually highly complex, with their parts having the same form as the entire figure. The study of fractals is related to powers of complex numbers and to the process of function iteration. Fractals have applications in many fields; examples include describing stock-market behavior, fluctuations in heart rhythms, turbulence in weather, and irregular coastlines and cloud formations.

An earlier mathematical curve, now classified as a fractal, was the Koch "snowflake" curve. This curve was created in 1904 by the Swedish mathematician Helge von Koch. To create a snowflake curve, a process of iteration is applied to an equilateral triangle. The curve has many properties that intrigue mathematicians.

You can use the following steps to create a Koch snowflake curve.

1. Draw a large equilateral triangle.

2. On each side of your triangle, draw an equilateral triangle with sides $\frac{1}{3}$ as long as the sides of the original triangle. Locate these triangles centrally on each side.

3. On the sides of the figure you constructed for Exercise 2, append triangles, again $\frac{1}{3}$ the size of the segments to which they are appended.

4. Repeat the process to produce a snowflake curve. The process could be carried on indefinitely.

5. Read about Mandelbrot or Koch and write a report about either of their careers. **See students' reports.**

e following materials may be used as models or manipulatives in
apter 6.

cientific calculator (Lesson 6-1)
eoboard (Lesson 6-2)

Lab Activity, pp. 55-56

Name _____ Activity 20 Worksheet

Radical Roots of Polynomials

1. Using one-inch ceramic tiles, make a square with 4, 9, 16, and 25 tiles. Complete the chart below based on your models.

Number of tiles used in model	4	9	16	25
Draw the model.				
Area of the square				
Length of a side				

2. Make a square using one 2-inch tile and five 1-inch tiles. Draw a picture of the model.

Make a square using four 2-inch tiles and nine 1-inch tiles. Draw a picture of the model.

3. Complete the following chart for the given measures of large and small tiles squares.

Large Square Sides	Small Square Sides	Model Side	Model Area	Prime Factors of Area
x by x	1 by 1	$x + 1$	$(x + 1)^2$	$(x + 2)(x + 1)$
x by x	2 by 2			
$2x$ by $2x$	x by x			
$3xy$ by $3xy$	xy by xy			
b^2 by b^2	3 by 3			

Find each square root.

4. $\sqrt{100}$ _____   5. $\sqrt{81}$ _____

6. $\sqrt{0.04}$ _____   7. $\sqrt{\frac{9}{121}}$ _____

8. $\sqrt{4x^2}$ _____   9. $\sqrt{24x^4}$ _____

10. $\sqrt{224x^4y^5}$ _____   11. $\sqrt{729x^8y^7}$ _____

oks/Periodicals

rdner, Martin. *Mathematical Puzzles.* Thomas Y. Crowell Company,
1961.

derson, K. *Trivia Math: Algebra*. Creative Publication.

ckenbach, E.F., and R. Bellman. *An Introduction to Inequalities.*
Mathematical Association of America.

ms/Videotapes/Videodiscs

stering Algebra, Merit Audio Visual, P.O. Box 392, New York,
NY 10024

ftware

ebra Drill & Practice II, Conduit Educational Software, University of
lowa, Oakdale Campus, Iowa City, IA 52242-0001

actical Algebra II, Algebra Word Problems II, Intellectual Software (IS),
Division of Queue, Inc., 338 Commerce Dr., Fairfield, CT 06430

thematics Exploration Toolkit, IBM, 4111 Northside Pkwy. NW,
P.O. Box 2150, Atlanta, GA 30327-3015

Background Information

Abstract reasoning ability and three-dimensional spatial visualization and analysis are essential to the role of the air traffic controller. This not only requires an understanding of coordinate systems, algebraic equations, and analytic geometry, but the knowledge and ability to apply these must become second nature. Application of these math concepts must be very rapid. Competition for air traffic controller jobs is expected to remain keen, increasing at only 5% to 13% through the 1990s. The high pay and liberal benefits attract many applicants.

Irrational and Complex Numbers

CHAPTER OBJECTIVES

In this chapter, you will:

- Simplify radical expressions.
- Simplify expressions with rational exponents.
- Solve equations containing radicals.
- Add, subtract, multiply, and divide complex numbers.

If two stations are 25 miles apart and the range of the radar at the stations is the same, how far must the radar be able to reach?

Diagram of Instrument Controlled Flight

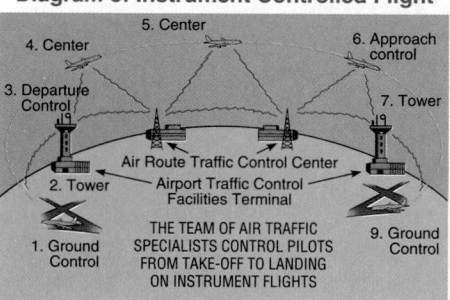

4. Center
5. Center
6. Approach control
3. Departure Control
7. Tower
Air Route Traffic Control Center
Airport Traffic Control Facilities Terminal
2. Tower
1. Ground Control
THE TEAM OF AIR TRAFFIC SPECIALISTS CONTROL PILOTS FROM TAKE-OFF TO LANDING ON INSTRUMENT FLIGHTS
9. Ground Control

250

CAREERS IN AIR TRAFFIC CONTROL

When you were a child, did you ever want to grow up to be an airplane pilot, commanding the wide, blue skies? That's still an attractive career, but you might find it even more appealing to be the person who commands the pilots: the air traffic controller.

Air traffic controllers usually control several planes at once and must be able to make quick decisions about completely different activities. For instance, a small owner-operated plane may be requesting wind and weather information at the same time that a jumbo jet asks for directions on its landing approach. While instructing these pilots, the controller would also be keeping an eye on other planes in his or her assigned airspace, such as those in a holding pattern waiting for permission to land, and making sure they are a safe distance apart.

Can you visualize three-dimensional spaces? Are you articulate enough to give pilots directions quickly and clearly? Do you have a good memory? Are you decisive? Could you pass physical, psychological, and drug-screening tests? Then you just might make a top-notch air traffic controller.

Chapter Project

Materials: graph paper, pencils, clock or watches

Organize students into cooperative groups. Assign one student in each group to be the air traffic controller and others to be pilots of incoming flights. Have each divide graph paper into a coordinate graph with point 0,0 at the center to represent an airport. The goal is for the controller to safely guide each pilot to point 0,0. Each pilot selects a starting x,y position in one of the four quadrants. The controller then assigns each pilot a direction in degrees and a speed. Speed can be simulated by intervals of 5, 10, 15, or 20 seconds. A pilot at point 5,5, and given a direction of 45 and a speed of 5 seconds, for example, moves toward 0,0 along a 45-degree angle in quadrant one, one square at a time, every 5 seconds. Each time a pilot moves he/she calls out the new position to the controller. The controller marks each pilot's position on a master graph. A controller may change a pilot's direction or speed at any time, for instance, to avoid a collision.

Connections and Applications

Lesson	Connections (C) and Applications (A)	Examples	Exercises
6-1	A: Manufacturing	6	
	Physics		64
	Aerospace		65
	Engineering		
	Business		72
6-2	C: Geometry		53
	A: Physics	10	56
	Manufacturing		55
6-3	A: Sports	4	55
	Automotive		54
	Engineering		
6-4	A: Music	8	68
	Personal		69
	Finance		
	Archaeology		70
6-5	C: Statistics		8
	Geometry		9
6-6	A: Physics	3	
	Electricity		44
	Medicine		45
6-7	A: Firefighting	4	
	Air Traffic		52
	Control		
	Energy		53
	Aerospace		54
	Engineering		
6-8	A: Electronics	5	
	Electricity		52
	Health		67
6-9	C: Geometry	4	47-50
	Fractal		67
	Geometry		
	A: Electrical		68
	Engineering		
	Chemistry		73
6-10	A: Electronics	5	
	Electrical		64
	Engineering		
	Chemistry		68

MORE ABOUT AIR TRAFFIC CONTROL

Degree Required:

- Bachelor's Degree in General Studies Program, and Intensive Training Program at FAA Academy

Some air traffic controllers like:

- good opportunities for advancement
- the satisfaction of doing challenging work
- good salaries and benefits

Related Math Subjects:

- Advanced Algebra
- Trigonometry
- Applied Math

Some air traffic controllers dislike:

- having to pass an annual physical exam to keep their job
- an irregular work schedule
- working under extremely stressful conditions
- having to keep up with technological advances

For more information about careers in the field of Air Traffic Control, write to:

Air Traffic Control Association
2020 North 14th Street
Arlington, VA 22201

251

252 Chapter 6

Lesson Resources

Reteaching Master 6-1
Practice Master 6-1
Enrichment Master 6-1
Lab Manual, pp. 55–56

 Transparency 6-1 contains the 5-Minute Check and a teaching aid for this lesson.

INTRODUCING THE LESSON

 5-Minute Check

(over Chapter 5)
Simplify.

1. $(5m^6 + 3m^3 + 9m + 5) + (9m^6 - 2m^4 + 3m - 7)$
   $14m^6 - 2m^4 + 3m^3 + 12m - 2$

Factor.

2. $2y^3 - 98y$ $2y(y + 7)(y - 7)$
3. $8a^3 + 27$ $(2a + 3)(4a^2 - 6a + 9)$
4. Evaluate. Express answer in both scientific and decimal notation.
   $\frac{15 \times 10^4}{6 \times 10^{-2}}$ 2.5×10^6
   $2,500,000$
5. Divide using synthetic division.
   $(m^3 - 3m^2 - 18m + 40) \div (m + 4)$ $m^2 - 7m + 10$

Motivating the Lesson

Have students find the length of the sides of a cube with a volume of 64 cubic feet. What does it mean to have a volume in cubic feet?

TEACHING THE LESSON

Teaching Tip ❶   The other powers do not have special names since they are not figures such as squares and cubes.

Teaching Tip ❷   Stress that the inverse of raising a number to the *n*th power is finding an *n*th root. The power and inverse keys on a calculator may be used to find roots.

Objectives
6-1A
6-1B

After studying this lesson, you should be able to:
- simplify radicals having various indices, and
- use a calculator to estimate roots of numbers.

Application

A carton shaped like a cube has sides 14 inches long. The volume of the carton is $14 \cdot 14 \cdot 14$ or 14^3 cubic inches (in^3). Can you see why we call 14 to the third power 14 *cubed*? Why do you think we call raising a number to the second power *squaring* the number? Why do you suppose that there are not special names for raising a number to any other power? **Teaching Tip ❶**

Raising a number to the *n*th power means using that number as a factor *n* times.

$7^3 = 7 \cdot 7 \cdot 7$ or 343   *7 is used as a factor 3 times, n = 3.*
$2^4 = 2 \cdot 2 \cdot 2 \cdot 2$ or 16   *2 is used as a factor 4 times, n = 4.*
$5^n = \underbrace{5 \cdot 5 \cdot 5 \cdot \ldots \cdot 5}_{n \text{ factors}}$ *5 is used as a factor n times.*

As you know, finding the square root of a number and squaring a number are inverse operations. To find the square root of *n*, you must find a number whose square is *n*. For example, a square root of 25 is 5 since $5^2 = 25$. Since $(-5)^2 = 25$, -5 is also a square root of 25.   **Teaching Tip ❷**

Square Root	**For any real numbers *a* and *b*, if $a^2 = b$, then *a* is a square root of *b*.**

Since finding the square root of a number and squaring a number are inverses, it makes sense that the inverse of raising a number to the *n*th power is finding the **nth root** of the number. For example, to find the cube root of 27, you must find a number whose cube is 27.

$$a^3 = 27 \qquad a \cdot a \cdot a = 27$$

Since $3 \cdot 3 \cdot 3 = 27$, 3 is a cube root of 27.   *Is −3 a cube root of 27? Why or why not?*

nth Root	**For any real numbers *a* and *b*, and any positive integer *n*, if $a^n = b$, then *a* is an *n*th root of *b*.**

ALTERNATE TEACHING STRATEGIES

Using Discussion

The set of real numbers is the union of the rational and the irrationals. Sometimes square roots result in irrational numbers. For example, $\sqrt[3]{28}$ is approximately 3.037. Discuss the appropriate symbol to use when finding roots. The equals symbol is used only for exact roots. The approximate sign, $\approx$, is used for rounded roots.

The symbol $\sqrt[n]{}$ indicates an *n*th root.

$$\underset{\text{index}}{\nearrow}\ \sqrt[n]{512}\ \underset{\substack{\uparrow \\ \text{radicand}}}{\nwarrow\ \text{radical sign}}$$

When no index is given, the radical sign indicates a nonnegative square root.

Some numbers have more than one *n*th root. As we just saw, 25 has two square roots, 5 and –5. When there is more than one root, the nonnegative root is called the **principal root.** The symbol $\sqrt[n]{b}$ stands for the principal root. If *n* is odd and *b* is negative, there will be no nonnegative root. So, in this case, the principal root is negative.

$\sqrt{49}\ = 7$	$\sqrt{49}$ indicates the principal square root of 49.
$-\sqrt{49}\ = -7$	$-\sqrt{49}$ indicates the opposite of the principal square root of 49.
$\pm\sqrt{49}\ = \pm 7$	$\pm\sqrt{49}$ indicates both square roots of 49. *± means positive or negative.*
$\sqrt[3]{-64}\ = -4$	$\sqrt[3]{-64}$ indicates the principal cube root of –64.
$-\sqrt[4]{81}\ = -3$	$-\sqrt[4]{81}$ indicates the opposite of the principal fourth root of 81.

The chart below gives a summary of the real *n*th roots of a number *b*.

The Real *n*th Roots of *b*, $\sqrt[n]{b}$ or $-\sqrt[n]{b}$

	$b > 0$	$b < 0$	$b = 0$
n even	one positive root one negative root	no real roots	one real root, 0
n odd	one positive root no negative roots	no positive roots one negative root	

Example 1

Find $\pm\sqrt{81n^2}$.

$$\pm\sqrt{81n^2} = \pm\sqrt{(9n)^2}$$
$$= \pm 9n$$

The square roots of $81n^2$ are $\pm 9n$. **Teaching Tip ❸**

Example 2

Find $-\sqrt{(x + 1)^4}$.

$$-\sqrt{(x + 1)^4} = -\sqrt{[(x + 1)^2]^2}$$
$$= -(x + 1)^2$$

The opposite of the principal square root of $(x + 1)^4$ is $-(x + 1)^2$.

LESSON 6-1 ROOTS OF REAL NUMBERS 253

Chalkboard Examples

For Example 3

a. Find $\sqrt[3]{125a^6}$. $5a^2$

b. Find $\sqrt[3]{-m^3n^3}$. $-mn$

c. Find $\sqrt[5]{32x^5y^{10}}$. $2xy^2$

For Example 4

a. Find $\sqrt[4]{(an)^4}$. $|an|$

b. Find $\sqrt[6]{(xy^2)^6}$. $|x|y^2$

c. Find $\sqrt[6]{(3-y^2)^{18}}$. $|3-y^2|^3$

For Example 5

Use a calculator to find a decimal approximation.

a. $\sqrt{973}$ 31.193

b. $\sqrt[3]{-870}$ -9.546

c. $\sqrt[5]{837}$ 3.842

Teaching Tip **④** The values will be the positive or negative as needed.

Teaching Tip **⑤** Students should exercise caution when using 🔘 or 〔INV〕〔y^x〕 because some calculators compute these values in a manner that has approximation errors. The display may show a number that is slightly more or less than the actual value.

Example 3

Find $\sqrt[3]{8n^9}$.

$$\sqrt[3]{8n^9} = \sqrt[3]{(2n^3)^3}$$
$$= 2n^3$$

The principal cube root of $8n^9$ is $2n^3$.

Example 4

Find $\sqrt[4]{m^4}$.

Since $m^4 = m \cdot m \cdot m \cdot m$, m is a fourth root of m^4. Since the index is even, the principal root is nonnegative. However, since m *may* be negative, we must take the absolute value of m to identify the principal root.

$$\sqrt[4]{m^4} = |m|$$

When you find the nth root of an even power and an odd power is the result, you must take the absolute value of the result to ensure that the value is nonnegative. If the result is an even power or you find the nth root of an odd power, there is no need to take the absolute value. *Why?*

Teaching Tip ④

$$\sqrt{(-6)^2} = |-6| \text{ or } 6 \qquad \sqrt{(-4)^6} = |(-4)^3| \text{ or } 64$$

Expressions such as $\sqrt{64}$ and $\sqrt[3]{-\frac{1}{8}}$ name rational numbers. There is no need to take the absolute value.

$$\sqrt{64} = 8 \qquad \sqrt[3]{-\frac{1}{8}} = -\frac{1}{2}$$

As you learned in Chapter 1, real numbers that cannot be expressed as terminating or repeating decimals are **irrational numbers**. $\sqrt{2}$ and $\sqrt{3}$ are examples of irrational numbers. Decimal approximations for irrational numbers, such as 3.14 for π, are often used in applications. You can use a calculator to find decimal approximations. *If you do not have a calculator, refer to the Tables Appendix.*

Example 5

Use a calculator to find a decimal approximation for $\sqrt[3]{339}$.

Method 1 Use the root key. *It may be a second function key.*

ENTER: 339 〔$\sqrt[x]{y}$〕 3 〔=〕 `6.972682649`

Method 2 Use the power and reciprocal keys. **Teaching Tip ⑤**

ENTER: 339 〔y^x〕 3 〔$1/x$〕 〔=〕 `6.972682649`

Check: 6.972682649 〔y^x〕 3 〔=〕 `339` ✓

$\sqrt[3]{339}$ is approximately 6.97.

Additional Answers

1. An absolute value is not necessary if the root is a positive number regardless of the value of the variable.

2. because $(-2n^3)^3 \neq 8n^9$

3. Taking an nth root and raising to the nth power are inverse operations.

4. No, if $x < 0$, then $\sqrt[4]{(-x)^4} = -x$.

5. No, if $x < 0$, then $\sqrt[5]{(-x)^5} = -x$.

Example 6

APPLICATION

Manufacturing

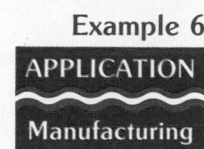

Educational Enterprises makes children's toys for use in preschools. One of their most popular items is a set of multicolored blocks designed to teach colors and shapes. The volume of the materials required to make each cubic block is 60 cubic centimeters. What is the surface area that needs to be printed on each block?

Let s represent the length of an edge of a block.

$V = s^3$	*The volume of a cube is the cube*
$60 = s^3$	*of the length of an edge.*
$\sqrt[3]{60} = s$	*Take the cube root of each side.*
$3.91 \approx s$	*Use a calculator to find an approximation for $\sqrt[3]{60}$.*

The length of an edge of a block is about 3.91 centimeters.

Each face of the block will have an area of s^2 square centimeters.

$$s^2 = (3.91)^2 \text{ or } 15.29$$

Since there are six faces, the total surface area to be painted is 6(15.29) or about 91.74 square centimeters.

CHECKING FOR UNDERSTANDING

Communicating Mathematics

Read and study the lesson to answer these questions. **1–5. See margin.**

1. Explain why it is not always necessary to take the absolute value of a result to indicate the principal root.

2. Why is $-2n^3$ not a second answer in Example 3?

3. Explain why you can use the inverse key with the power key to find an nth root on your calculator.

4. Does $\sqrt[4]{(-x)^4} = x$ no matter what value x represents? Explain.

5. Does $\sqrt[5]{(-x)^5} = x$ no matter what value x represents? Explain.

Guided Practice

Simplify.

6. $\sqrt{144}$ **12**

7. $-\sqrt{121}$ **−11**

8. $\sqrt[3]{8}$ **2**

9. $\sqrt[3]{y^3}$ **y**

10. $\sqrt[4]{16}$ **2**

11. $-\sqrt[4]{x^4}$ **−|x|**

12. $\sqrt[4]{t^8}$ **t^2**

13. $\sqrt[3]{-125}$ **−5**

14. $\sqrt[5]{32n^5}$ **2n**

15. $\sqrt{16a^2b^4}$ **4|a|b^2**

16. $\sqrt{(y+1)^2}$ **|y + 1|**

17. $\sqrt{x^2 + 6x + 9}$ **|x + 3|**

Use a calculator to approximate each value to three decimal places.

18. $\sqrt{3.2}$ **1.789**

19. $\sqrt{55}$ **7.416**

20. $\sqrt[3]{9.8}$ **2.140**

21. $-\sqrt[3]{47}$ **−3.609**

22. $-\sqrt[3]{670}$ **−8.750**

23. $\sqrt{64}$ **8.000**

RETEACHING THE LESSON

The problem at the right shows that given any two people you can show that they are the same age!

What is wrong with the solution?
See the Error Analysis.

Y = your age, M = my age

Average $A = \dfrac{(M + Y)}{2}$ or $2A = M + Y$

$2A(M - Y) = (M + Y)(M - Y)$
$2AM - 2AY = M^2 - Y^2$
$Y^2 - 2AY = M^2 - 2AM$
$Y^2 - 2AY + A^2 = M^2 - 2AM + A^2$
$(Y - A)(Y - A) = (M - A)(M - A)$
$(Y - A)^2 = (M - A)^2$
$Y - A = M - A$ or $Y = M$
You and I are the same age!

Closing the Lesson

Speaking Activity Have students discuss when they need to use absolute value signs in simplifying a radical.

APPLYING THE LESSON

Homework Exercises

Assignment Guide

Basic: 24–50, 63–64, 66–72
Average: 30–56, 63–72
Enriched: 36–72

Teaching Tip ⑥ Some calculators might have problems calculating odd roots of negative numbers. The display may show an error. In this case, have students calculate the root of the positive number and change the sign of the result.

Practice Masters Booklet, p. 41

EXERCISES

Practice Use a calculator to find each value to three places. Check your approximation by using the power key.   **Teaching Tip ⑥**

A 24. $\sqrt{83}$ 9.110   25. $-\sqrt{99}$ –9.950   26. $\sqrt{9.5}$ 3.082

27. $\sqrt[3]{23}$ 2.844   28. $\sqrt[3]{8.1}$ 2.008   29. $-\sqrt[3]{-41}$ 3.448

Simplify.

30. $\pm\sqrt{81}$ ± 9 31. $\sqrt{196}$ 14   32. $\sqrt{256}$ 16

33. $\sqrt[4]{81}$ 3   34. $-\sqrt[3]{27}$ –3   35. $\sqrt[3]{-216}$ –6

B 36. $\sqrt[5]{-1}$ –1   37. $\sqrt[3]{-1000}$ –10   38. $\pm\sqrt{0.49}$ ± 0.7

51. $|3x + y|$
52. $|a + b|$
53. $s + t$
54. $2x - y$
55. $|r + s|$
56. $2m - 3$
57. $|x + 5|$
58. $|x + 3|$
59. $|3a + 1|$
60. $|2y + 3|$
61. $|s - t|$
62. $|2x + 3y|$

39. $\sqrt[3]{0.125}$ 0.5   40. $\sqrt{121n^2}$ $11|n|$ 41. $\sqrt{25y^6}$ $5|y^3|$

42. $\sqrt{(3s)^4}$ $9s^2$ 43. $\pm\sqrt{576}$ ± 24 44. $\sqrt{676}$ 26

45. $\sqrt{64a^2b^4}$ $8|a|b^2$ 46. $-\sqrt{144b^2c^6}$ $-12|bc^3|$ 47. $\sqrt[3]{-8b^3c^3}$ $-2bc$

48. $\pm\sqrt[3]{27r^3s^3}$ $\pm 3rs$ 49. $\sqrt[3]{64a^6b^3}$ $4a^2b$ 50. $\sqrt[4]{625n^8m^4}$ $5n^2|m|$

C 51. $\sqrt{(3x + y)^2}$ 52. $\sqrt{(a + b)^2}$ 53. $\sqrt[3]{(s + t)^3}$

54. $\sqrt[3]{(2x - y)^3}$ 55. $\sqrt[4]{(r + s)^4}$ 56. $\sqrt[5]{(2m - 3)^5}$

57. $\sqrt{x^2 + 10x + 25}$ 58. $\sqrt{x^2 + 6x + 9}$ 59. $\sqrt{9a^2 + 6a + 1}$

60. $\sqrt{4y^2 + 12y + 9}$ 61. $\sqrt{s^2 - 2st + t^2}$ 62. $\sqrt{4x^2 + 12xy + 9y^2}$

Critical Thinking 63. Under what conditions is $\sqrt[n]{(-x)^n} = x$?
When n is even and $x > 0$, or when n is any number and $x = 0$.

Applications 64. **Physics** The formula for finding the time, t, it takes an object dropped from a height of h feet to reach the ground is $t = \sqrt{\dfrac{2h}{g}}$, where g represents the acceleration due to gravity. All objects in free fall near the earth's surface have an acceleration due to gravity of 32 feet per second squared. If a ball is dropped from a window 64 feet high, how long will it take for it to reach the ground?
2 seconds

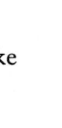

256   CHAPTER 6   IRRATIONAL AND COMPLEX NUMBERS

NAME _____ DATE _____

6-1 **Practice Worksheet**

Roots of Real Numbers
Simplify.

1. $\sqrt[5]{32}$ 2   2. $-\sqrt[4]{256}$ –4

3. $\sqrt{x^2 + 10x + 25}$ $|x + 5|$ 4. $\sqrt[4]{(m + 4)^4}$ $|m + 4|$

5. $\sqrt[5]{-64r^8w^{15}}$ $-4r^2w^5$ 6. $\sqrt{49m^2t^8}$ $7|m|t^4$

7. $\sqrt[4]{81}$ –3   8. $\sqrt[3]{-64}$ –4

9. $\sqrt{(2x)^8}$ $16x^4$ 10. $-\sqrt[4]{625}$ –5

11. $\sqrt[3]{216}$ 6   12. $\sqrt{676x^4y^6}$ $26x^2|y^3|$

13. $\sqrt[3]{(2x + 1)^3}$ $2x + 1$ 14. $\sqrt[3]{-32x^3y^{15}}$ $-2xy^2$

15. $-\sqrt{144m^8n^6}$ $-12m^4|n^3|$ 16. $\sqrt[3]{-27x^3y^{12}}$ $-3x^3y^4$

17. $\sqrt[5]{243x^{10}}$ $3x^2$ 18. $-\sqrt{49a^{10}b^{16}}$ $-7|a^5|b^8$

19. $\sqrt[4]{(x - 5)^8}$ $(x - 5)^2$ 20. $\sqrt[3]{343d^6}$ $7d^2$

21. $\sqrt{0.81}$ 0.9   22. $-\sqrt{0.0016}$ –0.04

23. $\sqrt[3]{0.512}$ 0.8   24. $-\sqrt[4]{0.6561}$ –0.9

Use a calculator to find each value to three places. Check your approximation by using the power key.

25. $\sqrt{7.8}$ 2.793   26. $-\sqrt{89}$ –9.434

27. $\sqrt[3]{25}$ 2.924   28. $\sqrt[5]{-4}$ –1.587

---

65. Aerospace Engineering Scientists expect that in future space stations artificial gravity will be created by rotating all or part of the space station. The formula $N = \frac{1}{2\pi}\sqrt{\frac{a}{r}}$ gives the number of rotations, N, required per second to maintain an acceleration of gravity of a meters per second squared on a satellite with a radius of r meters. The acceleration of gravity on Earth is 9.8 m/s². How many rotations per minute will produce an artificial gravity that is equal to half of the gravity on Earth in a space station with a 25 m radius? **about 4.2 rotations per minute**

Mixed Review

66. $t^2 - 2t + 1$

67. $x^2 - x + 7 + \dfrac{3}{5x - 3}$

Divide using synthetic division. (Lesson 5-7)

66. $(t^3 - 3t + 2) \div (t + 2)$ **67.** $(5x^3 - 8x^2 + 38x - 18) \div (5x - 3)$

68. Evaluate $(4.5 \times 10^4)(3.33 \times 10^2)$. Express the answer in both scientific and decimal notation. **(Lesson 5-1)** 1.4985×10^7; **14,985,000**

69. Solve $\begin{cases} x + y + z = 0 \\ 2x + 4y + z = -1 \\ x - 2y - z = -2 \end{cases}$ using an augmented matrix. **(Lesson 4-8)** **(-1, 0, 1)**

70. State the dimension of the matrix $\begin{bmatrix} 3 & 2 & 0 \\ -2 & 10 & 6 \end{bmatrix}$. Then find its determinant, if it exists. **(Lesson 4-1)** 2×3, **no determinant**

71. In which octant does the point $(3, 9, -2)$ lie? **(Lesson 3-8) 4**

72. Business The Burrough's Department Store parking garage charges $1.50 for each hour or fraction of an hour for parking. What type of function does this relationship represent? **(Lesson 2-7) a step function**

LANGUAGE CONNECTION

In mathematics, many words have specific definitions. However, when these words are used in everyday language, they frequently have a different meaning. Study each pair of sentences. How do the meanings of the word in boldface differ?

1a. Plants receive nourishment and water from their **roots.**
1b. The square **roots** of 36 are 6 and -6.

2a. This soup tastes **odd.**
2b. For any number a and any integer n greater than 1, if n is **odd**, then $\sqrt[n]{a^n} = a$.

Write two sentences for each word, one that uses the everyday meaning of the word and one that uses the mathematical meaning. **See students' work.**

1. negative   2. power   3. rational   4. coordinate

5. degree   6. absolute   7. identity   8. real

EXTENDING THE LESSON

Math Power: Reasoning

Simplify $\sqrt{8x^3 + 36x^2 + 54x + 27}$.
$(2x + 3)\sqrt{2x + 3}$

Language Connection

Discuss with students how the meanings of *root* and *odd* mean similar things in everyday life. How do you think the mathematicians decided on the names for the math topics?

Enrichment Masters Booklet, p. 36

Products and Quotients of Radicals

Lesson Resources

Reteaching Master 6-2
Practice Master 6-2
Enrichment Master 6-2
Technology Master, p. 6

 Transparency 6-2 contains the 5-Minute Check and a teaching aid for this lesson.

INTRODUCING THE LESSON

 5-Minute Check

(over Lesson 6-1)
Simplify.

1. $\pm\sqrt{81a^4b^6}$ $\pm 9a^2|b^3|$

2. $\sqrt[3]{-27a^3y^9}$ $-3ay^3$

3. $\sqrt[4]{16x^4y^8}$ $2|x|y^2$

4. $\sqrt{m^2 - 8m + 16}$ $|m - 4|$

5. $\sqrt{4a^4 + 20a^2c^2 + 25c^4}$
   $2a^2 + 5c^2$

Motivating the Lesson

Discuss $|a - b| = b - a$. What must be true? Discuss the use of absolute value for real roots.

1. An even root of an odd power will not require an absolute value symbol.

2. If $\sqrt[n]{x^p}$ is an even root of an even power, then absolute value is needed.

3. If $\sqrt[n]{x^p}$ is an odd root, then absolute value is not needed.

TEACHING THE LESSON

Teaching Tip ❶ Remind students that $2\sqrt{2} \neq \sqrt{4}$ and $4\sqrt{6} \neq \sqrt{24}$. From this they can generalize that $\sqrt{a}\sqrt{b} = \sqrt{ab}$ and $(c\sqrt{a})(d\sqrt{b}) = cd\sqrt{ab}$.

Objectives After studying this lesson, you should be able to:

6-2A ■ simplify radical expressions using multiplication and division, and

6-2B ■ rationalize the denominator of a fraction containing a radical expression.

Application

A group of graduate students from Purdue University is conducting research on marine life on a small island in the Pacific. An airplane must drop their supplies on the island since there is no clearing large enough for it to land. The airplane is flying at a speed of 484 feet per second at an altitude of 5000 feet. Where should the pilot let the supplies drop so that they land near the camp?

One of the formulas we need to solve this problem is $t = \sqrt{\dfrac{2h}{g}}$, where t represents time, h represents the height of the object when it is dropped, and g represents acceleration due to gravity. Do you think that $t = \dfrac{\sqrt{2} \cdot \sqrt{h}}{\sqrt{g}}$ is an equivalent formula? Let's do some investigation of multiplication and division of radicals to find out.

Try evaluating these roots in two ways. The first way is to find the root and then multiply. The second way is to multiply and then find the root. Then compare the results.

Method 1	*Method 2*
$\sqrt{9} \cdot \sqrt{16} = 3 \cdot 4$ or 12	$\sqrt{9} \cdot \sqrt{16} = \sqrt{144}$ or 12
$\sqrt[3]{-8} \cdot \sqrt[3]{27} = -2 \cdot 3$ or -6	$\sqrt[3]{-8} \cdot \sqrt[3]{27} = \sqrt[3]{-216}$ or -6

The result is the same using either method. These examples demonstrate the following property of radicals.

Product Property of Radicals

> **For any real numbers a and b, and any integer n, $n > 1$,**
>
> **1. If n is even, then $\sqrt[n]{ab} = \sqrt[n]{a} \cdot \sqrt[n]{b}$ as long as a and b are both nonnegative, and**
>
> **2. If n is odd, then $\sqrt[n]{ab} = \sqrt[n]{a} \cdot \sqrt[n]{b}$.**

When you simplify a square root, first write the prime factorization of the radicand. Then use the product property to isolate the perfect squares. Then simplify each radical.

258 CHAPTER 6 IRRATIONAL AND COMPLEX NUMBERS

ALTERNATE TEACHING STRATEGIES

Using Models

Use a geoboard as a model for the coordinate plane. Ask students to make a square.

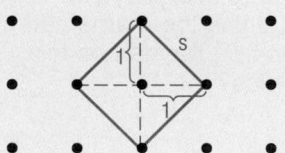

The length of each side of the square can be found by applying the Pythagorean Theorem, $1^2 + 1^2 = s^2$. Thus, $s = \sqrt{2}$ cm. If two of the right triangles are put together to form a square, the area of each square is 1 cm². So, the area of the large square is 2 cm². The area can also be represented by $A = s^2 = (\sqrt{2})^2$. Thus, $(\sqrt{2})^2 = \sqrt{2} \cdot \sqrt{2} = 2$.

Example 1

Simplify $\sqrt{24a^3b^2}$.

$$\sqrt{24a^3b^2} = \sqrt{2^2 \cdot 2 \cdot 3 \cdot a^2 \cdot a \cdot b^2} \qquad \text{\textit{The prime factorization of 24 is } } 2^3 \cdot 3.$$
$$= \sqrt{2^2} \cdot \sqrt{2} \cdot \sqrt{3} \cdot \sqrt{a^2} \cdot \sqrt{a} \cdot \sqrt{b^2} \qquad \text{\textit{Product property of radicals}}$$
$$= 2a|b|\sqrt{6a}$$

If $a < 0$, then $\sqrt{a^3}$ has no real roots, so we must assume that $a \geq 0$. Since $a \geq 0$, we don't need to write $\sqrt{a^3} = |a|\sqrt{a}$. However, b could be negative so we must write $\sqrt{b^2}$ as $|b|$.

Simplifying nth roots is very similar to simplifying square roots. Find the factors that are nth powers and use the product property.

Example 2

Simplify $\sqrt[3]{40x^3y^5}$.

$$\sqrt[3]{40x^3y^5} = \sqrt[3]{2^3 \cdot 5 \cdot x^3 \cdot y^3 \cdot y^2} \qquad \text{\textit{Factor into cubes where possible.}}$$
$$= \sqrt[3]{2^3} \cdot \sqrt[3]{5} \cdot \sqrt[3]{x^3} \cdot \sqrt[3]{y^3} \cdot \sqrt[3]{y^2} \qquad \text{\textit{Product property of radicals}}$$
$$= 2xy\sqrt[3]{5y^2}$$

Example 3

Simplify $\sqrt[4]{3n} \cdot \sqrt[4]{5n^7}$.

$$\sqrt[4]{3n} \cdot \sqrt[4]{5n^7} = \sqrt[4]{3n \cdot 5n^7} \qquad \text{\textit{Product property of radicals}}$$
$$= \sqrt[4]{15n^8}$$
$$= \sqrt[4]{15} \cdot \sqrt[4]{n^4} \cdot \sqrt[4]{n^4} \qquad \text{\textit{Factor into fourth powers where possible.}}$$
$$= n^2\sqrt[4]{15} \qquad \text{\textit{Why aren't absolute values required?}}$$

When you multiply rational numbers and radicals, multiply the rationals and the radicals separately and then simplify the product.

Example 4

Simplify $3\sqrt{2} \cdot 4\sqrt{10}$.   **Teaching Tip ❶**

$$3\sqrt{2} \cdot 4\sqrt{10} = 3 \cdot 4 \cdot \sqrt{2} \cdot \sqrt{10} \qquad \text{\textit{Commutative property of multiplication}}$$
$$= 12\sqrt{20}$$
$$= 12 \cdot \sqrt{2^2} \cdot \sqrt{5} \qquad \text{\textit{Product property of radicals}}$$
$$= 12 \cdot 2 \cdot \sqrt{5} \text{ or } 24\sqrt{5}$$

Take a look at the division of radicals to see if there is a quotient property similar to the product property of radicals. What do you think we'll discover?

$$\qquad \text{\textit{Method 1}} \qquad\qquad \text{\textit{Method 2}}$$
$$\frac{\sqrt{81}}{\sqrt{9}} = \frac{9}{3} \text{ or } 3 \qquad \sqrt{\frac{81}{9}} = \sqrt{9} \text{ or } 3$$
$$\frac{\sqrt[3]{-216}}{\sqrt[3]{27}} = \frac{-6}{3} \text{ or } -2 \qquad \sqrt[3]{\frac{216}{27}} = \sqrt[3]{-8} \text{ or } -2$$

Were you right about a quotient property of radicals?

Chalkboard Examples

For Example 1
Simplify.

a. $\sqrt{30a^3}$ $a\sqrt{30a}$
b. $\sqrt{64a^2b^3c}$ $8|ab|\sqrt{bc}$
c. $\sqrt{54x^4y^5z^7}$ $3x^2y^2z^3\sqrt{6yz}$

For Example 2
Simplify.

a. $\sqrt[3]{54a^3b^7}$ $3ab^2\sqrt[3]{2b}$
b. $\sqrt[4]{32x^8y^6}$ $2x^2|y|\sqrt[4]{2y^2}$
c. $\sqrt{60xy^3}$ $2|y|\sqrt{15xy}$

For Example 3
Simplify.

a. $\sqrt{10x^2y} \cdot \sqrt{40xy^3}$
  $20xy^2\sqrt{x}$
b. $\sqrt{12m^2n} \cdot \sqrt{6mn^2}$
  $6mn\sqrt{2mn}$
c. $\sqrt[4]{4t^3} \cdot \sqrt[4]{8t^2v^5}$ $2tv\sqrt[4]{2tv}$

For Example 4
Simplify.

a. $2\sqrt{2} \cdot 4\sqrt{6}$ $16\sqrt{3}$
b. $\sqrt{10}(\sqrt{2} + \sqrt{6})$
  $2\sqrt{5} + 2\sqrt{15}$
c. $4\sqrt{3}(\sqrt{27} + 4\sqrt{3})$ 84

For Example 5
Simplify.

a. $\sqrt{\dfrac{5}{4}}$ $\dfrac{\sqrt{5}}{2}$

b. $\sqrt[3]{\dfrac{16}{125}}$ $\dfrac{2\sqrt[3]{2}}{5}$

c. $\dfrac{20\sqrt{8}}{2\sqrt{2}}$ 20

For Example 6
Simplify.

a. $\dfrac{5}{2\sqrt{2}}$ $\dfrac{5\sqrt{2}}{4}$

b. $\dfrac{5}{7\sqrt{3}}$ $\dfrac{5\sqrt{3}}{21}$

c. $\dfrac{6}{2\sqrt{3}}$ $\sqrt{3}$

For Example 7
Simplify.

a. $\sqrt{\dfrac{4}{ab^2}}$ $\dfrac{2\sqrt{a}}{a|b|}$

b. $\dfrac{6}{\sqrt{2kn^3}}$ $\dfrac{3\sqrt{2kn}}{|k|n^2}$

c. $\sqrt{\dfrac{52}{7x}}$ $\dfrac{2\sqrt{91x}}{7x}$

Quotient Property of Radicals	For any real numbers a and b, $b \neq 0$, and any integer n, $n > 1$, $\sqrt[n]{\dfrac{a}{b}} = \dfrac{\sqrt[n]{a}}{\sqrt[n]{b}}$ if all roots are defined.

Example 5

a. Simplify $\sqrt[3]{\dfrac{3}{8}}$.

$\sqrt[3]{\dfrac{3}{8}} = \dfrac{\sqrt[3]{3}}{\sqrt[3]{8}}$ *Quotient property of radicals*

$= \dfrac{\sqrt[3]{3}}{2}$

b. Simplify $\dfrac{12\sqrt{18}}{4\sqrt{6}}$.

$\dfrac{12\sqrt{18}}{4\sqrt{6}} = \dfrac{12}{4} \cdot \sqrt{\dfrac{18}{6}}$

$= 3\sqrt{3}$

Fractions are usually written without radicals in the denominator. Radicals are not usually left in fraction form either. The process of eliminating radicals from the denominator or fractions from the radicand is called **rationalizing the denominator.**

To rationalize a denominator, you must multiply the numerator and denominator by a quantity so that the radicand has an exact root. Study the examples below.

If the denominator were $\sqrt{ab^2c^3}$ you would multiply the numerator and the denominator by $\sqrt{ac}$.

Other multipliers are also possible, but $\sqrt{ac}$ is the simplest multiplier you can use.

$\sqrt{ab^2c^3} \cdot \sqrt{ac} = \sqrt{a^2b^2c^4} = a|b|c^2$ *Note that all of the factors in $\sqrt{a^2b^2c^4}$ are perfect squares.*

If the denominator were $\sqrt[3]{2mn^2p^4}$, you would multiply the numerator and denominator by $\sqrt[3]{2^2m^2np^2}$.

$\sqrt[3]{2mn^2p^4} \cdot \sqrt[3]{2^2m^2np^2} = \sqrt[3]{2^3m^3n^3p^6} = 2mnp^2$ *Note that all of the factors in $\sqrt[3]{2^3m^3n^3p^6}$ are perfect cubes.*

Example 6

Simplify $\dfrac{5}{2\sqrt{3}}$.

$\dfrac{5}{2\sqrt{3}} = \dfrac{5}{2\sqrt{3}} \cdot \dfrac{\sqrt{3}}{\sqrt{3}}$ *Since $\dfrac{\sqrt{3}}{\sqrt{3}} = 1$, the value of $\dfrac{5}{2\sqrt{3}}$ is not changed.*

$= \dfrac{5\sqrt{3}}{2\sqrt{3} \cdot 3}$

$= \dfrac{5\sqrt{3}}{2\sqrt{3^2}}$ or $\dfrac{5\sqrt{3}}{6}$

A radical expression is simplified when the following conditions are met.

1. The index, n, is as small as possible. **Teaching Tip ❷**
2. The radicand contains no factor (other than one) which is the nth power of an integer or polynomial.
3. The radicand contains no fractions.
4. No radicals appear in the denominator.

Example 7

Simplify $\sqrt[3]{\dfrac{2}{3t}}$.

$$\sqrt[3]{\dfrac{2}{3t}} = \dfrac{\sqrt[3]{2}}{\sqrt[3]{3t}} \cdot \dfrac{\sqrt[3]{3^2t^2}}{\sqrt[3]{3^2t^2}}$$ *Why is $\dfrac{\sqrt[3]{3^2t^2}}{\sqrt[3]{3^2t^2}}$ used to rationalize the denominator?*

$$= \dfrac{\sqrt[3]{2 \cdot 3^2t^2}}{\sqrt[3]{3^3t^3}} \text{ or } \dfrac{\sqrt[3]{18t^2}}{3t}$$

Example 8

APPLICATION

Physics

The formula for finding centripetal force, F_c, the inward force that must be applied to keep an object moving in a circle, is $F_c = \dfrac{mv^2}{r}$. Let m represent the mass of the object, v represent the velocity, and r represent the radius of the circular path. Solve the formula for the velocity and write the result in simplified form.

$$F_c = \dfrac{mv^2}{r}$$

$$\dfrac{F_c r}{m} = v^2$$ *Multiply each side by $\dfrac{r}{m}$.*

$$\sqrt{\dfrac{F_c r}{m}} = v$$ *Find the square root of each side.*

$$\sqrt{\dfrac{F_c r}{m}} \cdot \dfrac{\sqrt{m}}{\sqrt{m}} = v$$ *Rationalize the denominator.*

$$\dfrac{\sqrt{F_c rm}}{m} = v$$

CHECKING FOR UNDERSTANDING

Communicating Mathematics

Read and study the lesson to answer these questions.

1. **product and quotient properties of racials.**

1. What property or properties make the alternative formula that is given in the beginning of the lesson equivalent to the original formula?

2. Why is the product property of radicals for odd indices different than the product property for even indices? **See margin.**

LESSON 6-2   PRODUCTS AND QUOTIENTS OF RADICALS   261

RETEACHING THE LESSON

Here's an activity that provides support for the convention of rationalizing denominators. Have students find approximate values of the equivalent expressions $\dfrac{2}{\sqrt{3}}$ and $\dfrac{2\sqrt{3}}{3}$ using calculators.

Additional Answers

2. If a and b were allowed to be negative when n is even, they would have no real roots. a and b may be negative when n is odd because negative radicands can have real roots if n is odd.

3. It meets all criteria for simplified expressions.

Chapter 6   261

Closing the Lesson

Writing Activity Have students write a paragraph explaining how to determine if a radical expression is in simplified form.

APPLYING THE LESSON

Homework Exercises

Assignment Guide
Basic: 20–43, 54–55, 57–62
Average: 25–48, 54–62
Enriched: 29–62

Teaching Tip ❸ Remind students that the radical expression must be simplified.

Practice Masters Booklet, p. 42

NAME _____ DATE _____

6-2 Practice Worksheet

Products and Quotients of Radicals

Simplify.

1. $\sqrt[3]{-432}$ $-6\sqrt[3]{2}$
2. $\sqrt{540}$ $6\sqrt{15}$
3. $\sqrt{5}(\sqrt{10} - \sqrt{45})$ $5\sqrt{2} - 15$
4. $\sqrt[3]{6}(4\sqrt[3]{12} + 5\sqrt[3]{9})$ $8\sqrt[3]{9} + 15\sqrt[3]{2}$
5. $(2\sqrt[3]{24})(7\sqrt[3]{18})$ $84\sqrt[3]{2}$
6. $\sqrt[4]{32x^4y^5n^{10}}$ $2|x|yn^2\sqrt[4]{2yn^2}$
7. $\sqrt{1792}$ $16\sqrt{7}$
8. $\sqrt[3]{-6750}$ $-15\sqrt[3]{2}$
9. $\sqrt{3x^2y^3} \cdot \sqrt{75xy^5}$ $15|x|y^4\sqrt{x}$
10. $\sqrt[3]{9t^5v^5} \cdot \sqrt[3]{6tv^4}$ $3t^2v^4\sqrt[3]{2}$
11. $\sqrt{60} \cdot \sqrt{105}$ $30\sqrt{7}$
12. $\sqrt[3]{3600} \cdot \sqrt[3]{165}$ $30\sqrt[3]{22}$
13. $\frac{\sqrt{35}}{\sqrt{7}}$ $\sqrt{5}$
14. $\frac{\sqrt[3]{42}}{\sqrt[3]{7}}$ $\sqrt[3]{6}$
15. $\sqrt{\frac{3}{5}}$ $\frac{\sqrt{15}}{5}$
16. $\sqrt{\frac{6}{w}}$ $\frac{\sqrt{6w}}{w}$
17. $\sqrt{\frac{5}{27}}$ $\frac{\sqrt{15}}{3}$
18. $\sqrt[3]{\frac{8}{9a^2}}$ $\frac{\sqrt[3]{72a}}{3a}$
19. $\frac{\sqrt{20}}{\sqrt{5}}$ 2
20. $\sqrt{\frac{11}{9}}$ $\frac{\sqrt{11}}{3}$
21. $\sqrt[3]{\frac{2}{9}}$ $\frac{\sqrt[3]{6}}{3}$
22. $\sqrt{\frac{9}{25}}$ $\frac{\sqrt{45}}{5}$
23. $\frac{\sqrt[3]{16}}{\sqrt[3]{4}}$ $\sqrt[3]{4}$
24. $\frac{\sqrt[3]{9}}{\sqrt[3]{4}}$ $\frac{\sqrt[3]{18}}{2}$

---

3. Explain why $\frac{\sqrt{3x}}{x}$ is in simplified form. **See margin.**

4. Explain how to simplify $\frac{4}{\sqrt{2}}$. **Multiply by $\frac{\sqrt{2}}{\sqrt{2}}$ to get $2\sqrt{2}$.**

Guided Practice   Simplify.

5. $\sqrt{27}$ $3\sqrt{3}$
6. $\sqrt{32}$ $4\sqrt{2}$
7. $\sqrt{98y^4}$ $7y^2\sqrt{2}$
8. $\sqrt{50x^2}$ $5|x|\sqrt{2}$
9. $\sqrt[3]{16}$ $2\sqrt[3]{2}$
10. $\sqrt[4]{48}$ $2\sqrt[4]{3}$
11. $\sqrt{y^3}$ $y\sqrt{y}$
12. $\sqrt{a^5}$ $a^2\sqrt{a}$
13. $\sqrt[4]{t^5}$ $t\sqrt[4]{t}$

State the fraction that each radical expression should be multiplied by to rationalize the denominator. Then simplify.

14. $\frac{6}{\sqrt{2}}$ $\frac{\sqrt{2}}{\sqrt{2}}$; $3\sqrt{2}$
15. $\frac{1}{\sqrt{3}}$ $\frac{\sqrt{3}}{\sqrt{3}}$, $\frac{\sqrt{3}}{3}$
16. $\frac{1}{\sqrt{x}}$ $\frac{\sqrt{x}}{\sqrt{x}}$, $\frac{\sqrt{x}}{x}$
17. $\frac{3}{\sqrt{b}}$ $\frac{\sqrt{b}}{\sqrt{b}}$, $\frac{3\sqrt{b}}{b}$
18. $\frac{3}{\sqrt[3]{4}}$ $\frac{\sqrt[3]{2}}{\sqrt[3]{2}}$, $\frac{3\sqrt[3]{2}}{2}$
19. $\frac{7}{\sqrt[3]{9}}$ $\frac{\sqrt[3]{3}}{\sqrt[3]{3}}$, $\frac{7\sqrt[3]{3}}{3}$

EXERCISES

Practice   Simplify.   **Teaching Tip ❸**

Practice answers (margin):
26. $2|a|b\sqrt{2b}$
27. $4xy\sqrt{x}$
28. $3|m|n\sqrt[4]{n}$
36. $-60\sqrt{30}$
37. $48\sqrt{7}$
38. 22
39. $3\sqrt{2} - 2\sqrt{3}$
40. $3x^2z^2\sqrt{5}$
41. $3a^2b\sqrt[4]{b}$
46. $7\sqrt{2} + 7\sqrt{3}$
47. $\sqrt{ab} + a\sqrt{b}$
48. $r + r\sqrt{rs}$

20. $5\sqrt{50}$ $25\sqrt{2}$
21. $4\sqrt{54}$ $12\sqrt{6}$
22. $\sqrt[3]{32}$ $2\sqrt[3]{4}$
23. $\sqrt[3]{56}$ $2\sqrt[3]{7}$
24. $\sqrt{162}$ $9\sqrt{2}$
25. $\sqrt{675}$ $15\sqrt{3}$
26. $\sqrt{8a^2b^3}$
27. $\sqrt{8x^2y} \cdot \sqrt{2xy}$
28. $\sqrt[4]{81m^4n^5}$

B
29. $\frac{\sqrt{10}}{\sqrt{5}}$ $\sqrt{2}$
30. $\frac{\sqrt{12}}{\sqrt{3}}$ 2
31. $\frac{\sqrt{22}}{\sqrt{2}}$ $\sqrt{11}$
32. $\sqrt[3]{-192}$ $-4\sqrt[3]{3}$
33. $6\sqrt{216}$ $36\sqrt{6}$
34. $3\sqrt{242}$ $33\sqrt{2}$
35. $\sqrt[4]{112}$ $2\sqrt[4]{7}$
36. $(-3\sqrt{24})(5\sqrt{20})$
37. $(4\sqrt{18})(2\sqrt{14})$
38. $\sqrt[3]{121} \cdot \sqrt[3]{88}$
39. $\sqrt{3}(\sqrt{6} - 2)$
40. $\sqrt{3x^2z^3} \cdot \sqrt{15x^2z}$
41. $\sqrt[4]{a^5b^3} \cdot \sqrt[4]{81a^3b^2}$
42. $\sqrt{\frac{7}{4}}$ $\frac{\sqrt{7}}{2}$
43. $\frac{\sqrt[3]{81}}{\sqrt[3]{9}}$ $\sqrt[3]{9}$
44. $\sqrt{\frac{1}{3}}$ $\frac{\sqrt{3}}{3}$
45. $\sqrt{\frac{5}{12a}}$ $\frac{\sqrt{15a}}{6a}$
46. $\sqrt{7}(\sqrt{14} + \sqrt{21})$

C
47. $\sqrt{a}(\sqrt{b} + \sqrt{ab})$
48. $\sqrt{r}(\sqrt{r} + r\sqrt{s})$
49. $\sqrt[3]{\frac{54}{125}}$ $\frac{3\sqrt[3]{2}}{5}$
50. $\sqrt[4]{\frac{5}{16}}$ $\frac{\sqrt[4]{5}}{2}$
51. $\sqrt{\frac{5}{32x}}$ $\frac{\sqrt{10x}}{8x}$
52. $\sqrt[4]{\frac{2}{3}}$ $\frac{\sqrt[4]{54}}{3}$

CONNECTION
Geometry

53. Find the radius, r, of a sphere whose surface area S is 616 square inches. Use the formula $r = \frac{1}{2}\sqrt{\frac{S}{\pi}}$ **7 inches**

Critical Thinking

54. Is the statement "All real numbers can be written as a radical." *true* or *false*? Justify your answer. **true; Every integer can be written as the square root of a square.**

Applications

55. **Manufacturing** Find the length in inches that a pendulum should be for a complete swing to take one second. Use the formula $T = 2\pi\sqrt{\dfrac{L}{384}}$, where T represents time in seconds, and L represents the length of the pendulum. **9.73 inches**

56. **Physics** Sharon and Anthony dropped a stone from a 150-foot cliff. Find the time, t, in seconds that it will take for the stone to reach the ground. Let $t = \dfrac{1}{4}\sqrt{s}$, where s represents the distance in feet the stone will fall. **3.06 seconds**

Mixed Review

Simplify. **(Lesson 6-1)**

57. $\sqrt{(5b)^4}$ **$25b^2$**

58. $-\sqrt{121b^2c^6}$ **$-11|bc^3|$**

59. Evaluate $(9 \times 10^3)^{-1}(3.5 \times 10^{-2})$. Express the answer in both scientific and decimal notation. **(Lesson 5-2)** **$3.\overline{8} \times 10^{-6}$; $0.0000038\overline{8}$**

60. Can a 3×4 matrix have an inverse? Explain your answer. **(Lesson 4-5) No, only square matrices have inverses.**

61. Find the x-, y-, and z-intercepts for the equation $3x + 6y - 8z = 24$. **(Lesson 3-8) $x = 8$, $y = 4$, $z = -3$**

62. If $h(x) = [3x - 1]$, find $h(-2.1)$. **(Lesson 2-7) -8**

~~~ BIOLOGY CONNECTION ~~~

Nature, seldom content with simple shapes alone, has created all kinds of intricate mathematical designs. The spirals of the shell of a chambered nautilus, for example, is an equiangular spiral. In the cutaway drawing at the right, notice that the outreaching radii form right angles with the chords along the curve and each chord has a value of 1. The Pythagorean Theorem allows us to calculate the measure of the hypotenuse. Notice the pattern of radicals that results with each additional chamber of the nautilus. This pattern was first documented by Jacob Bernoulli (1654–1705). He was so impressed with this spiral that he had it engraved on his tombstone with the inscription *Eadem mutata resurgo* (I shall arise, the same, though changed).

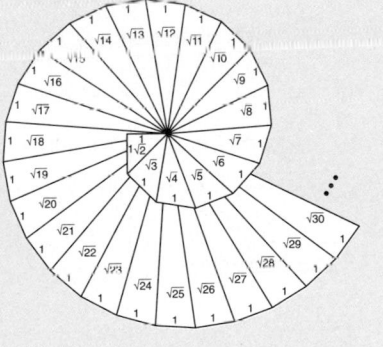

EXTENDING THE LESSON

Math Power: Connections

Find the radius, r, of a sphere whose volume, V, is 490 cubic meters. Use $V = \dfrac{4}{3}\pi r^3$, where $\pi \approx 3.14$. **$r \approx 4.89$ meters**

Biology Connection

Have students discuss each of the radicals on the shell. Have them draw the chords and show the pattern that exists. The students should research the life of Jacob Bernoulli. What did he add to the study of mathematics?

Enrichment Masters Booklet, p. 37

INTRODUCING THE LESSON

 5-Minute Check

(over Lesson 6-2)
Simplify.

1. $\sqrt[4]{81a^8b^5c^3}$ $3a^2b\sqrt[4]{bc^3}$

2. $6\sqrt{2}(4\sqrt{3} - 3\sqrt{8})$
   $24\sqrt{6} - 72$

3. $\sqrt[3]{\dfrac{9}{4m^2}}$ $\dfrac{\sqrt[3]{18m}}{2m}$

Other Prerequisite Skills
Simplify.

4. $(9a^2b + 6a - 12) - (7a - 8a^2b + 4)$
   $17a^2b - a - 16$

5. $(6a - 2)(4a + 3)$
   $24a^2 + 10a - 6$

Motivating the Lesson

Solve $\sqrt{4} + \sqrt{16}$ by finding the square root of the values.
$\sqrt{4} + \sqrt{16} = 2 + 4$
$\qquad\qquad = 6$

Solve the above expression by adding the radicands.
$\sqrt{4} + \sqrt{16} = \sqrt{20}$
$\qquad\qquad = 2\sqrt{5}$

Are they equal?   **no**
Discuss which is correct.

6-3 Computing with Radicals

Objective 6-3

After studying this lesson, you should be able to:
- add, subtract, multiply, and divide radical expressions.

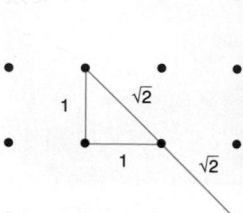

The geometric dot paper at the right shows the construction of a segment that is $\sqrt{2}$ units long. This can be verified by using the Pythagorean Theorem. The segment in green is also $\sqrt{2}$ units long. Estimate the sum of the two lengths. Based on your estimate, do you think $\sqrt{2} + \sqrt{2} = \sqrt{2 + 2}$ or 2?

$a^2 + b^2 = c^2$
$1^2 + 1^2 = c^2$
$\pm\sqrt{2} = c$

As you have just observed, $\sqrt{a} + \sqrt{b} \neq \sqrt{a + b}$ just like $a^2 + b^2 \neq (a + b)^2$. Adding radicals is like adding other monomials. You wouldn't say $x^2 + x^2 = (x + x)^2$. You know that $x^2 + x^2 = 2x^2$ because you add like terms. So you must add like terms with radicals also. Two radical expressions are called **like radical expressions** if both the indices and the radicands are alike. Some examples of like and unlike radical expressions are given below.

$2\sqrt[4]{3}$ and $5\sqrt[4]{3}$ are like expressions.   *Both the indices and radicands are alike.*

$\sqrt[3]{21}$ and $\sqrt[4]{21}$ are not like expressions.   *The indices are not alike.*

$6x\sqrt{5}$ and $6\sqrt{5x}$ are not like expressions.   *The radicands are not alike.*

$\sqrt[4]{7x}$ and $\sqrt[3]{7y}$ are not like expressions.   *Neither the indices nor the radicands are alike.*

To add or subtract radicals, just combine like terms as you do when you add or subtract other monomials.

Example 1

Simplify $4 + 3\sqrt{5} + 7 + 2\sqrt{5}$.

$\begin{aligned}
4 + 3\sqrt{5} + 7 + 2\sqrt{5} &= (4 + 7) + (3\sqrt{5} + 2\sqrt{5}) \\
&= (4 + 7) + (3 + 2)\sqrt{5} \qquad \text{\textit{$3\sqrt{5}$ and $2\sqrt{5}$ are like}} \\
&= 11 + 5\sqrt{5} \qquad\qquad\qquad \text{\textit{expressions.}}
\end{aligned}$

Example 2

Simplify $4\sqrt{27} + 3\sqrt{3} - \sqrt{48}$.   Teaching Tip ①

$\begin{aligned}
4\sqrt{27} + 3\sqrt{3} - \sqrt{48} &= 4\sqrt{3^2 \cdot 3} + 3\sqrt{3} - \sqrt{4^2 \cdot 3} \quad \text{\textit{Simplify each radical.}} \\
&= 4\sqrt{3^2}\sqrt{3} + 3\sqrt{3} - \sqrt{4^2}\sqrt{3} \\
&= 4 \cdot 3\sqrt{3} + 3\sqrt{3} - 4\sqrt{3} \\
&= 12\sqrt{3} + 3\sqrt{3} - 4\sqrt{3} \\
&= 11\sqrt{3} \qquad\qquad\qquad \text{\textit{Combine like expressions.}}
\end{aligned}$

Using Cooperative Groups

Divide the class into groups of four. Give each group four problems that involve radicals. Each of the four operations should be used. Have each group explain how to do the problems step by step. You could have the groups present one problem. The groups should make sure that every person in the group understands each problem before presenting them.

Example 3

Simplify $\sqrt[3]{32x} + \sqrt[3]{108x}$.

$$\sqrt[3]{32x} + \sqrt[3]{108x} = \sqrt[3]{2^3 \cdot 4x} + \sqrt[3]{3^3 \cdot 4x} \qquad \textit{Simplify each radical.}$$

$$= \sqrt[3]{2^3} \cdot \sqrt[3]{4x} + \sqrt[3]{3^3} \cdot \sqrt[3]{4x} \qquad \textit{Product of powers property}$$

$$= 2\sqrt[3]{4x} + 3\sqrt[3]{4x}$$

$$= 5\sqrt[3]{4x}$$

Example 4

APPLICATION

Sports

FYI · · ·

The world record high dive was made by Randal Dickison at Ocean Park, Hong Kong on April 6, 1985. It was 174 feet 8 inches.

Two cliff divers are performing in a diving show. One is diving from a cliff 128 feet high, and the other is diving from a cliff 32 feet high. They start to dive at the same time. Use the formula $t = \sqrt{\dfrac{2s}{g}}$, where s represents the distance in feet, t represents time in seconds, and g represents the acceleration due to gravity, to find how much longer it will take the diver on the higher cliff to enter the water. Assume that the acceleration due to gravity is 32 feet per second squared and that air resistance is not a factor.

Find the time for the diver from a 128-foot cliff to enter the water.

$$t = \sqrt{\frac{2s}{g}}$$

$$= \sqrt{\frac{2(128)}{32}} \qquad \begin{array}{l}\textit{Substitute 128 for s}\\ \textit{and 32 for g.}\end{array}$$

$$= \sqrt{8} \text{ or } 2\sqrt{2}$$

The time is $2\sqrt{2}$ seconds.

Find the time for the diver from a 32-foot cliff to enter the water.

$$t = \sqrt{\frac{2s}{g}}$$

$$= \sqrt{\frac{2(32)}{32}} \qquad \begin{array}{l}\textit{Substitute 32 for s}\\ \textit{and 32 for g.}\end{array}$$

$$= \sqrt{2}$$

The time is $\sqrt{2}$ seconds.

Now find the difference of the two times.

$$2\sqrt{2} - \sqrt{2} = \sqrt{2} \approx 1.41$$

It will take the diver on the higher cliff about 1.41 seconds longer to enter the water.

We combine radicals like monomials when we add and subtract. We can multiply radicals like binomials using the FOIL method.

Example 5

Simplify $(3 + \sqrt{2})(\sqrt{10} + \sqrt{5})$.

$$\begin{array}{ccccc} & F & O & I & L \\ (3 + \sqrt{2})(\sqrt{10} + \sqrt{5}) = & 3\sqrt{10} & + 3\sqrt{5} & + \sqrt{2} \cdot \sqrt{10} & + \sqrt{2} \cdot \sqrt{5} \end{array}$$

$$= 3\sqrt{10} + 3\sqrt{5} + \sqrt{20} \qquad + \sqrt{10}$$

$$= 3\sqrt{10} + 3\sqrt{5} + 2\sqrt{5} \qquad + \sqrt{10}$$

$$= 4\sqrt{10} + 5\sqrt{5}$$

Teaching Tip ❶ Remind students they need to find like terms. To determine if the terms are like they need to simplify them first.

Chalkboard Examples

For Example 1
Simplify.

a. $2\sqrt{3} + 5 + 7\sqrt{3} - 2$
   $9\sqrt{3} + 3$

b. $10\sqrt{2} - 3\sqrt{2} + 7 + 6\sqrt{2}$
   $13\sqrt{2} + 7$

For Example 2
Simplify.

a. $3\sqrt{27} - 7\sqrt{3} - \sqrt{12}$ 0

b. $5\sqrt{6} - 3\sqrt{24} + \sqrt{150}$
   $4\sqrt{6}$

For Example 3
Simplify.

a. $\sqrt[3]{16a} + 4\sqrt[3]{54a}$ $14\sqrt[3]{2a}$

b. $5\sqrt[3]{40x} - 7\sqrt[3]{5x}$ $3\sqrt[3]{5x}$

For Example 4
Find the difference in time for the two divers if one falls 80 feet and the other falls 20 feet. Assume the acceleration due to gravity is 32 feet per second squared and that air resistance is not a factor.
$0.5\sqrt{5}$ seconds

For Example 5
Simplify.

a. $(\sqrt{6} + \sqrt{3})(\sqrt{3} + \sqrt{2})$
   $3\sqrt{2} + 2\sqrt{3} + 3 + \sqrt{6}$

b. $(2\sqrt{3} + 4\sqrt{5})(\sqrt{3} + 6\sqrt{5})$
   $126 + 16\sqrt{15}$

Teaching Tip ❷ To generalize this expression we find $(a + \sqrt{b})(a - \sqrt{b})$. This equals $a^2 - b$. Here b does not need an absolute value sign if b is positive.

Teaching Tip ❸ Remind students to simplify the expression by using the rules to rationalize the denominators.

Reteaching Masters Booklet, p. 38

Example 6 | Simplify $(5 - \sqrt{3})(5 + \sqrt{3})$. **Teaching Tip ❷**

$(5 - \sqrt{3})(5 + \sqrt{3}) = 25 + 5\sqrt{3} - 5\sqrt{3} - \sqrt{3 \cdot 3}$
$\qquad = 25 - \sqrt{3^2}$
$\qquad = 25 - 3$
$\qquad = 22$

Binomials, like those in Example 6, of the form $a\sqrt{b} + c\sqrt{d}$ and $a\sqrt{b} - c\sqrt{d}$ where a, b, c, and d are rational numbers called **conjugates** of each other. The product of conjugates is always a rational number. We can use conjugates to rationalize a binomial denominator containing a radical.

Example 7 | Simplify $\dfrac{2 + \sqrt{5}}{5 - 2\sqrt{5}}$.

$\dfrac{2 + \sqrt{5}}{5 - 2\sqrt{5}} = \dfrac{2 + \sqrt{5}}{5 - 2\sqrt{5}} \cdot \dfrac{5 + 2\sqrt{5}}{5 + 2\sqrt{5}}$ *The conjugate of $5 - 2\sqrt{5}$ is $5 + 2\sqrt{5}$.*

$\qquad = \dfrac{10 + 4\sqrt{5} + 5\sqrt{5} + 2\sqrt{5 \cdot 5}}{25 - (2\sqrt{5})^2}$

$\qquad = \dfrac{10 + 4\sqrt{5} + 5\sqrt{5} + 10}{25 - 4(5)}$

$\qquad = \dfrac{20 + 9\sqrt{5}}{5}$

CHECKING FOR UNDERSTANDING

Communicating Mathematics

Read and study the lesson to answer these questions.

1. Are $3\sqrt{7}$ and $4\sqrt[3]{7}$ like radical expressions? If not, why not?

1. No; they have different indices.

2. What is the conjugate of $-4 - 2\sqrt{2}$? $\mathbf{-4 + 2\sqrt{2}}$

3. Why is the product of conjugates always a rational number? *Hint: Find the product of the two general conjugates given in the definition of conjugates.* **See margin.**

4. What expression would you multiply $\dfrac{1 - \sqrt{3}}{5 + 2\sqrt{3}}$ by to rationalize the denominator? $\dfrac{5 - 2\sqrt{3}}{5 - 2\sqrt{3}}$

Guided Practice

Name the conjugate of each expression.

5. $5 - \sqrt{7}$ $\mathbf{5 + \sqrt{7}}$
6. $1 + \sqrt{3}$ $\mathbf{1 - \sqrt{3}}$
7. $\sqrt{3} + \sqrt{10}$ $\mathbf{\sqrt{3} - \sqrt{10}}$
8. $\sqrt{3} + 5$ $\mathbf{\sqrt{3} - 5}$
9. $2 - 2\sqrt{3}$ $\mathbf{2 + 2\sqrt{3}}$
10. $\sqrt{7} - 3\sqrt{5}$ $\mathbf{\sqrt{7} + 3\sqrt{5}}$

RETEACHING THE LESSON

Have students complete the chart.

x	$\sqrt{x^2}$	$(\sqrt{x})^2$	$\sqrt[3]{x^3}$	$(\sqrt[3]{x})^3$
1	1	1	1	1
-1	1	—	-1	-1
64	64	64	64	64
-64	64	—	-64	-64

Now generalize the results.

$\sqrt[\text{even}]{\text{negative}}$ = no real root

$\sqrt[n]{x^n} = x$

$(\sqrt[n]{x})^n = x$

Simplify.

11. $5\sqrt{3} - 4\sqrt{3}$ $\sqrt{3}$
12. $7\sqrt[3]{y} - 4\sqrt[3]{y}$ $3\sqrt[3]{y}$
13. $8\sqrt[3]{6} + 3\sqrt[3]{6}$ $11\sqrt[3]{6}$

14. $\sqrt[5]{3} + 4\sqrt[5]{3}$ $5\sqrt[5]{3}$
15. $2\sqrt{2} + \sqrt{8}$ $4\sqrt{2}$
16. $\sqrt[3]{40} - 2\sqrt[3]{5}$ 0

Checking for Understanding
Exercises 1–16 are designed to help you assess understanding through reading, writing, and speaking. You should work through Exercises 1–4 with your students, and then monitor their work on Exercises 5–16.

Error Analysis
Students often overlook the conditions necessary for $\sqrt[n]{ab} = \sqrt[n]{a} \cdot \sqrt[n]{b}$; namely, that if n is even, then a and b must both be non-negative. Consider this counterexample: $\sqrt{(-4)(-9)} = \sqrt{-4} \cdot \sqrt{-9}$, but $\sqrt{-4}$ and $\sqrt{-9}$ are not real numbers. $\sqrt{(-4)(-9)} = \sqrt{36}$ or 6.

Closing the Lesson
Writing Activity Have students write a step-by-step process for adding and subtracting radical expressions.

EXERCISES

Practice   Simplify.

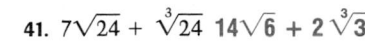

17. $-3\sqrt{5} + 5\sqrt{2} + 4\sqrt{20} - 3\sqrt{50}$ $5\sqrt{5} - 10\sqrt{2}$ **Teaching Tip ③**
18. $5\sqrt{2} + 3\sqrt{2} - 8$ $8\sqrt{2} - 8$
19. $8\sqrt{3} - 3\sqrt{75}$ $-7\sqrt{3}$
20. $3\sqrt{7} - 5\sqrt{28}$ $-7\sqrt{7}$
21. $(3 + \sqrt{5})(4 + \sqrt{5})$ $17 + 7\sqrt{5}$
22. $(5 + \sqrt{3})(3 - \sqrt{3})$ $12 - 2\sqrt{3}$
23. $(3x + \sqrt{5y})(3x - \sqrt{5y})$ $9x^2 - 5y$
24. $(6 - \sqrt{2})(6 + \sqrt{2})$ 34
25. $(4 + \sqrt{3})^2$ $19 + 8\sqrt{3}$
26. $(a + \sqrt{b})^2$ $a^2 + 2a\sqrt{b} + b$

27. $4\sqrt{5} + 23\sqrt{6}$

27. $5\sqrt{20} + \sqrt{24} - \sqrt{180} + 7\sqrt{54}$
28. $7\sqrt[3]{5t} + 4\sqrt[3]{5t}$ $11\sqrt[3]{5t}$
29. $\sqrt[3]{54} - \sqrt[3]{128}$ $-\sqrt[3]{2}$
30. $8\sqrt[3]{2x} + 3\sqrt[3]{2x} - 8\sqrt[3]{2x}$ $3\sqrt[3]{2x}$
31. $\sqrt[3]{48} - \sqrt[3]{6}$ $\sqrt[3]{6}$
32. $7\sqrt[3]{2} + 6\sqrt[3]{150}$ $7\sqrt[3]{2} + 6\sqrt[3]{150}$
33. $5\sqrt[3]{135} - 2\sqrt[3]{81}$ $15\sqrt[3]{5} - 6\sqrt[3]{3}$
34. $(5 + \sqrt{2})(3 + \sqrt{2})$ $17 + 8\sqrt{2}$

35. $25 - 5\sqrt{2} + 5\sqrt{6} - 2\sqrt{3}$

35. $(5 + \sqrt{6})(5 - \sqrt{2})$
36. $(8 - \sqrt{3})(6 + \sqrt{3})$ $45 + 2\sqrt{3}$
37. $(7 + \sqrt{11y})(7 - \sqrt{11y})$ $49 - 11y$
38. $(\sqrt{3} + \sqrt{5})(\sqrt{3} - \sqrt{5})$ $1 + \sqrt{15}$
39. $\dfrac{1}{3 + \sqrt{5}}$ $\dfrac{3 - \sqrt{5}}{4}$
40. $\dfrac{7}{4 - \sqrt{3}}$ $\dfrac{28 + 7\sqrt{3}}{13}$

41. $7\sqrt{24} + \sqrt[3]{24}$ $14\sqrt{6} + 2\sqrt[3]{3}$
42. $\sqrt{98} - \sqrt{72} + \sqrt{32}$ $5\sqrt{2}$
43. $7\sqrt[4]{2} + 8\sqrt[4]{2}$ $15\sqrt[4]{2}$
44. $\sqrt[4]{x^2} + \sqrt[4]{x^6}$ $(1 + |x|)\sqrt[4]{x^2}$

45. $|y| + y^2 + y^4$
46. $28 + 2\sqrt{10}$
47. $m^3 + 4$
48. $8 + s$

45. $\sqrt[4]{y^4} + \sqrt[3]{y^6} + \sqrt{y^8}$
46. $(4\sqrt{5} - 3\sqrt{2})(2\sqrt{5} + 2\sqrt{2})$
47. $(m + \sqrt[3]{4})(m^2 - m\sqrt[3]{4} + \sqrt[3]{16})$
48. $(2 + \sqrt[3]{s})(4 - 2\sqrt[3]{s} + \sqrt[3]{s^2})$
49. $\dfrac{\sqrt{x + 1}}{\sqrt{x - 1}}$ $\dfrac{\sqrt{x^2 - 1}}{x - 1}$
50. $\dfrac{\sqrt{3} + n\sqrt{6}}{4 - \sqrt{n}}$

51. $\sqrt{\dfrac{2}{5}} + \sqrt{40} + \sqrt{10}$ $\dfrac{16\sqrt{10}}{5}$
52. $\sqrt[3]{\dfrac{2}{3}} + \sqrt[3]{144} - \sqrt[3]{243}$ $\dfrac{7\sqrt[3]{18}}{3} - 3\sqrt[3]{9}$

50. $\dfrac{4\sqrt{3} + 4n\sqrt{6} + \sqrt{3n} + n\sqrt{6n}}{16 - n}$

Critical Thinking   53. As you recall, a set is closed under an operation if the result of performing the operation on any two elements of the set is an element of the set. Is the set of irrational numbers closed under any of the four basic operations? **No, all of these operations can have a rational number as a result.**

LESSON 6-3 COMPUTING WITH RADICALS **267**

Additional Answers

3. The product is a difference of two squares.
$(a\sqrt{b} + c\sqrt{d})(a\sqrt{b} - c\sqrt{d}) = (a\sqrt{b})^2 - (c\sqrt{d})^2$
$= a^2b - c^2d$
As long as a, b, c, and d are rational, the product of the conjugates will be.

Homework Exercises

See assignment guide on page 267.

Chapter 6, Quiz A, (Lessons 6-1 through 6-3), is available in the Evaluation Masters Booklet, p. 79.

Applications

54. **Automotive Engineering** An automotive engineer is trying to design a safer car. The maximum force a road can exert on the tires of the car being redesigned is 2000 pounds. What is the maximum velocity in ft/s at which this car can safely round a turn of radius 320 feet? Use the formula

$v = \sqrt{\dfrac{F_c r}{100}}$, where F_c is the force the road exerts on the car and r is the radius of the turn. **80 feet per second or about 55 miles per hour**

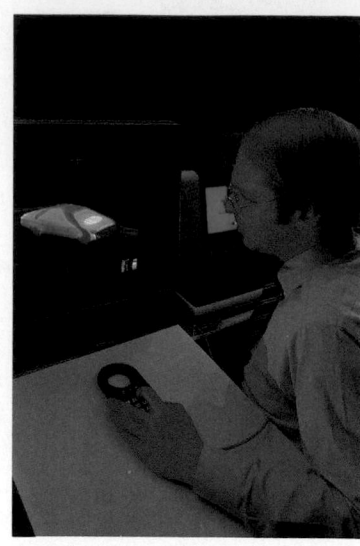

55. **Sports** Casey hit a foul-ball straight up over the plate. It reached a height of 112 feet. How long does the catcher have to get ready to catch the ball before it reaches the ground? The formula for the total time is

$t = 2\sqrt{\dfrac{2h}{g}}$, where h is the height of the ball and g is the acceleration due to gravity. Assume that the acceleration due to gravity is 32 feet per second squared. $2\sqrt{7}$ **or 5.3 seconds**

Mixed Review

Simplify. **(Lesson 6-2)**

56. $5\sqrt{54}$ **$15\sqrt{6}$**

57. $\sqrt[4]{5m^3n^5} \cdot \sqrt[4]{125m^2n^3}$ **$5mn^2\sqrt[4]{m}$**

58. Factor $1 - 8a^3$. **(Lesson 5-5)** **$(1 - 2a)(1 + 2a + 4a^2)$**

59. Simplify $c^3 \cdot c^2 \cdot c^4$. **(Lesson 5-1)** **c^9**

60. State the dimension of the matrix $\begin{bmatrix} -1 & 1 & 7 \\ 0 & 4 & 0 \\ 2 & 2 & 3 \end{bmatrix}$. Then evaluate its determinant (if one exists). **(Lesson 4-1)** **3×3; -68**

61. Find the maximum and minimum values of the function $f(x, y) = x - y$ defined for the polygonal region having vertices with coordinates $(0, 0)$, $(0, 5)$, $(3, 4)$, and $(6, 0)$. **(Lesson 3-6)** **maximum: 6 at (6, 0); minimum: -5 at (0, 5)**

EXTENDING THE LESSON

Math Power: Reasoning

Given $\sqrt{-49a^3b^4} = -7ab^2\sqrt{-a}$, is this equation correct?
Yes, it is.
Prove your answer.

Enrichment Masters Booklet, p. 38

6-4 Rational Exponents

Objectives After studying this lesson, you should be able to:

6-4A ▪ write expressions with rational exponents in simplest radical form and vice versa, and

6-4B ▪ evaluate expressions in either exponential or radical form.

Application

Nina deposited $500 in her account at First Atlanta Bank on March 1. Her account earns 8% interest per year. If she withdraws the money to pay for her college tuition at the beginning of September, how much interest has she earned? The bank uses the formula $A = P(1 + r)^t$ for finding the amount of money (A) in a compound interest account at the end of t years if P is the original amount of money deposited and r is the annual interest rate.

Nina had her money in the bank six months. But, t is expressed in years. So substituting $\frac{1}{2}$ for t, we must evaluate $A = 500(1 + 0.08)^{\frac{1}{2}}$ to find the amount of interest she earned. But how do we evaluate a fractional exponent? Assume that fractional exponents behave as integral exponents. Then, $5^1 = 5^{\left(\frac{1}{2}\right) \cdot 2}$ or $\left(5^{\frac{1}{2}}\right)^2$.

So, $5^{\frac{1}{2}}$ is a number that when squared equals 5. Since you know that, $(\sqrt{5})^2$ also equals 5, then $5^{\frac{1}{2}} = \sqrt{5}$. This suggests the following definition.

Definition of $b^{\frac{1}{n}}$

> For any real number b and for any integer n, $n > 1$,
> $$b^{\frac{1}{n}} = \sqrt[n]{b}$$
> except when $b < 0$ and n is even.

Teaching Tip ❶ From the definition, we can say that $7^{\frac{1}{4}} = \sqrt[4]{7}$ and $(-8)^{\frac{1}{3}} = \sqrt[3]{-8}$ or -2. The expression $(-16)^{\frac{1}{4}}$ is not defined since $-16 < 0$ and 4 is even. Can you tell why we need this restriction?

Example 1 Evaluate $64^{\frac{1}{3}}$.

Here are two methods of solution.

Method 1 $64^{\frac{1}{3}} = \sqrt[3]{64}$
$= \sqrt[3]{4^3}$
$= 4$

Method 2 $64^{\frac{1}{3}} = (4^3)^{\frac{1}{3}}$
$= 4^{3\left(\frac{1}{3}\right)}$
$= 4^1$ or 4

LESSON 6-4 RATIONAL EXPONENTS **269**

ALTERNATE TEACHING STRATEGIES

Using Questioning

The following statement is true:
$1^n \cdot 1^{\frac{1}{n}} = 1^1$. Is $2^n \cdot 2^{\frac{1}{n}} = 2^1$ a true statement?

No, $2^n \cdot 2^{\frac{1}{n}} = 2^{n+\frac{1}{n}} = 2^{\frac{n^2+1}{n}}$.

$\frac{n^2 + 1}{n} \neq 1$ for any real number n.

Using Logical Thinking

Evaluate $f(2)$ if $f(x) = x^{-\frac{1}{2}} + x^{-4}$.

$\frac{8\sqrt{2} + 1}{16}$

For what values of x would the equation not be defined? Why? **x must be greater than 0**

Lesson Resources

Reteaching Master 6-4
Practice Master 6-4
Enrichment Master 6-4

Transparency 6-4 contains the 5-Minute Check and a teaching aid for this lesson.

INTRODUCING THE LESSON

🕐 5-Minute Check

(over Lesson 6-3)
Simplify.

1. $7\sqrt{2} + 4\sqrt{18} - \sqrt{50}$
   $14\sqrt{2}$
2. $\sqrt[3]{192t} - \sqrt[3]{24t} + \sqrt[3]{5t}$
   $2\sqrt[3]{3t} + \sqrt[3]{5t}$
3. $(3\sqrt{5} \quad \sqrt{3})(3\sqrt{5} + \sqrt{3})$
   42
4. $(5\sqrt{6} + \sqrt{3})(2\sqrt{6} - 4\sqrt{3})$
   $48 - 54\sqrt{2}$
5. $\frac{4\sqrt{3} - 7}{5\sqrt{3} + 6}$ $\frac{102 - 59\sqrt{3}}{39}$

Motivating the Lesson

Review the properties of exponents before discussing this lesson. If $(2^2)(2^4) = 2^6$, how can you rewrite $2^2 \times 2^{\frac{1}{2}}$? Discuss what students think $2^{\frac{1}{2}}$ means.

TEACHING THE LESSON

Teaching Tip ❶ Remind students that "$(-16)^{\frac{1}{4}}$ is not defined" means that $(-16)^{\frac{1}{4}}$ is not a real number.

For Example 1

Evaluate.

a. $36^{\frac{1}{2}}$ 6

b. $64^{\frac{1}{3}}$ 4

c. $81^{\frac{1}{4}}$ 3

For Example 2

Evaluate.

a. $49^{-\frac{1}{2}}$ $\frac{1}{7}$

b. $\left(\frac{1}{8}\right)^{-\frac{1}{3}}$ 2

c. 4^{-1} $\frac{1}{4}$

For Example 3

Evaluate.

a. $36^{\frac{3}{2}}$ 216

b. $64^{\frac{5}{6}}$ 32

c. $27^{\frac{4}{3}}$ 81

For Example 4

Evaluate.

a. $27^{\frac{2}{3}} \cdot 27^{\frac{2}{3}}$ 81

b. $16^{\frac{3}{4}} \cdot 16^{\frac{1}{4}}$ 16

c. $81^{\frac{1}{2}} \cdot 81^{\frac{1}{4}}$ 27

Teaching Tip ❷ Remember when the base is negative the root must be odd. Otherwise, we have no principal root.

Example 2

Evaluate $625^{-\frac{1}{4}}$.

Method 1

$$625^{-\frac{1}{4}} = \frac{1}{625^{\frac{1}{4}}}$$

$$= \frac{1}{\sqrt[4]{625}} \qquad \text{Definition of } b^{\frac{1}{n}}$$

$$= \frac{1}{\sqrt[4]{5^4}}$$

$$= \frac{1}{5}$$

Method 2

$$625^{-\frac{1}{4}} = (5^4)^{-\frac{1}{4}}$$

$$= 5^{4\left(-\frac{1}{4}\right)} \qquad \textit{Raising a power to a power}$$

$$= 5^{-1}$$

$$= \frac{1}{5}$$

How can you evaluate an expression with a fractional exponent in which the numerator is not 1? Study the two methods shown below.

Method 1

$$6^{\frac{3}{2}} = \left(6^{\frac{1}{2}}\right)^3 \text{ or } (\sqrt{6})^3$$

Method 2

$$6^{\frac{3}{2}} = (6^3)^{\frac{1}{2}} \text{ or } \sqrt{6^3}$$

Since $(\sqrt{6})^3 = \sqrt{6} \cdot \sqrt{6} \cdot \sqrt{6}$ or $\sqrt{216}$ and $\sqrt{6^3} = \sqrt{6 \cdot 6 \cdot 6}$ or $\sqrt{216}$, $(\sqrt{6})^3$ and $\sqrt{6^3}$ have the same value.

Definition of Rational Exponents	For any nonzero real number b, and any integers m and n, with $n > 1$, $$b^{\frac{m}{n}} = \sqrt[n]{b^m} = (\sqrt[n]{b})^m$$ except when $b < 0$ and n is even.

Teaching Tip ❷ Why does the definition not apply when the index is even and the base is negative? Substitute different values in for b and n to discover the reason.

Example 3

Evaluate $8^{\frac{2}{3}}$.

Method 1 $8^{\frac{2}{3}} = (\sqrt[3]{8})^2$

$= (2)^2$

$= 4$

Method 2 $8^{\frac{2}{3}} = (2^3)^{\frac{2}{3}}$

$= 2^2$

$= 4$

Example 4

Evaluate $27^{\frac{1}{3}} \cdot 27^{\frac{4}{3}}$.

Method 1 $27^{\frac{1}{3}} \cdot 27^{\frac{4}{3}} = 27^{\frac{5}{3}}$

$= (\sqrt[3]{27})^5$

$= (3)^5$ or 243

Method 2 $27^{\frac{1}{3}} \cdot 27^{\frac{4}{3}} = 27^{\frac{5}{3}}$

$= (3^3)^{\frac{5}{3}}$

$= 3^5$ or 243

As you know, fractions are rational numbers that can also be written as decimal numbers. For example, $\frac{2}{3} = 0.\overline{6}$ and $\frac{3}{4} = 0.75$. We can use a calculator to evaluate expressions with fractional or decimal exponents.

Example 5

Use a calculator to evaluate $1331^{\frac{2}{3}}$.

ENTER: 1331 $\boxed{y^x}$ $\boxed{(}$ 2 $\boxed{\div}$ 3 $\boxed{)}$ $\boxed{=}$ 121

$1331^{\frac{2}{3}} = 121$ *To evaluate an expression with a decimal exponent, enter the decimal after the $\boxed{y^x}$ key.*

When simplifying a radical, find the smallest index possible.

Example 6

Express $\sqrt[6]{36}$ in simplest radical form.

In $\sqrt[6]{36}$, the index is 6. Methods 1 and 2 both illustrate using a smaller index.

Method 1 $\sqrt[6]{36} = 36^{\frac{1}{6}}$ *Method 2* $\sqrt[6]{36} = 36^{\frac{1}{6}}$
$= (36^{\frac{1}{2}})^{\frac{1}{3}}$ $= (6^2)^{\frac{1}{6}}$
$= (\sqrt{36})^{\frac{1}{3}}$ $= 6^{\frac{1}{3}}$ or $\sqrt[3]{6}$
$= 6^{\frac{1}{3}}$ or $\sqrt[3]{6}$

Example 7

Express $2^{\frac{1}{2}}a^{\frac{2}{3}}b^{\frac{5}{6}}$ in simplest radical form.

$2^{\frac{1}{2}}a^{\frac{2}{3}}b^{\frac{5}{6}} = 2^{\frac{3}{6}}a^{\frac{4}{6}}b^{\frac{5}{6}}$ *Rewrite all exponents using the least common denominator, 6.*
$= (2^3a^4b^5)^{\frac{1}{6}}$
$= \sqrt[6]{8a^4b^5}$

Example 8

APPLICATION
Music

The formula for the frequency, f, of a note is $f = (2L)^{-1}P^{\frac{1}{2}}m^{-\frac{1}{2}}$, where L is the length of the string, P is the stretching force on the string, and m is the mass of one centimeter of the string. Write the formula in simplest radical form.

$f = (2L)^{-1}P^{\frac{1}{2}}m^{-\frac{1}{2}}$
$= \left(\frac{1}{2L}\right)\sqrt{P}\left(\frac{1}{\sqrt{m}}\right)$ $(2L)^{-1} = \frac{1}{2L}; P^{\frac{1}{2}} = \sqrt{P}; m^{-\frac{1}{2}} = \frac{1}{\sqrt{m}}$
$= \left(\frac{1}{2L}\right)\left(\frac{\sqrt{P}}{\sqrt{m}}\right)$
$= \frac{1}{2L}\left(\frac{\sqrt{P}}{\sqrt{m}}\right)\left(\frac{\sqrt{m}}{\sqrt{m}}\right)$ *Rationalize the denominator.*
$= \frac{\sqrt{Pm}}{2Lm}$

Checking for Understanding

Exercises 1–21 are designed to help you assess understanding through reading, writing, and speaking. You should work through Exercises 1–3 with your students, and then monitor their work on Exercises 4–21.

Closing the Lesson

Modeling Activity Have students draw a model to show the equation

$$64^{\frac{1}{3}} = 4$$

The students can show a cube with sides equal to 4.

APPLYING THE LESSON

Homework Exercises

Assignment Guide

Basic: 22–51, 67–68, 71–76
Average: 28–57, 67–76
Enriched: 37–76
All: Mid-Chapter Review, 1–16

Reteaching Masters Booklet, p. 39

CHECKING FOR UNDERSTANDING

Communicating Mathematics

Read and study the lesson to answer these questions.

1. Why are fractional exponents not defined when the denominator of the exponent is even and the base is negative? **See margin.**

2. State an expression that is equivalent to $\sqrt[4]{33}$. $33^{\frac{1}{4}}$

3. Is $\sqrt[6]{256}$ in simplest radical form? If not, tell why and write the expression in simplest radical form. **No, because $256 = 2^6 \cdot 4$. $\sqrt[6]{256}$ $= 2\sqrt[6]{4}$ or $2\sqrt[3]{2}$, because $4^{\frac{1}{6}} = 2^{2\left(\frac{1}{6}\right)} = 2^{\frac{1}{3}}$.**

Guided Practice

Evaluate.

4. $9^{\frac{3}{2}}$ 27   5. $8^{\frac{2}{3}}$ 4   6. $4^{\frac{3}{2}}$ 8

7. $16^{\frac{3}{4}}$ 8   8. $64^{\frac{5}{6}}$ 32   9. $27^{-\frac{2}{3}}$ $\frac{1}{9}$

10. $\sqrt[3]{8^2}$ 4   11. $343^{\frac{2}{3}}$ 49   12. $\sqrt[4]{81}$ 3

13. $9^{\frac{1}{3}} \cdot 9^{\frac{3}{1}}$ 81   14. $16^{-\frac{3}{2}}$ $\frac{1}{64}$ 15. $36^{\frac{3}{4}} \div 36^{\frac{1}{4}}$ 6

Express in simplest radical form.

16. $\sqrt[6]{49}$ $\sqrt[3]{7}$ 17. $\sqrt[4]{36}$ $\sqrt{6}$ 18. $\sqrt[6]{81}$ $\sqrt[3]{9}$

19. $\sqrt[8]{16}$ $\sqrt{2}$ 20. $\sqrt[4]{25}$ $\sqrt{5}$ 21. $\sqrt[9]{64}$ $\sqrt[3]{4}$

EXERCISES

Practice

A

Express using rational exponents.

22. $\sqrt{14}$ $14^{\frac{1}{2}}$ 23. $\sqrt[3]{17}$ $17^{\frac{1}{3}}$ 24. $\sqrt[6]{32}$ $32^{\frac{1}{6}}$

25. $\sqrt[4]{y}$ $y^{\frac{1}{4}}$ 26. $\sqrt[3]{m}$ $m^{\frac{1}{3}}$ 27. $\sqrt{25a^3b^4}$ $5a^{\frac{3}{2}}b^2$

28. $\sqrt[3]{8x^3y^6}$ $2xy^2$ 29. $\sqrt[4]{27}$ $27^{\frac{1}{4}}$ 30. $\sqrt[4]{8x^3y^5}$ $8^{\frac{1}{4}}x^{\frac{3}{4}}y^{\frac{5}{4}}$

31. $\sqrt[3]{n^2}$ $n^{\frac{2}{3}}$ 32. $\sqrt[6]{b^3}$ $b^{\frac{1}{2}}$ 33. $\sqrt[3]{16a^5b^7}$ $16^{\frac{1}{3}}a^{\frac{5}{3}}b^{\frac{7}{3}}$

B

Express in simplest radical form.

34. $7^{\frac{1}{2}}$ $\sqrt{7}$ 35. $36^{\frac{1}{4}}$ $\sqrt{6}$ 36. $6^{\frac{1}{3}}$ $\sqrt[3]{6}$

37. $n^{\frac{3}{4}}$ $\sqrt[4]{n^3}$ 38. $x^{\frac{3}{2}}y^{\frac{5}{2}}$ $xy^2\sqrt{xy}$ 39. $2^{\frac{5}{3}}a^{\frac{7}{3}}$ $2a^2\sqrt[3]{4a}$

40. $(2m)^{\frac{1}{2}}m^{\frac{1}{2}}$ $m\sqrt{2}$ 41. $p^{\frac{5}{2}}q^{\frac{3}{4}}$ $p^2\sqrt[4]{p^2q^3}$ 42. $4^{\frac{1}{3}}x^{\frac{2}{3}}y^{\frac{4}{3}}$ $y\sqrt[3]{4x^2y}$

43. $(3r)^{\frac{2}{5}}s^{\frac{3}{5}}$ $\sqrt[5]{9r^2s^3}$ 44. $x^{\frac{4}{7}}y^{\frac{3}{7}}$ $\sqrt[7]{x^4y^3}$ 45. $5^{\frac{1}{3}}s^{\frac{2}{3}}t^{\frac{1}{3}}$ $\sqrt[3]{5s^2t}$

RETEACHING THE LESSON

Have students use both radicals and rational exponents to write dual solutions to simplifying or evaluating expressions. For example,

$$\sqrt[3]{8^2} = (8)^{\frac{2}{3}}$$
$$\sqrt[3]{64} \text{ or } (2^3)^{\frac{2}{3}}$$
$$\sqrt[3]{4^3} = 2^2$$
$$4 = 4$$

Additional Answer

1. If the base were negative and the denominator were even, then we would be taking an even root of a negative, which is undefined.

Evaluate each expression using a calculator.

46. $16^{0.25}$ **2**

47. $\left(\frac{1}{32}\right)^{\frac{1}{5}}$ **$\frac{1}{2}$**

48. $144^{\frac{1}{2}}$ **12**

49. $\sqrt[4]{256}$ **4**

50. $25^{2.5}$ **3125**

51. $27^{\frac{4}{3}}$ **81**

52. $\left(\frac{343}{64}\right)^{\frac{1}{3}}$ **$\frac{7}{4}$**

53. $(9^{0.75})^{\frac{2}{3}}$ **3**

54. $\left(\frac{216}{729}\right)^{\frac{2}{3}}$ **$\frac{4}{9}$**

55. $(0.008)^{\frac{1}{3}}$ **0.2**

56. $(0.125)^{\frac{2}{3}}$ **0.25**

57. $(6^{\frac{2}{3}})^3$ **36**

Express in simplest radical form.

58. $\sqrt[4]{9}$ **$\sqrt{3}$**

59. $x^{\frac{1}{3}}y^{\frac{1}{2}}$ **$\sqrt[6]{x^2y^3}$**

60. $a^{\frac{3}{4}}b^{\frac{1}{3}}c^{\frac{5}{6}}$ **$\sqrt[12]{a^9b^4c^{10}}$**

61. $\sqrt[6]{8}$ **$\sqrt{2}$**

62. $5a^{\frac{1}{2}}b^{\frac{1}{4}}$ **$5\sqrt[4]{a^2b}$**

63. $x^{\frac{5}{6}}y^{\frac{3}{2}}z^{\frac{7}{3}}$ **$yz^2\sqrt[6]{x^5y^3z^2}$**

64. $\sqrt[3]{2^5}\cdot\sqrt[4]{2}$ **$2\sqrt[12]{2^{11}}$**

65. $\sqrt{3}\cdot\sqrt[3]{3^2}$ **$3\sqrt[6]{3}$**

66. $\sqrt[3]{\sqrt{27}}$ **$\sqrt{3}$**

Critical Thinking

67. Does $\sqrt[n]{\sqrt[m]{b}} = \sqrt[m]{\sqrt[n]{b}}$? Justify your answer. **See margin.**

Applications

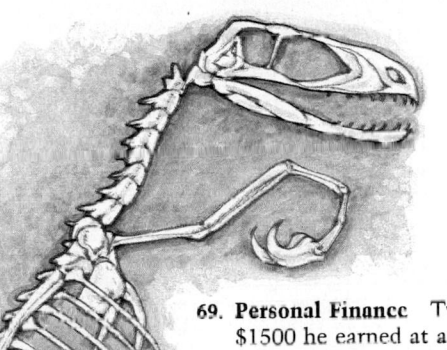

68. **Music** A technician is tuning a piano. The frequency of the A note above middle C is correctly set at 440 vibrations per second. The frequency f_n of a note n notes above A should be
$$f_n = 440\left(\sqrt[12]{2}\right)^{n-1}.$$
   a. At what frequency should the technician set the A that is one octave, or 12 notes, above the A above middle C? **831 vibrations per second**
   b. Middle C is nine notes below the A that has frequency 440 vibrations per second. What should the frequency of middle C be? **247 vibrations per second**

69. **Personal Finance** Two and one-half years ago, Connor deposited the $1500 he earned at a summer job in his bank account. His account earns 7.5% interest annually. Now, he is withdrawing the money and the interest to buy a car. Use the formula $A = P(1 + r)^t$, where A is the amount of money in the account after t years if the interest rate is r and the beginning balance is P, to find how much money Connor has to buy the car. **$1797.27**   **Teaching Tip ❸**

70. **Archaeology** Since carbon 14 is present in all living organisms and decays at a predictable rate after death, archaeologists use the amount of carbon 14 left in a fossil to estimate the age of the fossil. This is commonly called carbon dating. The approximate number of milligrams (A) of carbon 14 left in a fossil after 5000 years can be found using the formula $A = A_0(2.7)^{-\frac{3}{5}}$ where A_0 is the initial amount of carbon 14 in the organism. Find the amount of carbon 14 left in an organism that contained 500 milligrams of carbon 14. **276 milligrams**

LESSON 6-4 RATIONAL EXPONENTS 273

Additional Answer

67. yes, $\sqrt[n]{\sqrt[m]{b}} = (b^{\frac{1}{m}})^{\frac{1}{n}}$

$= b^{\frac{1}{m}\cdot\frac{1}{n}}$

$= b^{\frac{1}{n}\cdot\frac{1}{m}}$

$= (b^{\frac{1}{n}})^{\frac{1}{m}}$

$= \sqrt[m]{\sqrt[n]{b}}$

Teaching Tip ❸   The time is $2\frac{1}{2}$ years. Write this as a fraction before trying to solve the problem.

Practice Masters Booklet, p. 44

NAME _____ DATE _____

6-4 Practice Worksheet

Rational Exponents

Express using rational exponents.

1. $\sqrt[3]{26}$ **$26^{\frac{1}{3}}$**

2. $\sqrt[5]{8}$ **$8^{\frac{1}{5}}$ or $2^{\frac{3}{5}}$**

3. $\sqrt{36x^3y^4}$ **$6x^{\frac{3}{2}}y^2$ or $36^{\frac{1}{2}}x^{\frac{3}{2}}y^3$**

4. $\sqrt[3]{y^7}$ **$y^{\frac{7}{3}}$**

5. $\sqrt[5]{x^3}$ **$x^{\frac{3}{5}}$**

6. $\sqrt[3]{28x^2y^3t^{11}}$ **$28^{\frac{1}{3}}x^{\frac{2}{3}}yt^{\frac{11}{3}}$**

7. $3\sqrt[3]{27n^{10}w}$ **$3^{\frac{4}{3}}n^{\frac{5}{3}}w^{\frac{1}{4}}$ or $3\cdot27^{\frac{1}{4}}n^{\frac{5}{3}}w^{\frac{1}{4}}$**

8. $2\sqrt[5]{2z^{\frac{1}{3}}n^{13}}$ **$2^{\frac{6}{5}}z^{\frac{1}{3}}n^{0.13}$**

9. $4\sqrt{2a^{10}b^3}$ **$2^{\frac{5}{2}}a^5b^{\frac{3}{2}}$ or $4\cdot2^{\frac{1}{2}}a^5b^{\frac{3}{10}}$**

10. $\sqrt[3]{27m^5n^4}$ **$3m^2n^{\frac{4}{3}}$**

Express in simplest radical form.

11. $x^{\frac{3}{5}}\sqrt[5]{x^3}$

12. $27^{\frac{1}{4}}$ **$\sqrt{3}$**

13. $2^{\frac{5}{3}}a^{\frac{1}{3}}y^{\frac{1}{3}}$ **$y\sqrt[3]{32a^3y^2}$**

14. $(3w)^{\frac{1}{3}}m^{\frac{1}{3}}$ **$m^2\sqrt[3]{9w^2m}$**

15. $a^{\frac{1}{3}}g^{\frac{1}{3}}e^{\frac{1}{3}}$ **$\sqrt[15]{a^8g^3e^6}$**

16. $w^{\frac{1}{3}}n^{\frac{1}{3}}$ **$n\sqrt[21]{w^9n^{14}}$**

17. $\sqrt[6]{36}$ **$\sqrt[3]{6}$**

18. $\sqrt[10]{81}$ **$\sqrt[5]{9}$**

19. $m^{\frac{1}{3}}v^{\frac{1}{2}}z^{\frac{1}{3}}$ **$\sqrt[12]{m^4v^9z^{10}}$**

20. $27^{\frac{1}{3}}b^{\frac{1}{3}}c^{\frac{1}{3}}$ **$3c\sqrt[6]{27b^4c}$**

Evaluate each expression using a calculator.

21. $32^{\frac{2}{5}}$ **4**

22. $(25^{\frac{3}{2}})^{\frac{1}{3}}$ **5**

23. $(0.216)^{\frac{1}{3}}$ **0.6**

24. $\left(\frac{27}{125}\right)^{\frac{2}{3}}$ **0.36**

25. $\sqrt{2401}$ **7**

26. $36^{2.5}$ **7776**

71. Name the conjugate of the expression $5 + 3\sqrt{3}$. **(Lesson 6-3)** $5 - 3\sqrt{3}$

72. Simplify $\sqrt{108} - \sqrt{48} + (\sqrt{3})^3$. **(Lesson 6-3)** $5\sqrt{3}$

73. Use division to simplify $(a^2 - 5ab + 6b^2) \div (a - 3b)$. **(Lesson 5-6)**
$a - 2b$

74. Find the inverse of the matrix $\begin{bmatrix} 3 & 1 \\ 2 & -4 \end{bmatrix}$. **(Lesson 4-5)** $\frac{1}{14}\begin{bmatrix} 4 & 1 \\ 2 & -3 \end{bmatrix}$

75. The Worthington Public Library charges a fine of 5¢ per day for overdue books. What will the fine be on a book that is two weeks overdue? **(Lesson 2-2)** **70¢**

76. Simplify the expression $4(5x + 2y) + 9(x - 2y)$. **(Lesson 1-2)**
29x − 10y

Journal

Write how you would explain simplifying radical expressions to another student and write the examples you would use.

MID-CHAPTER REVIEW

Simplify. **(Lesson 6-1)**

1. $-\sqrt{81x^2}$ **−9|x|**

2. $\sqrt{a^2 + 14a + 49}$ **|a + 7|**

3. $\sqrt[3]{-64x^9}$ **−4x³**

4. $\sqrt{48m^2n^3}$ **4|m|n√3n**

Simplify. **(Lesson 6-2)**

5. $\sqrt{6}(\sqrt{3} + 5\sqrt{2})$ **3√2 + 10√3**

6. $\frac{5}{3\sqrt{5}}$ **$\frac{\sqrt{5}}{3}$**

7. $\frac{12}{\sqrt[3]{4x}}$ **$\frac{6\sqrt[3]{2x^2}}{x}$**

8. $\sqrt[4]{3b^6r^7} \cdot \sqrt[4]{81b^2r^2}$ **3b²r²√[4]{3r}**

9. **Physics** A pebble is dropped from a height of 200 feet. Use the formula $t = \frac{1}{4}\sqrt{s}$, where t is the number of seconds it takes for the pebble to reach the ground and s is the distance in feet it will fall, to find the time it will take for the pebble to reach the ground. **3.53 seconds**

Simplify. **(Lesson 6-3)**

10. $2\sqrt{18} + 3\sqrt{8} - 4\sqrt{50}$ **−8√2**

11. $(5 + \sqrt{3})(7 - 2\sqrt{3})$ **29 − 3√3**

12. $(11 - \sqrt{7})(11 + \sqrt{7})$ **114**

13. $\frac{1 + \sqrt{3}}{5 - 2\sqrt{3}}$ **$\frac{11 + 7\sqrt{3}}{13}$**

14. Evaluate $8^{\frac{2}{3}} \cdot 9^{\frac{1}{2}}$. **(Lesson 6-4)** **12**

15. Express $5^{\frac{2}{3}}x^{\frac{1}{2}}y^{\frac{3}{4}}$ in simplest radical form. **(Lesson 6-4)** **$\sqrt[12]{5^8x^6y^9}$**

16. Express $\sqrt[6]{27a^3b^4c^6}$ using rational exponents. **(Lesson 6-4)** **$3^{\frac{1}{2}}a^{\frac{1}{2}}b^{\frac{2}{3}}|c|$**

EXTENDING THE LESSON

Math Power: Problem Solving

Can π^π be evaluated? Why or why not? Defend your decision.

Mid-Chapter Review

The Mid-Chapter Review provides students with a brief review of the concepts and skills in Lessons 6-1 through 6-4. Lesson numbers are given at the end of problems or instruction lines so students may review concepts not yet mastered.

Enrichment Masters Booklet, p. 39

6-5 Problem-Solving Strategy: Identify Subgoals

Objective
6-5

After studying this lesson, you should be able to:

■ solve problems by identifying and achieving subgoals.

Like walking a mile, solving a problem is a series of small steps. If we can identify the steps, or subgoals, that need to be achieved in solving a problem, solving is a simpler process.

Example

Find the sum of the whole numbers from 1 through 200 that are not multiples of 4 or 9. You may use the formula $S = \frac{1}{2}n(n + 1)$ for the sum, S, of the integers 1 to n.

The first subgoal we can identify is to find the sum of the integers from 1 to 200. Use the formula provided.

$$S = \frac{1}{2}n(n + 1)$$
$$= \frac{1}{2}(200)(201) \qquad \text{\textit{Replace n with 200.}}$$
$$= 20{,}100$$

The second subgoal is to find the sum of the integers from 1 to 200 that are multiples of 4 and the sum of the integers that are multiples of 9.

The sum of the multiples of 4 is given by the following expression.

$$4 + 8 + 12 + \ldots + 200$$
$$= 4(1 + 2 + 3 + \ldots + 50) \qquad \text{\textit{Distributive property}}$$

Now use the formula for the sum of the integers 1 to 50.

$$4(1 + 2 + 3 + \ldots + 50)$$
$$= 4\left(\frac{1}{2}(50)(51)\right) \qquad \text{\textit{Replace n with 50.}}$$
$$= 5100$$

Use the same technique to find the sum of the multiples of 9.

$$9 + 18 + 27 + \ldots + 198$$
$$= 9(1 + 2 + 3 + \ldots + 22)$$
$$= 9\left(\frac{1}{2}(22)(23)\right) \text{ or } 2277$$

The final subgoal is to find the sum of the numbers between 1 and 100 that are not multiples of 4 or 9.

LESSON 6-5   PROBLEM SOLVING STRATEGY: IDENTIFY SUBGOALS   275

ALTERNATE TEACHING STRATEGIES

Mini-Math Lab

Have students conduct a survey of teachers. They should ask them how many students they have taught in their careers. The students should list the teachers surveyed by years taught and number of students taught. They should try to predict how many students a teacher will have in a career of 30 years. How did they arrive at their predictions?

Lesson Resources

Practice Master 6-5
Activity Master, p. 24

Transparency 6-5 contains the 5-Minute Check and a teaching aid for this lesson.

INTRODUCING THE LESSON

5-Minute Check

(over Lesson 6-4)
Evaluate.

1. $\sqrt[5]{-32}$ -2

2. $100^{-\frac{1}{2}}$ $\frac{1}{10}$

3. $16^{\frac{5}{4}}$ 32

4. $16^{\frac{1}{4}} \cdot 16^{\frac{1}{2}} \cdot 16^{\frac{3}{4}}$ 64

5. Express $3^{\frac{1}{3}} \cdot x^{\frac{5}{6}} \cdot y^{\frac{1}{4}}$ in simplest radical form. $\sqrt[12]{81x^{10}y^3}$

Motivating the Lesson

Have students try to solve this birthday problem.
What is the least number of people needed to insure a 50% probability that at least two of the people will have the same birthday? Suggest that students first find the probability of 2 persons having the same birthday, then 3 and so on. The answer is 24.

TEACHING THE LESSON

Teaching Tip **❶**   Why do you use 198 instead of 200? Make sure the students understand.

Chalkboard Example

For the Example
Find the sum of the whole numbers between 1 and 250 that are not multiples of 5 or 7.
21,570

Checking for Understanding
Exercises 1–4 are designed to help you assess understanding through reading, writing, and speaking. You should work through Exercises 1–3 with your students, and then monitor their work on Exercise 4.

Closing the Lesson
Writing Activity   Have students write a problem that uses sub-goals. Have a classmate solve the problem and explain the process.

APPLYING THE LESSON

Homework Exercises

Assignment Guide
Basic: 5–10
Average: 5–10
Enriched: 5–10

Chapter 6, Quiz B, (Lessons 6-4 through 6-5), is available in the Evaluation Masters Booklet, p. 79.

Teaching Tip ❷   When you add the multiples of 4 and 9, you include the multiples of both twice. What are the multiples of both?

Practice Masters Booklet, p. 45

If we subtract these two sums from the sum of all integers from 1 to 200, the numbers that are multiples of both 4 and 9 will be subtracted twice. So, we must find that sum and add it back so that those numbers are subtracted only once. The multiples of 36 are multiples of both 4 and 9.

Multiples of 36: 36 + 72 + 108 + 144 + 180 or 540

Solve the problem: 20,100 − 5100 − 2277 + 540 = 13,263

The sum of the whole numbers between 1 and 200 that are not multiples of 4 or 9 is 13,263

CHECKING FOR UNDERSTANDING

Communicating Mathematics
Read and study the lesson to answer these questions. **1–2. See margin.**

1. Why is it helpful to set subgoals when solving a problem?

2. Why did we need to add the sum of the multiples of 36 in the Example?

3. What is the sum of the integers from 1 through 300 that are not multiples of 4 or 9? **29,997**

Guided Practice

4. Find the value of the expression $\sqrt{\sqrt{\left(\sqrt{\left(\sqrt{\left(\sqrt{2^2}\right)^2}\right)^4}\right)^2}}$. Justify your answer.

2

EXERCISES

Solve. Use any strategy.

5. How many factors of 2000 are perfect squares? **6**

6. Find the sum $\frac{1}{2^1} + \frac{1}{2^2} + \frac{1}{2^3} + \ldots + \frac{1}{2^{10}}$. **1023 / 1024**

7. The proper divisors of a number are the factors of the number that are less than the number. What is the least natural number that has exactly nine proper factors? **48**

8. **Statistics**   The average of the ages of the first five presidents at the time of their inauguration is 58 years. If the sum of the ages of the first four presidents at their inauguration is 232, how old was the fifth president when he was inaugurated? **58**

9. **Geometry**   If the area of a 14 cm by 14 cm square is increased by 60 cm², what are the dimensions of the new square? **16 cm by 16 cm**

10. What positive number is equal to its square added to its opposite? **2**

COOPERATIVE LEARNING ACTIVITY

Work in groups. Each person in the group must understand the solution and be able to explain it to any person in the class.

How many zeros appear at the end of the product of the first 100 integers?   **21**

RETEACHING THE LESSON

Find the sum of all the odd integers between 100 and 300. Here are some approaches.
1. Find 101 + 103 + 105 + . . . + 297 + 299.
2. Sum of first 150 odds minus sum of first 50 odds
3. Sum of first 300 integers minus sum of first 150 evens minus sum of first 50 odds
20,000

Additional Answers
1. It breaks the problem down into smaller, simpler steps.
2. The multiples of 36 were subtracted twice—once in the multiples of 4 and once in the multiples of 9. We had to add them back in so that they were subtracted only once.

Simplifying Expressions with Rational Exponents

Objective
6-6

After studying this lesson, you should be able to:
- simplify expressions containing rational exponents.

Application

FYI …

NASA has launched more than 300 satellites since its start in 1958. Satellites are used for everything from observing weather patterns and providing communication links to monitoring the use of resources.

Aerospace engineers have found that the velocity necessary for a satellite to maintain a circular orbit around Earth is found by the formula

$v = R_e\sqrt{\dfrac{g}{r}}$, where R_e represents the radius of the Earth, g represents the acceleration due to gravity, and r represents the radius of the orbit. Can you rewrite the formula using positive rational exponents? That is, can you simplify the formula?

When you are asked to simplify an expression, you must write the expression with all positive exponents. Furthermore, any exponents in the denominator of a fraction must be positive *integers*.

Example 1

Remember $\dfrac{1}{5^{\frac{1}{2}}} = \dfrac{1}{\sqrt{5}}$.

Simplify each expression.

a. $\dfrac{1}{5^{\frac{1}{2}}}$

$\dfrac{1}{5^{\frac{1}{2}}} = \dfrac{1}{5^{\frac{1}{2}}} \cdot \dfrac{5^{\frac{1}{2}}}{5^{\frac{1}{2}}}$ Why $\dfrac{5^{\frac{1}{2}}}{5^{\frac{1}{2}}}$?

$= \dfrac{5^{\frac{1}{2}}}{5}$

b. $\dfrac{1}{7^{\frac{2}{3}}}$

$\dfrac{1}{7^{\frac{2}{3}}} = \dfrac{1}{7^{\frac{2}{3}}} \cdot \dfrac{7^{\frac{1}{3}}}{7^{\frac{1}{3}}}$ Why $\dfrac{7^{\frac{1}{3}}}{7^{\frac{1}{3}}}$?

$= \dfrac{7^{\frac{1}{3}}}{7}$

There is more than one way to simplify an expression. Choosing the multiplier carefully may allow you to simplify in fewer steps. Study Example 2 to learn how to choose the correct multiplier.

Lesson Resources

Reteaching Master 6-6
Practice Master 6-6
Enrichment Master 6-6

 Transparency 6-6 contains the 5-Minute Check and a teaching aid for this lesson.

INTRODUCING THE LESSON

5-Minute Check

(over Lesson 6-5)

1. Find the sum of the whole numbers between 0 and 150 that are not multiples of 2 or 9.
   5049

Other Prerequisite Skills

2. True or False. $a^x \cdot a^n = a$
   false

3. $\left(\dfrac{49}{81}\right)^{-\frac{1}{2}}$ $\dfrac{9}{7}$

4. $\dfrac{4\sqrt{3} - \sqrt{5}}{2\sqrt{3} + 3\sqrt{5}}$ $\dfrac{14\sqrt{15} - 39}{33}$

5. $(5\sqrt{6} - \sqrt{5})(2\sqrt{6} - 4\sqrt{5})$
   80 − 22√30

Motivating the Lesson

Have students review the meaning of rational exponents. They should also review the rules. Then have them rewrite the following expression using rational exponents.

$$\dfrac{2^{\frac{1}{2}} \cdot 2^{\frac{1}{5}}}{2^{\frac{1}{3}} \cdot 2^{\frac{1}{4}}} = 2^{\frac{7}{60}}$$

ALTERNATE TEACHING STRATEGIES

Using Applications

Have students find the total resistance of a parallel circuit with two resistors.

$$R^i = \left(\dfrac{1}{R_1} + \dfrac{1}{R_2}\right)^{-1}$$

Let $R_1 = 2$ and $R_2 = 4$.
What does the −1 power do to the equation?

Using Computers

Students can write a flow chart to show how to simplify the expressions with fractional exponents. Give the students an expression such as

$$\dfrac{x^{\frac{1}{4}} + x^{\frac{1}{2}}}{x^{\frac{1}{4}} - x}$$ to simplify.

Chalkboard Examples

For Example 1

Simplify.

a. $\dfrac{1}{a^{\frac{2}{3}}}$ $\dfrac{a^{\frac{1}{3}}}{a}$

b. $\dfrac{2}{3^{\frac{1}{2}}}$ $\dfrac{2 \cdot 3^{\frac{1}{2}}}{3}$

For Example 2

Simplify.

a. $\dfrac{5n}{n^{\frac{1}{5}}}$ $5n^{\frac{4}{5}}$

b. $\dfrac{x^{\frac{2}{3}}}{\sqrt[3]{x}}$ $x^{\frac{1}{3}}$

For Example 3

Solve $z = xy\left(\dfrac{9\pi^2 r^2}{n^2}\right)$ for n.

$n = \dfrac{3\pi r\sqrt{xyz}}{z}$

Reteaching Masters Booklet, p. 40

Example 2 | Simplify $\dfrac{1}{2^{\frac{3}{2}}}$.   **Teaching Tip ①**

Method 1

$\dfrac{1}{2^{\frac{3}{2}}} = \dfrac{1}{2^{\frac{3}{2}}}\left(\dfrac{2^{\frac{3}{2}}}{2^{\frac{3}{2}}}\right)$

$= \dfrac{2^{\frac{3}{2}}}{2^3}$ or $\dfrac{2^{\frac{1}{2}}}{2^2}$

Method 2

$\dfrac{1}{2^{\frac{3}{2}}} = \dfrac{1}{2^{\frac{3}{2}}}\left(\dfrac{2^{\frac{1}{2}}}{2^{\frac{1}{2}}}\right)$

$= \dfrac{2^{\frac{1}{2}}}{2^2}$

Notice that there are fewer steps in simplifying when the multiplier is in the form $\dfrac{2^{\frac{1}{2}}}{2^{\frac{1}{2}}}$.

An expression is simplified when it meets all of these conditions:
- it has no negative exponents,
- it has no fractional exponents in the denominator,
- it is not a complex fraction, and
- the index of any remaining radical is the least number possible.

Example 3

APPLICATION

Physics

A model airplane is fixed on a string so that it flies around in a circle. The designers of the plane would like to find the time it takes for the airplane to make a complete circle. They know that the formula $F_c = m\left(\dfrac{4\pi^2 r}{T^2}\right)$ describes the force required to keep the airplane going in a circle. m represents the mass of the airplane, r represents the radius of the circle, and T represents the time for a revolution. Solve the formula for T.

$F_c = m\left(\dfrac{4\pi^2 r}{T^2}\right)$

$T^2 = m\left(\dfrac{4\pi^2 r}{F_c}\right)$ *Multiply each side by $\dfrac{T^2}{F_c}$.*

$T = \sqrt{m\left(\dfrac{4\pi^2 r}{F_c}\right)}$ *Find the square root of each side.*

$= 2\pi\sqrt{\dfrac{mr}{F_c}}$ *Simplify.*

$= \dfrac{2\pi\sqrt{mrF_c}}{F_c}$ *Rationalize the denominator.*

Example 4 | Simplify $\dfrac{x^{\frac{1}{2}} - y^{\frac{1}{2}}}{x^{\frac{1}{2}} + y^{\frac{1}{2}}}$.

$\dfrac{x^{\frac{1}{2}} - y^{\frac{1}{2}}}{x^{\frac{1}{2}} + y^{\frac{1}{2}}} = \dfrac{x^{\frac{1}{2}} - y^{\frac{1}{2}}}{x^{\frac{1}{2}} + y^{\frac{1}{2}}} \cdot \dfrac{x^{\frac{1}{2}} - y^{\frac{1}{2}}}{x^{\frac{1}{2}} - y^{\frac{1}{2}}}$ *The conjugate of $x^{\frac{1}{2}} + y^{\frac{1}{2}}$ is $x^{\frac{1}{2}} - y^{\frac{1}{2}}$.*

$= \dfrac{x - 2x^{\frac{1}{2}}y^{\frac{1}{2}} + y}{x - y}$

RETEACHING THE LESSON

Ask students the following questions. By what can you multiply the denominator to eliminate the rational exponent? Then by what would you multiply the numerator to have an expression equivalent to the original? So you're really multiplying by a form of what number?   1

CHECKING FOR UNDERSTANDING

Communicating Mathematics

Read and study the lesson to answer these questions. **1–3. See margin.**

1. Under what conditions does a denominator need to be rationalized?

2. Is the expression $\dfrac{1}{q^{\frac{1}{2}}}$ simplified? If not, why not?

3. Explain your strategy for choosing the multiplier so that rationalizing a denominator will take the fewest steps.

Guided Practice

State a factor that can be used to rationalize the denominator of each expression. Then simplify.

11. $\dfrac{q^{\frac{1}{2}} + r^{\frac{1}{2}}}{q^{\frac{1}{2}} + r^{\frac{1}{2}}},\ \dfrac{q^{\frac{3}{2}} + qr^{\frac{1}{2}}}{q - r}$

12. $\dfrac{a^{\frac{1}{2}} - b}{a^{\frac{1}{2}} - b},$

$\dfrac{a^{\frac{3}{2}} - ab + a^{\frac{1}{2}}b - b^2}{a - b^2}$

4. $\dfrac{8}{3^{\frac{1}{2}}} \dfrac{3^{\frac{1}{2}}}{3^{\frac{1}{2}}},\ \dfrac{8 \cdot 3^{\frac{1}{2}}}{3}$

7. $\dfrac{1}{a^{\frac{1}{3}}} \dfrac{a^{\frac{2}{3}}}{a^{\frac{2}{3}}},\ \dfrac{a^{\frac{2}{3}}}{a}$

10. $m^{-\frac{3}{2}} \dfrac{m^{\frac{1}{2}}}{m^{\frac{1}{2}}},\ \dfrac{m^{\frac{1}{2}}}{m^2}$

13. $\dfrac{2}{t^{\frac{3}{2}} + s^{\frac{1}{2}}} \dfrac{t^{\frac{3}{2}} - s^{\frac{1}{2}}}{t^{\frac{3}{2}} - s^{\frac{1}{2}}},$
$\dfrac{2t^{\frac{3}{2}} - 2s^{\frac{1}{2}}}{t^3 - s}$

5. $\dfrac{16}{4^{\frac{3}{2}}} \dfrac{4^{\frac{1}{2}}}{4^{\frac{1}{2}}},\ 2$

8. $x^{-\frac{1}{5}} \dfrac{x^{\frac{4}{5}}}{x^{\frac{4}{5}}},\ \dfrac{x^{\frac{4}{5}}}{x}$

11. $\dfrac{q}{q^{\frac{1}{2}} - r^{\frac{1}{2}}}$

14. $\dfrac{3}{c^{\frac{3}{2}} + c^{\frac{1}{2}}} \dfrac{c^{\frac{3}{2}} - c^{\frac{1}{2}}}{c^{\frac{3}{2}} - c^{\frac{1}{2}}},$
$\dfrac{3c^{\frac{3}{2}} - 3c^{\frac{1}{2}}}{c^3 - c}$

6. $\dfrac{1}{y^{\frac{2}{3}}} \dfrac{y^{\frac{1}{3}}}{y^{\frac{1}{3}}},\ \dfrac{y^{\frac{1}{3}}}{y}$

9. $\dfrac{1}{t^{\frac{1}{2}} + 1} \dfrac{t^{\frac{1}{2}} - 1}{t^{\frac{1}{2}} - 1},\ \dfrac{t^{\frac{1}{2}} - 1}{t - 1}$

12. $\dfrac{a + b}{a^{\frac{1}{2}} + b}$

15. $\dfrac{w + 1}{w - w^{\frac{1}{2}}} \dfrac{w + w^{\frac{1}{2}}}{w + w^{\frac{1}{2}}},$
$\dfrac{w^2 + w^{\frac{3}{2}} + w + w^{\frac{1}{2}}}{w^2 - w}$

EXERCISES

Practice ▲A

Simplify.

16. $x^{-\frac{1}{4}} \dfrac{x^{\frac{3}{4}}}{x}$

19. $t^{-\frac{5}{6}} \dfrac{t^{\frac{1}{6}}}{t}$

22. $\dfrac{p^{\frac{3}{2}} - pq + p^{\frac{1}{2}}q - q^2}{p - q^?}$
22. $\dfrac{p + q}{p^{\frac{1}{2}} + q}$

25. $\dfrac{24}{6^{\frac{2}{3}}}\ 4 \cdot 6^{\frac{1}{3}}$

28. $\dfrac{xy}{\sqrt[3]{z}} \dfrac{xyz^{\frac{2}{3}}}{z}$

31. $\dfrac{3x + 4x^2}{x^{-\frac{2}{3}}}\ 3x^{\frac{5}{3}} + 4x^{\frac{8}{3}}$

17. $\dfrac{1}{s^{-\frac{4}{5}}} \dfrac{s^{\frac{1}{5}}}{s}$

20. $n^{-\frac{3}{2}} \dfrac{n^{\frac{1}{2}}}{n^2}$

23. $\dfrac{1}{t^{\frac{3}{2}} + t^{\frac{1}{2}}} \dfrac{t^{\frac{1}{2}}}{t(t + 1)}$

26. $\dfrac{15}{5^{\frac{2}{3}}}\ 3 \cdot 5^{\frac{1}{3}}$

29. $\dfrac{n^{\frac{3}{2}} + 3n^{-\frac{1}{2}}}{n^{\frac{1}{2}}} \dfrac{n^2 + 3}{n}$

32. $\left(r^{-\frac{1}{6}}\right)^{\frac{2}{3}} r^{\frac{1}{9}}$

18. $\dfrac{1}{y^{-\frac{2}{5}}} \dfrac{y^{\frac{3}{5}}}{y}$

21. $\dfrac{1}{x^{\frac{1}{2}} + 1} \dfrac{x^{\frac{1}{2}} - 1}{x - 1}$

24. $\dfrac{rt}{r^{\frac{1}{2}} + t^{\frac{1}{2}}} \dfrac{rt(r^{\frac{1}{2}} \ t^{\frac{1}{2}})}{r - t}$

27. $\dfrac{ab^{\frac{1}{2}}}{c^{\frac{3}{2}}} \dfrac{ab^{\frac{1}{2}}c^{\frac{1}{2}}}{c^2}$

30. $\dfrac{a^{\frac{5}{3}}b + 3a^{-\frac{1}{3}}}{a^{\frac{2}{3}}} \dfrac{a^2b + 3}{a}$

33. $\dfrac{3x}{y^{-\frac{3}{2}} \cdot \sqrt[3]{z}} \dfrac{3xy^{\frac{3}{2}}z^{\frac{2}{3}}}{z}$

▲B

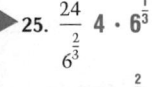

Journal

Write a few sentences about something new you learned in this lesson. Be sure to include examples.

Chalkboard Example

For Example 4
Simplify.

a. $\dfrac{1}{m^{\frac{5}{2}} + n^{\frac{3}{2}}}\quad \dfrac{m^{\frac{5}{2}} - n^{\frac{3}{2}}}{m^5 - n^3}$

b. $\dfrac{a}{a^{\frac{1}{2}} + b^{\frac{1}{2}}}\quad \dfrac{a(a^{\frac{1}{2}} - b^{\frac{1}{2}})}{a - b}$

Teaching Tip ❶ Why are there fewer steps? Point out that only the fractional part needs to be used as the multiplier.

EVALUATING THE LESSON

Checking for Understanding

Exercises 1–15 are designed to help you assess understanding through reading, writing, and speaking. You should work through Exercises 1–3 with your students, and then monitor their work on Exercises 4–15.

Assignment Guide

Basic: 16–36, 43–44, 46–50
Average: 21–39, 43–50
Enriched: 25–50

Practice Masters Booklet, p. 46

Additional Answers

1. when the denominator contains a radical or a term with a fractional or negative exponent

2. no; The exponent in the denominator should be a positive integer.

3. Choose a fraction equivalent to 1 that will make the denominator the least possible positive integer, while the exponents in the numerator are also positive.

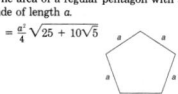

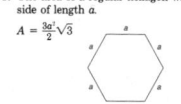

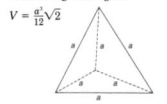

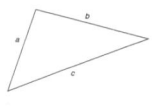

---

34. $\left(y^{\frac{1}{3}}\right)^{-\frac{3}{4}} \dfrac{y^{\frac{3}{4}}}{y}$

35. $\dfrac{r^{\frac{3}{2}}}{r^{\frac{1}{2}} + 2} \cdot \dfrac{r^2 - 2r^{\frac{3}{2}}}{r - 4}$

36. $\dfrac{s^{\frac{1}{2}} + t^{\frac{1}{2}}}{s^{\frac{1}{2}} - t^{\frac{1}{2}}} \cdot \dfrac{s + 2s^{\frac{1}{2}}t^{\frac{1}{2}} + t}{s - t}$

37. $\dfrac{b^{\frac{1}{2}}}{b^{\frac{3}{2}} - b^{\frac{1}{2}}} \cdot \dfrac{1}{b - 1}$

38. $\dfrac{s^{\frac{1}{2}} + 1}{s^{\frac{1}{2}} - 1} \cdot \dfrac{s + 2s^{\frac{1}{2}} + 1}{s - 1}$

39. $\left(\dfrac{x^{-2}y^{-6}}{9}\right)^{-\frac{1}{2}} 3xy^3$

40. $\dfrac{8^{\frac{1}{6}} - 9^{\frac{1}{4}}}{\sqrt{3} + \sqrt{2}}$ $2\sqrt{6} - 5$

41. $\dfrac{a^{-\frac{2}{3}}b^{\frac{1}{2}}}{b^{-\frac{3}{2}} \cdot \sqrt[3]{a}} \dfrac{b^2}{a}$

42. $\dfrac{x^{\frac{5}{3}} - x^{\frac{1}{3}}y^{\frac{4}{3}}}{x^{\frac{2}{3}} + y^{\frac{2}{3}}} x - x^{\frac{1}{3}}y^{\frac{2}{3}}$

Critical Thinking

43. Evaluate $-\dfrac{4}{9}x^9\left(\dfrac{3}{x^2} - \dfrac{1}{\sqrt[3]{2}}\right)$ when $x = \sqrt[6]{2}$. $-\dfrac{16}{9} \cdot 2^{\frac{1}{6}}$

Applications

44. **Electricity** The formula for finding the total resistance of a parallel circuit with four resistors is
$$R_t = \left(\dfrac{1}{R_1} + \dfrac{1}{R_2} + \dfrac{1}{R_3} + \dfrac{1}{R_4}\right)^{-1},$$
where R_t is the resistance of resistor t. Simplify the formula and find the total resistance for a circuit whose resistors have resistance of 16, 12, 8, and 24 ohms. **3.2 ohms**
$$R_t = \dfrac{R_1R_2R_3R_4}{R_2R_3R_4 + R_1R_3R_4 + R_1R_2R_4 + R_1R_2R_3}$$

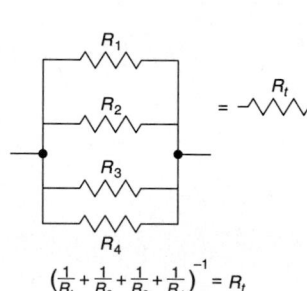

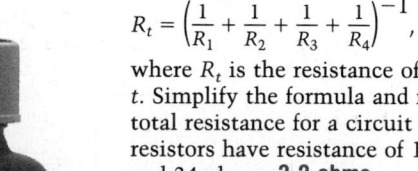

$\left(\dfrac{1}{R_1} + \dfrac{1}{R_2} + \dfrac{1}{R_3} + \dfrac{1}{R_4}\right)^{-1} = R_t$

45. **Medicine** A doctor has determined that 20 units of a medication are in a patient's system now. At the end of any hour there is one-third the medication left in his system that was there when the hour began. Assuming that no more injections of medication are made, write an expression for the amount of medication in the patient's system after t hours. $\dfrac{20}{3^t}$ **units** **Teaching Tip ❷**

Mixed Review

46. What fraction of the perfect squares between 0 and 100 are odd? (Lesson 6-5) $\dfrac{1}{2}$

47. How would you write the seventh root of 5 cubed using an exponent? (Lesson 6-4) $5^{\frac{3}{7}}$

48. Use synthetic division to find $(2x^3 - 2x^2 + 4) \div (x + 1)$. (Lesson 5-7) $2x^2 - 4x + 4$

49. Describe the graphs of two linear equations that are dependent. (Lesson 3-1) **They are the same line.**

50. Determine the slope of the line passing through the points $(9, 0)$ and $(4, -5)$ (Lesson 2-4) **1**

280 CHAPTER 6 IRRATIONAL AND COMPLEX NUMBERS

EXTENDING THE LESSON

Math Power: Reasoning

Have students work in groups to simplify the expression
$$\dfrac{2}{\sqrt{2} + \sqrt{3} + \sqrt{7}}. \quad \dfrac{4\sqrt{2} + 3\sqrt{3} - \sqrt{7} - \sqrt{42}}{5}$$

6-7 Solving Equations Containing Radicals

Objective 6-7

After studying this lesson, you should be able to:
- solve equations containing radicals.

Application

A jeweler is designing a pin in the shape of a parallelogram. The design consists of a square piece of black onyx and a piece of mother-of-pearl on either side. The pieces of mother-of-pearl are isosceles right triangles. A 10-centimeter piece of gold wire is to be placed around the outside of the pin. What are the lengths of the sides of the parallelogram?

Solving some equations involves the use of radical numbers in equations. Let's investigate this type of equation while we find the lengths of the sides of the parallelogram described above.

The drawing at the right models the shape of the pin.

Let x = the length of a side of the square.

Since we know that the triangles are right triangles, we can use the Pythagorean Theorem to find an expression for the length of an end of the parallelogram. *Since the triangle is isosceles, the legs are of equal length.*

$$a^2 + b^2 = c^2$$
$$x^2 + x^2 = c^2$$
$$2x^2 = c^2$$
$$\pm x\sqrt{2} = c$$

Since a measurement is positive, $x\sqrt{2}$ is the length of an end of the parallelogram.

The 10-cm-long gold wire represents the perimeter of the figure. The perimeter is $x + x + x\sqrt{2} + x + x + x\sqrt{2}$ or $4x + 2x\sqrt{2}$. So, $4x + 2x\sqrt{2} = 10$. We must use some of the properties of radical expressions to solve this equation.

$$4x + 2x\sqrt{2} = 10$$
$$x(4 + 2\sqrt{2}) = 10 \qquad \textit{Factor out } x.$$
$$x = \frac{10}{4 + 2\sqrt{2}} \qquad \textit{Divide each side by } 4 + 2\sqrt{2}.$$
$$= \left(\frac{10}{4 + 2\sqrt{2}}\right)\left(\frac{4 - 2\sqrt{2}}{4 - 2\sqrt{2}}\right) \qquad \textit{Rationalize the denominator.}$$
$$\qquad\qquad\qquad\qquad \textbf{Teaching Tip ❶}$$
$$= \frac{10 - 5\sqrt{2}}{2}$$

Using a calculator to evaluate this expression, we find that x is about 1.46 cm. So, the sides of the pin are $2x$ or about 2.92 cm and $x\sqrt{2}$ or 2.06 cm long.

LESSON 6-7   SOLVING EQUATIONS CONTAINING RADICALS   281

Using Models

Have students develop a sense of the geometric meaning of square roots. To find $\sqrt{13}$, draw a diagonal of a 2×3 rectangle.

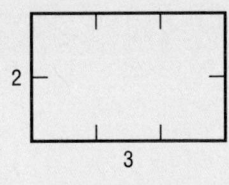

Another method: Construct a semicircle of diameter $2 + 3$ or 5. At the point of division between the 2 and 3, construct a perpendicular. This perpendicular is $\sqrt{6}$ units long.

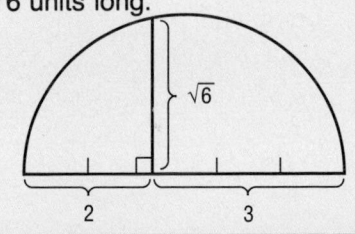

Lesson Resources
Reteaching Master 6-7
Practice Master 6-7
Enrichment Master 6-7
Activity Master, p. 6
Transparency 6-7 contains the 5-Minute Check and a teaching aid for this lesson.

INTRODUCING THE LESSON

⏱ 5-Minute Check

(over Lesson 6-6)

Simplify.

1. $\dfrac{6}{x^{\frac{5}{6}}}$ $\dfrac{6x^{\frac{1}{6}}}{x}$

2. $9^{-\frac{3}{2}}$ $\dfrac{1}{27}$

3. $\dfrac{9}{3^{\frac{2}{3}}}$ $3^{\frac{4}{3}}$

4. $\dfrac{x^{\frac{1}{2}} - y^{\frac{1}{2}}}{x^{\frac{1}{2}} + y^{\frac{1}{2}}}$ $\dfrac{x - 2x^{\frac{1}{2}}y^{\frac{1}{2}} + y}{x - y}$

5. $\dfrac{1}{a^{\frac{5}{2}} - b^{\frac{3}{2}}}$ $\dfrac{a^{\frac{5}{2}} + b^{\frac{3}{2}}}{a^5 - b^3}$

Motivating the Lesson

Review the properties of geometric figures such as rectangles and parallelograms. Have students use the Pythagorean Theorem to find the diagonals of the figures.

TEACHING THE LESSON

Teaching Tip ❶   Remind students they need to rationalize the denominator because there is a radical in the denominator.

Chalkboard Examples

For Example 1
Solve.

a. $x - 4 = x\sqrt{3}$ $-2 - 2\sqrt{3}$

b. $a\sqrt{3} + 2 = 2a\sqrt{3} + 7$
$\dfrac{-5\sqrt{3}}{3}$

For Example 2
Solve.

a. $\sqrt{2y - 1} - 3 = 0$ 5

b. $\sqrt{3t - 2} + 3 = 7$ 6

For Example 3
Solve.

a. $3 - \sqrt{x - 2} = 0$ 11

b. $12 - \sqrt{3m + 7} = 5$ 14

Example 1

Solve $x + 1 = x\sqrt{2}$.

$$x + 1 = x\sqrt{2}$$
$$1 = x\sqrt{2} - x$$
$$1 = x(\sqrt{2} - 1)$$
$$\frac{1}{\sqrt{2} - 1} = x$$
$$\frac{\sqrt{2} + 1}{\sqrt{2} + 1} \cdot \frac{1}{\sqrt{2} - 1} = x$$
$$\frac{\sqrt{2} + 1}{1} = x$$
$$\sqrt{2} + 1 = x$$

The solution is $\sqrt{2} + 1$.

Check:
$$x + 1 = x\sqrt{2}$$
$$(1 + \sqrt{2}) + 1 \stackrel{?}{=} (1 + \sqrt{2})\sqrt{2}$$
$$2 + \sqrt{2} = \sqrt{2} + 2 \ \checkmark$$

Sometimes variables appear in the radicand. Equations with radicals like this are called **radical equations.** To solve this type of equation, you will need to square (or sometimes cube) each side of the equation to remove the variable from the radical. Solving radical equations in this way sometimes yields **extraneous solutions,** solutions that do not satisfy the original equation. You must check all the possible solutions in the *original* equation and disregard the extraneous solutions. **Teaching Tip ❷**

Example 2

Solve $9 + \sqrt{x - 1} = 1$.

We need to remove the radical from this equation. We can achieve this subgoal by isolating the radical on one side of the equation.

$$9 + \sqrt{x - 1} = 1$$
$$\sqrt{x - 1} = -8 \qquad \textit{Isolate the radical.}$$
$$x - 1 = 64 \qquad \textit{Square each side.}$$
$$x = 65$$

The solution does not check.   The equation has no real solution.

Check: $9 + \sqrt{x - 1} = 1$
$$9 + \sqrt{65 - 1} \stackrel{?}{=} 1$$
$$9 + \sqrt{64} \stackrel{?}{=} 1$$
$$17 \neq 1$$

Example 3

Solve $5 - \sqrt{b + 2} = 0$.

$$5 - \sqrt{b + 2} = 0$$
$$5 = \sqrt{b + 2}$$
$$25 = b + 2 \qquad \textit{Square each side.}$$
$$23 = b$$

The solution is 23.

Check: $5 - \sqrt{b + 2} = 0$
$$5 - \sqrt{23 + 2} \stackrel{?}{=} 0$$
$$5 - \sqrt{25} \stackrel{?}{=} 0$$
$$0 = 0 \ \checkmark$$

Example 4

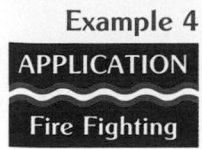

APPLICATION

Fire Fighting

The Durham City Fire Department is going to buy some new hoses. The hoses they buy must be powerful enough to propel water at least 75 feet into the air. The advertisement for the hose they are considering says that the water flows from the hose at a velocity as high as 72 feet per second. Use the formula $v = \sqrt{2gh}$, where v is the velocity of the water, g is the acceleration due to gravity, and h is the maximum height of the water flow, to determine whether this hose will be suitable. Assume that the acceleration due to gravity is 32 feet per second squared.

$$v = \sqrt{2gh}$$
$$72 = \sqrt{2(32)h} \qquad \text{Substitute the values into the formula.}$$
$$5184 = 64h \qquad \text{Square each side.}$$
$$81 = h \qquad \text{Check this solution.}$$

This hose will propel water up to 81 feet into the air, so it will be suitable.

Example 5

Solve $\sqrt[3]{4a - 1} - 3 = 0$.

$$\sqrt[3]{4a - 1} - 3 = 0$$
$$\sqrt[3]{4a - 1} = 3 \qquad \text{Isolate the radical.}$$
$$4a - 1 = 27 \qquad \text{Cube each side.}$$
$$4a = 28$$
$$a = 7$$

Check:
$$\sqrt[3]{4a - 1} - 3 = 0$$
$$\sqrt[3]{4(7) - 1} - 3 \overset{?}{=} 0$$
$$\sqrt[3]{27} - 3 \overset{?}{=} 0$$
$$0 = 0 \checkmark$$

The solution is 7.

Example 6

Solve $\sqrt{x + 8} - \sqrt{x + 35} = -3$.

$$\sqrt{x + 8} - \sqrt{x + 35} = -3$$
$$\sqrt{x + 8} = \sqrt{x + 35} - 3 \qquad \text{Isolate one radical.}$$
$$x + 8 = x + 35 - 6\sqrt{x + 35} + 9 \qquad \text{Square each side.}$$
$$-36 = -6\sqrt{x + 35} \qquad \text{Now isolate the radical again.}$$
$$6 = \sqrt{x + 35} \qquad \text{Divide each side by } 6.$$
$$36 = x + 35 \qquad \text{Square each side.}$$
$$x = 1$$

Check:
$$\sqrt{x + 8} - \sqrt{x + 35} = -3$$
$$\sqrt{1 + 8} - \sqrt{1 + 35} \overset{?}{=} -3$$
$$\sqrt{9} - \sqrt{36} \overset{?}{=} -3$$
$$3 - 6 \overset{?}{=} -3$$
$$-3 = -3 \checkmark$$

The solution is 1.

Chalkboard Examples

For Example 4
Solve for the variable.

a. $96 = \sqrt{4(64)h}$ **36**

b. $60 = \sqrt{6(25)x}$ **24**

For Example 5
Solve.

a. $\sqrt[3]{3y - 1} - 2 = 0$ **3**

b. $\sqrt[4]{2t + 1} - 1 = 2$ **40**

For Example 6
Solve.

a. $\sqrt{x + 3} + 2 = x - 1$ **6**

b. $5\sqrt{s - 2} = \sqrt{19s - 29} + 3$ **27**

EVALUATING THE LESSON

Checking for Understanding

Exercises 1–12 are designed to help you assess understanding through reading, writing, and speaking. You should work through Exercises 1–3 with your students, and then monitor their work on Exercises 4–12.

Reteaching Masters Booklet, p. 41

Example 7

Solve $r = \sqrt[3]{\dfrac{3w}{4\pi d}}$ for d.

$r = \sqrt[3]{\dfrac{3w}{4\pi d}}$

$r^3 = \dfrac{3w}{4\pi d}$ *Cube each side.*

$r^3 \cdot d = \dfrac{3w}{4\pi d} \cdot d$ *Multiply each side by d.*

$\dfrac{r^3 d}{r^3} = \dfrac{3w}{4\pi r^3}$ *Divide each side by r^3.*

$d = \dfrac{3w}{4\pi r^3}$

CHECKING FOR UNDERSTANDING

Communicating Mathematics

Read and study the lesson to answer these questions. 1–3. See margin.

1. What is an extraneous solution?

2. Look at Examples 2 and 3. Why do you think Example 2 had an extraneous solution and Example 3 did not?

3. Why do you need to isolate the radical before squaring to remove it?

Guided Practice

Solve each equation. Be sure to check for extraneous solutions.

4. $\sqrt{x} = 3$ **9**

5. $\sqrt{y} = 5$ **25**

6. $\sqrt{n} - 8 = 0$ **64**

7. $\sqrt{s} - 4 = 0$ **16**

8. $\sqrt{2y+7} = 3$ **1**

9. $\sqrt{3m+7} = 7$ **14**

10. $\sqrt[3]{x-2} = 3$ **29**

11. $\sqrt[4]{3w+7} = 2$ **3**

12. $y\sqrt{3} - y = 7$
   $\frac{7}{2}(\sqrt{3} + 1)$

EXERCISES

Practice

Solve each equation. Be sure to check for extraneous solutions.

A

13. $1 + x\sqrt{2} = 0$ $-\dfrac{\sqrt{2}}{2}$

14. $7 + 6n\sqrt{5} = 0$ $-\dfrac{7\sqrt{5}}{30}$

15. $6 + 2x\sqrt{3} = 0$ $-\sqrt{3}$

16. $2 + 5r\sqrt{10} = 0$ $-\dfrac{\sqrt{10}}{25}$

17. $x\sqrt{2} + 3x = 4$ $\dfrac{12 - 4\sqrt{2}}{7}$

18. $3x + 5 = x\sqrt{3}$ $\dfrac{-15 - 5\sqrt{3}}{6}$

19. $x - x\sqrt{5} = 2$ $\dfrac{1 + \sqrt{5}}{-2}$

20. $13 - 3p = p\sqrt{5}$ $\dfrac{39 - 13\sqrt{5}}{4}$

B

21. $\sqrt{a-4} - 3 = 0$ **13**

22. $\sqrt{x-5} - 7 = 0$ **54**

284   CHAPTER 6   IRRATIONAL AND COMPLEX NUMBERS

RETEACHING THE LESSON

An alternate approach to solving radical equations is to substitute a variable for each different radical expression.

$9 + \sqrt{x-1} = 1$
$9 + A = 1$
$A = -8$
$x - 1 = 64$
$x = 65$

Check for extraneous roots.

Additional Answers

1. A result found when solving the equation that does not satisfy the equation.

2. In example 2, squaring each side made the negative constant term a positive constant. We could have looked at $\sqrt{x-1} = -8$ and determined that there was no solution, since no real number has a principal square root of -8.

3. So that the radical is eliminated when you square.

Solve each equation. Be sure to check for extraneous solutions.

23. $\sqrt[3]{s+1} = 2$ **7**

24. $\sqrt[3]{n-1} = 3$ **28**

25. $\sqrt[4]{3q} - 2 = 0$ **$5\frac{1}{3}$**

26. $\sqrt[4]{4b} = 3$ **$20\frac{1}{4}$**

27. $\sqrt{2c+3} - 7 = 0$ **23**

28. $\sqrt{3z-5} - 3 = 1$ **7**

29. $\sqrt{4x+8} + 9 = 11$ **–1**

30. $\sqrt{1+2g} - 6 = -3$ **4**

31. $\sqrt{5y+1} + 6 = 10$ **3**

32. $\sqrt[4]{2d+3} + 5 = 4$ **no solution**

33. $\sqrt{3f+1} - 2 = 6$ **21**

34. $\sqrt[3]{x+5} + 6 = 4$ **–13**

▷C

35. $\sqrt{y+5} = \sqrt{2y-3}$ **8**

36. $\sqrt{x-4} = \sqrt{2x-3}$ **no solution**

37. $\sqrt{n+12} - \sqrt{n} = 2$ **4**

38. $\sqrt{x+6} - \sqrt{x} = \sqrt{2}$ **2**

39. $\sqrt{y-5} - \sqrt{y} = 1$ **no solution**

40. $\sqrt{c+4} = \sqrt{c+20} - 2$ **5**

42. no solution
41. $\sqrt{x-1} + \sqrt{x+3} = 5$ **5.41**

42. $\sqrt{4y+1} - \sqrt{4y-2} = 3$

44. no solution
43. $\sqrt{y+1} + \sqrt{y-3} = 5$ **7.41**

44. $\sqrt{x^2+5x} + x + 10 = 0$

46. no solution
45. $\sqrt{x+12} + 1 = \sqrt{x+21}$ **4**

46. $\sqrt{5y^2+7y-2} - y\sqrt{5} = -4$

Solve for the variable indicated.

47. $y = \sqrt{r^2 + s^2}$ for r
$r = \pm\sqrt{y^2 - s^2}$

48. $t = \sqrt{\dfrac{2s}{g}}$ for s $s = \dfrac{t^2 g}{2}$

49. $r = \sqrt[3]{\dfrac{2mM}{c}}$ for c $c = \dfrac{2mM}{r^3}$

50. $m^2 = \sqrt[3]{\dfrac{rp}{g^2}}$ for p $p = \dfrac{m^6 g^2}{r}$

Critical Thinking

51. For what values of a, b, and x will the equation $\sqrt{5x-7} + a = b$ have no real solution? **if $a > b$ and if $5x < 7$** **Teaching Tip ❸**

Applications

52. **Air Traffic Control** The radar used by the air traffic controllers at the Lake County Municipal Airport can receive signals from a circular area of 7854 square miles. Using the formula $A = \pi r^2$, where A represents the area of the circular region and r represents the radius of the region, find the greatest distance from which a signal can be received by the radar.
approximately 50 miles

53. **Energy** The energy of direct sunlight on a solar cell with an area of one square centimeter is converted into 0.01 watt of electrical energy. Suppose that a square solar cell must deliver 15 watts of energy. What dimensions should the cell have?

$10\sqrt{15}$ or about 38.73 centimeters on each side

LESSON 6-7 SOLVING EQUATIONS CONTAINING RADICALS 285

54. **Aerospace Engineering** The radius of the orbit of a satellite is found by

$$r = \sqrt[3]{\frac{GMt^2}{4\pi^2}},$$ where t represents the time it takes for the satellite to complete one orbit, G represents the constant of universal gravitation, and M is the mass of the central object. Solve the formula for t.

$$t = \frac{2\pi r\sqrt{GMr}}{GM}$$

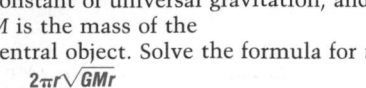

Mixed Review

Simplify. (Lesson 6-6)

55. $\dfrac{rs}{\frac{1}{r^2} + r^{\frac{3}{2}}} \cdot \dfrac{r^{\frac{1}{2}}s}{1 + r}$

56. $(\sqrt[6]{5}a^{\frac{7}{4}}b^{-\frac{2}{3}})^{12}$ $\dfrac{25a^{21}}{b^8}$

57. Find the degree of the polynomial $a^8 + a^7b + a^6b^2 - a^2b^6 - ab^7 - b^8$. (Lesson 5-4) **8**

58. Does the matrix $\begin{bmatrix} 3 & 4 & -2 \\ 0 & 1 & 0 \\ -1 & -1 & 4 \end{bmatrix}$ have an inverse? (Lesson 4-4) **yes**

59. The Woodward Park High School auditorium seats 150 people. Admission to the spring play is $2.00 for adults and $1.00 for students. The Drama Club has already sold fifty student tickets and the rest are to be sold at the door. How many of each type of ticket should be sold for the Drama Club to earn the maximum amount of money? (Lesson 3-7) **100 adults and 50 students**

60. Is the relation {(0, 0), (1, 0)} a function? Explain your answer. (Lesson 2-1) **Yes, each member of domain is paired with exactly one member of range.**

HISTORY CONNECTION

Johann Kepler (1571–1630) ranks foremost as the mathematician of the sky. He dreamed of a harmony in arithmetic, geometry, and music, and that every planet had its own tune. He described all of this in his 1618 book *Harmonica Mundi* (Harmony of the Worlds). While this may seem comical, he did disclose his third law of planetary motion in this text. This law which states that the square of the time of revolution of each planet is proportional to the cube of its mean distance from the sun, is still used to compare the distances and periods of the planets about the sun. One form of the law can be expressed using rational exponents.

$$\frac{T_a}{T_b} = \left(\frac{r_a}{r_b}\right)^{\frac{3}{2}},$$ where T_a and T_b are the planets' periods and r_a and r_b are their average distances from the sun.

286 CHAPTER 6 IRRATIONAL AND COMPLEX NUMBERS

EXTENDING THE LESSON

Math Power: Communication

Have students create three radical equations one with each of the following solutions:
1. 2 solutions
2. 1 solution
3. no solution
Have students describe the procedure used for developing the equations.

History Connection

The History Connection features introduce students to persons or cultures who were involved in the development of mathematics. You may want students to further research Kepler.

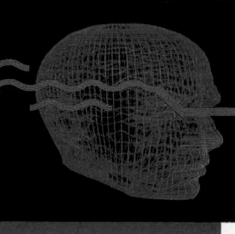

Technology

Solving Radical Equations

Using Technology
Objective This optional page shows how software can be used to perform mathematical computations and to enhance and extend mathematical concepts.

Teaching Suggestions
Point out to students that there are many effective ways to solve an equation. The order of the steps may vary. Encourage them to experiment. This would be a good time to introduce the UNDO command. UNDO displays the expression preceding the current expression. You also may wish to have students use the command SSTEPS which reveals the steps used by the computer to solve equations. Have students compare the steps they chose to those chosen by the computer and by other students. To use MET to solve equations involving higher roots, first convert the radical to a rational exponent. Use the RAISETO with reciprocal powers to clear the radical.

The *Mathematics Exploration Toolkit (MET)* can be used to solve equations that contain square roots. Some equations can be solved automatically with the SOLVEFOR command. Other equations require you to choose appropriate steps to simplify the equation before the computer can solve it. The computer does not check solutions obtained by squaring both sides of an equation. Therefore, some solutions found by the computer will *not* satisfy the original equation. The CALC commands (and their shortened forms) you can use are listed below.

ADD (add)	SUBTRACT (sub)	MULTIPLY (mul)
DIVIDE (div)	RAISETO (rai)	SIMPLIFY (simp)
STORE (sto)	SUBSTITUTE (subst)	& *enters a* $\sqrt{}$.

Example Solve $\sqrt{x+1} + \sqrt{x-4} = 5$.

ENTER: &(x + 3) + &(x − 4) = 5
       sto r
       rai 2
       simp, simp
       sub 2x
       simp
       add 3
       simp
       rai 2
       simp, simp
       sol x

$$\sqrt{x+1}+\sqrt{x-4}=5$$
saves the equation as r
$$(\sqrt{x+1}+\sqrt{x-4})^2=5^2$$
$$2\sqrt{x^2-3x-4}+2x-3=25$$
$$2\sqrt{x^2-3x-4}+2x-3-2x=25-2x$$
$$2\sqrt{x^2-3x-4}-3=-2x+25$$
$$2\sqrt{x^2-3x-4}-3+3=-2x+25+3$$
$$2\sqrt{x^2-3x-4}=-2x+28$$
$$(2\sqrt{x^2-3x-4})^2=(-2x+28)^2$$
$$4x^2-12x-16=4x^2-112x+784$$
$$x=8$$

Now check the computer's solution.

ENTER: r
       subst 8 x
       simp

$$\sqrt{x+1}+\sqrt{x-4}=5$$
$$\sqrt{9+1}+\sqrt{9-4}=5$$
$$5=5$$

The solution checks. The solution is $x = 8$.

EXERCISES

Use CALC commands to solve each equation. Check each solution.

1. $5x - 6\sqrt{x} + 1 = 0$ $\frac{1}{25}, 1$

2. $12 - 3\sqrt{x-5} = 0$ **21**

3. $\sqrt{4-x} + \sqrt{9-2x} = 0$
no solutions

4. $\sqrt{3x-2} - \sqrt{2x-3} = 1$ **2, 6**

Lesson Resources
Reteaching Master 6-8
Practice Master 6-8
Enrichment Master 6-8

Transparency 6-8 contains the 5-Minute Check and a teaching aid for this lesson.

INTRODUCING THE LESSON

 5-Minute Check

(over Lesson 6-7)
Solve.

1. $x + 2 = x\sqrt{3}$ $1 + \sqrt{3}$

2. $\sqrt{1 - 3y} - 3 = -10$
   no solution

3. $7 - \sqrt{5t + 4} = 0$ 9

4. $\sqrt[3]{5n + 2} + 2 = 0$ -2

5. $\sqrt{2x + 1} + \sqrt{4x - 2} = 4$ $\frac{3}{2}$

Motivating the Lesson

Have students solve the following equations.

1. $x^2 + 16 = 0$ **no real solution**
2. $5x^2 + 125 = 0$
   no real solution
3. $1 + x\sqrt{2} = 0$ $\frac{-\sqrt{2}}{2}$

What situations yield no real solutions? Can the equations be rewritten to have a similar expression?

TEACHING THE LESSON

Teaching Tip ❶   Emphasize that i is not a variable. It is a symbol that stands for a specific number.

Teaching Tip ❷   An imaginary number is any number in simplest form that contains the imaginary unit.

6-8   Pure Imaginary Numbers

Objectives
6-8A
6-8B
6-8C

After studying this lesson, you should be able to:
- simplify radicals containing negative radicands,
- multiply pure imaginary numbers, and
- solve quadratic equations that have pure imaginary solutions.

FYI ...

Girolamo Cardano began his career as a doctor and studied, taught, and wrote mathematics as a sideline. He held important positions at The Universities of Pavia and Bologna in Italy, and wrote many works on arithmetic, astronomy, physics, and medicine.

Until the sixteenth century, mathematicians were puzzled by square roots of negative numbers. As you know, some expressions have irrational solutions. For example, the solutions to $x^2 - 5 = 0$ are $\sqrt{5}$ and $-\sqrt{5}$. But the equation $x^2 = -1$ has no solution in the real numbers. This is because the square of a real number is nonnegative. However in 1545, the Italian mathematician Girolamo Cardano published *Ars Magna* in which he began working with what the great mathematician René Descartes later called **imaginary numbers**.

The number i is defined to be a solution to $x^2 = -1$ and is *not* a real number. It is called the **imaginary unit**. Using i as you would any constant, you can define square roots of negative numbers.   **Teaching Tip ❶**

Since $i = \sqrt{-1}$, it follows that $i^2 = -1$.

To avoid $\sqrt{2}(i)$ being read as $\sqrt{2i}$, write $\sqrt{2}(i)$ as $i\sqrt{2}$.

$(2i)^2 = 2^2i^2$ or -4 ➡ $\sqrt{-4} = \sqrt{4} \cdot \sqrt{-1}$ or $2i$
$(i\sqrt{2})^2 = i^2(\sqrt{2})^2$ or -2 ➡ $\sqrt{-2} = \sqrt{2} \cdot \sqrt{-1}$ or $i\sqrt{2}$

Teaching Tip ❷
Definition of Pure Imaginary Numbers

> **For any positive real number b,**
> $$\sqrt{-(b^2)} = \sqrt{b^2} \cdot \sqrt{-1} \text{ or } bi$$
> **where i is the imaginary unit, and bi is called a pure imaginary number.**

-bi is also a pure imaginary number since -bi = -1(bi).

Example 1

a. Simplify $\sqrt{-25}$.
$$\sqrt{-25} = \sqrt{25} \cdot \sqrt{-1}$$
$$= 5 \cdot \sqrt{-1}$$
$$= 5i$$

b. Simplify $\sqrt{-45}$.
$$\sqrt{-45} = \sqrt{45} \cdot \sqrt{-1}$$
$$= (\sqrt{9} \cdot \sqrt{5})i$$
$$= 3i\sqrt{5}$$

The commutative and associative properties for multiplication hold true for pure imaginary numbers.

Example 2

a. Simplify $2i \cdot 7i$.
$$2i \cdot 7i = (2 \cdot 7)(i \cdot i)$$
$$= 14i^2$$
$$= 14(-1) \quad i^2 = -1$$
$$= -14$$

b. Simplify $\sqrt{-5} \cdot \sqrt{-20}$.
$$\sqrt{-5} \cdot \sqrt{-20} = i\sqrt{5} \cdot i\sqrt{20}$$
$$= i^2\sqrt{100}$$
$$= -1 \cdot 10 \text{ or } -10$$

288   CHAPTER 6   IRRATIONAL AND COMPLEX NUMBERS

ALTERNATE TEACHING STRATEGIES

Using Charts

Show the students how the Argand plane can be used to "see" the powers of i. By rotating counter-clockwise from the real axis, you can generate all the powers of i and show you never need to use a power greater than 1. Use a chart to keep track as you rotate around the plane.

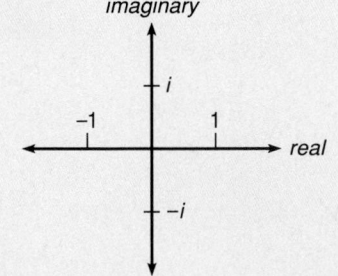

Simplify the successive powers of i. Do you see a pattern?

$i^1 = i$ $i^5 = i^4 \cdot i = 1 \cdot i = i$
$i^2 = -1$ $i^6 = i^4 \cdot 1^2 = 1 \cdot -1 = -1$
$i^3 = i^2 \cdot i = -1 \cdot i = -i$ $i^7 = 1^4 \cdot i^3 = 1 \cdot (-i) = -i$
$i^4 = i^2 \cdot i^2 = -1 \cdot (-1) = 1$ $i^8 = i^4 \cdot i^4 = 1 \cdot 1 = 1$

Example 3

Simplify i^{13}.

Method 1	Method 2
$i^{13} = i^4 \cdot i^4 \cdot i^4 \cdot i^1$	$i^{13} = i^{12} \cdot i^1$
$= 1 \cdot 1 \cdot 1 \cdot i$	$= (i^2)^6 \cdot i$
$= i$	$= (-1)^6 \cdot i$
	$= i$

Example 4

Solve $x^2 + 7 = 0$.

$x^2 + 7 = 0$
$\quad x^2 = -7$
$\quad\quad x = \pm\sqrt{-7}$ $\sqrt{-7} = \sqrt{7} \cdot \sqrt{-1}$
$\quad\quad\quad = \pm i\sqrt{7}$

The solutions, $i\sqrt{7}$ and $-i\sqrt{7}$, are both pure imaginary numbers.
Check these solutions.

Example 5

APPLICATION

Electronics

The reactance of an electrical circuit is represented by a pure imaginary number and is found by the formula $X = X_L - X_C$. X_L represents the inductive reactance and X_C represents the capacitive reactance. If the reactance of a circuit is $16i$ ohms and the capacitive reactance is $5i$ ohms, find the inductive reactance.

$X = X_L - X_C$
$16i = X_L - 5i$ *Substitute $16i$ for X and $5i$ for X_C.*
$21i = X_L$

The inductive reactance is $21i$ ohms.

CHECKING FOR UNDERSTANDING

Communicating Mathematics

1. A number that involves the square root of a negative number; no

Read and study the lesson to answer these questions.

1. What is an imaginary number? Is an imaginary number a real number?
2. Give examples of numbers that are pure imaginary numbers. $4i$, $-3i$
3. What is the pattern formed by the powers of i? **The values i, -1, $-i$, and 1 repeat in cycles of four.**

LESSON 6-8   PURE IMAGINARY NUMBERS   289

RETEACHING THE LESSON

Let w represent a whole number.
Evaluate

1. $i^{119} + i^{120} + i^{121} + i^{122}$.   0
2. $i^w + i^{w+1} + i^{w+2} + i^{w+3}$.   0
3. i^{4w+3}. $-i$
4. i^0 Hint: 1
   i^{-1} multiply $-i$
   i^{-2} by i^4 -1
   i^{-3} or 1. i
   i^{-4} 1

Checking for Understanding

Exercises 1–12 are designed to help you assess understanding through reading, writing, and speaking. You should work through Exercises 1–3 with your students, and then monitor their work on Exercises 4–12.

Closing the Lesson

Writing Activity Have the students show three methods of solutions for the expression i^{21}.

Practice Masters Booklet, p. 48

Guided Practice Simplify.

4. $\sqrt{-49}$ **7i**
5. $\sqrt{-36}$ **6i**
6. $4\sqrt{-3}$ **4i√3**
7. $\sqrt{-2} \cdot \sqrt{-2}$ **−2**
8. $6\sqrt{-4}$ **12i**
9. $\sqrt{-3} \cdot \sqrt{-3}$ **−3**
10. $\sqrt{-5} \cdot \sqrt{5}$ **5i**
11. $4 \cdot 5i$ **20i**
12. i^{10} **−1**

EXERCISES

Practice Simplify.

A
13. $\sqrt{-169}$ **13i**
14. $\sqrt{-100}$ **10i**
15. $\sqrt{-50}$ **5i√2**
16. $\sqrt{-98}$ **7i√2**
17. $\sqrt{-\frac{4}{9}}$ **2/3 i**
18. $\sqrt{-\frac{9}{25}}$ **3/5 i**
19. $\sqrt{-\frac{1}{5}}$ **i√5/5**
20. $\sqrt{-\frac{1}{2}}$ **i√2/2**
21. i^5 **i**

B
22. i^{11} **−i**
23. i^{91} **−i**
24. i^{244} **1** −7√2
25. $\sqrt{-8} \cdot \sqrt{-2}$ **−4**
26. $\sqrt{-3} \cdot \sqrt{-18}$ **−3√6**
27. $\sqrt{-14} \cdot \sqrt{-7}$
28. $(\sqrt{-5})^2$ **−5**
29. $(\sqrt{-12})^2$ **−12**
30. $(\sqrt{-3})^3$ **−3i√3**
31. $(\sqrt{-4})^3$ **−8i**
32. $\sqrt{9} \cdot \sqrt{-9}$ **9i**
33. $\sqrt{3} \cdot \sqrt{-27}$ **9i**
34. $\sqrt{-5} \cdot \sqrt{20}$ **10i**
35. $\sqrt{-8} \cdot \sqrt{6}$ **4i√3**
36. $(2i)(3i)^2$ **−18i**

C
37. $(-2\sqrt{-8})(3\sqrt{-2})$ **24**
38. $(4\sqrt{-12})(-2\sqrt{-3})$ **48**
39. $5i(-2i)^2$ **−20i**
40. $(3\sqrt{21})(-2\sqrt{-21})$ **−126i**

Solve each equation. **Teaching Tip ❸**

41. $a^2 + 16 = 0$ **±4i**
42. $x^2 + 64 = 0$ **±8i**
43. $m^2 + 121 = 0$ **±11i**
44. $n^2 + 169 = 0$ **±13i**
45. $3x^2 + 27 = 0$ **±3i**
46. $6y^2 = -96$ **±4i**
47. $t^2 + 12 = 0$ **±2i√3**
48. $3a^2 + 18 = 0$ **±i√6**
49. $4x^2 + 5 = 0$ **±i√5/2**
50. $5w^2 = -40$ **±2i√2**

Critical Thinking
51. Simplify $\sqrt{-81} \cdot \sqrt{-8} + \sqrt[3]{256}$. **−18√2 + 4 ∛4**

Application
52. **Electricity** The reactance of an electrical circuit is represented by a pure imaginary number, and is found by the formula $X = X_L - X_C$. X_L represents the inductive reactance and X_C represents the reactance from all capacitors.

a. The total reactance for the capacitors in a circuit is $6i$ ohms. If the reactance for the inductions is $14i$ ohms, find the total reactance of the circuit. **8i ohms**

b. A circuit has a total reactance of $8i$ ohms. If the reactance of the capacitors is $7i$ ohms, find the reactance of the inductions. **15i ohms**

Computer
Teaching Tip ❹

53. The BASIC program below simplifies powers of i. It uses the pattern of the powers discussed in Exercise 3. Lines 30–60 of the program find the remainder of the power divided by four and then lines 70–130 use that remainder to determine the value of the power.

```
10   PRINT "ENTER THE POWER"
20   INPUT N
30   IF N - 4 * INT(N/4) = THEN 70
40   IF N - 4 * INT(N/4) = 1 THEN 90
50   IF N - 4 * INT(N/4) = 2 THEN 110
60   IF N - 4 * INT(N/4) = 3 THEN 130
70   PRINT "i ^ ";N; " = 1"
80   GOTO 140
90   PRINT "i ^ ";N; " = i"
100  GOTO 140
110  PRINT "i ^ ";N; " = -1"
120  GOTO 140
130  PRINT "i ^ ";N; " = -i"
```

Enter the program and use it to simplify each power of i.

a. i^{17} i b. i^{34} -1
c. i^{59} $-i$ d. i^{92} 1
e. i^{103} $-i$ f. i^{300} 1
g. i^{997} i h. i^{2002} -1

Mixed Review

Solve each equation. **(Lesson 6-7)**

54. $2x + 7 = -x\sqrt{2}$ $\dfrac{7\sqrt{2} - 14}{2}$

55. $\sqrt{3y^2 + 11y - 5} = y\sqrt{3} + 1$ $\dfrac{6(11 + 2\sqrt{3})}{109}$

56. Simplify $\sqrt{(x - 2)^2}$. **(Lesson 6-1)** $|x - 2|$.

57. Factor $a^3 + 1$. **(Lesson 5-5)** $(a + 1)(a^2 - a + 1)$

58. Naren bought 2 slices of pizza, two cartons of milk, and one chocolate chip cookie for lunch at the Meadow Park High School cafeteria. He spent \$2.05 on his lunch. Ted brought a sandwich from home, so he just bought a carton of milk and 3 cookies. His total bill was 75¢. Sarah spent \$0.95 on one slice of pizza and a carton of milk. How much does a slice of pizza, a carton of milk, and a chocolate chip cookie cost? **(Lesson 4-7)** 65¢, 30¢, 15¢

59. Find the value of the determinant $\begin{vmatrix} 18 & -5 \\ -9 & 11 \end{vmatrix}$. **(Lesson 3-3)** 153

60. Health The optimum heart rate is the rate that a person should achieve during exercise for the exercise to be most beneficial. The prediction equation, $r = 0.6(220 - a)$, where a represents age, can be used to find a person's optimum heart rate, r. If Peggy is 20 years old, find her optimum heart rate. **(Lesson 2-2)** 120

LESSON 6-8   PURE IMAGINARY NUMBERS   291

EXTENDING THE LESSON

Math Power: Reasoning
Is i positive or negative?
Neither, since positive and negative are only defined for real numbers and i is not a real number.

APPLYING THE LESSON

Homework Exercises

Assignment Guide
Basic: 13–36, 51–52, 54–60
Average: 18–43, 51–60
Enriched: 25–60

Teaching Tip ❸   Remind students that they should check the solutions to make sure they are all true.

Teaching Tip ❹   Review with students how powers of i simplify to one of four expressions. Discuss the expression used in lines 30–60 to find the remainder of the power divided by four.
$$N - 4 * INT(N/4)$$
Remind them about the greatest lower integer function.

Enrichment Masters Booklet, p. 42

6-8   NAME _____ DATE _____
Enrichment Worksheet

Powers of i

Study the pattern that is formed when i is raised to the powers 1, 2, 3, 4, and so on.

$i^1 = i$
$i^2 = -1$
$i^3 = i^2(i) = -1(i) = -i$
$i^4 = i^2(i^2) = -1(-1) = 1$
$i^5 = i^4(i) = 1(i) = i$
$i^6 = i^4(i^2) = 1(-1) = -1$
$i^7 = i^4(i^3) = 1(-i) = -i$
$i^8 = i^4(i^4) = 1(1) = 1$

Notice that the four answers, i, -1, $-i$, and 1, are repeated for each group of four powers. You can use this pattern to find the value of i^n for any whole number n.

Example: Evaluate i^{28}.
$i^{28} = (i^4)^7 = 1^7 = 1$
If n is a multiple of four, the value of i^n is 1.

Example: Evaluate i^{43}.
$i^{43} = i^{40}(i^3) = (1)(i^3) = -i$
If n is not a multiple of four, rename i^n as a product $(i^a)(i^b)$ where a is the largest multiple of four less than n.

Evaluate.
1. i^9 i 2. i^{18} -1 3. i^{24} 1
4. i^{39} $-i$ 5. i^{101} i 6. i^{403} $-i$

Study this example where n is a negative number.
Example: Evaluate i^{-7}.
$i^{-7} = i^{-8}(i^1) = \frac{i}{i^8} = \frac{1}{1}(i) = i$

Evaluate.
7. i^{-1} $-i$ 8. i^{-10} -1 9. i^{-32} 1
10. i^{-18} -10 11. i^{-23} $-i$ 12. i^{-101} i

Lesson Resources

Reteaching Master 6-9
Practice Master 6-9
Enrichment Master 6-9
Technology Master, p. 23
Activity Master, p. 42
Multicultural Activity Master, p. 6

 Transparency 6-9 contains the 5-Minute Check and a teaching aid for this lesson.

INTRODUCING THE LESSON

 5-Minute Check

(over Lesson 6-8)

Simplify.

1. $\sqrt{-49}$ $7i$
2. $5i \cdot 4i$ -20
3. $\sqrt{-6} \cdot \sqrt{-15}$ $-3\sqrt{10}$
4. i^{15} $-i$
5. Solve $3n^2 + 36 = 0$. $\pm 2i\sqrt{3}$

Motivating the Lesson

Find an equation whose roots are $\pm 6i$. How do you start to write the equation? Is there more than one equation?

TEACHING THE LESSON

Teaching Tip ❶   If students are interested in learning more about fractal geometry, suggest the book *Fractals: Form, Chance, and Dimension* by Benoit Mandelbrot. Dr. Mandelbrot is the leader in research on fractals.

Teaching Tip ❷   Explain that the set of complex numbers has two independent subsets—the real numbers and the imaginary numbers.

Objective
6-9

After studying this lesson, you should be able to:
■ add, subtract, and multiply complex numbers.

FYI . . .

Research is still being conducted in the field of fractal geometry. So far, fractals have been used to simulate objects in nature, such as clouds and mountains. Their first application to science was to solve the problem of interference on transmission channels like telephone lines.

The picture at the right, called a fractal, was created with the aid of a computer. Many fractal objects are generated using functions that are iterated; that is, repeated over and over. The function is evaluated for some initial value of x, then the function is evaluated for the new value. Repeating this process and plotting the points produces interesting and sometimes beautiful pictures. Some of the most exciting fractals are created using this process with a number like $4 + 3i$ as the initial value. Numbers like $4 + 3i$ are called **complex numbers.**

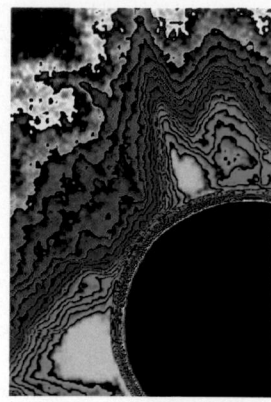

Teaching Tip ❶

Definition of a Complex Number

A complex number is any number that can be written in the form $a + bi$ where a and b are real numbers and i is the imaginary unit. a is called the real part, and bi is called the imaginary part.

A real number is also a complex number. For example, $\sqrt{3}$ can be expressed as $\sqrt{3} + 0i$. The imaginary part is 0. A complex number is real only if the imaginary part is zero.   **Teaching Tip ❷**

The Complex Numbers

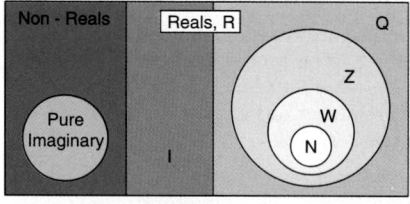

R = reals
I = irrationals
Q = rationals
Z = integers
W = wholes
N = naturals

The diagram at the left shows the relationship among the various sets of numbers that you have studied and the complex numbers.

Two complex numbers are equal if and only if their real parts are equal and their imaginary parts are equal. That is,

$$a + bi = c + di \text{ if and only if } a = c \text{ and } b = d.$$

Example 1

Find values for x and y such that $3x + 4yi = 12 + 8i$.

$3x + 4yi = 12 + 8i$
$3x = 12$ and $4y = 8$
$\quad x = 4 \qquad\qquad y = 2$

Check: $3x + 4yi = 12 + 8$
$3(4) + 4(2)i \stackrel{?}{=} 12 + 8i$
$12 + 8i = 12 + 8i \checkmark$

292   CHAPTER 6   IRRATIONAL AND COMPLEX NUMBERS

ALTERNATE TEACHING STRATEGIES

Using Cooperative Groups

Divide the class into groups. Have each group develop the properties for complex numbers. They should find the properties and provide an example of each. Each group should write a report on their findings. They should also include the structure of the complex numbers.

Using Critical Thinking

Review the properties of real numbers. Do the properties of real numbers apply to complex numbers? Show that commutativity applies to addition. Show that the associative property applies to multiplication. Why do you think these properties apply?

To add or subtract complex numbers, we must combine like terms; that is, combine the real parts and combine the imaginary parts.

Example 2

Simplify $(2 + 5i) + (4 - i)$.

$$(2 + 5i) + (4 - i) = (2 + 4) + (5i - i)$$
$$= 6 + 4i$$

Example 3

Simplify $(8 - 2i) - (6 - 4i)$.

$$(8 - 2i) - (6 - 4i) = (8 - 6) + (-2i - (-4i))$$
$$= 2 + 2i$$

The complex plane is also known as the Gaussian plane or an Argand diagram.

The complex numbers can be graphed on the complex plane, where the horizontal axis represents the real part of the complex number and the vertical axis represents the imaginary part. The complex numbers are represented by the segments whose endpoints are the origin and a point whose coordinates are the real part and the imaginary part of the complex number. Addition of complex numbers can also be represented by graphing. First, graph the two numbers to be added. Then complete the parallelogram that has two sides represented by the segments. The segment from the origin to the fourth vertex of the parallelogram represents the sum of the two original numbers.

Example 4

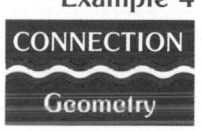

Geometry

This way of adding complex numbers assumes the numbers do not lie on the same line.

Graph $-4 + 3i$ and $5 + 2i$ on the complex plane. Find their sum geometrically.

Graph each complex number using the real part as the x-coordinate and the imaginary part as the y-coordinate. Connect each point to the origin.

Next, complete the parallelogram. The fourth vertex has coordinates $(1, 5)$ or $1 + 5i$.

Check by adding algebraically.
$$(-4 + 3i) + (5 + 2i) = (-4 + 5) + (3i + 2i)$$
$$= 1 + (3 + 2)i$$
$$= 1 + 5i \quad \text{It checks.}$$

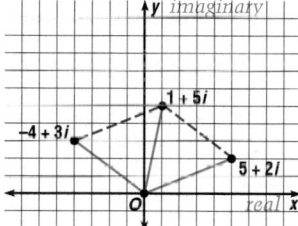

The green segment represents $1 + 5i$.

You can multiply complex numbers using the FOIL method.

Example 5

Simplify $(9 - 3i)(2 + 2i)$. **Teaching Tip ❸**

$$(9 - 3i)(2 + 2i) = \overset{F}{9 \cdot 2} + \overset{O}{9 \cdot 2i} + \overset{I}{(-3i) \cdot 2} + \overset{L}{(-3i) \cdot 2i}$$
$$= 18 + 18i - 6i - 6i^2$$
$$= (18 + 6) + (18i - 6i) \quad -6i^2 = 6$$
$$= 24 + 12i$$

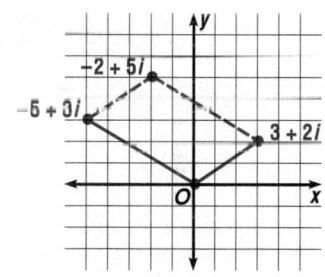

Example 6   Simplify $(-2 + 3i)(3 - i)$.

$(-2 + 3i)(3 - i) = (-2) \cdot 3 + (-2) \cdot (-i) + 3i \cdot 3 + 3i \cdot (-i)$
$= -6 + 2i + 9i - 3i^2$
$= (-6 + 3) + (2i + 9i)$ $-3i^2 = -3(-1) = 3$
$= -3 + 11i$

This chart summarizes addition, subtraction, and multiplication of complex numbers.

For any complex numbers $a + bi$ and $c + di$:
$(a + bi) + (c + di) = (a + c) + (b + d)i$
$(a + bi) - (c + di) = (a - c) + (b - d)i$
$(a + bi)(c + di) = (ac - bd) + (ad + bc)i$

CHECKING FOR UNDERSTANDING

Communicating Mathematics
1–3. See margin.

Read and study the lesson to answer these questions.

1. When are two complex numbers equal?
2. How are the complex and real numbers related?
3. State two phenomena that can be modeled by fractals.
4. What number does the segment from the origin to (4, 2) on the complex plane represent? $4 + 2i$

Guided Practice   Simplify.

5. $(4 - i) + (3 + 3i)$ $7 + 2i$
6. $(7 + 2i) + (2 + 8i)$ $9 + 10i$
7. $(5 + 2i) - (2 + 2i)$ 3
8. $(7 - 6i) - (5 - 6i)$ 2
9. $(7 + 3i) + (3 - 3i)$ 10
10. $(2 - 4i) + (2 + 4i)$ 4
11. $4(5 + 3i)$ $20 + 12i$
12. $-6(2 - 3i)$ $-12 + 18i$
13. $(2 + 4i)(1 + 3i)$ $-10 + 10i$
14. $(1 - 4i)(2 - 3i)$ $-10 - 11i$
15. $(4 + i)(4 - i)$ 17
16. $(4 - i)(3 + 2i)$ $14 + 5i$

Find the values of x and y for which each equation is true. Teaching Tip ❹

17. $x + yi = 2 - 3i$ $x = 2, y = -3$
18. $x - yi = 5 + 6i$ $x = 5, y = -6$
19. $x + 2yi = 3$ $x = 3, y = 0$
20. $x - yi = 4 + 5i$ $x = 4, y = -5$
21. $x - yi = 7 - 2i$ $x = 7, y = 2$
22. $2x + yi = 5i$ $x = 0, y = 5$

EXERCISES

Practice
🅰
Simplify.

23. $(4 + 2i) + (1 + 3i)$ $5 + 5i$
24. $(2 + 6i) + (4 + 3i)$ $6 + 9i$
25. $(11 + 5i) - (4 + 2i)$ $7 + 3i$
26. $(11 - \sqrt{-3}) - (-4 + \sqrt{-5})$
    $15 - i\sqrt{3} - i\sqrt{5}$
27. $(8 - 7i) + (-5 - i)$ $3 - 8i$
28. $(5 + \sqrt{-7}) + (-3 + \sqrt{-2})$
    $2 + i\sqrt{7} + i\sqrt{2}$

294   CHAPTER 6   IRRATIONAL AND COMPLEX NUMBERS

31. $5 - 3i\sqrt{3}$
32. $5 - i\sqrt{5}$
34. $-21 - 2i$

29. $(-6 - 2i) - (-8 - 3i)$ **2 + i**
30. $(3 - 11i) - (-5 + 4i)$ **8 - 15i**
31. $(1 - 5i\sqrt{3}) + (4 + 2i\sqrt{3})$
32. $(8 - 3i\sqrt{5}) + (-3 + 2i\sqrt{5})$
33. $3(4 - 5i) - 6(2 - i)$ **-9i**
34. $3(-5 - 2i) + 2(-3 + 2i)$
35. $(5 + 3i)(6 - i)$ **33 + 13i**
36. $(5 + i)(2 - 3i)$ **13 - 13i**
37. $(6 - 2i)^2$ **32 - 24i**
38. $(2 + i\sqrt{3})^2$ **1 + 4i\sqrt{3}**
39. $(7 - 2i)(4 - 3i)$ **22 - 29i**
40. $(7 - i\sqrt{2})(5 + i\sqrt{2})$ **37 + 2i\sqrt{2}**
41. $(3 + 4i)^2$ **-7 + 24i**
42. $(3 + 2i)^2$ **5 + 12i**
43. $(\sqrt{2} + i)(\sqrt{2} - i)$ **3**
44. $(2 - \sqrt{-3})(2 + \sqrt{-3})$ **7**
45. $(3 + 2i)(3 - 2i)$ **13**
46. $(3 + \sqrt{-2})(3 - \sqrt{-2})$ **11**

CONNECTION
Geometry

Graph each addend on the complex plane. Then find their sum geometrically.

47. $(-2 + i) + (4 + 4i)$ **2 + 5i**
48. $(9 + 4i) + (3 - 2i)$ **12 + 2i**
49. $(-1 - 5i) + (4 + 0i)$ **3 - 5i**
50. $(3 + 2i) + (-11 - 5i)$ **-8 - 3i**
47–50. For graphs, see Solutions Manual.

Find the values of x and y for which each equation is true.

51. $x = 6, y = \frac{7}{2}$
52. $x = 2, y = 4$
53. $x = -1, y = -3$
54. $x = 2, y = 3$

51. $3x + 2yi = 18 + 7i$
52. $3x + 5yi = 6 + 20i$
53. $(x - y) + (x + y)i = 2 - 4i$
54. $(2x + y) + (x - y)i = 7 - i$
55. $(x + 2y) + (2x - y)i = 5 + 5i$
$x = 3, y = 1$
56. $(x + 4y) + (2x - 3y)i = 13 + 7i$
$x = \frac{67}{11}, y = \frac{19}{11}$

Simplify.

Portfolio

Select an item from this chapter that you feel shows your best work and place it in your portfolio. Explain why you selected it.

57. $(1 + 2i)(3 - 4i)(2 + i)$ **20 + 15i**
58. $(3 + 3i)(6 - i)(5 + 2i)$ **75 + 117i**
59. $(2 - 3i)(7 + 5i)(7 - 5i)$ **148 -222i**
60. $(4 + 3i)(3 + i)(2 - 7i)$ **109 - 37i**
61. $(7 - i)(5 + 2i)(4 + 2i)$ **130 + 110i**
62. $(5 + i)(9 + 2i)(9 - 2i)$ **425 + 85i**

63. Write an expression for the additive inverse of the complex number $a + bi$. **-a - bi**
64. Show that 0 is the additive identity for the complex numbers.
65. Show that 1 is the multiplicative identity for the complex numbers. **See margin.**

Critical Thinking

66. Under which of the operations, addition, subtraction, or multiplication, are the imaginary numbers closed? Give examples to support your answer. **See margin.**

67. **(1 + i, -1 + 2i), (-1 + 2i, -4 - 4i), (-4 - 4i, -1 + 32i), (-1 + 32i, -1024 - 64i)**

Applications

67. Fractal Geometry Suppose the function $f(x) = x^2 - 1$ is to be iterated to produce a fractal. Find the first four points of the iteration if the initial value of x is $(1 + i)$.

68. Electrical Engineering The relationship between the flow of electricity, I, in a circuit, the resistance to the flow, Z, called impedance, and the electromotive force, E, called voltage, is given by the formula $E = I \cdot Z$. Electrical engineers use j to represent the imaginary unit. An electrical engineer is designing a circuit that is to have a current of $(6 - j8)$ amps. If impedance of the circuit is $(14 + j8)$ ohms, find the voltage. **(148 - j64) volts**

LESSON 6-9 COMPLEX NUMBERS 295

Additional Answers

64. $a + bi + 0 + 0i$
$= (a + 0) + (bi + 0i)$
$= a + (b + 0)i$
$= a + bi$
65. $(a + bi) \cdot 1$
$= (a \cdot 1) + (bi \cdot 1)$
$= a + bi$
66. The imaginary numbers are not closed under any of these operations.
Addition: $(2 + 3i) + (2 - 3i) = 4$
Subtraction: $(1 + 2i) - (3 + 2i) = -2$
Multiplication: $(3 + 2i)(3 - 2i) = 13$

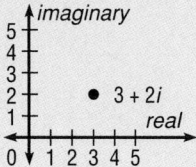

Homework Exercises

See assignment guide on page 294.

Additional Answers

75.

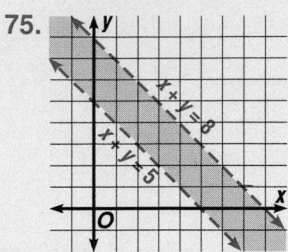

76.

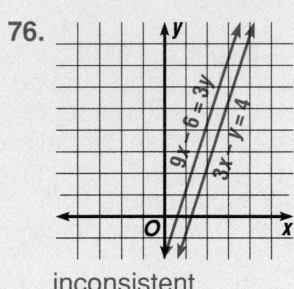

inconsistent

Enrichment Masters Booklet, p. 43

| 6-9 | NAME _____ DATE _____ |

Enrichment Worksheet

Graphing Complex Numbers

Every ordered pair of numbers (a, b) corresponds to exactly one complex number $a + bi$. Also, recall that every point in the coordinate plane corresponds to exactly one pair of numbers called the coordinates of the point.

Thus, a complex number $a + bi$ is associated with exactly one point of the plane called (a, b).

An arrow drawn from the origin to the point (a, b) represents the complex number $a + bi$.

In the grid below each exercise, graph the complex numbers. The first exercise is completed for you.

1. $2 + 3i$ and $1 - 2i$ **2.** $1 + 4i$ and $2 + i$ **3.** $-1 + 4i$ and $3 - 2i$

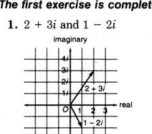   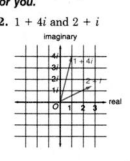   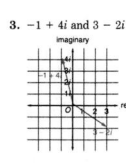

4. $2 + 0 \cdot i$ and $-1 + 3i$ **5.** $3i$ and $-3 - i$ **6.** -3 and $2 - 2i$

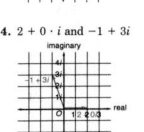   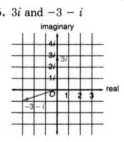   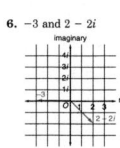

In each exercise, find the sum of the complex numbers in the exercise named. Then graph the sum in the grid for that exercise.

7. exercise 1 $3 + i$ **8.** exercise 2 $3 + 5i$ **9.** exercise 3 $2 + 2i$

10. exercise 4 $1 + 3i$ **11.** exercise 5 $-3 + 2i$ **12.** exercise 6 $-1 - 2i$

Mixed Review

69. Simplify $\sqrt{-\dfrac{1}{3}}$. **(Lesson 6-8)** $\dfrac{i\sqrt{3}}{3}$

70. Solve $3a^2 + 24 = 0$. **(Lesson 6-8)** $\pm 2i\sqrt{2}$

71. Simplify $\sqrt[4]{5} + 6\sqrt[4]{5} - 2\sqrt[4]{5}$. **(Lesson 6-3)** $5\sqrt[4]{5}$

72. Divide $(y^4 + 6y^3 - 7y^2 + 7y - 1) \div (y + 3)$ using synthetic division. **(Lesson 5-7)** $y^3 + 3y^2 - 16y + 55 - \dfrac{166}{y + 3}$

73. Chemistry The mass of a proton is 1.672×10^{-24} grams. If the mass of Earth's moon is 7.35×10^{22} kilograms, how many times greater is its mass than that of the proton? **(Lesson 5-2)** **approximately 4.4×10^{46}**

74. Find $\begin{bmatrix} 4 & 5 \\ 2 & -2 \\ 4 & 9 \end{bmatrix} + \begin{bmatrix} -3 & 2 \\ -1 & 4 \\ 4 & 4 \end{bmatrix}$. **(Lesson 4-3)** $\begin{bmatrix} 1 & 7 \\ 1 & 2 \\ 8 & 13 \end{bmatrix}$

75. Solve $\begin{cases} x + y < 8 \\ x + y > 5 \end{cases}$ by graphing. **(Lesson 3-4) See margin.**

76. Graph the system $\begin{cases} 3x - y = 4 \\ 9x - 6 = 3y \end{cases}$ and state its solution. Then state whether the system is *consistent and independent, consistent and dependent,* or *inconsistent.* **(Lesson 3-1) no solution, inconsistent For graph, see margin.**

77. Use the vertical line test to determine if the relation graphed at the right is a function. **(Lesson 2-1) no**

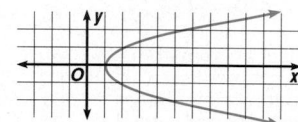

Benoit Mendelbroit

You have probably seen computer-generated images on television or in the movies that looked as if they were real pictures in nature. These images were generated using fractals. Fractal geometry was developed in 1980 by Benoit Mandelbroit, a research mathematician for IBM. Fractal geometry is based on complex numbers and their graphs. With fractal geometry, you can create the "irregular" shapes that appear in nature that you cannot create with traditional geometric shapes such as squares, rectangles, and circles.

296   CHAPTER 6   IRRATIONAL AND COMPLEX NUMBERS

EXTENDING THE LESSON

Math Power: Problem Solving

Find the values for x and y such that $\sqrt{x + 2} + 3iy = \sqrt{3x} + 4i$.

$x = 1$, $y = \dfrac{4}{3}$

What do you do first? Why? Justify your steps.

Technology Connection

Have students research the concept of fractal geometry. Have each student bring in three examples of the images. Also have students research the uses of fractal geometry.

6-10 Simplifying Expressions Containing Complex Numbers

Objective
6-10

After studying this lesson, you should be able to:
- simplify rational expressions containing complex numbers in the denominator.

As you know, two radical expressions of the form $a\sqrt{b} + c\sqrt{d}$ and $a\sqrt{b} - c\sqrt{d}$ are conjugates of each other. Since imaginary numbers also involve radicals, numbers of the form $a + bi$ and $a - bi$ are also called conjugates. Recall that the product of two radical conjugates is a rational number. Let's investigate the product of complex conjugates.

Example 1

Find the product of the conjugates $5 + 2i$ and $5 - 2i$.

$$
\begin{aligned}
(5 + 2i)(5 - 2i) &= 25 - 10i + 10i - 4i^2 \qquad \text{Use FOIL.} \\
&= 25 - 4i^2 \\
&= 25 - (-4) \qquad 4i^2 = -4 \\
&= 29
\end{aligned}
$$

In this case, the product is rational. Explore the general case.

Example 2

Find $(a + bi)(a - bi)$.

$$
\begin{aligned}
(a + bi)(a - bi) &= a^2 - abi + abi - b^2i^2 \qquad \text{Use FOIL.} \\
&= a^2 - b^2i^2 \\
&= a^2 - (-b^2) \qquad b^2i^2 = -b^2 \\
&= a^2 + b^2
\end{aligned}
$$

Since a and b are real, $a^2 + b^2$ will also be real.

To simplify expressions, we must eliminate all radicals in the denominator. Since i is a radical, all imaginary numbers must also be eliminated from denominators.

Example 3

Simplify $\dfrac{9 + 3i}{2i}$. **Teaching Tip ❶**

$$
\begin{aligned}
\frac{9 + 3i}{2i} &= \frac{9 + 3i}{2i} \cdot \frac{i}{i} \qquad \textit{Multiply by } \frac{i}{i} \textit{ to remove the } i \textit{ from the denominator.} \\
&= \frac{9i + 3i^2}{2i^2} \\
&= \frac{-3 + 9i}{-2} \text{ or } \frac{3 - 9i}{2}
\end{aligned}
$$

LESSON 6-10 SIMPLIFYING EXPRESSIONS CONTAINING COMPLEX NUMBERS 297

Lesson Resources

Reteaching Master 6-10
Practice Master 6-10
Enrichment Master 6-10

 Transparency 6-10 contains the 5-Minute Check and a teaching aid for this lesson.

INTRODUCING THE LESSON

 5-Minute Check

(over Lesson 6-9)
1. Find values for x and y such that $4x + 5yi = 12 + i$.
   $x = 3, y = \frac{1}{5}$

Simplify.

2. $(3 + 6i) + (7 - 9i)$
   $10 - 3i$
3. $(1 + 8i) - (5 - 4i)$
   $-4 + 12i$
4. $(7 + 6i)(4 - 2i)$ $40 + 10i$
5. $(8 + 3i)(8 - 3i)$ 73

Motivating the Lesson

Ask students to find a and b for each of the following:

1. $(8 + 2i)(a + bi) = 26 - 2i$
2. $(5 - 3i) + (a + bi) = 9 + i$
3. $(3 - 4i)^3 = a + bi$

What properties justify your steps?

TEACHING THE LESSON

Teaching Tip ❶   Note that $\dfrac{-i}{-i}$ could have been used to rationalize the denominator.

ALTERNATE TEACHING STRATEGIES

Using Discussion

Ask students the following questions and discuss.

1. What are the conjugates of $\dfrac{1}{3 + \sqrt{7}}$ and $\dfrac{2}{2 + \sqrt{5}}$?
2. What are the products of conjugates involving irrational numbers?
3. What can you hypothesize about the conjugates of complex numbers?

Using Computers

Have students write a program to solve complex number equations. Make sure they include the imaginary number cycle for the powers.

For Example 1
Simplify.

a. $(6 + 3i)(6 - 3i)$ **45**
b. $(9 - 7i)(9 + 7i)$ **130**

For Example 2
Simplify.

a. $(x + 2yi)(x - 2yi)$
   $x^2 + 4y^2$
b. $(3x - 8yi)(3x + 8yi)$
   $9x^2 + 64y^2$

For Example 3
Simplify.

a. $\dfrac{2 + 8i}{3i}$ $\dfrac{8 - 2i}{3}$

b. $\dfrac{3 + 7i}{2i}$ $\dfrac{7 - 3i}{2}$

For Example 4
Simplify.

a. $\dfrac{3 - 9i}{4 + 2i}$ $\dfrac{-3 - 21i}{10}$

b. $\dfrac{4 + 5i}{3 + 7i}$ $\dfrac{47 - 13i}{58}$

For Example 5
Find I if $E = (60 + j108)$ volts and
$Z = (6 - j4)$ ohms.
$\dfrac{-18 + j222}{13}$ **amps**

We use conjugates of radicals to rationalize the denominators of expressions with radicals in the denominator. We can also use conjugates of complex numbers to rationalize denominators of expressions with complex numbers in the denominator.

Example 4   Simplify $\dfrac{5 + i}{1 + 2i}$.

$$\frac{5 + i}{1 + 2i} = \frac{5 + i}{1 + 2i} \cdot \frac{1 - 2i}{1 - 2i} \qquad \text{\textit{1 + 2i and 1 − 2i are conjugates.}}$$

$$= \frac{5 - 10i + i - 2i^2}{1 - 4i^2} \qquad \text{\textit{(a + b)(a − b) = a}}^2 - b^2$$

$$= \frac{5 - 9i + 2}{1 + 4} \text{ or } \frac{7 - 9i}{5}$$

Example 5

APPLICATION

Electronics

Dr. Sharon Weisman is an electrical engineer designing the electrical circuits for a new office building. There are three basic things to be considered in an electrical circuit: the flow of the electrical current, I; the resistance to that flow, Z, called impedance; and electromotive force, E, called voltage. These quantities are related in the formula $E = I \cdot Z$. The current of the circuit Sharon is designing is to be $(35 - j40)$ amps. Electrical engineers use the letter j to represent the imaginary unit. Find the impedance of the circuit if the voltage is to be $(430 - j330)$ volts.

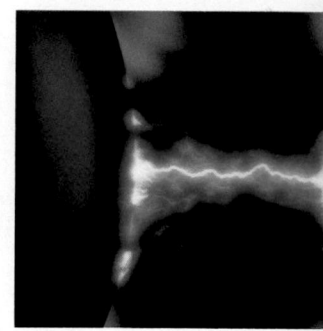

$$E = I \cdot Z$$

$$\frac{E}{I} = Z$$

$$\frac{(430 - j330)}{(35 - j40)} = Z$$

$$\frac{(430 - j330)}{(35 - j40)} \cdot \frac{(35 + j40)}{(35 + j40)} = Z \qquad \text{\textit{Rationalize the denominator.}}$$

$$\frac{15{,}050 + j17{,}200 - j11{,}550 - j^2 13{,}200}{1225 - j^2 1600} = Z \qquad j^2 = -1$$

$$\frac{28250 + j5650}{2825} = Z$$

$$10 + j2 = Z$$

The impedance will be $(10 + j2)$ ohms.

Example 6

Find the multiplicative inverse of $5 - 7i$.

The multiplicative inverse of $5 - 7i$ is $\dfrac{1}{5 - 7i}$.

Now simplify the expression.

$$\dfrac{1}{5 - 7i} = \dfrac{1}{5 - 7i} \cdot \dfrac{5 + 7i}{5 + 7i} \qquad \text{Multiply by conjugate}$$

$$= \dfrac{5 + 7i}{25 - 49i^2}$$

$$= \dfrac{5 + 7i}{74} \qquad i^2 = -1$$

Check: *The product of a number and its multiplicative inverse is 1.*

$$5 - 7i \cdot \dfrac{5 + 7i}{74} = \dfrac{25 + 49}{74}$$

$$= \dfrac{74}{74} \text{ or } 1 \checkmark$$

The inverse of $5 - 7i$ is $\dfrac{5 + 7i}{74}$.

Chalkboard Examples

For Example 6
Find the multiplicative inverse of the following complex numbers.

a. $\dfrac{3i}{2 - 4i}$ $\dfrac{-4 - 2i}{3}$

b. $7 + 2i$ $\dfrac{7 - 2i}{53}$

EVALUATING THE LESSON

Checking for Understanding
Exercises 1–16 are designed to help you assess understanding through reading, writing, and speaking. You should work through Exercises 1–4 with your students, and then monitor their work on Exercises 5–16.

Error Analysis
Students often think they have rationalized the denominator below:

$$\dfrac{1}{\sqrt[3]{2} + i\sqrt{3}} \cdot \dfrac{\sqrt[3]{2} - i\sqrt{3}}{\sqrt[3]{2} - i\sqrt{3}} = \dfrac{\sqrt[3]{2} - i\sqrt{3}}{\sqrt[3]{4} - i^2 \cdot 3}$$

$$\text{or} \quad \dfrac{\sqrt[3]{2} - i\sqrt{3}}{\sqrt[3]{4} + 3}$$

but they have only changed it to a real number. It is still not in simplest form.

Reteaching Masters Booklet, p. 44

CHECKING FOR UNDERSTANDING

Communicating Mathematics

2. the real number $a^2 + b^2$

3. The conjugate divided by the product of the number and its conjugate.

Guided Practice

Read and study the lesson to answer these questions.

1. What is the conjugate of the complex number $3 - 2i$? **$3 + 2i$**

2. Describe the product of the complex number $a + bi$ and its conjugate.

3. Study Example 6. Describe the multiplicative inverse of a complex number.

4. Does every complex number have a multiplicative inverse?
   No, all have inverses except 0.

Find the conjugate of each complex number.

5. $4 + i$ **$4 - i$**   6. $1 + 6i$ **$1 - 6i$**   7. $5 - 4i$ **$5 + 4i$**

8. $3 - 3i$ **$3 + 3i$**   9. $5i$ **$-5i$**   10. $6i$ **$-6i$**

11. $-10i$ **$10i$**   12. 9 **9**   13. $12 - i$ **$12 + i$**

Show that each pair of numbers are multiplicative inverses of one another.

14–16. See margin.

14. $2 + 3i; \dfrac{2 - 3i}{13}$ 15. $5 - 4i; \dfrac{5 + 4i}{41}$ 16. $6 + 8i; \dfrac{3 - 4i}{50}$

LESSON 6-10 SIMPLIFYING EXPRESSIONS CONTAINING COMPLEX NUMBERS   299

RETEACHING THE LESSON

In order to simplify each fraction, by what number would you multiply both the numerator and the denominator?

1. $\dfrac{1 + 3i}{4 + 2i}$ **$4 - 2i$**

2. $\dfrac{1 - 3i}{-4 + 2i}$ **$-4 - 2i$**

3. $\dfrac{a + bi}{c + di}$ **$c - di$**

Additional Answers

14. $2 + 3i \cdot \dfrac{2 - 3i}{13} = \dfrac{4 - 9i^2}{13}$

$$= \dfrac{4 + 9}{13}$$

$$= 1$$

15. $5 - 4i \cdot \dfrac{5 + 4i}{41} = \dfrac{25 - 16i^2}{41}$

$$= \dfrac{25 + 16}{41}$$

$$= 1$$

16. $6 + 8i \cdot \dfrac{3 - 4i}{50} = \dfrac{18 - 24i + 24i - 32i^2}{50}$

$$= \dfrac{18 + 32}{50}$$

$$= 1$$

NAME _____   **DATE** _____

6-10 **Reteaching Worksheet**

Simplifying Expressions Containing Complex Numbers

Complex numbers of the form $a + bi$ and $a - bi$ are called **conjugates** of each other. Notice that the product of complex conjugates is always a real number. Study the example to the left.

Example: Find $(5 + 2i)(5 - 2i)$.
$(5 + 2i)(5 - 2i) = 25 - 4i^2$
$= 25 - (-4)$
$= 29$

Sometimes rational expressions contain complex numbers. Since i represents a radical, rational numbers are usually written without imaginary numbers in the denominator. As with radicals, the denominator should be rationalized. Study the example to the right.

Example: Simplify $\dfrac{2 + 9i}{3i}$.
$\dfrac{2 + 9i}{3i} = \dfrac{2 + 9i}{3i} \cdot \dfrac{i}{i}$
$= \dfrac{2i + 9i^2}{3i^2}$
$= \dfrac{-9 + 2i}{-3}$ or $\dfrac{9 - 2i}{3}$

Find the product of each complex number and its conjugate.

1. $4 - 2i$ **20**   2. $9 - 2i$ **85**   3. $5 - 4i$ **41**

Find the multiplicative inverse of each complex number.

4. $4 - 2i$ $\dfrac{2 + i}{10}$ 5. $8 - 2i$ $\dfrac{4 + i}{34}$ 6. $6 + 3i$ $\dfrac{2 - i}{15}$

Simplify.

7. $(5 - 7i)(5 + 7i)$ **74**   8. $5 + (3 + i)$ $\dfrac{3 - i}{2}$ 9. $7 - 13i \div 2i$ $\dfrac{1}{2}$

10. $\dfrac{3 + i\sqrt{5}}{3 - i\sqrt{5}}$ $\dfrac{2 + 3i\sqrt{5}}{7}$ 11. $\dfrac{4 - i\sqrt{2}}{i\sqrt{2}}$ $-1 - 2\sqrt{2}i$ 12. $\dfrac{\sqrt{6} + i\sqrt{3}}{\sqrt{2} - i}$ $\dfrac{\sqrt{12} - \sqrt{3} + 2i\sqrt{6}}{3}$

EXERCISES

Practice   Find the product of each complex number and its conjugate.

A   17. $8-2i$ **68**   18. $3+7i$ **58**   19. $5-2i$ **29**

20. 5 **25**   21. $1+i$ **2**   22. $12+5i$ **169**

23. $9i$ **81**   24. $6+5i$ **61**   25. $-10i$ **100**

Simplify.

26. $\frac{4+5i}{1+i}$ $\frac{9+i}{2}$ 27. $\frac{3-2i}{1-i}$ $\frac{5+i}{2}$ 28. $\frac{1+i}{3+2i}$ $\frac{5+i}{13}$

29. $\frac{11+i}{2-i}$ $\frac{21+13i}{5}$ 30. $\frac{3+5i}{2i}$ $\frac{5-3i}{2}$ 31. $\frac{1-i}{4-5i}$ $\frac{9+i}{41}$

B   32. $\frac{5-6i}{-3i}$ $\frac{6+5i}{3}$ 33. $\frac{2+i}{5i}$ $\frac{1-2i}{5}$ 34. $\frac{4-7i}{-3i}$ $\frac{7+4i}{3}$

35. $\frac{5}{2+i}$ $2-i$ 36. $\frac{3}{4-i}$ $\frac{12+3i}{17}$ 37. $\frac{2}{6+5i}$ $\frac{12-10i}{61}$

38. $\frac{7}{\sqrt{2}-3i}$ $\frac{7\sqrt{2}+21i}{11}$ 39. $\frac{4}{\sqrt{3}+2i}$ $\frac{4\sqrt{3}-8i}{7}$ 40. $\frac{1+i\sqrt{2}}{1-i\sqrt{2}}$ $\frac{-1+2i\sqrt{2}}{3}$

41. $\frac{\sqrt{3}}{\sqrt{3}-i}$ $\frac{3+i\sqrt{3}}{4}$ 42. $\frac{2+i\sqrt{3}}{2-i\sqrt{3}}$ $\frac{1+4i\sqrt{3}}{7}$ 43. $\frac{3-i\sqrt{5}}{3+i\sqrt{5}}$ $\frac{2-3i\sqrt{5}}{7}$

Find the multiplicative inverse of each complex number.

44. $2+i$ $\frac{2-i}{5}$ 45. $3-4i$ $\frac{3+4i}{25}$ 46. $7-3i$ $\frac{7+3i}{58}$

47. $3+7i$ $\frac{3-7i}{58}$ 48. $2-5i$ $\frac{2+5i}{29}$ 49. $10-12i$ $\frac{5+6i}{122}$

C   50. $\frac{2i}{5-i}$ $\frac{-1-5i}{2}$ 51. $\frac{4i}{3+i}$ $\frac{1-3i}{4}$ 52. $\frac{-i}{2-3i}$ $3+2i$

53. $\frac{i}{8-2i}$ $-2-8i$ 54. $\frac{-3i}{3+4i}$ $\frac{-4+3i}{3}$ 55. $a+bi$ $\frac{a-bi}{a^2+b^2}$

Simplify.

56. $\frac{1-i\sqrt{3}}{2-i\sqrt{3}}$ $\frac{5-i\sqrt{3}}{7}$ 57. $\frac{2-i\sqrt{7}}{2+i\sqrt{7}}$ $\frac{-3-4i\sqrt{7}}{11}$ 58. $\frac{(2+3i)^2}{(3+i)^2}$ $\frac{16+63i}{50}$

59. $\frac{(3+3i)^2}{(1+i)^2}$ 9 60. $\frac{(4+3i)^2}{(3-i)^2}$ $\frac{-44+117i}{50}$ 61. $\frac{1-i}{(1+i)^2}$ $\frac{-1-i}{2}$

Critical Thinking   62. Show that $-\frac{1}{2}+\frac{1}{2}i\sqrt{3}$ is a cube root of 1.   *Hint: Find the cube of the number.* **See margin.**

63. Show that $1+i\sqrt{3}$ is a cube root of -8. **See margin.**

Additional Answers

62. $\left(-\frac{1}{2}+\frac{1}{2}i\sqrt{3}\right)^3$

$= \left(\frac{1}{4}-\frac{1}{2}i\sqrt{3}+\frac{3}{4}i^2\right)\left(-\frac{1}{2}+\frac{1}{2}i\sqrt{3}\right)$

$= \left(\frac{1}{4}-\frac{1}{2}i\sqrt{3}-\frac{3}{4}\right)\left(-\frac{1}{2}+\frac{1}{2}i\sqrt{3}\right)$

$= \left(-\frac{1}{2}-\frac{1}{2}i\sqrt{3}\right)\left(-\frac{1}{2}+\frac{1}{2}i\sqrt{3}\right)$

$= \frac{1}{4}-\frac{3}{4}i^2$

$= \frac{1}{4}+\frac{3}{4}$

$= 1$

63. $(1+i\sqrt{3})^3$

$= (1+i\sqrt{3})(1+i\sqrt{3})(1+i\sqrt{3})$

$= (1+2i\sqrt{3}+3i^2)(1+i\sqrt{3})$

$= (1+2i\sqrt{3}-3)(1+i\sqrt{3})$

$= (-2+2i\sqrt{3})(1+i\sqrt{3})$

$= -2-2i\sqrt{3}+2i\sqrt{3}+6i^2$

$= -2-6$

$= -8$

64. Electrical Engineering In an electrical circuit, the flow of the electrical current, I, the impedance, Z, and the voltage, E, are related by the formula $E = I \cdot Z$.

Find I given the following values.

a. $E = (70 + j226)$ volts, $Z = (6 + j8)$ ohms $\dfrac{557 + j199}{25}$ **amps**

b. $E = (85 + j110)$ volts, $Z = (3 - j4)$ ohms $\dfrac{-37 + j134}{5}$ **amps**

c. $E = (60 + j112)$ volts, $Z = (10 - j6)$ ohms $\dfrac{-9 + j185}{17}$ **amps**

Find Z given the following values.

d. $E = (-50 + j100)$ volts, $I = (-6 - j2)$ amps $\dfrac{5 - j35}{2}$ **ohms**

e. $E = (100 + j10)$ volts, $I = (-8 + j3)$ amps $\dfrac{-770 - j380}{73}$ **ohms**

f. $E = (-70 + j240)$ volts, $I = (-5 + j4)$ amps $\dfrac{1310 - j920}{41}$ **ohms**

Mixed Review

Simplify. (Lesson 6-9)

65. $(3 + 2i) + (4 + 5i)$ **$7 + 7i$**

66. $(4 + 3i)(16 - 28i)$ **$148 - 64i$**

67. Express $\sqrt[3]{\sqrt{64n^6}}$ in simplest radical form. **(Lesson 6-4)** **$2n$**

68. 1.9663 × 10⁶ wavelengths

69. yes, (–2, 4, 3)

68. Chemistry Wavelengths of light are measured in Angstroms. An Angstrom is 10^{-8} centimeters. The wavelength of cadmium's green line is 5085.8 Angstroms. How many wavelengths of cadmium's green line are there in one meter? **(Lesson 5-2)**

69. Determine whether the system
$$\begin{cases} 5a + b + 3c = 3 \\ 5a + b - c = -9 \\ a - b + 5c = 9 \end{cases}$$
has a unique solution. If so, solve the system using Cramer's Rule. **(Lesson 4-7)**

70. Use the strategy of solving a simpler problem to find the sum of the first 30 positive integers. **(Lesson 3-5)** **465**

71. Draw the graph of $3x + 8y < 11$. **(Lesson 2-8)** **See margin.**

72. Solve the equation $|x + 9| = 22$. **(Lesson 1-6)** **13, –31**

LESSON 6-10 SIMPLIFYING EXPRESSIONS CONTAINING COMPLEX NUMBERS 301

EXTENDING THE LESSON

Math Power: Reasoning

Can the product of a conjugate and its complex number be an irrational number? **Yes,**

$$\left(\sqrt[3]{2} + i\right)\left(\sqrt[3]{2} - i\right) = \sqrt[3]{4} + 1$$

is irrational.

Additional Answer

71.

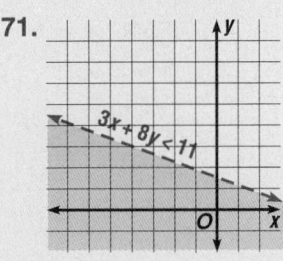

CHAPTER

6 SUMMARY AND REVIEW

VOCABULARY

Upon completing this chapter, you should be familiar with the following terms:

complex number	**292**	**258**	product property of radicals
conjugates	**266**	**288**	pure imaginary number
extraneous solutions	**282**	**259**	quotient property of radicals
imaginary number	**288**	**282**	radical equations
imaginary unit	**288**	**253**	radical sign
index	**253**	**253**	radicand
irrational numbers	**254**	**270**	rational exponents
like radical expressions	**264**	**260**	rationalizing the denominator
nth root	**252**	**252**	square root
principal root	**253**		

SKILLS AND CONCEPTS

OBJECTIVES AND EXAMPLES	REVIEW EXERCISES

Upon completing this chapter, you should be able to:

Use these exercises to review and prepare for the chapter test.

■ simplify radicals **(Lesson 6-1)**

$$\sqrt{36m^4n^6} = \sqrt{(6m^2n^3)^2}$$
$$= 6\ m^2|n^3|$$

Simplify. **3.** $|3p - 5q|$ **4.** $|2n + 3|$

1. $\sqrt{49x^2}$ $7|x|$ **2.** $\sqrt[3]{-64a^6b^9}$ $-4a^2b^3$

3. $\sqrt{(3p - 5q)^2}$ **4.** $\sqrt{4n^2 + 12n + 9}$

■ simplify radical expressions using multiplication and division, and rationalize the denominator of a fraction containing a radical expression **(Lesson 6-2)**

$$\sqrt{27a^3} = \sqrt{3^2} \cdot \sqrt{3} \cdot \sqrt{a^2} \cdot \sqrt{a}$$
$$= 3a\sqrt{3a}$$

Simplify.

5. $\sqrt{96}$ $4\sqrt{6}$ **6.** $\sqrt{50x^3y^2}$ $5x|y|\sqrt{2x}$

7. $\sqrt{6ab} \cdot \sqrt{3a}$ $3|a|\sqrt{2b}$ **8.** $\sqrt[3]{\dfrac{5}{27}}$ $\dfrac{\sqrt[3]{5}}{3}$

9. $\dfrac{15}{2\sqrt{5}}$ $\dfrac{3\sqrt{5}}{2}$ **10.** $\dfrac{4}{\sqrt[4]{2}}$ $2\sqrt[4]{8}$

11. $\sqrt{5}(2\sqrt{10} + 3\sqrt{2})$ $10\sqrt{2} + 3\sqrt{10}$

12. $\sqrt[3]{4}(2\ \sqrt[3]{4} - 5\ \sqrt[3]{2})$ $4\ \sqrt[3]{2} - 10$

- add, subtract, multiply, and divide radical expressions **(Lesson 6-3)**

$(2 + \sqrt{2})(3 + \sqrt{3})$
$= 6 + 2\sqrt{3} + 3\sqrt{2} + \sqrt{6}$

$\dfrac{2 - \sqrt{5}}{1 - 2\sqrt{5}} \cdot \dfrac{1 + 2\sqrt{5}}{1 + 2\sqrt{5}} = \dfrac{-8 + 3\sqrt{5}}{1 - 20}$
$= \dfrac{8 - 3\sqrt{5}}{19}$

Simplify. 16. $12\sqrt{5} - 6\sqrt{3} + 2\sqrt{15} - 3$

13. $5 + 2\sqrt{6} - 3\sqrt{6} + 9$ **$14 - \sqrt{6}$**
14. $3\sqrt{27} - 5\sqrt{3} + 2\sqrt{48}$ **$12\sqrt{3}$**
15. $7\sqrt[3]{24x^2} + \sqrt[3]{81x^2}$ **$17\sqrt[3]{3x^2}$**
16. $(6 + \sqrt{3})(2\sqrt{5} - \sqrt{3})$
17. $(5\sqrt{2} - \sqrt{3})(5\sqrt{2} + \sqrt{3})$ **47**
18. $\dfrac{4 - \sqrt{3}}{1 + 2\sqrt{3}}$ **$\dfrac{9\sqrt{3} - 10}{11}$**

- write expressions with rational exponents in simplest radical form and vice versa **(Lesson 6-4)**

$\sqrt{36a^2b^3} = 6|a|b^{\frac{3}{2}}$

$x^{\frac{4}{5}} = \sqrt[5]{x^4}$

Express using rational exponents.

19. $\sqrt[4]{r^3}$ **$r^{\frac{3}{4}}$**   20. $\sqrt[3]{8m^2n^7}$ **$2m^{\frac{2}{3}}n^{\frac{7}{3}}$**

Express in simplest radical form. $\sqrt[6]{2^4x^5y^3}$

21. $5^{\frac{1}{3}}$ **$\sqrt[3]{5}$**   22. $2^{\frac{2}{3}} \cdot x^{\frac{5}{6}} \cdot y^{\frac{1}{2}}$

- evaluate expressions in either exponential or radical form **(Lesson 6-4)**

$8^{-\frac{1}{3}} = \dfrac{1}{\sqrt[3]{8}} - \dfrac{1}{2}$

Evaluate.

23. $125^{\frac{1}{3}}$ **5**   24. $4^{-\frac{1}{2}}$ **$\dfrac{1}{2}$**

25. $16^{1.25}$ **32**   26. $8^{\frac{2}{3}} \cdot 8^{\frac{2}{3}}$ **16**

- simplify expressions containing rational exponents **(Lesson 6-6)**

$\dfrac{1}{4^{\frac{3}{2}}} = \dfrac{1}{4^{\frac{3}{2}}} \cdot \dfrac{4^{\frac{1}{2}}}{4^{\frac{1}{2}}} = \dfrac{4^{\frac{1}{2}}}{4^2} = \dfrac{4^{\frac{1}{2}}}{16}$

$\dfrac{1}{w \; y^{\frac{1}{2}}} \cdot \dfrac{w + y^{\frac{1}{2}}}{w + y^{\frac{1}{2}}} = \dfrac{w + y^{\frac{1}{2}}}{w^2 - y}$

Simplify

27. $\dfrac{1}{5^{\frac{1}{3}}}$ **$\dfrac{5^{\frac{2}{3}}}{5}$**   28. $\dfrac{2^{\frac{1}{2}}}{2^{\frac{2}{3}}}$ **$2^{\frac{1}{6}}$**

29. $a^{-\frac{3}{4}} \dfrac{a^{\frac{1}{4}}}{a}$ 30. $\dfrac{p^{\frac{1}{2}} - 2q^{\frac{1}{2}}}{p^{\frac{1}{2}} + q^{\frac{1}{2}}}$

$\dfrac{p - 3p^{\frac{1}{2}}q^{\frac{1}{2}} + 2q}{p - q}$

- solve equations containing radicals **(Lesson 6-7)**

$\sqrt{x + 1} - \sqrt{x + 3} = 1$
$\sqrt{x + 1} = \sqrt{x + 3} + 1$
$x + 1 = x + 3 + 2\sqrt{x + 3} + 1$
$\dfrac{-3}{2} = \sqrt{x + 3}$
$\dfrac{9}{4} = x + 3$
$-\dfrac{3}{4} = x$

However, this solution does not check so there is no solution.

Solve each equation.

31. $u + 3 - u\sqrt{2}$ **$3 + 3\sqrt{2}$**
32. $4x - \sqrt{2} = x\sqrt{3} + 2\sqrt{2}$ **$\dfrac{12\sqrt{2} + 3\sqrt{6}}{13}$**
33. $5 - \sqrt{3x + 4} = 0$ **7**
34. $\sqrt{x + 11} - \sqrt{15 + 2x} = 1$ **-7**
35. $\sqrt{x - 2} + \sqrt{7x - 6} = 8$ **6**
36. $\sqrt[3]{5n + 4} - 4 = 0$ **12**

Alternate Review Strategy

To provide a brief in-class review, you may wish to read the following questions to the class and require a verbal response.

1. Simplify $\sqrt{625c^2}$.   **$25|c|$**

2. Simplify $\dfrac{20}{\sqrt[3]{4}}$.   **$5\sqrt[3]{16}$**

3. Simplify $2\sqrt{8} + 3\sqrt{2} + 7\sqrt{32}$.   **$35\sqrt{2}$**

4. Express $7^{\frac{3}{4}}$ in simplest radical form.   **$\sqrt[4]{7^3}$**

5. Evaluate $16^{-\frac{1}{4}}$.   **$\dfrac{1}{2}$**

6. Simplify $\dfrac{c^{\frac{1}{2}} - d^{\frac{1}{2}}}{c^{\frac{1}{2}} + d^{\frac{1}{2}}}$.   **$\dfrac{c - 2(cd)^{\frac{1}{2}} + d}{c - d}$**

7. Solve $2x - \sqrt{3} = x\sqrt{5} + \sqrt{3}$.   **$-(4\sqrt{3} + 2\sqrt{15})$**

8. Simplify $(2i)^6$.   **-64**

9. Simplify $(2 + 5i) - (4 - 7i)$.   **$-2 + 12i$**

10. Find the conjugate of $5 - 2i$.   **$5 + 2i$**

The Cumulative Review shown below can be used to review skills and concepts presented thus far in the text. Standardized Test Practice Questions are also provided in the Evaluation Masters Booklet.

Evaluation Masters Booklet, pp. 81–82

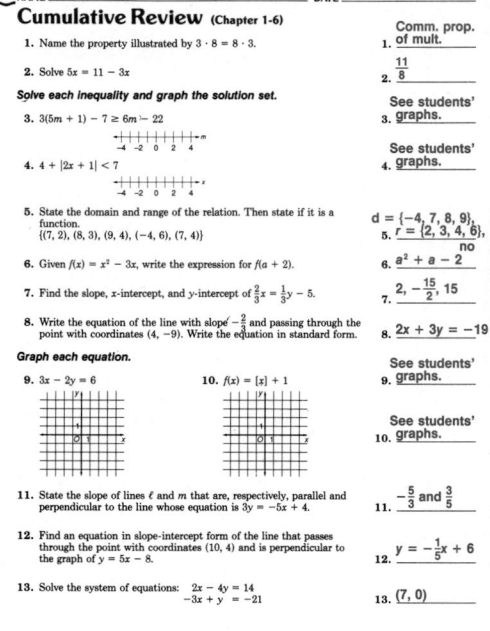

OBJECTIVES AND EXAMPLES	REVIEW EXERCISES

■ simplify radicals containing negative radicands and multiply pure imaginary numbers **(Lesson 6-8)**

$$\sqrt{-180} = \sqrt{36} \cdot \sqrt{5} \cdot \sqrt{-1}$$
$$= 6i\sqrt{5}$$

$$2i(i)^2 = 2i(-1) = -2i$$

Simplify.

37. $\sqrt{-121}$ $11i$ 38. $\sqrt{-32}$ $4i\sqrt{2}$

39. $5i(3i)$ -15 40. $(8i)^3$ $-512i$

■ add, subtract, and multiply complex numbers **(Lesson 6-9)**

$$(2 + 3i) + (4 - i) = 6 + 2i$$
$$(13 - 6i) - (10 - 4i) = 3 - 2i$$
$$(1 + 5i)(2 - 3i) = 2 + 7i + 15$$
$$= 17 + 7i$$

Simplify.

41. $(8 + 7i) + (13 - 2i)$ $21 + 5i$

42. $(29 - 37i) - (19 + 21i)$ $10 - 58i$

43. $(7 + 6i)(4 - 3i)$ $46 + 3i$

44. $(5 - 7i)^2$ $-24 - 70i$

■ simplify rational expressions containing complex numbers in the denominator **(Lesson 6-10)**

$$\frac{3 + 4i}{3 - 2i} \cdot \frac{3 + 2i}{3 + 2i} = \frac{1 + 18i}{13}$$

The multiplicative inverse of $2 + 5i$ is $\frac{1}{2 + 5i}$ or $\frac{2 - 5i}{29}$.

Find the conjugate of each complex number.

45. $8 - 13i$ $8 + 13i$ 46. $-3 + 11i$ $-3 - 11i$

Simplify.

47. $\frac{11 + 8i}{2i}$ $8 - \frac{11i}{2}$ 48. $\frac{2 + 3i}{2 - 3i}$ $\frac{-5 + 12i}{13}$

Find the multiplicative inverse of each complex number.

49. $8 - i$ $\frac{8 + i}{65}$ 50. $12i$ $\frac{i}{-12}$

∿∿∿ APPLICATIONS AND CONNECTIONS ∿∿∿

51. **Physics** Find the time, t (in seconds), that it takes for a freely falling object to fall a distance, s, of 200 feet. Use the formula $t = \frac{1}{4}\sqrt{s}$. **(Lesson 6-3)** $\frac{5\sqrt{2}}{2}$ or about 3.54 seconds

52. Find the sum of the numbers between 1 and 500 that are not multiples of 2 or 3. You may use the formula $S = \frac{n(n + 1)}{2}$ for the sum, S, of the integers 1 to n. **(Lesson 6-5)** 41,833

53. **Energy** A circular solar cell must deliver 18 watts of energy. If each square centimeter of the cell that is in sunlight produces 0.01 watt of energy, how long must the radius of the cell be? **(Lesson 6-7)** about 23.94 cm

54. **Electronics** The voltage, E, (in volts) of an electrical circuit is given by the formula $E = I \cdot Z$, where I represents the current, and Z represents the impedance. Find the voltage of a circuit with current $(20 + j12)$ amps and impedance $(15 + j3)$ ohms. **(Lesson 6-9)** $(264 + j240)$ volts

Simplify.

1. $\sqrt{324}$ **18**

2. $\sqrt{512}$ **$16\sqrt{2}$**

3. $\sqrt{169a^3b^2}$ **$13a|b|\sqrt{a}$**

4. $\sqrt[3]{-16y^3}$ **$-2y\sqrt[3]{2}$**

5. $\sqrt{9x^2 - 30xy + 25y^2}$ **$|3x - 5y|$**

6. $\sqrt{x^2(x-3)^2}$ **$|x(x-3)|$**

7. $\sqrt{5a^3} \cdot \sqrt{10ab^3}$ **$5a^2b\sqrt{2b}$**

8. $\sqrt{6}(3\sqrt{2} - 2\sqrt{12})$ **$6\sqrt{3} - 12\sqrt{2}$**

9. $\sqrt[3]{2}(\sqrt[3]{54} - 3\sqrt[3]{16})$ **$-3\sqrt[3]{4}$**

10. $5\sqrt{8} - 6\sqrt{50} + 4\sqrt{18}$ **$-8\sqrt{2}$**

11. $(5 + \sqrt{3})(7 - 2\sqrt{3})$ **$29 - 3\sqrt{3}$**

12. $(2\sqrt{5} - \sqrt{3})(2\sqrt{5} + \sqrt{3})$ **17**

13. $(\sqrt{2} - 3\sqrt{6})(\sqrt{3} + 6)$ **$-17\sqrt{6} - 3\sqrt{2}$**

14. $\dfrac{6}{\sqrt{3}}$ **$2\sqrt{3}$**

15. $\dfrac{3}{\sqrt[4]{54}}$ **$\dfrac{\sqrt[4]{24}}{2}$**

16. $\dfrac{3 - \sqrt{2}}{4 + \sqrt{2}}$ **$\dfrac{2 - \sqrt{2}}{2}$**

17. What fraction of the odd whole numbers less than 100 are perfect squares? **$\dfrac{1}{10}$**

Simplify.

18. $\dfrac{\frac{1}{4^3}}{4^{\frac{1}{3}}}$ **$\dfrac{4^{\frac{2}{3}}}{4}$**

19. $p^{-\frac{3}{4}}$ **$\dfrac{p^{\frac{1}{4}}}{p}$**

20. $\dfrac{3}{a^{-1} + b^{-2}}$ **$\dfrac{3ab^2}{a + b^9}$**

21. $\dfrac{m^{\frac{1}{2}}}{m^{\frac{1}{2}} - n^{\frac{1}{2}}}$ **$\dfrac{m + \sqrt{mn}}{m - n}$**

Solve each equation.

22. $\sqrt{3t - 2} = 5$ **9**

23. $\sqrt{x + 5} + \sqrt{x + 13} = 4$ **-4**

24. $\sqrt[3]{4n + 9} = 5$ **29**

25. $\sqrt{n^2 - 7} = \sqrt{4n + 25}$ **-4 or 8**

26. $x^2 + 100 = 0$ **$\pm 10i$**

27. $6x^2 + 42 = 0$ **$\pm i\sqrt{7}$**

Find the conjugate of each complex number.

28. $-8 + 5i$ **$-8 - 5i$**

29. $4i$ **$-4i$**

Find the multiplicative inverse of each complex number.

30. $3 - 9i$ **$\dfrac{1 + 3i}{30}$**

31. $11i$ **$-\dfrac{i}{11}$**

32. Write $5^{\frac{2}{3}}a^{\frac{1}{2}}b^{\frac{3}{8}}$ using a single radical. **$\sqrt[24]{5^{16}a^{12}b^9}$**

33. Write $\sqrt[6]{36x^5y^9z^4}$ in simplified form using rational exponents. **$6^{\frac{1}{3}}x^{\frac{5}{6}}y^{\frac{3}{2}}z^{\frac{2}{3}}$**

Bonus Find the least positive integer greater than 2 whose cube ends in 8. **12**

A **Test and Review Generator** is provided in Apple, IBM, and Macintosh versions. You may use this software to create your own tests or worksheets, based on the needs of your students.

The **Performance Assessment Booklet** provides an alternate asssessment for evaluating student progress. An assessment for this chapter can be found on pages 11–12.

The questions on these pages involve comparing two quantities, one in column A and one in column B. In certain questions, information related to one or both quantities is centered above them. All variables used represent real numbers.

Directions:

Write A if the quantity in Column A is greater.

Write B if the quantity in Column B is greater.

Write C if the quantities are equal.

Write D if there is not enough information to determine the relationship.

Column A	Column B
1. $\dfrac{8a + 12}{2}$ **C**	$4a + 6$
2. A $(-9)^{72}$	$(-9)^{83}$
3. A $\quad\quad -3 < n < 0$ $-3(n + n)$	$(n)(n)(n)$
4. D $\quad\quad n + 11 > 12$ $3n + 8$	$16 - 2n$
5. B $\quad\quad a < 0 < b$ $\dfrac{a}{2}$	b^2
6. D $\quad\quad x^2 > y^2$ $(y + 1)^2$	$(x + 1)^2$

Column A	Column B
7. B $\frac{1}{2}\%$ of 400	0.5×400
8. B $\quad\quad \dfrac{0.05}{x} = \dfrac{0.2}{0.6}$ x	0.2
9. D $\quad\quad 6 > b > -5$ $\dfrac{b}{5}$	$\dfrac{5}{b}$
10. B $\quad$ 30% of r is 6 The percent that 60 is of r.	The percent that r is of 6.
11. C $0.8 \times 6d$	$\frac{3}{5}$ of $8d$
12. A $23 - 4(2)0$	$6 + 10(3 - 2)$
13. D $\quad\quad \dfrac{x}{2} = z^2$ x	z
14. area of a circle with **A** diameter 10	area of a right triangle with hypotenuse 10
15. A $\quad\quad \dfrac{1}{3} < a < \dfrac{2}{3}$ $\quad\quad \dfrac{2}{3} < b < 1$ $a + b$	$a^2 + b^2$
16. B a if $3a < 23$	b if $23 < 3b$

Column A	Column B

17. The perimeter of the square and
A rectangle are equal.

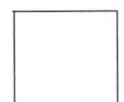 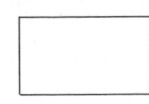

area of the square	area of the rectangle

18. $\dfrac{x}{y}$ $\dfrac{y}{x}$
D

19. $a > 0$

B $4a - 3a$ $4 \times 3a$

20. the slope of   the slope of
B $2x + 3y = 7$ $3x - 2y = 7$

21. $-x$ $\dfrac{1}{x}$
D

22.
B
$$\begin{bmatrix} 3 & -4 & 5 \\ -2 & 1 & -3 \\ 6 & -5 & -7 \end{bmatrix}$$

the signed minor of e_{23}	the signed minor of e_{32}

23. $5x - 2y = 4$

A the y-intercept of the line parallel to the given line and containing $(-2, 3)$ the y-intercept of the line perpendicular to given line and containing $(-2, 3)$

24. $r < 0$

A $\sqrt{r^2}$ $\sqrt[3]{r^3}$

TEST TAKING TIP

If the use of A's and B's in both the column names and answer choices is confusing, change the column names to another pair of letters or numbers, such as X and Y or I or II.

Perform any indicated mathematical operations. Change the common information by addition, subtraction, multiplication, or division when it is given as an equation or an inequality.

Remember that the figures are often not drawn to scale and may lead you to make assumptions which are not valid. Try many ways to illustrate the figures given to fit the situations given.

Column A	Column B

25. $x + 3y = 5$
B $y = 3x + 5$

     x y

26. $i^x = -i$
D
    x 6

7 Quadratic Equations

PREVIEWING THE CHAPTER

In this chapter students learn to solve quadratic equations by factoring, by graphing, by completing the square, and by using the quadratic formula. Students use the discriminant to determine the nature of the roots of a quadratic equation and then learn how to write a quadratic equation when two roots of the equation are known. The chapter concludes with a lesson where students solve nonquadratic equations using one or more of the methods they learned to use when solving quadratic equations.

Problem-Solving Strategy   Students use the strategy of *guess and check* to solve problems where they guess, check the guess, analyze the result, and continue to guess and check until they find the correct answer.

Lesson Objective Chart

Lesson (Pages)	Lesson Objectives	State/Local Objectives
7-1 (310-311)	**7-1:** Solve problems using the guess-and-check strategy.	
7-2 (316-321)	**7-2A:** Solve quadratic equations by graphing.	
	7-2B: Solve quadratic equations by factoring.	
7-3 (322-326)	**7-3:** Solve quadratic equations by completing the square.	
7-4 (327-331)	**7-4A:** Solve quadratic equations using the quadratic formula.	
	7-4B: Use the discriminant to determine the nature of the roots of a quadratic equation.	
7-5 (333-338)	**7-5A:** Find the sum and product of the roots of a quadratic equation.	
	7-5B: Find all possible integral roots of a quadratic equation.	
	7-5C: Find a quadratic equation to fit a given condition.	
7-6 (339-343)	**7-6A:** Solve third and fourth degree equations that contain a quadratic factor.	
	7-6B: Solve other nonquadratic equations that can be written in quadratic form.	

ORGANIZING THE CHAPTER

You may want to refer to the **Course Planning Calendar** on page T44.

Lesson (Pages)	Pacing Chart (days) Course I	II	III	Reteaching	Practice	Enrichment	Evaluation	Technology	Lab Manual	Activities Mixed Problem Solving	Applications	Cooperative Learning Activity	Multicultural	Transparencies
7-1 (310-311)	1	0.5	0.5		p. 51							p. 43		7-1
7-2 (316-321)	2	1.5	1.5	p. 45	p. 52	p. 45	Quiz A, p. 93	p. 24						7-2
7-3 (322-326)	1.5	1	1	p. 46	p. 53	p. 46	Quiz B, p. 93		pp. 57-58	p. 7				7-3
7-4 (327-331)	1.5	1	1	p. 47	p. 54	p. 47	Quiz C, p. 94 Mid-Chapter Test, p. 97	p. 7			p. 25			7-4
7-5 (333-338)	1.5	1.5	1	p. 48	p. 55	p. 48								7-5
7-6 (339-343)	1.5	1.5	1	p. 49	p. 56	p. 49	Quiz D, p. 94						p. 7	7-6
Review (344-346)	1	1	1	Multiple Choice Tests, Forms 1A and 1B, pp. 85-88 Free Response Tests, Forms 2A and 2B, pp. 89-92										
Test (349)	1	1	1	Cumulative Review, pp. 95-96 Standardized Test Practice Questions, p. 98										

Blackline Masters Booklets

Course I: Chapters 1-13; Course II: Chapters 1-15; Course III: Chapters 1-17

Other Chapter Resources

Student Edition

Chapter Opener, pp. 308-309
Cooperative Learning Activity, p. 311
Graphing Calculator Exploration,
   pp. 312-315
Journal Entries, pp. 326, 331
Mid-Chapter Review, p. 326
Technology, p. 332
History Connection, p. 338
Portfolio Suggestion, p. 343
Extended Project 2, pp. A6-A9

Teacher's Classroom Resources

Transparency 7-0
Real-World Applications
   Transparencies, 14, 15
Performance Assessment Booklet,
   pp. 13-14
Problem-of-the-Week Activity Cards,
   14, 15
Tech Prep Applications Booklet, pp. 13-14
Lesson Plans, pp. 51-56

Other Supplements

Glencoe Mathematics
   Professional Series

Software

Test and Review Generator Software
   (Apple, IBM, and Macintosh)
Interactive Software (Macintosh)
Teacher's Guide for Software
   Resources

ENHANCING THE CHAPTER

Cooperative Learning

Planning Teaching Materials

When groups have had substantial experience and exhibit reasonable competence in cooperative-learning skills, you may not have to give much special care to how you arrange materials. However, until this stage is achieved, you should consider how to distribute materials in order to communicate that the activity is to be a group and not an individual activity. One way to do this is to provide only one set of materials or one copy of the worksheet to the group. The members will quickly realize that they have to work together if they are to be successful in achieving the objective and receiving your recognition. A variation on this method is to provide each member of the group with a worksheet but tell the group that you will collect only one of them, chosen at random. This method also encourages members to help one another and to make sure that each member has and understands the correct answer. A third method, appropriate in some activities, is to give each member only part of the materials or resources required to complete the task. Thus, every member must participate if the whole group is to be successful.

Technology

The BASIC program in the Technology Feature of this chapter enables students to determine the nature of the roots of an equation using the discriminant. Have students relate the steps of the program to the algorithms presented in the chapter.

Critical Thinking

The acquisition of critical-thinking skills related to analysis and synthesis are vital for success in many algebraic situations. You can help students improve these skills by taking advantage of the problem-solving activities in Lesson 7-1 that involve the strategy *guess and check*. When working with this strategy, make students aware that you expect them to be able to explain, when their first guess is not the answer, how and why they chose each successive guess. Such analysis of the results of initial guesses to make more intelligent guesses will ensure success with this strategy when applied to real-life problems or to other algebraic content.

Cooperative Learning, p. 43

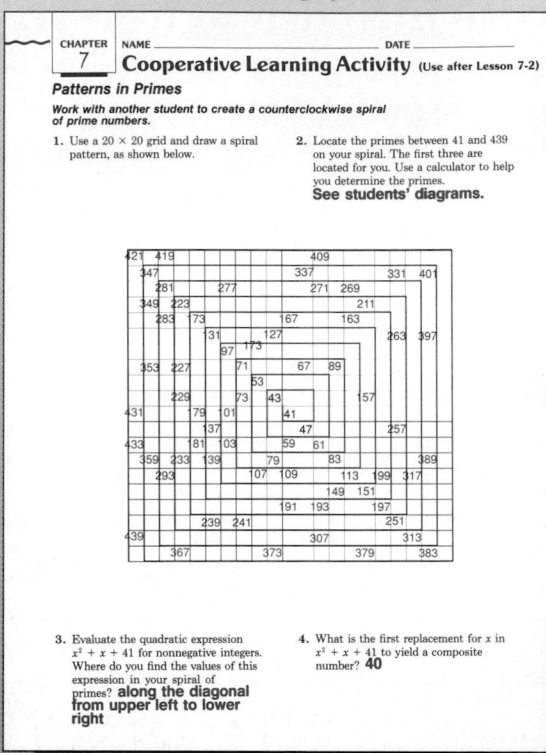

Technology, p. 7

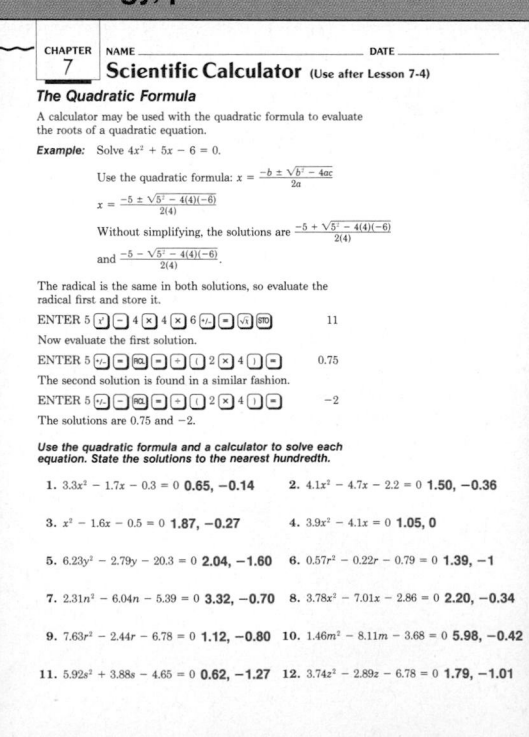

Problem of the Week Activity

The card shown below is one of two available for this chapter. It can be used as a class or small group activity.

Activity Card

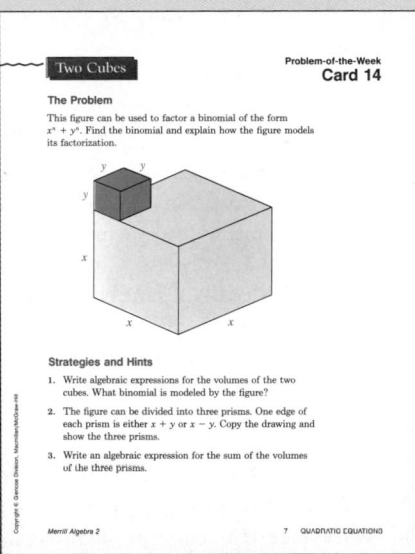

Manipulatives and Models

The following materials may be used as models or manipulatives in chapter 7.

- toothpicks (Lesson 7-1)
- algebra tiles (Lesson 7-2)
- ball (Lesson 7-2)
- stopwatch (Lesson 7-2)
- paper and scissors (Lesson 7-3)
- several different calculators (Lesson 7-3)

Outside Resources

Books/Periodicals

ApSimon, Hugh. *More Mathematical Byways.* Oxford University Press.

Cupillari, Antonella. *The Nuts and Bolts of Proofs.* Wadsworth Publishing Company.

Films/Videotapes/Videodiscs

Miscellaneous Quadratic Equations Solved by Factoring, Solving Quadratic Equations by the Quadratic Formula, and *Solving Quadratic Equations by Completing the Square,* parts of the Intermediate Algebra Series, Great Plains National Instructional TV Library (GPN), P.O. Box 80669, Lincoln, NE 68501

Software

Algebra Drill & Practice II, Conduit Educational Software, University of Iowa, Oakdale Campus, Iowa City, IA 52242-0001

Green Globs and Graphing Equations, WINGS for Learning/Sunburst Communications, 1600 Green Hills Rd., P.O. Box 660002, Scotts Valley, CA 95067-0002

Multicultural

Multicultural Activity, p. 7

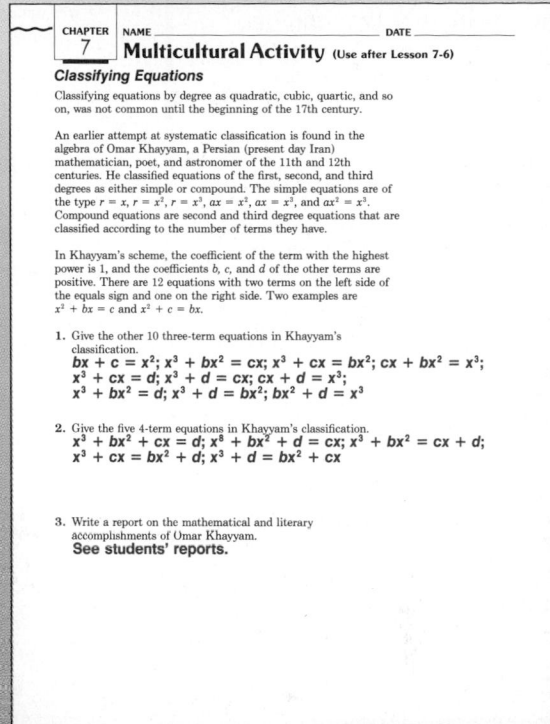

Lab Manual

Lab Activity, pp. 57-58

Background Information

City planners must be well versed in economics, statistics, and probability. They often design new transportation systems and parking facilities and, as a result, become heavily involved in the mathematics of architecture and engineering. City planners prepare detailed studies of current land use and budgets. Employment of city planners is expected to grow 14%–24% through the 1990s as a result of increased demand for environmental, economic, and energy production planning. Opportunities will be best in rapidly growing areas and older areas undergoing redevelopment.

Quadratic Equations

CHAPTER OBJECTIVES

In this chapter, you will:

- Solve quadratic equations by graphing, factoring, completing the square, and using the quadratic formula.
- Write quadratic equations when two roots of the equation are known.
- Solve nonquadratic equations by methods used to solve quadratic equations.

What trends do you foresee for city planners? Why do you think this trend is occurring?

Percentage of Population Living in Urban Areas

Legend:
- 2000
- 1990
- 1980
- 1970

(Regions: North America, Europe, Oceania, USSR, Latin America, East Asia, South Asia, Africa)

308

CAREERS IN CITY PLANNING

What kinds of cities will we need in the next century? The downtowns of many cities today are degenerating into vacant stores and uninhabited offices and apartments. City planners are replacing these areas with elegant convention centers, glassy hotels and office towers, and festive marketplaces. These features might entice suburban dwellers to leave their small shopping centers and fast food outlets to venture into the city.

What about the next century? Today most of us use our automobile to travel to the market or workplace. The concept of convenience has steered many city planners to expand cities as small, self-sufficient centers. With the increase in the price of oil, this trend will increase. Planners will design areas with apartments, houses, offices, factories, bike trails, lakes, medical facilities, schools, parks, shops and supermarkets, and sports facilities clustered together. In such neighborhoods, people can walk to any local destination and save their cars for long trips.

In designing such environments, city planners will create 3-D mathematical models on their computers. They'll consult with architects, public health officers, economists, and many other specialists. They will become experts in evaluating statistics as they study traffic patterns, weather, and demographics. Will you someday play a part in the design of your own children's hometown?

Chapter Project

Materials: paper and pencil, library resources

Organize students into cooperative groups of city planners. Assign each group the task of planning and designing the development of one of the following for a specific city, county, or region.

- Transportation system; for example, a monorail system
- Civic center
- Environmentally safe power plant
- Redevelopment of an older area
- New housing development
- Highways
- Sports arena
- Shopping center

Each group should research state and local housing and building codes, environmental requirements, land availability and usage, budgets, political feasibility, and so on. Have each group report its plans and designs to the class as a whole.

MORE ABOUT CITY PLANNING

Degree Required:

- Bachelor's Degree in City and Community Planning, Environmental Design

Related Math Subjects:

- Advanced Algebra
- Trigonometry
- Statistics/Probability
- Economics

Some city planners like:

- working for the community
- helping to improve the quality of life for citizens
- good salaries and benefits
- variety and challenge in their work

Some city planners dislike:

- keeping up with government rules and regulations and local building codes
- meeting deadlines
- attending meetings after regular work hours and on weekends

For more information on the various careers available in the field of city planning, write to:
American Institute of Certified Planners
1776 Massachusetts Avenue NW
Washington, DC 20036

309

Connections and Applications

Lesson	Connections (C) and Applications (A)	Examples	Exercises
7-2	C: Physics		46
	A: Physics	3	37
	City		48
	Planning		49
	Sports		55
	Electricity		
7-3	A: Physics	3	32
	Hobbies		31
	Safety		33
7-4	A: Gardening		37
	Astronomy		38
7-5	C: Geometry		54
	A: Sports	4	
	Aeronautics		45
	Horticulture		46
	Flight		47
	Business		53
7-6	C: Geometry		39
	A: Landscaping		47
	Aeronautics		48

PLAN
SOLVE
EXAMINE

7-1 Problem-Solving Strategy: Guess-and-Check

Lesson Resources

Practice Master 7-1
Activity Master, p. 43

 Transparency 7-1 contains the 5-Minute Check and a teaching aid for this lesson.

INTRODUCING THE LESSON

 5-Minute Check

(over Chapter 6)

1. Simplify $\sqrt[3]{2}\left(\sqrt[3]{24} - \sqrt[3]{4}\right)$.
   $2\sqrt[3]{6} - 2$

2. Evaluate $\left(\frac{1}{64}\right)^{-\frac{2}{3}}$.   16

3. Solve $\sqrt{r + 12} - \sqrt{r} = 2$.   4

4. Simplify $\frac{4 - 5i}{3 + 7i}$. $\frac{-23 - 43i}{58}$

Motivating the Lesson

Ask students to find the ways you can get 8 liters of water, given you have only two buckets. One of the buckets is 3 liters and the other bucket is 7 liters in capacity. Have students explain their method of solution. If someone says they guessed, point out that guessing is a valid method.

TEACHING THE LESSON

Chalkboard Example

For the Example

Find five consecutive integers such that the sum of the squares of the least and greatest is 208.
8, 9, 10, 11, 12 or –12, –11, –10, –9, –8

Objective

7-1

After studying this lesson, you will be able to:

■ solve problems using the guess-and-check strategy.

Application

Miss Grusselli owns a ranch in Colorado. She wants to fence off part of the ranch to make a corral for her horses. The fence used for horses is made of sections of wood planking nailed to posts. She has enough lumber to build 16 sections, but she also wants to have the maximum area for her horses. What should the dimensions of the rectangular corral be?

Let one unit represent each section of wood planking.

length (units)	width (units)	perimeter (units)	area (units²)	
7	1	16	7	
6	2	16	12	*This is getting closer. Guess again.*
5	3	16	15	*This is better. Guess again.*
4	4	16	16	*Better still! Is this it?*
4.5	3.5	16	15.75	

The last guess produced an area smaller than the area of the 4 × 4 rectangle. You might try other combinations to convince yourself that the 4 × 4 rectangle will be the figure that has the maximum area of a perimeter of 16 units.

Example

You need only divide by primes. What are the first five primes?

Find the least prime number greater than 720.

One way to solve this problem is to check each integer, beginning with 721, for prime divisors until you find a prime number. However, if you use known information, you can save time and effort. Obviously, any even integer greater than 720 is not prime. Since 720 is divisible by 3, every third integer greater than 720 will not prime. Any integer greater than 720 whose last digit is 5 or 0 is not prime. Thus, many possibilities are eliminated.

Try 721.   *Using a calculator is helpful.*
   $721 \div 7 = 103$ *not prime*

Try 727.
   $727 \div 7 \approx 103.9$ $727 \div 11 \approx 66.1$
   $727 \div 13 \approx 55.9$ $727 \div 17 \approx 42.8$
   $727 \div 19 \approx 38.3$ $727 \div 23 \approx 31.6$
   $727 \div 29 \approx 25.1$ *Why can you stop after this division?*

Thus, 727 is the least prime number greater than 720.

RETEACHING THE LESSON

Use the guess-and-check strategy to solve the following problem. A farmer wants to build a rectangular pen using a side of a barn and 60 feet of fence. Find the dimensions and area of the largest such pen.   **30 ft by 15 ft, 450 sq ft**
Notice that the largest pen is not a square as in the corral problem.

CHECKING FOR UNDERSTANDING

Communicating Mathematics

Read and study the lesson to answer these questions. **2. See margin. square, yes**

1. In the corral problem, what was the shape of the figure that had the maximum area for a perimeter of 16 units? For any given perimeter, is this type of figure always the rectangle with the maximum area?

2. What is the rule for easily checking if a number is divisible by 3 or by 5?

3. In the example, explain why you can stop dividing after you have tried 29. **See margin.**

Guided Practice

4. Rich and Peg raise dogs and puffins. They counted all the heads and got 120. They counted all the feet and got 400. How many dogs and how many puffins do they have? **80 dogs, 40 puffins**

EXERCISES

Strategies

Look for a pattern.
Solve a simpler problem.
Act it out.
Guess and check.
Draw a diagram.
Make a chart.
Work backwards.

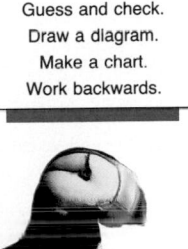

Solve. Use any strategy.

$$\begin{array}{r} ABCDE \\ \times 4 \\ \hline EDCBA \end{array}$$

5. Replace each letter with a whole number so that the multiplication problem at the right is correct. Each letter represents a different number. **A = 2, B = 1, C = 9, D = 7, E = 8**

6. At the conclusion of a committee meeting, a total of 153 handshakes were exchanged. Assuming each person shook hands with everyone else, how many people were at the meeting? **18**

7. With one straight vertical cut and one straight horizontal cut, divide this Greek cross into four pieces that can be assembled in a different way to form a square. **See margin.**

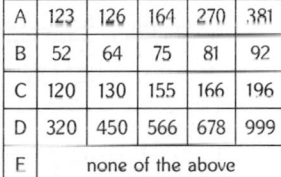

8. What row in the table contains the square of an integer and the cube of a different integer? **B**

A	123	126	164	270	381
B	52	64	75	81	92
C	120	130	155	166	196
D	320	450	566	678	999
E	none of the above				

COOPERATIVE LEARNING ACTIVITY

Work in groups. Each person in the group must understand the solution and be able to explain it to any person in the class.

A perfect number is one in which the number equals the sum of its factors, excluding itself. The first perfect number is 6.

The factors of 6 are 1, 2, 3, and 6. Now exclude the 6. The sum of the factors is $1 + 2 + 3$, or 6. Thus, 6 is a perfect number.

Find two other perfect numbers. **Answers will vary. Three other perfect numbers are 28, 496, and 8128.**

LESSON 7-1   PROBLEM-SOLVING STRATEGY: GUESS-AND-CHECK   311

EVALUATING THE LESSON

Checking for Understanding

Exercises 1–4 are designed to help you assess understanding through reading, writing, and speaking. You should work through Exercises 1–3 with your students, and then monitor their work on Exercise 4.

Closing the Lesson

Writing Activity Have students explain in writing the advantages and disadvantages of the guess-and-check strategy.

APPLYING THE LESSON

Homework Exercises

Assignment Guide

Basic: 5–8
Average: 5–8
Enriched: 5–8

Additional Answers

2. If the sum of the digits of a number is divisible by 3, the number is divisible by 3. If a number ends in 0 or 5, it is divisible by 5.

Practice Masters Booklet, p. 51

EXTENDING THE LESSON

Math Power: Problem Solving

If you have six toothpicks, how can you form four triangles so that they only touch at the end points? The toothpicks cannot cross. What problem-solving methods did you use? Why?

Additional Answers

3. Both prime factors cannot be greater than the square root of the number.

7. The solution is a hollow square.

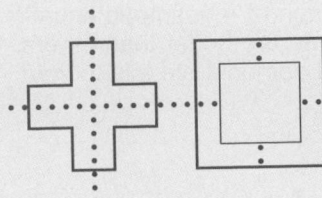

INTRODUCING THE LESSON

Objective: Graph and solve quadratic equations on a graphing calculator.

Motivating the Lesson
Draw the general shape of several graphs on the chalkboard or overhead. For example, draw an ellipse, a circle, a hyperbola, a parabola, and a cubic on different coordinate planes. Ask students which picture is the graph of a quadratic equation and why.
The parabola since it would graph equations of the form $y = ax^2 + bx + c$.

TEACHING THE LESSON

Teaching Tip ❶ On the TI-81, you can also clear the graphics screen by pressing [Y=] and "turning off" equations instead of clearing them. You can turn them off by using the [▼] and [▲] keys to move to the "=" and pressing [ENTER] to make the sign not black.

Teaching Tip ❷ You can also graph $y = x^2$ on the Casio by pressing [GRAPH] [x^2] [EXE], but the calculator will draw the graph in the viewing window of [⁻7, 7] by [⁻2, 29].

Teaching Tip ❸ Many students do not realize that a parabola does not have to "open" up. One can also open down, to the left, or to the right. These are *all* parabola.

Graphing Calculator Exploration: Quadratic Equations

The graphing calculator is a powerful tool for studying graphs of different equations. In this lesson we will study the graphs of equations of the form $y = ax^2 + bx + c$. These are called **quadratic equations.** The graphs of quadratic equations are called **parabolas.**

Example 1

Graph $y = x^2$ using the standard viewing window.

This equation is of the form $y = ax^2 + bx + c$, where $a = 1$, $b = 0$, and $c = 0$.

Teaching Tip ❶

First, clear the graphics screen. To clear the screen on the Casio fx-7000G, press [SHIFT] [Cls] then [EXE]. To clear the screen on the TI-81, press [Y=], then use the arrow keys and the [CLEAR] key to select and clear any equations from the Y= list.

Next, make sure that the range parameters are set for the standard viewing window and graph.

Teaching Tip ❷

Casio

ENTER: [GRAPH] [ALPHA] [X] [x^2] [EXE]

TI-81

ENTER: [Y=] [X|T] [x^2] [GRAPH]

Teaching Tip ❸

The graph of the equation is shaped like a cup. This is the general shape of a parabola. *Notice that $a > 0$.*

The standard viewing window allowed us to view a complete graph of $y = x^2$. As you recall from our earlier work on the graphing calculator, a graph is said to be complete if all of the important characteristics of the graph are displayed. In general, the important characteristics of a parabola are the x- and y-intercepts, a relative maximum or relative minimum point, that is, the top or bottom of the "cup", and the end behavior of the graph. The end behavior refers to the nature of the graph as the x values grow very large or very small.

312 CHAPTER 7 QUADRATIC EQUATIONS

ALTERNATE TEACHING STRATEGIES

Using Discussion
Have students experiment with different viewing windows. Many different viewing windows will contain a complete graph of a quadratic equation, however some are better than others. Discuss and demonstrate this to your students.

Using Discussion
If students graph the equation in a different viewing window, have them tell why they do or why they do not think it is a complete graph. Try to get them to go through a checklist of necessary characteristics in their explanation.

Example 2

Graph $y = -0.15x^2 + 30$.

The equation $y = -0.15x^2 + 30$ is in the form $y = ax^2 + bx + c$, where $a = -0.15$, $b = 0$, and $c = 30$.

Teaching Tip ❹

Let's try graphing in the standard viewing window. Clear the graphics window before graphing.

Casio

ENTER: [GRAPH] [(-)] 0.15 [ALPHA]

[×] [x^2] [+] 30 [EXE]

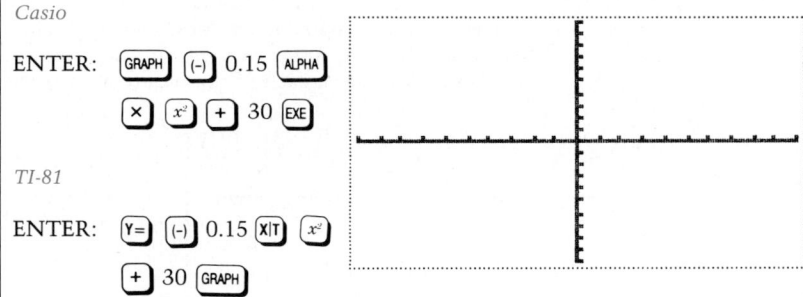

TI-81

ENTER: [Y=] [(-)] 0.15 [X|T] [x^2]

[+] 30 [GRAPH]

Nothing appears on the graphics screen. We must change the range parameters to be able to view a complete graph. Set the range parameters to [-20, 20] by [-5, 35] with scale factors of 5 for both axes and graph again.

Recall that [-20, 20] by [-5, 35] with scale factors of 5 for both axes represents Xmin = -20, Xmax = 20, Ymin = -5, and Ymax = 35, with Xscl = 5 and Yscl = 5.

There is no need to retype the equation after changing the range parameters. Simply press [EXE] on the Casio or [GRAPH] on the TI-81.

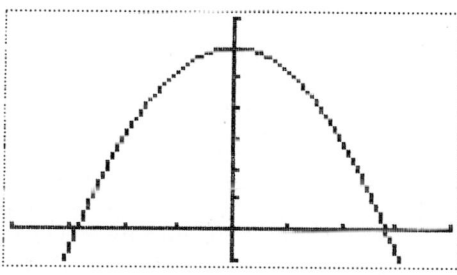

The graph of $y = -0.15x^2 + 30$ is a parabola that opens downward. *Notice that $a < 0$.*

You have solved quadratic equations of the form $0 = ax^2 + bx + c$ by factoring or by using the quadratic formula. You can also solve these equations graphically by using the graphing calculator.

GRAPHING CALCULATOR EXPLORATION: QUADRATIC EQUATIONS 313

Teaching Tip ❹ The standard viewing window is [-10, 10] by [-10, 10]. You can clear the graphics screen on the Casio by pressing [SHIFT] [Cls] [EXE]. You can clear the graphics screen on the TI-81 by pressing [Y=] and using the [▼] and [▲] keys and the [CLEAR] key to select and clear any equations.

More Examples

1. Graph $y = 2x^2$ using the standard viewing window.

   Casio: [GRAPH] 2 [ALPHA] [X]

   [x^2] [EXE]

   TI-81: [Y=] 2 [X|T] [x^2] [GRAPH]

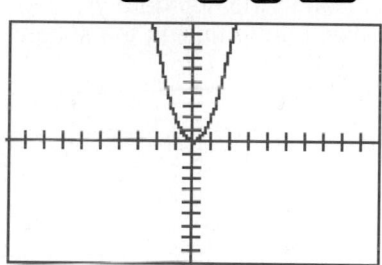

2. Graph $y = -0.25x^2 - 23$.

   Try the range [-20, 20] by a scale of 5 and [-50, 5] by a scale of 5.

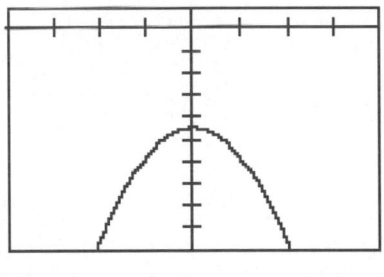

RETEACHING THE LESSON

If students are having problems understanding what a complete graph is, draw some functions on the chalkboard or overhead and ask them if they are or are not complete graphs. Help them to go through the criteria listed on the bottom of page 312 to verify if the graphs are complete graphs or not.

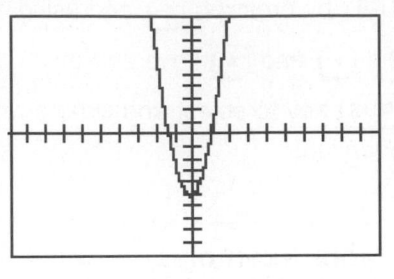
The graph of the quadratic equation $y = ax^2 + bx + c$ represents all of the values of x and y that satisfy the equation. When we solve the equation $0 = ax^2 + bx + c$, we are only interested in the values of x which make the value of the expression $ax^2 + bx + c$ equal to 0. These values are represented by the points at which the graph of the equation crosses the x-axis, since the y-values of these points are 0. These x-intercepts are the **solutions** or **roots** of the quadratic equation.

There are three possible outcomes when solving a quadratic equation. The equation will have either two real solutions, one real solution, or no real solutions. A graph of each of these outcomes is shown below.

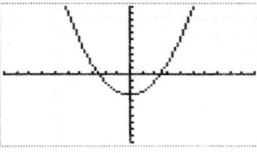 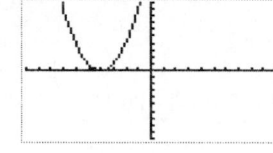 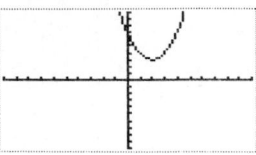

two real solutions   one real solution   no real solutions

Example 3

Solve $3x^2 + 6x - 1 = 0$ using the graphing calculator.

Set the range parameters to the standard viewing window and clear the graphics screen before graphing the equation.

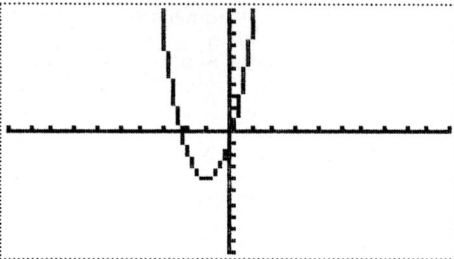

Teaching Tip ❺

Now use the zoom-in process that we used in the Graphing Calculator Exploration on page 105 to zoom in on each of the x-intercepts and determine the solutions. The solutions of this equation are 0.1547 and -2.1547, accurate to four decimal places.

It should be noted that solving quadratic equations graphically produces only approximate solutions. While approximations are usually adequate for most applications, if an exact solution is needed the equations should be solved by factoring or using the quadratic formula.

EXERCISES

Graph $y = x^2 - 6x + 7$ for each set of range parameter values. Then sketch the graph shown on the graphics screen, indicating the scales on each axis.

1–5. See students' work.

1. Xmin: -10, Xmax: 10, Xscl: 1, Ymin: -10, Ymax: 10, Yscl: 1

2. Xmin: -1, Xmax: 9, Xscl: 1, Ymin: 0, Ymax: 35, Yscl: 5

3. Xmin: -10, Xmax: 16, Xscl: 2, Ymin: -5, Ymax: 160, Yscl: 10

4. Xmin: -100, Xmax: 100, Xscl: 20, Ymin: -100, Ymax: 2000, Yscl: 400

5. Xmin: -25, Xmax: 25, Xscl: 5, Ymin: -50, Ymax: 1200, Yscl: 200

6. Which of the range parameter values used in Exercises 1 to 5 produced a complete graph of $y = x^2 - 6x + 7$? **1, 3, 4, 5**

7. How many solutions does the equation $0 = x^2 - 6x + 7$ have? **two**

Graph $y = -8x^2 - 1$ for each set of range parameter values. Then sketch the graph shown on the graphics screen, indicating the scales on each axis.

8–12. See students' work.

8. Xmin: -10, Xmax: 10, Xscl: 1, Ymin: -10, Ymax: 10, Yscl: 1

9. Xmin: -1, Xmax: 12, Xscl: 1, Ymin: 0, Ymax: 30, Yscl: 5

10. Xmin: -10, Xmax: 20, Xscl: 2, Ymin: -5, Ymax: 100, Yscl: 10

11. Xmin: -20, Xmax: 20, Xscl: 2, Ymin: -100, Ymax: 0, Yscl: 10

12. Xmin: -25, Xmax: 25, Xscl: 5, Ymin: -25, Ymax: 25, Yscl: 5

15–20. Answers may vary. Samples answers given. See student's graphs.

15. $[-10, 10]$ by $[-15, 30]$

16. $[-2, 6]$ by $[-2, 12]$

17. $[-15, 1]$ by $[-10, 30]$

18. $[-10, 5]$ by $[-30, 10]$

19. $[-10, 10]$ by $[-15, 10]$

20. $[-10, 10]$ by $[-5, 15]$

13. Which of the range parameter values used in Exercises 8 to 12 produced a complete graph of $y = -8x^2 - 1$? **8, 11, 12**

14. How many solutions does the equation $0 = -8x^2 - 1$ have? **no solutions**

Find and state an appropriate viewing window for viewing a completed graph of each function. Then sketch each graph as seen on the graphics screen.

15. $y = 3.2x^2 + 9.2$

16. $y = x^2 - 5x + 6$

17. $y = 6x^2 + 108x + 480$

18. $y = 2x^2 + 9x - 18$

19. $y = 2x^2 - x - 15$

20. $y = 1.3x^2 - 3.8x + 5.1$

21. 3.0000, -2.5000
22. 1.5000, 0.2460
23. no real solutions
24. 0.3333, -1.3600
25. -20.2000, -11.3400
26. -2.6000, 0.7142

Find the solutions of each quadratic equation accurate to four decimal places by using your graphing calculator.

21. $2x^2 - x - 15 = 0$

22. $0.2x^2 - 0.3492x - 0.0738 = 0$

23. $1.2x^2 - 3.6x + 5.8 = 0$

24. $3x^2 + 3.08x - 1.36 = 0$

25. $x^2 + 31.54x + 229.068 = 0$

26. $35x^2 + 66x - 65 = 0$

GRAPHING CALCULATOR EXPLORATION: QUADRATIC EQUATIONS **315**

EVALUATING THE LESSON

Closing the Lesson

Writing Activity Have students write an equation that has two real solutions, an equation that has one real solution, and an equation that has no real solutions. Have them use their graphing calculators to experiment with finding equations that fit each criteria.

Error Analysis

Students should get in a habit of writing only those digits that they are sure are correct. While they may know that solutions of 0.215 and -4.215 may be correct to three decimal places, the calculator may display seven or eight numbers to the right of the decimal point and all these may not be correct.

APPLYING THE LESSON

Homework Exercises

Assignment Guide
Basic: 1–7, 15–16, 21–22
Average: 8–14, 17–18, 23–24
Enriched: 8–14, 19–20, 25–26

EXTENDING THE LESSON

Math Power: Problem Solving

Ask students how they could find an equation of a parabola that opens to the left or to the right. (Example: $y^2 = x$.) Once they have found an equation, help them try to figure out how to graph this equation on their graphing calculators. You can do this by solving for y to obtain the solutions $y = \pm\sqrt{x}$. Then enter each solution as a separate equation and graph both. Since both calculators are *function* graphers, you cannot graph $y = \pm\sqrt{x}$ as one equation.

INTRODUCING THE LESSON

 5-Minute Check

(over Lesson 7-1)

1. Find the least prime number greater than 550. **557**

Other Prerequisite Skills

2. Factor $ab^2 - a^3$. **$a(b + a)$ $(b - a)$**
3. Factor $4z^2 - 20z + 21$. **$(2z - 3)(2z - 7)$**
4. Factor $3m^3 + 21m^2 + 36m$. **$3m(m + 3)(m + 4)$**
5. Find the degree of $6x^2y + 2xy^3 - 9x^2y^3$. **5**

Motivating the Lesson

Bring in a ball and a stopwatch. Throw the ball into the air. Have one of the students measure the time it takes the ball to return to your hand. Discuss what forces of nature affect the rising and falling of the ball. Discuss the equation $s = v_i t - \frac{1}{2}gt^2$, where s is the height of the ball at a given time, v_i is the initial velocity, t is time, and g is the acceleration of gravity.

7-2 Solving Quadratic Equations

Objectives

After studying this lesson, you should be able to:

7-2A ■ solve quadratic equations by graphing, and

7-2B ■ solve quadratic equations by factoring.

Application

Craig Hoffheimer wants to build a swimming pool surrounded by a sidewalk of uniform width. He wants the dimensions of the pool and sidewalk to be 16 meters by 20 meters. The pool has an area of 192 square meters. How wide should the sidewalk be?

A drawing will help in solving this problem.

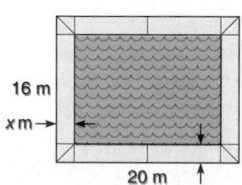

Let x meters be the width of the sidewalk. The length of the pool is $20 - 2x$ meters. The width of the pool is $16 - 2x$ meters.

The area of the pool can be expressed as the product of the length and width.

$$A = \ell w$$
$$= (20 - 2x)(16 - 2x) \quad \text{Substitute for } \ell \text{ and } w.$$
$$= 320 - 72x + 4x^2 \quad \text{Use FOIL.}$$
$$= 4x^2 - 72x + 320$$

The area of the pool can be expressed as $4x^2 - 72x + 320$ square meters. Since the area of the pool is 192 square meters, replacing A with 192 results in the equation $192 = 4x^2 - 72x + 320$.

Of course, Craig would probably never use a quadratic equation like $192 = 4x^2 - 72x + 320$ to express the area of a pool. However, in this chapter you will study many other formulas in science and business that involve this type of equation.

Teaching Tip ❶

A **quadratic equation** is an equation that can be written in the form $ax^2 + bx + c = 0$, where $a \neq 0$. We say that equations like this have a **degree** of 2 since the greatest exponent of the variable is 2. Notice that a quadratic equation only has one variable, and all the exponents are positive.

The values of the variable that satisfy an equation are called **roots** or **solutions** of the equation. There are several methods that you can use to find the roots of a quadratic equation.

ALTERNATE TEACHING STRATEGIES

Using Models

Algebra tiles can be used to represent the factorization of a trinomial. Red tiles are used to represent negative values. The model for factoring $x^2 - 2x - 15$ is shown. Notice that 3 pairs of tiles (3 positive, 3 negative) were added to form the representation.

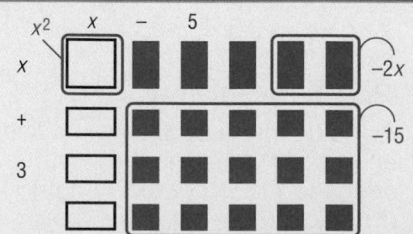

This model can now be used to solve $x^2 - 2x - 15 = 0$. One of the sides must represent 0. So, $x + 3 = 0$ or $x - 5 = 0$. Thus, the solutions are -3 or 5.

One way to determine the roots of a quadratic equation is to graph the related quadratic function. First, the quadratic equation must be written in the general form. The swimming pool equation needs to be rewritten.

$$192 = 4x^2 - 72x + 320$$
$$0 = 4x^2 - 72x + 128 \quad \text{\textit{Subtract 192 from each side.}}$$
$$0 = x^2 - 18x + 32 \quad \text{\textit{Divide each side by 4.}}$$

The related function for this equation is $y = x^2 - 18x + 32$.

To graph this function, first make a table of values that satisfy the function. Then graph these ordered pairs.

x	0	4	8	12	16	20
y	32	-24	-48	-40	0	72

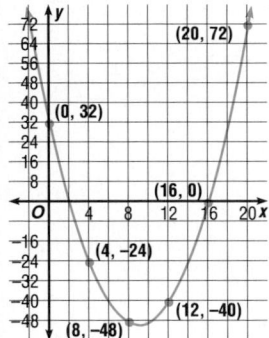

When you graph the ordered pairs, note that the points suggest the shape of a curve called a **parabola.** Notice this parabola crosses the x-axis twice and the function has a degree of 2. These intercept points are called the **zeros of a function.** For this function, the two points are $(2, 0)$ and $(16, 0)$. Remember that the quadratic equation is the related quadratic function with y equaling 0. The x values, 2 and 16, are the roots of the equation $0 = x^2 - 18x + 32$.

Teaching Tip ❷

Now let's solve the swimming pool problem. The solutions to the quadratic equation $0 = x^2 - 18x + 32$ are 2 and 16. The region containing the pool and sidewalk is only 16 meters wide. Therefore, the sidewalk itself cannot be 16 meters wide. The value of x appropriate for this problem is 2. So, the sidewalk should be 2 meters wide on each side of the pool.

You can use your graphing calculator and the TRACE function to find the zeros of the graphed function.

Another way of solving a quadratic equation is by **factoring.** The factoring method depends on the **zero product property.**

Zero Product Property	**For any real numbers a and b,** **if $ab = 0$, then $a = 0$ or $b = 0$.**

Let's factor the same equation we solved by graphing.

$$x^2 - 18x + 32 = 0 \quad \Rightarrow \quad (x - 16)(x - 2) = 0$$

Now set each factor equal to zero and solve.

$$x - 16 = 0 \qquad x - 2 = 0$$
$$x = 16 \qquad\quad x = 2$$

You see that the same two solutions occur.

LESSON 7-2 SOLVING QUADRATIC EQUATIONS 317

Teaching Tip ❶ Remind students that when writing an equation in this form they need to make sure the operations being performed are addition. However, the coefficient of any term may be negative.

Teaching Tip ❷ Remember that the sidewalk has a uniform width.

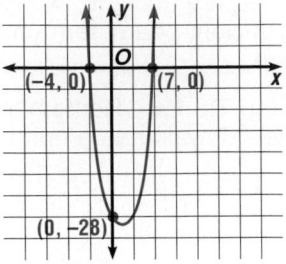
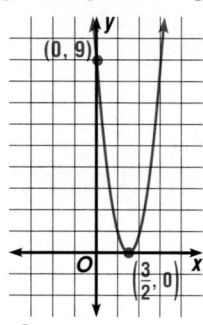
When using factoring to solve a real-life problem, you still need to examine each solution carefully to see if it is reasonable for that situation.

Example 1

Solve $x^2 - 2x - 15 = 0$ by graphing. Then verify your solutions by factoring.

Graph the related quadratic function $y = x^2 - 2x - 15$ by finding and graphing the ordered pairs that satisfy the function. Then graph the parabola suggested by the points.

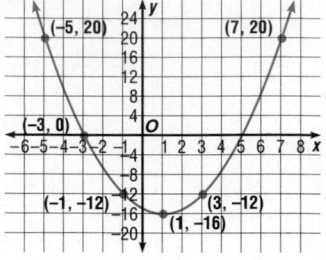

x	y
-7	48
-3	0
-1	-12
1	-16
3	-12
7	20

The table tells us one solution of $x^2 - 2x - 15 = 0$ is -3. The graph tells us that the other solution is 5. Let's check our solutions by using factoring.

To factor, you use the guess-and-check strategy.

$x^2 - 2x - 15 = 0$
$(x - 5)(x + 3) = 0$ *Factor.*
$x - 5 = 0$ or $x + 3 = 0$ *Zero product*
$x = 5$ or $x = -3$ *property*

The solutions are 5 and -3.

Check: $x^2 - 2x - 15 = 0$
$(5)^2 - 2(5) - 15 \stackrel{?}{=} 0$
$0 = 0$ ✓
$(-3)^2 - 2(-3) - 15 \stackrel{?}{=} 0$
$0 = 0$ ✓

No matter what method you use, you can always check your solutions by substituting the values into the equation and simplifying.

Quadratic equations always have two solutions. Sometimes those two solutions may be the same number. **Teaching Tip ❸**

Example 2

Solve $x^2 + 6x = -9$ by graphing and by factoring.

First rewrite the equation in quadratic form: $x^2 + 6x + 9 = 0$.

Notice the graph intersects the x-axis in one point. This means there is only one solution.

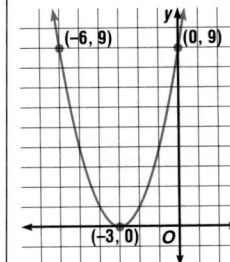

$x^2 + 6x + 9 = 0$
$(x + 3)(x + 3) = 0$

$x + 3 = 0$ or $x + 3 = 0$
$x = -3$ or $x = -3$

Notice that the graph has only one x-intercept, -3. Factoring yields one solution.

The only solution is -3.

318 CHAPTER 7 QUADRATIC EQUATIONS

Example 3

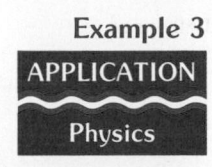

APPLICATION

Physics

FYI ...

Robert Goddard launched the first liquid-fuel rocket on March 16, 1926. It flew for 2.5 seconds and went 184 feet.

The graph shown is the graph of the function that describes the height at any given time. The <u>actual path</u> of the rocket is an entirely different parabola.

As an object is propelled upwards, gravity pulls it back to Earth. This relationship can be expressed by the formula $s = v_i t - \frac{1}{2}gt^2$, where s is the distance above the starting point, v_i is the initial velocity, t is time elapsed, and g is the acceleration of gravity. Find how long it will take a model rocket propelled into the air at an initial velocity of 80 ft/s to return to ground level, if the acceleration of gravity is 32 ft/s^2. *Since the rocket is returning to ground level, the distance above ground is 0.*

Substitute the values into the formula and solve the equation. Let's try factoring.

$s = v_i t - \frac{1}{2}gt^2$

$0 = (80)t - \frac{1}{2}(32)t^2$

$0 = 80t - 16t^2$

$0 = 16t(5 - t)$

$16t = 0 \qquad 5 - t = 0$
$\quad t = 0 \qquad \quad 5 = t$

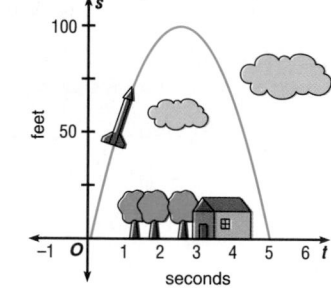

The solution of 0 seconds is the time when the rocket is launched. The solution of 5 seconds is the time elapsed when the rocket returns to the ground. The graph verifies this. So, it will take the rocket 5 seconds to return to the ground.

CHECKING FOR UNDERSTANDING

Communicating Mathematics

Read and study the lesson to answer each question.

1. In the swimming pool problem, what are the dimensions of the pool? Make a scale drawing of the pool and sidewalk. **16 m × 12 m; See students' work.**
2. Define each term and explain how they are related. **See margin.**

   a. solution b. root c. zero of a function d. x-intercept

3. What is the name of the graph of a quadratic function? **parabola**

4. Can a quadratic equation have more than two solutions? Why or why not? **no; The maximum number of zeros a quadratic equation can have is two.**
5. In Example 3, estimate the maximum height of the rocket. **100 ft**

Guided Practice

Determine if each equation is a quadratic equation. Write *yes* or *no*.

6. $4x^2 + 7x - 3 = 0$ **yes**
7. $5y^4 - 7y^2 = 0$ **no**
8. $\frac{1}{2}y^2 + \frac{3}{4} = 0$ **yes**
9. $z^2 + 7z - 3 = z^3$ **no**

10. Factor $12m^2 + 25m + 12$. **$(4m + 3)(3m + 4)$**

RETEACHING THE LESSON

Solve each equation by graphing.

$(x - 2)(x + 3) = 6$ **−4, 3**
$(x - 2)(x + 3) = -4$ **−2, 1**
$(x - 2)(x + 3) = 0$ **2, −3**
$(x - 2)(x + 3) = -6$ **0, −1**

First graph the related quadratic function $y = (x - 2)(x + 3)$. Then find where it intersects graphs of $y = 6, y = -4, y = 0,$ and $y = 10$.

Additional Answers

2a. value that satisfies an equation
b. value that satisfies a quadratic equation
c. the x-value of a function when $y = 0$
d. where the graph intersects the x-axis

All can name solutions of a quadratic equation.

Chalkboard Example

For Example 3
Using the information given in the example, find how long it will take a model rocket propelled into the air at an initial velocity of 136 ft/s to return to the ground level if the acceleration of gravity is 32 ft/s. After 4 seconds, how high is the rocket? **8.5 seconds, 288 feet**

Teaching Tip ❸ Remind students that not every solution to the equation will answer the question presented in an application problem.

EVALUATING THE LESSON

Checking for Understanding

Exercises 1–14 are designed to help you assess understanding through reading, writing, and speaking. You should work through Exercises 1–5 with your students, and then monitor their work on Exercises 6–14.

Reteaching Masters Booklet, p. 45

7-2 **Reteaching Worksheet**
NAME _____ DATE _____
Solving Quadratic Equations

The only way for the product of two numbers to equal 0 is for at least one of the factors to be 0. This fact is known as the **Zero Product Property.** You use this property when you solve equations by factoring.

Zero Product Property	For any real numbers a and b, if $ab = 0$, then $a = 0$ or $b = 0$

Example: Solve $x^2 - 4x = 12$ by factoring.
$x^2 - 4x - 12 = 0$ Rewrite the equation in standard form.
$(x - 6)(x + 2) = 0$ Factor.
$x - 6 = 0 \quad x + 2 = 0$ Use the Zero Product Property.
$x = 6 \qquad x = -2$ Set each factor equal to zero and solve.

Solve each equation by factoring.

1. $z^2 - 12z + 27 = 0$
   9, 3
2. $x^2 + 13x + 40 = 0$
   −8, −5
3. $x^2 - 7x - 44 = 0$
   11, −4
4. $x^2 + 3x - 130 = 0$
   −13, 10
5. $x^2 - 12x = -36$
   6
6. $3s^2 - 13s = 10$
   $\frac{-2}{3}$, 5
7. $16x^2 = 49$
   $\frac{7}{4}, \frac{-7}{4}$
8. $3s^2 - 13s = -10$
   $\frac{10}{3}$, 1
9. $4k^2 - 35k - 9 = 0$
   9, $-\frac{1}{4}$
10. $-2x^2 - 5x + 12 = 0$
   $\frac{3}{2}$, −4

Practice Masters Booklet, p. 52

Determine the solution of each equation from its related graph.

11.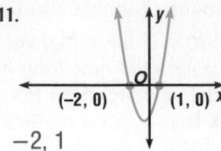

$(-2, 0)$ $(1, 0)$
$-2, 1$

12.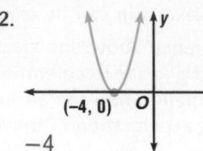

$(-4, 0)$
-4

13.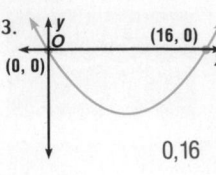

$(0, 0)$ $(16, 0)$
$0, 16$

14. What are the solutions of $(y - 3)(y + 7) = 0$? **3, −7**

EXERCISES

Practice

Solve each equation.

A

15. $(a + 6)(a + 2) = 0$ **−6, −2**   16. $z(z - 1)^2 = 0$ **0, 1**

17. $(3y + 7)(y + 5) = 0$ **−$\frac{7}{3}$, −5**   18. $(2x + 3)(3x - 1) = 0$ **−$\frac{3}{2}$, $\frac{1}{3}$**

Solve each equation by graphing. **19–24. See Solutions Manual for graphs.**

19. **−4, −2**
20. **−3, −1**
21. **−2**
22. **0, 3**
23. **−1.5, 3**
24. **−$\frac{1}{4}$, 3**

19. $d^2 + 6d + 8 = 0$ 20. $z^2 + 4z + 3 = 0$ 21. $c^2 + 4c + 4 = 0$

22. $n^2 - 3n = 0$ 23. $2w^2 - 3w = 9$ 24. $4s^2 - 11s = 3$

Solve each equation by factoring.

25. $y^2 - y = 12$ **4, −3**   26. $z^2 - 5z = 0$ **0, 5**   27. $p^2 - 12p + 36 = 0$ **6**

28. $r^2 + r = 30$ **5, −6**   29. $d^2 - 3d = 4$ **4, −1**   30. $3c^2 = 5c$ **0, $\frac{5}{3}$**

32. **−$\frac{1}{6}$, $\frac{1}{3}$**

B

31. $2q^2 + 11q = 21$ **$\frac{3}{2}$, −7**   32. $18u^2 - 3u = 1$ 33. $3t^2 + 4t = 15$ **$\frac{5}{3}$, −3**

34. $4y^2 = 25$ **$\frac{5}{2}$, −$\frac{5}{2}$**   35. $6r^2 + 7r = 3$ **$\frac{1}{3}$, −$\frac{3}{2}$**   36. $9y^2 + 16 = -24y$ **−$\frac{4}{3}$**

37. **Physics** A tennis ball is shot vertically upward from a launcher with an initial velocity of 64 feet per second. When will the ball return to the ground? How far off the ground will the ball be after 1 second? after 3 seconds?
4 seconds, 48 ft, 48 ft

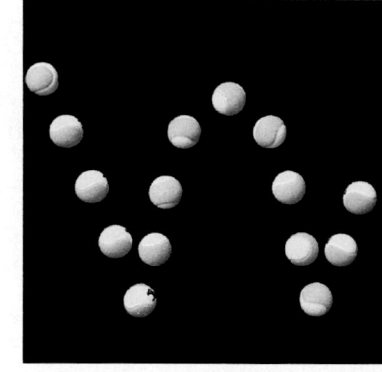

Solve each equation.

38. $4a^2 - 17a + 4 = 0$ **$\frac{1}{4}$, 4**

39. $b^2 + 3b = 40$ **5, −8**

40. $12m^2 + 25m + 12 = 0$ **−$\frac{3}{4}$, −$\frac{4}{3}$**

41. $18n^2 - 3n = 15$ **−$\frac{5}{6}$, 1**

C

42. $n^3 = 9n$ **0, 3, −3**

43. $a^3 = 81a$ **0, 9, −9**

44. $35z^3 + 16z^2 = 12z$ **0, −$\frac{6}{7}$, $\frac{2}{5}$**

45. $18r^3 + 16r = 34r^2$ **0, 1, $\frac{8}{9}$**

46. Physics Marsha hits a tennis ball upward from the top of a 90-foot-high cliff with an initial velocity of 16 ft/s. Marsha hit the ball when it was 6 feet above the top of the cliff.

a. Assume that the tennis ball will hit the ground below the cliff. Determine the equation for the height of the ball after t seconds. *Hint: If the initial height is 6 feet, how would you write a distance 90 feet below that height?* $s = 16t - 16t^2 + 96$

b. Graph your equation. **See margin.**

c. Find the number of seconds it will take the ball to hit the ground. **3 seconds**

Critical Thinking

47. Graph the function $y = x^2 + 2x + 4$. Based on this graph, what are the roots of $0 = x^2 + 2x + 4$? Explain your answer. **See margin.**

Teaching Tip ❹

Applications

48. City Planning In the Winton Woods Park, a playground is planned that is 30 m by 20 m. Due to a government grant, the plans are being revised to double the area of the playground by adding strips of the same width to a side and an end of the area to form a rectangle. Find the width of the strips. What are the dimensions of the new playground? **10 m, 40 m × 30 m**

49. Sports Plans for the rectangular Pinetown Ice-Skating Rink that is 30 m by 60 m have to be revised because of a budget cut. Strips of equal width will be removed from one end and one side of the plan to create an area of 1000 m². What are the dimensions of the new rink? **20 m × 50 m**

Mixed Review

50. Find two numbers whose sum is 81 and whose product is 1400. **(Lesson 7-1)** **56, 25**

51. Simplify $(3a)(5a^2b) + (6ab)(10a^2)$. **(Lesson 5-2)** $75a^3b$

52. Simplify $\sqrt{3mn^4} \cdot \sqrt{25m^6}$. **(Lesson 6-2)** $5m^3n^2\sqrt{3m}$

53. Solve $\begin{cases} 6x - 2y - 3z = -10 \\ -6x + y + 9z = 3 \\ 8x - 3y = -16 \end{cases}$. **(Lesson 3-9)** $\left(\frac{1}{4}, 6, -\frac{1}{6}\right)$

54. Sam bought 6 deluxe, 5 glazed, and 2 cake doughnuts for $4.00. If he had bought 4 deluxe, 2 glazed, and 7 cake doughnuts, the cost would have been $3.40. A deluxe doughnut costs 5 cents less than twice the cost of a cake doughnut. Find the cost of each type of doughnut. **(Lesson 1-5)** **deluxe, 35¢; glazed, 30¢; cake, 20¢**

55. Electricity Find the amount of current I (in amperes) produced if the electromotive force E is 1.5 volts, the circuit resistance R is 2.35 ohms, and the resistance r within a battery is 0.15 ohms, using the formula $I = \dfrac{E}{R + r}$. **(Lesson 1-1)** **0.6 amperes**

EXTENDING THE LESSON

Math Power: Reasoning

Find the length and width of a rectangle if its perimeter is 44 inches and its area is 117 square inches. List the strategy used and explain the steps taken.
$l = 13$ inches, $w = 9$ inches

Chapter 7, Quiz A, (Lessons 7-1 through 7-2), is available in the Evaluation Masters Booklet, p. 93.

Teaching Tip ❹ Students should be reminded that drawings can help in solving equations.

Additional Answers

46a. $h(t) = 16t - 16t^2 + 96$

46b.

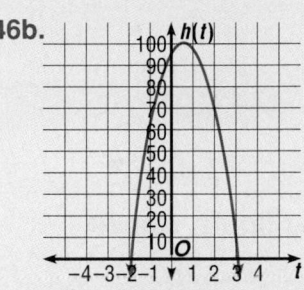

47. There would be no real roots since the graph does not intersect the x-axis.

Enrichment Masters Booklet, p. 45

7-3 Completing the Square

Objective
7-3

After studying this lesson, you should be able to:
- solve quadratic equations by completing the square.

Lesson Resources

Reteaching Master 7-3
Practice Master 7-3
Enrichment Master 7-3
Lab Manual, pp. 57–58
Activity Master, p. 7

 Transparency 7-3 contains the 5-Minute Check and a teaching aid for this lesson.

Application

The Finneytown Athletic Association owns a large lot. On a portion of the lot, a square athletic field has been maintained. Each side of the field is 110 feet long. The association would like to equally expand two of the sides of the field for parking spaces so that the entire region has an area of 14,000 ft². What is the width of the parking strips being added?

INTRODUCING THE LESSON

 5-Minute Check

(over Lesson 7-2)

1. Is $\frac{2}{3}c^3 - 3c^2 + 2c = 0$ a quadratic equation? **no**
2. Solve $(3y + 7)(y + 5) = 0$.
   $-\frac{7}{3}, -5$
3. Solve $x^2 + 10x + 25 = 0$ by graphing. -5

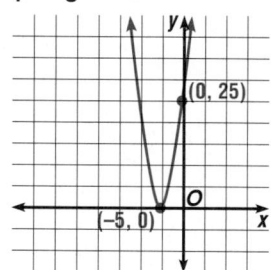

Solve each equation by factoring.

4. $2x^2 + 5x + 3 = 0$ $-\frac{3}{2}, -1$

5. $12p^2 + 8p = 15$ $\frac{5}{6}, -\frac{3}{2}$

Let s ft represent the width of each parking strip. After expansion, each side of the field would now be $110 + s$ feet long. The equation that expresses the area of the new field, which is still square, is $14,000 = (110 + s)^2$.

Remember that an equation like $100 = y^2$ can be solved by taking the square root of each side. The solutions are ± 10.

The equation $14,000 = (110 + s)^2$ can be solved in this same way.

$$14,000 = (110 + s)^2$$
$$\sqrt{14,000} = \sqrt{(110 + s)^2} \quad \text{\textit{Take the square root of each side.}}$$
$$\pm\sqrt{14,000} = 110 + s$$
$$\pm\sqrt{14,000} - 110 = s$$

Now use your calculator to find approximate values for s.

The $\boxed{\sqrt{x}}$ key may be a second function key.

ENTER: 14000 $\boxed{\sqrt{x}}$ $\boxed{-}$ 110 $\boxed{=}$ 8.321595662

ENTER: 14000 $\boxed{\sqrt{x}}$ $\boxed{+/-}$ $\boxed{-}$ 110 $\boxed{=}$ -228.3215957

Since our problem asks for a field measurement, the negative solution can be disregarded. The parking strip should be approximately 8.32 feet wide. Check this solution.

Quadratic equations can be solved in the same way as long as one side of the equation contains a perfect square. When the equation does not contain a perfect square, you can use a process called **completing the square** to create a perfect square. Notice the pattern in the following examples.

Teaching Tip ❶

Motivating the Lesson

Have students draw a square. Have them cut off the same amount on two adjoining sides. They should then determine the dimensions and area of the new square. Have them write an equation to solve the problem.

ALTERNATE TEACHING STRATEGIES

TEACHING THE LESSON

Teaching Tip ❶ Remind students what a perfect square trinomial is.

Using Calculators

Present several problems containing irrational roots. Demonstrate how to determine the square root of a number on different calculators. Then discuss that the radical values are the exact values and the values on the calculator are approximations. Discuss when the approximations are important.

Using Cooperative Groups

Divide the class into groups. Have each group solve $x^2 - 2x - 8 = 0$ in three ways. Discuss which way seems easier and why. Have the groups then make up problems that are easier to do the other two ways.

In a perfect square, there is a relationship between the coefficient of the middle term and the constant term.

$$(x + 7)^2 = x^2 + 14x + 49 \qquad\qquad (x + b)^2 = x^2 + 2bx + b^2$$

$$7 = \tfrac{1}{2}(14) \to 7^2 = 49 \qquad\qquad b = \tfrac{1}{2}(2b) \to (b)^2$$

To complete the square in the expression below, you would use the same process. Take half the coefficient of x and square it.

$$x^2 - 8x + \underline{\quad ? \quad}$$

$$\left(-\tfrac{8}{2}\right)^2 \to (-4)^2 \text{ or } 16 \qquad \text{The answer is } x^2 - 8x + 16.$$

$x^2 - 8x + 16$ is a perfect square trinomial.

In Example 1, follow through the steps that show how completing the square is used in solving a quadratic equation.

Example 1

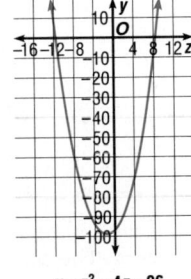

$y = z^2 + 4z - 96$

Solve $z^2 + 4z = 96$ by completing the square.

You must find the term that completes the square on the left side. Remember that whatever you add to one side of an equation, you must add to the other side also.

$$z^2 + 4z + \; ? \; = 96 + \; ?$$
$$z^2 + 4z + 4 = 96 + 4 \qquad \left(\tfrac{4}{2}\right)^2 = 4$$
$$(z + 2)^2 = 100 \qquad \text{\textit{Factor the perfect square trinomial.}}$$
$$z + 2 = \pm 10 \qquad \text{\textit{Take the square root of each side.}}$$

$$z + 2 = 10 \quad \text{or} \quad z + 2 = -10$$
$$z = 8 \quad \text{or} \qquad z = -12$$

The solutions are 8 and -12. **Teaching Tip ❷**

When the coefficient of the second degree term is not 1, you must first divide the equation by that coefficient before completing the square.

Example 2

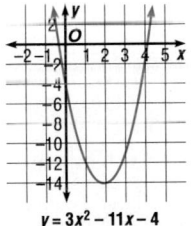

$y = 3x^2 - 11x - 4$

In Examples 1 and 2, both graphs cross the x-axis twice, so there are two solutions for each equation.

Solve $3x^2 - 11x - 4 = 0$ by completing the square.

$$3x^2 - 11x - 4 = 0$$

$$x^2 - \tfrac{11}{3}x - \tfrac{4}{3} = 0 \qquad \text{\textit{Divide each side by 3.}}$$

$$x^2 - \tfrac{11}{3}x = \tfrac{4}{3} \qquad \text{\textit{Isolate the constant on one side.}}$$

$$x^2 - \tfrac{11}{3}x + \tfrac{121}{36} = \tfrac{4}{3} + \tfrac{121}{36} \qquad \text{\textit{Add} } \left(-\tfrac{11}{3} \div 2\right)^2 \text{ \textit{or} } \tfrac{121}{36} \text{ \textit{to each side.}}$$

$$\left(x - \tfrac{11}{6}\right)^2 = \tfrac{169}{36} \qquad \text{\textit{Factor.}}$$

$$x - \tfrac{11}{6} = \pm\tfrac{13}{6} \qquad \text{\textit{Take the square root of each side.}}$$

$$x = \tfrac{11}{6} \pm \tfrac{13}{6} \qquad \text{\textit{Add} } \tfrac{11}{6} \text{ \textit{to each side.}}$$

$$x = 4 \quad \text{or} \quad x = -\tfrac{1}{3} \qquad \text{The solutions are 4 and } -\tfrac{1}{3}.$$

LESSON 7-3 COMPLETING THE SQUARE   323

Not all solutions to quadratic equations are rational numbers. When a solution is irrational, there are two ways you might express the value. The solution written with the radical is the *exact* answer. When you use your calculator to change the expression to an equivalent decimal, the solution is approximate. **Teaching Tip ❸**

Example 3

APPLICATION

Physics

FYI ···

The highest road-tested acceleration reported is 0–60 mph in 4.1 seconds for an MG Metro 6R4 International Rally Car.

The distance (s) an object travels can be computed when the initial speed (v_i), time elapsed (t), and the rate of constant acceleration (a) is known. The formula that relates these factors is $s = v_it + \frac{1}{2}at^2$. If a car has an initial speed of 20 m/s and a constant acceleration of 2 m/s², determine the amount of time it takes it to travel 145 m.

$$s = v_it + \frac{1}{2}at^2$$

$$145 = (20)t + \frac{1}{2}(2)t^2 \qquad \textit{Substitute the known values.}$$

$$145 = 20t + t^2 \qquad \textit{Complete the square by adding } \left[\frac{1}{2}(2b)\right]^2 \textit{ or 100.}$$

$$145 + 100 = t^2 + 20t + 100$$

$$245 = (t + 10)^2 \qquad \textit{Factor.}$$

$$\pm\sqrt{245} = t + 10 \qquad \textit{Take the square root of each side.}$$

$$\pm\sqrt{245} - 10 = t$$

The solutions are $\sqrt{245} - 10$, or about 5.65 seconds and $-\sqrt{245} - 10$, or about −25.65 seconds. Since negative time represents time before the car started, the second solution can be disregarded for this problem. The car traveled 145 m in about 5.65 seconds.

CHECKING FOR UNDERSTANDING

Communicating Mathematics

Read and study the lesson to answer each question.

1. In the athletic field problem, what would be the width of the parking strip if the area of the region were to be 13,000 ft²? **4.02 ft**

2. Why does a quadratic equation have two solutions but you sometimes may only use one of them to solve a problem? **See margin.**

3. Could you solve the equation in Example 1 by factoring? Explain your answer. **See margin.**

4. Could you solve the equation in Example 1 by graphing? Explain your answer. **See margin.**

Guided Practice

State whether each trinomial is a perfect square. Write *yes* or *no*.

5. $a^2 + 4a + 28$ **no**   6. $m^2 - 10m + 25$ **yes**   7. $a^2 - 3a + \frac{9}{2}$ **no**

324   CHAPTER 7   QUADRATIC EQUATIONS

Find the value of c that makes each trinomial a perfect square.

8. $x^2 + 2x + c$ **1**
9. $t^2 + 40t + c$ **400**
10. $x^2 + 18x + c$ **81**
11. $r^2 - 9r + c$ **$\frac{81}{4}$**
12. $a^2 - 100a + c$ **2500**
13. $x^2 + 15x + c$ **$\frac{225}{4}$**

Solve each equation by completing the square.

14. $y^2 - 2y = 24$ **6, -4**
15. $z^2 + 3z = 88$ **-11, 8**

EXERCISES

Practice

Solve each equation by completing the square.

 A

16. $x^2 + 8x - 84 = 0$ **6, -14**
17. $m^2 + 3m - 180 = 0$ **-15, 12**
18. $n^2 - 8n + 14 = 0$ **$4 \pm \sqrt{2}$**
19. $x^2 - 7x + 5 = 0$

19. $\frac{7 \pm \sqrt{29}}{2}$

B

20. $a^2 - 5a - 10 = 0$
21. $t^2 + 3t - 8 = 0$

20. $\frac{5 \pm \sqrt{65}}{2}$

22. $12r^2 - 17r - 5 = 0$ **$\frac{5}{3}, -\frac{1}{4}$**
23. $b^2 - \frac{3}{4}b + \frac{1}{8} = 0$ **$\frac{1}{2}, \frac{1}{4}$**

21. $\frac{-3 \pm \sqrt{41}}{2}$

24. $3t^2 + 4t - 15 = 0$ **$\frac{5}{3}, -3$**
25. $3z^2 - 12z + 4 = 0$ **$2 \pm \frac{2\sqrt{6}}{3}$**

26. $\frac{-1 \pm i\sqrt{17}}{6}$

C

26. $6s^2 + 2s + 3 = 0$
27. $ax^2 + c = 0$ **$\frac{\pm i\sqrt{ac}}{a}$**
28. $x^2 + bx + c = 0$ **$\frac{-b \pm \sqrt{b^2 - 4c}}{2}$**
29. $ax^2 + bx + c = 0$ **$\frac{-b \pm \sqrt{b^2 - 4ac}}{2a}$**

Critical Thinking

30. You have learned how to solve quadratic equations using three different methods. How do you know what is the best method to use for any given equation? Is any one method more useful than the other two? Explain your answer. **Answers will vary. See margin.**

Applications

31. **Hobbies** Jackie is in charge of building a set for the school play. She wants each rectangular window to have an area of 315 in². She also wants each window to be 6 in. taller than it is wide. What are the dimensions of the window? **21 × 15 in.**

32. **Physics** Michael drives a red sportscar on a race track at an initial velocity of 24 ft/s and begins to accelerate at a constant rate of 8 ft/s².

a. How long will it take him to travel a distance of 100 ft? *Round to the nearest tenth.* **2.8 s**

b. How long will it take him to travel a distance of 200 ft? *Round to the nearest tenth.* **4.7 s**

c. How long will it take him to travel a distance of 300 ft? *Round to the nearest tenth.* **6.2 s**

d. Study your answers in parts a–c. As the distance doubles, does the amount of time double? Explain your answer. **See margin.**

33. **Safety** Juanita is driving a truck at an initial velocity of 60 ft/s. She sees a stop sign 600 ft ahead of her. If she begins to decelerate at the rate of 3 ft/s², how long will it take her before she stops at the stop sign? *If acceleration is a positive number, what is deceleration?* **20 seconds**

LESSON 7-3 COMPLETING THE SQUARE 325

Additional Answers

4. Yes

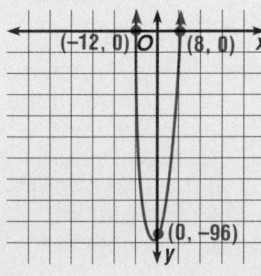

30. If the equation is easily factored, use factoring. If you have a graphing calculator, graphing might be easier. Completing the square is often longer, but it will always work.

32d. No, the formula is not a direct variation.

Additional Answers

37.

$$
\begin{array}{r}
a^2 - 6 \\
a - 5 \overline{\smash{\big)}\ a^3 - 5a^2 - 6a + 30} \\
\underline{a^3 - 5a^2} \\
-6a + 30 \\
\underline{-6a + 30} \\
0
\end{array}
$$

38.

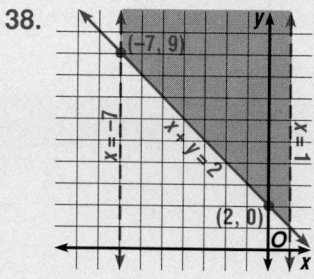

---

34. The BASIC program below determines if an equation written in standard form contains a perfect square trinomial. It uses the same process that you use when completing the square to determine if the expression is a perfect square trinomial.

```
10 PRINT "INPUT A, B, and C."        90 IF B^2 = 4*A*C THEN 120
20 INPUT A, B, C                    100 PRINT "NOT A PERFECT
30 PRINT "A", "B", "C",                      SQUARE"
   "4*A*C", "B^2"                   110 GOTO 140
40 PRINT A,B,C,4*A*C,B^2            120 PRINT A;"X^2 + ";B;
50 PRINT                                   "X + ";C;" = 0"
60 IF A<0 OR C<0 THEN 100           130 PRINT "(";SQR(A);
70 IF SQR(A) <> INT(SQR(A))                "X + ";SQR(C);")^2 = 0"
   THEN 100                         140 PRINT "X = ";-B/(2*A)
80 IF SQR(C) <> INT(SQR(C))         150 END
   THEN 100
```

Use the program above to guess-and-check values for k in each expression so that $ax^2 + bx + c$ is a perfect square trinomial.

a. $x^2 - 14x + k$ **49**   b. $x^2 + kx + 64$ **16**   c. $4x^2 + kx + 1$ **4**

d. $kx^2 - 20x + 4$ **25**   e. $16x^2 + 40x + k$ **25**   f. $4x^2 - 12x + k$ **9**

Mixed Review

35. Solve $x^2 - 20x = -75$ by factoring. (Lesson 7-2) **15, 5**

36. Solve $\sqrt{3w - 2} = 8$. (Lesson 6-7) **22**

37. Use long division to show that $a - 5$ is a factor of $a^3 - 5a^2 - 6a + 30$. (Lesson 5-6) **See margin.**

38. Solve $\begin{cases} |x + 3| < 4 \\ x + y \ge 2 \end{cases}$ by graphing. (Lesson 2-8) **See margin.**

39. Find the next number in the pattern 2, 8, 18, 32, 50, __?__. (Lesson 2-3)
72

～～ MID-CHAPTER REVIEW ～～

1. Find the least prime number greater than 840. (Lesson 7-1) **853**

Solve each equation by graphing. (Lesson 7-2) **2–3. For graphs, see Solutions Manual.**

2. $x^2 - 2x - 35 = 0$ **7, –5**   3. $m^2 + 6m = 27$ **–9, 3**

Solve each equation by factoring. (Lesson 7-2)

4. $4x^2 - 13x = 12$ $-\dfrac{3}{4}$, **4**   5. $4t^2 = 25$ $\pm\dfrac{5}{2}$ 6. $a^3 = 81a$ **0, ±9**

Solve each equation by completing the square. (Lesson 7-3)

7. $4x^2 + 19x - 5 = 0$ $\dfrac{1}{4}$, **–5**   8. $y^2 + 12y + 4 = 0$ **–6 ± 4√2**

9. **Photography** The edge of a metallic picture frame forms a rectangle 12 by 16 in. The frame is of uniform width and contains a picture whose area is 164 in². What is the approximate width of the frame? (Lesson 7-2) **0.52 in.**

EXTENDING THE LESSON

Math Power: Reasoning

Find the values of m that make $x^2 + (m + 5)x + (5m + 1)$ a perfect square. **$m = 7$ or $m = 3$**
How many roots would each related quadratic equation have? **1**

Mid-Chapter Review

The Mid-Chapter Review provides students with a brief review of the concepts and skills in Lessons 7–1 through 7–3. Lesson numbers are given at the end of problems or instruction lines so students may review concepts not yet mastered.

Objectives

After studying this lesson, you should be able to:

7-4A ■ solve quadratic equations using the quadratic formula, and

7-4B ■ use the discriminant to determine the nature of the roots of a quadratic equation.

In Lessons 7-2 and 7-3, you learned several ways to solve quadratic equations. Each has its limitations. You might ask, "Isn't there some formula that will work for any quadratic equation?" The answer is "yes" and that formula is called the **quadratic formula.** The formula is derived from solving the general form of a quadratic equation for x.

$$ax^2 + bx + c = 0 \quad (a \neq 0)$$ *Start with the general form of a quadratic equation.*

$$x^2 + \frac{b}{a}x + \frac{c}{a} = 0$$ *Divide by a so that the coefficient of x^2 is 1.*

$$x^2 + \frac{b}{a}x = -\frac{c}{a}$$ *Subtract $\frac{c}{a}$ from each side.*

    Complete the square by adding

$$x^2 + \frac{b}{a}x + \left(\frac{b}{2a}\right)^2 = -\frac{c}{a} + \left(\frac{b}{2a}\right)^2$$ $\left(\frac{b}{a} \div 2\right)^2$ *or* $\left(\frac{b}{2a}\right)^2$ *to each side.*

$$\left(x + \frac{b}{2a}\right)^2 = -\frac{c}{a} + \frac{b^2}{4a^2}$$ *Factor the left side.*

$$\left(x + \frac{b}{2a}\right)^2 = \frac{b^2 - 4ac}{4a^2}$$ *Add the fractions on the right side.*

$$\left|x + \frac{b}{2a}\right| = \sqrt{\frac{b^2 - 4ac}{4a^2}}$$ *Take the square root of each side.*

$$x + \frac{b}{2a} = \pm\frac{\sqrt{b^2 - 4ac}}{2a}$$ *Simplify.*

$$x = -\frac{b}{2a} \pm \frac{\sqrt{b^2 - 4ac}}{2a}$$ *Subtract $\frac{b}{2a}$ from each side.*

$$x = \frac{-b \pm \sqrt{b^2 - 4ac}}{2a}$$

This equation is known as the quadratic formula. **Teaching Tip**

Quadratic Formula	The solutions of a quadratic equation of the form $ax^2 + bx + c = 0$ with $a \neq 0$ are given by this formula. $$x = \frac{-b \pm \sqrt{b^2 - 4ac}}{2a}$$

LESSON 7-4 THE QUADRATIC FORMULA 327

ALTERNATE TEACHING STRATEGIES

Using Logical Reasoning

Have students explain the chart on page 330. Have them give three cases for each kind of root. Graph one of each of the examples. How can you tell from the graph what kind of roots there are?

Using Connections

Four methods of solving quadratic equations have been presented.

1. factoring
2. completing the square
3. quadratic formula
4. graphing

Have students state the advantages and disadvantages, if any, of each method. How are the methods related? If they could only remember one method, which one should it be and why?

Lesson Resources

Reteaching Master 7-4
Practice Master 7-4
Enrichment Master 7-4
Technology Master, p. 7
Activity Master, p. 25

Transparency 7-4 contains the 5-Minute Check and a teaching aid for this lesson.

INTRODUCING THE LESSON

 5-Minute Check

(over Lesson 7-3)

Find the value of c that makes each trinomial a perfect square.

1. $z^2 + 13z + c$ $\frac{169}{4}$

2. $t^2 - \frac{5}{8}t + c$ $\frac{25}{256}$

Solve each equation by completing the square.

3. $x^2 - 7x + 12 = 0$ $3, 4$

4. $n^2 - 5n + 14 = 0$ $\frac{5 \pm i\sqrt{31}}{2}$

5. $3c^2 - 14c + 8 = 0$ $4, \frac{2}{3}$

Motivating the Lesson

Give students the general equation $ax^2 + bx + c = 0$ where $(a \neq 0)$. Have students determine what they need to add to each side in order to complete the square. Have students then determine the value for several equations such as $x^2 + 5x + 6 = 0$ and $x^2 + 10x + 16 = 0$.

TEACHING THE LESSON

Teaching Tip ❶ Ask students to determine what the restrictions for the formula are.

Teaching Tip ❷ Each type of
scientific calculator has a different
system of storing information. Before covering calculator use, make
sure students are familiar with that
function on their calculator.

A photo editor at a magazine publisher has a 12.5 cm
by 8.4 cm photo of a rabbit sitting in the center of a
large field of grass. She wishes to get a print that has
half the area of the original photo and concentrates on
the rabbit. The layout artist needs to be told how much
of the grass section to crop, or cut off. If the same
amount is cropped from all edges of the photo, what are
the dimensions of the print?

The area of the original photo is (12.5)(8.4) or
105 cm². The problem states that the print has
half the area of the original, or $\frac{1}{2}$ (105) cm².
The print has a length of 12.5 − 2x cm
and a width of 8.4 − 2x cm.

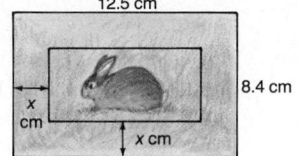

$$A = \ell w$$
$$\frac{1}{2}(105) = (12.5 - 2x)(8.4 - 2x) \qquad \textit{Substitute the known values.}$$
$$52.5 = 105 - 41.8x + 4x^2 \qquad \textit{Multiply.}$$
$$0 = 4x^2 - 41.8x + 52.5 \qquad \textit{Subtract 52.5 from each side.}$$

In the last step, the equation is written in the general form of a quadratic
equation. From this form, the values for a, b, and c can be defined for use in
the quadratic formula.

$$x = \frac{-b \pm \sqrt{b^2 - 4ac}}{2a}$$

$$x = \frac{-(-41.8) \pm \sqrt{(-41.8)^2 - 4(4)(52.5)}}{2(4)} \qquad a = 4, b = -41.8, c = 52.5$$

$$x = \frac{41.8 \pm \sqrt{(-41.8)^2 - 4(4)(52.5)}}{8}$$

Now you can use your calculator to help you find approximate solutions.
First evaluate the radical part of the formula and store the result in
memory. **Teaching Tip ❷**

ENTER: 41.8 [+/-] [x²] [−] 4 [×] 4 [×] 52.5 [=] [√x] [STO] 30.12042496

Now find the solutions.

ENTER: [(] 41.8 [+] [RCL] [)] [÷] 8 [=] 8.99005312

ENTER: [(] 41.8 [−] [RCL] [)] [÷] 8 [=] 1.45994688

The two solutions are approximately 8.99 cm and 1.46 cm. In this problem,
8.99 cm is not a reasonable solution. The new length of the print would
be 12.5 − 2(1.46), or 9.58 cm. The new width would be 8.4 − 2(1.46), or
5.48 cm.

Check: 9.58(5.48) = 52.4984 ≈ $\frac{1}{2}$(105). √

Example 1

Solve $t^2 - 3t - 28 = 0$.

This equation is already in general form. So you can use the quadratic formula directly. $a = 1, b = -3, c = -28$

$$t = \frac{-b \pm \sqrt{b^2 - 4ac}}{2a}$$

$$t = \frac{-(-3) \pm \sqrt{(-3)^2 - 4(1)(-28)}}{2(1)}$$

$$t = \frac{3 \pm \sqrt{121}}{2} \text{ or } \frac{3 \pm 11}{2}$$

$$t = \frac{3 + 11}{2} \text{ or } 7 \quad \text{and} \quad t = \frac{3 - 11}{2} \text{ or } -4.$$

The solutions are 7 and -4. *Check these solutions.*

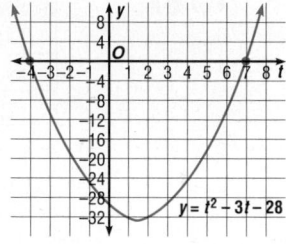

The related function shows that there are 2 solutions.

Example 2

Solve $x^2 - 8x + 16 = 0$. $a = 1, b = -8, c = 16$

$$x = \frac{-b \pm \sqrt{b^2 - 4ac}}{2a}$$

$$x = \frac{-(-8) \pm \sqrt{(-8)^2 - 4(1)(16)}}{2(1)}$$

$$x = \frac{8 \pm 0}{2}$$

$$x = \frac{8 + 0}{2} \text{ or } 4 \quad \text{and} \quad x = \frac{8 - 0}{2} \text{ or } 4$$

There is one distinct solution, 4.

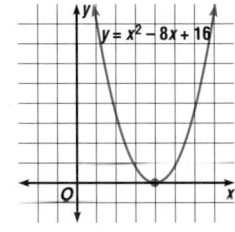

The related function shows that there is 1 solution.

Example 3

Solve $3p^2 - 5p + 9 = 0$. $a = 3, b = -5, c = 9$

$$x = \frac{-b \pm \sqrt{b^2 - 4ac}}{2a}$$

$$x = \frac{-(-5) \pm \sqrt{(-5)^2 - 4(3)(9)}}{2(3)}$$

$$x = \frac{5 \pm \sqrt{-83}}{6}$$

Since the radical contains a negative value, the solutions will be imaginary.

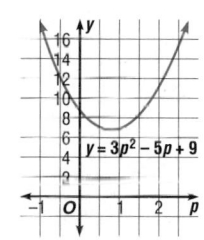

The related function does not intersect the horizontal axis.

The solutions are imaginary.

The solutions are $\dfrac{5 + i\sqrt{83}}{6}$ and $\dfrac{5 - i\sqrt{83}}{6}$.

Imaginary solutions appear in conjugate pairs.

These three examples demonstrate a pattern that is useful in determining the nature of the roots of a quadratic equation. In the quadratic formula, the expression under the radical sign, $b^2 - 4ac$, is called the **discriminant.** The discriminant tells the nature of the roots of a quadratic equation.

RETEACHING THE LESSON

Have students verify by substitution that both solutions to the general quadratic equation $ax^2 + bx + c = 0$ are indeed roots. To make the check less cumbersome, use D for the discriminant until the radicals are cleared.

Chalkboard Examples

For Example 1
Solve each equation.

a. $t^2 - 10t + 24 = 0$ **6, 4**

b. $2y^2 + 4y - 30 = 0$ **3, -5**

For Example 2
Solve each equation.

a. $4y^2 + 4y + 1 = 0$ $-\dfrac{1}{2}$

b. $3x^2 - 18x + 27 = 0$ **3**

For Example 3
Solve each equation.

a. $x^2 - 3x + 7 = 0$
$$\frac{3 + i\sqrt{19}}{2}, \frac{3 - i\sqrt{19}}{2}$$

b. $5m^2 + 7m = -3$
$$\frac{7 + i\sqrt{11}}{10}, \frac{7 - i\sqrt{11}}{10}$$

Reteaching Masters Booklet, p. 47

Equation	Value of the Discriminant	Roots	Nature of the Roots
Ex. 1 $t^2 - 3t - 28 = 0$	121 or $(11)^2$	7, -4	2 real roots
Ex. 2 $x^2 - 8x + 16 = 0$	0	4	1 real root
Ex. 3 $3p^2 - 5p + 9 = 0$	-83	$\frac{5 \pm i\sqrt{83}}{6}$	2 imaginary roots

The chart shows that if the value of the discriminant is a perfect square or 0, the roots are real and rational. Other positive discriminants will yield irrational roots. A negative discriminant means the roots will be imaginary.

Example 4

Find the value of the discriminant of each equation and then describe the nature of its roots.

a. $2x^2 + x - 3 = 0$
   $a = 2, b = 1, c = -3$
   $b^2 - 4ac = (1)^2 - 4(2)(-3)$
   $= 1 + 24$
   $= 25$

   The value of the discriminant is a positive and a perfect square. So, $2x^2 + x - 3 = 0$ has two real roots and they are rational.

b. $x^2 + 8 = 0$
   $a = 1, b = 0, c = 8$
   $b^2 - 4ac = (0)^2 - 4(1)(8)$
   $= 0 - 32$
   $= -32$

   The value of the discriminant is negative. So, $x^2 + 8 = 0$ has two imaginary roots.

CHECKING FOR UNDERSTANDING

Communicating Mathematics

Read and study the lesson to answer each question.

1. In the photo problem, why was 8.99 cm eliminated as a reasonable answer? **8.99 cm is larger than the width.**

2. The two solutions for the photo problem were stated to be *approximately* 8.99 and 1.46. Why was the word approximately used? **The decimal value of $\sqrt{907.24}$ is not an exact number.**

3. When the discriminant is a positive number, there will be __?__ __?__ roots. **2 real**

4. When the discriminant is __?__, there will be one real root. **0**

5. When the discriminant is a negative number, there will be __?__ __?__ roots. **2 imaginary**

Guided Practice

State the values of a, b, and c for each quadratic equation. Then find the value of the discriminant, and solve the equation. **See margin.**

6. $y^2 + 6y + 9 = 0$

7. $a^2 = 16$

8. $5x^2 + 16x + 3 = 0$

9. $6a^2 + 2a + 1 = 0$

10. $-3x^2 + x - 2 = 0$

11. $3a^2 - a + 3 = 0$

Additional Answers

6. $a = 1, b = 6, c = 9$; 0; -3

7. $a = 1, b = 0, c = -16$; 64; ± 4

8. $a = 5, b = 16, c = 3$; 196; $-\frac{1}{5}, -3$

9. $a = 6, b = 2, c = 1$; -20; $\frac{-1 \pm i\sqrt{5}}{6}$

10. $a = -3, b = 1, c = -2$; -23; $\frac{-1 \pm i\sqrt{23}}{-6}$

11. $a = 3, b = -1, c = 3$; -35; $\frac{1 \pm i\sqrt{35}}{6}$

12. 16; 2 R,Q; -8, -4

13. 0; 1 R,Q; 2

14. 12; 2 R,I; $2 \pm \sqrt{3}$; 3.73, 0.27

15. 144; 2 R,Q; 7, -5

16. 0; 1 R,Q; 5

17. 16; 2 R,Q; $-\frac{3}{2}, -\frac{1}{2}$

18. 73; 2 R,I; $\frac{-11 \pm \sqrt{73}}{6}$; -0.41, -3.26

Practice

12. 16; 2 R,Q; −8, −4
13. 0; 1 R,Q; 2

Find the value of the discriminant for each quadratic equation. Fully describe the nature of its roots. Then solve the equation. Express irrational roots as exact and then use your calculator to give an approximation. **12–18, 28–33. See margin.**

A 12. $a^2 + 12a + 32 = 0$ 13. $y^2 − 4y + 4 = 0$

14. $x^2 − 4x + 1 = 0$ 15. $x^2 − 2x − 35 = 0$

16. $x^2 − 10x + 25 = 0$ 17. $4x^2 + 8x + 3 = 0$

18. $3x^2 + 11x + 4 = 0$ 19. $4y^2 + 16y + 15 = 0$

B 20. $m^2 − 2m + 5 = 0$ 21. $y^2 − 6y + 13 = 0$

22. $c^2 − 12c + 42 = 0$ 23. $a^2 = 6a$ **36; 2 R,Q; 0, 6**

24. $3m^2 = 108m$ **11,664; 2 R,Q; 0, 36** 25. $4x^2 − 8x + 13 = 0$

26. $x^2 − x + 1 = 0$ 27. $n^2 + 4n + 29 = 0$

28. $2a^2 − 13a = 7$ 29. $a^2 + a − 5 = 0$

C 30. $11m^2 − 12m = 10$ 31. $4a^2 + 3a − 2 = 0$

32. $t^2 − 16t + 4 = 0$ 33. $2x^2 + 5x = 9$

19. 16; 2 R,Q; $-\frac{3}{2}$, $-\frac{5}{2}$
20. −16; 2 Im; $1 \pm 2i$ 21. −16; 2 Im; $3 \pm 2i$ 22. −24; 2 Im; $6 \pm i\sqrt{6}$ 25. −144; 2 Im; $\frac{2 \pm 3i}{2}$

Critical Thinking

26. −3, 2 Im; $\frac{1 \pm i\sqrt{3}}{2}$
27. −100; 2 Im; $-2 \pm 5i$

Find three values for k for each equation so that it will have one real root, two real roots, and two imaginary roots. **34–36. Answers will vary.**

34. $x^2 + 3x + k = 0$ 35. $kx^2 + 3x − 2 = 0$ 36. $2x^2 − 5x − k = 0$

Applications

37. **Gardening** The Hillcrest Garden Club wants to double the area of its rectangular rose bed. Strips of the same width will be added to one end and one side to form a rectangle. If the bed is now 17.5 m by 12.2 m, what are the dimensions of the new bed? **18.2 m × 23.5 m Teaching Tip ④**

38. **Astronomy** The acceleration due to gravity on the surface of Earth is 9.8 m/s². The acceleration due to gravity on the surface of Mars is 3.7 m/s² and on Venus it is 8.9 m/s². How long will it take a ball thrown upward to return to the ground on each of these planets if the initial velocity is 25 m/s? **Earth, 5.1 s; Mars, 13.5 s; Venus, 5.6 s**

Mixed Review

40. 8, −3; See Solutions Manual for graph. $-7 \pm \sqrt{61}$

39. Solve $x^2 + 14x − 12 = 0$ by completing the square. **(Lesson 7-3)**

40. Solve $d^2 − 5d − 24 = 0$ by graphing. **(Lesson 7-2)**

41. Simplify $(4a + 7)(3a − 9)$. **(Lesson 5-2)** $12a^2 − 15a − 63$

42. Write $\begin{cases} h + t + u = 10 \\ h − u = 1 \\ h = t + u \end{cases}$ as an augmented matrix. **(Lesson 4-7) See margin.**

43. Given $f(x, y) = 3x + 2y$; find $f(5, −2)$. **(Lesson 3-6) 11**

EXTENDING THE LESSON

Math Power: Reasoning

Show that if a and c have different signs, then $ax^2 + bx + c = 0$ ($a \neq 0$) has two real roots. Since $ac < 0$, then $-4ac > 0$. Thus, $b^2 − 4ac > 0$ and $ax^2 + bx + c = 0$ has two real roots.

Additional Answers

28. 225; 2 R, Q; 7, $-\frac{1}{2}$

29. 21; 2 R, I; $\frac{-1 \pm \sqrt{21}}{2}$; 1.79, −2.79

30. 584; 2 R, I; $\frac{6 \pm \sqrt{146}}{11}$; 1.64, −0.55

31. 41; 2 R, I; $\frac{-3 \pm \sqrt{41}}{8}$; 0.43, −1.18

32. 240; 2 R, I; $8 \pm 2\sqrt{15}$; 15.75, 0.25

33. 97; 2 R, I; $\frac{-5 \pm \sqrt{97}}{4}$; 1.21, −3.71

Closing the Lesson

Speaking Activity Present several quadratic equations to the class. Have students determine the discriminant of each equation. They should be able to describe the nature of the roots for each problem.

APPLYING THE LESSON

Homework Exercises

Assignment Guide

Basic: 12–29, 34–37, 39–43
Average: 16–31, 34–43
Enriched: 18–43

Chapter 7, Quiz C, (Lesson 7-4), is available in the Evaluation Masters Booklet, p. 94.

Teaching Tip ④ Review the formula for a free falling body.

$$s = v_i t − \frac{1}{2}gt^2$$

Additional Answer

42. $\begin{bmatrix} 1 & 1 & 1 & 10 \\ 1 & 0 & 1 & 1 \\ 1 & -1 & -1 & 0 \end{bmatrix}$

Enrichment Masters Booklet, p. 47

Using Technology

Objective This optional page shows how the BASIC programming language can be used to perform mathematical computations and to enhance and extend mathematical concepts.

Teaching Suggestions

Have students modify the program to tell if real roots are rational or irrational. The following steps could be added to the program to accomplish this task.

```
81  IF SQR (D) − INT ( SQR
      (D)) = 0 THEN GOTO 90
85  PRINT "TWO IRRATIONAL
      ROOTS";X;" ";Y
87  GOTO 150
90  PRINT "TWO RATIONAL
      ROOTS";X;" ";Y
```

Additional Answers

4. 1st: Discriminant, −8;
Two complex roots,
2 + 1.41i, 2 − 1.41i
2nd: Discriminant, −8;
Two complex roots,
−2 + 1.41i, −2 − 1.41i
The roots are additive inverses of one another.

5. 1st: Discriminant, 100;
Two real rational roots, 5, −5
2nd: Discriminant, 80;
Two real irrational roots,
2.236, −2.236
3rd: Discriminant, 768;
Two real irrational roots,
0.866, −0.866
The roots are additive inverses of one another.

6. 1st: Discriminant, 121;
Two real rational roots, 7, −4
2nd: Discriminant, 484;
Two real rational roots, 7, −4
3rd: Discriminant, 3025;
Two real rational roots, 7, −4
When coefficients are multiplied by the same value, the roots remain the same but the discriminant changes.

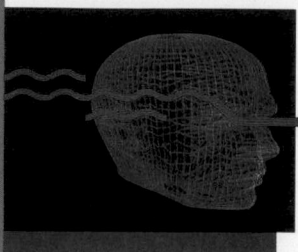

Technology
Discriminants and Roots

▶ **BASIC**
Spreadsheets
Software

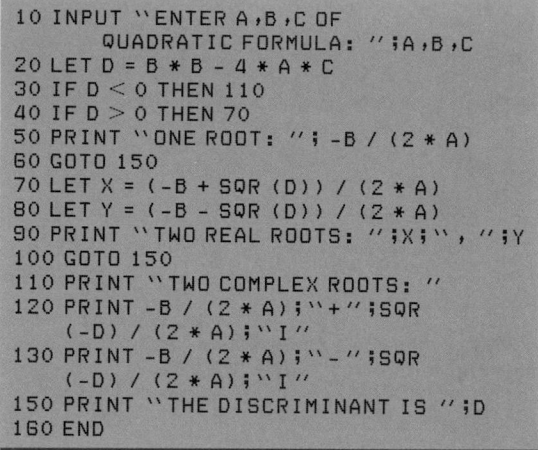

```
10 INPUT "ENTER A,B,C OF
        QUADRATIC FORMULA: ";A,B,C
20 LET D = B * B − 4 * A * C
30 IF D < 0 THEN 110
40 IF D > 0 THEN 70
50 PRINT "ONE ROOT: "; −B / (2 * A)
60 GOTO 150
70 LET X = (−B + SQR (D)) / (2 * A)
80 LET Y = (−B − SQR (D)) / (2 * A)
90 PRINT "TWO REAL ROOTS: ";X;", ";Y
100 GOTO 150
110 PRINT "TWO COMPLEX ROOTS: "
120 PRINT −B / (2 * A);"+";SQR
        (−D) / (2 * A);"I"
130 PRINT −B / (2 * A);"−";SQR
        (−D) / (2 * A);"I"
150 PRINT "THE DISCRIMINANT IS ";D
160 END
```

The BASIC program at the left utilizes the discriminant to determine the type of roots an equation has and what those roots are. In order to use the program, you must have the quadratic equation written in standard form.

Example $3x^2 + 16x = -5$
$3x^2 + 16x + 5 = 0$

$a = 3$, $b = 16$, and $c = 5$

To run the program to solve this equation, type RUN and then enter the values for a, b, and c when the ? prompt appears on the screen. The screen should print the following information.

```
TWO REAL ROOTS: −.33333333, −5
THE DISCRIMINANT IS 196.
```

EXERCISES

Use the BASIC program to find the roots of each quadratic equation. Describe the types of roots each equation has. If the roots are real, determine if they are rational or irrational.

1. $6n^2 + 8n + 1 = 0$
   −0.1396, −1.1937; R; I

2. $3y^2 + 3y = -2$
   −0.5 ± 0.645i; Im

3. $x^2 = 6x - 13$
   3 ± 2i; Im

Find the value of the discriminant and the roots of each equation. Make a conjecture about the roots and discriminants of each group of equations.

4–7. See margin.

4. $m^2 - 4m + 6 = 0$
   $m^2 + 4m + 6 = 0$

5. $x^2 - 25 = 0$
   $2x^2 - 10 = 0$
   $16x^2 - 12 = 0$

6. $x^2 - 3x - 28 = 0$
   $2x^2 - 6x - 56 = 0$
   $5x^2 - 15x - 140 = 0$

7. $x^2 + 4x + 4 = 0$
   $x^2 - 10x + 25 = 0$
   $4x^2 + 32x + 64 = 0$

332   CHAPTER 7   QUADRATIC EQUATIONS

Additional Answers

7. 1st: Discriminant, 0;
One real rational root, −2
2nd: Discriminant, 0;
One real rational root, 5
3rd: Discriminant, 0;
One real rational root, −4
A zero discriminant implies there is one real root.

7-5 Sum and Product of Roots

Objectives

After studying this lesson, you should be able to:

7-5A ■ find the sum and product of the roots of a quadratic equation,

7-5B ■ find all possible integral roots of a quadratic equation, and

7-5C ■ find a quadratic equation to fit a given condition.

There are times when you may know the roots of a quadratic equation but you don't know the equation itself. For example, suppose the roots of a quadratic equation are -7 and 5, and you want to find the equation.

Remember when you used factoring to solve an equation. You eventually solved two equations set equal to zero to find the two solutions. You can use the process in reverse to find the equation when you know the solutions.

$x = 5$	$x = -7$	*Start with the solutions.*
$\underline{x - 5 = 0}$	$\underline{x + 7 = 0}$	*Find equations set equal to 0.*

$$(x - 5)(x + 7) = 0 \qquad \textit{Use the zero product property.}$$
$$x^2 + 2x - 35 = 0 \qquad \textit{Find the quadratic equation by multiplying.}$$

The last step shows the general form of a quadratic equation whose roots are 5 and -7. These roots, their sum, and their product can lead you to the equation in another way. Study the pattern shown below.

$$x^2 \qquad + \quad 2x \quad + \quad (-35) = \quad 0$$
$$\uparrow \qquad\qquad \uparrow \qquad\quad \uparrow$$
$$1 \qquad\quad \frac{-(-7 + 5)}{1} \quad \frac{7(5)}{1}$$

This pattern can be generalized for any quadratic equation by using the roots as defined by the quadratic formula. Let s_1 and s_2 represent solutions, or roots.

Teaching Tip ❶

$$s_1 = \frac{-b + \sqrt{b^2 - 4ac}}{2a} \qquad s_2 = \frac{-b - \sqrt{b^2 - 4ac}}{2a}$$

$$s_1 + s_2 = \frac{-b + \sqrt{b^2 - 4ac}}{2a} + \frac{-b - \sqrt{b^2 - 4ac}}{2a}$$

$$= \frac{-b + (-b) + \sqrt{b^2 - 4ac} - \sqrt{b^2 - 4ac}}{2a}$$

$$= \frac{-2b + 0}{2a} \text{ or } -\frac{b}{a}$$

$$s_1 s_2 = \frac{-b + \sqrt{b^2 - 4ac}}{2a} \cdot \frac{-b - \sqrt{b^2 - 4ac}}{2a}$$

$$= \frac{b^2 - (b^2 - 4ac)}{4a^2} \qquad \textit{Use the distributive property.}$$

$$= \frac{b^2 - b^2 + 4ac}{4a^2}$$

$$= \frac{4ac}{4a^2} \text{ or } \frac{c}{a}$$

LESSON 7-5　SUM AND PRODUCT OF ROOTS　**333**

ALTERNATE TEACHING STRATEGIES

Using Questioning

Suppose you know that a and b are roots of a quadratic equation and you're asked to find the equation.

■ What strategy could you use? Working backwards
■ If a and b are roots, what two equations can you write? $x - a = 0$, $x - b = 0$

■ From these two equations, what equation can you write? $(x - a)(x - b) = 0$
■ What property did you use? Zero product property
■ How do you find the quadratic equation? Multiply the binomial factors.

7-5 Lesson Notes

Lesson Resources

Reteaching Master 7-5
Practice Master 7-5
Enrichment Master 7-5

 Transparency 7-5 contains the 5-Minute Check and a teaching aid for this lesson.

INTRODUCING THE LESSON

🕐 5-Minute Check

(over Lesson 7-4)
Determine the roots of the quadratic equation $m^2 - 8m + 15 = 0$

1. by completing the square. **3, 5**
2. by using the quadratic formula. **3, 5**

Find the value of the discriminant. Describe the nature of the roots. Then solve the equation.

3. $x^2 - 9x + 21 = 0$ **-3;** **2 imaginary roots;** $\frac{9 \pm i\sqrt{3}}{2}$
4. $5x^2 - x - 4 = 0$ **81; 2 real-rational roots; 1,** $-\frac{4}{5}$

Motivating the Lesson

Divide the class into four groups. Have each group graph one of the following equations and determine the roots.

$5x^2 + x - 4 = 0$
$x^2 + 2x - 8 = 0$
$2x^2 + 4x - 16 = 0$
$8 - 2x - x^2 = 0$

Discuss how different equations have the same roots and differently shaped graphs.

TEACHING THE LESSON

Teaching Tip ❶　The product of these two terms is the difference of squares.

Chapter 7　**333**

Chalkboard Examples

For Example 1

Solve each function. Then use the sum and product of the roots to check your solutions.

a. $3x^2 - 10x + 3 = 0$ $3, \frac{1}{3}$;

$s_1 + s_2 = \frac{10}{3} = -\frac{b}{a}$

$s_1 s_2 = 1 = \frac{c}{a}$

b. $y^2 - 10y = 11$ $11, -1$;

$s_1 + s_2 = 10 = -\frac{b}{a}$

$s_1 s_2 = -11 = \frac{c}{a}$

For Example 2

Write a quadratic equation that has the given roots.

a. $-\frac{3}{8}$ and 5 $8x^2 - 37x - 15 = 0$

b. $\frac{1}{3}$ and $\frac{1}{2}$ $6x^2 - 5x + 1 = 0$

Teaching Tip ➋ Emphasize that fractions for the sum and product must be written with the same denominator. Then, a, b, and c are recognizable. Do not simplify unless it is necessary.

Sum and Product of Roots	If the roots of $ax^2 + bx + c = 0$ with $a \neq 0$ are s_1 and s_2, then $s_1 + s_2 = -\dfrac{b}{a}$ and $s_1 s_2 = \dfrac{c}{a}.$

Example 1

Solve $3x^2 - 16x - 12 = 0$. Then use the sum and product of the roots to check your solution.

$$x = \frac{-b \pm \sqrt{b^2 - 4ac}}{2a}$$

$$= \frac{-(-16) \pm \sqrt{(-16)^2 - 4(3)(-12)}}{2(3)}$$ *In the equation $3x^2 - 16x - 12 = 0$, $a = 3$, $b = -16$, and $c = -12$.*

$$= \frac{16 \pm \sqrt{400}}{6} \quad \text{or} \quad \frac{16 \pm 20}{6}$$

The roots are $\dfrac{16 + 20}{6}$ and $\dfrac{16 - 20}{6}$ or 6 and $-\dfrac{2}{3}$.

Check: *The sum of the roots, $s_1 + s_2$, should be $-\dfrac{b}{a}$ or $\dfrac{16}{3}$.*   *The product of the roots, $s_1 s_2$, should be $\dfrac{c}{a}$ or -4.*

$$\left[6 + \left(-\frac{2}{3}\right)\right] = \frac{16}{3} \qquad\qquad 6\left(-\frac{2}{3}\right) = -4$$

The solutions are correct.

Example 2

Write a quadratic equation that has roots $-\dfrac{5}{4}$ and $\dfrac{16}{5}$.   **Teaching Tip ➋**

Find the sum and product of the roots. Express the two fractions with the same denominator.

$$s_1 + s_2 = -\frac{5}{4} + \frac{16}{5} = \frac{39}{20} \quad -\frac{b}{a} \qquad s_1 s_2 = \left(-\frac{5}{4}\right)\left(\frac{16}{5}\right) = -\frac{80}{20} \quad \frac{c}{a}$$

Therefore, $a = 20$, $b = -39$, and $c = -80$.

The equation is $20x^2 - 39x - 80 = 0$.

The method used in Example 2 can also be used with equations whose roots are imaginary.

Example 3

Find a quadratic equation that has roots $5 + 2i$ and $5 - 2i$.

$$s_1 + s_2 = (5 + 2i) + (5 - 2i) \qquad s_1 s_2 = (5 + 2i)(5 - 2i)$$
$$= 10 \quad -\frac{b}{a} = \frac{10}{1} \qquad\qquad = 25 + 4 \text{ or } 29 \quad \frac{c}{a} = \frac{29}{1}$$

Therefore, $a = 1$, $b = -10$, and $c = 29$.

The equation is $x^2 - 10x + 29 = 0$.

Example 4

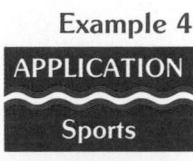

APPLICATION

Sports

FYI …

The most money won by a woman in a single year is $2,173,556, won in 1984 by Martina Navratilova.

Claire Homan is practicing her lobs for a tennis tournament. In analyzing her style of play, she must use some physics. Her coach videotapes her practice with a special camera that also records the elapsed time (in seconds) of each frame of film. When reviewing the film, he notes that the ball she lobs is approximately the same distance above the ground after 0.5 second and after 1.5 seconds. At what speed was she hitting the ball? If Claire hits the ball when it is 7 feet in the air, how far above the ground is it at 0.5 second and 1.5 seconds?

You can use the formula you learned in Lesson 7-2 for a free falling object affected by gravity to solve this problem. This formula can be rewritten as a quadratic equation in general form.

$$s = v_i t - \frac{1}{2}gt^2 \quad \Rightarrow \quad 0 = \left(-\frac{1}{2}g\right)t^2 + (v_i)t + (-s)$$
$$\qquad\qquad\qquad\qquad\uparrow\qquad\uparrow\qquad\uparrow$$
$$\qquad\qquad\qquad\qquad a\qquad b\qquad c$$

Since the acceleration of gravity is 32 ft/s^2, $a = -16$.
The two solutions for t are 0.5 and 1.5.

$$s_1 + s_2 = -\frac{b}{a} \qquad s_1 \cdot s_2 = \frac{c}{a}$$
$$0.5 + 1.5 = -\frac{b}{-16} \qquad 0.5 \cdot 1.5 = \frac{c}{-16}$$
$$2 = \frac{b}{16} \qquad\qquad 0.75 = \frac{c}{-16}$$
$$32 = b \qquad\qquad\qquad -12 = c$$

The equation is $0 = -16t^2 + 32t - 12$. It can also be written as $12 = 32t - 16t^2$, so that it has the same form as the original equation.

From this form, you can see that v_i is 32. So, she hits the ball at a speed of 32 ft/s. The value of s in this equation is 12, but recall that she hits the ball when it is 7 feet in the air. The actual height of the ball at 0.5 and 1.5 seconds is $12 + 7$ or 19 feet.

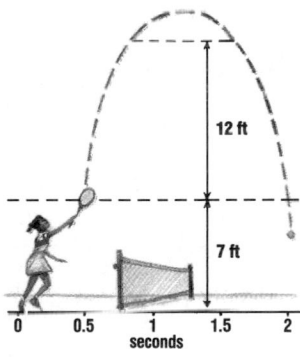

12 ft

7 ft

0   0.5   1   1.5   2
seconds

Remember that this graph shows the graph of the formula and <u>not</u> the actual path of the ball.

LESSON 7-5 SUM AND PRODUCT OF ROOTS 335

You can also use the sum or product to find missing values for a, b, or c when one of the roots is known.

Example 5

Find k such that -3 is a root of $x^2 + kx - 24 = 0$.

Let $s_1 = -3$. Solve $s_1 s_2 = \dfrac{c}{a}$ for s_2. Then solve for k.

$$-3s_2 = \frac{-24}{1} \qquad s_1 + s_2 = -\frac{b}{a}$$
$$s_2 = 8 \qquad -3 + 8 = -\frac{k}{1}$$
$$-5 = k$$

The value of k is -5.   *Check this result.*

CHECKING FOR UNDERSTANDING

Communicating Mathematics

Read and study the lesson to answer each question.

1. What property allows you to conclude that if the roots of a quadratic equation are 5 and -7, then $(x - 5)(x + 7) = 0$? **zero product property**

2. The product of the roots of a quadratic equation is equal to ___?___ expressed in terms of a, b, and c. **$\frac{c}{a}$**

3. The sum of the roots of a quadratic equation is equal to ___?___ expressed in terms of a, b, and c. **$-\frac{b}{a}$**

4. The sum of the roots of $5x^2 - 14x - 20 = 0$ would be
   a. -14 b. $-\frac{14}{5}$ c. $\frac{14}{5}$ **c**

5. The product of the roots of $5x^2 - 14x - 20 = 0$ would be
   a. -20 b. -4 c. 4 **b**

Guided Practice

State the sum and the product of the roots of each quadratic equation.

6. $2x^2 + 8x - 3 = 0$ **−4, −$\frac{3}{2}$**

7. $4x^2 + 3x - 12 = 0$ **−$\frac{3}{4}$, −3**

8. $2x^2 + 7 = 0$ **0, $\frac{7}{2}$**

9. $5x^2 = 3$ **0, −$\frac{3}{5}$**

10. $x^2 + 4x - \frac{5}{3} = 0$ **−4, −$\frac{5}{3}$**

11. $3x^2 - \frac{x}{5} - \frac{4}{5} = 0$ **$\frac{1}{15}$, −$\frac{4}{15}$**

Solve each equation. Then find the sum and the product of the roots to check your solutions.

12. $x^2 + x - 6 = 0$ **−3, 2**

13. $m^2 + 5m + 6 = 0$ **−3, −2**

14. $s^2 + 5s - 24 = 0$ **−8, 3**

15. $a^2 - 9a + 20 = 0$ **5, 4**

EXERCISES

Practice

Solve each equation. Then find the sum and the product of the roots to check your solutions.

A

19. $\frac{5 \pm \sqrt{17}}{4}$

16. $x^2 + 6x - 7 = 0$ **-7, 1**

17. $2z^2 - 5z - 3 = 0$ **3, $-\frac{1}{2}$**

18. $y^2 + 5y + 6 = 0$ **-3, -2**

19. $2c^2 - 5c + 1 = 0$

22. $x^2 - 10x + 24 = 0$

20. $6t^2 + 28t - 10 = 0$ **-5, $\frac{1}{3}$**

21. $4a^2 + 21a = 18$ **$\frac{3}{4}$, -6**

23. $x^2 - 6x - 16 = 0$

24. $x^2 - 36 = 0$

Write a quadratic equation that has the given roots.

25. $2x^2 - 7x + 3 = 0$

26. $3x^2 - 17x + 10 = 0$

22. 6, 4

23. 8, -2

24. 6, -6

25. 3, $\frac{1}{2}$

27. $25x^2 - 4 = 0$

B

26. 5, $\frac{2}{3}$

27. $-\frac{2}{5}, \frac{2}{5}$

28. $\frac{5}{8}, \frac{1}{4}$

29. $\sqrt{3}, 2\sqrt{3}$

28. $32x^2 - 28x + 5 = 0$

29. $x^2 - (3\sqrt{3})x + 6 = 0$

Solve each equation. Then use the sum and the product of the roots to check your solutions.

30. $9n^2 - 1 = 0$ **$\pm\frac{1}{3}$**

31. $s^2 - 16 = 0$ **±4**

32. $2x^2 - 7x = 15$ **5, $-\frac{3}{2}$**

33. $15c^2 - 2c - 8 = 0$ **$\frac{4}{5}, -\frac{2}{3}$**

34. $7s^2 + 5s - 1 = 0$ **$\frac{-5 \pm \sqrt{53}}{14}$**

35. $12x^2 + 19x + 4 = 0$ **$-\frac{1}{4}, -\frac{4}{3}$**

C

Write a quadratic equation that has the given roots.

36. $x^2 - 4x + 1 = 0$

37. $x^2 + 36 = 0$

38. $8x^2 - 20x + 17 = 0$

39. $2x^2 - 2x - 3 = 0$

36. $2 \pm \sqrt{3}$

37. $-6i, 6i$

38. $\frac{5 - 3i}{4}, \frac{5 + 3i}{4}$

39. $\frac{1 + \sqrt{7}}{2}, \frac{1 - \sqrt{7}}{2}$

Find k such that the number given is a root of the equation.

40. 1; $x^2 + kx - 5 = 0$ **4**

41. 3; $x^2 + kx - 21 = 0$ **4**

42. 3; $x^2 + 6x - k = 0$ **27**

43. $-\frac{3}{2}; 2x^2 + kx - 12 = 0$ **-5**

Critical Thinking

44. Suppose you were given the equation $x^2 + bx + 12 = 0$ and told that b was an integer. List all the possible integral roots of that equation. **12, 1; -12, -1; 2, 6; -2, -6; 3, 4; -3, -4**

Applications

45. **Aeronautics** Determine the initial velocity of a model rocket if it returns to Earth 15 seconds after takeoff. Use the formula $s = v_i t - \frac{1}{2}gt^2$, where $g = 32$ ft/s². *Remember that the rocket starts on Earth when $t = 0$.* **240 ft/s**

46. **Horticulture** Helene Jonson has a rectangular garden 25 ft by 50 ft. She wishes to increase the garden on all sides by an equal amount. The area of the garden will be increased by 400 ft². By how much will each dimension be increased? **2.5 ft** Teaching Tip ❸

Homework Exercises

Assignment Guide

Basic: 16–35, 44–45, 48–54
Average: 20–39, 44–54
Enriched: 26–54

Teaching Tip ❸ Have students make a drawing in order to help solve the problem.

Practice Masters Booklet, p. 55

NAME _____ DATE _____

7-5 Practice Worksheet

Sum and Product of Roots

Solve each equation. Then find the sum and the product of the roots to check your solutions.

1. $x^2 - 7x + 4 = 0$ $\frac{7 \pm \sqrt{33}}{2}$; 7; 4

2. $x^2 + 3x + 6 = 0$ $\frac{-3 \pm \sqrt{15}i}{2}$; -3, 6

3. $2n^2 + 5n + 6 = 0$ $\frac{-5 \pm \sqrt{23}i}{4}$; $-\frac{5}{2}$; 3

4. $7x^2 - 5x = 0$ 0, $\frac{5}{7}$; $\frac{5}{7}$; 0

5. $4r^2 - 9 = 0$ $\frac{3}{2}, -\frac{3}{2}$; 0; $-\frac{9}{4}$

6. $-5x^2 - x + 4 = 0$ $-1, \frac{4}{5}$; $-\frac{1}{5}$; $-\frac{4}{5}$

7. $3x^2 + 8x = 3$ $\frac{1}{3}, -3$; $-\frac{8}{3}$; -1

8. $\frac{2}{3}x^2 - \frac{1}{2}x - 1 = 0$ $\frac{3 \pm \sqrt{105}}{8}$; $\frac{3}{4}$; $-\frac{3}{2}$

Write a quadratic equation that has the given roots.

9. 7, -3 $x^2 - 4x - 21 = 0$

10. 4, $\frac{1}{3}$ $3x^2 - 13x + 4 = 0$

11. $-\frac{2}{3}, -\frac{4}{5}$ $15x^2 + 22x + 8 = 0$

12. $-2\sqrt{5}, 4\sqrt{5}$ $x^2 - 2\sqrt{5}x - 40 = 0$

13. $3 - \sqrt{6}, 3 + \sqrt{6}$ $x^2 - 6x + 3 = 0$

14. $7 - 2i, 7 + 2i$ $x^2 - 14x + 53 = 0$

15. $7i, -7i$ $x^2 + 49 = 0$

16. $\frac{2 + \sqrt{10}}{5}, \frac{2 - \sqrt{10}}{5}$ $25x^2 - 20x - 6 = 0$

17. $2 + i\sqrt{11}, 2 - i\sqrt{11}$ $x^2 - 4x + 15 = 0$

18. $\frac{1 + 6i}{4}, \frac{1 - 6i}{4}$ $16x^2 - 8x + 37 = 0$

Find k such that the number given is a root of the equation.

19. 7; $2x^2 + kx - 21 = 0$ **-11**

20. -2; $x^2 - 13x + k = 0$ **-30**

47. **Flight** Sam shot his model rocket up into the air and counted the seconds it stayed in flight. He noticed that the rocket seemed to be at the same height as the top of a television antenna at 1 and 3 seconds. Find the initial speed of the model rocket and the height of the television antenna. **64 ft/s, 48 ft**

Mixed Review

48. $\dfrac{5 \pm i\sqrt{7}}{4}$

48. Solve $2x^2 - 5x + 4 = 0$ using the quadratic formula. (**Lesson 7-4**)

49. Solve $\sqrt[3]{2x + 1} = 3$. (**Lesson 6-7**) **13**

50. Simplify $\dfrac{(3 + \sqrt{5})}{(1 + \sqrt{2})}$. (**Lesson 6-2**) $-3 + 3\sqrt{2} - \sqrt{5} + \sqrt{10}$

51. Factor $ab + 7a + 4b + 28$. (**Lesson 5-5**) $(b + 7)(a + 4)$

52. $\begin{bmatrix} 1 & 0 & 0 \\ 0 & 1 & 0 \\ 0 & 0 & 1 \end{bmatrix}$

52. Write the identity matrix for a 3×3 matrix. (**Lesson 4-4**)

53. **Business** Derringer Cleaners charges $52 to clean a prom dress. If the equation relating time spent (in hours) to total charge (in dollars) is $C = 12 + 20t$, find the time spent cleaning the dress. (**Lesson 2-1**) **2 hours**

54. **Geometry** A piece of wire was cut into two pieces. One was bent into a square and the other into an equilateral triangle. The side of the equilateral triangle has the same whole-number length (in cm) as the side of the square. If the length of the piece of wire is less than 50 cm, find all possible measurements for the sides of the figures. (**Lesson 1-5**) **1 cm, 2 cm, 3 cm, 4 cm, 5 cm, 6 cm, 7 cm**

~~~~~~ **HISTORY CONNECTION** ~~~~~~

Archaeologists in an ancient area of the Middle East have found artifacts that show the Babylonians solved mathematical problems. They completed these calculations in words. Algebraic symbols were not in general usage until the middle of the 17th century A.D. The tablet shown at the right contains one quadratic equation and its solution written sometime between 1900 and 1600 B.C. The tablet explains the solution to a problem about a rectangle whose area is 60 square units.

The solution to the problem, when translated into English, involves a version of a quadratic equation in the form $x^2 + ax = b$, $b > 0$. If y is the length of the rectangle and x is the width, then $y = x + 7$ and $xy = 60$. When solved, we find the rectangle's dimensions are 5×12 units.

EXTENDING THE LESSON

Math Power: Reasoning

Find k such that $\dfrac{-13}{3}$ is a root of $3x^2 - kx - (k + 73) = 0$. $k = 5$ Have students give the justification for the steps in their solution.

History Connection

The History Connection features introduce students to persons or cultures who were involved in the development of mathematics. You may want students to further research the Babylonians or to research the development of quadratic equations.

Quadratic Techniques to Solve Polynomial Equations

Objectives   After studying this lesson, you should be able to:

7-6A   ■ solve third and fourth degree equations that contain a quadratic factor, and

7-6B   ■ solve other nonquadratic equations that can be written in quadratic form.

The problem below demonstrates solving an equation that is not a quadratic equation itself, but contains a factor that is a quadratic. The methods you have learned are used to solve the quadratic part of that equation. **Teaching Tip ❶**

Connection   A rectangular prism has a base that is b mm long. The width of the base is 2 mm less than its length. The height is 3 mm greater than the length of the base. The measure of the volume is 6 times the measure of the length of the base. Find the dimensions of the prism.

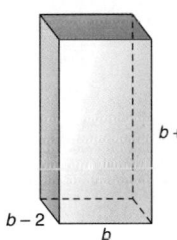

The volume of a prism is the product of the length, width, and height of the prism. That is, $V = \ell wh$.

$\ell = b,\ w = b - 2,\ h = b + 3,\ V = 6b$

$V = \ell wh$

$6b = (b)(b - 2)(b + 3)$	*Substitute values for ℓ, w, h.*
$6b = b^3 + b^2 - 6b$	*Multiply.*
$0 = b^3 + b^2 - 12b$	*Subtract $6b$ from each side.*
$0 = b(b^2 + b - 12)$	*Factor out the common factor, b.*
$0 = b(b - 3)(b + 4)$	*Factor the quadratic term.*

Now use the zero product property.

$b = 0$ or $b + 4 = 0$ or $b - 3 = 0$
$b = 0$ $\qquad\quad$ $b = -4$ $\qquad\quad$ $b = 3$

Since this problem deals with measures of a prism, we can eliminate 0 and -4 as reasonable solutions.

$\ell = b = 3$
$w = b - 2 = 3 - 2$ or 1
$h = b + 3 = 3 + 3$ or 6

The dimensions of the prism are 3 mm × 1 mm × 6 mm.

Check: The width, ℓ, is 2 less than 3, the length.
$\qquad\quad$ The height, 6, is 3 more than 3, the length.
$\qquad\quad$ $V = 3 \cdot 1 \cdot 6$ or 18, which is 6 times the length.

LESSON 7-6   QUADRATIC TECHNIQUES TO SOLVE POLYNOMIAL EQUATIONS   339

Lesson Resources

Reteaching Master 7-6
Practice Master 7-6
Enrichment Master 7-6
Multicultural Activity Master, p. 7

 Transparency 7-6 contains the 5-Minute Check and a teaching aid for this lesson.

INTRODUCING THE LESSON

🕐 5-Minute Check

(over Lesson 7-5)

Find the sum and product of the roots of the quadratic equations.

1. $4x^2 - 2x + 3 = 0$ $\frac{1}{2}; \frac{3}{4}$

2. $12x^2 + 19x + 4 = 0$ $-\frac{19}{12}; \frac{1}{3}$

3. Find the sum and product of the roots of $y^2 + 9y + 25 = 0$. Then solve the equation.
   $-9; 25; \dfrac{-9 \pm i\sqrt{19}}{2}$

Find the quadratic equation with the given roots.

4. $3, -1$ $x^2 - 2x - 3 = 0$
5. $2 + \sqrt{5}, 2 - \sqrt{5}$
   $x^2 - 4x - 1 = 0$

Motivating the Lesson

Divide the class into groups. Have them solve the following problem. A square room has a rug in the middle of the room. If there is a 4-foot edge around the entire rug and the rug has an area of 400 square feet, what are the measurements of the sides of the room? **28 feet**

TEACHING THE LESSON

Teaching Tip ❶   Review the meaning of quadratic form.

ALTERNATE TEACHING STRATEGIES

Using Models

Have students make 3 or 4 rectangular prisms. They should measure the sides and determine the volume. Then they should write a problem like the one on page 339. Have another student solve the problem using algebraic methods.

Chalkboard Examples

For Example 1

a. Solve $x^4 + 3x^3 - 18x^2 = 0$.
   0, -6, 3
b. Solve $x^4 - 7x^2 + 12 = 0$.
   2, -2, $\sqrt{3}$, $-\sqrt{3}$

For Example 2

a. Solve $x^{\frac{2}{3}} - 8x^{\frac{1}{3}} + 15 = 0$.
   125, 27

b. Solve $y^{\frac{4}{3}} - 13y^{\frac{2}{3}} + 36 = 0$.
   8, 27

Some equations are not quadratic but can be written in a form that resembles a quadratic equation. For example, the equation $x^4 - 20x^2 + 64 = 0$ can be written as $(x^2)^2 - 20(x^2) + 64 = 0$. Equations that can be written in this way are said to be equations in **quadratic form**.

Definition of Quadratic Form	For any numbers a, b, and c, except $a = 0$, an equation that may be written as $a[f(x)]^2 + b[f(x)] + c = 0$, where $f(x)$ is some expression in x, is in quadratic form.

Once an equation is written in quadratic form, it can be solved by the methods you have aleady learned to use for solving quadratic equations.

Example 1

Solve $x^4 - 13x^2 + 36 = 0$.

$$x^4 - 13x^2 + 36 = 0$$
$$(x^2)^2 - 13(x^2) + 36 = 0$$
$$(x^2 - 9)(x^2 - 4) = 0$$
$$(x + 3)(x - 3)(x + 2)(x - 2) = 0$$

$$x + 3 = 0 \qquad x - 3 = 0$$
$$x = -3 \qquad x = 3$$

$$x + 2 = 0 \qquad x - 2 = 0$$
$$x = -2 \qquad x = 2$$

The graph of $y = x^4 - 13x^2 + 36$ crosses the x-axis 4 times. There will be 4 real solutions.

The solutions or roots are -3, 3, -2, and 2.

Recall that $(a^m)^n = a^{mn}$ for any positive number a and any rational numbers n and m. This property of exponents that you learned in Chapter 5 is often used when solving equations.

Example 2

Solve $x^{\frac{1}{2}} - 6x^{\frac{1}{4}} + 8 = 0$.

$$x^{\frac{1}{2}} - 6x^{\frac{1}{4}} + 8 = 0$$
$$(x^{\frac{1}{4}})^2 - 6(x^{\frac{1}{4}}) + 8 = 0 \quad \text{$f(x)$ is $x^{\frac{1}{2}}$.}$$
$$(x^{\frac{1}{4}} - 2)(x^{\frac{1}{4}} - 4) = 0 \quad \text{Factor to solve for $f(x)$.}$$
$$x^{\frac{1}{4}} - 2 = 0 \quad \text{or} \quad x^{\frac{1}{4}} - 4 = 0$$
$$x^{\frac{1}{4}} = 2 \qquad x^{\frac{1}{4}} = 4$$
$$(x^{\frac{1}{4}})^4 = (2)^4 \qquad (x^{\frac{1}{4}})^4 = 4^4$$
$$x = 2^4 \text{ or } 16 \qquad x = 4^4 \text{ or } 256$$

Check:
$$x^{\frac{1}{2}} - 6x^{\frac{1}{4}} + 8 = 0$$
$$16^{\frac{1}{2}} - 6(16^{\frac{1}{4}}) + 8 \stackrel{?}{=} 0$$
$$4 - 6(2) + 8 \stackrel{?}{=} 0$$
$$0 = 0 \checkmark$$

$$256^{\frac{1}{2}} - 6(256^{\frac{1}{4}}) + 8 \stackrel{?}{=} 0$$
$$16 - 6(4) + 8 \stackrel{?}{=} 0$$
$$0 = 0 \checkmark$$

The solutions are 16 and 256.

Example 3

Solve $t^{\frac{2}{3}} = 16$.

$t^{\frac{2}{3}} = 16$

$\left(t^{\frac{2}{3}}\right)^3 = (16)^3$ *Cube each side.*

$t^2 = 16^3$ or 4^6

$t = \pm(4^6)^{\frac{1}{2}}$ *Why ±?*

$t = \pm4^3$ or ±64

Check:

$t^{\frac{2}{3}} = 16$

$64^{\frac{2}{3}} \stackrel{?}{=} 16$

$(\sqrt[3]{64})^2 \stackrel{?}{=} 16$

$4^2 \stackrel{?}{=} 16$

$16 = 16$ ✓

$t^{\frac{2}{3}} = 16$

$(-64)^{\frac{2}{3}} \stackrel{?}{=} 16$

$(\sqrt[3]{-64})^2 \stackrel{?}{=} 16$

$(-4)^2 \stackrel{?}{=} 16$

$16 = 16$ ✓

The solutions are 64 and −64.

The quadratic formula can also be used to solve equations that are in quadratic form.

Example 4

Solve $x - 7\sqrt{x} - 8 = 0$.   **Teaching Tip ②**

$x - 7\sqrt{x} - 8 = 0$

$(\sqrt{x})^2 - 7(\sqrt{x}) - 8 = 0$ $f(x)$ is $\sqrt{x}$.

$\sqrt{x} = \dfrac{-b \pm \sqrt{b^2 - 4ac}}{2a}$

$= \dfrac{-(-7) \pm \sqrt{(-7)^2 - 4(1)(-8)}}{2(1)}$ $a = 1,$ $b = -7,$ $c = -8$

$= \dfrac{7 \pm \sqrt{81}}{2}$ or $\dfrac{7 \pm 9}{2}$

$\sqrt{x} = 8$ or $\sqrt{x} = -1$ There is no real number x such that $\sqrt{x} = -1$.

$x = 64$ The only solution is 64.

Check: $x - 7\sqrt{x} - 8 = 0$

$64 - 7\sqrt{64} - 8 \stackrel{?}{=} 0$

$64 - 7 \cdot 8 - 8 \stackrel{?}{=} 0$

$0 = 0$ ✓

Some cubic equations can be solved using the quadratic formula. First a binomial factor must be found.

Example 5

Solve $x^3 - 27 = 0$.

$x^3 - 27 = 0$ *The left side is the difference of cubes.*

$(x - 3)(x^2 + 3x + 9) = 0$ *Factor.*

$x - 3 = 0$ or $x^2 + 3x + 9 = 0$ *Zero product property*

$x = 3$ or $x = \dfrac{-3 \pm \sqrt{(3)^2 - 4(1)(9)}}{2(1)}$

$= \dfrac{-3 + \sqrt{-27}}{2}$

$= \dfrac{-3 \pm 3i\sqrt{3}}{2}$

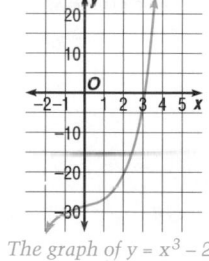

The graph of $y = x^3 - 27$ crosses the x-axis once. There will be 1 real root.

The solutions are 3, $\dfrac{-3 + 3i\sqrt{3}}{2}$, and $\dfrac{-3 - 3i\sqrt{3}}{2}$.

LESSON 7-6   QUADRATIC TECHNIQUES TO SOLVE POLYNOMIAL EQUATIONS   341

Chalkboard Examples

For Example 3

a. Solve $y^{\frac{2}{5}} = 9$.   **243**

b. Solve $p^{-2} = 169$. $\dfrac{1}{13}$

For Example 4

a. Solve $y - 8\sqrt{y} + 7 = 0$.
1, 49

b. Solve $s - 13\sqrt{s} + 36 = 0$.
81, 16

For Example 5

Solve $t^3 = 216$.   **6, −3 + 3i √3, −3 − 3i √3**

Teaching Tip ②   Put in quadratic form and identify the constant values.

Reteaching Masters Booklet, p. 49

Checking for Understanding

Exercises 1–20 are designed to help you assess understanding through reading, writing, and speaking. You should work through Exercises 1–6 with your students, and then monitor their work on Exercises 7–20.

Error Analysis

Remind students that the radical sign indicates only the positive square root. Caution students to be careful to watch when squaring both sides of any equation. Note that $-4 \neq 4$ but $(-4)^2 = (4)^2$.

Closing the Lesson

Writing Activity Given $x^4 - 20x^2 + 64 = 0$, have students determine the maximum and minimum number of roots.
4 real roots or as few as 0 real roots Then discuss different ways to solve the equation.

Practice Masters Booklet, p. 56

CHECKING FOR UNDERSTANDING

Communicating Mathematics

Read and study the lesson to answer each question.

1. Why were the roots 0 and −4 disregarded as possible solutions for measures of a prism? **Dimensions cannot be 0 or negative.**

2. What is the actual volume of the prism in the problem at the beginning of the lesson? **18 mm³**

3. 2 of the solutions are imaginary; they cannot be graphed.

3. In Example 5, three solutions are shown but the graph of the related function crosses the *x*-axis once. Explain this discrepancy.

4. The maximum number of solutions a quadratic equation can have is ___?___. **2**

5. If $pqr = 0$, what property allows us to say that at least one of the three factors is equal to zero? **zero product property**

6. Give two examples of equations that are not quadratic, but can be written in quadratic form. **Answers will vary.**

7. $x^2(x^2 + 5x + 6) = 0$ 8. $x(x^2 + 10x + 16) = 0$ 9. $m(3m^2 - 2m + 7) = 0$
10. $a(a^4 - a^2 + 81) = 0$ 11. $d(25d^2 - 30d + 9) = 0$ 12. $t(16t^3 - 40t + 25) = 0$

Guided Practice

Factor each equation. Is one of the factors a quadratic? Write *yes* or *no*.

7. $x^4 + 5x^3 + 6x^2 = 0$ **yes**   8. $x^3 + 10x^2 + 16x = 0$ **yes**

9. $3m^3 = 2m^2 - 7m$ **yes**   10. $a^3 = 81a + a^5$ **no**

11. $25d^3 + 9d = 30d^2$ **yes**   12. $16t^4 = 40t^2 - 25t$ **no**

State whether each equation can be written in quadratic form.

13. $x^4 + 5x^2 + 3 = 0$ **yes**   14. $6x^4 + 7x = 8$ **no**

15. $6n^4 + 8n^2 = 0$ **yes**   16. $2p + 5\sqrt{p} = 9$ **yes**

Solve each equation.

17. $r^{\frac{1}{3}} = 2$ **8**   18. $x^{\frac{1}{4}} = 3$ **81**   19. $p^{\frac{3}{2}} - 8 = 0$ **4**   20. $k^{\frac{3}{4}} = 27$ **81**

21. $(x^{\frac{1}{2}})^2 - 10(x^{\frac{1}{2}}) + 25 = 0$ 22. $(x^{\frac{1}{3}})^2 - 7(x^{\frac{1}{3}}) + 12 = 0$ 23. $z^2(z^2 + 6z + 8) = 0$

EXERCISES

24. $(y^{\frac{1}{4}})^2 - 10(y^{\frac{1}{4}}) + 16 = 0$ 25. $(r^{\frac{1}{3}})^2 - 5(r^{\frac{1}{3}}) + 6 = 0$

Practice

Write each equation so that it contains a quadratic factor or is in quadratic form.

21. $x - 10x^{\frac{1}{2}} + 25 = 0$ 22. $x^{\frac{4}{3}} - 7x^{\frac{2}{3}} + 12 = 0$

23. $z^4 + 6z^3 + 8z^2 = 0$ 24. $y^{\frac{1}{2}} - 10y^{\frac{1}{4}} + 16 = 0$

25. $r^{\frac{2}{3}} - 5r^{\frac{1}{3}} + 6 = 0$ 26. $s^{\frac{2}{3}} - 9s^{\frac{1}{3}} + 20 = 0$

27. $x^{\frac{1}{2}} + 7x^{\frac{1}{4}} + 12 = 0$ 28. $9y^3 + 16y = -24y^2$

26. $(s^{\frac{1}{3}})^2 - 9(s^{\frac{1}{3}}) + 20 = 0$ 27. $(x^{\frac{1}{4}})^2 + 7(x^{\frac{1}{4}}) + 12 = 0$ 28. $y(9y^2 + 24y + 16) = 0$

Solve each equation.

29. $x^4 + 5x^3 + 6x^2 = 0$ **0, −3, −2**   30. $x^3 + 10x^2 + 16x = 0$ **0, −2, −8**

31. $16x^4 - x^2 = 0$ **0, $\pm\frac{1}{4}$**   32. $a^3 = 81a$ **0, ±9**

342   CHAPTER 7   QUADRATIC EQUATIONS

Additional Answers

51.
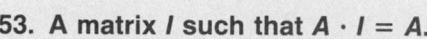

```
−3 | 2   15    22   −15
   |     −6   −27    15
   ---------------------
     2    9    −5  |  0
```

53. A matrix *I* such that $A \cdot I = A$.

$$I_{3\times3} = \begin{bmatrix} 1 & 0 & 0 \\ 0 & 1 & 0 \\ 0 & 0 & 1 \end{bmatrix}$$

54.
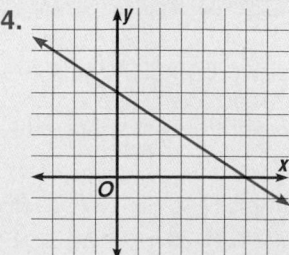

Solve each equation.

B 33. $s^3 = 8$ **$-1 \pm i\sqrt{3}, 2$**   34. $s^4 = 25$ **$\pm\sqrt{5}, \pm i\sqrt{5}$**

35. $b^4 - 5b^2 + 4 = 0$ **$\pm 2, \pm 1$**   36. $y^4 - 3y^2 + 2 = 0$ **$\pm 1, \pm\sqrt{2}$**

37. $a^3 = 125$ **$5, \dfrac{-5 \pm 5i\sqrt{3}}{2}$**   38. $m - 9\sqrt{m} + 8 = 0$ **64, 1**

CONNECTION
Geometry

39. A rectangular prism has a width of w inches. The length is 3 inches more than the width. The height is 4 inches more than the width. The measure of the volume of the prism is 32 times the measure of the length. Find the dimensions of the prism and its volume. **$w = 4$ in., $\ell = 7$ in., $h = 8$ in., $V = 224$ in^3**

Solve each equation. **Teaching Tip ❸**

C 40. $r^{\frac{2}{3}} - 12r^{\frac{1}{3}} + 20 = 0$ **8, 1000**   41. $x^{\frac{2}{3}} - 8x^{\frac{1}{3}} + 15 = 0$ **27, 125**

42. $m - 11m^{\frac{1}{2}} + 30 = 0$ **25, 36**   43. $y^3 - 16y^{\frac{3}{2}} + 64 = 0$ **4**

44. $3g^{\frac{2}{3}} - 10g^{\frac{1}{3}} + 8 = 0$ **$8, \dfrac{64}{27}$**   45. $3m + m^{\frac{1}{2}} - 2 = 0$ **$\dfrac{4}{9}$**

Critical Thinking 46. How would you solve the equation $|a - 4|^2 - 7|a - 4| = -6$? Write an explanation. Then solve the equation. **Explanations will vary. $a = 10, 5, 3, -2$**

Applications 47. **Landscaping** A rectangular lawn has dimensions 24 m by 32 m. A walkway of uniform width will be constructed along the inside edges of all four sides of the lawn. The remaining lawn will have an area of 425 m^2. How wide is the walkway? **3.5 m**

48. **Aeronautics** As an object moves farther from Earth, its weight decreases. The force of gravity decreases with the square of the distance from the center of Earth. The radius R of Earth is about 3960 miles. Let w_E be the weight of a body on Earth, w_S be the weight of a body a certain distance from the center of Earth, and r be the distance of the object above Earth's surface. The formula relating these is $(R + r)^2 = \dfrac{R^2 \cdot w_E}{w_S}$. Determine how far above Earth's surface a 135-pound astronaut is if she weighs 12.5 pounds in space. **155.35 miles**

Mixed Review 49. Solve $x^2 - 3x + 1 = 0$. Then find the sum and the product of the roots to check your solutions. (**Lesson 7-5**) **$\dfrac{3 \pm \sqrt{5}}{2}$**

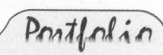
Portfolio

Select an item that shows something new you learned in this chapter and place it in your portfolio.

50. Simplify $\sqrt{600}$. (**Lesson 6-1**) **$10\sqrt{6}$**

51. Use synthetic division to show that $x + 3$ is a factor of $2x^3 + 15x^2 + 22x - 15$. (**Lesson 5-7**) **See margin.**

52. Factor $6a^2 + a - 35$. (**Lesson 5-5**) **$(3a - 7)(2a + 5)$**

53. Define and give an example of an identity matrix. (**Lesson 4-4**) **See margin.**

54. Graph $2x + 3y = 12$. (**Lesson 2-2**) **See margin.**

LESSON 7-6 USING QUADRATIC TECHNIQUES TO SOLVE POLYNOMIALS 343

EXTENDING THE LESSON

Math Power: Reasoning

Solve $\sqrt{y^4 + 48} = 4y$.
Solve using two methods. Why are the solutions all positive?
$y = 2, 2\sqrt{3}$
Because when substituted into the original equation, the negative values do not check.

The Chapter Summary and Review begins with an alphabetical listing of the new terms that were presented in the chapter. Have students define each term and provide an example of it, if appropriate.

The Skills and Concepts presented in the chapter are reviewed using a side-by-side format. Encourage students to refer to the Objectives and Examples on the left as they complete the Review Exercises on the right.

The Chapter Summary and Review ends with exercises that review Applications and Connections.

Additional Answers

2.

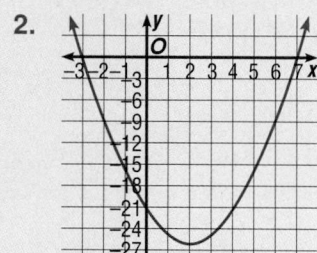

3.

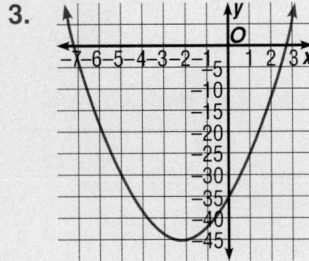

CHAPTER 7 SUMMARY AND REVIEW

VOCABULARY

Upon completing this chapter you should be familiar with the following terms:

completing the square	322	340	quadratic form
degree	316	327	quadratic formula
discriminant	329	316	roots
factoring	317	316	solutions
parabola	317	317	zero product property
quadratic equation	316	317	zeros of a function

SKILLS AND CONCEPTS

OBJECTIVES AND EXAMPLES

Upon completing this chapter, you should be able to:

- solve problems using the guess-and-check strategy **(Lesson 7-1)**

Find two integers whose sum is 8 and whose product is 16.

Guess: 2, 6   Check: $2(6) = 12$, not 16
Guess: 4, 4   Check: $4(4) = 16$ ✓

- solve quadratic equations by factoring or by graphing **(Lesson 7-2)**

Solve $x^2 + 4x + 3 = 0$.
$(x + 3)(x + 1) = 0$
$x = -3$ and $x = -1$

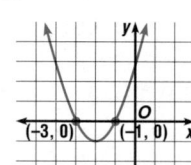

REVIEW EXERCISES

Use these exercises to review and prepare for the chapter test.

1. Write an 8-digit number using each of the digits 1, 2, 3, and 4 twice so that the 1s are separated by 1 digit, the 2s are separated by 2 digits, the 3s are separated by 3 digits, and the 4s are separated by 4 digits. **41312432**

Solve each equation by graphing the related quadratic function. **For graphs, see margin.**

2. $g^2 - 4g - 21 = 0$ **7, –3**
3. $(x + 7)(2x - 5) = 0$ **–7, $\frac{5}{2}$**

Solve each equation by factoring.

4. $2x^2 + 5x + 3 = 0$ **–1, $-\frac{3}{2}$**
5. $4p^2 + 9 = 12p$ **$\frac{3}{2}$**
6. $2x^2 - 8x = 0$ **0, 4**
7. $8b^2 + 10b = 3$ **$\frac{1}{4}, -\frac{3}{2}$**

Alternate Review Strategy

To provide a brief in-class review, you may wish to read the following questions to the class and require a verbal response.

- solve quadratic equations by completing the square (**Lesson 7-3**)

Solve $x^2 + 6x = 12$.

$x^2 + 6x + \underline{\ ?\ } = 12 + \underline{\ ?\ }$
$x^2 + 6x + 9 = 12 + 9$
$(x + 3)^2 = 21$
$x + 3 = \pm\sqrt{21}$ or $x = -3 \pm\sqrt{21}$

Solve each equation by completing the square.

8. $x^2 + 20x + 75 = 0$ **-5, -15**
9. $x^2 - 5x - 24 = 0$ **-3, 8**
10. $2t^2 + t - 21 = 0$ **$-\frac{7}{2}$, 3**
11. $r^2 + 4r = 96$ **-12, 8**

1. Find two integers whose sum is 23 and whose product is 132.
 11, 12
2. Solve $3x^2 + 8x + 4 = 0$ by factoring. $x = -\frac{2}{3}, -2$
3. Solve $x^2 + 3x - 28 = 0$ by completing the square.
 $x = 4, -7$

- solve quadratic equations using the quadratic formula (**Lesson 7-4**)

If $ax^2 + bx + c = 0$, where $a \neq 0$,

$x = \dfrac{-b \pm \sqrt{b^2 - 4ac}}{2a}$.

Solve each equation by using the quadratic formula.

12. $3x^2 - 11x + 10 = 0$ **2, $\frac{5}{3}$**
13. $2p^2 - 5p + 4 = 0$ **13. $\frac{5 \pm i\sqrt{7}}{4}$**
14. $4x^2 - 40x + 25 = 0$ **14. $\frac{10 \pm 5\sqrt{3}}{2}$**
15. $y^2 + 3y = 0$ **0, -3**

4. Solve $2x^2 + 5x - 7 = 0$ by using quadratic formula.
 $x = 1, -\frac{7}{2}$
5. Find the value of the discriminant of $3x^2 + 3x - 1 = 0$. Describe the roots completely. Then find the roots.
 21, 2 real roots, $x = \frac{-3 \pm \sqrt{21}}{6}$

- use the discriminant to determine the nature of the roots of a quadratic equation (**Lesson 7-4**)

Discriminant	Description of Roots
positive	2 real roots
0	1 real root
negative	2 imaginary roots

Find the value of the discriminant of each equation. Describe the roots completely. Then find the roots. **See margin.**

16. $n^2 = 8n - 16$
17. $7b^2 = 4b$
18. $2y^2 + 6y + 5 = 0$

6. Find the sum and product of the roots of $5m^2 - 7m + 4 = 0$.
 sum $= \frac{7}{5}$ product $= \frac{4}{5}$
7. Find a quadratic equation that has the roots 4 and -5.
 $x^2 + x - 20 = 0$
8. Solve $m^3 - 4m^2 + 16m = 0$.
 $m = 0, 2 \pm 2i\sqrt{3}$

- find the sum and product of the roots of a quadratic equation (**Lesson 7-5**)

For $ax^2 + bx + c = 0$ with roots s_1 and s_2,

$s_1 + s_2 = -\dfrac{b}{a}$ and $s_1 s_2 = \dfrac{c}{a}$.

Solve each equation. Find the sum and product of the roots of each quadratic equation.

19. $x^2 - 12x - 45 = 0$ **-3, 15; 12, -45**
20. $2m^2 - 10m + 9 = 0$ **20. $\frac{5 \pm \sqrt{7}}{2}$; 5, $\frac{9}{2}$**
21. $3s^2 - 11 = 0$
 21. $\frac{\pm\sqrt{33}}{3}$; 0, $-\frac{11}{3}$
22. $2x^2 = 3 - 3x$ **22. $\frac{-3 \pm \sqrt{33}}{4}$; $-\frac{3}{2}$, $-\frac{3}{2}$**

- find the quadratic equation given its roots (**Lesson 7-5**)

$s_1 = 7 \quad s_2 = 8$
$s_1 + s_2 = \dfrac{15}{1} = -\dfrac{b}{a}$
$s_1 s_2 = \dfrac{56}{1} = \dfrac{c}{a}$

Therefore, $a = 1$, $b = -15$, $c = 56$.
The equation is $x^2 - 15x + 56 = 0$.

Find a quadratic equation that has the given roots.

23. 4, -6
24. $\frac{3}{4}, \frac{1}{3}$
25. $5 \pm 3i$
26. $2 \pm \sqrt{3}$

23. $x^2 + 2x - 24 = 0$
24. $12x^2 - 13x + 3 = 0$
25. $x^2 - 10x + 34 = 0$
26. $x^2 - 4x + 1 = 0$

Additional Answers

16. **0, 1 real root, rational, 4**
17. **16, 2 real roots; rational;**
 $\frac{4}{7}$, 0
18. **-4; 2 imaginary roots; $\frac{-3 \pm i}{2}$**

The Cumulative Review shown below can be used to review skills and concepts presented thus far in the text. Standardized Test Practice Questions are also provided in the Evaluation Masters Booklet.

Evaluation Masters Booklet, pp. 95–96

■ solve nonquadratic equations using quadratic techniques. (**Lesson 7-6**)

$x^3 - 3x^2 - 54x = 0$
$x(x - 9)(x + 6) = 0$
$x = 0 \quad x = 9 \quad x = -6$

$y - 4\sqrt{y} - 45 = 0$
$(\sqrt{y})^2 - 4(\sqrt{y}) - 45 = 0$
$(\sqrt{y} - 9)(\sqrt{y} + 5) = 0$
$y = 81 \qquad \sqrt{y} + 5 = 0$ has no real solution.

Solve each equation.

27. $3x^3 + 4x^2 - 15x = 0$　$\frac{5}{3}$, **−3, 0**

28. $m^4 + 3m^3 = 40m^2$　**0, 5, −8**

29. $a^3 - 64 = 0$　**4, −2 ± 2i√3**

30. $r + 9\sqrt{r} = -8$　**∅**

31. $x^4 - 8x^2 + 16 = 0$　**2, −2**

32. $x^{\frac{2}{3}} - 9x^{\frac{1}{3}} + 20 = 0$　**64, 125**

～～～APPLICATIONS AND CONNECTIONS～～～

33. **Decorating** Tonniann and Glenn have a family room with a 9 ft by 12 ft rug. A strip of floor of the same width shows on all sides of the rug. If the area of the room is 270 ft², how wide is the strip? (**Lesson 7-2**) **3 feet**

34. **Space Exploration** The Apollo 11 spacecraft propelled the first men to the moon and contained three stages of rockets. The first stage dropped off 2 min 40 s after takeoff and the second stage ignited. The initial velocity of the second stage was 2760 m/s with a constant acceleration of 200 m/s². How long did it take the second stage to travel 7040 m? (**Lesson 7-3**) **about 2.35 seconds**

35. **Aeronautics** A rocket is fired upward from a platform 288 ft above ground level with an initial velocity of 960 ft/s. Find the number of seconds it will take the rocket to reach ground level. (**Lesson 7-4**) **60.3 seconds**

36. **Geometry** Sue, Darlene, and Jeanne mow lawns to earn extra money. Jeanne is going to mow one-third of a 100 ft by 120 ft lawn by mowing a strip of uniform width around the outer edge of the lawn. What is the width of the strip? (**Lesson 7-5**) **10 ft**

Additional Answers, p. 347

7. 0; 1 real, rat'l; $\frac{5}{3}$

8. −8; 2 imag; $\frac{2 \pm i\sqrt{2}}{3}$

9. −15; 2 imag; $\frac{-3 \pm i\sqrt{15}}{4}$

10. 1505; 2 real, irr.; $\frac{-35 \pm \sqrt{1505}}{28}$

11. −20; 2 imag; $\frac{1 \pm i\sqrt{5}}{6}$

12. 289; 2 real, rat'l; 4, $-\frac{5}{3}$

13. 0; 1 real, rat'l; 2

14. 44; 2 real, irr.; $\frac{2 \pm \sqrt{11}}{7}$

15. 5184; 2 real, rat'l; ±9

Solve each equation by graphing. **For graphs, see Solutions Manual.**

1. $a^2 + 8a - 33 = 0$ **3, −11**
2. $7m^2 - 21m = 0$ **0, 3**
3. $5x^2 - 125 = 0$ **5, −5**

Solve each equation by factoring.

4. $6y^2 - y = 15$ **$\frac{5}{3}$, $-\frac{3}{2}$**
5. $3b^2 + b = 14$ **2, $-\frac{7}{3}$**
6. $12p^2 - 5p = 3$ **$\frac{3}{4}$, $-\frac{1}{3}$**

Find the value of the discriminant of each equation. Describe the roots completely. Then solve each equation. **7–15. See margin.**

7. $9a^2 - 30a + 25 = 0$
8. $3x^2 - 4x + 2 = 0$
9. $2x^2 + 3x + 3 = 0$
10. $14r^2 + 35r - 5 = 0$
11. $6t^2 = 2t - 1$
12. $3x^2 - 7x = 20$
13. $n^2 - 4n + 4 = 0$
14. $7k^2 = 4k + 1$
15. $4x^2 = 324$

Find the sum and the product of the roots for each quadratic equation.

16. $2z^2 - 3z - 12 = 0$ **$\frac{3}{2}$, −6**
17. $2x^2 = 3 - 3x$ **$-\frac{3}{2}$, $-\frac{3}{2}$**
18. $n + 7 = 4n^2$ **$\frac{1}{4}$, $-\frac{7}{4}$**

Find a quadratic equation having the given roots.

19. $0, -3$
    $x^2 + 3x = 0$
20. $\frac{4}{3}, \frac{2}{3}$
    $9x^2 - 18x + 8 = 0$
21. $5 + 2i, 5 - 2i$
    $x^2 - 10x + 29 = 0$
22. 8 **$x^2 - 16x + 64 = 0$**

Solve each equation. **23. 0, −4 ± √34**
24. **±√6, ±√3**
26. **$-\frac{27}{8}$, 64**

23. $p^3 + 8p^2 = 18p$
24. $r^4 - 9r^2 + 18 = 0$
25. $2d + 3\sqrt{d} = 9$ **$\frac{9}{4}$**
26. $2m^{\frac{2}{3}} - 5m^{\frac{1}{3}} - 12 = 0$
27. $x^{\frac{1}{2}} - 15x^{\frac{1}{4}} + 50 = 0$ **625, 10,000**
28. $x^3 + 27 = 0$ **$-3, \dfrac{3 \pm 3i\sqrt{3}}{2}$**

29. The Dolphin Pool Company will build a pool for Sally Wadman having a surface area of 600 ft². Ms. Wadman's pool, along with a deck of uniform width, will have dimensions 30 ft by 40 ft. What will be the width of the deck around the pool? **5 ft**

30. A cannonball is shot upward from the upper deck of a fort with an initial velocity of 192 ft/s. The deck is 32 ft above the ground. How long will it take the cannonball to return to the ground? **about 12.16 seconds**

Bonus
In the figure at the right, the shaded rectangle created by the dotted line is similar to the rectangle with the dimensions 1 by x. Write a proportion and solve for x to find the ratio relating the sides of the two rectangles. Round to the nearest thousandth. **$\ell : w = 1 : 0.618$**

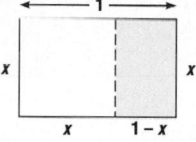

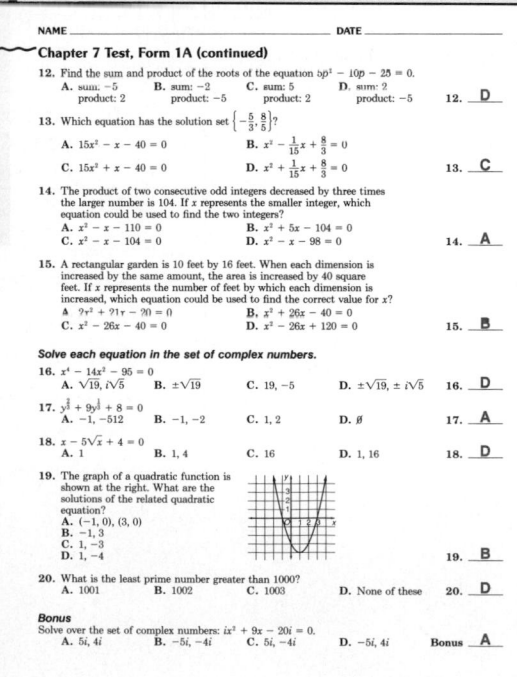

CHAPTER 8

Quadratic Relations and Functions

PREVIEWING THE CHAPTER

The focus of this chapter is on quadratic functions and inequalities. Students begin by identifying and writing equations in quadratic form. They graph quadratic equations for parabolas and learn to designate the vertex, axis of symmetry, and direction of the opening. Students then examine numerous applications of quadratic equations and conclude their work in this chapter by solving quadratic inequalities in one variable.

Problem-Solving Strategy   Students learn to use the strategy *make a table* to organize given data, identify missing data, or to look for a pattern in order to solve problems.

Lesson Objective Chart

Lesson (Pages)	Lesson Objectives	State/Local Objectives
8-1 (353-355)	**8-1A:** Write functions in quadratic form.	
	8-1B: Identify the quadratic term, the linear term, and the constant term of a quadratic function.	
8-2 (356-358)	**8-2:** Solve problems by using tables.	
8-3 (360-364)	**8-3:** Graph quadratic equations of the form $y = (x - h)^2 + k$, and identify the vertex and the equations of the axis of symmetry of a parabola.	
8-4 (366-372)	**8-4A:** Graph equations of the form $y = a(x - h)^2 + k$, and identify the vertex, the equation of the axis of symmetry, and the direction of the opening.	
	8-4B: Determine the equation of a parabola from given information about the graph.	
8-5 (373-378)	**8-5:** Solve problems using quadratic equations.	
8-6 (379-382)	**8-6:** Graph quadratic inequalities.	
8-7 (383-387)	**8-7:** Solve quadratic inequalities in one variable.	

ORGANIZING THE CHAPTER

You may want to refer to the **Course Planning Calendar** on page T44.

Lesson (Pages)	Pacing Chart (days) Course			Reteaching	Practice	Enrichment	Evaluation	Technology	Lab Manual	Mixed Problem Solving	Applications	Cooperative Learning Activity	Multicultural	Transparencies
	I	II	III											
8-1 (353-355)	1	1	0.5	p. 50	p. 57	p. 50								8-1
8-2 (356-358)	1	1	0.5		p. 58		Quiz A, p. 107		pp. 41-42	p. 8				8-2
8-3 (360-364)	1.5	1	1	p. 51	p. 59	p. 51		p. 8				p. 44		8-3
8-4 (366-372)	1.5	1.5	1	p. 52	p. 60	p. 52	Quiz B, p. 107 Mid-Chapter Test, p. 111	p. 25			p. 26			8-4
8-5 (373-378)	1.5	1.5	1	p. 53	p. 61	p. 53	Quiz C, p. 108						p. 0	8-5
8-6 (379-382)	1	1	1	p. 54	p. 62	p. 54								8-6
8-7 (383-387)	1.5	1	1	p. 55	p. 63	p. 55	Quiz D, p. 108							8-7
Review (388-390)	1	1	1	Multiple Choice Tests, Forms 1A and 1B, pp. 99-102 Free Response Tests, Forms 2A and 2B, pp. 103-106										
Test (391)	1	1	1	Cumulative Review, pp. 109-110 Standardized Test Practice Questions, p. 112										

Blackline Masters Booklets — **Activities**

Course I: Chapters 1-13; Course II: Chapters 1-15; Course III: Chapters 1-17

Other Chapter Resources

Student Edition

Chapter Opener, pp. 394-395
Graphing Calculator Exploration, pp. 350-352
Cooperative Learning Activity, p. 358
Graphing Calculator Exploration, p. 359
Technology, p. 365
Mid-Chapter Review, p. 372
History Connection, p. 382
Journal Entries, pp. 354, 382
Portfolio Suggestion, p. 387
College Entrance Exam Preview, pp. 392-393
Extended Project 2, pp. A6-A9

Teacher's Classroom Resources

Transparency 8-0
Real-World Applications Transparencies, 16, 17
Performance Assessment Booklet, pp. 15-16
Problem-of-the-Week Activity Cards, 16, 17
Tech Prep Applications Booklet, pp. 15-16
Lesson Plans, pp. 57-63

Other Supplements

Glencoe Mathematics Professional Series

Software

Test and Review Generator Software (Apple, IBM, and Macintosh)
Interactive Software (Macintosh)
Teacher's Guide for Software Resources

ENHANCING THE CHAPTER

Cooperative Learning

Assigning Roles to Students

Keep in mind that past and current experiences of most students involve competitive rather than cooperative activities. Therefore, remember to be patient as well as persistent in your efforts to develop cooperative interdependence. One way to enhance group skills is to assign each student in the group a specific role. Examples of such roles include a *checker*, who makes sure all members know and can explain the responses, an *encourager*, who motivates silent or reluctant members to participate, a *praiser*, who commends members for good ideas or contributions, a *prober*, who asks questions about or calls for further clarifications of ideas that have been proposed, a *materials handler*, who obtains the necessary items for the activity and then returns them to their proper place, a *recorder*, who writes the group's ideas or answers on paper, and a *help asker*, who requests assistance from the teacher when the group needs it. Other roles may suggest themselves to you to meet certain needs of a particular activity or student. For example, a group member who has difficulty remaining quiet can be assigned the role of *noise monitor*, who uses a non-verbal signal to remind the members to quiet down.

Technology

The BASIC program in the Technology Feature of this chapter enables students to graph a parabola after being given the graphing parameters needed to sketch the graph. Have students compare the results of this program to the actual graphs obtained with a graphing calculator.

Critical Thinking

Grasp every opportunity to eliminate from the minds of students any notion that success in mathematics is achieved by memorizing a series of arbitrary tricks and stratagems. Utilize discussions during which students explain their reasoning, justify their responses, and relate concepts and skills to other areas of mathematics as well as to other content areas and real-life experiences. Also, encourage students to always suggest alternative procedures. When working with the content in this chapter, for example, you may wish to have students research and report on the history of quadratic equations during which they will discover that such equations were solved arithmetically by the ancient Egyptians and geometrically by Euclid.

Cooperative Learning, p. 44

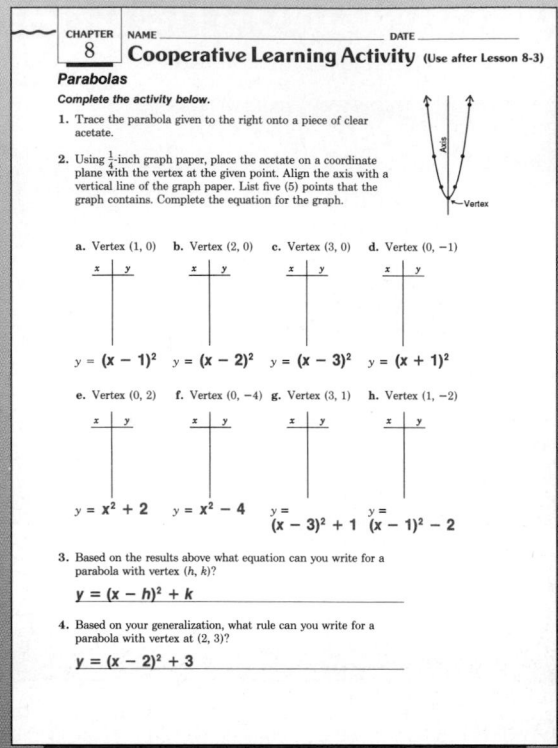

Technology, p. 25

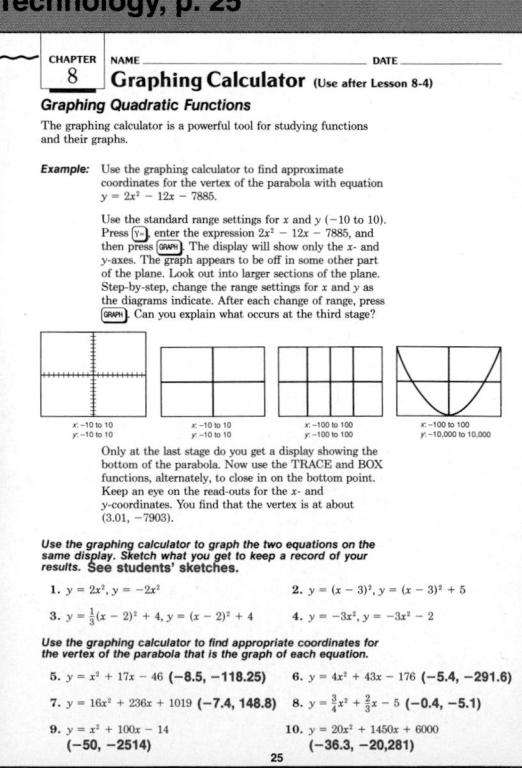

Problem of the Week Activity

The card shown below is one of two available for this chapter. It can be used as a class or small group activity.

Activity Card

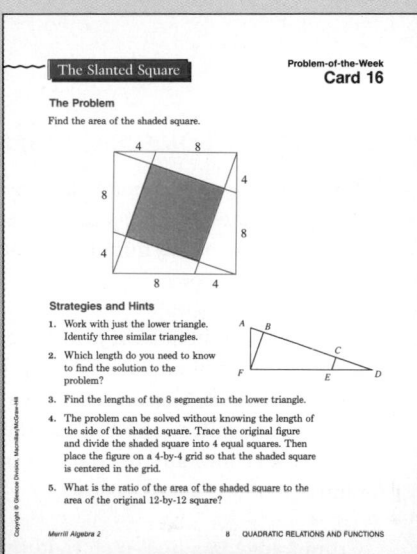

Manipulatives and Models

The following materials may be used as models or manipulatives in Chapter 8.

geoboard (Lesson 8-1)
coin (Lesson 8-2)
paper chains (Lesson 8-2)
ball (Lesson 8-3)
graphing calculator (Lesson 8-4)
paper and scissors (Lesson 8-5)

Outside Resources

Books/Periodicals

Cole, R.J. *Vector Methods*. Van Nostrand Reinhold Company.

Ekeland, Ivar. *Mathematics and the Unexpected*. The University of Chicago Press.

Films/Videotapes/Videodiscs

Quadratic Functions Part 1 and *Part 2*, Maryland Center for Public Broadcasting, Program Sales Department, Owings Mill, MD 21117

Software

Graphic Wiz and *Bradford GraphMaker*, William K. Bradford Publishing Company, 310 School St., Acton, MA 01720

Mathematics Exploration Toolkit, IBM, 4111 Northside Pkwy. NW, P.O. Box 2150, Atlanta, GA 30327-3015

Multicultural

Multicultural Activity, p. 8

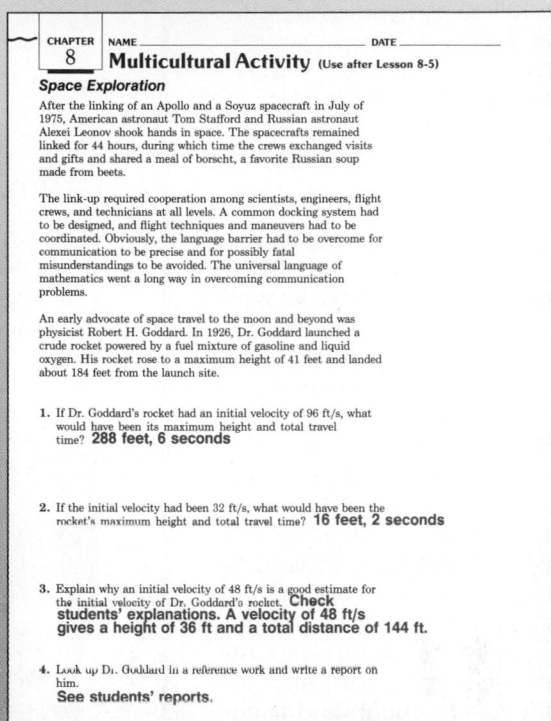

Lab Manual

Lab Activity, pp. 41-42

Using the Chapter Opener

Transparency 8–0 is available in the Transparency Package. It provides a full-color visual and motivational activity that you can use to engage students in the mathematical content of the chapter.

Background Information

Criminologists apply scientific principles and hi-tech instruments to the examination and identification of evidence related to crimes. They test and classify explosives, firearms, and other weapons, and interpret laboratory findings on drugs and poisons. The tool of such scientific examination and technology is mathematics, lots of mathematics. Criminologists must be able to interpret statistical data, analyze probabilities, perform the complex calculations required by hi-tech devices, select mathematical methods and models, and come up with thorough and accurate answers.

Quadratic Relations and Functions

CHAPTER OBJECTIVES

In this chapter, you will:
- Graph quadratic functions.
- Solve problems using quadratic equations.
- Solve quadratic inequalities.

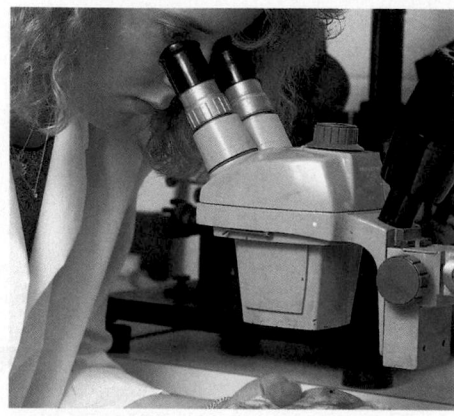

Which type of crime has escalated in the past twenty years?

Crime rate In the United States
Rate per 100,000 population

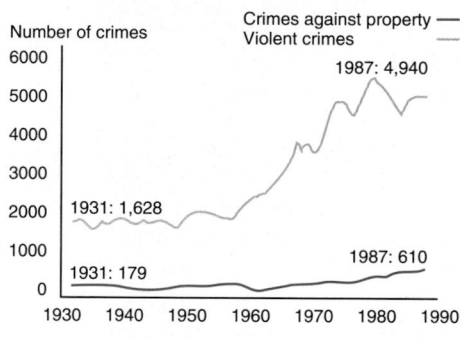

- Crimes against property —
- Violent crimes —

Number of crimes

1987: 4,940

1931: 1,628

1931: 179

1987: 610

1930 1940 1950 1960 1970 1980 1990

348

CAREERS IN FORENSIC SCIENCE

Every 10 seconds, a premise somewhere in the United States is burglarized. Every 22 seconds, a car is stolen. Every 25 minutes, someone is murdered.

If you want to help fight crime, perhaps you'll select the career of criminalist, also known as forensic scientist. A criminalist uses scientific techniques to collect and analyze the physical evidence of crimes and testifies about his or her findings in court.

Criminology is a high-tech field these days. A hundred years ago, a real-life counterpart of the fictional Sherlock Holmes could scrape up a bit of cigarette ash with a trusty penknife and briefly examine it with a hand-held magnifying glass before declaring "Aha! The villain has delivered himself into our hands!" Today, that same bit of ash would have to be analyzed by a spectrophotometer and a gas chromatograph. In the case of blood and other body fluids, the criminalist prepares a DNA profile and does a protein marker analysis to help identify the criminal. Even fingerprints can be lifted by the laser today. It's a demanding job, but one that is filled with mystery, discovery, and satisfaction.

Chapter Project

Materials: Paper and pencil, library resources, play props

Organize students into pairs of criminologists. Assign each pair the task of selecting and researching at least one of the following areas of crime investigation.

- Fingerprinting, including "DNA fingerprinting"
- Blood analysis
- Toxicology
- Firearms and/or explosives
- Handwriting
- Plaster imprints
- Hi-tech instrumentation

Then have two or more pairs of students combine their research

and report it to the class in the form of a play that they have written and rehearsed. The play should present a crime (real or fictitious) to the class in the setting of a courtroom with one student playing the criminologist and testifying as the expert witness. Other students are to fill roles as prosecuting and defense attorneys, witnesses, victims, and so on.

MORE ABOUT FORENSIC SCIENCE

Degree Required:

- Bachelor's degree in biochemistry, biophysics, or chemistry, with study in forensic science

Some criminalists like:

- doing work that is challenging and intellectually stimulating
- the great deal of variety in their work
- good pay

Related Math Subjects:

- Advanced Algebra
- Trigonometry
- Probability/Statistics
- Calculus

Some criminalists dislike:

- the stiff competition for jobs
- having to testify in court
- the difficulty to advance beyond a certain level

For more information about the various careers available in the field of Forensic Science, write to:

American Academy of Forensic Sciences
218 East Cache LaPoudre
Colorado Springs, CO 80903

Connections and Applications

Lesson	Connections (C) and Applications (A)	Examples	Exercises
8-1	C: Geometry		31, 33-34, 37-38
	A: Entertainment	2	41
	Business		40
	Physics		47
8-2	A: Business	1	
8-3	C: Geometry	3	
	A: Physics		47
	Sports		48
8-4	A: Sports	4	
	Architecture		44
8-5	C: Geometry		12-13, 22
	A: Business	2	6, 26
	Physics		25
8-6	C: Geometry	2	28
	A: Forensic Science		30
	Sports		31
	Astronomy		36
8-7	C: Physics	1	
	Number Theory		56
	A: Sports		47
	Landscaping		48
	Business		49

349

Objective: Graph and explore similarities between parabolas on a graphing calculator.

Motivating the Lesson

Ask each student to sketch a parabola in a standard viewing window drawn on a piece of paper. Then draw a standard viewing window on the chalkboard or overhead and have each student draw his or her parabola on it. Explain that all of these are related and are members of the family of parabolas.

Teaching Tip ❶ Make sure all three graphs are turned on (or the "=" is black) when you graph the functions.

Teaching Tip ❷ This is [SHIFT] [Cls] [EXE] .

Graphing Calculator Exploration: Families of Parabolas

In geometry, a collection of related geometric configurations is referred to as a *family*. Likewise, there are families of parabolas. The equations of the parabolas in these families are closely related. In the general form of a quadratic equation, $y = a(x - h)^2 + k$, the parameters are a, h, and k. Changing a parameter in an equation results in a different parabola in the family.

Example 1

Graph the following equations on one set of axes and describe the similarities and differences between the graphs. $y = x^2$, $y = x^2 + 3$, $y = x^2 - 5$. *The k values for these equations are 0, 3, and -5 respectively.*

Graph each of the equations. Make sure your calculator is set for the standard viewing window. *If you are using a TI-81, make sure all old equations are cleared from the Y = list before graphing.*

Casio

ENTER: [GRAPH] [ALPHA] [X] [x²] [:] [GRAPH]
[ALPHA] [X] [x²] [+] 3 [:] [GRAPH]
[ALPHA] [X] [x²] [−] 5 [EXE]

TI-81 **Teaching Tip ❶**

ENTER: [Y=] [X|T] [x²] [ENTER] [X|T] [x²] [+] 3
[ENTER] [X|T] [x²] [−] 5 [GRAPH]

The graphs are all the same shape, all open upward, and all have their vertex on the y-axis. The graphs have different vertical positions.

Example 1 shows that changing the k value in an equation translates the parabola vertically. If $k > 0$, the parabola is translated k units upward and if $k < 0$, it is translated k units downward. How do you think changing the value of h will change the graphs in a family of parabolas?

Example 2

Graph the following equations on one set of axes and describe the similarities and differences between the graphs. $y = x^2$, $y = (x - 4)^2$, $y = (x + 2)^2$ *The h values for these equations are 0, 4, and -2 respectively.*

Graph the equations. *If you are using a Casio fx-7000G, be sure to clear the graphics screen before graphing.* **Teaching Tip ❷**

Casio

ENTER: [GRAPH] [ALPHA] [X] [x²] [:] [GRAPH] [(] [ALPHA] [X] [−] 4 [)]
[x²] [:] [GRAPH] [(] [ALPHA] [X] [+] 2 [)] [x²] [EXE]

ALTERNATE TEACHING STRATEGIES

Using Connections

The graphing calculator gives an opportunity to investigate transformations. The values of h and k define a translation. Many students will have difficulty understanding why the parabola will move to the right or in a positive direction if the value of h in $x - h$ is positive and to the left or in a negative direction if h is negative. Try to explain using the base equation. If h is positive the $x - h$ will remain this way, but if h is negative, we will be looking at $x - (-h)$ or $x + h$.

TI-81

ENTER:

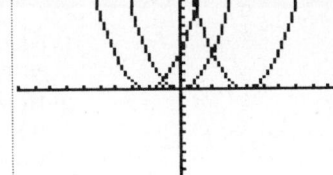

GRAPH

The graphs have the same shape, all open upward, and all have their vertices on the x-axis. The graphs have different horizontal positions.

Example 2 demonstrates that changing the h value in $y = a(x - h)^2 + k$, translates the graph horizontally. If $h > 0$, the graph translates to the right h units and if $h < 0$, the graph translates to the left h units.

Changing the value of a in the equation $y = a(x - h)^2 + k$ affects the direction of opening and the shape of the graph. If $a > 0$, the graph opens upward and if $a < 0$ the graph opens downward. If $|a| < 1$ the graph is wider than the graph of $y = x^2$ and if $|a| > 1$ the graph is narrower than the graph of $y = x^2$. Graphs of equations with a values with the same absolute value, such as $y - 3x^2$ and $y = 3x^2$ have the same shape.

Example 3

Graph the following equations on one set of axes and describe the similarities and differences between the graphs $y = x^2$, $y = -x^2$, $y = 0.5x^2$, $y = -2x^2$:

Casio

ENTER: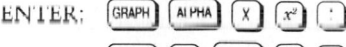

TI 81

ENTER:

The graphs of $y = x^2$ and $y = 0.5x^2$ open upward, and the graphs of $y = -x^2$ and $y = -2x^2$ open downward. The graphs of $y = x^2$ and $y = -x^2$ have the same shape. The graph of $y = 0.5x^2$ is wider than the graph of $y = x^2$. The graph of $y = -2x^2$ is narrower than the graph of $y = -x^2$, or the graph of $y = x^2$.

GRAPHING CALCULATOR EXPLORATION: FAMILIES OF PARABOLAS   351

RETEACHING THE LESSON

You may want to graph fewer than four equations at once for Example 3. It may be difficult for students to see and remember which graph corresponds to each equation. Try graphing $y = x^2$ with each graph separately.

More Examples

1. Graph the following equations on one set of axes and describe the similarities and differences between the graphs.

$y = x^2$, $y = x^2 + 4$,
$y = x^2 - 2.5$

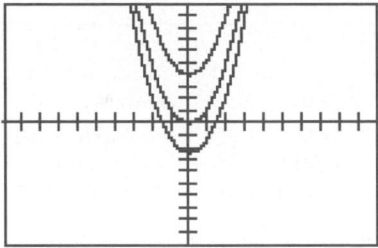

2. Graph the following equations on one set of axes and describe the similarities and differences between the graphs.

$y = x^2$, $y = (x - 2)^2$,
$y = (x - (-3))^2$

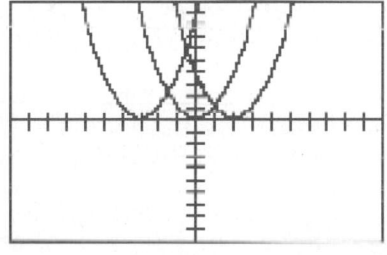

EVALUATING THE LESSON

Closing the Lesson

Writing Activity Have each student write and graph an equation that moves a parabola in a specific direction and changes shape from the graph of $y = x^2$. For example, tell students that you want an equation that will move the graph of $y = x^2$ up, to the right, and skinnier. One equation would be $y = 3(x - 2)^2 + 3$, but students' answers will vary.

Homework Exercises

Assignment Guide

Basic: 1–3, 5–35 odd
Average: 1–3, 4–36 even
Enriched: 1–3, 4–36 even

Additional Answers

1. translates the graph vertically
2. translates the graph horizontally
3. They have the same shape and vertex, but one opens upward and one opens downward.
4. 8 units to the left
5. 5 units to the right
6. 6 units below
7. 8 units above
8. 2 units to the right
9. 7 units below
10. 10 units to the right, 9 units above
11. 6 units to the left, 5 units below
12. 11 units to the right, 7 units below
13. 9 units to the left, 4 units above
14. narrower
15. wider
16. opens upward not downward
17. narrower
18. narrower, opens downward not upward
19. wider, opens downward not upward
20. wider
21. 8 units to the right, narrower

28. $|h|$ units to the left or right
29. $|k|$ units above or below
30. $|k|$ units above or below
31. $|h|$ units to the left or right
32. $|h|$ units to the left or right and $|k|$ units above or below
33. narrower if $|a| > 1$, wider if $|a| < 1$, opens downward not upward if $a < 0$
34. narrower if $|a| > 1$, wider if $|a| < 1$, opens downward not upward if $a < 0$
35. narrower if $|a| > 1$, wider if $|a| < 1$, opens downward not upward if $a < 0$
36. $|h|$ units to the left or right, $|k|$ units above or below, narrower if $|a| > 1$, wider if $|a| < 1$, opens downward not upward if $a < 0$

EXERCISES

1. Describe the effect that changing the value of k in an equation of the form $y = a(x - h)^2 + k$ has on the graph of the equation. **See margin.**
2. How does changing the value of h in an equation of the form $y = a(x - h)^2 + k$ affect the graph of the equation? **See margin.**
3. How do the graphs of $y = a(x - h)^2 + k$ and $y = -a(x - h)^2 + k$ compare? **See margin.**

Use your graphing calculator to graph each pair of equations on the same set of axes. Then compare the graph of the first equation to the graph of the second equation. **See margin.**

4. $y = (x + 8)^2$, $y = x^2$
5. $y = (x - 5)^2$, $y = x^2$
6. $y = x^2 - 6$, $y = x^2$
7. $y = x^2 + 8$, $y = x^2$
8. $y = (x - 2)^2 + 8$, $y = x^2 + 8$
9. $y = (x - 4)^2 - 7$, $y = (x - 4)^2$
10. $y = (x - 10)^2 + 9$, $y = x^2$
11. $y = (x + 6)^2 - 5$, $y = x^2$
12. $y = (x - 11)^2 - 7$, $y = x^2$
13. $y = (x + 9)^2 + 4$, $y = x^2$
14. $y = 2x^2$, $y = x^2$
15. $y = 0.75x^2$, $y = x^2$
16. $y = 3x^2$, $y = -3x^2$
17. $y = 5x^2 + 1$, $y = x^2 + 1$
18. $y = -\frac{5}{3}x^2$, $y = x^2$
19. $y = -0.55x^2 - 10$, $y = x^2 - 10$
20. $y = 0.375(x + 2)^2$, $y = (x + 2)^2$
21. $y = \frac{19}{6}(x - 8)^2$, $y = x^2$
22. $y = -7(x - 13)^2$, $y = (x - 13)^2$
23. $y = \frac{6}{7}(x + 5)^2$, $y = x^2$
24. $y = 3(x - 9)^2 + 5$, $y = (x - 9)^2 + 5$
25. $y = -0.1(x + 1)^2 + 3$, $y = (x + 1)^2 + 3$
26. $y = \frac{5}{2}(x - 3)^2 - 9$, $y = x^2$
27. $y = -\frac{3}{4}(x + 12)^2 - 12$, $y = x^2$

Use the results of Exercises 4–27 to answer each question. Assume that a, h, and k are real numbers and $a \neq 0$. **See margin.**

28. How does the graph of $y = (x - h)^2$ compare to the graph of $y = x^2$?
29. How does the graph of $y = x^2 + k$ compare to the graph of $y = x^2$?
30. How does the graph of $y = (x - h)^2 + k$ compare to the graph of $y = (x - h)^2$?
31. How does the graph of $y = (x - h)^2 + k$ compare to the graph of $y = x^2 + k$?
32. How does the graph of $y = (x - h)^2 + k$ compare to the graph of $y = x^2$?
33. How does the graph of $y = ax^2$ compare to the graph of $y = x^2$?
34. How does the graph of $y = ax^2 + k$ compare to the graph of $y = x^2 + k$?
35. How does the graph of $y = a(x - h)^2 + k$ compare to the graph of $y = (x - h)^2 + k$?
36. How does the graph of $y = a(x - h)^2 + k$ compare to the graph of $y = x^2$?

352　CHAPTER 8　QUADRATIC RELATIONS AND FUNCTIONS

EXTENDING THE LESSON

Math Power: Connections

Try to think of other families of geometric shapes or families of graphs, such as triangles, squares, ovals, cubics, and so on. Discuss how some families contain other families, like the rectangle family contains the square family. Try to get the students to experiment with graphing different equations, such as cubic equations, or odd-powered equations.

Additional Answers

22. narrower, opens downward not upward
23. 5 units to the left, wider
24. narrower
25. wider, opens downward not upward
26. 3 units to the right, 9 units below, narrower
27. 12 units to the left, 12 units below; wider, opens downward not upward

8-1 Quadratic Functions

Objectives

8-1A
- write functions in quadratic form, and

8-1B
- identify the quadratic term, the linear term, and the constant term of a quadratic function.

After studying this lesson, you should be able to:

Application

Mike and Rich are conducting a physics experiment. They will launch a model rocket and use a formula to find the maximum height that the rocket reaches based on the time that it takes for it to land. The rocket they are launching is to have an initial velocity of 160 feet per second. According to the formula, the height of the rocket, $h(t)$, t seconds after it is launched is given by the function $h(t) = 160t - 16t^2$. This function is a quadratic function. You will graph and solve this function in Lesson 8-3.

Definition of Quadratic Function	A quadratic function is a function described by an equation that can be written in the form $f(x) = ax^2 + bx + c$ where $a \neq 0$.

In a quadratic function, ax^2 is called the **quadratic term**, bx is the **linear term**, and c is the **constant term**.

Example 1

Write $f(x) = (x + 2)^2 - 6$ in quadratic form. Identify the quadratic term, the linear term, and the constant term.

$f(x) = (x + 2)^2 - 6 \ \blacktriangleright \ x^2 + 4x + 4 - 6 \ \text{ or } \ x^2 + 4x - 2$

The quadratic term is x^2, the linear term is $4x$, and the constant term is -2.

Example 2

APPLICATION

Entertainment

FYI ...

The *Return of the Jedi* holds the record for the highest gross movie ticket sales for one day, $8,440,105.

The four theaters in the Studio 25 Cinema have 125 seats each. Based on previous experience, the owner estimates that for each 50¢ increase in the ticket price 20 fewer people will attend a show. Each showing is sold out at the current price of $5.00 a seat. Define a variable and write a quadratic function to describe the Cinema's income after any number of price increases.

Let n represent the number of 50¢ price increases. So, $5.00 + 0.50n$ is the ticket price after n increases.

There are 4 × 125 or 500 seats in the cinema. $500 - 20n$ is the number of people who will attend a show after n price increases.

Income = (ticket price)(number of people attending)

$$I(n) = (5.00 + 0.50n)(500 - 20n)$$
$$= 2500 - 100n + 250n - 10n^2$$
$$= 2500 + 150n - 10n^2$$

RETEACHING THE LESSON

To help identify terms and coefficients of quadratic functions, use the table below.

quadratic	terms		
function	quad.	linear	const.

Replace "terms" with "coefficients" in a similar table.

TEACHING THE LESSON

Chalkboard Examples

For Example 1

Express the following function in quadratic form. Then identify the quadratic, linear, and constant terms.
$f(x) = 3(x + 2)^2$
$f(x) = 3x^2 + 12x + 12$; $3x^2$; $12x$; 12

For Example 2

Kwan Lee has 140 feet of fence to put around a rectangular garden. She will use the side of her house for one side of the garden. Define a variable and write a quadratic function to describe the area of her garden.
s = length of side adjacent to the house; $f(s) = 140s - 2s^2$

Practice Masters Booklet, p. 57

NAME _____ DATE _____

8-1 Practice Worksheet

Quadratic Functions

Write each function in quadratic form.

1. $f(x) = (x + 7)^2$
   $f(x) = x^2 + 14x + 49$

2. $f(x) = (4x - 3)^2$
   $f(x) = 16x^2 - 24x + 9$

3. $f(x) = -3(2x + 1)^2$
   $f(x) = -12x^2 - 12x - 3$

4. $f(x) = 6(3x + 1)^2 + 4$
   $f(x) = 54x^2 + 36x + 10$

5. $f(x) = \frac{1}{2}(4x - 5)^2 - 3$
   $f(x) = 8x^2 - 20x + \frac{19}{2}$

6. $f(x) = -\frac{2}{3}(x - 6)^2 + 4$
   $f(x) = -\frac{2}{3}x^2 + 8x - 20$

7. $f(x) = 2(3x - 1)^2 + 6$
   $f(x) = 18x^2 - 12x + 8$

8. $f(x) = -3(x + 7)^2 - 8$
   $f(x) = -3x^2 - 42x - 155$

9. $f(x) = \frac{1}{2}(2x - 6)^2 + 4$
   $f(x) = 2x^2 - 12x + 22$

10. $f(x) = -\frac{3}{4}(2x + 8)^2 - 1$
    $f(x) = -3x^2 - 24x - 49$

Define a variable and write a quadratic function to describe each situation.

11. the product of two numbers whose difference is 6
    Let x = the larger number; $f(x) = x^2 - 6x$

12. the area of a rectangle whose perimeter is 20 feet
    Let x = the length; $f(x) = -x^2 + 10x$

13. A movie theatre averages 160 customers per show. The charge is $6.00 per person. The owner estimates that for each $0.50 decrease in price, 20 more people will attend each show. Write a quadratic function to describe the owner's ticket income after the price is decreased.
    Let x = the number of $0.50 decreases;
    $f(x) = -10x^2 + 40x + 960$

14. Wanda wants to put fencing around a rectangular garden. One side of the garden is her house. She has 70 feet of fencing for the other 3 sides. Write a quadratic function to describe the area of the garden.
    Let x = the length of the two sides that are the same; $f(x) = -2x^2 + 70x$

CHECKING FOR UNDERSTANDING

Communicating Mathematics

Read and study the lesson to answer these questions.

1. Name the quadratic term, the linear term, and the constant term of the quadratic function found in Example 2. **Q: $-10n^2$, L: $150n$, C: 2500**

2. Explain the steps you would use to write $f(x) = 4(x - 1)^2 - 1$ in quadratic form. **See margin.**

3. Is the equation $f(x) = 3(x - 2)^2 + 5$ in quadratic form? If not, write the function in quadratic form. **no; $3x^2 - 12x + 17$**

Guided Practice

State whether each equation describes a quadratic function.

4. $f(x) = x^2 - 5x + 2$ **yes**

5. $m(x) = -4x^2 - 6x - 2$ **yes**

6. $g(x) = 3x + 3$ **no**

7. $f(x) = (x - 4)^2$ **yes**

8. $f(x) = 2(x + 5)^2 + 7$ **yes**

9. $p(x) = x$ **no**

10. $g(x) = -\frac{1}{3}x + \frac{4}{5}$ **no**

11. $f(x) = \frac{1}{x^2} + \frac{1}{x} = 1$ **no**

Journal
Tell what your favorite sport is and how mathematics is used in it.

For each function, identify the quadratic term, the linear term, and the constant term.

12. $f(x) = x^2 + x - 4$ **x^2; x; -4**

13. $g(x) = 5x^2 - 7x + 2$ **$5x^2$; $-7x$; 2**

14. $g(n) = 3n^2 - 1$ **$3n^2$; 0; -1**

15. $f(n) = \frac{1}{3}n^2 + 4$ **$\frac{1}{3}n^2$; 0; 4**

16. $n(x) = -4x^2 - 8x - 9$ **$-4x^2$; $-8x$; -9**

17. $f(z) = z^2 + 3z$ **z^2; $3z$; 0**

18. $f(x) = (x + 3)^2$ **x^2; $6x$; 9**

19. $f(t) = (3t + 1)^2 - 8$ **$9t^2$; $6t$; -7**

20. $g(x) = x^2 - 2x + 1$

21. $f(x) = x^2 - 6x + 9$

22. $f(m) = 4m^2 - 20m + 25$

23. $h(x) = 9x^2 + 12x + 4$

EXERCISES

Practice

24. $f(r) = 3r^2 - 12r + 12$

25. $f(x) = -16x^2 + 64x - 64$

26. $g(x) = 32x^2 + 16x + 2$

27. $f(x) = 4x^2 + 8x + 14$

Write each function in quadratic form.

20. $g(x) = (x - 1)^2$

21. $f(x) = (x - 3)^2$

22. $f(m) = (2m - 5)^2$

23. $h(x) = (3x + 2)^2$

24. $f(r) = 3(r - 2)^2$

25. $f(x) = -4(2x - 4)^2$

26. $g(x) = 2(4x + 1)^2$

27. $f(x) = 4(x + 1)^2 + 10$

28. $f(x) = -3(2x + 2)^2 + 6$
    $f(x) = -12x^2 - 24x - 6$

29. $g(x) = \frac{1}{6}(6x + 12)^2 + 5$
    $g(x) = 6x^2 + 24x + 29$

Define a variable and write a quadratic function to describe each situation.

30–36. See margin.

CONNECTION
Geometry

30. the product of two numbers whose sum is 45

31. the area of a circle in terms of its radius

32. the product of two numbers whose difference is 15

33. the area of an isosceles right triangle in terms of the measure of its legs

34. the area of a rectangle whose perimeter is 30 centimeters

35. the sum of the squares of two numbers whose sum is 10

36. the sum of the squares of two numbers whose difference is 18

354   CHAPTER 8   QUADRATIC RELATIONS AND FUNCTIONS

Additional Answers

2. $f(x) = 4(x - 1)^2 - 1$
   $= 4(x^2 - 2x + 1) - 1$
   $= 4x^2 - 8x + 4 - 1$
   $= 4x^2 - 8x + 3$

30. n = one of the numbers;
    product = $45n - n^2$

31. r = the radius; area = πr^2

32. n = one of the numbers;
    product = $n^2 + 15n$

33. s = the measure of the length of a leg; area = $\frac{1}{2}s^2$

34. l = the length; area = $15l - l^2$

35. x = one of the numbers;
    sum = $2x^2 - 20x + 100$

36. x = the lesser number;
    sum = $2x^2 + 36x + 324$

39. $x = 2n + 1$
    $x^2 - 1 = (2n + 1)^2 - 1$
    $= 4n^2 + 4n + 1 - 1$
    $= 4n^2 + 4n$
    $= 4n(n + 1)$

This number is divisible by 4 since $4n$ is. We can rewrite the number as $4(n)(n + 1)$. Since either n or $(n + 1)$ must be even, this product must contain another factor of 2. Therefore, it must be divisible by 4×2 or 8.

CONNECTION
Geometry

37. Mr. Gordon bought 100 feet of fencing material to build a kennel for his dog. Write a quadratic function to represent the area of the kennel. **w = the width of the kennel; area = $50w - w^2$**

38. Cheryl is going to wallpaper her bedroom walls. The perimeter of the room is $4x + 10$ feet. Write a quadratic function to represent the amount of wallpaper in square feet Cheryl will need if the height of the walls is x feet. **$a(x) = 4x^2 + 10x$**

Critical Thinking

39. Prove that $x^2 - 1$ is always divisible by 8 if x is an odd number.
Hint: Substitute $2n + 1$ for x, since $2n + 1$ is always odd.
See margin.

Applications

40. **Business** Ernie Burton runs a shuttle bus between the airport and the convention center. About 300 passengers ride the shuttle per week. He plans to raise the $8.00 charge. But, based on past experience, he estimates that he will lose 20 passengers per week to the competition for each $1 he increases the fare. Write a quadratic function to describe Mr. Burton's income after he raises the fare. **$I(p) = 2400 + 140p - 20p^2$**

41. **Entertainment** The Darien High School winter play brought in $800 last year. This year, the drama teacher intends to raise the $4.00 ticket price. It is estimated that for each 25¢ increase in the price 10 fewer people will come to the play. Write a quadratic function to describe the income after the price increase. **$I(p) = 800 + 10p - 2.5p^2$**

Mixed Review

42. Express the equation $x^6 + 3x^3 - 10 = 0$ in quadratic form. (**Lesson 7-6**)
$1(x^3)^2 + 3(x^3) - 10 = 0$

43. Solve the equation $a - 4a^{\frac{1}{2}} + 3 = 0$.
(**Lesson 7-6**) **1 or 9**

44. Find the product of the complex number $2 + 9i$ and its conjugate. (**Lesson 6-10**) **85**

45. Evaluate the expression $(0.0016)^{\frac{1}{4}}$.
(**Lesson 6-4**) **0.2**

46. Divide $(x^3 - 2.8)$ by $(x + 0.4)$ using synthetic division. (**Lesson 5-7**)
$x^2 - 0.4x + 0.16 - \dfrac{2.864}{x + 0.4}$

47. **Physics** Light from a laser will travel about 300,000 kilometers per second. How many kilometers will it travel in a day? (**Lesson 5-1**)
2.592×10^{10} km/day

48. Use a matrix equation to solve
$\begin{cases} 4x + y = -5 \\ x + 4y = 10 \end{cases}$. (**Lesson 4-6**) **(-2, 3)**

LESSON 8-1 QUADRATIC FUNCTIONS **355**

EVALUATING THE LESSON

Checking for Understanding

Exercises 1–19 are designed to help you assess understanding through reading, writing, and speaking. You should work through Exercises 1–3 with your students, and then monitor their work on Exercises 4–19.

Closing the Lesson

Writing Activity Have students write a sentence or two explaining why $a \neq 0$ is in the quadratic form.

APPLYING THE LESSON

Homework Exercises

Assignment Guide

Basic: 20–33, 39–40, 42–48
Average: 23–36, 39–48
Enriched: 26–48

Enrichment Masters Booklet, p. 50

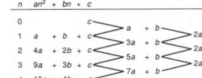

8-1 **Enrichment Worksheet**
NAME _____ DATE _____

Quadratic Formulas for Sequences

An ordinary arithmetic sequence is formed using a rule such as $bn + c$. The first term is c, b is called the common difference, and n takes on the values 0, 1, 2, 3, and so on. The value of term $n + 1$ equals $b(n + 1) + c$ or $bn + b + c$. So, the value of a term is a function of the term number.

Some sequences use quadratic functions. A method called *finite differences* can be used to find the values of the terms. Notice what happens when you subtract twice as shown in this table.

n	$an^2 + bn + c$		
0	c	$a + b$	
1	$a + b + c$	$3a + b$	$2a$
2	$4a + 2b + c$	$5a + b$	$2a$
3	$9a + 3b + c$	$7a + b$	$2a$
4	$16a + 4b + c$		

A sequence that yields a common difference after two subtractions can be generated by a quadratic expression. For example, the sequence 1, 5, 12, 22, 35, . . . gives a common difference of 3 after two subtractions. Using the table above, you write and solve three equations to find the general rule. The equations are $1 = c$, $5 = a + b + c$, and $12 = 4a + 2b + c$.

Solve each problem.

1. Refer to the sequence in the example above. Solve the system of equations for a, b, and c and then find the quadratic expression for the sequence. Then write the next three terms.
$\frac{3}{2}n^2 + \frac{5}{2}n + 1$; 51, 70, 92

2. The number of line segments connecting n points forms the sequence 0, 0, 1, 3, 6, 10, . . . , in which n is the number of points and the term value is the number of line segments. What is the common difference after the second subtraction? Find a quadratic expression for the term value.
$1; \frac{1}{2}n^2 - \frac{1}{2}n$

3. The maximum number of regions formed by n chords in a circle forms the sequence 1, 2, 4, 7, 11, 16, . . . (A chord is a line segment joining any two points on a circle.) Draw circles to illustrate the first four terms of the sequence. Then find a quadratic expression for the term value.

    $\frac{1}{2}n^2 + \frac{1}{2}n + 1$

EXTENDING THE LESSON

Math Power:
Problem Solving

A photography store owner can sell 21 cameras at $120.00 each. She estimates that for each $5.00 decrease in price she will sell three more cameras. She buys the cameras from a wholesale dealer at a rate $75.00 each. If she sells as many cameras as she buys, write a quadratic function to describe the owner's profit after she decreases the price. **profit = $945 + 30n - 15n^2$**

8-2 Lesson Notes

Lesson Resources
Practice Master 8-2
Lab Manual, pp. 41–42
Activity Master, p. 8

 Transparency 8-2 contains the 5-Minute Check and a teaching aid for this lesson.

INTRODUCING THE LESSON

 5-Minute Check

(over Lesson 8-1)

1. Write the function $f(x) = (x - 3)^2 + 5$ in quadratic form. $f(x) = x^2 - 6x + 14$
2. Identify the quadratic, linear, and constant terms for the function in Exercise 1. x^2; $-6x$; 14
3. Write $f(x) = -3(x + 0.25)^2 + 0.2$ in quadratic form. $f(x) = -3x^2 - 1.5x + 0.0125$
4. A recording studio makes 120 records a day, with a profit of $3.20 per record. If production increases, profit increases by 5¢ per record. Define a variable and write a quadratic equation to describe the total profit in cents. Let $n =$ number of records over 120 produced; $f(n) = 5n^2 + 920n + 38,400$

Motivating the Lesson

Toss a coin 50 times and tally the number of heads. Have students do this problem without keeping a table. They may use markers or have someone keep track by counting. Show them how a table could have made keeping their counts easier.

8-2 Problem-Solving Strategy: Make a Table

Objective 8-2

After studying this lesson, you should be able to:
■ solve problems by using tables.

Organizing data into a table can be very helpful when solving problems. You can use a table to organize given data and identify missing data, to organize your results, or to look for a pattern.

Example 1

APPLICATION

Business

FYI · · ·

The highest bridge is the Royal Gorge over the Arkansas River in Colorado. It is 1053 ft above the water level.

The toll to cross the bridge over the Rushing River is 50¢. One of the lanes has an automatic gate for exact change only. If the automatic gate will not accept pennies, how many combinations of coins must the gate be programmed to accept?

The total of the change must always be 50¢. So make a table to show all of the combinations of coins with a total value of 50¢. We'll start with the larger coins and work toward the smaller ones. **Teaching Tip ❶**

Half-Dollars	Quarters	Dimes	Nickels
1	0	0	0
0	2	0	0
0	1	2	1
0	1	1	3
0	1	0	5
0	0	5	0
0	0	4	2
0	0	3	4
0	0	2	6
0	0	1	8
0	0	0	10

There are 11 combinations that the gate must be programmed to accept.

Example 2

What is the ones' digit of 7^{100}?

Let's make a table and look for a pattern. Use the y^x key on your calculator to find the powers of 7.

n	7^n	Ones' digit
1	7	7
2	49	9
3	343	3
4	2401	1
5	16,807	7
6	117,649	9
7	823,543	3
8	5,764,801	1
9	40,353,607	7

To find 7^4, ENTER: 7 y^x 4 $=$ 2401.

The ones' digits repeat in a cycle of four: 7–9–3–1, 7–9–3–1, ... Every fourth power of 7 has a ones' digit of 1, so the ones' digit of 7^{100} will be 1.

Teaching Tip ❷

356   CHAPTER 8   QUADRATIC RELATIONS AND FUNCTIONS

ALTERNATE TEACHING STRATEGIES

Using Manipulatives

Give each student a set of four paper chains of three links each. Have them try to find a way to link all four of the chains, cutting and retaping only three links. Have them use a table to keep track of their tries.

Using Computers

Have students write a BASIC program to find the ones digit of the second example. They should include a printout of the results to prove that the ones digit for 7^{100} is 1. Have them find the ones digit for 7^{202}.

CHECKING FOR UNDERSTANDING

Communicating Mathematics

1. **organize data and find what's missing; organize results; look for patterns**

Read and study the lesson to answer these questions.

1. Name some ways you can use a table to help solve a problem.
2. If a driver has 3 dimes, 1 quarter, and 5 pennies, can she use the exact change only toll gate at the Rushing River? **no**
3. What is the ones' digit of 7^{125}? **7**
4. Can you see a pattern in the tens' digits of the powers of 7? **yes; It is also in a cycle of four: 0, 4, 4, 0, ...**

Guided Practice

Make a table to help you answer the following.

5. If the toll over the Rushing River is raised to 60¢, how many combinations of coins must the gate be programmed to accept? **15**
6. Clay bought a pen at the school book store for 69¢. He gave the clerk \$1.00 and received 7 coins in change. What coins might he have received? **1 quarter and 6 pennies or 6 nickels and 1 penny**
7. What is the tens' digit of 11^{10}? **0**

EXERCISES

Strategies

Look for a pattern.
Solve a simpler problem.
Act it out.
Guess and check.
Draw a diagram.
Make a chart.
Work backwards.

Solve. Use any strategy.

8. Darren and Emily are playing a game of darts with the target shown at the right. If they each throw three darts in a round, in how many ways could a player score 90 points in one round? Assume that all of the darts hit the target.

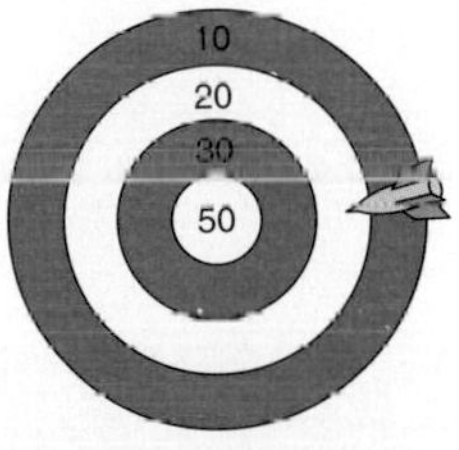

9. What is the remainder of the division $5^{100} \div 7$?
10. A new high school is being built in West Union City. The building will be built around a courtyard with walkways constructed as shown at the right. If the walkways are to be 4 feet wide, how many square feet of sod should the contractor order to cover the grassy area in the courtyard? **225 ft²**

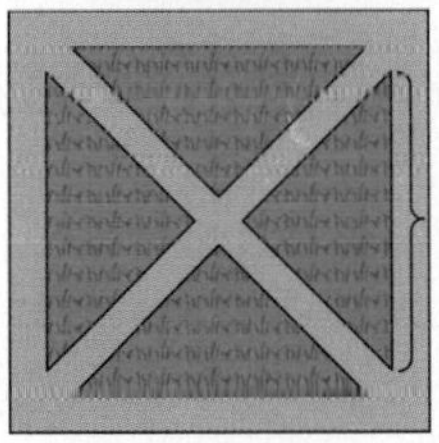

11. In how many ways can you write 53 as the sum of two prime numbers? **0**
12. The difference of the squares of two consecutive integers is 1993. What is the sum of the two integers? **1993 or −1993**
13. Find the least positive integer that is divisible by 2, 3, 7, 10, 15, 20, and 21. **420**

8. (1) 1–50, 1–30, 1–10 (2) 1–50, 2–20s (3) 3–30s

9. Remainders of successive powers of 5 divided by 7 repeat in a cycle of six: 5, 4, 6, 2, 3, 1, ... So $5^{100} \div 7$ will have a remainder of 2.

TEACHING THE LESSON

Chalkboard Examples

For Example 1

The basketball team won 4 of its first 6 games. Use a table to determine the total number of different won-lost patterns possible. **15 patterns**

For Example 2

Multiply 4 × 6, 14 × 16, 24 × 26, and 34 × 36. Use a table and this data to discover a pattern and predict the product of 64 × 66. **All products end in 24. Digits to the left of tens place are determined by adding consecutively larger multiples of 2 to the previous answers.**

Teaching Tip 1 You may want to show students how to set up a table by finding the ways to make change for a smaller amount such as 25¢.

Teaching Tip 2 Point out to students that if they divide the power of 7 by 4 the remainders can be used to find the ones' digit.

Practice Masters Booklet, p. 58

NAME ____________ DATE ________

8-2 Practice Worksheet

Problem Solving Strategy: Make a Table

Use any strategy.

1. A toll on a tollroad is 40¢. The automatic lane takes exact change only. If the automatic gate will take pennies, how many combinations of coins must the gate be programmed to accept? **31 combinations**
2. What is the ones' digit of 8^{30}? **4**
3. The difference of the squares of two consecutive integers is 853. What is the sum of the two integers? **853**
4. Find the least positive integer that is divisible by 2, 5, 7, 15, 21, 24, 25, and 30. **4200**

RETEACHING THE LESSON

Give the integral lengths of the sides of every possible triangle that has a perimeter of 15. Hint: Recall the triangle inequality.
7 triangles: 1-7-7, 2-6-7, 3-5-7, 3-6-6, 4-4-7, 4-5-6, and 5-5-5

EVALUATING THE LESSON

Checking for Understanding
Exercises 1–7 are designed to help you assess understanding through reading, writing, and speaking. You should work through Exercises 1–4 with your students, and then monitor their work on Exercises 5–7.

Closing the Lesson
Speaking Activity Have students explain when they might use a table to solve a problem.

APPLYING THE LESSON

Homework Exercises

Assignment Guide
Basic: 8–18
Average: 8–18
Enriched: 8–18

Chapter 8, Quiz A, (Lessons 8-1 through 8-2), is available in the Evaluation Masters Booklet, p. 107.

Additional Answer
18. 198 + 199 + 200 + 201 + 202; 55 + 56 + 57 + 58 + 59 + 60 + 61 + 62 + 63 + 64 + 65 + 66 + 67 + 68 + 69 + 70; 28 + 29 + 30 + 31 + 32 + 33 + 34 + 35 + 36 + 37 + 38 + 39 + 40 + 41 + 42 + 43 + 44 + 45 + 46 + 47 + 48 + 49 + 50 + 51 + 52

---

14. Three soccer teams, the Hornets, the Warriors, and the Vikings, play each other in the Central State League. The following table shows the results of the games played so far this season. Copy and complete the table and find the score of each game.

	Games Played	Wins	Losses	Ties	Goals Scored	Goals Against
Hornets	2	2	0	0	7	1
Warriors	2	0	1	1	2	4
Vikings	2	0	1	1	3	7

Hornets vs. Warriors: 2 to 0, Warriors vs. Vikings: 2 to 2; Vikings vs. Hornets: 1 to 5

15. Place four coins on your desk with tails up as shown at the right. Choose any three of the coins and turn them over. Continue choosing three coins and turning them over until all of the coins are heads-up. What is the fewest number of such moves that results in all heads-up? **4**

16. **Sample answers:**
$$\begin{array}{r} 154 \\ +782 \\ \hline 936 \end{array} \qquad \begin{array}{r} 215 \\ +478 \\ \hline 693 \end{array}$$

16. Find the digit represented by each different letter in the problem at the right. Each of the digits 1–9 is used exactly once.

$$\begin{array}{r} ABC \\ +DEF \\ \hline GHI \end{array}$$

17. The number 25 is a square. When each of its digits is increased by one, the result is also a square, namely 36. There is one four-digit number with the same property. What is it? **2025**

18. Use a calculator to find three different ways to express 1000 as the sum of two or more consecutive positive integers. **See margin.**

COOPERATIVE LEARNING ACTIVITY

Work in groups. Each person in the group must understand the solution and be able to explain it to any person in class.

Arrange nine coins as shown at the right with the center coin tails-up and the rest heads-up. A move consists of turning over the three coins in any row, column, or diagonal. In how many moves can you make all of the coins heads-up? **See margin.**

EXTENDING THE LESSON

Math Power: Problem Solving
What is the least power of 7, 9, and 11 for which they have the same ones digit? What is the next greater power? What is the pattern? **4, 8, every 4th power**

Answer to Cooperative Learning Activity
THH TTH TTT HHH HHH
HHH→HTH→HHH→HHH→HHH
HHT HTT TTT TTT HHH

Graphing Calculator Exploration: Locating the Vertex of a Parabola

The vertex of a parabola is the maximum or minimum point on the parabola. Finding the approximate coordinates of the vertex of a parabola on a graphing calculator is a simple process. **Teaching Tip ❶**

Teaching Tip ❷

To use the graphing calculator to find the vertex of a parabola, use the tracing and zoom-in features of the calculator, with which you are already familiar. The vertex is located at the maximum point of the parabola if it opens downward and at the minimum point if it opens upward. Once you have graphed the parabola in an appropriate viewing window, use the tracing function to move the cursor close to the vertex. Move the cursor back and forth over the vertex while you watch the y-values. Find the point with the highest, or lowest, y-value. This is the vertex. Now, use the zoom-in process to determine the coordinates with your desired accuracy.

Example

Use the tracing function to determine the coordinates of the vertex of the parabola with equation $y = (x - 2)^2 - 3$.

First graph the parabola. *Use the standard viewing window.*

Casio

ENTER:  2
 3 EXE

TI-81

ENTER: Y= (X|T) − 2) x^2
− 3 GRAPH

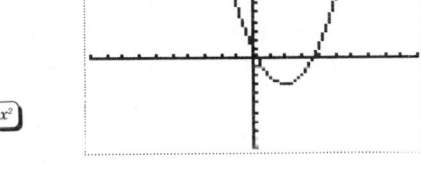

Now use the tracing and zoom-in functions to determine the coordinates of the vertex. The coordinates of the vertex to two decimal places are (2.00, −3.00). *You may wish to review the Graphing Calculator Exploration on pages 104–107 to refresh your memory on the zoom-in process.*

EXERCISES

Graph each equation on your graphing calculator. Then use the tracing function to approximate the coordinates of the vertex of the graph to two decimal places.

4. (43.50, −1915.25)
5. (30.20, −4881.20)

6. (−0.75, 3.25)
7. (37.00, 92.50)
8. (3.50, 11.50)

1. $y = 2(x - 10)^2 + 14$ **(10, 14)**
3. $y = x^2 - 14x + 70$ **(7, 21)**
5. $y = 5x^2 - 302x - 321$
7. $y = 0.5x^2 - 37x + 777$
9. $y = \frac{2}{3}x^2 - \frac{3}{4}x + 6$ **(0.56, 5.79)**

2. $y = (x + 8)^2 - 5$ **(−8, −5)**
4. $y = x^2 - 87x - 23$
6. $y = 12x^2 + 18x + 10$
8. $y = 10x^2 - 70x + 134$
10. $y = 0.5x^2 + 0.29x + 8.9$ **(−0.28, 8.85)**

RETEACHING THE LESSON

Have students experiment with the zoom box if you have TI-81 or TI-82 graphing calculators. Have them make long skinny boxes around the vertex and then have them make short wide boxes around the vertex. Point out that when they zoom in when using a box, the screen will look like it does in the box. So if the graph looks like a straight line in the box, it will look like a straight line when they zoom in.

Graphing Calculator Exploration

INTRODUCING THE LESSON

Objective: Graph and trace to find vertices of parabolas on a graphing calculator.

Motivating the Lesson
Ask students if every parabola has a vertex. **yes** Why? **The closed end of a parabola always contains a maximum or minimum value of the x- or y-coordinate. This is the vertex of the parabola.** Do any parabolas have more than one vertex? **no**

TEACHING THE LESSON

Teaching Tip ❶ Emphasize that there will only be *one* vertex since all parabolas extend to positive infinity or negative infinity in the other direction.

Teaching Tip ❷   will let you read the y values on the Casio. The TI-81 will display both values.

EVALUATING THE LESSON

Closing the Lesson
Modeling Activity Make transparencies of the standard viewing window and several different parabolas. Then give students an equation and have them graph it on their calculators. Once they have done this, have them select a parabola transparency and place the vertex of that parabola at the right place on the transparency viewing window.

APPLYING THE LESSON

Homework Exercises

Assignment Guide
All: 1–10

8-3 Graphing Quadratic Functions

Lesson Resources

Reteaching Master 8-3
Practice Master 8-3
Enrichment Master 8-3
Technology Master, p. 8
Activity Master, p. 44

 Transparency 8-3 contains the 5-Minute Check and a teaching aid for this lesson.

INTRODUCING THE LESSON

 5-Minute Check

(over Lesson 8-2)

1. Use a table to find the number of ways you can make change for a quarter if you have to use at least one nickel. **9 ways**

Other Prerequisite Skills

2. Graph $2x + 3y = 5$.

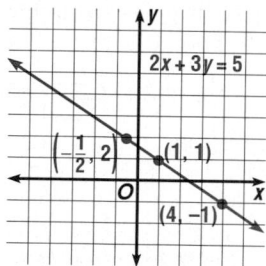

3. Write $f(x) = 3(x - 4)^2 + 2$ in quadratic form.
$f(x) = 3x^2 - 24x + 50$

Motivating the Lesson

Have students launch rockets in a field outside school. One person should keep the time from launch to touch down. Several people should draw the path of the rockets. What happens to the rocket at the top before it starts to come back down?

Objective
8-3

After studying this lesson, you should be able to:

- graph quadratic equations of the form $y = (x - h)^2 + k$, and identify the vertex and the equation of the axis of symmetry of a parabola.

Application

After launching the model rocket described in Lesson 8-1, and measuring the amount of time that the rocket was in flight with a stopwatch at 10 seconds, Mike and Rita graphed the function describing the flight of the rocket. The height of the rocket, $h(t)$, t seconds after being launched is given by the quadratic function $h(t) = 160t - 16t^2$.

Teaching Tip ❶

First they created a table of values.

Next they plotted the points $(t, h(t))$.

t	$160t - 16t^2$	$h(t)$
0	$160(0) - 16(0)^2$	0
1	$160(1) - 16(1)^2$	144
2	$160(2) - 16(2)^2$	256
3	$160(3) - 16(3)^2$	336
4	$160(4) - 16(4)^2$	384
5	$160(5) - 16(5)^2$	400
6	$160(6) - 16(6)^2$	384
7	$160(7) - 16(7)^2$	336
8	$160(8) - 16(8)^2$	256
9	$160(9) - 16(9)^2$	144
10	$160(10) - 16(10)^2$	0

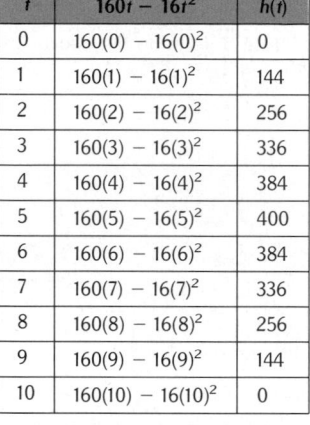

Finally, they connected the points in a smooth curve. The resulting graph is called a **parabola.**

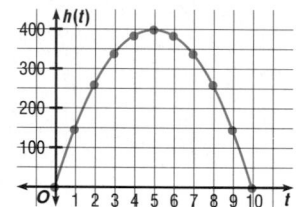

Notice how the height of the rocket is zero again 10 seconds after launching. This means that the rocket has returned to the ground. It appears that the rocket reached its maximum height of 400 feet after 5 seconds. Evaluate $h(t)$ for other values of t between 4 and 6 to check this conclusion.

The graph of any quadratic function is a parabola. All parabolas have an **axis of symmetry.** The axis of symmetry is the line about which the parabola is symmetric. That is, if you could fold the coordinate plane along the axis of symmetry the portions of the parabola on each side of the line would match. The line of symmetry is named by the equation of the line. All parabolas have a **vertex** as well. The vertex is the point of intersection of the parabola and the axis of symmetry.

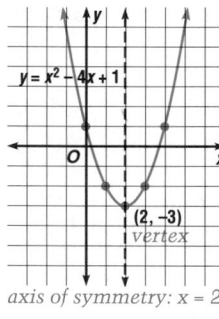

axis of symmetry: x = 2

360 CHAPTER 8 QUADRATIC RELATIONS AND FUNCTIONS

ALTERNATE TEACHING STRATEGIES

Using Models

To help students understand the concept of an axis of symmetry, have them copy the sketches of the graphs for the examples in the lesson. Fold the paper along the axis of symmetry to check the symmetry of each parabola.

Mini-Math Lab

Divide students into groups of four.

Give each group a ball. Have them determine the speed of the ball as thrown by one of the persons in the group. They can estimate this speed by throwing the ball against the wall of the gym with one of the other students timing it. Keeping the speed consistent have the same student throw the ball into the air. Find an equation to describe the height at time t.

The graphs of $y = x^2$, $y = (x - 2)^2$, $y = x^2 + 3$, and $y = (x - 2)^2 + 3$ are shown below on the same set of axes. Study these graphs.

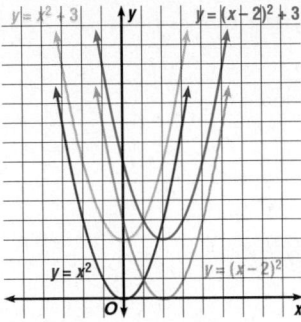

Equation	Vertex	Axis of Symmetry
$y = x^2$	(0, 0)	$x = 0$
$y = (x - 2)^2$	(2, 0)	$x = 2$
$y = x^2 + 3$	(0, 3)	$x = 0$
$y = (x - 2)^2 + 3$	(2, 3)	$x = 2$

Notice that the graphs all have the same shape. The difference is their position.

We can express the equations for these parabolas in the general form $y = (x - h)^2 + k$. When a quadratic function is written in this form, the values of h and k are easy to determine.

$y = x^2$ ➧ $y = (x - 0)^2 + 0$ ➧ $h = 0, k = 0$

$y = (x - 2)^2$ ➧ $y = (x - 2)^2 + 0$ ➧ $h = 2, k = 0$

$y = x^2 + 3$ ➧ $y = (x - 0)^2 + 3$ ➧ $h = 0, k = 3$

$y = (x - 2)^2 + 3$ ➧ $y = (x - 2)^2 + 3$ ➧ $h = 2, k = 3$

Teaching Tip ❷ Compare the values for h and k for each equation with the coordinates of the vertex of each graph given above. Also, compare each equation for the axis of symmetry with each value for h. What pattern do you notice?

$y = (x - h)^2 + k$	
Vertex	(h, k)
Axis of Symmetry	$x = h$

In Chapter 4 you learned that a translation moves a figure on the coordinate plane without changing its size. As the value of h and k change, the graph of $y = (x - h)^2 + k$ is the graph of $y = x^2$ translated $|h|$ units left or right and $|k|$ units up or down. If h is positive, the parabola is translated to the right. If h is negative, it is translated to the left. Likewise, for k, the translation is up if k is positive and down if k is negative.

Example 1

Name the vertex and the axis of symmetry for the graph of $y = (x + 8)^2 - 1$. How is this graph different from the graph of $y = x^2$?

Rewrite the equation in the form $y = (x - h)^2 + k$.

$$y = (x - (-8))^2 + (-1)$$

From this equation, $h = -8$, $k = -1$.

So, the vertex is $(-8, -1)$ and the axis of symmetry is $x = -8$. The shape of the graph is the same as the shape of the graph of $y = x^2$, but it is translated 8 units left and 1 unit down.

LESSON 8-3 GRAPHING QUADRATIC FUNCTIONS 361

Teaching Tip ❶ Problems to find the maximum height will be solved in Lesson 8-5.

Teaching Tip ❷ Point out to students the vertex is (h, k), the axis of symmetry is $x = h$, and all these graphs have the same shape.

Chalkboard Example

For Example 1
Name the vertex and axis of symmetry for the graph of $f(x) = (x + 11)^2 + 4$.
$(-11, 4)$; $x = -11$

For Example 2

Name the vertex and axis of symmetry for the graph of $f(x) = (x + 2)^2 + 1$. Then draw the graph. $(-2, 1); x = -2$

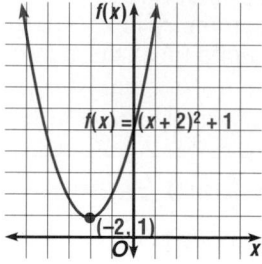

$f(x) = (x + 2)^2 + 1$

$(-2, 1)$

For Example 3

Write a function for the area of a triangle if the height is 3 cm greater than the base. Then draw the graph. $A = f(b) = \dfrac{b^2}{2} + \dfrac{3b}{2}$

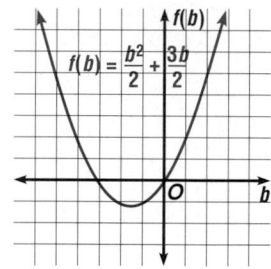

$f(b) = \dfrac{b^2}{2} + \dfrac{3b}{2}$

Reteaching Masters Booklet, p. 51

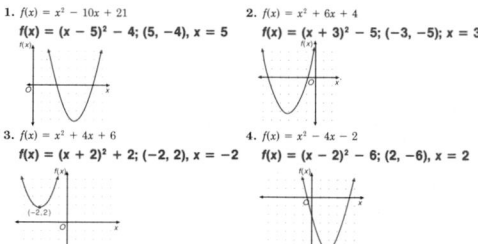

Example 2

Name the vertex and the axis of symmetry for the graph of $f(x) = (x + 1)^2 + 3$. Then draw the graph.

This function can be rewritten as $f(x) = (x - (-1))^2 + 3$.

So, $h = -1$ and $k = 3$.
The vertex is $(-1, 3)$ and the axis of symmetry is $x = -1$.

Finding several points on the graph makes graphing easier.

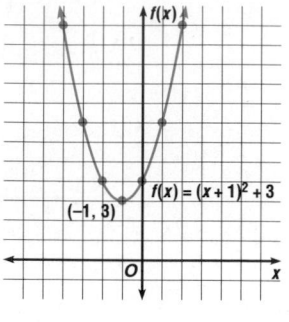

$f(x) = (x + 1)^2 + 3$

$(-1, 3)$

x	$(x + 1)^2 + 3$	$f(x)$
-4	$(-4 + 1)^2 + 3$	12
-3	$(-3 + 1)^2 + 3$	7
-2	$(-2 + 1)^2 + 3$	4
-1	$(-1 + 1)^2 + 3$	3
0	$(0 + 1)^2 + 3$	4
1	$(1 + 1)^2 + 3$	7
2	$(2 + 1)^2 + 3$	12

Notice that points with the same y-coordinates are the same distance from the axis of symmetry, $x = -1$.

Example 3

CONNECTION

Geometry

Write a function to represent the area of all the rectangles whose length is 2 centimeters more than their width. Graph the function. **Teaching Tip ③**

Let $w = $ the width of the rectangle and $w + 2 = $ the length.
$$\text{Area} = f(w) = w(w + 2)$$
$$= w^2 + 2w$$

Now rewrite the equation in the form $y = (x - h)^2 + k$. To do this we must complete the square.
$$f(w) = (w^2 + 2w + 1) - 1$$
$$= (w + 1)^2 - 1$$
$$= (w - (-1))^2 + (-1)$$
From this equation, $h = -1$ and $k = -1$.
Therefore, the vertex is $(-1, -1)$ and the axis of symmetry is $x = -1$.
Find other points on the graph.

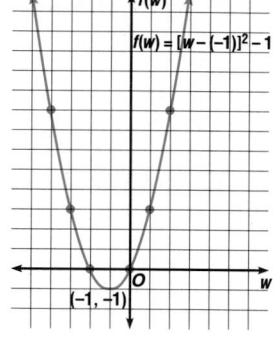

$f(w) = [w - (-1)]^2 - 1$

$(-1, -1)$

w	$(w + 1)^2 - 1$	$f(w)$
-4	$(-4 + 1)^2 - 1$	8
-3	$(-3 + 1)^2 - 1$	3
-2	$(-2 + 1)^2 - 1$	0
0	$(0 + 1)^2 - 1$	0
1	$(1 + 1)^2 - 1$	3
2	$(2 + 1)^2 - 1$	8

Only the points with nonnegative coordinates make sense as measures for the sides of a rectangle.

RETEACHING THE LESSON

Graph several equations of the form $y = (x - h)^2 + k$ on an overhead transparency. Then superimpose (slide) the graph of $y = x^2$ over each parabola graphed to show that they have the same shape. Point out for each parabola that (h, k) are the coordinates of its vertex.

CHECKING FOR UNDERSTANDING

Communicating Mathematics

1. yes; Justification may vary.

3. A sample answer is $f(x) = (x - (-1))^2 - 1$.

4. See margin.

Read and study the lesson to answer these questions.

1. Did the model rocket described in the beginning of the lesson reach its maximum height 5 seconds after launch? Justify the answer.

2. The graph of a quadratic function is a ___?___. It is symmetric about a line called the ___?___. **parabola; axis of symmetry**

3. Write a quadratic function whose graph has a vertex in the third quadrant.

4. Compare the graphs of the functions $f(x) = (x - 2)^2 + 2$ and $f(x) = (x + 2)^2 + 2$.

5. Write the equation of the function whose graph is shown at the right.
$y = (x - (-2))^2 + 1$

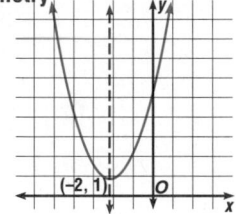

Guided Practice

6. $(0, 0)$, $x = 0$
7. $(4, 0)$, $x = 4$
8. $(-6, 0)$, $x = -6$
9. $(0, 3)$, $x = 0$
10. $(0, -9)$, $x = 0$
11. $(6, 4)$, $x = 6$
12. $(-10, -7)$, $x = -10$
13. $\left(\frac{1}{5}, 1\right)$, $x = \frac{1}{5}$
14. $(-1.5, -3.2)$, $x = -1.5$

Name the vertex and the axis of symmetry for the graph of each equation.

6. $f(x) = x^2$
7. $g(x) = (x - 4)^2$
8. $f(x) = (x + 6)^2$
9. $h(x) = x^2 + 3$
10. $f(x) = x^2 - 9$
11. $y = (x - 6)^2 + 4$
12. $y = (x + 10)^2 - 7$
13. $y = \left(x - \frac{1}{5}\right)^2 + 1$
14. $f(x) = (x + 1.5)^2 - 3.2$

Write the equation of the quadratic function for each graph.

19. $f(x) = (x - 2)^2$, $(2, 0)$, $x = 2$
20. $f(x) = [x - (-3)]^2$, $(-3, 0)$, $x = -3$
21. $f(x) = (x - 0)^2 + 9$, $(0, 9)$, $x = 0$
22. $f(x) = (x - 0)^2 + (-7)$, $(0, -7)$, $x = 0$

15.
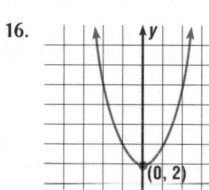
$y = [x - (-2)]^2 + 0$

16.
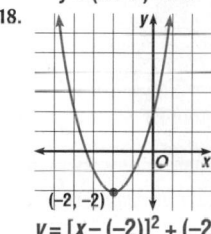
$y = (x + 0)^2 + 2$

17.
$y = (x - 2)^2 + 2$

18.
$y = [x - (-2)]^2 + (-2)$

EXERCISES

Practice A

23. $f(x) = [x - (-5)]^2 - 25$, $(-5, -25)$, $x = -5$
24. $f(x) = (x - 6)^2 - 36$, $(6, -36)$, $x = 6$

Write each equation in the form $f(x) = (x - h)^2 + k$. Then name the vertex and the axis of symmetry for the graph of each function.

19. $f(x) = x^2 - 4x + 4$
20. $f(x) = x^2 + 6x + 9$
21. $f(x) = x^2 + 9$
22. $f(x) = x^2 - 7$
23. $f(x) = x^2 + 10x$
24. $f(x) = x^2 - 12x$

LESSON 8-3 GRAPHING QUADRATIC FUNCTIONS 363

Additional Answer

4. The graphs have the same shape. The vertex of $f(x) = (x - 2)^2 + 2$ is $(2, 2)$ and the vertex of $f(x) = (x + 2)^2 + 2$ is $(-2, 2)$.

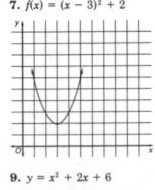
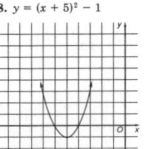

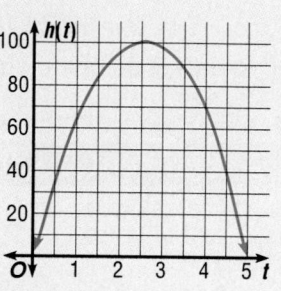

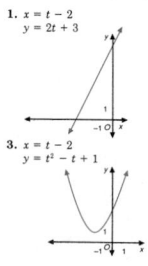
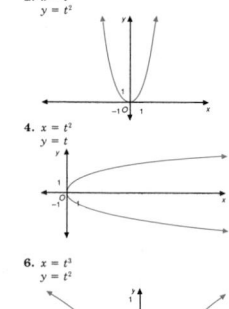
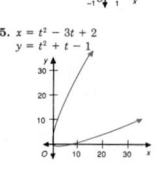
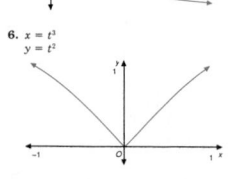
Write each equation in the form $f(x) = (x - h)^2 + k$. Then name the vertex and the axis of symmetry for the graph of each function.

25. $f(x) = x^2 + 8x + 20$

26. $f(x) = x^2 - 3x + 3$

Graph each equation. **27–42. See Solutions Manual.**

27. $y = (x - 5)^2$

28. $y = (x + 7)^2$

29. $f(x) = x^2 + 6$

30. $g(x) = x^2 - 4$

31. $y = (x - 3)^2 + 5$

32. $f(x) = (x - 8)^2 + 3$

33. $g(x) = (x + 2)^2 - 3$

34. $y = (x + 4)^2 + 1$

35. $f(x) = (x - 1)^2 - 4$

36. $y = (x + 11)^2 - 1$

37. $y = x^2 + 6x + 2$

38. $f(x) = x^2 + 10x + 27$

39. $g(x) = x^2 - 2x + 7$

40. $y = x^2 + 3x$

41. $h(x) = x^2 - 5x$

42. $f(x) = x^2 - x - 3$

Critical Thinking Complete the following table for parabolas with equations of the form $y = (x - h)^2 + k$.

	Axis of Symmetry	Contains the Point	Vertex	Equation of the Parabola
43.	$x = 0$	$(2, -1)$	$(0, -5)$	$y = x^2 - 5$
44.	$x = -2$	$(-5, 9)$	$(-2, 0)$	$y = (x + 2)^2$
45.	$x = -3$	$(1, 18)$	$(-3, 2)$	$y = (x + 3)^2 + 2$
46.	$x = 1$	$(-1, -2)$	$(1, -6)$	$y = (x - 1)^2 - 6$

Applications

47. **Physics** An arrow is shot upward with an initial velocity of 80 feet per second. The height of the arrow, $h(t)$, in terms of the time since the arrow was released t, is $h(t) = 80t - 16t^2$.
   a. Draw the graph of the function relating the height of the arrow to the time. **See margin.**
   b. How long after the arrow is released does it reach its maximum height? What is that height? **2.5 seconds; 100 feet**

48. **Sports** Shawn hit a foul ball straight up over home plate. The height of the ball over the level of the bat, $h(t)$, is given by the function $h(t) = 48t - 16t^2$, where t is the time in seconds after the ball left the bat.
   a. Draw the graph of the function relating the height of the ball over the level of the bat to the time. **See margin.**
   b. If the catcher is going to attempt to catch the ball, how long does she have to get ready? **3 seconds**
   c. Where is the ball when the height found by the function is zero? **at the level of the bat where the foul ball was hit**

Mixed Review

49. Identify the quadratic term, the linear term, and the constant term of the function $f(x) = 4x^2 - 8x - 2$. **(Lesson 8-1)** $4x^2$; $-8x$; -2

50. $x^2 - x - 56 = 0$

50. Find a quadratic equation having 8 and -7 as roots. **(Lesson 7-5)**

51. Simplify $\sqrt[3]{2}(3\sqrt[3]{4} + 2\sqrt[3]{32})$. **(Lesson 6-2)** **14**

52. Find the degree of the polynomial $16x^4yz + 12x^2y^3z - 24x^3y^2z - 18xy^4z$. **(Lesson 5-4)** **6**

53. Determine the slope of the line that passes through the points $(9, 3)$ and $(-3, 9)$. **(Lesson 2-4)** $-\dfrac{1}{2}$

EXTENDING THE LESSON

Math Power: Reasoning

Write an equation of the parabola that passes through $(5, 20)$ and $(36, -11)$ if the equation is in the form $y = (x - h)^2 + k$.
$y = (x - 21)^2 - 236$

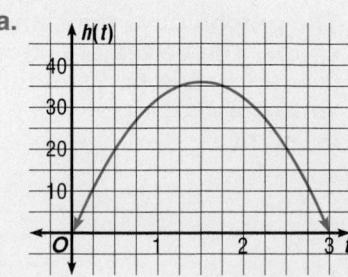

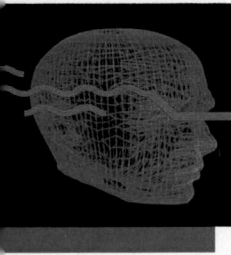

Technology
Quadratic Functions

▶ BASIC
Spreadsheets
Software

In order to enter the correct data, the quadratic function must be in the form $f(x) = ax^2 + bx + c$.

The BASIC program below can be used to find the vertex, axis of symmetry, and direction of the opening for the graph of any quadratic function. The program also lists six points on the graph, which are three points on either side of the axis of symmetry.

```
10    INPUT "ENTER THE COEFFICIENTS OF THE EQUATION:";
      A, B, C
20    LET H = -B/(2*A)
30    LET K = A*H*H+B*H+C
40    PRINT "THE VERTEX IS (";H;",";K;")."
50    PRINT "THE AXIS OF SYMMETRY IS X = ";H;"."
60    IF A > 0, THEN 80
70    PRINT "THE GRAPH OPENS DOWNWARD.": GOTO 90
80    PRINT "THE GRAPH OPENS UPWARD."
90    PRINT "HERE ARE THE COORDINATES OF SIX ADDITIONAL
      POINTS ON THE GRAPH:"
100   FOR N = H - 3 TO H + 3
110   IF H = INT(H) THEN 130
120   IF N = H - 3 THEN 170
130   LET X = INT(N)
140   IF X = H THEN 170
150   LET Y = A*X*X+B*X+C
160   PRINT "(";X;",";Y;")."
170   NEXT N
180   END
```

Run the program for the function $f(x) = 2x^2 - 5x + 3$.

```
RUN
ENTER THE COEFFICIENTS OF THE EQUATION: 2, -5, 3
THE VERTEX IS (1.25, -0.125).
THE AXIS OF SYMMETRY IS X = 1.25.
THE GRAPH OPENS UPWARD.
HERE ARE THE COORDINATES OF SIX ADDITIONAL POINTS ON THE
GRAPH
(-1, 10)        (0, 3)(1, 0)        (2,1)
(3, 6)          (4, 15)
```

EXERCISES

1-4. **See margin.
For graphs, see
students' work.**

Use the program to find the vertex, axis of symmetry, direction of opening, and additional points on the graph of each function. Then graph the function.

1. $f(x) = x^2 - 28x + 186$

2. $f(x) = -x^2 - 16x + 36$

3. $f(x) = -5x^2 + 22x - 3$

4. $f(x) = 10x^2 - 37x - 7$

Using Technology

Objective This optional page shows how the BASIC programming language can be used to perform mathematical computations and to enhance and extend mathematical concepts.

Teaching Suggestions

The program is designed to generate ordered pairs that have integral x-coordinates, even if the x-coordinate of the vertex is not an integer. Discuss with students how the program generates the six ordered pairs when the x-coordinate of the vertex is an integer and when it is not an integer.

Additional Answers

1. **vertex: (14, -10)
   axis of symmetry: $x = 14$
   opens upward
   (11, -1), (12, -6), (13, -9),
   (15, -9), (16, -6), (17, -1)**

2. **vertex: (-8, 100)
   axis of symmetry: $x = -8$
   opens downward
   (-11, 91), (-10, 96), (-9, 99),
   (-7, 99), (-6, 96), (-5, 91)**

3. **vertex: (2.2, 21.2)
   axis of symmetry: $x = 2.2$
   opens downward
   (0, -3), (1, 14), (2, 21), (3, 18),
   (4, 5), (5, -18)**

4. **vertex: (1.85, -41.225)
   axis of symmetry: $x = 1.85$
   opens upward
   (-1, 40), (0, -7), (1, -34),
   (2, -41), (3, -28), (4, 5)**

Lesson Resources
Reteaching Master 8-4
Practice Master 8-4
Enrichment Master 8-4
Technology Master, p. 25
Activity Master, p. 26

Transparency 8-4 contains the
5-Minute Check and a teaching aid
for this lesson.

INTRODUCING THE LESSON

 5-Minute Check

(over Lesson 8-3)

Use the function $f(x) = x^2 - 8x + 9$ to solve Exercises 1–4.

1. Write the function in the form
   $f(x) = (x - h)^2 + k$.
   $f(x) = (x - 4)^2 + (-7)$
2. Name the vertex and axis of
   symmetry of the graph of the
   function. **(4, -7); x = 4**

Other Prerequisite Skills

3. Identify the quadratic, linear,
   and constant terms.
   x^2; $-8x$; 9
4. Find the value of $f(x)$ if
   $x = 3$. **-6**

Motivating the Lesson

Have students use graphing calculators to graph the equations $y = -4(x - 5)^2$ and $y = 5(x + 3)^2 - 1$ on the same screen. What do you notice about the graphs? In which direction does each parabola open? Graph $y = (x - 1)^2 + 7$ and $y = 2(x - 1)^2 + 7$. What do you notice about the openings? Can you make any generalizations from your observations?

8-4 Analyzing Graphs of Quadratic Functions

Objectives

After studying this lesson, you should be able to:

8-4A ■ graph equations of the form $y = a(x - h)^2 + k$ and identify the vertex, the equation of the axis of symmetry, and the direction of the opening, and

8-4B ■ determine the equation of a parabola from given information about the graph.

Application

Athletic Advantage Inc. makes athletic shoes for aerobics and running. Their sales manager has determined that their profit, $P(x)$, on x pairs of shoes can be found by $P(x) = -x^2 + 90x - 500$.

You know that the graph of any quadratic function is a parabola. We've studied graphs of equations of the form $y = (x - h)^2 + k$. Some other quadratic functions can be written in the form $y = a(x - h)^2$. Let's compare the graph of the profit function given above to some other graphs we've already studied.

First, write the equation in the form $y = a(x - h)^2 + k$. We'll do this by completing the square.

$$P(x) = -x^2 + 90x - 500$$
$$= -1(x^2 - 90x) - 500$$
$$= -1(x^2 - 90x + 2025) + 2025 - 500 \quad \textit{Add and subtract } \left(\frac{90}{2}\right)^2 \textit{ or 2025 to}$$
$$= -1(x - 45)^2 + 1525 \qquad\qquad\qquad \textit{obtain an equivalent equation.}$$

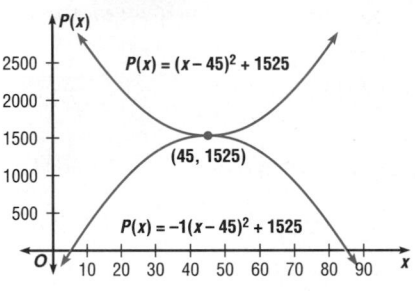

Now graph $P(x) = -1(x - 45)^2 + 1525$ and $P(x) = (x - 45)^2 + 1525$ on the same coordinate plane and compare the graphs.

The graphs have the same vertex and are shaped the same, but the graph of $P(x) = -1(x - 45)^2 + 1525$ opens downward and the graph of $P(x) = (x - 45)^2 + 1525$ opens upward.

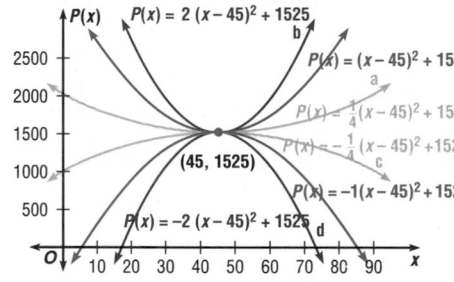

Graph the following functions to further investigate the relationships between similar functions. What do you find?

a. $P(x) = \frac{1}{4}(x - 45)^2 + 1525$ $a = \frac{1}{4}$

b. $P(x) = 2(x - 45)^2 + 1525$ $a = 2$

c. $P(x) = -\frac{1}{4}(x - 45)^2 + 1525$ $a = -\frac{1}{4}$

d. $P(x) = -2(x - 45)^2 + 1525$ $a = -2$

ALTERNATE TEACHING STRATEGIES

Using Critical Thinking

Have students think about each question when they graph a parabola.

1. Is the equation in the form
   $y = a(x - h)^2 + k$?
2. What are the values of a, h, and k?

3. How do these values affect the way the graph is shaped and the direction in which it is opening?
4. How do these affect where it is located?

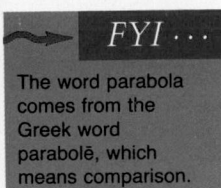
All of the graphs for quadratic functions **a**, **b**, **c**, and **d** have the vertex (45, 1525) and the axis of symmetry $x = 45$. When a is negative, the graph opens downward. When a is positive, the graph opens upward. As the value of $|a|$ increases the graph becomes narrower.

The following chart summarizes the characteristics of the graph of $y = a(x - h)^2 + k$. **Teaching Tip ❶**

$y = a(x - h)^2 + k$	a is positive	a is negative
Vertex	(h, k)	(h, k)
Axis of Symmetry	$x = h$	$x = h$
Direction of Opening	upward	downward
As the value of $|a|$ increases, the graphs of $y = a(x - h)^2 + k$ narrow.		

Teaching Tip ❷

Example 1

Name the vertex, axis of symmetry, and direction of opening for the graph of $f(x) = -4(x - 9)^2$.

This function can be written in the form $f(x) = -4(x - 9)^2 + 0$.

From this equation, $a = -4$, $h = 9$, and $k = 0$.

So, the vertex is (9, 0), the axis of symmetry is $x = 9$, and since a is negative, the graph opens downward.

Example 2

Graph $f(x) = -2x^2 - 8x - 1$.

Write the equation in the form $f(x) = a(x - h)^2 + k$ by completing the square.

$$f(x) = -2x^2 - 8x - 1$$
$$= -2(x^2 + 4x) - 1$$
$$= -2(x^2 + 4x + 4) - 1 - (-2)(4)$$
$$= -2(x + 2)^2 + 7$$
$$= -2(x - (-2))^2 + 7$$

From the equation, $h = -2$, $k = 7$, and $a = -2$.
So, the vertex is $(-2, 7)$ and the axis of symmetry is $x = -2$.
Since $a = -2$, the graph opens downward and is narrower than the graph of $f(x) = (x + 2)^2 + 7$.

x	$-2(x + 2)^2 + 7$	$f(x)$
-4	$-2(-4 + 2)^2 + 7$	-1
-3	$-2(-3 + 2)^2 + 7$	5
-2	$-2(-2 + 2)^2 + 7$	7
-1	$-2(-1 + 2)^2 + 7$	5
0	$-2(0 + 2)^2 + 7$	-1

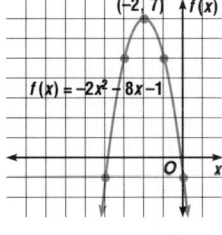

TEACHING THE LESSON

Teaching Tip ❶   You may want to verify the conclusions in this chart by looking at each graph on page 366 and identifying the values a, h, and k.

Teaching Tip ❷   Point out that this statement also means that as the value of $|a|$ decreases, the graphs of $y = a(x - h)^2 + k$ widen.

Chalkboard Examples

For Example 1
Name the vertex, axis of symmetry, and direction of opening for the graph of $f(x) = \frac{2}{3}(x + 11)^2 + 8$.
$(-11, 8)$; $x = -11$; up

For Example 2
Graph the function $f(x) = 2(x + 4)^2 - 3$.

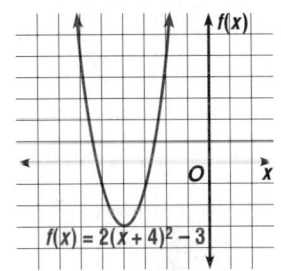

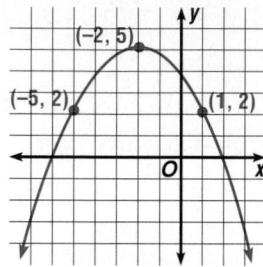
Example 3

Write the equation of the parabola shown below.

The vertex of the parabola is (4, −1). So $h = 4$, and $k = -1$.

Substitute the values of h and k and the coordinates of one other point on the graph into the general form of the equation and solve for a. *Use (3, 2).* **Teaching Tip ❸**

$$y = a(x - h)^2 + k$$
$$2 = a(3 - 4)^2 + (-1) \quad \textit{Substitute 4 for } h, -1 \textit{ for}$$
$$3 = a(-1)^2 \qquad\qquad\quad k, 3 \textit{ for } x, \textit{ and } 2 \textit{ for } y.$$
$$3 = a$$

The equation of the parabola is $y = 3(x - 4)^2 - 1$ or $y = 3x^2 - 24x + 47$.

Example 4

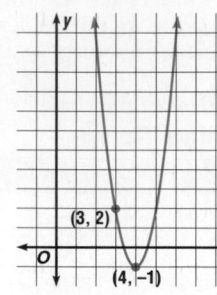

APPLICATION

Sports

In the finals of the softball tournament, Jenny hit a homerun to win the game. The ball she hit traveled in a path described by the function $f(x) = -0.004x^2 + x + 4$, where x represents the number of feet the ball has traveled from the plate and $f(x)$ represents the height of the ball in feet. Name the vertex, axis of symmetry, and direction of opening for the graph of this function. Then graph.

First, write the equation in standard form by completing the square.

$$y = -0.004x^2 + x + 4$$
$$= -0.004(x^2 - 250x) + 4$$
$$= -0.004(x^2 - 250x + 15,625) + 4 - (-0.004)(15,625)$$
$$= -0.004(x - 125)^2 + 66.5$$

From this equation, $a = -0.004$, $h = 125$, and $k = 66.5$.
So, the vertex is (125, 66.5), the axis of symmetry is $x = 125$, and since a is negative the graph opens downward.

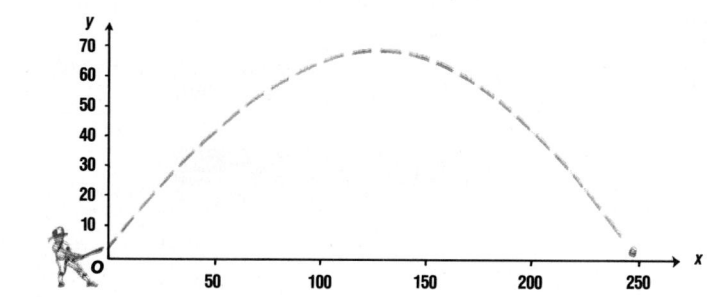

Example 5 | Graph $f(x) = \frac{1}{3}(x - 1)^2 + 3$.

From this equation, $h = 1$, $k = 3$, and $a = \frac{1}{3}$. Therefore, the vertex is $(1, 3)$ and the axis of symmetry is $x = 1$. Since $a = \frac{1}{3}$, the graph opens upward and is wider than the graph of $f(x) = (x - 1)^2 + 3$.

Find some points on the graph, plot, and connect to form a smooth graph.

x	$\frac{1}{3}(x - 1)^2 + 3$	$f(x)$
-3	$\frac{1}{3}(-3 - 1)^2 + 3$	$8\frac{1}{3}$
-2	$\frac{1}{3}(-2 - 1)^2 + 3$	6
1	$\frac{1}{3}(1 - 1)^2 + 3$	3
4	$\frac{1}{3}(4 - 1)^2 + 3$	6
5	$\frac{1}{3}(5 - 1)^2 + 3$	$8\frac{1}{3}$

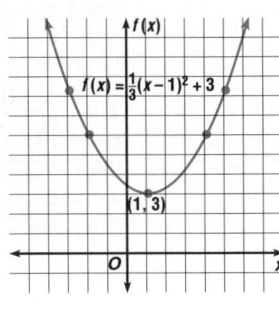

Example 6 | Write the equation of the parabola that passes through the points $(0, -2)$, $(2, -2)$, and $(3, 4)$.

Each point should satisfy the equation of the parabola. Using the form of the equation $y = ax^2 + bx + c$, find a, b, and c by substituting the coordinates of the points into the general form of the equation.

$-2 = a(0)^2 + b(0) + c$ ➡ $-2 = c$

$-2 = a(2)^2 + b(2) + c$ ➡ $-2 = 4a + 2b + c$

$4 = a(3)^2 + b(3) + c$ ➡ $4 = 9a + 3b + c$

Now solve the system of equations. From the first equation, $c = -2$, so substitute -2 for c in the other two equations.

$-2 = 4a + 2b - 2$ ➡ $0 = 4a + 2b$

$4 = 9a + 3b - 2$ ➡ $6 = 9a + 3b$

Solve using elimination.

$0 = 4a + 2b$ Multiply by -3. $0 = -12a - 6b$

$6 = 9a + 3b$ 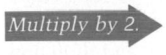 Multiply by 2. $\underline{12 = 18a + 6b}$

$12 = 6a$

$2 = a$

Now substitute 2 for a and solve for b.

$0 = 4(2) + 2b$

$-4 = b$

The solution to the system is $(2, -4, -2)$. So the equation of the parabola is $y = 2x^2 - 4x - 2$. *Check this solution by graphing.*

Chalkboard Examples

For Example 5
Graph $f(x) = x^2 + 8x + 15$.

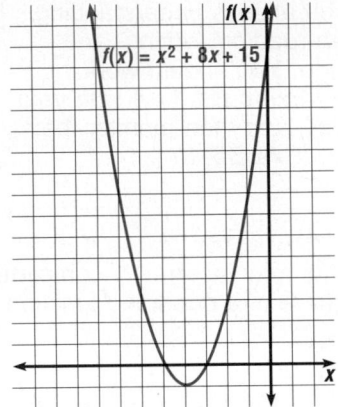

For Example 6
Write an equation of the parabola that passes through $(9, -3)$, $(6, 3)$, and $(4, 27)$.
$f(x) = 2(x - 8)^2 - 5$.

Checking for Understanding

Exercises 1–14 are designed to help you assess understanding through reading, writing, and speaking. You should work through Exercises 1–4 with your students, and then monitor their work on Exercises 5–14.

Error Analysis

Students may incorrectly complete the square in a quadratic function when $a \neq 1$.

$$f(x) = 2x^2 - 8x - 1$$
$$f(x) = 2(x^2 - 4x) - 1$$
$$f(x) = 2(x^2 - 4x \underline{+ 4}) - 1 \underline{- 4}$$

Because 4 is added inside the parentheses, it is multiplied by 2. Thus, 8 is being added and 8 should be subtracted, not 4.

Closing the Lesson

Modeling Activity Have students draw the four parabolas, such that all have the same vertex, two open downward, and two open upward. Make sure students can tell you the equation of each graph.

Reteaching Masters Booklet, p. 52

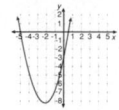
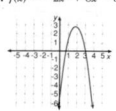
370   Chapter 8

CHECKING FOR UNDERSTANDING

Communicating Mathematics

Read and study the lesson to answer these questions.

1. How can you tell if the graph of a function in the form $y = a(x - h)^2 + k$ will open upward or downward?
   If $a > 0$ it will open up. If $a < 0$ it will open down.

2. As $|a|$ decreases what happens to the graph of $y = a(x - h)^2 + k$?
   The graph gets wider.

3. Explain the difference between the graph of $y = 2(x - 5)^2 + 3$ and $y = -2(x - 5)^2 + 3$. **See margin.**

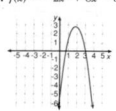

4. The equation $y = 2(x - 5)^2 + 3$ is graphed at the left. Describe the differences between this graph and the graph of $y = \frac{1}{2}(x - 5)^2 + 3$. **See margin.**

Guided Practice

5. $(9, 0)$, $x = 9$, up
6. $(-3, 0)$, $x = -3$, down
7. $(0, -6)$, $x = 0$, up
8. $(0, 6)$, $x = 0$, down
9. $(-3, -1)$, $x = -3$, up
10. $(2, -2)$, $x = 2$, down
11. $\left(-2, \frac{-4}{3}\right)$, $x = -2$, up
12. $\left(\frac{1}{2}, \frac{1}{4}\right)$, $x = \frac{1}{2}$, up

Name the vertex, axis of symmetry, and the direction of opening for the graph of each equation.

5. $y = 3(x - 9)^2$

6. $f(x) = -2(x + 3)^2$

7. $y = 5x^2 - 6$

8. $g(x) = -3x^2 + 6$

9. $y = 5(x + 3)^2 - 1$

10. $y = -2(x - 2)^2 - 2$

11. $y = (x + 2)^2 - \frac{4}{3}$

12. $h(x) = 3\left(x - \frac{1}{2}\right)^2 + \frac{1}{4}$

13. Write the equation of a parabola with position 4 units above the parabola with equation $f(x) = -2x^2$. $f(x) = -2x^2 + 4$

14. Write the equation of a parabola with position 1 unit to the right and 8 units below the parabola with equation $f(x) = 5x^2$. $f(x) = 5(x - 1)^2 - 8$

EXERCISES

Practice
A

Write each equation in the form $f(x) = a(x - h)^2 + k$. Then name the vertex, axis of symmetry, and direction of opening for the graph of each equation.
15–22. See margin.

15. $f(x) = x^2 - 4x + 5$

16. $f(x) = -x^2 - 2x + 2$

17. $f(x) = -3x^2 + 12x$

18. $f(x) = 4x^2 + 24x$

19. $f(x) = 3x^2 - 18x + 11$

20. $f(x) = -2x^2 - 20x - 50$

21. $f(x) = -\frac{1}{2}x^2 + 5x - \frac{27}{2}$

22. $f(x) = \frac{1}{3}x^2 - 4x + 15$

370   CHAPTER 8   QUADRATIC RELATIONS AND FUNCTIONS

RETEACHING THE LESSON

Given either the vertex and one point, three points, or the vertex and the value of a, write the equation of the parabola in the form $y = a(x - h)^2 + k$. Then check to see if the graph of the equation fits the given features of the parabola by using a graphing calculator or graphing software.

Additional Answers

3. They have the same vertex and axis of symmetry. They are the same shape, but the graph of $y = 2(x - 5)^2 + 3$ opens upward and the graph of $y = -2(x - 5)^2 + 3$ opens downward.

4. They have the same vertex and axis of symmetry. They both open upward, but the graph of $y = 2(x - 5)^2 + 3$ is much more narrow than the graph of $y = \frac{1}{2}(x - 5)^2 + 3$.

Write the equation of each parabola shown.

23.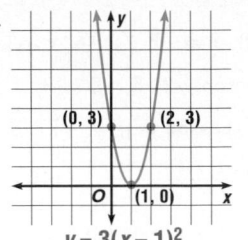
(0, 3) (2, 3)
(1, 0)
$y = 3(x - 1)^2$

24.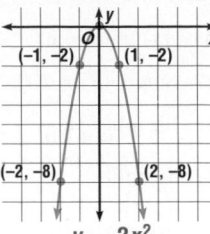
(-1, -2) (1, -2)
(-2, -8) (2, -8)
$y = -2x^2$

25.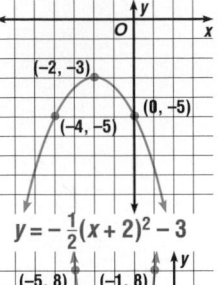
(-2, -3)
(0, -5)
(-4, -5)
$y = -\frac{1}{2}(x + 2)^2 - 3$

26.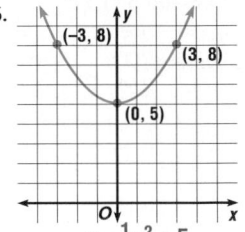
(-3, 8) (3, 8)
(0, 5)
$y = \frac{1}{3}x^2 + 5$

27.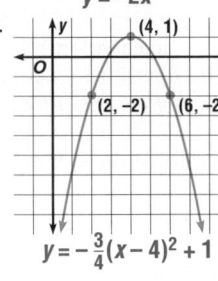
(4, 1)
(2, -2) (6, -2)
$y = -\frac{3}{4}(x - 4)^2 + 1$

28.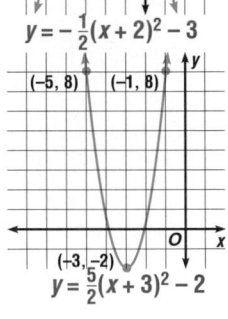
(-5, 8) (-1, 8)
(-3, -2)
$y = \frac{5}{2}(x + 3)^2 - 2$

Teaching Tip ❹

29. $y = 2x^2 - x$
30. $y = 3x^2 - 4x + 7$

Write the equation of a parabola that passes through the given points.

29. (0, 0), (2, 6), (-1, 3)

30. (1, 6), (-2, 27), (2, 11)

31. (2, -3), (0, -1), $\left(-1, 1\frac{1}{2}\right)$
$y = \frac{1}{2}x^2 - 2x - 1$

32. (1, 0), (3, 38), (-2, 48)
$y = 7x^2 - 9x + 2$

Graph each equation. **33–42. See Solutions Manual.**

33. $f(x) = 2(x + 3)^2 - 5$

34. $f(x) = 3x^2 + 18x + 27$

35. $f(x) = \frac{1}{2}(x + 3)^2 - 5$

36. $f(x) = \frac{1}{3}(x - 1)^2 + 2$

37. $f(x) = x^2 + 6x + 2$

38. $f(x) = -2x^2 + 16x - 31$

39. $f(x) = -5x^2 - 40x - 80$

40. $f(x) = 2x^2 + 8x + 10$

41. $f(x) = -9x^2 - 18x - 6$

42. $f(x) = -0.25x^2 - 2.5x - 0.25$

Critical Thinking

43. Given $f(x) = ax^2 + bx + c$ with $a \neq 0$, complete the square and rewrite the equation in the form $f(x) = a(x - h)^2 + k$. State an expression for h and k in terms of a, b, and c.

$$h = -\frac{b}{2a}, \quad k = \frac{4ac - b^2}{4a} \text{ or } c - \frac{b^2}{4a}$$

Application

44. Architecture The Gateway Arch of the Jefferson National Expansion Memorial in St. Louis is shaped like the parabola whose equation is $f(x) = \frac{1}{315}(-2x^2 + 1260x)$.

  a. Write the equation of the arch in the form $f(x) = a(x - h)^2 + k$.

  b. If the bases of the arch are 630 feet apart, how tall is the arch? **630 ft**

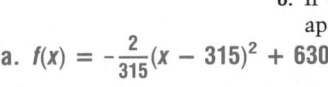
44a. $f(x) = -\frac{2}{315}(x - 315)^2 + 630$

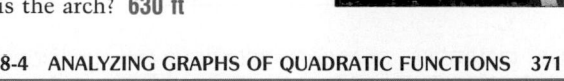
LESSON 8-4 ANALYZING GRAPHS OF QUADRATIC FUNCTIONS **371**

Additional Answers

15. $f(x) = (x - 2)^2 + 1$
(2, 1); $x = 2$; up

16. $f(x) = -(x + 1)^2 + 3$
(-1, 3); $x = -1$; down

17. $f(x) = -3(x - 2)^2 + 12$
(2, 12); $x = 2$; down

18. $f(x) = 4(x + 3)^2 - 36$
(-3, -36); $x = -3$; up

19. $f(x) = 3(x - 3)^2 - 16$
(3, -16); $x = 3$; up

20. $f(x) = -2(x + 5)^2$
(-5, 0); $x = -5$; down

21. $f(x) = -\frac{1}{2}(x - 5)^2 - 1$
(5, -1); $x = 5$; down

22. $f(x) = \frac{1}{3}(x - 6)^2 + 3$
(6, 3); $x = 6$; up

APPLYING THE LESSON

Homework Exercises

Assignment Guide

Basic: 15–36, 43–52
Average: 19–39, 43–52
Enriched: 23–52
All: Mid-Chapter Review, 1–13

Chapter 8, Quiz B, (Lessons 8-3 through 8-4), is available in the Evaluation Masters Booklet, p. 107.

Teaching Tip ❹ Remind students to review Example 6 if they have difficulty finding the equations.

Practice Masters Booklet, p. 60

8-4 Practice Worksheet

Analyzing Graphs of Quadratic Functions

Write each equation in the form $f(x) = a(x - h)^2 + k$. Then name the vertex, axis of symmetry, and direction of opening for the graph of each equation.

1. $f(x) = -6x^2$
$f(x) = -6x^2$;
(0, 0); $x = 0$; down

2. $y = -2x^2 - 16x - 32$
$f(x) = -2(x + 4)^2$;
(-4, 0); $x = -4$; down

3. $h(x) = \frac{2}{3}x^2 + 4x + 6$
$f(x) = \frac{2}{3}(x + 3)^2$;
(-3, 0); $x = -3$; up

4. $y = 2x^2 + 16x + 29$
$f(x) = 2(x + 4)^2 - 3$;
(-4, -3);
$x = -4$; up

5. $g(x) = -9x^2 + 12x - 4$
$g(x) = -9\left(x - \frac{2}{3}\right)^2$;
$\left(\frac{2}{3}, 0\right)$;
$x = \frac{2}{3}$; down

6. $y = -3x^2 + 6x - 5$
$f(x) = -3(x - 1)^2 - 2$;
(1, -2);
$x = 1$; down

Write the equation of a parabola that passes through the given points.

7. (0, 1), (2, -1), (1, 3)
$f(x) = -3x^2 + 5x + 1$

8. (0, 0), (2, 3), (-1, 4)
$f(x) = \frac{11}{6}x^2 - \frac{13}{6}x$

Graph each equation.

9. $y = -2x^2 + 1$
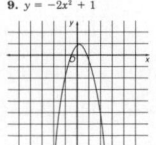

10. $f(x) = -3x^2 + 6x - 5$
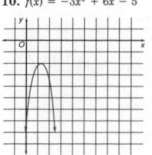

Additional Answer

52.

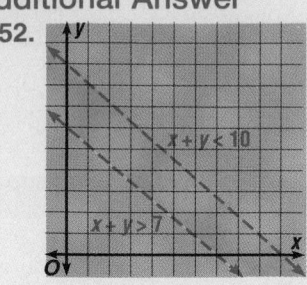

Answers to Mid-Chapter Review

3. Let n = one of the numbers; product = $50n - n^2$

4. Let l = the length; area = $21l - l^2$

6. They have the same shape, but the graph of $y = (x - 7)^2$ is shifted 7 units to the right.

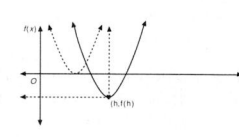

Mixed Review Name the vertex and the axis of symmetry for the graph of each equation. (Lesson 8-4)

45. $f(x) = (x + 2)^2$ **(-2, 0), $x = -2$** **46.** $y = (x - 3)^2 - 11$ **(3, -11), $x = 3$**

47. Solve $8s^2 = 200$. (Lesson 7-2) **5, -5**

48. Simplify $(1 - \sqrt{3})^2$. (Lesson 6-3) **$4 - 2\sqrt{3}$**

49. Simplify $\dfrac{18x^3yz^2 + 27x^2yz + 45x^2y^2z^2}{9xyz}$. (Lesson 5-6) **$2x^2z + 3x + 5xyz$**

50. State whether the expression $3xy + x$ is a monomial. If it is, name its coefficient and degree. (Lesson 5-1) **no**

51. Determine whether the system $\begin{cases} 5x + y - z = 0 \\ 2x - y = 7 \\ 3y + 5z = 0 \end{cases}$ has a unique solution. (Lesson 4-7) **yes**

52. Solve the system $\begin{cases} x + y > 7 \\ x + y < 10 \end{cases}$ by graphing. (Lesson 3-4) **See margin.**

~ MID-CHAPTER REVIEW ~

Express each function in quadratic form. (Lesson 8-1)

1. $g(x) = (x + 2)^2$ **$g(x) = x^2 + 4x + 4$**   **2.** $f(x) = 3(x - 5)^2 + 4$ **$f(x) = 3x^2 - 30x + 79$**

Define a variable and write an equation to describe each situation. (Lesson 8-1)

3. the product of two numbers whose sum is 50 **See margin.**

4. the area of a rectangle whose perimeter is 42 centimeters **See margin.**

5. You want to make a rectangular potholder with the maximum surface on each side. However, you only have 36 inches of piping to put around the edge of the potholder. Make a table to determine the best dimensions for the potholder. (Lesson 8-2) **9 in. × 9 in.**

6. Compare the graphs of $y = (x - 7)^2$ and $y = x^2$. (Lesson 8-3) **See margin.**

Name the vertex and axis of symmetry for each equation. (Lesson 8-3)

7. $f(x) = 3(x - 2)^2 - 4$ **(2, -4), $x = 2$**
8. $y = (x + 4)^2$ **(-4, 0), $x = -4$**
9. $y = x^2 + 4x + 10$ **(-2, 6), $x = -2$**
10. $g(x) = x^2$ **(0, 0), $x = 0$**

11. Write the equation of the parabola that is 2 units to the right of the parabola whose equation is $y = (x + 2)^2 + 3$. (Lesson 8-4) **$y = x^2 + 3$**

Write each equation in the form $f(x) = a(x - h)^2 + k$. Then name the vertex, axis of symmetry, and direction of opening for the graph of each equation. (Lesson 8-4)

12. $f(x) = x^2 + 6x + 3$ **$f(x) = (x + 3)^2 - 6$**
 (-3, -6), $x = -3$, up

13. $f(x) = -9x^2 - 18x - 10$ **$f(x) = -9(x + 1)^2 - 1$, (-1, -1), $x = -1$, down**

EXTENDING THE LESSON

Math Power: Reasoning

Describe the graph of $f(x) = ax^2 + bx + \dfrac{b^2}{4a}$ where $a \neq 0$.

A parabola in the form $f(x) = a\left(x + \dfrac{b}{2a}\right)^2$; The vertex is $\left(-\dfrac{b}{2a}, 0\right)$. The axis of symmetry is $x = -\dfrac{b}{2a}$. The graph opens upward if $a > 0$ and downward if $a < 0$. The graph is tangent to the x-axis.

Mid-Chapter Review

The Mid-Chapter Review provides students with a brief review of the concepts and skills in Lessons 8-1 through 8-4. Lesson numbers are given at the end of problems or instruction lines so students may review concepts not yet mastered.

Applications of Quadratic Equations

Objective
8-5

After studying this lesson, you should be able to:
- solve problems using quadratic equations.

Application

Ken Virkus has 1200 feet of fencing material to build a pen for his sheep and goats. The pen will be a rectangle with a divider down the middle as shown at the right.

What is the maximum area for the pen? What are the dimensions of the pen with the maximum area?

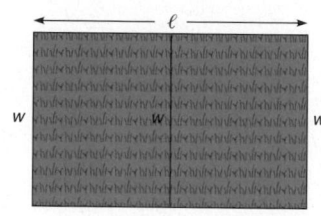

Let w = the width of the pen and ℓ represent the length. So, $2\ell + 3w = 1200$. To express the area in one variable, solve for ℓ in terms of w.

Teaching Tip ❶

$$2\ell + 3w = 1200$$
$$\ell = \frac{1200 - 3w}{2}$$
$$\ell = 600 - 1.5w$$

The area of the two pens is represented by $A = w(600 - 1.5w)$. Simplify the expression $w(600 - 1.5w)$ and complete the square. **Teaching Tip ❷**

$$A = w(600 - 1.5w)$$
$$= 600w - 1.5w^2$$
$$= -1.5(w^2 - 400w)$$
$$= -1.5(w^2 - 400w + 40,000) - (-1.5)(40,000)$$
$$= -1.5(w - 200)^2 + 60,000$$

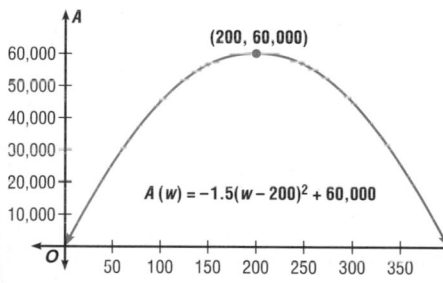

$A(w) = -1.5(w - 200)^2 + 60,000$

The graph of this equation is a parabola with vertex (200, 60,000). Since the parabola opens downward, the vertex is a maximum point. The first coordinate of the maximum point represents the width of the rectangular pen. The length is $600 - 1.5(200)$ or 300 feet. The second coordinate of the maximum point represents the maximum area of the pen, 60,000 square feet.

Many problems ask you to find a **maximum** or **minimum value.** If you can write a quadratic function to describe the situation in these problems, you can probably solve it by finding the coordinates of the vertex of the function. The vertex of a parabola that opens downward represents a maximum point of the function. The vertex of a parabola opening upward represents a minimum point of the function.

LESSON 8-5 APPLICATIONS OF QUADRATIC EQUATIONS **373**

ALTERNATE TEACHING STRATEGIES

Using Discussion
Students should discuss the following questions.

1. Does every quadratic relation have a maximum or minimum value?
2. Does every quadratic function have a maximum or minimum value?
3. What coordinate of the vertex represents the maximum or minimum value?

8-5 Lesson Notes

Lesson Resources
Reteaching Master 8-5
Practice Master 8-5
Enrichment Master 8-5
Multicultural Activity Master, p. 8

 Transparency 8-5 contains the 5-Minute Check and a teaching aid for this lesson.

INTRODUCING THE LESSON

🕐 **5-Minute Check**

(over Lesson 8-4)
Use $f(x) = 5(x + 3)^2 - 1$ to solve Exercises 1–4.

1. Name the vertex of the graph of the function. **(−3, −1)**
2. Name the axis of symmetry of the graph of the function. **x = −3**
3. Name the direction of opening for the graph of the function. **upward**
4. Graph the function.

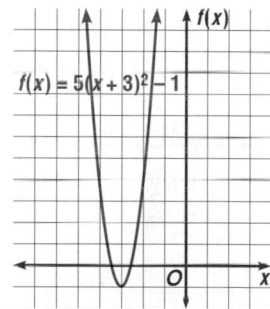

$f(x) = 5(x + 3)^2 - 1$

5. Write the equation of the parabola passing through (0, 3), (1, 0), and (2, 3). **$f(x) = 3(x - 1)^2$**

Motivating the Lesson
Give each student an $8\frac{1}{2}'' \times 11''$ piece of paper. Have them make a tray by cutting congruent squares from each corner. Then fold the sides up and tape them. Have each student determine the volume of his or her tray. Put a chart on the chalkboard to keep track of the dimensions and volume for each tray. Is there a maximum volume?

Teaching Tip ① Remind students that the perimeter of the rectangle will be 1200 feet.

Teaching Tip ② Have students refer to Lesson 7-3 to review completing the square.

Chalkboard Examples

For Example 1
Find two numbers whose sum is 26 and whose product is a maximum.   **13, 13**

For Example 2
A hot dog vendor sells an average of 160 hot dogs per day for $1.00 each. He needs to raise the price, but the other vendors tell him that for every nickel increase in price, he'll lose 5 customers. What should the price be to maximize profit?   **$1.30**

Example 1

Find two numbers whose difference is 48 and whose product is a minimum.

Explore   Let n represent the lesser number. Then $n + 48$ represents the greater number.

Plan   Product $= n(n + 48)$
               $= n^2 + 48n$

Solve   This is the equation of a quadratic function. Write the equation in the form $y = a(x - h)^2 + k$ to find the vertex. Let y represent the product of the two numbers.

$y = n^2 + 48n$
$\quad = n^2 + 48n + \left(\dfrac{48}{2}\right)^2 - \left(\dfrac{48}{2}\right)^2$ *Complete the square.*
$\quad = (n + 24)^2 - 576$

The vertex is $(-24, -576)$. So, the minimum product, -576, occurs when n is -24. When $n = -24$, $n + 48 = -24 + 48$ or 24.

Examine   Let's check some other pairs of numbers with a difference of 48 to see that their product is not less than -576.

$(-23)(25) = -575 \qquad (-20)(28) = -560 \qquad (-15)(33) = -495$

Example 2

APPLICATION

Business

A ferry transports tourists to the Middle Bass Island on Lake Erie during the summer months. The one-way fare is $6.00 a person and 200 people ride the ferry each day. The owner estimates that for every $0.50 the fare is raised, they will lose 10 customers. What should the fare be for the greatest income for the ferry owner?

Let p represent the number of $0.50 price increases.
Then $6 + 0.5p$ represents the fare and $200 - 10p$ represents the number of passengers.

Income = (number of passengers) × (fare)
Income $= (200 - 10p) \qquad\quad × (6 + 0.5p)$
$\qquad\quad = 1200 + 100p - 60p - 5p^2$
$\qquad\quad = 1200 + 40p - 5p^2$

Complete the square to find the vertex of the parabola.
Income $= 1200 + 40p - 5p^2$
$\qquad\quad = -5(p^2 - 8p) + 1200$
$\qquad\quad = -5(p^2 - 8p + 16) + 1200 - (-5)(16)$ *Complete the square.*
$\qquad\quad = -5(p - 4)^2 + 1280$

The vertex is $(4, 1280)$. So the maximum income, $1280, occurs when the owner raises the fare 4 times. The total increase will be $4(0.50)$ or $2.00. Therefore, a fare of $6.00 + $2.00 or $8.00 will maximize the owner's income.

374   CHAPTER 8   QUADRATIC RELATIONS AND FUNCTIONS

CHECKING FOR UNDERSTANDING

Communicating Mathematics

Read and study the lesson to answer these questions.

1. Describe a situation where someone would want to find the maximum value of a function. **sample answers: income and area**

2. Why does the vertex of a parabola represent a maximum value when the parabola opens downward and a minimum value when the parabola opens upward? **No values will be higher, or lower, than the vertex.**

3. Does the quadratic function $f(x) = 3(x - 3)^2 + 5$ have a minimum value? If so, where does the minimum value occur? **yes, at (3, 5)**

4. Look back at Example 2. How many price increases should the owner of the ferry make if they would lose 20 people for every $0.50 increase in fare? What would the fare be after that change? **no increases—decrease the price one time by $0.50 for a fare of $5.50.**

Guided Practice

5. Find two numbers whose difference is -20 and whose product is a minimum.

   a. Let x represent the lesser number. Write an expression for the greater number. **x + 20**
      5b. **x(x + 20) or x² + 20x**

   b. Write an expression for the product of the two numbers.

   c. Draw a graph relating the lesser number to the product of the two numbers. Place x on the horizontal axis and the product on the vertical axis. **See margin.**

   d. What are the two numbers? **−10 and 10**

6. **Business** The circulation of the Charlotte Arts Council Newsletter is 50,000. Due to increased production costs, the council must increase the current price of 40¢ a copy. According to a recent survey, the circulation of the newsletter will decrease 5000 for each 10¢ increase in price.

   a. Let p represent the number of 10¢ price increases. Write an algebraic expression to describe the decreased circulation after the price increase. **50,000 − 5000p**
      6b. **0.40 + 0.10p**

   b. Write an algebraic expression for the increased price per copy.

   c. The Arts Council's income from the newsletter is the product of the number of copies sold and the price per copy. This is a function of the number of price increases. Write an equation to describe the function.

   d. Draw a graph relating the Arts Council's income to the number of price increases. Use the number of price increases for the x-axis and the income in dollars for the y-axis. **See margin.**

   e. What price per copy will maximize the Arts Council's income from the newsletter? **70¢**

6c. See margin.

LESSON 8-5 APPLICATIONS OF QUADRATIC EQUATIONS 375

Checking for Understanding

Exercises 1–6 are designed to help you assess understanding through reading, writing, and speaking. You should work through Exercises 1–4 with your students, and then monitor their work on Exercises 5–6.

Closing the Lesson

Writing Activity Have students write a word problem that uses maximum or minimum values.

Additional Answers

5c.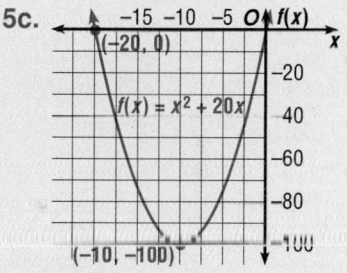

6c. income
$$= (50,000 - 5000p)(0.40 + 0.10p)$$
$$= 20,000 + 5000p - 2000p - 500p^2$$
$$= 20,000 + 3000p - 500p^2$$
$$= -500(p - 3)^2 + 24,500$$

6d.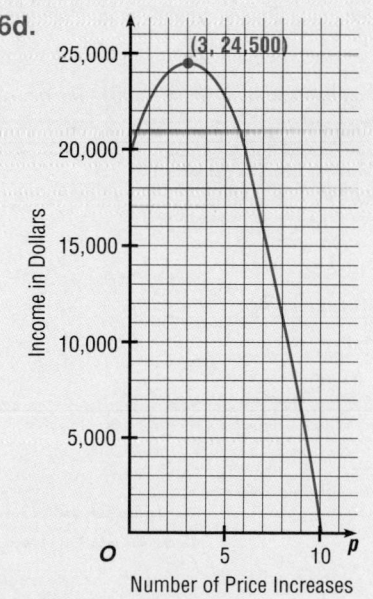

Homework Exercises

Assignment Guide
Basic: 7–20, 27–28, 30–35
Average: 9–23, 27–35
Enriched: 12–35

Chapter 8, Quiz C, (Lesson 8-5), is available in the Evaluation Masters Booklet, p. 108.

Teaching Tip ❸ Drawing a picture of the situation may help in developing an equation for the problem.

Reteaching Masters Booklet, p. 53

EXERCISES

Practice

Solve each problem.

A

7. Find two numbers whose sum is 36 and whose product is a maximum. **18, 18**

8. Find two numbers whose difference is 40 and whose product is a minimum. **−20, 20**

9. $\dfrac{37}{2}, \dfrac{37}{2}$

9. Find two numbers whose sum is 37 and whose product is a maximum.

10. $-\dfrac{25}{2}, \dfrac{25}{2}$

10. Find two numbers whose difference is 25 and whose product is a minimum.

11. −8, −8

11. The sum of x and y is −16. Find x and y so that xy is a maximum.

B

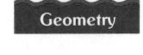

CONNECTION
Geometry

12. A rectangle has a perimeter of 40 meters. Find the dimensions of the rectangle with the maximum area. **10 m × 10 m**

13. Find the dimensions and maximum area of a rectangle whose perimeter is 24 inches. **6 in. by 6 in.; 36 sq.in.**

Teaching Tip ❸

Application

14. Melissa Hart plans to put a fence around her rectangular garden. She has 150 feet of fencing material to make the fence. If there is to be a 10 foot opening left for an entrance on one side of the garden, what dimensions should the garden be for maximum area? **40 ft by 40 ft**

15. Marc Jesson has 120 feet of fence to make a rectangular kennel for his dogs. If the house is to be used as one side of the kennel, what would be the length and width for maximum area? **60 ft × 30 ft**

16. A tour bus carries tourists through the historic district of Savannah, Georgia, serving 300 customers a day. The charge is $8.00 per person. The company owner estimates that the company would lose 20 passengers a day for each $1 increase in the fare. What charge would be most profitable for the tour bus company? **$11.50**

17. The Hoosier Commuter Airline transports about 800 passengers a week between Chicago and Fort Wayne. A round-trip ticket is $300. The company executives estimate that for each $5 increase in the ticket price, 10 passengers would be lost to the competition. What ticket price would maximize income for the company? **$350**

18. An object is fired upwards from the top of a 200 foot tower at a velocity of 80 feet per second. The height of the object t seconds after firing is given by the formula $h(t) = -16t^2 + 80t + 200$. Find the maximum height reached by the object and the time that that height is reached.

19. The Center Stage Community Theater can seat 500 people. They sold out for every performance last season. They intend to raise the $3.00 admission price for the upcoming season. They estimate that for every $0.20 increase in price, 25 fewer people will attend a performance. What ticket price will maximize the theater's income? **$3.50**

18. **300 ft, 2.5 seconds**

20. It costs the Fresh Air Fan Company $(20x + 1000)$ dollars to produce x ceiling fans. They sell the fans for $(300 - 2x)$ dollars each. How many fans should the company produce each month to maximize their profit? **70**

RETEACHING THE LESSON

A theater seats 975 people. It is filled to capacity for each show. Tickets cost $4.75 per person. The owner estimates that for each $0.30 price increase, 32 fewer people will attend. Write the equation that can be used to find the ticket price to maximize her income.

$$y = (975 - 32p)(4.75 + 0.30p)$$

21. Lian is making a box to collect paper for the school paper drive. She cuts a 5 centimeter square from each corner of a rectangular piece of cardboard and folds the sides up to make the box. If the perimeter of the bottom of the box must be 50 centimeters, what should the length, width, and height of the box be for maximum volume? **12.5 cm by 12.5 cm by 5 cm**

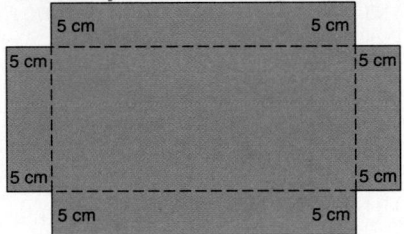

22. A rectangle is inscribed in an isosceles triangle. The base of the triangle is 8 inches and the height is 10 inches. Find the dimensions of the inscribed rectangle with maximum area. **5 in. by 4 in.**

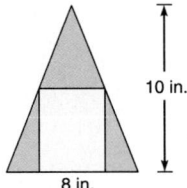

10 in.

8 in.

23. Zach and Amy cut a 32-inch piece of wire into two pieces. Amy bent one piece into a square and Zach bent the other into a rectangle that is 2 inches longer than it is wide. How long should they have cut each piece so that the sum of the areas of the square and the rectangle are minimized? **16 inches**

24. Two hundred people came to last year's winter play at Meadowbrook High School. The ticket price was $2. Since the Drama Club is planning a trip to a Broadway play, they would like to price the tickets so that they earn the maximum amount of money possible. They estimate that for each 25¢ increase in the price, 10 fewer people will come to the play. How much should the tickets be? **$3.50**

25. Physics A ball is thrown straight up with an initial velocity of 64 feet per second. The height of the ball t seconds after it is thrown is given by the formula $h(t) = 64t - 16t^2$. What is the height of the ball after 1.5 seconds? What is its maximum height? After how many seconds will it return to the ground? **60 ft; 64 ft; 4 seconds**

26. Business The Images Camera Shop can sell 21 KS-2 Cameras a month at $120 each. The owner estimates that for each $5 decrease in price they could sell three more of these cameras a month. The cameras cost the store $75 each. If the store sells all of the cameras bought each month, what should they charge for a camera to maximize profit? What is the maximum profit? **$115; $960**

Critical Thinking

27. Find two numbers whose sum is a and whose product is a maximum. $\dfrac{a}{2}, \dfrac{a}{2}$

LESSON 8-5   APPLICATIONS OF QUADRATIC EQUATIONS   377

Computer When an object is hurled upward, its height s, above the ground is given as a function of time by the formula $s = -16t^2 + v_0 t + s_0$. The height is in feet and the time is in seconds. The initial velocity is symbolized by v_0 and s_0 is the initial height. The BASIC program below finds the height and the time, given the initial velocity and initial height. **Teaching Tip 4**

```
10   PRINT "ENTER THE INITIAL VELOCITY."
20   INPUT VO
30   PRINT "ENTER THE INITIAL HEIGHT."
40   INPUT SO
50   PRINT
60   PRINT "TIME", "HEIGHT"
70   DEFFNS(T) = -16*T^2 + VO*T + SO
80   LET T = 0
90   PRINT T, FNS(T)
100  LET T = T + 1
110  IF FNS(T) < 0 THEN 130
120  GOTO 90
130  END
```

28. Enter an initial velocity of 256 feet per second and an initial height of 0 feet.

    a. How long will the object be airborne? **16 seconds**

    b. What is the greatest height the object will reach? **1024 feet**

    c. When will the object be at a height of 768 feet? **4 and 12 seconds**

29. Suppose a baseball is thrown upward from a height of six feet at an initial velocity of 88 feet per second.

    a. How far off the ground will the ball be after one second? **78 feet**

    b. About how long will the ball be in the air? **between 5 and 6 seconds**

    29c. about 3 seconds   c. At about what time will the ball reach its greatest height?

    d. Approximately what is the greatest height the ball will reach? **126 feet**

Mixed Review

30. What is the remainder of the division $8^{100} \div 5$? **(Lesson 8-2) 1**

31. Write the equation of a parabola with position 3 units to the right of the parabola with equation $f(x) = x^2$. **(Lesson 8-4) $f(x) = (x - 3)^2$**

32. Find a value of c that makes $x^2 - 8x + c$ a perfect square. **(Lesson 7-3) 16**

33. Simplify $(3 + 2i)(4 - i)$. **(Lesson 6-9) $14 + 5i$**

34. Factor $9x^2 - 12x + 4$. **(Lesson 5-6) $(3x - 2)^2$**

35. State the row operations you would use to obtain a zero in the second column of row one of $\begin{bmatrix} -2 & 1 & 0 \\ 0 & 4 & 12 \end{bmatrix}$. **(Lesson 4-7) Answers may vary.**

EXTENDING THE LESSON

Math Power: Problem Solving

Find the dimensions and area of the largest pen that can be formed with 120′ of flexible fence in each of the following shapes.

a. triangle   **40′, 40′, 40′; $400\sqrt{3}$ sq ft**

b. rectangle   **30′ by 30′; 900 sq ft**

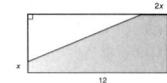
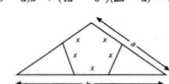
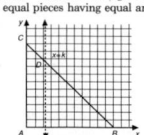
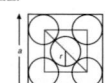

Graphing Quadratic Inequalities

Objective
8-6

After studying this lesson, you should be able to:
- graph quadratic inequalities.

Application

Discovery Audio Inc. makes compact disks. According to their recent sales figures, their profit can be found by the inequality $P(x) \leq -0.003x^2 + 9x - 1500$, where x is the number of CDs sold in a week. The relation is an inequality because it is based on the list price of the CDs, and the company often charges record stores less than list price when they buy in great quantities.

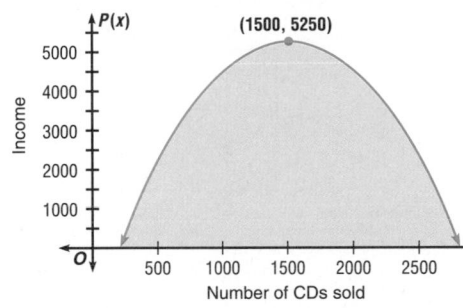

Number of CDs sold

Notice that the boundary is solid. You can determine whether the boundary is solid or broken the same way that you do with a linear inequality.

The graph of this inequality is the part of the plane enclosed by the parabola whose equation is $P(x) = -0.003x^2 + 9x - 1500$. The parabola is the **boundary** of each region. Points on the parabola represent the profit if all of the CDs are sold at list price. Points in the interior of the curve represent profits if some of the CDs were sold for a price below list price.

Teaching Tip ❶

Example 1

Graph $y \leq -3x^2 + 12x - 2$.

Complete the square on the right side.

$$y \leq -3x^2 + 12x - 2$$
$$y \leq -3(x^2 - 4x) - 2$$
$$y \leq -3(x^2 - 4x + 4) - 2 - (-3)(4)$$
$$y \leq -3(x - 2)^2 + 10$$

The boundary is a parabola with vertex $(2, 10)$ that opens downward. Test points not on the parabola to see whether points above or below the parabola belong to the graph. **Teaching Tip ❷**

Region below parabola

Test $(2, 0)$: $y \leq -3x^2 + 12x - 2$
$$0 \leq -3(2)^2 + 12(2) - 2$$
$$0 \leq -12 + 24 - 2$$
$$0 \leq 10$$

belongs

Region above parabola

Test $(5, 0)$: $y \leq -3x^2 + 12x - 2$
$$0 \leq -3(5)^2 + 12(5) - 2$$
$$0 \leq -75 + 60 - 2$$
$$0 \leq -17$$

does not belong

LESSON 8-6 GRAPHIC QUADRATIC INEQUALITIES **379**

8-6 Lesson Notes

Lesson Resources
Reteaching Master 8-6
Practice Master 8-6
Enrichment Master 8-6

 Transparency 8-6 contains the 5-Minute Check and a teaching aid for this lesson.

INTRODUCING THE LESSON

⏱ 5-Minute Check
(over Lesson 8-5)

1. Find two numbers whose sum is 12 and whose product is a maximum. **6, 6**
2. Find two numbers whose difference is 64 and whose product is a minimum. **−32, 32**
3. A rectangle has a perimeter of 36 cm. Find the dimensions of the rectangle with the maximum area. **9 cm by 9 cm**
4. Find the area of the rectangle in Exercise 3. **81 cm²**
5. Marci has 78 inches of molding to make into a picture frame. What dimensions should the frame be if the picture is the maximum size for the frame? **19.5 in. by 19.5 in.**

Motivating the Lesson
Have students graph $3x + 8 \geq y$. Ask them to discuss each step in determining the type of line the boundary should be and which part of the graph should be shaded. Ask them what they think they should do if the boundary of an inequality was a parabola.

ALTERNATE TEACHING STRATEGIES

Using Logical Reasoning
Have the students draw a graph for $y > x^2 + 2x + 1$.

1. What would be the first step in graphing the inequality?
2. How can you decide which side of the boundary to shade without testing a point? Can you decide without testing a point?
3. Which point would be the easiest to test in each case? Why?

Teaching Tip ❶ Emphasize that the process for graphing quadratic inequalities is the same process as the process for graphing linear inequalities.

Teaching Tip ❷ Ask students if this graph has a maximum or minimum. How can they determine this from the graph?

Chalkboard Examples

For Example 1

Graph $y < x^2 + 3x - 4$.

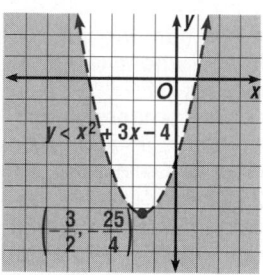

For Example 2

A flower bed is 3 ft longer than it is wide. Find the possible dimensions if the area of the flower bed is at least 40 square feet. **length ≥ 8 ft; width 3 ft less than the length**

Reteaching Masters Booklet, p. 54

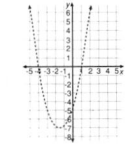
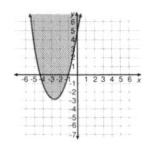 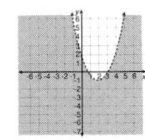
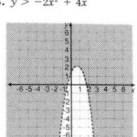 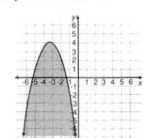

Shade the region below the parabola. Since the inequality contains a "less than or equal" symbol, the boundary is included. So the graph of the parabola itself is solid.

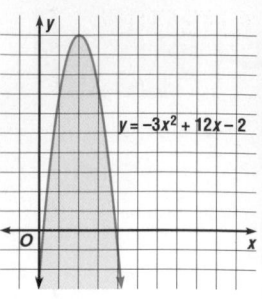

$y = -3x^2 + 12x - 2$

Example 2

CONNECTION

Geometry

A rectangle is 2 inches longer than it is wide. Find the possible dimensions if the area of the rectangle is more than 224 square inches.

Draw a diagram of the rectangle.

Let w represent the width of the rectangle. The length would be represented by $w + 2$. Thus, the area of the rectangle is $w(w + 2)$.

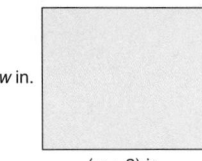

w in.

$(w + 2)$ in.

So, $w(w + 2) > 224$.

$$w(w + 2) > 224$$
$$w^2 + 2w > 224$$
$$w^2 + 2w - 224 > 0$$
$$(w^2 + 2w + 1) - 224 - 1 > 0$$
$$(w + 1)^2 - 225 > 0$$

The boundary of the graph of this relation is a parabola with vertex $(-1, -225)$ that opens upward. Test a point off of the boundary to determine which region should be included in the graph.

Test $(0, 0)$: $w(w + 2) > 224$
$$0(0 + 2) > 224$$
$$0 > 224$$

Since $(0, 0)$ is above the parabola and it does not satisfy the inequality, the region below the parabola is included in the graph.

The graph includes points that have negative values. Since lengths and areas cannot be negative, these values should be disregarded in determining the solution. So allowing only positive values, the width of the rectangle should be greater than 14 and the length should be greater than 16.

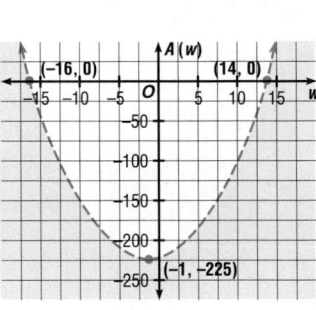

$(-16, 0)$ $(14, 0)$

$(-1, -225)$

RETEACHING THE LESSON

Each parabola itself is correctly graphed. Determine if the boundary and shaded portion are correct for the inequality given.

1. $y \geq x^2$

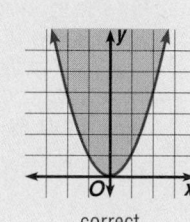

correct

2. $y \leq x^2 + 3$

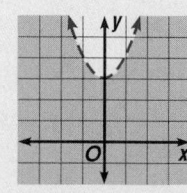

boundary incorrect

3. $y > -x^2 - 4$

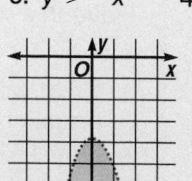

shading incorrect

CHECKING FOR UNDERSTANDING

Communicating Mathematics

Read and study the lesson to answer these questions.

1. Should the boundary of the graph of $y < 2x^2 + 3x - 5$ be solid or broken? Explain. **See margin.**

2. The equation $y = x^2 - 6x + 5$ is graphed at the right. If you were to graph the inequality $y \geq x^2 - 6x + 5$, would you include the region above or below the parabola? Explain why.

2. See margin.

3. Why were the points with negative coordinates disregarded in Example 2?
   Lengths and areas cannot be negative.

$y = x^2 - 6x + 5$

Guided Practice

Determine if the ordered pair is a solution of the given inequality.

4. $y > x^2$, $(3, 2)$ **no**

5. $y > (x - 2)^2$, $(0, 5)$ **yes**

6. $y \geq x^2 - 16$, $(-3, 0)$ **yes**

7. $y \leq -3x^2 + 5$, $(2, -7)$ **yes**

8. $y \leq 2(x + 3)^2$, $(-2, 3)$ **no**

9. $y \geq 5x^2 - 6x$, $(1, 1)$ **yes**

10. $y \geq 4x^2 - 8x - 13$, $(3, -1)$ **yes**

11. $y < -0.5x^2 + 9x - 2$, $(16, 15)$ **no**

EXERCISES

Practice

Draw the graph of each inequality. **12–27. See Solutions Manual.**

A

12. $y \leq (x + 3)^2$

13. $y > x^2 + 2x + 1$

14. $y \geq x^2 + 8x + 16$

15. $y > x^2 - 10x + 25$

16. $y \geq x^2 - 49$

17. $y \leq x^2 - 16$

B

18. $y \geq x^2 + 3x - 18$

19. $y \leq x^2 - 13x + 36$

20. $y > x^2 + x - 30$

21. $y > x^2 - x - 20$

22. $y \leq x^2 + 6x + 8$

23. $y < 2x^2 + x - 3$

C

24. $y > 4x^2 - 8x + 3$

25. $y \leq -x^2 - 7x + 10$

26. $y < 3x^2 + 5x + 2$

27. $y > -4x^2 - 3x - 6$

CONNECTION
Geometry

28. A rectangle is 5 centimeters longer than it is wide. Find the possible dimensions if the area of the rectangle is more than 104 square centimeters.
The width is greater than 8 centimeters.

Critical Thinking

29. Find the intersection of the graphs of $y \geq x^2 - 3$ and $y \leq x^2 + 3$. **See margin.**

Applications

30. **Forensic Science** A criminalist is investigating a shooting of a police helicopter. A weapon was found with a suspect's fingerprints. The criminalist has deduced that the weapon is capable of firing with an initial velocity of 1100 feet per second, so the height of the bullet t seconds after firing is found by the function $h(t) = -16t^2 + 1100t$. The helicopter was flying at an altitude of 7000 feet at the time it was shot. Tell how you can determine whether it is possible that this gun shot the helicopter.
Use the function to determine if the bullet can reach a height of 7000 ft.

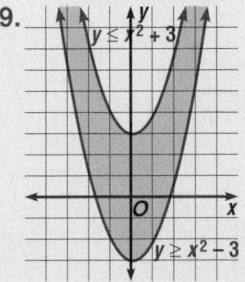

LESSON 8-6 GRAPHING QUADRATIC INEQUALITIES 381

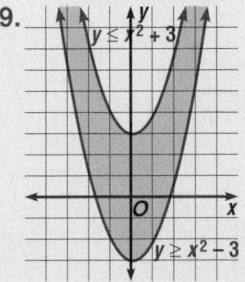
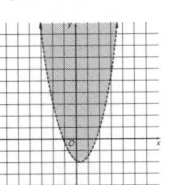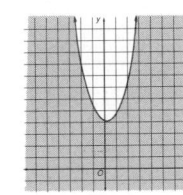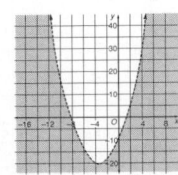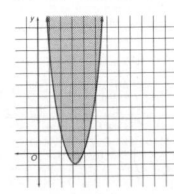

Homework Exercises

See assignment guide on page 381.

Substitute values for *x* and *f*(*x*). 30 ≠ -460.3. The ball hits the ground about 337 ft from the plate.

31. **Sports** Kristin's homerun hit traveled in a path described by the function $f(x) = -0.003x^2 + x + 4$ where *x* represents the number of feet the ball has traveled from the plate and $f(x)$ represents the height of the ball. If the scoreboard is 30 feet high and 410 feet from the plate, show that Kristin's homerun ball did not hit the scoreboard.

Mixed Review

32. The cruise ship *The Silver Dollar* was rented to take 100 passengers to the Green Mountain Resort. The fare is $5 per person. The owner of the cruise ship has agreed to reduce the fare by 2¢ per passenger for every passenger over 100 in the group. How many passengers will produce a maximum profit for the owner? **(Lesson 8-5) 175**

33. Find two numbers whose difference is -40 and whose product is a minimum. **(Lesson 8-5) -20, 20**

34. Solve the equation $y^2 - 16y + 10$ using the quadratic formula. **(Lesson 7-4) $8 \pm 3\sqrt{6}$**

35. Simplify $\sqrt{\dfrac{8}{9}}$. **(Lesson 6-2) $\dfrac{2\sqrt{2}}{3}$**

36. **Astronomy** Venus has an average distance of 1.08×10^8 kilometers from the Sun. Saturn has an average distance of 1.428×10^9 kilometers from the Sun. About how much closer to the Sun is Venus? **(Lesson 5-1) 1.32×10^9 kilometers**

Journal
Use graphs of quadratic equations to draw a sketch of a roller coaster ride. Be use to include the equation of each graph.

HISTORY CONNECTION

Hypatia (370–415 A.D.) was the first recorded woman mathematician. Her beauty and talents were legendary at a time when Greek mathematics was neither appreciated nor encouraged. Her lectures at the University of Alexandria were well attended by scholars from Europe, Asia, and Africa. She often spoke about the works of Diophantus and other Greek scholars and wrote a text called *On the Conics of Appollonius,* in which she described graphs such as the parabola.

The diagram at the right illustrates her definition of a parabola as the path of all points the same distance from a fixed point called the focus *F* and a fixed line. A group of concentric circles is drawn with *F* as their center. The fixed line is line 0. Lines parallel to line 0 are drawn tangent to each circle. If you connect the points where the circles intersect the parallel lines, the parabola is formed.

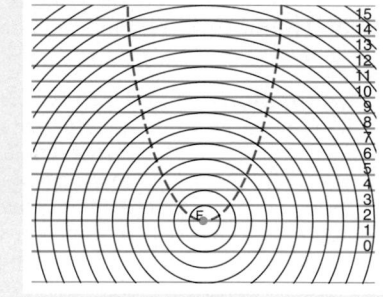

382 CHAPTER 8 QUADRATIC RELATIONS AND FUNCTIONS

EXTENDING THE LESSON

Math Power: Problem Solving

Solve $(x - 3)(x + 4)(x - 1) > 0$. **-4 < x < 1 or x > 3**

History Connection

The History Connection features introduce students to persons or cultures who were involved in the development of mathematics. You may want students to further research Hypatia or to research the study of other graphs.

Enrichment Masters Booklet, p. 54

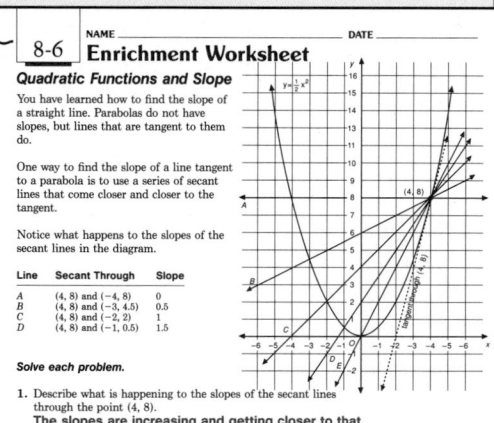

Solving Quadratic Inequalities

Objective
8-7
After studying this lesson, you should be able to:
■ solve quadratic inequalities in one variable.

Application

The Corporate Commuter Airline, CCA, transports 500 people a week from Atlanta to Washington, D.C. The round trip fare is currently $400. CCA is in a fare war with competing airlines, and company officials estimate that for every $10 decrease in the fare at most 25 passengers will choose them over their competitor. If it costs $144,000 a week to run the airline, how many $10 decreases could the airline make and not lose money?

There are many different changes in the airfare that Corporate Commuter could make that would make the airline remain profitable, since quadratic inequalities have an infinite number of solutions. Let's graph the inequality for the situation described above to find the solution.

First write the inequality. Let x represent the number of $10 price decreases and y represent the profit.

Profit = (number of passengers)(fare) − cost   *Since it is "at most 25 passengers,"*
$y \leq (500 + 25x)(400 - 10x) - 144,000$ *this is an inequality.*
$y \leq 200,000 - 5000x + 10,000x - 250x^2 - 144,000$
$y \leq -250x^2 + 5000x + 56,000$
$y \leq -250(x^2 - 20x + 100) + 56,000 + 25,000$ *Complete the square.*
$y \leq -250(x - 10)^2 + 81,000$

Now graph the inequality. It is a parabola with vertex (10, 81,000) that opens downward. The axis of symmetry is $x = 10$.

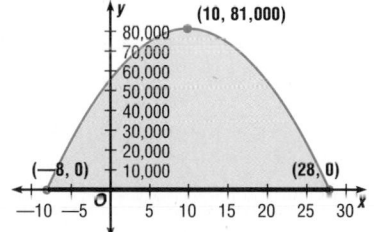

We are looking for all the points where Corporate Commuter is not losing money. That would be where the profit is greater than or equal to 0. Each point on the x-axis has a y-coordinate of 0. So the points on the x-axis that satisfy $y \leq -250(x - 10)^2 + 81,000$ are solutions to the inequality $0 \leq -250(x - 10)^2 + 81,000$. Those solutions are $\{x | -8 \leq x \leq 28\}$. **Teaching Tip ❶**

LESSON 8-7   SOLVING QUADRATIC INEQUALITIES   383

ALTERNATE TEACHING STRATEGIES

Using Communication
Discuss how a company makes a profit. From the given information, when will the Corporate Commuter Airline, CCA, lose money? Why is it possible for the airline to lose money even though they are getting more passengers? How could you change the problem so the company will not lose money?

Lesson Resources
Reteaching Master 8-7
Practice Master 8-7
Enrichment Master 8-7

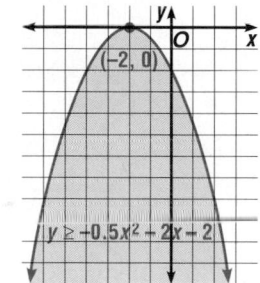 Transparency 8-7 contains the 5-Minute Check and a teaching aid for this lesson.

INTRODUCING THE LESSON

5-Minute Check
(over Lesson 8-6)

1. Graph $y \leq -0.5x^2 - 2x - 2$.

Other Prerequisite Skills

2. Solve $(x - 1)^2 - 25$.   **6, −4**
3. Solve $x^2 + 4x - 96 = 0$.
   8, −12
4. Solve $2x(x - 4) = 3(1 - x)$.
   3, $-\frac{1}{2}$

Motivating the Lesson
It costs the Fresh Fan Company $(20x + 1000)$ dollars to produce a ceiling fan. They sell each fan for $(300 - 2x)$ dollars. If they sell 150 fans will they make a profit? If they sell 200 fans do they make a profit?

TEACHING THE LESSON

Teaching Tip ❶   Ask students to explain how a negative number can express the number of decreases in fare.

We could also solve the inequality algebraically.

$0 \le -250x^2 + 5000x + 56{,}000$ *The company is not losing money as long as profit is greater than or equal to 0.*

$0 \le -250(x^2 - 20x - 224)$ *Factor.*

$0 \le -250(x - 28)(x + 8)$

$0 \ge (x - 28)(x + 8)$ *Divide each side by -250 and reverse the inequality.*

The product of two numbers is negative if one number is negative and one is positive, so we can write the following.

$(x - 28)$ is negative.		$(x + 8)$ is negative.
$x - 28 \le 0$ and $x + 8 \ge 0$		$x - 28 \ge 0$ and $x + 8 \le 0$
$x \le 28$ and $x \ge -8$	or	$x \ge 28$ and $x \le -8$
$-8 \le x \le 28$		never true

The graphs of $x \ge 28$ and $x \le -8$ never intersect, so $x \ge 28$ and $x \le -8$ can never be true.

Solving $0 \le -250x^2 + 5000x + 56{,}000$ either graphically or algebraically produces the solution $\{x|-8 \le x \le 28\}$. So, Corporate Commuter would not lose money if they lower their fare between -8 and 28 times inclusive.
If they were to lower the fare -8 times, they would actually be increasing the $10 fare 8 times.

Example 1

A ball is thrown upward with an intial velocity of 64 feet per second. The formula $h(t) = 64t - 16t^2$ gives the height of the ball after t seconds. During what time span is the ball in flight?

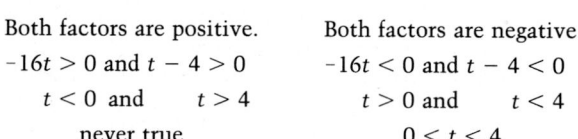

The ball is in flight as long as its height is greater than 0. We can find the times that the ball is in flight by solving the inequality $0 < 64t - 16t^2$.

$$0 < 64t - 16t^2$$
$$0 < -16t(t - 4)$$

The product of two numbers is positive if both of the numbers are positive or both are negative.

Both factors are positive.	Both factors are negative.
$-16t > 0$ and $t - 4 > 0$	$-16t < 0$ and $t - 4 < 0$
$t < 0$ and $t > 4$	$t > 0$ and $t < 4$
never true	$0 < t < 4$

The solution set is $\{t|0 < t < 4\}$. So the ball is in flight between 0 and 4 seconds after it is thrown.

Example 2

Solve $(x - 7)(x + 2) > 0$.

Teaching Tip ❷

Another way that you can solve quadratic inequalities is by using three test points. First solve the equation $(x - 7)(x + 2) = 0$.

$$(x - 7)(x + 2) = 0$$
$$x - 7 = 0 \text{ or } x + 2 = 0$$
$$x = 7 \qquad x = -2 \qquad \textit{These solutions are called \underline{critical points}.}$$

The points 7 and -2 separate the x-axis into three parts: $x < -2$, $-2 < x < 7$, and $x > 7$.

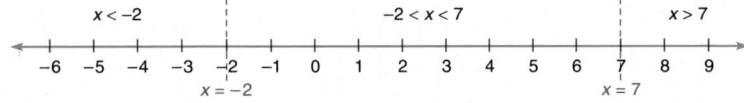

Choose a value from each of the parts and substitute it into $(x - 7)(x + 2) > 0$. Make a table to organize your results.

Part of x-axis	Point, x	$(x - 7)(x + 2)$	Is $(x - 7)(x + 2) > 0$?
$x < -2$	-3	$((-3) - 7)((-3) + 2) = 10$	yes
$-2 < x < 7$	0	$(0 - 7)(0 + 2) = -14$	no
$x > 7$	8	$(8 - 7)(8 + 2) = 10$	yes

The parts of the x-axis whose points are solutions to $(x - 7)(x + 2) > 0$ belong to the solution set. So the solution set is $\{x|x < -2 \text{ or } x > 7\}$.

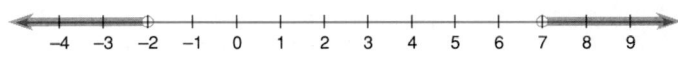

CHECKING FOR UNDERSTANDING

Communicating Mathematics

Read and study the lesson to answer these questions.

1. Why might the Corporate Commuter Airline want to charge a fare that will not give maximum profit? **sample answer: to undercut the competition**

2. What is the solution set for the inequality graphed at the right? $\{x|x < -5 \text{ or } x > 3\}$

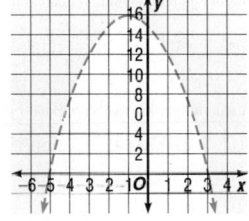

3. What points would you test to find the solution to $(x + 8)(x - 10) > 0$? **sample answer: any number less than -8, one greater than 10, and one between -8 and 10**

RETEACHING THE LESSON

An alternate strategy to solve polynomial inequalities is to use a sign chart of the factors and product.

Example: $(x - 7)(x + 2) > 0$

value of x	-6	-4	-2	0	1	3	5	7	9
sign of $(x - 7)$	$-$	$-$	$-$	$-$	$-$	$-$	$-$	0	$+$
sign of $(x + 2)$	$-$	$-$	0	$+$	$+$	$+$	$+$	$+$	$+$
sign of product	$+$	$+$	0	$-$	$-$	$-$	$-$	0	$+$
points on graph where product is > 0									

Teaching Tip ❷ Ask students why they should use three test points and from where should they be picked.

EVALUATING THE LESSON

Checking for Understanding
Exercises 1–16 are designed to help you assess understanding through reading, writing, and speaking. You should work through Exercises 1–3 with your students, and then monitor their work on Exercises 4–16.

Reteaching Masters Booklet, p. 55

Closing the Lesson

Speaking Activity Explain two methods for solving quadratic inequalities.

Guided Practice

4. one > 0 and one < 0
5. both > 0 or both < 0
6. both > 0 or both < 0
7. one ≥ 0 and one ≤ 0
8. one > 0 and one < 0
9. both > 0 or both < 0
10. one ≥ 0 and one ≤ 0
11. one ≥ 0 and one ≤ 0

State the signs of the factors of each quadratic inequality.

4. $(x - 9)(x + 1) < 0$
5. $(x + 5)(x - 9) > 0$
6. $(x + 11)(x - 1) > 0$
7. $(x - 8)(x - 2) \leq 0$
8. $(x + 20)(x - 20) < 0$
9. $(x + 1)(x - 3) > 0$
10. $x^2 + 6x - 27 \leq 0$
11. $x^2 + 9x + 20 \leq 0$
12. $x^2 - x - 90 > 0$ both > 0 or both < 0
13. $2x^2 + 3x + 1 \leq 0$ one ≥ 0 and one ≤ 0

State the solution set for each inequality graphed below.

14.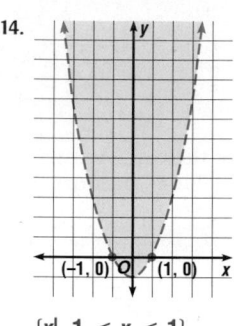

15. 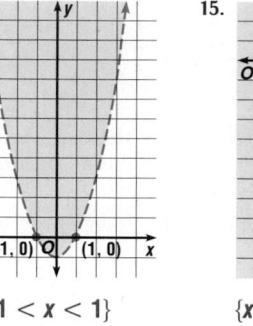 (3, 0) (6, 0)

16.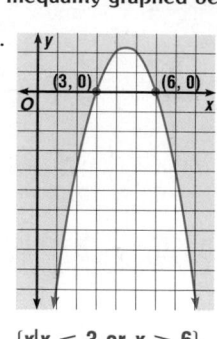

$\{x|-1 < x < 1\}$ $\{x|x \leq 3 \text{ or } x \geq 6\}$ $\varnothing$

EXERCISES

Practice

19. $\{n|n \geq 2.5 \text{ or } n \leq -3.8\}$ Ⓐ
20. $\{x|-7 < x < 3\}$
21. $\{q|q \geq 4 \text{ or } q \leq -6\}$
22. $\{m|m > 2 \text{ or } m < -3\}$ Ⓑ
24. $\left\{s|s < -\frac{4}{3} \text{ or } s > \frac{1}{2}\right\}$
31. $\left\{x|x > \frac{5\sqrt{2}}{2} \text{ or } x < \frac{-5\sqrt{2}}{2}\right\}$
34. $\left\{v|v = \frac{1}{3}\right\}$
36. $\left\{g|-\frac{1}{2} < g < 3\right\}$
37. $\left\{x|x > \frac{1}{3} \text{ or } x < -2\right\}$

Solve each inequality. 17. $\{x|x > -2 \text{ or } x < -9\}$ 18. $\{a|3 \leq a \leq 10\}$

17. $(x + 2)(x + 9) > 0$
18. $(a - 10)(a - 3) \leq 0$
19. $(n - 2.5)(n + 3.8) \geq 0$
20. $x^2 + 4x - 21 < 0$
21. $q^2 + 2q \geq 24$
22. $m^2 + m - 6 > 0$
23. $2b^2 - b < 6$ $\left\{b|-\frac{3}{2} < b < 2\right\}$
24. $6s^2 + 5s > 4$
25. $p^2 - 4p \leq 5$ $\{p|-1 \leq p \leq 5\}$
26. $x^2 - 4x \leq 0$ $\{x|0 \leq x \leq 4\}$
27. $w^2 \geq 2w$ $\{w|w \leq 0 \text{ or } w \geq 2\}$
28. $c^2 \leq 49$ $\{c|-7 \leq c \leq 7\}$
29. $d^2 \geq 3d + 28$ $\{d|d \leq -4 \text{ or } d \geq 7\}$
30. $b^2 \geq 10b - 25$ $\{\text{all reals}\}$
31. $2x^2 > 25$
32. $t^2 + 12t \leq -27$ $\{t|-9 \leq t \leq -3\}$
33. $f^2 + 12f + 36 < 0$ $\varnothing$ Ⓒ
34. $9v^2 - 6v + 1 \leq 0$
35. $8d + d^2 \geq -16$ $\{\text{all reals}\}$
36. $2g^2 - 5g - 3 < 0$
37. $-5x - 3x^2 < -2$
38. $n^2 \leq 3$ $\{n|-\sqrt{3} \leq n \leq \sqrt{3}\}$
39. $4t^2 - 9 < -4t$ $\left\{t|\frac{-1 - \sqrt{10}}{2} < t < \frac{-1 + \sqrt{10}}{2}\right\}$
40. $-2 > -6r - 9r^2$ $\left\{r|r > \frac{-1 + \sqrt{3}}{3} \text{ or } r < \frac{-1 - \sqrt{3}}{3}\right\}$

Critical Thinking

Solve each inequality. 41–46. See margin.

41. $(x - 1)(x - 3)(x + 4) > 0$
42. $(x - 8)(x + 2)(x + 4) \leq 0$
43. $(x - 3)(x + 6)(x + 2) < 0$
44. $(x + 5)(x + 6)(x + 7) \geq 0$
45. $(x + 5)(x + 1)(x - 4)(x - 6) > 0$
46. $(x - 2)(x + 2)(x - 1)(x + 3) \geq 0$

386   CHAPTER 8   QUADRATIC RELATIONS AND FUNCTIONS

Additional Answers

41. $\{x|-4 < x < 1 \text{ or } x > 3\}$
42. $\{x|x \leq -4 \text{ or } -2 \leq x \leq 8\}$
43. $\{x|x < -6 \text{ or } -2 < x < 3\}$
44. $\{x|-7 \leq x \leq -6 \text{ or } x \geq -5\}$
45. $\{x|x < -5 \text{ or } -1 < x < 4 \text{ or } x > 6\}$
46. $\{x|x \leq -3 \text{ or } -2 \leq x \leq 1 \text{ or } x \geq 2\}$

47. **Sports** The instant replay facility at the Superdome was moved because it was hit by a high punt kicked by Oakland Raider Ray Guy. The original position of the facility was 90 feet above the playing field. Colin, a high school punter, can kick a football with an initial velocity of 65 feet per second. The height of the football t seconds after he kicks it is found by the function $h(t) = -16t^2 + 65t$. If Colin were to have kicked a football in the Superdome before the instant replay facility was moved, would he have been able to hit it? **no**

48. **Landscaping** Mr. and Mrs. Ortiz are making an English garden in their backyard which they plan to surround with decorative stones. They have enough stones to enclose a rectangular garden with a perimeter of 68 feet. They would like the area of the garden to be at least 240 square feet. What could the width of the garden be? **$10 \leq w \leq 24$**

49. **Business** Judy runs a shuttle bus for the Department of Recreation. She charges \$1 per person to ride from the High School to the Community Recreation Center. About 100 students ride the shuttle bus each week. Judy estimates that for every 20¢ she lowers the fare 5 more students would ride each week. If the cost of running the shuttle is \$66 a week, how many 20¢ decreases in fare could Judy make without having to subsidize the shuttle bus program?
Let n = number of decreases; $-17 \leq n \leq 2$; up to 2 decreases in fare

Mixed Review

50. Is $(4, -4)$ a solution to the quadratic inequality $y \leq -x^2 + 5x$? (**Lesson 8-6**) **yes**

51. Graph $y > x^2 - 7x + 10$. (**Lesson 8-6**) **See margin.**

52. Identify the quadratic term, the linear term, and the constant term of the function $f(x) = x^2 + 3x - 2$. (**Lesson 8-1**) **x^2; $3x$; -2**

53. Solve $d^{\frac{1}{3}} = 4$. (**Lesson 7-6**) **64**

54. Simplify $(\sqrt{3a} + \sqrt{2b})(\sqrt{15a} - \sqrt{3b})$. (**Lesson 6-3**)
$3a\sqrt{5} = 3\sqrt{ab} + \sqrt{30ab} - b\sqrt{6}$

55. Factor $a^2 - b^2 + 8b - 16$. (**Lesson 5-5**) **$(a - b + 4)(a + b - 4)$**

56. **Number Theory** The sum of the digits of a three digit number is 13. The tens' digit is 1 less than the ones' digit. The hundreds' digit is 2 less than twice the sum of the ones' and tens' digits. Find the number. (**Lesson 4-4**) **823**

LESSON 8-7 SOLVING QUADRATIC INEQUALITIES 387

Portfolio

Review the items in your portfolio. Make a table of contents of the items, noting why each item was chosen. Replace any items that are no longer appropriate.

EXTENDING THE LESSON

Math Power: Reasoning

Solve $(x - 1)^3(x + 1) \leq (x - 1)(x + 1)^3$.
$\{x \mid -1 \leq x \leq 0 \text{ or } x \geq 1\}$

Additional Answer

51.
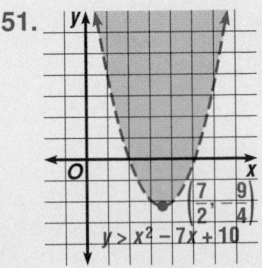
$y > x^2 - 7x + 10$

Enrichment Masters Booklet, p. 55

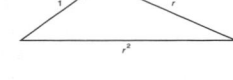

8-7 **Enrichment Worksheet**
NAME _____ DATE _____

Quadratic Relationships in Triangles

The **triangle inequality** states that the sum of any two sides of a triangle is greater than the length of the third side. For the triangle in the diagram, the sides measure 1, r, and r^2.

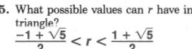

Solve each problem.

1. Write an inequality comparing the sum of the two shorter sides to the longest side.
$1 + r > r^2$

2. Solve the inequality from problem 1 for r.
$r < \frac{1 + \sqrt{5}}{2}$

3. Compare the sum of the two longer sides to the shortest side.
$r^2 + r > 1$

4. Solve the inequality in problem 3 for r.
$r > \frac{-1 + \sqrt{5}}{2}$

5. What possible values can r have in the triangle?
$\frac{-1 + \sqrt{5}}{2} < r < \frac{1 + \sqrt{5}}{2}$

6. A Golden Rectangle has sides r and 1 that satisfy the proportion $r : 1 = (r + 1) : r$. Solve for r and relate this answer to the results of problem 5.
$r = \frac{1 + \sqrt{5}}{2}$; the range of values for r in the triangle lies between $\frac{1 + \sqrt{5}}{2}$ and $\frac{-1 + \sqrt{5}}{2}$.

Look for the so-called golden ratio, $\frac{1 + \sqrt{5}}{2}$, to appear as you solve the following problems. Triangles ABC and A'B'C' are both isosceles, with AY = XB and A'Y' = X'B'.

7. Write a proportion showing that the sides of triangles ABC and ACX form equal ratios. Use b for the length of the long side of triangle ABC.
$\frac{b}{b} = \frac{b - a}{a}$

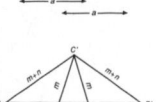

8. Let the ratio $b{:}a$ equal r. Solve the proportion in problem 7 for r.
$\frac{a}{a} = \frac{b}{a} - 1$, so $\frac{1}{r} = r - 1$; $r = \frac{1 + \sqrt{5}}{2}$

9. Show that triangles ABC and $A'B'C'$ are similar by finding the ratio r' in the triangle $A'B'C'$.
$\frac{m + n}{2m + n} = \frac{m}{m + n}$; for $r' = \frac{2m + n}{m + n}$,
$\frac{m + n}{2m + n} = \frac{2m + n}{m + n} - \frac{m + n}{m + n}$ and $\frac{1}{r'} = r' - 1$.

So, $r = r'$ and the figures are similar.

388 Chapter 8

Using the Chapter Summary and Review

The Chapter Summary and Review begins with an alphabetical listing of the new terms that were presented in the chapter. Have students define each term and provide an example of it, if appropriate.

The Skills and Concepts presented in the chapter are reviewed using a side-by-side format. Encourage students to refer to the Objectives and Examples on the left as they complete the Review Exercises on the right.

The Chapter Summary and Review ends with exercises that review Applications and Connections.

Additional Answers

7.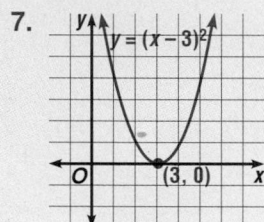

8.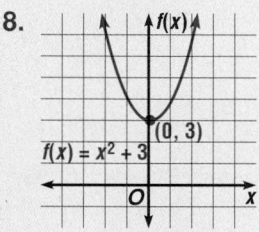

17.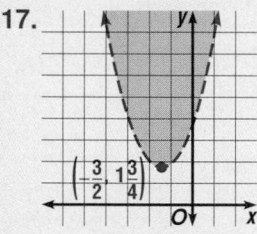

VOCABULARY

Upon completing this chapter, you should be familiar with the following terms:

axis of symmetry	360	373	minimum value
boundary	379	360	parabola
constant term	353	353	quadratic function
half plane	379	353	quadratic term
linear term	353	360	vertex
maximum value	373		

SKILLS AND CONCEPTS

OBJECTIVES AND EXAMPLES	REVIEW EXERCISES

Upon completing this chapter, you should be able to:

Use these exercises to review and prepare for the chapter test.

■ write functions in quadratic form **(Lesson 8-1)**

Express each function in quadratic form.

1. $f(x) = (x + 2)^2$ $f(x) = x^2 + 4x + 4$

2. $h(x) = 2(x - 4)^2 + 6$ $h(x) = 2x^2 - 16x + 38$

Express $g(x) = (3x - 1)^2$ in quadratic form.

$$g(x) = 9x^2 - 6x + 1$$

■ identify the quadratic term, the linear term, and the constant term of a quadratic function   **(Lesson 8-1)**

For each function, identify the quadratic term, the linear term, and the constant term.

3. $f(x) = 3x^2 + 2x - 1$ $3x^2; 2x; -1$

4. $g(x) = x^2 + 4x - 2$ $x^2; 4x; -2$

For $f(x) = 2x^2 + x - 5$, the quadratic term is $2x^2$, the linear term is x, and the constant term is -5.

OBJECTIVES AND EXAMPLES

■ graph quadratic equations of the form $y = (x - h)^2 + k$ (**Lesson 8-3**)

Graph $y = (x + 1)^2 - 1$.

The vertex is $(-1, -1)$.
The axis of symmetry is $x = -1$.

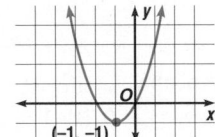

(-1, -1)

■ identify the vertex and the equation of the axis of symmetry of a parabola (**Lesson 8-3**)

The function $f(x) = x^2 - 2x + 3$ written in the form $f(x) = (x - h)^2 + k$ is $f(x) = (x - 1)^2 + 2$. The vertex is $(1, 2)$. The axis of symmetry is $x = 1$.

■ graph equations of the form $y = a(x - h)^2 + k$ and identify the vertex, the equation of the axis of symmetry, and the direction of the opening (**Lesson 8-4**)

The function $f(x) = 2x^2 - 8x + 9$ written in the form $f(x) = a(x - h)^2 + k$ is $f(x) = 2(x - 2)^2 + 1$. The vertex is $(2, 1)$. The axis of symmetry is $x = 2$. The graph opens upward.

14. $g(x) = \frac{1}{3}(x + 3)^2 + 4$, **(-3, 4)**, $x = -3$, **up**

■ solve problems using quadratic equations (**Lesson 8-5**)

If you are asked to find a maximum or minimum value, write a quadratic function to describe the situation by finding the coordinates of the vertex of the functions.

REVIEW EXERCISES

Write the equation of each parabola if its equation has the form $y = (x - h)^2 + k$.

5.
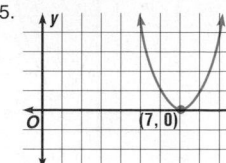
(7, 0)
$y = (x - 7)^2$

6.
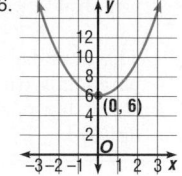
(0, 6)
$y = x^2 + 6$

Graph each equation. **See margin.**

7. $y = (x - 3)^2$ **8.** $f(x) = x^2 + 3$

Write each equation in the form $f(x) = (x - h)^2 + k$. Then name the vertex and the axis of symmetry for the graph of each function.

9. $f(x) = x^2 - 2x + 1$
$f(x) = (x - 1)^2$, **(1, 0)**, $x = 1$
10. $g(x) = x^2 + 6x + 3$
$g(x) = (x + 3)^2 - 6$, **(-3, -6)**, $x = -3$

Write each equation in the form $f(x) = a(x - h)^2 + k$. Then name the vertex, axis of symmetry, and direction of opening for the graph of each equation.

11. $f(x) = x^2 - 2x + 4$
$f(x) = (x - 1)^2 + 3$, **(1, 3)**, $x = 1$, **up**
12. $h(x) = -3x^2 + 18x$
$h(x) = -3(x - 3)^2 + 27$, **(3, 27)**, $x = 3$, **down**
13. $f(x) = -2x^2 - 40x + 10$
$f(x) = -2(x + 10)^2 + 210$, **(-10, 210)**, $x = -10$, **down**
14. $g(x) = \frac{1}{3}x^2 + 2x + 7$

15. Find two numbers whose difference is 5 and whose product is a minimum. $\frac{5}{2}$, $-\frac{5}{2}$

16. Geometry Find the dimensions and maximum area of a rectangle whose perimeter is 80 cm. **20 cm × 20 cm, 400 cm²**

Additional Answers

18.
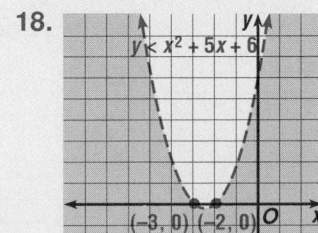
$y < x^2 + 5x + 6$
(-3, 0) (-2, 0)

19.
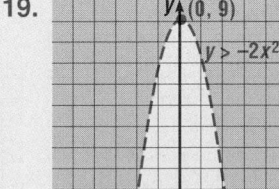
(0, 9)
$y > -2x^2 + 9$

20.
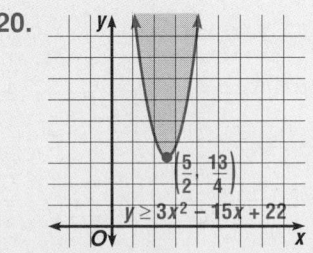
$\left(\frac{5}{2}, \frac{13}{4}\right)$
$y \geq 3x^2 - 15x + 22$

The Cumulative Review shown below can be used to review skills and concepts presented thus far in the text. Standardized Test Practice Questions are also provided in the Evaluation Masters Booklet.

Evaluation Masters Booklet, pp. 109–110

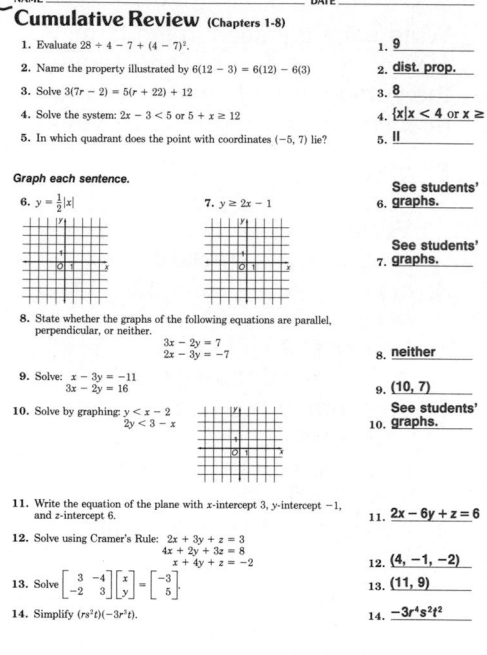
OBJECTIVES AND EXAMPLES	REVIEW EXERCISES

■ graph quadratic inequalities (Lesson 8-6)

Graph $y \geq (x - 2)^2 + 1$.

The boundary is a parabola with vertex (2, 1) that opens upward.

Draw the graph of each inequality. See margin.

17. $y > x^2 + 3x + 4$

18. $y < x^2 + 5x + 6$

19. $y > -2x^2 + 9$

20. $y \geq 3x^2 - 15x + 22$

■ solve quadratic inequalities in one variable. (Lesson 8-7)

To solve an inequality, either graph the inequality or use three test points to determine the solutions.

Solve each inequality.

21. $(x - 10)(x + 1) < 0$ {x|−1 < x < 10}

22. $x^2 + 8x - 9 > 0$ {x|x < −9 or x > 1}

23. $6 - 5a - 4a^2 \leq 0$ {a|a ≥ ¾ or a ≤ −2}

24. $m^2 - 20m \geq -100$ {all reals}

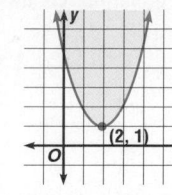

APPLICATIONS AND CONNECTIONS

25. Make a table to help you find the remainder of the division $6^{100} \div 5$. (Lesson 8-2) **1**

26. **Art** Morgan needs to paint a landscape for art class. She has 6 feet of framing material to frame the finished painting. What should the dimensions of her canvas be for the painting to be of maximum area? (Lesson 8-5) **1.5 ft × 1.5 ft**

27. **Business** Quick Cab Co. runs a taxi cab service between the airport and the business district. The charge for one-way service is $11.50. The owners estimate the 30 passengers will be lost each day for each $1.50 increase in the fare. If they currently service 320 passengers per day, what fare should they charge for maximum income? (Lesson 8-5) **$13.75**

28. **Construction** Kipp has 80 feet of fencing material to make a kennel for his springer spaniel puppies. The fence that already runs around his backyard will be used as one side of the kennel. What should the dimensions of the kennel be if Kipp wants to give the puppies as much area as possible? What is the area of the completed kennel? (Lesson 8-5) **20 ft by 40 ft; 800 square feet**

29. **Physics** The Empire State Building is 1250 feet high. If an object is thrown upward from the top of the building at an initial velocity of 35 feet per second, its height t seconds after it is thrown is given by the function $h(t) = -16t^2 + 35t + 1250$. How long will it be before the object hits the ground? (Lesson 8-5) **10 seconds**

Additional Answers, p. 391

21.
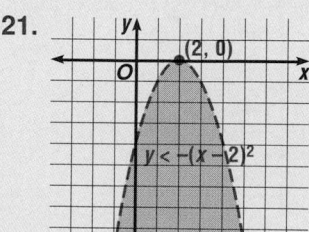
$y < -(x - 2)^2$

22.
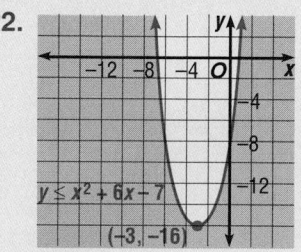
$y \leq x^2 + 6x - 7$

Bonus
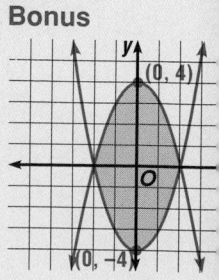

Express each function in quadratic form.

1. $f(x) = (x + 2)^2 + 4$ $f(x) = x^2 + 4x + 8$

2. $f(x) = 2(x - 3)^2 + 5$ $f(x) = 2x^2 - 12x + 23$

Write the equation of each parabola shown.

3.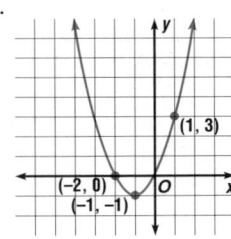

4.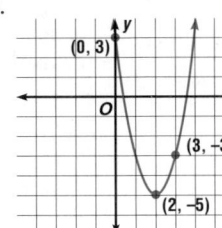

5.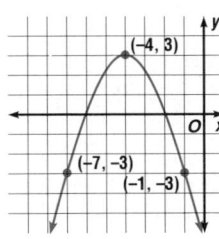

Graph each equation. Then name the vertex, the axis of symmetry, and the direction of opening for each graph. For graphs see Solutions Manual.

6. $y = (x + 3)^2$ **(-3, 0), $x = -3$, up**

7. $f(x) = -(x - 2)^2$ **(2, 0), $x = 2$, down**

8. $y = (x + 2)^2 + 1$ **(-2, 1), $x = -2$, up**

9. $f(x) = -2(x + 4)^2 + 6$ **(-4, 6), $x = -4$, down**

10. $g(x) = x^2 + 3x + 6$ $\left(-\frac{3}{2}, \frac{15}{4}\right)$**, $x = \frac{-3}{2}$, up**

11. $y = \frac{1}{2}(x + 6)^2 - 3$ **(-6, -3), $x = -6$, up**

12. $h(x) = 2x^2 + 8x + 9$ **(-2, 1), $x = -2$, up**

13. $y = x^2 - 8x + 9$ **(4, -7), $x = 4$, up**

14. $f(x) = -x^2 - 10x + 10$ **(-5, 35), $x = -5$, down**

15. $y = -\frac{2}{3}x^2 + 4x - 3$ **(3, 3), $x = 3$, down**

16. Make a table to help you find the ones digit of 8^{50}. **4**

17. Find two numbers whose difference is -22 and whose product is a minimum. **-11, 11**

18. **Geometry** A rectangle has a perimeter of 60 cm. Find the dimensions of the rectangle with the maximum area. **15 cm × 15 cm, 225 cm²**

19. **Geometry** Corey is building a fence around the vegetable garden with 60 feet of chicken wire. The side of the barn will serve as one side of the fence. Find the dimensions of the garden with the maximum area. **30 ft × 15 ft, 450 ft²**

20. **Physics** The initial velocity of a rocket shot straight upward is 40 ft/s. The height of the rocket after t seconds is given by the formula $h(t) = -16t^2 + 40t$. What is the maximum height the rocket reaches? When will it land? **25 ft, 2.5 seconds**

Draw the graph of each inequality. See margin.

21. $y < -(x - 2)^2$

22. $y \leq x^2 + 6x - 7$

Solve each inequality.

23. $(x + 6)(x - 3) < 0$ $\{x | -6 < x < 3\}$

24. $3x^2 + 2x - 5 \geq 0$ $\left\{x | x \geq 1 \text{ or } x \leq -1\frac{2}{3}\right\}$

25. $a^2 - 8a \geq 16$ **{all reals}**

Bonus Graph all points bounded by the graphs of $y = x^2 - 4$ and $y = -x^2 + 4$. **See margin.**

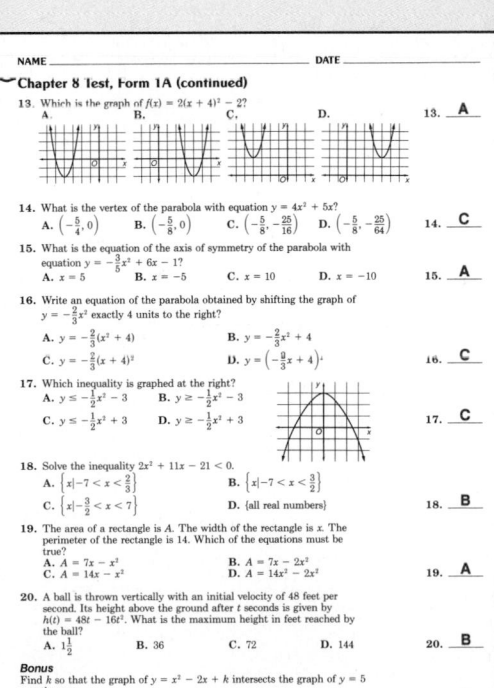

CHAPTER 8

College Entrance Exam Preview

The test questions on these pages deal with expression and equations.

Directions: Choose the one best answer. Write A, B, C, or D.

1. If $10 - 4y = 18 + 2y$, then what is the value of $3y$?
A
   (A) -4 (B) -3 (C) $\frac{-4}{3}$ (D) $\frac{4}{3}$

2. If it takes 6 hours for 4 people to paint a room, how many hours will it take 5 people, working at the same rate, to paint a room that is the same size?
B
   (A) $3\frac{1}{3}$ (B) $4\frac{4}{5}$ (C) $6\frac{1}{2}$ (D) $7\frac{1}{2}$

3. In a college lecture hall, the number of seats in each row is 25 less than the number of rows. If there are 350 seats in all, find the number of rows.
D
   (A) 10   (B) 14   (C) 25   (D) 35

4. A grocery store sold 500 candy bars for $255.00. A small candy bar sells for 40¢ and a large bar sells for 65¢. How many of the small bars were sold?
D
   (A) 55   (B) 77   (C) 220   (D) 280

5. A bottle of type B perfume costs two dollars more than 2 bottles of type C perfume. If the total cost of one bottle of each type is $32, how much more does type B cost then type C?
B
   (A) 10   (B) 12   (C) 22   (D) 32

6. If $x > 1$, which of the following increases as x increases?
C
   I. $x - \frac{1}{x}$
   II. $\frac{1}{x^2 - x}$
   III. $4x^3 - 2x^2$
   (A) I only
   (B) II only
   (C) I and III only
   (D) I, II, and III

7. Evaluate $3x^3 - 2x^2 + x - 1$ if $x = -1$.
A
   (A) -7 (B) -3 (C) -2 (D) -1

8. Eight pencils and five pens cost $5.41, while nine pencils and three pens cost $3.75. What is the cost of a pencil?
A
   (A) 12¢   (B) 15¢   (C) 38¢   (D) 89¢

9. John sold 3 less than twice the number of pizzas that Sam sold. If Sam sold x pizzas, how many more did John sell?
D
   (A) $3x - 3$ (B) $2x - 3$
   (C) $x + 3$ (D) $x - 3$

10. What is the value of $(x - y)^3$ if $y = x + 3$?
A
   (A) -27 (B) 0   (C) 6   (D) 9

11. What is the value of xy in the equation $21xy + 77 = 32xy$?
D
   (A) $\frac{-1}{7}$ (B) $\frac{1}{7}$ (C) -7 (D) 7

12. If $a^3 = 7$, then what is the value of $4a^6$?

C (A) 28   (B) 56   (C) 196   (D) 1372

13. Which is the equation of the line that
B passes through $(2, -5)$ and is parallel to
the graph of $y - 3x = 2$?

(A) $y = -3x - 11$ (B) $y = 3x - 11$
(C) $y = 3x - 5$ (D) $y = x - 7$

14. $q * t$ is defined as $q^2 + t^2 + qt$. What is
B the value of $4 * (-2)$?

(A) 4   (B) 12   (C) 26   (D) 28

15. What is the value of c if $3x^2 - 12x + c$
A is a perfect square?

(A) 12   (B) 16   (C) 36   (D) 144

16. How many real roots does the equation
B $2x^2 - 5x - 7 = 0$ have?

(A) one   (B) two   (C) none
(D) cannot be determined

17. The number of days in w weeks, d days,
C and h hours is

(A) $7w + d + 24h$ (B) $\dfrac{w + d}{7} + 24h$
(C) $7w + d + \dfrac{h}{24}$ (D) $7w + \dfrac{d - h}{24}$

18. Simplify $\dfrac{\sqrt{108}}{\sqrt{24}}$.
D

(A) $\dfrac{3}{\sqrt{2}}$ (B) $\dfrac{6\sqrt{3}}{2\sqrt{6}}$ (C) $\dfrac{\sqrt{3}}{2}$ (D) $\dfrac{3\sqrt{2}}{2}$

19. If x, y, and z are three odd consecutive
C integers and $x < y < z$, then
$(x - y)(x - z)(y - z) =$

(A) -6 (B) 6   (C) -16 (D) 16

TEST TAKING TIP

College entrance exams often introduce non standard symbols such as * or @ to define an expression. Do not be confused by such symbols. Substitute the values given into the expression.

20. If $x @ y = x^2 - y^2$ then $3 @ (-2) =$
A

(A) 5   (B) 10   (C) 13   (D) 25

21. Jana has scores of 89, 92, 76, and 85 on
B four tests. What must she score on the
next test if she wishes her average to
be 86?

(A) 90   (B) 88   (C) 86   (D) 84

22. A truck and a train leave from the same
C terminal at 9:35 A.M. If the truck travels
at 52 mph and the train travels at 84
mph, how far apart, to the nearest mile,
are they at 3:20 P.M.?

(A) 782   (B) 384   (C) 184   (D) 174

23. The cost of two audio tapes is the same
B as two-thirds the cost of a compact disk.
Mel purchased three audio tapes and
two compact disks for $45. What is the
cost of two audio tapes?

(A) $5   (B) $10   (C) $15   (D) $20

24. If $a + b = 7$ and $a^2 - b^2 = -7$, then
B $b - a =$

(A) -1 (B) 1   (C) 0   (D) 7

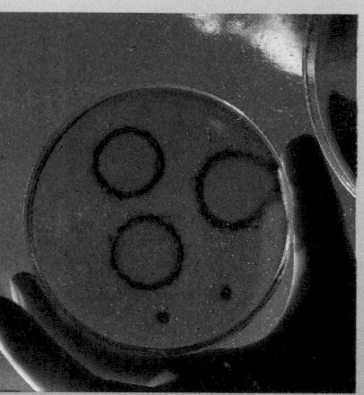

PREVIEWING THE CHAPTER

This chapter opens with the development of the formulas for finding the distance between two points and finding the midpoint of a line segment. Students then learn to identify and graph parabolas, circles, ellipses, and hyperbolas from their equations. They also learn to write the equations for these same curves given certain properties or the graph of the curve. Conic sections are classified, and students learn to identify a conic section from its quadratic equation written in standard form. Graphs and algebraic methods then are used to solve systems where one or more of the equations are quadratic equations.

Problem-Solving Strategy Students learn that they sometimes can model or simulate a situation to make a problem easier to solve.

Lesson Objective Chart

Lesson (Pages)	Lesson Objectives	State/Local Objectives
9-1 (396-399)	**9-1A:** Find the distance between two points in the coordinate plane.	
	9-1B: Find the midpoint of a line segment in the coordinate plane.	
9-2 (400-404)	**9-2A:** Write equations of parabolas.	
	9-2B: Graph parabolas from given information.	
9-3 (405-408)	**9-3A:** Write equations of circles.	
	9-3B: Draw a circle having certain properties.	
9-4 (409-415)	**9-4A:** Write equations of ellipses.	
	9-4B: Draw an ellipse having certain properties.	
9-5 (416-422)	**9-5A:** Write equations of hyperbolas.	
	9-5B: Draw hyperbolas.	
9-6 (423-424)	**9-6:** Use a simulation to help solve problems.	
9-7 (427-430)	**9-7A:** Write the equation of a conic section in standard form.	
	9-7B: Identify a conic section from its equation.	
9-8 (432-436)	**9-8:** Graph systems of quadratic equations and identify the solution sets.	
9-9 (439-443)	**9-9A:** Solve systems of equations algebraically.	
	9-9B: Solve systems of inequalities involving quadratics graphically.	

ORGANIZING THE CHAPTER

You may want to refer to the **Course Planning Calendar** on page T44.

Lesson (Pages)	Pacing Chart (days) Course			Reteaching	Practice	Enrichment	Evaluation	Technology	Lab Manual	Mixed Problem Solving	Applications	Cooperative Learning Activity	Multicultural	Transparencies
	I	II	III											
9-1 (396-399)	1	1	1	p. 56	p. 64	p. 56			pp. 39-40					9-1
9-2 (400-404)	1.5	1	1	p. 57	p. 65	p. 57	Quiz A, p. 121				p. 27	p. 45		9-2
9-3 (405-408)	1	1	0.5	p. 58	p. 66	p. 58		p. 9						9-3
9-4 (409-415)	2	1.5	1	p. 59	p. 67	p. 59	Quiz B, p. 121			p. 9				9-4
9-5 (416-422)	2	1.5	1	p. 60	p. 68	p. 60	Mid-Chapter Test, p. 120							9-5
9-6 (423-424)	1	1	1		p. 69									9-6
9-7 (427-430)	1	1	0.5	p. 61	p. 70	p. 61	Quiz C, p. 122	p. 26	pp. 59-60				p. 9	9-7
9-8 (432-436)	1	1	1	p. 62	p. 71	p. 62								9-8
9-9 (439-443)	1.5	1	1	p. 63	p. 72	p. 63	Quiz D, p. 122							9-9
Review (444-446)	1	1	1	Multiple Choice Tests, Forms 1A and 1B, pp. 113-116 Free Response Tests, Forms 2A and 2B, pp. 117-120 Cumulative Review, pp. 123-124 Standardized Test Practice Questions, p. 126										
Test (447)	1	1	1											

Course I: Chapters 1-13; Course II: Chapters 1-15; Course III: Chapters 1-17

Other Chapter Resources

Student Edition

Chapter Opener, pp. 394-395
Journal Entries, pp. 399, 435
History Connection, p. 408
Mid-Chapter Review, p. 415
Application, p. 422
Cooperative Learning Activity, p. 424
Graphing Calculator Exploration, pp. 425-426
Technology, p. 431
Graphing Calculator Exploration, pp. 437-438
Portfolio Suggestion, p. 443
Extended Project 3, pp. A10-A13

Teacher's Classroom Resources

Transparency 9-0
Real-World Applications Transparencies, 18, 19
Performance Assessment Booklet, pp. 17-18
Problem-of-the-Week Activity Cards, 18, 19
Tech Prep Applications Booklet, pp. 17-18
Lesson Plans, pp. 64-72

Other Supplements

Glencoe Mathematics Professional Series

Software

Test and Review Generator Software (Apple, IBM, and Macintosh)
Interactive Software (Macintosh)
Teacher's Guide for Software Resources

ENHANCING THE CHAPTER

Cooperative Learning

Describing the Student's Responsibilities to the Group

It is important students understand that they are expected not merely to work in a group but to work *cooperatively* in a group. Each member must accept responsibility for learning the assigned material and for making sure every other member of the group also learns the material. One way to encourage this attitude is to have the group generate a single product, report, or set of answers that each member must sign to indicate agreement with the responses and the ability to justify or explain why the responses are appropriate. Be alert to other ways to encourage group members to count on each other to look for ways to help one another do better. For example, when you give a quiz or test, you might inform the group that each member will earn his or her own individual score and will also earn bonus points based on how much the group's average score exceeds a preset level of performance.

Technology

The Technology Feature after Lesson 9-7 employs the *Mathematical Exploration Toolkit* to determine the number of solutions of a quadratic system. MET includes a powerful graphing utility with special commands to graph the conic sections. Unlike most graphing calculators, equations need not be in function form. The commands SCAN and ZOOM provide a way to obtain accurate estimates of solutions. The Guided Explorations that accompany MET include lessons specifically for circles, ellipses, and hyperbolas. Refer to the MET manual for teaching suggestions and blackline masters of student worksheets.

Critical Thinking

To encourage students to develop their critical-thinking skills, use questioning techniques that stimulate thought and investigation, such as, "What do you think will happen if ...?", "What patterns do you see?", "How can you tell?", "Can you think of an example when ...?", and so on. For example, ask students what they think will happen when |x| gets extremely large in the standard equation for an hyperbola. (The hyperbola is virtually indistinguishable from its asymptotes.) Get them to suggest ways to explore the question, make a conjecture, and demonstrate their conclusion. Begin a collection of similar questions that can be used to stimulate students' thinking as you read professional books or journals such as *The Mathematics Teacher*.

Cooperative Learning, p. 45

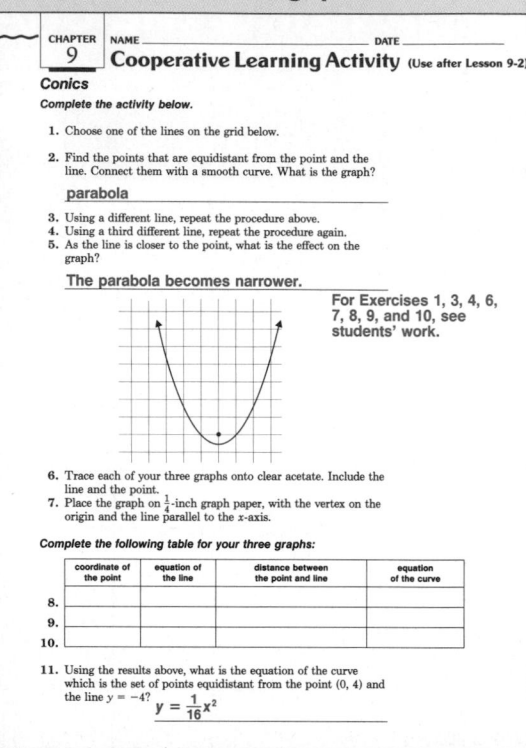

Technology, p. 9

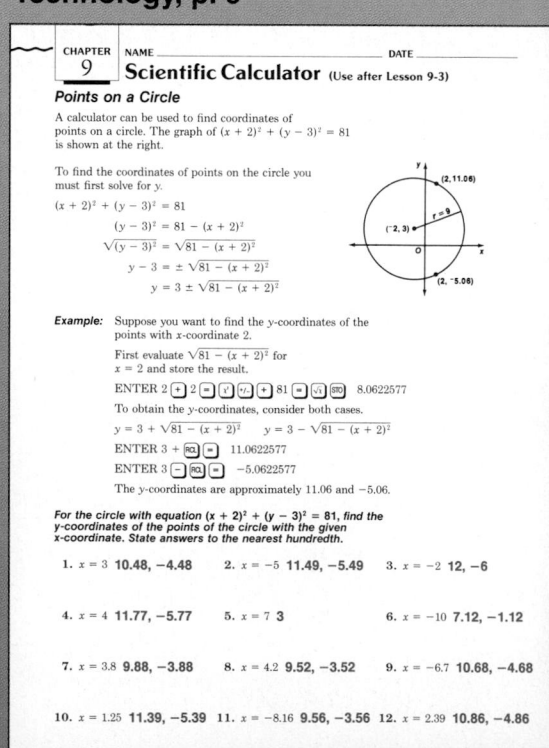

...e card shown below is one of two available for this chapter. It can ...used as a class or small group activity.

...ctivity Card

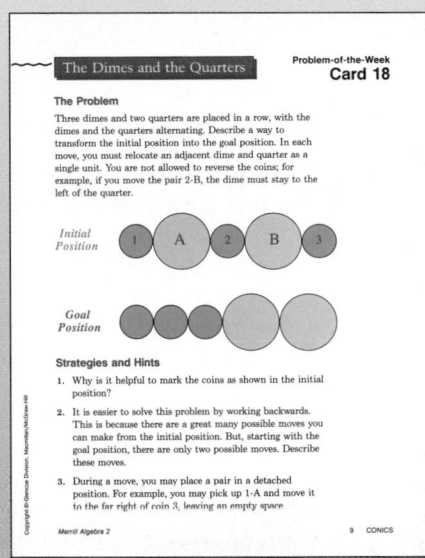

The Dimes and the Quarters

Problem-of-the-Week
Card 18

The Problem

Three dimes and two quarters are placed in a row, with the dimes and the quarters alternating. Describe a way to transform the initial position into the goal position. In each move, you must relocate an adjacent dime and quarter as a single unit. You are not allowed to reverse the coins; for example, if you move the pair 2-B, the dime must stay to the left of the quarter.

Initial Position

Goal Position

Strategies and Hints

1. Why is it helpful to mark the coins as shown in the initial position?

2. It is easier to solve this problem by working backwards. This is because there are a great many possible moves you can make from the initial position. But, starting with the goal position, there are only two possible moves. Describe these moves.

3. During a move, you may place a pair in a detached position. For example, you may pick up 1-A and move it to the far right of coin 3, leaving an empty space.

Merrill Algebra 2   9   CONICS

Manipulatives and Models

...ne following materials may be used as models or manipulatives in ...hapter 9.

- geoboard (Lesson 9-1)
- wax paper (Lesson 9-2)
- string (Lesson 9-3 and 9-7)
- ...ack (Lesson 9-3)
- flashlight (Lesson 9-4)
- circular key ring (Lesson 9-5)
- wood (Lesson 9-7)

- drill (Lesson 9-7)
- geometric figures (Lesson 9-7)
- graphing calculator (Lesson 9-8)
- twelve 1-cm squares (Lesson 9-9)

Outside Resources

...ooks/Periodicals

...ray, Jeremy. *Ideas of Space*. Clarendon Press.

...osamentier, Alfred and William Wernick. *Advanced Geometric Constructions*. Dale Seymour Publications.

...ilms/Videotapes/Videodiscs

...onic Sections, Phoenix/BFA Films and Video, Inc., 468 Park Ave., New YorK, NY 10016

...athematical Curves, Churchill Films, 12210 Nebraska Ave., Los Angeles, CA 90025

...oftware

...raphs of Lines and Hyperbola, Intellectual Software (IS), Division of Queue, Inc., 338 Commerce Dr., Fairfield, CT 06430

...athTools for Advanced Algebra, William K. Bradford Publishing Company, 310 School St., Acton, MA 01720

...athematics Exploration Toolkit, IBM, 4111 Northside Pkwy. NW, P.O. Box 2150, Atlanta, GA 30327-3015

Multicultural Activity, p. 9

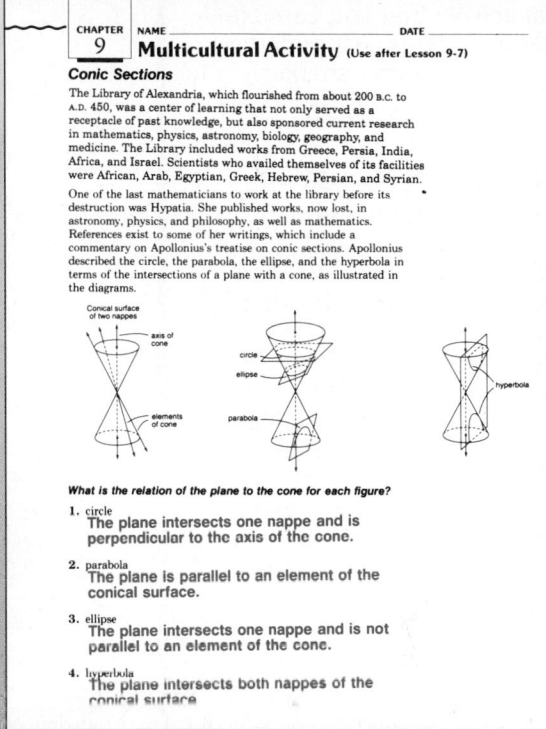

CHAPTER 9 NAME _____ DATE _____
Multicultural Activity (Use after Lesson 9-7)

Conic Sections

The Library of Alexandria, which flourished from about 200 B.C. to A.D. 450, was a center of learning that not only served as a receptacle of past knowledge, but also sponsored current research in mathematics, physics, astronomy, biology, geography, and medicine. The Library included works from Greece, Persia, India, Africa, and Israel. Scientists who availed themselves of its facilities were African, Arab, Egyptian, Greek, Hebrew, Persian, and Syrian.

One of the last mathematicians to work at the library before its destruction was Hypatia. She published works, now lost, in astronomy, physics, and philosophy, as well as mathematics. References exist to some of her writings, which include a commentary on Apollonius's treatise on conic sections. Apollonius described the circle, the parabola, the ellipse, and the hyperbola in terms of the intersections of a plane with a cone, as illustrated in the diagrams.

What is the relation of the plane to the cone for each figure?

1. circle
   The plane intersects one nappe and is perpendicular to the axis of the cone.

2. parabola
   The plane is parallel to an element of the conical surface.

3. ellipse
   The plane intersects one nappe and is not parallel to an element of the cone.

4. hyperbola
   The plane intersects both nappes of the conical surface.

Lab Activity, pp. 39-40

Name _____ Activity 12 Worksheet

The Pythagorean Theorem

1. Cut three squares from graph paper with sides of length 3, 4, and 5. What is the area of each square?

   Write an equation to show that the sum of the areas of two of the squares is equal to the area of the third square.

2. Place the three squares on a sheet of paper so that their sides form a triangle. What type of triangle is it?

   Write an equation to show the relationship among the squares of the sides of the triangle. Let a and b represent the length of the legs and c the length of the hypotenuse.

3. Find the squares of the numbers from 1 to 30. Use your calculator.

   $1^2 = $_____ $7^2 = $_____ $13^2 = $_____ $19^2 = $_____ $25^2 = $_____
   $2^2 = $_____ $8^2 = $_____ $14^2 = $_____ $20^2 = $_____ $26^2 = $_____
   $3^2 = $_____ $9^2 = $_____ $15^2 = $_____ $21^2 = $_____ $27^2 = $_____
   $4^2 = $_____ $10^2 = $_____ $16^2 = $_____ $22^2 = $_____ $28^2 = $_____
   $5^2 = $_____ $11^2 = $_____ $17^2 = $_____ $23^2 = $_____ $29^2 = $_____
   $6^2 = $_____ $12^2 = $_____ $18^2 = $_____ $24^2 = $_____ $30^2 = $_____

4. Find four sets of three squares each such that the sum of two of the squares equals the third.

5. Find the length of the hypotenuse of the right triangle given the lengths of its other sides. Use a calculator.

   a. 15 feet, 36 feet
   b. 7.5 meters, 10 meters
   c. 8 inches, 9 inches

Background Information

Medical technologists perform complicated chemical, biological, hematological, microscopic, and bacteriological tests. Such tests require a high degree of mathematical precision and accuracy. Medical technologists use computerized instruments, microscopes, cell counters, and other sophisticated laboratory equipment. They not only perform tests, but they also interpret the results and relay them to physicians. Employment of medical technologists is expected to grow 14% to 24% through the 1990s because of the growing need for lab testing.

CHAPTER OBJECTIVES

In this chapter, you will:
- Find the distance between two points in a plane.
- Find the midpoint of a segment.
- Identify and graph conic sections from their equations.
- Solve quadratic systems of equations and inequalities.

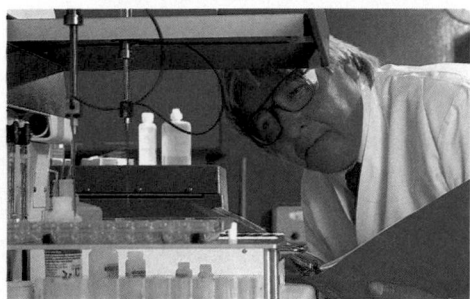

Point A indicates average glucose (blood sugar) level. The red line shows your glucose level after eating an apple. The blue line shows the level after eating a candy bar. Which item will give you more energy over a longer period of time?

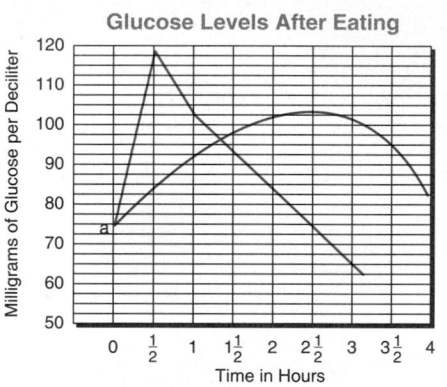

Glucose Levels After Eating

CAREERS IN MEDICAL TECHNOLOGY

Would you like to be an unseen member of a life-saving team? If you choose this career, you won't be in the spotlight—in fact, the people whose lives you help to save may never see you or know your name. But your special knowledge and careful work will be essential to the doctors and nurses who do see the patients. You'll be a medical technologist.

Medical technologists run many complicated tests. Those who work in large labs may specialize, but if you are a medical technologist in a small lab, you may perform all these functions and more:
- run chemical tests to determine blood sugar levels or cholesterol levels,
- examine tissues to detect the presence of infections or diseases,
- examine blood, tissue, and other body substances with a microscope,
- make cultures of body fluid or tissue samples to determine the presence of viruses, bacteria, fungi, parasites, or other microorganisms, and
- type and cross-match blood samples for transfusions.

No matter what kinds of test you may run, it's always satisfying to know that because of your work the patient's medical picture has become less of a mystery.

394

Chapter Project

Materials: paper, pencil, graph paper, library resources

Organize students into cooperative groups of medical technology researchers. Assign each group the task of researching one or more of the following specialized areas of medical technologists.

- Clinical chemistry technologist
- Microbiology technologist
- Histology technologist
- Phlebotomists and blood bank technologist
- Immunology technologist
- Cytotechnologist

Instruct each pair or group to report its research results, being

sure to include mathematical requirements and samples of results, graphs, and interpretations. Then have each group identify a local technologist in its area of research, include that person's resume in its report, and invite that person to make a brief presentation to the class.

MORE ABOUT MEDICAL TECHNOLOGY

Degree Required:

- Bachelor's Degree in one of the Life Sciences

Some medical technologists like:

- being an important part of the medical field
- the opportunity to work part-time
- working with a minimum of supervision
- being able to specialize in a field of their choice

Related Math Subjects:

- Advanced Algebra
- Trigonometry
- Statistics
- Probability
- Calculus

Some medical technologists dislike:

- working in an environment that may have unpleasant odors
- the possibility of infection if cultures are not handled properly
- working nights, weekends, and holidays

For more information on the various careers available in the field of Medical Technology, write to:

American Society for Medical Technology
2021 "L" Street, NW, Suite 400
Washington, D.C. 20036

395

Connections and Applications

Lesson	Connections (C) and Applications (A)	Examples	Exercises
9-1	C: Geometry A: Transportation	2,3	31-36 38
	Manufacturing		39
9-2	C: Geometry A: Communications	3	53
	Electronics Engineering		49 50
9-3	A: Seismology Air Traffic Control	1	57
	Physics City Planning		58 59
9-4	A: Aeronautics History	1	42
9-5	A: Astronomy Chemistry Sports	2	50 51
9-6	A: Marketing	1	
9-7	C: Probability A: Aeronautics Astronomy	2	34 32
9-8	A: Aeronautics Sports Seismology	2	42 43
9-9	A: Aviation Gardening Seismology	3	50 51

Lesson Resources

Reteaching Master 9-1
Practice Master 9-1
Enrichment Master 9-1
Lab Manual, pp. 39–40

 Transparency 9-1 contains the 5-Minute Check and a teaching aid for this lesson.

INTRODUCING THE LESSON

 5-Minute Check

(over Chapter 8)

1. Express $f(x) = -4(2x - 1)^2$ in quadratic form.
   $f(x) = -16x^2 + 16x - 4$
2. Name the vertex and axis of symmetry for the graph of $f(x) = (x - 2)^2 + 6$.
   $(2, 6); x = 2$
3. Name the direction of opening for the graph of
   $f(x) = -\frac{4}{5}(x + 2)^2 - 3$.
   downward
4. Write an equation of the parabola that passes through $(0, 15)$, $(-1, 8)$, and $(-6, 3)$.
   $f(x) = x^2 + 8x + 15$

Motivating the Lesson

If Annie lives 5 miles from Becky and Becky lives 3 miles from Connie, how far does Annie live from Connie?

Here we need to see a sketch or arrive at a series of possible answers. What is most important is to realize that there are a multitude of answers as the problem is stated.

TEACHING THE LESSON

Teaching Tip ❶ A good way to introduce distance is with the use of the geoboard. Using an overhead projector geoboard, squares can easily be counted and distance calculated using the Pythagorean Theorem.

Objectives

After studying this lesson, you should be able to:

9-1A ■ find the distance between two points in the coordinate plane, and
9-1B ■ find the midpoint of a line segment in the coordinate plane.

Application

Mike and Nita are going on a camping vacation to the Great Smoky Mountains National Park. The park appears as B4 on their map. They live in Wilmington, which appears as L1 on the map. If each side of a grid square represents 30 miles, about how far will they have to drive to get to the park?

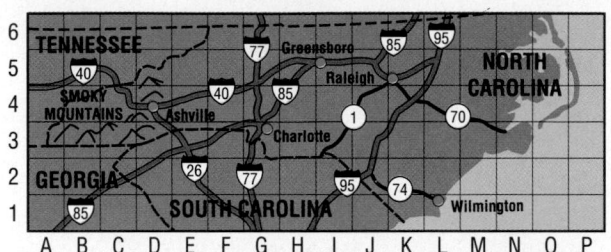

We can look at the map as a coordinate plane. On a coordinate plane, the location of the park would be represented by the ordered pair (2, 4) instead of B4. The location of Wilmington would be represented by (12, 1) instead of L1. To find the distance between two points on a coordinate plane we can use the Pythagorean Theorem. **Teaching Tip ❶**

First plot the points and draw vertical and horizontal segments from each point to form a right triangle. Then use the Pythagorean Theorem to find the length of the segment between the two points.

The square of the measure of the hypotenuse of a right triangle equals the sum of the squares of the measures of the other two sides.

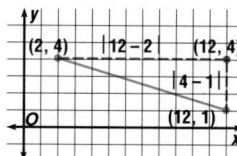

Recall that you can find the distance between two points on a number line using absolute value. That is, the distance between two points whose coordinates are a and b is $|a - b|$ or $|b - a|$. So the length of the horizontal leg is $|12 - 2|$ or 10 units, and the length of the vertical leg is $|4 - 1|$ or 3 units.

$$d^2 = 10^2 + 3^2$$
$$d^2 = 109$$
$$d = \sqrt{109}$$
$$d \approx 10.44 \quad \textit{Distance is positive.}$$

So Mike and Nita would have to drive about 10.44×30 or 313.2 miles to get to the park. Of course, the distance we found is in a straight line, and since the roads will not be straight from Wilmington to the park, their actual driving distance will be longer.

396   CHAPTER 9   CONICS

ALTERNATE TEACHING STRATEGIES

Using Cooperative Groups

Divide the class into groups of four. Give each group a geoboard. Have them make several right triangles. Have them find the length of the hypotenuse of the right triangles formed. Then have them generalize the results. Discuss the results and the formula on page 397.

Using Computers

Have students write a BASIC computer program to find the distance between two points. Then run the program for Exercises 13–18. Alter the program to include the slopes of two points.

Suppose (x_1, y_1) and (x_2, y_2) name two points in the plane. If we form a right triangle by drawing a vertical line through (x_1, y_1) and a horizontal line through (x_2, y_2), the lines will intersect at point (x_1, y_2). *Why?*

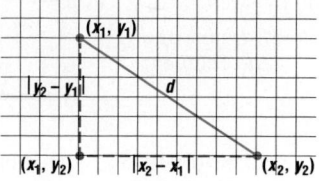

Use the Pythagorean Theorem to find the distance.

$$d^2 = |x_2 - x_1|^2 + |y_2 - y_1|^2$$
$$d^2 = (x_2 - x_1)^2 + (y_2 - y_1)^2 \qquad \textit{Why can } (x_2 - x_1)^2 \textit{ be substituted for } |x_2 - x_1|^2?$$
$$d = \sqrt{(x_2 - x_1)^2 + (y_2 - y_1)^2}$$

Distance Formula for Two Points in a Plane	**The distance between two points with coordinates (x_1, y_1) and (x_2, y_2) is given by $d = \sqrt{(x_2 - x_1)^2 + (y_2 - y_1)^2}$.**

Example 1

Use the distance formula to find the distance between $(-3, 2)$ and $(9, 4)$.

$$\begin{aligned} d &= \sqrt{(x_2 - x_1)^2 + (y_2 - y_1)^2} \\ &= \sqrt{((-3) - 9)^2 + (2 - 4)^2} \\ &= \sqrt{(-12)^2 + (-2)^2} \\ &= \sqrt{144 + 4} \\ &= \sqrt{148} \text{ or } 2\sqrt{37} \qquad \text{The distance is } 2\sqrt{37} \text{ or about 12.17 units.} \end{aligned}$$

Example 2

Geometry

Show that $P(4, 2)$ is the midpoint of the segment from $A(9, 3)$ to $B(-1, 1)$.

First we must prove that point P is on segment AB. It is sufficient to show that segments AP and AB have the same slope. *Why?*

$$\text{slope of } \overline{AP} = \frac{3 - 2}{9 - 4} \qquad \text{slope of } \overline{AB} = \frac{3 - 1}{9 - (-1)}$$
$$= \frac{1}{5} \qquad\qquad\qquad = \frac{2}{10}$$
$$\qquad\qquad\qquad\qquad = \frac{1}{3}$$

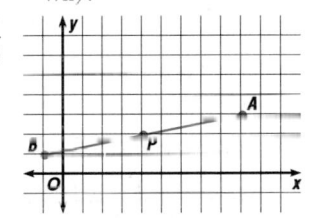

Next we need to show that the distance from A to P equals the distance from B to P.

distance from A to P

$$\begin{aligned} d_{\overline{AP}} &= \sqrt{(9 - 4)^2 + (3 - 2)^2} \\ &= \sqrt{5^2 + 1^2} \\ &= \sqrt{25 + 1} \text{ or } \sqrt{26} \end{aligned}$$

distance from B to P

$$\begin{aligned} d_{\overline{BP}} &= \sqrt{(-1 - 4)^2 + (1 - 2)^2} \\ &= \sqrt{(-5)^2 + (-1)^2} \\ &= \sqrt{25 + 1} \text{ or } \sqrt{26} \end{aligned}$$

Since the distances are equal, P is the midpoint.

RETEACHING THE LESSON

The formula for the coordinates of the midpoint of a line segment can be developed from $x_m = x_1 + \dfrac{x_2 - x_1}{2}$ and $y_m = y_1 + \dfrac{y_2 - y_1}{2}$

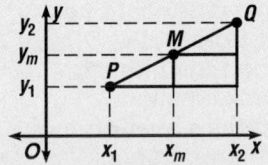

Chalkboard Examples

For Example 1
Use the distance formula to find the distance between two points with coordinates $(4, 4)$ and $(-6, -2)$. $2\sqrt{34}$

For Example 2
Show that $P(5.5, 5.5)$ is the midpoint of the segment from $A(4, 2)$ to $B(7, 9)$.   slope $AP =$ slope $AB = \frac{7}{3}$; $AP = BP = \dfrac{\sqrt{58}}{2}$

Reteaching Masters Booklet, p. 56

NAME _____   DATE _____
9-1   Reteaching Worksheet
The Distance and Midpoint Formulas

For number lines, you can use absolute value and averages to find distances and locate midpoints. You can do the same in the coordinate plane, though to find distances you need to use the Pythagorean Theorem.

Number Line	Coordinate Plane
A: coordinate a	P: coordinates (x_1, y_1)
B: coordinate b	Q: coordinates (x_2, y_2)
distance: $AB = |a - b|$ or $|b - a|$	distance: $PQ = \sqrt{(x_2 - x_1)^2 + (y_2 - y_1)^2}$
midpoint: $\frac{a + b}{2}$ (average)	midpoint: $\left(\frac{x_1 + x_2}{2}, \frac{y_1 + y_2}{2}\right)$

Example: Find the distance from P to Q and the midpoint of $\overline{PQ}$ if P has coordinates $(-2, 7)$ and Q has coordinates $(9, 3)$.

You can choose either point for (x_1, y_1).

Use the other point for (x_2, y_2). Let (x_1, y_1) be $(-2, 7)$. Then (x_2, y_2) is $(9, 3)$.

distance $PQ = \sqrt{(x_2 - x_1)^2 + (y_2 - y_1)^2}$
$= \sqrt{(9 - (-2))^2 + (3 - 7)^2}$
$= \sqrt{121 + 16}$
$= \sqrt{137}$

midpoint of $\overline{PQ} = \left(\frac{x_1 + x_2}{2}, \frac{y_1 + y_2}{2}\right)$
$\left(\frac{(-2) + 9}{2}, \frac{7 + 3}{2}\right)$
$\left(\frac{7}{2}, 5\right)$

Use the distance formula to find the distance between each pair of points.

1. $(-3, 4), (6, -11)$
   $3\sqrt{34}$
2. $(13, 9), (11, 15)$
   $2\sqrt{10}$
3. $(-15, -7), (2, 12)$
   $5\sqrt{26}$
4. $\left(\frac{1}{2}, 2\right), \left(-\frac{1}{2}, 1\right)$
   $\sqrt{2}$
5. $\left(\frac{1}{4}, \frac{1}{4}\right), \left(\frac{1}{2}, \frac{1}{4}\right)$
   $\frac{1}{4}\sqrt{2}$
6. $(1.0, -0.31), (-0.2, 0.19)$
   1.3

Find the midpoint of each line segment whose endpoints are given below.

7. $(3, 5), (-6, 11)$
   $\left(-\frac{3}{2}, 8\right)$
8. $(8, -15), (-7, 13)$
   $\left(\frac{1}{2}, -1\right)$
9. $(2.5, -6.1), (7.9, 13.7)$
   $(5.2, 3.8)$
10. $(-7, -6), (-1, 24)$
    $(-4, 9)$
11. $(3, -10), (30, -20)$
    $\left(\frac{33}{2}, -15\right)$
12. $(-9, 1.7), (-11, 1.3)$
    $(-10, 1.5)$

EVALUATING THE LESSON

Checking for Understanding

Exercises 1–12 are designed to help you assess understanding through reading, writing, and speaking. You should work through Exercises 1–3 with your students, and then monitor their work on Exercises 4–12.

Error Analysis

Students may subtract the coordinates of a point in different orders when using the distance formula. It is important that the coordinates be subtracted in the correct order, $(x_2 - x_1)$ and $(y_2 - y_1)$, regardless of which point is chosen to be (x_1, y_1).

Practice Masters Booklet, p. 64

Midpoint of a Line Segment	If a line segment has endpoints at (x_1, y_1) and (x_2, y_2) then the midpoint of the line segment has coordinates $\left(\dfrac{x_1 + x_2}{2}, \dfrac{y_1 + y_2}{2}\right)$.

Example 3

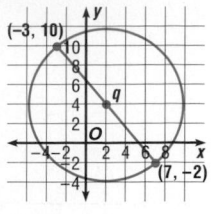

CONNECTION
Geometry

Find the center of the circle Q with a diameter whose endpoints are (−3, 10) and (7, −2).

The center of the circle will be the midpoint of the diameter.

$$(x, y) = \left(\frac{-3 + 7}{2}, \frac{10 + (-2)}{2}\right)$$
$$= \left(\frac{4}{2}, \frac{8}{2}\right)$$
$$= (2, 4) \quad \text{The center of circle } Q \text{ is } (2, 4).$$

CHECKING FOR UNDERSTANDING

Communicating Mathematics

1. Squaring the quantity will make it positive, so the absolute value is unnecessary.

Read and study the lesson to answer these questions.

1. Why were we able to substitute $(x_2 - x_1)^2$ for $|x_2 - x_1|^2$ when we derived the distance formula?

2. Is a point that is equidistant from two points always the midpoint of the segment between them? Explain your answer. **See margin.**

3. Could you find one endpoint of a segment given the other endpoint and the midpoint? If so, demonstrate by finding the endpoint of the segment with one endpoint (3, 7) and midpoint (0, −2). **See margin.**

Guided Practice

The coordinates of two points on the number line are given. Find the distance between each pair of points.

4. −8, 9 **17 units** 5. −3, 0 **3 units** 6. −30, −15 **15 units**

7. −12.2, −3.3 **8.9 units** 8. 4.4, −8.1 **12.5 units** 9. $10\frac{2}{3}, -6\frac{1}{8}$ $16\frac{19}{24}$ **units**

Use the distance formula to find the distance between each pair of points.

10. $(6, 3), (6, -1)$ **4 units** 11. $(9, 5), (4, -7)$ **13 units** 12. $(0, -5), (10, -3)$ **2√26 units**

EXERCISES

Practice

Use the distance formula to find the distance between each pair of points.

A
13. $(4, 8), (8, 8)$ **4 units** 14. $(0, 5), (-4, -2)$ **√65 units**
15. $(9, 0), (6, 7)$ **√58 units** 16. $(-4, 9), (1, -3)$ **13 units**
17. $(-4, -10), (-3, -11)$ **√2 units** 18. $\left(1, \frac{1}{2}\right), \left(\frac{1}{3}, -2\right)$ $\frac{\sqrt{241}}{6}$ **units**
19. $(-0.5, 1), (-2.2, -0.3)$ **√4.58 units** 20. $(3, 3), (\sqrt{3}, \sqrt{3})$ **2√6 − 3√3 units**

B
21. $(-2\sqrt{7}, 10), (4\sqrt{7}, 8)$ **16 units** 22. $(2\sqrt{3}, 4\sqrt{3}), (2\sqrt{3}, -\sqrt{3})$ **5√3 units**

Additional Answers

2. No. The point is only the midpoint if it lies on the segment. A point could be equidistant from both points and not lie on the line segment between them.

3. Yes. Set up the equation for the midpoint and solve.

$$(0, -2) = \left(\frac{3 + x}{2}, \frac{7 + y}{2}\right)$$

So, $0 = \dfrac{3 + x}{2}$ $-2 = \dfrac{7 + y}{2}$

$0 = 3 + x$ $-4 = 7 + y$
$x = -3$ $y = -11$

The second endpoint is (−3, −11).

35. $AB = \sqrt{(-3 - (-1))^2 + (0 - 4)^2}$
$= \sqrt{(-2)^2 + (-4)^2}$
$= \sqrt{4 + 16}$
$= \sqrt{20}$

$AC = \sqrt{(-3 - 1)^2 + (0 - (-2))^2}$
$= \sqrt{(-4)^2 + 2^2}$
$= \sqrt{16 + 4}$
$= \sqrt{20}$

Since $AB = AC$, $\triangle ABC$ is isosceles.

Find the value of c such that each pair of points is 5 units apart.

23. $(7, 2)$, $(3, c)$ **5 or –1**

24. $(-7, 7)$, $(c, 11)$ **–4 or –10**

25. $(13, 10.1)$, $(9, c)$ **7.1 or 13.1**

26. $(1.2, 5.9)$, $(c, 1.9)$ **4.2 or –1.8**

Find the midpoint of each line segment whose endpoints are given below.

27. $(8, 3)$, $(16, 7)$ **$(12, 5)$**

28. $(5, 9)$, $(12, 18)$ **$\left(\frac{17}{2}, \frac{27}{2}\right)$**

29. $\left(\frac{1}{4}, 3\right)$, $\left(\frac{7}{8}, -\frac{1}{2}\right)$ **$\left(\frac{9}{16}, \frac{5}{4}\right)$**

30. $(-4.3, 2.8)$, $(2.7, 4.9)$ **$(-0.8, 3.85)$**

CONNECTION
Geometry

Solve. Use a drawing.

C ▶31. Find the center of the circle whose diameter has endpoints $(9, 0)$ and $(11, -14)$. **$(10, -7)$**

32. Find the perimeter of a quadrilateral with vertices at $(4, 5)$, $(-4, 6)$, $(-5, -8)$, and $(6, 3)$. **$13\sqrt{2} + \sqrt{65} + \sqrt{197}$ units**

33. Triangle MNO has vertices $M(3, 5)$, $N(-2, 8)$, and $O(7, -4)$. Find the coordinates of the midpoint of each side. **See margin.**

Journal
Draw a rectangle on a piece of graph paper. Tell how you could find the point where the diagonals meet by using the formulas in this lesson.

34. Find the lengths of the diagonals of the parallelogram with vertices at $(-14, 8)$, $(6, 8)$, $(-12, -2)$, and $(8, -2)$. **$2\sqrt{106}$ and $2\sqrt{146}$ units**

35. Show that the triangle with vertices $A(-3, 0)$, $B(-1, 4)$ and $C(1, -2)$ is isosceles. **See margin.**

36. Triangle XYZ is a right triangle with vertices at $X(0, 1)$, $Y(4, 1)$, and $Z(0, 7)$. Show that the midpoint of the hypotenuse is the same distance from each vertex. **See margin.**

Critical Thinking

Teaching Tip ②

37. Find the coordinates of a point one fourth of the distance from $A(11, 2)$ to $D(3, 2)$. **$(5, 1)$**

Applications

38. **Transportation** A semi-truck traveled 23 miles south on I-71 before turning west on I-70. After traveling 85 miles on I-70, about how far is it from its starting point? **about 88 miles**

39. **Manufacturing** The hole in a record album needs to be placed in the center of the record. If the record is 12 inches in diameter, and the hole is $\frac{1}{4}$ inch in diameter, how far from the edge should the edge of the hole be placed? **$5\frac{7}{8}$ inches**

—— 12 in. ——

Mixed Review

Solve each inequality. (Lesson 8-9)

40. $(x + 3)(x + 7) > 0$

41. $(a - 1.5)(a + 2.5) \geq 0$

40. $\{x \mid x > -3 \text{ or } x < -7\}$
41. $\{a \mid a \geq 1.5 \text{ or } a \leq -2.5\}$

42. Solve the equation $y^4 - y^2 - 30 = 0$. (Lesson 7-6) **$\pm i\sqrt{5}, \pm\sqrt{6}$**

43. Find values of x and y for which the sentence $2x + 5yi = 4 + 15i$ is true. (Lesson 6-9) **$x = 2, y = 3$**

44. Factor $3m^3 + 24p^3$. (Lesson 5-6) **$3(m + 2p)(m^2 - 2mp + 4p^2)$**

EXTENDING THE LESSON

Math Power: Reasoning
Show that the points at $A(5, -1)$, $B(3, 2)$, and $C(9, 6)$ are vertices of a right triangle.

$AB = \sqrt{13}$, $BC = 2\sqrt{13}$,
$AC = \sqrt{65}$, hypotenuse $= \sqrt{65}$
$(\sqrt{65})^2 = (\sqrt{13})^2 + (2\sqrt{13})^2$
$\quad 65 = 13 + 52$
$\quad 65 = 65$
Satisfies the Pythagorean Theorem.

Additional Answers
33. midpoint of $\overline{MN} = \left(\frac{1}{2}, \frac{13}{2}\right)$

midpoint of $\overline{MO} = \left(5, \frac{1}{2}\right)$

midpoint of $\overline{NO} = \left(\frac{5}{2}, 2\right)$

36. midpoint of hypotenuse $= (2, 4)$
distance from $(2, 4)$ to $X = \sqrt{13}$ units
distance from $(2, 4)$ to $Y = \sqrt{13}$ units
distance from $(2, 4)$ to $Z = \sqrt{13}$ units

Closing the Lesson
Writing Activity Find three points that form the vertices of a right triangle where no sides are parallel to either axis. Explain how you determined that the three points were vertices of a right triangle.

APPLYING THE LESSON

Homework Exercises

Assignment Guide
Basic: 13–30, 37–38, 40–44
Average: 16–33, 37–44
Enriched: 19–44

Teaching Tip ② You may want to give students the hint that the midpoint is half the distance.

Enrichment Masters Booklet, p. 56

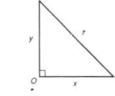

9-1 NAME _____ DATE _____
Enrichment Worksheet

Reading Algebra

If two mathematical problems have basic structural similarities, they are said to be **analogous.** Using analogies is one way of discovering and proving new theorems.

The following paragraph discusses a three-dimensional analogy to the Pythagorean Theorem.

01 Consider a tetrahedron with three perpendicular faces that meet at vertex O.
02 Suppose you want to know how the areas A, B, and C of the three faces that meet at vertex O are related to the area D of the face opposite vertex O.
03 It is natural to expect a formula analogous to the Pythagorean Theorem $z^2 = x^2 + y^2$, which is true for a similar situation in two dimensions.
04 To explore the three-dimensional case, you might guess a formula and then try to prove it.
05 Two reasonable guesses are $D^3 = A^3 + B^3 + C^3$ and $D^2 = A^2 + B^2 + C^2$.

Refer to the paragraph to answer the questions.

1. Use sentence 01 and the top diagram. The prefix *tetra-* means four. Write an informal definition of tetrahedron.
   a three-dimensional figure with four faces

2. Use sentence 02 and the top diagram. What are the lengths of the sides of each face of the tetrahedron?
   a, b, and c; a, q, and r; b, p, and q.

3. Rewrite sentence 01 to state a two-dimensional analogue.
   Consider a triangle with two perpendicular sides that meet at vertex C.

4. Refer to the top diagram and write expressions for the areas A, B, and C mentioned in sentence 02.
   Possible answer: $A = \frac{1}{2}pr$, $B = \frac{1}{2}pq$, $C = \frac{1}{2}rq$

5. To explore the three-dimensional case, you might begin by expressing a, b, and c in terms of p, q, and r. Use the Pythagorean Theorem to do this.
   $a^2 = q^2 + r^2$, $b^2 = r^2 + p^2$, $c^2 = p^2 + q^2$

6. Which guess in sentence 05 seems more likely? Justify your answer.
   See students' explanations.

Lesson Resources

Reteaching Master 9-2
Practice Master 9-2
Enrichment Master 9-2
Activity Masters, pp. 27, 45

 Transparency 9-2 contains the 5-Minute Check and a teaching aid for this lesson.

INTRODUCING THE LESSON

 5-Minute Check

(over Lesson 9-1)

1. Use the Pythagorean Theorem to find the distance between two points with coordinates (9, 7) and (6, 3). **5**
2. Use the distance formula to find the distance between two points with coordinates (6, 4) and (1, 1). $\sqrt{34}$
3. Find the midpoint of the line segment whose endpoints are (11, 8) and (1, 4). **(6, 6)**
4. Show that $P(4, 3)$ is the midpoint of the segment from $A(-2, 7)$ to $B(10, -1)$. **slope**

   $AP = $ **slope** $AB = -\frac{2}{3}$;

   $AP = BP = 2\sqrt{13}$
5. Find the center of the circle with a diameter whose endpoints are (13, 12) and (6, 7). **(9.5, 9.5)**

Motivating the Lesson

Ask the class how an auto headlight works. The picture on the first page of this lesson should help. Be sure they understand that any other point as a light source (focus) will cause the rays to be directed differently. This is how low beam and high beam can be created within the same headlight reflector. Bring in a double filament headlight bulb to show how the focus is in different positions.

9-2 Parabolas

Objectives

After studying this lesson, you should be able to:

9-2A ■ write equations of parabolas, and

9-2B ■ graph parabolas from given information.

Application

FYI · · ·

Drawings showing the reflective properties of a parabola were found among the papers of Leonardo Da Vinci, a gifted scientist and architect as well as a noted sculptor and painter.

The shape of the reflectors in flashlights and searchlights is based on the **parabola.** If you were to cut one of these reflectors down the middle, the cross section would look like the diagram at the right. The light source is placed at a point where the light is reflected in parallel rays. So, the light coming out of the reflector is a straight beam.

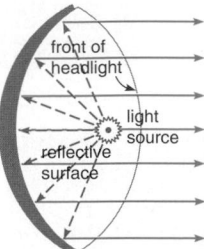

The point where the light source is placed is called the **focus.** A parabola can be defined in terms of the location of its focus and a line called the **directrix.**

Definition of a Parabola	A parabola is the set of all points in a plane that are the same distance from a given point called the *focus* and a given line called the *directrix.*

The directrix is named by the equation of the line.

The parabola at the right has focus (5, 3) and directrix $y = -1$. We can use the distance formula with the definition of a parabola to find the equation of this parabola. Let (x, y) be a point on the parabola. The distance from this point to the focus must be the same as its distance from the directrix.

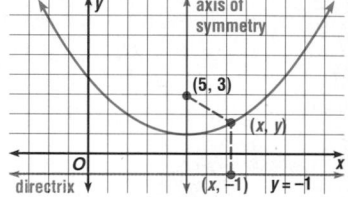

distance between (x, y) and $(5, 3) = $ distance between (x, y) and $(x, -1)$

$$\sqrt{(x - 5)^2 + (y - 3)^2} = \sqrt{(x - x)^2 + (y - (-1))^2}$$
$$(x - 5)^2 + (y - 3)^2 = (x - x)^2 + (y + 1)^2$$
$$(x - 5)^2 + y^2 - 6y + 9 = y^2 + 2y + 1$$
$$(x - 5)^2 + 8 = 8y$$
$$\frac{1}{8}(x - 5)^2 + 1 = y$$

The equation of a parabola with focus (5, 3) and directrix $y = -1$ is $y = \frac{1}{8}(x - 5)^2 + 1$. The axis of symmetry of this parabola is $x = 5$. Notice that the axis of symmetry and the directrix are perpendicular. The point of intersection of the axis of symmetry and the parabola is called the **vertex.** The vertex of this parabola is (5, 1).

ALTERNATE TEACHING STRATEGIES

Mini Math Lab

Draw a coordinate grid on graph paper with the x values going from -12 to 12 and the y values going from 4 to -22. For positive x values draw segments that connect the points $(n, 0)$ and $(12, -2n)$. For negative values of x draw segments that connect the points $(n, 0)$ and $(-12, 2n)$. What figure is suggested? Have students experiment with other ordered pairs.

Using Logical Reasoning

As the distance between the focus and the directrix increases, what happens to the shape of the parabola? **It widens.** Knowing this, have students explain how the parabolic reflector works to produce the sound for football games.

Teaching Tip ❶

The line segment through the focus of a parabola and perpendicular to the axis of symmetry whose endpoints are on the parabola is called the **latus rectum**. In the figure at the right the latus rectum is $\overline{AB}$. The length of the latus rectum of the parabola whose equation is $y = a(x - h)^2 + k$ is $\left|\dfrac{1}{a}\right|$ units. The endpoints of the latus rectum are $\left|\dfrac{1}{2a}\right|$ units from the focus.

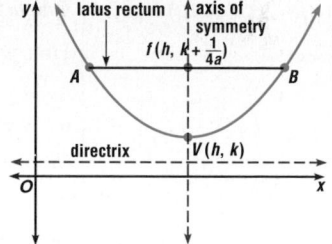

You can write the equation for a parabola in the form $y = a(x - h)^2 + k$ or in the form $x = a(y - k)^2 + h$. Either form gives us valuable information about the graph of the parabola.

Information about Parabolas		
form of equation	$y = a(x - h)^2 + k$	$x = a(y - k)^2 + h$
axis of symmetry	$x = h$	$y = k$
vertex	(h, k)	(h, k)
focus	$\left(h, k + \dfrac{1}{4a}\right)$	$\left(h + \dfrac{1}{4a}, k\right)$
directrix	$y = k - \dfrac{1}{4a}$	$x = h - \dfrac{1}{4a}$
direction of opening	upward if $a > 0$, downward if $a < 0$	right if $a > 0$, left if $a < 0$
length of latus rectum	$\left|\dfrac{1}{a}\right|$ units	$\left|\dfrac{1}{a}\right|$ units

Example 1

Graph $y = \dfrac{1}{8}(x - 1)^2 + 4$.

Use the chart above to find as much information about the graph as possible. Use the information to graph the parabola.

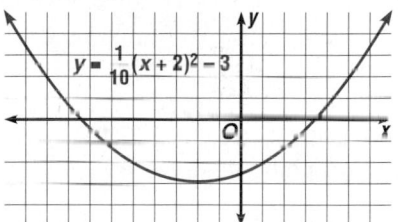

vertex:	$(1, 4)$
axis of symmetry:	$x = 1$
focus:	$(1, 4 + 2)$ or $(1, 6)$
directrix:	$y = 4 - 2$ or $y = 2$
direction of opening:	upward since $a > 0$
length of latus rectum:	$\left|\dfrac{1}{\frac{1}{8}}\right|$ or 8 units

$\dfrac{1}{4a} = \dfrac{1}{4\left(\frac{1}{8}\right)}$ or 2

Teaching Tip ❶   The latus rectum is sometimes called the focal chord. It is helpful in determining the shape of the curve.

Chalkboard Examples

For Example 1

Graph $y = \dfrac{1}{10}(x + 2)^2 - 3$. Use the chart to find out as much about the graph as possible. vertex: $(-2, -3)$; axis of symmetry: $x = -2$; focus: $\left(-2, -\dfrac{1}{2}\right)$; directrix: $y = -5.5$; direction of opening: upward; length of latus rectum: 10 units

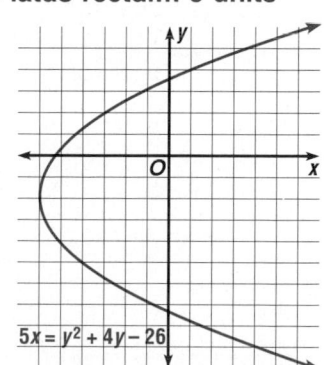

For Example 2

Graph $5x = y^2 + 4y - 26$. Use the chart to find out as much about the graph as possible. vertex: $(-6, -2)$; axis of symmetry: $y = -2$; focus: $\left(-4\dfrac{3}{4}, -2\right)$; directrix: $x = -7.25$; direction of opening: to the right; length of latus rectum: 5 units

EVALUATING THE LESSON

Checking for Understanding

Exercises 1–17 are designed to help you assess understanding through reading, writing, and speaking. You should work through Exercises 1–3 with your students, and then monitor their work on Exercises 4–17.

Closing the Lesson

Speaking Activity For those with graphing calculators:

1. Graph $y = ax^2$ for various values of a. Then discuss findings.
2. Graph $y = x^2 + bx$ for various values of b. Then discuss findings.

Reteaching Masters Booklet, p. 57

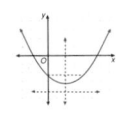
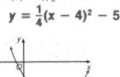 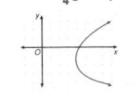
Example 2 Graph $6x = y^2 - 6y + 39$.

First write the equation in the form $x = a(y - k)^2 + h$.

$6x = y^2 - 6y + 39$
$6x = y^2 - 6y + \Box - \Box + 39$ *Complete the square.*
$6x = y^2 - 6y + \left(\frac{6}{2}\right)^2 - \left(\frac{6}{2}\right)^2 + 39$
$6x = (y - 3)^2 + 30$
$\ \ x = \frac{1}{6}(y - 3)^2 + 5$

vertex: $(5, 3)$ focus: $\left(6\frac{1}{2}, 3\right)$
axis of symmetry: $y = 3$
directrix: $x = 3\frac{1}{2}$
direction of opening: right $(a > 0)$
length of
latus rectum: $\left|\frac{1}{\frac{1}{6}}\right|$ or 6 units

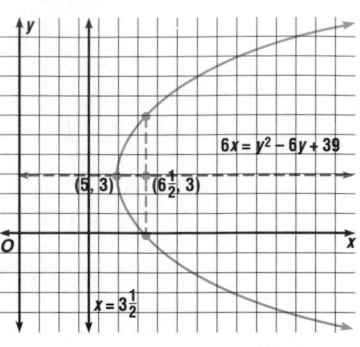

Example 3

APPLICATION
Communication

A microphone is placed at the focus of a parabolic reflector to collect sounds for the television broadcast of a football game. The focus of the parabola that is the cross section of the reflector is 5 inches from the vertex. The latus rectum is 20 inches long. Assuming that the focus is at the origin and the parabola opens to the right, write the equation of the cross section.

focus: $(0, 0)$ *Since the parabola opens to*
vertex: $(-5, 0)$ *the right, the vertex must*
                    be to the left of the focus.

measure of latus rectum $= 20 = \left|\frac{1}{a}\right|$, so $a = \frac{1}{20}$

Write the equation using the form $x = a(y - k)^2 + h$.

$x = \frac{1}{20}y^2 - 5$

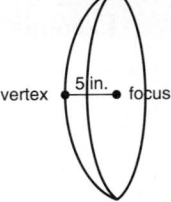

vertex •—5 in.—• focus

CHECKING FOR UNDERSTANDING

Communicating Mathematics

1. **Answers may vary. Sample answers are car headlights, flashlights, sound collectors, and satellite dishes.**

Read and study the lesson to answer these questions.

1. Name some uses for parabolic reflectors.

2. Describe the relationships between the directrix, the vertex, the axis of symmetry, and the latus rectum. **See margin.**

402 CHAPTER 9 CONICS

RETEACHING THE LESSON

Given the focus and the directrix, find the equation of a parabola in two ways. First use the definition of a parabola and the distance formula to find the equation. Second, use formulas for the focus and directrix to find values of h, k and a, and then write the equation.

Additional Answers

2. **The directrix and the latus rectum are parallel and are both perpendicular to the axis of symmetry. The vertex lies on the axis of symmetry and is the midpoint of the shortest segment between the latus rectum and the directrix.**

3. **vertex $(-1, -2)$, axis of symmetry $y = -2$, focus $\left(-\frac{7}{8}, -2\right)$, directrix $x = -\frac{9}{8}$**

3. The graph of the parabola whose equation is $x = 2(y + 2)^2 - 1$ is shown at the right. Name the vertex, the axis of symmetry, the focus, and the directrix of the parabola. **See margin.**

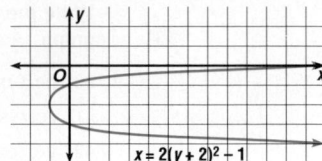
$x = 2(y + 2)^2 - 1$

Guided Practice

Find the value of c that makes each trinomial a perfect square.

4. $x^2 - 6x + c$ **9**   5. $y^2 + 4y + c$ **4**   6. $a^2 - 8a + c$ **16**

7. $n^2 - 10n + c$ **25**   8. $q^2 + 3q + c$ $\frac{9}{4}$ 9. $s^2 - 7s + c$ $\frac{49}{4}$

Express each equation in the form $y = a(x - h)^2 + k$.

10. $12y = x^2$ $y = \frac{1}{12}x^2$ 11. $x^2 = -4y$ $y = -\frac{1}{4}x^2$

12. $y = x^2 + 8x + 20$ 13. $y = x^2 + 4x + 1$
$y = (x + 4)^2 + 4$ $y = (x + 2)^2 - 3$

Name the vertex, axis of symmetry, focus, directrix, and direction of opening of the parabola whose equation is given. Then find the length of the latus rectum. **14–17. See Solutions Manual for graphs.**

14. (0, 0); $y = 0$; $\left(\frac{3}{2}, 0\right)$; $x = -\frac{3}{2}$; right; 6

14. $y^2 = 6x$ 15. $(x + 2)^2 = y - 3$

16. $6x = (y + 2)^2$ 17. $x^2 = (y - 1)$

15. (−2, 3); $x = -2$; $\left(-2, 3\frac{1}{4}\right)$; $y = 2\frac{3}{4}$; up; 1

16. (0, −2); $y = -2$; $\left(\frac{3}{2}, -2\right)$; $x = -\frac{3}{2}$; right; 6

17. (0, 1); $x = 0$; $\left(0, \frac{5}{4}\right)$; $y = \frac{3}{4}$; up; 1

EXERCISES

Practice

Name the vertex, axis of symmetry, focus, directrix, and direction of opening of the parabola whose equation is given. Then find the length of the latus rectum and graph the parabola. **18–31. See margin. See Solutions Manual for graphs.**

A 18. $-8y = x^2$ 19. $4(y - 2) = (x - 4)^2$

20. $(x + 3)^2 = \frac{1}{4}(y - 2)$ 21. $\frac{1}{2}(y + 1) = (x - 8)^2$

22. $4(x - 2) = (y + 3)^2$ 23. $(y - 8)^2 = -4(x - 4)$

B 24. $y = x^2 + 8x + 20$ 25. $x = y^2 - 14y + 25$

26. $y = x^2 - 6x + 33$ 27. $y = \frac{1}{2}x^2 - 3x + \frac{19}{2}$

28. $y = x^2 + 4x + 1$ 29. $x = \frac{1}{4}y^2 - \frac{1}{2}y - 3$

30. $x = 5y^2 - 25y + 60$ 31. $y = 3x^2 - 24x + 50$

The focus and directrix of a parabola are given. Write an equation for each parabola. Then draw the graph. **32–39. See Solutions Manual for graphs.**

32. (3, 8), $y = 4$ $y = \frac{1}{8}(x - 3)^2 + 6$ 33. (8, 0), $y = 4$ $y = \frac{-1}{8}(x - 8)^2 + 2$

34. (5, 5), $y = -3$ $y = \frac{1}{16}(x - 5)^2 + 1$ 35. (6, 2), $x = 4$ $x = \frac{1}{4}(y - 2)^2 + 5$

36. (4, −3), $y = 6$ 37. (3, −1), $x = -2$

36. $y = \frac{-1}{18}(x - 4)^2 + \frac{3}{2}$ 38. (3, 0), $x = -2$ $x = \frac{1}{10}y^2 + \frac{1}{2}$ 39. (10, −3), $x = 5$

37. $x = \frac{1}{10}(y + 1)^2 + \frac{1}{2}$ 39. $x = \frac{1}{10}(y + 3)^2 + 7\frac{1}{2}$

LESSON 9-2 PARABOLAS 403

Additional Answers

24. (−4, 4); $x = -4$; $\left(-4, \frac{17}{4}\right)$; $y = \frac{15}{4}$; up; 1

25. (−24, 7); $y = 7$; $\left(-23\frac{3}{4}, 7\right)$; $x = -24\frac{1}{4}$; right; 1

26. (3, 24); $x = 3$; $\left(3, 24\frac{1}{4}\right)$; $y = 23\frac{3}{4}$; up; 1

27. (3, 5); $x = 3$; $\left(3, 5\frac{1}{2}\right)$; $y = 4\frac{1}{2}$; up; 2

28. (−2, −3); $x = -2$; $\left(-2, -\frac{11}{4}\right)$; $y = -\frac{13}{4}$; up; 1

29. $\left(-\frac{13}{4}, 1\right)$; $y = 1$; $\left(-\frac{9}{4}, 1\right)$; $x = -\frac{17}{4}$; right; 4

30. $\left(\frac{115}{4}, \frac{5}{2}\right)$; $y = \frac{5}{2}$; $\left(\frac{144}{5}, \frac{5}{2}\right)$; $x = \frac{287}{10}$; right; $\frac{1}{5}$

31. (4, 2); $x = 4$; $\left(4, 2\frac{1}{12}\right)$; $y = 1\frac{11}{12}$; up; $\frac{1}{3}$

APPLYING THE LESSON

Homework Exercises

Assignment Guide

Basic: 18–39, 48–57
Average: 21–43, 48–57
Enriched: 24–57

Additional Answers

18. (0, 0); $x = 0$; (0, −2); $y = 2$; down; 8

19. (4, 2); $x = 4$; (4, 3); $y = 1$; up; 4

20. (−3, 2); $x = -3$; $\left(-3, 2\frac{1}{16}\right)$; $y = 1\frac{15}{16}$; up; $\frac{1}{4}$

21. (8, −1); $x = 8$; $\left(8, -\frac{7}{8}\right)$; $y = -\frac{9}{8}$; up; $\frac{1}{2}$

22. (2, −3); $y = -3$; (3, −3); $x = 1$; right; 4

23. (4, 8); $y = 8$; (3, 8); $x = 5$; left; 4

Practice Masters Booklet, p. 65

Chapter 9, Quiz A, (Lessons 9-1 through 9-2), is available in the Evaluation Masters Booklet, p. 121.

Teaching Tip ❷ Have students graph the two points. They should be able to draw the two parabolas that are formed.

c Write the equation of each parabola described below. Then draw the graph. 40–47. See Solutions Manual for graphs.

42. $y = \frac{-1}{6}(x + 7)^2 + 4$

43. $x = \frac{1}{4}(y - 3)^2 + 4$

44. $y = \frac{-1}{6}(x - 11)^2 + \frac{1}{2}$

45. $x = -\frac{1}{4}(y - 6)^2 + 4$

$y = \frac{x^2}{12}$

$x = \frac{-1}{8}(y + 1)^2 + 5$

40. vertex $(0, 0)$, focus $(0, 3)$

41. vertex $(5, -1)$, focus $(3, -1)$

42. vertex $(-7, 4)$, axis $x = -7$, measure of latus rectum 6, $a < 0$

43. vertex $(4, 3)$, axis of symmetry $y = 3$, measure of latus rectum 4, $a > 0$

44. focus $(11, -1)$, directrix $y = 2$ 45. focus $(3, 6)$, directrix $x = 5$

46. focus $(7, -7)$, directrix $x = -2$ 47. focus $(-1, 2)$, directrix $y = -1$

$x = \frac{1}{18}(y + 7)^2 + \frac{5}{2}$ $y = \frac{1}{6}(x + 1)^2 + \frac{1}{2}$

Critical Thinking
Teaching Tip ❷

48. There are two parabolas that have vertex $(-3, -4)$ and pass through the point $(-1, 4)$. Find their equations. $y = 2(x + 3)^2 - 4$ and

$x = \frac{1}{32}(y + 4)^2 - 3$

Applications

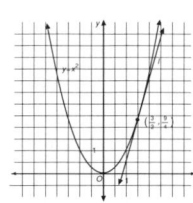

49. **Electronics** The headlights on a car contain parabolic reflectors. A special light bulb with two filaments is used to produce the high and low beams. The filament placed at the focus produces the high beam and low beam is produced by the filament placed off of the focus. If the equation of the parabola that is the cross section of the reflector is $y = \frac{1}{10}x^2$, where should the filament for the high beam be placed?

$\left(0, 2\frac{1}{2}\right)$

50. **Engineering** The shape taken by the supporting cables for a suspension bridge is actually a catenary curve, which very closely approximates a parabola. The cables for a certain bridge are 75 feet above the road at the towers and 10 feet above it at the center of the bridge. Find the equation of the path of the supporting cables if the distance between the towers is 250 feet. $y = \frac{13}{3125}(x - 125)^2 + 10$

Mixed Review

51. Use the distance formula to find the distance between $(9, 6)$ and $(8, 0)$. (**Lesson 9-1**) $\sqrt{37}$ **units**

$\left(\frac{3}{2}, -\frac{5}{2}\right)$

52. Find the midpoint of the segment whose endpoints are $(9, 3)$ and $(-6, -8)$. (**Lesson 9-1**)

53. **Geometry** A wire 36 centimeters long is cut into two pieces and each piece is bent into a square. How long should each piece be cut so that the sum of the areas of the two squares is minimal? (**Lesson 8-5**) **18 cm**

54. Find two consecutive integers whose product is 7832. (**Lesson 7-2**) **88 and 89 or −88 and −89**

55. Simplify $\frac{\frac{3}{4}}{x^{\frac{3}{5}}}$. (**Lesson 6-4**) $\frac{3x^{\frac{1}{5}}}{x}$

56. Divide $(a^4 - 5a^3 - 13a^2 + 53a + 60)$ by $(a + 1)$ using synthetic division. (**Lesson 5-7**) $a^3 - 6a^2 - 7a + 60$

57. State whether the expression $-24p^4q$ is a monomial. If it is, name its coefficient and degree. (**Lesson 5-1**) **yes, −24, 5**

EXTENDING THE LESSON

Math Power: Reasoning

Write the equation of the parabola whose latus rectum has endpoints at $(6, 0)$ and $(-6, 0)$, and $a > 0$.

$y = \frac{1}{12}x^2 - 3$

Enrichment Masters Booklet, p. 57

9-2   NAME _____ DATE _____
Enrichment Worksheet

Tangents to Parabolas

A line that intersects a parabola in exactly one point without crossing the curve is a **tangent** to the parabola. The point where a tangent line touches a parabola is the **point of tangency**. The line perpendicular to a tangent to a parabola at the point of tangency is called the **normal** to the parabola at that point. In the diagram, line l is tangent to the parabola that is the graph of $y = x^2$ at $\left(\frac{3}{2}, \frac{9}{4}\right)$. The x-axis is tangent to the parabola at O, and the y-axis is the normal to the parabola at O.

Solve each problem.

1. Find an equation for line l in the diagram. Hint: A nonvertical line with an equation of the form $y = mx + b$ will be tangent to the graph of $y = x^2$ at $\left(\frac{3}{2}, \frac{9}{4}\right)$ if and only if $\left(\frac{3}{2}, \frac{9}{4}\right)$ is the only pair of numbers that satisfies both $y = x^2$ and $y = mx + b$.
$m = 3, b = -\frac{9}{4}, y = 3x - \frac{9}{4}$

2. If a is any real number, then (a, a^2) belongs to the graph of $y = x^2$. Express m and b in terms of a to find an equation of the form $y = mx + b$ for the line that is tangent to the graph of $y = x^2$ at (a, a^2).
$m = 2a, b = a^2, y = (2a)x + (-a^2)$ or $y = 2ax - a^2$

3. Find an equation for the normal to the graph of $y = x^2$ at $\left(\frac{3}{2}, \frac{9}{4}\right)$.
$y = -\frac{1}{3}x + \frac{11}{4}$

4. If a is a nonzero real number, find an equation for the normal to the graph of $y = x^2$ at (a, a^2).
$y = \left(-\frac{1}{2a}\right)x + \left(a^2 + \frac{1}{2}\right)$

Objectives
After studying this lesson, you should be able to:
9-3A ■ write equations of circles, and
9-3B ■ draw a circle having certain properties.

Application
Dean and Shina are flying a model airplane on a line. They control the flight of the plane with the 25-foot connecting wire. The plane's path is a circle with radius 25 feet and the controller at the center.

The measure of a radius is also called a radius.

A circle is the set of all points in a plane that are equidistant from a given point, called the **center.** Any segment whose endpoints are the center and a point on the circle is a **radius** of the circle.

Let's use the distance formula and the definition of a circle to find the equation of a circle with radius 8 units and center $(4, -5)$. Let (x, y) represent any point on the circle.

distance between (x, y) and $(4, -5) = 8$

$$\sqrt{(x - 4)^2 + (y - (-5))^2} = 8 \qquad \textit{Apply the distance formula.}$$
$$(x - 4)^2 + (y - (-5))^2 = 64 \qquad \textit{Square each side.}$$
$$(x - 4)^2 + (y + 5)^2 = 64 \qquad \textit{Simplify.}$$

Teaching Tip ❶
The equation of the circle with center $(4, -5)$ and radius 8 units is $(x - 4)^2 + (y + 5)^2 = 64$.

Equation of a Circle with Center (h, k)	The equation of a circle with center (h, k) and radius r units is $(x - h)^2 + (y - k)^2 = r^2.$

Example 1

APPLICATION

Seismology

An earthquake observation station that is located 30 miles east and 25 miles north of the central station detected that an earthquake occurred in the area. It is estimated that the epicenter was 50 miles away. Write the equation of the set of points that could be the epicenter and graph the solution set.

Assume that the central station is located at the origin. Any point that is 50 miles away from the station could be the epicenter. So the circle whose center is the observation station and whose radius is 50 miles is the solution set. The center of the circle is $(30, 25)$. The equation of the circle is $(x - 30)^2 + (y - 25)^2 = 50^2.$

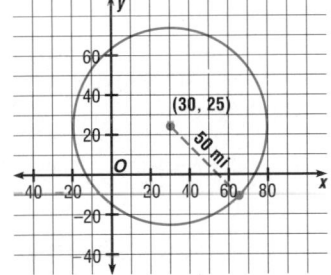

(30, 25)

50 mi.

Lesson Resources
Reteaching Master 9-3
Practice Master 9-3
Enrichment Master 9-3
Technology Master, p. 9

Transparency 9-3 contains the 5-Minute Check and a teaching aid for this lesson.

INTRODUCING THE LESSON

⏱ 5-Minute Check

(over Lesson 9-2)
Use the equation $x = 3(y - 1)^2 + 15$ for Exercises 1–5.

1. Name the vertex and axis of symmetry of its graph. $(15, 1); y = 1$
2. Name the focus and directrix of its graph. $\left(15\frac{1}{12}, 1\right); x = 14\frac{11}{12}$
3. Toward what direction does its graph open? **right**
4. What is the length of the latus rectum of its graph? $\frac{1}{3}$ **units**
5. Graph the equation.

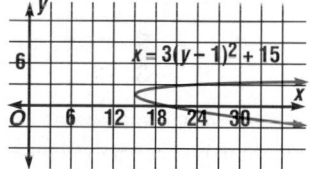

$x = 3(y - 1)^2 + 15$

Motivating the Lesson
Have students use a pencil, a piece of string, and a tack to make a circle. Place the tack on a piece of graph paper at a particular point. Draw the circle. Have students pick some points on the circle and find the distance from the center to each point.

TEACHING THE LESSON

Teaching Tip ❶ You may want to substitute (h, k) for the center, $(4, -5)$, and r for the radius, 8, to derive the general equation of a circle.

ALTERNATE TEACHING STRATEGIES

Using Discussion
Ask students the following questions to start a discussion.

1. What are circles and their components?
2. How can we relate distance formulas to finding the radius? **Given the coordinates of a point on the circle and the coordinates of the center, you can find the length of the radius.**
3. Is a circle the graph of a function? **No, there are two points for most x-value with a point on the circle.**

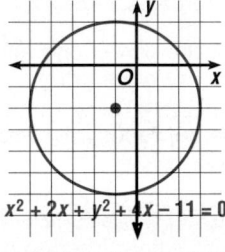
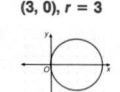 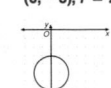 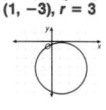
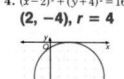 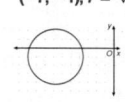 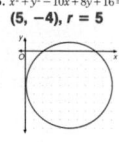

Teaching Tip ②   The equation $x^2 + y^2 + 2x - 12y = 35$ also describes a circle. If we were to complete the square for each variable and write the equation in the form $(x - h)^2 + (y - k)^2 = r^2$, the result would be $(x + 1)^2 + (y - 6)^2 = 72$. This circle has center $(-1, 6)$ and radius $\sqrt{72}$ or $6\sqrt{2}$ units.

Example 2   Find the center and radius of the circle whose equation is $x^2 + y^2 - 3x + 8y = 20$. Then graph the circle.

$$x^2 + y^2 - 3x + 8y = 20$$
$$x^2 - 3x + \square + y^2 + 8y + \blacksquare = 20 + \square + \blacksquare$$
$$x^2 - 3x + \frac{9}{4} + y^2 + 8y + 16 = 20 + \frac{9}{4} + 16$$
$$\left(x - \frac{3}{2}\right)^2 + (y + 4)^2 = \frac{153}{4}$$

The circle has center $\left(\frac{3}{2}, -4\right)$ and radius $\sqrt{\frac{153}{4}} = \frac{3\sqrt{17}}{2}$ or about 6.2 units.

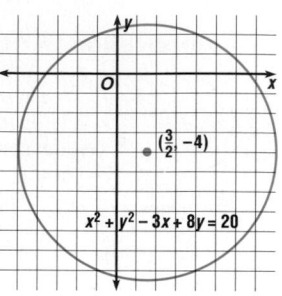

$x^2 + y^2 - 3x + 8y = 20$

CHECKING FOR UNDERSTANDING

Communicating Mathematics

Read and study the lesson to answer these questions.

1. If the restriction "in a plane" were taken out of the definition of the circle, would the figure change? If so, how? **Yes, it would be a sphere.**

2. Describe the similarities and differences between the graphs of $(x + 3)^2 + (y - 4)^2 = 16$ and $(x - 3)^2 + (y - 2)^2 = 16$. **See margin.**

3. Concentric circles are circles with the same center, but not necessarily the same radius. Write the equations of two concentric circles. Graph the circles. **See margin.**

4. The circle whose equation is $(x - a)^2 + (y - b)^2 = 25$ has its center in the second quadrant. What do you know about a and b? **$a < 0, b > 0$**

5. Find the equation of the circle graphed at the right. State the center and radius of the circle. **$(x - 12)^2 + (y + 3)^2 = 121; (12, -3); 11$**

Guided Practice

State whether the graph of each equation is a circle or a parabola.

6. $x^2 + y^2 = 36$ **circle**

7. $x^2 + 4x + 4 = 9y + 27$ **parabola**

8. $y^2 = 6x - 4$ **parabola**

9. $x^2 + y^2 = 7x - 5$ **circle**

10. $y^2 + y + x^2 = 12 - 3x$ **circle**

11. $y^2 = 5x$ **parabola**

RETEACHING THE LESSON

Given the coordinates of three points on a circle, find the center of the circle, its radius, and its equation. Verify that the three given points do indeed lie on the circle. If needed, remind students that the center lies on the perpendicular bisectors of chords.

Additional Answers

2. They have the same radius, 4, but different centers, $(-3, 4)$ and $(3, 2)$.

3. Answers may vary. A sample answer is $x^2 + y^2 = 9$ and $x^2 + y^2 = 16$.

State the center and radius of each circle whose equation is given.

12. $x^2 + y^2 = 49$ **(0, 0), 7**

13. $x^2 + (y - 3)^2 = 36$ **(0, 3), 6**

15. $\left(-2, \frac{2}{3}\right), 2\sqrt{2}$

14. $(x - 4)^2 + (y - 1)^2 = 9$ **(4, 1), 3**

15. $(x + 2)^2 + \left(y - \frac{2}{3}\right)^2 = 8$

16. $(4, 0), \frac{4}{5}$

16. $(x - 4)^2 + y^2 = \frac{16}{25}$

17. $x^2 + (y + 5)^2 = \frac{81}{64}$

17. $(0, -5), \frac{9}{8}$

Find the center and radius of each circle whose equation is given. Then draw the graph. **For graphs, see Solutions Manual.**

18. $x^2 + y^2 = 9$ **(0, 0), 3**

19. $(x + 5)^2 + y^2 = 64$ **(-5, 0), 8**

20. $(x + 6)^2 + (y - 5)^2 = 16$ **(-6, 5), 4**

21. $(x - 3)^2 + (y + 2)^2 = 169$
(3, -2), 13

EXERCISES

Practice

Find the center and radius of each circle whose equation is given. Then draw the graph. **For graphs, see Solutions Manual.**

26. **(3, 1), 5**

22. $x^2 + (y - 4)^2 = 49$ **(0, 4), 7**

23. $x^2 + (y + 2)^2 = 4$ **(0, -2), 2**

27. **(-2, 1), 9**

24. $(x - 3)^2 + y^2 = 16$ **(3, 0), 4**

25. $x^2 + y^2 = 144$ **(0, 0), 12**

28. **(-3, -7), 9**

26. $(x - 3)^2 + (y - 1)^2 = 25$

27. $(x + 2)^2 + (y - 1)^2 = 81$

29. **(4, 9), 2**

28. $(x + 3)^2 + (y + 7)^2 = 81$

29. $(x - 4)^2 + (y - 9)^2 = 4$

30. **(-3, 1), 5**

30. $x^2 + y^2 + 6x - 2y - 15 = 0$

31. $x^2 + y^2 - 18x - 18y + 53 = 0$

32. $x^2 + y^2 + 14x + 6y = 23$

33. $x^2 + y^2 + 8x - 6y = 0$

31. **(9, 9), $\sqrt{109}$**

34. $x^2 - 12x + 84 = -y^2 + 16y$

35. $x^2 + y^2 = 4x + 9$

32. **(-7, -3), 9**

33. **(-4, 3), 5**

36. $x^2 + y^2 - 6y - 16 = 0$

37. $3x^2 + 3y^2 + 6y + 9x = 2$

34. **(6, 8), 4**

38. $x^2 + y^2 + 9x - 8y + 4 = 0$

39. $4x^2 + 4y^2 + 36y + 5 = 0$

35. **(2, 0), $\sqrt{13}$**

40. $x^2 + y^2 + 4x - 8 = 0$

41. $x^2 + y^2 + 2x + 4y - 9 = 0$

36. **(0, 3), 5**

37–41. **See margin.**

42. $x^2 + 14x + y^2 + 6y + 50 = 0$

43. $x^2 + y^2 + 2x - 10 = 0$

44. $(x - 4)^2 +$
$(y - 1)^2 = 16$

(-7, -3), $2\sqrt{2}$

(-1, 0), $\sqrt{11}$

Write an equation for each circle whose center and radius are given.

45. $x^2 + (y - 3)^2 = 49$

46. $(x - 5)^2 + y^2 = 64$

44. (4, 1), 4 units

45. (0, 3), 7 inches

46. (5, 0), 8 meters

47. $(x + 1)^2 +$
$(y + 5)^2 = 4$

47. (-1, -5), 2 cm

48. $(-8, 7), \frac{1}{2}$ km

49. $(-3, -9), \frac{5}{6}$ yd

48. $(x + 8)^2 +$
$(y - 7)^2 = \frac{1}{4}$

Write the equation of each circle described below. **See margin.**

49. $(x + 3)^2 +$
$(y + 9)^2 = \frac{25}{36}$

50. The circle has center (4, -2) and passes through (5, 3).

51. The circle has center (3, 3) and passes through the origin.

52. The endpoints of a diameter of the circle are (2, 5) and (2, -1).

53. The endpoints of a diameter of the circle are (-4, 12) and (2, 0).

54. The circle has center (-3, 8) and is tangent to the x-axis.
A circle tangent to a line intersects that line in exactly one point.

55. The center of the circle is (4, -3) and the circle is tangent to the y-axis.

Critical Thinking

56. Write the equation of a circle that is tangent to both the x- and y-axes.
Answers may vary. A sample answer is $(x - 1)^2 + (y - 1)^2 = 1$.

LESSON 9-3 CIRCLES 407

Additional Answers

37. $\left(-\frac{3}{2}, -1\right), \frac{\sqrt{141}}{6}$

38. $\left(-\frac{9}{2}, 4\right), \frac{\sqrt{129}}{2}$

39. $\left(0, -\frac{9}{2}\right), \sqrt{19}$

40. (-2, 0), $2\sqrt{3}$

41. (-1, -2), $\sqrt{14}$;

50. $(x - 4)^2 + (y + 2)^2 = 26$
51. $(x - 3)^2 + (y - 3)^2 = 18$
52. $(x - 2)^2 + (y - 2)^2 = 9$
53. $(x + 1)^2 + (y - 6)^2 = 45$
54. $(x + 3)^2 + (y - 8)^2 = 64$
55. $(x - 4)^2 + (y + 3)^2 = 16$

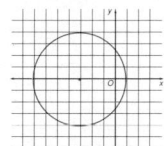
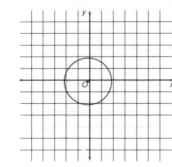
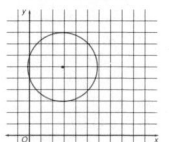
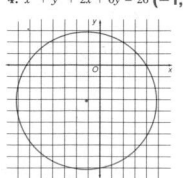

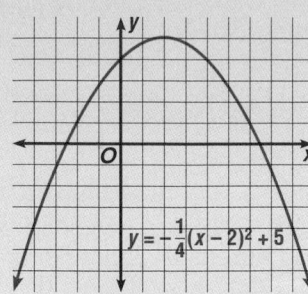
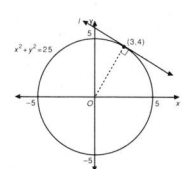
Applications

57. **Air Traffic Control**   The control tower for the municipal airport is located at (4, 16) on the county map. The radar used in tracking airplanes can detect a plane up to 13 miles away. Write an equation for the position of the most distant plane that the tower can detect in terms of the county map. $(x - 4)^2 + (y - 16)^2 = 169$

58. **Physics**   The model plane described in the beginning of the lesson makes one revolution in 8 seconds. How fast is the model traveling in feet per second?   (*Hint: Recall that the formula for the circumference of a circle is $C = 2\pi r$.*)   **about 19.6 feet per second**

59. **City Planning**   The officials of the city of Westerville are planning the placement of some new fire stations. They want to ensure that all areas of the city are within 5 miles of a fire station. If the city is approximately 10 miles square, will they be able to cover the entire city with two fire stations?   *Hint: Draw a diagram.*   **no**

61. $y = -\frac{1}{4}(x - 2)^2 + 5$; **See margin for graph.**

Mixed Review

60. Change the equation $y^2 = 6x$ to the form $x = a(y - k)^2 + h$. **(Lesson 9-2)** $x = \frac{1}{6}y^2$

61. Write an equation for the parabola with focus (2, 4) and directrix $y = 6$. Then draw the graph.   **(Lesson 9-2)**

62. Is (3, −5) a solution for the inequality $y \geq x^2 - 16$?   **(Lesson 8-7) yes**

63. Express the equation $y^{-6} + 4y^{-3} - 32 = 0$ in quadratic form.   **(Lesson 7-6)** $1(y^{-3})^2 + 4(y^{-3}) - 32 = 0$

64. Solve $3x\sqrt{3} + 2 = 0$.   **(Lesson 6-7)** $\frac{-2\sqrt{3}}{9}$

65. Factor $4k^2 + 26k + 30$.   **(Lesson 5-5)** $2(2k + 3)(k + 5)$

66. Find the inverse (if one exists) of the matrix $\begin{bmatrix} 8 & 0 \\ -1 & -4 \end{bmatrix}$.   **(Lesson 4-5)** $\begin{bmatrix} \frac{1}{8} & 0 \\ -\frac{1}{32} & -\frac{1}{4} \end{bmatrix}$

~~~ HISTORY CONNECTION ~~~

The Dogon of Mali

Some 500 to 700 years ago, the astronomer priests of the Dogon of the Republic of Mali in West Africa began accumulating detailed observations and knowledge of the universe that equal modern science. They knew, in detail, of the elliptical paths of the planets, the rings of Saturn, the moons of Jupiter, and the spiral structure of the Milky Way Galaxy. They knew that Earth's moon was barren and described it as dry and dead. Amazingly enough, all these observations were made with the naked eye without the aid of modern tools.

Every 60 years, when the orbits of Jupiter and Saturn converse, the Dogon held a ceremony to the star Sirius. Actually they celebrated Sirius B, a smaller star, that revolves around Sirius A, the brightest star in the sky. They knew that this dwarf star had an elliptical orbit around Sirius A which took 50 years to complete. Modern scientists have not been able to confirm or deny this incredible observation. They know only of Sirius B's existence, which can only be seen with high-powered telescopes.

EXTENDING THE LESSON

Math Power: Problem Solving

Write an equation of the circle described below.

center on the x-axis, radius 5 units long, and passes through (2, −2)
center at $(2 + \sqrt{21}, 0)$ or $(2 - \sqrt{21}, 0)$

Equation:
$2 + \sqrt{21} \approx 6.6$
$2 - \sqrt{21} \approx -2.6$
$(x - 6.6)^2 + y^2 = 25$
or $(x + 2.6)^2 + y^2 = 25$

History Connection

The History Connection features introduce students to persons or cultures who were involved in the development of mathematics. You may want students to further research Sirius B.

Ellipses

Objectives

After studying this lesson, you should be able to:

9-4A ▪ write equations of ellipses, and

9-4B ▪ draw an ellipse having certain properties.

Application

You will read more about this chamber later in this lesson.

The Statuary Hall in The United States Capitol is shaped like an **ellipse**. In this chamber, a person standing at one of two points called the **foci** of the ellipse can hear someone who is standing on the other **focus point** whispering, even though that point is more than 80 feet away.

Definition of Ellipse

> An ellipse is the set of all points in a plane such that the sum of the distances from two given points in the plane, called the *foci*, is constant.

You can draw an ellipse using two tacks and a piece of string. Push the two tacks into a piece of cardboard. Tie a knot in the piece of string and loop it around the tacks as shown at the right. Place your pencil in the loop and draw around the tacks, making sure to keep the string tight. The foci of your ellipse are the points where the tacks are placed.

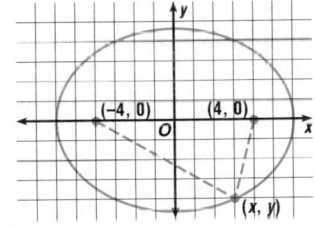

The ellipse at the left has foci $(-4, 0)$ and $(4, 0)$, and the sum of the distances to any point (x, y) on the ellipse to the foci is 12 units. Let's use the distance formula and the definition of an ellipse to find the equation of this ellipse.

Let (x, y) be any point on the ellipse. The sum of the distance between (x, y) and $(-4, 0)$ and the distance between (x, y) and $(4, 0)$ is 12 units.

$$\underset{\substack{\text{distance between}\\(x, y) \text{ and } (-4, 0)}}{} + \underset{\substack{\text{distance between}\\(x, y) \text{ and } (4, 0)}}{} = 12$$

$$\sqrt{(x + 4)^2 + y^2} + \sqrt{(x - 4)^2 + y^2} = 12$$

$$\sqrt{(x + 4)^2 + y^2} = 12 - \sqrt{(x - 4)^2 + y^2} \quad \textit{Now square each side.}$$

$$(x + 4)^2 + y^2 = 144 - 24\sqrt{(x - 4)^2 + y^2} + (x - 4)^2 + y^2$$

$$4x - 36 = -6\sqrt{(x - 4)^2 + y^2} \quad \textit{Simplify.}$$

$$16x^2 - 288x + 1296 = 36[(x - 4)^2 + y^2] \quad \textit{Square each side.}$$

$$720 = 20x^2 + 36y^2 \quad \textit{Simplify.}$$

$$1 = \frac{x^2}{36} + \frac{y^2}{20} \quad \textit{Divide by 720.}$$

The equation of the ellipse with foci $(-4, 0)$ and $(4, 0)$ and with 12 units as the sum of the distances from the foci is $\frac{x^2}{36} + \frac{y^2}{20} = 1$.

ALTERNATE TEACHING STRATEGIES

Using Models

Use the procedure described for drawing an ellipse to show students that as the foci of an ellipse get closer together, the shape of the ellipse approaches the shape of a circle. As a result of this activity, students will see that when the foci and the center become one point, the figure is a circle.

1. Under what conditions is the graph of $\frac{x^2}{a^2} + \frac{y^2}{b^2} = 1$ a circle?
   when $a = b$

2. What happens to the foci and the center of this ellipse? **They become one point—the center of the circle since $c^2 = a^2 - b^2 = 0$.** Note that a circle, then, is a special case of an ellipse.

INTRODUCING THE LESSON

Lesson Resources

Reteaching Master 9-4
Practice Master 9-4
Enrichment Master 9-4
Activity Master, p. 9

Transparency 9-4 contains the 5-Minute Check and a teaching aid for this lesson.

🕐 5-Minute Check

(over Lesson 9-3)

Write equations for the circles whose centers and radii are given in Exercises 1–2.

1. $C(5, 0); r = 6$
   $(x - 5)^2 + y^2 = 36$

2. $C(-3, -2); r = \frac{3}{2}$
   $(x + 3)^2 + (y + 2)^2 = \frac{9}{4}$

3. Graph the equation $x^2 + (y - 3)^2 = 16$.

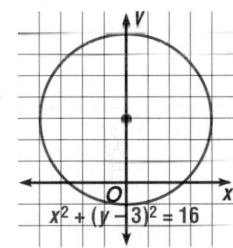

$x^2 + (y - 3)^2 = 16$

4. Simplify $(3\sqrt{2} + \sqrt{3})^2$.
   $21 + 6\sqrt{6}$

5. Simplify $rs/(r^{1/2} + r^{3/2})$.
   $\dfrac{r^{\frac{1}{2}}s}{(1 + r)}$

Motivating the Lesson

Bring in a flashlight. Show how to form a circle (beam perpendicular to the wall), ellipse (beam at an angle to the wall) and parabola (place flashlight parallel to wall). Discuss what happens as you move the flashlight slowly through the different positions.

For $\dfrac{x^2}{36} + \dfrac{y^2}{20} = 1$, the length of the major axis is $2a$ or $2\sqrt{36}$ or 12. The length of the minor axis is $2\sqrt{20}$ or $4\sqrt{5}$.

Chalkboard Example

For Example 1

For intramural games, an elliptical track is used. There is a timekeeper at each focus. The major axis is 400 meters and the timekeepers are both 120 meters from the center of the ellipse. Assuming the center is the origin and the foci lie on the x-axis, find the equation for the path of a runner on the track.

$$\frac{x^2}{40,000} + \frac{y^2}{25,600} = 1$$

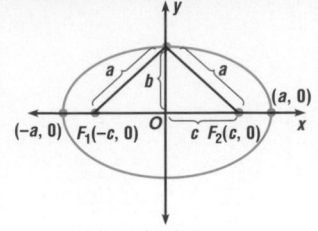

The length of the major axis is 2a. The length of the minor axis is 2b. Notice a > b.

There are two axes of symmetry in an ellipse. The points where the ellipse intersects the axes define two line segments whose endpoints lie on the ellipse. The longer segment is called the major axis and the shorter is the minor axis. The foci always lie on the major axis. The intersection of the two axes is the **center** of the ellipse. **Teaching Tip** ❶

Study the ellipse at the left. The sum of the distances from the foci to any point on the ellipse is $2a$ units. The distance from the center to either focus is c units. By using the Pythagorean Theorem, we can conclude that $b^2 = a^2 - c^2$. If we found the equation of this general ellipse, we would find the standard equation of an ellipse.

Standard Equation of Ellipse with Center at the Origin

For ellipses, $a^2 > b^2$

> If an ellipse has foci at $(-c, 0)$ and $(c, 0)$ and if the sum of the distances from the foci to any point on the ellipse is $2a$ units,
> then the standard equation of the ellipse is $\dfrac{x^2}{a^2} + \dfrac{y^2}{b^2} = 1$, where $b^2 = a^2 - c^2$.
>
> If an ellipse has foci at $(0, -c)$ and $(0, c)$ and if the sum of the distances from the foci to any point on the ellipse is $2a$ units,
> then the standard equation of the ellipse is $\dfrac{x^2}{b^2} + \dfrac{y^2}{a^2} = 1$, where $b^2 = a^2 - c^2$.

Example 1

APPLICATION
Aeronautics

A satellite is in an elliptical orbit with the center of Earth at one focus. The major axis of the orbit is 28,900 miles long and the center of the Earth is 8000 miles from the center of the ellipse. Assuming that the center of the ellipse is the origin and the foci lie on the x-axis, write the equation of the path of the satellite.

We know the length of the major axis is 28,900. So we can find a.

$$2a = 28,900$$
$$a = 14,450$$

Since Earth is at a focus point and it is 8000 miles from the center, $c = 8000$.

$$b^2 = a^2 - c^2$$
$$b^2 = 14,450^2 - 8000^2$$
$$b^2 = 144,802,500$$

Now we can write the equation.

$$\frac{x^2}{a^2} + \frac{y^2}{b^2} = 1$$

$$\frac{x^2}{(14,450^2)} + \frac{y^2}{144,802,500} = 1$$

$$\frac{x^2}{208,802,500} + \frac{y^2}{144,802,500} = 1$$

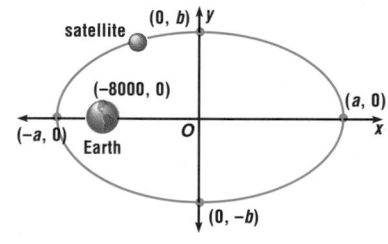

Example 2

Write the equation of the ellipse shown below.

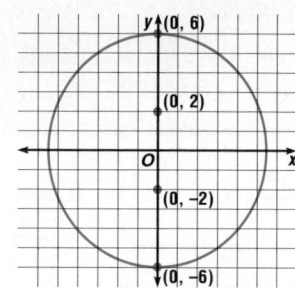

First find the length of the major axis. The distance between $(0, -6)$ and $(0, 6)$ is 12 units.

$$2a = 12$$
$$a = 6$$

Since the foci are at $(0, -2)$ and $(0, 2)$, $c = 2$.

$$b^2 = a^2 - c^2$$
$$b^2 = 6^2 - 2^2$$
$$b^2 = 32$$

Now write the equation.

$$\frac{x^2}{b^2} + \frac{y^2}{a^2} = 1 \qquad \textit{The major axis is vertical.}$$

$$\frac{x^2}{32} + \frac{y^2}{6^2} = 1 \quad \text{or} \quad \frac{x^2}{32} + \frac{y^2}{36} = 1$$

In the equation of an ellipse, $a^2 > b^2$. So it is easy to decide whether the foci are on the x-axis or the y-axis just by looking at the equation. If a^2 is the denominator of the x^2 term, the foci are on the x-axis. If a^2 is the denominator of the y^2 term, the foci are on the y-axis.

Example 3

Find the foci and the lengths of the major and minor axes of the ellipse whose equation is $4x^2 + y^2 = 16$. Then draw the graph.

$$4x^2 + y^2 = 16 \qquad \textit{Write the equation in standard form.}$$
$$\frac{x^2}{4} + \frac{y^2}{16} = 1$$

Since $16 > 4$, the foci are on the y-axis, $a = 4$, and $b = 2$.

$$b^2 = a^2 - c^2$$
$$4 = 16 - c^2$$
$$c^2 = 12$$
$$c = \sqrt{12} \text{ or } 2\sqrt{3} \qquad 2\sqrt{3} \approx 3.5$$

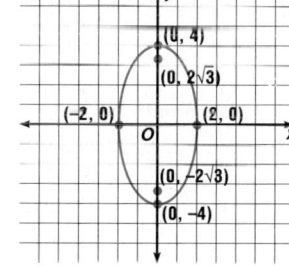

The foci are at $(0, 2\sqrt{3})$ and $(0, -2\sqrt{3})$. The major axis is $2a$ or 8 units long and the minor axis is $2b$ or 4 units long.

An equation in the form $\frac{x^2}{a^2} + \frac{y^2}{b^2} = 1$ or $\frac{x^2}{b^2} + \frac{y^2}{a^2} = 1$ represents an ellipse with center at the origin. If an ellipse has center at a point (h, k), its equation would be similar with $(x - h)$ replacing x and $(y - k)$ replacing y.

LESSON 9-4 ELLIPSES **411**

Chalkboard Examples

For Example 2
Write the equation of the ellipse with foci at $(0, \pm \sqrt{33})$ shown below.

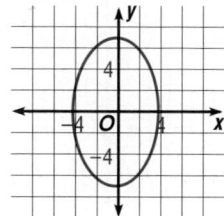

$$\frac{x^2}{16} + \frac{y^2}{49} = 1$$

For Example 3
Find the foci and the lengths of the major and minor axes of the ellipse whose equation is $64x^2 + 9y^2 = 576$. Then draw the graph.

foci: $(0, \sqrt{55})$, $(0, -\sqrt{55})$
major axis length: 16
minor axis length: 6

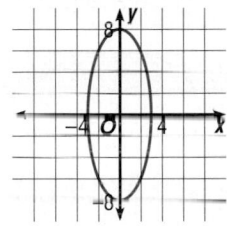

Graph $\dfrac{(x+1)^2}{4} + \dfrac{(y+2)^2}{9} = 1$.

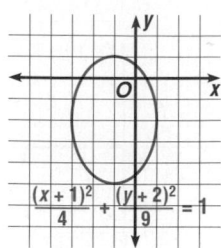

For Example 5

Find the center, the foci, and the lengths of the major and minor axes of the ellipse whose equation is $16y^2 + 9x^2 - 96y - 90x = -225$. Then draw the graph.

center: (5, 3)
foci: $(5 + \sqrt{7}, 3)$, $(5 - \sqrt{7}, 3)$
major axis length: 8
minor axis length: 6

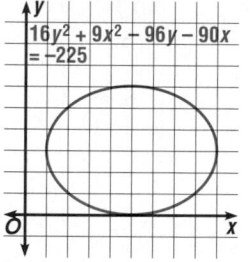

Checking for Understanding

Exercises 1–17 are designed to help you assess understanding through reading, writing, and speaking. You should work through Exercises 1–3 with your students, and then monitor their work on Exercises 4–17.

Standard Equation of Ellipse with Center at (h, k)

For ellipses $a^2 > b^2$.

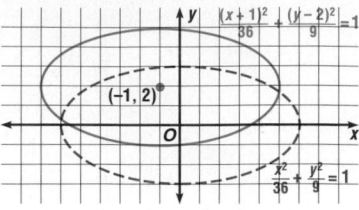

The equation of an ellipse whose center is at (h, k) and with a horizontal major axis is $\dfrac{(x-h)^2}{a^2} + \dfrac{(y-k)^2}{b^2} = 1$.

The equation of an ellipse whose center is at (h, k) and with a vertical major axis is $\dfrac{(x-h)^2}{b^2} + \dfrac{(y-k)^2}{a^2} = 1$.

Example 4

Graph $\dfrac{(x+1)^2}{36} + \dfrac{(y-2)^2}{9} = 1$.

The graph is the same shape as the graph of $\dfrac{x^2}{36} + \dfrac{y^2}{9} = 1$, but with center translated 1 unit to the left and 2 units up. The center is at $(-1, 2)$ instead of the origin.

The graph of $2x^2 + y^2 - 4x + 8y - 6 = 0$ is an ellipse. Complete the square for each variable, like you did with equations of circles, to write the equation in standard form.

$$2x^2 + y^2 - 4x + 8y - 6 = 0$$
$$2(x^2 - 2x + \square) + y^2 + 8y + \blacksquare = 6 + 2\square + \blacksquare \qquad \textit{Complete the square.}$$
$$2(x^2 - 2x + 1) + y^2 + 8y + 16 = 6 + 2(1) + 16$$
$$2(x - 1)^2 + (y + 4)^2 = 24$$
$$\frac{(x-1)^2}{12} + \frac{(y+4)^2}{24} = 1$$

The ellipse has center at $(1, -4)$. Since $24 > 12$, $a^2 = 24$ and $b^2 = 12$ and it has a vertical major axis. So the major axis is $2a$ or $2\sqrt{24}$ (or $4\sqrt{6}$) units long and the minor axis is $2b$ or $2\sqrt{12}$ (or $4\sqrt{3}$) units long.

Example 5

Find the center, foci, and lengths of the major and minor axes of the ellipse whose equation is $x^2 + 25y^2 - 8x + 100y + 91 = 0$. Then draw the graph.

$$x^2 + 25y^2 - 8x + 100y + 91 = 0$$
$$x^2 - 8x + \square + 25(y^2 + 4y + \blacksquare) = -91 + \square + 25(\blacksquare) \qquad \textit{Complete the square.}$$
$$x^2 - 8x + 16 + 25(y^2 + 4y + 4) = -91 + 16 + 25(4)$$
$$(x - 4)^2 + 25(y + 2)^2 = 25$$
$$\frac{(x-4)^2}{25} + \frac{(y+2)^2}{1} = 1$$

The ellipse has center at $(4, -2)$. Since $25 > 1$, a^2 must be 25. So $a = 5$, $b = 1$, and the major axis is parallel to the x-axis.

$$b^2 = a^2 - c^2$$
$$1 = 25 - c^2$$
$$c^2 = 24$$
$$c = \sqrt{24} \text{ or } 2\sqrt{6} \qquad 2\sqrt{6} \approx 4.9$$

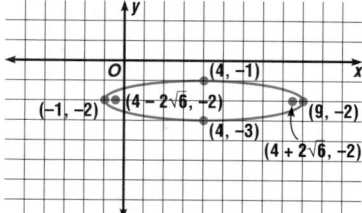

The foci are $2\sqrt{6}$ units to the left and right of the center. The foci are at $(4 + 2\sqrt{6}, -2)$ and $(4 - 2\sqrt{6}, -2)$ or about $(8.9, -2)$ and $(-0.9, -2)$. The length of the major axis is $2a$ or 10 units and the minor axis is $2b$ or 2 units.

CHECKING FOR UNDERSTANDING

Communicating Mathematics

1. **The result is a circle. A circle is a special ellipse.**

Read and study the lesson to answer these questions.

1. Use the string and tack technique to draw an ellipse with the two foci at one point. What do you observe? What can you conclude?

2. How can you tell which axis is the major axis from the equation of an ellipse? **See margin.**

3. Describe the graph of the equation $\dfrac{x^2}{4} + \dfrac{(y-2)^2}{1} = 1$. **See margin.**

Guided Practice

8. $\dfrac{x^2}{4} + \dfrac{y^2}{16} = 1$

9. $\dfrac{x^2}{12} + \dfrac{y^2}{28} = 1$

10. $\dfrac{(x+1)^2}{4} + \dfrac{(y-3)^2}{1} = 1$

11. $\dfrac{(x+3)^2}{9} + \dfrac{(y-5)^2}{4} = 1$

12. $\dfrac{(x+4.5)^2}{42.25} +$
$\dfrac{(y+1)^2}{25.35} = 1$

13. $\dfrac{(x-3)^2}{16} +$
$\dfrac{(y+2)^2}{9} = 1$

Name the center of the ellipse with each equation and state whether the major axis is horizontal or vertical.

4. $\dfrac{x^2}{12} + \dfrac{y^2}{8} = 1$ **(0, 0), H**

5. $\dfrac{x^2}{5} + \dfrac{y^2}{24} = 1$ **(0, 0), V**

6. $\dfrac{x^2}{64} + \dfrac{(y-3)^2}{36} = 1$ **(0, 3), H**

7. $\dfrac{(x-11)^2}{121} + \dfrac{(y+8)^2}{144} = 1$ **(11, -8), V**

Write the equation of each ellipse in standard form.

8. $8x^2 + 2y^2 = 32$

9. $7x^2 + 3y^2 = 84$

10. $x^2 + 4y^2 + 2x - 24y + 33 = 0$

11. $4x^2 + 9y^2 + 24x - 90y = -225$

12. $6x^2 + 10y^2 + 54x + 20y = 122$

13. $9x^2 + 16y^2 - 54x + 64y + 1 = 0$

Find the center, foci, and lengths of the major and minor axes for each ellipse whose equation is given. Then draw the graph. **For graphs, see Solutions Manual.**

14. $\dfrac{x^2}{9} + \dfrac{y^2}{36} = 1$ **(0, 0); (0, $\pm 3\sqrt{3}$); 12, 6**

15. $\dfrac{x^2}{36} + \dfrac{y^2}{16} = 1$ **(0, 0); ($\pm 2\sqrt{5}$, 0); 12, 8**

16. $3x^2 + 9y^2 = 27$ **(0, 0); ($\pm \sqrt{6}$, 0); 6, $2\sqrt{3}$**

17. $16x^2 + 9y^2 = 144$ **(0, 0); (0, $\pm \sqrt{7}$); 8, 6**

EXERCISES

Practice

Write the equation of each ellipse.

18.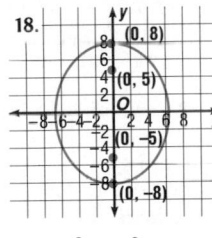

$\dfrac{x^2}{39} + \dfrac{y^2}{64} = 1$

19.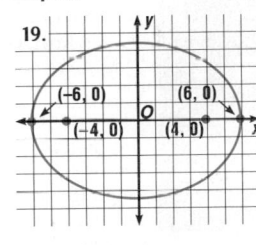

$\dfrac{x^2}{36} + \dfrac{y^2}{20} = 1$

20. $\dfrac{(x-5)^2}{64} + \dfrac{(y-4)^2}{9} = 1$

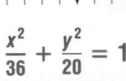

RETEACHING THE LESSON

Given the foci and the sum of the distances from the foci to any point on an ellipse, find the standard form of its equation in two ways. First use the definition of an ellipse and the distance formula to find the equation. Then use relationships to find h, k, b, and c.

Additional Answers

2. The major axis is parallel or equal to the axis named in

the term with the greater denominator. For example, in the equation $\dfrac{(x-3)^2}{39} + \dfrac{y^2}{22} = 1$, the x is in the term with the greater denominator, so the major axis is parallel or equal to the x-axis.

3. An ellipse with a major axis that is 4 units long and parallel to the x-axis. The minor axis is 2 units long. The center is (0, 2) and the foci are $(\sqrt{3}, 2)$, $(-\sqrt{3}, 2)$.

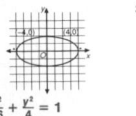
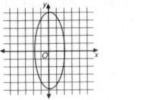
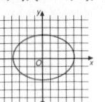

Chapter 9, Quiz B, (Lessons 9-3 through 9-4), is available in the Evaluation Masters Booklet, p. 121.

Teaching Tip ② Remind students to complete the square for Exercises 31–34.

Additional Answer

41. For $k > 0$, as k increases the shape remains similar and the size increases.

B Find the center, foci, and lengths of the major and minor axes for each ellipse whose equation is given. Then draw the graph. **See Solutions Manual for graphs.**

21. $\frac{x^2}{25} + \frac{y^2}{9} = 1$ (0, 0); (±4, 0); 10, 6   **22.** $\frac{x^2}{5} + \frac{y^2}{10} = 1$ (0, 0); (0, ±√5); 2√1 2√5

24. (0, 0); (±3√5, 0), 18, 12

23. $x^2 + 9y^2 = 9$ (0, 0); (±2√2, 0); 6, 2   **24.** $36x^2 + 81y^2 = 2916$

25. (0, 0); (0, ±√6); 6; 2√3

25. $27x^2 + 9y^2 = 81$ **26.** $\frac{(x+3)^2}{36} + \frac{(y-4)^2}{9} = 1$

26. (−3, 4); (−3 ± 3√3, 4); 12, 6

27. $\frac{(x-8)^2}{4} + \frac{(y+8)^2}{1} = 1$ **28.** $\frac{(x+2)^2}{20} + \frac{(y+3)^2}{40} = 1$

29. $\frac{(x+8)^2}{121} + \frac{(y-7)^2}{64} = 1$

27. (8, −8); (8 ± √3, −8); 4, 2

Teaching Tip ②

30. $\frac{(x-4)^2}{16} + \frac{(y+1)^2}{9} = 1$

31. $4x^2 + 9y^2 + 16x - 18y - 11 = 0$ **32.** $9x^2 + 16y^2 - 18x + 64y = 71$

33. $7x^2 + 3y^2 - 28x - 12y + 19 = 0$ **34.** $16x^2 + 25y^2 + 32x - 150y = 159$
(2, 2); (2, 4), (2, 0); 2√7, 2√3   (−1, 3); (2, 3), (−4, 3); 10, 8

C Write the equation of each ellipse described below.

28. (−2, −3); (−2, −3 ± 2√5); 4√10, 4√5

35. The endpoints of the major axis are at (0, 10) and (0, −10). The foci are at (0, 8) and (0, −8). $\frac{x^2}{36} + \frac{y^2}{100} = 1$

36. The foci are at (12, 0) and (−12, 0). The endpoints of the minor axis are at (0, 5) and (0, −5). $\frac{x^2}{169} + \frac{y^2}{25} = 1$

29. (−8, 7); (−8 ± √57, 7); 22, 16

30. (4, −1); (4 ± √7, −1); 8, 6

37. The major axis is 16 units long and parallel to the x-axis. The center is (5, 4) and the minor axis is 9 units long. $\frac{(x-5)^2}{64} + \frac{4(y-4)^2}{81} = 1$

38. The endpoints of the major axis are at (2, 12) and (2, −4). The endpoints of the minor axis are at (4, 4) and (0, 4). $\frac{(x-2)^2}{4} + \frac{(y-4)^2}{64} = 1$

31. (−2, 1); (−2 ± √5, 1); 6, 4

39. The major axis is 12 units long and parallel to the y-axis. The minor axis is 8 units long and the center is at (−2, 3). $\frac{(x+2)^2}{16} + \frac{(y-3)^2}{36} = 1$

32. (1, −2); (1 ± √7, −2); 8, 6

40. The endpoints of the minor axis are at (−2, 5) and (−2, −1). The endpoints of the major axis are at (−9, 2) and (5, 2). $\frac{(x+2)^2}{49} + \frac{(y-2)^2}{9} = 1$

Critical Thinking

41. Describe the changes in the shape and size of the ellipse whose equation is $x^2 + 4y^2 = k$ as you increase the value of k. **See margin.**

Applications

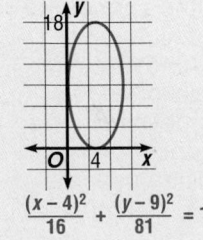

42. History The elliptical chamber in the United States Capitol Building is 46 feet wide and 96 feet long.

a. Write an equation to describe the shape of the room. Assume that it is centered at the origin and the major axis is horizontal. $\frac{x^2}{2304} + \frac{y^2}{529} = 1$

b. John Quincy Adams discovered that he could overhear the conversations being held at the opposing party leader's desk if he stood in a certain spot in the elliptical chamber. Describe the position of the desk and how far away Adams had to stand to overhear. **The desk is on one focus point; about 84 feet**

414   CHAPTER 9   CONICS

Practice Masters Booklet, p. 67

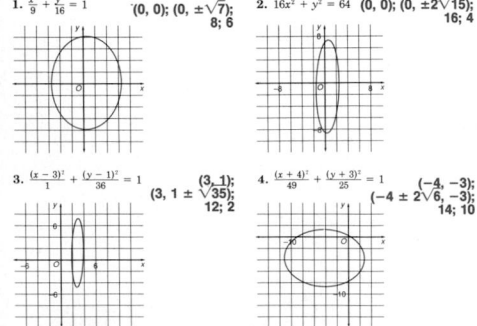

EXTENDING THE LESSON

Math Power: Reasoning

An ellipse with center at (4, 9) is tangent to the coordinates axes. Write the equation of the ellipse and draw the graph.

$\frac{(x-4)^2}{16} + \frac{(y-9)^2}{81} = 1$

43. Write an equation for the circle whose center is (6, 2) and whose radius is 5 units. (**Lesson 9-3**) $(x - 6)^2 + (y - 2)^2 = 25$

45. $f(x) =$ $(x + 1)^2 - 3$; $(-1, -3)$; $x = -1$; **up**

44. Write an equation for the circle with center at (1, 5) that passes through the origin. (**Lesson 9-3**) $(x - 1)^2 + (x - 5)^2 = 26$

45. Write the equation $f(x) = x^2 + 2x - 2$ in the form $f(x) = a(x - h)^2 + k$. Then name the vertex, axis of symmetry, and direction of opening for the parabola it describes. (**Lesson 8-3**)

46. State whether $x^2 + 8x + 64$ is a perfect square. (**Lesson 7-3**) **no**

47. Find the product of $7 - 7i$ and its conjugate. (**Lesson 6-10**) **98**

48. Rose, Lars, Kris, and Jim were ready to begin playing a game of cards. Lars started shuffling the deck, but dropped the cards. Rose, Kris, and Jim picked up the cards for him. Rose said she had twice as many cards as Jim. If Rose were to give Kris five cards, Kris would have five times as many cards as Jim. Without counting the cards, Lars said he would get a second deck of cards because the deck they were using could not be complete. Find all the possible numbers of cards that might have been in the incomplete deck. (**Lesson 1-5**) **19, 27, 35, 43, 51**

MID-CHAPTER REVIEW

Use the distance formula to find the distance between each pair of points. (**Lesson 9-1**)

1. (-2, 7), (4, -1) **10 units**

2. (0, 5), (6, 3) $2\sqrt{10}$ **units**

Find the midpoint of the line segment whose endpoints are given below. (**Lesson 9-1**)

3. (3, -1), (5, -7) **(4, -4)**

4. (8, 0), (-5, 12) $\left(\frac{3}{2}, 6\right)$

Name the vertex, axis of symmetry, focus, directrix, and direction of opening of the parabola whose equation is given. Then find the length of the latus rectum and graph. (**Lesson 9-2**)

5. $-12y = x^2$ **See margin.**

6. $8x = y^2 + 4y + 28$ **See margin.**

The focus and directrix of a parabola are given. Write an equation for each parabola. Then draw the graph. (**Lesson 9-2**) **See margin.**

7. (3, 5), $y = 1$

8. (0, 4), $x = 1$

State whether the graph of each equation is a circle or a parabola. (**Lesson 9-3**)

9. $x^2 + y = 8$ **parabola**

10. $x^2 = 16 - y^2$ **circle**

State the center and radius of each circle whose equation is given. (**Lesson 9-3**)

11. $x^2 + y^2 = 27$ **(0, 0), $3\sqrt{3}$ units**

12. $(x + 3)^2 + (y - 1)^2 = 81$ **(-3, 1), 9 units**

Write the equation of each ellipse in standard form. (**Lesson 9-4**) **13–14. See margin.**

13. $12x^2 + 6y^2 = 168$

14. $8x^2 + 4y^2 - 16x - 20y = 7$

15. Write the equation of an ellipse whose foci are at (3, 8) and (3, -6). The major axis is 18 units long. (**Lesson 9-4**)

15. $\frac{(x - 3)^2}{32} + \frac{(y - 1)^2}{81} = 1$

Mid-Chapter Review

The Mid-Chapter Review provides students with a brief review of the concepts and skills in Lessons 9-1 through 9-4. Lesson numbers are given at the end of problems or instruction lines so students may review concepts not yet mastered.

Enrichment Masters Booklet, p. 59

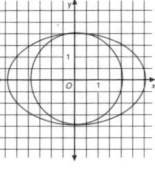
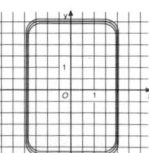

Lesson Resources

Reteaching Master 9-5
Practice Master 9-5
Enrichment Master 9-5

Transparency 9-5 contains the 5-Minute Check and a teaching aid for this lesson.

INTRODUCING THE LESSON

 5-Minute Check

(over Lesson 9-4)

Use the equation $\dfrac{x^2}{16} + \dfrac{y^2}{4} = 1$ for Exercises 1–5.

1. Find the center of the graph of the equation. **(0, 0)**
2. Find the foci of the graph of the equation. **$(2\sqrt{3}, 0), (-2\sqrt{3}, 0)$**
3. Find the length of the major axis. **8**
4. Find the length of the minor axis. **4**
5. Graph the equation.

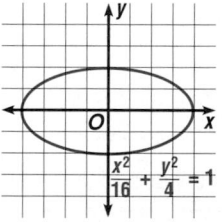

$\dfrac{x^2}{16} + \dfrac{y^2}{4} = 1$

Motivating the Lesson

Explore the effect of rotating a circle in space. Use a circular ring (like a key ring) and place it on an overhead projector. Lift one edge to form an ellipse. Ask students what could be done to form a hyperbola.

9-5 Hyperbolas

Objectives

After studying this lesson, you should be able to:

9-5A ■ write equations of hyperbolas, and
9-5B ■ draw hyperbolas.

Application

The orbits of some comets and satellites are shaped like a **hyperbola.** You can see the shape of a hyperbola by placing a table lamp near the wall and observing the shape the light makes. The comets or satellites that have orbits like this follow one branch of the curve and are said to be in an open or escape orbit.

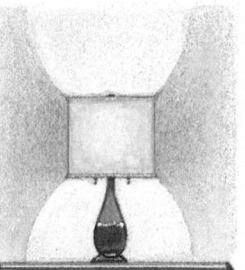

Definition of Hyperbola

A hyperbola is the set of all points in a plane such that the absolute value of the difference of the distances from any point on the hyperbola to two given points in the plane, called the *foci*, is constant.

The hyperbola at the left has foci at $(-10, 0)$ and $(10, 0)$. The absolute value of the difference of the distances from the two foci is 16. Let's use the distance formula and the definition of a hyperbola to find the equation of a hyperbola.

Let (x, y) be any point on the hyperbola. The distance between (x, y) and $(-10, 0)$ *minus* the distance between (x, y) and $(10, 0)$ is ± 16 units.

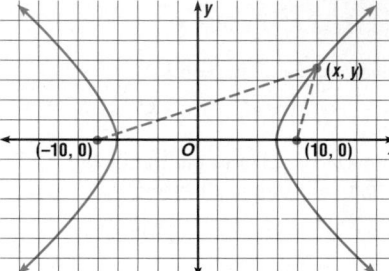

$\begin{array}{ll} \sqrt{(x+10)^2 + y^2} - \sqrt{(x-10)^2 + y^2} = \pm 16 & \\ \sqrt{(x+10)^2 + y^2} = \pm 16 + \sqrt{(x-10)^2 + y^2} & \textit{Add } \sqrt{(x-10)^2 + y^2} \textit{ to each side.} \\ (x+10)^2 + y^2 = 256 \pm 32\sqrt{(x-10)^2 + y^2} + (x-10)^2 + y^2 & \textit{Square each side.} \\ 5x - 32 = \pm 4\sqrt{(x-10)^2 + y^2} & \textit{Simplify.} \\ 25x^2 - 320x + 1024 = 16[(x-10)^2 + y^2] & \textit{Square each side.} \\ 9x^2 - 16y^2 = 576 & \textit{Simplify.} \\ \dfrac{x^2}{64} - \dfrac{y^2}{36} = 1 & \textit{Divide each side by 576.} \end{array}$

The equation of the hyperbola with foci at $(-10, 0)$ and $(10, 0)$ and with 16 as the absolute value of the difference between the distances from the two foci is $\dfrac{x^2}{64} - \dfrac{y^2}{36} = 1$. **Teaching Tip ❶**

416 CHAPTER 9 CONICS

ALTERNATE TEACHING STRATEGIES

Using Charts

When working with hyperbolas, it may help students to make comparisons. Have them make charts for the vertices, foci, slope of the asymptotes, and the direction of the transverse axis.

Using Questioning

What is the difference between an ellipse and a hyperbola? **The lengths of a, b, and c are related differently. For a hyperbola you use $a^2 + b^2 = c^2$. For an ellipse you use $b^2 = a^2 - c^2$.** Why are the asymptotes important for graphing a hyperbola? **The lines approach the asymptotes as the branches go out from the vertex.**

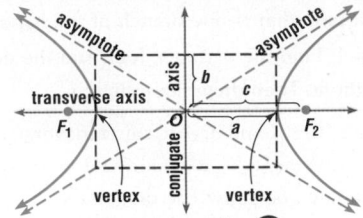

Let's take a close look at the parts of a hyperbola. The midpoint of the segment connecting the foci of a hyperbola is the center of the hyperbola. The point on each branch of the hyperbola that is nearest the center is a **vertex**. As a hyperbola recedes from the center, the branches approach lines called the **asymptotes**.

Teaching Tip ②

A hyperbola has many similarities to an ellipse. The distance to the center from a vertex of a hyperbola is a units and the distance from a focus to the center is c units. It has two axes of symmetry. One axis is the **transverse axis,** which is the segment of length $2a$ units whose endpoints are the vertices of the hyperbola. The **conjugate axis** is the segment of length $2b$ units that is perpendicular to the transverse axis at the center. However, the lengths of a, b, and c are related differently for a hyperbola than for an ellipse. For a hyperbola, $a^2 + b^2 = c^2$. **Teaching Tip ③**

Standard Equation of Hyperbola with Center at the Origin	If a hyperbola has foci at $(-c, 0)$ and $(c, 0)$ and if the absolute value of the difference of the distances from any point on the hyperbola to the two foci is $2a$ units, then the standard equation of the hyperbola is $\dfrac{x^2}{a^2} - \dfrac{y^2}{b^2} = 1$, where $c^2 = a^2 + b^2$. If a hyperbola has foci at $(0, -c)$ and $(0, c)$ and if the absolute value of the difference of the distances from any point on the hyperbola to the two foci is $2a$ units, then the standard equation of the hyperbola is $\dfrac{y^2}{a^2} - \dfrac{x^2}{b^2} = 1$, where $c^2 = a^2 + b^2$.

Example 1

Write the equation of the hyperbola shown below.

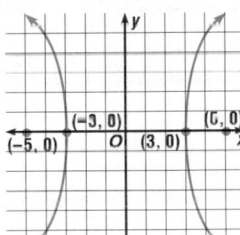

The distance from the center to a vertex is a units and the distance from the center to a focus is c units, so $a = 3$ and $c = 5$.

Use the formula $c^2 = a^2 + b^2$ to find b^2.

$$c^2 = a^2 + b^2$$
$$5^2 = 3^2 + b^2$$
$$b^2 = 16$$

The equation is $\dfrac{x^2}{9} - \dfrac{y^2}{16} = 1$.

Sketching the asymptotes of a hyperbola makes graphing it easier. The chart below shows the equations of asymptotes for different hyperbolas.

Equation of Hyperbola	$\dfrac{x^2}{a^2} - \dfrac{y^2}{b^2} = 1$	$\dfrac{y^2}{a^2} - \dfrac{x^2}{b^2} = 1$
Equations of Asymptotes	$y = \pm\dfrac{b}{a}x$	$y = \pm\dfrac{a}{b}x$
Transverse Axis	horizontal	vertical

Teaching Tip ① Use the hyperbola on page 416 in conjunction with the equation of the hyperbola defined on page 417. This hyperbola is of the form $\dfrac{x^2}{a^2} - \dfrac{y^2}{b^2} = 1$.

The figure on page 417 can be used to show that $c^2 = a^2 + b^2$ follows from the Pythagorean Theorem.

Teaching Tip ② You may want to introduce the latus rectum as an aid to graphing. The latera recta are segments perpendicular to the transverse axis that pass through the foci. Each latus rectum is $\dfrac{2b^2}{a}$ units long. The distance from the focus to the point of intersection with the branch of the hyperbola is $\dfrac{b^2}{a}$ units.

Teaching Tip ③ The relationship between a, b, and c, is different for ellipses and hyperbolas. In an ellipse, $b^2 = a^2 - c^2$. In a hyperbola, $b^2 = c^2 - a^2$.

Chalkboard Example

For Example 1

Write the equation of the hyperbola shown below.

$$\dfrac{y^2}{9} - \dfrac{x^2}{40} = 1$$

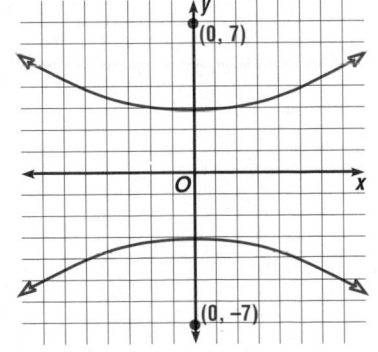

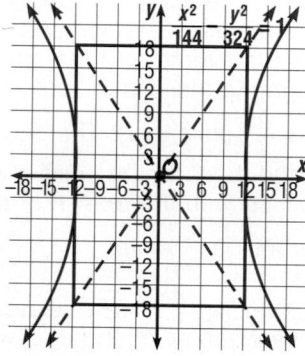
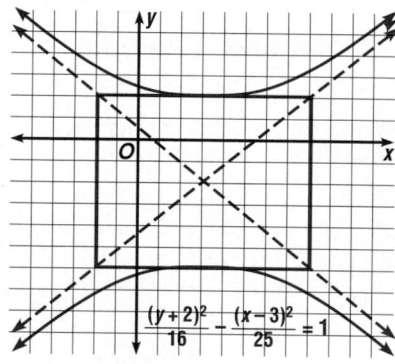
Example 2

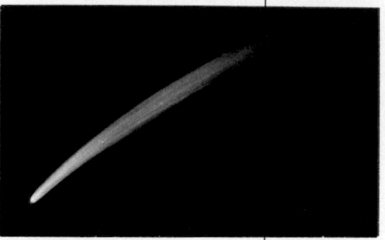

APPLICATION

Astronomy

A comet travels along a path that is one branch of the hyperbola whose equation is $\dfrac{y^2}{225} - \dfrac{x^2}{400} = 1$. Find the vertices, foci, and the equations of the asymptotes of the hyperbola. Then draw the graph.

The hyperbola has center (0, 0) and a vertical transverse axis. The equations of the asymptotes are $y = \pm\dfrac{3}{4}x$, since $a = 15$ and $b = 20$. Sketch a $2a$ by $2b$ rectangle and draw the diagonals.

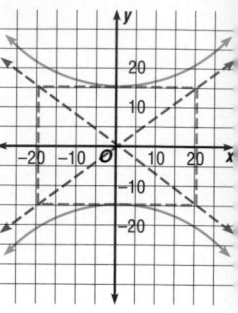

Since $a = 15$, the distance from the center to each vertex is 15 units. The vertices are (0, 15) and (0, −15).

To locate the foci, find the value of c.

$$c^2 = a^2 + b^2$$
$$c^2 = 225 + 400$$
$$c^2 = 625$$
$$c = 25$$

So the foci are at (0, 25) and (0, −25).

So far we have discussed equations of hyperbolas centered at the origin. A hyperbola with center (h, k) that is the same shape as one centered at the origin can be described by the standard equation with $(x - h)$ replacing x and $(y - k)$ replacing y.

Standard Equation of Hyperbola with Center at (h, k)

> The equation of a hyperbola whose center is at (h, k) and with a horizontal transverse axis is $\dfrac{(x - h)^2}{a^2} - \dfrac{(y - k)^2}{b^2} = 1$.
> The equation of a hyperbola whose center is at (h, k) and with a vertical transverse axis is $\dfrac{(y - k)^2}{a^2} - \dfrac{(x - h)^2}{b^2} = 1$.

You can find the slopes of the asymptotes for hyperbolas with centers other than the origin in the same way as you found the slopes for hyperbolas centered at the origin. Remember that the asymptotes always pass through the center of the hyperbola.

Example 3

Graph $\dfrac{(x - 1)^2}{9} - \dfrac{(y + 4)^2}{16} = 1.$

The graph has the same shape as the graph of $\dfrac{x^2}{9} - \dfrac{y^2}{16} = 1$, but has center (1, −4).

The slopes of the asymptotes are $\pm\dfrac{4}{3}$.

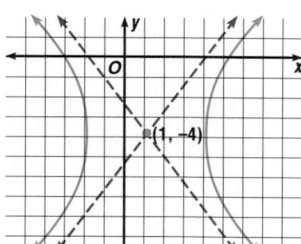

418   CHAPTER 9   CONICS

Example 4 | The graph of $16x^2 - y^2 + 96x + 8y + 112 = 0$ is a hyperbola. Write the equation in standard form and find the vertices, foci, and slopes of the asymptotes of the hyperbola. Then draw the graph.

Complete the square for each variable to write the equation in standard form.

$$16x^2 - y^2 + 96x + 8y + 112 = 0$$
$$16(x^2 + 6x + \square) - (y^2 - 8y + \blacksquare) = -112 + 16\square + (-\blacksquare) \quad \text{Complete the square.}$$
$$16(x^2 + 6x + 9) - (y^2 - 8y + 16) = -112 + 16(9) - 16$$
$$16(x + 3)^2 - (y - 4)^2 = 16$$
$$\frac{(x + 3)^2}{1} - \frac{(y - 4)^2}{16} = 1$$

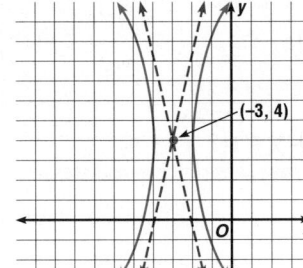

The hyperbola has center at $(-3, 4)$ and a horizontal transverse axis. Since $a = 1$ and $b = 4$, the slopes of the asymptotes are 4 and -4.

The distance from the center to each vertex is 1 unit, since $a = 1$. So, the vertices are at $(-2, 4)$ and $(-4, 4)$.

To locate the foci, find c.

$$c^2 = a^2 + b^2$$
$$c^2 = 1^2 + 4^2$$
$$c = \sqrt{17}$$

The foci are $\sqrt{17}$ units to the left and to the right of the center. So, the foci are at $(-3 + \sqrt{17}, 4)$ and $(-3 - \sqrt{17}, 4)$ or about $(1.1, 4)$ and $(-7.1, 4)$.

CHECKING FOR UNDERSTANDING

Communicating Mathematics

See margin.

Read and study the lesson to answer these questions.

1. Name some similarities and differences between the hyperbola and the ellipse.

2. The graph of $\frac{x^2}{4} + \frac{y^2}{1} = 1$ is an ellipse and the graph of $\frac{x^2}{4} - \frac{y^2}{1} = 1$ is a hyperbola. How can you determine that from their equations? **See margin.**

3. Describe the graph of the equation $\frac{(y - 2)^2}{25} - \frac{x^2}{4} = 1$. **See margin.**

4. Write the equation of the hyperbola shown at the right. State its vertices, foci, and the slopes of its asymptotes.

$\frac{y^2}{16} - \frac{x^2}{9} = 1$; (0, 4), (0, -4); (0, 5), (0, -5); $\pm\frac{4}{3}$

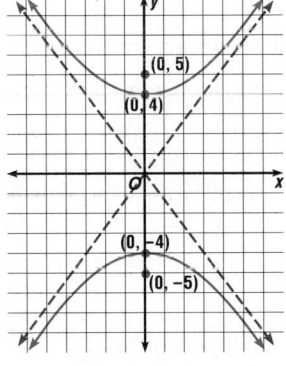

LESSON 9-5 HYPERBOLAS 419

Additional Answers

1. **Answers may vary. A sample answer is:**
   Similarities: two axes of symmetry, can be defined by two foci, distance from center to vertices is 2a
   Differences: standard equation of hyperbola contains subtraction and ellipse contains addition; ellipse is a closed figure and the hyperbola is not, relationship of a, b, and c is different, hyperbola has asymptotes

2. **The equation of an ellipse contains addition and the equation of a hyperbola contains subtraction. That comes from the definitions of both curves.**

3. **A hyperbola with center at (0, 2), a vertical transverse axis, and vertices at (0, 7) and (0, -3). The slopes of the asymptotes are $\frac{5}{2}$ and $-\frac{5}{2}$ and the foci are at $(0, 2 + \sqrt{29})$ and $(0, 2 - \sqrt{29})$ or about (0, 7.4) and (0, -3.4).**

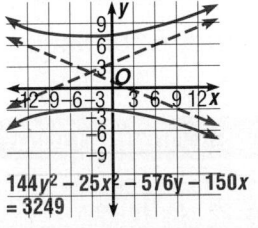

Closing the Lesson

Writing Activity Find the values of a and b for which the asymptotes of $\dfrac{x^2}{a^2} - \dfrac{y^2}{b^2} = 1$ are perpendicular. Explain how you found these values. **If $y = \dfrac{b}{a}x$ and $y = \dfrac{-b}{a}x$ are perpendicular, then $\dfrac{b}{a} = -\dfrac{1}{\frac{-b}{a}}$, or $\dfrac{b}{a} = \dfrac{a}{b}$. Since a and b are positive, $a = b$.**

APPLYING THE LESSON

Homework Exercises

Assignment Guide
Basic: 19–43, 49–56
Average: 22–46, 49–56
Enriched: 25–56

Teaching Tip ❹ Is the transverse axis vertical or horizontal in each case?

Reteaching Masters Booklet, p. 60

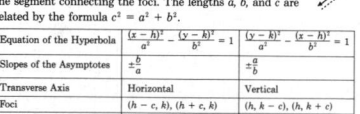

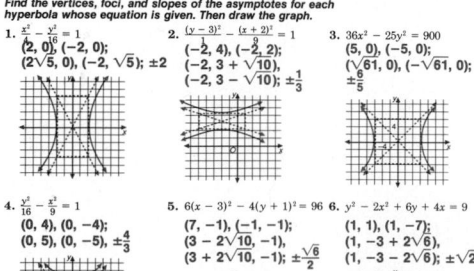

Guided Practice

State whether the graph of each function is an ellipse or a hyperbola.

5. ellipse
6. hyperbola
7. hyperbola
8. ellipse
9. hyperbola
10. ellipse

5. $\dfrac{x^2}{10} + \dfrac{y^2}{18} = 1$

6. $\dfrac{y^2}{1} - \dfrac{x^2}{8} = 1$

7. $\dfrac{x^2}{24} - \dfrac{y^2}{36} = 1$

8. $\dfrac{y^2}{49} + \dfrac{x^2}{49} = 1$

9. $\dfrac{y^2}{20} - \dfrac{x^2}{32} = 1$

10. $\dfrac{x^2}{100} + \dfrac{y^2}{25} = 1$

Write the equation of each hyperbola in standard form.

11. $\dfrac{x^2}{5} - \dfrac{y^2}{10} = 1$

12. $\dfrac{y^2}{34} - \dfrac{x^2}{6} = 1$

13. $\dfrac{(y-1)^2}{168} - \dfrac{(x-2)^2}{42} = 1$

14. $\dfrac{(x+7.5)^2}{11.25} - \dfrac{(y-2.5)^2}{2.8125} = 1$

11. $2x^2 - y^2 = 10$

12. $6y^2 - 34x^2 = 204$

13. $(y-1)^2 - 4(x-2)^2 = 168$

14. $3x^2 - 12y^2 + 45x + 60y = -60$

Find the vertices, foci, and slopes of the asymptotes for each hyperbola whose equation is given. Then draw the graph. See Solutions Manual for graphs.

15. $\dfrac{x^2}{16} - \dfrac{y^2}{4} = 1$ $(\pm 4, 0);$ $(\pm 2\sqrt{5}, 0); \pm\frac{1}{2}$

16. $\dfrac{x^2}{6} - \dfrac{y^2}{2} = 1$

17. $\dfrac{x^2}{9} - \dfrac{y^2}{4} = 1$ $(\pm 3, 0); (\pm\sqrt{13}, 0); \pm\frac{2}{3}$

18. $x^2 - y^2 = 4$

16. $(\pm\sqrt{6}, 0); (\pm 2\sqrt{2}, 0); \pm\frac{\sqrt{3}}{3}$

18. $(\pm, 0); (\pm 2\sqrt{2}, 0) \pm 1$

EXERCISES

Practice

Write the equation of each hyperbola.

A

25. $(\pm 6, 0);$ $(\pm\sqrt{37}, 0); \pm\frac{1}{6}$

26. $(0, \pm 4);$ $(0, \pm\sqrt{41}); \pm\frac{4}{5}$

27. $(\pm 3, 0);$ $(\pm\sqrt{34}, 0); \pm\frac{5}{3}$

28. $(0, \pm 9);$ $(0, \pm\sqrt{106}); \pm\frac{9}{5}$

29. $(\pm 2, 0);$ $(\pm\sqrt{13}, 0); \pm\frac{3}{2}$

30. $(\pm 9, 0);$ $(\pm\sqrt{117}, 0); \pm\frac{2}{3}$

19.
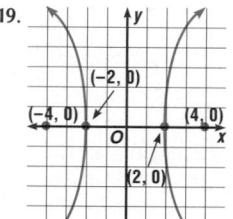
$\dfrac{x^2}{4} - \dfrac{y^2-3}{12} = 1$

20.
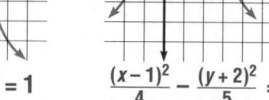
$\dfrac{(x-1)^2}{4} - \dfrac{(y+2)^2}{5} = 1$

21.
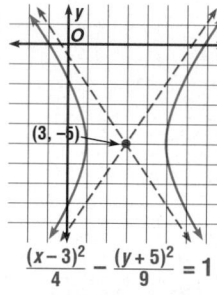
$\dfrac{(x-3)^2}{4} - \dfrac{(y+5)^2}{9} = 1$

22.
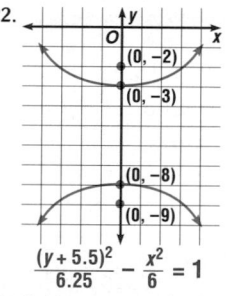
$\dfrac{(y+5.5)^2}{6.25} - \dfrac{x^2}{6} = 1$

23.
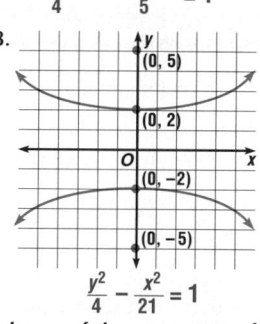
$\dfrac{y^2}{4} - \dfrac{x^2}{21} = 1$

24.
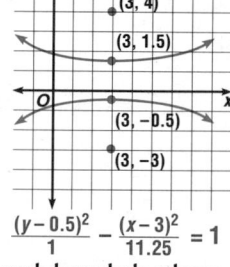
$\dfrac{(y-0.5)^2}{1} - \dfrac{(x-3)^2}{11.25} = 1$

Find the vertices, foci, and slopes of the asymptotes for each hyperbola whose equation is given. Then draw the graph. See Solutions Manual for graphs.

B

25. $\dfrac{x^2}{36} - \dfrac{y^2}{1} = 1$

26. $\dfrac{y^2}{16} - \dfrac{x^2}{25} = 1$

27. $\dfrac{x^2}{9} - \dfrac{y^2}{25} = 1$

28. $\dfrac{y^2}{81} - \dfrac{x^2}{25} = 1$

29. $\dfrac{x^2}{4} - \dfrac{y^2}{9} = 1$

30. $\dfrac{x^2}{81} - \dfrac{y^2}{36} = 1$

Teaching Tip ❹

RETEACHING THE LESSON

Given the foci and the difference of the distances from the foci to any point on a hyperbola, find the standard form of its equation in two ways. First use the definition of a hyperbola and the distance formula to find the equation. Then use given values to find h, k, a, and b.

$(\pm 3, 0); (\pm 5, 0); \pm\frac{4}{3}$ $(0, \pm 10); (0, \pm 2\sqrt{61}); \pm\frac{5}{6}$

31. $(0, \pm 3\sqrt{2})$; $(0, \pm\sqrt{38})$; $\pm\frac{3\sqrt{10}}{10}$

34. $(\pm\sqrt{2}, 0)$; $(\pm\sqrt{3}, 0)$; $\pm\frac{\sqrt{2}}{2}$

35. $(0, \pm 6)$; $(0, \pm 3\sqrt{5})$; ± 2

31. $\frac{y^2}{18} - \frac{x^2}{20} = 1$ 32. $\frac{x^2}{9} - \frac{y^2}{16} = 1$ 33. $\frac{y^2}{100} - \frac{x^2}{144} = 1$

34. $x^2 - 2y^2 = 2$ 35. $y^2 = 36 + 4x^2$

36. $\frac{(x+6)^2}{36} - \frac{(y+3)^2}{9} = 1$ 37. $\frac{(y-3)^2}{25} - \frac{(x-2)^2}{16} = 1$

38. $\frac{(y-4)^2}{16} - \frac{(x+2)^2}{9} = 1$ 39. $\frac{(x+1)^2}{4} - \frac{(y+3)^2}{9} = 1$

40. $(x+3)^2 - 4(y-2)^2 = 4$ 41. $5x^2 - 4y^2 - 40x - 16y = 36$

C 42. $y^2 - 4x^2 - 2y - 16x + 1 = 0$ 43. $y^2 - 3x^2 + 6y + 6x = 18$

36. $(0, -3)$, $(-12, -3)$; $(-6 \pm 3\sqrt{5}, -3)$; $\pm\frac{1}{2}$

37. $(2, -2)$, $(2, 8)$; $(2, 3 \pm\sqrt{41})$; $\pm\frac{5}{4}$

38. $(-2, 0)$, $(-2, 8)$; $(-2, -1)$, $(-2, 9)$; $\pm\frac{4}{3}$

39. $(1, -3)$, $(-3, -3)$; $(-1 \pm\sqrt{13}, -3)$; $\pm\frac{3}{2}$

40. $(-5, 2)$; $(-1, 2)$; $(-3 \pm\sqrt{5}, 2)$; $\pm\frac{1}{2}$

Write the equation of each hyperbola described below.

44. A hyperbola is centered at the origin with a horizontal transverse axis. The value of $a = 1$ and $b = 4$. $\frac{x^2}{1} - \frac{y^2}{16} = 1$

45. The center is at (5, 4) and it has a vertical transverse axis. The value of $a = 2$ and $b = 6$. $\frac{(y-4)^2}{4} - \frac{(x-5)^2}{36} = 1$

46. The equations of the asymptotes are $3x - 2y = 0$ and $3x + 2y = 0$. It has a horizontal transverse axis and passes through (2, 0). $\frac{x^2}{4} - \frac{y^2}{9} = 1$

An equation of the form $xy = c$ is a hyperbola with the x- and y-axes as asymptotes. 47–48. See margin.

47. Sketch the graph of $xy = 3$. 48. Sketch the graph of $xy = -1$.

Critical Thinking

49. The asymptotes of a hyperbola are given by the equations $5x + 3y = -1$ and $5x - 3y - 11$. Find the equation of the hyperbola if it passes through the point (4, −2). $\frac{(x-1)^2}{9} - \frac{(y+2)^2}{25} = 1$

Applications

41. $(4 \pm 2\sqrt{5}, -2)$; $(4 \pm 3\sqrt{5}, -2)$; $\pm\frac{\sqrt{5}}{2}$

42. $(-4, 1)$, $(0, 1)$; $(-2 \pm 2\sqrt{5}, 1)$; ± 2

43. $(1, -3 \pm 2\sqrt{6})$; $(1, -3 \pm 4\sqrt{2})$; $\pm\sqrt{3}$

50. **Chemistry** Boyle's Law states that if the temperature of a gas is constant, then the pressure exerted by the gas varies inversely as the volume. Symbolically, $PV = k$, where P represents the pressure, V represents the volume, and k is a constant. The constant for a certain gas is 22,000. Graph $PV = k$ for this gas. **See students' graphs.**

51. **Sports** One lap of the Indianapolis 500 is $2\frac{1}{2}$ miles. Since you know that rate multiplied by time equals distance, you could find the speed at which a car is traveling if you timed one lap. Graph the combinations of times and speeds a car could have for one lap of the Indy 500. **See students' graphs.**

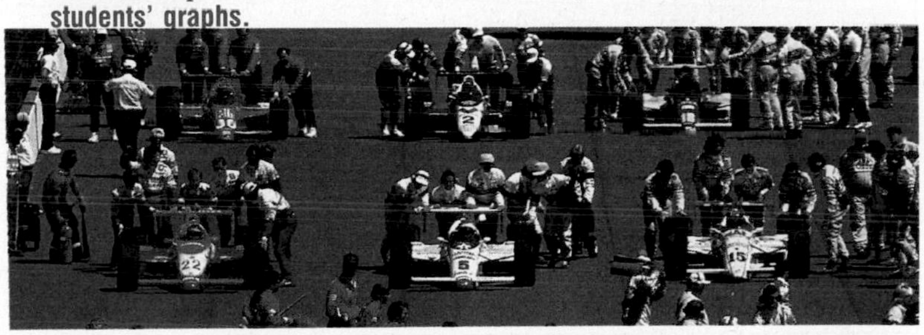

Additional Answers

47.

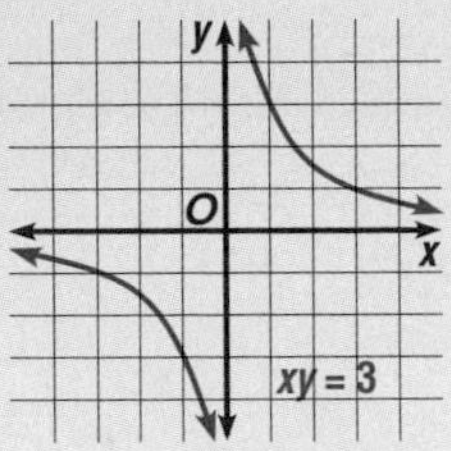

48.

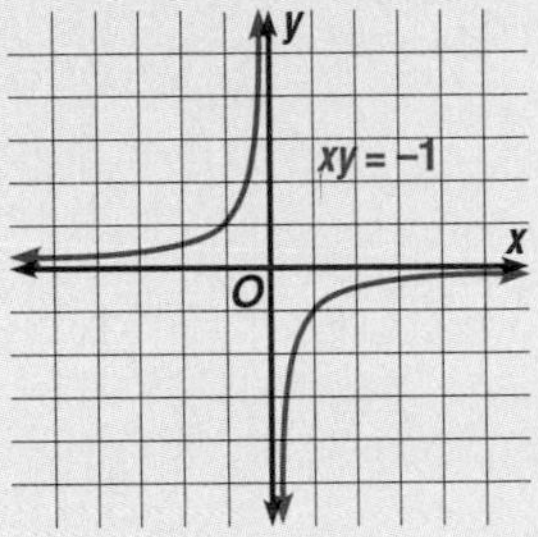

Practice Masters Booklet, p. 68

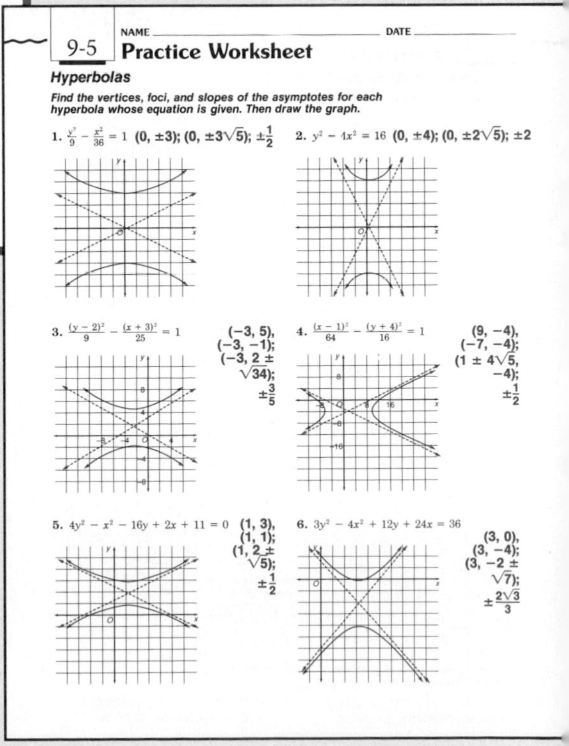
NAME ____ DATE ____

9-5 **Practice Worksheet**

Hyperbolas

Find the vertices, foci, and slopes of the asymptotes for each hyperbola whose equation is given. Then draw the graph.

1. $\frac{y^2}{9} - \frac{x^2}{36} = 1$ **(0, ±3); (0, ±3√5); ±½**

2. $y^2 - 4x^2 = 16$ **(0, ±4); (0, ±2√5); ±2**

3. $\frac{(y-2)^2}{9} - \frac{(x+3)^2}{25} = 1$ **(−3, 5), (−3, −1); (−3, 2 ± √34); ±3/5**

4. $\frac{(x-1)^2}{64} - \frac{(y+4)^2}{16} = 1$ **(9, −4), (−7, −4); (1 ± 4√5, −4); ±½**

5. $4y^2 - x^2 - 16y + 2x + 11 = 0$ **(1, 3), (1, 1); (1, 2 ± √5); ±½**

6. $3y^2 - 4x^2 + 12y + 24x = 36$ **(3, 0), (3, −4); (3, −2 ± √7); ±2√3/3**

52. Find the center, foci, and lengths of the major and minor axes of the ellipse whose equation is $\frac{x^2}{4} + \frac{y^2}{25} = 1$. Then graph the ellipse. **(Lesson 9-4)** **(0, 0); (0, ±√21); 10 units, 4 units; See students' graphs.**

53. Write the equation of the ellipse whose foci are at (5, 4) and (−3, 4). The major axis is 10 units long. **(Lesson 9-4)** $\frac{(x-1)^2}{25} + \frac{(y-4)^2}{9} = 1$

54. Solve the inequality $x^2 \leq 6$. **(Lesson 8-7)** $\{x|-\sqrt{6} \leq x \leq \sqrt{6}\}$

55. State the sum and product of the roots of the equation $2x^2 + 4x = 6$. **(Lesson 7-5)** **−2, −3**

56. State a factor that can be used to rationalize the denominator of $\frac{10}{5^{\frac{2}{3}}}$. **(Lesson 6-6)** $\frac{5^{\frac{1}{3}}}{5^{\frac{1}{3}}}$

~ APPLICATION ~

Most of us are familiar with the mathematical shapes used in architecture. We are used to seeing squares, rectangles, pyramids, and spheres. But some of the more recent architects use designs that are not recognizable. One such example is St. Mary's Cathedral in San Francisco. Its design is called a **hyperbolic paraboloid.** The cathedral was designed by Paul Ryan and John Lee. Pier Nervi of Rome and Pietro Bellaschi of M.I.T. were engineering consultants on the project. When Nervi was asked what Michelangelo would have thought of the cathedral, he replied, "He could not have thought of it. This design comes from geometric theories, not then proven."

A hyperbolic paraboloid combines a parabola revolved about its axis of symmetry and a three-dimensional hyperbola. The top of St. Mary's is a 2135 cubic foot hyperbolic paraboloid cupola with concrete pylons extending 94 feet into the ground. Each pylon carries a weight of 9 million pounds. The walls are made from 1680 prepounded concrete coffers involving 128 different sizes. The dimensions of the square foundation measure 255 feet by 255 feet. The equation for a hyperbolic paraboloid is $\frac{y^2}{b^2} - \frac{x^2}{a^2} = \frac{z}{c}$, where $a > 0$, $b > 0$, and $c \neq 0$. Since a hyperbolic paraboloid is a three-dimensional figure, z represents values on the third axis.

EXTENDING THE LESSON

Math Power: Reasoning

If the difference of the distances from any point on the hyperbola to the two foci, (−12, 0) and (12, 0), is 20 units, what is the equation of the hyperbola? $\frac{x^2}{100} - \frac{y^2}{44} = 1$

Application

Mathematics plays a large role in the designs of most buildings. You may wish to have students research unique designs that are also functional. One of the most famous is the flying buttresses of Notre Dame Cathedral.

Enrichment Masters Booklet, p. 60

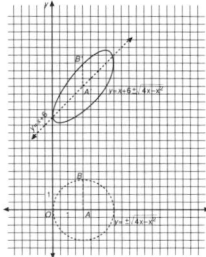
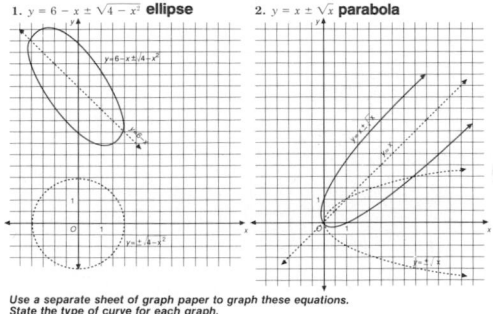

9-6

Problem-Solving Strategy: Use a Model

Objective 9-6

After studying this lesson, you should be able to:
- use a simulation to help solve problems.

Sometimes solving a problem directly is impractical. In these cases, it helps to devise a way of modeling, or simulating, a situation to make the problem easier to solve.

Example

APPLICATION

Marketing

HealthWise Cereal has placed contest tickets that are printed with two letters from the name of the cereal in their cereal boxes. To win a $50 prize, you must collect all five different tickets whose letters spell the name of the cereal. The total number of each kind of ticket is the same. How many boxes would you expect to have to buy to win the contest?

It would be expensive and inconvenient, but you could buy hundreds of boxes of cereal to see how many it took to win. Instead, you could simulate these purchases by assigning each of the tickets a number from 1 to 5. Then roll a die to determine how many boxes you would need to buy. If you roll a 6, you ignore it. You keep rolling until all 5 numbers appear. In the following trials, the first time each number occurs is shown in blue.

	Number of boxes to win
5 1 4 3 4 3 5 3 3 1 4 2	12
4 3 2 5 5 4 4 4 3 2 4 4 1	13
1 2 1 5 5 5 4 3	8
3 5 5 4 1 3 1 1 3 1 2	11
4 3 5 1 3 4 3 4 4 5 4 1 1 3 2	14

Take an average to find an estimate of the number of boxes you would have to buy.

$$\frac{12 + 13 + 8 + 11 + 14}{5} = 11.6 \approx 12$$

Our estimate is that you would have to buy 12 boxes to win the contest. *When you simulate a situation in this way, the more trials you conduct, the better your estimation.*

CHECKING FOR UNDERSTANDING

Communicating Mathematics

Read and study the lesson to answer these questions.

1. When is it helpful to use simulation to help solve a problem?

1. When it is difficult or impossible to solve a problem directly.

2. What is the least number of boxes of HealthWise that you could have to buy to win their contest? **5, you could get all five tickets right away.**

3. Conduct more trials for the Example using your own die. How do your results compare with the results above? with other students' results? **See students' work.**

LESSON 9-6 PROBLEM-SOLVING STRATEGY: USE A MODEL 423

Checking for Understanding

Exercises 1–4 are designed to help you assess understanding through reading, writing, and speaking. You should work through Exercises 1–3 with your students, and then monitor their work on Exercise 4.

Closing the Lesson

Modeling Activity Have students write a problem that would be helped in the solution by modeling. Share the problems with the class. Compare what type of models were used to solve the problems.

APPLYING THE LESSON

Homework Exercises

Assignment Guide
Basic: 5–9
Average: 5–9
Enriched: 5–9

Teaching Tip ❶ If students list the number of chimes for one cycle, it will help them to see what is happening for all the hours.

Practice Masters Booklet, p. 69

9-6 NAME _____ DATE _____

Practice Worksheet

Problem Solving Strategy: Use a Simulation

Solve. Use any strategy.

1. Yummy cereal puts six different prizes in their boxes of cereal, one per box. If each prize is assigned a number 1 through 6, use the following trials to predict how many boxes of cereal you would have to buy before you get all six prizes.

Trials	Number of boxes
1: 1 2 3 6 5 2 3 5 1 4	10
2: 1 1 2 5 6 2 1 4 5 6 1 3	12
3: 3 2 6 1 3 5 4	7
4: 5 6 5 4 5 3 1 5 6 4 6 3 2	13
5: 4 3 4 5 5 6 4 3 3 3 6 5 2 2 2 1	16
6: 4 2 3 4 5 3 2 4 4 1 3 2 5 4 4 3 6	17

13 boxes

a. What device could you use to simulate this solution? **die**

b. Would more trials permit better predictions? **yes**

2. Maria's batting average is 0.2000. Use 0 and 1 to represent hits and 2-9 to represent misses. Use the following trials to predict how many hits Maria will get if she is at bat 50 times.

Trials	Hits	Times at bat
1: 1 9 0 2 4 6 7 9 8 5 1	3	11
2: 4 3 2 5 7 9 8 6 1 2 0	2	11
3: 4 3 8 9 7 1 4 0 2 7 9 8 6 2	2	14
4: 5 6 9 3 8 7 2 4 5 6 9 8 7 9 4	0	15
5: 8 9 5 6 7 4 3 5 7 9 8 4 7 1	1	14

about 6 hits

Strategies
Look for a pattern.
Solve a simpler problem.
Act it out.
Guess and check.
Draw a diagram.
Make a chart.
Work backwards.

4. **Statistics** Miguel had been making only 50% of his free throws all season. During a practice session, Kristin noticed something about Miguel's shooting style and suggested a way he might correct it. Miguel tried the new technique and hit 9 of his next 10 free throws. Did Kristin's suggestion help Miguel's game? **Answers will vary depending on simulation.**

a. With Miguel's old style of shooting, he has a 50% chance of sinking a single shot. Use a coin to simulate 10 free throws. Heads represents a made shot and tails represents a miss. If tossing the coin simulates ten of Miguel's shots, how many would he have made?

b. Use the coin to simulate 10 sets of 10 free throws and average the results. How many does Miguel hit on average?

EXERCISES

Solve. Use any strategy.

5. How many triangles are in the figure at the right? **20**

6. The Chimes that ring on The Ohio State University campus ring every fifteen minutes. At one-quarter past the hour, they chime four notes, at half past they chime eight notes, and at one-quarter before the hour they chime twelve notes. On every hour, they chime sixteen notes and the number of the hour. How many notes will be struck by the chimes in one week? **7812 notes** Teaching Tip ❶

7. What is the 120th odd natural number? **239**

Answers may vary. Sample answer:

8. Write an expression whose value is 56 using five 4s. $44 + 4 \times 4 - 4.$

9. Karen was fouled at the final buzzer of the playoff basketball game. She will shoot free throws. She has a success rate of 67% at the free throw line. If her team is behind by one point, do you think she will be able to win the game with these free throws? Do you think she will be able to tie the game? **Answers may vary.**

∼∼∼ COOPERATIVE LEARNING ACTIVITY ∼∼∼

Work in groups. Each person in the group must understand the solution and be able to explain it to any person in class.

A parking lot attendant keeps the keys for the cars parked in the lot. The spaces in the lot are numbered and the keys are kept in a locked box with numbered pegs to correspond with the spaces. There are twelve cars parked in the lot when the attendant drops the key box and all of the keys are mixed up. If he places the keys on the numbered pegs in random order, how many do you think he will get in the right place? **Answers may vary.**

EXTENDING THE LESSON

Math Power: Problem Solving

There are 1000 lockers in Lincoln High. On the first day of school, the first student in the building closes all the doors. The second student opens every second door. The third student changes the position of every third door. This goes on for all 1000 students. Which doors will be closed?
the perfect squares

Cooperative Learning Activity

This activity provides students with an opportunity to *learn* things together, not just do things together. You may wish to refer to pages T6–T8 and page 6C for the various elements of cooperative groups and specific goals and strategies for using them.

Graphing Calculator Exploration: Conic Sections

Teaching Tip ❶

The parabola, circle, ellipse, and hyperbola are called the **conic sections.** You can use your graphing calculator to graph the conic sections. However, some special care must be taken when graphing the conic sections.

Most of the conic sections are relations, not functions. Since the graphing calculators will only plot functions, we must manipulate the equations before entering them into the calculator for graphing. For example, the equation for a circle, $x^2 + y^2 = 9$, cannot be entered directly, since both types of calculators require that the equation be entered in a "$y =$" format. We must put the equation into this format algebraically before entering it into the calculator.

Graph the circle whose equation is $x^2 + y^2 = 9$.

First put the equation in the "$y =$" format.

$$x^2 + y^2 = 9$$
$$y^2 = 9 - x^2 \qquad \textit{Subtract } x^2 \textit{ from each side.}$$
$$y = \pm\sqrt{9 - x^2} \qquad \textit{Take the square root of each side, including both the positive and negative roots.}$$

Now enter the equations as $y = \sqrt{9 - x^2}$ and $y = -\sqrt{9 - x^2}$ separately, since there is no $\pm$ on the calculator.
Make sure that the range parameters are set for the standard viewing window.

Casio

Teaching Tip ❷

ENTER:

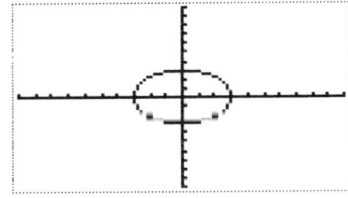

TI-81 **Teaching Tip ❸**

ENTER:

Sometimes the points near the x-axis or the vertices of a graph will not be graphed by a graphing calculator. These points are included in the graph, but the calculator cannot graph them accurately.

The graph appears to be an ellipse. The calculator screen must be set so that the units on the x- and y-axes are equal in length. This adjustment can be made on each of the calculators, so that the graph is not distorted.

GRAPHING CALCULATOR EXPLORATION: CONIC SECTIONS 425

INTRODUCING THE LESSON

Objective: Graph conic sections on a graphing calculator.

Motivating the Lesson

Write an equation of a conic section on the chalkboard or overhead. Tell students to graph it on their graphing calculators. Ask students if you *can* graph the equation. Tally how many students say yes and how many say no.

TEACHING THE LESSON

Teaching Tip ❶ A parabola is the only conic section that can be a function.

Teaching Tip ❷ A circle is not a function but a semi-circle can be. You are entering halves of the circle.

Teaching Tip ❸ Make sure both functions are turned on if you are using the TI-81.

RETEACHING THE LESSON

Have students graph the ellipse $\dfrac{x^2}{4} + \dfrac{y^2}{9} = 1$ in the standard viewing window. It will look like a circle. Then have them graph it in the default viewing window of [−4.7, 4.7] by [−3.1, 3.1] on the Casio or in the viewing window of [−7.5, 7.5] by [−5, 5] on the TI-81. Explain the importance of knowing your range values.

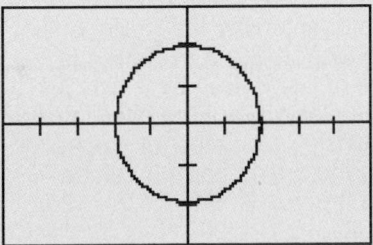

More Examples

Graph the hyperbola whose equation is $9x^2 - y^2 + 54x + 6y - 9 = 0$.

$$y = 3 \pm 3\sqrt{(x + 3)^2 - 9}$$

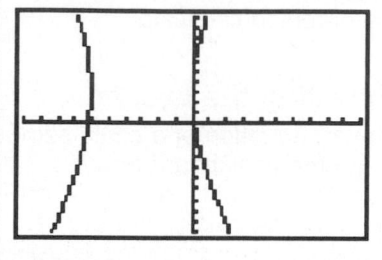

Teaching Tip ❹ The TI-81 will not "connect" the parts of the hyperbola because it is calculating the top half separately from the bottom half.

EVALUATING THE LESSON

Closing the Lesson

Writing Activity Have students solve and graph an equation of each type of conic section. Have them state their viewing windows for each graph.

APPLYING THE LESSON

Homework Exercises

Assignment Guide

All: 1–6

Casio

ENTER:

        RANGE   EXE

TI-81

ENTER: ZOOM 5

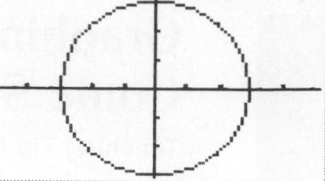

The graph now appears as a circle.

Sometimes a complete graph of an equation will not be shown on the square grid provided by the Casio system. In this case, simply reset the range parameters using multiples of the range setting values that the calculator set.

EXAMPLE

Graph the hyperbola $16x^2 - y^2 + 96x + 8y + 112 = 0$.

Solve the equation for y by completing the square. The result is
$$y = 4 \pm 4\sqrt{(x + 3)^2 - 1}.$$

Now enter the equations to graph the relation. **Teaching Tip ❹**
Multiply each of the range parameters in the Casio range by 4 to view a complete graph.

Casio

ENTER: GRAPH 4 + 4 √ ((
         ALPHA X + 3) x^2
         − 1) : GRAPH 4 − 4
         √ ((ALPHA X + 3
) x^2 − 1) EXE

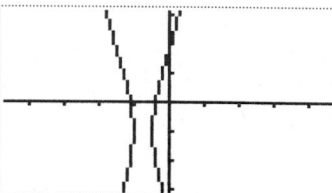

TI-81

ENTER: Y= 4 + 4 2nd √ (((X|T + 3) x^2 − 1) ENTER
        4 − 4 2nd √ (((X|T + 3) x^2 − 1) GRAPH

EXERCISES

Graph each of the following conic sections on your graphing calculator. Sketch the graph that appears on the graphics screen. **See student's graphs.**

1. $x = y^2 + 4y + 28$ **2.** $(x - 2)^2 + y^2 = 9$

3. $5x^2 + 15y^2 = 225$ **4.** $9x^2 - 4y^2 - 54x - 40y - 55 = 0$

5. $x^2 + y^2 + 7x - 5 = 0$ **6.** $y^2 - 20x^2 - 4x - 6y = 36$

EXTENDING THE LESSON

Math Power: Connections

Ask students why the graph of a circle looked like a circle in the range of [−4.7, 4.7] by [−3.1, 3.1] on the Casio graphing calculator. The Casio calculates 94 values along the x-axis and 62 values along the y-axis. 94 ÷ 4.7 = 20, and 62 ÷ 3.1 = 20.

What about the TI-81? The TI-81 calculates 94 values along both the x- and y-axes. The screen is 2.25″ wide and 1.5″ high. Since the calculator went to a range of [−15, 15] by [−10, 10] when you pressed ZOOM 5, the circle looked like a circle because 2.25 ÷ 15 = 0.15 and 1.5 ÷ 10 = 0.15.

Conic Sections

Objectives
9-7A
9-7B

After studying this lesson, you should be able to:
- write the equation of a conic section in standard form, and
- identify a conic section from its equation.

Application

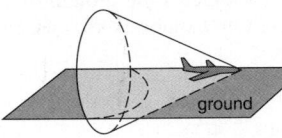

A supersonic jet has a shock wave in the shape of a cone. At the points where the wave hits the ground, a sonic boom is heard. If the jet is traveling parallel to the ground, the sonic boom is heard at points that form one branch of a hyperbola. What shape would the points form if the jet is not traveling parallel to the ground?

ground

By slicing a double cone in different directions, you can form parabolas, circles, ellipses and hyperbolas. For this reason, these curves are called conic sections.

FYI · · ·

Supersonic jets fly faster than the speed of sound. Capt. Charles Yeager became the first person to fly faster than the speed of sound on October 14, 1947.

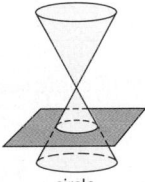

circle

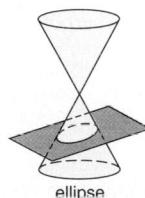

ellipse

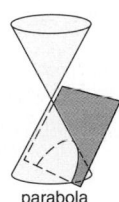

parabola

hyperbola

The conic sections can all be described by a quadratic equation.

Equation of a Conic Section

The equation of a conic section can be written in the form $Ax^2 + Bxy + Cy^2 + Dx + Ey + F = 0$ where A, B, and C are not all zero.

You can identify the conic section that is represented by a given equation by writing the equation in one of the standard forms you have learned. Study the table below to recall those forms.

Conic Section	Standard Form of Equation
parabola	$y = a(x - h)^2 + k$ or $x = a(y - k)^2 + h$
circle	$(x - h)^2 + (y - k)^2 = r^2$
ellipse	$\dfrac{(x - h)^2}{a^2} + \dfrac{(y - k)^2}{b^2} = 1$ or $\dfrac{(x - h)^2}{b^2} + \dfrac{(y - k)^2}{a^2} = 1$

Conic Section	Standard Form of Equation
hyperbola	$\dfrac{(x - h)^2}{a^2} - \dfrac{(y - k)^2}{b^2} = 1$ or $\dfrac{(y - k)^2}{a^2} - \dfrac{(x - h)^2}{b^2} = 1$ or $xy = c$, when $c \neq 0$

LESSON 9-7 CONIC SECTIONS 427

INTRODUCING THE LESSON

 5-Minute Check

(over Lesson 9-6)

1. Use a coin to model the number of boys and the number of girls predicted to be in a class of 26 students. **Answers will vary depending on simulation**

Other Prerequisite Skills

2. Find the value of c that makes $x^2 + 12x + c$ a perfect square. **36**
3. Find the axis of symmetry of the parabola whose equation is $y = 2x^2 - 6x + 4$. $x = \dfrac{3}{2}$
4. Find the distance between $(-4, 8)$ and $(1, -2)$. **$5\sqrt{5}$ units**
5. What figure is represented by the equation $x^2 + y^2 = 121$? **circle**

Motivating the Lesson

Conceal the top of the overhead projector from the students' view and use some of the following blocks and figures for them to identify.

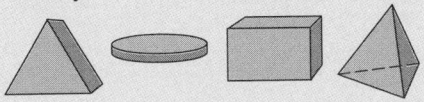

By placing the figures in different positions or on their sides, they will appear quite different. This helps a student to realize that a figure's appearance and properties can change. Do the same with a circular or elliptical ring.

ALTERNATE TEACHING STRATEGIES

Using Models

The following is an excellent project to learn some properties of 3-D geometric figures. Cut out two wooden circular disks about 8 inches in diameter. Drill holes around the perimeter. Connect with a rod about 15 inches long. Connect the two disks with string. Now, slowly revolve the disks and you will be forming a hyperboloid. Notice that the

strings are all straight and the figure has the appearance of being curved.

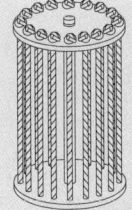

Chalkboard Examples

For Example 1
Determine if the graph of
$2x^2 + 3y^2 + 4x + 12y + 13 = 0$
is a parabola, a circle, an ellipse,
or a hyperbola.   **ellipse**

For Example 2
The shock wave generated by a
supersonic jet intersects the
ground in a curve whose equation
is $(y - 1)^2 = -5(x - 3)$. What
shape is the curve?   **parabola**

Teaching Tip ❶ The equation
may not always represent conic
sections. The equation may be an
example of a degenerate case or
it may not represent anything.

Checking for Understanding

Exercises 1–11 are designed to
help you assess understanding
through reading, writing, and
speaking. You should work
through Exercises 1–3 with your
students, and then monitor their
work on Exercises 4–11.

Reteaching Masters Booklet, p. 61

9-7 NAME _____ DATE _____
Reteaching Worksheet
Conic Sections

Parabolas, circles, ellipses, and hyperbolas are known as **conic
sections.** Any conic section in the coordinate plane can be described
by an equation of the form $Ax^2 + Bxy + Cy^2 + Dx + Ey + F = 0$,
where A, B, and C are not all zero. When $B = 0$, the coefficients of
x^2 and y^2 tell you what kind of conic section the equation will have
for its graph.

$A = C$	circle	$A \neq C$, but have opposite signs	hyperbola
$A \neq C$, but have same sign	ellipse	$A = 0$ or $C = 0$, but not both	parabola

Example: Write $x^2 = 4y^2 + 16$ in the form $Ax^2 + Bxy + Cy^2 + Dx + Ey + F = 0$. Tell what
kind of conic section the graph will be. Then change the equation to the standard
form for that conic section and graph the equation.

$x^2 = 4y^2 + 16$
$x^2 - 4y^2 = 16$
Since A and C have opposite signs, the graph will
be a hyperbola.
Next change $x^2 - 4y^2 = 16$ to the standard form
for a hyperbola. Divide each side by 16.
$\frac{x^2}{16} - \frac{y^2}{4} = 1$

**Write each equation in the form $Ax^2 + Bxy + Cy^2 + Dx + Ey
+ F = 0$. Tell what kind of conic section the graph will be. Then
change the equation to standard form for that conic section and
graph the equation.**

1. $x^2 - 2x + y^2 + 8y = 8$
   $x^2 + y^2 - 2x + 8y - 8 = 0$; circle;
   $(x - 1)^2 + (y + 4)^2 = 25$

2. $y = x^2 - 2x - 8$
   $x^2 - 2x - y - 8 = 0$; parabola;
   $y = (x - 1)^2 - 9$

3. $9(x + 4)^2 + 4(y - 1)^2 = 36$
   $9x^2 + 4y^2 + 72x - 8y + 112 = 0$;
   ellipse; $\frac{(x + 4)^2}{4} + \frac{(y - 1)^2}{9} = 1$

4. $x^2 = 2x + y^2 - 4y + 7$
   $x^2 - y^2 - 2x + 4y - 7 = 0$;
   hyperbola; $\frac{(x - 1)^2}{4} - \frac{(y - 2)^2}{4} = 1$

Example 1

Is the graph of $x^2 + y^2 - 8x + 6y + 24 = 0$ a parabola, a circle, an ellipse,
or a hyperbola?

Write the equation in standard form.

$x^2 + y^2 - 8x + 6y + 24 = 0$
$x^2 - 8x + \square + y^2 + 6y + \blacksquare = -24 + \square + \blacksquare$ *Complete the square.*
$x^2 - 8x + 16 + y^2 + 6y + 9 = -24 + 16 + 9$
$(x - 4)^2 + (y + 3)^2 = 1$ *h is 4, k is –3, and r is 1.*

The graph is a circle. It is also an ellipse, with *a* and *b* both equal to 1.

Example 2
APPLICATION
Aeronautics

The shock wave generated by a supersonic jet intersects the ground in a curve
whose equation is $x^2 + 10x + 5 = 4y^2 + 16y$. What shape is the curve?

$x^2 + 10x + 5 = 4y^2 + 16y$
$x^2 + 10x + \square + 4(y^2 + 4y + \blacksquare) = -5 + \square + (-4)\blacksquare$ *Complete the square.*
$x^2 + 10x + 25 - 4(y^2 + 4y + 4) = -5 + 25 - 4(4)$
$(x + 5)^2 - 4(y + 2)^2 = 4$

$\frac{(x + 5)^2}{4} - \frac{(y + 2)^2}{1} = 1$ *h is –5, k is –2, a is 2, and b is 1.*

The curve is a hyperbola.

You can easily determine the type of conic section represented by an
equation of the form $Ax^2 + Bxy + Cy^2 + Dx + Ey + F = 0$ when $B = 0$ by
looking at A and C.

- If $A = C$, the equation represents a circle.   **Teaching Tip ❶**
- If A and C have the same sign and $A \neq C$, the equation represents an
  ellipse.
- If A and C have opposite signs, the equation represents a hyperbola.
- If $A = 0$ or $C = 0$, but not both, the equation represents a parabola.

CHECKING FOR UNDERSTANDING

**Communicating
Mathematics**

1. **parabola, circle,
   ellipse, and
   hyperbola; They are
   formed by slicing a
   cone.**

Read and study the lesson to answer these questions.

1. Which curves are conic sections and why are they called conic sections?

2. If a supersonic jet were gaining in altitude, what curve would be formed
   by the points on the ground where the sonic boom could be
   heard? **parabola**

3. Explain why a circle is a special kind of ellipse. **See students' work.**

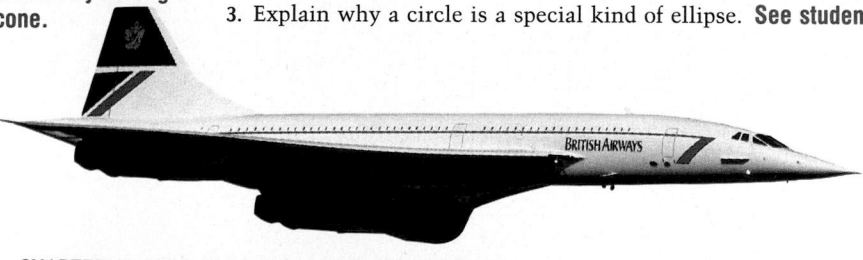

RETEACHING THE LESSON

The graph of every second degree
equation $Ax^2 + Bxy + Cy^2 +
Dx + Ey + F = 0$, is a conic sec-
tion (or a degenerated case). The
sign of the discriminant, $D = B^2 -
4AC$, can be used to determine
the conic section.

$D < 0$ ellipse (one point or 0)
$D = 0$ parabola (parallel lines)
$D > 0$ hyperbola (intersecting
          lines)

Additional Answer

28.

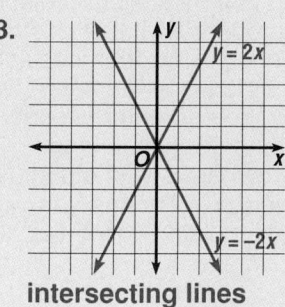

intersecting lines

Guided Practice

State whether the graph of each equation is a parabola, a circle, an ellipse, or a hyperbola.

4. $x^2 + y^2 = 81$ **circle**

5. $y = (x - 3)^2 + 25$ **parabola**

6. $x = (y + 4)^2 - 6$ **parabola**

7. $\dfrac{x^2}{8} - \dfrac{y^2}{10} = 1$ **hyperbola**

8. $\dfrac{x^2}{6} + \dfrac{y^2}{4} = 1$ **ellipse**

9. $\dfrac{(x - 4)^2}{9} - \dfrac{(y + 2)^2}{1} = 1$ **hyperbola**

10. $x^2 = 121 - y^2$ **circle**

11. $\dfrac{(y - 7)^2}{3} + \dfrac{(x + 2)^2}{2} = 1$ **ellipse**

12. $\dfrac{x^2}{2} + \dfrac{y^2}{4} = 1$; **ellipse**

13. $y = \dfrac{1}{8}x^2$; **parabola**

14. $x^2 + y^2 = 27$; **circle**

15. $\dfrac{x^2}{4} - \dfrac{y^2}{1} = 1$; **hyperbola**

16. $x^2 + y^2 = \dfrac{49}{13}$; **circle**

17. $\dfrac{y^2}{16} - \dfrac{x^2}{8} = 1$; **hyperbola**

EXERCISES

Practice

18. $\dfrac{x^2}{4} + \dfrac{(y + 1)^2}{3} = 1$; **ellipse**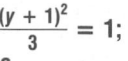

19. $y = \left(x + \dfrac{3}{2}\right)^2 - \dfrac{5}{4}$; **parabola**

20. $y = -1\left(x - \dfrac{1}{2}\right)^2 + \dfrac{9}{4}$; **parabola**

21. $\dfrac{(y - 5)^2}{16} - \dfrac{(x + 1)^2}{4} = 1$; **hyperbola**

22. $x^2 + (y - 4)^2 = 5$; **circle**

23. $x = \dfrac{1}{9}(y - 4)^2 + 4$; **parabola**

24. $\dfrac{(y + 4)^2}{2} - \dfrac{(x + 1)^2}{6} = 1$; **hyperbola**

25. $\dfrac{(x - 3)^2}{25} + \dfrac{(y - 1)^2}{9} = 1$; **ellipse**

Write the standard form of each equation. State whether the graph of the equation is a parabola, a circle, an ellipse, or a hyperbola. Then graph the equation. **See Solutions Manual for graphs.** Teaching Tip ❷

12. $4x^2 + 2y^2 = 8$

13. $x^2 = 8y$

14. $6x^2 + 6y^2 = 162$

15. $4y^2 - x^2 + 4 = 0$

16. $13x^2 + 13y^2 = 49$

17. $y^2 - 2x^2 - 16 = 0$

B

18. $3x^2 + 4y^2 + 8y = 8$

19. $y = x^2 + 3x + 1$

20. $x + 2 = x^2 + y$

21. $\dfrac{(y - 5)^2}{4} - (x + 1)^2 = 4$

22. $x^2 - 8y + y^2 + 11 = 0$

23. $(y - 4)^2 = 9(x - 4)$

24. $3y^2 + 24y - x^2 - 2x + 41 = 0$

25. $25y^2 + 9x^2 - 50y - 54x = 119$

26. $x^2 + y^2 = x + 2$

27. $6x^2 - 24x - 5y^2 - 10y - 11 = 0$

$\left(x - \dfrac{1}{2}\right)^2 + y^2 = \left(\dfrac{3}{2}\right)^2$; **circle**

$\dfrac{(x - 2)^2}{5} - \dfrac{(y + 1)^2}{6} = 1$; **hyperbola**

C

The graph of an equation of the form $Ax^2 + Bxy + Cy^2 + Dx + Ey + F = 0$ is either a conic section or a *degenerated case*. The degenerated cases for the conic sections are stated below. Graph each equation and identify the result. **28–30. See margin.**

28. $4x^2 - y^2 = 0$

29. $4y^2 + 3x^2 + 32y - 6x = -67$

30. $x^2 - x = 0$

Conic	Degenerated Case
ellipse or circle	isolated point
hyperbola	two intersecting lines
parabola	two parallel lines or one line

Critical Thinking

31. Graph $\dfrac{x^2}{4} - \dfrac{y^2}{9} = 1$. Then graph $\dfrac{x^2}{4} - \dfrac{y^2}{9} = c$ for several values of c that approach 0. What happens to the graphs as c approaches 0? Describe the graph if $c = 0$. **See students' work for graphs. When $c = 0$, the graph is two intersecting lines.**

Additional Answers

29.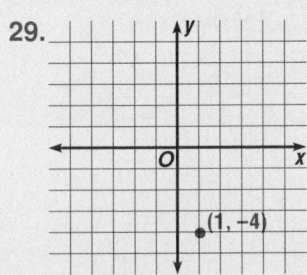

isolated point

30.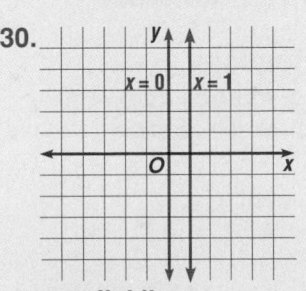

parallel lines

Closing the Lesson

Writing Activity Have students write a paragraph explaining the equations for the conic sections.

APPLYING THE LESSON

Homework Exercises

Assignment Guide

Basic: 12–27, 31–32, 34–38
Average: 15–28, 31–38
Enriched: 18–38

Chapter 9, Quiz C, (Lessons 9–5 through 9–7), is available in the Evaluation Masters Booklet, p. 122.

Teaching Tip ❷ Completing the square will be necessary in some cases.

Practice Masters Booklet, p. 70

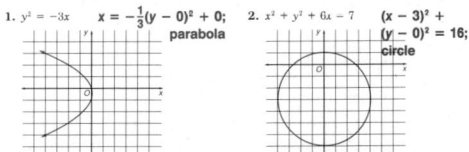

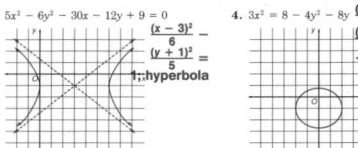

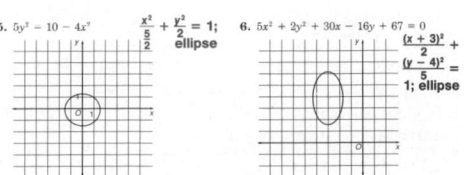

Applications

32. Astronomy   In the early 1600s, Johann Kepler studied the orbits of the planets and determined that they are elliptical. It is known now that orbits can take the shape of any of the conic sections. The equations of different orbits are given below. State the shape of each orbit.

a. $x^2 + y^2 = 75,000$ **circle**

b. $y - x^2 = 3x + 5$ **parabola**

c. $x^2 + y^2 - 4x = 9$ **ellipse**

d. $x^2 + 5x = y^2 - 6y - 1$ **hyperbola**

Computer
Teaching Tip ❸

33. This BASIC program uses the general form for the equation of a conic section to determine if the graph of the equation is a conic section or a degenerate case.

```
10   PRINT "A*X^2 + C*Y^2 +
     D*X + E*Y + F = 0
20   PRINT "ENTER A, C, D, E, F
25   INPUT A,C,D,E,F
30   IF A <> 0 THEN 60
40   IF D = 0 THEN 100
50   GOTO 120
60   IF C <> 0 THEN 80
70   GOTO 120
80   LET F1 = D^2/(4*A) + E^2/
     (4*C)
90   IF F1 <> F THEN 120
100  PRINT "DEGENERATE
     CASE": GOTO 190
120  IF A = C THEN PRINT
     "CIRCLE": GOTO 190
140  IF A*C > 0 THEN PRINT
     "ELLIPSE": GOTO 190
160  IF A*C < 0 THEN PRINT
     "HYPERBOLA": GOTO 190
180  PRINT "PARABOLA"
190  END
```

Use the program to determine if each equation is a conic section equation or the degenerate case.

a. $12x^2 + 36x + 16y^2 + 32y - 5 = 0$ **ellipse**

b. $25x^2 - 4y^2 = 100$ **hyperbola**

c. $x^2 + 12x + y^2 - 8y = -44$ **circle**

d. $4x^2 + 24x + y^2 - 10y + 45 = 0$ **ellipse**

e. $(y + 3)^2 = -12(x - 2)$ **parabola**

f. $16x^2 + 8x + 16y^2 - 32y + 17 = 0$ **degenerate case**

Mixed Review

34. Probability   When Kesia and Jeff play darts, Kesia usually wins two out of three games. Jeff read a book on the game and practiced several days before their recent match. Jeff won all three games. Do you think the book and the practice helped Jeff's game?   **(Lesson 9-6) Answers may vary.**

35. Write the equation of the hyperbola with center $(-2, 2)$ and a vertical transverse axis. $a = 6$ and $c = 10$.   **(Lesson 9-5)** $\dfrac{(y - 2)^2}{36} - \dfrac{(x + 2)^2}{64} = 1$

36. Graph the equation $f(x) = 2x^2 + 3$.   **(Lesson 8-3) See margin.**

37. Solve the equation $6x^2 - 16x - 6 = 0$ using the quadratic formula.   **(Lesson 7-4)** $3, -\dfrac{1}{3}$

38. Simplify $\sqrt[3]{-27r^3s^3}$.   **(Lesson 6-2) $-3rs$**

430   CHAPTER 9   CONICS

EXTENDING THE LESSON

Math Power: Reasoning

Which coefficient(s) must be zero if $Ax^2 + Bxy + Cy^2 + Dx + Ey + F = 0$:

a. is to be a function?   **C**

b. is to be a line?   **A, B, and C**

Additional Answer

36.

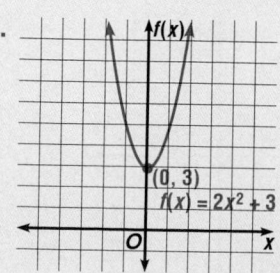

$f(x) = 2x^2 + 3$, $(0, 3)$

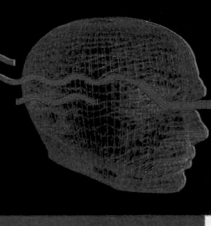

Technology

Conic Sections

BASIC
Spreadsheets
▶ Software

The *Mathematical Exploration Toolkit (MET)* can be used to graph a system of quadratic equations containing conic sections. From the graphs, you can determine the number of solutions the system has. The CALC commands (and their shortened forms) you can use are listed below.

CLEAR f (clr f)   CIRCLE (cir)   COLOR (col)
ELLIPSE (ell)   GRAPH (gra)   HYPERBOLA (hyp)
SCALE (sca)

The equations of circles, hyperbolas, and ellipses are entered using the values of the graphing parameters given in the general form of each conic section. That is, CIRCLE h k r, ELLIPSE h k a b, and HYPERBOLA h k a b are the commands used, replacing each variable with its numerical value from the general form. A parabola is entered either in the form $y = ax^2 + bx + c$ or $y = (x - h)^2 + k$.

Example   Find the number of solutions for the system $\begin{cases} y = (x - 1)^2 \\ (x - 1)^2 + (y - 2)^2 = 4 \end{cases}$.

ENTER:

clr f	clears the graphing window
sca 10	sets axes limits at -10 and 10 for x and y
y=(x-1)^2	$y = (x - 1)^2$
col 1	sets color to cyan (blue)
gra	graphs the parabola in blue
cir 1 2 2	$(x - 1)^2 + (y - 2) = 2^2$
col 2	sets color to magenta (red)
gra	graphs the circle in red

Since the graphs intersect at three points, there are three solutions.

EXERCISES

Graph each pair of equations on the same set of axes. Then determine the number of solutions the system has. **See student's graphs.**

1. $\dfrac{(x - 2)^2}{3^2} + \dfrac{(y + 1)^2}{4^2} = 1$

   $\dfrac{(x + 1)^2}{2^2} - \dfrac{(y - 2)^2}{3^2} = 1$

2. $\dfrac{(x - 2)^2}{9} - \dfrac{(y + 1)^2}{16} = 1$

   $x^2 + (y + 1)^2 = 25$

3. $\dfrac{(x + 1)^2}{4} + \dfrac{(y - 2)^2}{9} = 1$

   $y = -2(2x + 1)^2 + 3$

4. $y = x^2 + 2x - 3$

   $16y^2 - 9x^2 = 144$

Using Technology

Objective   This optional page shows how graphing software can be used to perform mathematical computations and to enhance and extend mathematical concepts.

Teaching Suggestions

Remind students that the equations must first be put into graphing form in order to determine the values of the parameters. You may want to extend this lesson to estimating the solutions of quadratic systems. The SCAN commands place a cursor in the graphing window. The coordinates of the cursor point are displayed. SCAN also provides a way to view a portion of the graph more closely. Consult the MET manual for examples.

Lesson Resources

Reteaching Master 9-8
Practice Master 9-8
Enrichment Master 9-8

 Transparency 9-8 contains the 5-Minute Check and a teaching aid for this lesson.

INTRODUCING THE LESSON

5-Minute Check

(over Lesson 9-7)
State whether the graph of each equation is a hyperbola, a parabola, a circle, an ellipse, or none of these.

1. $\dfrac{(x-1)^2}{25} + (y+5)^2 = 1$
   ellipse
2. $x^2 + y^2 = -9$ **none**
3. $x^2 - 4y^2 = 4$ **hyperbola**
4. $x^2 + 2x - 7 = y$ **parabola**
5. $x^2 - 8x - 3 = 4 - 6y - y^2$
   circle

Motivating the Lesson

Use a coordinate grid on an over-head projector. Draw intersecting curves and have students practice trying to estimate the points of intersection. This is the thrust of this lesson.

9-8 Graphing Quadratic Systems

Objective 9-8

After studying this lesson, you should be able to:
- graph systems of quadratic equations and identify the solution sets.

Application

An important concept in chemistry, Boyle's Law, states that if the temperature of a gas is constant, the pressure exerted by the gas varies inversely as the volume. So, $PV = k$, where P represents pressure in kilopascals, V represents volume in cubic decimeters, and k is a constant. A medical technologist provides oxygen for patients with respiratory problems through a tank containing compressed oxygen. The constant for oxygen at 25°C is 504. The volume of the tank is 12 cubic decimeters. What is the pressure of the oxygen in the tank?

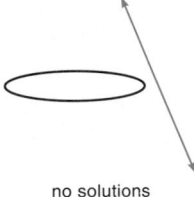

Since a negative pressure or volume is impossible, we will only consider positive values of P and V.

We can solve the system of equations described by graphing to find the pressure in the tank. First write the system of equations.

$PV = k$ — *Boyle's Law*
$PV = 504$ — *The constant for oxygen at 25°C is 504.*
$V = 12$ — *The volume of the tank is 12 dm³.*

Now graph.

The point where the line intersects the hyperbola is the solution.

The pressure is 42 kilopascals when the volume is 12 cubic decimeters.

If the graphs of a system of equations are a conic section and a straight line, the system will have zero, one, or two solutions.

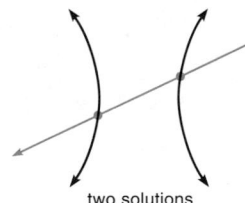

no solutions   one solution   two solutions

ALTERNATE TEACHING STRATEGIES

Using Calculators

In order to make the solutions easier to find, students can use graphing calculators. Remind them it may be necessary to experiment with different sets of range parameter values before finding the ones that will produce a complete graph.

Example 1
Teaching Tip ❶

Graph the following system of equations and find its solution.

$$x^2 + y^2 = 9$$
$$x - y = 3$$

The graph of $x^2 + y^2 = 9$ is a circle centered at the origin with a radius of 3 units.

The graph of $x - y = 3$ is a line with slope 1 and y-intercept -3.

The solutions of the system are $(3, 0)$ and $(0, -3)$.   *Check.*

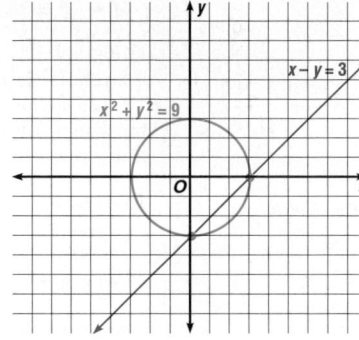

If the graphs of the system of equations are two conic sections, the system will have zero, one, two, three, or four solutions.

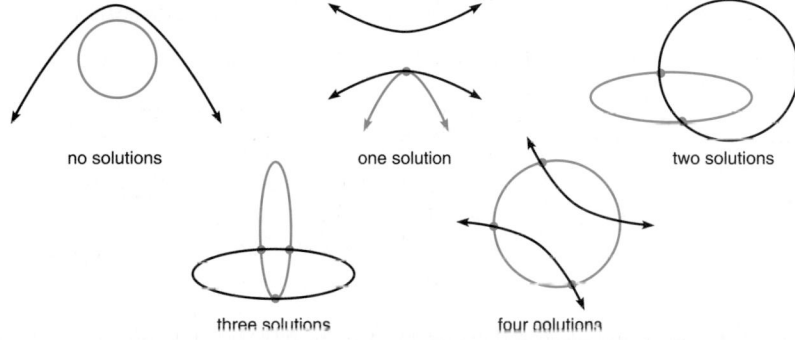

no solutions   one solution   two solutions

three solutions   four solutions

Example 2

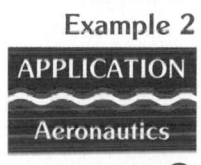

APPLICATION

Aeronautics

Teaching Tip ❷

The elliptical orbit of a comet that orbits the Sun is described by the equation $\frac{x^2}{9.61} + \frac{y^2}{4.84} = 1$. If NASA were to launch a satellite whose orbit would be $\frac{x^2}{7.84} + \frac{y^2}{5.76} = 1$, would the satellite be in danger of colliding with the comet?

The graph of each equation is an ellipse with center at the origin. The vertices of the comet's orbit are $(0, 2.2)$, $(0, -2.2)$, $(3.1, 0)$, and $(-3.1, 0)$. The vertices of the satellite's orbit are $(0, 2.4)$, $(0, -2.4)$, $(2.8, 0)$, and $(-2.8, 0)$.

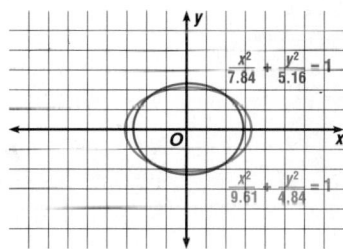

Since the orbits of the comet and the satellite intersect, there is a danger of the two colliding.

Chalkboard Examples

For Example 1
Graph the following system of equations and then find any solutions.

$$y = (x - 2)^2 + 1$$
$$y = {}^-4x + 5 \qquad (0, 5)$$

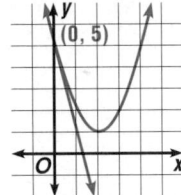

For Example 2
At a track meet, runners are using an elliptical track and shot putters are using a circle with a radius of 30 m. If the equation describing the ellipse is $\frac{x^2}{3600} + \frac{y^2}{900} = 1$, and the equation for the circle is $(x - 50)^2 + (y - 50)^2 = 900$, is there any chance of a runner being hit by a shot?   **yes**

Teaching Tip ❶   Encourage students to check the solutions by substituting the values into both equations.

Teaching Tip ❷   You may want students to guess the coordinates of the intersection.

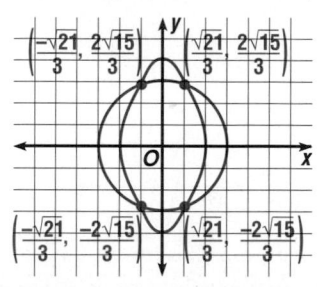
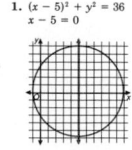
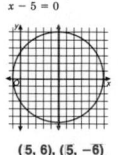
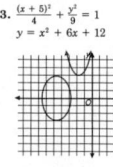
Example 3

Graph the following system of equations and find its solutions.

$4y = 25 - x^2$
$x^2 - y^2 = 36$

The graph of $4y = 25 - x^2$ is a parabola with vertex at $(0, 6.25)$. It opens downward and has x-intercepts at $(5, 0)$ and $(-5, 0)$.

The graph of $x^2 - y^2 = 36$ is a hyperbola with x-intercepts at $(6, 0)$ and $(-6, 0)$. The asymptotes are $y = \pm x$.

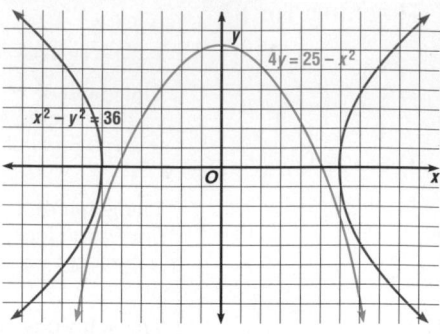

Since the two curves do not intersect, the system has no solutions.

CHECKING FOR UNDERSTANDING

Communicating Mathematics

Read and study the lesson to answer these questions.

1. How many solutions could there be to a system of equations whose graphs are a parabola and a hyperbola? Draw a diagram of each situation. **0, 1, 2, 3, or 4; See students' work.**

2. Describe and sketch an example of the graphs of a system of equations with no solutions, if the graph of each equation is a conic section. **They do not intersect; See students' work.**

3. Could the graphs of two hyperbolas intersect in just one point? If so, draw a sketch of the situation. **yes; See students' work.**

4. Use Boyle's Law to find the pressure in a 15 cubic deciliter tank of oxygen. Assume that the temperature is 25°C. **33.6 kilopascals**

Guided Practice

If possible, draw a sketch of the graphs of a system of equations for each situation described below. **5., 7., 8. See students' work.**

5. a hyperbola and a circle that intersect in 2 points

6. two circles that intersect in 3 points **not possible**

7. two parabolas that intersect in 4 points

8. a hyperbola and an ellipse that do not intersect

See Solutions Manual for graphs.

Graph each system of equations. Then find the solutions of each system.

9. $x^2 + y^2 = 16$
   $y = 2$ **$(\pm 2\sqrt{3}, 2)$**

10. $x + y = -7$ **(-4, -3), (-3, -4)**
    $x^2 + y^2 = 25$

11. $x + y + 1 = 0$
    $(y - 1)^2 = x + 4$ **(0, -1), (-3, 2)**

12. $3y = 6 - 5x$ **(0, 2)**,
    $\dfrac{x^2}{16} + \dfrac{y^2}{4} = 1$ **(2.2, -1.7)**

RETEACHING THE LESSON

In solving quadratic systems by graphing, the shape and range of each equation's graph are first identified. To help with the tedious work of making tables of sample (x, y) pairs, use a simple computer program to generate the tables.

Practice   Graph each system of equations. Then find the solutions of each system.

A ▶

13. $y = x + 2$
    $y = x^2$ **(-1, 1), (2, 4)**

14. $y = 3x$
    $y = x^2 - 4$ **(4, 12), (-1, -3)**

15. $x^2 + 4y^2 = 20$
    $x = y$ **(2, 2), (-2, -2)**

16. $x^2 - y^2 = 9$
    $2y = x - 3$ **(3, 0), (-5, -4)**

B ▶

17. $y = 6$
    $y^2 = x^2 + 9$ **(±5.2, 6)**

18. $y^2 = 100 - x^2$
    $x - y = 2$ **(8, 6), (-6, -8)**

19. $y = 7 - x$
    $y^2 + x^2 = 9$ **no solution**

20. $y = x - 6$
    $\dfrac{x^2}{4} + \dfrac{y^2}{1} = 1$ **no solution**

21. $x + 2y = 1$
    $x^2 + 4y^2 = 25$ **(4, -1.5), (-3, 2)**

22. $x^2 - 4y^2 = 16$
    $3x - y = 3$ **no solution**

23. $x - y = -2$
    $\dfrac{(x-2)^2}{16} + \dfrac{y^2}{16} = 1$ **(-2, 0), (2, 4)**

24. $y + x^2 = 0$
    $x + y = -2$ **(-1, -1), (2, -4)**

25. $\dfrac{x^2}{36} - \dfrac{y^2}{4} = 1$
    $x = y$ **no solution**

26. $(x - 1)^2 + 4(y - 1)^2 = 20$
    $y = x$ **(3, 3), (-1, -1)**

27. $5x^2 + y^2 = 30$ **(±1, 5),**
    $9x^2 - y^2 = -16$ **(±1, -5)**

28. $3x + 5y = 44$ **(3, 7), (8, 4)**
    $\dfrac{(x-3)^2}{25} + \dfrac{(y-4)^2}{9} = 1$

29. $x - y = 3$ **(3, 0), (-3, -6)**
    $(x - 3)^2 + (y + 6)^2 = 36$

30. $y = -2x^2$
    $x^2 + y^2 = 5$ **(1, -2), (-1, -2)**

31. $9x^2 + 4y^2 = 36$
    $9x^2 - 4y^2 = 36$ **(±2, 0)**

32. $3x^2 - y^2 = 9$ **(±2, 1.7),**
    $x^2 + 2y^2 = 10$ **(±2, -1.7)**

C ▶

33. $y = x^2 + 3$ **(0, 3),**
    $x^2 + 4y^2 = 36$ **(±2.4, -2.8)**

34. $y^2 = x^2 - 25$
    $x^2 - y^2 = 7$ **no solution**

35. $x^2 + y^2 = 64$
    $\dfrac{x^2}{64} + \dfrac{y^2}{1} = 1$ **(±8, 0)**

36. $y^2 = 16 - x^2$
    $x^2 + y^2 = 9$ **no solution**

37. $(x - 2)^2 + (y - 2)^2 = 1$
    $x^2 = 4 - 4y^2$ **no solution**

38. $y^2 = x^2 - 7$ **(±4, 3),**
    $x^2 + y^2 = 25$ **(±4, -3)**

39. $y^2 - x^2 = 16$
    $x^2 - y^2 = 16$ **no solution**

40. $x^2 + 2y^2 = 16$ **(±2.4, 2.2)**
    $y^2 + 2x^2 = 17$ **(±2.4, -2.2)**

Critical Thinking   41. Solve the following system of equations by graphing.

$$x - y = -10$$
$$y^2 = 16(x + 10) \quad \textbf{(-10, 0), (6, 16)}$$

Closing the Lesson

Speaking Activity What is the greatest number of solutions that can be found for the intersection of a line with any conic section?
2
Describe several examples of an intersection of a line and a hyperbola.

APPLYING THE LESSON

Homework Exercises

Assignment Guide

Basic: 13–32, 41–48
Average: 15–36, 41–48
Enriched: 19–48

Practice Masters Booklet, p. 71

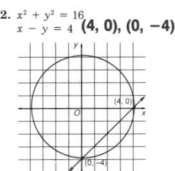
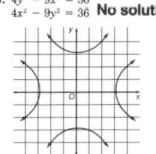
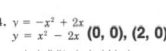
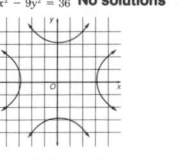
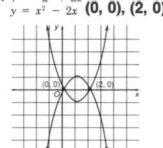
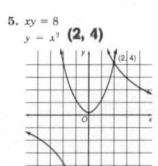
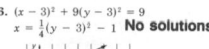
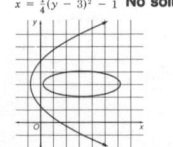

9 8   Practice Worksheet
Graphing Quadratic Systems

Graph each system of equations. Then find the solutions of each system.

1. $y = x^2$
   $y = -x + 2$ **(-2, 4), (1, 1)**

2. $x^2 + y^2 = 16$
   $x - y = 4$ **(4, 0), (0, -4)**

3. $4y^2 - 9x^2 = 36$
   $4x^2 - 9y^2 = 36$ **No solutions**

4. $y = -x^2 + 2x$
   $y = x^2 - 2x$ **(0, 0), (2, 0)**

5. $xy = 8$
   $y = x^3$ **(2, 4)**

6. $(x - 3)^2 + 9(y - 3)^2 = 9$
   $x = \frac{1}{4}(y - 3)^3 - 1$ **No solutions**

Applications

42. Sports When Greg Norman drives a golf ball, its path is shaped like a parabola. On the 18th fairway, there is a tree that is 60 feet tall.

a. When he drives the ball along the part of the fairway where the tree is, describe three possible heights the ball might reach in terms of the tree. **a parabola not as high, one as high, or one higher than the tree**

b. In each situation, how many times during its path will the ball be as high as the tree? **not as high = 0, as high = 1, higher than = 2**

43. Seismology Two tracking stations have detected an earthquake. The first station determined that the epicenter was 25 miles away. The second station determined that the epicenter was 42 miles away. If the first station is located at the origin and the second station is 50 miles due east of the first station, where could the epicenter have been? **approximately (13.6, 21) or (13.6, −21): that is 13.6 miles east and 21 miles north or south**

Mixed Review

44. State whether the graph of $\frac{(x+3)^2}{1} - \frac{(y-4)^2}{9} = 1$ is a parabola, a circle, an ellipse, or a hyperbola. **(Lesson 9-7) hyperbola**

45. Write the standard form of the equation $x^2 + 4y^2 = 4$. Graph the equation and state whether the graph is a parabola, a circle, an ellipse, or a hyperbola. **(Lesson 9-7)** $\frac{x^2}{4} + \frac{y^2}{1} = 1$; **See students' graphs; ellipse**

46. State whether the equation $f(x) = -3x^2 - 8x + 7$ describes a quadratic function. **(Lesson 8-1) yes**

47. Solve the equation $x^2 + 5x - 14 = 0$ by completing the square. **(Lesson 7-3) −7, 2**

48. Simplify $(2p^3 + 7p^2 - 29p + 29) \div (2p - 3)$. **(Lesson 5-6)**
$$p^2 + 5p - 7 + \frac{8}{2p - 3}$$

436   CHAPTER 9   CONICS

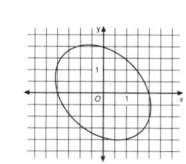
EXTENDING THE LESSON

Math Power: Reasoning

Solve the system of equations by graphing.
$9(x - 2)^2 + 6(y - 3)^2 \leq 54$
$2y = x + 3$

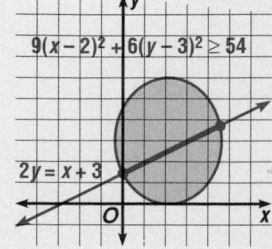

Graphing Calculator Exploration: Solving Quadratic Systems

As you know, the graphing calculator is capable of graphing several equations on the screen at one time. You can use this capability with the tracing function to determine the approximate solutions of a system of quadratic equations.

Example 1

Graph the following system of equations and find its solutions to two decimal places.

$$4y = 25 - x^2$$
$$x^2 - y^2 = 36$$

First solve each equation for y. **Teaching Tip ❶**

$$4y = 25 - x^2$$
$$y = \frac{1}{4}(25 - x^2)$$

$$x^2 - y^2 = 36$$
$$x^2 - 36 = y^2$$
$$\pm\sqrt{x^2 - 36} = y$$

Now graph the equations. *Make sure your calculator is set for a square viewing window.*

Casio

ENTER:

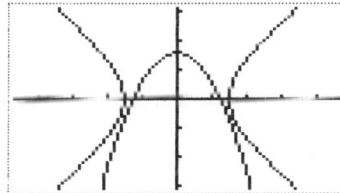

TI-81

ENTER: [Y=] .25 [(] 25 [-] [X|T] [x²]

[)] [ENTER] [2nd] [√] [(] [X|T]

[x²] [-] 36 [)] [ENTER] [(-)]

[2nd] [Y-VARS] [▼] [ENTER] [GRAPH]

The Y-VARS menus allows you to reuse the equations in the Y = list without retyping them.

There are no intersection points, so there are no real solutions to this system of equations.

INTRODUCING THE LESSON

Objective: Graph and solve quadratic systems on a graphing calculator.

Motivating the Lesson

Write two conic section equations on the chalkboard or overhead. Then ask students how they would solve them graphically. Try to get them to apply what they learned in previous graphing calculator explorations.

TEACHING THE LESSON

Teaching Tip ❶ You will be entering three equations on your calculator.

More Examples

1. Graph the following system of equations and find its solutions to two decimal places.
   $$y^2 - 16 = -x^2$$
   $$x^2 + 16 = y^2$$

   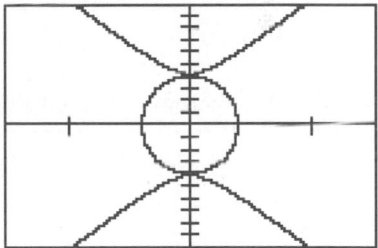

2. Graph the following system of equations and find its solutions to two decimal places.
   $$3x^2 + y^2 = 18$$
   $$4y^2 = 16 - 4x^2$$

   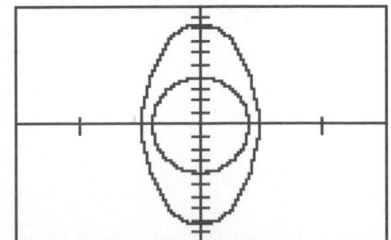

RETEACHING THE LESSON

Go through solving the equations very carefully with students. Some may have the most trouble in this area. Emphasize that you can tell what shape the conic section will be by looking at the equation. Try to get students to guess the shape before they graph it.

Teaching Tip ❷ The [Y-VARS] menu allows you to "plug in" one of the functions already entered on the calculator into another function. Here, since the second function is the opposite of the first function, you are entering, Y_1.

Teaching Tip ❸ On the TI-81, you can use several zoom techniques.

EVALUATING THE LESSON

Closing the Lesson

Writing Activity Divide the class into small groups and give each group two types of conic sections, making sure no two groups have the same two types of conics. Then tell them to write two equations for those conics, graph the conics, and solve the system of equations by graphing.

APPLYING THE LESSON

Homework Exercises

Assignment Guide

All: 1–6

Example 2 Graph the following system of equations and find its solutions to two decimal places.

$$6x^2 + y^2 = 30$$
$$8x^2 - 2y^2 = 4$$

Solve each equation for y.

$$6x^2 + y^2 = 30 \qquad\qquad 8x^2 - 2y^2 = 4$$
$$\quad y^2 = 30 - 6x^2 \qquad\qquad 8x^2 - 4 = 2y^2$$
$$\quad y = \pm\sqrt{30 - 6x^2} \qquad\qquad 4x^2 - 2 = y^2$$
$$\qquad\qquad\qquad\qquad\qquad \pm\sqrt{4x^2 - 2} = y$$

Graph the equations.

Casio

ENTER:

TI-81

Teaching Tip ❷

ENTER:

The points near the axes are part of the graph, but are not drawn by the graphing calculator.

Teaching Tip ❸ Now use the zoom-in technique that we used to find the solution of a system of linear equations to find the solutions. The solutions are (1.78, 3.28), (1.78, −3.28), (−1.78, 3.28), and (−1.78, −3.28) to the nearest two decimal places. *Notice the symmetry of these points.*

EXERCISES

Use your graphing calculator to graph each system of equations and find the solutions to two decimal places. **See margin.**

1. $x^2 + y^2 = 25$
   $y - x^2 = 1$

2. $x^2 + 2y^2 = 10$
   $3x^2 - y^2 = 9$

3. $x^2 + y^2 = 16$
   $x^2 + y^2 = 9$

4. $y = x^2 - 6$
   $9x^2 - 4y^2 = 36$

5. $(x - 1)^2 + y^2 = 9$
   $x^2 + 64y^2 = 64$

6. $x^2 + 4y^2 = 16$
   $(x - 2)^2 + y^2 = 16$

438   CHAPTER 9   CONICS

EXTENDING THE LESSON

Math Power: Reasoning

Have students make conjectures as to how many solutions different quadratic systems can have. For example, an hyperbola and a parabola can have none, one, two, three, four, or an infinite number of solutions.

Additional Answers

1. (1.90, 4.62), (−1.90, 4.62)
2. (2.00, 1.73), (2.00, −1.73),
   (−2.00, 1.73), (−2.00, −1.73)
3. no solutions
4. (3.08, 3.52), (−3.08, 3.52),
   (2.17, −1.27), (−2.17, 1.27)
5. (3.86, 0.87), (3.86, −0.87),
   (−1.83, 0.97), (−1.83, −0.97)
6. (−1.54, 1.84), (−1.54, −1.84)

Objectives
9-9A
9-9B

After studying this lesson, you should be able to:
- solve systems of equations algebraically, and
- solve systems of inequalities involving quadratics graphically.

You have learned how to solve systems of linear equations algebraically.
You can use similar methods to solve systems of quadratic equations.

Example 1

Find the solutions of the following system of equations.
$$4x^2 + 4y^2 = 65$$
$$6x - 2y = 5$$

The graphs of the equations are a circle
and a line. There are two solutions to the
system. *Estimate the solutions from the graph.*

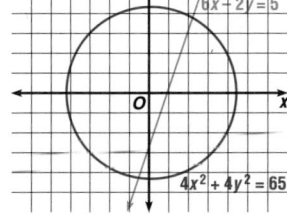

Let's use the substitution method to find
the solutions. First, rewrite $6x - 2y = 5$ as
$y = 3x - \frac{5}{2}$.

$$4x^2 + 4y^2 = 65$$
$$4x^2 + 4\left(3x - \frac{5}{2}\right)^2 = 65 \qquad \text{\textit{Substitute} } 3x - \frac{5}{2} \text{ \textit{for} } y.$$
$$4x^2 + 4\left(9x^2 - 15x + \frac{25}{4}\right) = 65$$
$$4x^2 + 36x^2 - 60x + 25 = 65$$
$$40x^2 - 60x - 40 = 0$$
$$2x^2 - 3x - 2 = 0$$
$$(2x + 1)(x - 2) = 0$$

$$2x + 1 = 0 \qquad \text{or} \qquad x - 2 = 0 \qquad \text{\textit{Zero product property}}$$
$$x = -\frac{1}{2} \qquad\qquad x = 2$$

Now solve for y.

$$y = 3x - \frac{5}{2} \qquad\qquad y = 3x - \frac{5}{2}$$
$$y = 3\left(-\frac{1}{2}\right) - \frac{5}{2} \qquad\qquad y = 3(2) - \frac{5}{2}$$
$$y = -4 \qquad\qquad y = \frac{7}{2}$$

The solutions are $\left(-\frac{1}{2}, -4\right)$ and $\left(2, \frac{7}{2}\right)$. *Compare to your estimate.*
Are these solutions reasonable?

LESSON 9-9 SOLVING QUADRATIC SYSTEMS 439

ALTERNATE TEACHING STRATEGIES

Using Connections

In tracking the epicenter of an
earthquake, scientists take readings
from several locations. Three locations
are sufficient to find the center. Why?
Two points will give two intersection
points but three circles can yield one
intersection point. Have students
research the locating of the epicenter of
an earthquake.

9-9 Lesson Notes

Lesson Resources
Reteaching Master 9-9
Practice Master 9-9
Enrichment Master 9-9

 Transparency 9-9 contains the
5-Minute Check and a teaching aid
for this lesson.

INTRODUCING THE LESSON

5-Minute Check

(over Lesson 9-8)

1. What conic section is
   represented by the equation
   $\frac{x^2}{9} - \frac{y^2}{36} = 1$? **hyperbola**
2. What conic section is
   represented by the equation
   $(x - 5)^2 + y^2 = 64$? **circle**
3. Graph the equations from
   Exercises 1 and 2 on the same
   coordinate plane.

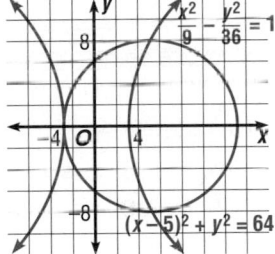

4. What are the solutions to this
   system of equations?
   (−3, 0), (5, 8), and (5, −8)

Motivating the Lesson

Place twelve 1-cm squares on the
overhead projector. The total area
is 12 cm². Arrange them as 1 by
12, then 2 by 6, then 3 by 4. Ask
the students to notice that the
area remains constant but the perimeter changes. What is the
greatest possible perimeter and
the least possible perimeter? Try
the same idea with a piece of
string. Here, the perimeter remains constant and the area
changes. What observations can
they make?

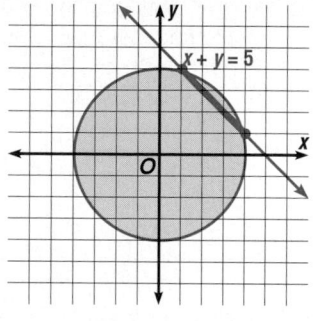
Example 2

Find the solutions to the following system of equations.
$$5x^2 + y^2 = 30$$
$$6x^2 - 2y^2 = 4$$

The graphs of the equations are an ellipse and a hyperbola. The graphs show that there are four solutions to the system.

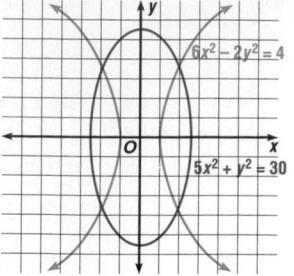

Use the elimination method to solve.

$$
\begin{array}{l}
5x^2 + y^2 = 30 \quad \text{\textit{Multiply by 2}} \quad\quad 10x^2 + 2y^2 = 60\\
6x^2 - 2y^2 = 4 \quad\quad\quad\quad\quad\quad\quad\quad \underline{ 6x^2 - 2y^2 = 4}\\
\quad\quad\quad\quad\quad\quad\quad\quad\quad\quad\quad\quad\quad 16x^2 = 64\\
\quad\quad\quad\quad\quad\quad\quad\quad\quad\quad\quad\quad\quad\quad x^2 = 4\\
\quad\quad\quad\quad\quad\quad\quad\quad\quad\quad\quad\quad\quad\quad\; x = \pm 2
\end{array}
$$

Substitute 2 and -2 for x to solve for y.

$$
\begin{array}{ll}
5x^2 + y^2 = 30 & \quad\quad 5x^2 + y^2 = 30\\
5(2)^2 + y^2 = 30 & \quad\quad 5(-2)^2 + y^2 = 30\\
y^2 = 10 & \quad\quad\quad\quad y^2 = 10\\
y = \pm\sqrt{10} & \quad\quad\quad\quad y = \pm\sqrt{10}
\end{array}
$$

The solutions are $(2, \sqrt{10})$, $(2, -\sqrt{10})$, $(-2, \sqrt{10})$, and $(-2, -\sqrt{10})$.

Example 3

APPLICATION

Aviation

The radar at the Municipal Airport can detect planes up to 45 miles away. The airport is located at (0, 0) on a map. If a plane is traveling on a straight path given by the equation $2x + y = 12$, show when the plane is within the range of the radar.

The area where the radar can detect the plane can be described by the inequality $x^2 + y^2 \leq 45^2$. To find the area where the plane is within the range of the radar, graph both the inequality that describes the range of the radar and the equation that describes the path of the plane and find the intersection of the two graphs.

Teaching Tip ❶

The graph of $x^2 + y^2 \leq 45^2$ is a circle and its interior. This region is shaded on the graph at the right. The graph of $2x + y = 12$ is a line with slope -2 and y-intercept 12. The intersection of the line and the shaded region is the graph of the area where the plane is in the range of the radar. It is indicated by the thick line segment.

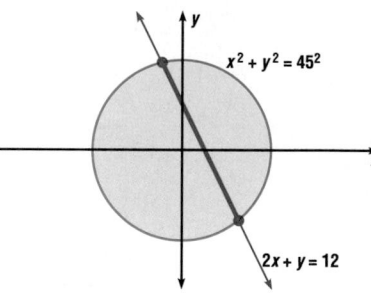

Example 4

Solve the following system of inequalities by graphing.

$$x^2 + y^2 < 9$$
$$y < -x^2$$

The graph of $x^2 + y^2 < 9$ is the interior of the circle $x^2 + y^2 = 9$. This region is shaded blue.

The graph of $y < -x^2$ is all of the points within the parabola $y = -x^2$. This region is shaded yellow.

The intersection of these two graphs represents the solutions for the system of inequalities. The points on the curves themselves are not solutions.

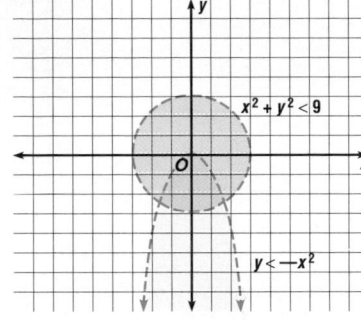

CHECKING FOR UNDERSTANDING

Communicating Mathematics

1. Answers may vary. A typical answer is when the solutions are not integers.

Read and study the lesson to answer these questions.

1. When would you choose to solve a system of quadratic equations algebraically rather than graphically?

2. If you were to solve a system of quadratic equations and the solution were an imaginary number, what can you conclude about the graphs of the equations of the system? **They do not intersect.**

3. The blue region of the graph at the right represents the solution of $x^2 + y^2 \le 25$ and the yellow region represents the solution of $4y + x^2 \le 25$. What does the green region represent? **the solution of the system of inequalities or the points that are solutions to both inequalities**

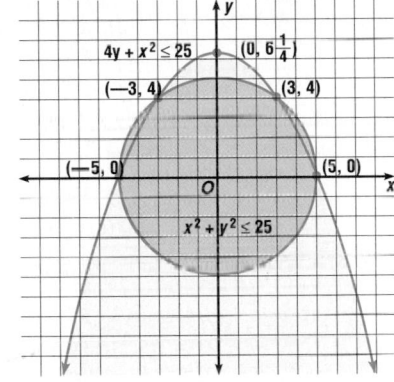

Guided Practice

4–9. Answers may vary. Typical answers are given.

State which method, substitution or elimination, you would use to solve each system of quadratic equations. Then solve each system.

4. $x^2 + y^2 = 25$
   $y - x = 1$ **substitution; (3, 4), (−4, −3)**

5. $x^2 + 2y^2 = 10$
   $3x^2 - y^2 = 9$ **elimination; $(2, \pm\sqrt{3})$, $(-2, \pm\sqrt{3})$**

6. $x^2 - y^2 = 25$ **elimination;**
   $4y^2 + x^2 = 25$ **(5, 0), (−5, 0)**

7. $3x - 4y^2$
   $4y^2 - 2x^2 = 16$ **substitution; no solutions**

8. $y = 3x^2 + 2$ **substitution;**
   $x^2 - 3y^2 = 27$ **no solutions**

9. $x^2 + y^2 = 81$
   $x = 2y^2 - 162$ **substitution; $(0, \pm9)$, $\left(-\frac{1}{2}, \pm\frac{\sqrt{323}}{2}\right)$**

LESSON 9-9 SOLVING QUADRATIC SYSTEMS 441

Chalkboard Example

For Example 4

Solve the following system of inequalities by graphing.

$$10 \ge (x - 5)^2 + 2y$$
$$y \ge -2x + 9$$

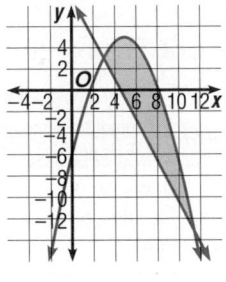

EVALUATING THE LESSON

Checking for Understanding

Exercises 1–12 are designed to help you assess understanding through reading, writing, and speaking. You should work through Exercises 1–3 with your students, and then monitor their work on Exercises 4–12.

Reteaching Masters Booklet, p. 63

9-9 Reteaching Worksheet

Solving Quadratic Systems

You can use algebra to find exact solutions for systems of quadratic equations. For systems of inequalities it is usually best to interpret the inequalities geometrically and show the solution set with a graph.

Example: Use algebra to find the solutions of the system $\begin{cases} x^2 + y^2 = 25 \\ y - x = 1. \end{cases}$

Solve $y - x = 1$ to get $y = x + 1$.

$x^2 + (x + 1)^2 = 25$	Substitute $x + 1$ for y.
$2x^2 + 2x - 24 = 0$	Simplify. Add -25 to both sides.
$2(x + 4)(x - 3) = 0$	Factor.
$x + 4 = 0$ or $x - 3 = 0$	Zero Product Property
$x = -4$ or $x = 3$	Solve for x.
$y = -3$ $y = 4$	Substitute for x in $y = 1 + x$.

The solutions are $(-4, -3)$ and $(3, 4)$.

Example: Solve the system $\begin{cases} x^2 + y^2 \le 25 \\ \left(x - \frac{5}{2}\right)^2 + y^2 \ge \frac{25}{4} \end{cases}$ by graphing.

The graph of $x^2 + y^2 \le 25$ consists of all points on or inside the circle with center $(0, 0)$ and radius 5. The graph of $\left(x - \frac{5}{2}\right)^2 + y^2 \ge \frac{25}{4}$ consists of all points on or outside the circle with center $\left(\frac{5}{2}, 0\right)$ and radius $\frac{5}{2}$. The solution of the system is the set of points in both regions.

Solve each system of equations.

1. $x^2 + y^2 = 9$
   $x^2 + y = 3$
   (0, 3), $(\sqrt{5}, -2)$, $(-\sqrt{5}, -2)$

2. $x^2 + (y - 5)^2 = 25$
   $y = -x^2$
   (0, 0)

3. $y = x^2 - 1$
   $y - x = 3$
   (2, −1), (−1, −4)

Solve each system of inequalities by graphing.

4. $x^2 + y^2 \le 169$
   $x^2 + 9y^2 \ge 225$

5. $\frac{x^2}{16} + \frac{y^2}{4} \le 1$
   $y > \frac{1}{2}x - 2$

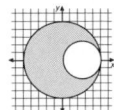 

RETEACHING THE LESSON

After students solve a quadratic system algebraically, have them predict or sketch the graph of the quadratic system. Then use a graphing utility (graphing calculator or computer program) to see the solutions.

Speaking Activity Describe what you would do to decide which method to use to solve a system of equations.

APPLYING THE LESSON

Homework Exercises

Assignment Guide

Basic: 13–38, 49–58
Average: 18–43, 49–58
Enriched: 23–58

Chapter 9, Quiz D, (Lessons 9-8 through 9-9), is available in the Evaluation Masters Booklet, p. 122.

Practice Masters Booklet, p. 72

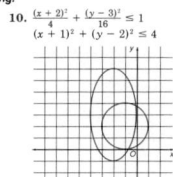

Write the system of inequalities represented by each graph.

10.

$x^2 + y^2 \geq 16$
$x + y = 2$

11.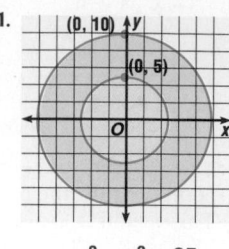

$x^2 + y^2 \geq 25$
$x^2 + y^2 \leq 100$

12.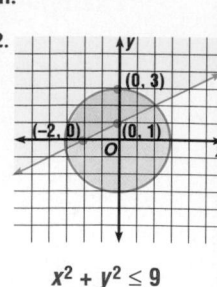

$x^2 + y^2 \leq 9$
$y \geq \frac{1}{2}x + 1$

EXERCISES

Practice Solve each system of equations.

A

13. $y = x + 2$
$y = x^2$ **(2, 4)**, **(-1, 1)**

14. $\dfrac{x^2}{20} + \dfrac{y^2}{5} = 1$
$y = x$ **(2, 2)**, **(-2, -2)**

15. $y^2 = x^2 - 9$
$2y = x - 3$ **(3, 0)**, **(-5, -4)**

16. $y = x^2 - 4$
$y = 3x$ **(4, 12)**, **(-1, -3)**

17. $x + y + 7 = 0$
$x^2 + y^2 = 25$ **(-4, -3)**, **(-3, -4)**

18. $x^2 + 4y^2 = 16$
$5x + 2y = 4$ **(0, 2)**, $\left(\dfrac{20}{13}, -\dfrac{24}{13}\right)$

19. $y = 6$
$x^2 - y^2 + 9 = 0$ **(±3√3, 6)**

20. $x + 4 = (y - 1)^2$
$x + y + 1 = 0$ **(-3, 2)**, **(0, -1)**

21. $x + y = 7$
$x^2 + y^2 = 9$ **no solutions**

22. $x - 2 = y$
$x^2 + y^2 = 100$ **(8, 6)**, **(-6, -8)**

B

23. $x^2 + 4y^2 = 4$
$y = x - 6$ **no solutions**

24. $(x - 2)^2 + y^2 = 16$
$y - x = 2$ **(-2, 0)**, **(2, 4)**

25. $y = -\dfrac{1}{2}x + \dfrac{1}{2}$
$x^2 + 4y^2 = 25$ $\left(4, -\dfrac{3}{2}\right)$, **(-3, 2)**

26. $3x - y = 3$
$x^2 - 4y^2 = 16$ **no solutions**

27. $x^2 + y = 0$
$x + y = -2$ **(-1, -1)**, **(2, -4)**

28. $x^2 - 9y^2 = 36$
$x = y$ **no solutions**

29. $5x^2 + y^2 = 30$
$y^2 - 16 = 9x^2$ **(1, ±5)**, **(-1, ±5)**

30. $(x - 3)^2 + (y + 6)^2 = 36$
$x - y = 3$ **(3, 0)**, **(-3, -6)**

31. $3x + 5y = 44$
$\dfrac{(x - 3)^2}{25} + \dfrac{(y - 4)^2}{9} = 1$ **(3, 7)**, **(8, 4)**

32. $x^2 + y^2 = 64$
$x^2 + 64y^2 = 64$ **(±8, 0)**

Solve each system of inequalities by graphing. **See Solutions Manual.**

33. $x^2 + y^2 < 25$
$4x^2 - 9y^2 < 36$

34. $x^2 + y^2 \geq 49$
$\dfrac{x^2}{16} - \dfrac{y^2}{1} \geq 1$

35. $\dfrac{x^2}{25} - \dfrac{y^2}{16} \geq 1$
$y \leq x - 2$

36. $x^2 + y^2 \geq 4$
$x^2 + y^2 \leq 36$

37. $(y - 3)^2 \geq x + 2$
$x^2 \leq y + 4$

38. $9x^2 + y^2 < 81$
$x^2 + y^2 \geq 16$

---

39. $y = x + 3$
$x^2 + y^2 < 25$

40. $y^2 < x$
$x^2 - 4y^2 < 16$

41. $x^2 + y^2 < 25$
$x + 2y > 1$

42. $x + y = 4$
$9x^2 - 4y^2 \geq 36$

43. $4x^2 + 9y^2 \geq 36$
$4y^2 + 9x^2 \leq 36$

44. $4x^2 + (y - 3)^2 \leq 16$
$x - 2y = -1$

45. $(x + 2)^2 + 16(y + 3)^2 \geq 16$
$x + y = 0$

46. $x = 2$
$4x^2 + 9y^2 \leq 36$

47. $x = 4$
$x^2 + y^2 \geq 16$

48. $y = 6$
$y^2 \leq 36 - x^2$

Critical Thinking

Solve each system of equations.

49. $x + y^2 = 2$ **(−2, −2), (0, $\sqrt{2}$)**
$2y - 2\sqrt{2} = x(\sqrt{2} + 2)$

50. $x^2 + y^2 = 1$
$y = 3x + 1$
$x^2 + (y + 1)^2 = 4$ **(0, 1)**

Teaching Tip ❷

Applications

51. Gardening Rob and Clarice are going to build a fence around their vegetable garden. They have 88 feet of fencing material and plan to have a garden with an area of 480 square feet. What will the dimensions of their garden be? **20 ft by 24 ft**

52. Seismology Three tracking stations have detected an earthquake in the area. The first station is located at the origin on the map. Each grid on the map represents one square mile. The second and third tracking stations are located at (0, 30) and (35, 18) respectively. The epicenter was 50 miles from the first station, 40 miles from the second station, and 13 miles from the third station. Where was the epicenter of the earthquake? **(40, 30) on the map**

Mixed Review

53. Graph the following system of equations. Then find the solutions. **(Lesson 9-8)**
$16x^2 = 4y^2 + 64$
$49x^2 = 4(y^2 - 49)$ **no solution**

54. Name the vertex, axis of symmetry and direction of opening of the parabola whose equation is $f(x) = 4(x - 8)^2$. **(Lesson 9-2) (8, 0); $x = 8$; up**

55. Cartography Edison is located at (9, 3) on the road map. Kettering is located at (12, 5) on the same map. Each side of a grid on the map represents 10 miles. Use the distance formula to approximate the distance between Edison and Kettering. **(Lesson 9-1) 36 miles**

56. Solve the equation $2x^2 + 15x + 7 = 0$. **(Lesson 7-2) −7, $-\frac{1}{2}$**

57. Simplify $\dfrac{2 + \sqrt{6}}{2 - \sqrt{6}}$. **(Lesson 6-3) −5 − 2$\sqrt{6}$**

58. Simplify $(2xy^2)^3 + (2xy^2)^2(6xy^2)$. **(Lesson 5-1) 32$x^3y^6$**

EXTENDING THE LESSON

Math Power:
Problem Solving

Find a such that there is a unique point of intersection of the two circles represented by $x^2 + y^2 = 4$ and $(x - 2)^2 + (y - 2)^2 = a$.
$a = 12 - 8\sqrt{2}$ or $a = 12 + 8\sqrt{2}$

Teaching Tip ❷ Drawing a sketch of the garden may help to see the relationship.

Enrichment Masters Booklet, p. 63

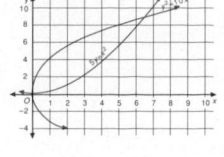

9-9 **Enrichment Worksheet**

NAME _____ DATE _____

Ancient Problems: Duplication of the Cube

One of the problems that attracted the interest of the early Greek mathematicians is the duplication of the cube. In this case, "duplication" does not mean making an exact copy. The problem is to find the side of a cube whose volume is double that of a given cube.

Geometric construction, using only a compass and a straightedge, was the only method the Greeks had to solve the problem. It turns out that, under these restrictions, there is no way to solve the problem. However, it can be solved using conic sections. The duplication of the cube can be written algebraically as $x^3 = 2a^3$, where a is the length of a side of the given cube.

Solve each problem.

1. The first mathematician to make some progress on the duplication of the cube was Hippocrates of Chios, who lived around 420 B.C. He transformed the problem into a three-part proportion, $a:x = x:y = y:2a$. Use the proportion to write a system of quadratic equations. Then show the system is equivalent to the algebraic statement of the problem.
$ay = x^2$ and $2ax = y^2$; $y = \frac{x^2}{a}$, $2ax = \frac{x^4}{a^2}$, so $2a^3 = x^3$

2. About 340 B.C. Menaechmus found that the solution is the intersection of the parabolas $y^2 = 2ax$ and $x^2 = ay$. Graph the parabolas and estimate the solution if a equals 5 units. **x ≈ 6.5**

3. In the 1600s, Descartes pointed out a slightly different solution. He used the system
$x^2 = ay$
$x^2 + y^2 = ay + bx$
In Descartes' solution, $b = 2a$. Graph the system and estimate the solution if a equals 4 units. **x ≈ 5**

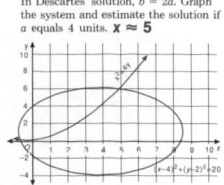

CHAPTER 9 SUMMARY AND REVIEW

VOCABULARY

Upon completing this chapter, you should be familiar with the following terms:

asymptotes	417	400	focus
center	405	416	hyperbola
circle	405	401	latus rectum
conic sections	407	410	major axis
conjugate axis	417	398	midpoint formula
directrix	400	410	minor axis
distance formula	397	400	parabola
ellipse	409	405	radius
foci	409	417	transverse axis

SKILLS AND CONCEPTS

OBJECTIVES AND EXAMPLES	REVIEW EXERCISES

Upon completing this chapter, you should be able to:

Use these exercises to review and prepare for the chapter test.

■ use the distance formula to find the distance between a pair of points. **(Lesson 9-1)**

Find the distance between (3, −2) and (0, 2).

$$d = \sqrt{(x_2 - x_1)^2 + (y_2 - y_1)^2}$$
$$= \sqrt{(0 - 3)^2 + [2 - (-2)]^2}$$
$$= \sqrt{25} \text{ or } 5$$

Find the distance between each pair of points.

1. (−8, −7), (−2, −1) $\mathbf{6\sqrt{2}}$
2. (3, 6), (7, −8) $\mathbf{2\sqrt{53}}$
3. (−2.4, 0.6), (1.7, 0.8) $\mathbf{\sqrt{16.85}}$
4. (2√3, 4√3), (2√3, −√3) $\mathbf{5\sqrt{3}}$

■ use the midpoint formula to find the midpoint of a segment.   **(Lesson 9-1)**

Find the midpoint of the segment whose endpoints are (−8, 7) and (2, 15).

$$M = \left(\frac{x_1 + x_2}{2}, \frac{y_1 + y_2}{2}\right)$$
$$= \left(\frac{-8 + 2}{2}, \frac{7 + 15}{2}\right) \text{ or } (-3, 11)$$

Find the midpoint of each line segment with endpoints having the following coordinates.

5. (17, −8), (−13, 1) $\left(\mathbf{2, -\frac{7}{2}}\right)$
6. (0.2, 0.6), (0.3, 0.4) $\mathbf{(0.25, 0.5)}$
7. (5, 2), (−3, 1) $\left(\mathbf{1, \frac{3}{2}}\right)$
8. (2, 2), (√2, √2) $\left(\mathbf{1 + \frac{\sqrt{2}}{2}, 1 + \frac{\sqrt{2}}{2}}\right)$

Additional Answers

9.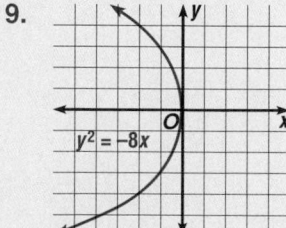

10.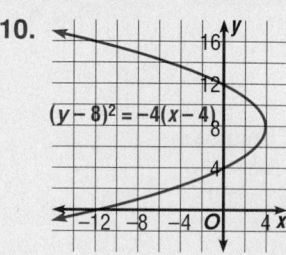

OBJECTIVES AND EXAMPLES	REVIEW EXERCISES

- graph parabolas. (Lesson 9-2)

Graph $x^2 = 4y$.

Rewrite as $y = \frac{1}{4}x^2$.

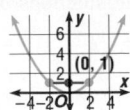

vertex: $(0, 0)$

axis of symmetry: $x = 0$

focus: $(0, 1)$

directrix: $y = -1$

direction of opening: up

length of latus rectum: $\left|\dfrac{1}{\frac{1}{4}}\right|$ or 4 units

Name the vertex, axis of symmetry, focus, directrix, and direction of opening of the parabola whose equation is given. Then find the length of the latus rectum and draw the graph. 9–10. See margin for graph.

9. $y^2 = -8x$

10. $(y - 8)^2 = -4(x - 4)$

9. $(0, 0)$; $y = 0$; $(-2, 0)$; $x = 2$; left; 8

10. $(4, 8)$; $y = 8$; $(3, 8)$; $x = 5$; left; 4

11–16. For graphs, see Solutions Manual.

- graph circles. (Lesson 9-3)

The equation of a circle with radius r and center (h, k) is $(x - h)^2 + (y - k)^2 = r^2$.

Find the center and radius of each circle whose equation is given. Then draw the graph.

11. $x^2 + y^2 = 121$ 12. $(x - 3)^2 + (y + 7)^2 = 81$

   $(0, 0)$; 11 $(3, -7)$; 9

- graph ellipses. (Lesson 9-4)

An ellipse is the set of all points in a plane such that the sum of the distances from two given points in the plane, called the foci, is constant.

Find the center, foci, and lengths of the major and minor axes for each ellipse whose equation is given. Then draw the graph.

13–14. See margin.

13. $9x^2 + 16y^2 = 144$

14. $\dfrac{(x - 3)^2}{25} + \dfrac{(y + 1)^2}{4} = 1$

- graph hyperbolas. (Lesson 9-5)

Graph $\dfrac{x^2}{16} - \dfrac{y^2}{81} = 1$.

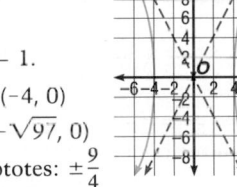

vertices: $(4, 0)$, $(-4, 0)$

foci $(\sqrt{97}, 0)$, $(-\sqrt{97}, 0)$

slopes of asymptotes: $\pm\dfrac{9}{4}$

Find the vertices, foci, and slopes of the asymptotes for each hyperbola whose equation is given. Then draw the graph. 15.–16. See margin.

15. $49x^2 - 16y^2 = 784$

16. $25(y + 6)^2 - 20(x - 1)^2 = 500$

- identify a conic section from its equation. (Lesson 9-7)

$Ax^2 + Bxy + Cy^2 + Dx + Ey + F = 0$

relationship of A and C	graph
$A = C$	circle
$A \neq C$, but have same sign	ellipse
A and C have opposite signs	hyperbola
$A = 0$ or $C = 0$ but not both	parabola

State whether the graph of each equation is a parabola, a circle, an ellipse, or a hyperbola.

17. $(x - 1)^2 = 4y$ **parabola**

18. $4x^2 + 5y^2 = 20$ **ellipse**

19. $3x^2 - 16 = -3y^2$ **circle**

20. $3y^2 - 7x^2 = 21$ **hyperbola**

To provide a brief in-class review, you may wish to read the following questions to the class and require a verbal response.

1. Find the distance between $(-4, 3)$ and $(-2, 1)$. $2\sqrt{2}$

2. Find the midpoint of $(-4, 3)$ and $(-2, 1)$. $(-3, 2)$

3. Name the vertex, axis of symmetry, focus, directrix, and direction of the opening of the parabola, $y = 4(x - 3)^2 + 1$.

   $(3, 1)$; $x = 3$; $\left(3, \dfrac{17}{16}\right)$; $y = \dfrac{15}{16}$; **upward**

4. Find the center and the radius of $(x - 4)^2 + (y + 3)^2 = 25$. $(4, -3)$; 5

5. Find the center, foci, and lengths of the major and minor axes for $\dfrac{(x - 4)^2}{9} + \dfrac{(y + 6)^2}{16} = 1$.

   $(4, -6)$; $(4, -6 + \sqrt{7})$, $(4, -6 - \sqrt{7})$; 8; 6

6. Find the vertices, foci, and slopes of the asymptotes for $\dfrac{x^2}{4} - \dfrac{y^2}{25} = 1$. $(2, 0)$, $(-2, 0)$;

   $(\sqrt{29}, 0)$, $(-\sqrt{29}, 0)$; $\dfrac{5}{2}$, $-\dfrac{5}{2}$

7. George and Mary want to have two children, both girls. If they have two children, what is the probability that they have two girls? **25%**

8. State whether $x = (y - 6)^2 - 8$ is a parabola, a circle, an ellipse, or a hyperbola. **parabola**

9. Find the solution for $y = x - 4$ and $y = x^2$. **no solution**

10. Find the solutions for $x + y = 8$ and $y = x^2 + 2$. $(-3, 11)$, $(2, 6)$

Additional Answers

13. $(0, 0)$; $(\pm\sqrt{7}, 0)$; 8, 6

14. $(3, -1)$; $(3 \pm \sqrt{21}, -1)$; 10, 4

15. $(\pm 4, 0)$; $(\pm\sqrt{65}, 0)$; $\pm\dfrac{7}{4}$

16. $(1, -6 \pm 2\sqrt{5})$;

    $(1, -6 \pm 3\sqrt{5})$; $\pm\dfrac{2\sqrt{5}}{5}$

The Cumulative Review shown below can be used to review skills and concepts presented thus far in the text. Standardized Test Practice Questions are also provided in the Evaluation Masters Booklet.

Evaluation Masters Booklet, pp. 123–124

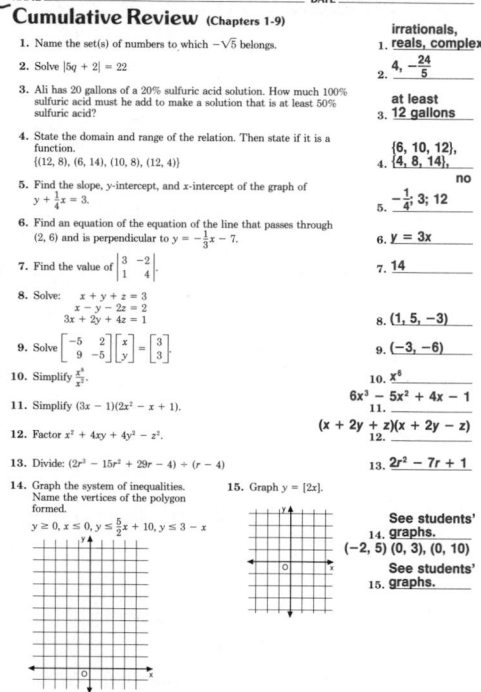

OBJECTIVES AND EXAMPLES	REVIEW EXERCISES

■ solve systems of quadratic equations. (Lesson 9-8 and 9-9)

A system of equations whose graphs are a line and a conic section can have zero, one, or two solutions. A system of equations whose graphs are two conic sections can have zero, one, two, three, or four solutions.

For graphs, See Solutions Manual.
Graph each system of equations. Then find the solutions of each system.

21. $(x - 2)^2 + y^2 = 16$
    $y - x = 2$
    (−2, 0), (2, 4)

22. $x^2 - y^2 = 16$
    $y^2 - x^2 = 16$
    no solutions

Solve each system of equations. **See margin.**

23. $x + y = 4$
    $y = x^2$

24. $x + y = 1$
    $x^2 + y^2 = 9$

■ solve systems involving quadratic inequalities by graphing. (Lesson 9-9)

Graph the solution set of the following system of inequalities.
$x^2 + y^2 \geq 5$
$2x - 3y = 5$

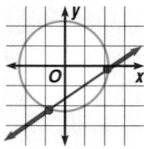

Solve each system of inequalities by graphing. **25–26. See margin**

25. $x^2 + y^2 < 25$
    $x + y > 5$

26. $y \geq x^2 + 4$
    $x^2 + y^2 < 49$

APPLICATIONS AND CONNECTIONS

27. **Aviation** An air traffic control tower is located at $(12, 25)$ on a county map. The radar equipment can detect planes up to 48 miles away. Assuming that each side of a grid on the map represents one mile, write an equation for the position of the most distant plane that the tower can detect in terms of the county map. (Lesson 9-1) **$(x - 12)^2 + (y - 25)^2 = 2304$**

28. **Sports** Elliptipool is a game like pool that is played on the elliptical table. The table has one pocket that is located at one focus of the ellipse. How could a player strike a ball and be guaranteed that the ball will go in the pocket? (Lesson 9-4) **Make it pass over the other focus.**

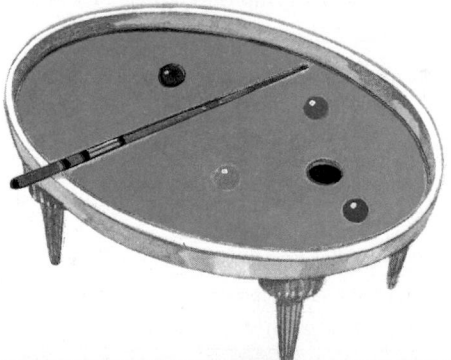

29. **Aerospace** The path of a comet can be described by the equation $4x^2 - 9y^2 = 36$. Describe this orbit. (Lesson 9-5) **a hyperbola with foci $(\pm\sqrt{13}, 0)$, vertices $(\pm 3, 0)$, and asymptotes $y = \pm\frac{3}{2}$**

30. **Probability** Mr. and Mrs. Porter would like to have two children, a boy and a girl. Use coins to determine how likely it is that they will have a boy and then a girl. (Lesson 9-6) **about 25%**

Additional Answers

23. **(1.6, 2.4), (−2.6, 6.6)**
24. **(−1.6, 2.6), (2.6, −1.6)**
25.

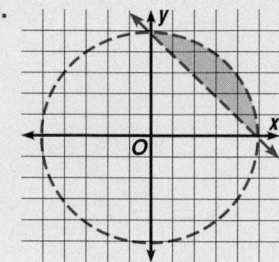

26.

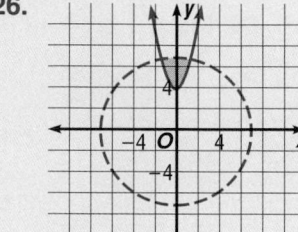

Use the distance formula to find the distance between each pair of points.

1. (6, 3), (-6, 0) $\sqrt{153}$

2. (9, -11), (-7, 18) $\sqrt{1097}$

Find the midpoint of each line segment whose endpoints are given below.

3. (6, 12), (-12, 22) **(-3, 17)**

4. (-3.2, 2.1), (9.8, -0.6) **(3.3, 0.75)**

State whether the graph of each equation is a parabola, a circle, an ellipse, or a hyperbola. Then draw the graph. **5-16. See Solutions Manual for graphs.**

5. $y = 3x^2$ **parabola**

6. $x^2 + 4x = -(y^2 - 6)$ **circle**

7. $9x^2 + 49y^2 = 441$ **ellipse**

8. $4x^2 - y^2 = 4$ **hyperbola**

9. $x^2 + 4x + y^2 - 8y = 2$ **circle**

10. $(x + 3)^2 = 8(y + 2)$ **parabola**

11. $9x^2 + 9y^2 = 9$ **circle**

12. $y - x^2 = x + 3$ **parabola**

13. $2x^2 - 13y^2 + 5 = 0$ **hyperbola**

14. $16(x - 3)^2 + 81(y + 4)^2 = 1296$ **ellipse**

15. $4x^2 - y^2 - 16$ **hyperbola**

16. $x^2 + 5y^2 = 16$ **ellipse**

17. **Statistics** Paul makes two of every three free throws that he attempts. He has been fouled and is to shoot two free throws. Do you think he will make them both? **probably, 67% chance each time**

Solve each system of equations.

18. $y = -(x + 1)$
$x^2 + y^2 = 25$ **(-4, 3), (3, -4)**

19. $9x^2 - 16y^2 = 144$
$x^2 + y^2 = 16$ **(4, 0), (-4, 0)**

Solve each system of inequalities by graphing. **20-21. See Solutions Manual.**

20. $x^2 + y < 2$
$x^2 + y^2 < 49$

21. $y = 5 - x$
$x^2 + y^2 \geq 49$

Find the equation for each conic section described below.

22. A parabola has vertex at (6, -1) and focus at (3, -1). $x = -\dfrac{1}{12}(y + 1)^2 + 6$

23. **Geometry** A diameter of a circle has endpoints at (-2, 3) and (4, 5). $(x - 1)^2 + (y - 4)^2 = 10$

24. An ellipse has center at (3, 1). Its major axis is 12 units long and is parallel to the y-axis. Its minor axis is $8\sqrt{2}$ units long. $\dfrac{(y - 1)^2}{36} + \dfrac{(x - 3)^2}{32} = 1$

25. The center of a hyperbola is (2, -4). The transverse axis is horizontal and is 6 units long. The conjugate axis is 10 units long. $\dfrac{(x - 2)^2}{9} - \dfrac{(y + 4)^2}{25} = 1$

Bonus
Solve the following system of equations.

$x^2 + 4y^2 = 4$
$(x - 1)^2 + y^2 = 1$ $\left(2, 0\right), \left(\dfrac{2}{3}, \dfrac{2\sqrt{2}}{3}\right), \left(\dfrac{2}{3}, \dfrac{-2\sqrt{2}}{3}\right)$

Using the Chapter Test

This page may be used as a test or as a review. In addition, two multiple-choice tests and two free-response tests are provided in the Evaluation Masters Booklet. Chapter 9 Test, Form 1A is shown below.

Evaluation Masters Booklet, pp. 113-114

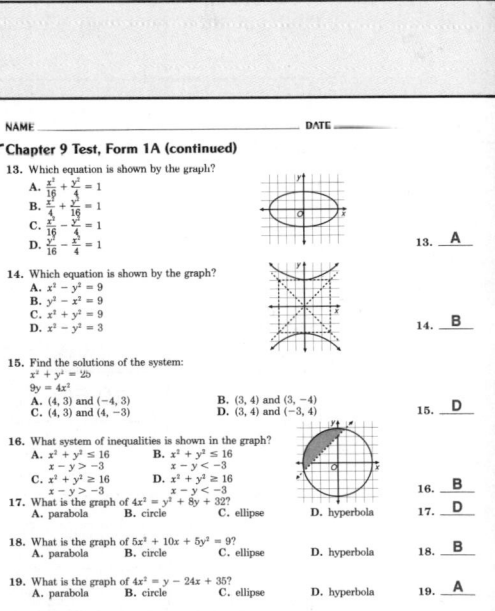

A **Test and Review Generator** is provided in Apple, IBM, and Macintosh versions. You may use this software to create your own tests or worksheets, based on the needs of your students.

The **Performance Assessment Booklet** provides an alternate assessment for evaluating student progress. An assessment for this chapter can be found on pages 17-18.

10 Polynomial Functions

PREVIEWING THE CHAPTER

The chapter opens with a lesson on evaluating polynomial functions. Then important topics from number theory are introduced as students learn to use the Factor Theorem and synthetic division to find factors of polynomials and the Rational Zero Theorem to identify all possible rational zeros of a polynomial function. Zeros are approximated and polynomial functions are graphed with the use of synthetic division to find significant points. Students find the composition of functions and then learn to identify and graph the inverse of a function.

Problem-Solving Strategy   Students learn that certain problems can be solved by using two or more strategies.

Lesson Objective Chart

Lesson (Pages)	Lesson Objectives	State/Local Objectives
10-1 (450-456)	**10-1A:** Evaluate polynomial functions.	
	10-1B: Identify general shapes of the graphs of polynomial functions.	
10-2 (459-464)	**10-2:** Find factors of polynomials using the Factor Theorem and synthetic division.	
10-3 (465-467)	**10-3:** Solve problems by using more than one strategy.	
10-4 (468-474)	**10-4:** Find the number of positive real zeros, negative real zeros, and complex zeros for a polynomial function.	
10-5 (475-480)	**10-5A:** Identify all possible rational zeros of a polynomial function using the Rational Zero Theorem.	
	10-5B: Find zeros of polynomial functions.	
10-6 (481-485)	**10-6A:** Approximate the real zeros of polynomial functions.	
	10-6B: Graph polynomial functions using synthetic division to find significant points.	
10-7 (487-490)	**10-7:** Find the composition of functions.	
10-8 (491-495)	**10-8A:** Determine the inverse of a function or relation.	
	10-8B: Graph a function and its inverse.	

ORGANIZING THE CHAPTER

You may want to refer to the **Course Planning Calendar** on page T44.

Lesson (Pages)	Pacing Chart (days) Course I	II	III	Reteaching	Practice	Enrichment	Evaluation	Technology	Lab Manual	Activities Mixed Problem Solving	Applications	Cooperative Learning Activity	Multicultural	Transparencies
10-1 (450-456)	1.5	1.5	1	p. 64	p. 73	p. 64								10-1
10-2 (459-464)	1.5	1.5	1	p. 65	p. 74	p. 65	Quiz A, p. 135							10-2
10-3 (465-467)	1	1	0.5		p. 75									10-3
10-4 (468-474)	2	2	1.5	p. 66	p. 76	p. 66	Quiz B, p. 135 Mid-Chapter Test, p. 139	p. 10				p. 46	p. 10	10-4
10-5 (475-480)	1.5	1	1	p. 67	p. 77	p. 67				p. 10				10-5
10-6 (481-485)	1.5	1	1	p. 68	p. 78	p. 68	Quiz C, p. 136	p. 27						10-6
10-7 (487-490)	1	1	1	p. 69	p. 79	p. 69					p. 28			10-7
10-8 (491-495)	1	1	1	p. 70	p. 80	p. 70	Quiz D, p. 136		pp. 61-62					10-8
Review (496-498)	1	1	1	Multiple Choice Tests, Forms 1A and 1B, pp. 127-130 Free Response Tests, Forms 2A and 2B, pp. 131-134 Cumulative Review, pp. 137-138 Standardized Test Practice Questions, p. 140										
Test (499)	1	1	1											

Course I: Chapters 1-13; Course II: Chapters 1-15; Course III: Chapters 1-17

Other Chapter Resources

Student Edition

Chapter Opener, pp. 448-449
History Connection, p. 456
Graphing Calculator Exploration, pp. 457-458
Cooperative Learning Activity, p. 467
Journal Entries, pp. 474, 490
Mid-Chapter Review, p. 474
Language Connection, p. 480
Technology, p. 486
Portfolio Suggestion, p. 495
College Entrance Exam Preview, pp. 500-501
Extended Project 3, pp. A10-A13

Teacher's Classroom Resources

Transparency 10-0
Real-World Applications Transparencies, 20, 21
Performance Assessment Booklet, pp. 19-20
Problem-of-the-Week Activity Cards, 20, 21
Tech Prep Applications Booklet, pp. 19-20
Lesson Plans, pp. 73-80

Other Supplements

Glencoe Mathematics Professional Series

Software

Test and Review Generator Software (Apple, IBM, and Macintosh)
Interactive Software (Macintosh)
Teacher's Guide for Software Resources

ENHANCING THE CHAPTER

Cooperative Learning

Explaining the Task

To make sure that students focus on the relevant concepts and skills throughout the session, it is important that you provide them with a clear understanding of the academic task that they are to complete. Be sure to clearly explain the objectives that are to be achieved and the procedures that students are expected to follow. Review and define pertinent concepts and, when possible, connect the task and objectives to students' previously-acquired knowledge and experience. Then, provide examples to help students comprehend what it is they are to do and to learn. Finally, ask the class specific questions about the assignment to make sure all students understand what the assignment is and how they are to proceed. Although students in a cooperative-learning group can ask one another about that which they do not understand, you can help make sure that such questions are appropriately and productively related to the new content by beginning every session with a clear definition of the task and procedures.

Cooperative Learning, p. 46

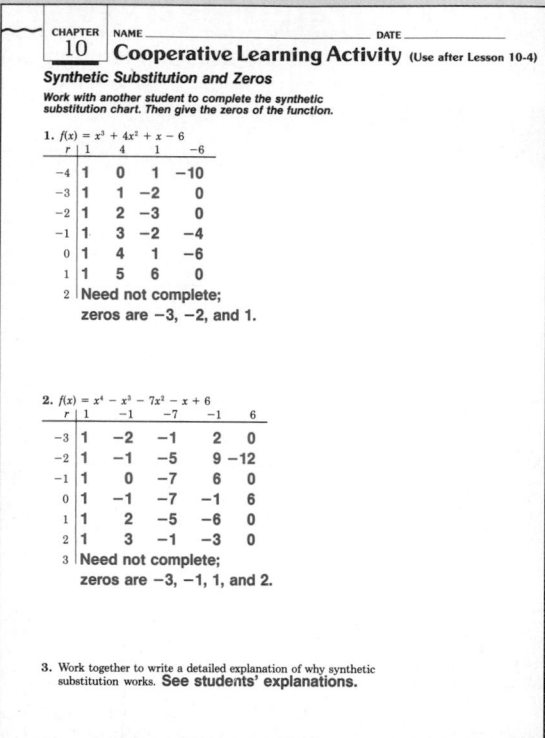

Technology

The Technology Feature after Lesson 10-6 shows students how to use the features of a spreadsheet program to evaluate a function and approximate zeros. A program for evaluating a certain function is given and students are asked to modify the program to find the values of other functions.

Technology, p. 27

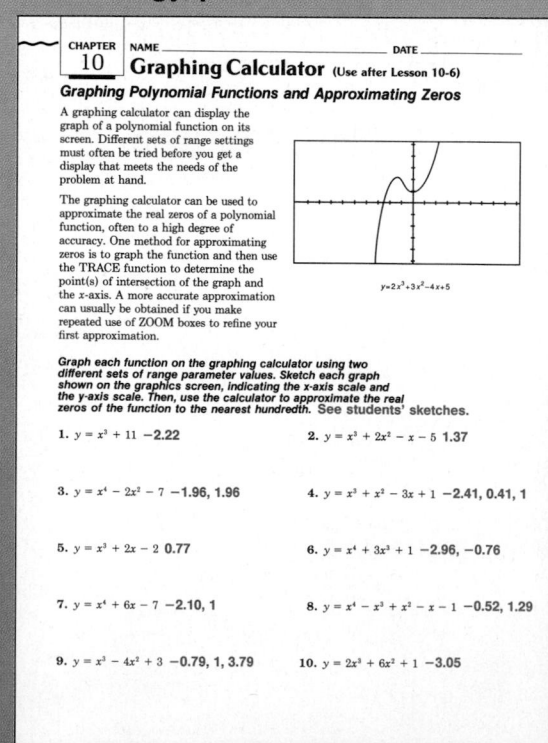

Critical Thinking

Everyday problems outside the classroom frequently require skills in divergent thinking to solve. This often is contrary to the classroom experiences of many students. For example, when faced with a problem in a classroom situation, students most often focus on what *is* the solution rather than on what *is not* the solution. To help develop divergent thinking, provide a straight-back chair as a model and have students draw it, not by drawing the chair but by drawing what is *not* the chair. They will recognize that this consists primarily of geometric figures which if drawn correctly will result in a fairly professional drawing of the chair.

The card shown below is one of two available for this chapter. It can
be used as a class or small group activity.

Activity Card

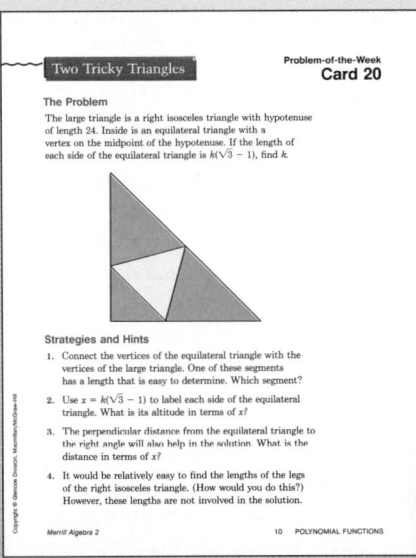

Multicultural Activity, p. 10

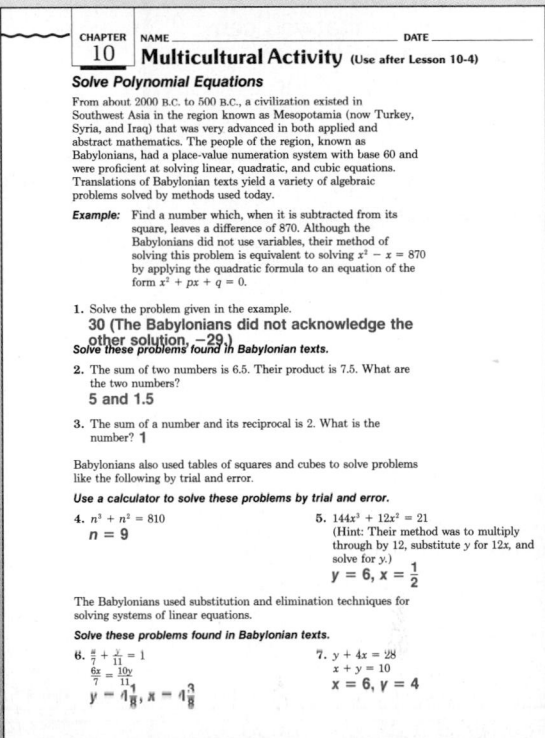

Manipulatives and Models

The following materials may be used as models or manipulatives in
Chapter 10.

- scientific calculator (Lesson 10-2)
- coins (Lesson 10-3)
- various containers (Lesson 10-5)
- tag board (Lesson 10-7)
- thermometers (Lesson 10-7)
- graph paper (Lesson 10-8)

Lab Manual

Lab Activity, pp. 61-62

Outside Resources

Books/Periodicals

Davis, Philip J. *The Mathematics of Matrices.* John Wiley and Sons, Inc.

Cushbaugh, Warren. *Polyominoes.* Charles Scribner's Sons.

Films/Videotapes/Videodiscs

*Addition & Subtraction of Rational Expressions, Multiplication & Division
of Rational Expressions,* and *Equations Involving Rational Expressions,*
parts of the Intermediate Algebra Series, Great Plains National
Instructional TV Library (GPN), P.O. Box 80669, Lincoln, NE 68501

Software

Superplot, EduSoft, P.O. Box 2560, Berkeley, CA 94702

Super Graph, Ventura Educational Systems, 3440 Brokenhill St.,
Newbury Park, CA 91320

Mathematics Exploration Toolkit, IBM, 4111 Northside Pkwy. NW,
P.O. Box 2150, Atlanta, GA 30327-3015

Background Information

Financial planners may prepare financial reports; oversee accounting, audit, and budget departments; or, monitor and control the flow of cash receipts and disbursements and other financial investments. Some become involved in international accounting. Financial analysis and management have been revolutionized by technological improvements in computers and data processing equipment. Mathematics is the foundation upon which the field of financial planning is based. Throughout the 1990s, there will continue to be a growing need for skilled financial planning with variety and complexity.

Chapter Project

Materials: paper, graph paper, pencil, newspapers, and library resources

Organize students into three, or multiples of three, groups of financial planners. Instruct students that each group represents an independent firm of financial planners. Assign each group to an imaginary client whom you categorize as either a "low-risk" investor, a "moderate-risk" investor, or a "high-risk" investor. The object of the project is for each "firm" to put together a mix of investments

CHAPTER

10 Polynomial Functions

CHAPTER OBJECTIVES

In this chapter, you will:

- Find factors and zeros of polynomials.
- Approximate real zeros of and graph polynomial functions.
- Find the composition of functions.
- Determine the inverse of a function or relation.

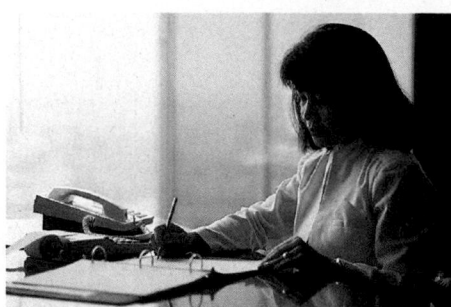

The diagram below shows sources of money flowing into a person's life and where it goes. Which of these inflows and outflows do you have? Which ones do you anticipate once you are living on your own?

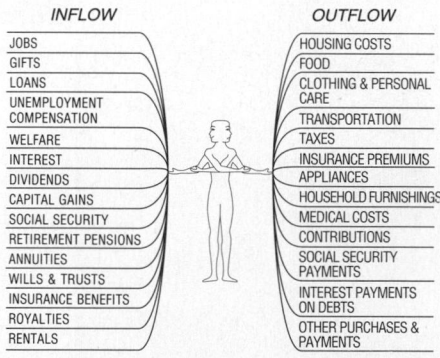

CAREERS IN FINANCIAL PLANNING

Does money fascinate you? Well, of course. But here's the question that separates future financial planners from everyone else: Would you rather save money and watch it grow than buy things with it? If you can honestly say yes, then financial planning may be for you. A good financial planner sees money as a garden to tend, not a treasure to spend.

Some financial planners work for institutions such as banks, credit unions, savings and loan associations, and finance companies. There they meet with individuals and families. They help their clients analyze cash flow (where it comes from, where it goes), taxes, savings, real estate, retirement plans, planning for college educations, investments, insurance, debts—in short, everything financial. Some people are rather haphazard about these matters. It's the financial planner's job to bring all the loose ends together into one big picture: the client's future financial security.

Other financial planners work for large corporations, setting and implementing financial policy for the firms.

Whatever the level, financial planners watch the money. If you think you could be responsible for the health and growth of major money, then you might want to think seriously about this career.

448

that will provide the greatest return on its client's capital. Have each group research each of the following investments: banking, insurance, real estate, and securities. Assign each group the responsibility of developing a financial mix of investments

appropriate to its client's level of risk. Have each group begin with the same amount of investment capital, say $100,000. Have each group follow and calculate the status of its investment mix on a daily and weekly basis and report the status weekly.

Lesson	Connections (C) and Applications (A)	Examples	Exercises
10-1	A: Biology	2	
	Energy		58
	Art		59
	Sports		65
10-2	A: Financial		43
	Planning		
	Physics		44
10-4	A: Manufac-		35, 36
	turing		
	Health		40
10-5	C: Geometry	2	36
	A: Manufac-		45
	turing		
	Food		46
	Production		
10-6	A: Aerospace		34
	Engineer-		
	ing		
	Pharmacy		35
10-7	A: Chemistry		34
	Business		35
10-8	C: Geometry		28
	A: Business		39

MORE ABOUT FINANCIAL PLANNING

Degree Required:

- Bachelor's Degree in accounting

Some financial planners like:

- seeing people succeed financially as a result of their advice
- challenge and variety in working with people
- potentially high salary

Related Math Subjects:

- Algebra
- Advanced Math
- Probability/Statistics

Some financial planners dislike:

- the competition
- economic uncertainties
- constant changes in federal and state regulations on finance

For more information on the various careers available in the field of Financial Planning, write to:

American Economics Association
1313 21st Avenue, South
Nashville, TN 37212

449

INTRODUCING THE LESSON

 5-Minute Check

(over Chapter 9)

1. Find the distance between (3, 6) and (7, −8). $2\sqrt{53}$
2. Find the midpoint of the line segment whose endpoints are $A(17, -8)$ and $B(-13, 1)$.
$\left(2, -\dfrac{7}{2}\right)$
3. State whether the graph of $(x - 3)^2 = 4y - 4$ is a parabola, a circle, an ellipse, or a hyperbola. **parabola**
4. Find the solution of the system of equations.
$(x - 2)^2 + y^2 = 16$
$y - x = 2$ **(−2, 0), (2, 4)**
5. Find the equation of the parabola with vertex at (6, −1) and focus at (3, −1).
$x = -\dfrac{1}{12}(y + 1)^2 + 6$

Motivating the Lesson

Have students list objects that increase in value over time. Such items should include stamps, antique cars, and paintings with high rates of appreciation such as 10% to 20%. Discuss how to compute the total value of an object using the formula $A = P(1 + r)^t$ where P is the original amount, A is the amount of money at the end of a specified time, t is time in years, and r is the yearly interest rate.

10-1 Polynomial Functions

Objectives

After studying this lesson, you should be able to:

10-1A ▪ evaluate polynomial functions, and

10-1B ▪ identify general shapes of the graphs of polynomial functions.

Application

The number of times that a cricket chirps in an hour is a function of the temperature described by $f(t) = \dfrac{t}{0.2} - 32$, where $f(t)$ is the number of chirps in relation to the temperature t in degrees Celsius. The brightness of the light that fireflies produce is also a function of the temperature. An approximate formula for the intensity of their light, $I(t)$, in lumens is $I(t) = 10 + 0.3t + 0.4t^2 - 0.01t^3$, where t represents the temperature in degrees Celsius. The expression $10 + 0.3t + 0.4t^2 - 0.01t^3$ is a **polynomial in one variable.**

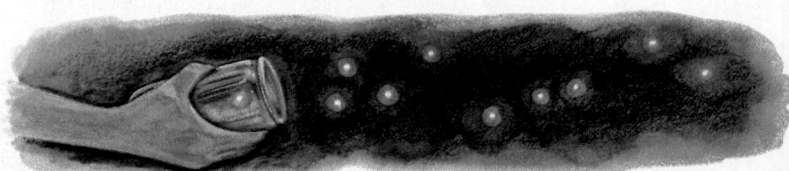

Definition of Polynomial in One Variable

A polynomial in one variable, x, is an expression of the form $a_0x^n + a_1x^{n-1} + ... + a_{n-2}x^2 + a_{n-1}x + a_n$. The coefficients a_0, a_1, a_2, ..., a_n represent complex numbers (real or imaginary), a_0 is not zero, and n represents a nonnegative integer.

Teaching Tip ❶

Example 1

 FYI ...

A lumen is a unit of the rate of flow of light energy from a source. A typical 100-watt light bulb emits 1750 lumens.

Determine if each expression is a polynomial in one variable.

a. $8x^5 + 6x^4 - 2x^2 + x - 9$

   This is a polynomial in one variable, x.

b. $8a^2b^4 + 2ab^2 - 1$

   This is not a polynomial in one variable. It contains two variables, a and b.

c. $x^2 + 2x - \dfrac{1}{x}$

   This is not a polynomial in one variable, because the term $\dfrac{1}{x}$ cannot be written in the form x^n with n a nonnegative integer.

d. $10 - 2a + 6a^2$

   This is a polynomial in one variable, a.

450   CHAPTER 10   POLYNOMIAL FUNCTIONS

ALTERNATE TEACHING STRATEGIES

Using Critical Thinking

Explain the difference between an odd degree function, $f(x) = x^3 + 3x^2 + 4x - 5$, and an odd function, $f(x) = f(-x)$. Also explain the difference between an even degree function, $f(x) = x^4 - 2x^3 + 4x^2 + 3x - 2$, and an even function, $f(x) = -f(x)$.

Using Connections

Students should be able to distinguish among integers, the rational numbers, and irrational numbers in the set of real numbers, and the real numbers and imaginary numbers in the set of complex numbers. There will be certain situations in which rational zeros and real zeros are discussed. They need to know the difference.

In Chapter 7, we said that the degree of a quadratic equation is 2. The degrees of other polynomials can also be found. The degree of a polynomial in one variable is the greatest exponent of its variable.

9 has degree 0. *Remember that $9 = 9x^0$.*
$x + 1$ has degree 1. *Remember $x = x^1$.*
$2x^2 + 4x - 8$ has degree 2.
$7x^6 - 1$ has degree 6.
$a_0x^n + a_1x^{n-1} + ... + a_{n-2}x^2 + a_{n-1}x + a_n$ has degree n.

Some of the polynomials in one variable have special names. As you know, a polynomial in one variable of degree 0 is called a **constant.** Polynomials in one variable of degree 1 are **linear expressions,** of degree 2 are **quadratic expressions,** and of degree 3 are **cubic expressions.**

When a polynomial equation is used to represent a function, it is a **polynomial function.** For example, the equation $f(x) = 3x^2 - 8x + 7$ represents a quadratic polynomial function, and the equation $p(x) = 2x^3 + 6x^2 - 5x + 3$ represents a cubic polynomial function. These and other polynomial functions can all be defined by the following general rule.

Definition of Polynomial Function	A polynomial function can be described by an equation of the form $P(x) = a_0x^n + a_1x^{n-1} + ... + a_{n-2}x^2 + a_{n-1}x + a_n$. The coefficients $a_0, a_1, ... , a_{n-1}$, and a_n represent real numbers, a_0 is not zero, and n represents a nonnegative integer.

The graphs of several polynomial functions are shown below. Notice how many times the graph of each function intersects the x-axis. In each case, this is the maximum number of real zeros the function may have.

constant function
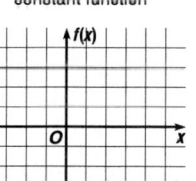

linear function
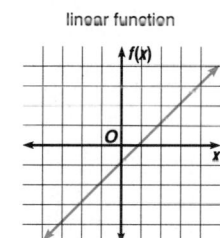

quadratic function
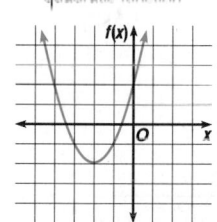

cubic function
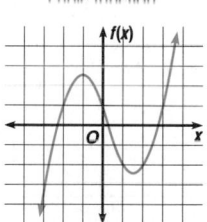

If you know an element in the domain of any polynomial function, you can find the corresponding value in the range. Remember that if $f(x)$ is the function and 4 is an element in the domain, the corresponding element in the range is $f(4)$. Its value is found when the function is evaluated for $x = 4$.

LESSON 10-1   POLYNOMIAL FUNCTIONS   451

Teaching Tip **❶**   You may want to list several polynomials and state the values of n, a_0, ... a_n for each polynomial to help students understand the notation.

Chalkboard Example

For Example 1
Determine if each expression is a polynomial in one variable.

a. $x^2 + 2xy + y^2$ **no**

b. $2a^2 - 2a + \frac{1}{4}$ **yes**

c. $12 - \frac{2}{n} + n^2$ **no**

Example 2

Using the polynomial function for the intensity of the light of a firefly that was given at the beginning of the lesson, find the intensity of the light emitted by a firefly when the temperature is 20°C.

$$I(t) = 10 + 0.3t + 0.4t^2 - 0.01t^3$$
$$I(20) = 10 + 0.3(20) + 0.4(20)^2 - 0.01(20)^3 \quad \text{Substitute 20 for } t.$$
$$I(20) = 10 + 6 + 160 - 80 \quad \text{Evaluate.}$$
$$I(20) = 96$$

The intensity of the light at 20°C is 96 lumens.

Example 3

Find $p(a + 1)$ if $p(x) = 4x - x^2 + 2x^3$.

$$p(a + 1) = 4(a + 1) - (a + 1)^2 + 2(a + 1)^3 \quad \text{Substitute } a + 1 \text{ for } x.$$
$$= 4a + 4 - (a^2 + 2a + 1) + 2(a^3 + 3a^2 + 3a + 1)$$
$$= 2a^3 + 5a^2 + 8a + 5$$

Example 4

Find $4[p(x)] + 3[p(x + 2)]$ if $p(x) = x^3 + 2x^2 - 4$.

$$4[p(x)] + 3[p(x + 2)]$$
$$= 4[x^3 + 2x^2 - 4] + 3[(x + 2)^3 + 2(x + 2)^2 - 4]$$
$$= 4x^3 + 8x^2 - 16 + 3[(x^3 + 6x^2 + 12x + 8) + (2x^2 + 8x + 8) - 4]$$
$$= 4x^3 + 8x^2 - 16 + 3[x^3 + 8x^2 + 20x + 12]$$
$$= 7x^3 + 32x^2 + 60x + 20$$

The coefficient of the term with the highest degree in a polynomial function is called the leading coefficient. The general shapes of the graphs for polynomial functions with positive leading coefficients and degree greater than 0 are shown below.

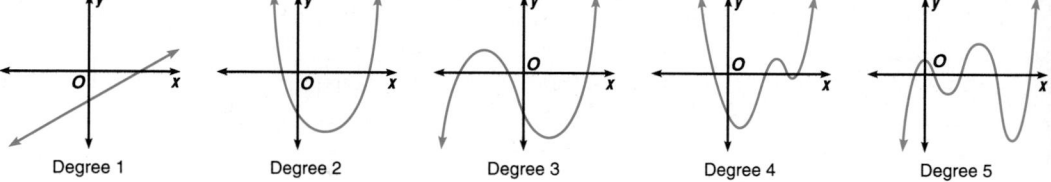

Degree 1   Degree 2   Degree 3   Degree 4   Degree 5

Study the graphs of the odd degree functions. The leftmost points of the graphs of odd degree functions have negative values for *y*. The rightmost points of the graphs of those functions have positive values for *y*.

Now study the graphs of the even degree functions. The leftmost points of the graphs have positive values for y as do the rightmost points of the graphs.

Another pattern can be observed in the graphs of polynomial functions. The simplest polynomial graphs are those with equations in the form $f(x) = x^n$, where n is a positive number. Observe the general shape of even degree polynomial functions and odd degree polynomial functions.

even degree polynomial functions

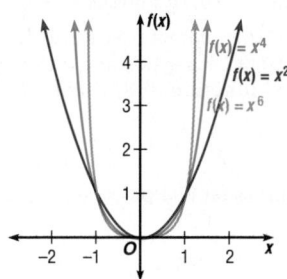

odd degree polynomial functions

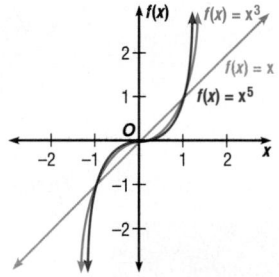

Note that these even degree functions intersect the x-axis once. An even degree function may or may not intersect the x-axis depending on its location in the coordinate plane. However, an odd degree function will always cross the x-axis at least once. Remember that where the graph crosses the x-axis is called a zero of the function. On the coordinate plane, these zeros are real numbers.

Example 5

Determine if each graph represents an odd degree function or an even degree function. Then state how many real zeros each function has.

a.
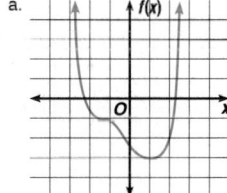

b.
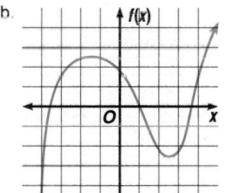

c.
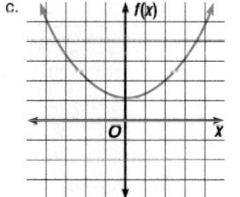

Graph	leftmost y values	rightmost y values	degree of function	times graph crosses x-axis	number of real zeros
a.	pos.	pos.	even	2	2
b.	neg.	pos.	odd	3	3
c.	pos.	pos.	even	0	0

For Example 5

Determine if each graph represents an odd degree function or an even degree function. Then state the number of real zeros.

a.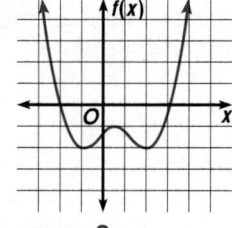

even; 2

b.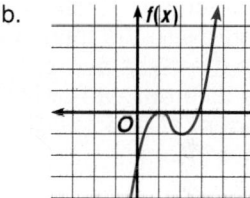

odd; 2

EVALUATING THE LESSON

Checking for Understanding
Exercises 1–21 are designed to help you assess understanding through reading, writing, and speaking. You should work through Exercises 1–4 with your students, and then monitor their work on Exercises 5–21.

Closing the Lesson
Speaking Activity Have students form small groups. Give each group the same principal and a different rate of interest and ask them to determine the amount of the total investment. Each group will then share the total investment with the class and discuss how the different rates with the same amount of principal will provide greater income.

APPLYING THE LESSON

Homework Exercises

Assignment Guide
Basic: 22–48, 57–65
Average: 24–52, 57–65
Enriched: 26–65

Reteaching Masters Booklet, p. 64

CHECKING FOR UNDERSTANDING

Communicating Mathematics

Read and study the lesson to answer these questions.

1. Write two expressions, one that is a polynomial in one variable and one that is not. Explain why one is a polynomial in one variable and one is not. **Answer may vary.**
2. Is $f(x) = x^3 - 2x + 4$ a polynomial expression or a polynomial function? **2. polynomial function**
3. What would the intensity of the light emitted by a firefly be if the temperature is 15°C? **70.75 lumens**
4. What are some of the characteristics of the graphs of odd degree polynomial functions? How do they differ from the graphs of even degree polynomial functions? **See margin.**

Guided Practice

Determine if each expression is a polynomial in one variable. If it is, state its degree.

5. $3x^3 - 4x^5 - 6x^2 + 3x$ **yes, 5**   6. $3a + 5b - 1$ **no**
7. 14 **yes, 0**   8. $x^2 - 8x + 9$ **yes, 2**
9. $xy\sqrt{2} + 3$ **no**   10. $6n^3 - 4n + 9$ **yes, 3**
11. $\frac{9}{t} + t + 3$ **no**   12. $13x^2 - 3x + 14$ **yes, 2**
13. $x^3 + 5x^2 + x\sqrt{3} + 2$ **yes, 3**   14. $(8 + 2i)x^2 + (1 - i)x - 8$ **no**

Find $p(2)$ for each function $p(x)$.

15. $p(x) = 4x + 2$ **10**   16. $p(x) = 2x^2 + 6x - 8$ **12**
17. $p(x) = 4x^3 - 2x^2 + x - 1$ **25**   18. $p(x) = \frac{x^2}{4} - 4x + 11$ **4**

Determine whether the degree of the function represented by each graph is even or odd. How many real zeros does each polynomial function have?

19. 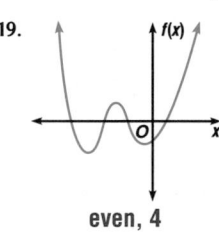   20. 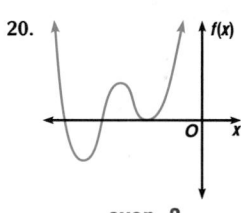   21.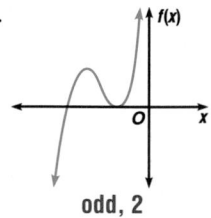

even, 4   even, 3   odd, 2

EXERCISES

Practice

Ⓐ Find $p(2)$ for each function, $p(x)$.

22. $p(x) = 2x^4 - 3x^3 + 8$ **16**   23. $p(x) = -3x^4 + 1$ **-47**
24. $p(x) = x^5 - x^2$ **28**   25. $p(x) = -x^6 + 12$ **-52**

RETEACHING THE LESSON

To focus on the scheme for naming coefficients in a polynomial, ask for the exponent of x for the term with coefficient a_r, $(a_r x^?)$.
$n - r$
Contrast the scheme given with
$b_n x^n + b_{n-1} x^{n-1} + b_{n-2} x^{n-2} + \ldots b_r x^r + \ldots b_1 x + b_0$.

Additional Answer

4. The leftmost values of y on the graph of an odd degree function are negative and the rightmost are positive. Even degree functions have positive values for y, both leftmost and rightmost.

Find $f(-5)$ for each function $f(x)$.

26. $f(x) = 3 - 2x$ **13**
27. $f(x) = 6x + 9$ **-21**
28. $f(x) = 3x^2$ **75**
29. $f(x) = x^2 - 2x + 1$ **36**
30. $f(x) = x^3 + 4x^2 + x + 15$ **-15**
31. $f(x) = x^4 + 10x$ **575**
32. $f(x) = \frac{x^4}{25} - 2$ **23**
33. $f(x) = 30 - \frac{x^3}{6}$ **$\frac{305}{6}$**

Find $f(x + h)$ for each function $f(x)$. **37–39. See margin.**

34. $f(x) = x + 1$ **$x + h + 1$**
35. $f(x) = 2x - 3$ **$2x + 2h - 3$**
36. $f(x) = 4x^2$ **$4x^2 + 8xh + 4h^2$**
37. $f(x) = x^2 - 2x + 5$
38. $f(x) = x^2 - \frac{1}{2}x$
39. $f(x) = x^3 + 4x$
40. $f(x) = \frac{4}{3}x^3 - 1$
41. $f(x) = 2x^3 - x^2 + 4$

$\frac{4}{3}x^3 + 4hx^2 + 4h^2x + \frac{4}{3}h^3 - 1$ **$2x^3 + 6hx^2 + 6h^2x + 2h^3 - x^2 - 2hx - h^2 + 4$**

Find $4[p(x)]$ for each function $p(x)$.

42. $p(x) = 2x - 4$ **$8x - 16$**
43. $p(x) = x^2 + 5$ **$4x^2 + 20$**
44. $p(x) = 6x^3 - 4x^2 + 2$
   $24x^3 - 16x^2 + 8$
45. $p(x) = \frac{x^3}{4} + \frac{x^2}{16} - 2$
   $x^3 + \frac{x^2}{4} - 8$

Determine whether the degree of the function repeated by each graph is even or odd. How many real zeros does each polynomial function have?

46.
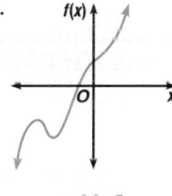
odd, 1

47.
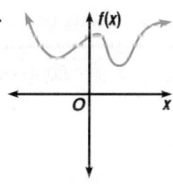
even, 0

48.
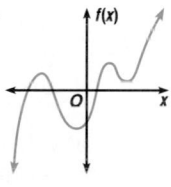
odd, 3

Find $2[f(x + 3)]$ for each function $f(x)$.

49. $f(x) = 3x + 8$ **$6x + 34$**
50. $f(x) = x^2 - 8$ **$2x^2 + 12x + 2$**
51. $f(x) = x^2 + 6x - 18$
   $2x^2 + 24x + 18$
52. $f(x) = \frac{1}{2}x^2 - \frac{3}{4}$ **$x^2 + 6x + \frac{15}{2}$**

Teaching Tip ❷

Find $2[p(x)] - 3[p(x + 1)]$ for each function $p(x)$.   **$-x^2 + x + 2$**

53. $p(x) = 5x - 7$ **$-5x - 8$**
54. $p(x) = x^2 - 7x + 16$
55. $p(x) = x^3 + 1$
   $-x^3 - 9x^2 - 9x - 4$
56. $p(x) = (x - 2)^3$
   $-x^3 - 3x^2 + 15x - 13$

LESSON 10-1 POLYNOMIAL FUNCTIONS 455

Additional Answers

37. $x^2 + 2xh + h^2 - 2x - 2h + 5$

38. $x^2 + 2xh + h^2 - \frac{1}{2}x - \frac{1}{2}h$

39. $x^3 + 3hx^2 + 3h^2x + h^3 + 4x + 4h$

Practice Masters Booklet, p. 73

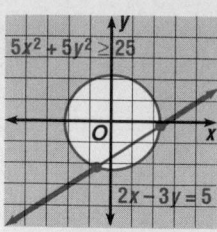
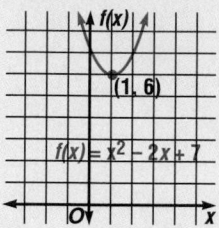
Critical Thinking

57. A super ball dropped from a height of 36 inches rebounds three-fourths of the distance of the previous bounce. Write an expression to represent the distance traveled by the ball in n bounces. Justify your answer.
   $d = 36 + 2[36(0.75) + 36(0.75)^2 + 36(0.75)^3 + ... + 36(0.75)^{n-1}]$

Applications

58. **Energy**   The power generated by a windmill is a function of the speed of the wind. The approximate power is given by the function $P(s) = \dfrac{s^3}{1000}$, where s represents the speed of the wind in kilometers per hour. Find the units of power generated by a windmill when the wind speed is 25 kilometers per hour.   **15.625 units**

59. **Art**   Joyce Cafaro purchases works of art for an art gallery. Two years ago she bought a painting for $20,000 and last year she bought one for $35,000. If these paintings appreciate at 14% per year, how much are these two pieces worth now?   **$65,892**

Mixed Review

60. Solve $\begin{cases} x^2 + y^2 = 5 \\ 2x^2 + y = 0 \end{cases}$.   **(Lesson 9-9)** $(1, -2), (-1, -2)$

61. Solve $\begin{cases} 5x^2 + 5y^2 \geq 25 \\ 2x - 3y = 5 \end{cases}$ by graphing.   **(Lesson 9-9)**   **See margin.**

62. Graph $f(x) = x^2 - 2x + 7$.   **(Lesson 8-3)**   **See margin.**

63. State whether the equation $5x^4 + 6x^3 = 9$ is in quadratic form. **(Lesson 7-6)**   **no**

64. Find values of x and y for which the equation $x + 2yi = 3$ is true. **(Lesson 6-9)** $x = 3, y = 0; x = 0, y = -\dfrac{3}{2}i$

65. **Sports**   Karl caught three times as many fish as Adam, and ten more fish than Sally. If the total number of fish caught was less than 100, what is the greatest number of fish that Karl could have caught? **(Lesson 2-6)**   **45 fish**

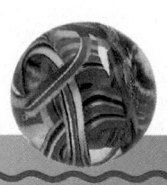

HISTORY CONNECTION

Karl Friedrich Gauss (1777–1855) was more than a famous adult mathematician. He displayed his mathematical talents as a child. His father, a gardener and bricklayer, taught Gauss his numbers at an early age. At the age of three, Gauss is said to have found a mathematical error in his father's ledgers of the total of his laborers' salaries. At the age of 10, when he entered school, his teacher asked the students to find the sum of 81297 + 81495 + 81693 + ... + 100899 to overwhelm them with the power of mathematics. Young Gauss stated the correct answer almost at the same time the teacher finished writing the problem on the board. While Gauss was brilliant, he did not like to publicize his thoughts. Many of the mathematical discoveries accredited to Gauss came from his diary, which was found after his death on February 23, 1855.

EXTENDING THE LESSON

Math Power: Reasoning

Find $\dfrac{f(x + h) - f(x)}{h}$ if $f(x) = x^4$.

$4x^3 + 6x^2h + 4xh^2 + h^3$

History Connection

The History Connection features introduce students to persons or cultures who were involved in the development of mathematics. You may want students to further research Gauss or to research other mathematicians who displayed advanced mathematical talents at an early age.

Graphing Calculator Exploration: Graphing Polynomial Equations

You can use your graphing calculator to graph polynomial functions and approximate the real zeros of a function. When using your calculator to approximate zeros, it is important to view a complete graph of the function before zooming-in on a certain point. Otherwise, zeros may be overlooked because they were not in the viewing window. Remember that a complete graph of the function shows all the characteristics of the graph, such as all x- and y-intercepts, relative maximum and minimum points, and the end behavior of the graph.

Example 1

Graph the function $f(x) = 3x^3 + 2x^2 - 8x + 7$, so that a complete graph appears in the viewing window. Then approximate each of the real zeros to the nearest hundredth.

Let's try graphing in the standard viewing window.

Casio

ENTER:  3

TI-81

ENTER:  3 + 2

/ GRAPH

Teaching Tip ②

This viewing window will not accommodate a complete graph. Change the viewing window to [4, 4] by [10, 30] with a scale factor of 1 for the x-axis and 2 for the y-axis and graph again by pressing EXE on the Casio or GRAPH on the TI-81.

This window can accommodate a complete graph.

According to the graph, there is one real zero to this function. There are three zeros for any third degree function, so two of the zeros for this function must be imaginary.

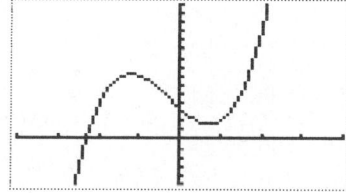

Use the tracing and the zoom-in features of the calculator to approximate the zero. The zero is approximately −2.28. *Check this result.*

GRAPHING CALCULATOR EXPLORATION: GRAPHING POLYNOMIAL EQUATIONS   457

INTRODUCING THE LESSON

Objective: Graph polynomial equations on a graphing calculator and approximate the real zeros of the equations.

Motivating the Lesson

Graph the equation $y = 5x^3 + 6x^2 - 4x + 12$ in the standard viewing window on a demonstration computer or graphing calculator overhead. Or have students graph it on their calculators. Is it really a line? **no** How do you know? **Because the highest power of the equation is x^3.** Then have your students change the y-max to 25. Now is it a line?

TEACHING THE LESSON

Teaching Tip ❶ Another way to raise x to the third power on the TI-81 is MATH 3.

Teaching Tip ❷ There are many viewing windows that will contain a complete graph. This is not the only one.

More Examples

Graph the function $y = -9x^3 + 21x^2 + x - 13$ so that a complete graph appears in the viewing window. Then approximate each of the real zeros to the nearest hundredth.
One viewing window is [−3, 3] by [−30, 10] with a scale factor of 1 for x and 5 for y. Zeros are −0.71, 1.00, and 2.04.

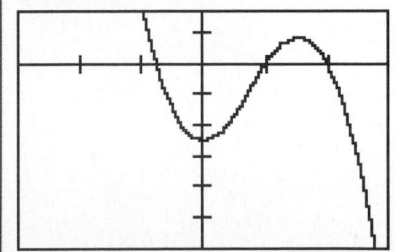

RETEACHING THE LESSON

If students are having difficulty understanding what a "real zero" is or why it is called a "real zero" tell them you are looking for points where the polynomial equals zero, or where $y = 0$. This is the same thing as setting the equation equal to zero and solving it.

Writing Activity Have students write a polynomial equation that has at least one real zero. Then have them graph the equation and approximate all the real zeros that it has. Also have them give a viewing window that shows a complete graph.

Homework Exercises

Assignment Guide

Basic: 1–14
Average: 2–28 even
Enriched: 7–29 odd, 30–32

When using your graphing calculator to approximate real zeros, it is helpful to know that a function with degree n has n zeros. This is a corollary to the Fundamental Theorem of Algebra, which you will study in Lesson 10-4. Since an nth degree function has n zeros, a function with degree 5 has 5 zeros. So, if you can see five x-intercepts in the viewing window you have all of the zeros in the window. However, these zeros may not all be real. Complex zeros occur in pairs of conjugates, so a fifth degree function may have five, three, or one real zero.

EXERCISES

Graph each function so the complete graph is shown. Then sketch the graph of the function and state how many real zeros the function has.

1–10. See students graphs.

1. $f(x) = x^3$ **1**
2. $g(x) = 4x^4 + 3$ **0**
3. $h(x) = 3x^3 + 2x - 1$ **1**
4. $r(x) = 6x^4 - 3x^2 + 7$ **0**
5. $m(x) = 7x^5 - 8x^4 + 1$ **3**
6. $f(x) = x^5 - 9x^4 + 6x^3 + x + 4$ **3**
7. $g(x) = -4x^4 + 9x + 2$ **2**
8. $h(x) = 2x^{11} + 6x^5 - 1$ **1**
9. $f(x) = x^4 + x^3 - 37x^2 - 64x + 84$ **4**
10. $n(x) = 7x^9 + 4x^7 - 3x^5 + 9x^3 - 1$ **1**

Graph each function so the complete graph is shown. Then approximate each of the real zeros to the nearest hundredth.

11. $f(x) = x^3 - 3$ **1.44**
12. $g(x) = x^3 - 5$ **1.71**
13. $g(x) = x^3 - 4x + 4$ **-2.38**
14. $h(x) = -7x^3 - 6x + 1$ **0.162**
15. $f(x) = x^3 - 2x^2 + 6$ **-1.34**
16. $f(x) = x^3 - x^2 + 1$ **-0.75**
17. $f(x) = x^5 - 6$ **1.43**
18. $nx = x^4 + 3x^3 - 4x^2 - 7$
19. $m(x) = 3x^4 - x^2 + x - 1$
20. $g(x) = x^4 - 4x^3 - 4x^2 + 24x - 6$
21. $p(x) = x^4 - x^2 + 6$ **no real zeros**
22. $p(x) = 2x^5 + 3x - 2$ **0.61**
23. $r(x) = x^4 - x^2 - 6$ **1.73, -1.73**
24. $f(x) = x^3 + 2x^2 - 3x - 5$
25. $g(x) = x^5 - x^3 - x + 1$
26. $h(x) = 3x^3 - 16x^2 + 12x + 6$
27. $f(x) = x^4 - 4x^2 + 3$
28. $c(x) = x^4 - 10x^2 + 21$
29. $m(x) = x^5 - 3x^4 + x^3 + 5x^2 - 6x - 1$ **-1.33, -0.15, 2.09**
30. $n(x) = x^4 - 9x^3 + 25x^2 - 24x + 6$ **0.38, 1.27, 2.62, 4.73**
31. $q(x) = x^5 + 4x^4 - x^3 - 9x^2 + 3$ **-3.60, -1.62, -0.66, 0.62, 1.31**
32. $r(x) = x^5 + 2x^4 - 10x^3 - 20x^2 + 9x + 15$
    -2.93, -2.19, -0.83, 0.93, 3.10

18. -4.08, 1.54
19. -1, 0.72
20. -2.38, 0.27
24. -2.38, -1.27, 1.65
25. -1.38, 0.82, 1
26. -0.34, 1.38, 4.39
27. -1.73, -1, 1, 1.73
28. -2.65, -1.73, 1.73, 2.65

Math Power:
Problem Solving

Explore finding the complex zeros of a cubic equation. Graph the equation $y = 4x^3 - 11x^2 + 9$ in the viewing window of $[-5, 5]$ by $[-10, 25]$. Then trace to find the real zero at $x = -3$. Then divide the equation by $x + 3$ (since $x + 3 = 0$) and you are left with $4x^2 - x + 3 = 0$. Use the quadratic formula to solve for x and obtain the solutions $x = \frac{1 \pm \sqrt{-47}}{8}$ or $\frac{1 \pm i\sqrt{47}}{8}$. Explain that these are complex roots because the radical contains a negative number. This can help demonstrate why complex zeros occur in pairs.

10-2 The Remainder and Factor Theorems

Objective
10-2

After studying this lesson, you should be able to:
- find factors of polynomials using the Factor Theorem and synthetic division.

Application

Chris Sabo of the Cincinnati Reds hits a high fastball straight up over home plate. The function that describes the height of the ball after t seconds is $h(t) = -16t^2 + 80t + 5$. The graph at the right shows this function. The roots of the function tell at what times the ball is theoretically on the ground. Notice that when $t = 0$, the height of the ball is 5 feet. This is the point at which he hit the ball.

Suppose we find the height of the ball after 4 seconds.

$h(t) = -16t^2 + 80t + 5$
$h(4) = -16(4^2) + 80(4) + 5$ *Replace t with 4.*
$= -256 + 320 + 5$
$= 69$

After 4 seconds, the height of the ball is 69 feet.

Now let's divide the polynomial in the function by $t - 4$, and compare the remainder to $h(4)$.

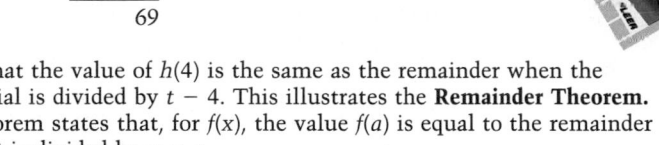

long division

$$
\begin{array}{r}
-16t + 16 \\
t - 4 \overline{\smash{)}\, -16t^2 + 80t + 5} \\
\underline{-16t^2 + 64t} \\
16t + 5 \\
\underline{16t - 64} \\
69
\end{array}
$$

synthetic division

$$
\begin{array}{r|rrr}
4 & -16 & 80 & 5 \\
 & & -64 & 64 \\
\hline
 & -16 & 16 & 69
\end{array}
$$

Notice that the value of $h(4)$ is the same as the remainder when the polynomial is divided by $t - 4$. This illustrates the **Remainder Theorem.** This theorem states that, for $f(x)$, the value $f(a)$ is equal to the remainder when $f(x)$ is divided by $x - a$.

LESSON 10-2 THE REMAINDER AND FACTOR THEOREMS   459

ALTERNATE TEACHING STRATEGIES

Using Discussion

You may want students to use calculators when performing the synthetic substitution computations. Discuss the fact that the degree of the depressed polynomial is always one less than the original polynomial if dividing by a first-degree binomial.

INTRODUCING THE LESSON

5-Minute Check
(over Lesson 10-1)

1. Find $f(4)$ if $f(x) = 3x^2 + 4x - 5$.   **59**
2. Find $3 \cdot p(x - 1)$ if $p(x) = x^2 - 4x - 9$. $3x^2 - 18x - 12$

Other Prerequisite Skills

3. Divide 4285 by 24. $178\frac{13}{24}$
4. Divide $(5m^3 - 3m^2 + 2m - 5) : (m + 2)$ using synthetic division. $5m^2 - 13m + 28 \quad \dfrac{61}{m+2}$
5. If a whole number is divided by 23, what is the greatest possible remainder?   **22**

Motivating the Lesson

Have students do two problems of division. One problem should be long division with whole numbers and the other problem should be long division with variables. Compare the steps of each problem.

If a polynomial $f(x)$ is divided by $x - a$, the remainder is the constant $f(a)$, and

$$\text{dividend} = \text{quotient} \cdot \text{divisor} + \text{remainder}$$
$$f(x) = q(x) \cdot (x - a) + f(a)$$

where $q(x)$ is a polynomial with degree one less than the degree of $f(x)$.

Teaching Tip ❶ Another way of interpreting the Remainder Theorem is:

For any polynomial $f(x)$, $f(a)$ is always the same value as the remainder when $f(x)$ is divided by $x - a$.

Chalkboard Examples

For Example 1

Show that $f(0)$ is the remainder when $f(x)$ is divided by x if $f(x) = x^3 - x^2 + x + 1$.

$$
\begin{array}{r|rrrr}
0 & 1 & -1 & 1 & 1 \\
  &   & 0 & 0 & 0 \\
\hline
  & 1 & -1 & 1 & \boxed{1}
\end{array}
$$

$f(0) = 0^3 - 0^2 + 0 + 1 = 1$
The result is the same as the remainder.

For Example 2

a. If $f(x) = x^4 - 6x^3 + 8x^2 + 5x + 13$, find $f(4)$.   **33**
b. If $f(x) = 3x^5 - 5x^3 + 57$, find $f(-2)$.   **1**

Example 1

Let $f(x) = 2x^4 + x^3 - 3x^2 - 5$. Show that $f(2)$ is the remainder when $f(x)$ is divided by $x - 2$.

Use synthetic division to divide by $x - 2$.

$$
\begin{array}{r|rrrrr}
2 & 2 & 1 & -3 & 0 & -5 \\
  &   & 4 & 10 & 14 & 28 \\
\hline
  & 2 & 5 & 7 & 14 & \boxed{23}
\end{array}
$$ *Long division could also be used.*

The quotient is $2x^3 + 5x^2 + 7x + 14$ with a remainder of 23.

Now find $f(2)$.
$$f(2) = 2(2)^4 + (2)^3 - 3(2)^2 - 5$$
$$= 32 + 8 - 12 - 5 \text{ or } 23$$

Thus, $f(2) = 23$, the same number as the remainder after division by $x - 2$.

As illustrated in Example 1, synthetic division can be used to find the value of a function. Synthetic division, when used to find the value of a function, is often called **synthetic substitution**. This is a very convenient way of finding the value of a function, especially when the degree of the polynomial is greater than two.

Example 2

If $f(x) = x^4 - 10x^3 + x^2 - 8x + 1$, find $f(10)$.

When $f(x)$ is divided by $x - 10$, the remainder is $f(10)$.

$$
\begin{array}{r|rrrrr}
10 & 1 & -10 & 1 & -8 & 1 \\
   &   & 10 & 0 & 10 & 20 \\
\hline
   & 1 & 0 & 1 & 2 & \boxed{21}
\end{array}
$$

Check: *Use direct substitution.*
$$f(10) = (10)^4 - 10(10)^3 + (10)^2 - 8(10) + 1$$
$$21 \overset{?}{=} 10{,}000 - 10{,}000 + 100 - 80 + 1$$
$$21 = 21 \checkmark$$

By *synthetic substitution*, $f(10) = 21$.

Consider $f(x) = x^4 + x^3 - 13x^2 - 25x - 12$. If $f(x)$ is divided by $x - 4$, then the remainder is zero. Therefore, 4 is a zero of $f(x)$.

$$
\begin{array}{r|rrrrr}
4 & 1 & 1 & -13 & -25 & -12 \\
  &   & 4 & 20 & 28 & 12 \\
\hline
  & 1 & 5 & 7 & 3 & \boxed{0}
\end{array}
$$

Check:
$$f(4) = (4)^4 + (4)^3 - 3(4)^2 - 25(4) - 12$$
$$0 = 256 + 64 - 208 - 100 - 12$$
$$0 = 0 \checkmark$$

From the results of the division and by using the Remainder Theorem, we can make the following statement.

$$\underset{\text{dividend}}{x^4 + x^3 - 13x^2 - 25x - 12} \underset{=}{=} \underset{\text{quotient} \cdot \text{divisor}}{(x^3 + 5x^2 + 7x + 3)(x - 4)} \underset{+ \text{remainder}}{+ \quad 0}$$

Since the remainder is zero, $x - 4$ is a factor of $x^4 + x^3 - 13x^2 - 25x - 12$. This illustrates the **Factor Theorem,** which is a special case of the Remainder Theorem.

The Factor Theorem	**The binomial $x - a$ is a factor of the polynomial $f(x)$ if and only if $f(a) = 0$.**

Suppose you wanted to find the zeros of $f(x) = x^3 + 3x^2 - 6x - 8$. From the graph at the right you find that the graph crosses the x-axis at -4, -1, and 2. These are the zeros of the function. Using these zeros and the zero product property, we can express the polynomial in factored form:

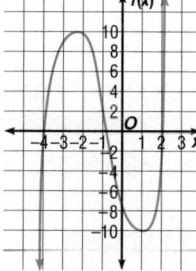

$$f(x) = (x + 4)(x + 1)(x - 2)$$

Many polynomial functions are not easily graphed and once graphed, the exact zeros are often difficult to determine. The Factor Theorem can help in finding all the factors of a polynomial. Suppose we wanted to determine if $x + 2$ is a factor of $x^3 - x^2 - 10x - 8$ and, if it is, what the other factors are.

Let $f(x) = x^3 - x^2 - 10x - 8$. If $x + 2$ is a factor of the polynomial, then -2 is a zero. Use the Factor Theorem.

$$
\begin{array}{r|rrrr}
-2 & 1 & -1 & -10 & -8 \\
   &   & -2 & 6 & 8 \\
\hline
   & 1 & -3 & -4 & 0 \\
\end{array}
$$

Since the remainder is 0, $x + 2$ is a factor of the polynomial. Further, since $x - 2$ is a factor of the polynomial, it follows that the remainder is 0.

When you divide a polynomial by one of its binomial factors, the quotient is called a **depressed polynomial.** In the polynomial above, $x^3 - x^2 - 10x - 8$ can be factored as $(x + 2)(x^2 - 3x - 4)$. The polynomial $x^2 - 3x - 4$ is the depressed polynomial, which also may be factorable.

$$x^2 - 3x - 4 = (x - 4)(x + 1)$$

So, $x^3 - x^2 - 10x - 8 = (x + 2)(x - 4)(x + 1)$.

EVALUATING THE LESSON

Checking for Understanding

Exercises 1–13 are designed to help you assess understanding through reading, writing, and speaking. You should work through Exercises 1–5 with your students, and then monitor their work on Exercises 6–13.

Error Analysis

Given two linear factors of $p(x)$, students sometimes divide $p(x)$ by one factor and then divide $p(x)$ again by the other factor. The second known factor should be divided into the depressed polynomial. Another error some students make is to not check for multiple factors.

Reteaching Masters Booklet, p. 65

Example 3 Show that $x + 2$ is a factor of $x^3 - 2x^2 - 5x + 6$. Then find any remaining factors.

−2| 1 −2 −5   6
   | −2   8 −6
   1 −4   3 | 0

The remainder is 0, so $x + 2$ is a factor of $x^3 - 2x^2 - 5x + 6$.

So, $x^3 - 2x^2 - 5x + 6 = (x^2 - 4x + 3)(x + 2)$.

Can the depressed polynomial be factored?

$x^2 - 4x + 3 = (x - 3)(x - 1)$

So, $x^3 - 2x^2 - 5x + 6 = (x - 3)(x - 1)(x + 2)$.

The graph of the polynomial function crosses the x-axis at 3, 1, and −2.

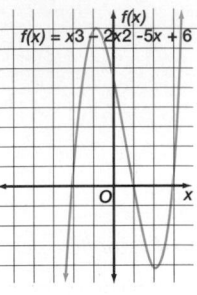

CHECKING FOR UNDERSTANDING

Communicating Mathematics

Read and study the lesson to answer each question.

1. When the polynomial function $f(x)$ is divided by $x - 4$, the remainder is 12. What is $f(4)$? **12**

2. What is a depressed polynomial? **See margin.**

3. If the divisor is a factor of a polynomial, then what is the remainder after division? **0**

4. In the baseball problem, approximately how long did the catcher have to get under the ball to catch the pop-up for an out? **about 5 seconds**

5. Suppose a depressed polynomial is a quadratic. What methods could you use to determine if the polynomial can be factored? **Answers will vary: quadratic formula, synthetic substitution, guess-and-check factoring, completing the square**

Guided Practice State the degree of each polynomial. Then state the degree of the depressed polynomial that would result from dividing the polynomial by one of its binomial factors in the form $x - a$.

6. $7x^3 - 4x^2 + 3x - 5$ **3, 2**   7. $x^5 - 3x^2 + 4$ **5, 4**
8. $x^2 - 2x - 9$ **2, 1**   9. $x^6 - 3x^5 + 5x^4 + 9$ **6, 5**

Use synthetic substitution to find $g(2)$ for each function g.

10. $g(x) = x^2 - 5$ **−1**   11. $g(x) = x^3 - 3x^2 + 4x + 8$ **12**
12. $g(x) = x^4 - 5x + 2$ **8**   13. $g(x) = x^2 - 4x + 4$ **0**

RETEACHING THE LESSON

1. Factor $p(x) = x^3 - 9x^2 + 26x - 24$ if $p(4) = 0$.
   $p(x) = (x - 4)(x - 2)(x - 3)$

2. Factor $p(x) = x^4 + x^3 - 31x^2 - 25x + 150$ if $p(2) = 0$.
   $p(x) = (x - 2)(x + 3)(x + 5)(x - 5)$

Additional Answer

2. the resulting polynomial after a polynomial undergoes division by a binomial of the form $x - r$

EXERCISES

Practice

Divide using synthetic division and write your answer in the form *dividend = quotient · divisor + remainder*. Is the binomial a factor of the polynomial? **14–21. See margin.**

14. $(x^3 - 4x^2 + 2x - 6) \div (x - 4)$ 15. $(x^3 - 8x^2 + 2x - 1) \div (x + 1)$

16. $(2x^3 + 8x^2 - 3x - 1) \div (x - 2)$ 17. $(x^4 - 16) \div (x - 2)$

18. $(x^3 + 27) \div (x + 3)$ 19. $(6x^3 + 9x^2 - 6x + 2) \div (x + 2)$

20. $(x^3 - 64) \div (x - 4)$ 21. $(4x^4 - 2x^2 + x + 1) \div (x - 1)$

Use synthetic substitution to find $f(2)$ and $f(-1)$ for each function f.

22. $f(x) = x^3 - 2x^2 - x + 1$ **-1, -1**   23. $f(x) = x^3 + 2x^2 - 3x + 1$ **11, 5**

24. $f(x) = 2x^2 - 8x + 6$ **-2, 16**   25. $f(x) = x^3 - 8x^2 - 2x + 5$ **-23, -2**

26. $f(x) = 3x^4 + 8x^2 - 1$ **79, 10**   27. $f(x) = x^4 + x^3 + x^2 + x + 1$ **31, 1**

Given a polynomial and one of its factors, find the remaining factors of the polynomial. Some factors may not be binomials. **Teaching Tip ❷**

28. x + 1, x + 2
29. x − 3, x − 1
30. x − 1, x + 6
31. x − 1, x + 2
32. x + 1, x − 3
33. x − 2,
**   x² + 2x + 4**

28. $x^3 + 2x^2 - x - 2; x - 1$ 29. $x^3 - 6x^2 + 11x - 6; x - 2$

30. $2x^3 + 17x^2 + 23x - 42; 2x + 7$ 31. $x^3 - 3x + 2; x - 1$

32. $x^3 - x^2 - 5x - 3; x + 1$ 33. $x^4 + 2x^3 - 8x - 16; x + 2$

34. $8x^4 + 32x^3 + x + 4; 2x + 1$ 35. $16x^5 - 32x^4 - 81x + 162; x - 2$
x + 4, 4x² − 2x + 1   **2x − 3, 2x + 3, 4x² + 9**

Use the graph of the polynomial function to determine at least one of the binomial factors of the polynomial. Then find all factors of the polynomial.

36. $x^5 + x^4 - 3x^3 - 3x^2 - 4x - 4$ 37. $x^5 + x^4 - x - 1$

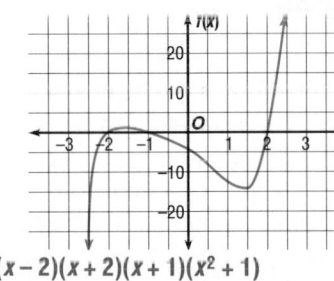   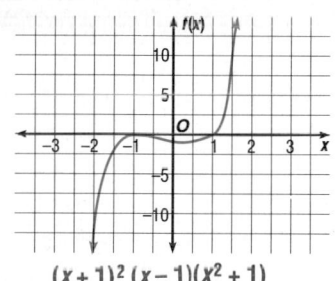

$(x-2)(x+2)(x+1)(x^2+1)$ $(x+1)^2(x-1)(x^2+1)$

Find values for k so that each remainder is 3.

38. $(x^2 + kx - 17) \div (x - 2)$ **8**   39. $(x^2 - x + k) \div (x - 1)$ **3**

40. $(x^3 + 4x^2 + x + k) \div (x + 1)$ **1**   41. $(x^2 + 5x + 7) \div (x + k)$ **1, 4**

Additional Answers

14. $(x^3 - 4x^2 + 2x - 6) =$ $(x^2 + 2)(x - 4) + 2$; no
15. $(x^3 - 8x^2 + 2x - 1) =$ $(x^2 - 9x + 11)(x + 1) - 12$; no
16. $(2x^3 + 8x^2 - 3x - 1) =$ $(2x^2 + 12x + 21)(x - 2) + 41$; no
17. $(x^4 - 16) = (x^3 + 2x^2 + 4x + 8)(x - 2) + 0$; yes
18. $(x^3 + 27) = (x^2 - 3x + 9)(x + 3) + 0$; yes
19. $(6x^3 + 9x^2 - 6x + 2) =$ $(6x^2 - 3x)(x + 2) + 2$; no
20. $(x^3 - 64) = (x^2 + 4x + 16)(x - 4) + 0$; yes
21. $(4x^4 - 2x^2 + x + 1) =$ $(4x^3 + 4x^2 + 2x + 3)(x - 1) + 4$; no

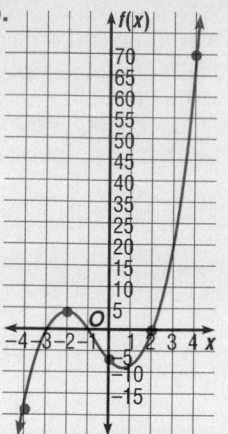
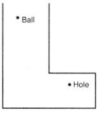
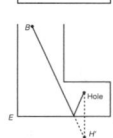 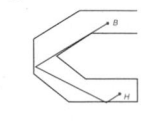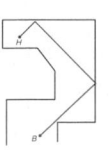
Critical Thinking

43a. $A = 1000(1 + r)^6$
$+ 1000(1 + r)^5$
$+ 1000(1 + r)^4$
$+ 1200(1 + r)^3$
$+ 1200(1 + r)^2$
$+ 2000(1 + r)$

42. Consider the function $f(x) = x^3 + 2x^2 - 5x - 6$.

a. Use synthetic substitution to find the values of $f(-4)$, $f(-2)$, $f(0)$, $f(2)$, and $f(4)$. **$f(-4) = -18$, $f(-2) = 4$, $f(0) = -6$, $f(2) = 0$, $f(4) = 70$**

b. On a coordinate plane, graph the ordered pairs of the form $(x, f[x])$ you found and connect them to make a smooth curve. **See margin.**

c. How many times does the graph cross the x-axis? Does this result agree with what you learned in Lesson 10-1 about the graphs of polynomial functions? **3 times, yes**

Applications

43. Financial Planning Jo Phillips, a financial advisor, is helping Ramon's parents develop a plan to save money for his college education. Ramon will start college in six years. According to Ms. Phillips's plan, Ramon's parents will save $1000 each year for the next three years. The fourth and fifth years they will save $1200 each year. The last year before he starts college, they will save $2000.

a. In the formula $A = P(1 + r)^t$, $A =$ the balance, $P =$ the amount invested, $r =$ the interest rate, and $t =$ the number of years the money has been invested. Use this formula to write a polynomial equation to describe the balance of the account when Ramon starts college.

b. Find the balance of the account if the interest rate is 6%. **$8916.76**

44a. when the rocket is on the ground

44. Physics A model rocket is shot straight up with an initial velocity of 64 meters per second. The height (in meters) of the rocket after t seconds is given by the function $h(t) = 64t - 4.9t^2$.

a. What do the solutions of the equation represent?

b. How long is the rocket in flight? **about 13 seconds**

Mixed Review

45. Find $f(2)$ for the function $f(x) = -3x^3 + 2$. **(Lesson 10-1)** **–22**

46. Find $3[p(x - 1)]$ for the function $p(x) = x^2 - 4$. **(Lesson 10-1)** **$3x^2 - 6x - 9$**

47. Find the center and radius of the circle whose equation is $(x + 4)^2 + y^2 = 49$. **(Lesson 9-3)** **(–4, 0); 7**

48. Solve the inequality $(y - 12)(y - 5) \leq 0$. **(Lesson 8-7)** **$\{y \mid 5 \leq y \leq 12\}$**

49. Solve the equation $169 = 9x^2$. **(Lesson 7-1)** **$\frac{13}{3}, -\frac{13}{3}$**

50. Evaluate $\dfrac{3^0 y + 4y^{-1}}{y^{-\frac{2}{3}}}$ when $y = 8$. **(Lesson 6-6)** **34**

51. Find the product $7\begin{bmatrix} 4 & 0 \\ 3 & -1 \end{bmatrix}$. **(Lesson 4-3)** **$\begin{bmatrix} 28 & 0 \\ 21 & -7 \end{bmatrix}$**

EXTENDING THE LESSON

Math Power: Reasoning

If $p(x) = 2x^3 + k^2x^2 - 4kx + 5$, find values for k so that $p(-1) = 0$.

–3 or –1

10-3 Problem-Solving Strategy: Combining Strategies

Objective
10-3

After studying this lesson, you should be able to:

■ solve problems by using more than one strategy.

Application

Suppose you wanted to know what is the largest amount of United States coins that you could have and still not be able to make correct change for a $1 bill. There are several ways you could attack this problem.

■ Make a list of all possible change combinations.
■ Make a table to record how many of each type of coin.
■ Work backwards by having change for $1 and then determine what coins you could substitute and/or add but still not have change for $1.
■ Model the problem with real coins, play money, or game pieces.

Whatever method you use, you will discover that two possibilities exist, both of which equal $1.19. They are

1 quarter, 9 dimes, 4 pennies and 3 quarters, 4 dimes, 4 pennies.

Many problems, like the one above, can be solved by using any one of a number of different strategies. Sometimes it takes more than one strategy to solve a problem.

Example

Mikhail has $3.21 to spend on pens. He knows the price of each pen is greater than 50¢. When he goes to the store, he is able to spend the exact amount of money he has on several pens. How many pens did he purchase? How much did each pen cost if each pen has the same price?

Let's find what strategies we can use to attack this problem. We could *list all the possibilities* of prices and then find multiples of each price. This strategy would work but it would be very time consuming.

We could *work backwards* from the total $3.21. If he bought 7 pens at 50¢, the total would be $3.50. This exceeds the maximum. So we know the number of pens has to be less than 7. From the problem, we know he bought more than 1 pen. So the answer must be either 2, 3, 4, 5, or 6.

Since we know that Mikhail spent all his money and each pen has the same price, we know that 321 is a multiple of some number. 321 is an odd number so we can *eliminate the possibility* of an even answer. This means the answer could be 3 or 5. 321 is a multiple of 3 and is not a multiple of 5. So 3 is the number of pens Mikhail bought, and by dividing we find that each pen costs $1.07.

LESSON 10-3 PROBLEM-SOLVING STRATEGY: COMBINING STRATEGIES 465

ALTERNATE TEACHING STRATEGIES

Mini-Math Lab
Give each group of students 7 coins that look alike but one of which is lighter in weight. Also give them a scale. Can they determine the fake coin in two weighings? Explain your solution.

Lesson Resources
Practice Master 10-3

Transparency 10-3 contains the 5-Minute Check and a teaching aid for this lesson.

INTRODUCING THE LESSON

5-Minute Check
(over Lesson 10-2)

1. If $f(x) = x^3 + 4x^2 + 3x - 2$, find $f(3)$. **70**
2. If $f(x) = x^4 - 4x^2 + 4$, find $f(-3)$. **49**
3. Divide $(x^3 - 4x^2 - 22x + 36)$ by $(x - 5)$. Write your answer in the form *dividend = quotient · divisor + remainder*.
   $x^3 - 4x^2 - 22x + 36 = (x^2 + x - 17)(x - 5) - 49$
4. Is $(x - 7)$ a factor of $x^3 - 2x^2 - 39x + 28$? **yes**
5. Is $(x + 2)$ a factor of $6x^3 + 9x^2 - 6x + 2$? **no**

Motivating the Lesson
Ask students if any of them work crossword puzzles or jigsaw puzzles. Ask them how they go about solving each type of puzzle. Make a list of all of the different strategies that are used.

TEACHING THE LESSON

Chalkboard Example
For the Example
A math quiz had 30 problems. Students received 2 points for each correct answer. They also lost 1 point for each incorrect or missing answer. Mike scored 24 points on the quiz. How many problems did Mike answer correctly? **18 problems**

Checking for Understanding

Exercises 1–4 are designed to help you assess understanding through reading, writing, and speaking. You should work through Exercises 1–3 with your students, and then monitor their work on Exercise 4.

Closing the Lesson

Writing Activity Write a paragraph explaining how strategies can be combined to solve a problem.

Teaching Tip ❶ You may want to remind students of the matrix logic lesson in Chapter 4.

Homework Exercises

Assignment Guide

Basic: 5–14
Average: 5–14
Enriched: 5–14

CHECKING FOR UNDERSTANDING

Communicating Mathematics

Read and study the lesson to answer each question. **1–3. See students' work.**

1. List all the problem solving strategies you can.

2. Which of these strategies do you think could be combined?

3. Which strategies would you use to solve the U.S. coin problem? Explain why you chose those strategies.

Guided Practice

4. Your algebra final exam has 120 questions. Your score is based on 1 point for each correct answer minus one-fourth point for each incorrect answer. Suppose you answered all the questions and got a score of 100 points. How many correct answers did you have? **104**

EXERCISES

Strategies

Look for a pattern.
Solve a simpler problem.
Act it out.
Guess and check.
Draw a diagram.
Make a chart.
Work backwards.

Solve. Use any strategy.

5. There are between 50 and 80 books on the shelf in the computer room. Exactly 20% of the books are on using BASIC and exactly one-seventh of the books are on fractal geometry. If possible, determine how many books there are in all. **70**

6. The square of an integer is a four-digit number whose digits are all even. Find the greatest such number. **92, the square is 8464**

7. Darcy is a math major at Indiana University. She is studying for finals with her friends, Janna and Ray at the university library. Janna is an English major and Ray is a sociology major. Ray said, "Isn't it funny that one of us is studying English, one math, and one sociology, but none of us is studying the subject that is our major?" The person studying English said, "So what?" Who is studying each subject? **Darcy—English, Janna—sociology, Ray—math** **Teaching Tip ❶**

8. Place addition signs in the left side of the equation below so that a true sentence results. **Answers will vary. See margin.**

$$9 \ 8 \ 7 \ 6 \ 5 \ 4 \ 3 \ 2 \ 1 = 99$$

9. Square $ABCD$ has an area of x square units. Each vertex is joined to the midpoint of one opposite side.

   a. What figure is formed in the center of the square? **a square**

   b. What is the area of this figure? $\frac{x}{5}$ **square units**

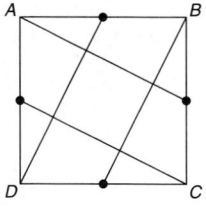

466 CHAPTER 10 POLYNOMIAL FUNCTIONS

Dr. Wise has three sons at three different colleges, each with a different major. John is not at Ohio State. Doug is not at Yale. The son at Ohio State is not majoring in history. The son at Yale is majoring in math. Doug is not majoring in biology. What is Tom majoring in and where? **biology at Ohio State**

Additional Answer

8. **Sample answers are 9 + 8 + 7 + 65 + 4 + 3 + 2 + 1 = 99 and 9 + 8 + 7 + 6 + 5 + 43 + 21 = 99.**

10. After half of the people at a Spanish Club meeting left, one-third of those remaining began to plan the club's Cinco de Mayo (5th of May) celebration. The other 18 people were cleaning up the room. How many people attended that meeting? **54**

11. In the figure at the right, assume all vertical lines are parallel, all angles are right angles, and all horizontal lines are equally distant. What part of the figure is shaded? **one-fourth**

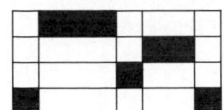

12. You are lost in the wilderness and are trying to get to the nearest town. You know that the people from the nearby village of Nallini are famous for always lying. The people from the village of Yassini always tell the truth. You have come to a fork in the road and there is a person from each of the two villages standing there. You don't know which person is which, so you choose one, point to the right, and ask "If I asked him whether or not this road leads to the nearest town, would he say yes?" "Yes he would" she replied. Should you head right or left at the fork? **left**

13. cube 1: 0, 1, 2, 6, 7, 8; cube 2: 1, 2, 0, 3, 4, 5. Nine can be formed by upside down 6.

13. The desk calendar shown at the right uses four cubes to show the month and the day. The two cubes in the center can be combined to make any date from 01 to 31. The cube on the right has 3 sides printed with the digits 3, 4, and 5. What digits are shown on the other sides and on the other cube? **Teaching Tip ❷**

14.

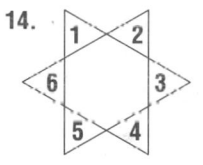

14. Arrange exactly six straws of the same length to form six congruent triangles.

COOPERATIVE LEARNING ACTIVITY

Work in groups. Each person in the group must understand the solution and be able to explain it to any person in class.

The polynomial equation below has at least one root that is an integer. Factor the polynomial completely and find all the roots of the equation.

$$x^6 + 2x^5 - 26x^4 - 28x^3 + 145x^2 + 26x - 120 = 0$$

$(x + 5)(x - 4)(x + 3)(x - 2)(x + 1)(x - 1);$ **-5, 4, -3, 2, -1, 1**

LESSON 10-3   PROBLEM-SOLVING STRATEGY: COMBINING STRATEGIES   467

EXTENDING THE LESSON

Math Power: Problem Solving

What would be the third entry in the 82nd row of this triangular number pattern?

```
            1
         2  3  4
      5  6  7  8  9
  10 11 12 13 14 15 16
               ⋮
```

The total number of numbers in 81 rows equals the sum, 1 + 3 + 5 + ... + (2n − 1), where n = 81. Hence the total number of these numbers is 81² or 6561. Add 3 to get the 3rd term in the 82nd row, which is 6564.

Cooperative Learning Activity

This activity provides students with an opportunity to *learn* things together, not just do things together. You may wish to refer to pages T6–T8 and page 6C for the various elements of cooperative groups and specific goals and strategies for using them.

Practice Masters Booklet, p. 75

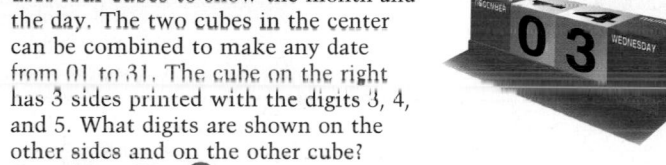

10-3 NAME _____ DATE _____
Practice Worksheet
Problem Solving
Use any strategy.

1. Alyson purchased a total of 12 muffins at a bakery and paid $7.80 (not including tax). Some of the muffins were bran muffins and cost $0.60 apiece. The other muffins were banana nut muffins and cost $0.75 apiece. How many muffins of each kind did she buy?
   8 bran muffins, 4 banana nut muffins

2. On the first day of school, Kyle lost his class schedule. He remembers that Math is not the first class. History is before English and Band. Band is after History and English. Neither Math or English is the fourth class, and Math is before English. Reconstruct Kyle's class schedule.
   1st: History
   2nd: Math
   3rd: English
   4th: Band

INTRODUCING THE LESSON

 5-Minute Check

(over Lesson 10-3)

1. In a certain basketball league, all field goals count two points each. In a recent game, Joe had one more field goal than Rob. Together they scored 38 points in field goals. How many field goals did each have? **Rob 9; Joe 10**

Motivating the Lesson

Bring in library books and encyclopedias containing biographies of two famous mathematicians, Gauss (1777–1855) and Descartes (1596–1650). One excellent book is *Men of Mathematics* by E. T. Bell. Have half of the students read about Gauss and the other half read about Descartes. Have them list their accomplishments.

10-4 Roots and Zeros

Objective 10-4

After studying this lesson, you should be able to:
- find the number of positive real zeros, negative real zeros, and complex zeros for a polynomial function.

Application

As part of an art class project, Carl is designing a carton for repackaging candy bars that the junior class will sell to raise money for the prom. The volume of the carton must be 120 in³. To hold the correct number of candy bars, the carton must be 3 inches longer than it is wide. The height of the carton should be 2 inches less than the width. Using these restrictions, Carl must determine the dimensions of the carton.

We can find the dimensions of the carton Carl is making by writing a polynomial equation. Then we can use the Factor Theorem and synthetic substitution.

First define each dimension of the carton in terms of the width w.

w = width $w + 3$ = length $w - 2$ = height

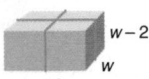

Let $V(w)$ be the function defining the volume.

$$V(w) = (w + 3)(w)(w - 2) \quad \text{\textit{volume} = lwh}$$
$$120 = w^3 + w^2 - 6w \quad \text{\textit{Substitute 120 for V(w) and multiply.}}$$
$$0 = w^3 + w^2 - 6w - 120 \quad \text{\textit{Subtract 120 from each side.}}$$

We will use a shortened form of synthetic substitution for several values of w to search for the solutions for $0 = w^3 + w^2 - 6w - 120$. The values for w are in the first column of the chart. Beside each value is the last line of the synthetic substitution. Recall that the first three numbers are the coefficients of the depressed polynomial. The last number in each row is the remainder. Study the chart below.

w	1	1	-6	-120
-1	1	0	-6	-114
0	1	1	-6	-120
1	1	2	-4	-124
2	1	3	0	-120
3	1	4	6	-102
4	1	5	14	-64
5	1	6	24	0
6	1	7	36	96

A remainder of 0 occurs when $r = 5$. This means that $w - 5$ is a factor of the polynomial. The depressed polynomial is $w^2 + 6w + 24$.

ALTERNATE TEACHING STRATEGIES

Using Communication

The number of real zeros of a polynomial function and the number of x-intercepts is the same for all polynomial functions. Point out that the zeros are used to write the factors of the polynomial. When there are 3 complex zeros of a function, the resulting polynomial would have degree 3.

The polynomial $w^3 + w^2 - 6w - 120$ can be factored as $(w - 5)(w^2 + 6w + 24)$. The trinomial $w^2 + 6w + 24$ cannot be factored.

$0 = w^3 + w^2 - 6w - 120$
$0 = (w - 5)(w^2 - 6w - 24)$ *How do you know w − 5 is a factor?*

Use the zero product property.

$w - 5 = 0$ or $w^2 - 6w + 24 = 0$
$w = 5$ $w = \dfrac{-(-6) \pm \sqrt{(-6)^2 - 4(1)(24)}}{2(1)}$ *Use the quadratic formula.*

$= \dfrac{6 \pm \sqrt{-60}}{2}$

$= \dfrac{6 \pm 2i\sqrt{15}}{2}$ or $3 \pm i\sqrt{15}$

Since imaginary solutions are not applicable to building a carton, use $w = 5$. The dimension of Carl's carton should be 5 inches wide by 5 + 3 or 8 inches long by 5 − 2 or 3 inches high. *Do these dimensions produce the correct volume?*

In Chapter 7, you learned that a **zero** of a function $f(x)$ is any value a such that $f(a) = 0$. This zero is also the **root** or solution of the equation formed when $f(x) = 0$. When the function is graphed, the real zeros of the function will be the x-intercepts of the graph. So you see these terms are interrelated.

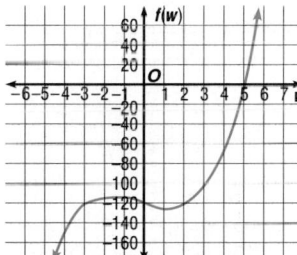

In the equation $w^3 + w^2 - 6w - 120 = 0$, the roots are 5, $3 + i\sqrt{15}$, and $3 - i\sqrt{15}$. One root is real and two are imaginary. The graph of $f(w) = w^3 + w^2 - 6w - 120$, shown at the left, crosses the x-axis only once, verifying that there is only one real root.

When you solve a polynomial equation you may have one or more real roots, or no real roots (the roots are imaginary). Remember that real numbers and imaginary numbers belong to the set of complex numbers. So, all polynomial equations have at least one root in the set of complex numbers. This is stated the **Fundamental Theorem of Algebra.** **Teaching Tip** ❶

Fundamental Theorem of Algebra	**Every polynomial equation with degree greater than zero has at least one root in the set of complex numbers.**

LESSON 10-4 ROOTS AND ZEROS **469**

TEACHING THE LESSON

Teaching Tip ❶ Remind students that the set of complex numbers includes the real numbers.

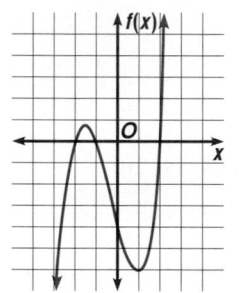
The following corollary of the Fundamental Theorem of Algebra is an even more powerful tool for problem solving.

Corollary	**A polynomial equation of the form $P(x) = 0$ of degree n has exactly n roots in the complex numbers.**

Example 1

FYI · · ·

Karl Friedrich Gauss (1777–1855) is credited with the first proof of the Fundamental Theorem of Algebra.

Find all roots of $0 = x^3 + 3x^2 - 6x - 8$.

We can find the roots of the equation by combining some of the strategies listed in Lesson 10-3. Let's list some of the possibilities for roots and then eliminate those that are not. Suppose we begin with integral values from -5 to 5 and use the shortened form of synthetic substitution. Because this polynomial has a degree of 3, the equation has 3 roots. However all of them may not be real.

You can use your calculator to find $f(a)$ quickly. To find $f(-5)$, duplicate the process of synthetic substitution on your calculator.

$$\underline{-5}\,|\quad 1\qquad 3\qquad -6\qquad -8\qquad \text{is processed by:}$$

ENTER: 5 [+/-] [STO] [×] 1 [+] 3 [=]   *After* [=] *the display is* -2.

[×] [RCL] [+] 6 [+/-] [=]   *After* [=] *the display is* 4.

[×] [RCL] [+] 8 [+/-] [=] -28

The display shown after each [=] gives the second, third, and fourth coefficients of the depressed polynomial. To evaluate $f(x)$ for other values for x, simply change the first number entered in the series of keystrokes shown above.

r	1	3	-6	-8
-5	1	-2	4	-28
-4	1	-1	-2	0
-3	1	0	-6	10
-2	1	1	-8	8
-1	1	2	-8	0
0	1	3	-6	-8
1	1	4	-2	-10
2	1	5	4	0

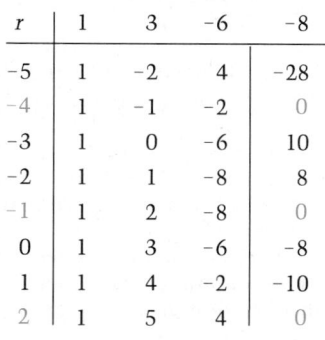

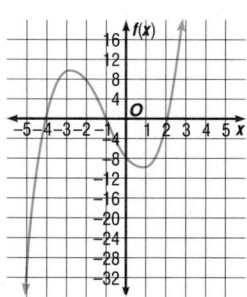

The zeros occur at $x = -4$, $x = -1$, and $x = 2$. The graph of the function verifies that there are three real roots.

Remember when you solved quadratic equations like $x^2 + 4 = 0$, there were always two imaginary roots. In this case, $2i$ and $-2i$ are the roots. These numbers are conjugate pairs. In any polynomial function, if an imaginary number is a zero of that function, its conjugate is also a zero.

Complex Conjugates Theorem	**Suppose a and b are real numbers with $b \neq 0$. Then, if $a + bi$ is a zero of a polynomial function, then $a - bi$ is also a zero of the function.**

Chalkboard Example

For Example 2
Given a function and one of its zeros, find the remaining zeros of the function.

a. $f(x) = x^3 - 7x^2 + 16x - 10$; $3 - i$ $3 + i$, 1
b. $g(x) = x^3 - 4x^2 + 6x - 4$; 2 $1 + i$; $1 - i$

Example 2
Teaching Tip ❷

Find all zeros of $f(x) = x^3 - 11x^2 + 40x - 50$ if $3 + i$ is one zero of $f(x)$.

Since $3 + i$ is a zero, $3 - i$ is also a zero. So, both $x - (3 + i)$ and $x - (3 - i)$ are factors of the polynomial $x^3 - 11x^2 + 40x - 50$.

$f(x) = [x - (3 + i)][x - (3 - i)](\underline{})$
    $= (x^2 - 6x + 10)(\underline{})$

Since $f(x)$ has a degree of 3, there are three factors. Use division to find the other factor.

$$
\begin{array}{r}
x - 5 \\
x^2 - 6x + 10 \overline{) x^3 - 11x^2 + 40x - 50} \\
\underline{x^3 - 6x^2 + 10x} \\
-5x^2 + 30x - 50 \\
\underline{-5x^2 + 30x - 50} \\
0
\end{array}
$$

Thus, $f(x) = (x^2 - 6x + 10)(x - 5)$.

Since $x - 5$ is a factor, 5 is a zero. The three zeros are $3 + i$, $3 - i$, and 5.

Teaching Tip ❷   Synthetic division cannot be used since the divisor is not in the form $x - r$.

French mathematician René Descartes made more discoveries about the zeros of polynomial functions. His rule of signs is given below.

Descartes' Rule of Signs	**If $P(x)$ is a polynomial whose terms are arranged in descending powers of the variable,** ■ **the number of positive real zeros of $y = P(x)$ is the same as the number of changes in sign of the coefficients of the terms, or is less than this by an even number, and** ■ **the number of negative real zeros of $y = P(x)$ is the same as the number of changes in sign of the coefficients of the terms of $P(-x)$, or is less than this number by an even number.**

When using Descartes' rule of signs, the coefficients are ignored.

LESSON 10-4   ROOTS AND ZEROS   471

Teaching Tip ❸ Once the number of positive and negative real zeros has been determined, students must consider 0 as a zero of the function before counting the imaginary zeros.

Reteaching Masters Booklet, p. 66

Example 3

State the number of positive and negative real zeros for $g(x) = 3x^4 - x^3 + 8x^2 + x - 7$.

Count the number of changes in sign for the coefficients of $g(x)$.

$$g(x) = 3x^4 \quad - \quad x^3 \quad + \quad 8x^2 \quad + \quad x \quad - \quad 7$$

$$3 \qquad -1 \qquad 8 \qquad 1 \qquad -7$$

yes   yes   no   yes   *3 sign changes*

There are either 3 positive real zeros or 1 (which is $3 - 2$) positive real zero.

Now find $g(-x)$ and count the number of changes in signs for its coefficients.

$$g(-x) = 3(-x)^4 \; - \; (-x)^3 \; + \; 8(-x)^2 \; + \; (-x) \; - \; 7$$
$$g(-x) = 3x^4 \; + \; x^3 \; + \; 8x^2 \; - \; x \; - \; 7$$

$$3 \qquad 1 \qquad 8 \qquad -1 \qquad -7$$

no   no   yes   no   *1 sign change*

There is exactly 1 negative real zero.

The function $g(x)$ has either 3 or 1 positive real zeros and exactly 1 negative real zero.

Using a graphing calculator or sketching the graph may help in determining the nature of the zeros of a function.

In Example 3, $g(x)$ has a degree of 4, so it has 4 zeros. Using the information in the example, you can make a chart of the possibilities for these zeros. **Teaching Tip ❸**

Number of Positive Real Zeros	Number of Negative Real Zeros	Number of Imaginary Zeros	
3	1	0	*3 + 1 + 0 = 4*
1	1	2	*1 + 1 + 2 = 4*

Example 4

Write the polynomial function of least degree with integral coefficients whose zeros are 6 and $4 - 2i$.

If $4 - 2i$ is a zero, then $4 + 2i$ is also a zero.   *Why?*

Use the zero product property to write a polynomial equation that has these zeros as roots.
$$0 = (x - 6)[x - (4 - 2i)][x - (4 + 2i)] \qquad \textit{Why is } x - 6 \textit{ a factor?}$$
Thus, $f(x) = (x - 6)[x - (4 - 2i)][x - (4 + 2i)]$
$$= (x - 6)(x^2 - 8x + 20)$$
$$= x^3 - 14x^2 + 68x - 120$$

472   CHAPTER 10   POLYNOMIAL FUNCTIONS

RETEACHING THE LESSON

Have each student pick three positive integers less than or equal to 6. Have them write the factors of the polynomial equation having these roots. Have them find the unfactored polynomial equation. Then have students exchange equations and solve the one they get.

CHECKING FOR UNDERSTANDING

Communicating Mathematics

Read and study the lesson to answer these questions.

1. How many zeros does $f(x) = x^4 - 1$ have? **4**

2. If one zero of a polynomial is $2 + i$, name one other zero. What are these zeros called? **$2 - i$, conjugates**

3. A polynomial has degree 4 and one positive real zero. Describe the other possible zeros. Justify your answer. **See margin.**

4. Describe how you can use Descartes' Rule of Signs to help you find the zeros of a polynomial function. **You know what kind of numbers you are looking for, so your search is easier.**

5. $f(-x) = -3x^5 + 7x^2 + 8x + 1$ **6.** $f(-x) = x^4 + 2x^3 + x^2 - 1$

Guided Practice Find $f(-x)$ for each function $f(x)$ given.

5. $f(x) = 3x^5 + 7x^2 - 8x + 1$ 6. $f(x) = x^4 - 2x^3 + x^2 - 1$

7. $f(x) = 4x^4 - 3x^3 + 2x^2 - x + 1$ 8. $f(x) = x^7 - x^3 + 2x - 1$
$f(-x) = 4x^4 + 3x^3 + 2x^2 + x + 1$ $f(-x) = -x^7 + x^3 - 2x - 1$

State the number of positive real zeros, negative real zeros, and imaginary zeros for each function.

9. **0; 3 or 1; 0 or 2**   9. $f(x) = x^3 + x^2 + x + 1$ 10. $f(x) = -x^4 - x^2 - x - 1$

10. **0; 2 or 0; 2 or 4**

11. **1; 3 or 1; 0 or 2**   11. $f(x) = x^4 + x^3 - 7x - 1$ 12. $f(x) = x^{10} - 1$

12. **1; 1; 8**   13. **2 or 0; 2 or 0; 0, 2, or 4**   14. **1; 3 or 1; 0 or 2**   15. **0; 1; 2**

16. **2 or 0; 1; 2 or 4**

EXERCISES

Practice For each function, state the number of positive real zeros, negative real zeros, and imaginary zeros.

13. $f(x) = 3x^4 + 2x^3 - 3x^2 - 4x + 1$ 14. $f(x) = x^4 + x^3 + 2x^2 - 3x - 1$

15. $f(x) = x^3 + 1$ 16. $f(x) = x^5 - x^3 - x + 1$

17. $f(x) = x^{10} - x^8 + x^6 - x^4 + x^2 - 1$ 18. $f(x) = x^{14} + x^{10} - x^9 + x - 1$

 5, 3, or 1; 5, 3, or 1; 0, 2, 4, 6, or 8   **3 or 1; 1; 10 or 12**

Given a function and one of its zeros, find all of the zeros of the function.

19. **4, $1 + i$, $1 - i$**

20. **-4, $1 + 2i$, $1 - 2i$**   19. $g(x) = x^3 - 6x^2 + 10x - 8; 4$ 20. $f(x) = x^3 + 2x^2 - 3x + 20; -4$

21. **$-\frac{3}{2}$, $1 + 4i$, $1 - 4i$**   21. $h(x) = 2x^3 - x^2 + 28x + 51; -\frac{3}{2}$ 22. $h(x) = 2x^3 - 17x^2 + 90x - 41; \frac{1}{2}$

22. **$\frac{1}{2}$, $4 + 5i$, $4 - 5i$**   23. $f(x) = 4x^4 + 17x^2 + 4; 2i$ 24. $f(x) = x^3 + 6x^2 + 21x + 26; -2$

23. **$2i$, $-2i$, $\frac{i}{2}$, $-\frac{i}{2}$**   25. $f(x) = x^3 - 3x^2 + 9x + 13; 2 + 3i$ **$2 + 3i$, $2 - 3i$, -1**

24. **-2, $-2 + 3i$, $-2i - 3i$**   26. $g(x) = x^3 - 10x^2 + 34x - 40; 3 - i$ **$3 - i$, $3 + i$, 4**

27. $g(x) = x^4 - 6x^3 + 12x^2 + 6x - 13; 3 + 2i$ **$3 - 2i$, $3 + 2i$, -1, 1**

Write the polynomial function of least degree with integral coefficients that has the given zeros. **28–33. See margin.**

28. $2, 1 - i$ 29. $3, 2i$ 30. $-1, 1, 2 - i$

 31. $-2 - i, 1 + 3i$ 32. $4, i, -1 + i$ 33. $3i, -2i, 1 - i$

Additional Answers

3. one negative real zero and two imaginary zeros or three negative real zeros; there must be four zeros and the imaginary zeros occur in pairs

28. $f(x) = x^3 - 4x^2 + 6x - 4$

29. $f(x) = x^3 - 3x^2 + 4x - 12$

30. $f(x) = x^4 - 4x^3 + 4x^2 + 4x - 5$

31. $f(x) = x^4 + 2x^3 + 7x^2 + 30x + 50$

32. $f(x) = x^5 - 2x^4 - 5x^3 - 10x^2 - 6x - 8$

33. $f(x) = x^6 - 2x^5 + 15x^4 - 26x^3 + 62x^2 - 72x + 72$

Checking for Understanding

Exercises 1–12 are designed to help you assess understanding through reading, writing, and speaking. You should work through Exercises 1–4 with your students, and then monitor their work on Exercises 5–12.

Error Analysis

Some students may try to apply the Complex Conjugates Theorem to equations with complex coefficients. However, the Complex Conjugates Theorem is true only for polynomial equations with real coefficients. For example, if $x - 2 + i = 0$, then $x = 2 - i$. But $x \neq 2 + i$.

Assignment Guide

Basic: 13–30, 31–35, 37–40
Average: 16–31, 34–40
Enriched: 19–40
All: Mid-Chapter Review, 1–10

Practice Masters Booklet, p. 76

Closing the Lesson

Speaking Activity Divide the class into two groups, those who gathered information on Gauss and those who gathered information on Descartes. Select one person to be the leader of each group and another to be the recorder. Allow each person in the group to share one accomplishment of the mathematician that they researched. Then have each group share the information with the rest of the class.

APPLYING THE LESSON

Homework Exercises

See assignment guide on page 473.

Chapter 10, Quiz B, (Lessons 10-3 through 10-4), is available in the Evaluation Masters Booklet, p. 135.

Enrichment Masters Booklet, p. 66

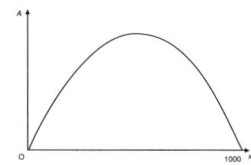

10-4 **Enrichment Worksheet**

NAME _____ DATE _____

Using Maximum Values

Many times maximum solutions are needed for different situations. For instance, what is the area of the largest rectangular field that can be enclosed with 2000 feet of fencing?

Let x and y denote the length and width of the field, respectively.

Perimeter: $2x + 2y = 2000 \rightarrow y = 1000 - x$
Area: $A = xy = x(1000 - x) = -x^2 + 1000x$

This problem is equivalent to finding the highest point on the graph of $A(x) = -x^2 + 1000x$ shown on the right.

Complete the square for $-x^2 + 1000x$.
$A = -(x^2 - 1000x + 500^2) + 500^2$
$= -(x - 500)^2 + 500^2$

Because the term $-(x - 500)^2$ is either negative or 0, the greatest value of A is 500^2. The maximum area enclosed is 500^2 or 250,000 square feet.

Solve each problem.

1. Find the area of the largest rectangular garden that can be enclosed by 300 feet of fence. **5625 sq ft**

2. A farmer will make a rectangular pen with 100 feet of fence using part of his barn for one side of the pen. What is the largest area he can enclose? **1250 sq ft**

3. An area along a straight stone wall is to be fenced. There are 600 meters of fencing available. What is the greatest rectangular area that can be enclosed? **45,000 m²**

Critical Thinking

34. If $f(x) = x^3 + kx^2 - 7x - 15$, find the value of k so that $-2 - i$ is a zero of $f(x)$. **1**

Applications

35. **Manufacturing** The volume of a fudge tin must be 120 cubic centimeters. The tin is 7 centimeters longer than it is wide and six times longer than it is tall. Find the dimensions of the tin.
35. 5 cm by 12 cm by 2 cm

36. **Manufacturing** The height of a certain juice can is 4 times the radius of the top of the can. Determine the dimensions of the can if the volume is approximately 17.89 cubic inches. *Hint: The volume of a right circular cylinder = $\pi r^2 h$.* **$r = 1.125$ in., $h = 4.5$ in.**

Mixed Review

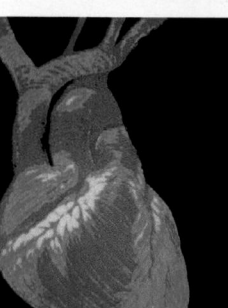

Journal
Explain how sketching the graph or using a graphing calculator can help you in determining the number of zeros of a function.

37. Use synthetic substitution to find $f(3)$ and $f(-2)$ for $f(x) = 2x^2 - 8x + 6$. **(Lesson 10-2) 0, 30**

38. $y = -\dfrac{x^2}{16}$

38. Write the equation of the parabola with vertex at $(0, 0)$ and focus at $(0, -4)$. **(Lesson 9-2)**

39. Write the function $f(x) = x^2 + 6$ in the form $f(x) = (x - h)^2 + k$. Then name the vertex and axis of symmetry for the graph of the function. **(Lesson 8-2) $f(x) = x^2 + 6$; (0, 6), $x = 0$**

40. **Health** On the average, an adult heart beats about once every $\dfrac{5}{6}$ second. If Diane is 18 years old, about how many beats has her heart made? **(Lesson 5-1) 681,177,600 or 6.811776 × 10⁸**

MID-CHAPTER REVIEW

Find each value if $p(x) = 6x^3 - 3x^2 + 4x - 9$. **(Lesson 10-1) $6x^3 + 15x^2 + 16x - 2$**

1. $p(-3)$ **−210**   2. $p(a^2)$ **$6a^6 - 3a^4 + 4a^2 - 9$**   3. $p(x + 1)$

Given a polynomial and one of its factors, find the remaining factors of the polynomial. **(Lesson 10-2)**

4. $x^3 + x^2 - 24x + 36; x + 6$ **$x - 3, x - 2$**   5. $2x^3 + 13x^2 + x - 70; x - 2$ **$2x + 7, x + 5$**

6. Four positive two-digit even numbers xy have a fifth power that ends in the digits xy. Find them. **(Lesson 10-3) 24, 32, 68, 76**

For each function, state the number of positive real zeros, negative real zeros, and imaginary zeros. **(Lesson 10-4)**

7. $f(x) = x^3 - 7x^2 - 6x + 3$ **2 or 0; 1; 0 or 2**   8. $g(x) = 2x^4 - x^3 - 9x - 12$ **1; 1; 2**

Write the polynomial function of least degree with integral coefficients that has the given zeros. **(Lesson 10-4)**
$$f(x) = x^4 + 7x^3 + 13x^2 - 23x - 78$$

9. $1, 1 - i$ **$f(x) = x^3 - 3x^2 + 4x - 2$**   10. $-3, 2, -3 + 2i$

474   CHAPTER 10   POLYNOMIAL FUNCTIONS

EXTENDING THE LESSON

Math Power: Reasoning
If $g(x) = x^3 + kx^2 - 7x - 15$, find the value of k so that $-2 + i$ is a zero of $g(x)$. **1**

Mid-Chapter Review
The Mid-Chapter Review provides students with a brief review of the concepts and skills in Lessons 10-1 through 10-4. Lesson numbers are given at the end of problems or instruction lines so students may review concepts not yet mastered.

The Rational Zero Theorem

Objectives

After studying this lesson, you should be able to:

10-5A ▪ identify all possible rational zeros of a polynomial function using the Rational Zero Theorem, and

10-5B ▪ find zeros of polynomial functions.

Application

The largest pyramid at Gizeh, Egypt was built by Khufu, a king of the fourth dynasty. The pyramid has a square base and has a volume of 2645 cubic dekameters. The height of the pyramid is approximately 8 dekameters less than the length of a side of the square base. What are the dimensions of the pyramid?   *1 dekameter = 10 meters*

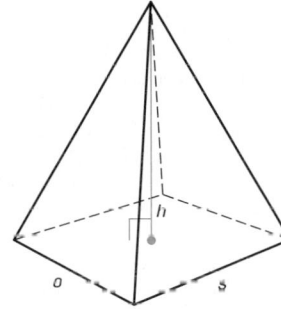

The formula for the volume of a pyramid is $V = \frac{1}{3}Bh$, where B represents the area of the base and h represents the height. Let's set up an equation to find the dimensions of the pyramid.

Let s represent the length of one side of the base of the pyramid. Then the height is $s - 8$.

$$V = \frac{1}{3}Bh$$

$$2645 = \frac{1}{3}(s^2)(s - 8) \qquad V = 2645,\ B = s^2,\ h = s - 8$$

$$7935 = s^4 - 8s^4 \qquad \textit{Multiply each side by 3.}$$

$$0 = s^3 - 8s^2 - 7935$$

We could use synthetic substitution to test possible zeros. But the numbers are so large that we might have to test hundreds of possible zeros before we find one. In situations like this, the **Rational Zero Theorem** can give us some direction in testing possible zeros. This theorem is stated below.

Rational Zero Theorem

Let $f(x) = a_0x^n + a_1x^{n-1} + \dots + a_{n-1}x + a_n$ represent a polynomial function with integral coefficients. If $\frac{p}{q}$ is a rational number in simplest form and is a zero of $y = f(x)$, then p is a factor of a_n and q is a factor of a_0.

A corollary to the Rational Zero Theorem, called the **Integral Zero Theorem**, states that if the coefficients of the polynomial function are integers such that $a_0 = 1$ and $a_n \neq 0$, any rational zeros of the function must be factors of a_n.

LESSON 10-5   THE RATIONAL ZERO THEOREM   475

ALTERNATE TEACHING STRATEGIES

Using Problem Solving

Have students find a counterexample for the converse of the Rational Zero Theorem. In other words, just because p is a factor of a_0 and q is a factor of a_n, $\frac{p}{q}$ may not be a zero. The theorem states only that $\frac{p}{q}$ is a zero, p and q will be of the form described.

Lesson Resources

Reteaching Master 10-5
Practice Master 10-5
Enrichment Master 10-5
Activity Master, p. 10

 Transparency 10-5 contains the 5-Minute Check and a teaching aid for this lesson.

INTRODUCING THE LESSON

5-Minute Check

(over Lesson 10-4)

1. How many zeros does the polynomial $f(x) = 3x^4 - x^3 + 8x^2 + x - 7$ have?   **4**
2. Find $f(-x)$ for $f(x) = x^3 - 3x^2 + 4x - 2$.   **$-x^3 - 3x^2 - 4x - 2$**
3. Is $\frac{2}{3}$ a zero of $f(x) = 3x^4 + 7x^3 - 25x + 14$?   **yes**
4. Given $2 + I$ is a zero of $f(x) = x^3 - 7x^2 + 17x - 15$, find all of its zeros.   **$2 + i, 2 - i, 3$**
5. Write the polynomial function of least degree with integral coefficients whose zeros are $\frac{3}{2}$ and $-1 + 5i$.   **$2x^3 + x^2 + 46x - 78$**

Motivating the Lesson

Divide the class into groups. Give each group of students a container to find its volume. Have them write a problem using their container that defines the dimensions in relationship to one of the sides. They should then write the equation. Discuss the solutions to the equations.

Let $V(s)$ be the related function for $0 = s^3 - 8s^2 - 7935$. In $V(s) = s^3 - 8s^2 - 7935$, all coefficients are integers, $a_0 = 1$, and $a_n = 7935$. According to the Integral Zero Theorem, any rational zeros must be factors of 7935. So the possible zeros are ± 1, ± 3, ± 5, ± 15, ± 23, ± 69, ± 115, ± 345, ± 529, ± 1587, ± 2645, and ± 7935. Since we know that the length must be positive, we will only try positive factors.

According to Descartes' rule of signs, there will be only one positive real root and no negative real roots. We can use synthetic substitution to test for possible zeros and we can stop testing when we find the first zero. Let's make a chart.

Since $s - 8 = h$ and h must be positive, we need only consider values for s that are greater than 8.

s	1	-8	0	-7935
15	1	7	105	-6360
23	1	15	345	0

A zero occurs when $s = 23$. Thus, $s - 23$ is a factor of the polynomial and 23 is a root of the equation.

Since Descartes' rule told us there was only one real root, 23 is the only possible measure for the side of the pyramid. The length of one side of the base of the pyramid at Gizeh, Egypt is 23 dekameters, and the height is $23 - 8$ or 15 dekameters.

Example 1 | List all of the possible rational zeros of $f(x) = 2x^3 - x^2 - 34x - 56$.

Since $a_0 \neq 1$, we cannot use the Integral Zero Theorem.

If $\frac{p}{q}$ is a rational root, then p is a factor of 56 and q is a factor of 2.

All of the possible values of p are ± 1, ± 2, ± 4, ± 7, ± 8, ± 14, ± 28, and ± 56.

All of the possible values of q are ± 1 and ± 2.

So all of the possible rational zeros are:

$$\pm\frac{1}{1}, \pm\frac{1}{2}, \pm\frac{2}{1}, \pm\frac{2}{2}, \pm\frac{4}{1}, \pm\frac{4}{2}, \pm\frac{7}{1}, \pm\frac{7}{2}, \pm\frac{8}{1}, \pm\frac{8}{2}, \pm\frac{14}{1}, \pm\frac{14}{2}, \pm\frac{28}{1}, \pm\frac{28}{2}, \pm\frac{56}{1}, \text{ and } \pm\frac{56}{2}$$

or ± 1, $\pm\frac{1}{2}$, ± 2, ± 4, ± 7, $\pm\frac{7}{2}$, ± 8, ± 14, ± 28, and ± 56.

476   CHAPTER 10   POLYNOMIAL FUNCTIONS

Example 2

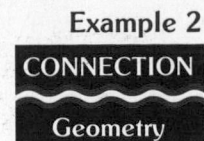

CONNECTION

Geometry

The volume of a rectangular solid is 72 cubic units. The width is twice the height and the length is 7 units more than the height. Find the dimensions of the solid.

Let h = the height of the solid.

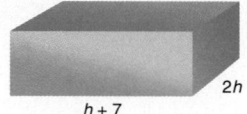

$$\text{volume} = (2h)(h + 7)(h)$$
$$72 = 2h^3 + 14h^2 \qquad \text{Substitute 72 for volume.}$$
$$0 = 2h^3 + 14h^2 - 72 \qquad \text{Subtract 72 from each side.}$$
$$0 = h^3 + 7h^2 - 36 \qquad \text{Divide each side by 2.}$$

All of the possible rational zeros are ± 1, ± 2, ± 3, ± 4, ± 6, ± 9, ± 12, ± 18, and ± 36. Since a measure must be positive and according to Descartes' Rule of Signs there is one positive real zero, we can stop testing possible zeros when we find the first one. Let's make a table and test each possible rational zero.

$\frac{p}{q}$	1	7	0	-36
1	1	8	8	-28
2	1	9	18	0

The zero is 2. So the solid is 4 units by 9 units by 2 units.

You have learned many rules to help you determine the number and characteristics of the zeros of a function. Example 3 shows how many of them can be used.

Example 3

Find all zeros of $f(x) = 2x^4 - 9x^3 + 2x^2 + 21x - 10$.

- From the corollary to the Fundamental Theorem of Algebra we know there are exactly 4 complex zeros.

- According to Descartes' rule of signs there are either 3 or 1 positive real zeros and exactly 1 negative real zero.

- Now use the Factor Theorem to determine that the possible rational zeros are $\pm\frac{1}{2}$, ± 1, ± 2, $\pm\frac{5}{2}$, ± 5, and ± 10.

- Use synthetic substitution and a chart to find at least one zero.

$\frac{p}{q}$	2	-9	2	21	-10	
$\frac{1}{2}$	2	-8	-2	20	0	One zero is $\frac{1}{2}$.

EVALUATING THE LESSON

Checking for Understanding
Exercises 1–12 are designed to help you assess understanding through reading, writing, and speaking. You should work through Exercises 1–4 with your students, and then monitor their work on Exercises 5–12.

Closing the Lesson
Writing Activity Have students determine the zeros of a third degree equation and sketch a graph of the function.

The depressed polynomial after division by $x - \frac{1}{2}$ is $2x^3 - 8x^2 - 2x + 20$. Now use a synthetic division chart with this polynomial.

x	2	−8	−2	20
1	2	−6	−8	12
2	2	−4	−10	0

Another zero is 2.

The depressed polynomial is $2x^2 - 4x - 10$. Use the quadratic formula to find other possible zeros.

$$x = \frac{-(-4) \pm \sqrt{(-4)^2 - 4(2)(-10)}}{2(2)}$$

$$= \frac{4 \pm \sqrt{96}}{4}$$

$$= \frac{4 \pm 4\sqrt{6}}{4} \text{ or } 1 \pm \sqrt{6}$$

The zeros are $\frac{1}{2}$, 2, $1 + \sqrt{6}$, and $1 - \sqrt{6}$. The approximate values of the irrational roots are 3.45 and −1.45. So, there are 3 positive zeros and 1 negative zero.

The graph of the function shown at the right crosses the x-axis 4 times, confirming that there are 4 real zeros.

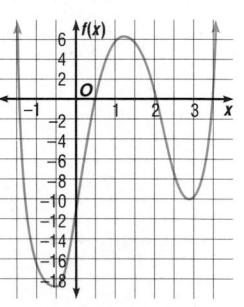

CHECKING FOR UNDERSTANDING

Communicating Mathematics

Read and study the lesson to answer these questions.

1. When can you use the Rational Zero Theorem to determine the possible rational zeros for a polynomial function?

2. Why is it helpful to use the Rational Zero Theorem while finding the zeros of a polynomial function?

3. Describe the possible rational zeros when the leading coefficient, a_0, of a polynomial function is one. **all the factors of a_n**

4. Write a polynomial function with four possible rational roots. **Answers may vary. A sample answer is $f(x) = x^4 + x^3 + x^2 + x + 3$.**

1. When coefficients are integers
2. You limit the number of possible solutions.

Guided Practice

State all possible rational zeros for each function.

5. $f(x) = x^3 + x + 2$ **±1, ±2**

6. $g(x) = x^3 + 3x^2 - 6x + 5$ **±1, ±5**

7. ±1, ±2, ±3, ±6
7. $f(x) = x^3 + 8x + 6$

8. $h(x) = x^4 - 9x - 3$ **±1, ±3**

9. ±1, ±2, ±5, ±10
9. $p(x) = x^5 - 10$

10. $d(x) = x^3 + 6x^2 - 3x + 1$ **±1**

11. $g(x) = 3x^3 - 5x^2 - x + 4$

$$\pm 1, \pm 2, \pm 4, \pm\frac{1}{3}, \pm\frac{2}{3}, \pm\frac{4}{3}$$

12. $f(x) = 2x^4 + 4x^3 - x^2 - 3$

$$\pm 1, \pm 3, \pm\frac{1}{2}, \pm\frac{3}{2}$$

478   CHAPTER 10   POLYNOMIAL FUNCTIONS

RETEACHING THE LESSON

Have students pick four numbers, two of which are fractions, to use as roots of a polynomial equation. Have them find the equation that has these roots. Have students exchange equations and solve.

APPLYING THE LESSON

Homework Exercises

Assignment Guide

Basic: 13–37, 45–46, 48–51
Average: 17–40, 45–51
Enriched: 21–51

Practice

State all possible rational zeros for each function.

13. $g(x) = x^3 + 2x^2 - 3x + 5$
14. $n(x) = x^3 - 7x + 12$

16. ±1, ±$\frac{1}{3}$, ±3

15. $f(x) = x^5 + 6x^3 - 12x + 18$
16. $h(x) = 3x^3 - 5x^2 - 11x + 3$

17. ±1, ±2, ±$\frac{1}{2}$, ±$\frac{1}{3}$,

17. $p(x) = 6x^3 + 6x^2 - 15x - 2$
18. $f(x) = 3x^4 + 15$

±$\frac{1}{6}$, ±$\frac{2}{3}$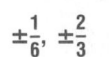

19. $f(x) = 4x^6 + 6x^4 - 4x^2 - 6$
20. $g(x) = 9x^6 - 5x^3 + 27$

18. ±1, ±$\frac{1}{3}$, ±3, ±5,

Find all the rational zeros for each function.

                          -2, -4, 7

±$\frac{5}{3}$, ±15

21. $f(x) = x^3 + x^2 - 80x - 300$
22. $g(x) = x^3 - x^2 - 34x - 56$

19. ±1, ±$\frac{1}{2}$, ±$\frac{1}{4}$, ±2,

23. $g(x) = x^3 - 3x - 2$ **-1, -1, 2**
24. $h(x) = x^4 - 3x^3 + x^2 - 3x$ **0, 3**

±3, ±$\frac{3}{2}$, ±$\frac{3}{4}$, ±6

25. $f(x) = x^4 - 3x^3 - 53x^2 - 9x$ **0, 9**
26. $h(x) = 2x^3 - 11x^2 + 12x + 9$

27. $p(x) = 6x^3 + 11x^2 - 3x - 2$
28. $g(x) = x^4 + 10x^3 + 33x^2 + 38x + 8$

20. ±1, ±$\frac{1}{3}$, ±$\frac{1}{9}$, ±3,

29. $f(x) = x^4 + x^2 - 2$ **1, -1**
30. $p(x) = x^4 + x^3 - 9x^2 - 17x - 8$

±9, ±27

31. $g(x) = x^3 + 4x^2 - 3x - 18$
32. $f(x) = x^4 - 13x^2 + 36$

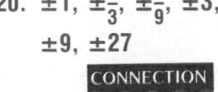

33. $h(x) = x^3 - x^2 - 40x + 12$ **-6**
34. $g(x) = 48x^4 - 52x^3 + 13x - 3$

35. $p(x) = x^5 - 6x^3 + 8x$ **0, 2, -2**
36. $f(x) = 2x^5 - x^4 - 2x + 1$

37. A rectangular solid has a volume of 144 cubic units. The width is twice the height and the length is 2 units more than the width. Find the dimensions of the solid. **6 units by 8 units by 3 units**

21. **-5, -6, 10**

Find all zeros of each function. **38–44. See margin.**

26. **3, 3, -$\frac{1}{2}$**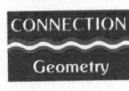

38. $f(x) = 8x^3 - 36x^2 + 22x + 21$

27. $\frac{1}{2}$, -$\frac{1}{3}$, -2

39. $g(x) = 6x^3 + 5x^2 - 9x + 2$

40. $g(x) = 12x^4 + 4x^4 - 3x^3 - x$

28. **-2, -4**

41. $p(x) = 6x^4 + 22x^3 + 11x^2 - 38x - 40$

30. **-1, -1**

42. $h(x) = 5x^4 - 29x^3 + 55x^2 - 28x$

31. **2, -3, -3**

43. $g(x) = 9x^5 - 94x^3 + 27x^2 + 40x - 12$

32. **2, -2, 3, -3**

44. $p(x) = x^5 - 2x^4 - 12x^3 - 12x^2 - 13x - 10$

34. -$\frac{1}{2}$, $\frac{1}{3}$, $\frac{1}{2}$, $\frac{3}{4}$

36. $\frac{1}{2}$, -1, 1

Critical Thinking

45. Suppose k and $2k$ are zeros of $f(x) = x^3 + 4x^2 + 9kx - 90$. Find k and all three zeros of $f(x)$. **k = -3; -3, -6, 5**

                          5 in. by 5 in. by 8 in.

Applications

46. **Manufacturing** The volume of a milk carton is 200 cubic inches. The base of the carton is square and the height is 3 inches more than the length of the base. What are the dimensions of the carton?

47. **Food Production** I.C. Dreams makes ice cream cones shaped like geometric cones. The volume of a cone is about 5.24 cubic inches, and its height is 4 inches more than the radius of the opening of the cone. Determine the dimensions of the cone. *Hint: The formula for the volume of a cone is* $V = \frac{1}{3}\pi r^2 h$. **radius = 1 in. and height = 5 in.**

Additional Answers

38. $-\frac{1}{2}, \frac{3}{2}, \frac{7}{2}$

39. $\frac{2}{3}, \frac{-3 \pm \sqrt{17}}{4}$

40. $0, -\frac{1}{3}, \frac{1}{2}, -\frac{1}{2}$

41. $-2, \frac{4}{3}, \frac{-3 \pm i}{2}$

42. $0, \frac{4}{5}, \frac{5 \pm i\sqrt{3}}{2}$

43. $3, \frac{2}{3}, -\frac{2}{3}, \frac{-3 \pm \sqrt{13}}{2}$

44. $-1, -2, 5, i, -i$

2 or 0; 1; 2 or 4

48. State the possible number of positive real zeros, negative real zeros, and imaginary zeros of the function $f(x) = 3x^5 - 8x^2 + 1$. **(Lesson 10-3)**

49. Write the polynomial function of least degree with integral coefficients that has -2 and $2 + 3i$ as zeros. **(Lesson 10-3)**

$f(x) = x^3 - 2x^2 + 5x + 26$

50. Graph the system $\begin{cases} 4x^2 + 9y^2 = 36 \\ 4x^2 - 9y^2 = 36 \end{cases}$. Then find the solutions. **(Lesson 9-8)**

$(\pm 3, 0)$ **For graphs, see Solutions Manual.**

51. A possible solution for the system $\begin{cases} 2x - 4y - z = 6 \\ 3x + 4y + 3z = -1 \\ x + y + z = 0 \end{cases}$ is $(1, -1, 0)$.

Determine if this ordered triple is a solution. **(Lesson 3-9) yes**

~~~~ LANGUAGE CONNECTION ~~~~

Study the mathematical terms used in the statements below.

$x^3 - 7x + 6$ is a **polynomial expression,** or a **polynomial.** Its factors are $(x - 2)$, $(x - 1)$, and $(x + 3)$. *When a polynomial is divided by one of its factors, the remainder is zero.*

$x^3 - 7x + 6 = 0$ is a polynomial equation. The **factored form** of the equation is $(x - 2)(x - 1)(x + 3) = 0$. Its **roots,** or **solutions,** are 2, 1, and -3. *When a root of an equation is substituted for the variable, the two sides are equal.*

$f(x) = x^3 - 7x + 6$ is a **polynomial function.** The **zeros** of the function are 2, 1, and -3. *When a zero of a function is substituted for the variable, the result is zero.*

The function $f(x) = x^3 - 7x + 6$ may be expressed as $y = x^3 - 7x + 6$. When a value is substituted for x, exactly one value is obtained for y. Each ordered pair (x, y) is a **solution** to the equation $y = x^3 - 7x + 6$. *We do not use the term root for solutions that are ordered pairs.*

Choose the correct term in parentheses to complete each statement.

1. $x - 2$ is a (*factor*, root) of the polynomial $x^2 - 4x + 4$.
2. 2 is a (root, *zero*) of the function $f(x) = x^2 - 4x + 4$.
3. $(2, 0)$ is a (*solution*, root) of the equation $y = x^2 - 4x + 4$.
4. 2 is a (*root*, zero) of $x^2 - 4x + 4 = 0$.
5. $y - 6$ is a (*factor*, solution) of $y^2 - 5y - 6$.
6. The zeros of the (*function*, expression) $f(y) = y^2 - 5y - 6$ are 6 and -1.
7. The roots of the (polynomial, *equation*) $y^2 - 5y - 6 = 0$ are 6 and -1.
8. 7 is a (factor, *zero*) of $f(k) = k - 7$.
9. 7 is a (*solution*, factor) of $k - 7 = 0$.
10. $(3, -4)$ is a (*solution*, root) of $y = k - 7$.
11. $f(k) = k - 7$ is a(n) (*function*, expression).
12. The factors of the (equation, *expression*) $x^2 - 1$ are $x - 1$ and $x + 1$.

480 **CHAPTER 10 POLYNOMIAL FUNCTIONS**

EXTENDING THE LESSON

Math Power: Communication

Do all polynomial functions with real coefficients have at least one real root if they have odd degree? **Yes, complex numbers appear in pairs (conjugates), so if there are an odd number of roots at least one must be real.**

Language Connection

The Language Connection feature offers students a chance to test their understanding of the vocabulary in this chapter. These terms are often misused by students.

Enrichment Masters Booklet, p. 67

10-6 Graphing Polynomial Functions and Approximating Zeros

Objectives
After studying this lesson, you should be able to:

10-6A   ■ approximate the real zeros of polynomial functions, and

10-6B   ■ graph polynomial functions to find significant points.

Application
The space shuttle has an external tank for the fuel that the main engines need for the launch. About eight minutes into the flight, the fuel is gone and the tank is released. This tank is shaped like a capsule, a cylinder with a hemispherical dome at either end. The cylindrical part of the tank has a volume of 1170 cubic meters and a height of 17 meters more than the radius of the tank. What are the dimensions of the tank to the nearest tenth of a meter?

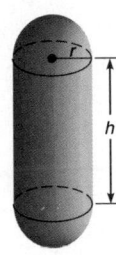

Let's begin searching for the dimensions of the tank by writing a polynomial equation describing the volume of the tank

Let r = the radius of the tank and $r + 17$ = the height. *Use the formula for the volume of a cylinder.*

$$V = \pi r^2 h$$
$$V = \pi r^2 (r + 17) \qquad \text{\textit{Replace h with r + 17.}}$$
$$1170 = \pi r^3 + 17\pi r^2 \qquad \text{\textit{Replace V with 1170.}}$$
$$0 = \pi r^3 + 17\pi r^2 - 1170 \qquad \text{\textit{Subtract 1170 from each side.}}$$
$$0 = r^3 + 17r^2 - \frac{1170}{\pi} \qquad \text{\textit{Divide each side by π.}}$$
$$0 = r^3 + 17r^2 - 372 \qquad \text{\textit{Round to the nearest integer.}}$$

Let $V(r) = r^3 + 17r^2 - 372$. According to Descartes' rule of signs, there is one positive real zero and two or zero negative real zeros. The possible rational zeros are $\pm 1, \pm 2, \pm 3, \pm 4, \pm 6, \pm 12, \pm 31, \pm 62, \pm 93, \pm 124, \pm 186,$ and ± 372, but upon inspection none of these values is a zero. Let's evaluate some values of $V(r)$. Zero separates the positives from the negatives. If you find a sign change in your list of $V(r)$ values a zero must lie somewhere between those two values.

LESSON 10-6   GRAPHING POLYNOMIAL FUNCTIONS AND APPROXIMATING ZEROS   **481**

ALTERNATE TEACHING STRATEGIES

Using Computers
Computer spreadsheets can be developed that will generate the tables for the determination of real roots instantaneously. Computer function graphers and graphing calculators have trace functions that allow approximate zeros to be determined from the graph. If computers and software are available, have students write the spreadsheets and then work some of the problems on them.

Lesson Resources
Reteaching Master 10-6
Practice Master 10-6
Enrichment Master 10-6
Technology Master, p. 27

    Transparency 10-6 contains the 5-Minute Check and a teaching aid for this lesson.

INTRODUCING THE LESSON

🕐 5-Minute Check
(over Lesson 10-5)

1. *True* or *False*. If the graph of $f(x)$ does not cross the x-axis, then $f(x)$ has at least one real zero.   **false**

2. If $3 + 2i$ is a zero of a polynomial function, name another zero of the function.   **3 − 2i**

3. State the number of positive real zeros, negative real zeros, and imaginary zeros for the function $g(x) = x^4 + x^3 - 9x^2 - 17x - 8$.   **1; 3 or 1; 0 or 2**

4. Find all possible rational zeros for the function $p(x) = 6x^3 + 4x^2 - 14x + 4$. $\pm 1; \pm \frac{1}{2};$ $\pm \frac{1}{3}; \pm \frac{1}{6}; \pm 2; \pm \frac{2}{3}; \pm 4; \pm \frac{4}{3}$

5. Find all zeros for the function $f(x) = x^3 - 3x^2 - 53x - 9$.   **9; −3 + 2√2; −3 − 2√2**

Motivating the Lesson
Have students sketch the graphs given the following conditions:

1. third degree with one real zero
2. third degree with two real zeros
3. third degree with three real zeros

Discuss the similarities and differences in this family of graphs.

Chalkboard Example

For Example 1
Approximate to the nearest tenth the real zeros for the function. Then draw the graph.
$g(x) = -2x^3 - 5x^2 + 3x + 2$
The real zeros are approximately −2.9, −0.4, and 0.8.

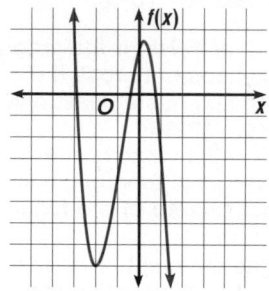

r	$V(r)$	r	$V(r)$	r	$V(r)$	r	$V(r)$
−16	−116	−10	328	−4	−164	2	−296
−15	78	−9	276	−3	−246	3	−192
−14	216	−8	204	−2	−312	4	−36
−13	304	−7	118	−1	−356	5	178
−12	348	−6	24	0	−372	6	456
−11	354	−5	−72	1	−354	7	804

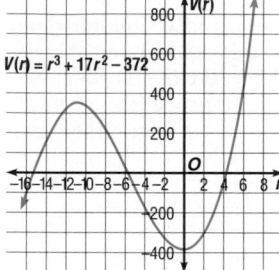

Teaching Tip ❶

Use the values from the charts to plot points on a graph. Then sketch the graph of the function $V(r)$ by connecting those points with a smooth curve. The graph will cross the r-axis somewhere between the pairs of r values where the corresponding $V(r)$ values change sign. Since r-intercepts are zeros of the function, there is a zero between each pair of these r values. This strategy is the **location principle.**

Note that the function has an odd degree so its leftmost points have negative values for $V(r)$ and the rightmost points have positive values. There are 3 r-intercepts, indicating there are 3 real zeros. The zeros are close to −15, −6, and 4.

The Location Principle	Suppose $y = f(x)$ represents a polynomial function and a and b are two numbers such that $f(a) < 0$ and $f(b) > 0$. Then the function has at least one real zero between a and b.

Since we would like to approximate the dimensions of the shuttle tank to the nearest tenth of a meter, we will have to repeat the process of evaluating $V(r) = r^3 + 17r^2 - 372$ for successive values of r expressed in tenths. The measure must be positive, so we will evaluate only the r values between 4 and 5. Start with the values closest to 4 since we know that $V(4)$ is closer to 0 than is $V(5)$. Using a calculator will help find these values more easily.

r	$r^3 + 17r^2 - 372$	$V(r)$
4	$4^3 + 17(4)^2 - 372$	−36
4.1	$(4.1)^3 + 17(4.1)^2 - 372$	−17.309
4.2	$(4.2)^3 + 17(4.2)^2 - 372$	1.968

To evaluate $V(4.1)$:

ENTER: 4.1 y^x 3 $+$ 17

$\times$ 4.1 x^2 $-$

372 $=$ −17.309

The positive zero of $V(r)$ is between 4.1 and 4.2, but it is closer to 4.2. So, to the nearest tenth, the radius of the cylinder is 4.2 meters. The height of the cylinder is 17 + 4.2 or 21.2 meters.

Example 1

Approximate the zeros of $f(x) = x^3 + 4x^2 + x - 2$. Then draw the graph.

According to Descartes' Rule of Signs, there is 1 positive real root and 2 or 0 negative real roots. Let's evaluate several successive values of x to locate the zeros. Then plot the points and connect them to form a smooth graph.

x	f(x)
−4	−6
−3	4
−2	4
−1	0
0	−2
1	4

x	f(x)
−3.5	0.625
−3.6	−0.416
−3.7	−1.593
0.5	−0.375
0.6	0.256

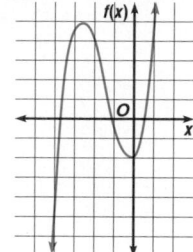

One zero is −1. One other zero lies between −4 and −3 and is approximately −3.6. The other zero lies between 0 and 1 and is approximately 0.6.

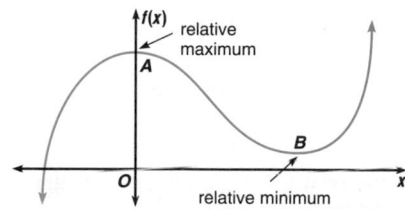

The sideways s-shaped graph at the left shows the shape of the graph of a general third degree polynomial function. Point A on the graph is a **relative maximum** of the cubic function since no other nearby points have a greater y-coordinate. Likewise, point B is a **relative minimum.** You can use this information to help graph functions that have imaginary zeros.

Example 2

Graph $f(x) = x^3 - 6x - 9$.

$f(x) = x^3 - 6x - 9$
$f(x) = (x - 3)(x^2 + 3x + 3)$ The function has one real zero, 3.

x	f(x)	
−3	−18	
−2	5	*indicates a relative maximum*
−1.5	−3.375	
−1	4	
0	−9	
1	14	
1.5	−14.625	*indicates a relative minimum*
2	−13	
3	0	← *3 is a zero.*
4	31	

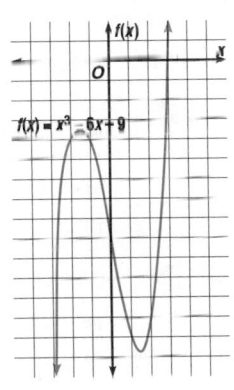

The graph of this cubic polynomial function has a *sideways* S shape. Thus, it has one relative maximum and one relative minimum. The values of $f(-1.5)$ and $f(1.5)$ were computed to approximate the maximum and minimum more closely.

LESSON 10-6 GRAPHING POLYNOMIAL FUNCTIONS AND APPROXIMATING ZEROS 483

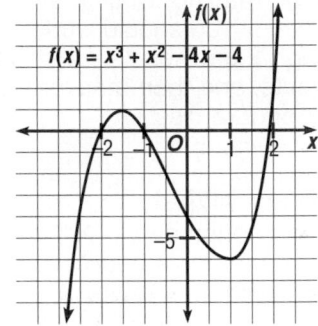
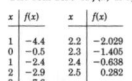
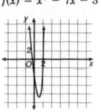
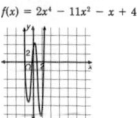

RETEACHING THE LESSON

Consider $p(x) = 40x^3 - 182x^2 + 273x - 135$. Use Descartes' Rule of Signs to find how many positive real zeros are possible. **3 or 1** How many negative real zeros are possible? **0** Find $p(0)$, $p(1)$, $p(2)$, and $p(3)$. Locate all intervals where zeros may occur. **one between 1 and 2** Find $p(1.1)$, $p(1.2)$, ..., $p(1.9)$. Locate all intervals where zeros may occur. **Actual zeros are 1.25, 1.5, and 1.8.**

Checking for Understanding
Exercises 1–5 are designed to help you assess understanding through reading, writing, and speaking. You should work through Exercises 1–4 with your students, and then monitor their work on Exercise 5.

Error Analysis
Students often overlook the possibility of real roots between integers m and $m + 1$ where $f(m)$ and $f(m + 1)$ have the same sign. Contrast this with the situation where for all x_1 and x_2 in $[m, m + 1]$, $f(x_1)$ and $f(x_2)$ have the same sign.

Practice Masters Booklet, p. 78

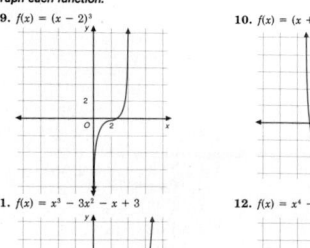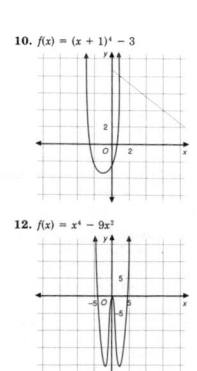
CHECKING FOR UNDERSTANDING

Communicating Mathematics

Read and study the lesson to answer these questions.

1. Why did we not choose one of the negative zeros for the height of the space shuttle tank cylinder? **A negative height makes no sense.**

2. Explain how to use the location principle. **See margin.**

3. Sketch a graph of a third degree polynomial with 1 real zero and two imaginary zeros. **See students' work.**

4. State the degree of the polynomial whose graph is shown at the right. Describe the zeros of the function. **degree 4 with 2 real roots (1 pos., 1 neg.) and 2 imag. roots**

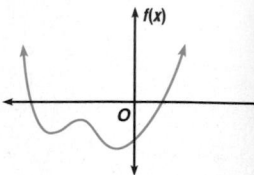

Guided Practice

5b. −3 and −2, −2 and −1, 1 and 2, 2 and 3, −2.6, −1.2, 1.2, 2.6

5. Consider the function $f(x) = x^4 - 8x^2 + 10$. **See margin.**

   a. Evaluate $f(x)$ for successive integers between −4 and 4 inclusive.

   b. Between what successive integers do the zeros appear? Approximate those zeros to the nearest tenth.

   c. State the ranges of x values where the values of $f(x)$ are negative and ranges where the values of $f(x)$ are positive. **See margin.**

   d. State the relative maximum(s) and relative minimum(s) if the data you found indicates that there are any. **minimums at 2 and −2, maximum at 0**

   e. Graph the function. **See Solutions Manual.**

EXERCISES

Practice

Approximate to the nearest tenth the real zeros of each function.

6. $f(x) = x^3 - 2x^2 + 6$ **−1.3**

7. $g(x) = 2x^5 + 3x - 2$ **0.6**

9. 1.6, −1.3, −2.4

8. $g(x) = x^5 - 6$ **1.4**

9. $h(x) = x^3 + 2x^2 - 3x - 5$

10. $n(x) = x^3 - x^2 + 1$ **−0.8**

11. $f(x) = x^3 + 1$ **−1**

12. $h(x) = 3x^3 - 16x^2 + 12x + 6$ **−0.3, 4.3, 1.4**

13. $f(x) = x^4 - 4x^2 + 6$ **no real zeros**

Graph each function. **14–25. See Solutions Manual. Teaching Tip ❷**

14. $f(x) = x^3$

15. $f(x) = 3x^5$

16. $f(x) = 4x^6$

17. $f(x) = x^3 - x^2 - 4x + 4$

18. $f(x) = x^3 - x$

19. $f(x) = x^3 - x^2 - 8x + 12$

20. $f(x) = x^4 - 81$

21. $f(x) = x^3 + 5$

22. $f(x) = 15x^3 - 16x^2 - x + 2$

23. $f(x) = x^4 - 10x^2 + 9$

24. $f(x) = -x^3 - 13x - 12$

25. $f(x) = -x^3 - 4x^2 - 8x - 8$

Additional Answers
2. List values for x and then find $f(x)$. Wherever a sign change occurs in $f(x)$ values, a zero lies between those two x values.

5a.

x	−4	−3	−2	−1	0
$f(x)$	138	19	−6	3	10

x	1	2	3	4
$f(x)$	3	−6	19	138

5c. negative between −2.5 and −1.2 and between 1.2 and 2.5; positive between −1.2 and 1.2, less than −2.5, and greater than 2.5

26–31. See Solutions Manual for graphs.

Approximate to the nearest tenth the real zeros of each function. Then use the functional values to graph the function.

.4, 1.3, 2.6, 4.7

3.6, −1.6, −0.7, 0.6, 1.3

26. $g(x) = x^4 - 9x^3 + 25x^2 - 24x + 6$ 27. $h(x) = x^5 + 4x^4 - x^3 - 9x^2 + 3$

28. $f(x) = x^3 - 3x^2 - 2$ **3.2**

29. $r(x) = x^3 - 3x - 4$ **2.2**

30. $f(x) = x^4 + 7x + 1$ **−1.9, −0.1**

31. $g(x) = x^5 + x^4 - 2x^3 + 1$ **−2.0**

Critical Thinking

32. Study the graphs for Exercises 14–31. Make a general statement comparing the graphs of functions of even degree with those of functions of odd degree. **Answers may vary. See margin.**

33. The function that represents the volume of a pyramid with a height of the same measure as the side of its square base is $V(s) = \frac{1}{3}s^3$.

   a. Graph the function. **See Solutions Manual.**

   b. Find the zeros of the function. **0**

   c. Find the maximum and minimum of the function. **There are none.**

   d. Make a conjecture about how all of this data relates. **See margin.**

Applications

34. **Aerospace Engineering** Use the information about the space shuttle fuel tank given in the beginning of the lesson to find the volume of the two hemispheres on the ends of the tank. Then determine the total volume of the tank to the nearest cubic meter. *Hint: The column of a sphere is given by the formula $V = \frac{4}{3}\pi r^3$.* **310 m³; 1480 m³**

35. **Pharmacy** A syringe is to deliver an injection of 2 cubic centimeters of medication. If the plunger is pulled out two centimeters to have the proper dosage, approximate the radius of the inside of the syringe to the nearest hundredth of a centimeter. *Hint: The volume of a cylinder is given by the formula $V = \pi r^2 h$.* **0.56 centimeters**

Mixed Review

36. **CDT—compact discs; CD—tapes; T—compact discs and tapes**

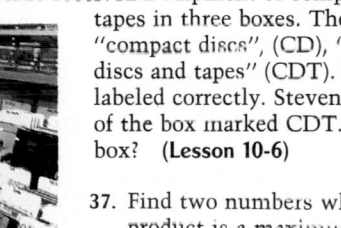

36. The Muzik Maze received a shipment of compact discs and cassette tapes in three boxes. The boxes are labeled "compact discs", (CD), "tapes", (T), and "compact discs and tapes" (CDT). None of the boxes are labeled correctly. Steven pulled a compact disc out of the box marked CDT. What is in each box? **(Lesson 10-6)**

37. Find two numbers whose sum is 60 and whose product is a maximum. **(Lesson 8-5) 30 and 30**

38. Factor $x^2y^2 - 25x^2$. **(Lesson 5-5)** $x^2(y + 5)(y - 5)$

39. State whether $y = \frac{1}{x}$ is a linear function. **(Lesson 2-2) no**

LESSON 10-6   GRAPHING POLYNOMIAL FUNCTIONS AND APPROXIMATING ZEROS   485

EXTENDING THE LESSON

Math Power: Reasoning

Suppose the graph $f(x)$ has 2 relative maxima and one relative minimum. What is the minimum degree of $f(x)$? **fourth degree**

Additional Answers

32. **A typical answer is that the ends of an even degree graph both point up or down and the ends of an odd degree function point in opposite directions.**

33d. **All three zeros occur at 0. However, since $V \neq 0$, we are not interested in zeros. There is no maximum or minimum volume for any value of s.**

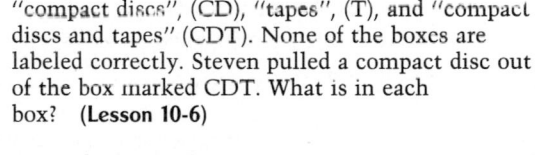
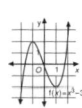
Chapter 10   485

Using Technology

Objective This optional page shows how spreadsheets can be used to perform mathematical computations and to enhance and extend mathematical concepts.

Teaching Suggestions

If spreadsheet software is available, have students enter the program for evaluating the function $f(x) = x^3 - 4x + 3$. Have students change the values in cells A3 to A11 to determine the zeros of the function to the nearest thousandth.

You may wish to have students modify the spreadsheet program to determine the zeros of other functions.

Point out to students that a spreadsheet program may also be used to determine ordered pairs for graphing functions.

Technology

Zeros of Polynomial Functions

Spreadsheet programs can be used to make tables and perform calculations. We can use these capabilities to find approximations for the zeros of polynomial functions.

The spreadsheet program below left is set up to find the values of the function $f(x) = x^3 - 4x + 3$ for values of the domain between -4 and 4. A printout of this program is shown below right. By finding these values, you can use the location principle to determine where zeros occur. Then the spreadsheet can be modified to find function values to get closer approximations of the zeros.

Polynomial Functions		
	A	**B**
1	FUNCTION	F(X) = X³ − 4X + 3
2	X	F(X)
3	-4	A3^3−4*A3+3
4	-3	A4^3−4*A4+3
5	-2	A5^3−4*A5+3
6	-1	A6^3−4*A6+3
7	0	A7^3−4*A7+3
8	1	A8^3−4*A8+3
9	2	A9^3−4*A9+3
10	3	A10^3−4*A10+3
11	4	A11^3−4*A11+3

```
= = = = = = = = = = = = = = = = = = =
       POLYNOMIAL FUNCTIONS
= = = = = = = A = = = = = = B = = = = = =
  1:   FUNCTION   F(X) = X³ - 4X + 3
  2:        X              F(X)
  3:       -4              -45
  4:       -3              -12
  5:       -2               3
  6:       -1               6
  7:        0               3
  8:        1               0
  9:        2               3
 10:        3              18
 11:        4              51
= = = = = = = = = = = = = = = = = = = = =
```

According to the location principal, there is a zero between -3 and -2, 1 is a zero, and there may be a zero between 0 and 1 or between 1 and 2. If you change the values in cells A3 to A11, you can evaluate the function for values in these ranges to determine the zeros more accurately. The zeros of the function are 1 and approximately -2.303 and 1.303.

EXERCISE

1. Describe how you could modify the spreadsheet program to find values for different functions. **Change cells B3 to B11 to evaluate the values in cells A3 to A11 appropriately.**

10-7 Composition of Functions

Objective
10-7

After studying this lesson, you should be able to:
- find the composition of functions.

Application

Bill Leshnock is an employee at Pogue's Department Store. As one of his benefits, he receives a 20% employee discount on his purchases at the store. During the Midnight Sale, Bill bought a leather jacket that was on sale for 30% off. The original price of the jacket was $299. How much did Bill pay?

To find how much Bill paid, we will have to first take 30% off of the price of the jacket and then take 20% off of that discounted price. This example illustrates the **composition of functions.**

Teaching Tip ❶

Composition of Functions

> Suppose f and g are functions such that the range of g is a subset of the domain of f. Then the composite function, $f \circ g$, can be described by the equation $[f \circ g](x) = f[g(x)]$.

$[f \circ g](x)$ and $f[g(x)]$ are both read "f of g of x."

Use the information given about Bill's purchase to find how much he paid for the leather jacket. Let x = the original price.

Let $f(x) = x - 0.2x$ *20% employee discount*
Let $g(x) = x - 0.3x$ *30% off sale price*

$[f \circ g](x) = f[g(x)]$

$\qquad = f(x - 0.3x)$ *Substitute x − 0.3x for g(x).*

$\qquad = f[299 - 0.3(299)]$ *Replace x with 299.*

$\qquad = f(209.30)$ *Simplify.*

$\qquad = 209.30 - 0.2(209.30)$ *Evaluate f when x is 239.20.*

$\qquad = 167.44$

Bill paid $167.44 for his leather jacket.

LESSON 10-7 COMPOSITION OF FUNCTIONS **487**

ALTERNATE TEACHING STRATEGIES

Using Models

Have students use differently colored cards or markers to create cards to illustrate the domain and range of each function in Example 2 on page 488. Then have students match the cards to show the mapping of $f \circ g$, as shown at the right. Then have them use the cards to show the mapping of $g \circ f$.

		Domain of g
5		4
−3		8	Range of g
−3	2	8	Domain of f
4	5	4	Range of f

Thus, $f \circ g = \{(5, 4), (4, 4)\}$

10-7 Lesson Notes

Lesson Resources
Reteaching Master 10-7
Practice Master 10-7
Enrichment Master 10-7
Activity Master, p. 28

 Transparency 10-7 contains the 5-Minute Check and a teaching aid for this lesson.

INTRODUCING THE LESSON

🕐 **5-Minute Check**

(over Lesson 10-6)

1. Graph $f(x) = x^4 - 17x^2 + 16$.

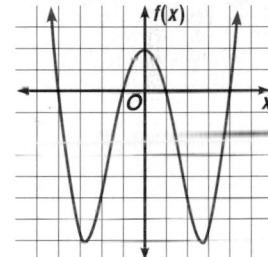

Other Prerequisite Skills
2. If $p(x) = x^2 + x - 6$, find $p(4)$. **14**
3. If $f(x) = x^2 + 5x - 3$, find $f(x - 3)$. **$x^2 - x - 9$**
4. If $g(x) = x^2 - 3$, find $2[g(x - 1)]$. **$2x^2 - 4x - 4$**
5. If $h(x) = x - 2$, find $3[h(x) - 2[h(x + 1)]]$. **$-3x$**

Motivating the Lesson
Bring in a Kelvin thermometer, a Celsius thermometer, and a Fahrenheit thermometer. Also bring in a hot plate, a container for water, and water for the container. Heat the water, taking the temperature of the water on all three scales as it rises. Write a formula to convert the temperature from one scale to the other.

Chapter 10 **487**

Teaching Tip ❶ Emphasize that the function symbol "closest" to the variable is applied first, rather than working from left to right. Thus, g is applied to x first when evaluating $(f \circ g)(x)$.

Chalkboard Examples

For Example 1

a. If $f(x) = x + 1$ and $g(x) = 3x - 4$, find $[f \circ g](x)$. $3x - 3$
b. If $g(x) = x^2 - 2$, and $f(x) = x + 1$, find $g[f(x)]$.
   $x^2 + 2x - 1$

For Example 2

If $f = \{(2, 1), (3, 2), (-1, 6)\}$ and $g = \{(2, 2), (6, -1), (1, 3)\}$, find $f \circ g$ and $g \circ f$.

$f \circ g = \{(2, 1), (6, 6), (1, 2)\}$
$g \circ f = \{(2, 3), (3, 2), (-1, -1)\}$

Reteaching Masters Booklet, p. 69

Example 1 | If $f(x) = x^2 + 6$ and $g(x) = 3x - 4$, find $[f \circ g](x)$.

$[f \circ g](x) = f[g(x)]$
$\quad = f[3x - 4]$ *Substitute $3x - 4$ for $g(x)$.*
$\quad = (3x - 4)^2 + 6$ *Evaluate f when x is $3x - 4$.*
$\quad = 9x^2 - 24x + 22$ *Simplify.*

The graphs of each function are shown at the right.

$f(x)$ is quadratic.
$g(x)$ is linear.
$[f \circ g](x)$ is quadratic.

What type of function would $[g \circ f](x)$ be?

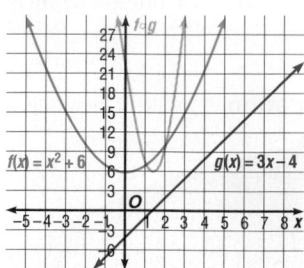

The composition of functions can be shown by mappings. Suppose $f = \{(3, 4), (9, -1), (0, 3)\}$ and $g = \{(4, 9), (3, 3), (-1, 0)\}$. The composition of these functions is shown below.

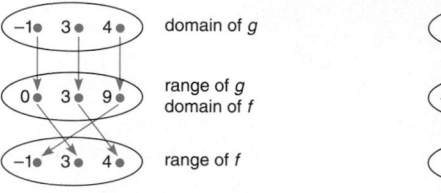
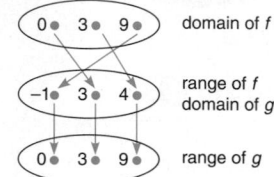

Example 2 | If $f = \{(2, 5), (8, 4), (-3, 4)\}$ and $g = \{(5, -3), (4, 8)\}$, find $f \circ g$ and $g \circ f$.

$f[g(5)] = f(-3)$ $g[f(2)] = g(5)$ $g[f(-3)] = g(4)$
$\quad = 4$ $\quad = -3$ $\quad = 8$

$f[g(4)] = f(8)$ $g[f(8)] = g(4)$
$\quad = 4$ $\quad = 8$

$f \circ g = \{(5, 4), (4, 4)\}$ $g \circ f = \{(2, -3), (8, 8), (-3, 8)\}$

The composition of two functions may not exist. Look back at the definition of the composition of functions. It defines the composition of functions f and g, $f \circ g$, when the range of g is a subset of the domain of f. If this condition is not met, the composition is not defined.

488   CHAPTER 10   POLYNOMIAL FUNCTIONS

Given $f(x)$ and $g(x)$, have students compute the value obtained by applying g, then f to a value of x in two ways. Find $f[g(3)]$ and $[f \circ g](3)$.

For example, $f(x) = 2x + 3$, $g(x) = x^2 - x - 2$:

$f(g(3))$ $[f \circ g](x) = 2x^2 - 2x - 1$
$f(3^2 - 3 - 2)$
$f(4)$ $[f \circ g](3) = 2 \cdot 9 - 6 - 1$
11 $[f \circ g](3) = 11$

Example 3

If $h = \{(2, 4), (6, 8), (4, 6), (8, 10)\}$ and $k = \{(6, 5), (4, 5), (10, 12), (8, 12)\}$, find $h \circ k$ and $k \circ h$ if they exist.

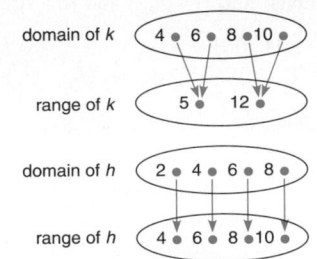

$h \circ k$ does not exist.
The range of k is not a subset of the domain of h.

$k \circ h = \{(2, 5), (4, 5), (6, 12), (8, 12)\}$

Chalkboard Example

For Example 3
If $f = \{(1, 3), (2, 7), (3, -2)\}$ and $g = \{(7, 11), (3, -6), (-2, -3)\}$, find $f \circ g$ and $g \circ f$ if they exist.
$f \circ g$ does not exist. The range of g is not a subset of the domain of f.
$g \circ f = \{(1, -6), (2, 11), (3, -3)\}$

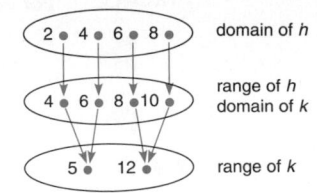

EVALUATING THE LESSON

Checking for Understanding
Exercises 1–12 are designed to help you assess understanding through reading, writing, and speaking. You should work through Exercises 1–4 with your students, and then monitor their work on Exercises 5–12.

Closing the Lesson

Writing Activity Write an explanation of how to find $f \circ g$ and $g \circ f$. Include the domain and range of each function and the composite.

Practice Masters Booklet, p. 79

CHECKING FOR UNDERSTANDING

Communicating Mathematics

Read and study the lesson to answer these questions.

1. Find the price Bill Leshnock would pay for a pair of jeans that are on sale 50% off. The regular price of the jeans is $35.99. **$14.40**

2. Would Bill get a greater discount on the jeans if the 20% employee discount was taken before the 50% off sale price? **no**

3. What is meant by the expression $[f \circ g](x)$?

4. Show that if $f(x) = x^2$ and $g(x) = x + 2$, $[f \circ g](x) \neq [g \circ f](x)$? **See margin.**

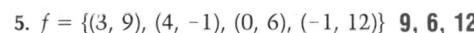 **3. *f* composition *g* or the function *f* performed on the function *g***

Guided Practice

For each function, f, find $f(3)$, $f(0)$, and $f(-1)$.

5. $f = \{(3, 9), (4, -1), (0, 6), (-1, 12)\}$ **9, 6, 12**

6. $f(x) = x - 5$ **-2, -5, -6**

7. $f(x) = x^2 + 3x + 2$ **20, 2, 0**

8. $f(x) = |x - 3|$ **0, 3, 4**

9. $f(x) = x^2 - x^5$ **-234, 0, 2**

For each pair of functions find $[f \circ g](2)$ and $[g \circ f](2)$.

10. $f(x) = x + 4$
    $g(x) = x - 7$
    -1, -1

11. $f(x) = x^2 + 1$
    $g(x) = x + 1$ **10, 6**

12. $f(x) = x^3 + 4$
    $g(x) = x + 3$
    129, 15

Additional Answer

4. $[f \circ g](x) = f[g(x)]$
   $= f[x + 2]$
   $= (x + 2)^2$
   $= x^2 + 4x + 4$

   $[g \circ f](x) = g[f(x)]$
   $= g[x^2]$
   $= (x^2) + 2$
   $= x^2 + 2$

   $[f \circ g](x) \neq [g \circ f](x)$

Homework Exercises

Assignment Guide

Basic: 13–30, 33–34, 36–39
Average: 14–31, 33–39
Enriched: 16–39

Teaching Tip ② Instead of finding the composite function and then substituting 2 for x, suggest that students find $f(2)$ [or $g(2)$] first and then use that value for $g(x)$ [or $f(x)$] in the next stage of evaluation.

Additional Answer

36.

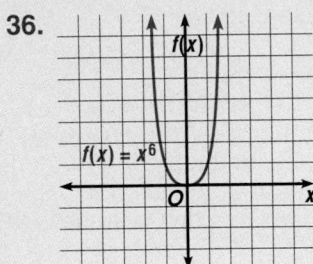

$f(x) = x^6$

Enrichment Masters Booklet, p. 69

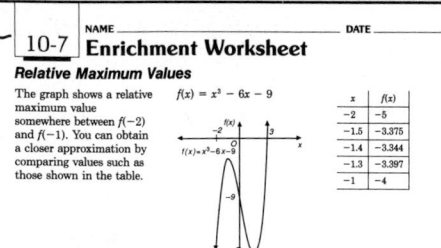
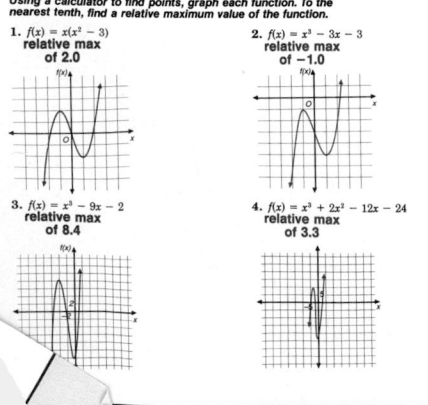

NAME _____ DATE _____

10-7 Enrichment Worksheet

Relative Maximum Values

The graph shows a relative maximum value $f(x) = x^3 - 6x - 9$
somewhere between $f(-2)$
and $f(-1)$. You can obtain
a closer approximation by
comparing values such as
those shown in the table.

x	$f(x)$
-2	-5
-1.5	-3.375
-1.4	-3.344
-1.3	-3.397
-1	-4

To the nearest tenth a relative maximum value for $f(x)$ is -3.3.

Using a calculator to find points, graph each function. To the
nearest tenth, find a relative maximum value of the function.

1. $f(x) = x(x^2 - 3)$
relative max of 2.0

2. $f(x) = x^3 - 3x - 3$
relative max of -1.0

3. $f(x) = x^3 - 9x - 2$
relative max of 8.4

4. $f(x) = x^3 + 2x^2 - 12x - 24$
relative max of 3.3

Chapter 10

EXERCISES

Practice

Ⓐ For each pair of functions, find $[f \circ g](2)$ and $[g \circ f](2)$. **Teaching Tip ②**

13. $f(x) = x^3$
$g(x) = x^2$ **64, 64**

14. $f(x) = x$
$g(x) = -x$ **−2, −2**

15. $f = \{(3, 2), (1, -7), (2, 0)\}$
$g = \{(2, 1), (0, 11)\}$ **−7, 11**

Ⓑ For each pair of functions, find $g[h(x)]$ and $h[g(x)]$.

16. $x + 13, x + 13$
17. $10x, 10x$
18. $x^2 - 1,$
$x^2 - 2x + 1$

16. $g(x) = x + 4$
$h(x) = x + 9$

17. $g(x) = 2x$
$h(x) = 5x$

18. $g(x) = x - 1$
$h(x) = x^2$

19. $g(x) = -x$
$h(x) = -x$ **x, x**

20. $g(x) = x + 1$
$h(x) = x^3$

21. $g(x) = |x|$
$h(x) = x - 3$

$x^3 + 1, x^3 + 3x^2 + 3x + 1$ $|x - 3|, |x| - 3$

If $f(x) = x^2$, $g(x) = 3x$, and $h(x) = x - 1$, find each value.

22. $g[f(1)]$ **3**
23. $[f \circ h](3)$ **4**
24. $[h \circ f](3)$ **8**
25. $[g \circ f](-2)$ **12**
26. $g[h(-2)]$ **−9**
27. $f[h(-3)]$ **16**
28. $g[f(x)]$ **3x²**
29. $[f \circ g](x)$ **9x²**
30. $[f \circ (g \circ h)](x)$
$9x^2 - 18x + 9$

Ⓒ Express $g \circ f$ and $f \circ g$, if they exist, as a set of ordered pairs.

31. $f = \{(1, 1), (0, -3)\}$
$g = \{(1, 0), (-3, 1), (2, 1)\}$
$f \circ g = \{(1, -3), (-3, 1), (2, 1)\}$
$g \circ f = \{(1, 0), (0, 1)\}$

32. $f = \{(3, 8), (4, 0), (6, 3), (7, -1)\}$
$g = \{(0, 4), (8, 6), (3, 6), (-1, -8)\}$
$g \circ f = \{(3, 6), (4, 4), (6, 6), (7, -8)\}$
$f \circ g$ doesn't exist

Journal
Make up a number puzzle like the one at the beginning of the lesson. Be sure to try it out on another person to see if it works.

Critical Thinking

33. Name two functions f and g such that $f[g(x)] = g[f(x)]$. **Sample answers are $f(x) = 2x$, $g(x) = 4x$; $f(x) = -x$, $g(x) = -x$.**

Applications

34. Chemistry While performing an experiment, Joyce needs to record the temperature of a solution at different times. She needs to record the temperature in degrees Kelvin, but only has a thermometer with a Fahrenheit scale. Joyce knows that a Kelvin temperature is 273 degrees greater than a Celsius temperature and that the formula $C = \frac{5}{9}(F - 32)$ converts a Fahrenheit temperature to Celsius. What will she record when the thermometer reads 59°F? **288°K**

35. Business The Clothes Rack adds a 75% markup to the wholesale price of merchandise to determine the selling price. If a jacket that costs $100 wholesale is on sale for 20% off, what would a customer pay for it? **$140**

Mixed Review

36. Graph the function $f(x) = x^6$. **(Lesson 10-6) See margin.**

37. Approximate to the nearest tenth the real zeros of the function $g(x) = x^4 - 4x^2 + 3$. **(Lesson 10-6) 1, −1, 1.7, −1.7**

38. Write an equation for the circle that has a diameter whose endpoints are $(4, -3)$ and $(8, 5)$. **(Lesson 9-3) $(x - 6)^2 + (y - 1)^2 = 20$**

39. Evaluate the expression $x(x^2 + 2x + 3)$ if $x = 5$. **(Lesson 1-2) 190**

EXTENDING THE LESSON

Math Power: Reasoning

How can you determine from the graph of a relation whether its inverse will be a function?

If any horizontal line drawn on the graph of the relation passes through no more than one point on that graph, then the inverse of the relation is a function.

10-8 Inverse Functions and Relations

Objectives After studying this lesson, you should be able to:

10-8A ■ determine the inverse of a function or relation, and

10-8B ■ graph a function and its inverse.

Application

Meredith read about a number game in her Scholastic magazine and decided to try it out on her twin brother Christopher. Christopher was perplexed because his sister could guess what number he was thinking of every time. Suppose Christopher was thinking of the number 47. Here are Meredith's instructions to him.

Verbal directions	Number	Functional representation
Think of a number.	47	$f(x) = x$
Double the number.	94	$g(x) = 2[f(x)] = 2x$
Now add 8.	102	$h(x) = g(x) + 8 = 2x + 8$
Tell me your final answer and I'll tell you your number.		

Not to be outdone by his sister, Christopher tried to figure out this puzzle. In algebra class, the solution dawned on him. Subtraction is the inverse operation of addition and division is the inverse operation of multiplication. She must use these inverses to determine the original number.

The chart below shows the inverse of the puzzle shown above.

Verbal directions	Number	Functional representation
Tell me a number	102	$p(x) = x$
Subtract 8 from the number.	94	$r(x) - p(x) = 8 = x - 8$
Now divide by 2.	47	$t(x) = \dfrac{r(x)}{?} = \dfrac{x - 8}{?}$

The functions $h(x) = 2x + 8$ and $t(x) = \dfrac{x - 8}{2}$ are **inverse functions.**

Definition of Inverse Functions	Two functions, f and g, are inverse functions if and only if both their compositions are the identity function. That is, $[f \circ g](x) = x$ and $[g \circ f](x) = x$.

ALTERNATE TEACHING STRATEGIES

Using Manipulatives

Cut a piece of graph paper into four equal parts. Distribute one of the quarter sheets to each student. Have them graph a function ($y = 2x - 4$) and its inverse ($y = \frac{1}{2}x + 2$) on the same grid. Have them graph $y = x$ and fold the paper about this line. They should observe that the two graphs are reflections of each other. They can then connect the concept of inverse functions and their graphs.

10-8 Lesson Notes

Lesson Resources
Reteaching Master 10-8
Practice Master 10-8
Enrichment Master 10-8
Lab Manual, pp. 61–62

 Transparency 10–8 contains the 5-Minute Check and a teaching aid for this lesson.

INTRODUCING THE LESSON

5-Minute Check

(over Lesson 10–7)

1. If $f(x) = x + 3$ and $g(x) = x^2 - 2$, find $g[f(x)]$.
   $x^2 + 6x + 7$
2. If $f(x) = x^2 - 3x + 7$ and $g(x) = x + 4$, find $(f \circ g)(x)$.
   $x^2 + 5x + 11$
3. If $f(x) = \{(2, 1), (3, 4), (6, -2)\}$ and $g(x) = \{(1, 5), (4, 7), (-2, -3)\}$, find $f \circ g$ and $g \circ f$ if they exist.
   $f \circ g$ **does not exist.**
   $g \circ f = \{(2, 5), (3, -7), (6, -3)\}$

Other Prerequisite Skills

4. Solve $y = 3x + 7$ for x.
   $x = \dfrac{y - 7}{3}$
5. Solve $y = x^2 + 4$ for x.
   $x = \pm\sqrt{y - 4}$

Motivating the Lesson

Discuss the following questions.

1. Why is 0 the additive identity?
   Any number plus 0 equals the number itself.
2. Why is 1 the multiplicative identity? **Any number times 1 equals the number itself.**
3. Tell what it means for two numbers to be additive inverses of one another. **Their sum is zero.**
4. Tell what it means for two numbers to be multiplicative inverses of one another. **Their product is 1.**

Chalkboard Example

For Example 1

Find the inverse of $f(x) = x + 3$. Then show that f and its inverse are inverse functions and graph both functions. $f^{-1}(x) = x - 3$ **They are inverse functions because $[f \circ f^{-1}](x) = [f^{-1} \circ f](x) = x$.**

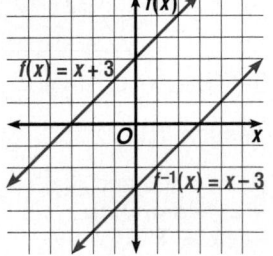

You can determine if two functions are inverse functions by finding both their compositions. Consider $h(x) = 2x + 8$ and $t(x) = \dfrac{x - 8}{2}$.

$$
\begin{aligned}
[h \circ t](x) &= h[t(x)] \\
&= h\!\left(\frac{x - 8}{2}\right) \\
&= 2\!\left(\frac{x - 8}{2}\right) + 8 \\
&= x
\end{aligned}
\qquad
\begin{aligned}
[t \circ h](x) &= t[h(x)] \\
&= t(2x + 8) \\
&= \frac{(2x + 8) - 8}{2} \\
&= x
\end{aligned}
$$

The identity function is $f(x) = x$. Since both $[h \circ t](x)$ and $[t \circ h](x)$ equal x, $h(x)$ and $t(x)$ are inverse functions. That is, h is the inverse of t and t is the inverse of h. We can write this using this notation.

$$ h = t^{-1} \quad \text{and} \quad t = h^{-1} $$

The symbol h^{-1} is read "h inverse" or "the inverse of h." By the definition of inverse functions we can write $[h \circ h^{-1}](x) = x$ and $[h^{-1} \circ h](x) = x$. *The -1 is <u>not</u> an exponent.*

The ordered pairs of inverse functions are related. The functions $f(x) = 4x + 5$ and $f^{-1}(x) = \dfrac{x - 5}{4}$ are inverse functions. Evaluate $f(5)$. Then find $f^{-1}[f(5)]$.

$$ f(5) = 4(5) + 5 \text{ or } 25 \qquad\qquad f^{-1}(25) = \frac{(25) - 5}{4} \text{ or } 5 $$

The ordered pair $(5, 25)$ belongs to f.

The ordered pair $(25, 5)$ belongs to f^{-1}.

The graphs of the two functions are shown at the left.

So, the inverse of a function can be found by reversing the order of the coordinates of each ordered pair that satisfies the function.

Property of Inverse Functions	**Suppose f and f^{-1} are inverse functions. Then $f(a) = b$ if and only if $f^{-1}(b) = a$.**

To find the inverse of a function f, you can interchange the variables in the equation, $y = f(x)$. This results in the inverse of the function $f(x)$.

Example

Find the inverse of $f(x) = 2x + 1$. Then show that f and its inverse are inverse functions and graph both functions.

Rewrite $f(x)$ as $y = 2x + 1$. Then interchange the variables and solve for y.

$$ x = 2y + 1 \qquad \textit{Interchange variables x and y.} $$
$$ x - 1 = 2y \qquad \textit{Solve for y.} $$
$$ \frac{x - 1}{2} = y \qquad \textit{Notice that the equation defines a function.} $$

The inverse of f is $f^{-1}(x) = \dfrac{x - 1}{2}$.

Now show that the compositions of f and f^{-1} are identity functions.

$[f \circ f^{-1}](x) = f[f^{-1}(x)]$

$\quad = f\left(\dfrac{x-1}{2}\right)$

$\quad = 2\left(\dfrac{x-1}{2}\right) + 1$

$\quad = x$

$[f^{-1} \circ f](x) = f^{-1}[f(x)]$

$\quad = f^{-1}(2x + 1)$

$\quad = \dfrac{(2x + 1) - 1}{2}$

$\quad = x$

The functions are inverses, since both $[f \circ f^{-1}](x)$ and $[f^{-1} \circ f]x$ equal x.

Now graph both functions.

Suppose the plane containing the graphs could be folded along the line $g(x) = x$. Then the graphs would coincide.

The graphs of a function and its inverse are mirror images, or reflections, of each other with respect to the graph of the identity function. The line whose equation is $g(x) = x$ is the line of symmetry.

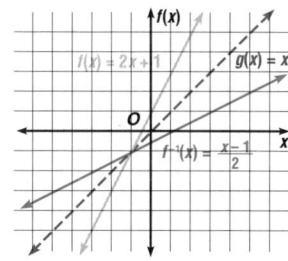

Teaching Tip ❶

In the Example, f and f^{-1} were both functions. However, the inverse of a function is not always a function. For example, the inverse of $f(x) = x^2$ is $f^{-1} = \pm\sqrt{x}$, which is not a function but a relation. You may recall that a relation is a set of ordered pairs. The order of the coordinates in each ordered pair of a relation can be reversed to create a new relation. This new set of ordered pairs and the original relation are inverse relations.

Definition of Inverse Relations	Two relations are inverse relations if and only if whenever one relation contains the element (a, b), the other relation contains the element (b, a).

CHECKING FOR UNDERSTANDING

Communicating Mathematics

Read and study the lesson to answer these questions.

1. How can you find the inverse of a function? **See margin.**

2. Give an example of a function whose inverse is not a function. $f(x) = x^2$.

3. Are the functions $f(x) = 5x^2 + 6$ and $g(x) = \dfrac{x^2 - 6}{5}$ inverse functions? Explain your answer. **No, $f \circ g \neq x$.**

LESSON 10-8   INVERSE FUNCTIONS AND RELATIONS   493

RETEACHING THE LESSON

Note that just as a rational number and its additive inverse yield the additive identity, the composition of a function and its inverse yield the identify function. Show that the inverse of a function can be found by reversing the order of each pair in the given function.

Additional Answer

1. Switch x and y in the equation and solve for y.

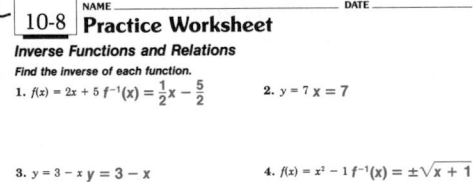

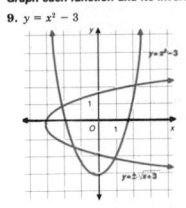
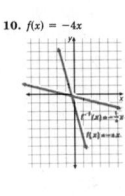

Guided Practice

Find the inverse of each relation and determine whether the inverse is a function.

4. {(2, 3), (2, 4)}, **no**   4. {(3, 2), (4, 2)}   5. {(−1, −2), (−3, −2), (−1, −4), (0, 6)}
5. {(−2, −1), (−2, −3), (−4, −1), (6, 0)}, **no**   6. {(3, 8), (4, −2), (5, −3)}   7. {(2, 4), (−3, 1), (2, 8)}
6. {(8, 3), (−2, 4), (−3, 5)}, **yes**   8. {(1, 3), (1, −1), (1, −3), (1, 1)}   9. {(6, 11), (−2, 7), (0, 3), (−5, 3)}
7. {(4, 2), (1, −3), (8, 2)}, **yes**   {(3, 1), (−1, 1), (−3, 1), (1, 1)}, **yes**   {(11, 6), (7, −2), (3, 0), (3, −5)}, **no**

Find the inverse of each function.

10. $y = 3x$ $y = \frac{x}{3}$ 11. $f(x) = x - 5$ $f^{-1}(x) = x + 5$ 12. $y = -3x + 1$ $y = -\frac{1}{3}x + \frac{1}{3}$

EXERCISES

Practice Find the inverse of each function. 14. $g^{-1}(x) = \frac{1}{4}x - 1$ 15. $f^{-1}(x) = 2x - 4$

A
13. $y = 8$ $x = 8$ 14. $g(x) = 4x + 4$ 15. $f(x) = \frac{1}{2}x + 2$

16. $h(x) = x^3$ $h^{-1}(x) = \sqrt[3]{x}$ 17. $y = x^2 - 9$ $y = \pm\sqrt{x + 9}$ 18. $f(x) = (x - 9)^2$ $f^{-1}(x) = \pm\sqrt{x} + 9$

B Graph each function and its inverse. **19–27. See Solutions Manual.**

19. $f(x) = x$ 20. $y = 3x$ 21. $y = -2x - 1$

22. $f(x) = \frac{2x - 1}{3}$ 23. $f(x) = 5x + 3$ 24. $g(x) = x - 2$

25. $g(x) = (x - 4)^2$ 26. $y = x^2 + 1$ 27. $y = (x + 2)^2 - 3$

CONNECTION **Geometry**

28. The vertices of square *ABCD* form the relation {(2, 4), (8, 4), (2, −2), (8, −2)}. Find the inverse of this relation and determine if the resulting ordered pairs are also the vertices of a square. {(4, 2), (4, 8), (−2, 2), (−2, 8)}, **a square**

C Determine whether each pair of functions are inverse functions.

29. $f(x) = x + 6$ $g(x) = x - 6$ **yes**   30. $f(x) = -2x + 3$ $g(x) = 2x - 3$ **no**   31. $f(x) = 4x - 5$ $g(x) = \frac{x + 5}{4}$ **yes**

32. $f(x) = x$ $g(x) = -x$ **no**   33. $f(x) = \frac{x - 2}{3}$ $g(x) = 3x - 2$ **no**   34. $f(x) = \frac{x - 1}{2}$ $g(x) = 2x + 1$ **yes**

Sketch the graph of the inverse of each relation. Then determine if the inverse is a function. **Teaching Tip** ❷

35.   36.   37.

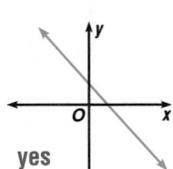
yes
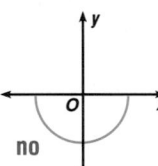
no
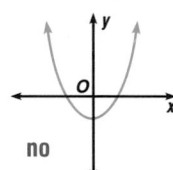
no

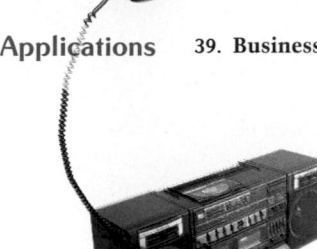

38. Find a function that is its own inverse. Can you find more than one? **Answers may vary. A sample answer is $f(x) = x$ and $f^{-1}(x) = x$ or $f(x) = -x$ and $f^{-1}(x) = -x$.**

Applications

39. Business Sales associates at Egan Electronics earn $7.00 an hour plus a 3% commission on the merchandise they sell. Write a function to describe their income and find how much merchandise they must sell in order to earn $400 in a 40-hour week. **$I(m) = 280 + 0.03m$; $4000**

40. Consumerism Mr. and Mrs. Pearson bought a stereo on sale from Egan Electronics. They used a $50 gift certificate to help pay for the stereo. The final bill was $453.20 plus tax. If the stereo was on sale 20% off, what is its regular price? **$629.00**

Computer

41. The DEFFN command in BASIC is used to enter a formula to be evaluated for many numbers. In this program the functions are $f(x) = 2x - 1$ and $g(x) = x^2 + 1$. The computer prints the values of $f(x)$, $g(x)$, $f[g(x)]$, and $g[f(x)]$. You can change lines 10 and 20 to use this program with any pair of functions.

```
10  DEFFNF(X) = 2*X -1
20  DEFFNG(X) = X^2 + 1
30  PRINT "ENTER A NUMBER."
40  INPUT X
50  PRINT "F(X) = ";FNF(X)
60  PRINT "G(X) = ";FNG(X)
70  PRINT "F[G(X)]
       = ";FNF(FNG(X))
80  PRINT "G[F(X)]
       - ";FNG(FNF(X))
90  END
```

Teaching Tip ❸

Use the BASIC program and a chart to determine if each pair of functions are inverses of each other.

a. $f(x) - x + 1$
$g(x) = x - 1$
yes

b. $f(x) = x + 4$
$g(x) = x - 4$
yes

c. $f(x) - \frac{1}{5}(x + 7)$
$t(x) = -5x + 7$
no

43. $g \cdot f = \{(2, 5), (3, -7), (6, -3)\}$; $f \circ g$ does not exist

Mixed Review

42. If $f(x) = 3x$ and $g(x) = x - 1$, find $f[g(x)]$. **(Lesson 10-7)** $3x - 3$

43. If $f = \{(2, 1)(3, 4)(6, -2)\}$ and $g = \{(1, 5), (4, -7), (-2, -3)\}$, express $g \circ f$ and $f \circ g$ as sets of ordered pairs, if they exist. **(Lesson 10-7)**

44. State whether $f(x) = \frac{1}{x^2} + \frac{1}{x} + 1$ describes a quadratic function. Explain your answer. **(Lesson 8-1)** **No, because of variable in denominator**

45. Simplify $\dfrac{x^{\frac{1}{3}}}{x^{\frac{2}{3}} - x^{-\frac{1}{3}}}$. **(Lesson 6-6)** $\dfrac{x^{\frac{2}{3}}}{x - 1}$

46. Divide $3a^4 - 2a^3 + 5a^2 - 4a - 2$ by $3a + 1$. **(Lesson 5-6)** $a^3 - a^2 + 2a - 2$

LESSON 10-8 INVERSE FUNCTIONS AND RELATIONS 495

Portfolio

Select some of your work from this chapter that shows how you used a calculator or computer. Place it in your portfolio.

EXTENDING THE LESSON

Math Power: Reasoning

The function $y = x$ is its own inverse. Write another function that is its own inverse.

Sample answer: $y = 2 - x$

The Chapter Summary and Review begins with an alphabetical listing of the new terms that were presented in the chapter. Have students define each term and provide an example of it, if appropriate.

The Skills and Concepts presented in the chapter are reviewed using a side-by-side format. Encourage students to refer to the Objectives and Examples on the left as they complete the Review Exercises on the right.

The Chapter Summary and Review ends with exercises that review Applications and Connections.

CHAPTER 10 **SUMMARY AND REVIEW**

VOCABULARY

Upon completing this chapter you should be familiar with the following terms:

Complex Conjugates Theorem	471	451	polynomial function
composition of functions	487	450	polynomial in one variable
depressed polynomial	461	475	Rational Zero Theorem
Descartes' rule of signs	471	483	relative maximum
Factor Theorem	461	483	relative minimum
Fundamental Theorem of Algebra	469	459	Remainder Theorem
Integral Zero Theorem	475	469	root of polynomial equation
inverse function	491	460	synthetic substitution
inverse relation	493	469	zero of polynomial function
Location Principle	482		

SKILLS AND CONCEPTS

OBJECTIVES AND EXAMPLES	REVIEW EXERCISES

Upon completing this chapter, you should be able to:
- evaluate polynomial functions. **(Lesson 10-1)**

Find $p(a + 1)$ if $p(x) = 5x - x^2 + 3x^3$.

$p(a + 1) = 5(a + 1) - (a + 1)^2 +$
$\qquad 3(a + 1)^3$
$\qquad = 5a + 5 - (a^2 + 2a + 1)$
$\qquad + 3(a^3 + 3a^2 + 3a + 1)$
$\qquad = 3a^3 + 8a^2 + 12a + 7$

Use these exercises to review and prepare for the chapter test.

Find $p(x - 2)$ for each function $p(x)$.

1. $p(x) = 6x + 3$ **2.** $p(x) = x^2 + 5$
   $\mathbf{6x - 9}$ $\mathbf{x^2 - 4x + 9}$

Find $f(x + h)$ for each function $f(x)$.

3. $f(x) = x^2 - x$ **4.** $f(x) = 2x^3 - 1$
   $\mathbf{x^2 + 2xh + h^2}$ $\mathbf{2x^3 + 6x^2h +}$
   $\mathbf{- x - h}$ $\mathbf{6xh^2 + 2h^3 - 1}$

- find factors of polynomials using the Factor Theorem and synthetic division. **(Lesson 10-2)**

The Factor Theorem states that the binomial $x - a$ is a factor of the polynomial $f(x)$ if and only if $f(a) = 0$.

Given a polynomial and one of its factors, find the remaining factors of the polynomial. Some factors may not be binomials.

5. $x^3 + 5x^2 + 8x + 4;\ x + 1$ $\mathbf{x + 2, x + 2}$
6. $x^4 - 6x^3 + 22x + 15;\ x + 1$
   $\mathbf{x + 1, x - 3, x - 5}$

- find the number of real positive zeros, real negative zeros, and complex zeros for a polynomial function. **(Lesson 10-4)**

State the number of positive real zeros and negative real zeros for $f(x) = 5x^4 + 6x^3 - 8x + 12$.

Since $f(x)$ has 2 sign changes, there are 2 or 0 real positive zeros.

$f(-x) = 5x^4 - 6x^3 + 8x + 12$

Since $f(-x)$ has 2 sign changes, there are 2 or 0 negative real zeros.

For each function, state the number of positive real zeros, negative real zeros, and complex zeros. **7. 3 or 1; 1; 2 or 0**

7. $f(x) = 2x^4 - x^3 + 5x^2 + 3x - 9$
8. $f(x) = 7x^3 + 5x - 1$ **1; 0; 2**
9. $f(x) = -4x^4 - x^2 - x - 1$ **0; 0 or 2; 4 or 2**
10. $f(x) = x^4 + x^3 - 7x + 1$
2 or 0; 2 or 0; 4, 2, or 0

- find zeros of polynomial functions **(Lesson 10-5)**

The Rational Zero Theorem states that if $\frac{p}{q}$ is a rational number in simplest form and a zero of the function $f(x) = a_0x^n + a_1x^{n-1} + ... + a_{n-1}x + a_n$, then p is a factor of a_n and q is a factor of a_0.

Find all the rational zeros for each function.

11. $f(x) = 2x^3 - 13x^2 + 17x + 12$ $-\frac{1}{2}, 3, 4$
12. $g(x) = x^4 + 5x^3 + 15x^2 + 19x + 8$ -1
13. $h(x) = x^3 - 3x^2 - 10x + 24$ $-3, 2, 4$
14. $f(x) = 2x^3 - 5x^2 - 28x + 15$ $-3, 5, \frac{1}{2}$

- approximate the real zeros of polynomial functions and graph. **(Lesson 10-6)**

The Location Principle states that if $y = f(x)$ represents a polynomial function, and a and b are two numbers such that $f(a) < 0$ and $f(b) > 0$, then the function has at least one zero between a and b.

Approximate to the nearest tenth the real zeros of each function. Then use the functional values to graph the function.

15. $f(x) = x^3 - x^2 + 1$ -0.8
16. $g(x) = 4x^3 + x^2 - 11x + 3$ $-1.9, 0.3, 1.4$
15–16. See margin for graphs.

- find the composition of functions. **(Lesson 10-7)**

If $f(x) = x^2 - 2$ and $g(x) = 8x - 1$, find $[f \circ g](x)$ and $[g \circ f](x)$.

$[f \circ g](x) = (8x - 1)^2 - 2$
$= 64x^2 - 16x + 1 - 2$
$= 64x^2 - 16x - 1$
$[g \circ f](x) = 8(x^2 - 2) - 1$
$= 8x^2 - 17$

For each pair of functions, f and g, find $[f \circ g](x)$ and $[g \circ f](x)$.

17. $f(x) = 2x - 1$ **18.** $f(x) = x^2 + 2$
$g(x) = 3x + 4$ $g(x) = x - 3$
19. If $f = \{(2, 1), (-1, 6), (3, 2)\}$ and $g = \{(2, 2), (6, -1), (1, 5)\}$, express $f \circ g$ and $g \circ f$, if they exist, as sets of ordered pairs. $f \circ g$
does not exist, $g \circ f = \{(2, 5), (-1, -1), (3, 2)\}$
17. $[f \circ g](x) = 6x + 7$, $[g \circ f](x) = 6x + 1$
18. $[f \circ g](x) = x^2 - 6x + 11$, $[g \circ f](x) = x^2 - 1$

Alternate Review Strategy

To provide a brief in-class review, you may wish to read the following questions to the class and require a verbal response.

1. Find $g(3)$ for $g(x) = 2x + 12$. **18**
2. Find $f(x + h)$ for $f(x) = 3x^3 - 2$.
   $f(x + h) = 3(x + h)^3 - 2$
3. For $f(x) = x^3 + 2x^2 - 5x - 6$, state the number of possible positive and negative real roots. **1; 2 or 0**
4. Find all the possible rational zeros for $f(x) = 2x^4 + x^3 + 4x^2 + x + 4$. **$\pm1; \pm2; \pm4; \pm\frac{1}{2}$**
5. Approximate to the nearest tenth the real zeros of $f(x) = x^2 - x - 5$. **2.8; -1.8**
6. Determine whether $f(x) = x + 6$ and $g(x) = x - 6$ are inverse functions. **yes**
7. Determine whether $f(x) = 4x^2$ and $g(x) = \frac{\sqrt{x}}{5}$ are inverse functions. **no**
8. The volume of a rectangular solid is 750 cubic units. The length of the box is 3 units times the width. The height is 2 units times the width. Find the dimensions of the box. **$5 \times 15 \times 10$**

Additional Answers

15.

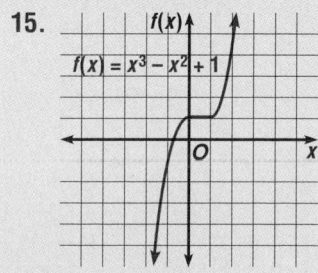

$f(x) = x^3 - x^2 + 1$

16.

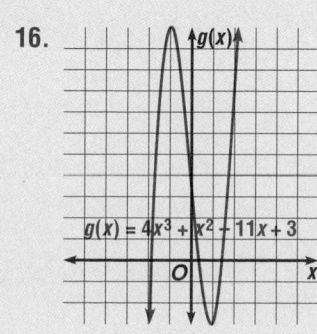

$g(x) = 4x^3 + x^2 - 11x + 3$

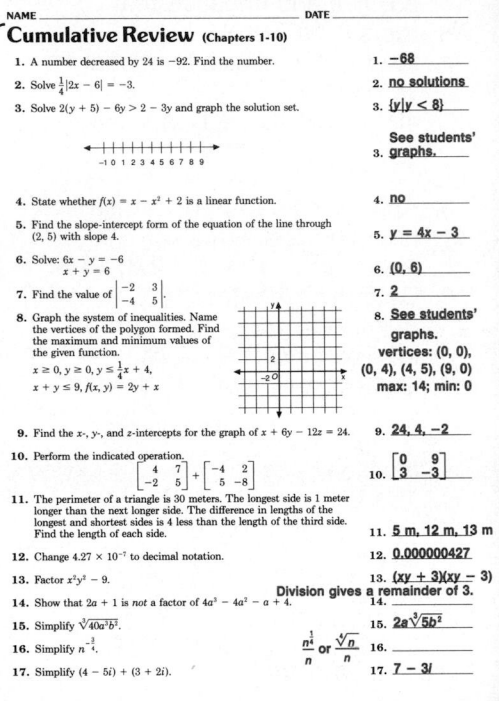

OBJECTIVES AND EXAMPLES	REVIEW EXERCISES

■ determine the inverse of a function or relation. (Lesson 10-8)

Two functions are inverses if and only if both of the compositions are the identity function. If one function contains the element (a, b), then the other contains (b, a).

Determine whether each pair of functions are inverse functions. **21. yes**

20. $f(x) = 3x - 4$
    $g(x) = \frac{x - 4}{3}$ **no**

21. $f(x) = -2x - 3$
    $g(x) = \frac{-x - 3}{2}$

APPLICATIONS AND CONNECTIONS

22. **Investments** Four years ago, Mr. and Mrs. Moon bought an apartment building for $200,000. Two years ago, they bought an office building for $500,000. They bought an ocean-front beach house for $100,000 last year. (Lesson 10-2) **See margin.**

  a. Assuming that the investments have appreciated at a rate of x% per year, write a polynomial function to represent the current worth of their investments.

  b. Find the total worth of their investments if they appreciated at a rate of 12% per year. **about $1,053,904**

24. **Manufacturing** The DrinKone Company makes paper cups that are cone shaped. The volume of a cone is about 7.07 cubic inches. The diameter of the top of the cone is equal to the height of the cone. Determine the dimensions of the cone. (Lesson 10-5) *Hint: The formula for the volume of a cone is $V = \frac{1}{3}\pi r^2 h$* **radius = 1.5 inches, height = 3 inches**

25. **Geometry** The volume of a rectangular solid is 2475 cubic units. The length of the box is three units more than twice the width of the box. The height is two units less than the width. Find the dimensions of the box. (Lesson 10-4) **9 by 11 by 25 units**

23. **Education** Craig, Vanessa, Devin, and Anita attend Harding High School. Each will be attending a different school next year. They will attend the DeVry Institute of Technology, Judson College, The Juilliard School, and Case Western Reserve. The student attending DeVry will study electronics and the student attending Juilliard will study the cello. The student attending Judson has not chosen a major and the student attending Case Western Reserve will study chemical engineering. Neither Devin nor Anita can play an instrument. Vanessa will study electronics next year, but Anita has not yet decided what to study. Who will be attending which school? (Lesson 10-3) **See margin.**

26. **Business** The CD Menagerie adds a 100% markup to the wholesale price of compact discs before placing them in the store for sale. If a CD is on sale for 20% off and the customer pays $12 for it, what is its wholesale price? (Lesson 10-7) **$7.50**

Additional Answers

22a. $E(x) = 200,000(1 + 0.01x)^4 + 500,000(1 + 0.01x)^2 + 100,000(1 + 0.01x)$

23. **Craig: Julliard; Vanessa: DeVry; Devin: Case Western Reserve; Anita: Judson**

Answers for Chapter Test

3. $a^3 - 3a^2 + 2a + 7$
4. $-a^3 + 4a^2 - 5a + 2$
5. $(x^2 + 6x - 3) = (x + 5)(x + 1) - 8$; no
6. $(x^3 + 8x + 1) = (x^2 - 2x + 12)(x + 2) - 23$; no
7. $(x^3 - x^2 - 5x - 3) = (x^2 - 2x - 3)(x + 1) + 0$; yes
8. $(x^4 + x^3 + x^2 + x + 1) = (x^3 + x)(x + 1) + 1$; no
9. 2 or 0; 1; 0 or 2
10. 1; 3 or 1; 0 or 2
13. 4; $-2 \pm 3i$
14. 2; $-\frac{3}{4}$; $-2 \pm i\sqrt{5}$

Find $f(3)$ for each function f.

1. $f(x) = x^3 - 27$ **0**

2. $f(x) = 2x^4 - 3x^3 + 8$ **89**

Find $f(a - 1)$ for each function f. **3–4. See margin.**

3. $f(x) = x^3 - x + 7$

4. $f(x) = x^2 - x^3$

Divide using synthetic division and write your answer in the form *dividend = quotient · divisor + remainder*. Is the binomial a factor of the polynomial? **5–8. See margin.**

5. $(x^2 + 6x - 3) \div (x + 1)$

6. $(x^3 + 8x + 1) \div (x + 2)$

7. $(x^3 - x^2 - 5x - 3) \div (x + 1)$

8. $(x^4 + x^3 + x^2 + x + 1) \div (x + 1)$

For each function, state the number of positive real zeros, negative real zeros, and complex zeros. **9–10. See margin.**

9. $g(x) = x^3 - x^2 - 14x + 24$

10. $f(x) = x^4 + x^3 - 9x^2 - 17x - 8$

Find all the rational zeros for each function.

11. $f(x) = x^3 - 3x^2 - 53x - 9$ **9**

12. $h(x) = 6x^3 + 4x^2 - 14x + 4$ **-2, $\frac{1}{3}$, 1**

Find all zeros of each function. **13–14. See margin.**

13. $g(x) = x^3 - 3x - 52$

14. $h(x) = 4x^4 + 11x^3 + 10x^2 - 69x - 54$

15. Tara, Alan, and Lee each have an after school job. They are a cashier, a pizza delivery person, and a typist. Tara never took typing and cannot drive. Lee works in a busy lawyer's office. Who has what job? **Tara–cashier, Alan–delivery person, Lee–typist**

Approximate to the nearest tenth the real zeros of each function. Then use the functional values to graph the function. **16–17. See Solutions Manual.**

16. $f(x) = x^3 + 6x^2 + 6x - 4$

17. $g(x) = x^3 + 3x^2 - 2x + 1$

If $f(x) = 2x$ and $g(x) = x^2 - 1$, find each value.

18. $[f \circ g](4)$ **30**

19. $[g \circ f](x)$ **$4x^2 - 1$**

20. Find the inverse of the function $f(x) = x^2 + 2$. **$f^{-1}(x) = \pm\sqrt{x - 2}$**

Bonus
Suppose $f = \{(0, -3), (2, 5), (-1, 1), (3, 2)\}$, $g = \{(-1, 2), (2, 2), (1, 4), (4, 3), (0, -1)\}$, and $h = \{(4, 2), (1, 0), (-3, 4), (3, -1)\}$. Find $f \circ g \circ h$. **$\{(4, 5), (1, 1), (-3, 2), (3, 5)\}$**

Using the Chapter Test

This page may be used as a test or as a review. In addition, two multiple-choice tests and two free-response tests are provided in the Evaluation Masters Booklet. Chapter 10 Test, Form 1A is shown below.

Evaluation Masters Booklet, pp. 127–128

NAME _____ DATE _____

Chapter 10 Test, Form 1A

Write the letter for the correct answer in the blank at the right of each problem.

1. What is $g(-2)$ if $g(x) = x^3 + 3x - 5$?
A. -19 B. -3 C. 9 D. -7 1. **A**

2. What is $p(x + 4)$ if $p(x) = x^2 - 3x + 5$?
A. $x^2 - 11x + 9$ B. $x^2 - 11x + 33$
C. $x^2 + 5x + 9$ D. $x^2 + 5x + 33$ 2. **C**

3. What is $2f(x) - f(x - 1)$ if $f(x) = x^2 - 10$?
A. $3x^2 - 2x - 9$ B. $3x^2 + 2x - 9$
C. $x^2 - 2x - 9$ D. $x^2 + 2x - 11$ 3. **D**

4. Use the Factor Theorem and synthetic division to determine which of the following is a factor of $x^3 - 2x^2 + 3x - 6$.
A. $x + 2$ B. $x - 1$ C. $x + 1$ D. $x - 2$ 4. **D**

5. What is the remainder for $(x^3 + 2x^2 - 4x - 3) \div (x - 5)$?
A. 152 B. -58 C. 192 D. -198 5. **A**

6. What are the factors of $x^3 + 3x^2 - x - 3$? (Use synthetic division.)
A. $(x - 1)(x - 3)(x + 3)$ B. $(x + 1)(x - 1)(x + 3)$
C. $(x + 1)(x - 3)(x + 3)$ D. $(x + 1)(x - 1)(x - 3)$ 6. **B**

7. What is the value for k so that the remainder for $(x^3 + 4x^2 - 3x + k) \div (x + 1)$ is 4?
A. -4 B. -2 C. 2 D. 4 7. **B**

8. What are all the rational zeros for $f(x) = x^4 + 2x^3 - 19x - 20$?
A. $\pm 1, \pm 2, \pm 4, \pm 5, \pm 10, \pm 20$ B. $\pm 2, \pm 5, \pm 10$
C. $-5, -1, 4$ D. $-4, 1, 5$ 8. **C**

9. According to Descartes' Rule of Signs, how many rational zeros for $f(x) = 6x^3 + 5x^2 - 8x - 3$?
A. $-\frac{3}{2}, -\frac{1}{3}, 1$ B. $-3, -1, 1$
C. $\pm\frac{2}{3}, \pm\frac{1}{3}, \pm 1, \pm 2, \pm 3, \pm 6$ D. $\pm\frac{1}{6}, \pm\frac{1}{3}, \pm\frac{1}{2}, \pm\frac{3}{2}, \pm 1, \pm 6$ 9. **D**

10. How many positive real zeros does $f(x) = x^5 - 2x^3 + 5x^2 - x^2 + 5$ have?
A. 3 or 1 B. 5 or 3 or 1 C. 4 or 2 or 0 D. 4 or 2 or 1 10. **C**

11. How many negative real zeros does $f(x) = x^5 - 3x^4 + x^3 + 4x^2 + 5x - 1$ have?
A. 3 or 1 B. 2 or 0 C. 5 or 1 D. 5 or 3 or 1 11. **B**

12. How many imaginary zeros does $f(x) = 3x^3 + 5x^2 - x + 1$ have?
A. 4 B. 2 or 0 C. 3 D. 3 or 1 12. **B**

NAME _____ DATE _____

Chapter 10, Form 1A (continued)

13. What are all the zeros for $f(x) = x^3 + x^2 - 15x + 25$ if $2 + i$ is one zero?
A. $2 + i, 2 - i, -5$ B. $2 + i, 2 - i, 5$
C. $2 + i, 2 - i, -5, 5$ D. $2 + i, -5, 5$ 13. **A**

14. What is the simplest polynomial equation with integral coefficients that has roots -2 and $2 + i$?
A. $x^3 + 2x^2 + 13x - 8 = 0$ B. $x^3 + 6x^2 + 13x + 10 = 0$
C. $x^3 - 2x^2 - 3x + 10 = 0$ D. $x^3 - 6x^2 + 13x - 10 = 0$ 14. **C**

15. What are the real zeros for $f(x) = x^3 + 2x^2 - 4$? (Approximate the zeros to the nearest tenth.)
A. 1.1 B. 1.2 C. 1.0 D. 1.2 and -2 15. **A**

16. Which of the following could be a function for the graph?
A. $f(x) = x^3 - x^2 - x + 1$
B. $f(x) = -x^3 + x^2 + x - 1$
C. $f(x) = x^3 - 2x^2 - 4x + 8$
D. $f(x) = -x^3 + 2x^2 + 4x - 8$ 16. **D**

17. If $f(x) = x^2 - 1$ and $g(x) = x + 3$, what is $[g \circ f](-3)$?
A. -1 B. 11 C. -7 D. 35 17. **B**

18. What is the inverse of $f(x) = x^2 + 3$?
A. $f^{-1}(x) = \pm\sqrt{x + 3}$ B. $f^{-1}(x) = \pm\sqrt{x - 3}$
C. $f^{-1}(x) = \frac{1}{x^2 + 3}$ D. $f^{-1}(x) = -\frac{1}{x^2 + 3}$ 18. **B**

19. Which is the graph of the inverse of $y = x^2 - 1$?
A. B. C. D. 19. **C**

20. Boris, Nell, and Tosha have different hobbies. One collects stamps, one collects postcards, and one collects shells. Tosha's collection will not fit in a book. Boris does not collect stamps. What does Nell collect?
A. stamps B. shells C. coins D. none of these 20. **A**

Bonus
Find all integer values of k so that $x^3 + (k + 3)x^2 + k = 0$ has exactly one positive real root.
A. $\{0\}$ B. $\{-2\}$ C. $\{k | k \geq -1\}$ D. $\{k | k \leq -1\}$ Bonus **D**

A **Test and Review Generator** is provided in Apple, IBM, and Macintosh versions. You may use this software to create your own tests or worksheets, based on the needs of your students.

The **Performance Assessment Booklet** provides an alternate asssessment for evaluating student progress. An assessment for this chapter can be found on pages 19–20.

Some test questions on these pages deal with coordinates and geometry. The figures shown may not be drawn to scale.

Directions: Choose the one best answer. Write A, B, C, or D.

1. **B** What is the length of the diagonal of a square, if the area is $25x^2$?

   (A) $5x$ (B) $5x\sqrt{2}$

   (C) $10x$ (D) $5x^2$

2. **A** What percent of rectangle $ACDF$ is shaded?

   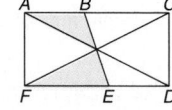

   (A) 25   (B) 30   (C) $33\frac{1}{3}$ (D) 50

3. **C** In $1\frac{1}{2}$ hours, the minute hand of a clock rotates through an angle of how many degrees?

   (A) 60°   (B) 180°   (C) 540°   (D) 720°

4. **C** The three straight lines intersect at the same point.

   $a + b =$

   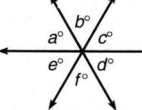

   (A) $b + f$ (B) $e + d$

   (C) $f + d$ (D) $c + e$

5. **B** Line p is parallel to line q.

   $c - a =$

   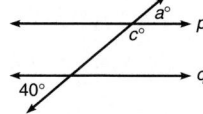

   (A) 0°   (B) 100°   (C) 120°   (D) 150°

6.

   C On line segment PR in the figure above, $PQ = 8$ and $QR = 6$. What is the length of the segment joining the midpoints of segments PQ and QR?

   (A) 3   (B) 4   (C) 7   (D) 14

7.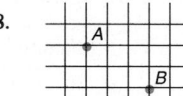

   D In the triangle above, $4x =$

   (A) 18   (B) 32   (C) 40   (D) 72

8.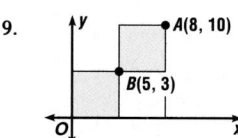

   D Above is a section of a graph without the x- and y-axes. If A has coordinates $(4, 6)$, state the coordinates of B.

   (A) $(4, 7)$ (B) $(4, 1)$

   (C) $(9, 2)$ (D) $(7, 4)$

9.
   A Point A in the figure above has coordinates $(8, 10)$ and point B has coordinates $(5, 3)$. What is the total area of the shaded region?

   (A) 36 square units   (B) 40 square units

   (C) 70 square units   (D) 80 square units

10. If $\ell_1 \perp \ell_2$, what is
D the value of $a + b$?

(A) 45

(B) 90

(C) 110

(D) cannot be determined

11.
B

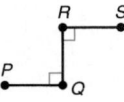

$\overline{QR} \perp \overline{RS}$
$\overline{QR} \perp \overline{PQ}$
$PQ = 10$
$QR = 7$
$RS = 14$

What is the shortest distance from
P to S?

(A) 24   (B) 25   (C) 28   (D) 31

12. What is the area of the triangle with
C vertices at $(4, -2)$, $(-2, 3)$, and $(4, 3)$?

(A) 60 square units   (B) 30 square units

(C) 15 square units   (D) 7.5 square units

13. The area of the
B circle enclosed
in the square is
8π. What is the
area of the
square?

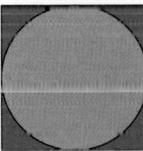

(A) 64 square units   (B) 32 square units

(C) 16 square units   (D) 8 square units

14. The length of a side of a rectangle is
D $(3x + 4)$ in. The length of the adjacent
side is nine less than twice the length
of the first side. What is the area of the
rectangle in terms of x?

(A) $6x^2 - 19x - 36$ in^2

(B) $6x^2 + 8x - 12$ in^2

(C) $18x^2 + 18x - 8$ in^2

(D) $18x^2 + 21x - 4$ in^2

---

15. The ratio of the circumference of a
C circle to its radius is

(A) π (B) $\dfrac{\pi}{2}$ (C) 2π (D) $\dfrac{2}{\pi}$

PREVIEWING THE CHAPTER

The chapter begins with a lesson where students find the asymptotes for the graph of a rational function and use them to sketch the graph. Next, students solve problems involving direct, inverse, and joint variation. Then, students learn how to add, subtract, multiply, and divide rational expressions and then apply these skills to solve rational equations. The chapter concludes with students applying their new-found knowledge and skills to solve real-world problems.

Problem-Solving Strategy   Students learn to draw a sketch of the situation or make a graph to organize and better visualize the data in order to solve problems.

Lesson Objective Chart

Lesson (Pages)	Lesson Objectives	State/Local Objectives
11-1 (506-509)	**11-1:** Locate the asymptotes and sketch the graph of a rational function.	
11-2 (510-515)	**11-2:** Solve problems involving direct, inverse, and joint variation.	
11-3 (516-521)	**11-3A:** Simplify rational expressions.	
	11-3B: Simplify complex fractions.	
11-4 (522-526)	**11-4A:** Find the least common denominator of two or more algebraic expressions.	
	11-4B: Add and subtract rational expressions.	
11-5 (527-530)	**11-5:** Solve rational equations.	
11-6 (532-534)	**11-6:** Solve problems by organizing data.	
11-7 (535-539)	**11-7:** Use rational expressions to solve problems.	

ORGANIZING THE CHAPTER

You may want to refer to the **Course Planning Calendar** on page T44.

Lesson Planning Guide — Blackline Masters Booklets

Lesson (Pages)	Course I	Course II	Course III	Reteaching	Practice	Enrichment	Evaluation	Technology	Lab Manual	Mixed Problem Solving	Applications	Cooperative Learning Activity	Multicultural	Transparencies
11-1 (506-509)	1	1	1	p. 71	p. 81	p. 71		p. 28					p. 11	11-1
11-2 (510-515)	1.5	1.5	1	p. 72	p. 82	p. 72	Quiz A, p. 149	p. 11		p. 11				11-2
11-3 (516-521)	2	1.5	1.5	p. 73	p. 83	p. 73								11-3
11-4 (522-526)	1.5	1	1	p. 74	p. 84	p. 74	Quiz D, p. 149 Mid-Chapter Test, p. 153							11-4
11-5 (527-530)	1	1	1	p. 75	p. 85	p. 75	Quiz C, p. 150				p. 29			11-5
11-6 (532-534)	1	1	0.5		p. 86							p. 47		11-6
11-7 (535-539)	1	1	1	p. 76	p. 87	p. 76	Quiz D, p. 150							11-7
Review (540-542)	1	1	1	Multiple Choice Tests, Forms 1A and 1B, pp. 141-144 Free Response Tests, Forms 2A and 2B, pp. 145-148										
Test (543)	1	1	1	Cumulative Review, pp. 151-152 Standardized Test Practice Questions, p. 154										

Course I: Chapters 1-13; Course II: Chapters 1-15; Course III: Chapters 1-17

Other Chapter Resources

Student Edition
Chapter Opener, pp. 502-503
Graphing Calculator Exploration, pp. 504-505
Fine Arts Connection, p. 515
Mid-Chapter Review, p. 521
Journal Entries, pp. 530, 534
Technology, p. 531
Cooperative Learning Activity, p. 534
Portfolio Suggestion, p. 539
Extended Project 3, pp. A10-A13

Teacher's Classroom Resources
Transparency 11-0
Real-World Applications Transparencies, 22, 23
Performance Assessment Booklet, pp. 21-22
Problem-of-the-Week Activity Cards, 22, 23
Tech Prep Applications Booklet, pp. 21-22
Lesson Plans, pp. 81-87

Other Supplements
Glencoe Mathematics Professional Series

Software
Test and Review Generator Software (Apple, IBM, and Macintosh)
Interactive Software (Macintosh)
Teacher's Guide for Software Resources

ENHANCING THE CHAPTER

Cooperative Learning

Establishing Individual Accountability

It is important for the success of a cooperative-learning session that students recognize their individual responsibility to the whole group. Not only is it unfair when only a few members of the group do all the work, it is contrary to the purpose of a cooperative-learning group; that is, to enhance the learning of each and every member. One way to encourage every-member participation is to make positive and rewarding comments about the members' contributions to the group. Another way is to evaluate the performance of each member of the group. Some tactics that can be used are to ask a reluctant participant to paraphrase what another member has just said, to ask a member if they agree with a statement just made by another member, and to say at the outset that you will randomly select a member from the group to explain the group's answers. Since the members of a group quickly observe who is a participant and who is not, another successful tactic is to assign the role of *encourager* to one of the members of the group. This student's main responsibility is to encourage each and every member of the group to participate.

Technology

The Technology Feature after Lesson 11-5 employs the *Mathematical Exploration Toolkit* to simplify phrases involving rational expressions. MET requires using the FACTOR command before a REDUCE command. Sums, differences, products, and quotients must first be combined into one rational expression. Therefore, students will gain practice making the same decision used when factoring by hand.

Critical Thinking

Students will live and work in a world that already provides them with easy access to powerful personal computers and software programs that provide interactive processes for finding and understanding solutions to business problems. Such programs require the user to employ higher-level thinking skills for successful implementation. As part of their preparation for this world, students should be given opportunities not only to answer but also to ask "What if" questions. Use the problems in this chapter to provide opportunities for students to create new conditions, including reversals where instead of finding the solution, the student gives a different solution and asks how the conditions must be changed to achieve the given results.

Cooperative Learning, p. 47

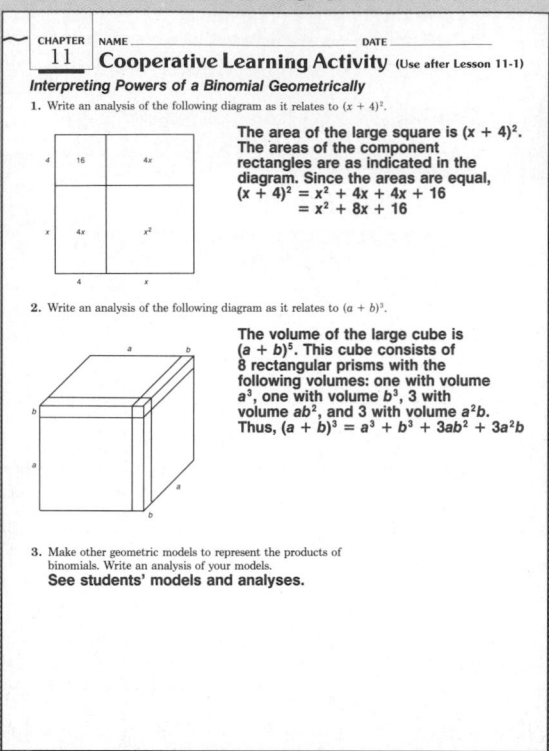

Technology, p. 11

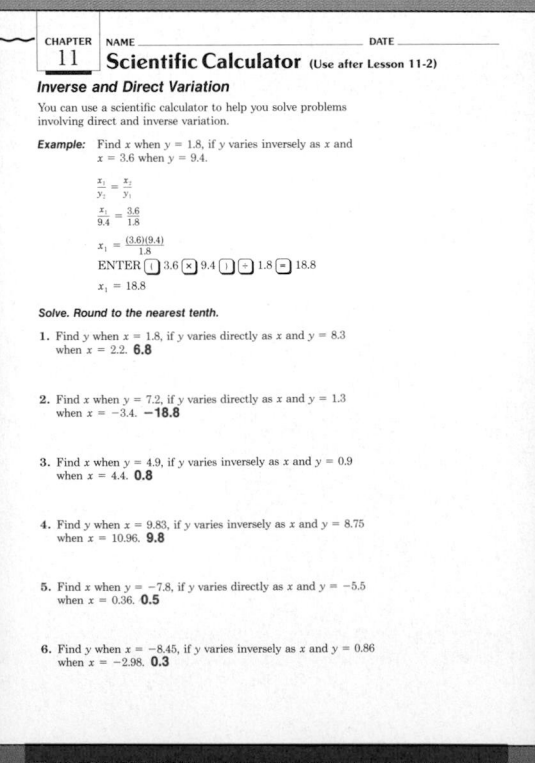

Problem of the Week Activity

The card shown below is one of two available for this chapter. It can be used as a class or small group activity.

Activity Card

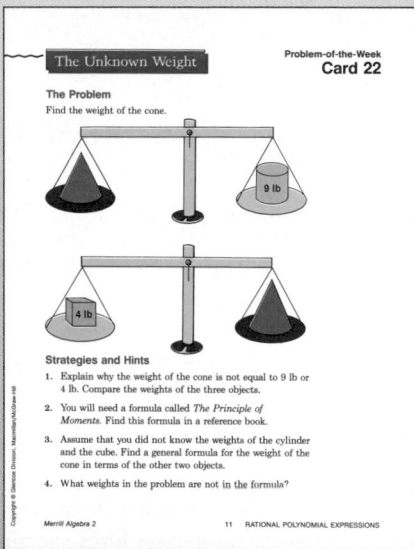

The Unknown Weight

Problem-of-the-Week
Card 22

The Problem
Find the weight of the cone.

Strategies and Hints

1. Explain why the weight of the cone is not equal to 9 lb or 4 lb. Compare the weights of the three objects.

2. You will need a formula called *The Principle of Moments*. Find this formula in a reference book.

3. Assume that you did not know the weights of the cylinder and the cube. Find a general formula for the weight of the cone in terms of the other two objects.

4. What weights in the problem are not in the formula?

Merrill Algebra 2   11   RATIONAL POLYNOMIAL EXPRESSIONS

Manipulatives and Models

The following materials may be used as models and manipulatives in Chapter 11.

- small electric appliances (Lesson 11-1)
- balance (Lesson 11-1)
- metric measuring cups (Lesson 11-1)
- graphing calculator (Lesson 11-1)
- balloon (Lesson 11-2)
- golf tees (Lesson 11-4)
- coins (Lesson 11-4)
- newspaper (Lesson 11-6)
- Periodic Table (Lesson 11-6)
- paper cups (Lesson 11-7)
- gallon container (Lesson 11-7)
- sand (Lesson 11-7)

Outside Resources

Books/Periodicals

Levita, Kathleen and Hilbert. *Logic and Boolean Algebra.* Barron's Educational Series, Inc.

Reid, Constance. *From Zero to Infinity.* Thomas Y. Crowell Company.

Films/Videotapes/Videodiscs

Polynomials, part of the Project Mathematics Series, The National Council of Teachers of Mathematics (NCTM), 1096 Association Dr., Reston, VA 22091-1593

Software

Algebra Drill & Practice III, Conduit Educational Software, University of Iowa, Oakdale Campus, Iowa City, IA 52242

Quadratic Equations I, Intellectual Software (IS), Division of Queue, Inc., 338 Commerce Dr., Fairfield, CT 06430

Multicultural

Multicultural Activity, p. 11

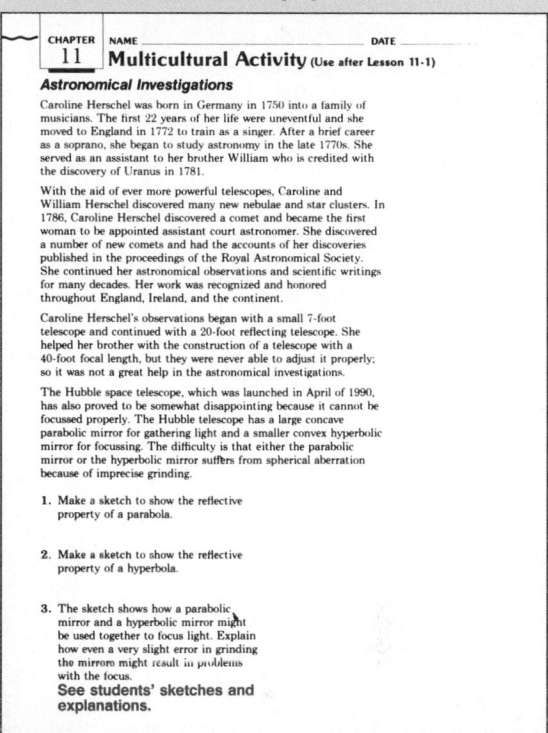

CHAPTER 11   NAME _____ DATE _____

Multicultural Activity (Use after Lesson 11-1)

Astronomical Investigations

Caroline Herschel was born in Germany in 1750 into a family of musicians. The first 22 years of her life were uneventful and she moved to England in 1772 to train as a singer. After a brief career as a soprano, she began to study astronomy in the late 1770s. She served as an assistant to her brother William who is credited with the discovery of Uranus in 1781.

With the aid of ever more powerful telescopes, Caroline and William Herschel discovered many new nebulae and star clusters. In 1786, Caroline Herschel discovered a comet and became the first woman to be appointed assistant court astronomer. She discovered a number of new comets and had the accounts of her discoveries published in the proceedings of the Royal Astronomical Society. She continued her astronomical observations and scientific writings for many decades. Her work was recognized and honored throughout England, Ireland, and the continent.

Caroline Herschel's observations began with a small 7-foot telescope and continued with a 20-foot reflecting telescope. She helped her brother with the construction of a telescope with a 40-foot focal length, but they were never able to adjust it properly; so it was not a great help in the astronomical investigations.

The Hubble space telescope, which was launched in April of 1990, has also proved to be somewhat disappointing because it cannot be focussed properly. The Hubble telescope has a large concave parabolic mirror for gathering light and a smaller convex hyperbolic mirror for focussing. The difficulty is that either the parabolic mirror or the hyperbolic mirror suffers from spherical aberration because of imprecise grinding.

1. Make a sketch to show the reflective property of a parabola.

2. Make a sketch to show the reflective property of a hyperbola.

3. The sketch shows how a parabolic mirror and a hyperbolic mirror might be used together to focus light. Explain how even a very slight error in grinding the mirror might result in problems with the focus.
See students' sketches and explanations.

Applications

Application, p. 29

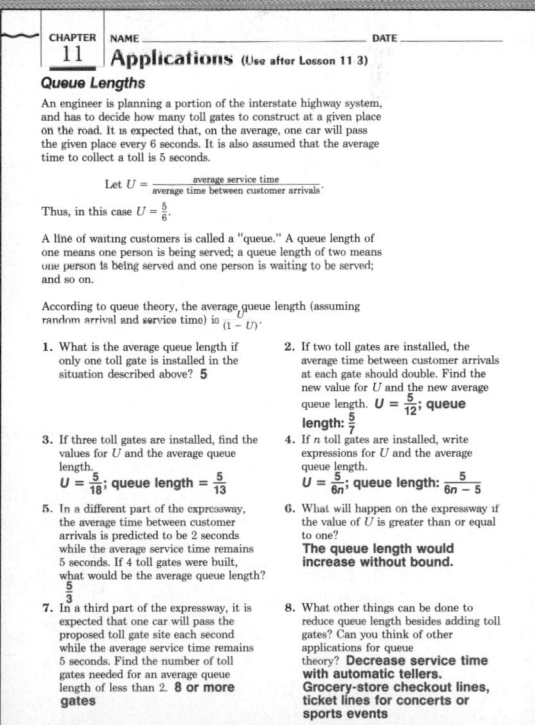

CHAPTER 11   NAME _____ DATE _____

Applications (Use after Lesson 11-3)

Queue Lengths

An engineer is planning a portion of the interstate highway system, and has to decide how many toll gates to construct at a given place on the road. It is expected that, on the average, one car will pass the given place every 6 seconds. It is also assumed that the average time to collect a toll is 5 seconds.

Let $U = \dfrac{\text{average service time}}{\text{average time between customer arrivals}}$.

Thus, in this case $U = \frac{5}{6}$.

A line of waiting customers is called a "queue." A queue length of one means one person is being served; a queue length of two means one person is being served and one person is waiting to be served; and so on.

According to queue theory, the average queue length (assuming random arrival and service time) is $\dfrac{U}{(1-U)}$.

1. What is the average queue length if only one toll gate is installed in the situation described above? **5**

2. If two toll gates are installed, the average time between customer arrivals at each gate should double. Find the new value for U and the new average queue length. $U = \frac{5}{12}$; queue length: $\frac{5}{7}$

3. If three toll gates are installed, find the values for U and the average queue length. $U = \frac{5}{18}$; queue length = $\frac{5}{13}$

4. If n toll gates are installed, write expressions for U and the average queue length. $U = \frac{5}{6n}$; queue length: $\frac{5}{6n-5}$

5. In a different part of the expressway, the average time between customer arrivals is predicted to be 2 seconds while the average service time remains 5 seconds. If 4 toll gates were built, what would be the average queue length? $\frac{5}{3}$

6. What will happen on the expressway if the value of U is greater than or equal to one? **The queue length would increase without bound.**

7. In a third part of the expressway, it is expected that one car will pass the proposed toll gate site each second while the average service time remains 5 seconds. Find the number of toll gates needed for an average queue length of less than 2. **8 or more gates**

8. What other things can be done to reduce queue length besides adding toll gates? Can you think of other applications for queue theory? **Decrease service time with automatic tellers. Grocery-store checkout lines, ticket lines for concerts or sports events**

11 Rational Polynomial Expressions

Using the Chapter Opener

Transparency 11–0 is available in the Transparency Package. It provides a full-color visual and motivational activity that you can use to engage students in the mathematical content of the chapter.

Background Information

Construction managers often plan a project in collaboration with engineers, architects, and other design professionals. Such planning often requires sophisticated analytical techniques to determine where construction activities might be disrupted, and includes flow charts, bar charts, and other graphic presentations. Construction managers use computers to evaluate various construction methods and to determine the most cost-efficient and timesaving plan. Employment opportunities are expected to increase 14% to 24% through the 1990s as projects grow in size and complexity.

CHAPTER OBJECTIVES

In this chapter, you will:
- Simplify rational expressions.
- Solve equations involving rational expressions.
- Graph rational functions.
- Solve problems involving direct, inverse, and joint variation.

Referring to the diagram below, when do you think an outbreak of flu would most handicap the construction team if it results in half of the workers being absent?

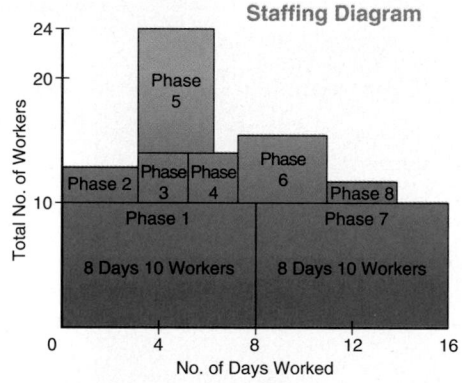

502

CAREERS IN CONSTRUCTION MANAGEMENT

The person who manages a construction project has one of the most creative, exciting, and important careers in the world. Before he or she starts, the property is undeveloped (or perhaps holds a structure that will be torn down). When he or she is finished, a new building stands in its place, ready for business.

Construction projects may be small (such as remodeling a home) or huge (such as building an industrial complex or a shopping mall). The construction manager hires and supervises the craftspeople such as electricians, plumbers, clerks, heavy-machinery operators, and engineers. He or she schedules their work and makes sure the needed tools and supplies are on hand for each step. When bad weather or accidents slow down the work, the construction manager reschedules. Obtaining all necessary permits and licenses is another of the manager's responsibilities, too—as well as monitoring compliance with safety codes and other union regulations. The construction manager regularly reviews the blueprints and specifications to be sure the work is right, and at the same time he or she keeps a close eye on the budget to avoid cost overruns. The manager prepares frequent—sometimes daily—progress reports. He or she also reports daily requirements for labor, material, and equipment at the construction site. It's not easy work. But it can be very rewarding.

Chapter Project

Materials: paper, pencil, set of blueprints

Locate and make copies of the blueprints for a simple house or other building. Check with the local library or a local builder for blueprints. Organize students into cooperative groups. Assign one group as construction managers, while each of the other groups represents at least one of the skilled trades necessary for the construction of the building project. Each group is to contact a local member of its skilled trade, conduct research, and schedule and estimate costs for all the work necessary for its role in construction. Each skilled-trade group will then give its report of costs and schedules to the group of construction managers. This final group will use the skilled-trade reports to develop a construction plan and schedule for the building project from beginning to completion.

Lesson	Connections (C) and Applications (A)	Examples	Exercises
11-1	A: Transporta-tion		28
	Auto Safety		29
11-2	C: Geometry	4	28,34
	A: Physics	3	37
	Cartography		21
	Manufactur-ing		22
	Auto Mechanics		38
	Tourism		39
11-3	C: Geometry	6	26,39
	Statistics		45
	A: Demograph-ics		46
	Real Estate		48
11-4	A: Photography		40
	Sports		41
	Auto Racing		42
	Landscaping		43
	Travel		49
11-5	C: Statistics		35,45
	Geometry		42
	A: Travel		34
11-6	C: Probability		7
	Geometry		10
	A: Commerce	1	
11-7	C: Number Theory		11-12, 17
	A: Zoology		8
	Oil Refining		9
	Construction		10
	Aviation		13
	Navigation		14
	Trucking		15
	Banking		16,19
	Chemistry		18

MORE ABOUT CONSTRUCTION MANAGEMENT

Degree Required:

- Bachelor's Degree in construction science

Some construction managers like:

- seeing the end-product of a project
- solving problems using technology
- high salary and good advancement opportunities

Related Math Subjects:

- Geometry
- Trigonometry
- Advanced Algebra
- Statistics and Probability

Some construction managers dislike:

- outdoor conditions they might encounter
- job uncertainty related to economic downturns

For more information on the various careers available in construction management, write to:

Construction Management Association of America
12355 Sunrise Valley Drive
Suite 640
Reston, VA 22091

503

Graphing Calculator Exploration: Graphing Rational Functions

A rational function is an equation of the form $f(x) = \frac{p(x)}{q(x)}$, where $p(x)$ and $q(x)$ are polynomial functions and $q(x) \neq 0$. A graphing calculator is a great tool for exploring the graphs of rational functions. These graphs have some features that never appear in the graphs of polynomial functions.

Teaching Tip ❶

The graphs of rational functions have *breaks in continuity*. This means that, unlike polynomial functions, which can be traced with a pencil never leaving the paper, a rational function is not traceable. Breaks in continuity can appear as vertical asymptotes or as *point discontinuity*. Point discontinuity is like a hole in a graph.

Example 1

Graph $y = \dfrac{x - 1}{x - 2}$. Use the viewing window [−5, 10] by [−5, 10] with scale factors of 1 for both axes.

Casio

ENTER: [Graph] [(] [ALPHA] [X] [−] 1 [)]
[÷] [(] [ALPHA] [X] [−] 2 [)] [EXE]

TI-81

ENTER: [Y=] [(] [X|T] [−] 1 [)] [÷] [(]
[X|T] [−] 2 [)] [GRAPH]

There is a break in continuity at $x = 2$. Looking back at the equation, we can see that when $x = 2$, the function is undefined. In this case, the graph has a vertical asymptote with equation $x = 2$. *Sometimes graphing calculators graph this line. This is for clarity, since the line is not part of the graph of the function.*

Example 2

Graph $y = \dfrac{x^2 - 4}{x + 2}$ in the standard viewing window.

Casio

ENTER: [Graph] [(] [ALPHA] [X] [x^2] [−]
4 [)] [÷] [(] [ALPHA] [X] [+]
2 [)] [EXE]

TI-81

ENTER: [Y=] [(] [X|T] [x^2] [−] 4 [)] [÷] [(] [X|T] [+] 2 [)] [GRAPH]

504   CHAPTER 11   RATIONAL POLYNOMIAL EXPRESSIONS

INTRODUCING THE LESSON

Objective: Graph rational functions on a graphing calculator and look for continuity.

Motivating the Lesson

Give each student a picture of the graph of a discontinuous rational function and ask them to find a way to trace the graph without lifting up their pencil or pen. Explain this as the "pencil test" for continuity.

TEACHING THE LESSON

Teaching Tip ❶   The function $q(x)$ cannot equal zero because then the denominator of the equation would also be zero and this would mean the function would be undefined.

Teaching Tip ❷   If you factor $x^2 - 4$ to $(x - 2)(x + 2)$, you can cancel $x + 2$ to obtain the equation $y = x - 2$. This is the graph that was drawn, except with a hole at $x = -2$.

Teaching Tip ❸   To find the horizontal asymptote, solve the equation for x to obtain $x = \dfrac{2y - 1}{y - 1}$.
You can see from the graph that there is also a break in continuity at $y = 1$ (since the denominator will be zero if y was 1).

Teaching Tip ❹   Stress the fact that you will never be able to trace *on* an asymptote, you can only trace *to* it. This is because there is no value for the function at that point so the calculator cannot trace on the function.

Teaching Tip ❺   The TI-81 will allow you to trace along parts of a function that are off the screen. The screen will change as you trace.

RETEACHING THE LESSON

If students are having difficulty with the concept of asymptote, have them calculate values that are very, very close to the asymptote value as well as the asymptote value itself. In some cases, the calculator may round off the solution, so according to it, the graph does hit the asymptote. Explain that you have reached the limits of machine precision when this happens. To do this, students may find it easier to change the range manually when they want to look at a point very close to an asymptote.

The graph looks like a line with a break in continuity at $x = -2$. This occurs because the function $y = \dfrac{x^2 - 4}{x + 2}$ reduces to $y = x - 2$, with the restriction that $x \neq -2$. *You may have to zoom-in to see the break in continuity.*

As you recall, a complete graph of a function includes all of the features of the graph, including the end behavior. The end behavior of some rational functions shows that the graphs approach horizontal asymptotes.

Example 3

Graph $y = \dfrac{9x + 1}{3x - 1}$. Use the viewing window [−5, 5] by [−5, 10] with scale factors of 1 on both axes. Then find the equation of the horizontal asymptote.

Casio

ENTER: [GRAPH] [(] 9 [ALPHA] [X] [+]

1 [)] [÷] [(] 3 [ALPHA] [X]

[−] 1 [)] [EXE]

TI-81

ENTER: [Y=] [(] 9 [X|T] [+] 1 [)] [÷]

[(] 3 [X|T] [−] 1 [)] [GRAPH]

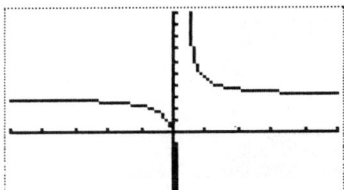

Now trace along the graph and observe the y-values as x grows smaller and as x grows larger. The y-values approach 3. Thus the equation of the horizontal asymptote is $y = 3$.

EXERCISES

Graph each equation on your graphing calculator so the complete graph is shown. Then sketch the graph. **See students' graphs.**

1. $y = \dfrac{1}{x}$

2. $y = \dfrac{1}{x^3}$

3. $y = \dfrac{-3x}{(x - 1)^2}$

4. $y = \dfrac{x^2 - 9}{x + 2}$

5. $y = \dfrac{2x}{x^2 + 4}$

6. $y = -\dfrac{x^2 - 9}{(x + 2)^3}$

7. $y = \dfrac{x + 5}{(x^2 - 16)(x + 1)}$

8. $y = \dfrac{x - 4}{x^3 + x^2 - 6x}$

9. $y = \dfrac{x - 4}{x^4 + 7x^3 - 36x}$

Use the tracing function on your graphing calculator to determine the equations of the horizontal asymptotes for the graph of each function.

10. $y = 0$
11. $y = \frac{1}{4}$

10. $f(x) = \dfrac{22}{x}$

11. $f(x) = \dfrac{x - 8}{4x}$

12. $f(x) = \dfrac{x}{x^2 - 4}$ $y = 0$

13. $f(x) = -\dfrac{6}{x^2}$ $y = 0$

14. $f(x) = -\dfrac{x^2 + 9}{3x^2}$ $y = \frac{1}{3}$

15. $f(x) = \dfrac{5x^2 - 8}{4x^2 + x}$ $y = \frac{5}{4}$

GRAPHING CALCULATOR EXPLORATION: GRAPHING RATIONAL FUNCTIONS   505

EXTENDING THE LESSON

Math Power: Problem Solving

Look at the function $y = \frac{1}{x}$. Make a table of values for x and y, making 1 the initial value of x and continuing with multiples of 10. Ask students what they notice about the y-values. Try to get them to formulate the hypothesis that as x increases, y decreases. What if x decreases?   **y will increase**

Then relate this knowledge to the graph of $y = \frac{1}{x}$, and compare this function to linear function values.

More Examples

1. Graph $y = \dfrac{x + 3}{x - 3}$. Use the viewing window [−10, 15] by [−10, 10] with a scale of 5 for x and a scale of 1 for y.

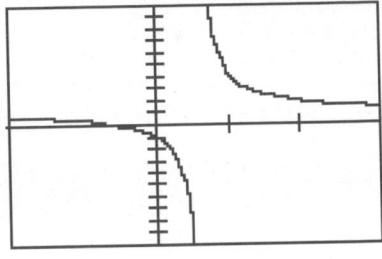

2. Graph $y = \dfrac{x^2 - 9}{x + 3}$ in the viewing window [−15, 15] by [−15, 15] with scale factors of 5 for both axes.

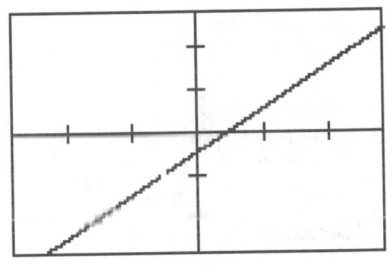

EVALUATING THE LESSON

Closing the Lesson

Speaking Activity   Have students graph a rational function on their graphing calculators and state a viewing window that gives a complete graph of the function (including the end behavior). Then have students state any asymptotes that occur in the graph of the function.

APPLYING THE LESSON

Homework Exercises

Assignment Guide
All: 1–15

Lesson Resources

Reteaching Master 11-1
Practice Master 11-1
Enrichment Master 11-1
Technology Master, p. 28
Multicultural Activity Master, p. 11

Transparency 11-1 contains the 5-Minute Check and a teaching aid for this lesson.

INTRODUCING THE LESSON

 5-Minute Check

(over Chapter 10)

1. Find $f(-3)$ if $f(x) = 3x^2 + 2x - 6$. **15**
2. Find $2[p(x)] + 3[p(x + 1)]$ if $p(x) = 2x^2 + 3x + 7$. **$10x^2 + 27x + 50$**
3. How many roots does $f(x) = 5x^6 + 4x^5 - x^3 + x^2 - 6$ have? **6**
4. How many positive real zeros are there for $f(x) = 4x^3 - 2x^2 - x + 7$? **0 or 2**
5. What are the possible rational zeros for $f(x) = x^3 + 9x^2 - 3x + 15$? **$\pm 1, \pm 3, \pm 5, \pm 15$**

Motivating the Lesson

Show students several small electrical appliances, such as a toaster, a lamp, and a curling iron. Tell them all operate on normal household power of 110 volts. Show them a chart (available from most electric companies) listing appliances and amount of current drawn during use. Ask students to guess how this amount of current is determined.

TEACHING THE LESSON

Teaching Tip ❶ Extend the lesson graph to show the branch that would have resulted had negative values been used.

Objective 11-1

After studying this lesson you should be able to:
■ locate the asymptotes and _____ the graph of a rational function.

Application

Electrical circuits operate according to Ohm's law which states that $\frac{V}{R} = I$.

V = electromotive force (in volts)
I = current (in amperes)
R = resistance of the circuit (in ohms).

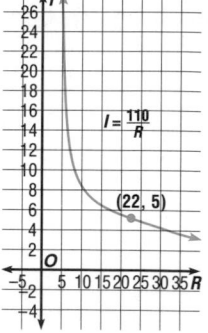

The resistance of an electric percolator is 22 ohms. Suppose you wanted to find what current it draws if you know that it has a voltage of 110. One way you could find this is by using the graph that represents Ohm's law if one of the values is known. The graph at the right shows $I = \frac{110}{R}$. The point $(22, 5)$ on the graph shows that when $R = 22$, $I = 5$. The current for the percolator is 5 amperes.

A **rational function** is an equation of the form $f(x) = \frac{p(x)}{q(x)}$, where $p(x)$ and $q(x)$ are polynomial functions and $q(x) \neq 0$. The equation $\frac{V}{R} = I$ is a rational function. Functions such as $f(x) = \frac{x}{x - 1}$, $f(x) = \frac{2}{x - 2}$, and $f(x) = \frac{4}{(x + 2)(x - 3)}$ are other examples of rational functions.

Teaching Tip ❶

The graph of a rational function has two or more branches. The graph above only shows one branch of the function because the negative values would have no real-world meaning in the formula $\frac{V}{R} = I$.

The branches of the graph of a rational function approach lines called **asymptotes.** If the function is not defined when $x = a$, the line with the equation $x = a$ is a vertical asymptote. In the example above, the function would not be defined if $R = 0$. So, the equation of one asymptote is $R = 0$. If the value of the function approaches b as the value of $|x|$ increases, the line with the equation $y = b$ is a horizontal asymptote. In the graph of $I = \frac{110}{R}$, the horizontal asymptote is at $I = 0$, because, as the values of R become greater, the value of I approaches 0.

Before graphing a rational function, it is helpful to graph the asymptotes of the function.

ALTERNATE TEACHING STRATEGIES

Mini-Math Lab

Have students use balances and metric measuring cups to find volumes of 20 grams of different liquids, such as water, cooking oil, alcohol, sugar water, and salt water. Have them use the rational function $D = \frac{m}{V}$ to find the density of each liquid and graph the data. From the graph, find the asymptotes. Compare and contrast this graph to that in the lesson application.

Example 1

Graph $f(x) = \dfrac{x}{x-1}$.

If $x = 1$, then $f(x)$ is undefined. Therefore, the equation of a vertical asymptote is $x = 1$. Study the pattern of values of $f(x)$ as the value of $|x|$ increases to determine the equation of the horizontal asymptote.

x	f(x)
2	2
5	1.25
10	1.111
100	1.010
1000	1.001
0	0
−10	0.9090
−100	0.9900
−1000	0.9990

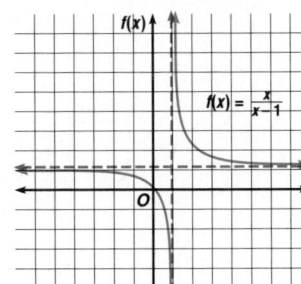

As the value of $|x|$ increases, it appears that the value of the function gets closer and closer to 1. The line with the equation $f(x) = 1$ is a horizontal asymptote of the function.

To graph the function, plot points on either side of each asymptote until the pattern is visible to sketch the graph. *Be sure to test values that are close to the asymptotes.*

Using a calculator can help you find values that pinpoint horizontal asymptotes more easily. The calculator can also help you find values quickly in order to graph ordered pairs of the function.

Example 2

Graph $f(x) = \dfrac{6}{(x-3)(x+4)}$.

The vertical asymptotes are the lines whose equations are $x - 3$ and $x = -4$. Use your calculator to find some values of $f(x)$, such as $f(10)$.

ENTER: $6 \div ((10 - 3) \times (10 +$
$4)) = 0.061224489$

The same pattern of keystrokes can be used to find other values of $f(x)$ that approach those of the horizontal asymptote.

A-11-507b

$f(10) = 0.061224489$
$f(100) = 0.000594766$
$f(1000) = 0.000005994$
$f(-10) = 0.076923076$
$f(-100) = 0.000606796$
$f(-1000) = 0.000006006$

As $|x|$ increases, it appears that the value of the function is approaching 0. The equation of the horizontal asymptote will be $f(x) = 0$. Plot points on either side of each asymptote. Then sketch the graph.

RETEACHING THE LESSON

A graphing calculator can be used to generate the graphs of rational functions. Students will be able to notice where the vertical and horizontal asymptotes of the graphs of these rational functions should occur. Range parameters should be chosen carefully.

Chalkboard Examples

For Example 1

Graph $f(x) = \dfrac{x-1}{x}$.

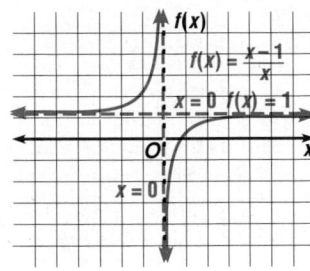

For Example 2

Graph $f(x) = \dfrac{-3}{x(x-3)}$.

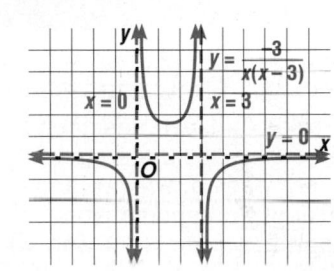

Reteaching Masters Booklet, p. 71

NAME _____ DATE _____

11-1 Reteaching Worksheet

Graphing Rational Functions

A rational function is an equation of the form $f(x) = \dfrac{p(x)}{q(x)}$ where $p(x)$ and $q(x)$ are polynomial functions and $q(x) \neq 0$. Functions such as $f(x) = \dfrac{x}{x-2}$ and $f(x) = \dfrac{3}{(x-4)(x-2)}$ are examples of rational functions.

The graph of a rational function has two or more branches. The branches of the graph approach lines called **asymptotes**. First graph the asymptotes. Then plot the points necessary to finish the graph.

Vertical Asymptote
The line with the equation $x = a$, if the rational function is undefined when x is a.

Horizontal Asymptote
The line with the equation $y = b$ if the value of the function approaches b as the value of $|x|$ increases.

Example: Graph $f(x) = \dfrac{x-1}{x}$.
The line with the equation $x = 0$ is a **vertical asymptote** because $f(x)$ is undefined when $x = 0$. As the value of $|x|$ increases, the value of the function approaches 1, as the table shows. The line with equation $y = 1$ is a **horizontal asymptote.**

x	f(x)
$\frac{1}{2}$	−1
1	0
2	$\frac{1}{2}$
4	$\frac{3}{4}$
10	$\frac{9}{10}$
$-\frac{1}{2}$	3
−1	2
−2	$\frac{3}{2}$
−4	$\frac{5}{4}$

Graph each rational function.

1. $f(x) = \dfrac{3}{x+1}$

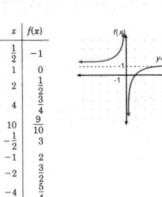

2. $f(x) = \dfrac{2}{x}$

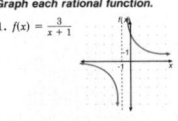

3. $f(x) = \dfrac{2x+1}{x-3}$

4. $f(x) = \dfrac{2}{(x+3)^2}$

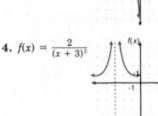

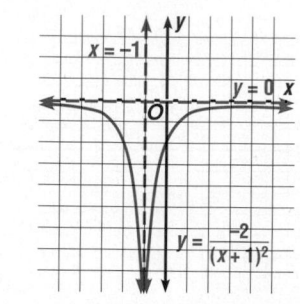
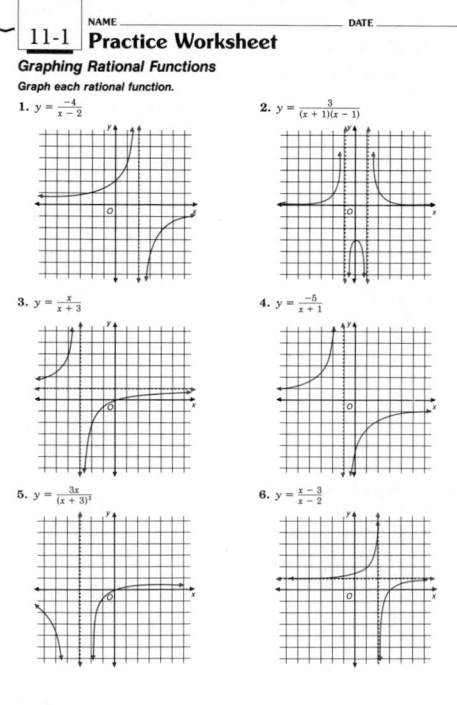

As you saw in Example 2, not all rational functions have graphs that are similar in appearance. Some contain no negative values for $f(x)$.

Example 3

Graph $f(x) = \dfrac{2}{(x-2)^2}$.

A vertical asymptote is the line whose equation is $x = 2$. Use your calculator to estimate the location of the horizontal asymptote. *Remember any value for x on either side of the asymptote may be used.*

$f(102) = 0.0002$
$f(1002) = 0.000002$
$f(10{,}002) = 0.00000002$

$f(-98) = 0.0002$
$f(-998) = 0.000002$
$f(-9998) = 0.00000002$

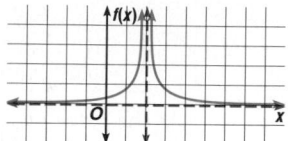

The pattern of values suggests that the equation of the horizontal asymptote will be $f(x) = 0$. Plot points on either side of the vertical asymptote. Then sketch the graph.

CHECKING FOR UNDERSTANDING

Communicating Mathematics

Read and study the lesson to answer each question.

1. What is the equation of the vertical asymptote of the graph of $f(x) = \dfrac{1}{x-3}$? **$x = 3$**

2. What is the equation of the horizontal asymptote of the graph of $f(x) = \dfrac{1}{x+2}$? Generate a table of values to support your answer.
   $y = 0$; For table, see students' work.

3. In Example 3, why do you think the values 102, 1002, 10,002, and so on were chosen? **See margin.**

4. In Example 3, why are there no negative values for $f(x)$? **See margin.**

Guided Practice

State the equations of the vertical and horizontal asymptotes for each rational function.

5. $f(x) = \dfrac{1}{x-3}$ **$x = 3, y = 0$**

6. $f(x) = \dfrac{6}{(x-6)^2}$ **$x = 6, y = 0$**

7. $f(x) = \dfrac{4}{(x-1)(x+5)}$
   $x = 1, x = -5, y = 0$

8. $f(x) = \dfrac{1}{2x}$ **$x = 0, y = 0$**

Additional Answers

3. With these values, the expressions in the denominator become powers of 10. The value of the fraction can be mentally calculated. For example,
$$\dfrac{2}{(102-2)^2} = \dfrac{2}{(100)^2} = \dfrac{2}{10{,}000} \text{ or } 0.0002.$$

4. The value of $x - 2$ when squared will always be positive.

EXERCISES

Practice Graph each rational function. **See Solutions Manual.** **Teaching Tip ❷**

A

9. $f(x) = \dfrac{1}{x}$

10. $f(x) = \dfrac{3}{x + 2}$

11. $f(x) = \dfrac{x}{x - 2}$

12. $f(x) = \dfrac{x - 5}{x + 1}$

13. $f(x) = \dfrac{x - 1}{x - 4}$

14. $f(x) = \dfrac{-4}{x - 1}$

B

15. $f(x) = \dfrac{x}{x + 1}$

16. $f(x) = \dfrac{-2}{(x - 3)^2}$

17. $f(x) = \dfrac{4x}{x - 1}$

18. $f(x) = \dfrac{-1}{x - 6}$

19. $f(x) = \dfrac{1}{(x + 2)^2}$

20. $f(x) = \dfrac{8}{(x - 1)(x + 3)}$

21. $f(x) = \dfrac{3}{(x - 4)^2}$

22. $f(x) = \dfrac{2}{(x - 2)(x + 1)}$

23. $f(x) = \dfrac{-5}{(x - 3)(x + 1)}$

C

24. $f(x) = \dfrac{x}{1 - x^2}$

25. $f(x) = \dfrac{x}{x^2 - 4}$

26. $f(x) = \dfrac{x - 1}{x^2 - 9}$

Critical Thinking

27. Study your graphs from Exercises 9-26. Make a conjecture on how many asymptotes there will be based on the number of factors in the numerator and denominator of the rational function. **See margin.**

Applications

28. **Transportation** A train travels at one velocity (V_1) for a given amount of time (t_1) and then another velocity (V_2) for a different amount of time (t_2). The average velocity is given by the formula $V = \dfrac{V_1 t_1 + V_2 t_2}{t_1 + t_2}$.

28a. See Solutions Manual.
  a. Draw the graph if $V_1 = 60$ mph, $V_2 = 40$ mph, and $t_2 = 8$ hours.
  b. Find V when $t_1 = 9$ hours. **V ≈ 50.60 mph**

29. **Auto Safety** If a car hits a tree, the objects in the car (including passengers) keep moving forward until an impact occurs. After impact, objects are repelled. Seatbelts and airbags limit how far you are jolted in this manner. The formula for the velocity you are thrown backward is
$V_f = \dfrac{m_1 - m_2}{m_1 + m_2} \cdot v_i$, where m_1 and m_2 are the masses of the two objects meeting and v_i is the initial velocity. **29a. See margin.**

  a. Graph the function if $m_2 = 7$ kg and $v_i = 5$ m/s.
  b. Find the value of V_f when the value of m_1 is 5 kg. **$V_f \approx -0.83$ m/s**

Mixed Review

30. Find the inverse of $f(x) = \dfrac{5x + 2}{2}$. **(Lesson 10-8)** $f^{-1}(x) = \dfrac{2x - 2}{5}$

31. Find the center and radius of a circle whose equation is $x^2 + y^2 = 25$. **(Lesson 9-3) (0, 0), 5**

32. Find $f(-2)$ for $f(x) = 2x^2 + 3x - 5$. **(Lesson 8-1) −3**

33. Solve $4y^2 - 8y - 7 = 0$ by completing the square. **(Lesson 7-3) $1 \pm \dfrac{\sqrt{11}}{2}$**

34. Factor $x^2 - x + 3xy - 3y$. **(Lesson 5-5) $(x + 3y)(x - 1)$**

EXTENDING THE LESSON

Math Power: Connections

Have students use physics and chemistry books to find other rational functions. Determine and graph asymptotes for each. Use theoretical data to graph the functions.

Additional Answer

27. **There will always be one horizontal asymptote. The degree of the denominator determines the number of vertical asymptotes.**

degree	asymptotes
1	1
2	(diff. factors) 2
2	(squared factor) 1
3	3
⋮	⋮

APPLYING THE LESSON

Homework Exercises

Assignment Guide

Basic: 9–23, 27–28, 30–34
Average: 12–24, 27–34
Enriched: 15–34

Teaching Tip ❷ Have students determine and graph asymptotes before plotting points.

Additional Answer

29a.

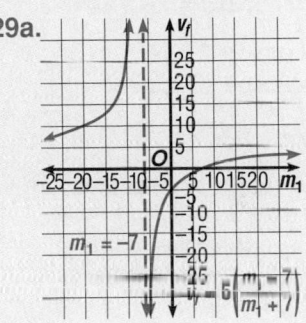

Enrichment Masters Booklet, p. 71

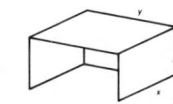
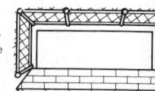

Lesson Resources

Reteaching Master 11-2
Practice Master 11-2
Enrichment Master 11-2
Technology Master, p. 11
Activity Master, p. 11

 Transparency 11-2 contains the 5-Minute Check and a teaching aid for this lesson.

INTRODUCING THE LESSON

 5-Minute Check

(over Lesson 11-1)

For Exercises 1–4, use
$f(x) = \dfrac{4}{(x+2)(x-3)}$.

1. How many asymptotes are there?   **3**
2. Write equations for any vertical asymptotes.
   x = -2, x = 3
3. Write equations for any horizontal asymptotes.
   y = 0
4. Graph the equation.

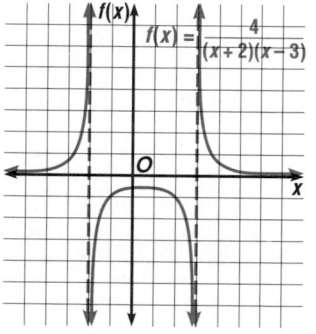

Motivating the Lesson

Measure the circumference of an inflated balloon. Immerse the balloon in a container of warm water for a few minutes and again measure the circumference. Repeat, using ice water. Have students look at the data. Ask how the last two measurements are related to the initial circumference.

11-2	# Direct, Inverse, and Joint Variation

Objective
11-2

After studying this lesson, you should be able to:
- solve problems involving direct, inverse, and joint variation.

Teaching Tip ❶

Application

The LEM (Lunar Exploration Module) used by astronauts to explore the moon's surface during the Apollo space missions weighs about 30,000 pounds on Earth. On the moon, there is less gravity so it weighs less, meaning that less fuel is needed to lift off from the moon's surface. The force of gravity on Earth is about six times as much as that on the moon. The relationship of the two gravities can be expressed in the equation $y = 6x$, where y represents the weight on Earth, and x represents the weight on the moon. The 6 is called the **constant of variation.**

To find out how much the LEM weighs on the moon, you can substitute 30,000 for y and solve the equation.

$$y = 6x$$
$$30{,}000 = 6x \qquad \textit{Substitute 30,000 for y.}$$
$$5000 = x \qquad \textit{Divide each side by 6.}$$

The LEM weighs approximately 5000 pounds on the moon.

The relationship described above is an example of a **direct variation.** This means that y is a multiple of x. To express a direct variation, we say that y *varies directly as x.*

Direct Variation	**y varies directly as x if there is some constant k such that $y = kx$. k is called the constant of variation.**

If you know that y varies directly as x and one set of corresponding values, you can use a proportion to find other unknown values.

$$y_1 = kx_1 \quad \text{and} \quad y_2 = kx_2$$
$$\frac{y_1}{x_1} = k \quad \text{and} \quad \frac{y_2}{x_2} = k$$
$$\text{Therefore, } \frac{y_1}{x_1} = \frac{y_2}{x_2}.$$

Using the properties of equality, you can find many other proportions that relate these same x-values and y-values.

510   CHAPTER 11   RATIONAL POLYNOMIAL EXPRESSIONS

ALTERNATE TEACHING STRATEGIES

Using Connections

Write variation equations. Name the type of variation represented.

1. Some points in a football game are based on the number of touchdowns scored.   **p = 6t; direct**

2. Refreshment receipts are based on the number of stands open, the attendance, and a price of 50¢ per item.   **r = 0.50na; joint**

3. The faster the wind blows, the lower attendance is.   **as = k, inverse**

Example 1

If y varies directly as x, and $y = 12$ when $x = 15$, find x when $y = 21$.

Use a proportion that relates the values.

$$\frac{y_1}{x_1} = \frac{y_2}{x_2}$$

$$\frac{12}{15} = \frac{21}{x_2} \qquad \textit{Substitute the known values.}$$

$$12x_2 = (15)(21) \qquad \textit{Cross multiply.}$$

$$x_2 = 26.25 \qquad \textit{Divide each side by 12.}$$

The value of x when $y = 21$ is 26.25.

Many quantities are **inversely proportional** or are said to **vary inversely** with each other. For example, if $xy = 12$, as x becomes greater, y becomes less.

Inverse Variation	**y varies inversely as x if there is some constant k such that $xy = k$.**

Just as with direct variation, a proportion can be used with indirect variation to solve problems where some quantities are known. The following proportion is only one of several that can be formed.

$$x_1y_1 = k \quad \text{and} \quad x_2y_2 = k$$

$$x_1y_1 = x_2y_2 \qquad \textit{Substitution property of equality}$$

Teaching Tip ❷ $\quad \dfrac{x_1}{y_2} = \dfrac{x_2}{y_1} \qquad \textit{Divide each side by } y_1y_2.$

Example 2

If y varies inversely as x, and $y = 3$ when $x = 4$, find y when $x = 18$.

$$\frac{x_1}{y_2} = \frac{x_2}{y_1}$$

$$\frac{4}{y_2} = \frac{18}{3} \qquad \textit{Substitute the known values.}$$

$$18y_2 = 12 \qquad \textit{Cross multiply.}$$

$$y_2 = \frac{12}{18} \text{ or } \frac{2}{3} \qquad \textit{Divide each side by 18.}$$

The value of y when $x = 18$ is $\frac{2}{3}$.

LESSON 11-2 DIRECT, INVERSE, AND JOINT VARIATION 511

TEACHING THE LESSON

Teaching Tip ❶ Relate this application to the feeling of weightlessness resulting from riding an amusement park ride that involves a great amount of centrifugal force.

Teaching Tip ❷ Write this equation on the chalkboard next to the corresponding equation for direct variation. Have students note similarities and differences.

Chalkboard Examples

For Example 1
If y varies directly as x, and $y = 6$ when $x = 11$, find y when $x = 3$.
$\dfrac{18}{11}$

For Example 2
If y varies inversely as x, and $y = 10$ when $x = 20$, find x when $y = 16$.   12.5

Chalkboard Examples

For Example 3

If temperature is constant, gas volume varies inversely with its pressure. If an air-filled balloon has a volume of 2.6 dm^3 when the pressure is 120 kilopascals, what is the pressure if the volume is 3.2 dm^3?   **97.5 kilopascals**

For Example 4

The volume (*V*) of a cone varies jointly as the square of the radius of the base (r^2) and the height (*h*). Find the equation of joint variation if *V* = 285, *r* = 4, and *h* = 17.   **$V = 1.05\,r^2h$**

(Note: 1.05 = $\pi/3$)

Teaching Tip ❸   Be sure students understand why joint variation is considered direct variation even though two of the variables are multiplied by each other.

EVALUATING THE LESSON

Checking for Understanding

Exercises 1–16 are designed to help you assess understanding through reading, writing, and speaking. You should work through Exercises 1–3 with your students, and then monitor their work on Exercises 4–16.

Example 3

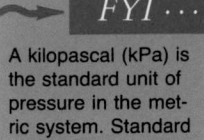

APPLICATION

Physics

FYI ...

A kilopascal (kPa) is the standard unit of pressure in the metric system. Standard atmospheric pressure is about 101.3 kPa.

The volume of any gas varies inversely with its pressure as long as the temperature remains constant. If a helium-filled balloon has a volume of 3.4 cubic decimeters at a pressure of 120 kilopascals, what is its volume at 101.3 kilopascals?

Let V_1 be the given volume of the helium, 3.4 cubic decimeters.
Let P_1 be the pressure of the helium at that volume, 120 kilopascals.
Let P_2 be the new pressure of the helium, 101.3 kilopascals.

Write a proportion for inversely proportional quantities. Then you can use your calculator to evaluate the proportion.

$$\frac{V_1}{P_2} = \frac{V_2}{P_1} \qquad \textit{Write a proportion.}$$

$$\frac{3.4}{101.3} = \frac{V_2}{120} \qquad \textit{Substitute the known values.}$$

$$\frac{(3.4)(120)}{101.3} = V_2 \qquad \textit{Solve for } V_2.$$

ENTER: ⎡ (⎤ 3.4 ⎡ × ⎤ 120 ⎡) ⎤ ⎡ ÷ ⎤ 101.3 ⎡ = ⎤ 4.027640671

The volume of helium at 101.3 kilopascals is about 4.03 cubic decimeters.
As the pressure decreases, the volume increases.

Teaching Tip ❸   Another type of variation is **joint variation.** This type of variation is a direct variation involving three variables as well as a constant.

Joint Variation	**y varies jointly as x and z if there is some number k such that $y = kxz$, where $x \neq 0$ and $z \neq 0$.**

Example 4

CONNECTION

Geometry

The area (*A*) of a triangle varies jointly as the base (*b*) and height (*h*). Find the equation of joint variation if *A* = 100, *b* = 25, and *h* = 8.

Write an equation for joint variation to find the constant of variation.

$A = kbh$ *Let y = A, x = b, and z = h.*

$100 = k(25)(8)$ *Substitute the known values.*

$100 = 200k$ *Multiply.*

$\dfrac{1}{2} = k$ *Divide each side by 200.*

The equation for the area of a triangle is $A = \dfrac{1}{2}\,bh$.

CHECKING FOR UNDERSTANDING

Communicating Mathematics

Read and study the lesson to answer each question.

1. What does k represent in each of the variation equations?

1. constant of variation

2. In which type of variation would the value of y become less as the value of x becomes greater? **inverse variation**

3. Why is joint variation considered to be a direct variation? **It is the direct variation with a product of two variables instead of a single variable.**

Teaching Tip ④

Guided Practice

State whether each equation represents a direct, inverse, or joint variation. Then name the constant of variation.

4. $xy = -3$ **I, -3**

5. $\dfrac{x}{y} = -6$ **D, $-\dfrac{1}{6}$**

6. $y = -4x$ **D, -4**

7. $\dfrac{x}{2} = y$ **D, $\dfrac{1}{2}$**

8. $y = 3xz$ **J, 3**

9. $a = 4b$ **D, 4**

10. $y = \dfrac{3}{x}$ **I, 3**

11. $a = kcb$ **J, k**

12. $\dfrac{3}{5}a = -\dfrac{5}{4}b$ **D, $-\dfrac{25}{12}$**

Write an equation for each statement and then solve the equation.

13. If y varies directly as x, and $y = 34$ when $x = 17$, find y when $x = 56$.
$y = 112$

14. $x = \dfrac{25}{6}$

14. If x varies inversely as y, and $y = 25$ when $x = 5$, find x when $y = 30$.

15. If y varies jointly as x and z, and $y = 60$ when $x = 5$ and $z = 4$, find y when $x = 4$ and $z = 10$. **$y = 120$**

16. If y varies directly as x and inversely as z, and $y = 40$ when $x = 20$ and $z = 2$, find y when $x = 60$ and $z = 4$. **$y = 60$**

EXERCISES

Practice

18. $w = -\dfrac{6}{5}$

19. $r = \dfrac{84}{11}$

20. $y = -\dfrac{3}{5}$

17. If y varies directly as x, and $y = 8$ when $x = 2$, find y when $x = 9$.
$y = 36$

18. If g varies directly as w, and $g = 10$ when $w = -3$, find w when $g = 4$.

19. If t varies inversely as r, and $r = 14$ when $t = -6$, find r when $t = -11$.

20. If y varies inversely as x, and $y = \dfrac{1}{5}$ when $x = 9$, find y when $x = -3$.

21. **Cartography** A map is scaled so that 1 cm represents 15 km. How far apart are two towns if they are 7.9 cm apart on the map? **118.5 km**

22. **Manufacturing** Six feet of steel wire weighs 0.7 kg. How much does 100 ft of the same steel wire weigh? **about 11.67 kg**

LESSON 11-2   DIRECT, INVERSE, AND JOINT VARIATION   513

RETEACHING THE LESSON

Solve direct and inverse variation problems using the definitions. For example, y varies directly with x, and $y = 42$ when $x = 14$. Find the constant of variation. Also find y when $x = 8$.

$y = kx$ $y = 3x$
$42 = k(14)$ $y = 3(8)$
$3 = k$ $y = 24$ when $x = 8$

11-2 Reteaching Worksheet

NAME _____ DATE _____

Direct, Inverse, and Joint Variation

Variables can be related by **direct**, **inverse**, and **joint** variation.

Direct Variation	Inverse Variation	Joint Variation
y varies directly as x if there is some constant k such that $y = kx$.	y varies inversely as x if there is some constant k such that $xy = k$.	y varies jointly as x and z if there is some number k such that $y = kxz$, where $x \neq 0$ and $z \neq 0$.

Examples:

If y varies directly as x and $y = 16$ when $x = 4$, find x when $y = 20$.

$\dfrac{y_1}{x_1} = \dfrac{y_2}{x_2}$
$\dfrac{16}{4} = \dfrac{20}{x_2}$
$16x_2 = (20)(4)$
$x_2 = 5$

The value of x is 5 when y is 20.

If y varies inversely as x and $y = 5$ when $x = 16$, find y when $x = 20$.

$\dfrac{x_1}{y_2} = \dfrac{x_2}{y_1}$
$\dfrac{16}{y_2} = \dfrac{20}{5}$
$80 = 20y_2$
$y_2 = 4$

The value of y is 4 when x is 20.

If y varies jointly as x and z and $y = 10$ when $x = 2$ and $z = 4$, find y when $x = 4$ and $z = 3$.

$\dfrac{y_1}{y_2} = \dfrac{x_1 z_1}{x_2 z_2}$
$\dfrac{10}{y} = \dfrac{2 \cdot 4}{4 \cdot 3}$
$120 = 8y$
$y = 15$

The value of y is 15 when $x = 4$ and $z = 3$.

Solve each problem.

1. Find y when $x = 15$, if y varies inversely as x and $x = 10$ when $y = 12$. **8**

2. Find y when $x = 8$, if x varies directly as y and $y = 9$ when $x = 6$. **12**

3. Find y when $x = 5$ and $z = 3$, if y varies jointly as $x = 3$ and $z = 2$ when $y = 18$. **45**

4. Find x when $y = 9$, if y varies directly as x and $x = 15$ when $y = 5$. **27**

5. Find y when $x = 6$ and $z = 8$, if y varies jointly as $x = 4$ and $z = 2$ when $y = 6$. **36**

6. Find x when $y = 27$, if y varies inversely as x and $x = 9$ when $y = 45$. **15**

7. Find x when $y = 1000$, if y varies directly as x and $y = 50$ when $x = 200$. **4000**

8. Find y when $x = 76$, if y varies inversely as x and $y = 100$ when $x = 38$. **50**

23. If y varies directly as x, and $x = 4$ when $y = 0.5$, find y when $x = 9$. **$y = 1.125$**

24. If y varies inversely as x, and $y = 1$ when $x = 44$, find x when $y = 40$. **$x = 1.1$**

25. Suppose y varies jointly as x and z. Find y when $x = 6$ and $z = 8$, if $y = 12$ when $z = 3$ and $x = 4$. **$y = 48$**

26. If y varies directly as x, and $y = -5$ when $x = 0.25$, find x when $y = -7$. **$x = 0.35$**

27. If y varies inversely as x, and $x = 20$ when $y = 10$, find x when $y = 14$. $x = \dfrac{100}{7}$

CONNECTION
Geometry

28. The area of a parallelogram varies jointly as its base and height. Parallelogram *DUCK* has a base of 15 meters, a height of 12 meters, and an area of 180 square meters. Find the height of parallelogram *DOVE* if its area is 1615 square meters and its base is 42.5 meters. **38 meters**

29. The Heavenly Hog has a 10 kg ham that serves 68 people. The Gourmet Diner has a 6 kg ham that serves 44 people. Which eating establishment serves larger portions? **Heavenly Hog**

30. If y varies inversely as x, and $y = \dfrac{4}{9}$ when $x = \dfrac{3}{8}$, find y when $x = \dfrac{2}{3}$. **$y = \dfrac{1}{4}$**

C

31. If g varies directly as h, and $g = \dfrac{3}{4}$ when $h = \dfrac{2}{5}$, find g when $h = 8$. **$g = 15$**

32. If y varies jointly as x and z, and $y = 25$ when $z = 5$ and $x = 1$, find y when $x = 8$ and $z = 12$. **$y = 480$**

33. If y varies jointly as x and z, and $y = 34$ when $z = 2$ and $x = 17$, find y when $x = 4$ and $z = 8$. **$y = 32$**

CONNECTION
Geometry

34. The area of a trapezoid varies jointly as the height and the sum of the bases. If the area of a trapezoid is 20 in², its bases are 3 in. and 5 in., and its height is 5 in., find the constant of variation. Then write the general equation for the area of a trapezoid.
$$k = \frac{1}{2}, \quad A = \frac{1}{2}(b_1 + b_2)h$$

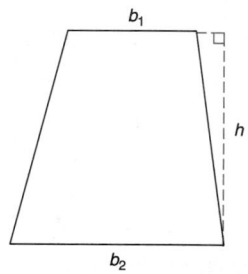

Critical Thinking

35. $y = \dfrac{343}{81}$

35. If y varies directly as x^2, and $y = 7$ when $x = 9$, find y when $x = 7$.

36. If y^2 varies inversely as x, and $y = 4$ when $x = 2$, find y when $x = 11$.
$$y = \pm\frac{4\sqrt{22}}{11}$$

Applications

37. **Physics** The current (I) in an electrical circuit varies inversely with the resistance (R) in the circuit.

   a. Use the chart below to write an equation relating the current and resistance. $I = \dfrac{6}{R}$

I (in amperes)	0.5	1.0	1.5	2.0	2.5	3.0	4.0	5.0
R (in ohms)	12	6.0	4.0	3.0	2.4	2.0	1.5	1.2

   b. What is the constant of variation? **6**

Practice Masters Booklet, p. 82

NAME _____ DATE _____

11-2 **Practice Worksheet**

Direct, Inverse, and Joint Variation

Write an equation for each statement and then solve the equation.

1. Find y when $x = 6$, if y varies directly as x and $y = 8$ when $x = 2$. **24**

2. Find y when $x = 1.5$, if y varies directly as x and $y = -16$ when $x = 6$. **−4**

3. Find y when $x = 4$, if y varies directly as x and $y = 7$ when $x = 1.5$. **$\dfrac{56}{3}$**

4. Find y when $x = 5$, if y varies directly as x and $y = 5$ when $x = 3.5$. **$\dfrac{50}{7}$**

5. Find x when $y = 3$, if y varies inversely as x and $x = 4$, when $y = 16$. **$\dfrac{64}{3}$**

6. Find x when $y = 5$, if y varies inversely as x and $x = 6$ when $y = -18$. **−21.6**

7. Find y when $x = 2\frac{1}{2}$, if y varies inversely as x and $x = 5$ when $y = 3$. **6**

8. Find y when $x = 10$, if y varies inversely as x and $x = 7.5$ when $y = 6$. **4.5**

9. Find y when $x = 4$ and $z = 15$, if y varies jointly as x and z and $y = 5$ when $z = 8$ and $x = 10$. **$\dfrac{15}{4}$**

10. Find y when $x = 12$ and $z = 2$, if y varies jointly as x and z and $y = 24$ when $z = 2$ and $x = 1$. **288**

11. Find y when $x = 6$ and $z = 8$, if y varies jointly as x and z and $y = 60$ when $x = 3$ and $z = 4$. **240**

12. Find y when $x = 4$ and $z = -1$, if y varies jointly as x and z and $y = 12$ when $x = -2$ and $z = 3$. **8**

38. **Auto Mechanics** When air is pumped into a tire, the pressure required varies inversely as the volume of the air. If the pressure is 30 lb/in² when the volume is 140 in³, find the pressure when the volume is 100 in³. **42 lb/in²**

39. **Tourism** In planning a trip you must know that the distance you travel varies jointly as the time and rate of speed. LaDonna Metcalf must travel 396 miles in 8 hours to meet a prospective client. She travels 6 hours at 55 mph. She stopped for a half hour to rest and eat lunch. What is the minimum speed at which she must travel to meet her appointment? **44 mph**

Mixed Review

40. Graph $y = \dfrac{-3x}{x-1}$. **(Lesson 11-1) See margin.**

41. Find all rational zeros of $f(a) = a^3 + 2a^2 - 11a - 12$. **(Lesson 10-4)** **-1, 3, -4**

42. Find the solution of $\begin{cases} 3x^2 - y^2 = 26 \\ 2 = y - x \end{cases}$. **(Lesson 9-9)** **(-3, -1), (5, 7)**

43. Define a variable and write a quadratic function to express the phrase, *the product of two numbers whose difference is 55.* **(Lesson 7-2)** **See margin.**

44. Simplify $3\sqrt{18} + 8\sqrt{8}$. **(Lesson 6-3)** **25√2**

45. Find $3\begin{bmatrix} -4 & 0 & 1 \\ 7 & -2 & 5 \\ 1 & 1 & 4 \end{bmatrix} + \begin{bmatrix} 8 & 0 & 6 \\ -5 & 2 & -1 \\ 4 & -4 & 7 \end{bmatrix}$. **(Lesson 4-3)** $\begin{bmatrix} -4 & 0 & 9 \\ 16 & -4 & 14 \\ 7 & -1 & 19 \end{bmatrix}$

46. Gladys is three times as old as Maria. In 10 years, Gladys will be twice as old as Maria. What are their ages now? **(Lesson 3-5)** **Gladys 30, Maria 10**

FINE ARTS CONNECTION

Those with a dislike for mathematics rarely see any beauty connected with it. The general population is often unaware of how much mathematics they see and use in everyday life. To help the nonmathematical-minded person relate to some complex mathematical relationships, Helaman R. P. Ferguson at Brigham Young University has found a way to communicate mathematics through sculpture.

The sculpture he calls *Umbilic Torus NC* looks like a twisted bronze ring inscribed with messages from some prehistoric culture. However, if you were to trace your finger along the ring's edge, you would find that your finger is carried around the ring three times before returning to its starting point. The form was created using matrices associated with homogeneous cubic polynomials in three variables.

When asked to explain his art, Ferguson said "Understanding the math would take years of training, but here a person can actually touch a theorem, and get a feel for math."

Umbilic Torus NC

EXTENDING THE LESSON

Math Power: Reasoning

A gas is kept at a constant temperature. As the volume occupied by the gas decreased from 60 ft³ to 40 ft³, the pressure increased by 2.5 pounds. If the pressure on the gas is increased by another 2.5 pounds, what is the volume now occupied by the gas? **30 ft³**

Fine Arts Connection

The Fine Arts Connection introduces students to another area in which mathematics plays a very important part. You may wish to discuss other areas in the arts such as music, painting, and design and how they depend upon mathematics. Students may wish to further research the involvement of mathematics in these areas.

 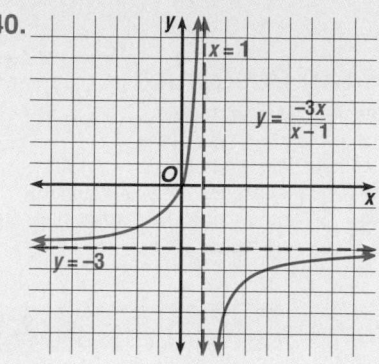

Lesson Resources
Reteaching Master 11-3
Practice Master 11-3
Enrichment Master 11-3

 Transparency 11-3 contains the 5-Minute Check and a teaching aid for this lesson.

Objectives

After studying this lesson, you should be able to:

11-3A ▪ simplify rational expressions, and

11-3B ▪ simplify complex fractions.

Operations with rational numbers and **rational algebraic expressions** are very similar. A rational number can be expressed as the quotient of two integers. A rational algebraic expression can be expressed as the quotient of two polynomials. In either case, the denominator can never be 0.

$$\frac{2}{3} \quad \frac{415}{100} \quad \frac{-6}{11}$$

$$\frac{6}{k} \quad \frac{2x}{x-5} \quad \frac{p^2-25}{p+6}$$

rational numbers   *rational algebraic expressions*

To write a fraction in simplest form, you divide both the numerator and denominator by their greatest common factor (GCF). To simplify a rational algebraic expression, you use similar properties.

Example 1

Simplify $\dfrac{2x(x-5)}{(x-5)(x^2-1)}$. Under what conditions is the expression undefined?

Look for common factors.

$$\frac{2x(x-5)}{(x-5)(x^2-1)} = \frac{2x}{x^2-1} \cdot \frac{x-5}{x-5} \qquad \textit{How is this similar to simplifying } \tfrac{4}{6}?$$

$$= \frac{2x}{x^2-1} \qquad \qquad \frac{x-5}{x-5} = 1$$

To find when the expression is undefined, completely factor the original denominator.

$$\frac{2x(x-5)}{(x-5)(x^2-1)} = \frac{2x(x-5)}{(x-5)(x-1)(x+1)}$$

The values that would make the denominator equal 0 are 5, 1, or -1. So, the expression is undefined when $x = 5$, $x = 1$, or $x = -1$.

Example 2

Simplify $\dfrac{z^2w - z^2}{z^3 - z^3w}$.

First factor the expression to find any common factors.

For what values is the expression undefined?

$$\frac{z^2w - z^2}{z^3 - z^3w} = \frac{z^2(w-1)}{z^3(1-w)} \qquad \textit{Factor the GCF of the numerator and then of the denominator.}$$

$$= \frac{z^2(-1)(1-w)}{z^3(1-w)} \qquad w - 1 = -1(-w+1) \textit{ or } -1(1-w)$$

$$= -\frac{1}{z} \qquad \qquad \textit{The GCF is } z^2(1-w).$$

5-Minute Check

(over Lesson 11-2)

For Exercises 1–3, tell what type of variation is represented in each.

1. $\dfrac{n_1}{x_2} = \dfrac{n_2}{x_1}$ **inverse**

2. $\dfrac{a_1}{c_1} = \dfrac{a_2}{c_2}$ **direct**

3. $V = \pi r^2 h$ **joint**

4. If y varies directly as x, and $x = 3$ when $y = -2$, find x when $y = 7$.   **-10.5**

5. If y varies inversely as x, and $y = 16$ when $x = 2$, find y when $x = 6$.   **$5\frac{1}{3}$**

Motivating the Lesson

Show students a sticker that gives the city and highway mileage rates for a new car. A consumer report comparing mileage ratings for different cars could also be used. Ask students how they think the rates were determined and why they differ.

Chalkboard Example

For Example 1

Simplify $\dfrac{2a^2(a^2+4)(b-3)}{8ab^2(a-2)(a^2+4)}$. When would the expression be undefined? $\dfrac{a(b-3)}{4b^2(a-2)}$; $a = 0$ or 2, $b = 0$

Using Cooperative Groups

Have students work in cooperative groups of four. Have one student name a rational algebraic expression. Have another student name another expression, using the same variable(s). Have the third student multiply the two expressions, and the fourth student divide them. Discuss procedures and solutions. Rotate and repeat.

Remember that to multiply two fractions you multiply the numerators and then multiply the denominators. To divide two fractions, you multiply by the multiplicative inverse, or reciprocal, of the divisor.

$$\frac{1}{2} \cdot \frac{8}{9} = \frac{1 \cdot \overset{4}{\cancel{8}} \cdot 4}{\underset{1}{\cancel{2}} \cdot 9} \text{ or } \frac{4}{9}$$

$$\frac{1}{3} \div \frac{5}{9} = \frac{1}{3} \cdot \frac{9}{5} = \frac{1 \cdot \overset{3}{\cancel{9}} \cdot 3}{\underset{1}{\cancel{3}} \cdot 5} \text{ or } \frac{3}{5}$$

The same procedures are used for multiplying and dividing rational expressions. These can be generalized by the following rules.

Multiplying and Dividing Rational Expressions

Teaching Tip ❶

> For all rational expressions $\frac{a}{b}$ and $\frac{c}{d}$,
>
> $\frac{a}{b} \cdot \frac{c}{d} = \frac{ac}{bd}$, if $b \neq 0$ and $d \neq 0$, and
>
> $\frac{a}{b} \div \frac{c}{d} = \frac{a}{b} \cdot \frac{d}{c} = \frac{ad}{bc}$, if $b \neq 0$, $c \neq 0$, and $d \neq 0$.

The following examples show how these rules are used with rational expressions.

Example 3

Find $\frac{4a}{5b} \cdot \frac{15b}{16a}$. Write the answer in simplest form.

$$\frac{4a}{5b} \cdot \frac{15b}{16a} = \frac{\overset{1}{\cancel{4}} \cdot \overset{1}{\cancel{15}} \cdot \overset{1}{\cancel{b}} \cdot \overset{1}{\cancel{a}}}{\underset{1}{\cancel{5}} \cdot \underset{1}{\cancel{b}} \cdot 4 \cdot \underset{1}{\cancel{a}}} \text{ or } \frac{3}{4}$$

For what values is the expression undefined?

Example 4

Find $\frac{4x^2y}{15a^3b^3} \div \frac{2xy^2}{5ab^3}$. Write the answer in simplest form.

$$\frac{4x^2y}{15a^3b^3} \div \frac{2xy^2}{5ab^3} = \frac{4x^2y}{15a^3b^3} \cdot \frac{5ab^3}{2xy^2}$$ *Multiply by the reciprocal of the divisor.*

$$= \frac{\overset{2}{\cancel{4}} \cdot \overset{1}{\cancel{5}} \cdot \overset{x}{\cancel{x^2}} \cdot \overset{1}{\cancel{y}} \cdot \overset{1}{\cancel{a}} \cdot \overset{1}{\cancel{b^3}}}{\underset{3}{\cancel{15}} \cdot \underset{1}{\cancel{2}} \cdot \underset{1}{\cancel{x}} \cdot \underset{y}{\cancel{y^2}} \cdot \underset{a^2}{\cancel{a^3}} \cdot \underset{1}{\cancel{b^3}}}$$ *Factor and divide.*

$$= \frac{2x}{3a^2y}$$ *Multiply.*

Chalkboard Examples

For Example 2

Simplify $\frac{y^3 - ay^2}{y^2 - ay}$. y

For Example 3

Find $\frac{7a}{9b} \cdot \frac{63b^3}{35a^2}$. Write the answer in simplest form. $\frac{7b^2}{5a}$

For Example 4

Find $\frac{14c^2d}{9m^3n^2} \div \frac{35cd^3}{24mn}$. Write the answer in simplest form. $\frac{16c}{15d^2m^2n}$

Teaching Tip ❶   You may want to show *why* dividing is the same as multiplying by the multiplicative inverse.

$\frac{a}{b} \div \frac{c}{d}$ can be written as $\dfrac{\frac{a}{b}}{\frac{c}{d}}$.

Now multiply by 1 in the form $\dfrac{\frac{d}{c}}{\frac{d}{c}}$.

$$\frac{\frac{a}{b}}{\frac{c}{d}} \cdot \frac{\frac{d}{c}}{\frac{d}{c}} = \frac{\frac{a}{b} \cdot \frac{d}{c}}{1}$$

$$= \frac{a}{b} \cdot \frac{d}{c}$$

Chalkboard Examples

For Example 5

Find $\dfrac{y + 2}{y^2 + 5y} \div \dfrac{y(y - 2)}{y^2 - 25}$. Write the answer in simplest form.

$\dfrac{(y + 2)(y - 5)}{y^2(y - 2)}$

For Example 6

A rectangular box has one side with an area of $(2x^2 + 7x - 15)$ in². The adjacent side has an area of $(3x^2 + 17x + 10)$ in². The height of the box is $(x + 5)$ in. Find the area of the bottom of the box.

$(6x^2 - 5x - 6)$ in²

For Example 7

Simplify $\dfrac{\dfrac{3 - x}{5}}{\dfrac{4 - x}{10}} \cdot \dfrac{2(3 - x)}{(4 - x)}$

Example 5

Find $\dfrac{x + 2}{x + 3} \div \dfrac{x^2 + x - 12}{x^2 - 9}$. Write the answer in simplest form.

$\dfrac{x + 2}{x + 3} \div \dfrac{x^2 + x - 12}{x^2 - 9} = \dfrac{x + 2}{x + 3} \cdot \dfrac{x^2 - 9}{x^2 + x - 12}$ *Multiply by the reciprocal of the divisor.*

$= \dfrac{(x + 2)\cancel{(x + 3)}\cancel{(x - 3)}}{\cancel{(x + 3)}(x + 4)\cancel{(x - 3)}}$ *Factor and divide.*

$= \dfrac{x + 2}{x + 4}$

Example 6

CONNECTION

Geometry

The bases of two parallelograms are also the edges of a rectangle C. Parallelogram A has an area of $12x^2 + 2x - 2$ ft² and height of $2x - 5$ ft. Parallelogram B has an area of $2x^2 - 3x - 5$ ft² and height of $3x - 1$ ft. Find the area of rectangle C.

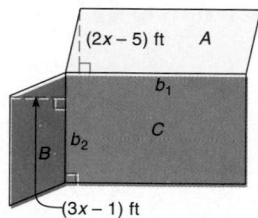

$(2x - 5)$ ft   A

b_1

C

B b_2

$(3x - 1)$ ft

The area of a parallelogram is found by using the formula $A = bh$. Since you know the area and height of each parallelogram, you can find the base measures, b_1 and b_2, by dividing the area by the height.

$b_1 = \dfrac{12x^2 + 2x - 2}{2x - 5}$ $b_2 = \dfrac{2x^2 - 3x - 5}{3x - 1}$

$\quad = \dfrac{(3x - 1)(4x + 2)}{2x - 5}$ $\quad = \dfrac{(2x - 5)(x + 1)}{3x - 1}$

The area of the rectangle is found by $A = bh$. In this case, b and h are the measures of the bases of the parallelograms. The area of rectangle C can be found by multiplying the bases.

$A = b_1 \cdot b_2$

$\quad = \dfrac{\cancel{(3x - 1)}(4x + 2)}{\cancel{2x - 5}} \cdot \dfrac{\cancel{(2x - 5)}(x + 1)}{\cancel{3x - 1}}$

$\quad = (4x + 2)(x + 1)$

$\quad = 4x^2 + 6x + 2$

The area of rectangle C is $4x^2 + 6x + 2$ ft².

A complex fraction is a rational expression whose numerator and/or denominator contains a rational expression. The expressions below are complex fractions. **Teaching Tip ❷**

$$\dfrac{\dfrac{z + 4t}{w}}{6z} \qquad \dfrac{8}{\dfrac{x}{3 - y}} \qquad \dfrac{\dfrac{1}{x} + 3}{\dfrac{2}{x} + 5} \qquad \dfrac{\dfrac{x^2 - 4}{2}}{\dfrac{2 - x}{5}}$$

Remember that a fraction is nothing more than a way to express a division problem. That is, $1 \div 3$ can be expressed as $\frac{1}{3}$. So to simplify any complex fraction, rewrite it as a division expression and use the rules for division.

Example 7

Simplify $\dfrac{\dfrac{x^2}{x^2 - 25y^2}}{\dfrac{x}{5y - x}}$. **Teaching Tip ❸**

Rewrite the complex fraction as a division expression.

$$\dfrac{\dfrac{x^2}{x^2 - 25y^2}}{\dfrac{x}{5y - x}} = \dfrac{x^2}{x^2 - 25y^2} \div \dfrac{x}{5y - x}$$

$$= \dfrac{x^2}{x^2 - 25y^2} \cdot \dfrac{5y - x}{x} \qquad \textit{Multiply by the reciprocal of the divisor.}$$

$$= \dfrac{\overset{x}{\cancel{x^2}}(-1)\overset{1}{\cancel{(x - 5y)}}}{\underset{1}{\cancel{x}}(x + 5y)\underset{1}{\cancel{(x - 5y)}}} \text{ or } \dfrac{-x}{x + 5y}$$

CHECKING FOR UNDERSTANDING

Communicating Mathematics

1. the greatest term that is a factor of each of a group of terms

7. $3x^2y^2$, $\dfrac{-y^3}{6x}$

9. $4x^5y$, $-2xy^2$

Guided Practice

10. a^3b^2, $-\dfrac{1}{b}$

11. $(m + 5)$, $\dfrac{1}{2}$

12. $9t^2u^3$, $\dfrac{-3t^4}{4u}$

Read and study the lesson to answer each question.

1. Define greatest common factor.

2. Suppose the numerator of a rational expression is a polynomial and the denominator of a rational expression is a different polynomial. Will factoring the polynomials necessarily provide a way to simplify the expression? Explain your answer. **See margin.**

3. What is the multiplicative inverse of $7a$? $\dfrac{1}{7a}$

4. What is the multiplicative inverse of $\dfrac{11b}{4c}$? $\dfrac{4c}{11b}$

5. What is the greatest common factor of $(ab - bc)$ and $(3xy + 4tr)$? **1**

Find the GCF of the numerator and denominator for each expression. Then simplify the expression.

6. $\dfrac{42y}{18xy}$ $6y$, $\dfrac{7}{3x}$

7. $\dfrac{-3x^2y^5}{18x^3y^2}$

8. $\dfrac{42y^2x}{18y^7}$ $6y^2$, $\dfrac{7x}{3y^5}$

9. $\dfrac{(-2x^2y)^3}{4x^5y}$

10. $\dfrac{a^3b^2}{(-ab)^3}$

11. $\dfrac{m + 5}{2m + 10}$

12. $\dfrac{(-3t^2u)^3}{(6tu^2)^2}$

13. $\dfrac{4x}{x^2 - x}$ x, $\dfrac{4}{x - 1}$

Teaching Tip ❸ Another way of simplifying the complex fraction in Example 7 is to multiply the numerator and denominator of the complex fraction by the LCM of the denominators of the separate fractions.

EVALUATING THE LESSON

Checking for Understanding

Exercises 1–16 are designed to help you assess understanding through reading, writing, and speaking. You should work through Exercises 1–5 with your students, and then monitor their work on Exercises 6–16.

Reteaching Masters Booklet, p. 73

NAME _____ DATE _____

11-3 Reteaching Worksheet

Multiplying and Dividing Rational Expressions

To simplify a rational algebraic expression, divide both numerator and denominator by their GCF. Multiply rational expressions by multiplying the numerators and denominators. Dividing by a rational expression is the same as multiplying by its multiplicative inverse.

Multiplying Rational Expressions:	**Dividing Rational Expressions**
For all rational expressions, $\frac{a}{b}$ and $\frac{c}{d}$, $b \neq 0$, and $d \neq 0$, $\frac{a}{b} \cdot \frac{c}{d} = \frac{ac}{bd}$.	For all rational expressions, $\frac{a}{b}$ and $\frac{c}{d}$, $b \neq 0$, $c \neq 0$, and $d \neq 0$, $\frac{a}{b} \div \frac{c}{d} = \frac{a}{b} \cdot \frac{d}{c}$.

A complex rational expression, also called a **complex fraction**, is an expression whose numerator or denominator, or both, contain rational expressions. To simplify a complex fraction, treat it as a division problem. Remember, all rational expressions must be reduced as much as possible.

Examples: Simplify each expression.

$$\dfrac{x^2 - 9}{x^2 + x - 12} \cdot \dfrac{x + 2}{x + 3} = \dfrac{(x + 3)(x - 3)}{(x + 4)(x - 3)} \cdot \dfrac{x + 2}{x + 3}$$
$$= \dfrac{(x + 3)(x - 3)(x + 2)}{(x + 4)(x - 3)(x + 3)}$$
$$= \dfrac{x + 2}{x + 4}$$

$$\dfrac{\frac{x^3}{y^2}}{\frac{x^2}{y^5}} = \dfrac{x^3}{y^2} \div \dfrac{x^2}{y^5} = \dfrac{x^3}{y^2} \cdot \dfrac{y^5}{x^2} = \dfrac{x^3 y^5}{x^2 y^2} = \dfrac{x y^3}{y} = \dfrac{x}{y}$$

Simplify each expression.

1. $\dfrac{c(c - 3)}{c^2 - 25} \cdot \dfrac{c^2 + 4c - 5}{c^2 - 4c + 3}$ $\dfrac{c}{c - 5}$

2. $\dfrac{(m - 3)^2}{m^2 - 6m + 9} \cdot \dfrac{m^3 - 9m}{m^2 - 9}$ m

3. $\dfrac{x^4 y^2 z^3}{x^3 - 4} \div \dfrac{x^6 y^4 z}{x + 2}$ $\dfrac{z^2}{(x - 2)x^4 y^2}$

4. $\dfrac{1}{x + 3} \div \dfrac{2x}{(x + 2)(x + 3)}$ $\dfrac{x + 2}{2x}$

5. $\dfrac{c^3 + 3c^2}{(c + 5)^2} \cdot \dfrac{c^2 - 25}{c^3}$ $\dfrac{(c + 3)(c - 5)}{c + 5}$

6. $\dfrac{\frac{x^2 - 4}{x + 3}}{\frac{x^2 - 4x + 4}{x^2 + 3x}}$ $\dfrac{x(x + 2)}{x - 2}$

7. $\dfrac{\frac{b^2 - 100}{b^3}}{3b^2 - 31b + 10}$ $\dfrac{2b + 20}{b^2(3b - 1)}$

8. $\dfrac{\frac{2x^2 + 9x + 9}{x + 1}}{\frac{10x^2 + 19x + 6}{5x^2 + 7x + 2}}$ $\dfrac{x + 3}{x + 3}$

9. $\dfrac{\frac{x^3 y^2 z}{a^2 b^3}}{\frac{a^2 x^2 y}{b^3}}$ $\dfrac{xyz}{a^4}$

RETEACHING THE LESSON

Compare multiplying and dividing rational expressions to multiplying and dividing fractions.

$$\dfrac{3}{4} \times \dfrac{5}{6} = \dfrac{3 \times 5}{4 \times 6} = \dfrac{15}{24} \text{ or } \dfrac{5}{8}$$

$$\dfrac{7}{8} \div \dfrac{7}{12} = \dfrac{\overset{1}{\cancel{7}}}{\underset{2}{\cancel{8}}} \times \dfrac{\overset{3}{\cancel{12}}}{\underset{1}{\cancel{7}}}$$

$$= \dfrac{3}{2} \text{ or } 1\dfrac{1}{2}$$

Additional Answer

2. No. For example,
$$\dfrac{x^2 - 4}{2x^2 + 12x + 18} = \dfrac{(x - 2)(x + 2)}{2(x + 3)(x + 3)}.$$
There are no common factors, so the expression is in simplest form.

Error Analysis

Students sometimes cancel matching expressions that are not factors.

For example:

$$\frac{2x + 5}{15} = \frac{2x + \cancel{5}^{1}}{\cancel{15}_{3}}$$

Point out that only factors can be cancelled (divided out) and 5 is not a factor of $2x + 5$.

Closing the Lesson

Writing Activity Using examples, have students write a sentence or two explaining any procedural differences between multiplying and dividing rational expressions.

APPLYING THE LESSON

Homework Exercises

Assignment Guide

Basic: 17–39, 44–45, 47–51
Average: 22–41, 44–51
Enriched: 24–51
All: Mid-Chapter Review, 1–8

Practice Masters Booklet, p. 83

---

14. $\frac{p^3}{2q} \div \frac{-p^2}{4q}$ **$-2p$**

15. $\frac{y^2}{x + 2} \div \frac{y}{x + 2}$ **y**

16. $\frac{3h}{h + 1} \div (h - 2)$

$$\frac{3h}{(h + 1)(h - 2)}$$

EXERCISES

Practice **Simplify each expression.**

17. $\frac{3ab}{4ac} \cdot \frac{6a^2}{3b^2}$ **$\frac{3a^2}{2bc}$**

18. $-\frac{3}{5a} \div \left(-\frac{9}{15ab}\right)$ **b**

19. $\frac{3d^3c}{a^4} \div \left(-\frac{6dc}{a^5}\right)$ **$\frac{-ad^2}{2}$**

20. $\frac{(cd)^3}{a} \cdot \frac{ax^2}{xc^2d}$ **cd^2x**

21. $\left(\frac{x^2}{y}\right)^2 \cdot \frac{5}{3x}$ **$\frac{5x^3}{3y^2}$**

22. $\frac{5}{m - 3} \div \frac{10}{m - 3}$ **$\frac{1}{2}$**

23. $\frac{(ab)^3}{d^3} \div \frac{a^2b^4}{(cd)^4}$ **$\frac{ac^4d}{b}$**

24. $\left(\frac{3a^3}{b^2}\right)^3 \cdot \frac{4b^2}{3a^7}$ **$\frac{36a^2}{b^4}$**

25. $\frac{x + y}{a} \div \frac{x + y}{a^2}$ **a**

26. The area of a triangle can be expressed as $4x^2 - 2x - 6$ square meters. The height of the triangle is $x + 1$ meters. Find the base of the triangle. **$8x - 12$ meters**

Simplify each expression.

27. $\frac{3x - 21}{x^2 - 49} \div \frac{3x}{x^2 + 7x}$ **1**

28. $\frac{2x + 2}{x^2 + 5x + 6} \div \frac{3x + 3}{x^2 + 2x - 3}$ **$\frac{2(x - 1)}{3(x + 2)}$**

29. $\frac{x^2 - y^2}{x + y} \cdot \frac{1}{x - y}$ **-1**

30. $\frac{a^2 + 2a - 15}{a - 3} \div \frac{a^2 - 4}{2}$

30. $\frac{2(a + 5)}{(a - 2)(a + 2)}$

31. $\frac{y^2 - y}{w^2 - y^2} \div \frac{y^2 - 2y + 1}{1 - y}$ **$\frac{-y}{w^2 - y^2}$**

32. $\frac{a^2 - b^2}{2a} \div \frac{a - b}{6a}$ **$3(a + b)$**

33. $\frac{(y - 2)^2}{(x - 4)^2} \cdot \frac{x - 4}{y - 2} \cdot \frac{y - 2}{x - 4}$

34. $\frac{x^2 - y^2}{y^2} \cdot \frac{y^3}{y - x}$ **$-y(x + y)$**

35. $\frac{x^2 + 3x - 10}{x^2 + 8x + 15} \cdot \frac{x^2 + 5x + 6}{x^2 + 4x + 4}$

35. $\frac{x - 2}{x + 2}$

36. $\frac{a^3 - b^3}{a + b} \cdot \frac{a^2 - b^2}{a^2 + ab + b^2}$

36. $(a - b)^2$

37. $\frac{w^2 - 11w + 24}{w^2 - 18w + 80} \cdot \frac{w^2 - 15w + 50}{w^2 - 9w + 20}$

37. $\frac{w - 3}{w - 4}$

38. $\frac{\frac{x^2 - y^2}{2}}{\frac{x - y}{4}}$ **$2(x + y)$**

39. The lengths of the sides of a right triangle can be expressed as $x + 2$ in., $x + 9$ in., and $x + 10$ in. Find the lengths of the sides. **5, 12, 13 inches**

Simplify each expression.

40. $\frac{\frac{w^2 + 2w + 1}{w + 1}}{3}$ **$3(w + 1)$**

41. $\frac{\frac{5a^2 - 20}{2a + 2}}{\frac{10a - 20}{4a}}$

42. $\frac{\frac{2y}{y^2 - 4}}{\frac{3}{y^2 - 4y + 4}}$

43. $\frac{\frac{p^2 + 7p}{3p}}{\frac{49 - p^2}{3p - 21}}$

41. $\frac{a(a + 2)}{a + 1}$

42. $\frac{2y(y - 2)}{3(y + 2)}$

43. **-1**

Critical Thinking 44. Simplify $\frac{(a^2 - 5a + 6)^{-1}}{(a - 2)^{-2}} \div \frac{(a - 3)^{-1}}{(a - 2)^{-2}}$. **$\frac{1}{a - 2}$** **Teaching Tip ❹**

Applications

45. Statistics After conducting a survey on raising taxes for schools in Worthington, a statistician said the number of women in favor of the tax levy could be expressed by $\dfrac{3 + 10t^2 - 17t}{5t^2 + 4t - 1}$. The number of men in favor of the levy can be expressed by $\dfrac{4t^2 - 9}{3 + 5t + 2t^2}$. Find the ratio of women to men in simplest form. What does this ratio mean? *A ratio is the quotient of two values.* **1; an equal number of men and women favor the tax.**

46. Demographics In the United States, the ratio of the number of females to the number of males is almost one. However, in sparsely populated parts of Alaska there are more men than women.

    a. If the ratio of men to women in one region of Alaska is expressed as $\dfrac{m^2 + 15m + 54}{m + 6}$ to $\dfrac{m + 9}{3}$, find how many men there are for each woman in that region. **There are 3 men for every woman.**

    b. Why do you think there are more men than women in these regions? **See margin.**

Mixed Review

47. If y varies inversely as x, and $y = -8$ when $x = 1.5$, find x when $y = -3$. **(Lesson 11-2)** $x = 4$

48. Real Estate Budget Realty charges a commission of $4800 on the sale of a $90,000 home. At that rate, how much commission would be charged on the sale of a $219,000 home? **(Lesson 11-2)** **$11,680**

49. State whether the graph of $4y^2 - x^2 - 24y + 6x = 11$ is a parabola, a circle, an ellipse, or a hyperbola. **(Lesson 9-7)** **hyperbola**

50. Find the sum, difference, and product for $6 + i$ and $5 - 2i$. **(Lesson 6-8)** $11 - i, 1 + 3i, 32 - 7i$

51. Suppose w is a number. Name the most sets of numbers to which it can belong. **(Lesson 6-1)** **See margin.**

MID-CHAPTER REVIEW

Graph each rational function. **(Lesson 11-1)** **1–3. For graphs, see Solutions Manual.**

1. $f(x) = \dfrac{2}{x - 5}$ **2.** $f(x) = \dfrac{2}{x^2 - 2x + 1}$ **3.** $f(x) = \dfrac{7}{(x - 2)(x - 3)}$

4. If y varies inversely as x, and $x = -8$ when $y = -2$, find x when $y = \dfrac{2}{3}$. **(Lesson 11-2)** $x = 24$

5. If m varies directly as n, and $n = \dfrac{1}{5}$ when $m = 11$, find m when $n = \dfrac{2}{5}$. **(Lesson 11-2)** $m = 22$

Simplify each expression. **(Lesson 11-3)**

6. $\dfrac{4ab}{2bc} \cdot \dfrac{11a^2b}{5b^2}$ $\dfrac{22a^3}{5bc}$

7. $\dfrac{7a + 49}{16} \cdot \dfrac{48}{6a + 42}$ $\dfrac{7}{2}$

8. $\dfrac{m^2 + 5m + 4}{6} \div \dfrac{m + 1}{18m + 24}$ $(m + 4)(3m + 4)$

Teaching Tip ④ Have students simplify both the dividend and the divisor so that only positive exponents are used in the actual division problem.

Additional Answers

46b. Answers will vary. Many areas of Alaska have unfavorable weather conditions and offer little employment for a single woman. Most women in these areas are wives of men employed in mining, fishing, or trapping.

51. Complex, Real, Rational, Integer, Whole, Natural

Enrichment Masters Booklet, p. 73

11-3 Enrichment Worksheet

Expansions of Rational Expressions

Many rational expressions can be transformed into a **power series.** A power series is an infinite series of the form $A + Bx + Cx^2 + Dx^3 + \ldots$. The rational expression and the power series normally can be said to have the same values only for certain values of x. For example, the following equation holds only for values of x such that $-1 < x < 1$.

$$\frac{1}{1-x} = 1 + x + x^2 + x^3 + \ldots \quad \text{for } -1 < x < 1$$

Example: Expand $\frac{2 + 3x}{1 + x + x^2}$ in ascending powers of x.

Assume that the expression equals a series of the form $A + Bx + Cx^2 + Dx^3 + \ldots$. Then multiply both sides of the equation by the denominator $1 + x + x^2$.

$$\frac{2 + 3x}{1 + x + x^2} = A + Bx + Cx^2 + Dx^3 + \ldots$$
$$2 + 3x = (1 + x + x^2)(A + Bx + Cx^2 + Dx^3 + \ldots)$$
$$2 + 3x = A + Bx + Cx^2 + Dx^3 + \ldots$$
$$\quad + Ax + Bx^2 + Cx^3 + \ldots$$
$$\quad + Ax^2 + Bx^3 + \ldots$$
$$2 + 3x = A + (B + A)x + (C + B + A)x^2 + (D + C + B + A)x^3 + \ldots$$

Now, match the coefficients of the polynomials.

$2 = A$
$3 = B + A$
$0 = C + B + A$
$0 = D + C + B + A$

Finally, solve for A, B, C, and D and write the expansion.

$A = 2, B = 1, C = -3,$ and $D = 0$

Therefore, $\frac{2 + 3x}{1 + x + x^2} = 2 + x - 3x^2 + \ldots$

Expand each rational expression to four terms.

1. $\frac{1 - x}{1 + x + x^2}$ $1 - 2x + x^2 + x^3 + \ldots$

2. $\frac{2}{1 - x}$ $2 + x + x^2 + x^3 + \ldots$

3. $\frac{1}{1 + x}$ $1 - x + x^2 - x^3 + \ldots$

EXTENDING THE LESSON

Math Power: Problem Solving

Simplify

$$\dfrac{\dfrac{9x^2 - 12x + 4}{6x^2 - 13x + 6}}{\dfrac{6x^2 + 13x + 6}{4x^2 - 9}} \div \dfrac{\dfrac{9x^2 - 4}{6x^2 - 5x - 6}}{\dfrac{6x^2 + 5x - 6}{4x^2 - 12x + 9}}.$$

$$\dfrac{(3x - 2)(2x + 3)}{(2x - 3)(3x + 2)} = \dfrac{6x^2 + 5x - 6}{6x^2 - 5x - 6}$$

Mid-Chapter Review

The Mid-Chapter Review provides students with a brief review of the concepts and skills in Lessons 11-1 through 11-3. Lesson numbers are given at the end of problems or instruction lines so students may review concepts not yet mastered.

Lesson Resources

Reteaching Master 11-4
Practice Master 11-4
Enrichment Master 11-4

 Transparency 11-4 contains the
5-Minute Check and a teaching aid
for this lesson.

INTRODUCING THE LESSON

5-Minute Check

(over Lesson 11-3)
Simplify each expression.

1. $\dfrac{x^2 + 10x + 25}{x^2 + 2x - 15} \cdot \dfrac{x + 5}{x - 3}$

2. $\dfrac{16ab^3}{25(4 - c)} \cdot \dfrac{5(c - 4)}{12a^2c^2} \quad \dfrac{-4b^3}{15ac^2}$

3. $\dfrac{x^2 - 16}{x^2 + 4x + 4} \cdot \dfrac{x + 2}{x - 4} \quad \dfrac{x + 4}{x + 2}$

4. $\dfrac{\frac{4 - y}{27}}{\frac{8 + y}{3}} \quad \dfrac{4 - y}{9(8 + y)}$

Motivating the Lesson

Show students several related objects. For example, 12 coins, consisting of 6 pennies, 4 dimes, and 2 nickels may be used. Ask questions about the objects. Sample: What part of the coins is made up of (a) dimes? $\frac{1}{3}$ (b) pennies? $\frac{1}{2}$

If you remove all the pennies and all the dimes, what part of the group have you removed altogether? $\frac{10}{12}$ or $\frac{5}{6}$

TEACHING THE LESSON

Teaching Tip ❶ Emphasize that students can use any common denominator, but the LCD requires the least simplification of the solution.

Adding and Subtracting Rational Expressions

Objectives
After studying this lesson, you should be able to:

11-4A ■ find the least common denominator of two or more algebraic expressions, and

11-4B ■ add and subtract rational expressions.

Application

Ansel Adams (1902–1984) was a famous American photographer known for his style of detailed, focused photos that showed its subjects simply and directly. Most of his photos are in black and white. To take sharp, clear pictures, Adams had to focus the camera precisely. The distance from the object to the lens (p) and the distance from the lens to the film (q) must be accurately calculated to insure this sharp image. The focal length of the lens is f. These measurements are demonstrated in the diagram below.

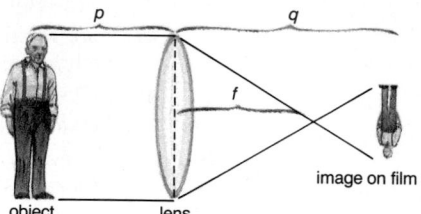

The formula that relates these measures is $\dfrac{1}{p} + \dfrac{1}{q} = \dfrac{1}{f}$.

Teaching Tip ❶

This formula involves addition of two rational expressions. Remember from arithmetic that to add (or subtract) fractions, they must first be written as equivalent fractions with a common denominator. The least common denominator (LCD) is usually used.

Specific case

$\dfrac{2}{3} + \dfrac{3}{5} = \dfrac{2 \cdot 5}{3 \cdot 5} + \dfrac{3 \cdot 3}{5 \cdot 3}$

Find equivalent fractions that have a common denominator.

$= \dfrac{10}{15} + \dfrac{9}{15}$

Teaching Tip ❷

Add the numerators.

$= \dfrac{19}{15}$

General case

$\dfrac{1}{p} + \dfrac{1}{q} = \dfrac{1 \cdot q}{p \cdot q} + \dfrac{1 \cdot p}{q \cdot p}$

$= \dfrac{q}{pq} + \dfrac{p}{pq}$

$= \dfrac{q + p}{pq}$

It is not necessary to rewrite the fraction $\frac{19}{15}$ as the mixed number $1\frac{4}{15}$.

ALTERNATE TEACHING STRATEGIES

Using Manipulatives

Using sets of golf tees of different colors, have students model problems involving addition and subtraction of rational expressions. (See Motivating the Lesson.)

Example 1 | Simplify $\dfrac{7x}{13y^2} + \dfrac{4y}{6x^2}$.

$\dfrac{7x}{13y^2} + \dfrac{4y}{6x^2} = \dfrac{7x}{13y^2} + \dfrac{2y}{3x^2}$ *Simplify the second term.*

$\qquad = \dfrac{7x(3x^2)}{13y^2(3x^2)} + \dfrac{2y(13y^2)}{3x^2(13y^2)}$ *The LCD is $39x^2y^2$. Find equivalent fractions that have this denominator.*

$\qquad = \dfrac{21x^3}{39x^2y^2} + \dfrac{26y^3}{39x^2y^2}$ *Simplify each numerator and denominator.*

$\qquad = \dfrac{21x^3 + 26y^3}{39x^2y^2}$ *Add the numerators.*

Sometimes the common denominator is not easily recognized, especially when working with algebraic rational expressions. Just as in arithmetic, the LCD must contain all prime factors of each denominator raised to the highest power that occurs in either denominator.

To add $\dfrac{5}{36}$ and $\dfrac{7}{24}$, it is helpful to factor each denominator.

$$36 = 2^2 \cdot 3^2 \qquad 24 = 2^3 \cdot 3$$

The prime factors are 2 and 3. The greatest power of 2 is 2^3, and the greatest power of 3 is 3^2. The LCD is $2^3 \cdot 3^2$ or 72.

The LCD for two algebraic rational expressions must also contain each factor of the denominator raised to its highest power.

Example 2 | Simplify $\dfrac{3y + 1}{2y - 10} + \dfrac{1}{y^2 - 2y - 15}$.

$\dfrac{3y + 1}{2y - 10} + \dfrac{1}{y^2 - 2y + 15} = \dfrac{3y + 1}{2(y - 5)} + \dfrac{1}{(y - 5)(y + 3)}$ *The LCD is $2(y - 5)(y + 3)$.*

$\qquad = \dfrac{3y + 1}{2(y - 5)} \cdot \dfrac{y + 3}{y + 3} + \dfrac{1}{(y - 5)(y + 3)} \cdot \dfrac{2}{2}$

$\qquad = \dfrac{(3y + 1)(y + 3) + 2}{2(y - 5)(y + 3)}$

$\qquad = \dfrac{3y^2 + 10y + 3 + 2}{2(y - 5)(y + 3)}$

$\qquad = \dfrac{3y^2 + 10y + 5}{2(y - 5)(y + 3)}$

Teaching Tip ❷   Be sure students understand that when both numerator and denominator are multiplied by the same number, the rational expression does not change in value, just in form (Multiplicative Identity Property).

Chalkboard Examples

For Example 1

Simplify $\dfrac{9}{10a} + \dfrac{4a}{5b}$. $\dfrac{9b + 8a^2}{10ab}$

For Example 2

Simplify $\dfrac{1}{4a^2 - 4a + 1} + \dfrac{1 - a}{1 - 2a}$.

$\dfrac{2a^2 - 3a + 2}{(2a - 1)^2}$

Teaching Tip ❸ Be sure students realize that the LCD is found in addition and subtraction problems so that parts of equal size can be added or subtracted. This is not needed for multiplication or division. Be sure students do not find a common denominator to multiply or divide.

Reteaching Masters Booklet, p. 74

In Example 2, you saw that the numerator was expressed as a trinomial, but the denominator was left as a product of factors. When you simplify the numerator, you sometimes discover that the polynomial contains a factor common to the denominator. Thus the rational expression can be further simplified.

Example 3 Simplify $\dfrac{w+12}{4w-16} - \dfrac{w+4}{2w-8}$.

$\dfrac{w+12}{4w-16} - \dfrac{w+4}{2w-8} = \dfrac{w+12}{4(w-4)} - \dfrac{w+4}{2(w-4)}$ *Factor each expression.*

$= \dfrac{(w+12) - (2)(w+4)}{4(w-4)}$ *Since 2 is a factor of 4, it is not necessary to include an extra factor of 2 in the LCD.*

$= \dfrac{w+12-2w-8}{4(w-4)}$

$= \dfrac{-w+4}{4(w-4)}$ *Combine like terms in the numerator.*

$= \dfrac{-1(w-4)}{4(w-4)}$ or $-\dfrac{1}{4}$

To simplify a complex fraction that contains sums or differences, you should first express the numerator and denominator as a single rational expression before you divide the two expressions.

Example 4 Simplify $\dfrac{\dfrac{1}{x} - \dfrac{1}{y}}{1 + \dfrac{1}{x}}$.

$\dfrac{\dfrac{1}{x} - \dfrac{1}{y}}{1 + \dfrac{1}{x}} = \dfrac{\dfrac{y}{xy} - \dfrac{x}{xy}}{\dfrac{x}{x} + \dfrac{1}{x}}$ *In the numerator, the LCD is xy.*

In the denominator, the LCD is x.

$= \dfrac{\dfrac{y-x}{xy}}{\dfrac{x+1}{x}}$ *Simplify the numerator and denominator.*

$= \dfrac{y-x}{xy} \div \dfrac{x+1}{x}$ *Write the complex fraction as a division problem.*

$= \dfrac{y-x}{xy} \cdot \dfrac{x}{x+1}$ *The GCF is x.*

$= \dfrac{y-x}{y(x+1)}$ or $\dfrac{y-x}{xy+y}$

Teaching Tip ❸

RETEACHING THE LESSON

Compare adding and subtracting rational expressions to adding and subtracting fractions.

$\dfrac{1}{15} + \dfrac{5}{6} = \dfrac{2}{30} + \dfrac{25}{30}$ The LCD is 30.

$= \dfrac{27}{30}$

CHECKING FOR UNDERSTANDING

Communicating Mathematics

Read and study the lesson to answer each question.

1. What does GCF represent? **greatest common factor**
2. What does LCD represent? **least common denominator**
3. What are equivalent fractions? **fractions that have the same value**
4. Two denominators of expressions to be added are $5(a + c)$ and $25a + 25b$. Tell how you would find the LCD. What is it? $\mathbf{25(a + c)(a + b)}$

Guided Practice

Find the LCD for each pair of denominators.

9. $x(x - 2)(x + 2)$
10. $(x + 2)(x + 1)(x - 1)$

5. 78, 39 **78**
8. $36x^2y$, $20xyz$ **$180x^2yz$**
11. $3x + 15$, $x^2 + 2x - 15$
   $\mathbf{3(x + 5)(x - 3)}$

6. 12, 27 **108**
9. $x(x - 2)$, $x^2 - 4$

7. 80, 125 **2000**
10. $(x + 2)(x + 1)$, $x^2 - 1$

12. $x^2 - 8x$, $y^2 - 8y$
   $\mathbf{xy(x - 8)(y - 8)}$

Simplify each expression.

13. $\dfrac{7}{ab} + \dfrac{9}{b}$ $\dfrac{7 + 9a}{ab}$

14. $\dfrac{11}{10} - \dfrac{7}{2a} - \dfrac{6}{5a}$ $\dfrac{11a - 47}{10a}$

15. $3t - 7 + \dfrac{3t + 1}{t - 5}$
   $\dfrac{3t^2 - 19t + 36}{t - 5}$

EXERCISES

Practice

Simplify each expression. **Teaching Tip**

 A

16. $\dfrac{3a + 2}{a + b} + \dfrac{4}{2a + 2b}$ $\dfrac{3a + 4}{a + b}$

17. $-\dfrac{18}{9xy} + \dfrac{7}{2x} - \dfrac{2}{3x^2}$ $\dfrac{-12x + 21xy - 4y}{6x^2y}$

18. $\dfrac{3}{4a} - \dfrac{2}{5a} - \dfrac{1}{2a}$ $-\dfrac{3}{20a}$

19. $\dfrac{7}{y - 8} - \dfrac{6}{8 - y}$ $\dfrac{13}{y - 8}$

20. $\dfrac{x}{x^2 - 9} + \dfrac{1}{2x + 6}$ $\dfrac{3(x - 1)}{2(x - 3)(x + 3)}$

21. $y - 1 + \dfrac{1}{y - 1}$ $\dfrac{y^2 - 2y + 2}{y - 1}$

22. $3m + 1 - \dfrac{2m}{3m + 1}$ $\dfrac{9m^2 + 4m + 1}{3m + 1}$

23. $\dfrac{x}{x + 3} - \dfrac{6x}{x^2 - 9}$ $\dfrac{x(x - 9)}{(x + 3)(x - 3)}$

B

24. $\dfrac{3}{a - 2} + \dfrac{2}{a - 3}$ $\dfrac{5a - 13}{(a - 2)(a - 3)}$

25. $\dfrac{6}{x^2 + 4x + 4} + \dfrac{5}{x + 2}$ $\dfrac{5x + 16}{(x + 2)^2}$

26. $\dfrac{8}{2y - 16} - \dfrac{y}{8 - y}$ $\dfrac{y + 4}{y - 8}$

27. $\dfrac{2a}{3a - 15} + \dfrac{-16a + 20}{3a^2 - 12a - 15}$ $\dfrac{2(a - 2)}{3(a + 1)}$

28. $\dfrac{7x + 38}{2(x - 7)(x + 4)}$

29. $\dfrac{-4x^2 - 5x - 2}{(x + 1)^2}$

30. $\dfrac{9m^2 - 42m + 81}{(m - 3)^2(m + 3)}$

32. $\dfrac{3x^2 - xy - y}{(x - y)(x + y)}$ C

33. $\dfrac{x^3 + 4x^2 + 7x + 17}{x^2 - 4}$

34. $\dfrac{6b^2 + 28b + 12}{(b - 7)(b + 7)(b + 2)}$

35. $\dfrac{2x^2 + x - 4}{(x - 1)(x - 2)}$

28. $\dfrac{5}{x^2 - 3x - 28} + \dfrac{7}{2x - 14}$

29. $\dfrac{x}{x^2 + 2x + 1} - \dfrac{x + 2}{x + 1} - \dfrac{3x}{x + 1}$

30. $\dfrac{m + 3}{m^2 - 6m + 9} - \dfrac{8m - 24}{9 - m^2}$

31. $\dfrac{m^2 + n^2}{m^2 - n^2} + \dfrac{m}{n - m} + \dfrac{n}{m + n}$ **0**

32. $\dfrac{x}{x - y} + \dfrac{y}{y^2 - x^2} + \dfrac{2x}{x + y}$

33. $\dfrac{x^2 - 3x + 1}{x^2 - 4} - \dfrac{x^2 + 2x + 4}{2 - x} - \dfrac{x - 4}{x - 2}$

34. $\dfrac{3b - 1}{b^2 - 49} - \dfrac{3b + 2}{14 + 5b - b^2}$

35. $\dfrac{x + 1}{x - 1} + \dfrac{x + 2}{x - 2} + \dfrac{x}{x^2 - 3x + 2}$

36. $\dfrac{(x + y)\left(\dfrac{1}{x} - \dfrac{1}{y}\right)}{(x - y)\left(\dfrac{1}{x} + \dfrac{1}{y}\right)}$ $\mathbf{-1}$

37. $\dfrac{\dfrac{1}{x + 5} + \dfrac{1}{x - 3}}{\dfrac{2x^2 - 3x - 5}{x^2 + 2x - 15}}$ $\dfrac{2}{2x - 5}$

LESSON 11-4 ADDING AND SUBTRACTING RATIONAL EXPRESSIONS **525**

Critical Thinking Simplify each expression.

38. $\dfrac{2x}{x^2 + 7x + 10} + \dfrac{x - 1}{x^2 - 25}$

$\dfrac{3x^2 - 9x - 2}{(x - 5)(x + 5)(x + 2)}$

39. $\dfrac{3x}{4x^2 - 1} + \dfrac{5}{2x^2 - x} + \dfrac{2x + 1}{2x^2 + 5x + 2}$

$\dfrac{7x^3 + 16x^2 + 24x + 10}{x(2x - 1)(2x + 1)(x + 2)}$

Applications

40. **Photography** Refer to the lens formula at the beginning of the lesson. Usha Smith has a camera with a focal length of 10 cm. When the lens is 12 cm from the film, the camera is focused to take a picture of her dog. How far from the lens is the dog? **60 cm**

41. **Sports** Ricki can throw a football at a speed of $\dfrac{4}{x + 2}$ mph. Juan can throw a football at a speed of $\dfrac{7}{x - 3}$ mph. How much greater is Ricki's speed than Juan's? $\dfrac{-3x - 26}{(x + 2)(x - 3)}$ **mph**

42. **Auto Racing** A Ferrari has a top speed of 189 mph. A Lamborghini can travel at a speed of $\dfrac{x}{x - 3}$ mph. If the Lamborghini is faster than the Ferrari, express the difference as a simplified rational expression.

$\dfrac{-188x + 567}{x - 3}$ **mph**

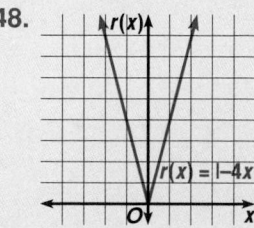

43. **Landscaping** A mad mathematics professor called the hardware store to find out how much fence he would need to outline his pentagon-shaped garden. He gave them the measures of each side as $\dfrac{1}{x}, \dfrac{2}{x - 2}, \dfrac{3}{x}, \dfrac{4}{x - 2}$, and $\dfrac{x}{x - 2}$. The manager of the store panicked until he found an algebra student to help him out. What was the total of the five sides of the garden? $\dfrac{x^2 + 10x - 8}{x(x - 2)}$

Mixed Review

44. Simplify $\dfrac{\dfrac{3x + 5}{3x + 1} - 2}{3 + \dfrac{3x}{1 - 2x}}$. (**Lesson 11-3**) $\dfrac{1 - 2x}{3x + 1}$

45. If $f(x) = 3x^2$ and $g(x) = x^2 - 1$, find $[f \circ g](2)$. (**Lesson 10-7**) **27**

46. Solve $x^2 - 8x + 7 \geq 0$. (**Lesson 8-7**) $\{x | x \leq 1 \text{ or } x \geq 7\}$

47. Solve $\sqrt{z + 12} - \sqrt{z} = 2$. (**Lesson 6-7**) **4**

48. Graph $r(x) = |-4x|$. (**Lesson 2-7**) **See margin.**

49. **Travel** The distance a car moves along the street in one revolution of the tires is directly proportional to the diameter of the tire. Mrs. Witmer's car travels about 88 inches in one revolution of the tires. Find the approximate diameter of the tire. (**Lesson 11-2**) **about 28 in.**

526 CHAPTER 11 RATIONAL POLYNOMIAL EXPRESSIONS

EXTENDING THE LESSON

Math Power: Reasoning

Simplify

$\dfrac{\dfrac{4}{x - 4} - \dfrac{1}{x + 2}}{\dfrac{3x^2 + 24x + 48}{2x^2 - 4x - 16}} + \dfrac{\dfrac{x - 4}{x - 4} + \dfrac{x - 5}{x + 4}}{\dfrac{x - 3}{x - 3} + \dfrac{x - 3}{x + 2}}$. **1**

Additional Answer

48.

Objective
11-5

After studying this lesson, you should be able to:

■ solve rational equations.

An equation that contains one or more rational expressions is called a **rational equation.** It is easiest to solve a rational equation if the fractions are eliminated. This can be done by multiplying each side of the equation by the least common denominator (LCD). Remember that when you multiply each side by the LCD, each term on each side must be multiplied by the LCD.

Application

Remember that the formula that relates the focal length f of a lens, the distance p from the lens to the object, and the distance q from the lens to the image on the film is $\frac{1}{p} + \frac{1}{q} = \frac{1}{f}$. Find q if $p = 45$ cm and $f = 5$ cm.

$$\frac{1}{p} + \frac{1}{q} = \frac{1}{f}$$

$$\frac{1}{45} + \frac{1}{q} = \frac{1}{5}$$

$$45q\left(\frac{1}{45} + \frac{1}{q}\right) = 45q\left(\frac{1}{5}\right)$$

$$45q\left(\frac{1}{45}\right) + 45q\left(\frac{1}{q}\right) = \frac{45q}{5}$$

$$q + 45 = 9q$$

$$45 = 8q$$

$$\frac{45}{8} = q \qquad \text{The value of } q \text{ is } \frac{45}{8} \text{ or } 5.625 \text{ cm.}$$

Check:

$$\frac{1}{p} + \frac{1}{q} = \frac{1}{f}$$

$$\frac{1}{45} + \frac{1}{\frac{45}{8}} \stackrel{?}{=} \frac{1}{5}$$

$$\frac{1}{45} + \left(1 \cdot \frac{8}{45}\right) \stackrel{?}{=} \frac{1}{5}$$

$$\frac{1}{45} + \frac{8}{45} \stackrel{?}{=} \frac{1}{5}$$

$$\frac{1}{5} = \frac{1}{5} \checkmark$$

In an equation, the LCD must be a common denominator for *all* denominators in the equation. This may involve finding the LCD for three or more denominators.

Example 1

Solve $\frac{9}{28} + \frac{3}{z+2} = \frac{3}{4}$.

The LCD for the three denominators is $28(z + 2)$.

$$\frac{9}{28} + \frac{3}{z+2} = \frac{3}{4}$$

$$28(z+2)\left(\frac{9}{28} + \frac{3}{z+2}\right) = 28(z+2)\left(\frac{3}{4}\right)$$

$$\frac{9}{28}(28)(z+2) + \left(\frac{3}{z+2}\right)(28)(z+2) = \left(\frac{3}{4}\right)(28)(z+2)$$

$$(9z + 18) + (84) = 21z + 42$$

$$60 = 12z$$

$$5 = z$$

Check: $\frac{9}{28} + \frac{3}{z+2} = \frac{3}{4}$

$$\frac{9}{28} + \frac{3}{5+2} \stackrel{?}{=} \frac{3}{4}$$

$$\frac{9}{28} + \frac{3}{7} \stackrel{?}{=} \frac{3}{4}$$

$$\frac{9}{28} + \frac{12}{28} \stackrel{?}{=} \frac{3}{4}$$

$$\frac{3}{4} = \frac{3}{4} \checkmark$$

ALTERNATE TEACHING STRATEGIES

Using Communication

Have students work with a partner. Have each group of two write a rational equation and take turns verbalizing each step needed to solve the equation and check the solution. Discuss any steps that are not commonly agreed upon.

Lesson Resources

Reteaching Master 11-5
Practice Master 11-5
Enrichment Master 11-5
Activity Master, p. 29

 Transparency 11-5 contains the 5-Minute Check and a teaching aid for this lesson.

INTRODUCING THE LESSON

5-Minute Check

(over Lesson 11-4)

Use the terms $\frac{2y}{y-3}$ and $\frac{3y-1}{y^2 + 2y - 15}$ to answer Exercises 1–3.

1. What is the LCD?
   $y^2 + 2y - 15$
2. What is the sum if the terms are added?
   $\frac{2y^2 + 13y - 1}{(y-3)(y+5)}$
3. What is the difference if the second term is subtracted from the first?
   $\frac{2y^2 + 7y + 1}{(y-3)(y+5)}$
4. Simplify $\frac{x - \frac{1}{x^2}}{x - \frac{1}{x}} \cdot \frac{x^2 + x + 1}{x(x+1)}$

Motivating the Lesson

Write several word phrases and several sentences on the chalkboard. Ask students to list general differences between phrases and sentences. Then write several algebraic expressions and equations and ask students how the relationship between expressions and equations compares to that between phrases and sentences.

Chalkboard Examples

For Example 1

Solve $\frac{6}{7} - \frac{3}{x-4} = \frac{7}{8}$. $x = -164$

For Example 2

Solve $\frac{7}{r+2} = \frac{6}{r-5}$. $r = 47$

For Example 3

Solve $\frac{x}{x+2} - \frac{x+2}{x-2} = \frac{x+3}{x-2}$.

$x = -1$ or $x = -10$

Teaching Tip ①   Ask students to look at Example 2 and name the value of m that would automatically be excluded as a solution.   3

Reteaching Masters Booklet, p. 75

NAME _____   DATE _____

11-5 **Reteaching Worksheet**

Solving Rational Equations

An equation that consists of one or more rational expressions is called a **rational equation.** One method of solving a rational equation is to multiply each side of the equation by the least common denominator (LCD) of *all* the denominators. Remember that a rational expression is undefined when the denominator is zero. Be sure to watch for solutions that would produce a denominator of zero. These solutions must be excluded from the final solution set.

Example: Solve $\frac{9}{10} + \frac{2}{x+1} = \frac{2}{5}$

$$\frac{9}{10} + \frac{2}{x+1} = \frac{2}{5}$$

$10(x+1)\left(\frac{9}{10} + \frac{2}{x+1}\right) = \left(\frac{2}{5}\right)(10)(x+1)$ Multiply each side by $10(x+1)$, the LCD for all three denominators.

$9(x+1) + 20 = 4(x+1)$

$9x + 9 + 20 = 4x + 4$

$5x = -25$

$x = -5$

The solution is -5.

Check: $\frac{9}{10} + \frac{2}{x+1} = \frac{2}{5}$
$\frac{9}{10} + \frac{2}{-5+1} = \frac{2}{5}$
$\frac{9}{10} + -\frac{1}{2} = \frac{2}{5}$
$\frac{2}{5} = \frac{2}{5}$

Solve each equation. Check your solutions.

1. $\frac{2y}{3} - \frac{y+3}{6} = 2$ 5

2. $\frac{4t-3}{5} - \frac{4-2t}{3} = 1$ 2

3. $\frac{2x+1}{3} - \frac{x-5}{4} = \frac{1}{2}$ $-\frac{13}{5}$

4. $\frac{3m+2}{5m} + \frac{2m-1}{2m} = 4$ $-\frac{1}{24}$

5. $\frac{4}{x-1} = \frac{x+1}{12}$ ± 7

6. $\frac{x}{x-2} + \frac{4}{x-2} = 10$ $\frac{8}{3}$

7. $\frac{3}{4} - \frac{3m}{4m+6} = 8$ $-\frac{87}{64}$

8. $\frac{10}{m^2-1} + \frac{2m-5}{m-1} = \frac{2m+5}{m+1}$ $\frac{5}{3}$

9. $\frac{7}{x+2} + \frac{3}{x-2} = \frac{1}{x-2}$ $\frac{10}{9}$

Remember that a rational expression is undefined when the value for a variable results in a denominator of zero. When solving rational equations, you should watch for solutions that would produce a denominator of zero. These values must be excluded from your list of solutions. This is one reason that checking your solutions in the *original* equation is so important.

Example 2

Solve $\frac{7}{m-3} = \frac{m+4}{m-3}$.

$$\frac{7}{m-3} = \frac{m+4}{m-3}$$

$$(m-3)\left(\frac{7}{m-3}\right) = (m-3)\left(\frac{m+4}{m-3}\right) \quad \text{The LCD is } m-3.$$

$$7 = m+4$$

$$3 = m$$

When you check your solution, you find that 3 produces a zero in the denominator. This value is not a solution. Since there are no other solutions to choose from, this equation has no solution.

Example 3

Solve $r + \frac{r^2-5}{r^2-1} = \frac{r^2+r+2}{r+1}$.

$$r + \frac{r^2-5}{r^2-1} = \frac{r^2+r+2}{r+1}$$

$$(r^2-1)\left(r + \frac{r^2-5}{r^2-1}\right) = (r^2-1)\left(\frac{r^2+r+2}{r+1}\right) \quad \text{The LCD is } (r^2-1).$$

$$(r^2-1)r + (r^2-1)\left(\frac{r^2-5}{r^2-1}\right) = (r-1)(r+1)\left(\frac{r^2+r+2}{r+1}\right)$$

$$r^3 - r + r^2 - 5 = (r-1)(r^2+r+2)$$

$$r^3 + r^2 - r - 5 = r^3 + r - 2$$

$$r^2 - 2r - 3 = 0$$

$$(r-3)(r+1) = 0$$

$$r - 3 = 0 \quad \text{or} \quad r + 1 = 0$$

$$r = 3 \qquad\qquad r = -1$$

Check: $r + \frac{r^2-5}{r^2-1} = \frac{r^2+r+2}{r+1}$

When you check the value of -1, you get a zero for the denominator. So, -1 must be eliminated from your list of solutions.

$$3 + \frac{3^2-5}{3^2-1} \stackrel{?}{=} \frac{3^2+3+2}{3+1}$$

$$3 + \frac{4}{8} \stackrel{?}{=} \frac{14}{4}$$

$$\frac{7}{2} = \frac{7}{2} \checkmark$$

The solution is 3.

RETEACHING THE LESSON

In Example 2, each side of the given equation is a fraction. For such equations, show students the following shortcut that they can cross multiply as shown.

$$\frac{5}{y+3} \underset{\displaystyle\nearrow}{\overset{\displaystyle\searrow}{}} \frac{3}{y-1}$$

$$5(y-1) = 3(y+3)$$

$$5y - 5 = 3y + 9$$

$$2y = 14$$

$$y = 7$$

CHECKING FOR UNDERSTANDING

Communicating Mathematics

Read and study the lesson to answer each question. **See margin.**

1. Explain why you multiply each side of an equation by the least common denominator as the first step in solving a rational equation.

2. Explain why the equation $x + \dfrac{1}{x-1} = 1 + \dfrac{1}{x-1}$ has no solution.

3. Explain how to find the LCD of a rational equation.

Guided Practice

Find the LCD for each equation. State what values should be excluded as solutions.

6. $(x+5)(x-3),$
   $3, -5$

4. $\dfrac{1}{5} = \dfrac{2}{10y}$ **10y, 0**

5. $\dfrac{1}{x} + \dfrac{1}{2} = \dfrac{2}{x}$ **2x, 0**

6. $\dfrac{9}{x+5} = \dfrac{6}{x-3}$

7. $\dfrac{3m}{2+m} - \dfrac{5}{7} = 4$
   $7(2+m), -2$

8. $\dfrac{1-b}{1+b} = \dfrac{2b}{2b+3}$
   $(1+b)(2b+3), -1, -\dfrac{3}{2}$

9. $\dfrac{6}{x} = \dfrac{9}{x^2}$ **x², 0**

Solve each equation.

10. $x + 3 = \dfrac{4}{x}$
    −4, 1

11. $r^2 + \dfrac{17r}{6} = \dfrac{1}{2}$
    $-3, \dfrac{1}{6}$

12. $\dfrac{2y}{3} - \dfrac{y+3}{6} = 2$ **5**

EXERCISES

Practice

Solve each equation. Check your solutions.

13. $\dfrac{y+1}{3} + \dfrac{y-1}{3} = \dfrac{4}{3}$ **2**

14. $\dfrac{2y-5}{6} - \dfrac{y-5}{4} = \dfrac{3}{4}$ **4**

15. $\dfrac{5+7p}{8} - \dfrac{3(5+p)}{10} = 2$ **5**

16. $8 - \dfrac{2-5x}{4} = \dfrac{4x+9}{3}$ **54**

17. $x + 5 = \dfrac{6}{x}$ **−6, 1**

18. $\dfrac{1}{y^2-1} = \dfrac{2}{y^2+y-2}$ **0**

19. $x + \dfrac{12}{x} - 8 = 0$ **2, 6**

20. $\dfrac{5}{6} - \dfrac{2m}{2m+3} = \dfrac{19}{6}$ $-\dfrac{21}{20}$

21. $\dfrac{1}{9} + \dfrac{1}{2a} = \dfrac{1}{a^2}$ $-6, \dfrac{3}{2}$

22. $\dfrac{1}{1-x} = 1 - \dfrac{x}{x-1}$ $\{x|x \neq 1\}$

23. $\dfrac{2p}{2p+3} - \dfrac{2p}{2p-3} = 1$ $\dfrac{-3 \pm 3\sqrt{2}}{2}$

24. $\dfrac{4}{x-2} - \dfrac{x+6}{x+1} = 1$ $\dfrac{1 \pm \sqrt{145}}{4}$

25. $\dfrac{x-4}{x-2} = \dfrac{x-2}{x+2} + \dfrac{1}{x-2}$ **14**

26. $\dfrac{x-3}{2x} = \dfrac{x-2}{2x+1} - \dfrac{1}{2} \pm \dfrac{\sqrt{6}}{2}$

27. $\dfrac{12}{x^2-16} - \dfrac{24}{x-4} = 3$ **−6, −2**

28. $\dfrac{6}{a-7} = \dfrac{a-49}{a^2-7a} + \dfrac{1}{a}$ **−14**

LESSON 11-5 SOLVING RATIONAL EQUATIONS **529**

Additional Answers

1. **By multiplying by the LCD, it removes the denominators making the equation easier to solve.**

2. **If you subtract $\dfrac{1}{x-1}$ from each side, you get x = 1. But x ≠ 1 because it gives 0 in the denominator.**

3. **Find an expression that contains each kind of factor present in each denominator with the factor raised to the highest power it has in any of the denominators.**

EVALUATING THE LESSON

Checking for Understanding

Exercises 1–12 are designed to help you assess understanding through reading, writing, and speaking. You should work through Exercises 1–3 with your students, and then monitor their work on Exercises 4–12.

Error Analysis

Students sometimes lose a solution to an equation when they divide each side of the equation by an expression that involves a variable. For example, if $x^2 = x$ is divided on each side by x, you obtain $x = 1$. The solution $x = 0$ is lost. To avoid this problem, students should check any numbers that make the divisor zero.

Assignment Guide

Basic: 13–28, 33–34, 36–45
Average: 16–30, 33–45
Enriched: 19–45

Practice Masters Booklet, p. 85

NAME _____ DATE _____

11-5 Practice Worksheet

Solving Rational Equations

Solve each equation. Check your solutions.

1. $\dfrac{12}{x} + \dfrac{3}{4} = \dfrac{3}{2}$ **16**

2. $\dfrac{x^2}{8} - 4 = \dfrac{x}{2}$ **−4, 8**

3. $\dfrac{x+10}{x^2-2} = \dfrac{4}{x}$ $-\dfrac{2}{3}, 4$

4. $\dfrac{x}{x+2} + x = \dfrac{5x+8}{x+2}$ **4**

5. $\dfrac{5}{x-5} = \dfrac{x}{x-5} - 1$ **all reals except 5**

6. $\dfrac{1}{3x-2} + \dfrac{b}{x} = 0$ $\dfrac{5}{8}$

7. $\dfrac{1}{x+3} = \dfrac{2}{x} - \dfrac{3}{4x}$ **−15**

8. $\dfrac{5}{x+6} = \dfrac{9x+6}{x^2+6x} + \dfrac{2}{x}$ **−3**

9. $\dfrac{6}{x-1} = \dfrac{4}{x-2} + \dfrac{2}{x+1}$ **∅**

10. $\dfrac{x+1}{x-3} = 4 - \dfrac{12}{x^2-2x-3}$ $-\dfrac{5}{3}, 5$

11. $\dfrac{1}{x-1} = \dfrac{2}{x+1} - \dfrac{1}{x+3}$ **∅**

12. $\dfrac{1}{x+2} + \dfrac{1}{x-2} = \dfrac{3}{x+1}$ $1 \pm \sqrt{13}$

Solve each equation. Check your solutions.

29. $\dfrac{2}{y+2} - \dfrac{y}{2-y} = \dfrac{y^2+4}{y^2-4}$ ∅

30. $\dfrac{t+4}{t} + \dfrac{3}{t-4} = \dfrac{-16}{t^2-4t}$ **−3**

31. $\dfrac{x+3}{x+2} = 2 - \dfrac{3}{x^2+5x+6}$ **0, −4**

32. $\dfrac{x}{x^2-1} + \dfrac{2}{x+1} = \dfrac{1}{2x-2}$ ∅

Critical Thinking

33. Find the values of A and B, if $\dfrac{A}{z+2} + \dfrac{B}{2z-3} = \dfrac{5z-11}{2z^2+z-6}$.

$A = 3, B = -1$

Applications

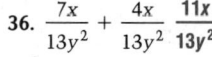

Journal

Tell why it is necessary to check your solutions when solving a rational equation. Give an example in your explanation.

34. **Travel** Alvin drove one-fourth of the way from Denver to Cheyenne at a speed of 40 mph in a snowstorm. He drove the rest of the way at a speed of 65 mph. What was his average speed for the entire trip?
58.75 mph

35. **Statistics** A number x is said to be the harmonic mean of y and z if $\dfrac{1}{x}$ is the average of $\dfrac{1}{y}$ and $\dfrac{1}{z}$.

a. Find y if $x = 8$ and $z = 20$. **5**

b. Find x if $y = 5$ and $z = 8$. **6.15**

Mixed Review

Simplify each expression. (Lesson 11-4)

36. $\dfrac{7x}{13y^2} + \dfrac{4x}{13y^2}$ $\dfrac{11x}{13y^2}$

37. $\dfrac{3}{x} + 4$ $\dfrac{3+4x}{x}$

38. $\dfrac{9}{4a} + \dfrac{-7}{5b}$ $\dfrac{45b-28a}{20ab}$

39. Find the equations of the asymptotes of the graph of $f(x) = \dfrac{-2x}{(x-1)(x-4)}$. (Lesson 11-1) $x = 1, x = 4, y = 0$

Find the solutions of each system of equations. (Lesson 9-9)

40. $x^2 + y^2 = 25$
$x = 2$ $(2, \pm\sqrt{21})$

41. $x - 2 = -2y$
$y - 1 = 2x + x^2$ $(0, 1), \left(-\dfrac{5}{2}, \dfrac{9}{4}\right)$

42. **Geometry** Find the coordinates of the midpoint of $\overline{AB}$ with $A(5, 5)$ and $B(\sqrt{5}, \sqrt{5})$. (Lesson 9-1) $\left(\dfrac{5+\sqrt{5}}{2}, \dfrac{5+\sqrt{5}}{2}\right)$

43. Graph $y < x^2 + x - 1$. (Lesson 8-6) **See margin.**

44. Simplify $(6 + \sqrt{3})(7 - \sqrt{2})$. (Lesson 6-3) $42 - 6\sqrt{2} + 7\sqrt{3} - \sqrt{6}$

45. **Statistics** The table below shows the number of miles driven per week by 10 people and the amount of fuel each used for that week. (Lesson 2-6)

Miles Driven	120	322	250	300	350	135	50	150	180	70
Fuel Used (gallons)	7.5	14	11	10	10	3.5	2.3	5	6.2	3.8

45a. For graph, see Solutions Manual. Equations will vary. Sample: $d = 25f$

a. Draw a scatter plot and find a prediction equation.

b. Estimate how much fuel a person who drives 280 miles a week would use. **about 11 gallons**

EXTENDING THE LESSON

Math Power: Problem Solving

Name all the excluded values of a for

$$\dfrac{a + 2 + \dfrac{2}{a+5}}{a + 6 + \dfrac{6}{a+1}} = \dfrac{a + 5 + \dfrac{3}{a+1}}{a - 1 - \dfrac{3}{a+1}}.$$

Then solve the equation.

$-5, -1, -4, -3, -2, 2; a = -\dfrac{11}{5}$

Additional Answer

43.

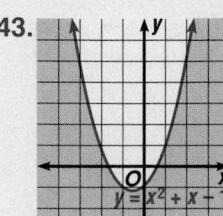

$y = x^2 + x - 1$

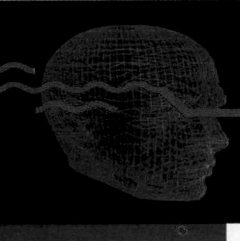

Technology

Rational Expressions

The *Mathematical Exploration Toolkit (MET)* can be used to simplify rational expressions. The CALC commands (and their shortened forms) you can use are listed below.

FACTOR (fac)   REDUCE (red)
SIMPLIFY (simp)   ^ *is used to enter an exponent.*

The SIMPLIFY command combines rational expressions. Once combined, use the FACTOR command to factor the numerator and denominator. In this form, the REDUCE command can be used to divide out any factors common to the numerator and denominator.

Example 1   Simplify $\dfrac{x^2-1}{x-1}$.

ENTER: $(x^2 - 1)/(x - 1)$

  fac

  red

$$\frac{x^2-1}{x-1}$$
$$\frac{(x-1)(x+1)}{x-1}$$
$$x+1$$

Example 2   Simplify $\dfrac{y^2-4}{y^2} \div \dfrac{y+2}{y}$.

ENTER: $((y^2 - 4)/y^2)/((y + 2)/y)$

  simp

  fac, fac

  red

$$\frac{y^2-4}{y^2} \cdot \frac{y}{y+2}$$
$$\frac{y^3-4y}{y^3 2y^2}$$
$$\frac{y(y-2)(y+2)}{yy(y+2)}$$
$$\frac{y-2}{y}$$

EXERCISES

Use CALC to simplify each rational expression.

1. $\dfrac{a^3-8}{a^2-4} \dfrac{a^2+2a+4}{a+2}$

2. $\dfrac{x^2-9}{x^2-6x+9} \dfrac{x+3}{x-3}$

3. $\dfrac{x^3-2x^2}{x^4-x^2} \dfrac{x-2}{(x+1)(x-1)}$

4. $\dfrac{2y^2-y-1}{y^2-1} \cdot \dfrac{y+1}{2y^2+y} \dfrac{1}{y}$

5. $\dfrac{x}{x-1} - \dfrac{x-1}{x} - \dfrac{1}{x^2-x} \dfrac{2}{x}$

Using Technology
Objective   This optional page shows how graphing software can be used to perform mathematical computations and to enhance and extend mathematical concepts.

Teaching Suggestions
Encourage students to experiment with the commands SIMPLIFY, FACTOR, and REDUCE. SIM-PLIFY will reduce expressions in which the denominator is a factor of the numerator even if the FAC-TOR command is not used first. Answers to the exercises are left in factored form. You may want students to use to SIMPLIFY com-mand to multiply the factors. Re-mind students that the command FSTEPS is available to reveal the steps used by the computer to factor.

11-6

11-6 Problem-Solving Strategy: Organizing Data

EXPLORE
PLAN
SOLVE
EXAMINE

Lesson Resources

Practice Master 11-6
Activity Master, p. 47

Transparency 11-6 contains the 5-Minute Check and a teaching aid for this lesson.

INTRODUCING THE LESSON

Objective 11-6   After studying this lesson, you should be able to:
- solve problems by organizing data.

Application   Two machines at the Vernon Wilson Chocolate Company can produce the same number of pounds of chocolate in one hour. Machine A produces 1.5-ounce pieces of candy, and machine B produces pieces twice that weight. If machine A produces 128 pieces of candy in one hour, how many pieces does machine B produce?

5-Minute Check

(over Lesson 11-5)

1. Solve $\frac{1}{y} + \frac{1}{3} = \frac{2}{y} - \frac{1}{4}$. $y = \frac{12}{7}$

2. Solve $\frac{p+1}{5} - \frac{3}{2p-1} = -1$.

   $p = \frac{3}{2}$ or $p = -7$

3. Solve $\frac{x}{x-2} + \frac{x}{x^2-4} = \frac{x+3}{x+2}$.

   $x = -3$

Other Prerequisite Skills

4. Solve $\frac{42}{71} = \frac{x}{43}$. $x = 25\frac{31}{71}$

5. 72 is what percent of 300?
   24 percent

Before trying to write an equation to solve this problem, first draw an illustration of the situation and then organize the data you have in the problem by labeling it on the illustration.   **Teaching Tip ❶**

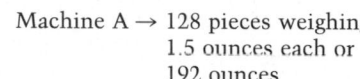

Machine A → 128 pieces weighing 1.5 ounces each or 192 ounces

Machine B → __?__ pieces weighing 2(1.5) ounces each or 3(?) ounces

Equal weight in one hour

We know the total output of machine B by weight is the same as machine A. So if we let x equal the number of pieces from machine B, we can write an equation.

$$\text{output of machine A} = \text{output of machine B}$$
$$192 = 3x$$
$$64 = x$$

Machine B produces 64 pieces in an hour.

Motivating the Lesson

From the sports section of a newspaper, read scores to the class. For example, you might read, "3 to 2, 6 to 8, and 9 to 0". Ask students what the scores mean to them. Elicit student responses and develop the concept that data must be organized to be meaningful.

There are many ways to organize the data in a given problem. You might use tables, different types of graphs, or diagrams. Your choice of display depends on the type of problem and your approach to solving it.

TEACHING THE LESSON

Teaching Tip ❶   Emphasize the importance of including all pertinent information in the illustration. Irrelevant facts need not be included.

ALTERNATE TEACHING STRATEGIES

Using Models

Divide students into five cooperative groups. Have each group display data in a different way, the choices being a table, a bar graph, a circle graph, a line graph, and a pictograph. Have each group create its own problem and model a solution using its data presentation. Students can use research, surveys, experimentation, or other data-collecting techniques.

APPLICATION

Commerce

The sources of oil (in thousands of 42-gallon barrels) imported daily by the United States in 1989 are listed below. What part of the total amount of oil is imported from each source?

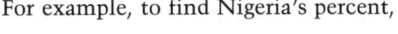

OPEC countries		Non-OPEC countries	
Nigeria	809	Canada	910
Saudi Arabia	1224	Mexico	763
Venezuela	867	United Kingdom	217
Other OPEC	772	Other	569

A circle graph is an excellent way to represent information that needs to be analyzed as parts of the whole. To show each source, you must find the total amount of oil imported and then calculate the percent each group represents.

The total is 6131 thousand barrels daily. Use your calculator to find the percent by dividing the number for each source by 6131.

For example, to find Nigeria's percent,

ENTER: 809 $\div$ 6131 $=$ 0.131952373

About 13% of our oil is imported from Nigeria. To find what part of the graph it occupies, multiply the percent by 360°.

ENTER: .13 $\times$ 360 $=$ 46.8

The central angle for Nigeria should be about 47°.

When completed, the graph should resemble the one above.

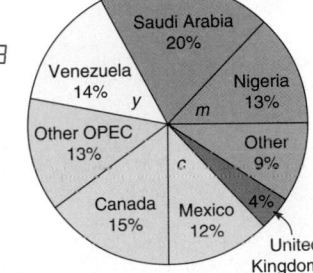

CHECKING FOR UNDERSTANDING

Communicating Mathematics

Read and study the lesson to answer each question.

1. Name some different ways to display data. **graphs, diagrams, tables**

2. How does drawing a sketch of the situation help you to organize your data? **A picture often gives a hint for the solution.**

3. Name as many different types of graphs as you can that might be used to display data. **line, histogram, circle, bar, pictograph**

Guided Practice

4. You are given the temperatures recorded every 10 minutes for a given day. What type of graph could you use to show this information? **bar graph or line graph**

RETEACHING THE LESSON

A man bought a horse for $60, sold it for $70, then bought it back for $80, and finally sold it for $90. Did he make or lose money, and how much?

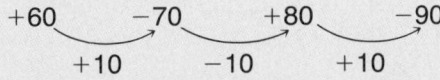

He made $10. Incorrect! Organize the data. Find and explain the correct answer.

Chalkboard Example

For the Example

Carbon-14 has a half-life of 5730 years. This means that if the amount of carbon-14 present in a living organism is measured now, half of that amount will be present in 5730 years. Use a bar graph to display the fraction of carbon-14 present originally and after four successive half-lives.

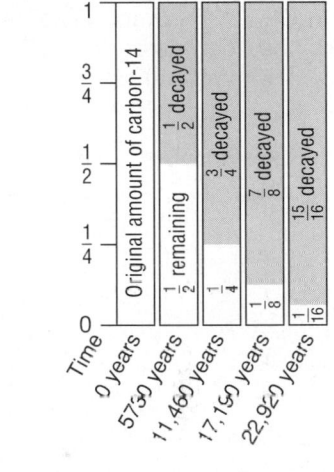

EVALUATING THE LESSON

Checking for Understanding

Exercises 1–5 are designed to help you assess understanding through reading, writing, and speaking. You should work through Exercises 1–3 with your students, and then monitor their work on Exercises 4–5.

Closing the Lesson

Modeling Activity Have students use a diagram to model the following problem. Al, Gene, and Mai were guessing what the temperature was that day. Al's guess was 6 C° below the actual temperature. Gene's guess was 2 C° above Al's guess and 8 C° below Mai's guess. Mai guessed that the temperature was 2°C. What was the actual temperature? **−2°C**

Homework Exercises

Assignment Guide

Basic: 6–10
Average: 6–10
Enriched: 6–10

Teaching Tip ❷ Emphasize that sketches can differ and still be effective in organizing data.

Additional Answer

5.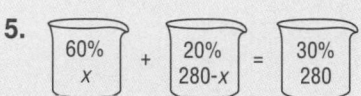

$$\frac{60\%}{x} + \frac{20\%}{280-x} = \frac{30\%}{280}$$

Practice Masters Booklet, p. 86

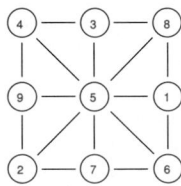

11-6 Practice Worksheet

NAME _____ DATE _____

Problem Solving Strategy: Organizing Data
Solve. Use any strategy.

1. Write the digits 1-9 in the circles so that the sum along any straight path is the same.

2. The sum of the last four digits of Kathy's telephone number is 7, and none of the digits is 0. If the probability of guessing Kathy's phone number is $\frac{1}{n}$, where n is the number of possible numbers, what is the probability of guessing Kathy's number on the first try? **$\frac{1}{20}$**

3. The view of the rectangular box at the right shows three faces of the box. The areas of two of the faces are 30 cm² and 48 cm². The volume of the box is 240 cm³. What is the area of the third face? **40 cm²**

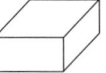

---

5. Dr. Xenon must make a 30% saline solution. He has one bottle of 60% saline solution and a bottle of 20% solution. He needs 280 mL of the 30% solution. Make a sketch to demonstrate the data in this problem. **See margin.**

EXERCISES

Solve. Use any strategy.

Strategies
Look for a pattern.
Solve a simpler problem.
Act it out.
Guess and check.
Draw a diagram.
Make a chart.
Work backwards.

6. Write the digits 1 through 8 in the squares so that no two consecutive numbers are next to each other either vertically, horizontally, or diagonally.

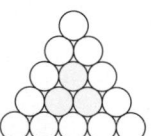

7. **Probability** The sum of the last four digits of Dan's telephone number is 6, and none of the digits is 0. If the probability of guessing Dan's phone number is $\frac{1}{n}$, where n is the number of possible numbers, what is the probability of guessing Dan's number on the first try? **$\frac{1}{10}$**

8. Fifteen balls are numbered 1 through 15 and arranged in a triangular format so that the three balls in the middle have a sum of 39 and the five balls on each side of the triangle have a sum of 39. Copy the sketch at the right and number each ball. **See margin.**

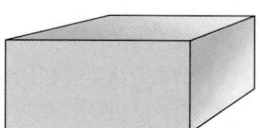

9. In the ancient land of Radico, a decree went out that each farmer should buy 100 head of livestock using exactly 100 radicands. In those days, cows cost 10 radicands each, pigs cost 3 radicands each, and geese cost 0.5 radicands each. Every farmer had to buy at least one of each type of livestock. What combination met with the decree? **5 cows, 1 pig, 94 geese**

10. **Geometry** The view of a rectangular box at the right shows 3 faces of the box. The areas of those faces are 24 in², 32 in², and 48 in². Find the volume of the box. **192 in³**

Journal
Show some other ways to organize data that are not presented in this lesson.

COOPERATIVE LEARNING ACTIVITY

Work in groups. Each person in the group must understand the solution and be able to explain it to any person in the class.

Refer to Exercise 5. Share your sketches of the problem and then find a solution to the problem using any method you wish. **70mL of 60%, 210 mL of 20%**

EXTENDING THE LESSON

Math Power: Connections
Have students use a Periodic Table of the elements, available in a physical science or chemistry book, to gather data on the elements. Have students each choose six elements and organize data about these elements in at least two different ways.

Additional Answer
8. Sample answer

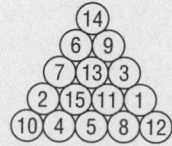

11-7 Applications of Rational Equations

Objective After studying this lesson, you should be able to:
11-7 ■ use rational expressions to solve problems.

Application

The Delaware Demolition Company wants to build a brick wall to hide the area where they store wrecked cars from public view. One bricklayer can build this wall in 5 days. Another bricklayer can do the job in 4 days. The Delaware Demolition Company decides to hire them both to work together. How long will it take the two bricklayers to finish this wall?

EXPLORE In one day, bricklayer A can complete $\frac{1}{5}$ of the wall. In 2 days, he can complete $\frac{1}{5} \cdot 2$ or $\frac{2}{5}$ of the wall. In t days, he can complete $\frac{1}{5} \cdot t$ or $\frac{t}{5}$ of the wall.

In one day, bricklayer B can complete $\frac{1}{4}$ of the wall. Using the same pattern as above, in t days she can complete $\frac{1}{4} \cdot t$ or $\frac{t}{4}$ of the wall.

PLAN In t days, bricklayer A can complete $\frac{t}{5}$ of the wall and, in that same time, bricklayer B can complete $\frac{t}{4}$ of the wall. Together, they can complete the entire wall.

$$bricklayer\ A\ +\ bricklayer\ B\ =\ entire\ wall$$
$$\frac{t}{5}\quad +\quad \frac{t}{4}\quad =\quad 1$$

SOLVE
$$\frac{t}{5} + \frac{t}{4} = 1$$
$$20\left(\frac{t}{5} + \frac{t}{4}\right) = 20(1) \qquad \textit{Multiply by the LCD.}$$
$$4t + 5t = 20 \qquad \textit{Distributive property}$$
$$9t = 20 \qquad \textit{Combine like terms.}$$
$$t = \frac{20}{9} \ \text{ or } \ 2\frac{2}{9} \qquad \textit{Divide each side by 9.}$$

The wall can be built in $2\frac{2}{9}$ days.

LESSON 11-7 APPLICATIONS OF RATIONAL EQUATIONS 535

ALTERNATE TEACHING STRATEGIES

Using Logical Reasoning
Emphasize a logical approach to each problem. Using examples, have cooperative groups of students ask and answer what the next logical step is in solving specific problems from start to finish.

Lesson Resources
Reteaching Master 11-7
Practice Master 11-7
Enrichment Master 11-7

 Transparency 11-7 contains the 5-Minute Check and a teaching aid for this lesson.

INTRODUCING THE LESSON

🕐 5-Minute Check
(over Lesson 11-6)
Have students express the data from the following bar graph.

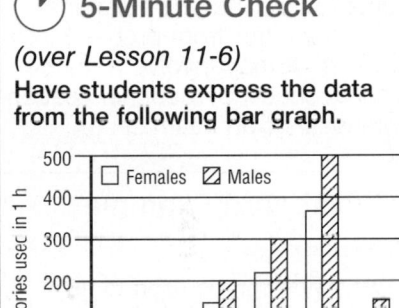

1. in a table

Calories Used in 1 Hour						
	Lying still	Sitting quietly	Walking slow	Walking fast	Swim-ming	Washing dishes
Female	65	80	150	220	370	105
Male	80	100	200	300	500	160

2. in a line graph

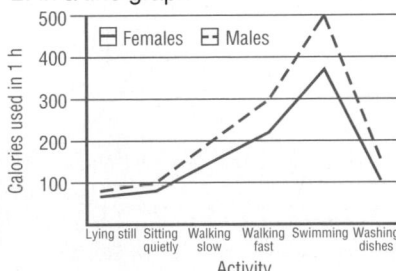

3. Which is the best display of the data? **bar graph**

Motivating the Lesson

You will need two paper cups, a gallon container, and at least a gallon of sand. Have one student use the cup to fill the container with sand as quickly as possible without spilling while he or she is being timed. Repeat, using another student. Ask students to predict how quickly the container could be filled if the two students worked together.

TEACHING THE LESSON

Teaching Tip ❶ Be sure students realize that the Examine step may differ from problem to problem. It may involve a mathematical check, a check for reasonableness, or an estimate.

Chalkboard Example

For the Example

Two pipes can be used to fill a water tank. One pipe alone can fill it in 27 minutes; the second pipe can fill it in 54 minutes. A third pipe, the drain pipe, can empty it in 36 minutes. If all valves are open when the tank is empty, how long will it take the tank to be filled? **36 minutes**

Teaching Tip ❷ Another way to solve the equation is to cross-multiply.

EXAMINE
Teaching Tip ❶

Bricklayer A builds $\frac{1}{5}t$ or $\frac{1}{5}\left(\frac{20}{9}\right)$ of the wall. $\frac{1}{5}\left(\frac{20}{9}\right) = \frac{4}{9}$

Bricklayer B builds $\frac{1}{4}t$ or $\frac{1}{4}\left(\frac{20}{9}\right)$ of the wall. $\frac{1}{4}\left(\frac{20}{9}\right) = \frac{5}{9}$

Since $\frac{4}{9} + \frac{5}{9} = \frac{9}{9}$ or 1, the solution checks.

Sometimes it is helpful to make a drawing when organizing the data given in the problem. In this way you can evaluate how to write an equation that helps you solve the problem.

Example

A car travels 300 km in the same time that a freight train travels 200 km. The speed of the car is 20 km/h more than the speed of the train. Find the speed of the car and the speed of the train.

EXPLORE You know the distances both vehicles traveled. You also know that both vehicles traveled the same amount of time, and that the speed of the car is 20 km/h faster than that of the train.

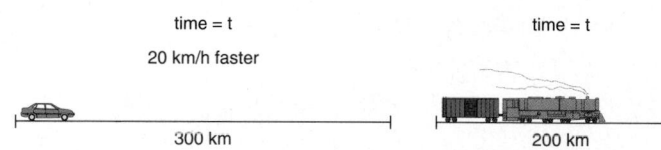

time = t
20 km/h faster

300 km

time = t

200 km

PLAN The formula that relates distance, time, and rate is $d = rt$. Since both vehicles travel the same time, you want to rewrite the formula in terms of t. That is, $\frac{d}{r} = t$. Then you can equate the formulas for the two vehicles in terms of t.

Let r be the speed of the train. The car goes 20 km/h faster so the speed of the car would be $r + 20$.

$$\underbrace{\frac{distance}{rate} = \frac{300}{r+20}}_{car's\ time} \quad = \quad \underbrace{\frac{distance}{rate} = \frac{200}{r}}_{train's\ time}$$

SOLVE

$$\frac{300}{r + 20} = \frac{200}{r}$$

$$\overset{1}{r(r+20)}\left(\frac{300}{r+20}\right) = \overset{1}{r(r+20)}\left(\frac{200}{r}\right)$$ *Multiply each side by the LCD.*

Teaching Tip ❷

$$300r = 200r + 4000$$

$$100r = 4000$$ *Subtract 200r from each side.*

$$r = 40$$ *Divide by 100.*

536 CHAPTER 11 RATIONAL POLYNOMIAL EXPRESSIONS

RETEACHING THE LESSON

Give students several work and distance problems, each with a proposed answer. The students' task is to check each answer with the conditions of the problem.

The speed of the freight train is 40 km/h, and the speed of the car is 40 + 20 or 60 km/h.

EXAMINE At 40 km/h, it takes the train $\frac{200}{40}$ or 5 hours to travel 200 km.

At 60 km/h, it takes the car $\frac{300}{60}$ or 5 hours to travel 300 km. Both vehicles travel their given distances in the same amount of time.

CHECKING FOR UNDERSTANDING

Communicating Mathematics

1. See margin.
1. See margin.
2. $\frac{1}{3}$ of the lawn

Read and study the lesson to answer each question.

1. What is the purpose of each step of the 4-step problem-solving plan?

2. If a girl can mow a lawn in 3 hours, what part of the lawn can she mow in one hour?

3. In the bricklayer problem, why was the sum of the rational expression equal to 1? **See margin.**

Guided Practice

4. $\frac{5}{12}\,p$
5. $\frac{x}{6} - \frac{x}{18} = 1$
6. $\frac{12}{1} = \frac{d}{5}$

Write an expression or equation for each problem. Then solve.

4. A pipe will fill a swimming pool in 12 hours. What part of the pool will be filled after 5 hours?

5. A tank can be filled in 6 hours and drained in 18 hours. If the drain is left open, how many hours will it take to fill an empty tank?

6. If Joe can travel at a speed of 12 mph on his bicycle, how far can he ride in 5 hours?

7. Salina drove 524 miles in 9 hours. What was her average speed per hour? $r = \frac{524}{9}$

EXERCISES

Applications

A

Solve each problem.

8. **Zoology** A panda can eat the eucalyptus leaves from a branch in 14 minutes. Together, two pandas can eat the leaves from that same branch in 9 minutes. How long would it have taken the second panda to eat the leaves from the branch by itself? **25.2 min**

9. **Oil Refining** An empty oil tank can be filled by pipeline in 10 hours. The tank can be emptied in 20 hours by opening a valve. If the valve is opened while the pipeline is filling the tank, how long will it take for the tank to fill? **20 h**

LESSON 11-7 APPLICATIONS OF RATIONAL EQUATIONS 537

Additional Answers

1. Explore: look at all information given in problem.
Plan: select a strategy and create a way to use the given information.
Solve: find a solution.
Examine: determine if the solution is valid.

3. The two bricklayers will complete parts of the wall. Together they will build a whole wall, represented by 1.

Closing the Lesson

Modeling Activity Have students write verbal problems involving transportation, and then use a diagram to model each problem.

APPLYING THE LESSON

Homework Exercises

See assignment guide on page 537.

Chapter 11, Quiz D, (Lessons 11-6 through 11-7), is available in the Evaluation Masters Booklet, p. 150.

Practice Masters Booklet, p. 87

11-7 Practice Worksheet

NAME _____ DATE _____

Applications of Rational Equations
Solve each problem.

1. It takes Angus three days to cultivate the garden. It takes Helga four days to do the same job. How long does it take them to do the job if they work together?
$1\frac{5}{7}$ **days**

2. A tank can be filled by a hose in 15 hours. It can be emptied by a drainpipe in 25 hours. If the drainpipe is open while the tank is being filled, how long does it take to fill the tank?
$37\frac{1}{2}$ **h**

3. Carlos can run to Ingrid's house in 30 minutes. Ingrid can run to Carlos' house in 40 minutes. If they start from their houses at the same time, in how many minutes will they meet?
$17\frac{1}{7}$ **min**

4. The denominator of a fraction is one less than three times the numerator. If 12 is added to both numerator and denominator, the resulting fraction has a value of $\frac{3}{4}$. Find the original fraction.
$\frac{3}{8}$

5. Increasing the average speed of a car by 12 mph results in a 189-mile trip taking an hour less than before. What was the original average speed of the car?
42 mi/h

6. In one hour, Steve drives 25 miles farther in his car than John can cycle on his bike. If it takes John $1\frac{1}{2}$ hours longer to cycle 75 miles than it takes Steve in his car, how fast can John cycle?
25 mi/h

---

10. **Construction** A painter works on a job for 10 days and is then joined by an associate. Together they finish the job in 6 more days. The associate could have done the job alone in 30 days. How long would it have taken the painter to do the job alone? **20 days**

11. **Number Theory** The ratio of 4 less than a number to 26 more than that number is 1 to 3. What is the number? **19**

12. **Number Theory** Five times the multiplicative inverse of a number is added to the number and the result is 10.5 What is the number? **10 or 0.5**

13. **Aviation** A plane flies 2000 miles from Chicago to Los Angeles with a 50 mph tail wind in $3\frac{1}{3}$ hours. Returning against the same wind, it takes 4 hours. What is the speed of the plane if there is no wind? **550 mph**

14. **Navigation** The speed of the current in the Puget Sound is 5 mph. A barge travels with the current 26 miles and returns in $10\frac{2}{3}$ hours. What is its speed in still water? **8 mph**

15. **Trucking** Two trucks can carry loads of coal in a ratio of 5 to 2. The smaller truck has a capacity 3 tons less than that of the larger truck. What is the capacity of the larger truck? **5 tons**

16. **Banking** The simple interest for one year on a sum of money is $108. Suppose the interest rate is increased by 2%. Then $450 less than the original sum could be invested and yield the same annual interest.

   a. How much is the original sum invested? **$1800**

   b. At what rate was the money invested? **6%**

17. **Number Theory** The denominator of a fraction is 1 less than twice the numerator. If 7 is added to both the numerator and denominator, the resulting fraction has a value of $\frac{7}{10}$. Find the original fraction. $\frac{7}{13}$

18. **Chemistry** A chemist needs to make 1000 mL of a 30% alcohol solution by mixing 25% and 55% solutions. How much of each should she use? **$166\frac{2}{3}$ mL of 55%, $833\frac{1}{3}$ mL of 25%**

19. **Banking** A sum of money is invested for one year at 8% simple interest rate. If the sum of money is increased by $200 and the interest rate is lowered to 6%, then the annual interest is increased by $1.

   a. How much is the original sum of money invested? **$550**

   b. What was the original amount of interest? **$44**

20. Pipe A can fill a tank in 4 hours and pipe B can fill the tank in 3 hours. With the tank empty, pipe A is turned on, and one hour later, pipe B is turned on. How long will pipe B run before the tank is full? $1\frac{2}{7}$ h

21. Pipe C can fill an empty tank in 6 hours and pipe D can empty the tank in 2 hours. With the tank empty, pipe C is turned on, and pipe D is left open. How long will it take to fill the tank? What is wrong with this problem? **It will never fill, because it empties faster than it fills.**

Computer

22. The Greek mathematician Euclid, who lived about 300 B.C., is credited with developing a method for finding the greatest common factor of two integers. This method is called the Euclidean Algorithm. For example, to find the GCF of 232 and 136, you use a process involving division by the remainder of a previous division. Study the following calculations.

dividend = quotient · divisor + remainder

$$232 = 1 \cdot 136 + 96$$
$$136 = 1 \cdot 96 + 40$$
$$96 = 2 \cdot 40 + 16$$
$$40 = 2 \cdot 16 + 8$$
$$16 = 2 \cdot 8 + 0$$

8 is the GCF of 232 and 136.

Teaching Tip ❸

The BASIC program at the right performs the Euclidean Algorithm. Use the program to find the GCF for each pair of integers.

a. 187, 221 **17**
b. 182, 1690 **26**
c. 4807, 5083 **23**
d. 1078, 1547 **7**
e. 41, 3 **1**
f. 199, 24 **1**
g. 766, 424 **2**
h. 197, 37 **1**

```
10   PRINT "ENTER THE GREATER NUMBER"
20   INPUT X
30   PRINT "ENTER THE LESSER NUMBER"
40   INPUT Y
50   IF INT (X / Y) = X / Y THEN 150
60   PRINT "DIVIDEND = QUOTIENT *
     DIVISOR + REMAINDER"
70   LET Q = INT (X / Y)
80   LET R = X - (Q * Y)
90   PRINT X;"=";Q;"*";Y;"+";R
100  IF R = 0 THEN 150
110  LET X = Y
120  LET Y = R
140  GOTO 70
150  PRINT Y;"IS THE GREATEST
     COMMON FACTOR."
180  END
```

Mixed Review

Simplify each expression. (Lessons 11-3, 11-4)

23. $\frac{x^2 - y^2}{x + y} \cdot \frac{1}{x - y}$ **1**

24. $\frac{4}{3a} - \frac{7}{5a} + \frac{1}{2a}$ **$\frac{13}{30a}$**

25. $\frac{13x^2}{40y} \div \frac{26x^2}{70y^3}$ **$\frac{7y^2}{8}$**

26. Write the simplest polynomial function with integral coefficients if two of its zeros are -2 and $4 + 3i$. (Lesson 10-3) $f(x) = x^3 - 6x^2 + 9x + 50$

27. Find the distance between points $X(3, 6)$ and $Y(7, -8)$. (Lesson 9-1) $2\sqrt{53}$

28. Use long division to find $(10s^3 - 3s^2 - 31s - 6) \div (2s + 3)$. (Lesson 5-6) $5s^2 - 9s - 2$

EXTENDING THE LESSON

Math Power: Problem Solving

A rectangular block has a height of 8 mm and a length that is 9 mm more than the width. A hole with a diameter of 5.04 mm is drilled $\frac{3}{4}$ of the way into the block, parallel to its height. The new volume of the block is 600 mm³.

What are the length and width of the block? Round the volume of the cylinder formed by drilling to the nearest whole number. Use 3.14 for π. **$L = 15$ mm; $W = 6$ mm**

Teaching Tip ❸ Line 50 of the program checks to see if the greater number is a multiple of the lesser. If so, the algorithm is circumvented since the lesser number is the GCF. Ask students to explain the purpose of line 50.

Extend the exercises with questions such as these. Encourage students to use the program to test their answers with large numbers.

1. Can two even integers be relatively prime? **no**
2. Can two prime numbers not be relatively prime? **no**
3. If two numbers are each divided by their GCF, are the quotients relatively prime? **yes**
4. What is obtained by dividing the product of two integers by their GCF? **LCM**

Additional Answers

1.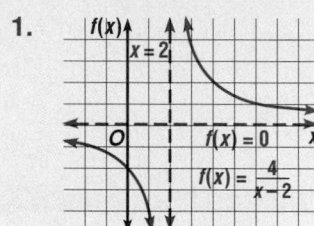

2.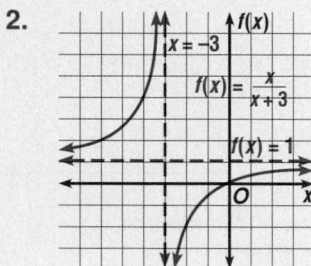

3.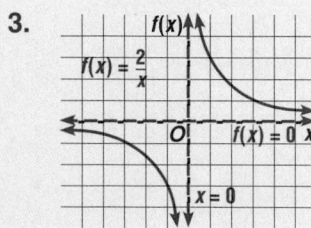

VOCABULARY

Upon completing this chapter you should be familiar with the following terms:

asymptote	506	512	joint variation
constant of variation	510	516	rational algebraic expression
direct variation	510	527	rational equation
inverse variation	511	506	rational function

SKILLS AND CONCEPTS

OBJECTIVES AND EXAMPLES	REVIEW EXERCISES

Upon completing this chapter, you should be able to:

- sketch the graph of a rational function (**Lesson 11-1**)

  Find the values for which the function is undefined to locate the vertical asymptotes. Then plot points on either side of the asymptotes.

  For $\frac{5}{(x-3)(x)} = y$, the vertical asymptotes have equations $x = 3$ and $x = 0$.

Use these exercises to review and prepare for the chapter test.

Graph each rational function. See margin.

1. $f(x) = \dfrac{4}{x-2}$ 2. $f(x) = \dfrac{x}{x+3}$

3. $f(x) = \dfrac{2}{x}$ 4. $f(x) = \dfrac{1}{2-x^2}$

5. $f(x) = \dfrac{5}{(x+1)(x-3)}$

- solve problems involving direct, inverse, and joint variation   (**Lesson 11-2**)

  7. $y = -37.5$

  direct: $y = kx$
  inverse: $xy = k$
  joint: $y = kxz$

6. If y varies directly as x, and $y = 21$ when $x = 7$, find x when $y = -5$. $x = \dfrac{-5}{3}$

7. If y varies inversely as x, and $y = 9$ when $x = 2.5$, find y when $x = -0.6$.

8. If y varies directly as x, and $x = 28$ when $y = 18$, find x when $y = 63$. $x = 98$

9. If y varies inversely as x, and $x = 28$ when $y = 18$, find x when $y = 63$. $x = 8$

10. If y varies jointly as x and z, and $x = 2$ and $z = 4$ when $y = 16$, find y when $x = 5$ and $z = 8$. $y = 80$

11. If y varies jointly as x and z, and $x = 4$ and $z = 2$ when $y = 25$, find x when $y = 12$ and $z = 20$. $x = 0.192$

Additional Answers

4.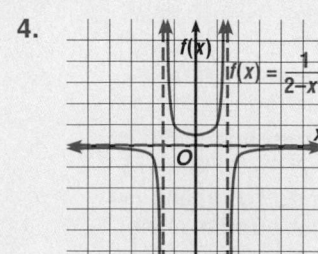

5.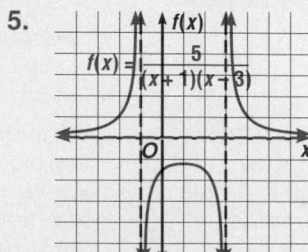

- multiply and divide rational expressions
(Lesson 11-3)

$$\frac{3x}{2y} \cdot \frac{8y^3}{6x^2} = \frac{\overset{1}{\cancel{3}} \cdot \overset{1}{\cancel{x}} \cdot \overset{4}{\cancel{8}} \cdot \overset{y^2}{\cancel{y^3}}}{\underset{1}{\cancel{2}} \cdot \underset{1}{\cancel{y}} \cdot \underset{2}{\cancel{6}} \cdot \underset{x}{\cancel{x^2}}} = \frac{2y^2}{x}$$

$$\frac{x^2 - 4}{x^2 - 9} \div \frac{x + 2}{x - 3} = \frac{x^2 - 4}{x^2 - 9} \cdot \frac{x - 3}{x + 2}$$

$$= \frac{(x + 2)(x - 2)\overset{1}{\cancel{(x - 3)}}}{(x + 3)\underset{1}{\cancel{(x - 3)}}\underset{1}{\cancel{(x + 2)}}}$$

$$= \frac{x - 2}{x + 3}$$

- simplify complex fractions
(Lesson 11-3)

Rewrite as a division expression.

$$\frac{\frac{1}{x}}{\frac{2x}{17}} = \frac{1}{x} \div \frac{2x}{17}$$

$$= \frac{1}{x} \cdot \frac{17}{2x} = \frac{17}{2x^2}$$

- add and subtract rational expression
(Lesson 11-4)

Rewrite all rational expressions as equivalent fractions with a common denominator.

$$\frac{3x}{x - y} + \frac{4x}{y - x} = \frac{3x}{x - y} + \frac{-4x}{x - y} = \frac{-x}{x - y}$$

Simplify each expression. $\dfrac{ay - 2a - 3y + 6}{a - x}$

12. $\dfrac{-4ab}{21c} \cdot \dfrac{14c^2}{22a^2}$ $\dfrac{-4bc}{33a}$ 13. $\dfrac{y - 2}{a - x} \cdot (a - 3)$

14. $\dfrac{x + y}{a} \div \dfrac{x + y}{a^2}$ a 15. $\dfrac{a^2 - b^2}{6b} \div \dfrac{a + b}{36b^2}$

$6b(a - b)$

16. $\dfrac{y^2 - y - 12}{y + 2} \div \dfrac{y - 4}{y^2 - 4y - 12}$

$(y + 3)(y - 6)$

Simplify each expression.

17. $\dfrac{\dfrac{1}{n^2 - 6n + 9}}{\dfrac{n + 3}{2n^2 - 18}}$ 18. $\dfrac{\dfrac{x^2 + 7x + 10}{x + 2}}{\dfrac{x^2 + 2x - 15}{x + 2}}$

$\dfrac{2}{n - 3}$ $\dfrac{x + 2}{x - 3}$

Simplify each expression. **See margin.**

19. $\dfrac{-9}{4a} + \dfrac{7}{3b}$ 20. $\dfrac{x + 2}{x - 5} + 6$

21. $\dfrac{x - 1}{x^2 - 1} + \dfrac{2}{5x + 5}$ 22. $\dfrac{7}{y} - \dfrac{2}{3y}$

23. $\dfrac{7}{y - 2} - \dfrac{11}{2 - y}$ 24. $\dfrac{14}{x + y} - \dfrac{9}{y^2 - x^2}$

25. $\dfrac{\dfrac{5x}{4}}{\dfrac{6x}{5}} + \dfrac{\dfrac{2x}{ab}}{\dfrac{3x}{a}}$ 26. $\dfrac{2a + 4}{\dfrac{a}{6 + \dfrac{2}{a^2}}}$

Additional Answers

19. $\dfrac{28a - 27b}{12ab}$ 20. $\dfrac{7(x - 4)}{x - 5}$

21. $\dfrac{7}{5(x + 1)}$ 22. $\dfrac{19}{3y}$

23. $\dfrac{18}{y - 2}$ 24. $\dfrac{14y - 14x - 9}{y^2 - x^2}$

25. $\dfrac{25b + 16}{24b}$ 26. $\dfrac{a^2 + 2a}{3a^2 + 1}$

Alternate Review Strategy

To provide a brief in-class review, you may wish to read the following questions to the class and require a verbal or written response.

1. Why is $f(x) = \dfrac{(x - 6)}{(x + 3)}$ an example of a rational function? **It is an equation of the form $f(x) = \dfrac{p(x)}{q(x)}$, p(x) and q(x) are both polynomial functions, and $q(x) \neq 0$.**

2. If y varies directly as x, and $y = 24$ when $x = 8$, find y when $x = 5$.   **15**

3. If y varies inversely as x, and $y = 2$ when $x = 14$, find y when $x = 7$.   **4**

4. What is the GCF of $n^2m^2 - 5m^2$ and $n^4 - 25$? $n^2 - 5$

5. What is the LCD of $9xy$ and $12y^2$? $36xy^2$

6. Simplify $\dfrac{(x + 2)}{7x} + \dfrac{(x - 3)}{14x^2}$.

$\dfrac{(2x^2 + 5x - 3)}{14x^2}$

7. By inspection, what values for y are excluded from a list of solutions for

$\dfrac{y}{(y - 6)} + \dfrac{(5y + 7)}{(3y + 6)} - \dfrac{2}{(9 - y)}$?

6, -2, 9

8. If a student were performing an experiment that required a temperature reading every two minutes, what type of graph would best be used to organize the data?   **line graph**

9. Joe can paint a room in 4 hours and Sue can paint the same room in 3 hours. How long will it take to paint the room if they work together?

$1\frac{5}{7}$ **hours**

10. What are the four steps to problem solving?   **explore, plan, solve, and examine**

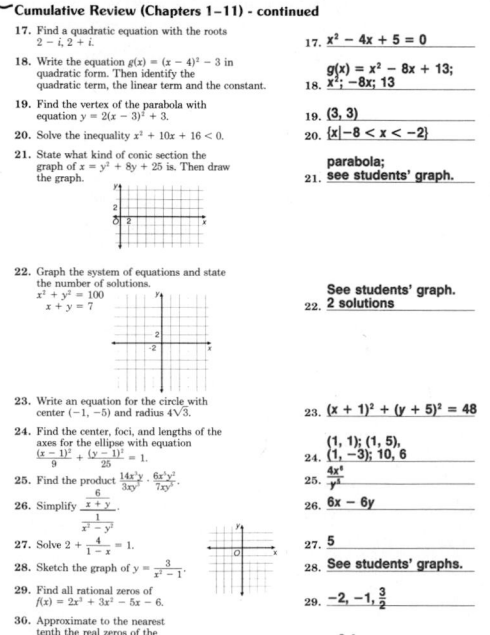

NAME _____ DATE _____
Cumulative Review (Chapters 1–11)

1. Evaluate $\frac{2a + 4a^2c}{b^3 + c}$ if $a = \frac{1}{2}$, $b = -3$, and $c = 6$. 1. $-\frac{1}{3}$

2. Bonnie has scored the following points in her first six basketball games: 12, 17, 8, 23, 16, 17. For her to average 16 points per game, how many points must she average in her next four games? 2. **at least 16.75 points**

3. If x and y are real numbers, does $x^2 + y^2 = 5$ represent a function? 3. **no**

4. Find the slope-intercept form of the equation for the line passing through $(-3, 7)$ with slope $-\frac{1}{3}$. 4. $y = -\frac{1}{3}x + 6$

5. State whether the graphs of the equations $3x - 2y = 1$ and $2x + 3y = -6$ are parallel, perpendicular, or neither. 5. **perpendicular**

6. Solve by graphing: $y \le 0$ 7. Graph $f(x) = x^3 - x$. 6. **See students' graphs.** 7. **See students' graphs.**
   $y \le 2x$

8. Solve using matrices: $3x + y - z = 4$ 8. $(2, -3, -1)$
   $x + 3y + z = -8$
   $5x - y - 2z = 15$

9. Simplify $\left(\frac{m^{-2}n^2p^3q^{-4}}{m^3n^2p^{-3}q}\right)^0$. 9. **1**

10. Simplify $(2r - s)(4r^2 + 2rs + s^2)$. 10. $8r^3 - s^3$

11. Factor $10x^2 - 45x - 90$. 11. $5(2x + 3)(x - 6)$

12. Express $16^{\frac{5}{4}}$ in simplest radical form. 12. $4\sqrt[4]{4}$

13. Solve $3x^2 + 8 = -16$. 13. $\pm 2i\sqrt{2}$

14. Simplify $\frac{3 + 2i}{5 - 3i}$. 14. $\frac{9 + 19i}{34}$

15. Solve $20x^2 - 3x - 2 = 0$ by factoring. 15. $\frac{2}{5}, -\frac{1}{4}$

16. Use the quadratic formula to solve $3x^2 - 7x + 4 = 0$. 16. $\frac{4}{3}, 1$

NAME _____ DATE _____
Cumulative Review (Chapters 1–11) - continued

17. Find a quadratic equation with the roots $2 - i$, $2 + i$. 17. $x^2 - 4x + 5 = 0$

18. Write the equation $g(x) = (x - 4)^2 - 3$ in quadratic form. Then identify the quadratic term, the linear term and the constant. 18. $g(x) = x^2 - 8x + 13$; x^2; $-8x$; 13

19. Find the vertex of the parabola with equation $y = 2(x - 3)^2 + 3$. 19. $(3, 3)$

20. Solve the inequality $x^2 + 10x + 16 < 0$. 20. $\{x | -8 < x < -2\}$

21. State what kind of conic section the graph of $x = y^2 + 8y + 25$ is. Then draw the graph. 21. **parabola; see students' graph.**

22. Graph the system of equations and state the number of solutions. 22. **See students' graph. 2 solutions**
    $x^2 + y^2 = 100$
    $x + y = 7$

23. Write an equation for the circle with center $(-1, -5)$ and radius $4\sqrt{3}$. 23. $(x + 1)^2 + (y + 5)^2 = 48$

24. Find the center, foci, and lengths of the axes for the ellipse with equation $\frac{(x - 1)^2}{9} + \frac{(y - 1)^2}{25} = 1$. 24. $(1, 1)$; $(1, 5)$, $(1, -3)$; 10, 6

25. Find the product $\frac{14x^3y}{3xy^5} \cdot \frac{6x^3y^2}{7xy^3}$. 25. $\frac{4x^4}{y^5}$

26. Simplify $\frac{x + y}{\frac{1}{x^3 - y^3}}$. 26. $6x - 6y$

27. Solve $2 + \frac{4}{1 - x} = 1$. 27. **5**

28. Sketch the graph of $y = \frac{3}{x^2 - 1}$. 28. **See students' graphs.**

29. Find all rational zeros of $f(x) = 2x^3 + 3x^2 - 5x - 6$. 29. $-2, -1, \frac{3}{2}$

30. Approximate to the nearest tenth the real zeros of the function $f(x) = x^3 - 4x + 4$. 30. -2.4

■ solve rational equations. (Lesson 11-5)

$$\frac{1}{x - 1} + \frac{2}{x} = 0$$

Multiply each side of the equation by the common denominator of the equation.

$$x(x - 1)\left[\frac{1}{x - 1} + \frac{2}{x}\right] = x(x - 1)(0)$$

Simplify the products.

$$\frac{x(x - 1)}{x - 1} + \frac{2x(x - 1)}{x} = 0$$

Solve the equation.

$$x + 2(x - 1) = 0$$
$$x + 2x - 2 = 0$$
$$3x = 2$$
$$x = \frac{2}{3}$$

Solve each equation.

27. $\frac{3}{y} + \frac{7}{y} = 9$ $\frac{10}{9}$

28. $1 + \frac{5}{y - 1} = \frac{7}{6}$ **31**

29. $\frac{3x + 2}{4} = \frac{9}{4} - \frac{3 - 2x}{6}$ **3**

30. $\frac{1}{r^2 - 1} = \frac{2}{r^2 + r - 2}$ **0**

31. $\frac{x}{x^2 - 1} + \frac{2}{x + 1} = 1 + \frac{1}{2x - 2}$ $\frac{3}{2}$

APPLICATIONS AND CONNECTIONS

32. **Meteorology** The temperature at noon on Monday was 54°F. On Tuesday, it was 33°F. The temperatures at noon on Wednesday through Sunday were 60°, 44°, 32°, 54°, and 78°, respectively. Make a drawing to organize this data and tell where the greatest change from day to day occurred. (Lesson 11-6)
   Drawings will vary. $T \to W = 27°$ difference

34. **Construction** Mike Welch can paint his house in 15 hours. His friend Joe can paint the house in 20 hours. If they work together, how long will it take them to paint the house? (Lesson 11-7) $8\frac{4}{7}$ **hours**

35. **Number Theory** One integer is 2 less than another integer. Three times the reciprocal of the lesser integer plus five times the reciprocal of the greater integer is $\frac{7}{8}$. What are the two integers? (Lesson 11-7) **8,10**

33. **Physics** The intensity of illumination on a surface varies inversely as the square of the distance from the light source. A surface is 12 meters from a light source. How far must the surface be from the source to receive twice as much illumination? (Lesson 11-7)
   $6\sqrt{2}$ **meters**

Answers for Chapter Test

16.
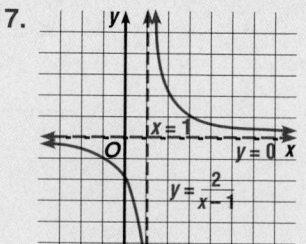

17.

18.
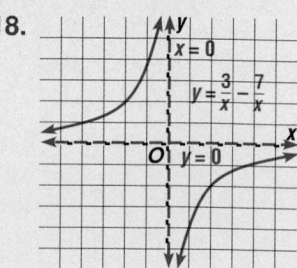

Simplify each expression. 7. $(x-1)(y+5)$

1. $\dfrac{7ab}{9c} \cdot \dfrac{81c^2}{91a^2b}$ $\dfrac{9c}{13a}$

2. $\dfrac{a^2-ab}{3a} \div \dfrac{a-b}{15b^2}$ $5b^2$

3. $\dfrac{7}{5a} - \dfrac{10}{3ab}$ $\dfrac{21b-50}{15ab}$

4. $\dfrac{6}{x-5} + 7a$ $\dfrac{6+7ax-35a}{x-5}$

5. $\dfrac{x^2-y^2}{a^2-b^2} \cdot \dfrac{a+b}{x-y}$ $\dfrac{x+y}{a-b}$

6. $\dfrac{x-y}{a-b} - \dfrac{x+y}{a+b}$ $\dfrac{2(bx-ay)}{a^2-b^2}$

7. $\dfrac{x^2-2x+1}{y-5} \div \dfrac{x-1}{y^2-25}$

8. $\dfrac{x+2}{x-1} + \dfrac{6}{7x-7}$ $\dfrac{7x+20}{7(x-1)}$

9. $\dfrac{y}{y-9} - \dfrac{-9}{9-y}$ 1

10. $\dfrac{\dfrac{x^2-1}{x^2-3x-10}}{\dfrac{x^2-12x+35}{x^2+3x+2}}$ $\dfrac{(x-1)(x+1)^2}{(x-7)(x-5)^2}$

11. $\dfrac{\dfrac{1}{x} - \dfrac{1}{2x}}{\dfrac{2}{x} + \dfrac{4}{3x}}$ $\dfrac{3}{20}$

12. $\dfrac{\dfrac{2}{x-4} + \dfrac{5}{x+1}}{\dfrac{3x}{x^2-3x-4}}$ $\dfrac{7x-18}{3x}$

Solve each equation.

13. $a - \dfrac{5}{a} = 4$ $-1, 5$

14. $\dfrac{3}{x} + \dfrac{x}{x+2} = \dfrac{-2}{x+2}$ -3

15. $\dfrac{y}{y-3} + \dfrac{6}{y+3} = 1$ 1

Graph each rational function. 16–18. See margin.

16. $y = \dfrac{3x}{x+2}$

17. $y = \dfrac{2}{x-1}$

18. $y = \dfrac{3}{x} - \dfrac{7}{x}$

19. Jesse Cruz can wordprocess 75 pages of manuscript in 8 hours. Tedra Szatro can produce the same number of pages in 13 hours. If they work together, how long will it take to process 75 pages?
$4\dfrac{20}{21}$ **hours**

20. Two barrels have capacities in the ratio of 7 to 4. The larger barrel holds 12 gallons less than two smaller barrels. How much will each barrel hold?
84 gal, 48 gal

21. Suppose y varies directly as x. If $y = 10$, then $x = -3$. Find y when $x = 20$. $-\dfrac{200}{3}$

22. Suppose y varies inversely as x. If $y = 9$, then $x = -\dfrac{2}{3}$. Find x when $y = -7$. $x = \dfrac{6}{7}$

23. Suppose y varies jointly as x and z. If $y = 45$ when $x = 3$ and $z = 5$, find y when $x = 2$ and $z = 4$ 24

24. Suppose y varies jointly as x and z. If $x = 10$ when $y = 250$ and $z = 5$, find x when $y = 2.5$ and $z = 4.5$. $\dfrac{1}{9}$

25. The city swimming pool can be filled from two sources, a well or city water. The pipe for the city water fills the pool in 6 hours. The pipe from the well fills the pool in 10 hours. How long will it take the pool to fill if both sources are piped in at the same time? Make an illustration of the problem. Then solve. **It will take $3\dfrac{3}{4}$ hours.**

Bonus

Simplify. $\dfrac{\dfrac{9x^2-12x+4}{6x^2-13x+6}}{\dfrac{6x^2+13x+6}{4x^2-9}} \div \dfrac{\dfrac{9x^2-4}{6x^2-5x-6}}{\dfrac{6x^2+5x-6}{4x^2-12x+9}}$

$\dfrac{6x^2+5x-6}{6x^2-5x-6}$

Using the Chapter Test

This page may be used as a test or as a review. In addition, two multiple-choice tests and two free-response tests are provided in the Evaluation Masters Booklet. Chapter 11 Test, Form 1A is shown below.

Evaluation Masters Booklet, pp. 141–142

NAME _____ DATE _____

Chapter 11 Test, Form 1A

Write the letter for the correct answer in the blank at the right of each problem.

1. Simplify $\dfrac{(4x^2a)^2}{12x^3a^4}$.
A. $\dfrac{x}{3a^3}$ B. $\dfrac{xa^2}{3}$ C. $\dfrac{4x}{3a^3}$ D. $\dfrac{4xa^2}{3}$ 1. **C**

2. Simplify $\left(\dfrac{3a^2}{b}\right)^2 \cdot \dfrac{b^3}{6}$.
A. $\dfrac{54a^4}{b^3}$ B. $\dfrac{3a^4b^2}{2}$ C. $\dfrac{a^2b^2}{2}$ D. $\dfrac{3a^4b}{2}$ 2. **D**

3. Simplify $\dfrac{t^2-2t-3}{t-1} \cdot \dfrac{3t-3}{4t+3}$.
A. $\dfrac{t^2-6t+9}{3t-3}$ B. $\dfrac{3(t-3)}{t^2-1}$ C. 3 D. $\dfrac{3}{t-1}$ 3. **D**

4. Simplify $\dfrac{a^2+b^2}{a^2-b^2} \cdot \dfrac{b-a}{b+a}$.
A. $\dfrac{a^2-ab+b^2}{a+b}$ B. $-\dfrac{a^2-ab+b^2}{a+b}$ C. $a+b$ D. $-(a+b)$ 4. **B**

5. Simplify $\dfrac{x^3y}{3z} \div \dfrac{6x^3}{6yz^2}$.
A. $\dfrac{2x^3}{5z^2}$ B. $\dfrac{2y^3z}{5x}$ C. $\dfrac{5y^2z}{18x}$ D. $\dfrac{2z}{5x}$ 5. **C**

6. Simplify $\dfrac{d^3}{d+4} \div \dfrac{d^3-4d}{d^2+8d+16}$.
A. $\dfrac{d^2+4d}{d-4}$ B. $\dfrac{d^2(d-4)}{(d+4)^2}$ C. $\dfrac{d^3}{d^2+8d+16}$ D. $\dfrac{d+4}{d-4}$ 6. **A**

7. The fraction in simplest form for $\dfrac{p^2-5p+6}{p^2+4p+4} \cdot \dfrac{p^2-4}{p^2+4p+3}$ has what denominator?
A. 2 B. p^2-p-2 C. $(p-1)(p-3)^2$ D. $p+2$ 7. **D**

8. If two fractions have denominators of x^2-4 and $x+2$, what is the least common denominator of the fractions?
A. $(x^2-4)(x+2)$ B. $(x+2)(x-2)$
C. x^3-8 D. x^2+x-2 8. **B**

9. Simplify $\dfrac{x}{x^2+2x+1} + \dfrac{3}{4x^2-4}$.
A. $\dfrac{4x^2-x+3}{4(x+1)^2(x-1)}$ B. $\dfrac{4x^2-7x+3}{4(x+1)(x-1)}$
C. $\dfrac{x+3}{5x^2+2x-3}$ D. $\dfrac{x^2+1}{4(x+1)^2(x+1)}$ 9. **A**

10. Simplify $w + 5 + \dfrac{1}{w-5}$.
A. $\dfrac{w^2-24}{w^2-25}$ B. $\dfrac{w+6}{w-5}$ C. $\dfrac{w^2-24}{w-5}$ D. $\dfrac{w^2-26}{w-5}$ 10. **C**

11. Simplify $\dfrac{8n}{n^2-4} - \dfrac{4}{n+2}$.
A. $\dfrac{4}{n+2}$ B. $\dfrac{4}{n-2}$ C. $\dfrac{4n-8}{(n+2)(n-2)}$ D. $\dfrac{4n+8}{(n+2)(n-2)}$ 11. **B**

NAME _____ DATE _____

Chapter 11 Test, Form 1A (continued)

12. Simplify $\dfrac{1-\dfrac{2}{x}}{1-\dfrac{1}{x}-\dfrac{2}{x^2}}$.
A. $\dfrac{x}{2}$ B. $\dfrac{x}{x+1}$ C. $\dfrac{(x-2)^2(x+1)}{x^3}$ D. $\dfrac{x+1}{x}$ 12. **B**

13. Solve $\dfrac{3k}{2+k} - \dfrac{5}{7} = 4$.
A. $\{-33\}$ B. $\{15\}$ C. $\{-3\}$ D. $\left\{-\dfrac{11}{2}\right\}$ 13. **D**

14. Solve $\dfrac{n}{n-3} + n = \dfrac{7n-18}{n-3}$.
A. $\{3\}$ B. $\{6\}$ C. $\{3, 6\}$ D. $\{-3, 6\}$ 14. **B**

15. Susan can do a certain job in 5 hours. Kim can do the same job in 3 hours. Working together, how many hours would they need to do the job?
A. $\dfrac{5}{3}$ hours   B. $\dfrac{15}{8}$ hours   C. $\dfrac{3}{5}$ hour   D. $\dfrac{8}{15}$ hour   15. **B**

16. Suppose y varies inversely as x. If $x = -6$, then $y = \dfrac{3}{8}$. Find y when $x = 4$.
A. $-\dfrac{9}{16}$ B. -9 C. $-\dfrac{1}{4}$ D. -64 16. **A**

17. Which method might be useful for organizing data in order to solve a problem?
A. Make a table.   B. Draw a circle graph.
C. Draw a line graph.   D. All of these   17. **D**

18. Which equation has the graph shown?
A. $y = (x-3)(x-1)$
B. $y = (x-3)(x+1)$
C. $y = \dfrac{3}{(x+3)(x-1)}$
D. $y = \dfrac{3}{(x-3)(x+1)}$ 18. **C**

19. Suppose y varies directly as x. If $y = 7$ when $x = -5$, what is the value of y when x is 20?
A. 28 B. -28 C. $\dfrac{7}{4}$ D. $-\dfrac{7}{4}$ 19. **B**

20. Suppose y varies jointly as x and z. If $y = 30$ when $x = 3$ and $z = 5$, find y when $x = 5$ and $z = 8$.
A. 40 B. 10 C. 2 D. 80 20. **D**

Bonus

Solve over the set of complex numbers: $\dfrac{3}{1+\dfrac{1}{\frac{1}{x}+1}} + \dfrac{2}{x-1} = 1$
A. $\dfrac{1 \pm i\sqrt{23}}{4}$ B. $-\dfrac{3}{2}, 1$ C. $-\dfrac{3}{2}$ D. $\varnothing$ Bonus **A**

A **Test and Review Generator** is provided in Apple, IBM, and Macintosh versions. You may use this software to create your own tests or worksheets, based on the needs of your students.

The **Performance Assessment Booklet** provides an alternate asssessment for evaluating student progress. An assessment for this chapter can be found on pages 21–22.

CHAPTER 12

Exponential and Logarithmic Functions

PREVIEWING THE CHAPTER

The chapter begins by extending the students familiarity with integers used as exponents to simplifying expressions and solving equations where real numbers are used as exponents. Students then make the connection between working with exponential equations and those in logarithmic form. The properties of logarithms are derived from the properties of exponents, and students learn how to employ common and natural logarithms to solve equations with variable exponents. The chapter concludes with examples of applications of logarithms.

Problem-Solving Strategy Students learn that estimation not only can be used to solve many problems but also can be used to provide a check on an answer when a more exact number is required as the solution.

Lesson Objective Chart

Lesson (Pages)	Lesson Objectives	State/Local Objectives
12-1 (546-550)	**12-1:** Simplify expressions and solve equations involving real exponents.	
12-2 (553-557)	**12-2A:** Write exponential equations in logarithmic form and vice versa.	
	12-2B: Evaluate logarithmic expressions.	
	12-2C: Solve equations involving logarithmic functions.	
12-3 (558-562)	**12-3:** Solve equations or simplify and evaluate expressions using properties of logarithms.	
12-4 (563-566)	**12-4A:** Identify the characteristic and the mantissa of a logarithm.	
	12-4B: Find common logarithms and antilogarithms.	
12-5 (567-570)	**12-5:** Find natural logarithms of numbers.	
12-6 (571-573)	**12-6:** Solve problems using estimation.	
12-7 (574-578)	**12-7:** Solve equations with variable exponents using logarithms.	
12-8 (580-585)	**12-8:** Use logarithms to solve problems.	

ORGANIZING THE CHAPTER

You may want to refer to the **Course Planning Calendar** on page T44.

Lesson Planning Guide / Blackline Masters Booklets

Lesson (Pages)	Pacing Chart (days) Course I	II	III	Reteaching	Practice	Enrichment	Evaluation	Technology	Lab Manual	Mixed Problem Solving	Applications	Cooperative Learning Activity	Multicultural	Transparencies
12-1 (546-550)	1.5	1	1	p. 77	p. 88	p. 77			pp. 63-64					12-1
12-2 (553-557)	1.5	1	1	p. 78	p. 89	p. 78	Quiz A, p. 163	p. 29						12-2
12-3 (558-562)	1.5	1.5	1	p. 79	p. 90	p. 79								12-3
12-4 (563-566)	1	1	1	p. 80	p. 91	p. 80	Quiz B, p. 163	p. 12						12-4
12-5 (567-570)	1	1	0.5	p. 81	p. 92	p. 81	Mid-Chapter Test, p. 167							12-5
12-6 (571-573)	1	1	0.5		p. 93		Quiz C, p. 164					p. 48		12-6
12-7 (574-578)	1.5	1	1	p. 82	p. 94	p. 82				p. 12				12-7
12-8 (580-585)	2	1.5	1	p. 83	p. 95	p. 83	Quiz D, p. 164				p. 30		p. 12	12-8
Review (586-588)	1	1	1	Multiple Choice Tests, Forms 1A and 1B, pp. 155-158 Free Response Tests, Forms 2A and 2B, pp. 159-162										
Test (589)	1	1	1	Cumulative Review, pp. 165-166 Standardized Test Practice Questions, p. 168										

Course I: Chapters 1-13; Course II: Chapters 1-15; Course III: Chapters 1-17

Other Chapter Resources

Student Edition
Chapter Opener, pp. 544-545
Journal Entries, pp. 550, 577
Graphing Calculator Exploration, pp. 551-552
Mid-Chapter Review, p. 566
History Connection, p. 570
Cooperative Learning Activity, p. 573
Biology Connection, p. 578
Technology, p. 579
Portfolio Suggestion, p. 585
College Entrance Exam Preview pp. 590-591
Extended Project 3, pp. A10-A13

Teacher's Classroom Resources
Transparency 12-0
Real-World Applications Transparencies, 24, 25
Performance Assessment Booklet, pp. 23-24
Problem-of-the-Week Activity Cards, 24, 25
Tech Prep Applications Booklet, pp. 23-24
Lesson Plans, pp. 88-95

Other Supplements
Glencoe Mathematics Professional Series

Software
Test and Review Generator Software (Apple, IBM, and Macintosh)
Interactive Software (Macintosh)
Teacher's Guide for Software Resources

ENHANCING THE CHAPTER

Cooperative Learning

Explaining the Criteria for Success

In addition to clearly explaining the specific tasks to be performed before the group begins its work, you should also clearly explain the criteria by which the final work will be evaluated. These criteria should be judiciously structured so that students may achieve them without penalizing or being penalized by other students in the group. The criteria also should be fashioned so that they are not only challenging but also realistic for each and every member of the group. For some types of activities, the criteria can be as explicit as a set number of problems to be answered correctly. For other types of activities, just completing the assignment or simply doing better this time than last time may be sufficient criteria for success. Although some teachers are successful in maintaining group interdependence when establishing different criteria for different members during a group-learning session, others find it better to reserve such differing criteria for whole-class activities, such as during the administration of a quiz or chapter test.

Technology

The Technology Feature after Lesson 12-7 investigates the use of a spreadsheet program for computing compound interest. A program for finding the value of an investment after 1 to 20 years is provided. If a spreadsheet program is available, students can use the program to find the value of various investments and to compare the effects of different interest rates.

Critical Thinking

Those who approach critical thinking from a theoretical basis often make it sound far more bewildering and complicated than it is. Critical thinking is not unlike anything else we do; that is, if we do it once, and then continue to do it, it becomes a natural part of our existence. For example, you did not have to understand the theory of how an automobile operates to learn how to drive, and after you drive for awhile, you make dozens of critical decisions without being aware of it, even on a short trip. To help students develop their critical-thinking skills, establish an environment where it becomes natural for them to expect additional questions such as, "Can you explain why ...", "What would happen next if ...", "What other ways could have been used to ...", and so on.

Cooperative Learning, p. 48

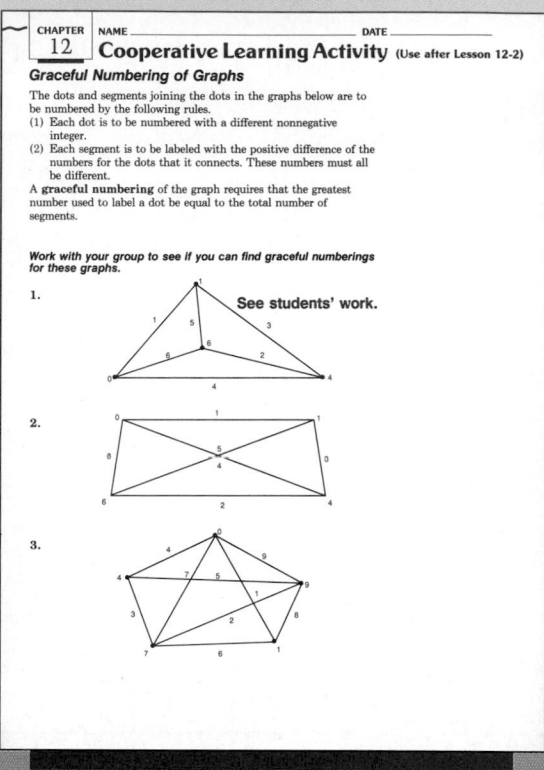

Technology, p. 29

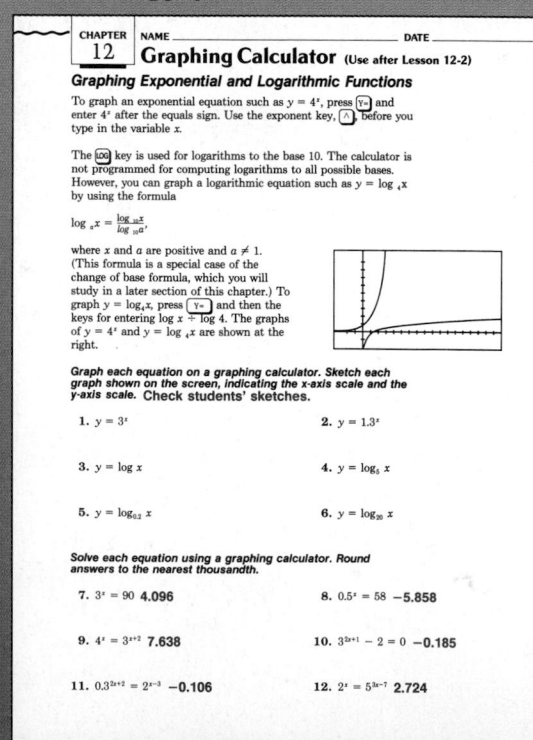

Problem of the Week Activity

The card shown below is one of two available for this chapter. It can be used as a class or small group activity.

Activity Card

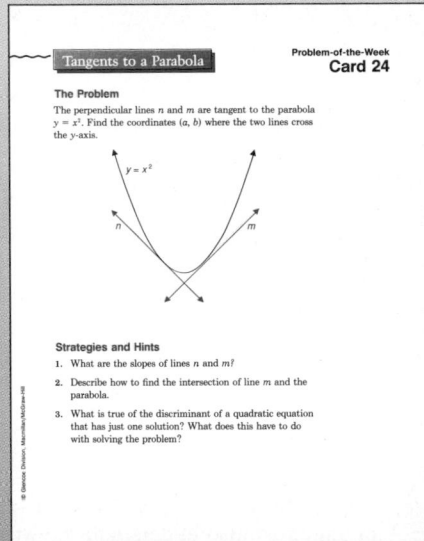

Tangents to a Parabola

Problem-of-the-Week
Card 24

The Problem

The perpendicular lines n and m are tangent to the parabola $y = x^2$. Find the coordinates (a, b) where the two lines cross the y-axis.

Strategies and Hints

1. What are the slopes of lines n and m?

2. Describe how to find the intersection of line m and the parabola.

3. What is true of the discriminant of a quadratic equation that has just one solution? What does this have to do with solving the problem?

Manipulatives and Models

The following materials may be used as models or manipulatives in Chapter 12.

- scientific calculator (all Lessons)
- graphing calculator (Lesson 12-1)
- superball (Lesson 12-2)
- pH paper (Lesson 12-3)
- bank brochures (Lesson 12-5)
- cash register receipts (Lesson 12-6)

Outside Resources

Books/Periodicals

Baker, Alan. *A Concise Introduction to the Theory of Numbers.* Cambridge University Press.

Emmett, E.R. *Brain Puzzler's Delight.* Emerson Book, Inc.

Films/Videotapes/Videodiscs

Powers and Roots, TPC Training Systems, 310 So. Michigan Ave., Chicago, IL 60604

Software

Quadratic Equations III, Intellectual Software (IS), Division of Queue, Inc., 338 Commerce Dr., Fairfield, CT 06430

Algebra II, Part I, IBM, 4111 Northside Pkwy. NW, P.O. Box 2150, Atlanta, GA 30327-3015

Multicultural

Multicultural Activity, p. 12

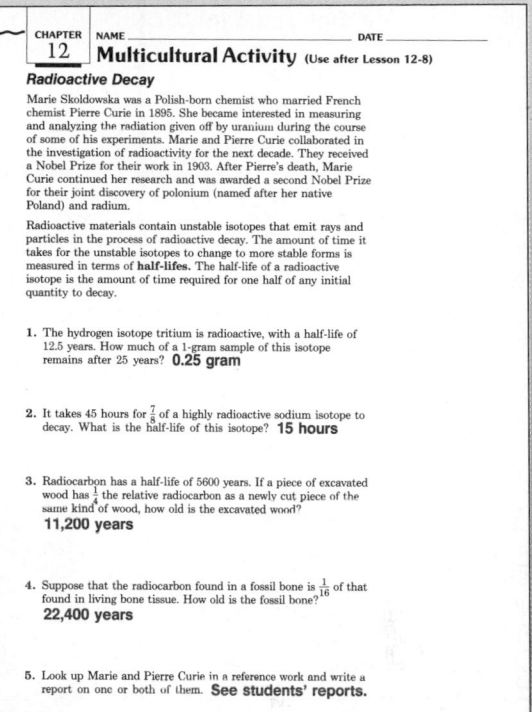

CHAPTER 12 NAME _____ DATE _____
Multicultural Activity (Use after Lesson 12-8)

Radioactive Decay

Marie Skolodowska was a Polish-born chemist who married French chemist Pierre Curie in 1895. She became interested in measuring and analyzing the radiation given off by uranium during the course of some of his experiments. Marie and Pierre Curie collaborated in the investigation of radioactivity for the next decade. They received a Nobel Prize for their work in 1903. After Pierre's death, Marie Curie continued her research and was awarded a second Nobel Prize for their joint discovery of polonium (named after her native Poland) and radium.

Radioactive materials contain unstable isotopes that emit rays and particles in the process of radioactive decay. The amount of time it takes for the unstable isotopes to change to more stable forms is measured in terms of **half-lives.** The half-life of a radioactive isotope is the amount of time required for one half of any initial quantity to decay.

1. The hydrogen isotope tritium is radioactive, with a half-life of 12.5 years. How much of a 1-gram sample of this isotope remains after 25 years? **0.25 gram**

2. It takes 45 hours for $\frac{7}{8}$ of a highly radioactive sodium isotope to decay. What is the half-life of this isotope? **15 hours**

3. Radiocarbon has a half-life of 5600 years. If a piece of excavated wood has $\frac{1}{4}$ the relative radiocarbon as a newly cut piece of the same kind of wood, how old is the excavated wood? **11,200 years**

4. Suppose that the radiocarbon found in a fossil bone is $\frac{1}{16}$ of that found in living bone tissue. How old is the fossil bone? **22,400 years**

5. Look up Marie and Pierre Curie in a reference work and write a report on one or both of them. **See students' reports.**

Lab Manual

Lab Activity, pp. 63-64

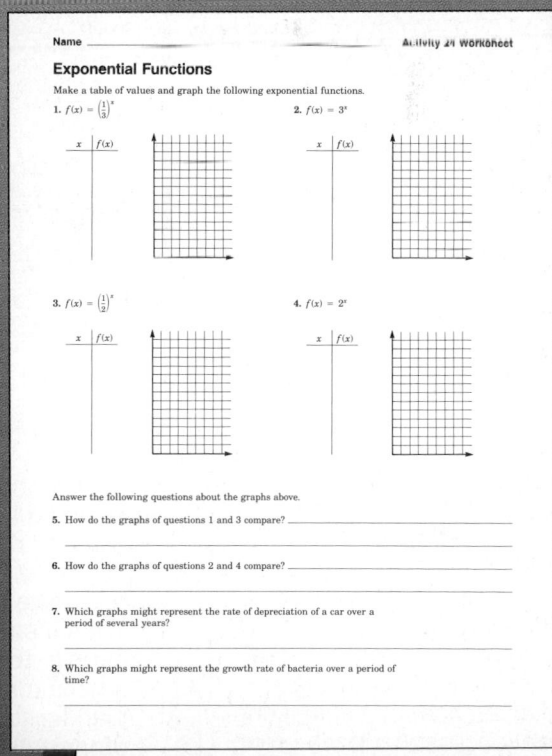

Name _____ Activity 24 Worksheet

Exponential Functions

Make a table of values and graph the following exponential functions.

1. $f(x) = \left(\frac{1}{3}\right)^x$ 2. $f(x) = 3^x$

3. $f(x) = \left(\frac{1}{2}\right)^x$ 4. $f(x) = 2^x$

Answer the following questions about the graphs above.

5. How do the graphs of questions 1 and 3 compare? _____

6. How do the graphs of questions 2 and 4 compare? _____

7. Which graphs might represent the rate of depreciation of a car over a period of several years? _____

8. Which graphs might represent the growth rate of bacteria over a period of time? _____

Transparency 12–0 is available in the Transparency Package. It provides a full-color visual and motivational activity that you can use to engage students in the mathematical content of the chapter.

Background Information

Systems analysts plan and develop methods for computerizing business and scientific tasks or for improving computer systems already in use. They discuss goals of the system with management and determine what information must be collected, how it is to be processed, and the type and frequency of reports to be produced. Analysts use techniques such as mathematical model building, sampling, and cost accounting to plan the system. Projected demand for systems analysts is expected to grow 35% or more through the 1990s as computer capabilities grow.

C H A P T E R

12 Exponential and Logarithmic Functions

CHAPTER OBJECTIVES

In this chapter, you will:
- Solve equations involving logarithmic and exponential functions.
- Find common and natural logarithms of numbers.
- Solve problems using estimation.
- Use logarithms to solve problems.

If the ant is $\frac{3}{8}$ inch long, estimate the size of the microchip.

CAREERS IN SYSTEMS ANALYSIS

The world depends on computers today, and it depends on them far more than anyone could have believed possible even thirty years ago. Research, business, government, education, art, sports, entertainment—almost every company in every field now has a computer system to help it function and grow. Thus it follows that the career of designing computer systems is a powerful one.

A systems analyst must understand the technical language of computer programming well enough to explain to the programmers what is needed. But he or she must also understand the workings of business. The systems analyst analyzes an organization's needs and then designs and creates a system of workers, information, materials, and computer technology that will meet those needs. Ideally, the machines and the people using them should work together like an artist's hand and mind. It costs a great deal to reorganize a company to the newest technology. If the system has not been designed correctly, there is little the computer programmer or the computer operator can do to make it meet the company's needs.

Some of today's systems analysts have an even bigger opportunity before them: the design and creation of robots. Robots are computers that can operate machines without direction from human operators. It's a challenging kind of system to analyze.

544

Chapter Project

Materials: paper, pencil, library resources

Organize students into cooperative groups of systems analysts. Assign each group the task of researching the data and information needs of a local business, scientific, service, or engineering organization. Instruct each group to (1) contact a manager within its selected local business, (2) determine its data and information needs, and (3) research available hardware and software programs. Then instruct each group to combine its research and develop and submit a computer networking plan for its respective business or organization. Each group is to include purpose, networking plan, hardware, software, and recommended operation. Finally, have each group present its plan to (1) the class and (2) its original contact person within the local business or organization for an evaluation of its plan.

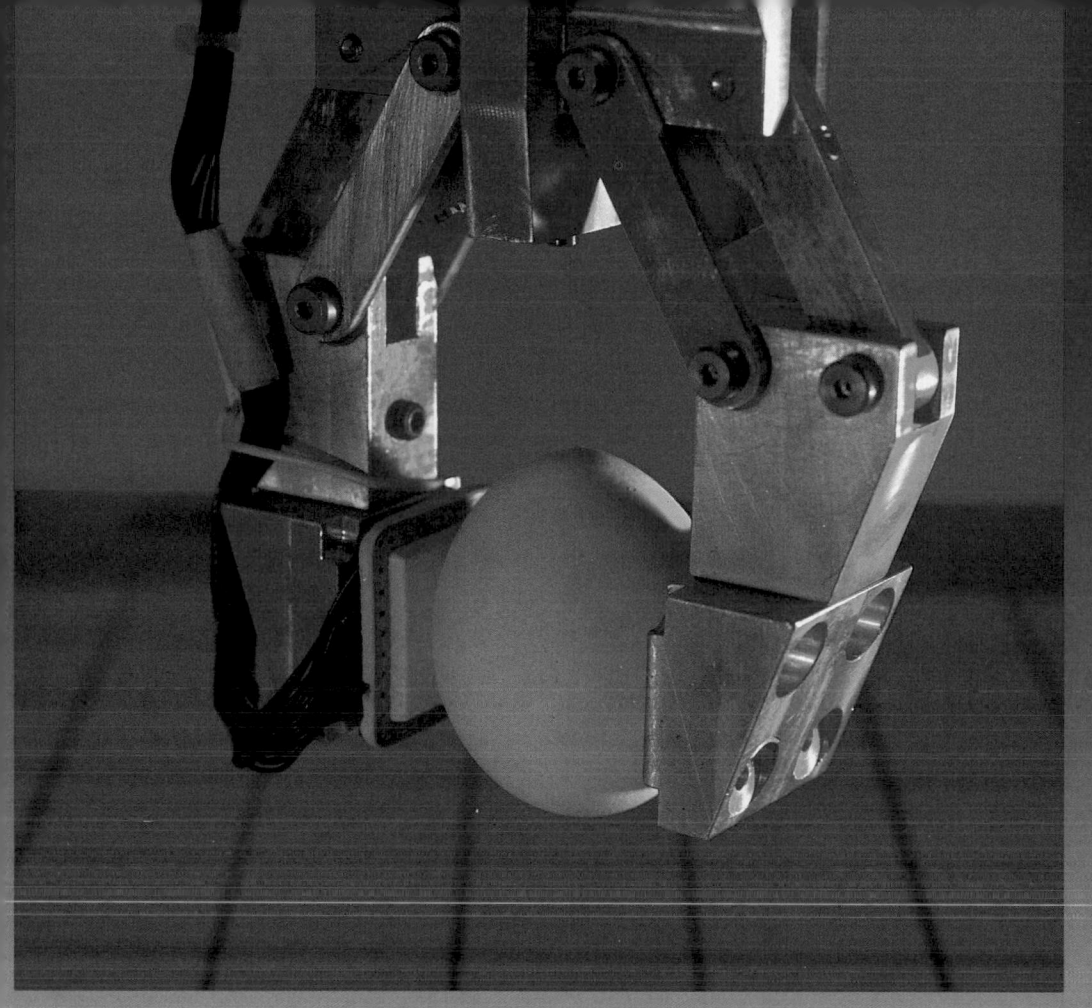

Lesson	Connections (C) and Applications (A)	Examples	Exercises

12-1	C: Geometry
	A: Biology
	   Communica-
	   tion
	   Finance
		1	55
			
			50
			
			51

12-2	A: Communica-
	   tions
	   Chemistry
	   Biology
		2	
			
			50
			51

12-3	A: Chemistry Medicine	2	 43
12-4	A: Physics Seismology	4	 33
12-5	A: Finance Chemistry	3, 4	32 33
12-6	C: Geometry A: Finance Aerospace	1 2 3	

12-7	A: Finance
	   Education
	   Business
	   Physics
	   Sports
		1	47
			48
			49
			53
			56

12-8	A: Chemistry
	   Business
	   Finance
	   Electronics
	   Real Estate
	   Photography
	   Physics
		1
		2
		3
			23
			
			22
			24
			36
			37

MORE ABOUT SYSTEMS ANALYSIS

Degree Required

- Bachelor's degree in Computer Science

Some systems analysts like:

- challenge and variety in their work
- good employment opportunities
- good salaries
- interaction with people in solving problems

Related Math Subjects:

- Advanced Algebra
- Geometry
- Statistics/Probability

Some systems analysts dislike:

- the need to update their knowledge with advances in technology
- working overtime to meet deadlines
- frustrating problems in computer programming

For more information on the various careers available in the field of Systems Analysis, write to:

Association of the Institute for
Certification of Computer Professionals
2200 East Devon Avenue
Suite 268
Des Plaines, IL 60018

545

Lesson Resources

Reteaching Master 12-1
Practice Master 12-1
Enrichment Master 12-1
Lab Manual, pp. 63–64

 Transparency 12-1 contains the 5-Minute Check and a teaching aid for this lesson.

INTRODUCING THE LESSON

 5-Minute Check

(over Chapter 11)

Simplify.

1. $\dfrac{x-3}{x+2} - \dfrac{x+1}{x-2}$ $\dfrac{-4(2x-1)}{(x+2)(x-2)}$

2. $\dfrac{b-1}{b} + \dfrac{b}{b+1}$ $\dfrac{2b^2-1}{b(b+1)}$

3. $\dfrac{x^2-y^2}{8x} \div \dfrac{x+y}{64x^2}$ $8x(x-y)$

4. Solve $\dfrac{2}{y} - \dfrac{4}{y} = 10$ $y = -\dfrac{1}{5}$

5. Suppose y varies directly as x. If $y = 8$, then $x = 2$. Find y when $x = 6$. $y = 24$

Motivating the Lesson

Show students a copy of a family tree. Ask students how many parents, grandparents, and great-grandparents a person has. Ask students to consider their answers to the previous questions and if they can think of a way to determine how many ancestors a person would have a certain number of generations ago.

12-1 Real Exponents and Exponential Functions

Objective 12-1

After studying this lesson, you should be able to:
- simplify expressions and solve equations involving real exponents.

Application

This bacteria is often referred to as e. coli.

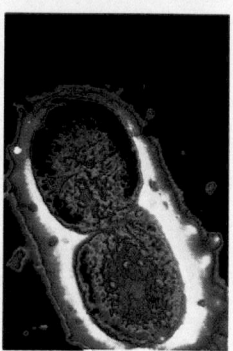

Mitosis is a process of cell duplication in which one cell divides into two. The *escherichia coli* is one of the fastest growing bacteria. It can reproduce itself in 15 minutes. If you begin with one escherichia coli cell, how many cells will there be in one hour?

Of course, in one hour there are four 15-minute intervals. After the first 15-minute interval, the cell will divide and form 2 cells. After the second 15-minute interval, each of the two cells will divide to form a total of 4 cells. After the third and fourth 15-minute intervals, 8 and 16 cells, respectively, will result.

This pattern can be summarized in the table at the right.

The total number of cells, y, can be expressed as a function of time where x is the number of 15-minute intervals. This function, $y = 2^x$, is an **exponential function**.

15-minute Intervals	Total Number of Cells	Pattern
0	1	2^0
1	2	2^1
2	4	2^2
3	8	2^3
4	16	2^4
.	.	.
.	.	.
.	.	.
x	y	2^x

Let's take a close look at the graph of $y = 2^x$, where x is a rational number. Make a table of values to help draw the curve. Of course, negative values for x have no meaning in mitosis. But, they must be included to show rational values for x.

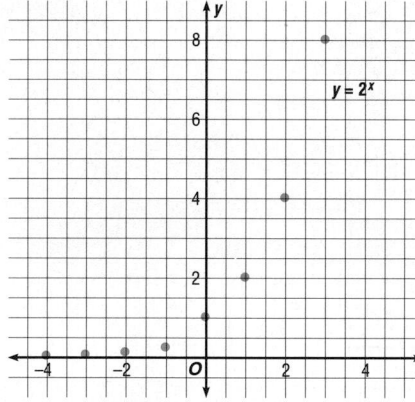

x	2^x or y	y (approx.)
-4	$2^{-4} = \frac{1}{16}$	0.06
-3	$2^{-3} = \frac{1}{8}$	0.12
-2	$2^{-2} = \frac{1}{4}$	0.25
-1	$2^{-1} = \frac{1}{2}$	0.5
$-\frac{1}{2}$	$2^{-\frac{1}{2}} = \frac{1}{2}\sqrt{2}$	0.7
0	$2^0 = 1$	1

x	2^x or y	y (approx.)
$\frac{1}{2}$	$2^{\frac{1}{2}} = \sqrt{2}$	1.4
1	$2^1 = 2$	2
$\frac{3}{2}$	$2^{\frac{3}{2}} = 2\sqrt{2}$	2.8
2	$2^2 = 4$	4
$\frac{5}{2}$	$2^{\frac{5}{2}} = 4\sqrt{2}$	5.7
3	$2^3 = 8$	8

546   CHAPTER 12   EXPONENTIAL AND LOGARITHMIC FUNCTIONS

ALTERNATE TEACHING STRATEGIES

Using Discussion

Before presenting the lesson, review basic rules for working with exponents. For example, compare the solution processes and results for $c^3 \cdot c^4$ and $(c^3)^4$, and $\dfrac{h^7}{h^5}$ and $\sqrt[5]{h^7}$.

Using Critical Thinking

Have students answer the following question. Suppose $a < b$ and $x > 0$. For which values of x is $x^a < x^b$?
$x > 1$

Since 2^x has not been defined when x is irrational, there are "holes" in the graph of $y = 2^x$. We can expand the domain of $y = 2^x$ to include the rational numbers and the irrational numbers. This will include all real numbers.

Consider the expression $2^{\sqrt{2}}$. Since $1.4 < \sqrt{2} < 1.5$, it makes sense that $2^{1.4} < 2^{\sqrt{2}} < 2^{1.5}$. By selecting closer approximations for $\sqrt{2}$, closer approximations for $2^{\sqrt{2}}$ will result.

$$2^{1.4} < 2^{\sqrt{2}} < 2^{1.5}$$
$$2^{1.41} < 2^{\sqrt{2}} < 2^{1.42}$$
$$2^{1.414} < 2^{\sqrt{2}} < 2^{1.415}$$
$$2^{1.4142} < 2^{\sqrt{2}} < 2^{1.4143}$$
$$2^{1.41421} < 2^{\sqrt{2}} < 2^{1.41422}$$

Teaching Tip ❶

So, approximate values for 2^x when x is irrational can be found by using rational approximations for x.

Definition of Irrational Exponents

If x is an irrational number and $a > 0$, then a^x is the real number between a^{x_1} and a^{x_2}, for all possible choices of rational numbers x_1 and x_2 such that $x_1 < x < x_2$.

Now since 2^x is defined when x is an irrational number, the domain of $y = 2^x$ is the set of all real numbers. There are no "holes" in the graph now. The graph is a smooth curve. You could use an accurate graph of $y = 2^x$ to estimate the value of 2^x when x is any real number.

Example 1

APPLICATION

Biology

Use the graph of $y = 2^x$ shown below to find the number of cells present in a sample after $\sqrt{3}$ fifteen-minute intervals. Then check your estimation using a calculator.

The value of x is $\sqrt{3}$ and $1.7 < \sqrt{3} < 1.8$.

From the graph, the value of y is approximately 3.3.

To check:

ENTER: 2 $\boxed{y^x}$ 3 $\boxed{\sqrt{x}}$ $\boxed{=}$

3.32199609

The calculator verifies our estimate from the graph. After $\sqrt{3}$ fifteen-minute intervals, there would be about 3 cells.

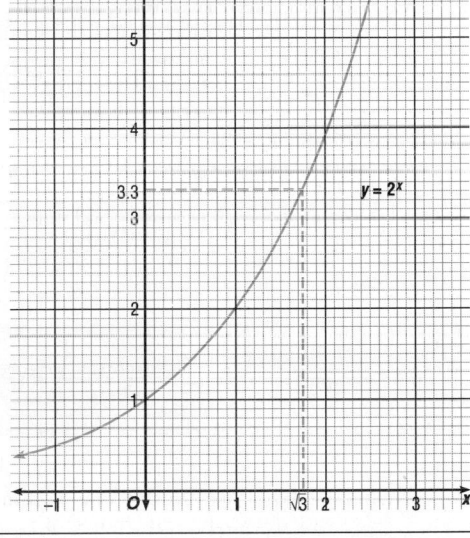

Teaching Tip ❶ Point out that you can quickly determine a decimal approximation for $2^{\sqrt{2}}$ on a calculator using the following sequence of keys.

2 $\boxed{y^x}$ 2 $\boxed{\sqrt{x}}$ $\boxed{=}$

You may want to have students verify the last inequality, $2^{1.41421} < 2^{\sqrt{2}} < 2^{1.41422}$ by using a calculator.

Chalkboard Example

For Example 1

Use the graph of $y = 2^x$ to evaluate $y = 2^{2.1}$ to the nearest tenth. Then check your estimation using a calculator.
$y \approx 4.3$
To check: $2^{2.1} \approx 4.28709385$

548 Chapter 12

Chalkboard Examples

For Example 2
Simplify.

a. $8^{\sqrt{6}} \cdot 4^{\sqrt{54}}$ $\mathbf{2^{9\sqrt{6}}}$

b. $27^{\sqrt{5}} \div 3^{\sqrt{5}}$ $\mathbf{3^{2\sqrt{5}}}$

For Example 3
Simplify.

a. $(4^{\sqrt{6}})^{\sqrt{12}}$ $\mathbf{4^{6\sqrt{2}}}$

b. $(x^{\sqrt{3}} - y^{\sqrt{3}})^2$
   $\mathbf{x^{2\sqrt{3}} - 2x^{\sqrt{3}}y^{\sqrt{3}} + y^{2\sqrt{3}}}$

For Example 4
Solve.

a. $3^4 = 27^{m-1}$ $\mathbf{m = \dfrac{7}{3}}$

b. $16^{2n+1} = \dfrac{1}{32}$ $\mathbf{n = -\dfrac{9}{8}}$

c. $\left(\dfrac{1}{25}\right)^{2n} = 5^{n-5}$ $\mathbf{n = 1}$

Teaching Tip ② Explain to students that a function, $y = f(x)$, is an increasing function if y increases as x increases. Also, a function, $y = f(x)$, is a decreasing function if y decreases as x increases.

Reteaching Masters Booklet, p. 77

All of the properties of rational exponents apply to real exponents as well.

Example 2 | Simplify $5^{\sqrt{2}} \cdot 5^{\sqrt{3}}$.

$5^{\sqrt{2}} \cdot 5^{\sqrt{3}} = 5^{\sqrt{2} + \sqrt{3}}$ *Recall the product of powers property, $a^m \cdot a^n = a^{m+n}$. Use your calculator to check this result.*

Example 3 | Simplify $(6^{\sqrt{5}})^{\sqrt{2}}$.

$(6^{\sqrt{5}})^{\sqrt{2}} = 6^{\sqrt{5} \cdot \sqrt{2}}$
$\qquad\qquad = 6^{\sqrt{10}}$ *Recall the power of a power property, $(a^m)^n = a^{mn}$.*

Definition of Exponential Function

An equation of the form $y = a^x$, where $a > 0$ and $a \neq 1$, is called an exponential function.

Teaching Tip ②

Several exponential functions have been graphed at the right. Compare the graphs of functions where $a > 1$ to those where $a < 1$. Notice that when $a > 1$ the value of y increases as the value of x increases. When $a < 1$, the value of y decreases as the value of x increases.

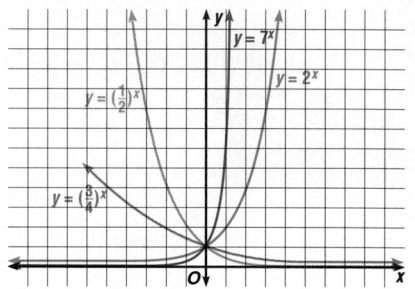

The following property is very useful when solving equations involving exponential functions.

Property of Equality for Exponential Functions

Suppose a is a positive number other than 1. Then $a^{x_1} = a^{x_2}$ if and only if $x_1 = x_2$.

Notice that a cannot equal 1. Since $1^x = 1$ for any real number, $1^{x_1} = 1^{x_2}$ for any choice of x_1 and x_2.

RETEACHING THE LESSON

Have students use graphing calculators to plot a graph of the equations $y = 3^x$, $y = \dfrac{1}{3}^x$, and $y = 5^x$. Using this graph, have students compare and contrast the relationships and then deduce where the graphs of $y = \dfrac{1}{5}^x$, $y = 7^x$, and $y = \dfrac{1}{4}^x$ would lie.

Example 4

Solve $9^3 = 3^{x^2}$ for x.

$9^3 = 3^{x^2}$

$(3^2)^3 = 3^{x^2}$ *Write each term with the same base; in this case, 3.*

$3^6 = 3^{x^2}$ *$(a^b)^c = a^{bc}$*

$6 = x^2$ *Property of equality for exponential functions*

$\pm\sqrt{6} = x$

Check: $9^3 = 3^{x^2}$

$9^3 \stackrel{?}{=} 3^{(\pm\sqrt{6})^2}$

$9^3 \stackrel{?}{=} 3^6$

$729 = 729 \checkmark$

CHECKING FOR UNDERSTANDING

Communicating Mathematics

Read and study the lesson to answer these questions.

1. Name three ways that you can find an approximate value for 2^x when x is an irrational number. **rational approximations, graph, calculator**

2. Use each of the three methods that you named to approximate $2^{\sqrt{5}}$. Which do you think is the most accurate? Why? **4.7111131; a calculator**

3. Why is 1 excluded as a value for a in the property of equality for exponential functions? **$1^{x_1} = 1^{x_2}$ for any x_1 and x_2**

Guided Practice

Use the graph of $y = 2^x$ on page 547 or a calculator to approximate each expression to the nearest tenth.

4. $2^{\sqrt{5}}$ **4.7**   5. $2^{0.7}$ **1.6**   6. $2^{-0.3}$ **0.8**

7. $2^{1.1}$ **2.1**   8. 2^{-1} **0.5**   9. $8^{\sqrt{2}}$ **18.9**

Use the rule of exponents to simplify each expression.

10. $7^{\sqrt{3}} \cdot 7^{\sqrt{3}}$ **$7^{3\sqrt{3}}$**   11. $(2^{\sqrt{3}})^{\sqrt{3}}$ **2^3**   12. $3(2^{\sqrt{2}})(2^{-\sqrt{2}})$ **3**

Solve each equation.

13. $5^x = 5^{-3}$ **−3**   14. $6^x = 216$ **3**   15. $7^y = \frac{1}{49}$ **−2**

16. $10^x = 0.001$ **−3**   17. $2^{2x} = \frac{1}{8}$ **$-\frac{3}{2}$**   18. $\left(\frac{1}{5}\right)^{b-3} = 125$ **0**

EXERCISES

Practice

Use the graph of $y = 2^x$ on page 547 or a calculator to evaluate each expression to the nearest tenth. **Teaching Tip ❸**

19. $2^{-1.1}$ **0.5**   20. $4^{-0.3}$ **0.7**   21. $16^{0.4}$ **3.0**

22. $8^{-0.3}$ **0.5**   23. $2^{\sqrt[3]{2}}$ **2.4**   24. $2^{\sqrt[3]{7}}$ **3.8**

Simplify each expression.

25. $(3^{\sqrt{8}})^{\sqrt{2}}$ **81**   26. $5^{\sqrt{3}} \cdot 5^{\sqrt{27}}$ **$5^{4\sqrt{3}}$**   27. $64^{\sqrt{7}} \div 2^{\sqrt{7}}$ **$2^{5\sqrt{7}}$**

28. $(y^{\sqrt{3}})^{\sqrt{27}}$ **y^9**   29. $(x^{\sqrt{2}})^{\sqrt{8}}$ **x^4**   30. $(m^{\sqrt{2}} + n^{\sqrt{2}})^2$

$m^{2\sqrt{2}} + 2(mn)^{\sqrt{2}} + n^{2\sqrt{2}}$

LESSON 12-1 REAL EXPONENTS AND EXPONENTIAL FUNCTIONS 549

EXTENDING THE LESSON

Math Power: Problem Solving

Have students graph several exponential functions on semilog paper. The vertical scale on this paper is adjusted so that graphs of exponential functions are straight lines. Ask students what is different about the graphs compared to those on regular graph paper.

B   Solve each equation.

31. $3^y = 3^{3y+1}$ $-\frac{1}{2}$
32. $5^{3y+4} = 5^y$ -2
33. $3^x = 9^{x+1}$ -2

34. $2^5 = 2^{2x-1}$ **3**
35. $8^{r-1} = 16^{3r}$ $-\frac{1}{3}$
36. $2^{x+3} = \frac{1}{16}$ -7

37. $9^{3y} = 27^{y+2}$ **2**
38. $\frac{1}{27} = 3^{x-5}$ **2**
39. $\left(\frac{1}{3}\right)^q = 3^{q-6}$ **3**

40. $25^{2m} = 125^{m-3}$ -9
41. $2^{2n-1} = 8^{n+7}$ -22
42. $2^{x^2+1} = 32$ ±2

43. $4^{x-1} = 8^x$ -2
44. $36^x = 6^{x^2-3}$ **3, -1**
45. $9^{x^2-2x} = 27^{x^2+1}$
$-1, -3$

C   Graph each equation. **See margin.**

46. $y = 4^x$
47. $y = 3^x$
48. $y = \left(\frac{1}{4}\right)^x$

Critical Thinking

49. Compare the graphs of $y = 4^x$ and $y = \left(\frac{1}{4}\right)^x$. What do you notice?
They are reflections over the y-axis.

Applications

50. Communication   Sally's office has a system to let people know when the department will have a meeting. Sally calls three people. Then those three people each call three other people, and so on until the whole department is notified. If it takes ten minutes for a person to call three people and all calls are completed within 30 minutes, how many people will be notified in the last round? **27**

51. Finance   Graham's grandparents started a savings account for him when he was born. They invested $100 in an account that pays 8% interest compounded annually. $y = 100 \times (1.08)^x$
   a. Write an exponential equation to express the amount of money in the account on Graham's xth birthday.
   b. How much is in the account on his 16th birthday? **$342.59**

Mixed Review

52. How much of a 60% saline solution must be added to a 35% saline solution to get 600 milliliters of a 50% solution? **(Lesson 11-7)** **360 mL**

53. Use synthetic substitution to find $f(3)$ and $f(-2)$ for the function $f(x) = x^3 + 8x + 1$. **(Lesson 10-2)** **52, -23**

54. Is $(4, 0)$ a solution for the inequality $y \leq x^2 - 7$? Explain your answer. **(Lesson 8-6)** **yes; $0 \leq 4^2 - 7$**

55. Geometry   The length of a rectangle is 2 units more than its width. The area of the rectangle is 1763 square units. What are the dimensions of the rectangle? **(Lesson 7-4)** **41 by 43 units**

56. Simplify $\dfrac{9x^{-\frac{4}{3}} - 4y^{-2}}{3x^{-\frac{2}{3}} + 2y^{-1}}$. **(Lesson 6-6)** $\dfrac{3x^{\frac{1}{3}}y - 2x}{xy}$

57. Factor $b(3b - 2y) - (3b - 2y)$. **(Lesson 5-5)** $(b - 1)(3b - 2y)$

Journal

Describe how the graph of an exponential function differs from the other curved graphs you have studied.

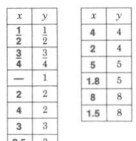
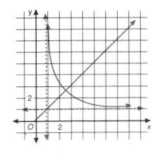
Additional Answers

46.
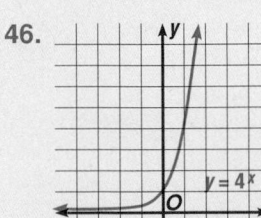

47.
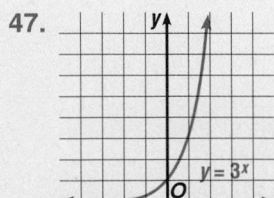

48.
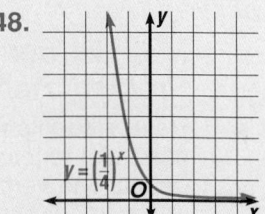

Graphing Calculator Exploration: Graphing Exponential and Logarithmic Functions

Teaching Tip ❶

You can draw graphs of exponential functions and logarithmic functions on your graphing calculator. As you know, an exponential function is a function of the form $y = a^x$, where $a > 0$ and $a \neq 1$. A logarithmic function is a function of the form $x = a^y$, where $a > 0$ and $a \neq 1$. It is denoted $y = \log_a x$, and is the inverse function of an exponential function.

Example 1

Graph the set of exponential equations, $y = 2^x$ and $y = \left(\frac{1}{2}\right)^x$, on the same set of axes. Use the viewing window [−5, 5] by [0, 10] with scale factors of 1 on both axes.

Graph the equations. *Be sure to set your range parameters before graphing.*

Casio

ENTER: [GRAPH] 2 [xʸ] [ALPHA] [X] [:] [GRAPH]
.5 [xʸ] [ALPHA] [X] [EXE]

TI-81

ENTER: [Y=] 2 [^] [X|T] [ENTER] .5 [^] [X|T] [GRAPH]

The set of functions has an axis of symmetry, the y-axis. The graphs have the point (0, 1) in common, and both have the x-axis as a horizontal asymptote. *Do you think that these characteristics are common to all exponential functions? Why?*

Teaching Tip ❷

The Casio graphing calculator has the graph of the logarithmic function $y = \log_{10} x$ built in. Try pressing [GRAPH] [LOG] [EXE] to view the graph.

Example 2

Graph the set of equations, $y = 2^x$ and $y = \log_2 x$, on the same set of axes. Use the viewing window [−2, 10] by [−2, 10] with scale factors of 1 on both axes.

To graph logarithmic functions with bases other than 10, you must use the change of base formula, $\log_a x = \dfrac{\log_{10} x}{\log_{10} a}$. You will use this formula more extensively in Lesson 12-7.

RETEACHING THE LESSON

Put five exponential functions on the chalkboard or overhead. Have students state the logarithmic inverse of each. Ask them what they think the graph will look like and check it with their calculator.

Graphing Calculator Exploration

INTRODUCING THE LESSON

Objective: Graph logarithmic and exponential functions on a graphing calculator.

Motivating the Lesson

Use paint and a piece of paper to illustrate the concept of axis of symmetry. Put paint on one side of a piece of paper. Then fold the paper in half and spread out the paint by pressing on the paper. Where the paper was folded is the axis of symmetry. Unfold the paper and the two sides will have the same design on them. Relate this to the axis of symmetry in graphing.

TEACHING THE LESSON

Teaching Tip ❶   Logarithmic and exponential functions are inverses of each other because the x- and y-values are interchanged.

Teaching Tip ❷   Check the range once you graph the function. Notice that $|{-1}| + |8.4| = 9.4$, which when divided by 94 (which is the number of points calculated to graph along the x-axis) is 0.1. This allows you to trace along the function by tenths.

More Examples

Graph the set of equations $y = 0.5^x$ and $y = \log_{.5} x$ on the same set of axes. Use the viewing window [−5, 5] by [−3, 5] with scale factors of 1 on both axes.

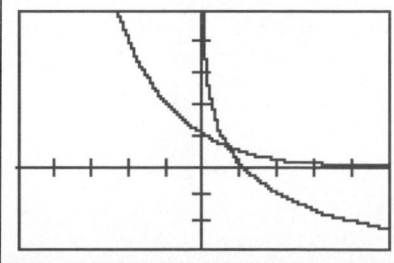

More Examples

Solve $2^{3x-1} = 4^x$.
$x = 1.00$
Viewing window $[-2, 2]$ by $[-3, 3]$.

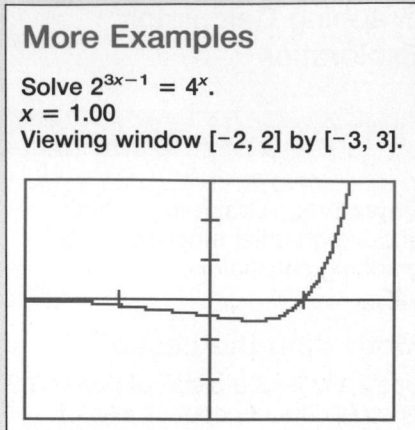

Teaching Tip ❸ The line of symmetry is given by the equation $y = x$.

EVALUATING THE LESSON

Closing the Lesson

Writing Activity Have each student write a logarithmic or exponential function. Then have them exchange theirs with another student and graph that function and its inverse on a graphing calculator.

APPLYING THE LESSON

Homework Exercises

Assignment Guide

All: 1–18

Casio

ENTER: [GRAPH] 2 [xʸ] [ALPHA] [X] [:]
[GRAPH] [LOG] [ALPHA] [X] [÷]
[LOG] 2 [EXE]

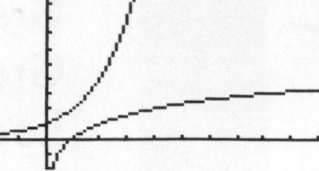

TI-81

ENTER: [Y=] 2 [^] [X|T] [ENTER] [LOG] [X|T] [÷] [LOG] 2 [GRAPH]

Notice that the graphs are reflections of each other over the line $y = x$.

Teaching Tip ❸

Example 3

Solve $4^{2x-5} = 3^x$.

There are two methods that you could use with your graphing calculator to find the solution to this equation. The first method is to graph the equations, $y = 4^{2x-5}$ and $y = 3^x$, and find the x-coordinate of the point of intersection. The second method is to graph the equation $y = 4^{2x-5} - 3^x$, and find the x-intercept. Let's try the second method. Use the viewing window $[-1, 5]$ by $[-35, 10]$.

Casio

ENTER: [GRAPH] 4 [xʸ] [(] 2 [ALPHA]
[X] [−] 5 [)] [−] 3 [xʸ]
[ALPHA] [X] [EXE]

TI-81

ENTER: [Y=] 4 [^] [(] 2 [X|T] [−]
5 [)] [−] 3 [^] [X|T] [GRAPH]

Now use the zoom-in process to estimate the solution. The solution is approximately 4.14   *Check this solution using the first method.*

EXERCISES

Graph each equation on your graphing calculator so the complete graph is shown. Then sketch the graph. **See students' graphs.**

1. $y = 10^x$ **2.** $y = 12.5^x$ **3.** $y = 0.1^x$

4. $y = \log_{20} x$ **5.** $y = \log_5 x$ **6.** $y = \log_{0.2} x$

Solve each equation using your graphing calculator. **10.** −0.28 **14.** 2, 4, −0.77

7. $0.5^x = 75$ **−6.23**   **8.** $25^{2x-1} = 512$ **1.47**   **9.** $10^{2x} = 17^{1-x}$ **0.38**

10. $0.3^{5x+1} = 0.7^{x-1}$ **11.** $5^x = 3^{x+2}$ **4.30**   **12.** $3.32^{3x-2} = 0.5$ **0.47**

13. $6^{x-1} = 10^x$ **−3.51**   **14.** $2^x = x^2$ **15.** $3^x = x^3$ **2.48, 3**

16. $0.35^{6-x} = 28$ **9.17**   **17.** $0.75^{x+3} = 4^{2x-1}$ **18.** $3^{4x-7} = 4^{2x+3}$ **7.30**
                                           0.17

EXTENDING THE LESSON

Ask students what the inverse of the graph of $\log_{10} x$ is. Students will have to look at the base of $\log_{10} x$, which is 10. They are inverses since if you interchange x and y, the equation $y = \log_{10} x$ is the inverse of $x = \log_{10} y$, which can be written as $y = 10^x$. Graph the two functions in the same viewing window. How can you tell that they actually are inverses of each other?
Because they are symmetric with respect to the line $y = x$.

12-2 Logarithms and Logarithmic Functions

Objectives

After studying this lesson, you should be able to:

12-2A
- write exponential equations in logarithmic form and vice versa,

12-2B
- evaluate logarithmic expressions, and

12-2C
- solve equations involving logarithmic functions.

Application

FYI ...

The 1989 earthquake started a wave of long-distance phone calls to the area. About 140 million calls were made the next day, the most ever for a single day.

The strength of an earthquake is measured using the Richter scale, which is based on powers of 10. The Richter scale is a **logarithmic scale.** This means that a 3 on the scale is 10 times stronger than a 2 and 100 times stronger than a 1. An earthquake that measured 6.9 on the Richter scale hit the San Francisco Bay area on October 17, 1989. This earthquake was $10^{6.9}$ or 7,943,280 times stronger than the weakest earthquake that a seismograph can detect.

The two tables below show two related exponential equations. You will recognize the equation in the table on the left as an exponential function.

Given the exponent, x, compute the power of 2, y.

x	$2^x = y$	y
-1	$2^{-1} = y$	?
2	$2^2 = y$	?
3	$2^3 = y$	?
6	$2^6 = y$	?

Given the power of 2, x, compute the exponent, y.

y	$2^y = x$	x
?	$2^y = \frac{1}{2}$	$\frac{1}{2}$
?	$2^y = 4$	4
?	$2^y = 8$	8
?	$2^y = 64$	64

In the relation shown in the table at the right, $2^y = x$, the exponent y is called the **logarithm,** base 2, of x. This relation is written as $\log_2 x = y$. This equation is read "the log base 2 of x is equal to y." The logarithm corresponds to the exponent. Study the diagram below.

Exponential Equation
$$n = b^p$$

Logarithmic Equation
$$p = \log_b n$$

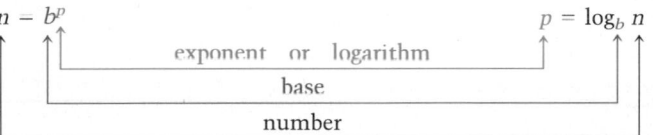

exponent or logarithm

base

number

Teaching Tip ❶

Definition of Logarithm

Suppose $b > 0$ and $b \neq 1$. For $n > 0$, there is a number p such that $\log_b n = p$ if and only if $b^p = n$.

LESSON 12-2   LOGARITHMS AND LOGARITHMIC FUNCTIONS   553

ALTERNATE TEACHING STRATEGIES

Using Cooperative Groups

Provide each group with a "superball." Have students assume the ball rebounds to 90 percent of its previous height on each bounce. If the ball is initially dropped from 8 feet, have students use the ball and logarithms to model the number of bounces it would take for the ball to rebound to a given height.
$h = 8 - 0.9^n$; $n = \log_{0.9} (8 - h)$

Lesson Resources

Reteaching Master 12-2
Practice Master 12-2
Enrichment Master 12-2
Technology Master, p. 29

 Transparency 12-2 contains the 5-Minute Check and a teaching aid for this lesson.

INTRODUCING THE LESSON

⏱ 5-Minute Check

(over Lesson 12-1)

Simplify.

1. $(2^{\sqrt{5}})^{\sqrt{5}}$ 2^5
2. $2^{\sqrt{2}} \cdot 16^{\sqrt{32}}$ $2^{17\sqrt{2}}$
3. $\dfrac{49^{\sqrt{2}}}{7^{\sqrt{12}}}$ $7^{2\sqrt{2}-2\sqrt{3}}$

Solve.

4. $(\sqrt{2})^{n+1} = 8^{n-1}$ $\dfrac{7}{5}$
5. $36^{3p-1} = 6^{4p+2}$ 2

Motivating the Lesson

Present the following problem. A large organization has 2500 members. To announce unscheduled meetings, the president calls 5 members, each of these call 5 members, and so on until all members are called. Assuming the president is level 1, how many levels of calls must be made? Have students discuss problems that would arise if they were to use a diagram to solve.

TEACHING THE LESSON

Teaching Tip ❶   Have students make flash cards with an exponential equation on one side and its corresponding logarithmic equation on the other side. Have students work in pairs and use the cards to reinforce the relationship of the two equations.

Exponential Equation	Logarithmic Equation
a. $5^2 = 25$	$\log_5 25 = 2$
b. $10^5 = 100{,}000$	$\log_{10} 100000 = 5$
c. $8^0 = 1$	$\log_8 1 = 0$
d. $2^{-4} = \frac{1}{16}$	$\log_2 \frac{1}{16} = -4$
e. $9^{\frac{1}{2}} = 3$	$\log_9 3 = \frac{1}{2}$

The chart at the left shows some equivalent exponential and logarithmic equations.

Examples 1 and 2 show how to find the value of a variable in a logarithmic equation $\log_b x = y$ when values for two of the variables are known.

Example 1

a. Solve $\log_3 243 = y$ for y.

$\log_3 243 = y$

$\qquad 3^y = 243$ — *Definition of logarithm*

$\qquad 3^y = 3^5$

$\qquad y = 5$ — *Property of equality for exponential functions*

b. Solve $\log_9 x = -3$ for x.

$\log_9 x = -3$

$\qquad 9^{-3} = x$ — *Definition of logarithm*

$\qquad x = \frac{1}{729}$

Example 2

APPLICATION
Communication

The superintendent of Fairborn School District has set up a telephone network to notify each faculty or staff member in the event of a school cancellation. She has estimated that each set of calls can be made in ten minutes and that the whole faculty and staff can be contacted in forty minutes. If 256 calls are made in the last round, how many people will each person call?

Since $40 \div 10 = 4$, there are 4 rounds of calls.

$\log_x 256 = 4$ — *The network contacts 256 people in the last round.*

$\qquad x^4 = 256$ — *Definition of logarithm*

$\qquad x = \sqrt[4]{256}$

$\qquad x = 4$ — *Since $b > 0$, -4 is not a solution.*

How many staff members does the superintendent have?

340

Each person contacts 4 people.

Let's look at the graphs of an exponential function and its corresponding logarithmic relation. The domain of the relation $y = \log_2 x$ is the set of all positive reals. The range is the set of all real numbers.

$y = 2^x$

x	-4	-3	-2	-1	0	1	2	3
y	$\frac{1}{16}$	$\frac{1}{8}$	$\frac{1}{4}$	$\frac{1}{2}$	1	2	4	8

$2^y = x$ or $y = \log_2 x$

x	$\frac{1}{16}$	$\frac{1}{8}$	$\frac{1}{4}$	$\frac{1}{2}$	1	2	4	8
y	-4	-3	-2	-1	0	1	2	3

The x and y values are reversed.

For every point (a, b) on $y = 2^x$, there is a point on $y = \log_2 x$ with coordinates (b, a).

554 CHAPTER 12 EXPONENTIAL AND LOGARITHMIC FUNCTIONS

Notice that the graphs are reflections of each other along the line $y = x$. The relations are inverses of each other. Using the vertical line test, you can see that no vertical line can intersect the graph of $y = \log_2 x$ in more than one place, so $y = \log_2 x$ is a **logarithmic function**.

Teaching Tip ❷

Definition of Logarithmic Function	An equation of the form $y = \log_b x$, where $b > 0$ and $b \neq 1$, is called a logarithmic function.

Since the exponential function and the logarithmic function are inverses of each other, their composites are the identity function. Let $f(x) = \log_b x$ and $g(x) = b^x$. For $f(x)$ and $g(x)$ to be inverses, it must be true that $f(g(x)) = x$ and $g(f(x)) = x$.

$$f(g(x)) = x \qquad\qquad g(f(x)) = x$$
$$f(b^x) = x \qquad\qquad g(\log_b x) = x$$
$$\log_b b^x = x \qquad\qquad b^{\log_b x} = x$$

Example 3

Evaluate each expression.

Teaching Tip ❸

a. $\log_8 8^4$

$\log_8 8^4 = 4 \qquad \log_b b^x = x$

b. $6^{(\log_6 (3x-1))}$

$6^{(\log_6 (3x-1))} = 3x - 1 \qquad b^{\log_b x} = x$

A property similar to the property of equality for exponential functions applies to the logarithmic functions.

Property of Equality for Logarithmic Functions	Suppose $b > 0$ and $b \neq 1$. Then $\log_b x_1 = \log_b x_2$ if and only if $x_1 = x_2$.

Example 4

Solve each of the following.

a. $\log_3 (3x - 6) = \log_3 (2x + 1)$

$\log_3 (3x - 6) = \log_3 (2x + 1)$
$\quad 3x - 6 = 2x + 1 \quad$ *Property of equality for logarithmic functions*
$\quad\quad\quad x = 7$

b. $\log_6 (3x - 1) = \log_6 (2x + 4)$

$\log_6 (3x - 1) = \log_6 (2x + 4)$
$\quad 3x - 1 = 2x + 4 \quad$ *Property of equality for logarithmic functions*
$\quad\quad\quad x = 5$

LESSON 12-2 LOGARITHMS AND LOGARITHMIC FUNCTIONS 555

RETEACHING THE LESSON

Have students graph the exponential equation $y = 4^x$ and the logarithmic equation $y = \log_4 x$ which is really $4^y = x$. Compare and contrast these graphs and discuss.

Chalkboard Examples

For Example 3
Evaluate $\log_5 5^8$.   8

For Example 4
Solve.

a. $\log_7 (2x + 1) = \log_7 (3x - 5)$ $x = 6$
b. $\log_8 (x^2 - 14) = \log_8 (5x)$
   $x = 7$ or $x = -2$
   The only solution is 7 since $\log_8 [5 \cdot -2]$ is not defined.

Teaching Tip ❸   Point out that $3x - 1$ can never be negative since $\log x$ is only defined for $x > 0$.

Reteaching Masters Booklet, p. 78

NAME _____ DATE _____
12-2 **Reteaching Worksheet**
Logarithms and Logarithmic Functions
Logarithmic functions are the inverses of exponential functions.

Exponential Equation	Logarithmic Equation
$n = b^p$	$p = \log_b n$

Definition of Logarithms	
Definition	Example
Suppose $b > 0$ and $b \neq 1$. For $n > 0$, there is a number p such that $\log_b n = p$ if and only if $b^p = n$.	Solve $\log_2 x = 3$ for x. $\log_2 x = 3$ $2^3 = x$ Definition of Logarithms $x = 8$

You can use the Property of Logarithmic Functions to solve exponential functions involving logarithms.

Property of Logarithmic Functions	
Definition	Example
Suppose $b > 0$ and $b \neq 1$. Then $\log_b x_1 = \log_b x_2$ if and only if $x_1 = x_2$.	Solve $\log_3 (2x - 4) = \log_3 (7x + 1)$. $\log_3 (2x - 4) = \log_3 (7x + 1)$ $2x - 4 = 7x + 1$ Property of Equality for $-5x = 5$ Logarithmic Functions $x = -1$

Evaluate each expression.

1. $\log_4 64$ **3**   2. $\log_2 64$ **6**   3. $\log_{10} 100{,}000$ **5**

4. $\log_5 625$ **4**   5. $\log_3 27$ **3**   6. $\log_{11} 121$ **2**

Solve each equation.

7. $\log_5 m = 4$ **625**   8. $\log_2 32 = 3x$ $\frac{5}{3}$ 9. $\log_3 2c = -2$ $\frac{1}{18}$

10. $\log_4 (3x - 1) = \log_4 (2x + 3)$ **4**   11. $\log_7 (x^2 - 6) = \log_7 (2x + 2)$ **4, -2**

Chapter 12 555

Checking for Understanding

Exercises 1–17 are designed to help you assess understanding through reading, writing, and speaking. You should work through Exercises 1–5 with your students, and then monitor their work on Exercises 6–17.

Closing the Lesson

Speaking Activity   Have students define number, base, and logarithm as they apply to exponential and logarithmic equations.

APPLYING THE LESSON

Homework Exercises

Assignment Guide

Basic: 18–44, 49–50, 52–58
Average: 24–58
Enriched: 24–58

Chapter 12, Quiz A, (Lessons 12-1 through 12-2), is available in the Evaluation Masters Booklet, p. 163.

Practice Masters Booklet, p. 89

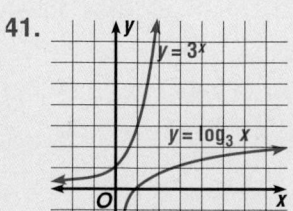

12-2 **Practice Worksheet**

Logarithms and Logarithmic Functions

Write each equation in logarithmic form.

1. $5^3 = 125$ $\log_5 125 = 3$ 2. $27^{\frac{4}{3}} = 81$ $\log_{27} 81 = \frac{4}{3}$

Write each equation in exponential form.

3. $\log_{10} 0.00001 = -5$ $10^{-5} = 0.00001$ 4. $\log_{\frac{3}{2}} \frac{\sqrt{6}}{3} = -\frac{1}{2}$ $\left(\frac{3}{2}\right)^{-\frac{1}{2}} = \frac{\sqrt{6}}{3}$

Evaluate each expression.

5. $\log_3 81$ **4**   6. $\log_{10} 0.0001$ **−4**

7. $\log_2 \frac{1}{16}$ **−4**   8. $\log_3 27$ **−3**

9. $\log_9 1$ **0**   10. $\log_8 4$ **$\frac{2}{3}$**

Solve each equation.

11. $\log_4 x = \frac{3}{2}$ **8**   12. $\log_n 16 = -4$ **$\frac{1}{2}$**

13. $\log_{\frac{1}{8}} = -3$ **2**   14. $\log_7 n = -\frac{1}{2}$ **$\frac{\sqrt{7}}{7}$**

15. $\log_{\sqrt{5}} y = \frac{4}{3}$ **$5^{\frac{2}{3}}$ or $\sqrt[3]{25}$**   16. $\log_n \sqrt[6]{9} = \frac{1}{6}$ **81**

17. $\log_5 (3x + 7) = \log_5 (7x + 4)$ **$\frac{3}{4}$**   18. $\log_7 (8x + 20) = \log_7 (x + 6)$ **−2**

19. $\log_3 (9x - 1) = \log_3 (4x - 16)$ **no solution**   20. $\log_{12}(x - 9) = \log_{12}(3x - 13)$ **no solution**

21. $\log_6 (x^2 - 30) = \log_6 6$ **±6**   22. $\log_4 (x^2 + 6) = \log_4 5x$ **2, 3**

CHECKING FOR UNDERSTANDING

Communicating Mathematics

1. the logarithm, base 2, of x

Read and study the lesson to answer these questions.

1. In the equation $2^y = x$, what is the exponent y called?

2. Give an example of a logarithmic function. **Sample answer:** $y = \log_2 x$.

3. The principal of Fairborn High School needed to contact each member of the Booster Association. She estimated that by using the network method to have each person call 4 people in ten minutes, each member could be contacted in one-half hour. How many members will be contacted in the last round of calls? **64**

4. In your own words, write a definition of a logarithm. **Answers may vary.**

5. How much stronger is an earthquake with a Richter scale rating of 7 than an aftershock with a rating of 4? **10^3 or 1000 times stronger**

Guided Practice   Write each equation in logarithmic form.

6. $2^3 = 8$ $\log_2 8 = 3$

7. $10^3 = 1000$ $\log_{10} 1000 = 3$

8. $6^{-3} = \frac{1}{216}$ $\log_6 \frac{1}{216} = -3$

Write each equation in exponential form.

9. $\log_2 64 = 6$ $2^6 = 64$

10. $\log_{10} 0.01 = -2$ $10^{-2} = 0.01$

11. $\log_9 27 = \frac{3}{2}$ $9^{\frac{3}{2}} = 27$

Solve each equation.

12. $\log_8 y = -2$ **$\frac{1}{64}$**

13. $\log_b 81 = 4$ **3**

14. $\log_{12} \frac{1}{12} = x$ **−1**

15. $\log_b 64 = 6$ **2**

16. $\log_{10} \frac{1}{1000} = x$ **−3**

17. $\log_4 y = 4$ **256**

EXERCISES

Practice

A

Evaluate each expression.

18. $\log_{10} 10000$ **4**   19. $\log_4 16$ **2**   20. $\log_{13} 169$ **2**

21. $\log_8 \frac{1}{64}$ **−2**   22. $\log_3 \frac{1}{243}$ **−5**   23. $\log_{25} 5$ **$\frac{1}{2}$**

Solve each equation.

24. $\log_{\frac{1}{2}} 8 = x$ **−3**   25. $\log_3 729 = x$ **6**   26. $\log_b 81 = 2$ **9**

B

27. $\log_3 y = 2$ **9**   28. $\log_5 x = -1$ **$\frac{1}{5}$**   29. $\log_b 18 = 1$ **18**

30. $\log_b 81 = 4$ **3**   31. $\log_5 x = -2$ **$\frac{1}{25}$**   32. $\log_3 (4 + y) = \log_3 (2y)$ **4**

556   CHAPTER 12   EXPONENTIAL AND LOGARITHMIC FUNCTIONS

Additional Answers

41.   42.   43.

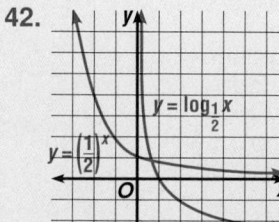

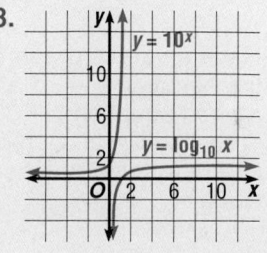

33. $\log_5 (2x - 3) = \log_5 (x + 2)$ **5**
34. $\log_8 (3y - 1) = \log_8 (y + 4)$ **2.5**
35. $\log_9 (5x - 1) = \log_9 (3x + 7)$ **4**
36. $\log_{10} (x - 1)^2 = \log_{10} 0.01$
37. $\log_2 (x^2 + 6x) = \log_2 (x - 4)$
38. $\log_{12} (7x - 3) = \log_{12} (5 - x^2)$ **1**
39. $\log_{10} (x^2 + 36) = \log_{10} 100$ **±8**
40. $\log_9 (x^2 + 9x) = \log_9 10$ **1, –10**

Graph each pair of equations on the same set of axes. **See margin.**

41. $y = \log_3 x$ and $y = 3^x$
42. $y = \log_{\frac{1}{2}} x$ and $y = \left(\frac{1}{2}\right)^x$
43. $y = 10^x$ and $y = \log_{10} x$
44. $y = 4^x$ and $y = \log_4 x$

C Show that each statement is true. **See margin.**

45. $\log_4 4 + \log_4 16 = \log_4 64$
46. $\log_4 16 = 2 \log_4 4$
47. $\log_2 8 \cdot \log_8 2 = 1$
48. $\log_{10} [\log_3 (\log_4 64)] = 0$

Critical Thinking

49. Show that $f(x) = \log_b x$ and $g(x) = b^x$ are inverse functions. **See margin.**

Applications

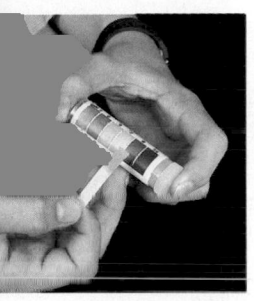

50. **Chemistry** The pH of a solution is a measure of its acidity. A low pH indicates an acidic solution, and a high pH indicates a basic solution. Neutral water has a pH of 7. The pH of a solution is related to the concentration of hydrogen ions by the formula pH $= \log_{10} \dfrac{1}{H^+}$, where H^+ represents the hydrogen atoms in gram atoms per liter. If the pH of a solution is 4, what is the concentration of hydrogen ions?
0.0001 gram atoms per liter

51. **Biology** An amoeba divides into two amoebas once every hour. How long would it take for a single amoeba to become a colony of 4096 amoebas? **12 hours**

Mixed Review

52. Simplify the expression $11^{\sqrt{5}} \cdot 11^{\sqrt{45}}$. **(Lesson 12-1)** $11^{4\sqrt{5}}$

53. Find the greatest common factor of the numerator and the denominator of $\dfrac{3x + 15}{9x + 45}$. Then simplify the expression. **(Lesson 11-1)** $x + 5; \dfrac{1}{3}$

54. State the number of positive real zeros, negative real zeros, and complex zeros for the function $f(x) = -x^3 + x^2 - x + 1$. **(Lesson 10-4)**

55. Find the vertices, foci, and slopes of the asymptotes for the hyperbola whose equation is $36y^2 - 81x^2 = 2916$. **(Lesson 9-5)**

56. State the sum and product of the roots of the quadratic equation $x^2 - 18x - 120 = 0$. **(Lesson 7-5)** **18, –120**

57. Find the product of $3 - 7i$ and its conjugate. **(Lesson 6-10)** **58**

58. The sum of the digits of a three-digit number is 22. The tens digit exceeds the hundreds digit by 1. When the digits are reversed, the new number is 297 greater than the original number. Find the number. **(Lesson 3-9)** **679**

EXTENDING THE LESSON

Math Power: Connections

Have students research radiocarbon dating. Have them write a short report on the subject, relating their findings to exponential functions and logarithms.

 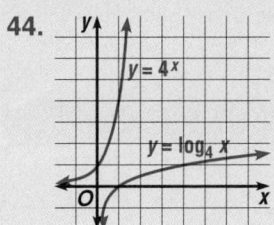
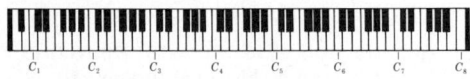

Lesson Resources

Reteaching Master 12-3
Practice Master 12-3
Enrichment Master 12-3

 Transparency 12-3 contains the 5-Minute Check and a teaching aid for this lesson.

INTRODUCING THE LESSON

🕐 5-Minute Check

(over Lesson 12-2)

Evaluate.

1. $\log_5 x = 3$ **125**
2. $\log_a \frac{1}{9} = -2$ **3**
3. Write $\log_4 64 = 3$ in exponential form.   **$4^3 = 64$**

Solve.

4. $\log_5 (4x) = \log_5 (x^2 - 5)$ **5**
5. $\log_6 (4x + 7) = \log_6 (6x - 9)$ **8**

Motivating the Lesson

Show students pictures of several severe earthquakes along with the magnitude of each quake on the Richter Scale. Tell students that the magnitude readings are base ten logarithms, and ask students if they know how the magnitudes can be compared.

TEACHING THE LESSON

Teaching Tip **❶**   As background, tell students that all rain is slightly acidic. Neutral water dissolves nitrogen and carbon oxides in the air, forming weak acids. These weak acids do not harm the environment.

12-3 Properties of Logarithms

Objective
12-3

After studying this lesson, you should be able to:
- solve equations or simplify and evaluate expressions using properties of logarithms.

Teaching Tip ❶

Application

FYI ...

A large portion of the acid rain is a result of the burning of fossil fuels. Finding other sources of energy will help solve the problem.

Acid rain is a serious problem in many parts of the world. It raises the pH level of lakes and streams, killing fish and other waterlife. The pH scale measures acidity and is a logarithmic scale. Lower pH numbers represent acids, and higher pH numbers represent bases. Acid rain has a pH of about 4.2, while neutral water has a pH of 7. So, acid rain is about 630 times more acidic than neutral water, since $10^{7-4.2} \approx 630$. The pH scale is an example of a logarithmic scale.

Since logarithms are exponents, the properties of logarithms can be derived from the properties of exponents that you already know.

The product of powers is found by adding exponents. So it makes sense that the logarithm of a product is found by adding the logarithms.

a. $\log_3 (9 \cdot 27)$
$= \log_3 (3^2 \cdot 3^3)$
$= \log_3 (3^{2+3})$
$= 2 + 3$

b. $\log_3 9 + \log_3 27$
$= \log_3 3^2 + \log_3 3^3$
$= 2 + 3$

So, $\log_3 (9 \cdot 27) = \log_3 9 + \log_3 27$. This illustrates the following property.

Product Property of Logarithms	For all positive numbers m, n and b, where $b \neq 1$, $\log_b mn = \log_b m + \log_b n$.

To prove this property, let $b^x = m$ and $b^y = n$.
Then $\log_b m = x$ and $\log_b n = y$.

$b^x b^y = mn$
$b^{x+y} = mn$ *Property of exponents*
$\log_b b^{x+y} = \log_b mn$ *Property of equality for logarithmic functions*
$x + y = \log_b mn$ *Definition of inverse functions*
$\log_b m + \log_b n = \log_b mn$ *Substitution property*

Example 1

Given $\log_2 5 = 2.322$, find each logarithm.

a. $\log_2 20 = \log_2 (2^2 \cdot 5)$
$= \log_2 2^2 + \log_2 5$
$= 2 + 2.322$ or 4.322

b. $\log_2 25 = \log_2 (5 \cdot 5)$
$= \log_2 5 + \log_2 5$
$= 2.322 + 2.322$ or 4.644

558   CHAPTER 12   EXPONENTIAL AND LOGARITHMIC FUNCTIONS

ALTERNATE TEACHING STRATEGIES

Mini-Math Lab

Provide students with some pH paper with a comparison pH chart and several different liquids, such as distilled water, tap water, pond water, and dilute solutions of baking soda and vinegar.

For each liquid, have students determine the pH. From the pH values, have students determine how much more acidic the lowest pH is than the highest pH.

To find the quotient of powers, you subtract the exponents. So, to find the logarithm of a quotient, you subtract logarithms.

a. $\log_3\left(\dfrac{81}{27}\right) = \log_3\left(\dfrac{3^4}{3^3}\right)$ **b.** $\log_3 81 - \log_3 27 = \log_3 3^4 - \log_3 3^3$
$= \log_3 (3^{4-3})$ $= 4 - 3$
$= 4 - 3$

So, $\log_3\left(\dfrac{81}{27}\right) = \log_3 81 - \log_3 27$. This illustrates the following property.

Quotient Property of Logarithms	For all positive numbers m, n, and b, where $b \neq 1$, $$\log_b \frac{m}{n} = \log_b m - \log_b n.$$

To prove this property, let $b^x = m$ and $b^y = n$.
Then $\log_b m = x$ and $\log_b n = y$.

$\dfrac{b^x}{b^y} = \dfrac{m}{n}$

$b^{x-y} = \dfrac{m}{n}$ *Property of exponents*

$\log_b b^{x-y} = \log_b \dfrac{m}{n}$ *Property of equality for logarithmic functions*

$x - y = \log_b \dfrac{m}{n}$ *Definition of inverse functions*

$\log_b m - \log_b n = \log_b \dfrac{m}{n}$ *Substitution property*

The following example illustrates the quotient property of equality for logarithms.

Example 2

APPLICATION

Chemistry

The pH of a solution is related to the number of gram atoms of hydrogen ions, H^+, by the formula $pH = \log_{10} \dfrac{1}{H+}$. If the pH level of a lake is 5, how much more acidic is it than neutral water, that has a pH of 7?

The pH of neutral water is 7. Since $\log_{10}\left(\dfrac{1}{10^{-7}}\right) = 7$, there are 10^{-7} gram atoms of hydrogen ions in a liter of neutral water. Similarly, since $\log_{10}\left(\dfrac{1}{10^{-5}}\right) = 5$, there 10^{-5} gram atoms of hydrogen ions in a liter of the lake water. If we divide these two numbers, we will find how much stronger the lake water is than neutral water.

$x = \dfrac{10^{-5}}{10^{-7}}$

$\log_{10} x = \log_{10} \dfrac{10^{-5}}{10^{-7}}$

$\log_{10} x = \log_{10} 10^{-5} - \log_{10} 10^{-7}$ **Check:** $x = \dfrac{10^{-5}}{10^{-7}}$

$\log_{10} x = -5 - (-7)$ $= 10^{-5-(-7)}$

$\log_{10} x = 2$ $= 10^2$

$x = 100$ $= 100\checkmark$

So the lake water is 100 times more acidic than the neutral water.

Example 3

Given $\log_{12} 9 = 0.884$ and $\log_{12} 18 = 1.163$, find each logarithm.

a. $\log_{12} \left(\frac{3}{4}\right)$

$$\log_{12} \left(\frac{3}{4}\right) = \log_{12} \left(\frac{9}{12}\right)$$
$$= \log_{12} 9 - \log_{12} 12$$
$$= 0.884 - 1$$
$$= -0.116$$

b. $\log_{12} 2$

$$\log_{12} 2 = \log_{12} \left(\frac{18}{9}\right)$$
$$= \log_{12} 18 - \log_{12} 9$$
$$= 1.163 - 0.884$$
$$= 0.279$$

The quotient property can be used to solve equations involving logarithms.

Example 4

Solve $\log_5 4 + \log_5 x = \log_5 36$.

$$\log_5 4 + \log_5 x = \log_5 36$$
$$\log_5 x = \log_5 36 - \log_5 4$$
$$\log_5 x = \log_5 \left(\frac{36}{4}\right) \quad \textit{Quotient property of logarithms}$$
$$\log_5 x = \log_5 9$$
$$x = 9 \quad \textit{Property of equality for logarithmic functions}$$

The power of a power is found by multiplying the two exponents. This suggests that the logarithm of a power is found by multiplying the logarithm and the exponent.

a. $\log_3 9^4$
$$= \log_3 (3^2)^4$$
$$= \log_3 3^{2 \cdot 4}$$
$$= 2 \cdot 4$$

b. $4 \log_3 9$
$$= (\log_3 9) \cdot 4$$
$$= (\log_3 3^2) \cdot 4$$
$$= 2 \cdot 4$$

So, $\log_3 9^4 = 4 \log_3 9$. This suggests the following property.

Power Property of Logarithms	For any real number p and positive numbers m and b where $b \neq 1$, $\log_b m^p = p \cdot \log_b m$.

In exercise 3, you will prove this property. Examples 5 and 6 illustrate how to use this property to solve equations involving logarithms.

Example 5

Solve $2 \log_6 4 - \frac{1}{3} \log_6 8 = \log_6 x$.

$$2 \log_6 4 - \frac{1}{3} \log_6 8 = \log_6 x$$
$$\log_6 4^2 - \log_6 8^{\frac{1}{3}} = \log_6 x \quad \textit{Power property of logarithms}$$
$$\log_6 16 - \log_6 2 = \log_6 x$$
$$\log_6 \left(\frac{16}{2}\right) = \log_6 x \quad \textit{Quotient property of logarithms}$$
$$\log_6 8 = \log_6 x$$
$$8 = x \quad \textit{Property of equality for logarithmic functions}$$

560   CHAPTER 12   EXPONENTIAL AND LOGARITHMIC FUNCTIONS

Example 6

Solve $\log_4 (x + 2) + \log_4 (x - 4) = 2$.

$$\log_4 (x + 2) + \log_4 (x - 4) = 2$$

$\log_4 (x + 2)(x - 4) = 2$ *Product property of logarithms*

$(x + 2)(x - 4) = 4^2$ *Definition of logarithm*

$$x^2 - 2x - 8 = 16$$
$$x^2 - 2x - 24 = 0$$
$$(x - 6)(x + 4) = 0$$
$$x - 6 = 0 \quad \text{or} \quad x + 4 = 0$$
$$x = 6 \quad \text{or} \quad x = -4$$

Check: $\log_4 (x + 2) + \log_4 (x - 4) = 2$ $\log_4 (x + 2) + \log_4 (x - 4) = 2$

$\log_4 (6 + 2) + \log_4 (6 - 4) = 2$ $\log_4 (-4 + 2) + \log_4 (-4 - 4) = 2$

$\log_4 8 + \log_4 2 = 2$ $\log_4 (-2) + \log_4 (-8) = 2$

$\log_4 16 = 2$ *Both $\log_4 (-2)$ and $\log_4 (-8)$ are*

$2 = 2\surd$ *undefined, so -4 is not a solution.*

The only solution is 6.

CHECKING FOR UNDERSTANDING

Communicating Mathematics

Read and study the lesson to answer these questions.

1. Does the more acidic of two solutions have a higher or lower pH? **lower**
2. Show that the acid rain described at the beginning of the lesson is about 630 times as acidic as neutral water. **See margin.**
3. Prove the power property of logarithms. **See margin.**

Guided Practice

Express each logarithm as the sum or difference of simpler logarithmic expressions.

4. $\log_8 x^3 y$ 5. $\log_5 (xy)^2$ 6. $\log_4 \dfrac{ab}{c}$ 7. $\log_2 rt^{\frac{1}{2}}$

$3 \log_8 x + \log_8 y$ $2 \log_5 x + 2 \log_5 y$ $\log_4 a + \log_4 b -$ $\log_2 r + \dfrac{1}{2} \log_2 t$

Evaluate each expression. $\log_4 c$

8. $8^{\log_8 3 + \log_8 2}$ **6**   9. $10^{4 \log_{10} 2}$ **16**   10. $9^{\log_9 12 - \log_9 4}$ **3**

Solve each equation.

11. $\log_3 7 + \log_3 x = \log_3 14$ **2**   12. $\log_2 10 - \log_2 t = \log_2 2$ **5**

EXERCISES

Practice

Use $\log_2 3 = 1.585$ and $\log_2 7 = 2.807$ to evaluate each expression.

13. $\log_2 49$ **5.614**   14. $\log_2 27$ **4.755**   15. $\log_2 \dfrac{7}{3}$ **1.222**

16. $\log_2 36$ **5.170**   17. $\log_2 0.75$ **−0.415**   18. $\log_2 48$ **5.585**

19. $\log_2 108$ **6.755**   20. $\log_2 \dfrac{36}{49}$ **−0.444**   21. $\log_2 \dfrac{7}{16}$ **−1.193**

Additional Answer

3. To prove this property, let $b^x = m$. Then $\log_b m = x$.

$$(b^x)^p = m^p$$
$b^{xp} = m^p$ **Power property of exponents**

$\log_b b^{xp} = \log_b m^p$ **Property of equality for logarithmic functions**

$xp = \log_b m^p$ **Definition of inverse functions**

$p \log_b m = \log_b m^p$ **Substitution property**

562 Chapter 12

Closing the Lesson

Speaking Activity Have students explain why $\log_5 8^2$ is equivalent to $2 \log_5 8$.

APPLYING THE LESSON

Homework Exercises

Assignment Guide
Basic: 13–37, 42–48
Average: 16–39, 42–48
Enriched: 19–48

Enrichment Masters Booklet, p. 79

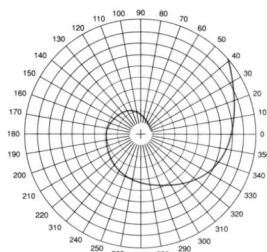

 Solve each equation.

22. $\log_2 3 + \log_2 7 = \log_2 x$ **21**

23. $\log_3 56 - \log_3 8 = \log_3 x$ **7**

24. $\log_3 14 + \log_3 y = \log_3 42$ **3**

25. $\log_9 x = \frac{1}{2} \log_9 144 - \frac{1}{3} \log_9 8$ **6**

26. $\log_{10} m = \frac{1}{2} \log_{10} 81$ **9**

27. $\log_7 m = \frac{1}{3} \log_7 64 + \frac{1}{2} \log_7 121$ **44**

28. 14 28. $\log_{10} 7 + \log_{10} (n - 2) = \log_{10} 6n$ 29. $3 \log_{10} x = \log_{10} 27$ **3**

30. 1 30. $\log_{10} (m + 3) - \log_{10} m = \log_{10} 4$ 31. $2 \log_3 x + \log_3 0.1 = \log_3 5 + \log_3 2$

31. 10 32. $3 \log_5 x - \log_5 4 = \log_5 16$ **4** 33. $\log_2 15 + \log_2 14 - \log_2 105 = \log_2 x$ **2**

34. $\log_{10} y + \log_{10} (y + 21) = 2$ **4** 35. $\log_4 (x + 3) + \log_4 (x - 3) = 2$ **5**

36. $\log_2 (y + 2) - 1 = \log_2 (y - 2)$ **6** 37. $\log_8 (n + 1) - \log_8 n = \log_8 4$ **$\frac{1}{3}$**

Solve for a. 38. $\frac{y}{3} + 1$

38. $\log_n a = \log_n (y + 3) - \log_n 3$

39. $\log_b 2a - \log_b x^3 = \log_b x$ **$\frac{x^4}{2}$**

40. $\log_x a^2 + 5 \log_x y = \log_x a$ **$\frac{1}{y^5}$**

41. $\log_b 4 + 2 \log_b a = 2 \log_b (n + 1)$
$\frac{1}{2}[n + 1]$

Critical Thinking

42. Explain why 1 is excluded from the possible values for b in each of the three properties you learned in this lesson. **Sample answer: Logarithms are undefined for base 1. If 1 were allowed, there would be multiple answers.**

Applications

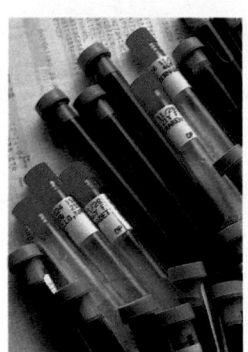

43. **Medicine** The pH of a person's blood can be found by using the Henderson-Hasselbach formula. The formula is pH $= 6.1 + \log_{10}\left(\frac{B}{C}\right)$, where B represents the concentration of bicarbonate, which is a base, and C represents the concentration of carbonic acid, which is acidic. Most people have a blood pH of about 7.4.

   a. Rewrite the formula to eliminate the logarithm of a quotient.
   pH $= 6.1 + \log_{10} B - \log_{10} C$

   b. As you know, a pH of 7 is neutral and lower pH numbers represent acidic solutions. The pH levels higher than 7 represent basic solutions. Is blood normally an acid, a base, or neutral? **a very weak base**

   c. If you have a scientific calculator, it will find logarithms base 10. Use your calculator to find the pH of a persons blood if the concentration of bicarbonate is 25 and the concentration of carbonic acid is 2. **7.197**

Mixed Review

44. Solve the equation $\log_{10} (3n) = \log_{10} (n + 2)$. **(Lesson 12-2) 1**

45. If $f = \{(0, 2), (1, 1), (3, 3), (4, -1)\}$ and $g = \{(0, 0), (1, 1), (2, 4), (3, 9)\}$, find $f \circ g$ and $g \circ f$ if they exist. **(Lesson 10-7) neither exist**

46. $4 \pm i\sqrt{6}$ 46. Use the quadratic formula to solve $x^2 - 8x + 22 = 0$. **(Lesson 7-4)**

47. Factor $3pq + 3ps + q^2 - s^2$. **(Lesson 5-5) $(q + s)(3p + q - s)$**

48. Solve the inequality $|x + 3| + |x - 3| > 8$. **(Lesson 1-8)**
$\{x|x > 4 \text{ or } x < -4\}$

562 CHAPTER 12 EXPONENTIAL AND LOGARITHMIC FUNCTIONS

EXTENDING THE LESSON

Math Power: Problem Solving

Solve $\frac{1}{2} \log_b (x + 2) + \frac{1}{2} \log_b (x - 22) = \frac{2}{3} \log_b 27$. **25**

Common Logarithms

Objectives
After studying this lesson, you should be able to:
12-4A ▪ identify the characteristic and the mantissa of a logarithm, and
12-4B ▪ find common logarithms and antilogarithms.

Logarithms can make certain computations easier. When logarithms are used, multiplication changes to addition and division changes to subtraction. For this reason, logarithms were used quite extensively for calculations before calculators became readily available. The most useful logarithms are base 10, since our number system is base 10. Base 10 logarithms are called **common logarithms.** These are usually written without the subscript 10, so $\log_{10} x$ is written as $\log x$.

Let's find the common logarithm of a number and explore common logarithms. Expressing a number in scientific notation is helpful when working with common logarithms.

Example 1

Given that log 8.1 = 0.9085, find the value of log 81,000.

$81,000 = 8.1 \times 10^4$ *Express 81,000 using scientific notation.*

$\log 81,000 = \log (8.1 \times 10^4)$
$= \log 8.1 + \log 10^4$
$= 0.9085 + 4$
$= 4.9085$

The log of 81,000 is 4.9085.   *Verify this with your calculator.*
Is $10^{4.9085} = 81,000$?

Teaching Tip ❶

Now look closely at the result of Example 1, 4.9085. It, like all common logarithms, is made up of two parts, the **characteristic** and the **mantissa.** The mantissa is the logarithm of a number between 1 and 10, in the case of Example 1 that number is 0.9085. The characteristic is the exponent of ten that is used when the number is expressed in scientific notation. In Example 1, the characteristic is 4.

$\log 81,000 = 4.9085$

characteristic   *mantissa*

The mantissa is the decimal post of a logarithm.

The mantissa is usually expressed as a positive number. This makes using a table of logarithms much easier. So to avoid negative mantissas, we rewrite the negative mantissa as the difference of a positive number and an integer, usually 10.

ALTERNATE TEACHING STRATEGIES

Using Calculators

Many students are quite proficient in general calculator use but have never used the [LOG] key to determine logarithms or antilogarithms. Using Examples 2 and 3, supervise students to be sure they understand how to use the calculator to determine common logarithms and antilogarithms. Provide additional practice, if needed.

Lesson Resources

Reteaching Master 12-4
Practice Master 12-4
Enrichment Master 12-4
Technology Master, p. 12

 Transparency 12-4 contains the 5-Minute Check and a teaching aid for this lesson.

INTRODUCING THE LESSON

⏱ 5-Minute Check

(over Lesson 12-3)
Solve.

1. $\log_4 48 - \log_4 x = \log_4 6$ **8**
2. $2 \log_7 3 + 3 \log_7 2 = \log_7 x$ **72**
3. $\log_4 (x + 2) + \log_4 (x - 4) = 2$ **6**

Other Prerequisite Skills

Express in scientific notation.
4. 8,130,000   **8.13×10^6**
5. 0.0325   **3.25×10^{-2}**

Motivating the Lesson

Show a pH meter or a picture of one to the students. Explain that the meter can measure pH more accurately than can pH paper. Ask students the following question. If a pH meter measures a pH to be 8.4, is there a way to determine how many hydrogen ions there are?

TEACHING THE LESSON

Teaching Tip ❶ You may want to use a calculator to reinforce the relationship between a number expressed in scientific notation and the characteristic of the logarithm of the number. Have the students find the logarithms of 5.94, 59.4, 594, and 5940 and compare the characteristics.

Example 2

Use your calculator to find log 0.0027. Write the result with a positive
mantissa. *If you do not have a scientific calculator, see the Appendix.*

The LOG key is used to find common logarithms.

ENTER: 0.0027 LOG ⁻2.5686362

The value of log 0.0027 is approximately −2.5686.

To write the logarithm with a positive mantissa, add and subtract 10.

(−2.5686 + 10) − 10 = 7.4314 − 10   *10 − 10 = 0 and a + 0 = a.*

The characteristic of the logarithm is 7 − 10 or −3. Thus, the mantissa is
0.4314.

Sometimes an application of logarithms requires that you use the inverse
of logarithms, exponentiation. When you are given a logarithm and asked to
find the number, you are finding the **antilogarithm.** That is, if log x = a,
then x = antilog a.

Example 3

Find the antilogarithm of 2.579 using a calculator.

To find an antilogarithm on your calculator, use the 10ˣ key. *If your
calculator does not have a 10ˣ key, use the INV key and then the LOG key.*

ENTER: 2.579 10ˣ = 379.31498

The antilogarithm of 2.579 is approximately 379.

Example 4

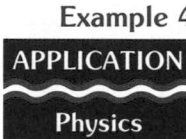

Physics

The intensity of sound in decibels, I_d, is related to
the intensity of sound in watts per square meter,
I, by the formula $I_d = 10 \log \dfrac{I}{10^{-12}}$. Sound
waves whose intensities reach more than 1 W/m^2
can cause damage to a person's hearing. If
the sound at a recent concert reached
110 decibels, were the listeners in danger of causing
damage to their hearing?

Use antilogarithms to find the value of I in the equation $I_d = 10 \log \dfrac{I}{10^{-12}}$.

$$I_d = 10 \log \frac{I}{10^{-12}}$$

$$110 = 10 \log \frac{I}{10^{-12}} \qquad \textit{Substitute 110 for } I_d.$$

$$11 = \log \frac{I}{10^{-12}} \qquad \textit{Divide each side by 10.}$$

$$\text{antilog } 11 = \text{antilog}\left(\log \frac{I}{10^{-12}}\right) \quad \textit{Take the antilogarithm of each side.}$$

$$10^{11} = \frac{I}{10^{-12}} \quad \textit{Definition of antilogarithm}$$

$$10^{11} \cdot 10^{-12} = I \quad \textit{Multiply each side by } 10^{-12}.$$

$$0.1 = I$$

The intensity of the music was 0.1 W/m^2, which is less than 1, so there was no danger of causing damage to their hearing.

CHECKING FOR UNDERSTANDING

Communicating Mathematics

Read and study the lesson to answer these questions.

1. What function are you performing when you take the antilogarithm of a value, such as x? **raising 10 to this power: antilog $x = 10^x$**

2. What base does the calculator key use? What are these logarithms called? **10; common logarithms**

3. For what values do you think the logarithms are programmed into calculators so that the value of any function using logarithms can be found? **logarithms of numbers $1 \le x < 10$ (the mantissas)**

Guided Practice

If log 573 = 2.7582, find each number.

4. characteristic of log 573 **2**   5. log 5.73 **0.7582**

If log 0.023 = -1.6383, find each number.

6. mantissa of log 0.023 **0.3617**   7. antilog 0.3617 **2.3**

EXERCISES

Practice

Use a calculator to find the logarithm of each number, rounded to four decimal places. Then state the characteristic.

 A

8. 53.7 **1.7300; 1**   9. 800.2 **2.9032; 2**   10. 2.25 **0.3522; 0**

11. 0.057 **-1.2441; -2**   12. 4.322 **0.6357; 0**   13. 0.295 **-0.5302; -1**

Use a calculator to find the antilogarithm of each logarithm, rounded to four decimal places.

14. 0.2586 **1.814**   15. 2.2249 **167.8**   16. 1.0024 **10.06**

B

17. -0.2586 **0.5513**   18. -2.0112 **0.0097**   19. -1.9725 **0.0107**

20. 8.1342 − 10 **0.0136**   21. 2.2675 − 3 **0.1851**   22. 4.9243 **84,000**

LESSON 12-4   COMMON LOGARITHMS   565

Closing the Lesson

Writing Activity Have students explain the difference in logarithms and antilogarithms.

APPLYING THE LESSON

Homework Exercises

See assignment guide on page 565.

Chapter 12, Quiz B, (Lessons 12-3 through 12-4), is available in the Evaluation Masters Booklet, p. 163.

Additional Answer

32. **Since calculators use logarithms, finding $(-3)^3$ would proceed as follows.**

$$x = (-3)^3$$
$$\log x = \log [(-3)^3]$$
$$\log x = 3 \log (-3)$$

Since the logarithm of -3 is undefined, the calculator sends an error message.

Enrichment Masters Booklet, p. 80

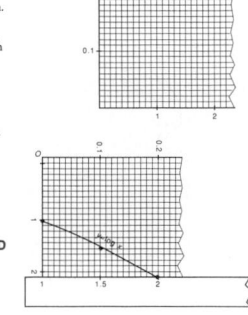

12-4 **Enrichment Worksheet**
NAME _____ DATE _____

The Slide Rule

Before the invention of electronic calculators, computations were often performed on a slide rule. A slide rule is based on the idea of logarithms. It has two movable rods labeled with C and D scales. Each of the scales is logarithmic.

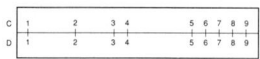

To multiply 2×3 on a slide rule, move the C rod to the right as shown below. You can find 2×3 by adding log 2 to log 3, and the slide rule adds the lengths for you. The distance you get is 0.788, or the logarithm of 6.

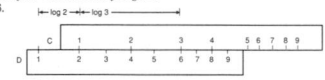

Follow the steps to make a slide rule.

1. Use graph paper that has small squares, such as 10 squares to the inch. Using the scales shown at the right, plot the curve $y = \log x$ for $x = 1, 1.5$, and the whole numbers from 2 through 10. Make an obvious heavy dot for each point plotted.

2. You will need two strips of cardboard. A 5-by-7 index card, cut in half the long way, will work fine. Turn the graph you made in problem 1 sideways and use it to mark a logarithmic scale on each of the two strips. The figures show the mark for 2 being drawn.

3. Explain how to use the slide rule to divide 8 by 2.
Line up the 2 on the C scale with the 8 on the D scale. The quotient is the number on the D scale below the 1 on the C scale.

Use a calculator to find the logarithm of each number, rounded to four decimal places. Then state the characteristic and the mantissa.

23. 98.29 **1.9925, 1, 0.9925**
24. 13.54 **1.1316, 1, 0.1316**
25. 827.1 **2.9156, 2, 0.9156**
26. 10^{-7} **-7, -7, 0**
27. 5.4265
28. 0.265
29. 0.005 **-2.3010, -3, 0.6990**
30. 6678 **3.8246, 3, 0.8246**
31. 1000 **3, 3, 0**

27. **0.7345, 0, 0.7345**
28. **-0.5768, -1, 0.4232**

Critical Thinking

32. Try to find $(-3)^3$ on your calculator. Some calculators will say "ERROR", even though $(-3)^3 = -27$. Can you think of a reason why they might do this? **See margin.**

33a. $10^{5.3}$ **or about 199,526 times more intense**

Applications

33. **Seismology** As you know, the Richter scale is a logarithmic scale. An earthquake that measures 6 on the Richter scale is 10^6 times as intense as the weakest earthquake perceptible by a seismograph.
   a. How much more intense is an earthquake that measures 5.3 on the Richter scale than the weakest perceptible earthquake?
   b. How much more intense was the San Francisco earthquake of 1989, a 6.9 on the Richter scale, than its strongest after shock, a 4.3 on the Richter scale? $10^{6.9-4.3} = 10^{2.6}$ **or about 398 times stronger**

Mixed Review

34. Solve the equation $2 \log_6 3 + 3 \log_6 2 = \log_6 x$. **(Lesson 12-3) 72**

35. If y varies inversely as x and when $y = 5$, $x = -2$, then find x when $y = 15$. **(Lesson 11-2)** $-\frac{2}{3}$

36. Find all zeros for the function $f(x) = 2x^3 + 9x^2 - 20x - 75$. **(Lesson 10-3)** $3, -5, -\frac{5}{2}$

37. State the dimension and evaluate the determinant (if one exists) for the matrix $\begin{bmatrix} 5 & 12 \\ 0 & -4 \end{bmatrix}$. **(Lesson 4-1)** $2 \times 2; -20$

~~~ MID-CHAPTER REVIEW ~~~

Solve each equation. **(Lesson 12-1)**

1. $12^5 = 12^{2x+1}$ **2**
2. $3^{x+3} = \frac{1}{81}$ **-7**
3. $5^{x^2-3} = 25^x$ **3, -1**

Evaluate each expression. **(Lesson 12-2)**

4. $\log_{10} 100$ **2**
5. $\log_{36} 6$ $\frac{1}{2}$
6. $\log_5 \frac{1}{125}$ **-3**

Solve each equation. **(Lesson 12-3)**

7. $\log_6 8 + \log_6 3 = \log_6 x$ **24**
8. $3 \log_2 x = \log_2 512$ **8**
9. $\log_2 (9x + 5) - \log_2 (x^2 - 1) = 2$ **3**

Use a calculator to find each value, round to four decimal places. **(Lesson 12-4)**

10. $\log 229$ **2.3598**
11. antilog -0.0951 **0.8033**
12. antilog $0.7935 - 3$ **0.0062**

13. **Seismology** The earthquake that occurred in San Francisco in 1989 registered a 6.9 on the Richter scale. In 1906, an earthquake occurred in San Francisco that is estimated to have registered an 8.3 on the Richter scale. How much more intense was the 1906 earthquake? **(Lesson 12-4)** $10^{8.3-6.9} = 10^{1.4}$ **or about 25 times more intense**

EXTENDING THE LESSON

Math Power: Communication

Have each student work with a partner to explain to each other how to solve $(x - 3) \log x \geq 0$. Then solve the inequality.
$0 < x \leq 1$ or $x \geq 3$

Mid-Chapter Review

The Mid-Chapter Review provides students with a brief review of the concepts and skills in Lessons 12-1 through 12-4. Lesson numbers are given at the end of problems or instruction lines so students may review concepts not yet mastered.

12-5 Natural Logarithms

Objective
12-5

After studying this lesson, you should be able to:
■ find natural logarithms of numbers.

Application

FYI ···

7% interest compounded continuously yields an interest rate of about

$7\frac{1}{4}$% per year.

Sean's grandparents opened a savings account for him when he was born. They placed $1000 in an account that paid 7% interest compounded continuously. The amount of money in the account, A, after t years is found by using the formula $A = Pe^{rt}$, where P represents the amount of principal, r represents the annual interest rate, and e is a special irrational number.

Sean is now 16 years old and would like to buy a used car that costs $2500. Does he have enough money in his savings account to buy it? *This problem will be solved in Example 3.*

Teaching Tip ❶

The number e, used in the interest formula, is used extensively in science and mathematics. It is an irrational number whose value is approximately 2.718. e is the base for the **natural logarithms,** which is abbreviated **ln.** So, the natural logarithm of e is 1. All of the properties of logarithms that you have learned apply to the natural logarithms as well. The key marked **LN** on your calculator is the natural logarithm key.

Example 1

> Use your calculator to find ln 3.965.
>
> ENTER: 3.965 **LN** 1.3775059
>
> The natural logarithm of 3.695 is approximately 1.3775.

You can take antilogarithms of natural logarithms as well. The symbol for the antilogarithm of x is antiln x.

Example 2

> Find each value.
>
> **a.** Find x if ln $x = 3.9824$.
>
>   ln $x = 3.9824$
> $x =$ antiln 3.9824
>
> ENTER: 3.9824 **e^** 53.645629
>
> *If your calculator has no* **e^** *key, use the* **INV** *key and then the* **LN** *key.*
>
> So x is approximately 53.6456.
>
> **b.** Find e if ln $e = 1$.
>
>   ln $e = 1$
> $e =$ antiln 1
>
> ENTER: 1 **e^** 2.7182818
>
> So e is approximately 2.7183.

LESSON 12-5 NATURAL LOGARITHMS 567

Lesson Resources

Reteaching Master 12-5
Practice Master 12-5
Enrichment Master 12-5

 Transparency 12-5 contains the 5-Minute Check and a teaching aid for this lesson.

INTRODUCING THE LESSON

5-Minute Check

(over Lesson 12-4)
Find the logarithm of each.

1. 58.2 **1.7649**
2. 0.3 **9.4771 − 10**

Find the antilogarithm of each.

3. 0.6304 **4.27**
4. 0.3194 − 2 **0.02087**
5. Use logarithms to find 150³.
   3,375,000

Motivating the Lesson

Show several different savings brochures from local banks or their ads from the newspaper. Ask students if any of them have savings accounts. Discuss different types of accounts, varying compounding periods, and why someone would choose one account over another. Ask students if they know how interest is determined.

TEACHING THE LESSON

Teaching Tip ❶ The natural logarithm of x is sometimes denoted $\log_e x$, but more often ln x.

ALTERNATE TEACHING STRATEGIES

Using Computers

Have students write a BASIC computer program to find t for the formula $A = Pe^{rt}$ when the initial amount (P), the constant (r), and the final amount (A) are given. A sample program is shown.

```
10 INPUT "ENTER THE INITIAL
   AMOUNT P:"; P
20 INPUT "ENTER THE CONSTANT
   R:"; R
30 INPUT "ENTER THE FINAL
   AMOUNT A:"; A
40 LET T = LOG (A/P)/R
50 PRINT: PRINT "TIME
   REQUIRED IS"; T; "UNITS."
60 END
```

The exponential equations in the following applications contain the number e. Equations involving e are easier to solve using natural logarithms, than using common logarithms since ln $e = 1$.

Example 3

APPLICATION
Finance

Use the formula $A = Pe^{rt}$, to determine whether Sean can buy a used car costing $2500 with the $1000 investment his grandparents made for him 16 years ago.

Use the formula $A = Pe^{rt}$.

$$A = Pe^{rt}$$
$$A = (1000)e^{(0.07)(16)}$$ *principal = $1000, rate = 7%, time = 16 years*
$$A = 1000e^{1.12}$$

$\ln A = \ln (1000e^{1.12})$ *Take the natural logarithm of each side.*
$\ln A = \ln 1000 + (1.12) \ln e$ *Power and product properties of logarithms*
$\ln A = \ln 1000 + 1.12$ *Since e is the base for natural logarithms, ln e = 1.*
$\ln A = 8.0277553$
$\quad A = 3064.85$ *Take the antiln of each side.*

Sean has $3064.85 in his account. This is more than enough to buy the car.

Natural logarithms can also be used to determine the amount you need to invest now in order to have a certain amount later.

Example 4

APPLICATION
Finance

Danica is saving money to go on a trip to Europe after her college graduation. She will finish college six years from now. If the six-year certificate of deposit that she buys now pays 8% interest compounded continuously, how much should she invest now in order to have $3000 for the trip?

Again, use the formula $A = Pe^{rt}$.

$$A = Pe^{rt}$$
$$3000 = Pe^{(0.08)(6)}$$
$$3000 = Pe^{0.48}$$
$$\ln 3000 = \ln (Pe^{0.48})$$
$$\ln 3000 = \ln P + (0.48) \ln e$$
$$\ln 3000 = \ln P + 0.48$$
$$7.5263676 ≈ \ln P$$
$$1856.35 ≈ P$$

Danica should invest $1856.35 to earn enough for the trip.

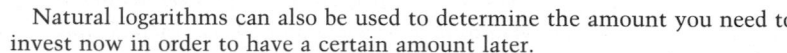

568   CHAPTER 12   EXPONENTIAL AND LOGARITHMIC FUNCTIONS

RETEACHING THE LESSON

Have students discuss the question, "If the natural logarithm of 3 is approximately 1.0986, then how would we use that information to give an antilogarithm statement?" **The antilogarithm of 1.0986 is approximately 3.**

CHECKING FOR UNDERSTANDING

Communicating Mathematics

Read and study the lesson to answer these questions.

1. What is the base of the natural logarithms? **the number e**
2. How much would Sean have in his savings account if the interest rate had been 7.25%? **$3189.93**
3. When should you choose to use natural logarithms instead of common logarithms to solve a problem? **Use natural logarithms when the base of an exponent to be simplified is e and common logarithms when the base is 10.**

Guided Practice

Teaching Tip

Use your calculator to find each value, rounded to four decimal places.

4. ln 2.58 **0.9478**
5. ln 4.28 **1.454**
6. ln 48.987 **3.892**
7. antiln 0.4253 **1.530**
8. antiln 1.7015 **5.482**
9. antiln −0.7876 **0.4549**

EXERCISES

Practice

A

Use your calculator to find each value, rounded to four decimal places.

10. ln 9.45 **2.246**
11. ln 7.21 **1.976**
12. ln 1.42 **0.3507**
13. antiln 0.469 **1.598**
14. antiln 0 **1**
15. antiln 2.2289 **9.290**

D

16. ln 56.9 **4.041**
17. ln 0.543 **−0.6106**
18. ln 65 **4.174**
19. ln e **1**
20. antiln 3.56 **35.16**
21. antiln 0.52 **1.682**
22. antiln 0.288 **1.334**
23. antiln −1.679 **0.1866**
24. ln 1000 **6.908**

C

Solve each equation.

25. $2000 = 5e^{0.045x}$ **133.1**
26. $2 = e^{5k}$ **0.1386**
27. $\ln 3.6 = \ln (e^{0.031t})$ **41.32**
28. $65 = e^{6n}$ **0.6957**
29. $25 = e^{0.075y}$ **42.92**
30. $\ln 40.5 = \ln (e^{0.21t})$ **17.6252**

Critical Thinking

31. The great Swiss mathematician Leonhard Euler, for whom the number e is named, defined e as the sum of the series $1 + \frac{1}{1} + \frac{1}{1 \cdot 2} + \frac{1}{1 \cdot 2 \cdot 3} + \frac{1}{1 \cdot 2 \cdot 3 \cdot 4} + \ldots$. Calculate e to the nearest ten-thousandth using this series. **2.7183**

Applications

32. **Finance** Mr. and Mrs. Grauser invested $500 at 6.5% compounded continuously.
    a. Find the value of the investment after 7 years. **$788.09**
    b. When will the Grausers' investment be tripled? **16.9 years**

LESSON 12-5 NATURAL LOGARITHMS 569

33. **Chemistry** Radium 226 decomposes radioactively. The amount of a radioactive substance present after t years is found by the formula $y = ne^{kt}$, where n is the initial amount of the substance and k is a constant. It takes 1800 years for half of a sample of Radium 226 to decompose.
   a. Use 100 grams as the original amount to find the constant k for this substance. **−0.000385**
   b. How much of a 1-gram sample of Radium 226 will remain after 10,000 years? **approximately 0.0213 grams**

Mixed Review

34. Use a calculator to find the common logarithm of 349.948, rounded to four decimal places. Then state the characteristic and the mantissa. (**Lesson 12-4**) **2.5440; 2; 0.5440**

35. Add $\dfrac{3}{x-2} + \dfrac{2}{x-3}$. (**Lesson 11-4**) $\dfrac{5x-13}{(x-2)(x-3)}$

36. Find the solutions of the system $\begin{array}{l} 2y^2 = 10 - x^2 \\ 3x^2 - 9 = y^2. \end{array}$ (**Lesson 9-9**) $(2, \pm\sqrt{3}), (-2, \pm\sqrt{3})$

37. Solve the inequality $x^2 \le 36$. (**Lesson 8-7**) $\{x | -6 \le x \le 6\}$

38. Carol and Frank want to buy some new living room furniture. A sofa, love seat, and coffee table cost $1230. The sofa costs twice as much as the love seat. The sofa and the coffee table cost $880. What are the prices of each piece of furniture? (**Lesson 3-9**) **sofa - $700, love seat - $350, coffee table - $180**

HISTORY CONNECTION

Logarithms were first described by **John Napier** (1550–1617 A.D.), a Scottish laird. This Baron of Murchiston managed his large estate, while pursuing writing and mathematics as a hobby. He first used the words "artifical number" to describe his system of exponential values. Later, when he published his findings in *Descripto* (1619), he used the word logarithm which he formed from the Greek words *logos* (meaning ratio) and *arithmos* (meaning number).

A Salvilian professor of geometry at Oxford University, **Henry Briggs** (1561–1639), read Napier's work and was enthusiastic in studying this further. It was Briggs who first used the terms *mantissa* and *characteristic*. The early logarithm tables printed both the mantissa and characteristic. It was not until the mid-18th century that tables containing only the mantissas were widely accepted.

John Napier

EXTENDING THE LESSON

Math Power: Connections
Have students research several radioactive elements and name the half-life for each. Using the formula $y = ne^{kt}$ (see Exercise 33), and assuming 100 g of each element is present initially, have students determine k for each of the elements.

History Connection
The History Connection features introduce students to persons or cultures who were involved in the development of mathematics. You may want students to further research Napier or Briggs.

Enrichment Masters Booklet, p. 81

12-6 Problem-Solving Strategy: Using Estimation

Objective
12-6

After studying this lesson, you should be able to:
- solve problems using estimation.

Sometimes solving a problem is a long process involving many steps. Occasionally we make a miscalculation, take a wrong turn, or even mis-key on a calculator and get an incorrect answer. This is why it is very helpful to estimate the solution to a problem before performing the calculations. Then if our solution is not close to the estimate, we know that we have made a mistake.

Teaching Tip ❶

Example 1

CONNECTION

Geometry

Find the approximate area of a regular hexagon whose sides are 29 cm long.

A regular hexagon can be inscribed in a circle. The figure shows the hexagon inscribed in a circle.

The diagonals of the hexagon form equilateral triangles, so the radius of the circle is also 29 cm.

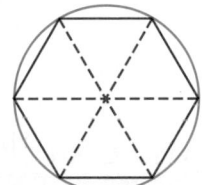

You can estimate that the size of the hexagon is a little less than the area of the circle, which is found using the formula $A = \pi r^2$. Use your calculator to find the area of the circle.

ENTER: $\boxed{\pi}$ $\boxed{\times}$ $\boxed{29}$ $\boxed{x^2}$ $\boxed{=}$ 2642.079422

The area of the circle is about 2642 cm^2. The area of the hexagon would be close to but less than 2642 cm^2. The actual area of the hexagon is $\frac{2523\sqrt{3}}{2}$ cm^2, which is about 2185 cm^2.

Example 2

APPLICATION

Finance

Ted invested $9300 in a two year certificate of deposit (CD) that has an annual yield of 9.57%. How much interest did he earn from the CD?

Ted will earn 9.57% each year. Since 10% of $9300 is $930, an estimate of Ted's earnings is 2×930 or $1860. *Will the actual value be greater or less than $1860?*

$I = Prt$ *Use the equation for simple interest.*
$I = (9300)(0.0957)(2)$
$I = 1780.02$

Ted will earn $1780.02 in interest. This is a reasonable answer according to our estimate.

LESSON 12-6 PROBLEM-SOLVING STRATEGY: USING ESTIMATION 571

ALTERNATE TEACHING STRATEGIES

Using Discussion
Provide students with copies of a cash register tape with the total removed. Have them estimate the total and then use calculators to determine the actual total. Discuss any differences in the estimate. Assume the total is $15.85 and you have $16.00. Is the significance of the estimate any different for this situation than it would be if you had $20.00?

INTRODUCING THE LESSON

Lesson Resources
Practice Master 12-6
Activity Master, p. 48

Transparency 12-6 contains the 5-Minute Check and a teaching aid for this lesson.

5-Minute Check
(over Lesson 12-5)

1. Find ln 5.46. ≈**1.697**
2. Find ln 0.083. ≈**−2.49**
3. Find x if ln x = 3.7.
   $x \approx$ **40.45**
4. Find x if ln x = 0.62.
   $x \approx$ **1.86**
5. Jane invests a sum of money at 8% interest compounded continuously. How much must she invest now to have a total of $10,000 in five years?
   $6703.20

Motivating the Lesson
Tell students that the Denver Broncos play in Mile High Stadium. Ask students if they think the stadium is at an altitude that is exactly one mile. Elicit student responses as to how close students think the altitude of the stadium would have to be to one mile to be called Mile High Stadium.

TEACHING THE LESSON

Teaching Tip ❶ Emphasize that students may differ in rounding and thus differ in their estimations. Estimations may be different and still be valid.

Teaching Tip ❷ Emphasize that common sense may give a valid estimate. Computation may not be necessary.

EVALUATING THE LESSON

Checking for Understanding

Exercises 1–5 are designed to help you assess understanding through reading, writing, and speaking. You should work through Exercises 1–3 with your students, and then monitor their work on Exercises 4–5.

Closing the Lesson

Speaking Activity Have students give one example of a situation in which an exact answer is needed and one in which an estimate is close enough.

Example 3

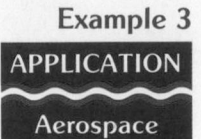

APPLICATION

Aerospace

Teaching Tip ❷

A satellite requires 10 watts of power to operate its equipment for one year. A power supply aboard the satellite generates power according to the equation $P = 50e^{-\frac{t}{250}}$, where P represents the power in watts and t represents the time in days. How much power will the power supply generate in one year?

Since the satellite requires 10 watts of power in a year, this is probably a good estimate of the power to be generated in one year.

$$P = 50e^{-\frac{t}{250}}$$
$$P = 50e^{-\frac{365}{250}} \qquad \text{There are 365 days in a year.}$$
$$\ln P = \ln 50 + \left(-\frac{365}{250}\right) \ln e$$
$$\ln P = 3.9120 - \frac{365}{250} \qquad \text{ln } e = 1$$
$$\ln P = 2.4520230$$
$$P = 11.611814$$

The power supply generates about 11.6 watts of energy in a year. This is a reasonable answer according to our estimate.

CHECKING FOR UNDERSTANDING

Communicating Mathematics

Read and study the lesson to answer these questions.

1. When might you use estimation in every day life? **See margin.**

2. When might you use estimation in solving mathematics problems? **See margin.**

3. Where would you look for a mistake if your estimate is very different than your solution? **Sample answers: computation errors, wrong procedures, or a mis-key on the calculator**

Guided Practice

Solve each problem using estimation.

4. Give an estimate of the area of a square with a side 9.39 inches long. Then find the actual area and compare your solution to your estimate. **estimate: more than 81 sq. in.; 88.1721 sq in.**

5. A roll of wallpaper will cover 75 square feet. The room Mary wishes to wallpaper is 9 feet wide and 12 feet long with a standard 8 foot ceiling.
   a. Estimate how many rolls of wallpaper she will need for the job. **5 rolls**
   b. Find the actual number of rolls Mary will need. **4.48 rolls**
   c. If she had bought the wallpaper according to your estimate, would she have bought the right amount? **Yes, since she can't buy 4.48 rolls, she must buy 5.**

572   CHAPTER 12   EXPONENTIAL AND LOGARITHMIC FUNCTIONS

RETEACHING THE LESSON

Have students brainstorm as to when estimation would be used in everyday life. Use these ideas to make-up hypothetical problems and have students estimate answers. Tell whether their actual answer will be higher or lower than the estimation and why.

Additional Answers

1. Answers may vary. Sample answers are adding prices of items at a store and figuring amounts of wallpaper or paint needed for a room.

2. To estimate an answer before performing the calculations so that you can check the reasonableness of a solution.

EXERCISES

Strategies

Look for a pattern.
Solve a simpler problem.
Act it out.
Guess and check.
Draw a diagram.
Make a chart.
Work backwards.

Solve. Use any strategy.

6. The sign in front of an Alaskan bank displays both Fahrenheit and Celsius temperatures. At what temperature are the readings the same? **–40°**

7. How can two fathers and two sons divide twenty-one $1 bills evenly among them? Each must receive an equal number of bills. **grandfather, father, and son each receive $7.**

8. A beautiful 9 × 12 meter rug was damaged by the moving company. After the damaged part was cut out, a 1 × 8 meter rectangular hole resulted in the very center of the rug. Using straight cuts, cut the remaining rug into two parts that, when sewn together, will form a square. **See margin.**

9. The following pattern contains all the digits from 0 through 9. Discover the pattern and complete the sequence.
8, 5, 4, 9, 1, __?__, __?__, __?__, __?__, __?__ **7, 6, 3, 2, 0 (alphabetical order)**

10. Keshia bought an eighteen month certificate of deposit with an annual yield of 8.79%. If the original investment was $1800, approximately how much interest did she earn? **$250**

11. Trace the square at the right. Then show at least five ways to divide the square into four congruent parts. **See margin.**

12. Use the following clues to find what year the first Super Bowl was played. **1967**
   (1) No digit is an 8.
   (2) The hundreds digit is 3 more than the tens digit.
   (3) The sum of the digits is 23.

COOPERATIVE LEARNING ACTIVITY

Work in groups. Each person in the group must understand the solution and be able to explain it to any person in class.

Leon is helping his younger sister with her homework. She is learning to simplify fractions and has simplified the fraction $\frac{154}{253}$ to $\frac{14}{23}$ by canceling out the two middle digits. Her procedure was wrong but the answer is correct. After Leon showed his sister how to simplify fractions correctly, he tried to find other fractions that would simplify correctly by illegally canceling. How many can you find? Can you generalize the form of these fractions? **See margin.**

LESSON 12-6   PROBLEM-SOLVING STRATEGY: USING ESTIMATION   573

EXTENDING THE LESSON

Math Power: Connections

Have each student choose a vocation and research when that person may estimate in doing his or her job, and when a definite figure is needed. For example, a carpenter may estimate the number of board feet needed or the number of pounds of nails to buy, but the measurements to which the board must be cut or the mileage to and from a job must be definite.

Cooperative Learning Activity

Some are $\frac{385}{682}$, $\frac{275}{374}$, and $\frac{572}{671}$; The sums of the ones and tens digits of the numerator and denominator of the reduced fraction are equal and less than 10. The fraction to be simplified is the original fraction multiplied by $\frac{11}{11}$. For example, for $\frac{14}{23}$:

$1 + 4 = 5$
$2 + 3 = 5$ and $5 < 10$
$\frac{14}{23} \times \frac{11}{11} = \frac{154}{253}$

Assignment Guide

Basic: 6–12
Average: 6–12
Enriched: 6–12

Chapter 12, Quiz C, (Lessons 12-5 through 12-6), is available in the Evaluation Masters Booklet, p. 164.

Additional Answers

8.

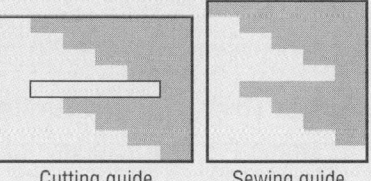

Cutting guide   Sewing guide

11. **Answers will vary. Sample answers are shown.**

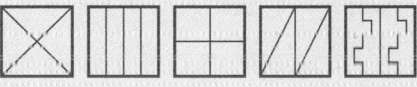

Practice Masters Booklet, p. 93

12-6 NAME _____ DATE _____
Practice Worksheet
Problem Solving Strategy: Using Estimation
Solve. Use any strategy.

1. Marita invested $5200 in a 2-year certificate of deposit that has an annual yield of 9.8%. Estimate the amount of interest she will earn and then check your estimate against the answer you obtain, using $I = prt$.
less than $1040; $1019.20

2. Jim wants to paint the walls of a room that is 15 feet wide and 20 feet long. The ceiling is 8 feet high. How many gallons of paint will he need if each gallon covers 350 square feet and he wants to give the room two coats of paint?
4 gallons

3. Use the following clues to find a year important in history.
   (1) The thousands digit is half the ones digit, which is half the hundreds digit.
   (2) The sum of the digits is 16.
   (3) No two digits are the same.
1492

INTRODUCING THE LESSON

5-Minute Check

(over Lesson 12-6)

1. Find the length of a side of a square if its area is 389 square centimeters. **19.723 cm**

Other Prerequisite Skills

2. Name the characteristic of log 87.32. **1**

Solve.

3. $4^x = 4^{3x+1}$ $-\dfrac{1}{2}$

4. $25^{2n} = 125^{n-3}$ **-9**

5. $m = \dfrac{\log 4}{\log 6 - \log 3}$ **2**

Motivating the Lesson

Have students survey the local banks and determine how often interest is compounded on different interest-bearing accounts. Ask students if they know how this affects how much they earn. Compare effective annual yields based on how frequently the investment is compounded.

TEACHING THE LESSON

Chalkboard Example

For Example 1

How long would it take to triple an investment of $500 at 8% interest compounded quarterly?

$A = P\left(1 + \dfrac{r}{n}\right)^{nt}$ **13.87 = t**

12-7 Exponential Equations

Objective
12-7

After studying this lesson, you should be able to:
- solve equations with variable exponents using logarithms.

Application

Jess Burgess is a systems analyst for an investment corporation. He is designing a computer program that will help financial planners analyze various investments and, as a result, choose wise investments for their clients. One of the things the computer program must be able to do is to find what the value of an investment that earns a given interest rate will be at some time in the future. The formula for finding that value is

$A = P\left(1 + \dfrac{r}{n}\right)^{nt}$, where A represents the value of the investment in the future, P is the original investment, r is the annual interest rate, t is the number of years of the investment, and n is the number of times the interest is compounded each year.

The value of an investment at some future date is one example of an **exponential equation.** Exponential equations are equations in which the variables appear as exponents. These equations can be solved using the property of equality for logarithmic functions.

Example 1

APPLICATION

Finance

Use the compound interest formula, $A = P\left(1 + \dfrac{r}{n}\right)^{nt}$, to find how long it would take for an investment of $2500 to triple if it is invested in an account that earns 6% interest compounded quarterly.

$$A = P\left(1 + \frac{r}{n}\right)^{nt} \qquad \textit{Compound interest formula}$$

$$7500 = 2500\left(1 + \frac{0.06}{4}\right)^{4t} \qquad \textit{P is \$2500, r is 0.06, n is 4, and A is 3P or \$7500.}$$

$$3 = (1.015)^{4t} \qquad \textit{Divide each side by 2500.}$$

$$\log 3 = \log (1.015)^{4t} \qquad \textit{Property of equality for logarithmic functions}$$

$$\log 3 = 4t \log (1.015) \qquad \textit{Power property of logarithms}$$

$$\frac{\log 3}{4 \log (1.015)} = t$$

$$t \approx 18.4472$$

The investment of $2500 would triple in a little less than $18\frac{1}{2}$ years.

ALTERNATE TEACHING STRATEGIES

Using Cooperative Groups

Have cooperative groups of students work through Examples 1–4. Have half of each group use a calculator and the other half use the table of common logarithms to solve the problem, then compare results. Each student should use the calculator on two examples and the table on the other two.

Example 2

Solve $4^x = 24$.

Teaching Tip ❶

$$4^x = 24$$

$$\log 4^x = \log 24 \qquad \textit{Property of equality for logarithmic functions}$$

$$x \log 4 = \log 24 \qquad \textit{Power property of logarithms}$$

$$x = \frac{\log 24}{\log 4} \qquad \textbf{Teaching Tip ❷}$$

$$x = \frac{1.3802}{0.6021}$$

$$x \approx 2.2923$$

The solution is approximately 2.2923. *Check this result.*

Example 3

Solve $7^{x-2} = 5^{3-x}$.

$$7^{x-2} = 5^{3-x}$$

$$\log 7^{x-2} = \log 5^{3-x} \qquad \textit{Property of equality for logarithmic functions}$$

$$(x - 2) \log 7 = (3 - x) \log 5 \qquad \textit{Power property of logarithms}$$

$$x \log 7 - 2 \log 7 = 3 \log 5 - x \log 5 \qquad \textit{Distributive property}$$

$$x \log 7 + x \log 5 = 3 \log 5 + 2 \log 7$$

$$x(\log 7 + \log 5) = 3 \log 5 + 2 \log 7 \qquad \textit{Distributive property}$$

$$x = \frac{3 \log 5 + 2 \log 7}{\log 7 + \log 5} \qquad \begin{array}{l}\textit{Use a calculator to perform}\\ \textit{calculations.}\end{array}$$

$$x = \frac{3(0.6990) + 2(0.8451)}{0.8451 + 0.6990}$$

$$x \approx 2.4527$$

The solution is approximately 2.4527. *Check this result.*

It is possible to evaluate expressions involving logarithms with different bases. Since your calculator isn't programmed with all of the possible bases for logarithms, the **change of base formula** is very helpful.

Change of Base Formula	For all positive numbers a, b and n, where $a \neq 1$ and $b \neq 1$, $$\log_a n = \frac{\log_b n}{\log_b a}.$$

Chalkboard Examples

For Example 2
Solve $7^x = 20$ using logarithms.
x ≈ 1.5395

For Example 3
Solve $3^{x-4} = 5^{x-1}$.
x ≈ −5.4502

Teaching Tip ❶ Note that $\frac{(\log 24)}{(\log 4)} \neq \log (24 - 4)$.

Teaching Tip ❷ In Examples 1, 2, and 3, the table of mantissas is used to find the value of the logarithms before evaluating the expressions. Emphasize that if a calculator is used and the answers rounded off only after the final step, then the answers may vary slightly from those given.

Example 4

Express each logarithm in terms of common logarithms. Then find its value.

a. $\log_4 22$ **b.** $\log_{12} 95$

$\log_a n = \dfrac{\log_b n}{\log_b a}$ *Change of base formula* $\log_a n = \dfrac{\log_b n}{\log_b a}$ *Change of base formula*

$\log_4 22 = \dfrac{\log 22}{\log 4}$ $a = 4, n = 22, b = 10$ $\log_{12} 95 = \dfrac{\log 95}{\log 12}$ $a = 12, n = 95, b = 10$

$= \dfrac{1.3424}{0.6021}$ $= \dfrac{1.9777}{1.0792}$

≈ 2.2295 ≈ 1.8326

The value of $\log_4 22$ is approximately 2.2295. The value of $\log_{12} 95$ is approximately 1.8326.

CHECKING FOR UNDERSTANDING

Communicating Mathematics

4. $\dfrac{\log 72}{\log 6}$; **2.3869**

5. $\dfrac{\log 100}{\log 8}$; **2.2146**

6. $\dfrac{\log 144}{2 \log 9}$; **1.1309**

Read and study the lesson to answer these questions.

1. Is $x^4 = 256$ an exponential equation? If not, why not? **See margin.**

2. When might the change of base formula come in handy? **When finding logarithms of different bases on the calculator.**

3. Could you use the change of base formula to express a logarithm in terms of natural logarithms? If not, why not? **yes**

Guided Practice

7. $\dfrac{\log 169}{\log 4}$; **3.7004**

8. $\dfrac{\log 90}{\log 6}$; **2.5114**

9. $\dfrac{\log 34}{2 \log 3}$; **1.6049**

State x in terms of common logarithms. Then find the value of x.

4. $6^x = 72$

5. $8^x = 100$

6. $9^{2x} = 144$

7. $x = \log_4 169$

8. $x = \log_6 90$

9. $3^x = \sqrt{34}$

10. $2^x = 5\sqrt{2}$ $\dfrac{\log 5}{\log 2} + \dfrac{1}{2}$; **2.8219**

11. $3^{-x} = 22$ $\dfrac{-\log 22}{\log 3}$; **−2.8136**

12. $2^{-x} = \sqrt[2]{7}$ $\dfrac{-\log 7}{2 \log 2}$; **−1.4037**

EXERCISES

Practice

25. **3.839**
26. **−0.3051**
27. **2.8446**
28. **4.8362**
29. **2.3059**
30. **±1.1024**

A

Approximate each logarithm to three decimal places.

13. $\log_5 15$ **1.683**

14. $\log_8 72$ **2.057**

15. $\log_{12} 169$ **2.064**

16. $\log_4 100$ **3.322**

17. $\log_{12} 15$ **1.090**

18. $\log_2 36$ **5.170**

19. $\log_{15} 5$ **0.594**

20. $\log_9 108$ **2.131**

21. $\log_{11} 104$ **1.937**

B

Use logarithms to solve each equation.

8.0086

22. $8^x = 45$ **1.8306**

23. $2^x = 27$ **4.7549**

24. $2.1^{x-5} = 9.32$

25. $7.6^{a-2} = 41.7$

26. $5^{x+2} = 15.3$

27. $x = \log_4 51.6$

28. $9^{x-4} = 6.28$

29. $x = \log_{20} 1000$

30. $25^{x^2} = 50$

31. $6^{x^2-2} = 48$ **±2.0397**

32. $4.3^{3x+1} = 78.5$ **0.6638**

33. $2.7^{x^2-1} = 52.3$ **±2.2325**

Additional Answer

1. **no; An exponential equation uses a variable as the exponent.**

34. 3.1507
35. 3.2838

37. −2.1507

40. 1.4125
41. 2.9172
42. 3.2598

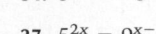

34. $5^{x-1} = 3^x$

35. $12^{x-4} = 4^{2-x}$

36. $7^{x-2} = 5^x$ **11.5665**

37. $5^{2x} = 9^{x-1}$

38. $2^{2x+3} = 3^{3x}$ **1.0890**

39. $2^{3y} = 3^{y+1}$ **1.1201**

40. $2^{5x-1} = 3^{2x+1}$

41. $4^{5y-6} = 3^{2y+5}$

42. $5^{4y+1} = 32^{2y}$

43. $24^{3x} = 6^{2x+1}$
0.3011

44. $2^n = \sqrt{3^{n-2}}$
−7.6377

45. $\sqrt[3]{4^{x-1}} = 6^{x-2}$
2.3475

Critical Thinking

46. Let x be any real number and a, b, and n be positive real numbers where $a \neq 1$ and $b \neq 1$. Show that if $x = \log_a n$, then $x = \dfrac{\log_b n}{\log_b a}$. **See margin.**

Applications

47. Finance Nalani saved $500 of the money she earned working at the Dairy Dream last summer. She deposited the money in a certificate of deposit that earns 8.75% interest compounded monthly. If she rolls over the CD at the same rate each year, when will Nalani's CD have a balance of $800? **5 years 5 months**

48. Education Dwain withdrew all of the $2500 in his savings account to pay the tuition for his first semester at college. The account had earned 12% interest compounded monthly, and no withdrawals or additional deposits were made.

about 5 years, 10 months ago

a. If Dwain's original deposit was $1250, how long ago did he open the account?

about 4 years, 3 months ago

b. If Dwain's original deposit was $1500, how long ago did he open the account?

49. Business The T.C. Company has a savings plan for their employees. The employee makes an initial contribution of $1000 and the company pays 8% interest compounded quarterly.

a. If an employee participating in the plan withdraws the balance of the account after five years, how much will the company have paid into the account? **$485.95**

b. If an employee participating in the plan withdraws the balance of the account after thirty-five years, how much will the company have paid into the account? **$14,996.47**

Additional Answer

46. $x = \log_a n$
$a^x = a^{\log_a n}$
$a^x = n$
$\log_b a^x = \log_b n$
$x \log_b a = \log_b n$
$x = \dfrac{\log_b n}{\log_b a}$

50. Solve the equation $\ln 9.5 = \ln (e^{0.2x})$. **(Lesson 12-5)** **11.26**

51. Write the equation $f(x) = x^2 + 16x + 67$ in the form $f(x) = (x - h)^2 + k$. Then name the vertex and axis of symmetry for the graph of the function. **(Lesson 8-2)** $f(x) = (x + 8)^2 + 3$; $(-8, 3)$; $x = -8$

52. State the sum and product of the roots of the equation $-5x^2 + x + 3 = 0$. **(Lesson 7-5)** $\dfrac{1}{5}, -\dfrac{3}{5}$

53. **Physics** The formula for the time, T, in seconds that it takes for a pendulum to make a complete swing (back and forth) is $T = 2\pi\sqrt{\dfrac{L}{32}}$, where L represents the length of the pendulum. Find the time for a complete swing of a pendulum whose length is 6 feet. *If your calculator does not have a π key, use 3.14 to approximate π.* **(Lesson 6-2)** **2.72 seconds**

54. Simplify $\dfrac{-3w^6t^7}{(-27w^3t^2)(wt)^2}$. **(Lesson 5-2)** $\dfrac{wt^3}{9}$

55. State the domain and range of the relation $\{(9, 3), (-8, 3), (1, -3), (0, 0)\}$. Then state if the relation is a function. **(Lesson 2-1)** **domain: $\{-8, 0, 1, 9\}$; range: $\{-3, 0, 3\}$; yes**

56. **Sports** The Wildcats play 84 games this season. It is now midseason and they have won 30 games. To win at least 60% of *all* of their games, how many of the remaining games must they win? **(Lesson 1-7)** **21 games**

BIOLOGY CONNECTION

Many problems involving estimation can be solved using **interpolation** and **extrapolation.** Interpolation is used to estimate a value between two known values. Extrapolation is used to estimate a value that is either greater than or less than two known values. Both use proportions to find the missing value. Environmentalists often use these methods to estimate wildlife populations.

The deer population in Deercreek Park is known for 1987 and 1992. The deer population in 1991 can be estimated using interpolation while the deer population for 1994 can be estimated using extrapolation.

Year	Population	Year	Population
$+3\begin{bmatrix}1987\\ \rightarrow 1991\\ 1992 \end{bmatrix}+5$	$+x\begin{bmatrix}4320\\ \rightarrow \text{unknown}\\ 6780 \end{bmatrix}+2460$	$+5\begin{bmatrix}1987\\ \rightarrow 1992\\ 1994 \end{bmatrix}+11$	$\begin{bmatrix}4320\\ 6780\\ \text{unknown} \end{bmatrix} \begin{matrix}+2460\\ +y\end{matrix}$

$$\dfrac{3}{5} = \dfrac{x}{2460}$$
$$x = 1476$$

$$\dfrac{11}{5} = \dfrac{y}{2460}$$
$$y = 5412$$

The deer population in 1991 is about 1476 more than 4320, or 5796 deer. The deer population for 1994 would be about 5412 more than 4320, or 9732 deer. *You could also round the numbers to have another estimate.*

578 CHAPTER 12 EXPONENTIAL AND LOGARITHMIC FUNCTIONS

Enrichment Masters Booklet, p. 82

EXTENDING THE LESSON

Math Power: Problem Solving

Have students solve $x^{\log x} = \dfrac{x^3}{100}$. **10 or 100**

Biology Connection

The Biology Connection feature shows students how mathematics is used to estimate wildlife population. Another method that can be used to estimate population is capture-recapture. You may want students to research the latter method and model it using small crackers or chips.

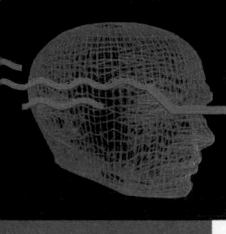

Technology

Compound Interest

You can use a spreadsheet to calculate how your funds are increasing due to interest that compounds. Use the formula $A = P\left(1 + \dfrac{r}{n}\right)^{nt}$, where A is the amount in the account after t years, with an initial ivestment of P dollars at an interest rate r, if the interest is compounded n times per year.

The spreadsheet below left is set up to find the value of an investment after 1 to 20 years. The principal is entered in cell B1, the number of times the interest is compounded per year is entered in cell B2, and the rate is entered in B3. Cells B5 to B24 contian a variation of the compound interest formula that will compute the balance in the account after successive years.

Below right is a partial printout from the spreadsheet on compound interest. It shows the amount accumulated in an account that bears 5.5% interest compounded monthly if the principal is $9500.

COMPOUND INTEREST		
	A	B
1	PRINCIPAL	
2	TIMES COMPOUNDED	
3	RATE	
4	YEAR	BALANCE
5	1	B1*(1 + B3/B2)† (B3*A5)
6	2	B1*(1 + B3/B2)│ (B3*A6)
24	20	B1*(1 + B3/B2)† (B3*∧24)

COMPOUND INTEREST		
	A	B
1:	PRINCIPAL	9500
2:	TIMES COMPOUNDED	12
3.	RATE	0.055
4:	YEAR	BALANCE
5:	1	10035.87
6:	2	10601.98
24:	20	28467.94

EXERCISES

1. Describe how you could modify the sprcadshcet program to print 50 years of account balances. **Continue column B to cell B54.**

2. Describe how you could modify the spreadsheet program to print comparisons of the amount accumulated in accounts of two different interest rates. **Add a column C similar to column B.**

Using Technology

Objective This optional page shows how spreadsheets can be used to perform mathematical computations and to enhance and extend mathematical concepts.

Teaching Suggestions

If a computer spreadsheet program is available, have students enter the program for finding compound interest. Have students enter various interest rates, principal values, and compounding periods and investigate the results. For example, which is a better investment, 6% interest compounded quarterly or 5.75% compounded monthly? **6% compounded quarterly**

Lesson Resources

Reteaching Master 12-8
Practice Master 12-8
Enrichment Master 12-8
Activity Master, p. 30
Multicultural Activity Master, p. 12

 Transparency 12-8 contains the 5-Minute Check and a teaching aid for this lesson.

INTRODUCING THE LESSON

 5-Minute Check

(over Lesson 12-7)

Express *x* in terms of common logarithms.

1. $7^x = \sqrt{11}$ $\dfrac{\log 11}{2 \log 7}$

2. $3^x = 4\sqrt{5}$ $\dfrac{\log 4}{\log 3} + \dfrac{\log 5}{2 \log 3}$

Solve each equation using logarithms.

3. $x = \log_{16} 232$ ≈ 1.964
4. $7^{2x} = 74$ ≈ 1.106
5. $32^{2y} = 5^{4y+1}$ ≈ 3.2598

Motivating the Lesson

Elicit student responses to the following question. Now that you have determined and used logarithms, in what situations would they be useful in solving problems?

TEACHING THE LESSON

Teaching Tip ❶ Remind students of the differences in common and natural logarithms, when each is used, and how the value of each is determined.

Objective 12-8

After studying this lesson, you should be able to:
- use logarithms to solve problems.

Application

Teaching Tip ❶

Bacteria reproduce by mitosis, a process by which a cell divides to produce two identical cells. Their growth can be described by the **general formula for growth and decay.** This is the exponential function $y = ne^{kt}$, where y is the final amount, n is the initial amount, k is a constant and t is the time. The *escherichia coli*, or *e. coli*, can reproduce in 15 minutes. If you began with just one bacterium, how many would there be in four hours?

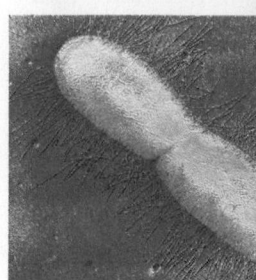

Use the general formula for growth and decay to find the number of bacteria present after four hours. First we must find the constant k when t is given in minutes. The constant will be positive since the number of bacteria is increasing. If the number were decreasing, as with radioactive decay, the value of k would be negative.

$$y = ne^{kt}$$
$$2 = 1e^{k(15)} \quad \textit{One bacterium can produce two in 15 minutes.}$$
$$2 = e^{15k}$$
$$\ln 2 = \ln e^{15k} \quad \textit{Take the natural logarithm of each side.}$$
$$\ln 2 = 15k \ln e \quad \textit{Power property of logarithms}$$
$$\ln 2 = 15k \quad \textit{ln e = 1}$$
$$\frac{\ln 2}{15} = k$$
$$\frac{0.6931}{15} = k$$
$$0.0462 \approx k \quad \textit{The constant is approximately 0.0462.}$$

Now apply the exponential growth and decay formula to find the number of bacteria present after four hours.

$$y = ne^{kt}$$
$$y = 1e^{(0.0462)(240)} \quad \textit{There are 240 minutes in four hours.}$$
$$y = e^{11.088} \quad \textit{Simplify.}$$
$$\ln y = \ln e^{11.088} \quad \textit{Take the natural logarithm of each side.}$$
$$\ln y = 11.088 \ln e \quad \textit{Power property of logarithms}$$
$$\ln y = 11.088 \quad \textit{Take the antiln of each side.}$$
$$y \approx 65382$$

There will be approximately 65,382 bacteria in four hours.

580   CHAPTER 12   EXPONENTIAL AND LOGARITHMIC FUNCTIONS

ALTERNATE TEACHING STRATEGIES

Using Charts

Using interest rates from a local bank and Example 3, have students create and complete a chart showing the amount of time it would take for investments to double at each (or some) of the listed interest rates. Use $600 and $1500 as the initial investments.

The general formula for growth and decay also describes the amount of decaying materials left after time. Study the example below.

Example 1

APPLICATION

Chemistry

Radioactive isotopes decay with time. In 9 years, just half of the mass of a 20-gram sample of an isotope remains. This period of time is called the half-life of the isotope. Find the constant k for this isotope when t is given in years.

$y = ne^{kt}$ *Since this problem involves decay, k will be negative.*

$10 = 20e^{k(9)}$ *Substitute 10 for y, 20 for n, and 9 for t.*

$0.5 = e^{9k}$

$\ln 0.5 = \ln e^{9k}$

$\ln 0.5 = 9k \ln e$

$\ln 0.5 = 9k$

$\dfrac{\ln 0.5}{9} = k$

$k \approx -0.0770$

The value of the constant for this isotope is approximately -0.0770.

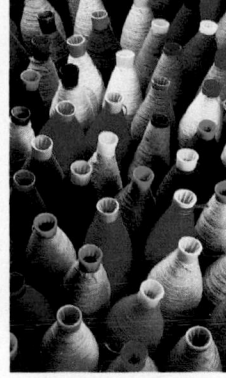

Teaching Tip ❷

Certain assets, such as cars, houses, and business equipment, depreciate or appreciate with time. The formula $V_n = P(1 + r)^n$, where V_n is the new value, P is the initial value, r is the fixed rate of appreciation or depreciation, and n is the number of years, can be used to compute the value of an asset. The value of r for a depreciating asset will be negative, and the value of r for an appreciating asset will be positive.

Example 2

APPLICATION

Business

Zoller Industries bought a piece of weaving equipment for $50,000. It is expected to depreciate at a steady rate of 10% each year. When will the value have depreciated to $25,000?

$V_n = P(1 + r)^n$

$25000 = 50000(1 - 0.10)^n$ *Substitute 25,000 for V_n,*

$0.5 = 0.9^n$ *50,000 for P,*

$\log 0.5 = \log 0.9^n$ *and $-.10$ for r.*

$\log 0.5 = n \log 0.9$

$\dfrac{\log 0.5}{\log 0.9} = n$

$n \approx 6.58$

The value of the equipment will be $25,000 in about $6\frac{1}{2}$ years.

LESSON 12-8 APPLICATIONS OF LOGARITHMS   581

For Example 3
Assume $100 is deposited in a savings account. The interest rate is 6% compounded continuously. When will the money be double the original amount?
in approximately 11.55 years

EVALUATING THE LESSON

Checking for Understanding

Exercises 1–7 are designed to help you assess understanding through reading, writing, and speaking. You should work through Exercises 1–3 with your students, and then monitor their work on Exercises 4–7.

Closing the Lesson

Speaking Activity Have students brainstorm a list of situations in which logarithms can be used to solve problems. Compare to any responses given at the beginning of the lesson.

You have studied compound interest where the interest is compounded at various intervals. When interest is compounded continuously, the formula for finding the amount in the account, A, after t years is $A = Pe^{rt}$, where P is the initial investment, and r is the annual interest rate.

Example 3
APPLICATION
Finance

FYI · · ·

You can estimate how long it will take for an investment to double by dividing the interest rate into 72. For example, an investment that pays 8% will double in about 9 years. This is known as the "Rule of 72."

The Saver's Club at Citizen's Fidelity Bank promises to double your money in $8\frac{1}{2}$ years. Assuming that the interest is compounded continuously, what is the interest rate?

$$A = Pe^{rt}$$
$$2 = 1e^{r(8.5)} \qquad \textit{Substitute 2 for A, 1 for P since the amount is doubled.}$$
$$2 = e^{8.5r}$$
$$\ln 2 = \ln e^{8.5r} \qquad \textit{Take the natural logarithm of each side.}$$
$$\ln 2 = 8.5r \ln e \qquad \textit{ln } a^b = b \ln a$$
$$\ln 2 = 8.5r$$
$$\frac{\ln 2}{8.5} = r$$
$$r \approx 0.0815$$

The interest rate is 8.15%.

CHECKING FOR UNDERSTANDING

Communicating Mathematics

Read and study the lesson to answer these questions.

1. Describe a situation where the constant k in the formula for growth and decay is positive and one where k is negative. Describe the situation if the value of k is zero. **See margin.**

2. The value of houses usually increase with time. Which formula would you use to find the value of a house that has appreciated 15% each year? $V_n = P(1 + r)^n$, **with** $r = 0.15$.

3. You are considering opening a savings account. Lake County Savings offers an account earning 8% interest compounded continuously and Beneficial Bank offers an account earning 8% compounded daily.

   a. Which account should you choose? **Based on interest alone, you should choose the account at Lake County Savings.**

   b. Are there any factors other than interest that you should consider when you choose between the two banks? **Other factors may include service charges, minimum balances, other services available like loans and safety deposit boxes.**

582 CHAPTER 12 EXPONENTIAL AND LOGARITHMIC FUNCTIONS

Additional Answer

1. **Answers may vary. Sample answers are bacteria growth and radioactive decay; If *k* is zero, then the population is not growing or decaying, the function is a constant function.**

Guided Practice Solve for each variable.

4. $40 = 200e^{7k}$ **-0.2299**
6. $200 = 100e^{.06t}$ **11.55**

5. $50000 = 25000(1 + 0.1)^n$ **7.27**
7. $2500 = 4e^{.58t}$ **11.1**

EXERCISES

Teaching Tip ③

Practice

Solve each problem.

A

8. For a certain strain of bacteria, k is 0.775 when t is measured in hours. How long will it take 2 bacteria to increase to 1000 bacteria? **8.02 hours**

9. Jackson deposited $100 in a savings account that pays 6% interest compounded continuously. He just withdrew the entire balance of $200. How long ago did he open the account? **about 11 years, 6 months**

B

10. The constant k for a radioactive substance is -0.08042 when t is measured in years. In how many years will a 250-gram sample reduce to 50 grams? **20.01 years**

11. A culture of a certain bacteria will grow from 500 to 4000 bacteria in 90 minutes. Find the constant k for this bacteria if k is in hours. **1.3863**

12. Charlotte invested $1000 in a certificate of deposit three years ago. The CD is now worth $1276. Assuming that the interest was compounded continuously, what was the interest rate? **8.12%**

13. A piece of office equipment valued at $25,000 depreciates at a steady rate of 10% annually. In how many years will it be worth $5000? **15.28 yr**

14. Keith has saved $2000 to buy a synthesizer that will cost about $2500. If he has the money in an account paying 7.25% compounded continuously, when will Keith be able to buy the synthesizer? **3.08 years**

C

15. Suppose you deposited $10 in a savings account that pays 8% interest compounded continuously. **28.78 years**
   a. In how many years will the account have a balance of $100?
   b. In how many years will the balance be $1000? **57.56 years**

16. The Holub's bought a condominium for $63,000. Assuming that its value will appreciate 8% a year, how much will the condo be worth in five years when the Holub's are ready to move? **$92,568**

17. Ten years ago, Cathy's mother bought a new car for $6000. Cathy is now going to buy the car for $600. Assuming a steady rate of depreciation what was the annual rate of depreciation? **20.56%**

RETEACHING THE LESSON

Population is another application of logarithms. Have the class orally work through the following problem: The population of Fargo, Ohio obeys the equation $y = ce^{kt}$ where c and k are constants and t is the time in years. If Fargo had 3000 residents in 1960 and 4200 in 1970, what was its population in 1980? **y = 5880 in 1980**

APPLYING THE LESSON

Homework Exercises

Assignment Guide

Basic: 8–16, 21–38
Average: 9–18, 21–38
Enriched: 10–38

Chapter 12, Quiz D, (Lessons 12-7 through 12-8), is available in the Evaluation Masters Booklet, p. 164.

Teaching Tip ③ You may also want students to identify the appropriate formula for solving each exercise.

Reteaching Masters Booklet, p. 83

12-8 NAME _____ DATE _____
Reteaching Worksheet
Applications of Logarithms
Many problems can be solved by applying the following formulas:

Growth and Decay Formula	$y = ne^{kt}$	y is the final amount, n is the initial amount, k is a constant, and t represents time.
Continuously Compounded Interest	$A = Pe^{rt}$	P is the initial investment, r is the annual interest rate, and t is the time in years.
Value of Equipment and Assets in Business	$V_n = P(1 + r)^n$	V_n is the new value, P is the initial value, r is the fixed rate of appreciation or depreciation, and n is the number of years.

Example: Find how long it will take money to double if it is invested at 8% annual interest, compounded continuously.

$A = Pe^{rt}$ Substitute 2 for A, 1 for P since the
$2 = 1e^{0.08t}$ amount is doubled. $r = 0.08$
$\ln 2 = \ln e^{0.08t}$ Take the natural log of each side.
$\ln 2 = 0.08t(\ln e)$ Power Property of Logarithms
$\ln 2 = 0.08t$
$\frac{\ln 2}{0.08} = t$
$8.6643 = t$

The money will double in approximately 8.66 years.

Solve each problem.

1. Carl plans to invest $500 at 8.25% interest, compounded continuously. How long will it take for his money to triple?
   13.316 years

2. A certain strain of bacteria grows from 40 to 326 in 120 minutes. Find k for the growth formula.
   0.0175

3. A $40,000 car depreciates at a constant rate of 12% per year. In how many years will the car be worth $12,000?
   9.42 years

18. A radioactive substance decays according to the equation $A = A_0 \times 10^{-0.024t}$, where t is in hours. Find the half-life of the substance, that is when $A = 0.5A_0$. **12.54 hours**

19. Colin has saved $500 of the money he earned working at Carousel Music Store. If he spends 10% of the money each week, after how many weeks will he have less than $1? *(Hint: Use $V_n = P(1 + r)^n$, where n is the number of weeks.)* **59 weeks**

20. A piece of machinery valued at $2,500 depreciates at a steady rate of 10% yearly. The owner of the business will replace the equipment when its value has depreciated to $500. In how many years will the equipment be replaced? **about $15\frac{1}{4}$ years**

Critical Thinking

21. Compare the formulas for exponential growth, $y = ne^{kt}$, and for continuously compounded interest, $A = Pe^{rt}$. Explain how the formulas are related. **Both equations find the final amount of something that is added to by the same rate over and over again.**

Applications

22. **Electronics** The output in watts of a power supply is given by $w = 50e^{-0.004t}$, where t is the time in days. In how many days will the power output be reduced to 20 watts? **229.07 days**

23. **Chemistry** Radium-226 decomposes radioactively. Its half-life, that is the time that it takes for half of the sample to decompose, is 1800 years. Find the constant k for this compound. Use 100 grams as the original amount. **−0.000385**

24. **Real Estate** Ten years ago, Mr. and Mrs. Oon bought a house for $49,000. Their home is now worth $120,000. Assuming a steady rate of growth, what was the annual rate of appreciation? **9.37%**

Teaching Tip ❹

Computer

This BASIC program determines the number of payments needed to accumulate an amount of money, given the amount of each payment, the annual interest rate, and the number of payments per year. The formula $S = R\left[\dfrac{(1 + I)^N - 1}{I}\right]$ finds the amount accumulated when payments are made at regular intervals and interest is compounded at the end of each payment period.

```
10  INPUT "ENTER THE AMOUNT TO BE
    ACCUMULATED: $"; S
20  INPUT "ENTER THE AMOUNT OF
    EACH PAYMENT: $"; R
30  INPUT "ENTER THE ANNUAL
    INTEREST RATE AS A PERCENT: ";
    IR
40  INPUT "ENTER THE NUMBER OF
    PAYMENTS PER YEAR: "; PAY
50  LET I = IR/(PAY*100):PRINT
60  LET N = LOG(S*I/R+1)/LOG(1+I)
70  IF N = INT(N+1) THEN 90
80  LET N = INT(N+1)
90  PRINT N; "PAYMENTS ARE NEEDED
    TO ACCUMULATE $"; S
100 END
```

584 CHAPTER 12 EXPONENTIAL AND LOGARITHMIC FUNCTIONS

Practice Masters Booklet, p. 95

NAME _____ DATE _____

12-8 Practice Worksheet

Applications of Logarithms

Solve each problem.

1. Suppose $500 is invested at 6% annual interest compounded twice a year. When will the investment be worth $1000?
11.72 years

2. Suppose $500 is invested at 6% annual interest compounded continuously. When will the investment be worth $1000?
11.55 years

3. An organism of a certain type can grow from 30 to 195 organisms in 5 hours. Find k for the growth formula.
0.3744

4. For a certain strain of bacteria, k is 0.825 when t is measured in days. How long will it take 20 bacteria to increase to 2000?
5.582 days

5. An investment service promises to triple your money in 12 years. Assuming continuous compounding of interest, what rate of interest is needed?
9.155%

6. A substance decomposes radioactively. Its half-life is 32 years. Find the constant k in the decay formula.
−0.02166

7. A piece of machinery valued at $250,000 depreciates at 12% per year by the fixed rate method. After how many years will the value have depreciated to $100,000?
7.168 years

8. Dave bought a new car 8 years ago for $5400. To buy a new car comparably equipped now would cost $12,500. Assuming a steady rate of increase, what was the yearly rate of inflation in car prices over the 8-year period?
11.06%

T

In the formula, R represents the amount of each payment, I represents the annual interest rate, N represents the number of payments, and S represents the amount of money accumulated immediately after the final payment. In the program, the formula is solved for N.

Use the program on the previous page to determine the number of payments needed to accumulate the indicated amount of money, given the amount of each payment, the annual interest rate, and the number of payments each year.

25. $4000; $300; 9%; 2 **11**

26. $7500; $400; 8.5%; 4 **16**

27. $8995; $156; 9.25%; 12 **48**

28. $14,600; $195; 8.75%; 12 **60**

29. $96,000; $850; 9.65%; 12 **81**

30. $90,000; $425; 9.65%; 26 **157**

31. Each month, Michael deposits $100 into an account that earns 8.75% compounded monthly. How many months will it take him to accumulate $3000 in his account? **28**

32. Every three months, Guillermo invests $300 in an account that pays 8.3% interest compounded quarterly. Joyce invests $98 each month in her account, which pays 9.3% interest compounded monthly. Who will accumulate $5000 more quickly? **Joyce**

Mixed Review

33. Approximate $\log_7 12$ to three decimal places. **(Lesson 12-7)** **1.277**

34. State all possible rational zeros for the function $f(x) = 3x^4 - 5x^2 + 4$. **(Lesson 10-5)** $\pm 1, \pm 2, \pm 4, \pm\frac{1}{3}, \pm\frac{2}{3}, \pm\frac{4}{3}$

35. For the function $f(x) = (x + 9)^2$, identify the quadratic term, the linear term, and the constant term. **(Lesson 8-1)** x^2, **18x**, **81**

36. **Photography** Shina Murakami is a professional photographer. She has a photograph that is 4 inches wide and 6 inches long. She wishes to make a print of the photograph for a competition. The area of the new print is to be five times the area of the original. If Ms. Murakami is going to add the same amount to the length and the width of the photograph, what will the dimensions of the new print be? **(Lesson 7-4)** **10 in. by 12 in.**

37. **Physics** Metal expands and contracts with changes in temperature. The change in the length of steel per degree Celsius is given by the constant 11×10^{-6}. Over a period of time, the temperature of a steel bridge 200 meters long varies by 70° Celsius. What is the change in the length of the bridge in centimeters? **(Lesson 5-1)** **15.4 cm**

38. Solve the inequality $3x + 1 < x + 5$. **(Lesson 1-7)** $\{x | x < 2\}$

LESSON 12-8 APPLICATIONS OF LOGARITHMS **585**

EXTENDING THE LESSON

Math Power: Connections

Have students solve the following problem. In 4 years, an investment of $750 grew to $1050. When will the investment be tripled, assuming continuous compounding? **13.06 years**

Enrichment Masters Booklet, p. 83

CHAPTER **12** SUMMARY AND REVIEW

VOCABULARY

Upon completing this chapter, you should be familiar with the following terms:

antilogarithm	564	546	exponential function
characteristic	563	553	logariths
common logarithm	563	555	logarithmic function
e	567	563	mantissa
exponential equation	574	567	natural logarithm

SKILLS AND CONCEPTS

OBJECTIVES AND EXAMPLES	REVIEW EXERCISES

Upon completing this chapter, you should be able to:

Use these exercises to review and prepare for the chapter test.

■ simplify expressions and solve equations involving real exponents **(Lesson 12-1)**

Simplify $(9^{\sqrt{5}})^{\sqrt{5}}$.
$$(9^{\sqrt{5}})^{\sqrt{5}} = 9^{\sqrt{5}\cdot\sqrt{5}}$$
$$= 9^5$$

Solve $9^{3r} = 27^{r-2}$.
$$9^{3r} = 27^{r-2}$$
$$(3^2)^{3r} = (3^3)^{r-2}$$
$$3^{6r} = 3^{3r-6}$$
$$6r = 3r - 6$$
$$r = -2$$

Simplify each expression.

1. $3^{\sqrt{2}}\, 3^{\sqrt{2}}$ $\mathbf{3^{2\sqrt{2}}}$ 2. $(9^{\sqrt{2}})^{\sqrt{2}}$ **81**

3. $\dfrac{49^{\sqrt{2}}}{7^{\sqrt{12}}}$ $\mathbf{7^{2\sqrt{2}-2\sqrt{3}}}$ 4. $(x^{\sqrt{5}})^{\sqrt{20}}$ $\mathbf{x^{10}}$

Solve each equation.

5. $2^{6x} = 4^{5x+2}$ **−1**   6. $(\sqrt{3})^{n+1} = 9^{n-1}$ $\mathbf{\frac{5}{3}}$

7. $49^{3p+1} = 7^{2p-5}$ $\mathbf{-\frac{7}{4}}$ 8. $9^{x^2} = 27^{x^2-2}$ $\mathbf{\pm\sqrt{6}}$

■ write exponential equations in logarithmic form and vice versa. **(Lesson 12-2)**

$$\log_7 343 = 3$$

Write $3^3 = 27$ in logarithmic form.
$$3^3 = 27$$
$$3 = \log_3 27$$

Write $\log_4 64 = 3$ in exponential form.
$$\log_4 64 = 3$$
$$64 = 4^3$$

Write each equation in logarithmic form.

9. $7^3 = 343$ 10. $5^{-2} = \frac{1}{25}$ $\log_5 \frac{1}{25} = -2$

11. $4^0 = 1$ $\log_4 1 = 0$ 12. $4^{\frac{3}{2}} = 8$ $\log_4 8 = \frac{3}{2}$

13. $4^3 = 64$ 15. $6^{-2} = \frac{1}{36}$

Write each equation in exponential form.

13. $\log_4 64 = 3$ 14. $\log_8 2 = \frac{1}{3}$ $8^{\frac{1}{3}} = 2$

15. $\log_6 \frac{1}{36} = -2$ 16. $\log_6 1 = 0$ $6^0 = 1$

■ evaluate logarithmic expressions and solve logarithmic equations. (**Lesson 12-2**)

Evaluate $\log_3 3^5$. $\log_3 3^5 = x$
$$3^x = 3^5$$
$$x = 5$$

Solve $\log_b 16 = 4$. $b^4 = 16$
$$b = \sqrt[4]{16}$$
$$b = 2$$

Evaluate each expression.

17. $\log_5 5^7$ **7**   18. $6^{\log_6 7}$ **7**

19. $\log_n n^3$ **3**   20. $n^{\log_n 3}$ **3**

Solve each equation.

21. $\log_b 9 = 2$ **3**   22. $\log_b 9 = \frac{1}{2}$ **81**

23. $\log_{16} 2 = x$ $\frac{1}{4}$ 24. $\log_4 x = -\frac{1}{2}$ $\frac{1}{2}$

■ solve equations involving logarithmic functions.   (**Lesson 12-2**)

For $b > 0$ and $b \neq 1$, $\log_b x_1 = \log_b x_2$ if and only if $x_1 = x_2$.

Solve $\log_3 10 = \log_3 (2x)$.
$$10 = 2x$$
$$5 = x$$

Solve each equation.

25. $\log_6 12 = \log_6 (5x - 3)$ **3**

26. $\log_4 (1 - 2x) = \log_4 (x + 10)$ **-3**

27. $\log_7 (x^2 + x) = \log_7 12$ **-4, 3**

28. $\log_2 (x - 1)^2 = \log_2 7$ $\mathbf{1 \pm \sqrt{7}}$

■ solve equations or simplify and evaluate expressions using the product, quotient, and power properties.   (**Lesson 12-3**)

For all positive numbers m, n and b, where $b \neq 1$.

$\log_b mn = \log_b m + \log_b n$

$\log_b \dfrac{m}{n} = \log_b m - \log_b n$

$\log_b m^n = n \log_b m$

Use $\log_9 7 = 0.8856$ and $\log_9 4 = 0.6309$ to evaluate each expression.

29. $\log_9 28$ **1.5165**   30. $\log_9 49$ **1.7712**

31. $\log_9 144$ **2.2618**   32. $\log_9 15.75$ **1.2547**

Solve each equation.

33. $\log_3 x - \log_3 4 = \log_3 12$ **48**

34. $\log_2 y = \frac{1}{3} \log_2 27$ **3**

35. $\log_5 7 + \frac{1}{2} \log_5 4 - \log_5 x$ **14**

36. $2 \log_2 x - \log_2 (x + 3) = 2$ **6**

■ identify the characteristic and mantissa of a logarithm.   (**Lesson 12-4**)

$\log 4{,}300 \approx 3.6336$

3 is the characteristic.
0.6335 is the mantissa.

If $\log 36.2 = 1.5587$, find each number.

37. the characteristic of $\log 36.2$ **1**

38. the mantissa of $\log 36.2$ **0.5587**

If $\log 0.00927 = -2.0329$, find each number.

39. the characteristic of $\log 0.00927$ **-3**

40. the mantissa of $\log 0.00927$ **0.9671**

Alternate Review Strategy

To provide a brief in-class review, you may wish to read the following questions to the class and require a verbal or written response.

1. Simplify $6^{\sqrt{3}} \cdot 6^{\sqrt{5}}$. $\mathbf{6^{\sqrt{3}+\sqrt{5}}}$
2. Simplify $(6^{\sqrt{3}})^{\sqrt{5}}$. $\mathbf{6^{\sqrt{15}}}$
3. Solve $\log_2 (x - 6) = \log_2 3$. $\mathbf{x = 9}$
4. Evaluate $\log_3 243$.   **5**
5. Solve $\log_b x - \log_b 6 = \log_b 4$.   **24**
6. Using a calculator, find the antilogarithm of 3.5431 to the nearest whole number.   **3492**
7. Find the value of $\ln 9.67$ to four decimal places.   **2.2690**
8. Estimate the amount of a 15 percent tip if the restaurant bill is \$39.67.   **\$6.00**
9. Express $\log_3 35$ in terms of common logarithms. $\dfrac{\log 35}{\log 3}$
10. In the formula for appreciation and depreciation, when is the rate positive and when is it negative?   **negative for depreciation; positive for appreciation**

The Cumulative Review shown below can be used to review skills and concepts presented thus far in the text. Standardized Test Practice Questions are also provided in the Evaluation Masters Booklet.

Evaluation Masters Booklet, pp. 165–166

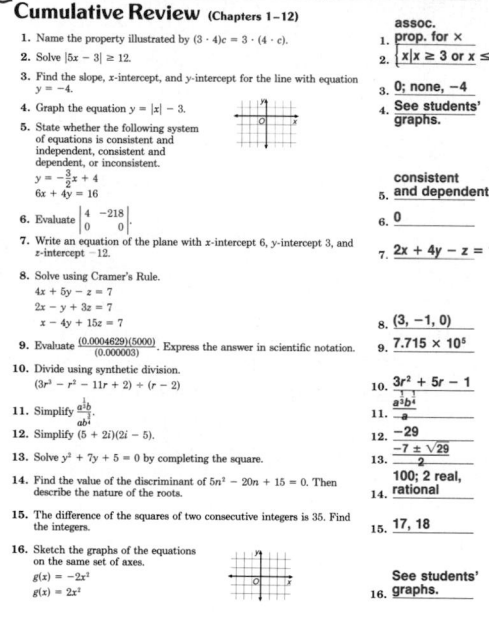

■ find common logarithms and antilogarithms. **(Lesson 12-4)**

Use the [LOG] key of your calculator to find common logarithms, the [10ˣ] key to find the antilogarithm.

Find the logarithm of each number

41. 0.003141 **−2.5029** 42. 50,030 **4.6992**

Find the antilogarithm of each logarithm.
0.0003609   **971.9**
43. 0.5574 − 4   44. 2.9876

■ find natural logarithms of numbers. **(Lesson 12-5)**

Use the [LN] key of your calculator to find common logarithms, the e^x key to find the antilogarithm.

Find each value.

45. ln 2.3 **0.8329**   46. ln 9.25 **2.2246**
47. antiln 1.9755 **7.21** 48. antiln 2.246 **9.45**

■ solve equations with variable exponents using logarithms. **(Lesson 12-7)**

$$3^{x-4} = 5^{x-1}$$
$$\log 3^{x-4} = \log 5^{x-1}$$
$$(x-4)\log 3 = (x-1)(\log 5)$$
$$x \log 3 - 4 \log 3 = x \log 5 - \log 5$$
$$x = \frac{4 \log 3 - \log 5}{\log 3 - \log 5}$$
$$x \approx -5.4502$$

Use logarithms to solve each equation.

49. $2^x = 53$ **5.7286**   50. $\log_4 11.2 = x$ **1.7427**

51. $2.3^{x^2} = 66.6$ **±2.2452**   52. $3^{4x-7} = 4^{2x+3}$ **7.3059**

53. $\sqrt{3^b} = 2^{b+1}$ **−4.8188**   54. $6^{3y} = 8^{y-3}$ **−1.8928**

55. $300 = 20e^{5t}$ **0.5416**

56. $500 = P(1 + 0.2)^5$ **200**

APPLICATIONS AND CONNECTIONS

57. **Business** A car valued at $14,000 depreciates 18% a year. After how many years will the value have depreciated to $1000? Estimate the answer and then check your estimate against the answer you obtain using $V = P(1 + r)^n$. **(Lesson 12-6)** **13.30 years**

58. **Science** For a certain strain of bacteria, k is 0.872 when t is measured in days. How long will it take 9 bacteria to increase to 738 bacteria? **(Lesson 12-8) 5.05 days**

59. **Finance** If $200 is invested at 6% annual interest compounded continuously when will the investment be worth $300? Use $A = Pe^{rt}$. **(Lesson 12-8) 6.76 years**

60. **Science** A bacteria culture grows from 400 to 5000 bacteria in 2 hours. Find the constant k for the growth formula $y = ne^{kt}$ where t is in hours. **(Lesson 12-8) 1.2629**

NAME _____ DATE _____
Cumulative Review (Chapters 1–12)

1. Name the property illustrated by $(3 \cdot 4)c = 3 \cdot (4 \cdot c)$.
1. **assoc. prop. for ×**

2. Solve $|5x - 3| \geq 12$.
2. $\{x \mid x \geq 3 \text{ or } x \leq -\frac{9}{5}\}$

3. Find the slope, x-intercept, and y-intercept for the line with equation $y = -4$.
3. **0; none, −4**

4. Graph the equation $y = |x| - 3$.
4. **See students' graphs.**

5. State whether the following system of equations is consistent and independent, consistent and dependent, or inconsistent.
$y = -\frac{3}{2}x + 4$
$6x + 4y = 16$
5. **consistent and dependent**

6. Evaluate $\begin{vmatrix} 4 & -218 \\ 0 & 0 \end{vmatrix}$.
6. **0**

7. Write an equation of the plane with x-intercept 6, y-intercept 3, and z-intercept −12.
7. **2x + 4y − z = 12**

8. Solve using Cramer's Rule.
$4x + 5y - z = 7$
$2x - y + 3z = 7$
$x - 4y + 15z = 7$
8. **(3, −1, 0)**

9. Evaluate $\frac{(0.0004629)(5000)}{(0.000003)}$. Express the answer in scientific notation.
9. **7.715 × 10⁵**

10. Divide using synthetic division.
$(3r^3 - r^2 - 11r + 2) \div (r - 2)$
10. **3r² + 5r − 1**

11. Simplify $\frac{a^{\frac{1}{3}}b}{ab^{\frac{1}{3}}}$.
11. **$\frac{a^{\frac{1}{3}}b^{\frac{2}{3}}}{a}$**

12. Simplify $(5 + 2i)(2i - 5)$.
12. **−29**

13. Solve $y^2 + 7y + 5 = 0$ by completing the square.
13. **$\frac{-7 \pm \sqrt{29}}{2}$**

14. Find the value of the discriminant of $5n^2 - 20n + 15 = 0$. Then describe the nature of the roots.
14. **100; 2 real, rational**

15. The difference of the squares of two consecutive integers is 35. Find the integers.
15. **17, 18**

16. Sketch the graphs of the equations on the same set of axes.
$g(x) = -2x^2$
$g(x) = 2x^2$
16. **See students' graphs.**

NAME _____ DATE _____
Cumulative Review (Chapters 1–12) - continued

17. Write the equation $f(x) = -3x^2 - 18x - 29$ in the form $f(x) = a(x - h)^2 + k$. Name the vertex, the axis of symmetry, and the direction of opening of the parabola that is the graph of the equation.
17. **$f(x) = -3(x + 3)^2 - 2$ (−3, −2); x = −3; down**

18. Solve $x^2 + 5x - 14 \geq 0$.
18. **$\{x \mid x \leq -7 \text{ or } x \geq 2\}$**

19. Use the distance formula to find the distance between the points $(2\sqrt{3}, 3\sqrt{3})$ and $(0, -\sqrt{3})$.
19. **$2\sqrt{15}$**

20. Find the vertices, foci, and slopes of the asymptotes for the hyperbola whose equation is $4x^2 - 25y^2 = 100$.
20. **(±5, 0), (±$\sqrt{29}$, 0), ±$\frac{2}{5}$**

21. State whether the graph of the equation is a circle, parabola, ellipse, or hyperbola: $\frac{x^2}{40} + \frac{y^2}{25} = 1$
21. **ellipse**

22. Find $p(x - 1)$ if $p(x) = x^2 - 1$.
22. **$p(x - 1) = x^2 - 2x$**

23. State the number of positive real zeros, negative real zeros, and imaginary zeros of $f(x) = x^4 + 1$.
23. **0 pos, 0 neg, 4 imag**

24. Graph the function $f(x) = 2x - 1$ and its inverse on the same set of axes.
24. **See students' graphs.**

25. Simplify $\frac{(1-r)^2}{16} \div \frac{r-1}{-40}$.
25. **$\frac{5-5r}{2}$**

26. Simplify $\frac{\frac{3a}{7a} + \frac{2a}{5}}{\frac{4a}{x} + \frac{10}{x}}$.
26. **$\frac{31}{28}$**

27. Solve $\frac{3}{a^2-1} = \frac{1}{a+1}$.
27. **4**

28. If y varies directly as x and $y = 16$ when $x = 2$, what is y when $x = 5$?
28. **40**

29. Simplify $5^{\sqrt{2}} \cdot 5^{\sqrt{5}}$.
29. **$5^{\sqrt{2}+\sqrt{5}}$**

30. Solve $\log_{\sqrt{2}} 16 = x$.
30. **8**

31. Find the log 0.0001582.
31. **0.1992 − 4 or −3.8008**

32. The number of bacteria of a certain type can increase from 80 to 164 in 3 hours. Find the value of k in the general formula for growth and decay, $y = ne^{kt}$.
32. **0.2393**

Write each equation in logarithmic form.

1. $6^4 = 1296$ $\log_6 1296 = 4$

2. $3^7 = 2187$ $\log_3 2187 = 7$

Write each equation in exponential form.

3. $\log_5 625 = 4$ $5^4 = 625$

4. $\log_8 16 = \frac{4}{3}$ $8^{\frac{4}{3}} = 16$

Evaluate each expression.

5. $\log_{12} 12^2$ **2**

6. $4^{\log_4 3}$ **3**

7. $\log_b b^{1.6}$ **1.6**

Solve each equation.

8. $9^x = 3^{3x-2}$ **2**

9. $27^{2p+1} = 3^{4p-1}$ **-2**

10. $\log_m 144 = -2$ $\frac{1}{12}$

11. $\log_2 128 = y$ **7**

12. $\log_3 x - 2\log_3 2 = 3\log_3 3$ **108**

13. $\log_{\sqrt{7}} x = 4$ **49**

14. $\log_5(8r - 7) = \log_5(r^2 + 5)$ **2, 6**

15. $\log_9(x + 4) + \log_9(x - 4) = 1$ **5**

Use $\log_4 7 = 1.4037$ and $\log_4 3 = 0.7925$ to evaluate each expression.

16. $\log_4 21$ **2.1962**

17. $\log_4 9$ **1.585**

18. $\log_4 36$ **2.585**

19. $\log_4 \frac{7}{12}$ **-0.3888**

Find each value, rounded to four decimal places.

20. $\log 769,000$
   5.0059

21. $\log 0.00535$
   0.7284 − 3

22. $\ln 9.6$
   2.2618

23. antilog -3.1649
   0.006841

24. antilog 6.3337
   2,156,000

25. antiln 0.4055
   1.5001

Use logarithms to solve each equation.

26. $7.6^{x-1} = 401$ **3.9910**

27. $\log_4 37 = x$ **2.6047**

28. $3^x = 5^{x-1}$ **3.1507**

29. $\sqrt{2^{b-4}} = 6^b$ **-0.9592**

30. $4^{2x-3} = 9^{x+2}$ **14.8659**

31. $45.9 = e^{0.75t}$ **5.1020**

32. **Finance** Suppose that a pilgrim ancestor of Jenny Chambers deposited $10 in a savings account at Provident Savings Bank. The annual interest rate was 4% compounded continuously. The account is now worth $75,000. How long ago was the account started? (Use $A = Pe^{rt}$.) **223 years**

33. **Biology** A certain culture of bacteria will grow from 500 to 4000 bacteria in 1.5 hours. Find the constant k for the growth formula. (Use $y = ne^{kt}$.) **1.3863**

Bonus Solve $\log x^2 = (\log x)^2$. **1 or 100**

This page may be used as a test or as a review. In addition, two multiple-choice tests and two free-response tests are provided in the Evaluation Masters Booklet. Chapter 12 Test, Form 1A is shown below.

Evaluation Masters Booklet, pp. 155–156

NAME _____ DATE _____

Chapter 12 Test, Form 1A

Write the letter for the correct answer in the blank at the right of each problem.

1. Simplify $32^{\sqrt{3}} \cdot 4^{\sqrt{3}}$.
   A. $2^{5\sqrt{3}+2\sqrt{3}}$ B. $128^{\sqrt{3}}$ C. $2^{10\sqrt{3}}$ D. $128^{\sqrt{3}+\sqrt{3}}$ 1. __A__

2. Solve $\left(\frac{1}{7}\right)^x = 7^{x+4}$.
   A. -2 B. 0   C. 2   D. 4   2. __A__

3. Write $7^3 = 343$ in logarithmic form.
   A. $\log_7 343 = 3$ B. $\log_3 343 = 7$
   C. $\log_7 3 = 343$ D. $\log_3 7 = 343$ 3. __A__

4. Write $\log_{10} 0.0001 = -4$ in exponential form.
   A. $0.0001^{-4} = 10$ B. $-4^{10} = 0.0001$
   C. $10^{-4} = 0.0001$ D. $10^{0.0001} = 4$ 4. __C__

5. Evaluate $\log_{16} 4$.
   A. 2   B. -2 C. $\frac{1}{2}$ D. $\frac{1}{4}$ 5. __C__

6. Solve $\log_x 9 = 2$.
   A. 3   B. 4.5   C. $-3, 3$ D. 81   6. __A__

7. Solve $\log_5 y = -3$.
   A. -15 B. -125 C. $\frac{1}{125}$ D. $\sqrt[3]{5}$ 7. __C__

8. Evaluate $\log_5 5^5$.
   A. 5   B. 6   C. 25   D. 36   8. __B__

9. Evaluate $7^{\log_7 25}$.
   A. 8   B. 7   C. 10   D. 48   9. __C__

10. Solve $\log_3(x^2 + 4x) = \log_3 12$.
    A. {2}   B. {6}   C. {-2, 6}   D. {-6, 2}   10. __D__

11. If $\log_5 6 = 1.631$ and $\log_5 4 = 1.262$, evaluate $\log_5 1.5$.
    A. 0.262   B. 0.631   C. 2.893   D. 0.369   11. __D__

12. Solve $\log_x y = \frac{1}{3}\log_x 125$.
    A. 5   B. 2   C. 375   D. $\frac{125}{3}$ 12. __A__

13. Solve $\frac{1}{2}\log_3 x = 4\log_3 9 - \log_3 4$.
    A. 2   B. 4   C. 16   D. 32   13. __C__

14. Solve $\log_4(m - 1) + \log_4(m - 1) = 2$.
    A. 3   B. 5   C. 9   D. $-3, 5$ 14. __B__

NAME _____ DATE _____

Chapter 12 Test, Form 1A (continued)

15. If $\log w = 7$ and $\log n = 4$, evaluate $\log \frac{w}{n}$.
    A. 3   B. 4   C. 1.75   D. 28   15. __A__

16. If $\log 0.048 = -1.3188$, what is the mantissa of $\log 0.048$?
    A. 0.3188   B. -1 C. -2 D. 0.6812   16. __D__

17. If $\log 48 = 1.6812$, what is the characteristic of $\log 48$?
    A. 0.3188   B. 1   C. 2   D. 0.6812   17. __B__

18. What is the logarithm of 84,300?
    A. $0.9258 - 4$ B. 9258   C. 0.9258   D. 4.9258   18. __D__

19. What is the antilog of $0.6405 - 1$?
    A. 0.437   B. 0.0437   C. 43.7   D. 43   19. __A__

20. Find $\ln 0.0622$, rounded to four decimal places.
    A. -1.2062 B. -2.7774 C. 0.2226   D. 0.7938   20. __B__

21. Find antiln 3.612, rounded to four significant digits.
    A. 0.004093   B. 37,040   C. 37.04   D. 4093   21. __C__

22. What is the approximate value of $\log_5 6$?
    A. 2   B. 0.7782   C. 0.6131   D. 1.6309   22. __D__

23. What is the approximate solution of $3^{x+1} = 5^x$?
    A. 2.1507   B. 141.4686   C. 0.4651   D. -0.4651 23. __A__

24. A certain strain of bacteria can grow from 50 to 180 bacteria in 4 hours. What is the approximate value of k for the growth formula $y = ne^{kt}$?
    A. 2.144   B. 0.3311   C. 2.09   D. 0.3202   24. __D__

25. Assume $50 is deposited in a savings account. If the interest rate is 11.5% compounded continuously, after how long will the amount of money in the account be double the original amount? ($A = Pe^{rt}$)
    A. 9.55 years   B. 1.53 years   C. 7.92 years   D. 8.35 years   25. __A__

Bonus
What is the solution set of $\log(x^2) = (\log x)^2$?
    A. {10, 100}   B. {1, 100}   C. {-1, 1}   D. {1}   Bonus __B__

A **Test and Review Generator** is provided in Apple, IBM, and Macintosh versions. You may use this software to create your own tests or worksheets, based on the needs of your students.

The **Performance Assessment Booklet** provides an alternate assessment for evaluating student progress. An assessment for this chapter can be found on pages 23–24.

The questions on these pages deal with rational expressions and radicals.

Directions: Choose the one best answer. Write A, B, C, or D.

1. If $\frac{x}{y} = z$ and $y = z$, find y in terms of x.

C

(A) y (B) $\pm\sqrt{y}$

(C) $\pm\sqrt{x}$ (D) $\pm\sqrt{xz}$

2. If the average of x and y equals the average of x, y, and z, then express z in terms of x and y.

C

(A) $x + y$ (B) $2(x + y)$

(C) $\frac{x + y}{2}$ (D) $\frac{x + y}{3}$

3. If the product of a number and $2b$ is increased by y, the result is p. Find the number in terms of b, y, and p.

C

(A) $2by - p$ (B) $\frac{2b}{y - p}$

(C) $\frac{p - y}{2b}$ (D) $\frac{y - b}{2b}$

4. If $\frac{1}{p} = \sqrt{0.25}$, then $p^2 =$

B

(A) 0.25   (B) 4

(C) 25   (D) 400

5. Of the following numbers, which is the greatest?

D

(A) $\frac{1}{3\sqrt{3}}$ (B) $\frac{1}{3}$

(C) $\frac{\sqrt{3}}{3}$ (D) $\sqrt{3}$

6. If $\frac{a + b}{a} = \frac{5}{4}$, then $\frac{b}{a} =$

A

(A) $\frac{1}{4}$ (B) $\frac{5}{4}$ (C) $\frac{7}{4}$ (D) $\frac{9}{4}$

7. Of the following, which is the closest to the value of $\frac{65.9 \times 0.49?}{3.3}$

A

(A) 10   (B) 80   (C) 100   (D) 450

8. The reciprocal of $\frac{5}{b - 1} + \frac{3}{b}$ is

C

(A) $\frac{b^2 - b}{15}$ (B) $\frac{b - 1}{2}$

(C) $\frac{b^2 - b}{8b - 3}$ (D) $\frac{2b - 1}{8}$

9. Simplify $\frac{1 \div \frac{1}{b}}{\frac{1}{b}}$.

D

(A) 1   (B) $\frac{1}{b}$ (C) b (D) b^2

10. If $4b - 3a = 0$, then what is the value of $\frac{16b^2}{a^2}$?

B

(A) $\frac{1}{9}$ (B) 9   (C) 16   (D) $\frac{256}{9}$

11. If $xyz = 8$ and $y = z$, then $x =$

B

(A) y^2 (B) $\frac{8}{y^2}$ (C) $8y^2$ (D) $\frac{1}{y^2}$

12. If $\frac{2b}{5a} = 12$, then $\frac{2b - 10a}{5a} =$

B

(A) 5   (B) 10   (C) 14   (D) 24

13. If $\frac{x}{6} + 4 = 1$, the value of $\frac{x}{3}$ is

C

(A) -36 (B) -18

(C) -6 (D) 6

14. If $3 + \frac{d}{4} = \frac{81}{2}$, then $d =$

D

(A) 10 (B) 80

(C) 100 (D) 150

15. Betty can mow the lawn in x hours. Ted

C can mow the same lawn in y hours. If they work together, how long will it take them to mow the lawn?

(A) $\frac{x+y}{2}$ (B) $\frac{1}{x+y}$

(C) $\frac{xy}{x+y}$ (D) $\frac{x+y}{xy}$

16. Mike saves c cents per week. In n weeks how much money, in terms of dollars, will he have saved?

C

(A) nc (B) $100nc$

(C) $\frac{nc}{100}$ (D) $\frac{n+c}{100}$

17. If $\frac{a}{b} = c$, then $\log c =$

B

(A) $\frac{\log a}{\log b}$

(B) $\log a - \log b$

(C) $\log (a - b)$

(D) $\frac{\log a}{b}$

18. Which of the following is not a real

C number?

(A) $\sqrt{(-3)^2}$ (B) $\sqrt[3]{(-3)^3}$

(C) $\sqrt{-(3)^2}$ (D) $\sqrt[3]{-(3)^3}$

19. Find the value of $(5\sqrt{3})^2$.

A

(A) 75 (B) 225 (C) $10\sqrt{6}$ (D) 150

20. A man owns $\frac{1}{4}$ of a business. He sells

C half of his share for \$12,000. What is the total value of the business?

(A) \$1500   (B) \$48,000

(C) \$96,000   (D) \$108,000

21. If a runner can cover 2 miles in

B 25 minutes, what is the rate in miles per hour?

(A) 5 (B) 4.8 (C) 3 (D) 0.8

22. If $x^2 + y^2 = 15$ and $(x + y)^2 = 35$, then

B $xy =$

(A) 5 (B) 10 (C) 20 (D) 40

23. If $5y + 1$ is an odd integer, what is the

B next consecutive odd integer?

(A) $3y + 1$ (B) $5y + 3$

(C) $7y + 1$ (D) $7y + 3$

CHAPTER 13

Sequences and Series

PREVIEWING THE CHAPTER

This chapter introduces arithmetic sequences and presents a formula for a general *n*th term of a sequence. Arithmetic series are defined and students find sums and specific terms in an arithmetic series. Introduced in a similar manner are geometric sequences and series. Then students study infinite geometric series and work with the formula for finding the sum of such series. The chapter concludes with attention to the Binomial Theorem where students expand powers of binomials using Pascal's triangle as well as the theorem and find specific terms of thc binomial expansion.

Problem-Solving Strategy   Students learn to *look for a pattern* in a series of numbers to find the next number and other numbers in the series.

Lesson Objective Chart

Lesson (Pages)	Lesson Objectives	State/Local Objectives
13-1 (594-595)	**13-1:** Find the next number in a sequence.	
13-2 (596-601)	**13-2A:** Find the *n*th term of an arithmetic sequence.	
	13-2B: Find the position of a given term in an arithmetic sequence.	
	13-2C: Find arithmetic means.	
13-3 (602-607)	**13-3A:** Find sums of arithmetic series and find specific terms in the series.	
	13-3B: Use sigma notation to express the sum.	
13-4 (608-614)	**13-4A:** Find the *n*th term of a geometric sequence.	
	13-4B: Find the position of a given term in a geometric sequence.	
	13-4C: Find geometric means.	
13-5 (615-619)	**13-5A:** Find sums of geometric series, and find specific terms in the series.	
	13-5B: Use sigma notation to express the sum.	
13-6 (620-624)	**13-6:** Find the sum of an infinite geometric series.	
13-7 (625-630)	**13-7A:** Expand powers of binomials using Pascal's triangle and the Binomial Theorem.	
	13-7B: Find specific terms of the binomial expansion.	

ORGANIZING THE CHAPTER

You may want to refer to the **Course Planning Guide** on page T44.

Lesson Planning Guide

Lesson (Pages)	Pacing Chart (days) Course I	II	III	Reteaching	Practice	Enrichment	Evaluation	Technology	Lab Manual	Mixed Problem Solving	Applications	Cooperative Learning Activity	Multicultural	Transparencies
13-1 (594-595)	1	0.5	0.5		p. 96		Quiz A, p. 177					p. 49		13-1
13-2 (596-601)	1.5	1	1	p. 84	p. 97	p. 84		p. 30						13-2
13-3 (602-607)	1.5	1.5	1	p. 85	p. 98	p. 85	Quiz B, p. 177	p. 13						13-3
13-4 (608-614)	1.5	1.5	1	p. 86	p. 99	p. 86	Mid-Chapter Test, p. 181				p. 31			13-4
13-5 (615-619)	1.5	1	1	p. 87	p. 100	p. 87	Quiz C, p. 178			p. 13			p. 13	13-5
13-6 (620-624)	1	1	1	p. 88	p. 101	p. 88								13-6
13-7 (625-630)	2	1.5	1.5	p. 89	p. 102	p. 89	Quiz D, p. 178							13-7
Review (632-634)	1	1	1	Multiple Choice Tests, Forms 1A and 1B, pp. 169-172 Free Response Tests, Forms 2A and 2B, pp. 173-176										
Test (635)	1	1	1	Cumulative Review, pp. 179-180 Standardized Test Practice Questions, p. 182										

Course I: Chapters 1-13; Course II: Chapters 1-15; Course III: Chapters 1-17

Other Chapter Resources

Student Edition

Chapter Opener, pp. 592-593
Cooperative Learning Activity, p. 595
Journal Entries, pp. 601, 624
Mid-Chapter Review, p. 607
Fine Arts Connection, p. 614
Portfolio Suggestion, p. 630
Technology, p. 631
Extended Project 3, pp. A10-A13

Teacher's Classroom Resources

Transparency 13-0
Real-World Applications
   Transparencies, 26, 27
Performance Assessment Booklet,
   pp. 25-26
Problem-of-the-Week Activity Cards,
   26, 27
Tech Prep Applications Booklet, pp. 25-26
Lesson Plans, pp. 96-102

Other Supplements

Glencoe Mathematics
Professional Series

Software

Test and Review Generator Software
   (Apple, IBM, and Macintosh)
Interactive Software (Macintosh)
Teacher's Guide for Software
   Resources

ENHANCING THE CHAPTER

Cooperative Learning

Monitoring Students' Behavior

Group-learning sessions are not opportunities for the teacher to relax and, in fact, often require more diligence and self-control of the teacher than other modes of instruction. The teacher should spend the time observing the groups as they work to identify problems they are having with the assignment and in working cooperatively. Keeping a written record of the observations made can provide the teacher with a useful guide for planning future activities, for assigning roles to different students, for defining additional goals to be achieved, and for conducting conferences with individual students or their parents. It is not necessary that the teacher be quiet during these observations. However, any intervention should not disrupt but enhance the groups' efforts. For example, praising positive group behavior, encouraging reluctant members to participate, and skillfully asking questions to advance the group when they seem to be at a deadend will go far in assuring successful and satisfying cooperative-learning sessions.

Cooperative Learning, p. 49

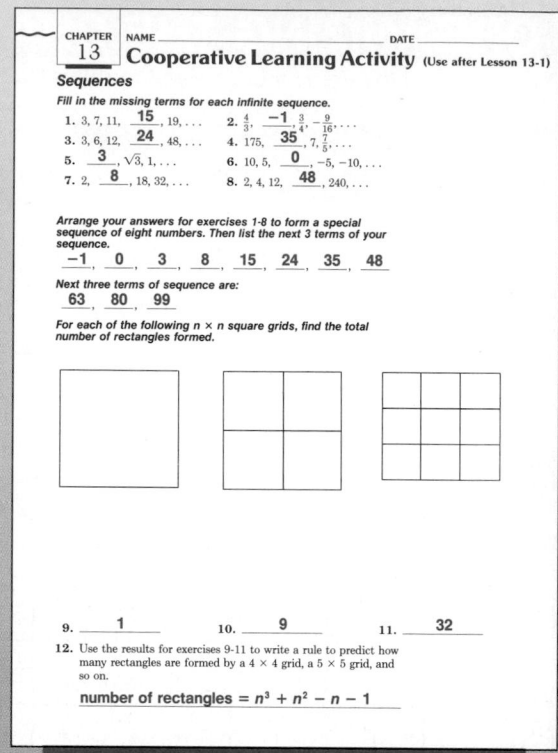

Technology

The Technology Feature after Lessons 13-7 shows students how to construct an amortization schedule using a spreadsheet program. A program for finding the portion of the payment that goes to interest and the portion that goes to paying back the principal. Students will investigate the nature of interest in a loan payment and will modify the given program to print the amortization schedule for a 30-year mortgage.

Technology, p. 13

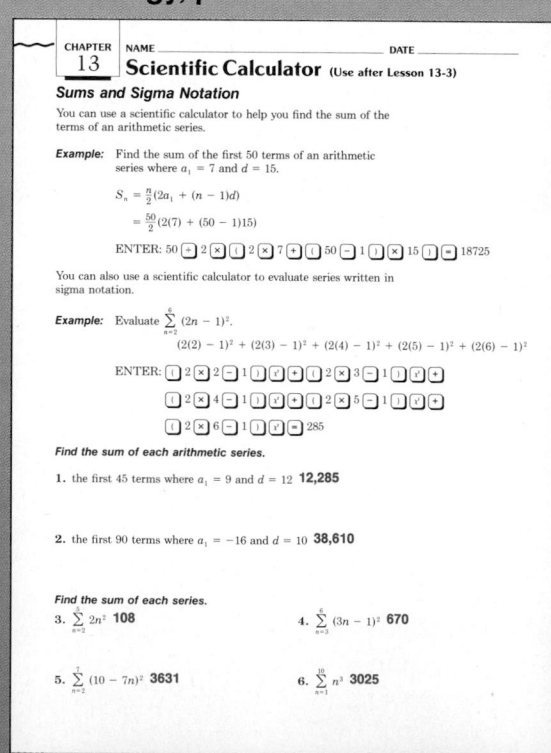

Critical Thinking

Complementing Bloom's research (1956) that led to his taxonomy is the research done by Williams (1969) in which he identified eight student behaviors involving creative thinking: the four cognitive factors are *fluency, flexibility, originality,* and *elaboration;* and the four affective factors are *risk taking, complexity, curiosity,* and *imagination.* Brainstorming activities, creative problem writing, paraphrasing and elaboration, making and testing predictions, justifying conclusions, and seeking many alternatives are just some ways to encourage positive behavior. Remember that all such behaviors are cultivated best when students are encouraged to explore, express different opinions, and define ideas in a non-judgmental environment.

Problem of the Week Activity

The card shown below is one of two available for this chapter. It can be used as a class or small group activity.

Activity Card

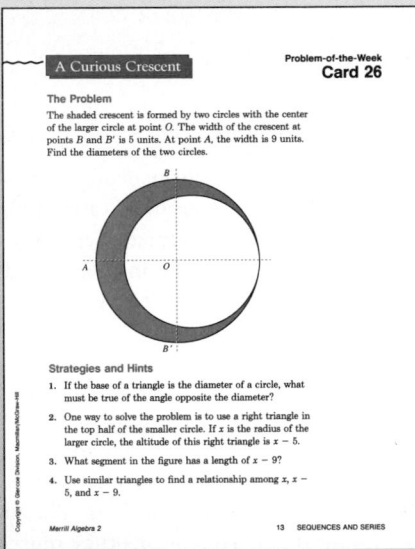

A Curious Crescent

Problem-of-the-Week
Card 26

The Problem
The shaded crescent is formed by two circles with the center of the larger circle at point O. The width of the crescent at points B and B' is 5 units. At point A, the width is 9 units. Find the diameters of the two circles.

Strategies and Hints
1. If the base of a triangle is the diameter of a circle, what must be true of the angle opposite the diameter?
2. One way to solve the problem is to use a right triangle in the top half of the smaller circle. If x is the radius of the larger circle, the altitude of this right triangle is $x - 5$.
3. What segment in the figure has a length of $x - 9$?
4. Use similar triangles to find a relationship among x, $x - 5$, and $x - 9$.

Merrill Algebra 2   13   SEQUENCES AND SERIES

Manipulatives and Models

The following materials may be used as models or manipulatives in Chapter 13.

- algebra tiles or counters (Lessons 13-1, 13-3, 13-5)
- jar (Lesson 13-3)
- pennies (Lesson 13-3)
- *Pit and the Pendulum* by Edgar Alan Poe (Lesson 13-6)

Outside Resources

Books/Periodicals

Asimov, Issac. *Asimov on Numbers.* Doubleday & Company, Inc.

Fleischmann, M., F.P.S., D.J. Tildesley, and R.C. Ball. *Fractals in the Natural Sciences.* Princeton University Press.

Films/Videotapes/Videodiscs

Dimension, AIMS Instructional Media, 9710 DeSoto Ave., Chatsworth, CA 91311

Software

Mathematics V.4: Advanced, Microsoft Corporation, 16011 NE 36th Way, Box 97017, Redmond, WA 98073-9717

Electronic Blackboard: Algebra, COMPress, 338 Commerce Dr., Fairfield, CT 06430-5540

Multicultural

Multicultural Activity, p. 13

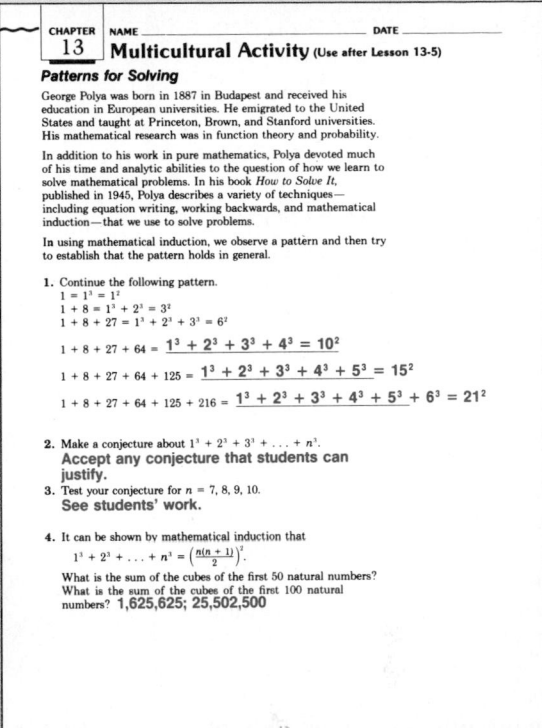

CHAPTER 13 NAME _____ DATE _____
Multicultural Activity (Use after Lesson 13-5)

Patterns for Solving

George Polya was born in 1887 in Budapest and received his education in European universities. He emigrated to the United States and taught at Princeton, Brown, and Stanford universities. His mathematical research was in function theory and probability.

In addition to his work in pure mathematics, Polya devoted much of his time and analytic abilities to the question of how we learn to solve mathematical problems. In his book *How to Solve It*, published in 1945, Polya describes a variety of techniques—including equation writing, working backwards, and mathematical induction—that we use to solve problems.

In using mathematical induction, we observe a pattern and then try to establish that the pattern holds in general.

1. Continue the following pattern.
$$1 = 1^3 = 1^2$$
$$1 + 8 = 1^3 + 2^3 = 3^2$$
$$1 + 8 + 27 = 1^3 + 2^3 + 3^3 = 6^2$$
$$1 + 8 + 27 + 64 = 1^3 + 2^3 + 3^3 + 4^3 = 10^2$$
$$1 + 8 + 27 + 64 + 125 = 1^3 + 2^3 + 3^3 + 4^3 + 5^3 = 15^2$$
$$1 + 8 + 27 + 64 + 125 + 216 = 1^3 + 2^3 + 3^3 + 4^3 + 5^3 + 6^3 = 21^2$$

2. Make a conjecture about $1^3 + 2^3 + 3^3 + \ldots + n^3$.
Accept any conjecture that students can justify.
3. Test your conjecture for $n = 7, 8, 9, 10$.
See students' work.
4. It can be shown by mathematical induction that
$$1^3 + 2^3 + \ldots + n^3 = \left(\frac{n(n+1)}{2}\right)^2.$$
What is the sum of the cubes of the first 50 natural numbers? What is the sum of the cubes of the first 100 natural numbers? **1,625,625; 25,502,500**

Applications

Application, p. 31

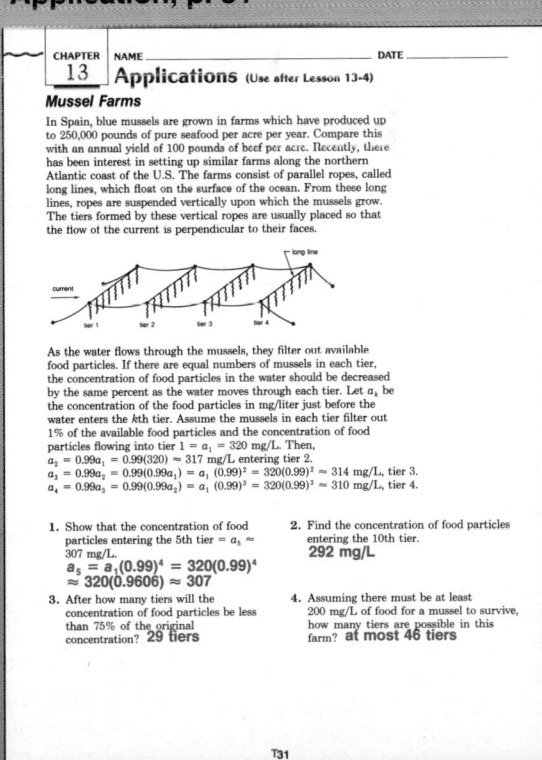

CHAPTER 13 NAME _____ DATE _____
Applications (Use after Lesson 13-4)

Mussel Farms

In Spain, blue mussels are grown in farms which have produced up to 250,000 pounds of pure seafood per acre per year. Compare this with an annual yield of 100 pounds of beef per acre. Recently, there has been interest in setting up similar farms along the northern Atlantic coast of the U.S. The farms consist of parallel ropes, called long lines, which float on the surface of the ocean. From these long lines, ropes are suspended vertically upon which the mussels grow. The tiers formed by these vertical ropes are usually placed so that the flow of the current is perpendicular to their faces.

As the water flows through the mussels, they filter out available food particles. If there are equal numbers of mussels in the water the concentration of food particles in the water should be decreased by the same percent as the water moves through each tier. Let a_k be the concentration of the food particles in mg/liter just before the water enters the kth tier. Assume the mussels in each tier filter out 1% of the available food particles and the concentration of food particles flowing into tier $1 = a_1 = 320$ mg/L. Then,
$a_2 = 0.99a_1 = 0.99(320) \approx 317$ mg/L entering tier 2.
$a_3 = 0.99a_2 = 0.99(0.99a_1) = a_1 (0.99)^2 = 320(0.99)^2 \approx 314$ mg/L, tier 3.
$a_4 = 0.99a_3 = 0.99(0.99a_1) = a_1 (0.99)^3 = 320(0.99)^3 \approx 310$ mg/L, tier 4.

1. Show that the concentration of food particles entering the 5th tier $= a_5 \approx 307$ mg/L.
$a_5 = a_1(0.99)^4 = 320(0.99)^4$
$\approx 320(0.9606) \approx 307$

2. Find the concentration of food particles entering the 10th tier. **292 mg/L**

3. After how many tiers will the concentration of food particles be less than 75% of the original concentration? **29 tiers**

4. Assuming there must be at least 200 mg/L of food for a mussel to survive, how many tiers are possible in this farm? **at most 46 tiers**

T31

Background Information
The special knowledge of the pharmacist is needed in advising physicians and other health professionals of the complexity and potential side effects of the large and growing number of pharmaceutical products on the market. Wide-spread use of computers allows pharmacists to create a computerized record of each patient's drug therapy. It is expected that employment of pharmacists will grow 14% to 24% through the 1990s as a result of the needs of a growing and aging population. In addition, scientific advances will bring more drugs onto the market requiring patient education.

C
H
A
P
T
E
R

13 Sequences and Series

CHAPTER OBJECTIVES

In this chapter you will:
- Find terms in arithmetic and geometric sequences.
- Find sums of arithmetic and geometric series.
- Use the Binomial Theorem to find terms of a binomial expansion.

Survey at least 20 people about how they treat their illnesses. How do your results compare with those in the chart?

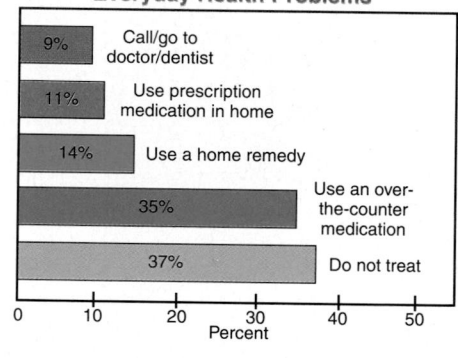

How Americans Handle Everyday Health Problems

- 9% Call/go to doctor/dentist
- 11% Use prescription medication in home
- 14% Use a home remedy
- 35% Use an over-the-counter medication
- 37% Do not treat

Percent: 0 10 20 30 40 50

592

CAREERS IN PHARMACOLOGY

Today's pharmacists don't do as much actual grinding, measuring, and mixing of ingredients to form powders, tablets, capsules, ointments, and solutions as they did in the early 1900's. Most medicines are produced by pharmaceutical companies.

Today's pharmacists now advise customers and physicians about the proper selection and use of medicines. There are so many pharmaceutical drugs on the market that most physicians are familiar with only a few hundred of them. Pharmacists must know all of them. This means they must be aware of all possible drug interactions and side effects. Computerized records help pharmacists keep track of their customers so that they can advise them more efficiently.

The job opportunities for a pharmacist may be as varied as the cities in which they work. A small town may only have one drugstore in which the pharmacist is the owner. This pharmacist may have to be on call to fill prescriptions in case of an emergency. Larger pharmacies may employ several pharmacists. Their duties may include supervision, inventory of counter merchandise, and even public health testing.

Chapter Project
Materials: paper, pencil, graph paper

Organize students into cooperative groups of research pharmacists. Instruct each group to select a category of over-the-counter drugs on which to conduct comparative research, prepare charts and graphs, and prepare a pharmaceutical report. Each group should visit a local pharmacy and record information as follows on

as many different brands within its respective category of drugs.
- Active ingredient (scientific name and amount)
- Directions
- Warnings
- Manufacturer
- Expiration date
- Cost
- Indications (what is the drug used for?)

Assign each group to report its findings to the class. The following is a partial list of categories of over-the-counter drugs.
- Painkillers and arthritis
- Gastrointestinal
- Coughs and colds
- Allergy drugs
- Eye drops and ointments

Connections and Applications

Lesson	Connections (C) and Applications (A)		Examples	Exercises
13-2	C:	Geometry		29
	A:	Flight	3	
		Skydiving		46
		Aeronautics		47
		Manufactur-ing		53
13-3	C:	Geometry		46
	A:	Design	3	
		Consumerism		40
		Education		41
13-4	C:	Geometry		49
	A:	Finance	4	40
		Physics	7	
		Aeronautics		41
		Demograph-ics		42
		Cinematogra-phy		43
13-5	A:	Chemistry	2	
		Recreation		44
		Communica-tions		45
		Meteorology		46
		Biology		48
13-6	A:	Physics	5	
		Aviation		39
		Sports		40
		Retailing		44
13-7	C:	Probability	6	
	A:	Sports		35
		Cooking		36

MORE ABOUT PHARMACOLOGY

Degree Required:

- Bachelor's Degree in Pharmacy, and a license from the state board

Some pharmacists like:

- pleasant working conditions
- working with people
- variety of specialties available to them

Related Math Subjects:

- Advanced Algebra
- Trigonometry
- Statistics/Probability

Some pharmacists dislike:

- having to work nights, weekends, and holidays
- the responsibility of being 100% accurate and being knowledgeable of all current developments

For more information on the various careers available in the field of Pharmacology, write to:

American Pharmaceutical Association and Academy of Pharmacy Practice and Management
2215 Constitution Avenue NW
Washington, DC 20037

593

INTRODUCING THE LESSON

⊘ 5-Minute Check

(over Chapter 12)

1. Write $5^3 = 125$ in logarithmic form. $\log_5 125 = 3$
2. Solve $\log_2 (3x - 2) = \log_2 (2x + 6)$. $x = 8$
3. Solve $\log_7 (m + 1) + \log_7 (m - 5) = 1$. $m = 6$
4. Find the antilogarithm of $0.4409 - 2$. 0.0276
5. Solve $8^{x-2} = 5^x$ using logarithms. 8.8486

Motivating the Lesson

Write the following sentence on the chalkboard. *Was it a cat I saw?* Then ask students if there is anything special about the sentence. Use student responses to develop the concept of the type of pattern called a palindrome, which reads the same forward and backward. Use the pattern to write other number and word palindromes.

TEACHING THE LESSON

Chalkboard Example

For Example 1
Find the next three terms in the sequence 2.1, 3.2, 4.3, 5.4, ...
6.5, 7.6, 8.7

For Example 2
Find the next three terms in the sequence 1, 4, 16, 64, ... 256, 1024, 4096

13-1 Problem-Solving Strategy: Look for a Pattern

Objective
13-1

After studying this lesson, you should be able to:
- find the next number in a sequence.

Application

The top view of a pine cone shows an example of a pattern often found in nature. The number of clockwise spirals is 13, and the number of counterclockwise spirals is 8. These are two numbers in a famous pattern of numbers called the **Fibonacci sequence,** named after its discoverer, Leonardo Fibonacci, who presented it in 1201. A sequence is an ordered set of numbers related mathematically. The first numbers of the Fibonacci sequence are shown below. The symbol ... means that the sequence continues indefinitely.

1, 1, 2, 3, 5, 8, 13, 21, 34, 55, 89, 144, ...

After the two first numbers, each number in the sequence is the sum of the two numbers that precede it. That is, $3 = 2 + 1$, $34 = 21 + 13$, and so on.

Example 1

Find the next three terms in the sequence 6, 10, 15, 21, 28, ...

One way to find a pattern in a sequence is to find the difference of consecutive terms.

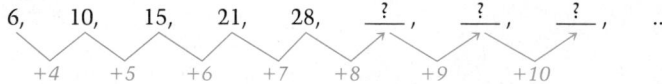

6,   10,   15,   21,   28,   ?,   ?,   ?,   ...
   +4   +5   +6   +7   +8   +9   +10

The difference increases by 1 for each term. The next three terms of this sequence are 36, 45, and 55.

Example 2

Find the next three terms in the sequence 1, 2, 6, 24, 120 ...

The pattern in this sequence is formed by multiplication. Each successive multiplier increases by 1.

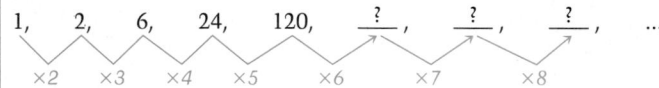

1,   2,   6,   24,   120,   ?,   ?,   ?,   ...
   ×2   ×3   ×4   ×5   ×6   ×7   ×8

The next three terms of this sequence are 720, 5040, and 40,320.

594   CHAPTER 13   SEQUENCES AND SERIES

RETEACHING THE LESSON

Patterns can be used involving letters as well as numbers. Have students find the next three terms of the following: *z, zx, zxt, zxtn, ...*
zxtnf, zxtnfv, zxtnfvj

CHECKING FOR UNDERSTANDING

Communicating Mathematics

Read and study the lesson to answer each question. 1–2. See margin.

1. In your own words, write a definition of *sequence*.
2. What operations can be used to form the pattern in a sequence?
3. For whom is the Fibonacci sequence named? **Leonardo Fibonacci**
4. Find other examples (besides the spirals of a pine cone) of the Fibonacci sequence in nature.
   sunflower, pineapple

Guided Practice

5. 1, 1, 2, 3, 5, 8, 13, 21, 34, 55, 89, 144, 233, 377, 610, 987, 1597, 2584, 4181, 6765

5. Find the first 20 terms of the Fibonacci sequence.
6. Observe the pattern in $4 \times 6 = 24$, $14 \times 16 = 224$, $24 \times 26 = 624$, and $34 \times 36 = 1224$. Without using a calculator or multiplication, write the product of 124×126. **15,624**

EXERCISES

Strategies

Look for a pattern.
Solve a simpler problem.
Act it out.
Guess and check.
Draw a diagram.
Make a chart.
Work backwards.

Solve. Use any strategy.

7. Find n if $n(n-1)(n-2)(n-3)(n-4) = 95,040$. **12**
8. The first fifty natural numbers are multiplied together. How many zeros appear as the last digits of the product? **10**
9. A bicycle is on sale at a 25% discount. It is reduced another 10% because of a coupon and another 3% for paying cash. These discounts are taken one after the other. If the final price of the bicycle is $195.89, what was the original price? **$299.18**
10. Trace the figure at the right without tracing over any segments you have already drawn. *Tracings which intersect at a point are allowed.* **See students' work.**

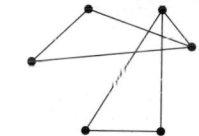

11. All the sides of a rectangle $ABCD$ have measures that are whole numbers. Find the greatest area possible for the rectangle if the perimeter is 42 cm. **110 cm²**

COOPERATIVE LEARNING ACTIVITY

Work in groups. Each person in the group must understand the solution and be able to explain it to any person in class.

The middle sapphire on a string of 33 sapphires is the largest and most expensive. Starting from one end, each sapphire is worth $100 more than the one before it up to and including the middle sapphire. From the other end, each sapphire is worth $150 more than the one before it, up to and including the middle sapphire. The string of sapphires is worth $65,000. What is the value of the middle sapphire? **$3000**

Checking for Understanding

Exercises 1–6 are designed to help you assess understanding through reading, writing, and speaking. You should work through Exercises 1–4 with your students, and then monitor their work on Exercises 5–6.

Closing the Lesson

Modeling Activity Have students use tiles or counters to model a sequence. Have another student determine the pattern used.

APPLYING THE LESSON

Homework Exercises

Assignment Guide

Basic: 7–11
Average: 7–11
Enriched: 7–11

Chapter 13, Quiz A, (Lesson 13–1), is available in the Evaluation Masters Booklet, p. 177.

Practice Masters Booklet, p. 96

13-1 **Practice Worksheet**

NAME _____ DATE _____

Problem Solving Strategy: Look for a Pattern
Solve. Use any strategy.

1. Find n if $n(n-1)(n-2)(n-3)(n-4) = 360,360$. **15**

2. Tires are on sale for 20% off. Karla has a coupon for 5% off. She gets another 4% off for not charging the tires on a credit card. These discounts are taken one after another. If the final price of a set of four tires is $162.85, what was the original price? **$223.20**

3. Find the missing terms in the sequence.
   4, 9, 25, 36, 49, **64**, **81**

4. Find the missing terms in the sequence.
   1, 1, 1, 3, 5, 9, 17, **31**, **57**

EXTENDING THE LESSON

Math Power: Connections

Show students an octave of keys on a keyboard or sketch the keys on the chalkboard or a transparency. Have them list ways the numbers in the Fibonacci sequence are used in that octave. **Answers may include 5 black keys, in sets of 2 and 3 keys, 8 white keys, and 13 keys total.**

Additional Answers

1. **Answers will vary. A group of ordered numbers in which each succeeding term is related to a previous term.**
2. **any mathematical operation or group of operations**

INTRODUCING THE LESSON

 5-Minute Check

(over Lesson 13-1)
Find the next three terms of each sequence.

1. 2, 4, 8, 16, ... **32, 64, 128**
2. 5, 12, 19, 26, ... **33, 40, 47**
3. −6.5, −1.5, 3.5, 8.5, ...
   13.5, 18.5, 23.5

Motivating the Lesson

Show students a savings passbook. Tell them a student saves $10 each week. If the starting February balance is $290, ask students to write a sequence that will give the balance each week of the month and at the first of March. Ask how the terms of this sequence are determined and how this differs from the way interest is determined on the account.

TEACHING THE LESSON

Teaching Tip ❶ This example assumes a constant acceleration and a changing velocity.

13-2 Arithmetic Sequences

Objectives

After studying this lesson, you should be able to:

- **13-2A** ■ find the nth term of an arithmetic sequence,
- **13-2B** ■ find the position of a given term in an arithmetic sequence, and
- **13-2C** ■ find arithmetic means.

Application

Emerson Fittipaldi is a professional race car driver from Brazil. As he drives out of a curve, he enters the straightaway at 119.9 mph. While on the straightaway, he steadily increases his speed by 78.3 mph. After 9 seconds, his speed is 198.2 mph. The chart below shows how his speed increased each second after entering the straightaway. **Teaching Tip ❶**

Number of seconds	0	1	2	3	4	5	6	7	8	9
Speed in mph	119.9	128.6	137.3	146.0	154.7	163.4	172.1	180.8	189.5	198.2

The graph shows the information from the table. If the points on the graph were connected, what kind of figure would you have? What type of equation does this represent? **a line; a linear equation**

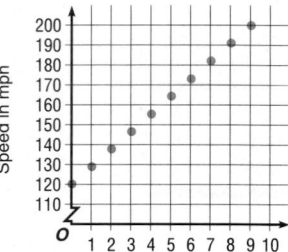

In the previous lesson, you learned to look for patterns in a list of numbers. The points in the graph represent the speeds at successive seconds. This set of numbers is another example of a *sequence*. Each number in a sequence is called a **term.** The first term is symbolized by a_1, the second term by a_2, and so on to a_n, the nth term.

The sequence shown in the chart above contains ten terms. Therefore, $a_1 = 119.9$ and $a_{10} = 198.2$. Each term of the sequence can be found by adding 8.7 to the previous term. A sequence of this type is called an **arithmetic sequence.** The number added to find the next term of an arithmetic sequence is called the **common difference** and is symbolized by the variable d.

Definition of Arithmetic Sequence	**An arithmetic sequence is a sequence in which each term, after the first, is found by adding a constant, called the common difference, to the previous term.**

596   CHAPTER 13   SEQUENCES AND SERIES

ALTERNATE TEACHING STRATEGIES

Using Applications

Have students list situations in which arithmetic sequences are used and write a sample sequence for each situation. For example, the sequence for money earned after each hour worked would be $4.25, $8.50, $12.75, ... if a person makes $4.25 per hour. The score for a team in a football game would be 0, 6, 12, ... if only touchdowns were scored.

To find the next terms in an arithmetic sequence, first find the common difference d by subtracting any term from its succeeding term. Then add the common difference to the last term to find successive terms.

Teaching Tip ❷

Example 1

Find the next four terms of the arithmetic sequence 33, 39, 45, ...

Find the common difference d by subtracting two consecutive terms.

$39 - 33 = 6$ and $45 - 39 = 6$ So, $d = 6$.

Now add 6 to the last term of the sequence, and then continue adding until the next four terms are found.

$$45 + 6 = 51$$
$$51 + 6 = 57$$
$$57 + 6 = 63$$
$$63 + 6 = 69$$

The next four terms of the sequence are 51, 57, 63, and 69.

There is a pattern in the way terms of an arithmetic sequence are formed. A formula to find any term of an arithmetic sequence can be found if you know the first term and the common difference. This type of formula is known as a **recursive formula**. Recursive means that each succeeding term is formulated from one or more previous terms. Let's use the terms of the sequence in Example 1.

a_1	a_2	a_3	a_4	a_5	...	a_n
33	39	45	51	57	...	a_n
$33 + 0(6)$	$33 + 1(6)$	$33 + 2(6)$	$33 + 3(6)$	$33 + 4(6)$	...	$33 + (n-1)(6)$
$a_1 + 0 \cdot d$	$a_1 + 1 \cdot d$	$a_1 + 2 \cdot d$	$a_1 + 3 \cdot d$	$a_1 + 4 \cdot d$	...	$a_1 + (n-1)d$

Why is the expression for a_n equal to $33 + (n - 1)6$?

The following formula generalizes this pattern for any sequence.

Formula for the nth Term of an Arithmetic Sequence

> The *n*th term, a_n, of an arithmetic sequence with first term a_1 and common difference d is given by
>
> $$a_n = a_1 + (n - 1)d.$$ **Teaching Tip ❸**

Teaching Tip ❷   Note that some sequences are infinite, such as this one, and some, such as that in the application, are not. The application sequence is limited by the speed limitations of the car and track.

Teaching Tip ❸   Point out that, although multiplication is used in the formula, the multiplication is just a quick way to add several differences. Addition is the operation used in arithmetic sequences.

Chalkboard Examples

For Example 2

What will her speed be after 20 seconds if her initial speed is 65 mph and her rate of acceleration is 4.8 mph?   **161 mph**

For Example 3

If an object free-falls, what is the distance it falls in the 12th second?   **368 feet**

For Example 4

a. Find the six arithmetic means between 12 and 47.   **17, 22, 27, 32, 37, 42**
b. Find the missing terms of the sequence __, 17, __, __, __, -7.   **23**, 17, **11**, **5**, **-1**, -7

Example 2

Suppose a race car driver increases her speed at a constant rate. What will her speed be after 15 seconds, if her initial speed is 85 mph and her rate of acceleration is 4.5 mph per second?

$a_1 = 85$ and $d = 4.5$ *Why does $a_1 = 85$ and $d = 4.5$?*

Find a_{16} using $a_n = a_1 + (n - 1)d$.   *Why do you need to find a_{16}?*

$a_n = a_1 + (n - 1)d$
$a_{16} = 85 + (16 - 1)(4.5)$
$a_{16} = 67.5$ or 152.5 Her speed will be 152.5 mph.

Example 3

APPLICATION

Flight

On a lengthy hot-air balloon flight, Hugo Furst floated into a warm air mass and began losing altitude. Because the air was too warm, he could not use his propane burner effectively to give him enough lift to clear a power line tower in front of him. So he threw an empty propane tank overboard to lighten the load. The distance the tank falls can be found using $d = 16t^2$, where d is the distance in feet and t is time elapsed in seconds. What would be the distance the tank falls *during* the 5th second?

Time elapsed (seconds)	Total distance fallen (ft)	Distance fallen since the last second (ft)	Difference from second to second
1	$16(1)^2 = 16$	$16 - 0 = 16$	
2	$16(2)^2 = 64$	$64 - 16 = 48$	$48 - 16 = 32$
3	$16(3)^2 = 144$	$144 - 64 = 80$	$80 - 48 = 32$
4	$16(4)^2 = 256$	$256 - 144 = 112$	$112 - 80 = 32$

The distances fallen in each second form the arithmetic sequence 16, 48, 80, ... The last column of the table tells that the common difference is 32. The first term is 16. Now use the formula for the *n*th term to find the distance fallen during the 5th second.

$a_n = a_1 + (n - 1)d$
$a_{10} = 16 + (5 - 1)(32)$

Now use your calculator to help you find this distance.

ENTER: 16 [+] [(] 5 [−] 1 [)] [×] 32 [=] 144

The propane tank fell 144 feet during the 5th second.

FYI …

The acceleration of gravity is the constant, 32 ft/s². Galileo Galilei (1564–1642) studied acceleration due to gravity by rolling metal balls down smooth ramps and timing them with a water clock.

598   CHAPTER 13   SEQUENCES AND SERIES

Sometimes you may know two terms of a sequence but they are not consecutive terms of that sequence. The terms between any two nonconsecutive terms of an arithmetic sequence are called **arithmetic means.** In the sequence below, 30, 39, and 48 are the three arithmetic means between 21 and 57.

$$12, 21, 30, 39, 48, 57, 66, 75, \ldots$$

Example 4

Find the four arithmetic means between 19 and 54.

You can use the nth term formula to find the common difference. In the sequence 19, ___, ___, ___, ___, 54, 19 is a_1 and 54 is a_6.

$a_n = a_1 + (n - 1)d$
$54 = 19 + (6 - 1)d$ *Substitute the known values.*
$54 = 19 + 5d$
$35 = 5d$
$7 = d$

Now use the value of d to find the four arithmetic means.

$19 + 7 = 26$ $26 + 7 = 33$ $33 + 7 = 40$ $40 + 7 = 47$

The arithmetic means are 26, 33, 40, and 47.

CHECKING FOR UNDERSTANDING

Communicating Mathematics

Read and study the lesson to answer each question. 1–3. See margin.

1. How would you determine if a list of numbers is an arithmetic sequence?

2. What is a common difference?

3. What is the formula for finding the nth term of an arithmetic sequence and what does each part of the formula represent?

4. What do you call the terms between any two nonconsecutive terms of an arithmetic sequence? **arithmetic means**

Teaching Tip ④

Guided Practice

Name the first five terms of each arithmetic sequence described.

5. 4, 7, 10, 13, 16
6. 7, 12, 17, 22, 27
7. 16, 14, 12, 10, 8

5. $a_1 = 4, d = 3$ 6. $a_1 = 7, d = 5$ 7. $a_1 = 16, d = -2$

8. $a_1 = 38, d = -4$ 9. $a_1 = \frac{3}{4}, d = -\frac{1}{4}$ 10. $a_1 = \frac{3}{8}, d = \frac{5}{8}$

   38, 34, 30, 26, 22 $\frac{3}{4}, \frac{1}{2}, \frac{1}{4}, 0, -\frac{1}{4}$ $\frac{3}{8}, 1, \frac{13}{8}, \frac{9}{4}, \frac{23}{8}$

Name the next four terms of each arithmetic sequence.

11. 17, 21, 25, 29
12. 20, 23, 26, 29
13. −13, −18, −23, −28

11. 5, 9, 13, ...   12. 11, 14, 17, ...   13. 2, −3, −8, ...

14. 21, 15, 9, ...   15. $\frac{1}{2}, \frac{3}{2}, \frac{5}{2}, \ldots$ 16. −5.4, −1.4, 2.6, ...
   3, −3, −9, −15 $\frac{7}{2}, \frac{9}{2}, \frac{11}{2}, \frac{13}{2}$ 6.6, 10.6, 14.6, 18.6

Additional Answers

1. Consider three consecutive terms of the sequence. Is the same number added to each term to get the next?

2. The difference between a term and its preceding term in an arithmetic sequence.

3. $a_n = a_1 + (n - 1)d$, where a_1 = the first term, n = the number of terms, d = common difference

Homework Exercises

Assignment Guide

Basic: 17–41, 44–46, 48–53
Average: 22–53
Enriched: 22–53

EXERCISES

Practice Find the *n*th term of each arithmetic sequence.

17. $a_1 = -1, d = -10, n = 25$ **–241** 18. $a_1 = -3, d = -9, n = 11$ **–93**
19. $a_1 = 7, d = 3, n = 14$ **46** 20. $a_1 = -7, d = 3, n = 17$ **41**
21. $a_1 = 2, d = \frac{1}{2}, n = 8$ **$11\frac{1}{2}$** 22. $a_1 = \frac{3}{4}, d = -\frac{5}{4}, n = 13$ **$-14\frac{1}{4}$**
23. $a_1 = 20, d = 4, n = 100$ **416** 24. $a_1 = 13, d = 3, n = 101$ **313**

Complete each statement.

25. 124 is the __?__ th term of –2, 5, 12, ... **19**
26. 142 is the __?__ th term of –3, 2, 7, ... **30**
27. –28 is the __?__ th term of 7, 2, –3, ... **8**
28. $-\frac{17}{4}$ is the __?__ th term of $2\frac{1}{4}$, 2, $1\frac{3}{4}$, ... **27**

CONNECTION
Geometry

29. Let $A = 24$, $B = 36$, and C = the arithmetic mean of A and B. Graph A, B, and C on a number line. What is the relationship of C to segment AB? **30, the midpoint**

B Find the indicated term in each arithmetic sequence.

30. a_{12} for –17, –13, –9, ... **27** 31. a_{21} for 10, 7, 4, ... **–50**
32. a_{32} for 4, 7, 10, 13, ... **97** 33. a_{10} for 8, 3, –2, ... **–37**

Find the missing terms in each arithmetic sequence. Then graph each sequence using the *x*-axis for the number of the term and the *y*-axis for the term itself. **For graphs, see Solutions Manual.**

34. **70, 85, 100**
35. $-\frac{13}{3}, -\frac{2}{3}$
36. $-\frac{38}{5}, -\frac{26}{5}, -\frac{14}{5}, -\frac{2}{5}$
37. **5, 8, 11, 14, 17**
38. **–13, 1, 8, 22**
39. **56, 42, 35**

34. 55, __?__ , __?__ , __?__ , 115 35. –8, __?__ , __?__ , 3
36. –10, __?__ , __?__ , __?__ , __?__ , 2 37. 2, __?__ , __?__ , __?__ , __?__ , __?__ , 20
38. __?__ , –6, __?__ , __?__ , 15, __?__ 39. __?__ , 49, __?__ , __?__ , 28

40. The last term of an arithmetic sequence is 207, the common difference is 3, and the number of terms is 14. What is the first term of the sequence? **168**

41. The third term of an arithmetic sequence is 14 and the ninth term is –1. Find the first four terms of the sequence. **19, 16.5, 14, 11.5**

C 42. The fifth term of an arithmetic sequence is 19 and the 11th term is 43. Find the first term and the 87th term. **3, 347**

43. Find three numbers that have a sum of 27, a product of 288, and form an arithmetic sequence. **2, 9, 16**

Critical Thinking 44. Use an arithmetic sequence to find how many multiples of seven are between 11 and 391. *Hint: What is the least multiple in that range? What is the greatest multiple?* **54**

Practice Masters Booklet, p. 97

45. In the Fibonacci sequence from Lesson 13-1, you learned that each term is found by adding a number to the previous numbers.

   a. Is the Fibonacci sequence an arithmetic sequence? Explain your answer. **no, the same number is not added to each term**

   b. Let $F_1 = 1$, $F_2 = 1$, $F_3 = 2$, $F_4 = 3$, and so on to identify each term of the Fibonacci sequence. Write an expression for F_n in terms of the preceding two terms. $F_n = F_{n-1} + F_{n-2}$

Applications

46. Skydiving During a free fall, a skydiver falls 16 feet in the first second, 48 feet in the second second, and 80 feet in the third second. If she continues to fall at this rate, how many feet will she fall during the 8th second? **240 ft**

47. Aeronautics A rocket rises 20 feet in the first second, 60 feet in the second second, and 100 feet in the third second. If it continues at this rate, how many feet will it rise in the 20th second? **780 ft**

Mixed Review

48. Find the next three terms of the following pattern a, ac, ace, $\underline{\ ?\ }$, $\underline{\ ?\ }$, $\underline{\ ?\ }$. **(Lesson 13-1)** **aceg, acegi, acegik**

49. Evaluate $\log_8 8^5$. **(Lesson 12-2)** **5**

50. Simplify $\dfrac{3x^2 - 5x + 2}{2x^2 - 5x - 3} + \dfrac{x^2 + x - 2}{2x^2 - x - 3}$. **(Lesson 11-3)** $\dfrac{(3x - 2)(x + 1)(2x - 3)}{(x + 2)(x - 3)(2x + 1)}$

51. Find $g[f(-2)]$ if $f(x) = 3x^2 + 12x - 5$ and $g(x) = x^3 + 5x^2 - 4x + 12$. **(Lesson 10-7)** **–3388**

52. Graph $y \le -x^2 + 8x - 11$. **(Lesson 8-6)** **See margin.**

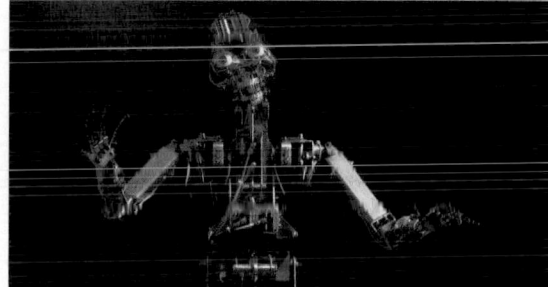

53. Manufacturing The Grasco Company makes widgets and gadgets. At least 500 widgets and 700 gadgets are needed to meet minimum, daily demands. The machinery can produce no more than 1200 widgets and 1400 gadgets per day. The combined number of widgets and gadgets that the packaging department can handle is 2300 per day. **(Lesson 2-6)**

   a. If the company sells widgets for 40¢ each and gadgets for 50¢ each, how many of each type should be produced for maximum daily income? **900 W, 1400 G**

   b. What is the maximum daily income? **$1060**

LESSON 13-2 ARITHMETIC SEQUENCES 601

EXTENDING THE LESSON

Math Power: Reasoning

Have students state a rule that defines a sequence with the first four terms as follows. 1, 0, 1, 0, ...

$$a_n = \frac{[1 + (-1)^{n-1}]}{2}$$

Additional Answer

52. $y \le -x^2 + 8x - 11$

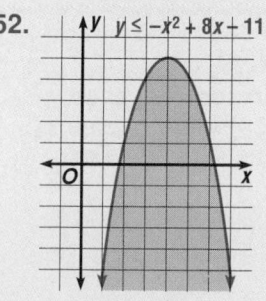

Enrichment Masters Booklet, p. 84

NAME _____ DATE _____

13-2 Enrichment Worksheet

Fibonacci Sequence

Leonardo Fibonacci first discovered the sequence of numbers named for him while studying rabbits. He wanted to know how many pairs of rabbits would be produced in n months, starting with a single pair of newborn rabbits. He made the following assumptions.

  1. Newborn rabbits become adults in one month.
  2. Each pair of rabbits produces one pair each month.
  3. No rabbits die.

Let F_n represent the number of pairs of rabbits at the end of n months. If you begin with one pair of newborn rabbits, $F_0 = F_1 = 1$. This pair of rabbits would produce one pair at the end of the second month, so $F_2 = 1 + 1$, or 2. At the end of the third month, the first pair of rabbits would produce another pair. Thus, $F_3 = 2 + 1$, or 3.

The chart below shows the number of rabbits each month for several months.

Month	Adult Pairs	Newborn Pairs	Total
F_0	0	1	1
F_1	1	0	1
F_2	1	1	2
F_3	2	1	3
F_4	3	2	5
F_5	5	3	8

Solve each problem.

1. Starting with a single pair of newborn rabbits, how many rabbits would there be at the end of 12 months? **233**

2. Write the first 10 terms of the sequence for which $F_0 = 3$, $F_1 = 4$, and $F_n = F_{n-2} + F_{n-1}$. **3, 4, 7, 11, 18, 29, 47, 76, 123, 199, 322**

3. Write the first 10 terms of the sequence for which $F_0 = 1$, $F_1 = 5$, and $F_n = F_{n-2} + F_{n-1}$. **1, 5, 6, 11, 17, 28, 45, 73, 118, 191, 309**

Lesson Resources

Reteaching Master 13-3
Practice Master 13-3
Enrichment Master 13-3
Technology Master, p. 13

 Transparency 13-3 contains the 5-Minute Check and a teaching aid for this lesson.

INTRODUCING THE LESSON

 5-Minute Check

(over Lesson 13-2)
Find the *n*th term of each arithmetic sequence.

1. $a_1 = 7$, $d = 3$, $n = 14$
   $a_n = 46$
2. $a_1 = 20$, $d = 4$, $n = 100$
   $a_n = 416$
3. Find the 12th term for the sequence $-17, -13, -9, \ldots$
   $a_{12} = 27$
4. Which term of the sequence $-2, 5, 12, \ldots$ is 124? **19**
5. Find the missing terms of the sequence $55, \underline{\quad}, \underline{\quad}, \underline{\quad}, 115$.
   70, 85, 100

Motivating the Lesson

Show students an empty jar and a container of pennies. Ask students if they were to place pennies in the jar according to an arithmetic sequence (give examples, such as 1 one day, 3 the next, then 5, ...), if there would be a way, other than counting the pennies, to determine the total number added after a certain number of additions.

13-3 Arithmetic Series

Objectives

After studying this lesson, you should be able to:

13-3A ■ find sums of arithmetic series and find specific terms in the series, and

13-3B ■ use sigma notation to express the sum.

Application

Skydivers fall greater distances each second they free fall. In Lesson 13-2, you learned that these free-fall distances form an arithmetic sequence.

$$16, 48, 80, 112, 144, 176, 208, \ldots$$

To find out what the total distance fallen by the skydiver is, you would add the terms in the sequence.

$$16 + 48 + 80 + 112 + 144 + 176 + 208 + \ldots$$

The indicated sum of the terms of a sequence is called a **series**. The series shown above is an **arithmetic series**.

The list below shows examples of arithmetic sequences and their corresponding arithmetic series.

Arithmetic Sequence	Arithmetic Series
$3, 6, 9, 12, 15$	$3 + 6 + 9 + 12 + 15$
$-8, -2, 4$	$-8 + (-2) + 4$
$\dfrac{4}{5}, \dfrac{8}{5}, \dfrac{12}{5}, \dfrac{16}{5}$	$\dfrac{4}{5} + \dfrac{8}{5} + \dfrac{12}{5} + \dfrac{16}{5}$
$a_1, a_2, a_3, a_4, \ldots, a_n$	$a_1 + a_2 + a_3 + a_4 + \cdots + a_n$

FYI ...

During a jump, sky-divers usually create a controlled free-fall by spreading their arms and legs. Even in a controlled free-fall, they may reach a speed of 146 ft/s or about 98 mph.

The symbol S_n is used to represent the sum of the first n terms of a series. For example, S_3 means the sum of the first three terms of a series. In the series $3 + 6 + 9 + 12 + 15$, S_3 would be $3 + 6 + 9$ or 18.

If a series has a large number of terms, it is not convenient to list all the terms and then find their sum. To develop a general formula for the sum of any arithmetic series, let's consider the series of skydiving distances.

$$16 + 48 + 80 + 112 + 144 + 176 + 208$$

602   CHAPTER 13   SEQUENCES AND SERIES

ALTERNATE TEACHING STRATEGIES

Using Manipulatives

Using coins, counters, or tiles, have students work in cooperative groups to model several arithmetic series. For each series, have students find the sum by using a sum formula and then check the results by counting.

Suppose we write S_7 in two different orders and find the sum.

$$\begin{aligned}
S_7 &= \ \ 16 + \ \ 48 + \ \ 80 + 112 + 144 + 176 + 208 \\
+ \ S_7 &= 208 + 176 + 144 + 112 + \ \ 80 + \ \ 48 + \ \ 16 \\
\hline
2 \cdot S_7 &= 224 + 224 + 224 + 224 + 224 + 224 + 224
\end{aligned}$$

7 sums of 224

$$2 \cdot S_7 = 7(224)$$
$$S_7 = \frac{7}{2}(224) \quad \textit{Divide each side by 2.}$$

Now let's analyze what these numbers represent in terms of S_n. In the equation $S_7 = \frac{7}{2}(224)$, 7 represents n, and 224 represents the sum of the first and last terms, $a_1 + a_n$. Thus, we can replace the equation with the formula $S_n = \frac{n}{2}(a_1 + a_n)$. This formula can be used to find the sum of any arithmetic series.

Sum of an Arithmetic Series	**The sum S_n of the first n terms of an arithmetic series is given by $S_n = \frac{n}{2}(a_1 + a_n)$.**

Example 1

Find the sum of the first 100 positive integers.

In this series, $a_1 = 1$ and $a_n = a_{100} = 100$.

$$S_n = \frac{n}{2}(a_1 + a_n)$$
$$S_{100} = \frac{100}{2}(1 + 100) \quad \textit{Substitute the known values.}$$
$$= 50(101) \quad \text{or} \quad 5050$$

The sum of the first 100 positive integers is 5050.

In Lesson 13-2, you learned that in an arithmetic sequence, $a_n = a_1 + (n - 1)d$. Using this formula and substitution gives us another version of the formula for the sum of an arithmetic sequence.

$$S_n : \frac{n}{2}(a_1 + a_n)$$
$$= \frac{n}{2}\{a_1 + [a_1 + (n - 1)d]\} \quad \textit{Substitute } a_1 + (n - 1)d \text{ for } a_n.$$
$$= \frac{n}{2}[2a_1 + (n - 1)d]$$

You can use this formula when you don't know the value of the last term.

Chalkboard Example

For Example 1
Find S_n for each described series.

a. first 50 positive integers **1275**

b. first 10 odd integers **100**

For Example 2

Find S_n for each described series.

a. first 60 terms where $a_1 = 15$ and $d = 80$ **142,500**
b. first 15 odd integers   **225**

For Example 3

A supermarket display consists of six rows of stacked boxes. The top row has 35 boxes. Each row has three less boxes than the one below it. How many boxes are in the display?   **255 boxes**

For Example 4

Find the first three terms of the series where $a_1 = 5$, $a_n = 100$, $S_n = 1050$.   **5, 10, 15**

Example 2

Find the sum of the first 50 terms of an arithmetic series where $a_1 = 5$ and $d = 25$.

The series is $5 + 30 + 55 + 80 + \ldots$ *Use the formula for S_n.*

$$S_n = \frac{n}{2}[2a_1 + (n - 1)d]$$

$$= \frac{50}{2}[2(5) + (50 - 1)25] \quad \textit{Substitute the known values.}$$

$$= 30{,}875$$

Example 3

APPLICATION

Design

A 24-hour Redimarket has its evening employees do most of the restocking of shelves and arranging of displays. At Thanksgiving the store creates large displays of those items most frequently bought at that time. Su Makita has the job of arranging the canned yams. He designs a display with 15 rows with each row having one less can than the row below it. If the bottom row has 27 cans, how many cans are in the display?

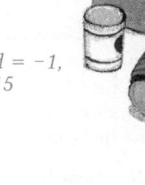

$$S_n = \frac{n}{2}[2a_1 + (n - 1)d] \quad \begin{smallmatrix} a_1 = 27,\ d = -1, \\ and\ n = 15 \end{smallmatrix}$$

$$= \frac{15}{2}[2(27) + (15 - 1)(-1)]$$

$$= 300$$

There are 300 cans of yams in the display.

It is sometimes necessary to use both sum formulas to solve a problem. You must analyze the information you are given and then decide which formula to use first.

Example 4

Find the first three terms of an arithmetic series where $a_1 = 17$, $a_n = 101$, and $S_n = 472$.

First, find n.

$$S_n = \frac{n}{2}(a_1 + a_n)$$

$$472 = \frac{n}{2}(17 + 101)$$

$$472 = 59n$$

$$n = 8$$

Next, find d.

$$a_n = a_1 + (n - 1)d$$

$$101 = 17 + (8 - 1)d$$

$$84 = 7d$$

$$12 = d$$

Now determine a_2 and a_3.

$$a_2 = 17 + 12 \text{ or } 29 \qquad a_3 = 29 + 12 \text{ or } 41$$

The first three terms are 17, 29, and 41.

Writing out a series is often time-consuming and lengthy. To simplify this, mathematicians use a more concise notation called **sigma** or **summation notation.**

$2 + 4 + 6 + 8 + \cdots + 20$ can be expressed as $\displaystyle\sum_{n=1}^{10} 2n$.   **Teaching Tip ❶**

$\displaystyle\sum_{n=1}^{10} 2n$ *is read the summation from 1 to 10 of 2n.*

When using sigma notation, the variable defined below the Σ (sigma) is called the **index of summation.** The upper number is the upper limit of the index. To generate the terms of the series, successively replace the index of summation with each value of n, in this series, 1, 2, 3, and so on through 10.

Example 5

Write the terms of $\displaystyle\sum_{k=2}^{6} (3k + 2)$ and find the sum.

In this series, replace k with 2 and then 3, 4, 5, and 6 to find the terms.

$$\sum_{k=2}^{6} (3k + 2) = \overset{k=2}{3(2) + 2} + \overset{k=3}{3(3) + 2} + \overset{k=4}{3(4) + 2} + \overset{k=5}{3(5) + 2} + \overset{k=6}{3(6) + 2}$$
$$= \quad 8 \quad + \quad 11 \quad + \quad 14 \quad + \quad 17 \quad + \quad 20$$
$$= 70$$

The sum is 70.

Just as a polynomial can be expressed in more than one form, the summation of a series can be expressed in different ways. The summation of the series in Example 5 is expressed as $\displaystyle\sum_{k=2}^{6} (3k + 2)$. It can also be expressed as $\displaystyle\sum_{k=2}^{6} [5 + 3(k - 1)]$.   *Verify that these two expressions are equivalent.*

CHECKING FOR UNDERSTANDING

Communicating Mathematics

Read and study the lesson to answer each question.

1. The indicated sum of terms of a sequence is called a __?__ . **series**
2. The sum of a series can be written in __?__ or __?__ notation. **sigma, summation**
3. What is the purpose of the index of summation?
   It tells which terms to add and how many.

Guided Practice

Find the sum of each series.

4. $4 + 7 + 10 + 13 + 16 + 19 + 22 + 25$ **116**
5. $1 + 5 + 9 + 13 + 17 + 21 + 25 + 29$ **120**

LESSON 13-3   ARITHMETIC SERIES   605

RETEACHING THE LESSON

Sam's parents decided when he was born to put $100 times his age away for him at every birthday through his 18th birthday. This will be a way to help save for college. How much money will they have saved after his 18th birthday, without taking into account interest earned? How much do you think would be saved if they put $200 times his age away every birthday? Check by mathematically working it out. Discuss.
$17,100; $34,200

Find S_n for each arithmetic series described. **11. 240**

6. $a_1 = 2, a_n = 200, n = 100$ **10,100**
7. $a_1 = 5, a_n = 100, n = 200$ **10,500**
8. $a_1 = 4, n = 15, d = 3$ **375**
9. $a_1 = 50, n = 20, d = -4$ **240**
10. $-3 + (-7) + (-11) + \ldots + a_{10}$ **−210**
11. $9 + 11 + 13 + 15 + \ldots$ for $n = 12$
12. the sum of the greatest 100 negative integers **−5050**
13. the sum of the first 100 positive even integers **10,100**

EXERCISES

Practice   Find S_n for each arithmetic series described.

14. $a_1 = 3, a_n = -38, n = 8$ **−140**
15. $a_1 = 85, n = 21, a_n = 25$ **1155**
16. $a_1 = 34, n = 9, a_n = 2$ **162**
17. $a_1 = 76, n = 16, a_n = 31$ **856**
18. $a_1 = 4, d = -1, n = 7$ **7**
19. $a_1 = 5, d = \frac{1}{2}, n = 13$ **104**

Find the sum of each arithmetic series.   **23. −220**

20. $6 + 12 + 18 + \ldots + 96$ **816**
21. $34 + 30 + 26 + \ldots + 2$ **162**
22. $7 + 14 + 21 + 28 + \ldots + 98$ **735**
23. $10 + 4 + (-2) + \ldots + (-50)$

24. $\sum_{n=1}^{25} 2n$ **650**
25. $\sum_{r=3}^{6} (r + 2)$ **26**
26. $\sum_{n=1}^{30} (2n - 1)$ **900**

27. $\sum_{n=21}^{75} (2n + 5)$ **5555**
28. $\sum_{n=10}^{50} (3n - 1)$ **3649**
29. $\sum_{j=1}^{6} (24 - 9j)$ **−45**

Find S_n for each arithmetic series described.

30. $a_1 = 91, d = -4, a_n = 15$ **1060**
31. $d = 5, n = 16, a_n = 72$ **552**
32. $d = -4, n = 9, a_n = 27$ **387**
33. $a_1 = -2, d = \frac{1}{2}, a_n = 5$ **$\frac{45}{2}$**

Find the first three terms of each arithmetic series.   **Teaching Tip ❷**

34. 7, 19, 31
35. 1, 5, 9
36. 18, 21, 24
37. 6, 36, 66

34. $a_1 = 7, a_n = 139, S_n = 876$
35. $n = 14, a_n = 53, S_n = 378$
36. $n = 21, a_n = 78, S_n = 1008$
37. $a_1 = 6, a_n = 306, S_n = 1716$

Critical Thinking

38. Evaluate $\sum_{a=3}^{6} (a - 2)^2$ and $\sum_{a=1}^{4} a^2$. What do you notice? **See margin.**

39. Write an argument to prove or disprove the statement
$$2\sum_{k=3}^{7} k^2 = \sum_{k=3}^{7} 2k^2.$$ **See margin.**

606   CHAPTER 13   SEQUENCES AND SERIES

40. Consumerism A pile of fireplace logs at the Garden Shop has 10 logs on the top layer, 11 logs in the next layer, and so on. The pile contains 13 layers. Write an expression that represents how many logs are in the pile, and then evaluate that expression.

41. Education Milford High School is planning a pep rally for their basketball team that is headed for the state tournament. The school wants to invite parents as well as students. Milford Auditorium has 21 seats in the first row. Each of the other rows has one more seat than the one in front of it and there are 30 rows of seats. If they anticipate 1200 people will come to the pep rally, will there be a seat for everyone? Justify your answer. **No, the auditorium only has 1065 seats.**

Teaching Tip ❸   40. Expressions will vary. 208 logs

Mixed Review

42. Find the 57th term of the arithmetic sequence 6, 15, 24, 33, ... **(Lesson 13-2) 510**

43. Solve $\log_5 (3x + 7) = \log_5 (x^2 - 4x - 1)$. **(Lesson 12-7)** $x = -1, 8$

44. Find $p(-4)$ if $p(x) = 3x^2 - 7x + 1$. **(Lesson 8-1) 77**

45. Solve $\begin{cases} x + 2y - 3z = -13 \\ 2x - y + 3z = 23 \\ 3x + y - 3z = -8 \end{cases}$ using augmented matrices. **(Lesson 4-8)** **(3, 1, 6)**

46. Geometry In isosceles triangle ABC, the length of each leg is 5 cm less than three times the length of its base. Find its dimensions if the perimeter of the triangle is 88 cm. **(Lesson 1-6) 37, 37, 14**

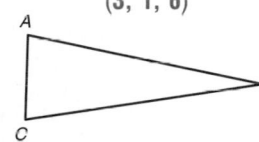

MID-CHAPTER REVIEW

1. If the first 27 terms in the sequence 3, 33, 333, 3333, 33,333, ... are added together, what is the digit in the hundreds place of their sum? **(Lesson 13-1) 3**

2. The Lucas sequence was developed from the Fibonacci sequence. In the Lucas sequence, $L_1 = F_1$ and $L_n = F_{n+1} + F_{n-1}$ for $n \geq 2$. Find the first 8 terms of the Lucas sequence. **1, 3, 4, 7, 11, 18, 29, 47**

3. Find the 12th term in the arithmetic sequence $\frac{3}{4}, \frac{3}{2}, \frac{9}{4}, ...$ **(Lesson 13-2) 9**

4. Find the 100th term in an arithmetic sequence where $a_1 = 20$ and $d = 4$. **(Lesson 13-2) 416**

5. Find S_n for $d = 5$, $n = 16$, and $a_n = 72$. **(Lesson 13-3) 552**

6. Find S_n for $a_1 = 9$, $d = -6$, and $n = 14$. **(Lesson 13-3) –420**

7. **Personal Finance** Louise McCall retired as a secretary at the lumberyard after 30 years of employment. If her salary was $4500 the first year, and she received an $820 raise at the end of each year of service, what was her total salary for those 30 years? **(Lesson 13-3)** **$491,700**

EXTENDING THE LESSON

Math Power: Problem Solving

The Cortez family moved to a new house six years ago. The value of the house increased 5 percent of the original price the first year, 10 percent the second year, 15 percent the third year, and so on for six years. If the value of the house today is $123,000, how much did the Cortez family pay for the house? **$60,000**

Mid-Chapter Review

The Mid-Chapter Review provides students with a brief review of the concepts and skills in Lessons 13–1 through 13–3. Lesson numbers are given at the end of problems or instruction lines so students may review concepts not yet mastered.

Enrichment Masters Booklet, p. 85

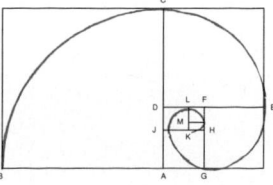

13-3 **Enrichment Worksheet**

NAME _____ DATE _____

Golden Rectangles

Use a straightedge, a compass, and the instructions below to construct a golden rectangle.

1. Construct square $ABCD$ with sides of 2 cm.

2. Construct the midpoint of $\overline{AB}$. Call the midpoint M.

3. Using M as the center, set your compass opening at MC. Construct an arc with center M that intersects $\overline{AB}$. Call the point of intersection P.

4. Construct a line through P that is perpendicular to $\overline{AB}$.

5. Extend $\overline{DC}$ so that it intersects the perpendicular. Call the intersection point Q. $APQD$ is a golden rectangle. Check this conclusion by finding the value of $\frac{QP}{AP}$. **0.62**

A figure consisting of similar golden rectangles is shown below. Use a compass and the instructions below to draw quarter-circle arcs that form a spiral like that found in the shell of a chambered nautilus.

6. Using A as a center, draw an arc that passes through B and C.

7. Using D as a center, draw an arc that passes through C and E.

8. Using F as a center, draw an arc that passes through E and G.

9. Continue drawing arcs, using H, K, and M as the centers.

Lesson Resources

Reteaching Master 13-4
Practice Master 13-4
Enrichment Master 13-4
Activity Master, p. 31

 Transparency 13-4 contains the 5-Minute Check and a teaching aid for this lesson.

INTRODUCING THE LESSON

 5-Minute Check

(over Lesson 13-3)

Find the sum, S_n, for each arithmetic series described.

1. $a_1 = 4$, $a_n = ^-16$, and $n = 5$ $S_5 = ^-30$
2. $a_1 = 3$, $a_n = 33$, and $n = 6$ $S_6 = 108$
3. Find the sum of the even integers from 2 through 1000. **250,500**
4. Find the sum of the series $^-4 + (^-1) + 2 + 5 + ... + 53$. $S = 490$
5. Find the sum of the series
$$\sum_{k=0}^{5} (5k - 7). \quad S = 33$$

Motivating the Lesson

Show students a picture of some bacteria growing in a petri dish. Remind students of examples in Chapter 12 where such organisms reproduce by dividing (mitosis). Ask students if they can name the number of organisms produced by 6 initial organisms reproducing one time. Ask how many would be produced by each of these new organisms reproducing.

Objectives

After studying this lesson, you should be able to:

13-4A ■ find the *n*th term of a geometric sequence,
13-4B ■ find the position of a given term in a geometric sequence, and
13-4C ■ find geometric means.

Application

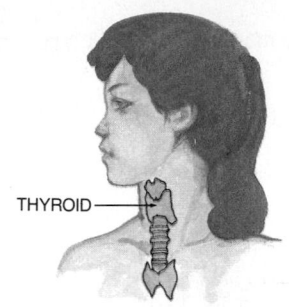

THYROID

Iodine-131 is used medically as a tracer isotope in monitoring the activity of the thyroid gland. A patient is given a compound containing the radioactive iodine. A physician uses a Geiger-Mueller counter to monitor the activity of the iodine in the thyroid. The amount of iodine retained by this gland is a measure of its ability to function.

Iodine-131 has a half-life of about 8 days. That means that approximately every 8 days, half the mass of iodine decays into another element. Then in the next 8 days, half of the remaining iodine decays, and so on.

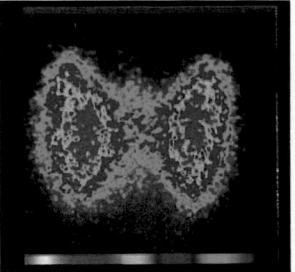

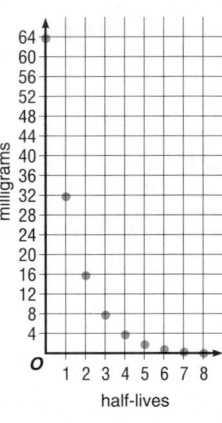

Iodine-131

Suppose a container held a mass of 64 milligrams of iodine-131. The graph shows the remaining mass of iodine after each half-life. What type of figure do these points suggest?

The pattern of masses forms a sequence of numbers known as a **geometric sequence**. The terms in this example are 64, 32, 16, 8, 4, 2, 1, 0.5, ... *What would be the next number in the sequence? How did you find it?*

Definition of Geometric Sequence	**A geometric sequence is one in which each term after the first is found by multiplying the previous term by a constant called the common ratio.**

In any geometric sequence, the **common ratio *r*** is found by dividing any term by the previous term.

ALTERNATE TEACHING STRATEGIES

Using Models

Use actual geometric sequences to model the information presented in the chart on page 609.

Using Cooperative Groups

Using groups of four students each, have one student write the first few terms of a geometric sequence. Have other students, in turn, name a_1, r, and a value for *n*. Have students collectively determine a value for a_n.

Example 1

Find the next two terms of the geometric sequence 4, 12, 36, ...

To find the common ratio, find the quotient of any two consecutive terms.

$\frac{12}{4} = 3$ $\frac{36}{12} = 3$ The common ratio is 3.   **Teaching Tip ❶**

The fourth term is 36(3) or 108.

The fifth term is 108(3) or 324.

The next two terms of the sequence are 108 and 324.

Successive terms of a geometric sequence are usually expressed as the product of r and the previous term. Thus, a geometric sequence is also a recursive sequence. Since each succeeding term contains a factor of r, each term can be expressed as a product of a_1 and a power of r. Notice each pattern of terms in the table below.

the sequence	a_1	a_2	a_3	a_4	...	a_n
terms expressed using the previous term and the common ratio	a_1	a_1r	a_2r	a_3r	...	$a_{n-1}r$
terms expressed using the first term and the common ratio	a_1	a_1r	a_1r^2	a_1r^3	...	a_1r^{n-1}

The nth term, a_n, in the last column can be expressed as either $a_{n-1}r$ or a_1r^{n-1}.

Formula for the nth term of a Geometric Sequence	**The nth term, a_n, of a geometric sequence with first term a_1 and common ratio r is given by either formula.** $a_n = a_{n-1}r$ or $a_n = a_1r^{n-1}$

Example 2

Write the first five terms of a geometric sequence in which $a_1 = 5$ and $r = 2$.

Since the first term is given, write each term using the formula $a_n = a_1r^{n-1}$.

a_1	a_2	a_3	a_4	a_5
5	$5(2^{2-1})$	$5(2^{3-1})$	$5(2^{4-1})$	$5(2^{5-1})$
5	$5(2^1)$	$5(2^2)$	$5(2^3)$	$5(2^4)$
5	10	20	40	80

The first five terms of the sequence are 5, 10, 20, 40, and 80.

LESSON 13-4   GEOMETRIC SEQUENCES   609

Teaching Tip ❶   Be sure students understand the importance of using consecutive terms, not just any two terms.

Chalkboard Examples

For Example 1
Find the common ratio and the next two terms for each geometric sequence.

a. 4, 16, 64, ...   256, 1024
b. 81, 27, 9, ...   3, 1

For Example 2
Write the first six terms of the described sequence.

a. $a_1 = 4$ and $r = 3$
   4, 12, 36, 108, 324, 972
b. $a_1 = 125$ and $r = -\frac{2}{5}$
   125, -50, 20, -8, $\frac{16}{5}$, $-\frac{32}{25}$

Chalkboard Examples

For Example 3

Find the *n*th term of the geometric sequence described using $a_n = a_1 r^{n-1}$.

a. $a_4 = 10, n = 5, r = \frac{1}{2}$ **5**

b. $a_6 = 5, n = 9, r = 3$ **135**

For Example 4

Find the amount of money Fred would earn on the 14th day of his plan.   **8192¢ or $81.92**

Example 3   **Find the seventh term, a_7, of a geometric sequence in which $a_3 = 96$ and $r = 4$.**

Method 1

The general form of the third term of a sequence is $a_1 r^2$.

Find a_1.   Then find a_7.

$a_3 = a_1 r^2$ $a_n = a_1 r^{n-1}$

$96 = a_1 (4^2)$ $a_7 = a_1 r^{7-1}$

$\dfrac{96}{16} = a_1$ $= 6(4^6)$

$6 = a_1$ $= 24{,}576$

Method 2

Begin with the third term and use r to find each successive term.

$a_4 = 96 \cdot 4 = 384$ *$a_4 = a_3 \cdot r$*

$a_5 = 384 \cdot 4 = 1536$

$a_6 = 1536 \cdot 4 = 6144$

$a_7 = 24{,}576$

The seventh term is 24,576.

Example 4

APPLICATION

Finance

Fred read about a "foolproof" way to become a millionaire. You save 1¢ on the first day. Then each day thereafter, save double the amount you saved the day before. Find the amount he should save on the 20th day of his plan.

In this sequence, $a_1 = 1$. Since the amount is twice that of the day before, $r = 2$.

$a_n = a_1 r^{n-1}$

$a_{20} = 1 \cdot 2^{20-1}$

$a_{20} = 524{,}288$

Is this foolproof way to become a millionaire a practical one?

On the 20th day, Fred should save 524,288¢ or $5242.88.

You learned that the missing terms between two nonconsecutive terms in an arithmetic sequence were called arithmetic means. Likewise, the missing term or terms between two nonconsecutive terms in a geometric sequence are called **geometric means**. In the sequence, 3, 12, 48, 192, 768, ..., the three geometric means between 3 and 768 are 12, 48, and 192. You can use the common ratio to find missing geometric means in a given sequence.

Example 5

Find the two geometric means between 81 and 3. The sequence is 81, ___, ___, 3, ...

Use the general formula for the nth term to find the value of r. Since $a_1 = 81$, $a_4 = 3$, and $n = 4$, $a_n = a_1 r^{n-1}$ becomes $a_4 = a_1 \cdot r^3$ or $3 = 81r^3$.

Teaching Tip ❷

$$3 = 81 \cdot r^3$$

$$\frac{1}{27} = r^3 \quad \textit{Divide each side by 81.}$$

$$\sqrt[3]{\frac{1}{27}} = \sqrt[3]{r^3} \quad \textit{Take the cube root of each side.}$$

$$\frac{1}{3} = r \qquad \frac{1}{27} = \frac{1^3}{3^3}$$

$$a_2 = 81\left(\frac{1}{3}\right) \text{ or } 27 \qquad a_3 = 81\left(\frac{1}{3}\right)^2 \text{ or } 9$$

The missing geometric means are 27 and 9.

Sometimes there is more than one way to find the missing geometric means for a sequence. If only two terms of the sequence are given, you may find that these terms actually are parts of two different sequences.

Example 6

Find the three geometric means between 6 and 96. Then graph the sequence using the x-axis for the number of the term and the y-axis for the term itself.

Approach the problem in the same way as you did in Example 5.

$$a_5 = a_1 r^{5-1} \quad a_n = a_1 r^{n-1}$$

$$96 = 6 \cdot r^4 \quad \textit{Substitute the known values.}$$

$$16 = r^4 \quad \textit{Divide each side by 6.}$$

$$\pm 2 = r \quad 2^4 = 16 \text{ and } (-2)^4 = 16$$

Since there are two values for r, two sequences exist.

r	a_1	a_2	a_3	a_4	a_5
$r = 2$	6	6(2) or 12	6(2²) or 24	6(2³) or 48	96
$r = -2$	6	6(-2) or -12	6(-2)² or 24	6(-2)³ or -48	96

The geometric means could be either 12, 24, and 48 or -12, 24, and -48.

Each sequence forms a different graph. Each graph represents a different polynomial which reflects the values of a_1 and r.

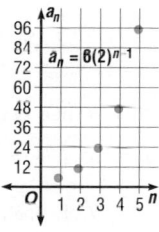

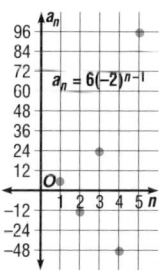

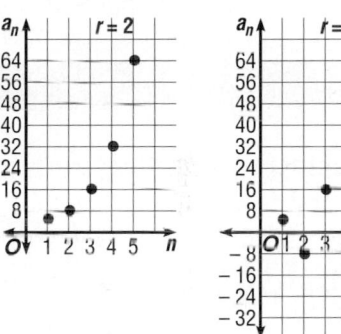
Teaching Tip ❷ Emphasize that r may be less than one, in which case sequence terms will be in decreasing instead of increasing order.

Example 7
APPLICATION
Physics

A vacuum pump removes $\frac{1}{5}$ of the air from a sealed container on each stroke of its piston. What percent of the air remains after five strokes of the piston?

Let 1 represent the original amount of air. After the first stroke, $1 - \frac{1}{5}$ or $\frac{4}{5}$ of the air remains. The second strike removes $\frac{1}{5}$ of the remaining air. Thus the amount that remains after two strokes is $\frac{4}{5}\left(1 - \frac{1}{5}\right) = \frac{4}{5} \cdot \frac{4}{5}$ or $\frac{16}{25}$. This pattern can be expressed as a geometric sequence.

number of strokes	0	1	2	3	4	5
sequence	1,	$\frac{4}{5}$,	$\frac{16}{25}$,	?,	?,	?
term	a_1	a_2	a_3	a_4	a_5	a_6

Now use the formula $a_n = a_1 r^{n-1}$ to find a_6, the amount of air left after five strokes.

$$a_n = a_1 \cdot r^{n-1}$$
$$a_6 = 1 \cdot \left(\frac{4}{5}\right)^5 \quad \text{or} \quad \frac{4^5}{5^5} \quad \textit{Substitute 1 for } a_1, \text{ 6 for } n, \text{ and } \tfrac{4}{5} \text{ for } r.$$
$$= \frac{1024}{3125} \quad \text{or about } 0.328 \quad \textbf{Teaching Tip ❸}$$

About 32.8% of the air remains after 5 strokes.

CHECKING FOR UNDERSTANDING

Communicating Mathematics

Read and study the lesson to answer each question.

1. What do you call the constant that, when multiplied by the previous term, yields the next term of the sequence? **common ratio**

2. Each term is derived from the previous term.

2. Why is a geometric sequence recursive?

3. What are the terms between any two nonconsecutive terms of a geometric sequence called? **geometric means**

4. What is a half-life? **the amount of time it takes for half the mass of an element to decay**

Guided Practice

Determine whether each sequence is geometric. If so, find the common ratio.

5. 4, 20, 100, 500 **yes, 5**   6. 2, 4, 6, 8 **no**   7. $\frac{3}{2}, \frac{9}{4}, \frac{27}{8}, \frac{81}{16}$ **yes, $\frac{3}{2}$**

8. 7, 14, 21, 28 **no**   9. 1, 4, 9, 16, 25 **no**   10. 9, 6, 4, $\frac{8}{3}$ **yes, $\frac{2}{3}$**

11. Find the first four terms of the geometric sequence in which $a_1 = 3$ and $r = -2$. **3, −6, 12, −24**

612   CHAPTER 13   SEQUENCES AND SERIES

RETEACHING THE LESSON

Have every student in each row of the class make up their own problems given a task. For example: Row 1—Every student is to make up their own geometric sequence, giving the first three terms and asking for the fourth term. Row 2—Every student is to make up their own geometric sequence giving the first and nth term and asking for the geometric mean, and so on. Have students exchange problems and solve.

EXERCISES

Practice

Find the next two terms of each geometric sequence.

12. 90, 30, 10, ...   13. 2, 6, 18, ...   14. 20, 30, 45, ...

15. 729, 243, 81, ...   16. $\frac{1}{27}, \frac{1}{9}, \frac{1}{3}, ...$ 17. $-\frac{1}{4}, \frac{1}{2}, -1, ...$

Find the first four terms of each geometric sequence described.

18. $a_1 = 3, r = -2$ 19. $a_1 = 27, r = -\frac{1}{3}$ 20. $a_1 = 12, r = \frac{1}{2}$

21. Graph the first eight terms of the sequence, −1, 2, −4, 8, ... Use the x-axis to represent n and the y-axis to represent a_n. **See Solutions Manual.**

Find the nth term of each geometric sequence described.

22. $a_1 = 4, n = 3, r = 5$ **100**   23. $a_1 = 2, n = 5, r = 2$ **32**

24. $a_1 = 7, n = 4, r = 2$ **56**   25. $a_1 = 243, n = 5, r = -\frac{1}{3}$ **3**

26. $a_3 = 32, n = 6, r = -\frac{1}{2}$ **−4**   27. $a_4 = 16, n = 8, r = \frac{1}{2}$ **1**

Find the missing geometric means. Then graph each sequence, using the x-axis for the number of the term and the y-axis for the term itself. For graphs, see Solutions Manual.

28. 3, ___, ___, ___, 48   29. 1, ___, ___, 8 **2, 4**

30. 8, ___, ___, ___, ___, $\frac{1}{4}$ 31. 3, ___, 75 **15 or −15**

32. 5, ___, ___, ___, 80   33. 7, ___, ___, ___, 112

34. ___, ___, −12, ___, ___, 96   35. ___, ___, ___, 24,
35. 3, 6, 12, 48, 96, 192 or −3, 6,   ___, ___, ___, 384
−12, −48, 96, −192

Write the formula for the nth term for each graphed sequence.

36.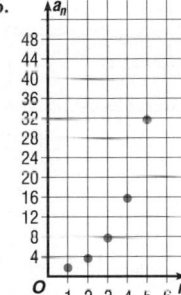

37.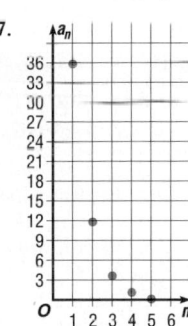

38.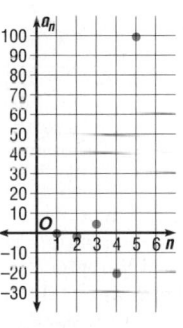

Critical Thinking

39. Write an argument to show that $a_n = a_{n-1}r$ and $a_n = a_1r^{n-1}$ are equivalent. **See margin.**

Additional Answer

39. In a geometric sequence, each subsequent term can be found by multiplying the preceding term by r. So $a_n = a_{n-1}r$, the preceding term times r, or $a_n - 1^r$. Since each term originally comes from the first term a_1, each succeeding term has one more factor of r than its preceding term. The second term has one factor of r, the third term has 2, and so on. So a_n would have $n - 1$ factors of r times a_1, or $a_n = a_1r^{n-1}$.

Error Analysis
When finding the geometric mean, have students check their answers by dividing some of the terms to see if they get the same r each time.

Closing the Lesson
Speaking Activity   Have students use examples to explain why either formula for a_n can be used to determine its value.

APPLYING THE LESSON

Homework Exercises

Assignment Guide
Basic: 12–33, 39–41, 44–49
Average: 17–36, 39–49
Enriched: 21–49

Practice Masters Booklet, p. 99

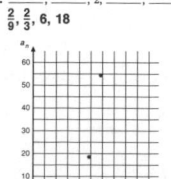
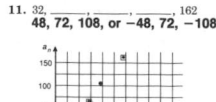
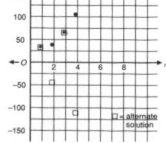

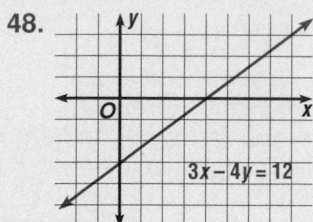
Applications

40. Physics A vacuum pump removes $\frac{1}{20}$ of the air in a sealed jar on each stroke of its pistons. How many strokes of the piston are required to remove 99% of the air from the jar?

  a. What methods could you use to solve the problem? **See margin.**

  b. Find the solution. **90**

41. Aeronautics A vacuum pump removes $\frac{1}{10}$ of the air from a space capsule on each stroke of its piston. What percent of the air remains after 10 strokes of the piston? **34.9%**

42. Demographics The population of Sunville increases by 10% each year. It currently has a population of 20,000. **32,200**

  a. Predict its population to the nearest 100 people 5 years from now.

  b. At this rate, in how many years will the population be at least 100,000? **17 years**

43. Cinematography To produce a vanishing effect on film, an animated character's image is filmed at 50%. Then each reduced image is filmed at 50% again. If this process of filming at 50% is repeated 8 more times, what is the area of the resulting image in comparison to the original image? $\frac{1}{1024}$ **or approximately 0.098% of the original**

Mixed Review

44. Find S_n for an arithmetic series in which $a_1 = 11$, $a_n = 44$, and $n = 23$. **(Lesson 13-3) 632.5**

  -3, 2, 5

45. Find all rational zeros of $f(x) = x^3 - 4x^2 - 11x + 30$. **(Lesson 10-3)**

46. Find $f(m + 2)$ if $f(x) = 2x^3 - 5x^2$. **(Lesson 8-1) $2m^3 + 7m^2 + 4m - 4$**

47. Factor $a^4 - 16b^8$. **(Lesson 5-5) $(a^2 + 4b^4)(a - 2b^2)(a + 2b^2)$**

48. Graph $3x - 4y = 12$. **(Lesson 2-4) See margin.**

49. Geometry The formula for the area of a regular hexagon is $A = \frac{1}{2}ap$, where a is the measure of the apothem and p is the perimeter of the hexagon. Find the area of a hexagon whose side is 6 inches long and whose apothem is 1.73 times the length of the side. **(Lesson 1-1)**
186.84 square inches

~~~~~ **FINE ARTS CONNECTION** ~~~~~

Music and mathematics are closely related. Have you ever wondered why a harp or pipe organ has a particular shape? Stringed instruments, like pianos and harps, and those formed from columns of air, like pipe organs, reflect the shape of an exponential curve. The length of each string or pipe is a term in an exponential sequence. The pitch of a string is determined by its thickness and tautness. The pitch of a pipe is determined by its thickness and diameter.

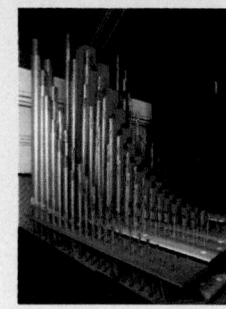

13-5   Geometric Series

Objectives

13-5A
13-5B

After studying this lesson, you should be able to:

- find sums of geometric series, and find specific terms in the series, and
- use sigma notation to express the sum.

Teaching Tip ❶

Application

Fred decided to try the foolproof way to become a millionaire by saving 1¢ on the first day and doubling the amount saved each day. On the first day, he placed a penny in a large glass bottle. The next day he placed 2 cents in the bottle, and so on. After a week, he wondered how much he had saved. How could he compute his savings without keeping extensive records?

The amounts saved in the first week were 1¢, 2¢, 4¢, 8¢, 16¢, 32¢, and 64¢. To find the total of this geometric sequence, you add these numbers. The sum of the terms of a geometric sequence is called a **geometric series.**

You can develop a formula for finding the sum of a geometric series. Let S_7 represent the sum of the first seven terms of the geometric series. In the series above, $a_1 = 1$ and $r = 2$.

$$S_7 = 1 + 2 + 4 + 8 + 16 + 32 + 64 \qquad \textit{Now multiply each side by 2.}$$
$$2S_7 = \quad 2 + 4 + 8 + 16 + 32 + 64 + 128 \qquad \textit{Align the terms.}$$
$$S_7 - 2S_7 = 1 + 0 + 0 + 0 + \ 0 + \ 0 + 0 + (-128) \qquad \textit{Subtract the two equations}$$

$$(1 - 2)S_7 = 1 - 128 \qquad \textit{Factor out } S_7.$$
$$S_7 = \frac{1 - 128}{1 - 2} \text{ or } 127 \qquad \textit{Divide each side by } 1 - 2.$$

Fred saved $1.27.

In Fred's problem, you can relate the equation $S_7 = \dfrac{1 - 128}{1 - 2}$ to terms of the series. Note that 1 is a_1, 128 is a_7, and 2 is r. If we substitute these values, the solution resembles a general formula.

$$S_7 = \frac{a_1 - a_8}{1 - r} \quad \text{or} \quad S_7 = \frac{a_1 - a_1 r^7}{1 - r} \qquad \textit{Remember, } a_8 = a_1 r^{8-1}.$$

Notice that we rewrote a_8 in terms of a_1 and r so that the formula contained as few different variables as possible. This can be generalized for the nth term.

Sum of a Geometric Series

> The sum, S_n, of the first n terms of a geometric series is given by the following formula.
>
> $$S_n = \frac{a_1 - a_1 r^n}{1 - r} \quad \text{or} \quad S_n = \frac{a_1(1 - r^n)}{1 - r} \text{ where } r \neq 1$$

The general formula for the sum of a geometric series limits the value of r. When you have a geometric series in which $r = 1$, the denominator would be zero, so S_n is found by the formula $S_n = n \cdot a_1$.

LESSON 13-5   GEOMETRIC SERIES   615

Lesson Resources

Reteaching Master 13-5
Practice Master 13-5
Enrichment Master 13-5
Activity Master, p. 13
Multicultural Activity Master, p. 13

 Transparency 13-5 contains the 5-Minute Check and a teaching aid for this lesson.

INTRODUCING THE LESSON

🕐 5-Minute Check

(over Lesson 13-4)

1. Find the next two terms of the geometric sequence 3, −12, 48, ...   **−192, 768**

Find the nth term of each geometric sequence.

2. $a_1 = -2, n = 5, r = 3$
$a_5 = $ **−162**
3. $a_1 = -5, n = 4, r = 2$
$a_4 = $ **−40**
4. Find the missing geometric means of the sequence 40, __, __, 135.   **60, 90**
5. A certain model automobile depreciates 20% of its value each year. If it costs $16,800 new, what is its value at the end of eight years? **$2818.57**

Motivating the Lesson

Refer to Motivating the Lesson for Lesson 13−4. Ask students how they would know how many organisms were present after a given number of divisions.

ALTERNATE TEACHING STRATEGIES

Mini-Math Lab

Using counters of one color to represent single digits and counters of another color to represent multiples of 10, have students model a sum for a given number of terms of a geometric series. Students may work independently or with a partner. Have students use the formula to check the modeled sum.

Chalkboard Examples

For Example 1

Find the sum of each geometric series.

a. $a_1 = 16$, $r = \frac{1}{2}$, $n = 7$

   $\frac{127}{4}$ or 31.75

b. $a_1 = 4$, $r = -\frac{1}{2}$, $n = 8$ $\frac{85}{32}$

For Example 2

How much Pu-236 is left after 5 half-lives?   3.125 g

For Example 3

Find the sum of a geometric series for which $a_1 = 4$, $a_n = 256$, and $r = 4$. $S_n = 340$

Example 1   **Find the sum of the first five terms of a geometric series for which $a_1 = 4$ and $r = -3$.**

Use the formula for the sum of a geometric series.

$$S_n = \frac{a_1 - a_1 r^n}{1 - r} \quad \Rightarrow \quad S_5 = \frac{4 - 4(-3)^5}{1 - (-3)}$$

$$= \frac{976}{4} \text{ or } 244$$

The sum of the first five terms is 244.

Example 2

The half-life of plutonium (Pu-236) is 2.85 years. Use a calculator to find how much of a 100 gram sample of Pu-236 is left after 10 half-lives.

To find the amount left, use the sum of a series to determine the amount that decays. Then subtract that amount from the initial amount, 100 grams. After the first half-life, 0.5(100) or 50 grams has decayed. So, $a_1 = 50$ and $r = 0.5$ in the series describing the total amount decayed.

$$S_n = \frac{a_1 - a_1 r^n}{1 - r} = \frac{50 - 50(0.5)^{10}}{1 - 0.5} \qquad a_1 = 50, \ r = 0.5, \ n = 10$$

ENTER: $($ 50 $-$ 50 $\times$ 0.5 $\boxed{y^x}$ 10 $)$ $\div$

$($ 1 $-$ 0.5 $)$ $=$ 99.90234375

Approximately $100 - 99.9$ or 0.1 gram of Pu-236 is left after 10 half-lives.

Another form of the formula for S_n can be developed and used when you don't know how many terms are in the series.

$$a_n = a_1 r^{n-1}$$
$$a_n \cdot r = a_1 r^{n-1} \cdot r \qquad \textit{Multiply each side by r.}$$
$$a_n r = a_1 r^n \qquad \qquad a_1 r^{n-1} \cdot r = a_1 \cdot r^{n-1+1}$$

Thus, we can substitute $a_n r$ into any formula containing $a_1 r^n$.

$$S_n = \frac{a_1 - a_1 r^n}{1 - r} \qquad \textit{Sum of a geometric series}$$

$$S_n = \frac{a_1 - a_n r}{1 - r} \qquad \textit{Substitute } a_n r \textit{ for } a_1 r^n. \qquad \textit{Remember, } r \neq 1.$$

Example 3   **Find the sum of a geometric series for which $a_1 = 48$, $a_n = 3$, and $r = -\frac{1}{2}$.**

Since we do not know the value of n, use $S_n = \dfrac{a_1 - a_n r}{1 - r}$.

$$S_n = \frac{a_1 - a_n r}{1 - r} = \frac{48 - 3\left(-\dfrac{1}{2}\right)}{1 - \left(-\dfrac{1}{2}\right)} \text{ or } 33$$

The sum is 33.

Example 4

Find a_1 in a geometric series where $S_7 = 3279$ and $r = 3$.

Use the sum formula and substitute in all values you know. Since we have S_7, we know $n = 7$.

$$S_7 = \frac{a_1 - a_1 r^7}{1 - r} \qquad S_n = \frac{a_1 - a_1 r^n}{1 - r}$$

$$3279 = \frac{a_1 - a_1 \cdot 3^7}{1 - 3} \qquad r = 3, \ S_7 = 3279$$

$$3279 = \frac{a_1(1 - 2187)}{-2} \qquad a_1 \text{ is a common factor.}$$

$$\frac{3279(-2)}{-2186} = a_1 \qquad \text{Solve for } a_1.$$

$$a_1 = 3$$

In Lesson 13-3, you learned that sigma notation can be used to express an arithmetic series. The same is true for a geometric series.

Example 5

Write the terms of $\sum_{j=1}^{5} 2(4)^{j-1}$ and find the sum.

$$\sum_{j=1}^{5} 2(4)^{j-1} = (2 \cdot 4^{1-1}) + (2 \cdot 4^{2-1}) + (2 \cdot 4^{3-1}) + (2 \cdot 4^{4-1}) + (2 \cdot 4^{5-1})$$
$$= 2(1) + 2(4) + 2(16) + 2(64) + 2(256)$$
$$= 2 + 8 + 32 + 128 + 512 \text{ or } 682$$

The sum is 682.

In Example 5, $a_1 = 2$, $n = 5$, and $r = 4$. The sum could also have been found by using the sum formula. So, $S_5 = \frac{2(1 - 4^5)}{1 - 4}$ or 682.

Example 6

Use sigma notation to express $1 - 3 + 9 - 27 + 81 - 243$.

This is the sum of the first six terms of a geometric series, so $n = 6$. The value of r is -3 and $a_1 = 1$. Use the formula for the nth term of a sequence to find a general form of each term.

$$a_n = a_1 r^{n-1}$$
$$a_n = 1(-3)^{n-1} \qquad a_1 = 1, \ r = -3$$

The sum of the terms from a_1 to a_6 is expressed in sigma notation as $\sum_{n=1}^{6} (-3)^{n-1}$.

RETEACHING THE LESSON

Have groups of students make up a geometric series and write it in sigma notation. Then have groups exchange problems and find the sum of the geometric series. Return to original groups to check answers.

Chalkboard Examples

For Example 4
In a certain geometric series, $S_8 = 13{,}120$ and $r = 3$, find a_1 for the series. $a_1 = 4$

For Example 5
Write $\sum_{s=5}^{8} \frac{1}{2}(3)^{2s-9}$ in expanded form and find the sum.

$$\sum_{s=5}^{8} \frac{1}{2}(3)^{2s-9} = \frac{3}{2} + \frac{27}{2} + \frac{243}{2} + \frac{2187}{2} = 1230$$

For Example 6
Use sigma notation to express $-3 + 2 - \frac{4}{3} + \frac{8}{9}$.

$$\sum_{n=1}^{4} -3\left(-\frac{2}{3}\right)^{n-1}$$

Reteaching Masters Booklet, p. 87

Checking for Understanding

Exercises 1–16 are designed to help you assess understanding through reading, writing, and speaking. You should work through Exercises 1–4 with your students, and then monitor their work on Exercises 5–16.

Closing the Lesson

Writing Activity   Have students compare and contrast arithmetic and geometric series.

APPLYING THE LESSON

Homework Exercises

Assignment Guide

Basic: 17–35, 43–44, 47–51
Average: 21–38, 43–51
Enriched: 25–51

Practice Masters Booklet, p. 100

NAME _____   DATE _____

13-5 Practice Worksheet

Geometric Series

Find the sum of each geometric series described.

1. $160 + 80 + 40 + \ldots, n = 6$ **315**
2. $a_1 = 5, r = -\frac{1}{2}, n = 7$ **$\frac{215}{64}$**

3. $a_2 = \frac{-3}{8}, a_3 = \frac{1}{4}, n = 5$ **$\frac{58}{144}$**
4. $a_3 = 8, a_5 = 2, n = 6$ **21 or 63**

Use sigma notation to express each series.

5. $54 + 18 + 6 + 2 + \frac{2}{3} + \frac{2}{9}$ **$\sum\limits_{n=1}^{6} 54\left(\frac{1}{3}\right)^{n-1}$**
6. $16 - 24 + 36 - 54 + 81 - 121.5 + 182.25$ **$\sum\limits_{n=1}^{7} 16\left(-\frac{3}{2}\right)^{n-1}$**

Find a_1 for each geometric series described.

7. $S_n = -55, r = -\frac{2}{3}, n = 5$ **−81**
8. $S_n = 2457, a_n = 3072, r = -4$ **−3**

9. A pile driver drives a post 9 feet into the ground on its first hit. Each additional hit drives the post $\frac{2}{3}$ the distance of the prior hit. Find the total distance the post has been driven after 4 hits. **$21\frac{2}{3}$ ft**

10. In problem 9, what is the greatest distance the pole could be driven into the ground? **27 ft**

11. Hugh Moore makes up a joke and tells it to his 5 closest friends on Sunday morning. Each of those friends tells his or her 5 closest friends on Monday morning, and so on. Assuming no duplication, how many people will have heard the joke by the end of Saturday? **97,655; 97,656 if Hugh is included**

CHECKING FOR UNDERSTANDING

Communicating Mathematics

2. $S_n = \dfrac{a_1 - a_1 r^n}{1 - r}$
$S_n = a_1 \cdot n$

Read and study the lesson to answer each question.

1. A geometric __?__ is the sum of the terms of a geometric sequence. **series**
2. The sum of a geometric series can be found by two formulas, __?__ and __?__ .
3. The formula for the sum of a geometric series states that $r \neq 1$. Why is this stipulation included? **because the denominator would be 0.**
4. Suppose the first and fifth terms of a geometric series are known and you are asked to find the three geometric means. How is it possible to get two correct sets of answers? **The value of r can be positive or negative.**

Guided Practice

5. 9; −2; −72; 4
6. 3; 0.5; 0.375; 4
7. 2; 4; 512; 5
8. −12; $-\frac{1}{2}$; $-\frac{3}{4}$; 5

For each geometric series, state the first term, the common ratio, the last term, and the number of terms.

5. $9 - 18 + 36 - 72$
6. $3 + 1.5 + 0.75 + 0.375$
7. $a_1 + 8 + 32 + 128 + a_5$
8. $a_1 + 6 - 3 + \frac{3}{2} + a_5$
9. In a certain geometric series, $a_1 = 20$, $a_4 = -\frac{5}{16}$, and the number of terms is 5. Find the common ratio and the last term. $-\frac{1}{4}, \frac{5}{64}$
10. In a certain geometric series, $a_2 = 6$ and $a_4 = 24$. Find the first term, the common ratio, and the sixth term. **3, 2, 96 or −3, −2, 96**

Find the sum of each geometric series.

                                                                              −364
11. $7 + 7 + 7 + \ldots$ to 9 terms **63**
12. $2 + (-6) + 18 + \ldots$ to 6 terms
13. $3 + 6 + 12 + \ldots$ to 6 terms **189**
14. $8 + 4 + 2 + \ldots$ to 6 terms $15\frac{3}{4}$
15. $\frac{1}{9} - \frac{1}{3} + 1 - \ldots$ to 5 terms $\frac{61}{9}$
16. $1296 - 216 + 36 - \ldots$ to 5 terms **1111**

EXERCISES

Practice

17. 176
19. 1,328,600

Find the sum of each geometric series described.

                                                                              93.75
A
17. $16 + 16 + 16 + \ldots$ to 11 terms.
18. $75 + 15 + 3 + \ldots$ to 10 terms.
19. $a_1 = 5, r = 3, n = 12$
20. $a_1 = 256, r = 0.75, n = 9$ **947.11**
21. $a_1 = 7, r = 2, n = 14$ **114,681**
22. $a_1 = 12, a_5 = 972, r = -3$ **732**
23. $a_1 = 16, r = -\frac{1}{2}, n = 10$ **10.66**
24. $a_1 = 625, r = \frac{2}{5}, n = 8$ **1040.98**

B
25. $a_1 = 1, a_5 = \frac{1}{16}, r = -\frac{1}{2}$ $\frac{11}{16}$
26. $a_1 = 243, r = -\frac{2}{3}, n = 5$ **165**
27. $a_1 = 343, a_4 = -1, r = -\frac{1}{7}$ **300**
28. $a_1 = 625, a_5 = 81, r = \frac{3}{5}$ **1441**
29. $a_1 = 125, a_5 = \frac{1}{5}, r = \frac{1}{5}$ $\frac{781}{5}$
30. $a_1 = 4, a_6 = \frac{1}{8}, r = \frac{1}{2}$ $\frac{63}{8}$

$$35. \sum_{n=1}^{6} 2(-3)^{n-1}$$

$$36. \sum_{n=1}^{6} 243\left(\frac{-2}{3}\right)^{n-1}$$

31. $a_2 = 1.5$, $a_5 = 0.1875$, $n = 9$ **5.99** 32. $a_3 = \frac{3}{4}$, $a_6 = \frac{3}{32}$, $n = 6$ $\frac{189}{32}$

33. $a_3 = \frac{5}{4}$, $a_4 = -\frac{5}{16}$, $n = 6$ $\frac{4095}{256}$ 34. $a_2 = -12$, $a_5 = -324$, $n = 10$ **−118,096**

Use sigma notation to express each series.

35. $2 - 6 + 18 - 54 + 162 - 486$

C 36. $243 - 162 + 108 - 72 + 48 - 32$

Find a_1 for each geometric series described.

37. $S_n = 244$, $r = -3$, $n = 5$ **4** 38. $S_n = 32$, $r = 2$, $n = 6$ $\frac{32}{63}$

39. $a_n = 324$, $r = 3$, $S_n = 484$ **4** 40. $S_n = 635$, $a_n = 320$, $r = 2$ **5**

41. $S_n = 15.75$, $r = 0.5$, $a_n = 0.25$ **8** 42. $S_n = 1022$, $r = 2$, $n = 9$ **2**

Critical Thinking 43. Use the formula for the nth term of a geometric sequence to show that, when $r = 1$, the sum of a geometric series is $S_n = n \cdot a_1$. **See margin.**

Applications 44. **Recreation** One minute after it is released, a hot air balloon rose 80 feet. In each succeeding minute the balloon rose only 60% as far as it rose in the previous minute.

a. Write a geometric sequence that describes the rise of the hot air balloon during the first 5 minutes. **80, 48, 28.8, 17.28, 10.368**

b. How far will the balloon rise in 6 minutes? **190.7 feet**

45. **Communications** The teaching staff of Fairmeadow High School informs its members of school cancellation by telephone. The principal calls 2 teachers, each of whom in turn calls 2 other teachers, and so on. In order to inform the entire staff, 6 rounds of calls are made. Counting the principal, find how many people are on staff at Fairmeadow High. **127**

46. **Meteorology** A 5-day rain caused the Olentangy River to rise. After the first day, the river rose one inch. Each day the rise in the river tripled. How much had the river risen after 5 days? **121 in. or about 10 ft**

Mixed Review 47. Find the missing terms of the geometric sequence __?__ , __?__ , 3, 9, 27. (Lesson 13-4) $\frac{1}{3}$, 1

48. **Biology** The number of a certain type of bacteria can increase from 80 to 164 in 3 hours. Find the approximate value of k in the growth formula. (Lesson 12-9) **0.2392**

49. **3 h 7 min** 49. Danny and Sonia run a lawn service during the summer. Sonia can cut the lawns of all customers in 15 hours. Danny can do the same in 12 hours. Sonia works alone for 8 hours, after which Danny joins her. How long will it take both of them to finish the job? (Lesson 8-5)

50. $n = m$ 50. What are the values of n and m if $A_{n \times m}$ has an inverse? (Lesson 4-4)

51. Solve $\begin{cases} 3x - 7y = -1 \\ 3x + 7y = 13 \end{cases}$ using Cramer's rule. (Lesson 3-3) **(2, 1)**

LESSON 13-5 GEOMETRIC SERIES 619

EXTENDING THE LESSON

Math Power: Reasoning

Have students determine a set of requirements for n, a_1, and r that will result in a negative S_n. Using their requirements, have them name sample values for n, a_1, and r, and find S_n. **Sample answer: n is even, a_1 is positive, and $r \le -1$; $n = 4$, $a_1 = 2$, and $r = -3$; $S_n = -40$**

Additional Answer

43. $S_n = a_1 + a_1r + a_1r^2 + a_1r^3 + \ldots + a_1r^{n-1}$
Substitute 1 for r.
$S_n = a_1 + a_1(1) + a_1(1^2) + a_1(1^3) + \ldots a_1(1^{1-1})$
$S_n = n$ addends of a_1 or $n \cdot a_1$

Chapter 13, Quiz C, (Lessons 13–4 through 13–5), is available in the Evaluation Masters Booklet, p. 178.

Enrichment Masters Booklet, p. 87

13-5 **Enrichment Worksheet**
NAME _____ DATE _____
Annuities

An annuity is a fixed amount of money payable at given intervals. For example, suppose you wanted to set up a trust fund so that $30,000 could be withdrawn each year for 14 years before the money ran out. Assume the money can be invested at 9%.

You must find the amount of money that needs to be invested. Call this amount A. After the third payment, the amount left is

$1.09[1.09A - 30,000(1 + 1.09)] - 30,000 = 1.09^2 A - 30,000(1 + 1.09 + 1.09^2)$.

The results are summarized in the table below.

Payment Number	Number of Dollars Left After Payment
1	$A - 30,000$
2	$1.09A - 30,000(1 + 1.09)$
3	$1.09^2 A - 30,000(1 + 1.09 + 1.09^2)$

1. Use the pattern shown in the table to find the number of dollars left after the fourth payment.
$1.09^3 A - 30,000(1 + 1.09 + 1.09^2 + 1.09^3)$

2. Find the amount left after the tenth payment.

The amount left after the 14th payment is $1.09^{13} A - 30,000(1 + 1.09 + 1.09^2 + \ldots + 1.09^{13})$. However, there should be no money left after the 14th and final payment.

$1.09^{13} A - 30,000(1 + 1.09 + 1.09^2 + \ldots + 1.09^{13}) = 0$

Notice that $1 + 1.09 + 1.09^2 + \ldots + 1.09^{13}$ is a geometric series where $a_1 = 1$, $a_n = 1.09^{13}$, $n = 14$ and $r = 1.09$.

Using the formula for S_n,

$1 + 1.09 + 1.09^2 + \ldots + 1.09^{13} = \frac{a_1 - a_1 r^n}{1 - r} = \frac{1 - 1.09^{14}}{1 - 1.09} = \frac{1 - 1.09^{14}}{-0.09}$.

3. Show that when you solve for A you get $A = \frac{30,000}{0.09}\left(\frac{1.09^{14} - 1}{1.09^{13}}\right)$.

$1.09^{13}A - 30,000\left(\frac{1 - 1.09^{14}}{-0.09}\right) = 0$ **results in stated expression for A.**

Therefore, to provide $30,000 for 14 years where the annual interest rate is 9%, you need $\frac{30,000}{0.09}\left(\frac{1.09^{14} - 1}{1.09^{13}}\right)$ dollars.

4. Use a calculator to find the value of A in problem 3. **$254,607**

In general, if you wish to provide P dollars for each of n years at an annual rate of $r\%$, you need A dollars where

$\left(1 + \frac{r}{100}\right)^{n-1} A - P\left[1 + \left(1 + \frac{r}{100}\right) + \left(1 + \frac{r}{100}\right)^2 + \ldots + \left(1 + \frac{r}{100}\right)^{n-1}\right] = 0$.

You can solve this equation for A, given P, n, and r.

Infinite Geometric Series

Lesson Resources

Reteaching Master 13-6
Practice Master 13-6
Enrichment Master 13-6

 Transparency 13-6 contains the 5-Minute Check and a teaching aid for this lesson.

INTRODUCING THE LESSON

 5-Minute Check

(over Lesson 13-5)

1. For the given geometric series, state the first term, the common ratio, the last term, and the number of terms.
$a_1 + (-6) + 18 + (-54) + 162 + a_6$ $a_1 = 2, r = -3,$
$a_6 = -486,$ 6 terms
2. Find the sum of the geometric series with $a_1 = 81$, $r = \frac{1}{3}$, $n = 7$. $121\frac{4}{9}$
3. Find the sum of the geometric series $2 + 4 + 8 + \ldots$ to ten terms.   2046
4. Find the sum of nine terms of the geometric series with $a_1 = -2$ and $r = -\frac{1}{4}$.
-1.600006
5. Use sigma notation to express the series $4 - 12 + 36 - 108 + 324$.
$\sum_{n=1}^{5} 4(-3)^{n-1}$

Motivating the Lesson

Read the Edgar Allen Poe short story, *The Pit and the Pendulum*, to the students. Discuss pendulums and how they relate to geometric sequences and series.

TEACHING THE LESSON

Teaching Tip ❶ Graphing the values may help students determine the limits.

Objective 13-6

Application

Teaching Tip ❶

Remember that |r| < 1 means -1 < r < 1.

Sum of an Infinite Geometric Series

After studying this lesson, you should be able to:
- find the sum of an infinite geometric series.

The first swing of a pendulum measures 25 cm. The lengths of the successive swings of the pendulum form the geometric sequence 25, 20, 16, 12.8, ...

Suppose this pendulum continues to swing back and forth indefinitely. Then the sequence shown above becomes an infinite geometric sequence.

25 cm
20 cm
16 cm
12.8 cm

The total distance the pendulum travels can be expressed as the **infinite geometric series**

$$25 + 20 + 16 + 12.8 + \ldots.$$

In this series, $a_1 = 25$ and $r = \frac{20}{25}$ or 0.8. So the series can be expressed as

$$25 + 25(0.8)^1 + 25(0.8)^2 + 25(0.8)^3 + 25(0.8)^4 + 25(0.8)^5 + 25(0.8)^6 + \ldots.$$

Use your calculator to *look for a pattern* in the values of 0.8^n as n increases.

$0.8^1 = 0.8$ $0.8^{10} \approx 0.1073742$ $0.8^{50} \approx 0.0000143$ $0.8^{70} \approx 0.0000002$

Use your calculator to *look for a pattern* as to how this affects a_n.

$a_1 = 25$ $a_{10} \approx 3.3554432$ $a_{50} \approx 0.000446$ $a_{70} \approx 0.00000514$

Use your calculator to *look for a pattern* in the values of S_n as n increases.

$S_1 = 25$ $S_{10} = \dfrac{25 - 25(0.8^{10})}{0.2}$ $S_{50} = \dfrac{25 - 25(0.8^{50})}{0.2}$ $S_{70} = \dfrac{25 - 25(0.8^{70})}{0.2}$
≈ 111.57823 ≈ 124.99822 ≈ 124.99998

The sum S_n appears to approach 125 as n becomes infinitely great. In an infinite geometric series where $|r| < 1$, as the value of n increases, the value of each term approaches zero. This implies that the sum converges to some number. This can be analyzed by observing how this affects the sum formula for a geometric series.

$$S_n = \frac{a_1 - a_1 r^n}{1 - r} \text{ as } n \text{ approaches infinity and } r^n \text{ approaches 0, } S_n = \frac{a_1}{1 - r}.$$

This is known as the sum of an infinite geometric series.

> The sum, S, of an infinite geometric series where $-1 < r < 1$ is given by the following formula.
>
> $$S = \frac{a_1}{1 - r}$$

620   CHAPTER 13   SEQUENCES AND SERIES

ALTERNATE TEACHING STRATEGIES

Using Questioning

While discussing the Application with students, ask them to verbalize a summary of each pattern shown by the calculator results. While solving the example problems with students, ask questions that will elicit student responses pertinent to each example.

An infinite geometric series in which $|r| > 1$ does not have a sum. For example, consider the series $1 + 2 + 4 + 8 + 16 + ...$, where $a_1 = 1$ and $r = 2$. The terms of this series keep increasing. So the sum becomes greater with each additional term and never approaches any particular number.

Example 1

Find the total distance traveled by the pendulum as it comes to rest.

$S = 25 + 20 + 16 + 12.8 + ...$, with $r = 0.8$ and $a_1 = 25$

$S = \frac{a_1}{1-r} = \frac{25}{1-0.8}$ or 125   *$a_1 = 25, r = 0.8$*

The pendulum travels 125 cm.

How does this compare with the pattern on page 620?

Example 2

Find the sum of the infinite geometric series $\frac{4}{3} - \frac{2}{3} + \frac{1}{3} - \frac{1}{6} + ...$

To find the value of r, divide any term by its preceding term.

$r = -\frac{2}{3} \div \frac{4}{3}$ **Teaching Tip ❷**

$= -\frac{2}{3} \cdot \frac{3}{4}$ or $-\frac{1}{2}$

Since $|r| < 1$, you can use the formula $S = \frac{a_1}{1-r}$.

$S = \frac{\frac{4}{3}}{1-\left(-\frac{1}{2}\right)} = \frac{\frac{4}{3}}{\frac{3}{2}}$ or $\frac{8}{9}$ The sum is $\frac{8}{9}$.

The sum of an infinite geometric series can be used to express a repeating decimal as a rational number in the form of $\frac{a}{b}$. Remember that repeating decimals such as $0.\overline{1}$ and $0.0\overline{43}$ represent 0.11111... and 0.0434343..., respectively.

Example 3

Express $0.\overline{1}$ as a rational number in the form $\frac{a}{b}$.   **Teaching Tip ❸**

First express $0.\overline{1}$ as an infinite geometric series.

$0.\overline{1} = 0.1 + 0.01 + 0.001 + 0.0001 + ...$

Each term is $\frac{1}{10}$ of the preceding term, so $r = 0.1$. Also $a_1 = 0.1$.

$S = \frac{a_1}{1-r}$

$= \frac{0.1}{1-0.1}$ *$a_1 = 0.1, r = 0.1$*

$= \frac{0.1}{0.9}$ or $\frac{1}{9}$ The decimal $0.\overline{1}$ can be expressed as $\frac{1}{9}$.

Chalkboard Examples

For Example 1

Find the sum of each infinite geometric series.

a. $a_1 = 6, r = \frac{1}{3}$ **9**

b. $a_1 = -4, r = -\frac{1}{2}$ $\mathbf{-2\frac{2}{3}}$

For Example 2

Find the sum of each infinite geometric series.

a. $8 + 4 + 2 + ...$ **16**

b. $1 - \frac{1}{3} + \frac{1}{9} - ...$ $\mathbf{\frac{3}{4}}$

For Example 3

Express $0.\overline{12}$ as a fraction. $\mathbf{\frac{4}{33}}$

Teaching Tip ❷ Remind students that any two consecutive terms can be used to determine r.

Teaching Tip ❸ Explain to students that if the repeating decimal has two or more digits that repeat, this number of digits is the basis for the series. For example, if the decimal is 0.171717 ..., 0.17 is a_1 and $r = 0.01$, watch for fractional values of r that are not less than 1.

The sum of an infinite geometric series can also be written using sigma notation. Since it is impossible to count the number of terms in an infinite series, the upper limit of the index is written as ∞, which is the symbol for **infinity.**

Example 4

Evaluate $\sum_{n=1}^{\infty} 36\left(-\frac{1}{3}\right)^{n-1}$.

$$\sum_{n=1}^{\infty} 36\left(-\frac{1}{3}\right)^{n-1} = 36\left(-\frac{1}{3}\right)^{1-1} + 36\left(-\frac{1}{3}\right)^{2-1} + 36\left(-\frac{1}{3}\right)^{3-1} + \dots$$

$$= 36 - 12 + 4 - \frac{4}{3} + \frac{4}{9} + \dots$$

Therefore, $a_1 = 36$ and $r = -\frac{1}{3}$. Now use the formula $s = \frac{a_1}{1 - r}$.

$$S = \frac{36}{1 - \left(-\frac{1}{3}\right)} = \frac{36}{\frac{4}{3}} \text{ or } 27$$

Therefore, $\sum_{n=1}^{\infty} 36\left(-\frac{1}{3}\right)^{n-1} = 27$.

Example 5

APPLICATION

Physics

To test its elasticity, a rubber ball is dropped into a 30-foot hollow tube that is calibrated so that the scientist can measure the height of each subsequent bounce. The scientist found that on each bounce, the ball rises to a height $\frac{2}{5}$ the height of the previous bounce. How far will the ball travel before it stops bouncing?

A diagram of the situation is helpful in exploring this problem.

This situation involves the sum of two infinite geometric series, one that contains the measures of the upward bounces and one that contains the measures of the downward bounces.

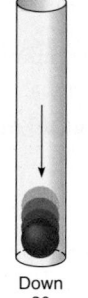 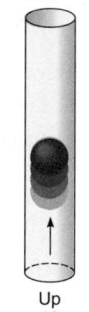 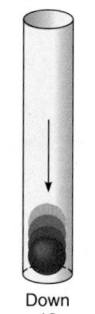 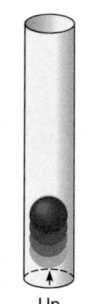 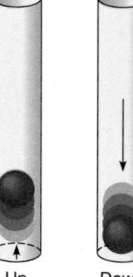

Down	Up	Down	Up	Down
30	12	12	4.8	4.8

Let S_D be the downward sum or $30 + 12 + 4.8 + 1.92 + \dots$.
Let S_U be the upward sum or $12 + 4.8 + 1.92 + \dots$.

$$S_D = \frac{30}{1 - 0.4} \qquad\qquad S_U = \frac{12}{1 - 0.4}$$

$$= \frac{30}{0.6} \text{ or } 50 \qquad\qquad = \frac{12}{0.6} \text{ or } 20$$

The ball will travel $50 + 20$ or 70 feet before it stops bouncing.

RETEACHING THE LESSON

Give students some possible values of r orally and ask if the geometric series with that r could be an infinite one. Have them explain why or why not.

CHECKING FOR UNDERSTANDING

Communicating Mathematics

Read and study the lesson to answer each question.   **1. See margin.**

1. Why are the series in this lesson called infinite geometric series?

2. Refer to the patterns of numbers shown on page 620.
   a. Describe the value of $(0.8)^n$ as n increases. **approaches 0**
   b. Describe the value a_n approaches as n increases. **approaches 0**
   c. Describe the value S_n approaches as n increases. **approaches 125**

3. What does the symbol ∞ represent? **infinity**

4. Under what condition can you find the sum of an infinite geometric series? **when $|r| < 1$**

Guided Practice

Find a_1 and r for each series. Then find the sum, if it exists.

5. $12 + 3 + \dfrac{3}{4} + \dfrac{3}{16} + \dots$ **$12, \frac{1}{4}, 16$**   6. $1 - 3 + 9 - 27 + \dots$ **$1, -3,$ no sum**

7. $1 - \dfrac{1}{3} + \dfrac{1}{9} - \dfrac{1}{27} + \dots$ **$1, -\frac{1}{3}, \frac{3}{4}$**   8. $\dfrac{1}{2} + \dfrac{1}{3} + \dfrac{2}{9} + \dfrac{4}{27} + \dots$ **$\frac{1}{2}, \frac{2}{3}, \frac{3}{2}$**

9. $48 + 16 + \dfrac{16}{3} + \dfrac{16}{9} + \dots$ **$48, \frac{1}{3}, 72$**   10. $1 + \dfrac{3}{2} + \dfrac{9}{4} + \dfrac{27}{8} + \dots$ **$1, \frac{3}{2},$ no sum**

Use the sum of an infinite geometric series to express each decimal as a rational number in the form $\dfrac{a}{b}$.

11. $0.\overline{7}$ **$\frac{7}{9}$**   12. $0.\overline{73}$ **$\frac{73}{99}$**   13. $0.\overline{152}$ **$\frac{152}{999}$**   14. $0.\overline{93}$ **$\frac{31}{33}$**

EXERCISES

Practice

Find the sum of each infinite geometric series, if it exists.   **20. does not exist**

15. $a_1 = 7, r = -\dfrac{3}{4}$ **4**   16. $a_1 = 6, r = \dfrac{11}{12}$ **72**   17. $a_1 = 18, r = -\dfrac{2}{7}$ **14**

18. $\dfrac{1}{3} + \dfrac{1}{9} + \dfrac{1}{27} + \dots$ **$\frac{1}{2}$**   19. $9 + 6 + 4 + \dots$ **27**   20. $2 + 6 + 18 + \dots$

21. $\dfrac{3}{4} + \dfrac{1}{2} + \dfrac{1}{3} + \dots$ **$\frac{9}{4}$**   22. $1 - \dfrac{1}{4} + \dfrac{1}{16} - \dots$ **$\frac{4}{5}$**   23. $12 - 4 + \dfrac{4}{3} - \dots$ **9**

24. $a_1 = 27, r = \dfrac{4}{5}$ **15**   25. $10 - \dfrac{5}{2} + \dfrac{5}{8} - \dots$ **8**   26. $12 + 6 + 3 + \dots$ **24**

27. $3 - 9 + 27 - \dots$ **does not exist**   28. $3 - 2 + \dfrac{4}{3} - \dots$ **$\frac{9}{5}$**   29. $10 - 1 + 0.1 - \dots$ **$\frac{100}{11}$**

Express each decimal as rational number in the form $\dfrac{a}{b}$.

30. $0.\overline{9}$ **1**   31. $0.\overline{31}$ **$\frac{31}{99}$**   32. $0.\overline{410}$ **$\frac{410}{999}$**   33. $0.4\overline{5}$ **$\frac{41}{90}$**

LESSON 13-6   INFINITE GEOMETRIC SERIES   623

Additional Answer

1. Because they are geometric series in which there is no "last" term, but the value of each term gets increasingly smaller.

EVALUATING THE LESSON

Checking for Understanding
Exercises 1–14 are designed to help you assess understanding through reading, writing, and speaking. You should work through Exercises 1–4 with your students, and then monitor their work on Exercises 5–14.

Error Analysis
Since r is fractional, watch that when finding r, the division is in the correct order. When dividing fractions, remember to multiply by the reciprocal.

Example: $\dfrac{1}{2} + \dfrac{1}{3} + \dfrac{2}{9} + \dots$

$r = \dfrac{1}{2} \div \dfrac{1}{3}$ $r = \dfrac{1}{3} \div \dfrac{1}{2}$ $r = \dfrac{1}{3} \div \dfrac{1}{2}$
no

$r = \dfrac{1}{3} \cdot \dfrac{2}{1}$ $r = \dfrac{1}{3} \cdot \dfrac{1}{2}$

$r = \dfrac{2}{3}$ $r = \dfrac{1}{6}$

yes   no

Assignment Guide
Basic: 15–34, 38–39, 41–45
Average: 19–35, 38–45
Enriched: 21–45

Practice Masters Booklet, p. 101

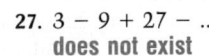

NAME _____ DATE _____

13-6 Practice Worksheet

Infinite Geometric Series

Find the sum of each infinite geometric series, if it exists.

1. $a_1 = 35, r = \frac{2}{7}$ **49**   2. $18 - 6 + 2 - \dots$ **$\frac{27}{2}$**

3. $\frac{4}{25} + \frac{2}{5} + 1 + \dots$ **does not exist**   4. $6 + 4 + \frac{8}{3} + \dots$ **18**

5. $10 + 1 + 0.1 + \dots$ **$\frac{100}{9}$**   6. $2 + 6 + 18 + \dots$ **does not exist**

7. $a_1 = 26, r = \frac{1}{2}$ **52**   8. $a_1 = 108, r = -\frac{3}{4}$ **$\frac{432}{7}$**

9. $a_1 = 42, r = \frac{6}{5}$ **does not exist**   10. $a_1 = 50, r = \frac{2}{5}$ **$\frac{250}{3}$**

Express each decimal as an infinite geometric series. Then find the ratio it represents.

11. $0.4\overline{9}$ **$0.49 + 0.009 + 0.0009 + \dots; \frac{1}{2}$**

12. $0.\overline{164}$ **$0.164 + 0.000164 + 0.000000164 + \dots; \frac{164}{999}$**

13. $0.2\overline{8}$ **$0.28 + 0.008 + 0.0008 + \dots; \frac{13}{45}$**

14. $0.6\overline{41}$ **$0.641 + 0.00041 + 0.0000041 + \dots; \frac{127}{198}$**

Find the first three terms of each infinite geometric series.

15. $S = 64, r = -\frac{3}{4}$ **$112 - 84 + 63$**   16. $S = 625, r = \frac{1}{5}$ **$500 + 100 + 20$**

17. $S = 90, r = -\frac{1}{2}$ **$135 - 67.5 + 33.75$**   18. $S = 4, r = \frac{1}{3}$ **$\frac{8}{3} + \frac{8}{9} + \frac{8}{27}$**

Closing the Lesson

Speaking Activity Have students explain why a sum can be found for some infinite geometric series and not for others.

APPLYING THE LESSON

Homework Exercises

See assignment guide on page 623.

Additional Answers

34a. $S_n = \dfrac{90}{1 - 0.9}$

38. Since $-1 < r < 1$, r^n produces a smaller and smaller number with each increase in the value of n. Eventually r^n approaches 0. Thus, $a_1 - a_1 r^n$ approaches $a_1 - a_1(0)$ or a_1. That is why the numerator of S_n becomes a_1 instead of $a_1 - a_1 r^n$.

Enrichment Masters Booklet, p. 88

---

34. Physics The end of a swinging pendulum 90 cm long travels 50 cm on its first swing. Each succeeding swing is 0.9 as long as the preceding one.

   a. Express the distance as an infinite geometric series. **See margin.**

   b. How far will the pendulum travel before coming to rest? **500 cm**

> **C** Find the first three terms of each infinite geometric series.

35. $S = 16$, $r = \dfrac{3}{4}$
   $4 + 3 + \dfrac{9}{4}$

36. $S = 28$, $r = -\dfrac{2}{7}$
   $36 - \dfrac{72}{7} + \dfrac{144}{49}$

37. $S = \dfrac{27}{4}$, $r = -\dfrac{1}{3}$
   $9 - 3 + 1$

Critical Thinking

38. Explain how $S_n = \dfrac{a_1 - a_1 r^n}{1 - r}$ becomes $S = \dfrac{a_1}{1 - r}$ when $-1 < r < 1$ and n approaches infinity. Give several real number examples to demonstrate your explanation. **See margin.**

Applications

39. Aviation A hot-air balloon rises 80 feet in the first minute of flight. If in each succeeding minute the balloon rises only 90% as far as in the previous minute, what will be its maximum altitude if it is allowed to rise without limit? **800 feet**

40. Sports A tennis ball fell 60 inches from the line judge's chair during intermission at Wimbledon. The ball rebounds $\frac{2}{3}$ that distance on the first bounce. It continues that pattern on each succeeding bounce before it comes to rest. Assuming that the ball bounces straight up and down, how far did it travel before it came to rest? **300 inches**

Mixed Review

41. Find the sum of $\displaystyle\sum_{s=1}^{4} 24\left(-\dfrac{1}{2}\right)^s$. **(Lesson 13-5)** **−7.5**

42. Find the missing geometric means in the sequence 3, __?__ , __?__ , __?__ , 48. **(Lesson 10-7)** **±6, 12, ±24**

43. If $f(x) = 2x + 3$, $g(x) = x - 1$, and $h(x) = x^2 + 4$, find $[g \circ h \circ f](2)$. **(Lesson 10-7)** **52**

44. Retailing A salesman receives $25 for every vacuum cleaner he sells. If he sells more than 10 vacuum cleaners, he will receive an additional $1.75 for each successive sale until he is paid a maximum of $46 per vacuum cleaner. How many must he sell to reach this maximum? **(Lesson 3-6)** **22**

45. Solve $2x - 4(x + 2) = -2x - 8$. **(Lesson 1-3)** **all reals**

EXTENDING THE LESSON

Math Power: Communication

Have each student write a short paragraph explaining why there is no infinite geometric series that has 6 as its first term and a sum of $\frac{3}{4}$. Have students share paragraphs and discuss any differences. **Paragraphs might include that r would need to be** -7 to satisfy $S = \dfrac{a_1}{(1 - r)}$, and this formula is only true for $-1 < r < 1$.

Objectives

13-7A   After studying this lesson, you should be able to:
 ■ expand powers of binomials using Pascal's triangle and the Binomial Theorem, and

13-7B   ■ find specific terms of the binomial expansion.

You have observed patterns in both geometric and arithmetic sequences. Another pattern can be observed when binomials, such as $(a + b)$, are raised to successive powers. The patterns of the coefficients and the exponents of the terms can be described in the **Binomial Theorem.** But first, let us observe some of the patterns that appear when $(a + b)^n$ is expanded for $n = 0, 1, 2, 3,$ and 4.

$$(a + b)^0 = 1a^0b^0$$
$$(a + b)^1 = 1a^1b^0 + 1a^0b^1$$
$$(a + b)^2 = 1a^2b^0 + 2a^1b^1 + 1a^0b^2$$
$$(a + b)^3 = 1a^3b^0 + 3a^2b^1 + 3a^1b^2 + 1a^0b^3$$
$$(a + b)^4 = 1a^4b^0 + 4a^3b^1 + 6a^2b^2 + 4a^1b^3 + 1a^0b^4$$

$a + b \neq 0$

Note that the coefficients are one. What is the pattern of the exponents of a and b in each line?

Look at the exponents in each term of the expansion of $(a + b)^4$. Notice that the sum of the exponents is 4, the exponent of the binomial. Look at the number of terms in each expression. Notice the number of terms is one more than the exponent of the binomial. Here is a list of patterns seen in the expansion of $(a + b)^n$.

1. The exponent of $(a + b)^n$ is the exponent of a in the first term and the exponent of b in the last term.

2. In successive terms, the exponent of a decreases by one. It is n in the first term and zero in the last term.

3. In successive terms, the exponent of b increases by one. It is zero in the first term and n in the last term.

4. The sum of the exponents of each term is n.

5. The coefficients are symmetric. They increase at the beginning and decrease at the end of the expansion.

FYI ...

Blaise Pascal (1623–1662) is best known for his accomplishments in science. Pascal's law is the principle used to operate hydraulic pumps, air compressors, and vacuum pumps.

$(a + b)^0$						1							
$(a + b)^1$					1		1						
$(a + b)^2$				1		2		1					
$(a + b)^3$			1		3		3		1				
$(a + b)^4$		1		4		6		4		1			
$(a + b)^5$	1		5		10		10		5		1		
$(a + b)^6$	1	6		15		20		15		6		1	

The coefficients form a pattern that is often displayed in a triangular formation. This is known as **Pascal's triangle.** Notice that each new row is formed by starting and ending with 1. Then each coefficient is the sum of the pair of coefficients above it in the previous row.

LESSON 13-7   THE BINOMIAL THEOREM   625

ALTERNATE TEACHING STRATEGIES

Using Discussion

In discussing the Binomial Theorem with students, be sure they understand the pattern. You may want to show them the first several terms on the chalkboard and have them name the next four terms. Use discussion to emphasize relationships between the Binomial Theorem, factorials, and sigma notation.

13-7   Lesson Notes

Lesson Resources
Reteaching Master 13-7
Practice Master 13-7
Enrichment Master 13-7

Transparency 13-7 contains the 5-Minute Check and a teaching aid for this lesson.

INTRODUCING THE LESSON

 5-Minute Check

(over Lesson 13-6)

1. Find the sum of the infinite geometric series $12 + 3 + \frac{3}{4} + \frac{3}{16} + ...$ **$S = 16$**

2. Find the sum of the infinite geometric series described by $a_1 = -2$ and $r = -\frac{1}{4}$.   **$S = -\frac{8}{5}$**

3. Find a common fraction equivalent to the repeating decimal $0.\overline{25}$.   **$\frac{25}{99}$**

4. Find the first three terms of the infinite geometric series with $S = 21$ and $r = \frac{1}{7}$.
$18 + \frac{18}{7} + \frac{18}{49}$

5. A hot air balloon rises 120 feet in its first minute of flight. In each succeeding minute, it rises only 80% as high as in the previous minute. What will be its maximum altitude if it rises freely?   **600 feet**

Motivating the Lesson
Ask students to name a busy intersection near the school. Ask them if there is a way to predict the traffic pattern if there are points of interest in all directions that a car can go from that intersection.

Teaching Tip ❶   Note that if b is negative, the theorem can still be used; just consider $(a - b)^n$ to be $[a + (-b)]^n$. Signs will alternate, being negative when the exponent of b is odd.

Example 1 | **Use the pattern in Pascal's triangle to write $(a + b)^7$ in expanded form.**

The next line of Pascal's triangle is

$$1 \quad 7 \quad 21 \quad 35 \quad 35 \quad 21 \quad 7 \quad 1. \qquad \textit{(a + b)}^7 \textit{ has 8 terms.}$$

$(a + b)^7$

$$= 1a^7b^0 + 7a^6b^1 + 21a^5b^2 + 35a^4b^3 + 35a^3b^4 + 21a^2b^5 + 7a^1b^6 + 1a^0b^7$$

$$= a^7 + 7a^6b + 21a^5b^2 + 35a^4b^3 + 35a^3b^4 + 21a^2b^5 + 7ab^6 + b^7$$

Another way to show the coefficients is by writing them in terms of the previous term, as you would in a sequence.

$(a + b)^0$			1	

Eliminate common factors that are shown in color. The coefficients are symmetrical.

$(a + b)^1$ 1 $\dfrac{1}{1}$

$(a + b)^2$ 1 $\dfrac{2}{1}$ $\dfrac{2 \cdot 1}{1 \cdot 2}$

$(a + b)^3$ 1 $\dfrac{3}{1}$ $\dfrac{3 \cdot 2}{1 \cdot 2}$ $\dfrac{3 \cdot 2 \cdot 1}{1 \cdot 2 \cdot 3}$

$(a + b)^4$ 1 $\dfrac{4}{1}$ $\dfrac{4 \cdot 3}{1 \cdot 2}$ $\dfrac{4 \cdot 3 \cdot 2}{1 \cdot 2 \cdot 3}$ $\dfrac{4 \cdot 3 \cdot 2 \cdot 1}{1 \cdot 2 \cdot 3 \cdot 4}$

This sequence pattern provides the coefficients of a binomial expansion without writing the previous rows of coefficients. This pattern is summarized in the **Binomial Theorem**.   **Teaching Tip ❶**

The Binomial Theorem	**If n is a positive integer, then** $(a + b)^n = 1a^nb^0 + \dfrac{n}{1}a^{n-1}b^1 + \dfrac{n(n-1)}{1 \cdot 2}a^{n-2}b^2 + \dots + 1a^0b^n.$

Example 2 | **Use the Binomial Theorem to express $(m + n)^8$ in expanded form.**

The expansion will have nine terms. Find the first five terms, using the Binomial Theorem and then use symmetry to find the remaining terms.

$(m + n)^8$

$$= m^8n^0 + \frac{8}{1}m^7n^1 + \frac{8 \cdot 7}{1 \cdot 2}m^6n^2 + \frac{8 \cdot 7 \cdot 6}{1 \cdot 2 \cdot 3}m^5n^3 + \frac{8 \cdot 7 \cdot 6 \cdot 5}{1 \cdot 2 \cdot 3 \cdot 4}m^4n^4 + \dots$$

$$= m^8 + 8m^7n + 28m^6n^2 + 56m^5n^3 + 70m^4n^4 + \dots$$

$$= m^8 + 8m^7n + 28m^6n^2 + 56m^5n^3 + 70m^4n^4 + 56m^3n^5 + 28m^2n^6 + 8mn^7 + n^8$$

Note that in terms having the same coefficients the exponents are reversed, as in $28m^6n^2$ and $28m^2n^6$.

The patterns in the products of the coefficients in Example 2 are parts of special products called factorials. The product $4 \cdot 3 \cdot 2 \cdot 1$ can be expressed as 4! and is read *4 factorial*. By definition, 0! = 1. For all positive values of n, $n! = n(n-1)(n-2)(n-3) \ldots (1)$.

Example 3

Evaluate $\frac{10!}{4!6!}$.

$$\frac{10!}{4!6!} = \frac{10 \cdot 9 \cdot 8 \cdot 7 \cdot 6 \cdot 5 \cdot 4 \cdot 3 \cdot 2 \cdot 1}{4 \cdot 3 \cdot 2 \cdot 1 \cdot 6 \cdot 5 \cdot 4 \cdot 3 \cdot 2 \cdot 1}$$

$$= \frac{10 \cdot 9 \cdot 8 \cdot 7}{4 \cdot 3 \cdot 2 \cdot 1} \text{ or } 210$$

Note that $10! = 10 \cdot 9 \cdot 8 \cdot 7 \cdot 6!$.

So $\frac{10!}{4!6!} = \frac{10 \cdot 9 \cdot 8 \cdot 7 \cdot 6!}{4!6!}$ or $\frac{10 \cdot 9 \cdot 8 \cdot 7}{4 \cdot 3 \cdot 2 \cdot 1}$

The $\boxed{x!}$ key may be the second function of another calculator key.

You can also evaluate this expression by using the $\boxed{x!}$ key on your calculator.

ENTER: $10 \boxed{x!} \boxed{\div} \boxed{(} 4 \boxed{x!} \boxed{\times} 6 \boxed{x!} \boxed{)} \boxed{=}$ `210`

In the Example 2, notice that products, such as $\frac{8 \cdot 7 \cdot 6}{1 \cdot 2 \cdot 3}$, can be written as a quotient of factorials. In this case, $\frac{8 \cdot 7 \cdot 6}{1 \cdot 2 \cdot 3} = \frac{8!}{3!5!}$. Using this same method, we can rewrite any binomial expansion using factorials.

$$(m + n)^8 = \frac{8!}{0!8!}m^8 + \frac{8!}{1!7!}m^7n + \frac{8!}{2!6!}m^6n^2 + \frac{8!}{3!5!}m^5n^3 + \frac{8!}{4!4!}m^4n^4 +$$

$$\frac{8!}{5!3!}m^3n^5 + \frac{8!}{6!2!}m^2n^6 + \frac{8!}{7!1!}m^1n^7 + \frac{8!}{8!0!}n^8$$

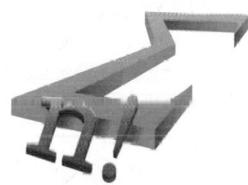

This same pattern can be used to write the expansion using sigma notation.

$$(m + n)^8 = \sum_{k=0}^{8} \frac{8!}{k!(8-k)!}m^{8-k}n^k$$

The Binomial Theorem can also be written both in factorial notation and in sigma notation.

$$(a + b)^n = \frac{n!}{0!(n-0)!}a^n + \frac{n!}{1!(n-1)!}a^{n-1}b^1 + \frac{n!}{2!(n-2)!}a^{n-2}b^2 + \ldots$$

$$= \sum_{k=0}^{n} \frac{n!}{k!(n-k)!}a^{n-k}b^k$$

LESSON 13-7   THE BINOMIAL THEOREM   627

628   Chapter 13

Example 4 | Express $(2s + t)^4$ using sigma notation. Then write the expansion.

$$(2s + t)^4 = \sum_{k=0}^{4} \frac{4!}{k!(4 - k)!} (2s)^{4-k}t^k \qquad \text{\textit{Now construct each term.}}$$

$$= \frac{4!}{0!(4 - 0)!} (2s)^{4-0}t^0 + \frac{4!}{1!(4 - 1)!} (2s)^{4-1}t^1 + \frac{4!}{2!(4 - 2)!} (2s)^{4-2}t^2 +$$

$$\frac{4!}{3!(4 - 3)!} (2s)^{4-3}t^3 + \frac{4!}{4!(4 - 4)!} (2s)^{4-4}t^4$$

$$= \frac{4 \cdot 3 \cdot 2 \cdot 1}{1 \cdot 4 \cdot 3 \cdot 2 \cdot 1} (2s)^4 + \frac{4 \cdot 3 \cdot 2 \cdot 1}{1 \cdot 3 \cdot 2 \cdot 1} (2s)^3t + \frac{4 \cdot 3 \cdot 2 \cdot 1}{2 \cdot 1 \cdot 2 \cdot 1} (2s)^2t^2 +$$

$$\frac{4 \cdot 3 \cdot 2 \cdot 1}{3 \cdot 2 \cdot 1 \cdot 1} (2s)t^3 + \frac{4 \cdot 3 \cdot 2 \cdot 1}{4 \cdot 3 \cdot 2 \cdot 1 \cdot 1} t^4$$

$$= 16s^4 + 32s^3t + 24s^2t^2 + 8st^3 + t^4$$

Sometimes a particular term in the expansion of a binomial is needed. Notice that in the sigma notation form of the Binomial Theorem, k is 0 for the first term, 1 for the second term, and so on. In general, the value of k is always one less than the number of the term you are seeking.

Example 5 | Find the sixth term of $(p + q)^{12}$.

First use the Binomial Theorem to write the general form of the expansion.

$$(p + q)^{12} = \sum_{k=0}^{12} \frac{12!}{k!(12 - k)!} p^{12-k}q^k$$

In the sixth term, $k = 5$ since k starts at 0.

The sixth term, $\dfrac{12!}{5!(12 - 5)!} p^{12-5}q^5$, is $\dfrac{12 \cdot 11 \cdot 10 \cdot 9 \cdot 8}{5 \cdot 4 \cdot 3 \cdot 2 \cdot 1} p^7q^5$ or $792p^7q^5$.

The Binomial Theorem can also be used to compute probability.

Example 6

APPLICATION

Probability

Sharon didn't study for her U.S. history quiz so she had to guess at all 10 true/false questions. What is the probability that exactly half of her answers are correct?

Let p be the probability that true is the correct answer and q be the probability that false is the correct answer. Since there are 10 questions, we can use the Binomial Theorem to find any term in the expansion of $(p + q)^{10}$.

$$(p + q)^{10} = \sum_{k=0}^{10} \frac{10!}{k!(10 - k)!} p^{10-k}q^k$$

Getting half the answers correct means that Sharon would get exactly 5 correct and 5 incorrect. So, the probability can be computed using the term where $k = 5$, the sixth term.

$$\frac{10!}{5!(10 - 5)!} p^5q^5 \text{ or } 252p^5q^5$$

628   CHAPTER 13   SEQUENCES AND SERIES

RETEACHING THE LESSON

Have students find the decimal expansion of a given expression using a specified number of terms and an indicated accuracy.

Example:
(1.05)⁵, 3 terms, hundredths
$(1.05)^5 = (1 + 0.05)^5$
$= 1^5 + 5 \cdot 1^4 \cdot (0.05) + \dfrac{5(4)}{1 \cdot 2} \cdot 1^3 \cdot (0.05)^2$

$(1.05)^5 \approx 1.28$

Additional Answers

1. For each coefficient add the pair of coefficients above its location.

3. The Binomial Theorem is a system by which the coefficients are part of a series and the exponents of the two variables in succeeding terms are related in ascending and descending orders.

Each question has two possible answers. Only one is correct. So the probability that *true* is the correct answer is 1 out of 2 or $\frac{1}{2}$. Likewise, the probability that *false* is the correct answer is also $\frac{1}{2}$. Evaluate the expression for the sixth term if $p = \frac{1}{2}$ and $q = \frac{1}{2}$.

$252p^5q^5$ ➡ $252\left(\frac{1}{2}\right)^5\left(\frac{1}{2}\right)^5 = 252\left(\frac{1}{32}\right)\left(\frac{1}{32}\right)$ or $\frac{63}{256}$

The probability that Sharon guesses exactly 5 answers correctly is $\frac{63}{256}$ or about 25%.

CHECKING FOR UNDERSTANDING

Communicating Mathematics

Read and study the lesson to answer each question.

1. Explain how to form additional rows of Pascal's triangle. **See margin.**
2. Without writing the expansion, tell how many terms are in the expansion of $(w + z)^{12}$. **13**   **See margin.**
3. In your own words, explain how the Binomial Theorem works.
4. If you guess at the answer to a true/false question, what is the probability you will guess correctly? $\frac{1}{2}$

Guided Practice

Use your calculator to evaluate each expression. **Teaching Tip ②**

5. $9!$ 6. $12!$ 7. $\frac{10!}{8!}$ **90**   8. $\frac{31!}{28!}$ 9. $\frac{6!}{3!}$ **120**   10. $\frac{10!}{4!6!}$

   362,880   **479,001,600**   **26,970**   **210**

State the number of terms in the expansion of each expression. Then find the fourth term of that expansion.

11. $(a + 3)^4$ 12. $(k + m)^7$ 13. $(b - z)^5$
    5, 108a   **8, 35k⁴m³**   **6, −10b²z³**

EXERCISES

Practice

Expand each binomial. **See margin.**

14. $(r + s)^6$ 15. $(y + p)^7$ 16. $(x - y)^3$
17. $(r - m)^6$ 18. $(2m + y)^5$ 19. $(3r + y)^4$
20. $(2b + x)^6$ 21. $(2x + 3y)^4$ 22. $(3x - 2y)^5$
23. $(2m - 3)^6$ 24. $\left(2 + \frac{x}{2}\right)^6$ 25. $\left(\frac{y}{3} + 3\right)^6$

Find the indicated term of each expansion.

26. seventh term of $(x - y)^{15}$ **5005x⁹y⁶** 27. fifth term of $(x + y)^7$ **35x³y⁴**
28. fourth term of $(2x + 3y)^9$ 29. eighth term of $(3a - 5b)^{11}$
    145,152x⁶y³   **−2,088,281,250a⁴b⁷**

LESSON 13-7   THE BINOMIAL THEOREM   629

Additional Answers

14. $r^6 + 6r^5s + 15r^4s^2 + 20r^3s^3 + 15r^2s^4 + 6rs^5 + s^6$
15. $y^7 + 7y^6p + 21y^5p^2 + 35y^4p^3 + 35y^3p^4 + 21y^2p^5 + 7yp^6 + p^7$
16. $x^3 - 3x^2y + 3xy^2 - y^3$
17. $r^6 - 6r^5m + 15r^4m^2 - 20r^3m^3 + 15r^2m^4 - 6rm^5 + m^6$
18. $32m^5 + 80m^4y + 80m^3y^2 + 40m^2y^3 + 10my^4 + y^5$
19. $81r^4 + 108r^3y + 54r^2y^2 + 12ry^3 + y^4$

20. $64b^6 + 192b^5x + 240b^4x^2 + 160b^3x^3 + 60b^2x^4 + 12bx^5 + x^6$
21. $16x^4 + 96x^3y + 216x^2y^2 + 216xy^3 + 81y^4$
22. $243x^5 - 810x^4y + 1080x^3y^2 - 720x^2y^3 + 240xy^4 - 32y^5$
23. $64m^6 - 576m^5 + 2160m^4 - 4320m^3 + 4860m^2 - 2916m + 729$

Teaching Tip ②   In solving Exercises 7–10, you may want to have students simplify each expression before solving. For example, $\frac{10!}{8!} = \frac{10 \cdot 9 \cdot 8!}{8!} = 10 \cdot 9 = 90$.

EVALUATING THE LESSON

Checking for Understanding

Exercises 1–13 are designed to help you assess understanding through reading, writing, and speaking. You should work through Exercises 1–4 with your students, and then monitor their work on Exercises 5–13.

Assignment Guide

Basic: 14–29, 34–35, 38–42
Average: 17–31, 34–42
Enriched: 20–42

Additional Answers

24. $64 + 96x + 60x^2 + 20x^3 + \frac{15}{4}x^4 + \frac{3}{8}x^5 + \frac{1}{64}x^6$

25. $\frac{1}{729}y^6 + \frac{2}{27}y^5 + \frac{5}{3}y^4 + 20y^3 + 135y^2 + 486y + 729$

Practice Masters Booklet, p. 102

NAME _____   DATE _____

13-7 Practice Worksheet

The Binomial Theorem

Use your calculator to evaluate each expression.

1. $7!$ **5040**   2. $6!4!$ **17,280**   3. $\frac{8!}{6!2!}$ **28**

4. $\frac{8!}{5!3!}$ **56**   5. $(3! - 2!)!$ **24**   6. $\left(\frac{9! + 11 + 3!}{2!}\right)!$ **24**

Expand each binomial.

7. $(x + 3)^4$ 8. $(2m - y)^4$
   $x^4 + 12x^3 + 54x^2 + 108x + 81$ $16m^4 - 32m^3y + 24m^2y^2 - 8my^3 + y^4$

9. $(2x - y)^5$ $32x^5 - 80x^4y +$ 10. $(r + 3)^5$ $r^5 + 15r^4 + 90r^3 +$
   $80x^3y^2 - 40x^2y^3 + 10xy^4 - y^5$ $270r^2 + 405r + 243$

11. $(n + v)^8$ $n^8 + 8n^7v + 28n^6v^2 +$ 12. $(x - y)^7$ $x^7 - 7x^6y + 21x^5y^2 -$
    $56n^5v^3 + 70n^4v^4 + 56n^3v^5 +$ $35x^4y^3 + 35x^3y^4 - 21x^2y^5 +$
    $28n^2v^6 + 8nv^7 + v^8$ $7xy^6 - y^7$

Find the indicated term of each expansion.

13. fourth term of $(x - 3y)^6$ 14. fifth term of $(2x - 1)^9$
    $-540x^3y^3$ $4032x^5$

15. seventh term of $(x + y)^{10}$ 16. tenth term of $(2x + y)^{12}$
    $210x^4y^6$ $1760x^3y^9$

17. Find the sixth element in the tenth row of Pascal's triangle. **126**

18. Find the ninth element in the fourteenth row of Pascal's triangle. **1287**

Simplify.

30. $\dfrac{k!}{(k-1)!}$ k

31. $\dfrac{(k+3)!}{(k+2)!}$ $k+3$

32. $\dfrac{3!4(k-3)!}{(k-2)!}$ $\dfrac{24}{k-2}$

33. $(k+1)!(k+2)$ $(k+2)!$

Critical Thinking

34. Ball bearings fall down a chute toward a tray. As they fall, they branch out. At each branch, there is an equal chance to go either way.

    a. If 16 ball bearings go through the chute, how many will be in the tray for each branch? **1, 4, 6, 4, 1**

    b. If 64 ball bearings go through the chute, how many will be in the tray for each branch? **4, 16, 24, 16, 4**

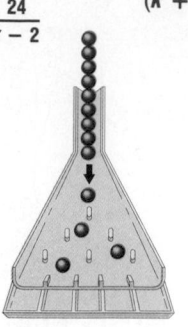

Applications

35. **Sports** In the high school football playoffs, Kyle had a success rate of 2 out of 3 passes completed in the first quarter. What is the likelihood of exactly 5 completions in six attempts? $26\frac{1}{3}\%$

36. **Cooking** In cooking class, Sonja had a success rate of 4 out of 5 for her souffles. One out of 5 collapse. For a party for her parents, she is preparing 6 souffles. What is the likelihood of exactly 4 of them being successes? **24.576%**

Computer

37. The BASIC program at the right generates the line of coefficients in Pascal's triangle for $(a + b)^n$. You must input the value of n when running the program.

Use the program to express each binomial in expanded form. See margin.

a. $(a + b)^4$ b. $(a + b)^{12}$

c. $(x - y)^6$ d. $(x - y)^{10}$

```
1    PRINT "ENTER THE VALUE
     OF N"
5    INPUT Y
10   FOR N = 0 TO Y
20   FOR R = 0 TO N
30   LET C = 1
40   IF N < N - R + 1 THEN 80
50   FOR X = N TO N - R + 1
     STEP - 1
60   LET C = C*X/(N - X + 1)
70   NEXT X
80   PRINT C;"  ";
90   NEXT R
100  PRINT
110  NEXT N
120  END
```

Mixed Review

38. Find the sum of the infinite series $\frac{2}{3} + \frac{1}{3} + \frac{1}{6} + ...$ (**Lesson 13-6**) $\frac{4}{3}$

39. **Finance** Suppose a pilgrim ancestor of Kevin White left $150 in a savings account and interest was compounded continuously at 4%. If the account is now worth $24,000,000, how long ago was the account started? Use $A = Pe^{rt}$. (**Lesson 12-8**) **about 300 years**

40. Simplify $\dfrac{1}{2x-3} - \dfrac{1}{3x-2}$. (**Lesson 11-4**) $\dfrac{x+1}{(2x-3)(3x-2)}$

41. For $f(x) = 7x^5 + 4x^4 - 3x^3 - 2x^2 + 7x + 1$, state the number of positive real zeros, negative real zeros, and imaginary zeros. (**Lesson 10-3**) **See margin.**

EXTENDING THE LESSON

Math Power: Problem Solving

Have students use an example and a calculator to verify the correctness of the binomial expansion. An example is to use the binomial expression $(0.3 + 0.7)^5$. Expand the expression, then evaluate both the expansion and the original expression to show that the evaluations are equal. In this case, both equal 1.

Additional Answers

37a. 1, 4, 6, 4, 1
37b. 1, 12, 66, 220, 495, 792, 924, 792, 495, 220, 66, 12, 1
37c. 1, −6, 15, −20, 15, −6, 1
37d. 1, −10, 45, −120, 210, −252, 210, −120, 45, −10, 1
41. 2 or 0 pos. real, 3 or 1 neg. real, 0, 2, or 4 imaginary

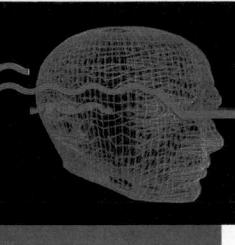

Technology

Amortization

BASIC
▶ Spreadsheets
Software

Mortgages for homes and other consumer loans are repaid in a series of equal payments made over a period of time. This is called **amortization**. The money from each of the payments is divided into an interest payment and a principal payment. The interest due for the period since the last payment is paid first, and then the balance of the payment goes toward reducing the principal. The spreadsheet program below constructs an amortization schedule for a two-year loan.

AMORTIZATION SCHEDULE			
	A	**B**	**C**	**D**
1		LOAN AMOUNT	PAYMENT	INTEREST RATE
2				
3	PAYMENT	INTEREST PAID	PRINCIPAL PAID	BALANCE DUE
4	0	0	0	B2
5	1	D2/12*D4	C2-B5	D4-C5
6	2	D2/12*D5	C2-B6	D5-C6
28	24	D2/12*D27	D27	$0

Sondra is taking out a two-year loan to buy a used car. The loan amount is $2500, the monthly payment is $115.94, and the interest rate is 10.5%. A portion of the amortization schedule for her loan is shown below.

```
= = = = = = = = = = = = = = = = = = = = = = = = = = = = = = = = = = =
                     AMORTIZATION SCHEDULE
= = = = A = = = = = = = B = = = = = = = = = C = = = = = = = = D = = = =
 1            LOAN AMOUNT       PAYMENT         INTEREST RATE
 2               2500            115.94            .105
 3  PAYMENT   INTEREST PAID   PRINCIPAL PAID    BALANCE DUE
 4    0           0               0               2500
 5    1          21.88           94.06           2405.94
 6    2          21.05           94.89           2311.05
28   24          1.01           114.92            $0
```

EXERCISES

1. Explain why the amount of interest paid per months grows smaller. It is figured on the balance of the account, which is growing smaller.

2. Explain how you could modify the spreadsheet program to make an amortization table for a 30-year mortgage. **1–2. See margin.**

The Chapter Summary and Review begins with an alphabetical listing of the new terms that were presented in the chapter. Have students define each term and provide an example of it, if appropriate.

The Skills and Concepts presented in the chapter are reviewed using a side-by-side format. Encourage students to refer to the Objectives and Examples on the left as they complete the Review Exercises on the right.

The Chapter Summary and Review ends with exercises that review Applications and Connections.

CHAPTER **13** # SUMMARY AND REVIEW

VOCABULARY

Upon completing this chapter you should be familiar with the following terms:

arithmetic means	599	615	geometric series
arithmetic sequence	596	605	index of summation
arithmetic series	602	620	infinite geometric series
Binomial Theorem	625	622	infinity (∞)
common difference	596	597	nth term
common ratio	608	625	Pascal's triangle
Fibonacci sequence	594	597	recursive formula
geometric means	610	605	sigma (or summation) notation (Σ)
geometric sequence	608	596	term

SKILLS AND CONCEPTS

OBJECTIVES AND EXAMPLES	REVIEW EXERCISES
Upon completing this chapter, you should be able to:	Use these exercises to review and prepare for the chapter test.

■ find the nth term of an arithmetic sequence. **(Lesson 13-2)**

The nth term of an arithmetic sequence with first term a_1 and common difference d is given by $a_n = a_1 + (n - 1)d$.

Find the indicated term in each arithmetic sequence.

1. a_5 for 6, 14, 22, ... **38**
2. a_{22} for -5, 2, 9, ... **142**
3. $a_1 = 5$, $d = -2$, $n = 9$ **-11**
4. $a_1 = -2$, $d = -3$, $n = 15$ **-44**

■ find the position of a term in an arithmetic sequence. **(Lesson 13-2)**

-3 is what term of 7, 5, 3 ...?
$-3 = 7 + (n - 1)(-2)$
$6 = n$ $\quad$ -3 is the 6th term.

Complete each statement.

5. 72 is the __?__ th term of -5, 2, 9, ... **12**
6. -37 is the __?__ th term of 1, -1, -3, -5, ... **20**
7. 49 is the __?__ th term of 4, 9, 14, ... **10**

■ find the arithmetic means of an arithmetic sequence. **(Lesson 13-2)**

Find the two arithmetic means between 4 and 25.
$25 = 4 + (4 - 1)d$ $\quad$ So, $7 = d$.
$4 + 7 = 11$ $\quad$ $11 + 7 = 18$
The arithmetic means are 11 and 18.

Find the arithmetic means in each sequence.

8. 12, ___, ___, 4 $\quad$ **$\frac{28}{3}, \frac{20}{3}$**
9. -7, ___, ___, ___, 9 $\quad$ **$-3, 1, 5$**
10. ___, 6, ___, ___, -3, ___ $\quad$ **9, 3, 0, -6**

- find the sums of arithmetic series and find specific terms. (**Lesson 13-3**)

The sum S_n of the first n terms of an arithmetic series is given by
$S_n = \frac{n}{2}(a_1 + a_n)$.

Find S_n for each arithmetic series.

11. $a_1 = 12$, $a_n = 117$, $n = 36$ **2322**
12. $4 + 10 + 16 + \ldots + 106$ **990**
13. Evaluate $\sum_{n=2}^{29}(3n + 1)$. **1330**
14. Find the first three terms of an arithmetic series if $a_1 = 3$, $a_n = 24$, and $S_n = 108$. **3, 6, 9**

- find the nth term of a geometric sequence and any missing geometric means. (**Lesson 13-4**)

The nth term a_n of a geometric sequence with first term a_1 and common ratio r is given by $a_n = a_{n-1}r$ or $a_n = a_1 r^{n-1}$.

17. −108, 324

Find the indicated term in each geometric sequence.

15. a_6 for $\frac{2}{3}, \frac{4}{3}, \frac{8}{3}, \ldots$ $\frac{64}{3}$
16. a_5 if $a_1 = 7$ and $r = 3$ **567**
17. the next two terms of $4, -12, 36, \ldots$
18. Find the geometric means of $7.5, \underline{}, \underline{}, \underline{}, 120$. **15, 30, 60**

- find sums of geometric series. (**Lesson 13-5**)

The sum, S_n, of the first n terms of a geometric series is given by $S_n = \frac{a_1 - a_1 r^n}{1 - r}$ or $S_n = \frac{a_1(1 - r^n)}{1 - r}$; $r \neq 1$.

Find the sum of each geometric series described.

19. $a_1 = 12$, $r = 3$, $n = 5$ **1452**
20. $a_1 = 625$, $a_n = 16$, $r = \frac{2}{5}$ **1031**
21. $a_1 = 4$, $r = -\frac{1}{2}$, $n = 6$ $\frac{21}{8}$

- find the first term of a described geometric series. (**Lesson 13-5**)

Find a_1 if $S_5 = 2.75$ and $r = -2$.
$\frac{11}{4} = \frac{a_1[1 - (-2)^5]}{1 - (-2)}$
$\frac{11}{4} = \frac{a_1(33)}{3}$
$\frac{1}{4} = a_1$

For the geometric series, find a_1.

22. $S_n = 1031$, $r = \frac{2}{5}$, $n = 5$ **625**
23. $S_n = 30$, $n = 4$, $r = -2$ **−6**
24. $S_n = -61$, $n = 5$, $r = -1$ **−61**

- find the sum of an infinite geometric series. (**Lesson 13-6**)

The sum, S, of an infinite geometric series where $-1 < r < 1$ is given by $S = \frac{a_1}{1 - r}$.

Find the sum of each infinite geometric series, if it exists.

25. $a_1 = -2$ and $r = -\frac{5}{8}$ $-\frac{16}{13}$
26. $\frac{1}{8} - \frac{3}{16} + \frac{9}{32} - \frac{27}{64} + \ldots$ **no sum**
27. Evaluate $\sum_{n=1}^{\infty} \frac{1}{2}\left(\frac{1}{3}\right)^{n-1}$. $\frac{3}{4}$
28. Express $0.\overline{09}$ as a rational number in the form $\frac{a}{b}$. $\frac{1}{11}$

Alternate Review Strategy

To provide a brief in-class review, you may wish to read the following questions to the class and require a verbal or written response.

1. What is the pattern in the following sequence? 16, 8, 4, 2 ... **Each term is divided by 2 to get the following**

2. Is the following an arithmetic sequence? Why? 2, 4, 8, 14, ... **No, d is not the same for each set of consecutive terms.**

3. What is the sum of the first seven terms of the following sequence? 4, 7, 10, 13, ... **91**

4. How is $\sum_{n=1}^{8}(2n + 5)$ read? **the summation from 1 to 8 of $(2n + 5)$**

5. What would the next term be in the sequence 5, 20, 80, ... ? **320**

6. Find the sum of $2 + 2 + 2 + \ldots$ to 16 terms. **32**

7. Use sigma notation to express $3 - 6 + 12 - 24$. $\sum_{n=1}^{4} 3(-2)^{n-1}$

8. What does the term infinity **there is no limit**

9. Write $0.\overline{6}$ as a ratio. $\frac{2}{3}$

10. What is the value of $4!$? **24**

OBJECTIVES AND EXAMPLES

- expand powers of binomials using Pascal's triangle and the Binomial Theorem. **(Lesson 13-7)**

If n is a positive integer, then

$$(a + b)^n = \sum_{k=0}^{n} \frac{n!}{k!(n-k)!} a^{n-k}b^k$$

- find specific terms of the binomial expansion. **(Lesson 13-7)**

The general form of the expansion of $(c + d)^{11}$ is

$$\sum_{k=0}^{11} \frac{11!}{k!(11-k)!} a^{11-k}b^k$$

REVIEW EXERCISES

Expand each binomial.

30. $x^4 - 8x^3 + 24x^2 - 32x + 16$

29. $(a + b)^3$
$a^3 + 3a^2b + 3ab^2 + b^3$

30. $(x - 2)^4$

31. $(3r + s)^5$
$243r^5 + 405r^4s + 270r^3s^2 + 90r^2s^3 + 15rs^4 + s^5$

Find the indicated term.

32. fourth term of $(x + 2y)^6$ $160x^3y^3$

33. second term of $(4x - 5)^{10}$
$-13,107,200x^9$

~~~ APPLICATIONS AND CONNECTIONS ~~~

34. Number Theory The Leibniz series is
$$\frac{\pi}{4} = 1 + \left(-\frac{1}{3}\right) + \frac{1}{5} + \left(-\frac{1}{7}\right) + \frac{1}{9} + \dots + \frac{(-1)^{n-1}}{2n-1} + \dots.$$ Use the first 10 terms of the series and your calculator to find a decimal approximation of π.
(Lesson 13-1) 3.041839619

36. Recreation One minute after it is released, a gas-filled balloon rises 100 feet. In each succeeding minute the balloon rises only 50% as far as it rose in the previous minute. How far will the balloon rise in 5 minutes?
(Lesson 13-3) 193.75 feet

37. Business Mr. Olsen invested in computer equipment worth $900,000. The equipment depreciates at the rate of 25% per year of the previous year's value. What will be the value of his equipment at the end of four years? **(Lesson 13-5)** $284,766

35. Physics A rocket rises 40 feet in the first second, 60 feet in the second second, and 80 feet in the third second. If it continues to rise at this rate, how many feet will it rise in the 10th second? **(Lesson 13-2)** 220 feet

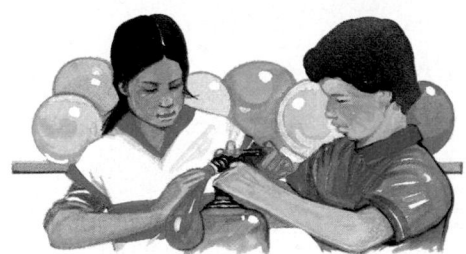

38. Fine Arts A layered sculpture is arranged so that there are 5 diamonds on the top design layer, 7 diamonds on the second layer, 9 diamonds on the third layer, and so on. How many diamonds are on the twentieth layer? **(Lesson 13-5)** 43

Worksheet (left column)

1. Find the pattern and complete the sequence 3, 3, 6, 18, 72, __?__ , __?__ , __?__ . **360, 2160, 15,120**

2. How many integers between 26 and 415 are multiples of 9? **44**

3. Find the next four terms of the arithmetic sequence 42, 37, 32, ... **27, 22, 17, 12**

4. Find the next two terms of the geometric sequence $\frac{1}{81}, \frac{1}{27}, \frac{1}{9}, ...$ **$\frac{1}{3}$, 1**

5. Find the 27th term of an arithmetic sequence if $a_1 = 2$ and $d = 6$. **158**

6. Find the sixth term of a geometric sequence if $a_1 = 5$ and $r = -2$. **–160**

7. Find the sum of the arithmetic series where $a_1 = 7$, $n = 31$, and $a_n = 127$. **2077**

8. Find the sum of the geometric series where $a_1 = 125$, $r = \frac{2}{5}$, and $n = 4$. **203**

9. Find the three arithmetic means between –4 and 16. **1, 6, 11**

10. Find the two geometric means between 7 and 189. **21, 63**

Find each sum.

11. $\sum_{k=3}^{15} (14 - 2k)$ **–52**

12. $\sum_{n=1}^{\infty} \frac{1}{3}(-2)^{n-1}$ **no sum**

13. Find the sum of the series $91 + 85 + 79 + ... + (-29)$. **651**

14. Find the sum of the geometric series $12 - 6 + 3 - \frac{3}{2} + ...$ **8**

15. Express $0.3\overline{2}$ as a rational number in the form $\frac{a}{b}$. **$\frac{29}{90}$**

16. Expand $(2s - 3t)^5$. **$32s^5 - 240s^4t + 720s^3t^2 - 1080s^2t^3 + 810st^4 - 243t^5$**

17. Find the third term of $(x + y)^8$ **$28x^6y^2$**

18. **Nature** The counterclockwise and clockwise spirals of a sunflower can be described by the sixth and seventh terms of the Fibonacci sequence. What are these two terms? **8, 13**

19. **Physics** A vacuum pump removes $\frac{1}{7}$ of the air from a jar on each stroke of its piston. What percent of the air remains after four strokes of the piston? **54%**

20. **Design** A landscaper is designing a wall of white brick and red brick. The pattern starts with 20 red bricks on the bottom row. Each row above it contains 3 fewer red bricks than the preceding row. If the top row contains no red bricks, how many rows are there and how many red bricks were used? **8 rows, 77 bricks**

Bonus
A side of an equilateral triangle is 20 inches long. The midpoints of its sides are joined to form a smaller equilateral triangle. If this process is continued infinitely, find the sum of the perimeters of the triangles. **120 inches**

CHAPTER 14

Statistics

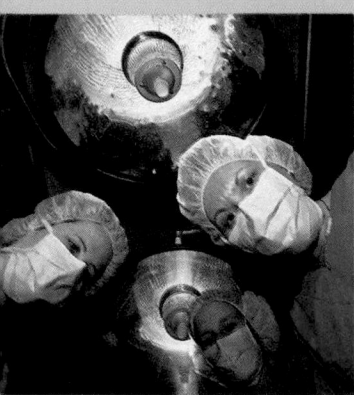

PREVIEWING THE CHAPTER

In this chapter students represent and interpret date using bar graphs, line graphs, circle graphs, line plots, stem-and-leaf plots, and box-and-whisker plots. Next, students use measures of central tendency — mean, median, mode — to interpret or describe data. They also find the range and interquartile range for a set of data and determine if any values in data are outliers. Then, students find the standard deviation for a set of data and solve problems involving normally distributed data.

Problem-Solving Strategy Students learn that solving problems can be facilitated when the *data is organized in a table* and presented in a graph because such data is easier to read and interpret.

Lesson Objective Chart

Lesson (Pages)	Lesson Objectives	State/Local Objectives
14-1 (638-641)	**14-1:** Solve problems by organizing data and making graphs.	
14-2 (642-647)	**14-2A:** Represent data using line plots and stem-and-leaf plots.	
	14-2B: Read and interpret data from line plots and stem-and-leaf plots.	
14-3 (648-652)	**14-3A:** Find the median, mode, and mean of sets of data.	
	14-3B: Use the median, mode, and mean to interpret data.	
14-4 (653-657)	**14-4A:** Find the range and interquartile range for a set of data.	
	14-4B: Determine if any values in a set of data are outliers.	
14-5 (658-662)	**14-5:** Represent data using box-and-whisker plots.	
14-6 (664-667)	**14-6:** Find the standard deviation for a set of data.	
14-7 (668-673)	**14-7:** Solve problems involving normally distributed data.	

ORGANIZING THE CHAPTER

You may want to refer to the **Course Planning Calendar** on page T44.

Lesson Planning Guide				Blackline Masters Booklets						Activities				
Lesson (Pages)	Pacing Chart (days) Course			Reteaching	Practice	Enrichment	Evaluation	Technology	Lab Manual	Mixed Problem Solving	Applications	Cooperative Learning Activity	Multicultural	Transparencies
	I	II	III											
14-1 (638-641)	–	1	1		p. 103							p. 50		14-1
14-2 (642-647)	–	1.5	1	p. 90	p. 104	p. 90	Quiz A, p. 191							14-2
14-3 (648-652)	–	1.5	1	p. 91	p. 105	p. 91	Quiz B, p. 191		pp. 43-44	p. 14				14-3
14-4 (653-657)	–	1	1	p. 92	p. 106	p. 92	Mid-Chapter Test, p. 195				p. 32			14-4
14-5 (658-662)	–	1	1	p. 93	p. 107	p. 93	Quiz C, p. 192	p. 14						14-5
14-6 (664-667)	–	1	1	p. 94	p. 108	p. 94								14-6
14-7 (668-673)	–	1	1	p. 95	p. 109	p. 95	Quiz D, p. 192	p. 31					p. 14	14-7
Review (674-676)	–	1	1	Multiple Choice Tests, Forms 1A and 1B, pp. 183-186 Free Response Tests, Forms 2A and 2B, pp. 187-190										
Test (677)	–	1	1	Cumulative Review, pp. 193-194 Standardized Test Practice Questions, p. 196										

Course I: Chapters 1-13; Course II: Chapters 1-15; Course III: Chapters 1-17

Other Chapter Resources

Student Edition

Chapter Opener, pp. 636-637
Cooperative Learning Activity, p. 641
Journal Entries, pp. 647, 657
Mid-Chapter Review, p. 657
Challenge, p. 662
Technology, p. 663
Portfolio Suggestion, p. 673
Application, p. 673
College Entrance Exam Preview pp. 678-679
Extended Project 4, pp. A14-A16

Teacher's Classroom Resources

Transparency 14-0
Real-World Applications Transparencies, 28, 29, 30
Performance Assessment Booklet, pp. 27-28
Problem-of-the-Week Activity Cards, 28, 29
Tech Prep Applications Booklet, pp. 27-28
Lesson Plans, pp. 103-109

Other Supplements

Glencoe Mathematics Professional Series

Software

Test and Review Generator Software (Apple, IBM, and Macintosh)
Interactive Software (Macintosh)
Teacher's Guide for Software Resources

ENHANCING THE CHAPTER

Cooperative Learning

Providing Task Assistance

When monitoring cooperative-learning groups as they do their work, you should resist temptation to intervene any more often than is absolutely necessary. Even when intervening, your role should be more that of an enhancer rather than an answerer. For example, when a group appears to be stuck, say something such as, "Let's do a little brainstorming about ..." or "What do you think would happen if you tried ..." and give a hint to get them moving again. Even when it may be necessary to clarify instructions or review procedures and strategies, encourage the group to work their way through the problem by recalling a specific instruction you gave before the session began and then ask, "Now who remembers what we said you should do next?" When students themselves seek assistance, they should first discuss among themselves and agree on the question that they want answered. The member whose role is *asker* should then address the question to you. You should respond only to the specific question, using terms relevant to the task, and then have one or more other members of the group paraphrase your answer to make sure that it is understood.

Technology

There are many software programs available that remove the tediousness of calculations and pencil-and-paper graphing. *Data Insights* by Sunburst Communications, Inc. provides a medium through which students can explore different types of statistical graphs and measures. The software allows students to customize each graph so that students feel a sense of involvement in their explorations. The menu-driven software is easily utilized without extensive teacher instruction.

Critical Thinking

The ability to evaluate data and make sound judgments or decisions involves a thorough understanding and fluency with the vocabulary and how language is used or misused. Students will enjoy applying the content of this chapter while engaging their critical-thinking skills to analyze propaganda, the most familiar type being TV advertising. For example, have students work in small groups to choose a current and popular ad, state what conclusion the advertiser wants the viewer to assume, identify the data supplied to support this conclusion (if any), list additional data that is required to actually support the conclusion, and describe other equally valid conclusions that could be made based on the same data along with an explanation.

Cooperative Learning, p. 50

CHAPTER 14 NAME _____ DATE _____
Cooperative Learning Activity (Use after Lesson 14-1)

Glyphs

A **glyph** is a pictorial representation of data using symbols to illustrate different variables of the data. The illustration to the right is an example of a glyph representing certain characteristics of a high school student. Use the chart below to read the glyph.

This is a sophomore whose favorite subject is math/science and whose favorite leisure activity is movies. He or she spends 60–90 minutes on homework each night and 10–17 hours on recreation each week.

GRADE LEVEL	FRESHMAN	SOPHOMORE	JUNIOR	SENIOR
HAIR				
FAVORITE SUBJECT	MATH/ SCIENCE	ENGLISH	SOCIAL STUDIES	PHYSICAL EDUCATION
RIGHT EYE				
NUMBER OF MINUTES OF HOMEWORK NIGHTLY	0-30	30-60	60-90	OVER 90
LEFT EYE				
NUMBER OF HOURS OF RECREATION WEEKLY	OVER 25	18-24	10-17	0-10
MOUTH				
FAVORITE LEISURE ACTIVITY	SPORTS	MOVIES	READING	TV
NOSE	Δ	▲	L	–

1. Write a description of the glyph shown to the right.

This is a freshman whose favorite subject

is English and whose favorite leisure

activity is sports. He or she spends

0–30 minutes on homework each night

and spends more than 25 hours on recreation

each week.

2. Draw glyphs to represent each member of your group.
See students' work.

Technology, p. 31

CHAPTER 14 NAME _____ DATE _____
Graphing Calculator (Use after Lesson 14-7)

Histograms

Histograms can be drawn on a graphing calculator. After entering the data, you simply select HIST from the menu and the calculator will draw a histogram of the data.

Example:

Construct a histogram of the data shown in the table at the right.

Press [2nd] [STAT].

Press [▶] twice and [ENTER] to select DATA from the menu.

DATA — Enter the data from the table as shown at the left. When you have entered all of the data, press [2nd] [STAT] to get back to the menu. Press [▶] once to call up the DRAW menu. Select 1: Hist by pressing [ENTER]. Press [ENTER] again to draw the histogram.

x1 = 1
y1 = 3
x2 = 2
y2 = 6
x3 = 3
y3 = 9
x4 = 4
y4 = 6
x5 = 5
y5 = 6
x6 = 6
y6 = 6
x7 = 7
y7 = 4

Percent of GNP	Number of Countries
1.0-1.9	3
2.0-2.9	6
3.0-3.9	9
4.0-4.9	6
5.0-5.9	6
6.0-6.9	6
7.0-7.9	4

Use a graphing calculator to construct a histogram of each set of data given. **See students' graphs.**

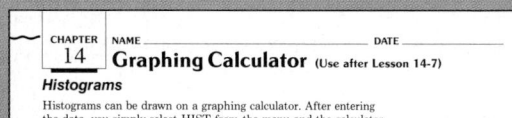

1.

Score	Number of Scores
1	0
2	1
3	1
4	1
5	2
6	5
7	6
8	7
9	5
10	1

2.

Percent of Packages	Number of People
1-2.9	5
3-4.9	6
5-6.9	6
7-8.9	8
9-10.9	10
11-12.9	9
13-14.9	8
15-16.9	2
17-18.9	1

Problem of the Week Activity

The card shown below is one of two available for this chapter. It can be used as a class or small group activity.

Activity Card

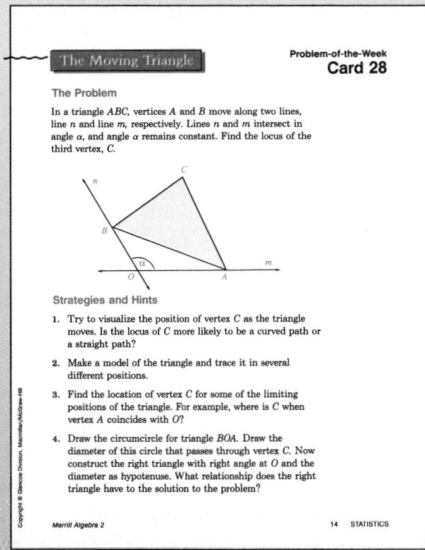

The Moving Triangle

Problem-of-the-Week
Card 28

The Problem

In a triangle ABC, vertices A and B move along two lines, line n and line m, respectively. Lines n and m intersect in angle α, and angle α remains constant. Find the locus of the third vertex, C.

Strategies and Hints

1. Try to visualize the position of vertex C as the triangle moves. Is the locus of C more likely to be a curved path or a straight path?

2. Make a model of the triangle and trace it in several different positions.

3. Find the location of vertex C for some of the limiting positions of the triangle. For example, where is C when vertex A coincides with O?

4. Draw the circumcircle for triangle BOA. Draw the diameter of this circle that passes through vertex C. Now construct the right triangle with right angle at O and the diameter as hypotenuse. What relationship does the right triangle have to the solution to the problem?

Merrill Algebra 2   14   STATISTICS

Manipulatives and Models

The following materials may be used as models or manipulatives in Chapter 14.

- foliage plant (Lesson 14-2)
- dice (Lesson 14-2)
- boxes of raisins (Lesson 14-2)
- newspaper (Lesson 14-3)
- consumer product catalogs (Lesson 14-3)
- ruler (Lesson 14-3)
- bulls-eye (Lesson 14-6)

- blindfold (Lesson 14-6)
- pennies (Lesson 14-7)
- container (Lesson 14-7)

Outside Resources

Books/Periodicals

Christensen, Helen, R.S.M. *Mathematical Modeling for the Marketplace.* Kendall/Hunt Publishing Company.

Slonim, Morris James. *Sampling In A Nutshell.* Simon and Schuster.

Films/Videotapes/Videodiscs

Statistics and Graphs, Parts 1 and 2, part of the Mainly Math Series, Great Plains National Instructional TV Library (GPN), P.O. Box 80669, Lincoln, NE 68501

Statistics: Decisions Through Data, Consortium for Mathematics and Its Applications (COMAP), Suite 210, 57 Bedford St., Lexington, MA 02173-4496

Software

Data Insights, WINGS for Learning/Sunburst Communications, 1600 Green Hills Rd., P.O. Box 660002, Scotts Valley, CA 95067-0002

TrueStat, TrueBASIC, Inc., 12 Commerce Ave., West Lebanon, NH 03766

Survey Kit, William K. Bradford Publishing Company, 310 School St., Acton, MA 01720

Multicultural

Multicultural Activity, p. 14

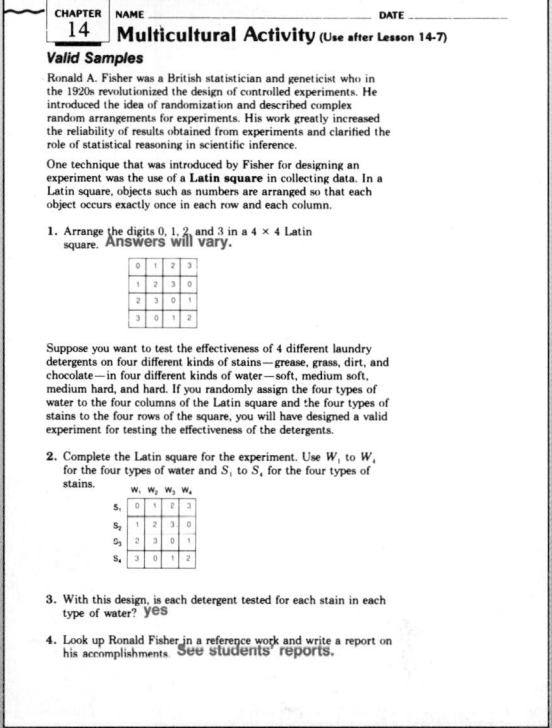

CHAPTER **14**   NAME _____ DATE _____

Multicultural Activity (Use after Lesson 14-7)

Valid Samples

Ronald A. Fisher was a British statistician and geneticist who in the 1920s revolutionized the design of controlled experiments. He introduced the idea of randomization and described complex random arrangements for experiments. His work greatly increased the reliability of results obtained from experiments and clarified the role of statistical reasoning in scientific inference.

One technique that was introduced by Fisher for designing an experiment was the use of a **Latin square** in collecting data. In a Latin square, objects such as numbers are arranged so that each object occurs exactly once in each row and each column.

1. Arrange the digits 0, 1, 2, and 3 in a 4 × 4 Latin square. **Answers will vary.**

0	1	2	3
1	2	3	0
2	3	0	1
3	0	1	2

Suppose you want to test the effectiveness of 4 different laundry detergents on four different kinds of stains—grease, grass, dirt, and chocolate—in four different kinds of water—soft, medium soft, medium hard, and hard. If you randomly assign the four types of water to the four columns of the Latin square and the four types of stains to the four rows of the square, you will have designed a valid experiment for testing the effectiveness of the detergents.

2. Complete the Latin square for the experiment. Use W_1 to W_4 for the four types of water and S_1 to S_4 for the four types of stains.

	W_1	W_2	W_3	W_4
S_1	0	1	2	3
S_2	1	2	3	0
S_3	2	3	0	1
S_4	3	0	1	2

3. With this design, is each detergent tested for each stain in each type of water? **yes**

4. Look up Ronald Fisher in a reference work and write a report on his accomplishments. **See students' reports.**

Lab Manual

Lab Activity, pp. 43-44

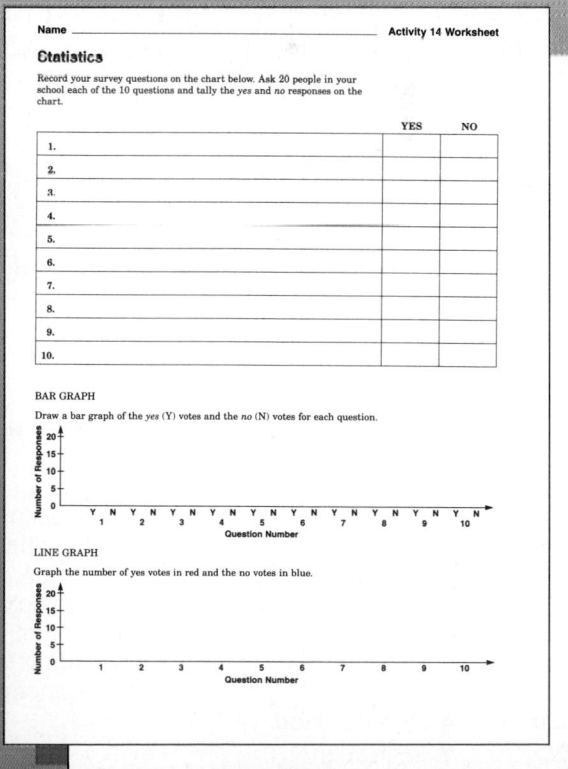

Name _____   Activity 14 Worksheet

Statistics

Record your survey questions on the chart below. Ask 20 people in your school each of the 10 questions and tally the *yes* and *no* responses on the chart.

	YES	NO
1.		
2.		
3.		
4.		
5.		
6.		
7.		
8.		
9.		
10.		

BAR GRAPH

Draw a bar graph of the *yes* (Y) votes and the *no* (N) votes for each question.

LINE GRAPH

Graph the number of yes votes in red and the no votes in blue.

CHAPTER OBJECTIVES

In this chapter you will:
- make bar graphs, line graphs, circle graphs, line plots, stem-and-leaf plots, and box-and-whisker plots.
- find the median, mean, mode, range, quartiles, interquartile range, standard deviation, and outliers of sets of data.
- solve problems involving normally distributed data.

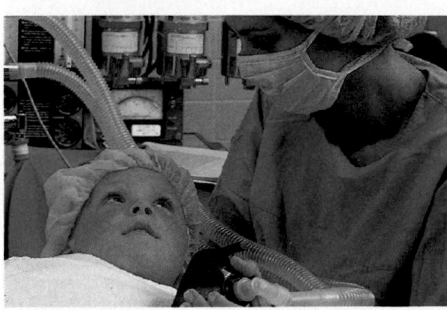

Anesthetics remain in the body long after a patient is awake. What concentration of this anesthetic should be kept in the patient's bloodstream during surgery?

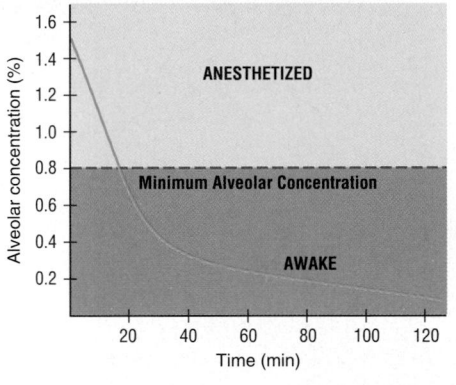

636

CAREERS IN ANESTHESIOLOGY

What kind of doctor spends the most time in the operating room? It isn't surgeons; it isn't even obstetricians. It's anesthesiologists. The doctor who gives the patient anesthesia ("relief from pain") really runs the operating room.

An anesthesiologist must be both a doctor with a broad knowledge of surgery and a clinical pharmacologist. More than any other doctor, the anesthesiologist must be a master of *pharmacodynamics*, the science dealing with reactions between drugs and living systems. For surgery to proceed safely, the patient must be in no pain or shock with all systems operating normally. However, a surgical operation is a violent physical invasion. The body could be excused for reacting as though attacked. The job of the anesthesiologist is to prevent such a reaction.

In most surgeries, he or she renders the patient unconscious as well as anesthetized. That means the anesthesiologist is then responsible for the patient's breathing, heartbeat, and all other life functions. He or she must thoroughly know the patient's medical history, the operation and its risks. Calculating and giving correct dosages of anesthetics is key to surgical success. In fact, it is the anesthesiologist who is legally responsible for the anesthetics given. That underlies the life-or-death consequences of mathematical accuracy.

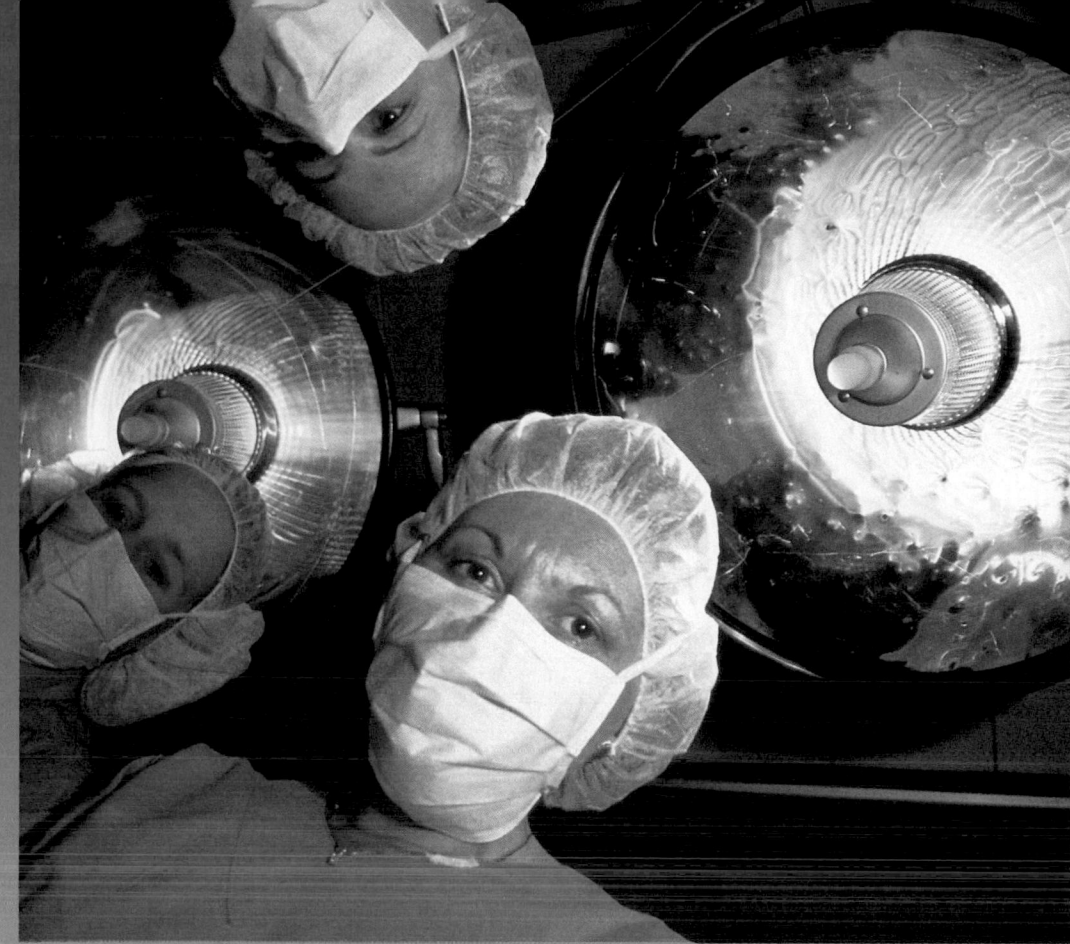

Lesson	Connections (C) and Applications (A)	Examples	Exercises
14-1	A: Sports	1	
	Education	2	
14-2	A: Education	1	
	Consumerism	2	
	Sports	3	10
	Meteorology	4	
	History		11
14-3	A: Business	1	
	Finance	2	
	Education	3	
	Health		25
14-4	A: Meteorology	1, 2	
	Sports	3	
	Business		29, 36
	Consumerism		30
14-5	A: Sports	1	16
	Consumerism		15
14-6	A: Horticulture	1	
	Entertainment	2	
	Business		18
	Astronomy		19
	C: Geometry		23
14-7	A: Medicine	1	
	Health	2	
	Education		12

MORE ABOUT ANESTHESIOLOGY

Degree Required:

- Medical Doctor plus five years of medical residency

Some anesthesiologists like:

- good working conditions
- the high salaries and prestige
- the satisfaction they derive from helping others

Related Math Subjects:

- Advanced Algebra
- Trigonometry
- Geometry
- Statistics/Probability

Some anesthesiologists dislike:

- being responsible for the life of a patient
- the long preparation to enter the field
- having to be available at all times

For more information on the various careers available in the field of anesthesiology, write to:

American Society of Anesthesiologists
515 Busse Highway
Park Ridge, IL 60068

637

14-1 Problem-Solving Strategy: Make a Graph

INTRODUCING THE LESSON

Motivating the Lesson

Give students slips of paper with data on each and tell them to organize the data. A sample data set would be peanut, elephant, apple, tree, 8 ounces, 2 tons, 0.25 ounce, 200 pounds, bark, skin, peel, and shell. Compare results.

TEACHING THE LESSON

Teaching Tip ❶   Review with students the type of information best suited to each type of graph.

Objective
14-1

After studying this lesson, you should be able to:
■ solve problems by organizing data and making graphs.

Application

Data is easier to read and interpret when it is organized. One way to organize data is by using tables. The following table shows the changes in population in some cities from the 1980 census to the 1990 census.

City	1990 population	Change from 1980
Boise, ID	123,059	+20.4%
Charleston, WV	56,012	−12.4%
Detroit, MI	970,156	−19.4%
Kansas City, MO	427,799	−4.5%
Louisville, KY	265,660	−11.1%
Newark, NJ	260,097	−27.3%
Oklahoma City, OK	441,154	+9.2%
Portland, ME	64,084	+4.1%
Sioux Falls, SD	100,281	+23.3%
Wilmington, DE	70,278	+0.1%

You can use the information in the table to quickly answer questions like:

■ Which city had the greatest percent change in population?   *Newark, NJ*
■ Which city had very little change in population?   *Wilmington, DE*
■ Which city has the greatest population?   *Detroit, MI*

The census, which provided the information for this table, is a survey that polls all residents of the United States. Some surveys only poll a **sample** of a population. For a survey to correctly represent the larger group, a representative sample that correctly represents the group should be taken randomly.   **Teaching Tip ❶**

The information gathered from a survey can be organized in a table or in different types of graphs. Study the graphs in the following examples.

ALTERNATE TEACHING STRATEGIES

Mini-Math Lab

Have students choose a topic and conduct a survey among members of the class. Use the results of the survey to predict what results would be obtained for the entire school. Display results in both a table and a graph. Discuss reasons why sampling one class only might not give a representative sampling of the entire school.

Bar graphs are useful for showing how quantities compare. Circle graphs are best for showing how parts are related to the whole.

Teaching Tip ②

Example 1

Use the data in the table to draw a bar graph and a circle graph.

Injuries to students 5–24 years old in organized sports programs (1988–1989)

Sport	Football	Basketball	Soccer	Baseball	Gymnastics
Number of Injuries	83,378	75,565	22,415	19,106	11,904

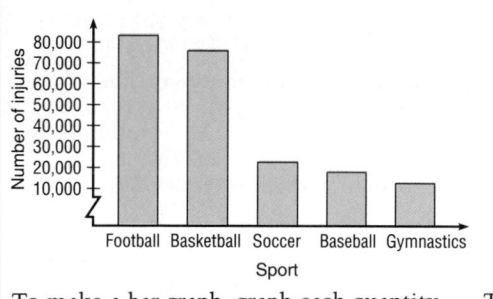

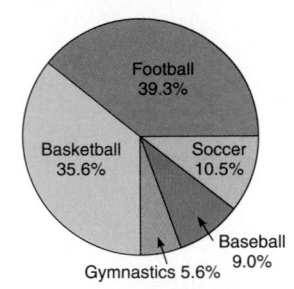

To make a bar graph, graph each quantity on the horizontal axis with the vertical axis showing the range.

To make a circle graph, find the percentage of the whole that each quantity represents. Then find the number of degrees each central angle should have.

Line graphs are usually used for showing changes over time. They make it easy to identify trends.

Teaching Tip ③

Example 2

Use the data in the table to draw a line graph.

High School Graduates (in thousands)

Year	1960	1965	1970	1975	1980	1985	1990
Number	1864	2665	2896	3140	3058	2683	2793

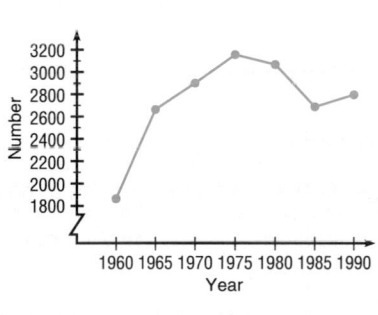

To make a line graph, plot each ordered pair on the graph. Then connect successive points with lines.

LESSON 14-1   PROBLEM SOLVING STRATEGY: MAKE A GRAPH   **639**

RETEACHING THE LESSON

Give a table of data to each pair of students. Have each pair graph their data. Have students exchange graphs with other pairs. Have each pair construct a table to fit the graph. Compare with original tables.

Chalkboard Examples

For Example 1

Use the data in the table to draw a bar graph.

Oil from Saudi Arabia
(Thousands of Barrels per day)

Year	1975	1977	1979	1981	1983	1985
Bar.	715	1380	1356	1129	337	168

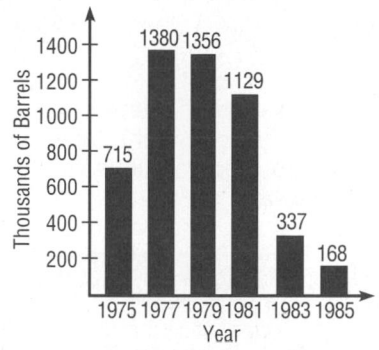

For Example 2

Use the data in the table to draw a line graph.

Average Motor Fuel Consumption in U.S.
gallons per automobile

Year	1960	1965	1970	1975	1980	1985
Consumption	661	667	738	712	603	549

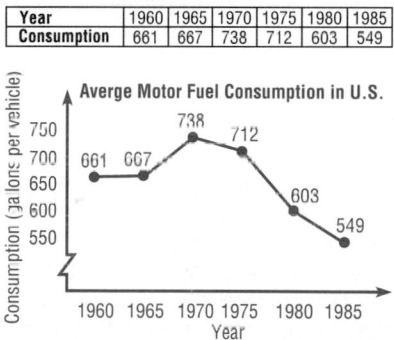

Teaching Tip ② Discuss with students that a line graph is usually used to display a numeric change and thus would not be a meaningful display of this data.

Teaching Tip ③ Discuss with students why a bar graph would also be useful for this situation but a circle graph would not.

Checking for Understanding

Exercises 1–5 are designed to help you assess understanding through reading, writing, and speaking. You should work through Exercises 1–4 with your students, and then monitor their work on Exercise 5.

Closing the Lesson

Modeling Activity Have students use the data in the table on this page to model various displays of data.

Homework Exercises

Assignment Guide

Basic: 6–14
Average: 6–14
Enriched: 6–14

Additional Answers

1. **Answers may vary. Samples are: bar—number of students of each grade in a school; circle—breakdown of ages of people in American population; line—profit of a company over 10 years**

3. **no; The people at home to answer the phone probably do not work outside the home.**

5c.

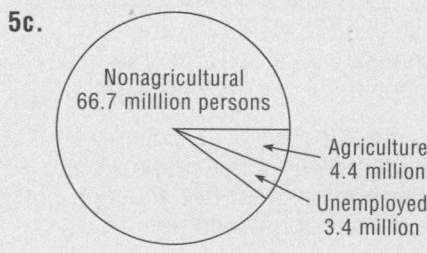

Civilian Labor Force, 1965

CHECKING FOR UNDERSTANDING

Communicating Mathematics

Read and study the lesson to answer these questions.

1. Describe a situation where you would use each type of graph—bar, circle, and line. **See margin.**

2. The circle graph at the right represents the cost of a $4 paperback book broken down by type. How much of the $4 goes to the bookstore? **$1.60**

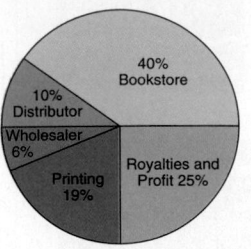

3. Would a daytime telephone poll be the best method for taking a survey on career choices? Why or why not? **See margin.**

4. Look through a newspaper or magazine to find different types of graphs. What type of graphs are used most often? Do you think the type of graph they chose is the best one for the information? **Answers may vary.**

Guided Practice

5. Use the data in the table to answer each of the following. The figures are given in millions of people.

Employment Status	1965	1975	1985
Employed in nonagricultural industries	66.7	82.4	104.0
Employed in agriculture	4.4	3.4	3.2
Unemployed	3.4	7.9	8.3
Total civilian labor force	74.5	93.7	115.5

a. How many people were employed in agriculture in 1975? **3,400,000**

b. What percentage of the civilian labor force was employed in nonagricultural industries in 1985? **90%**

c. Make a circle graph to show the breakdown of the civilian labor force in 1965. **See margin.**

EXERCISES

Solve. Use any strategy.

6. Jack and Kara are running laps around the Bradley Community Park track in opposite directions. Jack makes one lap every 55 seconds. He meets Kara every 30 seconds. How fast can Kara run one lap? **66 seconds**

7. Simplify $\dfrac{3^{x+3} - 3(3^x)}{3(3^{x+2})}$. $\dfrac{8}{9}$

Strategies

Look for a pattern.
Solve a simpler problem.
Act it out.
Guess and check.
Draw a diagram.
Make a chart.
Work backwards.

8. The Jackson Carton Co. makes cardboard cartons. Their medium size carton is 20% longer and 30% wider than their smallest carton. The cartons are the same height. How much greater is the volume of the medium size carton? **56% larger**

9. Find the real roots of $|x - 2|^2 - 2|x - 2| = 8$. **6, −2**

10. The average monthly automobile production in thousands in the United States for 1982 to 1988 is shown in the table below. Make a bar graph and a line graph of the data. **See Solutions Manual.**

Year	1984	1985	1986	1987	1988	1989	1990
Production	647.8	682.1	652.4	591.6	592.6	568.6	506.4

11. How many times do the hands of a clock cross in one day? **24 times**

12. The numbers of presidents of different political affiliations are listed in the table below. Make a circle graph of this data. **See Solutions Manual.**

Political Party	Democratic	Democratic-Republican	Federalist	Republican	Union	Whig
Number of Presidents	14	4	2	17	1	4

13. A palindrome is a word or number that is the same when read forwards and backwards. Some examples are TOOT, RADAR, 232, and 11899811. List all the two-, three-, and four-digit palindromes that are prime numbers. **See margin.**

14. How many divisions are *necessary* to determine whether or not a number is prime? **the number of primes less than the square root of the number**

COOPERATIVE LEARNING ACTIVITY

Work in groups. Each person in the group must understand the solution and be able to explain it to any person in class.

Start at the 0 at the top left-hand corner and move one square to a 1, then move two squares to a 2, then three squares to a 3, and so on. Make a path to the 8 in the bottom right-hand corner without revisiting any square. You may move only horizontally or vertically; diagonal moves are not allowed. **See margin.**

0	1	3	2	5	3	5	6
1	3	2	4	5	4	6	7
2	3	4	3	4	6	7	5
3	4	5	3	7	7	6	7
4	5	6	5	4	5	7	6
7	6	5	4	5	7	5	7
6	5	4	5	6	4	5	6
7	6	6	7	4	6	7	⑧

LESSON 14-1 PROBLEM SOLVING STRATEGY: MAKE A GRAPH   641

EXTENDING THE LESSON

Math Power: Communication

Have each student communicate his or her music preferences to a partner by use of data displays only. Have the partner then write what was communicated to him or her by the displays. Have the two students then discuss how effectively the information was communicated.

Cooperative Learning Activity

This activity provides students with an opportunity to *learn* things together, not just do things together. You may wish to refer to pages T6–T8 and page 6C for the various elements of cooperative groups and specific goals and strategies for using them.

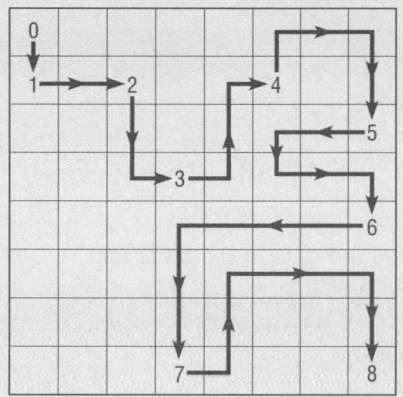
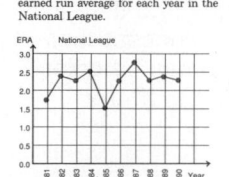

Lesson Resources

Reteaching Master 14-2
Practice Master 14-2
Enrichment Master 14-2

 Transparency 14-2 contains the 5-Minute Check and a teaching aid for this lesson.

INTRODUCING THE LESSON

 5-Minute Check

(over Lesson 14-1)
Use the data in the table for Exercises 1–3.

U.S. Population Distribution, by Age

Year	1900	1950	1985
Under 5	12.1%	10.7%	7.5%
5–19	32.3%	23.2%	22.3%
20–44	37.7%	37.6%	39.5%
45–64	13.7%	20.3%	18.8%
65 and over	4.2%	8.2%	11.9%

1. In which year did the people 65 and over make up a larger percentage of the U.S. population than those under age 5? **1985**
2. In 1950, what percent of the U.S. population was between the age of 20 and 64 years old? **57.9%**
3. What percentage decrease did the under 5 group have from 1900 to 1985? **4.6%**

Motivating the Lesson

Bring a foliage plant into the class. Ask students what the relationship is between the stems and the leaves. Develop the concept that, although the leaves may be different, several may come off the same stem.

14-2 Line Plots and Stem-and-Leaf Plots

Objectives

After studying this lesson, you should be able to:

14-2A ■ represent data using line plots and stem-and-leaf plots, and
14-2B ■ read and interpret data from line plots and stem-and-leaf plots.

Numerical data is often organized and displayed using either **line plots** or **stem-and-leaf plots.** In a line plot, data is recorded and displayed using a number line.

You can make a line plot of the enrollments of thirty small American colleges and universities as follows.

School	Enrollment (in hundreds)	School	Enrollment (in hundreds)
Amherst College	16	Northwestern University	74
Berea College	15	University of Notre Dame	75
Brown University	58	Oberlin College	29
Carnegie-Mellon University	43	Princeton University	46
Case Western Reserve University	30	Purdue University	29
University of Chicago	33	Rice University	26
Columbia University	29	University of Rochester	48
Dartmouth College	37	Smith College	27
Duke University	59	Southern Methodist University	57
Emory University	52	Stanford University	65
Georgetown University	59	Vanderbilt University	52
Grinnell College	13	Wake Forest University	35
Harvard University	66	Wellesley College	22
Johns Hopkins University	27	Williams College	20
Massachusetts Institute of Technology	42	Yale University	52

The data range from 13 to 75. The number line must be drawn long enough to contain all of these values. An "x" is used to indicate the enrollment of a school.

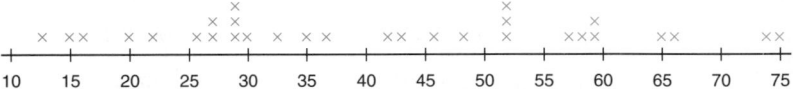

When making a stem-and-leaf plot, each piece of data is separated into two parts that are used to form the stem and leaf for the piece of data. The data is usually organized into two columns. The column on the left side is the stem, which usually consists of the digits in the greatest common place value used in all the data. For example, if the greatest common place value is hundreds, then the stem of 580 is 5 and the stem of 1293 is 12. The column on the right contains the leaves, which are 80 for 580 and 93 for 1293.

ALTERNATE TEACHING STRATEGIES

Using Manipulatives

Have each student roll two dice 20 times and determine the product of each result. Have students display these products in a stem-and-leaf plot. Have students compare plots and discuss similarities and differences and possible reasons for each. Ask students to explain why the plots might be more similar if the dice had been rolled 40 times.

Mini-Math Lab

Distribute small boxes of raisins or other such items to the students in the class. Have the students count the raisins in the box and record the data on a line plot. Discuss the information. What is the range of the data? How many raisins do most of the boxes contain?

Example 1

APPLICATION

Education

Make a stem-and-leaf plot of the enrollments of the colleges and universities listed on the previous page.

The data ranges from 13 to 75 and the greatest common place value of all the data is tens. So, the stems are the numbers from 1 to 7. To plot the number 16, use 1 as the stem and 6 as the leaf. We can organize the data in a stem-and-leaf plot in two different ways. The plot on the left shows the leaves in order of the given data and the plot on the right shows the leaves in numerical order.

Stem	Leaf
1	6 5 3
2	9 7 9 9 6 7 2 0
3	0 3 7 5
4	3 2 6 8
5	8 9 2 9 7 2 2
6	6 5 6 | 5 represents 65 hundred students.
7	4 5 **Teaching Tip ❶**

Stem	Leaf
1	3 5 6
2	0 2 6 7 7 9 9 9
3	0 3 5 7
4	2 3 6 8
5	2 2 2 7 8 9 9
6	5 6
7	4 5

Sometimes it is a good idea to break a stem into two parts so that the data is organized more conveniently.

Example 2

APPLICATION

Consumerism

Maria was browsing through the Shoe Shoppe catalog. The catalog contains 29 pairs of shoes that can be ordered through the mail. The prices are $53, $42, $49, $38, $39, $48, $37, $48, $37, $39, $58, $59, $32, $50, $59, $37, $36, $30, $40, $33, $30, $45, $40, $30, $35, $48, $37, $48, and $50. Make a stem-and-leaf plot of the shoe prices.

Since the data ranges from 30 to 59, the stems can be 3, 4, and 5. If we make the plot this way however, the stems 3 and 4 will have a great number of leaves. So, in order to make the stem-and-leaf plot easier to interpret, we will break each stem into two parts to represent the data.

Let 3 | represent prices from $30 to $34, and
3 • | represent prices from $35 to $39.

Stem	Leaf
3	0 0 0 2 3
•	5 6 7 7 7 7 8 9 9
4	0 0 2
•	5 8 8 8 8 9
5	0 0 3
•	8 9 9 *5 | 0 represents $50.*

Teaching Tip ❷

The leaves have been ordered from least to greatest.

Teaching Tip ❸

Sometimes data values have more than two digits. In these cases, it is sometimes necessary to round or truncate each piece of data before it can be plotted in a stem-and-leaf plot. This way each leaf will have only one digit. For example, if the greatest common place value is thousands, then the leaf for 1573 is 573. If 1573 is rounded to 1600, then the stem is 1 and the leaf is 6. If 1573 is truncated to 1500, then the stem is 1 and the leaf is 5.

TEACHING THE LESSON

Chalkboard Examples

For Example 1

The ages of the teachers at Darby Avenue School are 27, 52, 31, 22, 42, 43, 37, 52, 44, 36, 28, 35, 57, 36, 41, 34, 49, 28, 36, and 40. Make a line plot of the ages.

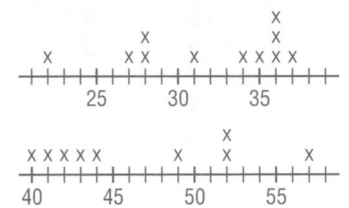

For Example 2

Each student in Mrs. Fogg's class walks to school. The times for each student, in minutes, are 27, 25, 5, 23, 7, 18, 23, 13, 14, 8, 10, 17, 12, 19, 19, 30, 18, 19, 14, 23, 9, 15, 23, 13, 29, 16, 27, 19, 22, 15, 16, 33. Make a stem-and-leaf plot of the times.

Stem	Leaf
0	
•	5 7 8 9
1	0 2 3 3 4 4
•	5 5 6 6 7 8 8 9 9 9 9
2	2 3 3 3 3
•	5 7 7 9
3	0 3

2 | 2 represents 22 minutes.

Teaching Tip ❶ Point out that students need to include this "key" in order to interpret the numbers from the stem-and-leaf plot.

Teaching Tip ❷ Encourage students to plot the numbers as they appear in the data and then reorder the data in ascending or descending order in a second stem-and-leaf plot.

Teaching Tip ❸ Be sure students know the difference in rounding and truncating. Plots using rounded and truncated data give the same general information.

For Example 3

The heights in feet of some mountains in the U.S. are 15,700, 16,390, 17,400, 20,320, 15,015, 16,550, 15,300, 18,008, 16,237, 15,638, and 16,286. Make a back-to-back stem-and-leaf plot of the rounded and truncated values of the data.

Rounded	Stem	Truncated
7 6 3 0	15	0 3 6 7
6 4 3 2	16	2 2 3 5
4	17	4
0	18	0
	19	
3	20	3

4 | 17 | represents 17,350 to 17,449 feet.

17 | 4 | represents 17,400 to 17,499 feet.

For Example 4

Make a back-to-back stem-and-leaf plot of the percent of TV households viewing network programs and syndicated programs.

Top 5 Regularly Scheduled Network Programs, 11/88	% of TV Households
Bill Cosby Show	27.9
A Different World	23.4
Cheers	22.8
Roseanne	22.3
Golden Girls	22.3

Top 5 Syndicated TV Programs, 11/88	% of TV Households
Wheel of Fortune	15.7
Jeopardy	13.2
Cosby Show	11.7
Oprah Winfrey Show	10.1
Star Trek	10.0

Network	Stem	Syndicated
.9	27	
.4	23	
.3 .3 .8	22	
	15	.7
	14	
	13	.2
	12	
	11	.7
	10	0 .1

Network programs are viewed by more households than syndicated programs.

Example 3

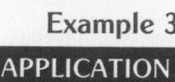

APPLICATION

Sports

The winners of the men's springboard diving competition at the Olympic Games are listed below. Make a stem-and-leaf plot of the rounded and of the truncated values of the points they received to win the competition.

Year	Winner	Points	Year	Winner	Points
1932	Michael Galitzen	161.38	1968	Bernard Wrightson	170.15
1936	Richard Degener	163.57	1972	Vladimir Vasin	594.09
1948	Bruce Harlan	163.64	1976	Phil Boggs	619.05
1952	David Browning	205.59	1980	Alexandr Portnov	905.02
1956	Robert Clotworthy	159.56	1984	Greg Louganis	754.41
1960	Gary Tobian	170.00	1988	Greg Louganis	730.80
1964	Ken Sitzberger	159.90	1992	Mark Lenzi	676.53

Round to the nearest 10. So, using rounded data, 7 | 3 represents 725 to 734 points.

Stem	Leaf
1	6 6 6 6 6 7 7
2	1
3	
4	
5	9
6	2 8
7	3 5
8	
9	1

Truncate after the ten. So, using truncated data, 7 | 3 represents 730 to 739 points.

Stem	Leaf
1	5 5 6 6 6 7 7
2	0
3	
4	
5	9
6	1 7
7	3 5
8	
9	0

Example 4

APPLICATION

Meteorology

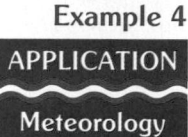

The average monthly temperatures in selected cities for January and July are given in the table below. Make a back-to-back stem-and-leaf plot of the rounded temperatures of the cities.

City	January Temp.	July Temp.	City	January Temp.	July Temp.
Baton Rouge, LA	50.8	82.1	Indianapolis, IN	26.0	75.1
Caribou, ME	10.7	65.1	Jacksonville, FL	53.2	81.3
Charlotte, NC	40.5	78.5	Juneau, AK	21.8	55.7
Chicago, IL	21.4	73.0	Roswell, NM	41.4	77.7
Dallas, TX	44.0	86.3	San Diego, CA	56.8	70.3
Denver, CO	29.5	73.4	Tulsa, OK	35.2	83.2

January Temperatures	Stem	July Temperatures
1	1	
1 2 6	2	
0 5	3	
1 1 4	4	
1 3 7	5	6
	6	5
	7	0 3 3 5 8 9
	8	1 2 3 6

6 | 2 | represents 26°F.

| 8 | 1 represents 81°F.

RETEACHING THE LESSON

Give students a list of test scores. Have them make a stem-and-leaf plot for the data. Then have them make a line plot for the same data. Put in cutoff lines for letter grades.

CHECKING FOR UNDERSTANDING

Communicating Mathematics

Read and study the lesson to answer these questions.

1. Describe a situation in which a line plot is an appropriate way to display data. **Answers may vary.**

2. Compare the two stem-and-leaf plots made in Example 3. How different are the two? Is one more accurate than the other? Explain your answer. **See margin.**

3. Name some collections of data for which a back-to-back stem-and-leaf plot is an appropriate way to display the data. **See margin.**

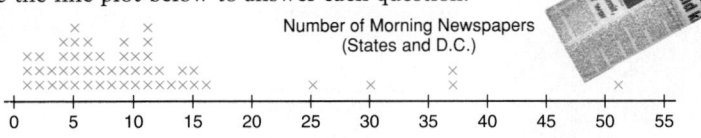

Guided Practice

4. Use the line plot below to answer each question.

Number of Morning Newspapers (States and D.C.)

```
        ×
       ××× ×  ××
     ×× ××××  ×××
    ××××××××××××  ×
    ×××××××××××××× ××        ×    ×        ×              ×
    ┼───┼───┼───┼───┼───┼───┼───┼───┼───┼───┼───┼───┼
    0   5  10  15  20  25  30  35  40  45  50  55
```

   a. What is the greatest number of newspapers in one state? **51**

   b. What is the least number of newspapers in one state? **1**

   c. How many states have 10 to 20 newspapers? **16**

   d. How many newspapers do most states have? **5 or 11**

5. Use the stem-and-leaf plot at the right to answer each question.

   a. What was the highest winning score? **299**

   b. What was the lowest winning score? **277**

   c. In 1986, Jane Geddes won the U.S. Women's Open Golf Championship with a score of 287. How many winners won with scores lower than Ms. Geddes'? **11**

   d. What scores did more of the winners earn than any other? **280, 290**

Winning Scores of U.S. Women's Open 1970–1992

Stem	Leaf
27	
●	7 8 9
28	0 0 0 3 3 4 4
●	5 7 7 8 9
29	0 0 0 2 2
●	5 5 9

29 | 0 represents a score of 290.

EXERCISES

Practice

6. Each number below represents the age of a U.S. president on his first inauguration.

▷ A

57	61	57	57	58	57	61	54	68	51	49
50	48	65	52	56	46	54	49	50	47	55
54	42	51	56	55	51	54	51	60	62	43
56	61	52	69	64	64	55	55	46		

   a. Make a line plot of the ages of U.S. presidents on their first inauguration. **See margin.**

LESSON 14-2 LINE PLOTS AND STEM-AND-LEAF PLOTS 645

Additional Answers

2. The two plots are not very different. The distributions are similar. Neither is more accurate than the other.

3. Answers may vary. A sample answer is populations of cities in the 1980 and the 1990 national census.

6a.

```
              ×  ×× ×
              ×  ××××   ×
         ×  ×××× ××××   × ×
        ××  ××××××× ××××× ××× ××   ××
        ┼┼┼┼┼┼┼┼┼┼┼┼┼┼┼┼┼┼┼┼┼┼┼┼┼┼┼┼┼┼┼
        40   45   50   55   60   65   70
```

Writing Activity Have students compare and contrast line plots and stem-and-leaf plots.

APPLYING THE LESSON

Homework Exercises
See assignment guide on page 645.

Chapter 14, Quiz A, (Lessons 14–1 through 14–2), is available in the Evaluation Masters Booklet, p. 191.

Additional Answer

7a.
Stem	Leaf
6	8
7	0 3
●	5 6 8 9
8	0 0 1 1 1 2 2 2

7 | 3 represents 73 games.

Practice Masters Booklet, p. 104

b. What was the age of the oldest president on his first inauguration? **69**

c. What was the age of the youngest president on his first inauguration? **42**

d. What is the difference in the ages of the youngest and oldest presidents? **27**

e. How many ages are given? **42**

f. Which age(s) occur most frequently? **51, 54, 55, 57**

g. How many presidents were in their 60s when they were first inaugurated? **10**

7. The following table gives scoring information for the top 15 scoring players in the National Basketball Association for 1991–92.

Player, Team	Games	Points	Average
Michael Jordan, Chicago	80	2404	30.1
Karl Malone, Utah	81	2272	28.0
Chris Mullin, Golden State	81	2074	25.6
Clyde Drexler, Portland	76	1903	25.0
Patrick Ewing, New York	82	1970	24.0
Tim Hardaway, Golden State	81	1893	23.4
David Robinson, San Antonio	68	1578	23.2
Charles Barkley, Philadelphia	75	1730	23.1
Mitch Richmond, Sacramento	80	1803	22.5
Glen Rice, Miami	79	1765	22.3
Ricky Pierce, Seattle	78	1690	21.7
Hakeem Olajuwon, Houston	70	1510	21.6
Brad Dougherty, Cleveland	73	1566	21.5
Scottie Pippen, Chicago	82	1720	21.0
Reggie Lewis, Boston	82	1703	20.8

a. Make a stem-and-leaf plot of the number of games played by each player. **See margin.**

b. Who played the most games? **Ewing, Pippen, and Lewis**

c. Who played the least games? **Robinson**

d. How many more games did the player with the most games play than the player with the least games? **14**

e. How many games did most of the players play? **81 or 82**

f. How many players played more than 80 games? **6**

g. Make a stem-and-leaf plot of the number of points scored by each player. Round scores to the nearest ten. **See margin.**

h. Who scored the most points? **Jordan**

i. Who scored the fewest points? **Olajuwon**

j. How many more points did the highest scoring player make than the lowest scoring player? **894**

k. How many players scored less than 2000 points? **12**

l. Make a stem-and-leaf plot of the average number of points scored per game. Round the number of points to the nearest whole number. **See margin.**

Additional Answers

7g.
Stem	Leaf
15	1 7 8
16	9
17	0 2 3 7
18	0 9
19	0 7
20	7
21	
22	7
23	
24	0

16 | 9 represents 1690 points.

7l.
Stem	Leaf
2	1 1 2 2 2 2 3 3 3 3 4
●	5 6 8
3	0

2 | 3 represents 23 points.

 m. Who had the highest per game average? **Jordan**

n. Who had the lowest per game average? **Lewis**

o. What is the difference between the averages of the players with the highest and lowest average? **9.3**

p. What is the most frequently occurring average? **none**

q. How many players averaged more than 25 points per game? **3**

8. The prize money earned in 1992 by the top five women and men tennis players is listed in the table below.

Player	Prize Money
Monica Seles	$1,732,352
Aranxa Sanchez Vicario	1,093,155
Steffi Graf	1,068,026
Gabriela Sabatini	824,065
Natalia Zvereva	519,144

Player	Prize Money
Jim Courier	$1,550,045
Stefan Edberg	1,367,029
Pete Sampras	1,131,372
Andre Agassi	1,000,484
Petr Korda	793,823

a. Make a back-to-back stem-and-leaf plot of the prize money for women and men. **See margin.**

b. What information about the relationship between the prize money available to women and men does it present? **See margin.**

Critical Thinking

9. Record the heights, to the nearest inch, of the students in your class. Make a stem-and-leaf plot and a line plot of the information. Also make a back-to-back stem-and-leaf plot comparing the heights of male and female students. What observations can you make? **Answers will vary.**

Applications

10. **Sports** Use the information about tennis players' earnings given above. Make a line plot. Who earned the most money? **See margin.**

11. **History** Use the information about the ages of the presidents given in Exercise 6 to make a stem-and-leaf plot. In what age range were most of the presidents when they were inaugurated? **See margin.**

Mixed Review

12. Use the information about tennis players' earnings given above to make a circle graph showing how much of the prize money was won by each player. (**Lesson 14-1**) **See margin.**

13. Name the first five terms of the arithmetic sequence described by $a_1 = 10$, $d = 2.2$ (**Lesson 13-1**) **10, 12.2, 14.4, 16.6, 18.8**

14. Evaluate the expression $9^{\log_9 2}$. (**Lesson 12-2**) **2**

15. Use synthetic substitution to find $f(3)$ and $f(-2)$ if $f(x) = x^4 + x^3 + x^2 + x + 1$. (**Lesson 10-2**) **121, 11**

$f(x) = 45x^2 - 60x + 24$

16. Express $f(x) = 5(3x - 2)^2 + 4$ in quadratic form. (**Lesson 8-1**)

17. The sum of Kari's age and her mother's age is 52. Kari's mother is 20 years older than Kari. How old is each? (**Lesson 3-2**) **36 and 16**

LESSON 14-2 LINE PLOTS AND STEM-AND-LEAF PLOTS **647**

Journal

Describe the patterns you might see when using a line plot or stem-and-leaf plot. Include some graphs in your description.

EXTENDING THE LESSON

Math Power: Connections

Have students keep records of high and low temperatures for two weeks. Have students make a back-to-back stem-and-leaf plot of the data.

Additional Answer

8a.

Men	Stem	Women
	17	3
	16	
5	15	
	14	
7	13	
	12	
3	11	
0	10	9 7
	9	
	8	2
9	7	
	6	
	5	2

$8 | 2$ represents $820,000.$

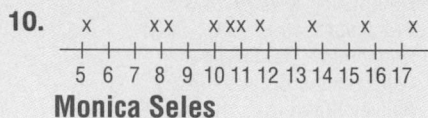

Additional Answers

8b. The men earned slightly more than the women.

10.

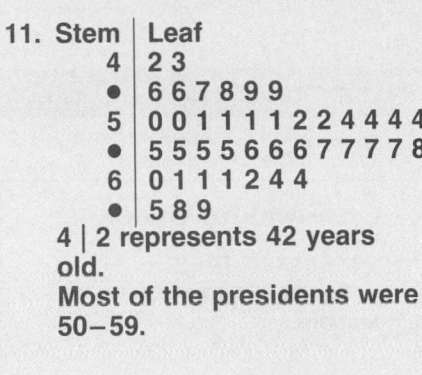

Monica Seles

11.

Stem	Leaf
4	2 3
●	6 6 7 8 9 9
5	0 0 1 1 1 1 2 2 4 4 4 4
●	5 5 5 5 6 6 6 7 7 7 7 8
6	0 1 1 1 2 4 4
●	5 8 9

$4 | 2$ represents 42 years old.
Most of the presidents were 50–59.

12.

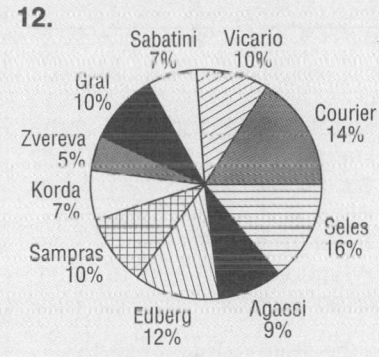

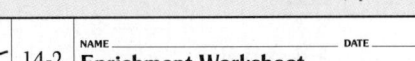

Enrichment Masters Booklet, p. 90

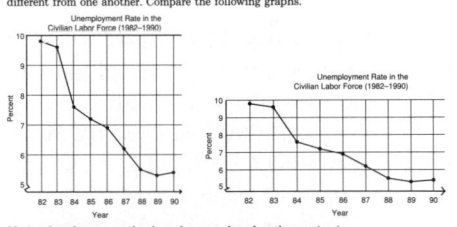

14-2 **Enrichment Worksheet**

Misuses of Statistics

Statistics can be misleading. Graphs for a set of data can look very different from one another. Compare the following graphs.

Notice that the two graphs show the same data, but the spacing in the vertical and horizontal scales differs. Scales can be cramped or spread out to make a graph that gives a certain impression. Which graph would you use to give the impression that the unemployment rate dropped dramatically from 1983 to 1990? **the first graph**

Suppose that a car company claims, "75% of people surveyed say that our car is better than the competition." If four people were asked which car they preferred and 75% agreed, how many people thought that *Our Car* was better? **3 people**

The advertisement was misleading in other ways as well. For example, who was surveyed—were the people company employees, or impartial buyers?

Suppose an advertiser claims that 90% of all of one brand of car sold in the last 10 years are still on the road.

1. If 10,000 cars were sold, how many are still on the road? **9,000**

2. If 1000 cars were sold, how many are still on the road? **900**

3. Find an example to show how you think averages could be used in a misleading way. **See students' work.**

4. A survey of a large sample of people who own small computers revealed that 85% of the people thought the instruction manuals should be better written. A manufacturer of small computers claimed that it surveyed many of the same people and found that all of them liked their manuals. Discuss the possible discrepancy in the results. **See students' work.**

Chapter 14 **647**

Lesson Resources

Reteaching Master 14-3
Practice Master 14-3
Enrichment Master 14-3
Lab Manual, pp. 43–44
Activity Master, p. 14

 Transparency 14-3 contains the 5-Minute Check and a teaching aid for this lesson.

INTRODUCING THE LESSON

 5-Minute Check

(over Lesson 14-2)

Use the line plot to answer the questions.

```
              x
      x       x
  x   x       x   x  x  x
  +--+--+--+--+--+--+--+--+
 10          20          30
```

1. List the data displayed in the line plot.   **10, 14, 14, 20, 20, 20, 24, 26, 28**
2. What is the data range?   **from 10 to 28**
3. Which value(s) appear most often?   **20**

Use the stem-and-leaf plot to answer the questions.

Stem	Leaf
8	3 7 8 | 3 = 83
9	4 4 8 8 9
10	0 5
11	1

4. What is the difference between the highest value and lowest value?   **28**
5. Which value(s) appear most frequently?   **94, 98**

Motivating the Lesson

Use an audio or video tape of a ball game or a sports section from a newspaper. Point out statistics determined by averaging. Examples might be earned run average, average number of points scored per game, or average number of yards rushing per game. Ask students what information this gives them.

Central Tendency: Median, Mode, and Mean

Objectives

After studying this lesson, you should be able to:

14-3A ■ find the median, mode, and mean of sets of data, and
14-3B ■ use the median, mode, and mean to interpret data.

Application

The table below shows the gross incomes for 1992 of some of the most successful entertainers or entertainment groups. What income is the most representative of the gross incomes listed?

Entertainer	Gross Income (in millions)	Entertainer	Gross Income (in millions)
Kevin Costner	$21	Eddie Murphy	$24
Robin Williams	20	Jack Nicholson	14
Bill Cosby	42	Arnold Schwarzenegger	28
Michael Douglas	14	U2	27
Madonna	24	Charles Schultz	24
Julio Iglesias	25	David Copperfield	20
Mel Gibson	22	Arsenio Hall	12
Guns N' Roses	26	Steven Spielberg	30
Michael Jackson	26	Tom Cruise	18
Steven King	15	Sylvester Stallone	16
Prince	35	Hammer	16
Garth Brooks	24	Oprah Winfrey	46

The average income is a value that is most representative of the entire set of incomes. The most commonly used averages are the **median, mode,** and **mean.** In this application, the most representative value is the value in the middle of the group.

Teaching Tip ❶   Teaching Tip ❷

Definition of Median, Mode, and Mean

Teaching Tip ❸

> The median of a set of data is the middle value. If there are two middle values, it is the value halfway between.
> The mode of a set of data is the most frequent value. Some sets of data have multiple modes and others have no mode.
> The mean of a set of data is the sum of all the values divided by the number of values.

Let's investigate the information on the entertainers' incomes.

median: To find the median, begin by arranging the data values in order from least to greatest.

The range of the data is 65 − 5, or 60.

12 14 14 15 16 16 18 20 20 21 22 24
24 24 24 25 26 26 27 28 30 35 42 46

ALTERNATE TEACHING STRATEGIES

Using Cooperative Groups

Have each cooperative group choose a type of consumer product. Using catalogs and advertisements, have students list prices for similar items. Have students determine the mean, median, and mode for the set of data. If students have difficulty collecting data on a product, you might suggest using grocery ads and choosing a health care product, such as shampoo.

Since there is an even number of values, we must find the number halfway between the two middle values. The middle values are 24 and 24. So, the median is $\frac{24 + 24}{2}$ or \$24 million.

mode: To find the mode of the entertainers' incomes, look for the most frequently occurring value. Since 24 occurs 4 times, the mode is 24 million dollars.

Some calculators have a $\boxed{\bar{x}}$ key that calculates the mean.

mean: The first step in finding the mean is to add all of the values. Then divide the sum by the number of values, which is 24.

$$\frac{\text{sum of values}}{\text{number of values}} = \frac{569}{24} \text{ or approximately 23.7 million dollars.}$$

As you can see, the median, mode, and mean are not always the same number. In this case, the median and the mode are the same and are greater than the mean. This means that a few people have incomes that are less than the rest. The median is the most representative average of the incomes. **Teaching Tip ❹**

Extreme values are those data values that are vastly different from the central group of data values. Every data value affects the value of the mean, so when extreme values are included in a set of data, the mean may become less representative of the set. However, the values of the median and the mode are not affected by extreme values in the set.

Example 1

APPLICATION
Business

The prices of some new cars are listed below. Determine the mean of the values in the left column and of the values in the right column. Determine the extent to which each mean is representative of the data.

Subaru Justy	\$7576	Toyota Tercel	\$8245
Hyundai Excel	7417	Ford Escort	8617
Pontiac Sunbird	9970	Chevrolet Cavalier	8882
Nissan Sentra	9458	Geo Storm	8677

$$\text{mean} = \frac{7576 + 7417 + 9970 + 9458}{4}$$
$$= \frac{34,421}{4} \text{ or \$8605.25}$$

$$\text{mean} = \frac{8245 + 8617 + 8882 + 8677}{4}$$
$$= \frac{34,421}{4} \text{ or \$8605.25}$$

This mean is not close to any one of the four data values. In this case, it is not a representative value.

There are no extreme values in this set. In this case, the mean is representative of the data.

In some sets of data any average, the mean, median, or mode, is representative of the data.

LESSON 14-3 CENTRAL TENDENCY: MEDIAN, MODE, AND MEAN 649

Teaching Tip ❶ Point out that the median divides the data so that there is an equal number of values above and below the median.

Teaching Tip ❷ A set of data has no mode if there are no repeated data. For example, the set {0, 1, 5, 3, −2} has no mode.

Teaching Tip ❸ The term *mean* is commonly referred to as the *average* or *arithmetic mean*.

Teaching Tip ❹ Be sure students understand that extreme values are those not within the normal range of values.

Chalkboard Example

For Example 1
Find the mean of {1, 2, 4, 93} and {23, 24, 26, 27}. Which is more representative?
mean 1: 25   mean 2: 25
Mean 2 is more representative.

Example 2

APPLICATION

Finance

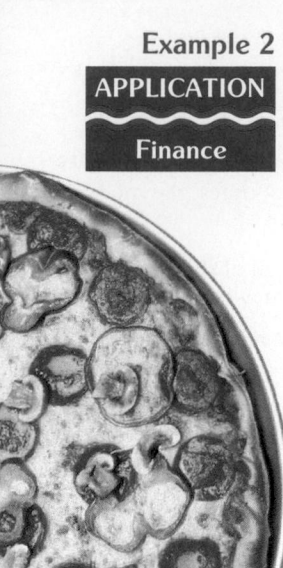

The Parents' Association of the Plain City School District is going to give a pizza party for the graduating senior class. They purchased 6 large cheese pizzas for $6.95 each, 15 large pepperoni pizzas for $8.25 each, 10 large sausage and pepper pizzas for $9.50 each, and 14 large vegetable pizzas for $11.95 each. Find the median, mode, and mean of the cost of the pizzas for the party.

Arrange the prices in order from least to greatest.

$ 6.95	6 pizzas
8.25	15 pizzas
9.50	10 pizzas
11.95	14 pizzas

Since this set of data has 45 values, there is one middle value. The 23rd value is the middle, so the median is $9.50.

Most of the pizzas the Parents' Association bought were $8.25, so this is the mode of the data.

Use your calculator to find the mean.

ENTER:  (6 × 6.95 + 15 × 8.25 + 10 × 9.50 + 14 × 11.95) ÷ 45 = 9.505555556

The mean is about $9.51.

In some applications, there is no mode and it may be impossible to compute the mean.

Example 3

APPLICATION

Education

There are seven problem-solving teams in Mr. George's Algebra 2 class. They were given a problem to solve, and their times for solving the problem are listed below. What is the average amount of time it takes a problem-solving team in Mr. George's class to solve a problem?

Students	Time
Marsha and Mike	12
Monica and Ethan	14
Becky and Kristin	15
Matt and Estevan	16
Byron and Kelly	18
Sam and Emily	19
Eric and Lydia	never finished

Since there are seven teams, the median is the time for the team with the fourth fastest time. That is Matt and Estevan. The median time is 16 minutes.

None of the times occur more than once, so there is no mode.

Because there is no time recorded for Eric and Lydia, we cannot determine the mean of the times.

Since no mode or mean can be determined, the median, 16 minutes, is the average time for the teams to solve a problem.

650   CHAPTER 14   STATISTICS

RETEACHING THE LESSON

Find the median, mode, and mean of these salaries given in thousands of dollars: 27, 28, 29, 30, 31, 32, 33, 40, 500, 500. **mean: 125,000, mode: 500,000, median: 31,500.**

True or False:

1. A half million dollars is the most common salary.   **T**
2. The median salary is $31,500.   **T**
3. The average salary is $125,000.   **T**

CHECKING FOR UNDERSTANDING

Communicating Mathematics

Read and study the lesson to answer these questions.

1. **Oprah Winfrey; Arsenio Hall**

1. Of the entertainers listed in the table at the beginning of the lesson, who had the greatest gross income in 1992? Who had the lowest?

2. What is the difference between the greatest income and the least income of the entertainers? **$34 million**

3. In your own words, tell the difference between the median, mode, and the mean. **See students' work.**

4. Describe some situations in which the median or the mode would be more representative of the data than the mean. **whenever extreme values are present that distort the arithmetic mean**

Guided Practice

Find the median, mode, and mean for each set of data.

5. {0, 2, 4, 4, 5}   **4; 4; 3**
6. {2, 4, 6, 8, 10}   **6; no mode; 6**
7. {9, 9, 9, 9, 9, 9}   **9; 9; 9**

8. {4, 1, 2, 1, 1}   **1; 1; 1.8**
9. {2, 56, 8, 43, 44}   **43; no mode; 30.6**
10. {239, 299, 318, 399, 399}   **318; 399; 330.8**

EXERCISES

Practice

Teaching Tip ⑤

Find the median, mode, and mean for each set of data. 11–16. See margin.

11. {4.8, 5.7, 2.1, 2.1, 4.8, 2.1}
12. {216, 399, 219, 179, 180, 399}
13. {11, 10, 13, 12, 12, 13, 15}
14. {80, 50, 65, 55, 70, 65, 75, 50}
15. {100, 45, 105, 98, 97, 101}
16. {2.0, 2.2, 2.1, 2.2, 2.4, 2.2, 2.3}

17. A die was tossed 25 times with the results shown below. Find the median, mode, and mean for the tosses. **4; 6; about 3.7**

| 5 | 6 | 1 | 3 | 5 | 6 | 1 | 6 | 6 | 6 | 3 | 4 | 5 |
| 6 | 1 | 2 | 4 | 2 | 1 | 4 | 2 | 5 | 4 | 4 | 1 | |

18. The height in feet of 20 of the highest mountains in the world are given below. Find the median, mode, and mean for the heights.

26,504	26,041	26,400	26,750	26,810
29,108	26,470	26,360	26,090	26,000
29,064	26,291	25,910	25,895	28,208
25,925	27,890	27,790	26,760	26,660

26,487; no mode; 26,846.3

19. Find the median, mode, and mean of the hourly wages of 200 employees. One hundred earn $5.00 per hour, ten earn $6.25 per hour, ten earn $7.75 per hour, twenty earn $4.50 per hour, and sixty earn $5.90 per hour. **$5.00; $5.00; $5.42**

20. The stem-and-leaf plot at the right shows the points scored by the winning teams in the first 25 Super Bowls. Find the median, mode, and mean for the scores. **27; 16, 27; 29**

Stem	Leaf
1	4 6 6 6
2	0 0 1 3 4 4 6 7 7 7
3	1 2 3 5 5 8 8 9
4	2 6 *1	4 represents 14 points.*
5	5

LESSON 14-3 CENTRAL TENDENCY: MEDIAN, MODE, AND MEAN 651

Additional Answers
11. 3.45; 2.1; 3.6
12. 217.5; 399; about 265.3
13. 12; 12 and 13; about 12.3
14. 65; 50 and 65; about 63.8
15. 99; no mode; 91
16. 2.2; 2.2; 2.2

EVALUATING THE LESSON

Checking for Understanding
Exercises 1–10 are designed to help you assess understanding through reading, writing, and speaking. You should work through Exercises 1–4 with your students, and then monitor their work on Exercises 5–10.

Closing the Lesson
Modeling Activity Have students use strips of paper of various lengths and a ruler to determine the mean, median, and mode of the lengths of the strips.

APPLYING THE LESSON

Homework Exercises

Assignment Guide
Basic: 11–20, 22–23, 25–28
Average: 14–28
Enriched: 14–28

Teaching Tip ⑤ A set of data that has two modes is said to have bimodal distribution.

Practice Masters Booklet, p. 105

14-3 **Practice Worksheet**

NAME _____ DATE _____

Central Tendency: Median, Mode, and Mean

The following chart gives the number of airline fatalities in the United States during the years 1981 to 1989.

	Fatalities		Fatalities
1981	4	1986	1
1982	233	1987	231
1983	15	1988	285
1984	4	1989	278
1985	197		

1. Find the mean of the data. **138.7**
2. Find the median of the data. **197**
3. Find the mode of the data. **4**

The following chart gives the average number of points per game scored by members of a basketball team during a recent year.

37.1	8.5	4.2
14.5	8.5	3.5
11.3	8.3	2.8
9.7	6.9	1.9

4. Find the mean of the data. **9.8**
5. Find the median of the data. **8.4**
6. Find the mode of the data. **8.5**

The following chart gives the number of students present at each of the monthly club meetings.

August	146	January	121
September	138	February	93
October	120	March	118
November	132	April	129
December	146	May	136

7. Find the mean of the data. **127.9**
8. Find the median of the data. **130.5**
9. Find the mode of the data. **146**

Chapter 14, Quiz B, (Lesson 14–3), is available in the Evaluation Masters Booklet, p. 191.

21. The union and the company executives are currently negotiating a raise in salaries for all of the MicroTech employees. Three of the employees have salaries of $300,000 each. However, a majority of the employees have salaries of about $30,000 per year.

mean; it is higher

   a. You are a vice-president and would like to show that the current salaries are reasonable. Would you quote the median, mode, or mean as the "average" salary to justify your claim? Why?

   b. You are the union representative for your department and maintain that a pay raise is in order. Which of the median, mode, or mean would you quote to justify your claim? Why? **mode; It is lower and is what most employees make. It reflects the most representative worker.**

Critical Thinking

22. Write the formula for the mean of a set of data using the summation symbol. *Hint: Let x_i represent the ith data value.*

$$\text{mean} = \frac{1}{n}\sum_{i=1}^{n} x_i$$

Applications

23. **Health** When physicians say that the typical adult female requires 44 grams of protein per day to maintain good health, do you think they are using the median, the mode, or the mean? Why? **See students' work.**

24. **Business** The back-to-back stem-and-leaf plot below shows the median weekly incomes of male and female workers in various occupations. Find the median, mode, and mean of the male workers' incomes and of the female workers' incomes. Compare the results.

Males	Stem	Females
	2	0 1 4 4
5 6	●	6 7 9
0	3	1
7	●	5 6
0 2 2 3	4	1 4
5 8	●	9
1	5	
	●	
	6	
6 7	●	

|2| 0 represents $200 per week.

male: $420; $420; $432.31; female: $290; $240; $313.08; Male workers make more than female workers.

Mixed Review

25. **Cartography** A map is scaled so that 1 inch represents 25 miles. How far apart are two towns if they are 8.2 inches apart on the map? (Lesson 11-2) **205 miles**

26. Write the equation of the parabola whose focus is (0, 3) and whose directrix is $y = -1$. (Lesson 9-2) $y = \frac{1}{8}x^2 + 1$

27. Find the product $6\begin{bmatrix} 5 & 6 \\ 0 & -2 \end{bmatrix}$. (Lesson 4-3) $\begin{bmatrix} 30 & 36 \\ 0 & -12 \end{bmatrix}$

28. Solve $\left| x - \frac{7}{3} \right| = 6$. (Lesson 1-6) $-\frac{11}{3}, \frac{25}{3}$

EXTENDING THE LESSON

Math Power: Connections

Using a page from a reading book, have students make a data table listing the frequency of use of each letter of the alphabet. Have students determine the mean, the median, and the mode for the set of frequencies.

Enrichment Masters Booklet, p. 91

14-4 Variation: Range, Interquartile Range, and Outliers

Objectives

14-4A

14-4B

After studying this lesson, you should be able to:
- find the range and interquartile range for a set of data, and
- determine if any values in a set of data are outliers.

Application

If the record low and high temperatures in each of the fifty states were all the same, there would be no point in studying about how the record temperatures vary. However, values in a set of data usually vary. Study the table of record high and low temperatures below. The variation within a set of data is called **dispersion**.

State	Low	High	State	Low	High	State	Low	High
AL	−27	112	LA	−16	114	OH	−39	113
AK	−80	100	ME	−48	105	OK	−27	120
AZ	−40	127	MD	−40	109	OR	−54	119
AR	−29	120	MA	−34	107	PA	−42	111
CA	−45	134	MI	−51	112	RI	−23	104
CO	−60	118	MN	−59	114	SC	−20	111
CT	−32	105	MS	−19	115	SD	−58	120
DE	−17	110	MO	−40	118	TN	−32	113
FL	−2	109	MT	−70	117	TX	−23	120
GA	−17	113	NE	−47	118	UT	−50	116
HI	14	100	NV	−50	122	VT	−50	105
ID	−60	118	NH	−46	106	VA	−29	110
IL	35	117	NJ	−34	110	WA	−48	118
IN	−35	116	NM	−50	116	WV	−37	112
IA	−47	118	NY	−52	108	WI	−54	114
KS	−40	121	NC	−29	109	WY	−63	114
KY	−34	114	ND	−60	121			

There are several ways to measure variation. The simplest is called the **range**.

Definition of Range	**The range of a set of data is the difference between the greatest and least values in the set.**

The greatest record high temperature is 134° in California, and the least record high temperature is 100° in Alaska. So the range of the record high temperatures is 134 − 100 or 34°.

Because the range is the difference between the greatest and least values in a set of data, it is affected by extreme values. In these cases it is not a good measure of variation.

14-4 VARIATION: RANGE, INTERQUARTILE RANGE, AND OUTLIERS 653

ALTERNATE TEACHING STRATEGIES

Using Questioning
On the chalkboard, list class scores from the last test or quiz, adjusting the order of the grades and providing no identification. Have students determine the range, median, quartiles, interquartile range, and any outliers for the set of data. If there is sufficient data, each student can also determine these values for his or her own grades for several tests or quizzes.

Lesson Resources
Reteaching Master 14-4
Practice Master 14-4
Enrichment Master 14-4
Activity Master, p. 32

 Transparency 14-4 contains the 5-Minute Check and a teaching aid for this lesson.

INTRODUCING THE LESSON

 5-Minute Check

(over Lesson 14-3)

Find the median of each set of data.

1. {3, 5, 8, 2, 1}   **3**
2. {22, 45, 67, 3, 98}   **45**
3. {146, 232, 79, 182}   **164**

Find the mean, median, and mode for each set of data.

4. {124, 155, 172, 117, 146, 138, 151, 160, 142}   **mean: 145; median: 146; mode: none**
5. {64, 87, 62, 87, 63, 98, 76, 54, 87, 58, 70, 76}   **mean: 73.5; median: 73; mode: 87**

Motivating the Lesson
Have the tallest person and the shortest person in the class stand side by side. Ask students to estimate the difference in the two heights. Measure and compare to the estimate. Ask students to list situations where knowing the difference in the greatest and least measurements might be important.

Chalkboard Examples

For Example 1

The mean daily temperatures in San Francisco for each month of the year are 49°, 52°, 53°, 55°, 58°, 61°, 62°, 63°, 64°, 61°, 55°, 49°. Find the quartiles and interquartile range for the temperatures.
median: 56.5°
lower quartile: 52.5°
upper quartile: 61.5°
interquartile range: 9°

For Example 2

Find any outliers for the daily temperatures in the previous example.

$$52.5 - (1.5)9 = 39$$
$$61.5 + (1.5)9 = 75$$

There are no outliers.

For Example 3

The stem-and-leaf plot below represents Nancy's average bowling score for each week of the winter bowling league. Find the interquartile range of the scores and find any possible outliers.

Stem	Leaf
12	5
13	7 8 8
14	0 2 2 4 8 9
15	1 3 3 4 7 8
16	2 5 6 6 7
17	0 1 2 2 2 9
18	5 6 6
19	0 2
20	9

18 | 5 = 185

lower quartile: 146
upper quartile: 172
interquartile range: 26
146 − (1.5)(26) = 107
172 + (1.5)(26) = 211
There are no outliers.

Teaching Tip ❶

Another commonly used measure of variation is called the **interquartile range.** The interquartile range is the difference between the upper and lower **quartiles.** Quartiles are the values in a set of data that separate the data into four equal parts. The median is one of the quartiles. It separates the data into two equal parts. The remaining two quartiles are the medians of two parts into which the median separates a set of data. The quartile that is less than the median is called the **lower quartile** (LQ) and the quartile that is greater than the median is called the **upper quartile** (UQ).

Example 1

Find the interquartile range of the record low temperatures of the United States.

First, place the temperatures in ascending order.

−80 −70 −63 −60 −60 −60 −59 −58 −54 −54 −52 −51 −50 −50 −50 −50
−48 −48 −47 −47 −46 −45 −42 −40 −40 −40 −40 −39 −37 −35 −35 −34
−34 −34 −32 −32 −29 −29 −29 −27 −27 −23 −23 −20 −19 −17 −17 −16
−2 14

The median is the value halfway between the 25th value, −40, and the 26th value, which is also −40. So the median is −40°.

The median separates the set of data into two sets that each contain 25 values. The median itself is not in either of these sets. The 13th value in each of these sets will be the quartile. The 13th value of the set that is below the median is −50, and the 13th value of the set that is above the median is −29°.

The lower quartile is −50 and the upper quartile is −29. So the interquartile range is −29 − (−50) or 21°.

Notice that the interquartile range in Example 1 is very small as compared to the range of the entire set of data. Since the interquartile range represents the range in which 50% of the data fall, this means that the data are clustered closely around the median of the set. Since most of the data are close to the median, values like −80° and 14° seem rather extreme. Very extreme values are called **outliers.**

Teaching Tip ❷

Definition of Outlier | **An outlier is any value in a set of data that is at least 1.5 interquartile ranges beyond the upper or lower quartile.**

Example 2

Find any outliers in the record low temperatures.

The interquartile range of the record low temperatures is 21°. Find the values that are 1.5 interquartile ranges beyond the upper and lower quartiles. The upper quartile is −29 and the lower quartile is −50.

$$-29 + 1.5(21) = 2.5° \qquad -50 - 1.5(21) = -81.5°$$

Any record low temperature that is above 2.5° or below −81.5° is an outlier. So, the only outlier is 14°, the record low for Hawaii.

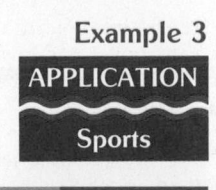

Example 3

APPLICATION

Sports

FYI · · ·

The fastest time for the Kentucky Derby, 119.4 seconds, was run by Secretariat in 1973.

The stem-and-leaf plot below represents the winning times at the Kentucky Derby from 1965 to 1990. Find the interquartile range of the times and determine if there are any outliers.

There are 26 leaves in this plot. The median is between the 13th and 14th times. Thus, the lower quartile is the 7th time, 121.8, and the upper quartile is the 21st time, 122.4.

Stem	Leaf
119	4
120	2 6
121	2 2 6 8 8 9
122	0 0 0 0 0 2 2 2 4 4 4 4 8
123	2 4 4
124	0

120 | 6 represents a time of 120.6.

The interquartile range is 122.4 − 121.8 or 0.6 seconds.

$$122.4 + 1.5(0.6) = 123.3 \qquad 121.8 - 1.5(0.6) = 120.9$$

Any time above 123.3 or below 120.9 is an outlier. So, 123.4, 123.4, 124.0, 120.2, 120.6, and 119.4 are outliers.

Teaching Tip ❷ Emphasize that while the range can be greatly affected by extreme values, the interquartile range usually is not.

EVALUATING THE LESSON

Checking for Understanding

Exercises 1–14 are designed to help you assess understanding through reading, writing, and speaking. You should work through Exercises 1–4 with your students, and then monitor their work on Exercises 5–14.

CHECKING FOR UNDERSTANDING

Communicating Mathematics

Read and study the lesson to answer these questions.

1. What is the range of the record low temperatures for the United States? **94°**

2. Which has the greater variation, the record high temperatures or the record low temperatures? **record low temperatures**

3. In your own words, describe an outlier. **See students' work.**

4. Give an example of a set of data that is greatly varied and a set that is not greatly varied. **See students' work.**

Guided Practice

Find the range for each set of data.

5. {250, 275, 325, 300, 200, 225, 175} **150**

6. {48, 36, 40, 37, 29, 45, 38, 51, 47, 38} **22**

7. {15, 13, 19, 7, 82, 8, 3, 22, 19, 31, 12, 9} **79**

8.
Stem	Leaf
4	1 3 9
5	2 3 6 9
6	4 4 5
7	2 4 7 **36**

4 | 1 represents 41.

9.
Stem	Leaf
3	0 0 1 2 4
●	5 6 6 6 8 9
4	1 1 3 4 4
●	5 5 6 **16**

3 | 4 represents 34.

10–14. Find the quartiles and the interquartile range for each set of data in Exercises 5–9. **See margin.**

LESSON 14-4   VARIATION: RANGE, INTERQUARTILE RANGE, AND OUTLIERS   655

RETEACHING THE LESSON

Find the range, quartiles, median, interquartile range and outliers for each set of data.
Set 1: Page 645, Exercise 6, Ages of U.S. Presidents on First Inauguration. **27; 51, 58; 55; 7; outlier 69**
Set 2: Page 642, Enrollments of Thirty Small American Colleges **62; 27, 57; 39.5; 30; no outliers**

Additional Answers

10. 200, 250, 300; 100
11. 37, 39, 47; 10
12. 8.5, 14, 20.5; 12
13. 50.5, 59, 68.5; 18
14. 34, 38, 44; 10

Reteaching Masters Booklet, p. 92

NAME _____   DATE _____

14-4 Reteaching Worksheet

Variation: Range, Interquartile Range, and Outliers

The **range** of a set of data is the difference between the greatest and least values in the set. It is affected by unusually extreme values. In such cases, it is not a good measure of variation.

Another commonly used measure of variation is the **interquartile range**. Quartiles are the values in a set of data that separate the data into four equal parts. The median is one of the quartiles. It separates the data into two equal parts. Each of these two sets of data also has a median. These two medians are called the **upper quartile** and **lower quartile**. The difference between the upper and lower quartile is called the *interquartile range*. It represents the middle 50%, or half, of the data. An **outlier** is any value in a set of data that is at least 1.5 interquartile ranges beyond the upper or lower quartiles.

Example: Find the range, quartiles, and interquartile range for {19, 13, 17, 21, 25, 29, 31, 35, 18, 16, 27, 29}.

First place the numbers in ascending order: 13, 16, 17, 18, 19, 21, 25, 27, 29, 29, 31, 35

The range is 35−13 or 22. The median is halfway between the 6th value, 21, and the 7th value, 25. So the median is 23. The median divides the data into two sets, each consisting of six numbers. The median of the lower half is 17.5. So the lower quartile is 17.5. The median of the upper half is 29. So the upper quartile is 29. Therefore, the interquartile range is 29−17.5 or 11.5.

Find the range, quartiles, and interquartile range for each set of data.

1. {12, 23, 34, 45, 56, 67, 78, 89}
   77; 28.5, 50.5, 72.5; 44

2. {135, 246, 357, 468, 579, 680, 713, 935, 824, 257, 385, 405}
   800; 307, 436.5, 696.5; 389.5

3. {62, 47, 59, 30, 21, 34, 21, 62, 62, 84, 21, 93, 62, 84, 93, 21}
   72; 25.5, 60.5, 73; 47.5

4. {23, 46, 49, 57, 51, 82, 49, 47, 54, 58}
   59; 47, 50, 57; 10

5.
Stem	Leaf
4	139
5	2369
6	445
7	247

5|2 represents 52'
   36; 50.5, 59, 68.5; 18

6.
Stem	Leaf
3	0012
●	566689
4	11344
●	56

3|4 represents 34
●|5 represents 35
   16; 33.5, 38, 43.5; 10

Chapter 14   655

656 Chapter 14

Error Analysis

Students may be tempted to divide the number of numbers by 4 to get the place or position of the lower quartile (LQ) and upper quartile (UQ). But LQ and UQ are defined as the medians of the two sets of equal size (order) determined by the median. Demonstrate with sets having 10 or 12 members.

Closing the Lesson

Speaking Activity Have students explain why not all extremes are considered outliers.

Homework Exercises

Assignment Guide

Basic: 15–26, 28–29, 31–36
Average: 17–36
Enriched: 17–36
All: Mid-Chapter Review, 1–7

Practice Masters Booklet, p. 106

EXERCISES

17. 170; 1025, 1075, 1125; 100
18. 45; 64, 73, 85; 21

Practice

Find the range, quartiles, and interquartile range for each set of data.

A

15. {4, 1, 3, 7, 7, 5, 4, 1, 8, 20, 2, 11, 7, 7, 1} **19; 2, 5, 7; 5**

16. {51, 57, 49, 47, 23, 82, 49, 47, 54, 58} **59; 47, 50, 57; 10**

17. {1055, 1075, 1095, 1125, 1005, 975, 1125, 1100, 1145, 1025, 1075}

18. {71, 81, 65, 95, 85, 59, 88, 66, 53, 75, 96, 57, 63, 76, 64, 82, 98, 65}

B

19. Stem | Leaf **See margin.**
    0 | 1 1 8 8 9
    1 | 4 5 5 7 7 7 9
    2 | 1 4 4 5 8 8 8 8 9
    3 | 0 1 3 6 6 7 8
    4 | 4 5 6 9   *2 | 4 represents 240.*

20. Stem | Leaf **See margin.**
    4 | 0
    5 | 7 9
    6 | 0 4 5 6 6 7 8 8
    7 | 0 1 1 2 2 3
    8 | 0 5 9   *5 | 9 represents 5.9.*

C

21–26. Find any outliers in each set of data in Exercises 15–20. **See margin.**

27. The prices of several zoom lenses available for use with a single-lens reflex camera are listed below.

$396 $290 $350 $298 $239 $200 $150 $235 $265 $175
$230 $150 $140 $275 $500 $275 $180 $350 $130 $180

Find the range, quartiles, and interquartile range of the prices. Then identify any outliers. **$370; $177.50, $237, $294; $116.50; $500**

Critical Thinking

28. Give an example of a set of data with a small interquartile range and a large range. Does the set have any outliers? **See students' work.**

Applications

29. **Business** The sales of the 15 largest American businesses are given below. Find the range, quartiles, and interquartile range for the sales figures. Then determine if there are any outliers. **102; 21, 34, 60; 39; 121**

Company	Sales (in billions)	Company	Sales (in billions)
Amoco	21	IBM	60
Chevron	25	Mobil	48
Chrysler	35	Occidental Petroleum	19
Du Pont	33	Philip Morris	26
Exxon	80	Proctor and Gamble	19
Ford Motor	92	Shell Oil	21
General Electric	49	Texaco	34
General Motors	121		

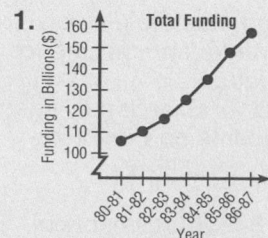

30. **Consumerism** The prices for several bike helmets are given below. Find the range, quartiles, and interquartile range for the prices. Then determine if there are any outliers.

$51 $40 $58 $60 $30 $45 $66
$40 $87 $65 $41 $60 $40 $35
$47 $49 $54 $50 $52 $47 $39
57; 40, 49, 59; 19; none

656 CHAPTER 14 STATISTICS

Additional Answers

19. 480; 160, 265, 345; 185
20. 4.9; 6.45, 6.8, 7.2; 0.75
21. 20
22. 23, 82
23. none
24. none
25. none
26. 4.0, 8.5, 8.9

Additional Answer to Mid-Chapter Review

1.

31. Find the median, mode, and mean of the prices of the bike helmets given in Exercise 30. **(Lesson 14-3)** 49; 40; 50.3

32. 2; 3; 162; 5

32. State the first term, the common ratio, the last term, and the number of terms for the geometric series $2 + 6 + 18 + 54 + 162$. **(Lesson 13-5)**

33. Find the inverse of the function $f(x) = 3x - 4$. **(Lesson 10-8)**

34. Solve $x\sqrt{5} + x = 3$. **(Lesson 6-7)**

$-6a^4b^4 + 12a^5b^3 - 21a^4b^2$

35. Simplify $3a^3b^2(-2ab^2 + 4a^2b - 7a)$. **(Lesson 5-4)**

36. **Business** The Friendly Fix-It Company charges $35 for any in-home repair. In addition, the technician charges $10 an hour after the first half-hour. How much will an in-home repair of t hours cost? **(Lesson 2-5)**

$$c = 10\left(t - \frac{1}{2}\right) + 35$$

33. $f^{-1}(x) = \dfrac{x + 4}{3}$ 34. $\dfrac{3\sqrt{5} - 3}{4}$

MID-CHAPTER REVIEW

Use the data in the table below for Exercises 1–7.

Funding for Public Education 1980 to 1987 (in thousands)

School Year	Federal	State	Local	Total
1980–81	$ 9,768,262	$50,182,659	$45,998,166	$105,949,087
1981–82	8,186,466	52,436,435	49,568,356	110,191,257
1982–83	8,339,990	56,282,157	52,875,354	117,497,502
1983–84	8,576,547	60,232,981	57,245,892	126,055,419
1984–85	9,106,660	67,168,684	61,020,425	137,294,678
1985–86	9,956,009	73,673,174	65,375,698	149,004,882
1986–87	10,145,899	79,022,572	69,659,003	158,827,473

6. $9,105,569,000; no mode; $9,154,106,000

1. Make a line graph of the total funding for public education from 1980 to 1987. **(Lesson 14-1)** **See margin.**

2. Make a bar graph to show the state funding of public education from 1980 to 1987. **(Lesson 14-1)** **See margin.**

3. Make a circle graph to show the sources of funding for public education for the 1985–86 school year. **(Lesson 14-1)** **See margin.**

4. Make a back-to-back stem-and-leaf plot of the rounded and truncated values of local funding for public education from 1980 to 1987. **(Lesson 14-2)** **See margin.**

5. Make a line plot of the values of state funding for public education from 1980 to 1987. **(Lesson 14-3)** **See margin.**

6. Find the median, mode, and mean values of the federal funding for public education from 1980 to 1987. **(Lesson 14-3)**

7. Find the range, quartiles, and interquartile range of the total funding for public education from 1980 to 1987. Then determine if there are any outliers. **(Lesson 14-4)**

$52,878,386,000; $110,191,257,000; $126,055,419,000; $149,004,882,000; $38,813,625,000; none

LESSON 14-4   VARIATION: RANGE, INTERQUARTILE RANGE, AND OUTLIERS   657

EXTENDING THE LESSON

Math Power: Reasoning

Have students set values for quartiles, range, and interquartile range then determine a set of data that would fit these values. Have students present this data in the form of a verbal problem.

Mid-Chapter Review

The Mid-Chapter Review provides students with a brief review of the concepts and skills in Lessons 14–1 through 14–4. Lesson numbers are given at the end of problems or instruction lines so students may review concepts not yet mastered.

Additional Answers

2.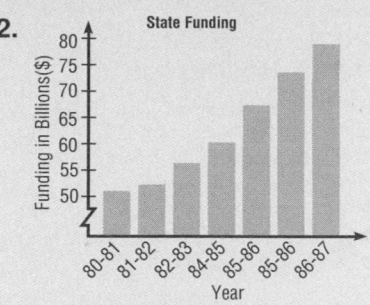

3. Sources of Funding for 1985-1986

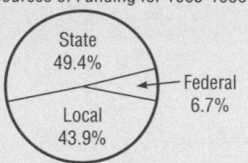

4.

rounded	stem	truncated
6	4	5 9
7 3 0	5	2 7
5 1	6	1 5 9
0	7	

**Using rounded data, 1 | 6 | represents $60,500,000,000 to $61,499,999,000.
Using truncated data, | 6 | 1 represents $61,000,000,000 to $61,999,999,000.**

5.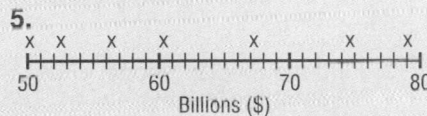

Enrichment Masters Booklet, p. 92

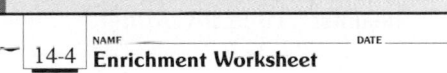

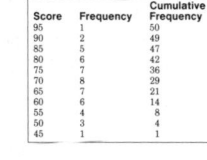

Lesson Resources

Reteaching Masters 14-5
Practice Master 14-5
Enrichment Master 14-5
Technology, p. 14

Transparency 14-5 contains the
5-Minute Check and a teaching aid
for this lesson.

INTRODUCING THE LESSON

 5-Minute Check

(over Lesson 14-4)

1. Find the difference between
   the greatest and least values
   of the set {18, 16, 24, 32, 50, 8,
   6, 19, 4}.　**46**
2. *True* or *False:* The value of the
   mean of a set of data is not
   affected by extreme values.
   false

   The heights, in inches, of
   students in a class are 62, 66, 64,
   65, 70, 66, 69, 63, 69, 68, 72, 70,
   58, 67, 65, 61, 64, 66, 63, 79, and
   59.

3. Find the median, mode, and
   mean of the heights.
   66; 66; 66
4. Find the range and
   interquartile range of the
   heights.　**21; 6**
5. Find any outliers in the
   heights.　**79 is an outlier.**

Motivating the Lesson

Display a set of data in a stem-
and-leaf plot. Ask students what
measures of central tendency and
variation can be easily determined
by the plot. Ask if there is a way
to display data that would readily
show the quartiles.

Objective
14-5

After studying this lesson, you should be able to:
- represent data using box-and-whisker plots.

Numerical data can be represented using a **box-and-whisker plot.** In a box-and-whisker plot, the quartiles and the extreme values of a set of data are displayed using a number line. The nutritional information for some sandwiches sold by leading fast food restaurants are listed below.

Sandwich	Calories per serving	Calories per Ounce	Sandwich	Calories per serving	Calories per Ounce
Arby's Ham and Cheese	380	69.1	Hardee's Big Cheese	495	82.5
Arby's Roast Beef	350	70	Hardee's Big Deluxe	675	75.8
Arby's Super Roast Beef	620	63.6	McDonald's Quarter Pounder	418	73.3
Burger King Hamburger	310	75.8	McDonald's Quarter Pounder with Cheese	518	76.7
Burger King Cheeseburger	360	78.4	McDonald's Big Mac	541	83.3
Burger King Whopper	760	72.8	Roy Roger's Hamburger	425	113.3
Dairy Queen's Hamburger	360	69.2	Roy Roger's Cheeseburger	475	126.7
Dairy Queen's Cheeseburger	410	71.9	Wendy's Hamburger	472	67.4
Friendly's Big Beef Hamburger	420	57.7	Wendy's Cheeseburger	577	68.7
Friendly's Big Beef Cheeseburger	480	61.5	Wendy's Double Hamburger	797	67

To make a box-and-whisker plot of the calories, first arrange the values in ascending order and find the quartiles.

310	350	360	360	380	410	418	420	425	472
475	480	495	518	541	577	620	675	760	797

The median is halfway between the 10th and 11th values.

$$\frac{472 + 475}{2} = 473.5$$

The lower quartile is between the 5th value, 380, and the 6th value, 410. The upper quartile is between the 15th value, 541, and the 16th value, 577.

lower quartile: $\frac{380 + 410}{2} = 395$　　　　upper quartile: $\frac{541 + 577}{2} = 559$

The extreme values are the least value, 310, and the greatest value, 797.

Abbreviations are often used for statistical terms:
LQ: lower quartile
UQ: upper quartile
LV: least value
GV: greatest value

To make the box-and-whisker plot, draw a number line and plot the quartiles, the median, and the extreme values.

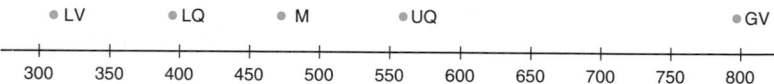

ALTERNATE TEACHING STRATEGIES

Using Charts

Have students use two box-and-whisker
plots to display the charted data from
page 653. You may want to divide the
class into cooperative groups and have
each group plot either the high or low
temperatures.

Using Connections

Have students collect local weather
data on wind speed, temperature, and
air pressure for several days. Display
these in box-and-whisker plots.

Draw a box to designate the interquartile range and mark the median by drawing a segment containing its point in the box. Draw segments (whiskers) connecting the lower quartile to the least value and the upper quartile to the greatest value.

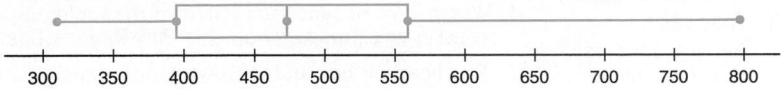

Box-and-whisker plots can be drawn horizontally, as above, or vertically. The plot of the calories of the sandwiches has been drawn vertically at the right. Notice that the box contains 50% of the data and each whisker contains 25% of the data.

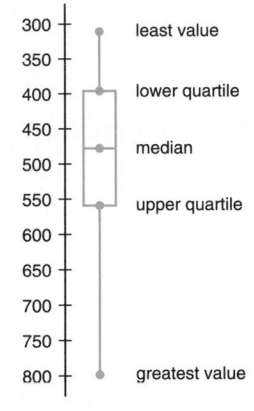

The interquartile range for the calories in the sandwiches was 559 − 395 or 164 calories. Since each calorie count was above 395 − 1.5(164) or 149 calories and below 559 + 1.5(164) or 805 calories, there were no outliers. However, outliers can be displayed on a box-and-whisker plot. Each outlier is represented by a point only, and the whisker is extended only to the last value of the data that is not an outlier.

Example 1

Sports

FYI...

The largest of the major league stadiums is Cleveland Stadium, home of the Cleveland Indians. Fenway Park, home of the Boston Red Sox, is the smallest major league stadium.

The seating capacities of the major league baseball stadiums are listed below. Find any outliers in the data. Then draw a box-and-whisker plot.

34,182	39,600	40,625	43,508	44,087	45,000	49,219	52,003
52,392	52,416	53,000	53,192	54,017	54,224	55,300	55,833
56,000	57,545	58,000	58,150	58,433	58,727	59,149	64,538
64,593	74,483

There are 26 values. The median is halfway between the 13th and 14th values. So the median is $\frac{54017 + 54224}{2}$ or 54,120.5. The lower quartile is the 7th value, 49,219, and the upper quartile is the 20th value, 58,150.

The interquartile range is 58,150 − 49,219 or 8931.
$$49,219 - 1.5(8931) = 35,822.5$$
$$58,150 + 1.5(8931) = 71,546.5$$
The values 34,182 and 74,483 are outliers.

Draw a number line and plot the quartiles and outliers. Also plot 39,600 and 64,593, since these are the last data values that are not outliers. Extend the whiskers to these points and leave the outliers as single points.

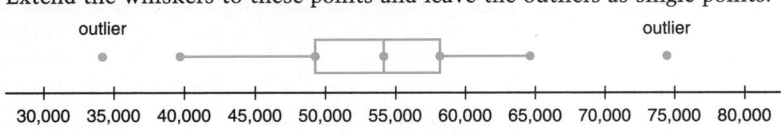

LESSON 14-5 BOX-AND-WHISKER PLOTS 659

Teaching Tip ❶ Point out that the length of each whisker and the length of the box indicates a range of values in the data and not the number of values.

Chalkboard Example

For Example 1
The stem-and-leaf plot below represents the scores on a 100-point test in Mr. Porter's science class. Find any outliers in the scores. Then draw a box-and-whisker plot of the scores.

Stem	Leaf
10	0
9	
8	0 0 2 3 3
7	1 1 2 4 7 7 8
6	0 1 3 3 6 8 9
5	2 7
4	5
3	1

4 | 5 = 45

median: 71
lower quartile: 62
upper quartile: 79
interquartile range: 17
79 + 1.5(17) = 104.5
62 − 1.5(17) = 36.5
outlier: 31
greatest value: 100
least value not an outlier: 45

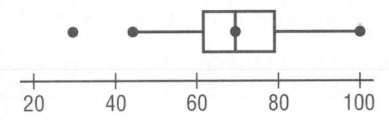

Checking for Understanding

Exercises 1–7 are designed to help you assess understanding through reading, writing, and speaking. You should work through Exercises 1–4 with your students, and then monitor their work on Exercises 5–7.

Closing the Lesson

Writing Activity Have students write a paragraph describing the data that is represented by a box-and-whisker plot in which the box is very short and the left whisker is longer than the right whisker.

APPLYING THE LESSON

Homework Exercises

Assignment Guide

Basic: 8–12, 14–15, 17–21
Average: 9–21
Enriched: 10–21

Chapter 14, Quiz C, (Lessons 14-4 through 14-5), is available in the Evaluation Masters Booklet, p. 192.

Reteaching Masters Booklet, p. 93

CHECKING FOR UNDERSTANDING

Communicating Mathematics
2. 25% each
3. Sample answers: quartiles, range, outliers, dispersion

Read and study the lesson to answer these questions.

1. Which type of sandwich listed in the table on page 658 had the highest number of calories per ounce? **Roy Roger's Cheeseburger**

2. The box in a box-and-whisker plot is separated by a line indicating the median. What portion of the data is represented by each part of the box?

3. What can you tell about a set of data from a box-and-whisker plot?

4. If the box of a box plot was very long, what could you tell about the set of data? **It is greatly dispersed.**

Guided Practice

5. Use box-and-whisker plot I to answer each question.

    I.

   a. What is the range of the data? **20**
   b. What is the median of the data? **26**
   c. What percent of the data is greater than 28? **25%**
   d. Between what two values of the data is the middle 50% of the data? **21 and 28**

6. Use box-and-whisker plot II to answer each question. **a. 50% b. 75%**

    II.

   a. What percent of the data is less than 76?
   b. What percent of the data is less than 92?
   c. What percent of the data is greater than 64 and less than 92? **50%**
   d. Under what conditions would a set of data have this type of box-and-whisker plot? **See margin.**

7. Use box-and-whisker plot III to answer each question.

    III.

   a. What is the range of the data? **210**
   670, 700 b. What values of the data are outliers?
   c. What percent of the data is greater than 560? **50%**
   d. What percent of the data is less than 580? **75%**

EXERCISES

Practice
A

8. The number of calories in a regular serving of french fries at different restaurants are listed below. Make a box-and-whisker plot of the data. **See margin.**

Restaurant	Calories	Restaurant	Calories
Burger Chef	250	Hardee's	239
Burger King	240	McDonald's	211
Carl's Jr.	220	Roy Rogers	240
Dairy Queen	200	Wendy's	327
Friendly's	125		

RETEACHING THE LESSON

Make a box-and-whisker plot for each set of data from the indicated exercises. Students should use their results when they originally worked the exercises.

1. Page 655, Exercise 6
2. Page 655, Exercise 15
3. Page 656, Exercise 18
4. Page 656, Exercise 20

See students' work.

Additional Answer

6d. The least value and the lower quartile are the same number.

9. Make a box-and-whisker plot of the calories per ounce of the sandwiches listed on page 658. **See margin.**

See margin.

10. The number of medals won by the top 16 countries at the 1992 Summer Olympics are given below. Make a box-and-whisker plot of the data.

Country	Number of Medals	Country	Number of Medals
Unified Team	112	Australia	27
United States	108	Spain	22
Germany	82	Japan	22
China	54	Britain	20
Cuba	31	Italy	19
Hungary	30	Poland	19
South Korea	29	Canada	18
France	29	Romania	18

See margin.

11. The amount of sodium, in milligrams, per serving of certain brands of peanut butter is given below. Make a box-and-whisker plot of the data.

195 210 180 225 255 225 195 225 203 225 195 195 188 191
210 233 225 248 225 210 240 180 225 240 180 225 240 240
195 189 178 255 225 225 225 194 210 225 195 188 205

12. Juanita's bowling scores for each week of her summer bowling league are given below.

153 167 154 172 167 166 201 158 166 134 163 167 188
187 144 154 176 170 129 139 190 221 165 160 171 170
149 168 197 161 166 165 169 200 204 151 178 161 162

a. Make a box-and-whisker plot of the data. **See margin.**

b. Make a stem-and-leaf plot of the same data. **See margin.**

c. Find the mode and median using the stem-and-leaf plot. How do these averages compare with the information from your box-and-whisker plot? **The medians should be the same. You cannot find a mode comparison.**

13. The table below shows the median ages of men and women at the time of their first marriage for the decades of 1890 through 1990.

Year	Men	Women	Year	Men	Women
1890	26.1	22.0	1950	22.8	20.3
1900	25.9	21.9	1960	22.8	20.3
1910	25.1	21.6	1970	23.2	20.8
1920	24.6	21.2	1980	24.7	22.0
1930	24.3	21.3	1990	26.2	25.1
1940	24.3	21.5			

a. Make a box-and-whisker plot for the men's and women's ages.

b. Compare the two plots. **a–b. See margin.**

c. Write a paragraph analyzing the trend suggested by the data. Include any reasons you might think exist for this trend. **See students' work.**

LESSON 14-5 BOX-AND-WHISKER PLOTS 661

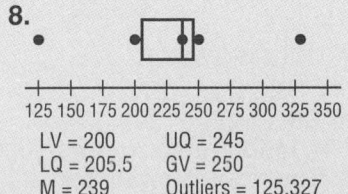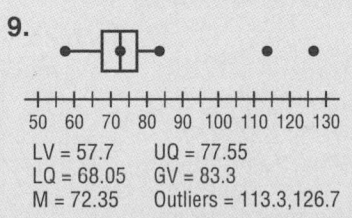
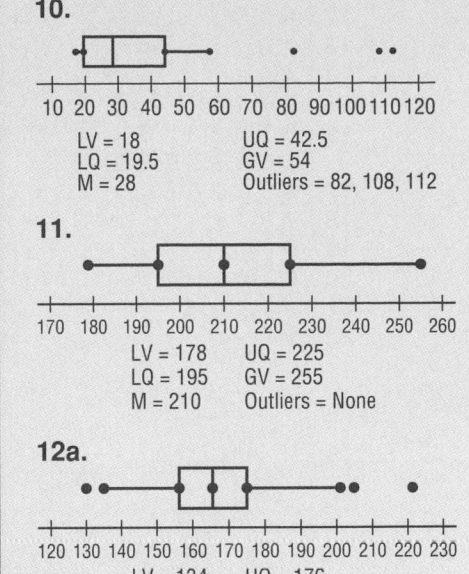
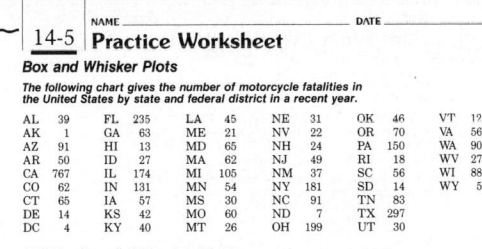
Chapter 14 661

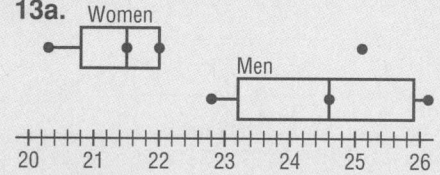
Critical Thinking   14. Describe a set of data for which the box-and-whisker plot has no
whiskers. **See margin.**

Applications   15. **Consumerism**   The prices of 14 video cameras are listed below. Make a
box-and-whisker plot of the prices. **See margin.**
$877 $819 $1100 $1450 $812 $973 $1399
$890 $1409 $949 $900 $775 $1299 $1399

16. **Sports**   The number of touchdown passes made by the top 20
quarterbacks in the National Football League through the 1991 season
are shown in the table below. Make a box-and-whisker plot of the
data. **See margin.**

Player	Passes	Player	Passes
Fran Tarkenton	342	John Brodie	214
Johnny Unitas	290	Terry Bradshaw	212
Dan Marino	266	Jim Hart	209
Sonny Jergensen	255	Roman Gabriel	201
Dan Fouts	254	Ken Anderson	197
John Hadl	244	Norm Snead	196
Joe Montana	242	Bobby Layne	196
Y. A. Tittle	242	Joe Ferguson	196
Len Dawson	239	Dave Krieg	195
George Blanda	236	Ken Stabler	194

Mixed Review   17. Use the information in the table for Exercise 16 to find the range,
quartiles, and interquartile range of the number of passes for
touchdowns made by the top 20 quarterbacks. Identify any
outliers.   **(Lesson 14-4) 152; 196, 210.5, 243; 47; 290 and 342**

18. Write the expression $\sum_{n=0}^{5} 4^{n-2}$ in expanded form and find the sum.

(Lesson 13-5) $\frac{1}{16} + \frac{1}{4} + 1 + 4 + 16 + 64; 85\frac{5}{16}$

19. Solve $\log_{10}(y - 1) + \log_{10}(y + 2) = \log_7 7$.   **(Lesson 12-3) 3**

20. Simplify $\frac{x^2 - y^2}{x} \div \frac{y - x}{x^2}$.   **(Lesson 11-3)** $-x^2 - xy$

21. Find the center and radius of the circle whose equation is $(x + 8)^2 + (y - 3)^2 = 25$. Then draw the graph.   **(Lesson 9-3)**
(−8, 3); 5; See Solutions Manual for graph.

CHALLENGE

Sequence A and Sequence B are both arithmetic
sequences that have infinitely many terms in common.
Find three of these common terms. **50, 134, 218**

A = 2, 14, 26, . . .   B = 1, 8, 15, . . .

EXTENDING THE LESSON

Math Power: Connections

Have students do research to find
the number of members of the
United States House of Representatives from each state. Have students determine the mean, mode,
quartiles, range, interquartile
range, and any outliers of this
data and display the data using a
box-and-whisker plot.

Additional Answers

15. **LV = 775, LQ = 877,
M = 961, UQ = 1399,
GV = 1450, outliers: none;
See Solutions Manual for
plot.**
16. **LV = 194, LQ = 196.5,
M = 225, UQ = 249,
GV = 290, outlier: 342; See
Solutions Manual for plot.**

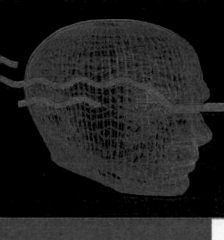

Technology
Statistical Graphs

BASIC
Spreadsheets
▶ Software

The table below shows the 1990 populations (in millions) of the ten largest cities in the world and the predicted populations for the year 2000.

City	Tokyo	Mexico City	Sao Paulo	Seoul	New York	Osaka	Bombay	Calcutta	Buenos Aires	Rio de Janeiro
1990	27.0	20.2	18.1	16.3	14.6	13.8	11.8	11.7	11.5	11.4
2000	30.0	27.9	25.4	22.0	14.6	14.3	15.4	14.1	12.9	14.2

There are many ways this data could be displayed. *Data Insights* software provides a quick way to display this data using your computer. You must first enter each group of data in a column shown on the screen. Then return to the main menu. The PLOT option allows you to select what type of display you wish to use. It also allows you to customize your graph with headings and your choice of numerical increments for the axes.

Four types of displays available are line plot, histogram, stem-and-leaf plot, and box plot (box-and-whisker plot). All of these, except the line plot, allow you to graph more than one set of data. When graphing box plots, you may also choose vertical or horizontal displays.

The graphs below are a histogram and a vertical box plot of the data in the table. *Data #1* are the 1990 figures, and *Data#2* are the 2000 figures.

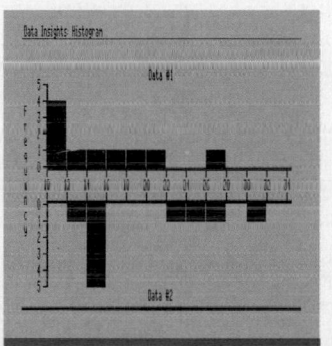
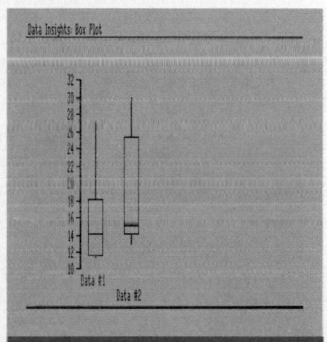

EXERCISES

Use the Data Insights software and the data from the table above to create each of the following graphs. **See margin.**

1. line plot of Data #1.
2. line plot of Data #2
3. horizontal box plot of both sets of data
4. stem-and-leaf plot of both sets of data

Additional Answers

1.
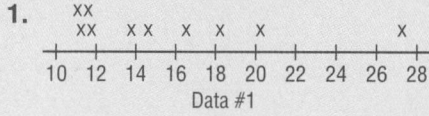
Data #1

2.
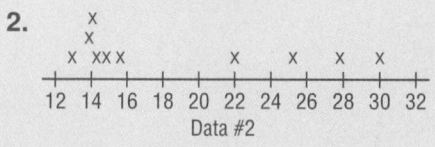
Data #2

3.
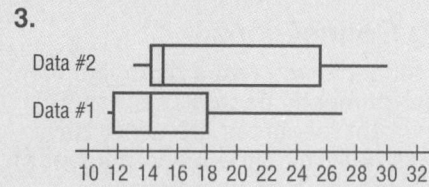

Using Technology
Objective This optional page shows how graphing software can be used to perform mathematical computations and to enhance and extend mathematical concepts.

Teaching Suggestions
Data Insights from Sunburst Communications software offers students a variety of ways to explore the same set of data. Students are required to enter the data in columns, much as they would with a spreadsheet. From that point on, they need only work from a menu to determine what type of graph they wish to examine. The PRINT feature allows them to print their graphs on paper. The software's STATISTICS option also calculates the other statistical measures presented in this chapter.

Additional Answer

1.

Data #2	Stem	Data #1
	11	4578
9	12	
	13	8
0321	14	6
4	15	
	16	3
	17	
	18	1
	19	
	20	2
	21	
0	22	
	23	
	24	
4	25	
	26	
9	27	0
	28	
	29	
0	30	30|0 = 30.0

14-6 Variation: Standard Deviation

Lesson Resources

Reteaching Master 14-6
Practice Master 14-6
Enrichment Master 14-6

 Transparency 14-6 contains the 5-Minute Check and a teaching aid for this lesson.

INTRODUCING THE LESSON

 5-Minute Check

(over Lesson 14-5)

Use the box-and-whisker plot to answer Exercises 1–5.

1. What is the range of the data? **36**
2. What is the median of the data? **90**
3. What is the interquartile range of the data? **16**

Other Prerequisite Skills

4. Find the median of the set {10, 8, 24, 32, 50, 8, 8}. **10**
5. Find the interquartile range of the set {10, 8, 24, 32, 50, 8, 8}. **24**

Motivating the Lesson

Draw or post a bull's-eye target on the chalkboard. Blindfold several student volunteers. One at a time, have each of these students make a mark where he or she thinks the bull's-eye is located. Elicit student responses regarding the variance of the marks from the bull's-eye. Ask if the location of the other rings gives us a reference for determining variance.

Objective 14-6

After studying this lesson, you should be able to:
- find the standard deviation for a set of data.

Standard deviation is the most commonly used measure of variation. It is used more often than the other measures of variation we discussed in Lesson 14-4, since it is closely tied to the normal distribution, which you will study in Lesson 14-7. Standard deviation is the average measure of how much each value in a set of data differs from the mean. Standard deviation is often symbolized by SD or the lower case Greek sigma, σ.

Definition of Standard Deviation

From a set of data with n values, if x_i represents a value such that i and n are positive integers and $1 \le i \le n$, and $\bar{x}$ represents the mean, then the standard deviation can be found as follows.

$$SD = \sqrt{\frac{\sum_{i=1}^{n}(x_i - \bar{x})^2}{n}}$$

To find the standard deviation of a set of data, follow these steps.

1. Find the mean.
2. Find the difference between each value in the set of data and the mean.
3. Square each difference.
4. Find the mean of the squares.
5. Take the principal square root of this mean.

Example 1

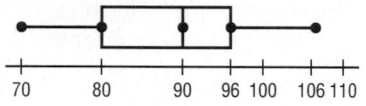
APPLICATION

Horticulture

Ramon is studying the effects of different fertilizers on tree growth. The trees he planted last year are now 49 cm, 54 cm, 61 cm, 49 cm, 54 cm, 51 cm, 56 cm, and 58 cm tall. Find the standard deviation of the heights.

First find the mean height of the trees.

$$\text{mean height} = \frac{49 + 54 + 61 + 49 + 54 + 51 + 56 + 58}{8} \text{ or } 54 \text{ cm} \quad \text{Thus, } \bar{x} = 54.$$

Then find the standard deviation.

$$SD = \sqrt{\frac{\sum_{i=1}^{n}(x_i - \bar{x})^2}{n}} = \sqrt{\frac{(-5)^2 + (0)^2 + (7)^2 + (-5)^2 + (0)^2 + (-3)^2 + (2)^2 + (4)^2}{8}}$$

$$= \sqrt{\frac{25 + 0 + 49 + 25 + 0 + 9 + 4 + 16}{8}}$$

$$= \sqrt{\frac{128}{8}} = \sqrt{16} \text{ or } 4 \quad \text{The standard deviation is 4 cm.}$$

ALTERNATE TEACHING STRATEGIES

Using Connections

Have students use research to find the number of moons each planet has. Be sure current resources are used. Have students determine the mean number of moons and the standard deviation.

Example 2

APPLICATION

Entertainment

The rental revenues for the top 16 videos of 1991 are given below. Use your calculator to find the standard deviation of the revenues.

Title	Revenue (in millions)	Title	Revenue (in millions)
The Addams Family	$55	Hot Shots!	$33
Backdraft	40	The Naked Gun 2½	44
Beauty and the Beast	39	Robin Hood: Prince of Thieves	86
Cape Fear	32	The Silence of the Lambs	60
City Slickers	61	Sleeping with the Enemy	46
Dances with Wolves	53	Star Trek VI: The Undiscovered Country	32
Home Alone	60	Teenage Mutant Ninja Turtles II	42
Hook	40	Terminator 2	112

You can use a calculator to perform the arithmetic needed to find the standard deviation. However, your calculator may have a statistics mode that simplifies this calculation. Press MODE and STAT to put your calculator in statistics mode. *The statistics functions are often second key functions.*

Enter the data by entering each number and then pressing the Σ+ key.

ENTER: 55 Σ+ 40 Σ+ 39 Σ+ . . . 112 Σ+   *Wrong entries can be deleted by using Σ−.*

Pressing n tells you how many entries you have.

To find the standard deviation, press σn .   `20.60406134`

The standard deviation is about $20 million dollars.

It is very important to keep the mean of a set in mind when studying the standard deviation of a set of data. For example, suppose that a company that sells video equipment found that the standard deviation of monthly prices for their equipment sold in the last two years was $50. If the mean of the prices over the last two years was $200, then the standard deviation indicates a great deal of variation. If the mean of the prices was $800, then the standard deviation indicates very little variation.

CHECKING FOR UNDERSTANDING

Communicating Mathematics

Read and study the lesson to answer these questions.

1. In your own words, explain standard deviation. **See students' work.**

2. A recent survey shows that the mean number of full-time employees in law enforcement in large cities is 2881 with a standard deviation of 515. What does the standard deviation say about the variation within the number of employees in the cities? **vary greatly**

RETEACHING THE LESSON

Find the mean and standard deviation for the set of data on page 645, Ages of U.S. Presidents on First Inauguration.
mean = 55
standard deviation = 6.15

TEACHING THE LESSON

Chalkboard Examples

For Example 1
Find the standard deviation for {200, 476, 721, 579, 152, 158}
≈223

For Example 2
The winning average speeds, in miles per hour, of the Daytona 500 from 1975 to 1988 are 154, 152, 153, 160, 144, 178, 170, 154, 156, 151, 172, 148, 177, and 138. Find the mean and the standard deviation.
mean = 157.64
standard deviation = 11.79

Reteaching Masters Booklet, p. 94

NAME _____ DATE _____

14-6 Reteaching Worksheet

Variation: Standard Deviation

The most commonly used measure of variation is called the **standard deviation.** The standard deviation for a set of data is an average measure of how much each value differs from the mean.

Definition of Standard Deviation

From a set of data within values, if x_i represents a value such that $1 \le i \le n$, and x represents the mean, then the standard deviation can be found as follows.

$$\text{standard deviation} = \sqrt{\frac{\sum_{i=1}^{n} (x_i - \bar{x})^2}{n}}$$

Example: Find the standard deviation for {2, 2, 4, 6, 8, 14}.

$$\bar{x} = \frac{2 + 2 + 4 + 6 + 8 + 14}{6} = 6 \qquad \text{Find the mean.}$$

$$\text{standard deviation} = \sqrt{\frac{\sum_{i=1}^{6} (x_i - \bar{x})^2}{6}} \qquad \begin{array}{l}\text{Apply the definition}\\\text{of standard deviation.}\end{array}$$

$$= \sqrt{\frac{(-4)^2 + (-4)^2 + (-2)^2 + (0)^2 + (2)^2 + (8)^2}{6}} \qquad \begin{array}{l}\text{Write the}\\\text{expression.}\end{array}$$

$$= \sqrt{\frac{16 + 16 + 4 + 0 + 4 + 64}{6}}$$

$$= \sqrt{17.33} \text{ or about } 4.2$$

The standard deviation is 4.2.

Find the standard deviation for each set of data.

1. {3, 5, 6, 7, 9, 11, 22}
   5.8

2. {6, 8, 9, 11, 12, 28, 34, 36}
   11.7

The average points scored per basketball game in the Eastern Conference and Western Conference of the National Basketball League are listed below.

| Eastern Conference | 114 | 107 | 103 | 104 | 104 | 105 | 109 |
| | 99 | 109 | 111 | 109 | 103 | 104 | 103 |

| Western Conference | 105 | 106 | 107 | 100 | 106 | 99 | 121 |
| | 116 | 107 | 114 | 118 | 107 | 104 | 102 |

3. Find the standard deviation of average points scored for the Eastern Conference.
   3.8

4. Find the standard deviation of average points scored for the Western Conference.
   6.5

5. Find the standard deviation for the average points scored for the entire National Basketball League.
   5.4

3. do not vary greatly

3. If the mean number of full-time employees in law enforcement in large cities had been 2881 with a standard deviation of 50, what would you say about the variation of the number of employees in the cities?

4. Use the information in Example 2 to find the standard deviation of the rental revenues of the top 10 videos for 1991. Do these revenues vary more or less than the revenues of the top 16?
10.2; These vary less.

Guided Practice

Find the mean and the standard deviation for each set of data.

Teaching Tip

5. {11, 7, 2, 4, 1} **5; 3.6**
6. {4, 6, 14, 8, 2, 2} **6; 4.2**
7. {300, 200, 225, 175, 325, 275, 250} **250; 50**
8. {29, 45, 38, 51, 47, 39, 37, 40, 36, 48} **41; 6.3**
9. {81, 95, 79, 85, 82, 90, 63, 84, 84, 85, 80, 72, 82, 85, 86} **82.2; 7.1**

EXERCISES

Practice

Find the standard deviation for each set of data.

10. {5, 7, 3, 4, 2, 4, 4, 4, 4, 5, 4, 3, 4, 3, 4} **1.1**
11. {1145, 1100, 1125, 1050, 1175, 835, 1075, 1095} **97.9**

12. Stem | Leaf **0.55**
3 | 0 0 1 2 4
● | 5 6 6 6 8 9
4 | 1 1 3 4 4
● | 5 5 6 7

3 | 4 *represents 3.4.*

13. Stem | Leaf **10.6**
4 | 1 3 9
5 | 2 3 6 9
6 | 4 4 5 7 8
7 | 2 4 7

5 | 2 *represents 52.*

14. The weights in pounds of the starting players for three area high schools' football teams are given below.

West High: 160, 180, 190, 200, 210, 170, 250, 220, 180, 200, 240
Ridgemont: 160, 190, 210, 230, 240, 220, 150, 190, 210, 160, 240
Grandview: 250, 170, 205, 220, 185, 215, 205, 210, 205, 185, 170

a. Find the standard deviation for the weights of the players on the West High team. **27**

b. Find the standard deviation for the weights of the players on the Ridgemont team. **31**

c. Find the standard deviation for the weights of the players on the Grandview team. **22**

d. Which of the teams has the most variation in weights? **Ridgemont**

15. Corporate Car Leasing leases cars to companies for use by employees. The mileages (miles per gallon) for the cars leased to three of their customers are listed below.

Parcels To Go: 22, 14, 33, 11, 25, 11, 22, 14, 36, 35, 28, 20, 36, 15, 21, 12, 22, 10

Selby Sales: 32, 16, 22, 24, 23, 13, 23, 31, 15, 21, 24, 27, 30, 21, 12, 24

T.C. Industries: 23, 28, 16, 30, 12, 22, 11, 33, 25, 28, 21, 25, 16, 30, 12, 29, 18, 24, 13, 25

    a. Find the standard deviation for the mileages for Parcels To Go. **8.8**

    b. Find the standard deviation for the mileages for Selby Sales. **5.9**

    c. Find the standard deviation for the mileages for T.C. Industries. **6.7**

    d. Which of the companies had the least variation in mileages? **Selby Sales**

16. The average points scored by the leading scorer in the NBA from 1960 to 1989 are given below. Make a stem-and-leaf plot of the data. Then find the mode, mean, quartiles, interquartile range, standard deviation, and any outliers in the data. **See margin.**

    37.9 38.4 50.4 44.8 36.5 34.7 33.5 35.6 27.1 28.4
    31.2 31.7 34.8 34.0 30.6 34.5 31.1 31.1 27.2 29.6
    33.1 30.7 32.3 28.4 30.6 32.9 30.3 37.1 35.0 32.5

Critical Thinking

17. Under what circumstances would the standard deviation of a set of data equal zero? **When all the data are equal**

Applications

18. **Business** The hourly wages of eight employees of the Sequoia Insurance Company are $4.45, $5.50, $5.50, $6.30, $7.80, $11.00, $12.20, and $17.20. Find the mean and the standard deviation of the wages of these employees. **$8.74; $4.11**

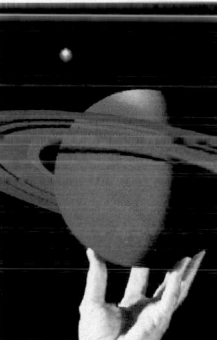

19. **Astronomy** An astronomer made ten measurements of the angular distance between two stars. The measurements were 11.20°, 11.17°, 10.92°, 11.06°, 11.19°, 10.97°, 11.09°, 11.05°, 11.22°, and 11.03°. Find the mean and the standard deviation of the measurements of the distance between the two stars. **11.09°; 0.097°**

Mixed Review

20. Solve $2.7^x = 52.3$ using logarithms.   (Lesson 12-7) **3.9839**

21. Find all rational zeros of the function $f(x) = x^4 - 6x^3 - 3x^2 - 24x - 28$. (Lesson 10-5) **7, -1**

22. Solve $x^2 - 7x - 8 \leq 0$.   (Lesson 8-7) **$\{x \mid -1 \leq x \leq 8\}$**

23. **Geometry** Find the length and width of a rectangle if its perimeter is 44 units and its area is 117 square units.   (Lesson 7-4) **9 by 13 units**

EXTENDING THE LESSON

Math Power:
Communication

Have students research standard deviation and use of quality control in production of consumer products. Have them write a short report including several common examples. For example, steel used for a specific purpose should contain a certain amount of carbon. Samples with carbon contents that vary more than a speci- fied standard deviation are rejected.

Additional Answer

16.

Stem	Leaf
27	1 2
28	4 4
29	6
30	3 6 6 7
31	1 1 2 7
32	3 5 9
33	1 5
34	0 5 7 8
35	0 6
36	5
37	1 9
38	4
39	
40	
41	
42	
43	
44	8
45	
46	
47	
48	
49	
50	4

36 | 5 represents 36.5 points.

28.4, 30.6, 31.1; 33.53; 30.6, 32.7, 35.0; 4.4; 4.8; 44.8, 50.4

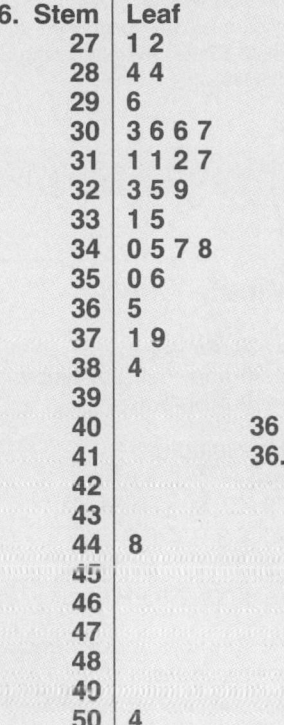

NAME _____   DATE _____

14-6 **Enrichment Worksheet**

Correlation

There is a useful number, called the **correlation coefficient,** that gives a measure of how well a group of data items is clustered around a line. If the values of y are almost in direct proportion to the values of x, then the data points in a graph will cluster around a line and the correlation coefficient, r, will be close to 1. If the values of y are inversely proportional to x and closely bunched around a line, the correlation coefficient r will be close to -1. If there is no close correlation, $r = 0$.

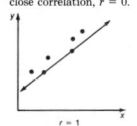 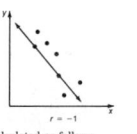 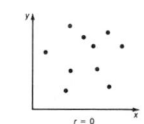

$r = 1$ $r = -1$ $r = 0$

The correlation coefficient is calculated as follows.

$$r = \frac{S_{xy}}{\sqrt{S_{xx} \cdot S_{yy}}}$$

$$S_{xx} = \Sigma x^2 - \frac{(\Sigma x)^2}{n}$$

$$S_{yy} = \Sigma y^2 - \frac{(\Sigma y)^2}{n}$$

$$S_{xy} = \Sigma xy - \frac{\Sigma x \Sigma y}{n}$$

Note: Σx^2 is shorthand for $\sum_{i=1}^{n} x_i^2$

Use the formula to find the correlation coefficient for the following students scores in math and English.

1.

Student	Math (x)	English (y)
1	82	79
2	53	50
3	61	87
4	74	96
5	51	73
6	51	73

0.572

2.

Student	Math (x)	English (y)
1	92	70
2	86	80
3	43	40
4	60	72
5	75	60
6	80	92

0.703

INTRODUCING THE LESSON

 5-Minute Check

(over Lesson 14-6)

Use the stem-and-leaf plot below to solve each problem.

Monthly Precipitation

Stem	Leaf
2	6 8
3	0 0 1 3 3 4 6 8
4	2 2

2 | 8 represents 2.8 inches.

1. Find the median, mode, and mean of the data.
   median: 3.3
   mode: 3.0, 3.3, 4.2
   mean: about 3.4
2. Determine the upper quartile and the lower quartile.
   UQ: 3.7   LQ: 3.0
3. Find the range and interquartile range of the data. **range: 1.6**
   interquartile range: 0.7
4. Determine if any value in the data is an outlier. **none**
5. Find the standard deviation of the data. **about 0.49**

Motivating the Lesson

Ask students if they have ever had a teacher who graded "on the curve". Ask if students know how the teacher knew how many students got each grade.

Objective
14-7

After studying this lesson, you should be able to:

■ solve problems involving normally distributed data.

Application

FYI ...

The gross national product of a nation is the total value of the goods and services produced in the nation during a specified period of time.

One way of analyzing data is to consider how frequently each value occurs. The table below shows the frequencies of the percentages of their gross national product that different industrialized countries spend on education in a year. The bar graph on the right shows the frequencies of the percentages in the table.

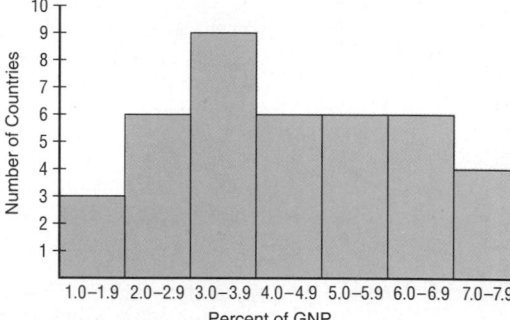

Percent of GNP	Number of Countries
1.0–1.9	3
2.0–2.9	6
3.0–3.9	9
4.0–4.9	6
5.0–5.9	6
6.0–6.9	6
7.0–7.9	4

Teaching Tip ❶

The bar graph shows a **frequency distribution** of the scores. That is, it shows how they are spread out over the range of 1.0% to 7.9%. A bar graph, like this one, that shows a frequency distribution is called a **histogram.**

Curves are often used to show frequency distributions, especially when the distribution contains a large number of values. While the curves may be of any shape, many distributions have graphs shaped like the one at the left. A distribution with this type of graph is called a **normal distribution.**

The curve of the graph of a normal distribution is symmetric and is often called a **bell curve.** The shape of the curve indicates that the frequencies in a normal distribution are concentrated around the center portion of the distribution. What does this tell you about the mean?

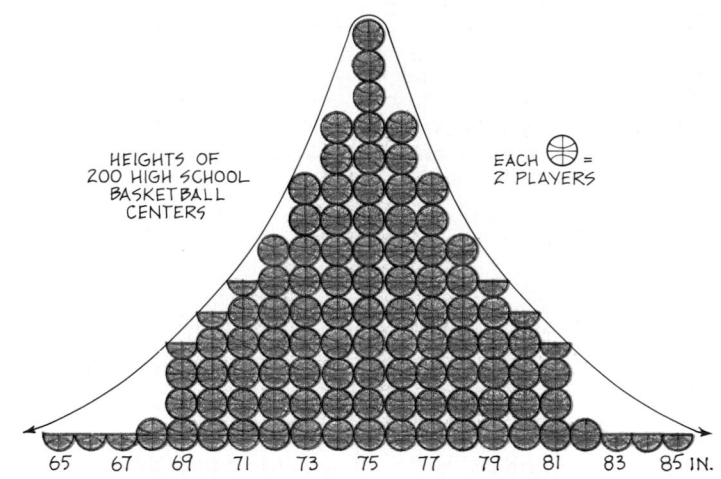

HEIGHTS OF 200 HIGH SCHOOL BASKETBALL CENTERS

EACH ⊕ = 2 PLAYERS

ALTERNATE TEACHING STRATEGIES

Using Cooperative Groups

Have cooperative groups of students draw a normal curve for and solve the following problem.
500 deer were tagged and their heights recorded. If the heights were normally distributed, the mean height was 4.5 feet, and the standard deviation was 0.5 feet, how many deer were taller than 5 feet? **80 deer**

Normal distributions have these properties:

1. The graph is maximized at the mean.
2. About 68% of the values are within one standard deviation from the mean.   *Of the 68%, 34% are greater than the mean and 34% are less.*
3. About 95% of the values are within two standard deviations from the mean.   *Of the 95%, 47.5% are greater than the mean and 47.5% are less.*
4. About 99% of the values are within three standard deviations from the mean.   *Of the 99%, 49.5% are greater than the mean and 49.5% are less.*

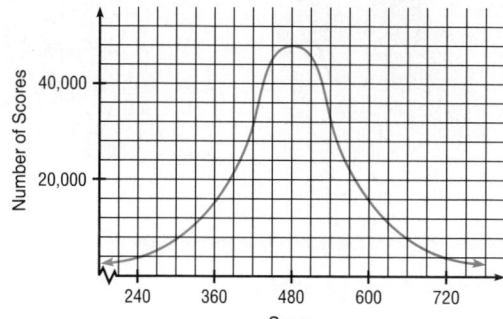

Suppose the scores on the mathematics component of the Scholastic Aptitude Test (SAT) of 1,000,000 students are recorded and the frequency of those scores is normally distributed. If the mean score is 480 and the standard deviation is 90, then the graph at the left approximates the curve for the frequency distribution of the scores.

As shown by the graph, the mean is the most frequent score. Of the 1,000,000 students, about 680,000 scored between 390 and 570 points. About 950,000 students scored between 300 and 660 points. About 990,000 students scored between 210 and 750 points.

Normal distributions occur quite frequently. In addition to test scores, the number of errors made by typists and the lengths of newborn babies can be represented by normal distributions. In all of these cases, the number of data must be sufficiently large for the distribution to be normal.

Example 1

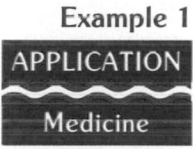
APPLICATION

Medicine

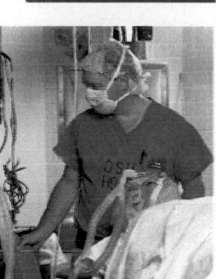

The correct number of milligrams of anesthetic an anesthesiologist must administer to a patient is normally distributed. The mean is 100 milligrams and the standard deviation is 20 milligrams. Of a sample of 200 patients, about how many people require less than 80 milligrams of anesthetic for a response?

This frequency distribution is shown by the following curve. The percentages represent the percentages of patients requiring the dosage within the given interval.

The percentage of people requiring less than 80 milligrams of anesthetic is 0.5% + 2% + 13.5% or 16%.

$200 \times 16\% = 32$

So about 32 of the 200 patients require less than 80 milligrams of anesthetic.

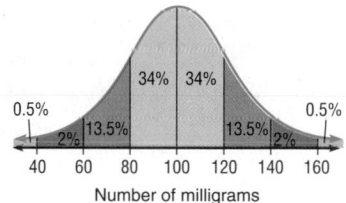

Number of milligrams

LESSON 14-7 THE NORMAL DISTRIBUTION 669

Example 2

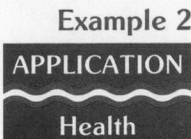

APPLICATION

Health

The lengths of babies born at the hospital in Neenah, Wisconsin in the last year were normally distributed. The mean length was 20.4 inches, and the standard deviation was 0.8 inches. What percentage of babies born in the hospital were born between 18.8 and 21.2 inches long?

Of the babies born at the hospital last year, 68% had lengths between 19.6 and 21.2 inches. Another 13.5% had lengths between 18.8 and 19.6 inches. Therefore, 68% + 13.5% or 81.5% of the babies were between 18.8 and 21.2 inches long.

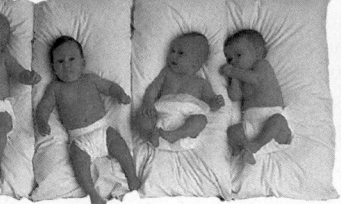
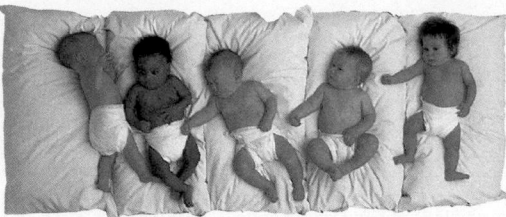
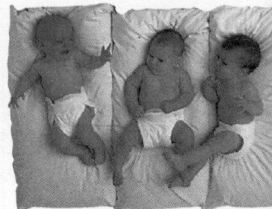

CHECKING FOR UNDERSTANDING

Communicating Mathematics

Read and study the lesson to answer these questions.

1. In your own words, define histogram. **See students' work.**

2. On the graph of the frequencies of percentages of gross national product spent on education, the percentages are graphed on the __?__ axis and the frequencies are graphed on the __?__ axis. *x; y*

3. Where is the concentration of values in a normal distribution? **the center**

4. Recently, Mrs. Sung gave a test in her trigonometry class. The scores were normally distributed with a mean of 85% and a standard deviation of 3%. What percentage of her class would you expect to have scored between 79% and 91% on the test? **95%**

5. A frequency distribution like the one graphed at the right is said to be skewed with a long tail to the right. Describe some situations when you would expect data to be distributed in this way. **See margin.**

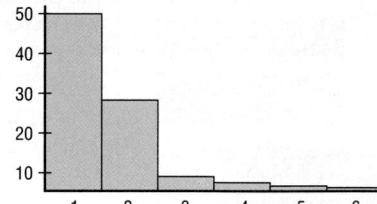

Guided Practice

340

475

495

6. Suppose 500 items are normally distributed.

a. How many items are within one standard deviation from the mean?

b. How many items are within two standard deviations from the mean?

c. How many items are within three standard deviations from the mean?

d. How many items are within one standard deviation less than the mean? **170**

e. How many items are within two standard deviations greater than the mean? **237.5**

EXERCISES

Closing the Lesson

Modeling Activity Have students model verbal problems using a normal curve.

Practice

7. The diameters of metal fittings made by a machine are normally distributed. The mean diameter is 7.5 cm, and the standard deviation is 0.5 cm.

   a. What percentage of the fittings have diameters between 7.0 cm and 8.0 cm? **68%**

   b. What percentage of the fittings have diameters between 7.5 cm and 8.0 cm? **34%**

   c. What percentage of the fittings have diameters greater than 6.5 cm? **97.5%**

   d. Of 100 fittings, how many will have a diameter between 6.0 cm and 8.5 cm? **97**

8. The lifetimes of 10,000 light bulbs are normally distributed. The mean lifetime is 300 days, and the standard deviation is 40 days.

   a. How many light bulbs will last between 260 and 340 days? **6800**

   b. How many light bulbs will last between 220 and 380 days? **9500**

   c. How many light bulbs will last less than 300 days? **5000**

   d. How many light bulbs will last more than 300 days? **5000**

   e. How many light bulbs will last more than 380 days? **250**

   f. How many light bulbs will last less than 180 days? **50**

9. Jalisa and Wes were conducting an experiment in statistics. They asked each student in their mathematics classes to toss a fair coin 100 times and record the number of heads they obtained. They found that the number of heads was almost distributed normally. The mean number of heads was 50 and the standard deviation was 5.

   a. What percentage of the students who tossed the coins obtained less than 50 heads? **50%**

   b. What percentage of the students who tossed the coins obtained between 35 and 45 heads? **15.5%**

   c. What percentage of the students who tossed the coins obtained between 40 and 60 heads? **95%**

10. The weights of boxes of cereal filled by a machine are normally distributed. The mean weight is 510 grams with a standard deviation of 4 grams.

    a. Of 1000 boxes, how many weigh at least 510 grams? **500**

    b. Of 1000 boxes, how many weigh between 502 and 514 grams? **815**

    c. A machine at the end of the production line checks the weight of the boxes before they are shipped to the stores. If a box weighs more than 522 grams, it is sent back to the beginning of the line to be emptied and reused. Of 1000 boxes, how many will be sent back for this reason? **5**

    d. The machine that checks the weight of the boxes sends back boxes that weigh less than 502 grams. Of 1000 boxes, how many will be sent back for this reason? **25**

RETEACHING THE LESSON

Give each pair of students a shaker of 20 pennies. Each group is to record the number of heads obtained in each of 5 throws. Find the standard deviation for the number of heads in 20 coins. How often are these outcomes expected: 5 heads, 2 heads, 0 heads?

Assignment Guide

Basic: 7–9, 11–12, 14–17
Average: 8–17
Enriched: 8–17

Chapter 14, Quiz D, (Lessons 14–6 through 14–7), is available in the Evaluation Masters Booklet, p. 192.

Reteaching Masters Booklet, p. 95

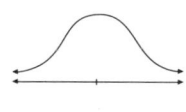

14-7 Reteaching Worksheet
The Normal Distribution

One way to analyze data is to consider the frequency with which each value occurs. Often this is done on a bar graph called a **histogram.** Often the frequency distributions are shown by curves of many different shapes. A curve that is bell-shaped and symmetric indicates a **normal distribution.**

Normal Distribution Properties

1. The graph is maximized at the mean.

2. About 68% of the items are within one standard deviation from the mean. Of the 68%, 34% are greater than the mean and 34% are less than the mean.

3. About 95% of the items are within two standard deviations from the mean. Of the 95%, 47.5% are greater than the mean and 47.5% are less than the mean.

4. About 99% of the items are within three standard deviations from the mean. Of the 99%, 49.5% are greater than the mean and 49.5% are less than the mean.

The number of hours that students studied for final exams was normally distributed. Of the 200 students surveyed, the mean number of hours they studied was 12 hours. The standard deviation was 3 hours.

1. Make the curve to represent the frequency distribution.

2. Of the 200 students surveyed, how many studied less than 9 hours? **32**

3. Of the 200 students surveyed, how many studied between 9 and 15 hours? **136**

4. Of the 200 students surveyed, how many studied at least 3 hours? **199**

5. What percentage of the students studied 3 hours or less? **0.5%**

6. What percentage of the students studied at least 9 hours? **84%**

7. How many students studied less than 12 hours? **100**

Critical Thinking

11. The scores for all American students taking the Scholastic Aptitude Test are normally distributed. Would you expect the scores of the students in your Algebra 2 class to be normally distributed? Explain your answer. **Answers may vary. A typical answer will be no, since the sample is so small.**

Applications

12. **Education** The table below shows the number of male and female students who scored within a particular range on the verbal component of the Scholastic Aptitude Test.

Score	Number of Males	Number of Females
200–249	20,993	26,576
250–299	35,900	45,677
300–349	61,662	76,402
350–399	83,187	97,328
400–449	97,269	108,582
450–499	85,904	89,576
500–549	68,284	67,544
550–599	44,932	41,513
600–649	25,139	21,404
650–699	14,974	11,364
700–749	5,500	3,986
750–800	621	365

a. Construct a histogram for the scores of male students. **See margin.**

b. Construct a histogram for the scores of female students. **See margin.**

c. Which of the two sets of data appears to be closer to a normal distribution? **male students scores**

d. Do you think that the scores for all students would be closer to a normal distribution than either of the separate sets? Explain your answer. **Answers may vary.**

Teaching Tip ➋

Computer

13. A claim appears in a consumers magazine that 30% of American households have at least one personal computer. Laura Chenault believes that this percentage is incorrect in her neighborhood. To prove her point, she conducted a survey in her neighborhood. She went to 20 households and asked if there was a personal computer at home. Eight of them answered *YES* and the rest answered *NO*.

The BASIC program at the top of the next page can be used to analyze the data to see if it provides enough evidence to accept or reject the claim that 30% of American households have at least one personal computer. This claim is what statisticians call a **null hypothesis.** The program results are reliable if the hypothetical percentages of *YES* and *NO* answers are greater than 5.

N = the number of people surveyed. C = the number of YES answers.
P = the percentage of American households with a personal computer.
Q = the percentage of American households without a personal computer.
Z = number of standard deviations from the mean to a YES answer.

```
10   READ P,Q,Z
20   DATA 0.3,0.7,1.96
30   INPUT "WHAT IS THE NUMBER
     OF PEOPLE SURVEYED?";N
40   INPUT "WHAT IS THE NUMBER
     OF YES ANSWERS?";C
50   LET X1 = N*P
60   LET X2 = N*Q
70   IF X1 < = 5 THEN 155
80   IF X2 < = 5 THEN 155
90   LET SD = SQR(X1*Q)
100  LET C1 = X1 + Z*SD
110  LET C2 = X1 - Z*SD
120  IF ABS(C-X1)>Z*SD THEN 150
130  PRINT "ACCEPT THE NULL
     HYPOTHESIS SINCE";C2;"<= "
     ;C;"< = ";C1;"."
140  GOTO 160
150  PRINT "REJECT THE NULL
     HYPOTHESIS SINCE ";C;" > ";
     C1;" OR ";C;" > ";C2;"."
151  GOTO 160
155  PRINT "RESULTS NOT RELIABLE."
160  END
```

Use the program to answer each question. **rejected**

a. If $N = 30$ and $C = 17$, is the null hypothesis rejected or accepted?

b. What would happen if you ran the program for $N = 10$? **See margin.**

c. A claim appears in a national newspaper that 45% of American homes have at least one VCR. To verify these statistics, a local paper interviewed 55 households and found only 30 of them had a VCR. Is the national claim correct for this small town? *Change line 20 to DATA 0.45, 0.55, 1.96.* **yes**

Mixed Review

14. Find the eighth, ninth, and tenth terms of the sequence for which $a_n = 2n + 1$. **(Lesson 13-2) 17, 19, 21**

15. Solve $\log_5 (4x) = \log_5 (x^2 - 5)$. **(Lesson 12-3) 5**

16. Simplify $\dfrac{a + 1}{a^2 - 1} + \dfrac{2}{4a - 4}$. **(Lesson 11-4)** $\dfrac{3}{2(a - 1)}$

$\dfrac{(x - 1)^2}{5} + \dfrac{(y - 2.5)^2}{10} = 1;$ **ellipse**

17. Write the standard form of the equation $8x^2 - 16x + 4y^2 - 20y = 7$. Graph the equation and state whether the graph of the equation is a parabola, a circle, an ellipse, or a hyperbola. **(Lesson 9-7) See students' graphs.**

APPLICATION

You should always carefully examine statistical data represented in magazines, advertising brochures, and newspapers. Data can be misrepresented in order to lead you to a desired conclusion. For example, a group wants to sponsor a rock concert in a public park. They conduct a survey and find that 8 out of 10 people surveyed approve of the concert. The city council approves the concert based on these results. However, upon scrutiny, you may find that the sample was composed of teenagers and those who do not live in the immediate area of the park. Thus the survey was not representative of everyone's views.

Also be aware of misleading graphs. A change in the scale of one of the axes can make a line graph look more dramatic. The choice of graph may make accurate interpretations more difficult. Look at the graph at the right. Is it a reliable graph? Explain your answer. **No, sum = 112%, most possible is 100%**

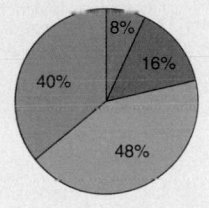

EXTENDING THE LESSON

Math Power: Problem Solving

The burning time of a fabricated fire log is normally distributed with a mean of 5 hours and a standard deviation of 0.25 hours. A camping store has 1000 logs to sell. How many of these logs will burn longer than 4.5 hours? **975**

Application

Statistics can be used to prove any point an individual wants to make. Have students make a line graph whose axes are delineated in units. Then have them graph the data again changing *one* of the axes to a scale of 1 square = 3 units. Ask them how this may affect the interpretation of the graph.

Additional Answers

12a.

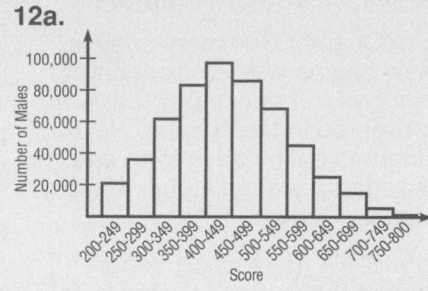

12b.

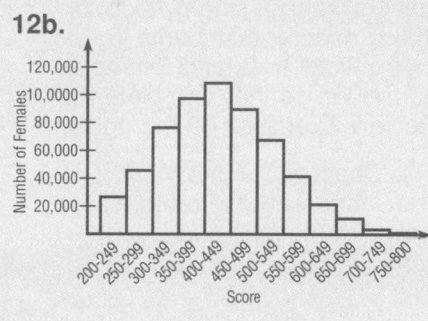

13b. X1 = 10 * 0.3 = 3
X2 = 10 * 0.7 = 7
Since X1 is less than 5, the procedure is stopped.

Enrichment Masters Booklet, p. 95

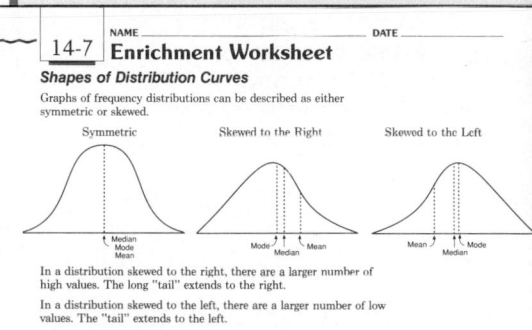

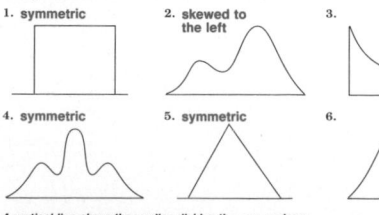

Using the Chapter Summary and Review

The Chapter Summary and Review begins with an alphabetical listing of the new terms that were presented in the chapter. Have students define each term and provide an example of it, if appropriate.

The Skills and Concepts presented in the chapter are reviewed using a side-by-side format. Encourage students to refer to the Objectives and Examples on the left as they complete the Review Exercises on the right.

The Chapter Summary and Review ends with exercises that review Applications and Connections.

Additional Answers

1.
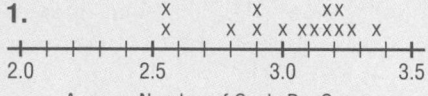
Average Number of Goals Per Game

2.

Stem	Leaf
25	3 3
26	
27	
28	1 9 9
29	
30	0 9
31	3 5 9
32	2 2 6
33	5

33 | 5 represents 3.35.

3. 7.1; none; about 6.7
4. 2.1; 2.1; about 3.4
5. 20,735.5; none; 21,479.7
6. 10; 10; about 12.6
7. 15; 84, 87, 90; 6; no outliers
8. 1.8; 0.3, 0.5, 0.7; 0.4; 1.9
9. 106; 94.5, 100, 105; 10.5; 19, 125
10. 90; 25, 50, 75; 50; no outliers
11. 47; 23.5, 35.5, 41.5; 18; no outliers

VOCABULARY

Upon completing this chapter you should be familiar with the following terms:

bell curve	668	648	mode
box-and-whisker plot	658	668	normal distribution
frequency distribution	668	654	outlier
histogram	668	654	quartile
interquartile range	654	653	range
line plot	642	638	sample
mean	648	664	standard deviation
median	648	642	stem-and-leaf plot

SKILLS AND CONCEPTS

OBJECTIVES AND EXAMPLES

Upon completing this chapter, you should be able to:

■ represent data using line plots and stem-and-leaf plots. **(Lesson 14-2)**

The prices of twelve toasters are listed below. Make a line plot and a stem-and-leaf plot of the prices.

$40 $45 $38 $40 $47 $39
$18 $18 $14 $25 $27 $25

Prices of toasters

Stem	Leaf	
1	4 8 8	
2	5 5 7	
3	8 9	
4	0 0 5 7	2	5 represents $25.

REVIEW EXERCISES

Use these exercises to review and prepare for the chapter test.

The table shows the average number of goals allowed by the top goaltenders in professional hockey. **See margin.**

Player	Avg	Player	Avg
Roy	2.53	Vernon	3.13
Luit	2.53	Essensa	3.15
Lemelin	2.81	Ranford	3.19
Puppa	2.89	Casey	3.22
Moog	2.89	Beaupre	3.22
Richter	3.00	Wamsley	3.26
Cloutier	3.09	Malarchuk	3.35

1. Make a line plot for the goals allowed per game averages for the goaltenders.

2. Make a stem-and-leaf plot of the goals allowed per game averages for the goaltenders.

- find the median, mode, and mean of a set of data. **(Lesson 14-3)**

Find the median, mode, and mean of the set {66, 67, 68, 69, 70, 73, 74, 76, 78, 78, 84}.

median: 6th value = 73   mode = 78

mean = $\dfrac{66 + 67 + \ldots + 78 + 84}{11}$ or 73

Find the median, mode, and mean for each set of data. 3–6. See margin.

3. {7.1, 5.0, 2.7, 9.1, 8.1, 6.3, 8.5}
4. {2.1, 4.8, 2.1, 5.7, 2.1, 4.8, 2.1}
5. {20,270, 29,002, 14,255, 18,700, 28,146, 22,835, 21,201, 15,781, 25,263, 19,344}
6. {3, 6, 7, 7, 7, 7, 9, 10, 10, 10, 10, 10, 13, 14, 14, 16, 17, 17, 19, 20, 21, 31}

- find the range, interquartile range, and outliers for a set of data. **(Lesson 14-4)**

Find the range, interquartile range, and any outliers for the scores in the stem-and-leaf plot below.

Stem	Leaf
6	0 1 2
7	2 2 8
8	0 2 3
9	9

greatest value = 99
least value = 60
range = 39

median = 6th score, 78
lower quartile = 3rd score, 62
upper quartile = 9th score, 83
interquartile range = 83 − 62 or 21
There are no outliers.

Find the range, quartiles, interquartile range, and any outliers for each set of data. 7–11. See margin.

7. {90, 92, 78, 93, 79, 85, 89, 88, 84, 86}
8. {0.4, 0.2, 0.5, 0.9, 0.3, 0.4, 0.5, 1.9, 0.5, 0.7, 0.8, 0.6, 0.2, 0.1, 0.4}
9. {100, 99, 93, 94, 96, 94, 95, 101, 109, 108, 104, 106, 125, 100, 104, 98, 19}
10. {10, 50, 90, 40, 60, 40, 50, 90, 0}
11.

Stem	Leaf
1	1 1 2 2 2
2	2 5 7 7
3	0 3 5 6 8
4	0 0 1 1 2 5
5	0 2 6 8

4 | 0 represents 40.

- represent data using a box-and-whisker plot. **(Lesson 14-5)**

Use the information in the stem-and-leaf plot above to make a box-and-whisker plot.

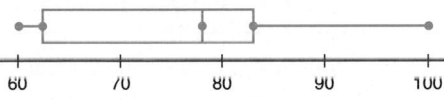

12. The value in millions of U.S. dollars of the exports of 12 industrialized countries for 1989 are listed below. Make a box-and-whisker plot of the data, labeling any outliers. **See margin.**

101,261	116,013	178,846	343,195
138,503	275,173	109,212	152,447
364,080	107,877	44,424	32,206

- find the standard deviation of a set of data. **(Lesson 14-6)**

To find the standard deviation of a set of data:

1. Find the mean.
2. Find the difference between each value in the set of data and the mean.
3. Square each difference.
4. Find the mean of the squares.
5. Take the principal square root of this mean.

Find the standard deviation for each set of data.

13. {5.2, 5.7, 6.0, 5.6, 2.4} **1.3**
14. {13.7, 15.0, 13.7, 16.9, 13.6, 14.3, 14.8, 14.8, 15.1, 15.4, 14.9} **0.9**
15. {2490, 3700, 4300, 2370, 4730, 3105, 4056, 2905, 2130, 2930, 2770, 3320, 3384, 4750, 3500, 4078} **784.6**
16. {797, 6481, 117, 3750, 500, 3842, 1748, 3359, 1375, 3662, 1876, 801, 200} **1819.8**

Alternate Review Strategy

To provide a brief in-class review, you may wish to read the following questions to the class and require a verbal response.

1. What form of data must be used in a circle graph? **percentages**
2. How do you know the meaning of the numbers forming the stem on a stem-and-leaf plot? **A key must be provided giving the place value represented by the stem number.**
3. Find the mean, the median, and the mode for the following set of data. {6, 4, 5, 12, 9, 36} **12, 7.5, no mode**
4. Which of the measures of central tendency is affected by extremes in the data? **mean**
5. What is the range of the following set of data? {2, −1, 0, 8, 3, 7} **9**
6. How is an outlier shown on a box-and-whisker plot? **as a point only and is not included in either the box or whiskers**
7. Find the standard deviation of the following set of data. {4, 6, 9, 5} **about 1.87**
8. Which would have greater variance, a base salary of $400 per month with a standard deviation of $40 or a base salary of $4000 per month with a standard deviation of $40? **a base salary of $400 per month with a standard deviation of $40**
9. What is a bar graph that shows a frequency distribution called? **a histogram**

Additional Answers

12.

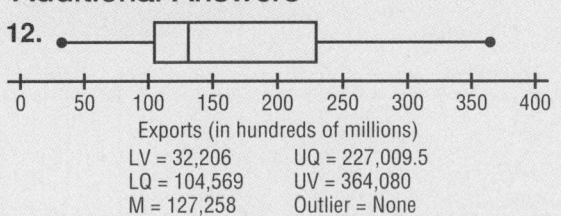

Exports (in hundreds of millions)

LV = 32,206	UQ = 227,009.5
LQ = 104,569	UV = 364,080
M = 127,258	Outlier = None

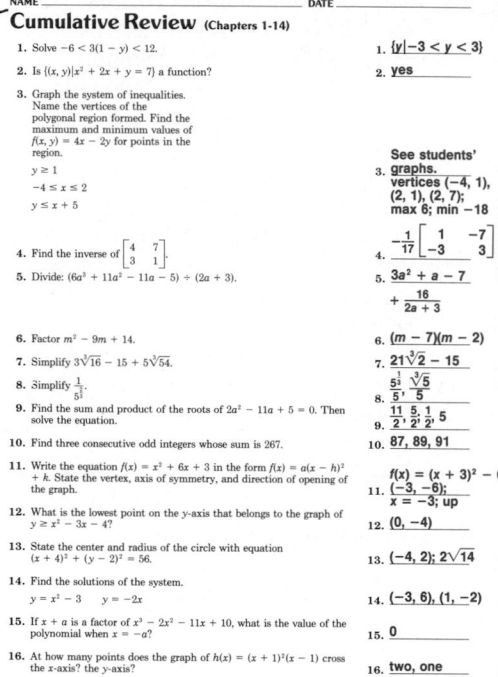

OBJECTIVES AND EXAMPLES

■ solve problems involving normally distributed data.

A Normal Distribution

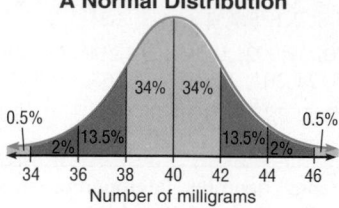

REVIEW EXERCISES

The number of hours of TV watched weekly by 3000 families is normally distributed. The mean is 22 hours and the standard deviation is 7.5 hours.

17. How many families watch at least 22 hours of TV per week? **1500**

18. How many families watch TV between 7 and 29.5 hours per week? **2445**

19. What percentage of the 3000 families watch more than 37 hours of TV a week? **2.5%**

~~~~~~ **APPLICATIONS AND CONNECTIONS** ~~~~~~

20. **Ecology** The weights in tons of different types of waste found in a landfill are given in the table below.

Type	Weight	Type	Weight
plastic	2,000	metal	2,125
yard debris	4,400	glass	1,750
food waste	1,850	other	2,875
paper	10,000		

a. Draw a circle graph to show the composition of the landfill. (**Lesson 14-1**) **See margin.**

b. Draw a bar graph to show how the weights of the types of waste compare. (**Lesson 14-1**) **See margin.**

22. **Safety** The numbers of job-related injuries at a construction site for each month of 1990 are listed below.

10	13	15	39	21	24
19	16	39	17	23	25

a. Make a stem-and-leaf plot of the numbers of injuries. (**Lesson 14-2**) **See Solutions Manual.**

b. Make a line plot of the numbers of injuries. (**Lesson 14-2**) **See Solutions Manual.**

c. Find the median, mode, and mean of the numbers of injuries. (**Lesson 14-3**) **20; 39; 21.75**

21. **Education** The numbers of books in the libraries of the top 12 college or university libraries in the United States are listed below.

11,781,270 8,718,619 7,561,615
7,366,672 6,237,521 6,066,136
5,976,588 5,894,135 5,753,147
5,144,830 5,063,051 4,908,985

a. Find the median, mode, and mean of the numbers of books. **6,021,362; (Lesson 14-3) no mode; 6,706,047.4**

b. Find the range, quartiles, interquartile range, and any outliers. (**Lesson 14-4**) **6,872,285; 5,448,988.5, 6,021,362, 7,464,143.5; 2,015,155; 11,781,270**

23. **Demographics** The monthly incomes of 10,000 workers in Gahanna are distributed normally. Suppose the mean monthly income is $1250 and the standard deviation is $250.

a. How many workers earn more than $1500 per month? (**Lesson 14-7**) **1600**

b. How many workers earn less than $750 per month? (**Lesson 14-7**) **250**

c. What percentage of the 10,000 workers earn between $500 and $1750 a month? (**Lesson 14-7**) **97%**

d. What percentage of the workers earn less than $1750 a month? (**Lesson 14-7**) **97.5%**

Additional Answers

20a.

20b.

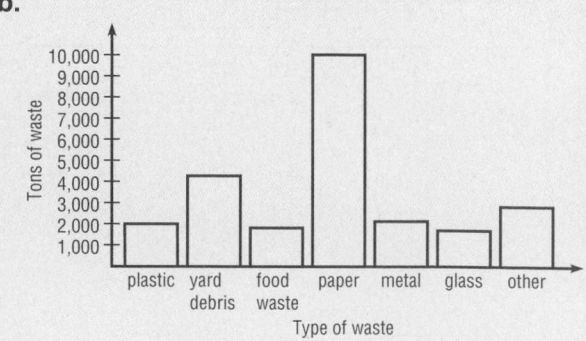

The following high temperatures were recorded during a cold spell in Cleveland lasting thirty-eight days. Use this data for Exercises 1–9.

29° 26° 17° 12° 5° 4° 25° 17° 23° 18° 13° 6° 25° 20° 27° 22° 26° 30° 31°
2° 12° 27° 16° 27° 16° 30° 6° 16° 5° 0° 5° 29° 18° 16° 22° 29° 8° 23°

1. Draw a circle graph to show how many days the temperature was 0° to 10°, 11° to 20°, 21° to 30°, and above 30°. **1, 2, 5, and 8. See Solutions Manual.**

2. Draw a line plot of the temperatures.

3. What is the range of the temperatures? **31°**

4. Find the median, mode, and mean of the temperatures. **18; 16; 17.97**

5. Make a stem-and-leaf plot of the temperatures.

6. Find the quartiles and the interquartile range of the temperatures. **12°, 18°, 26°; 14°**

7. Find any outliers in the temperatures. **none**

8. Make a box-and-whisker plot of the temperatures.

9. Find the standard deviation of the temperatures. **about 9.1**

10. Find the median, mode, and mean of the hourly wages of 200 workers. One hundred earn $5.00 an hour, ten earn $5.75 an hour, ten earn $6.75 an hour, twenty earn $4.50 an hour, and sixty earn $5.25 an hour. **$5.00; $5.00; $5.15**

12. **$90; $80, $90, and $120; $117.19**

Connie is buying a pair of headphones to use with her stereo receiver. The prices of the 21 different types of stereo headphones sold at the Stereo Studio are $100, $150, $75, $79, $149, $120, $80, $70, $400, $190, $50, $80, $148, $40, $85, $60, $160, $90, $90, $125, and $120.

11. Make a stem-and-leaf plot of the prices of the headphones. **See Solutions Manual.**

12. Find the median, mode, and mean of the prices of the headphones.

13. Find the range, quartiles, interquartile range, and any outliers of the prices.

14. Make a box-and-whisker plot of the prices. **See Solutions Manual.**

15. Find the standard deviation of the prices. **$74.01**

13. **$360; $77, $90, $148.50; $71.50; $400**

The scores on a college entrance exam are normally distributed. The mean score is 510, and the standard deviation is 80. **17. 34,000**

16. Of the 50,000 people who took the exam, how many scored above 510? **25,000**

17. Of the 50,000 people who took the exam, how many scored between 430 and 590?

18. What percentage of the people who took the exam scored below 670? **97.5%**

19. A student must score above 750 on the college entrance exam to qualify for a full scholarship at Carleton University. What percentage of the people who took the exam will qualify? **0.5%**

20. **Real Estate** Ten homes were sold in Oak Hills in January. Of these, one sold for $225,000, three sold for $100,000, and six sold for $85,000. Find the median, mode, and mean of the prices of these homes. Which "average" would you quote if you were an area home owner? **$85,000; $85,000, $103,500; mean**

Bonus The square of the standard deviation is called the variance. Find the variance of the prices of the headphones, given in Exercises 11–15. **$5476.92**

Using the Chapter Test

This page may be used as a test or as a review. In addition, two multiple-choice tests and two free-response tests are provided in the Evaluation Masters Booklet. Chapter 14 Test, Form 1A is shown below.

Evaluation Masters Booklet, pp. 183–184

NAME _____ DATE _____

Chapter 14 Test, Form 1A

Write the letter for the correct answer in the blank at the right of each problem. For questions 1 and 2 refer to the graph at the right.

1. How many of the women shown scored more points than Tonya?
   A. 0   B. 1   C. 2   D. 3   1. **C**

2. The team scored 54 points. How many points were scored by non-starting players?
   A. 10   B. 39   C. 15   D. 44   2. **C**

3. Of the running shoes sold at Foot Ease, 44% are black, 27% are white, 12% are navy, 9% are red, 4% are maroon, and 2% are pink. In a circle graph of the data, about how many degrees are needed for other colors?
   A. 2°   B. 0°   C. 9°   D. 7°   3. **D**

4. In a stem-and-leaf plot, 7 | 6 represents 7550 to 7649 people. How would 2683 be represented?
   A. 2 | 7   B. 3 | 0   C. 2 | 6   D. 2 | 68   4. **A**

The following line plot shows the average 1990 home attendance, rounded to the nearest thousand, for the 14 baseball teams of the American League in 1990. Values are rounded to the nearest thousand.

5. The Toronto Blue Jays' average home attendance was highest. What was it?
   A. 25,000   B. 30,000   C. 45,360   D. 46,000   5. **D**

6. What is the mode of the data?
   A. 25,000   B. 25,500   C. 27,000   D. 27,214   6. **A**

7. What is the range of the data?
   A. 10,000   B. 22,000   C. 30,000   D. 32,000   7. **D**

The stem-and-leaf plot at the right gives the combined score SAT test results for 23 students. 89 | 2 represents 892.

8. What is the median score?
   A. 899   B. 890   C. 896   D. 908   8. **C**

9. What is the interquartile range?
   A. 23.75   B. 27   C. 29   D. 31.67   9. **B**

10. Find the standard deviation of {3, 3, 5, 6, 8, 8, 9, 9, 9, 10}.
    A. √6   B. √2.2   C. √2   D. √7   10. **A**

NAME _____ DATE _____

Chapter 14 Test, Form 1A (continued)

Matt's scores on six weekly quizzes are 8, 7, 9, 8, 9, 10.

11. What is the mode of the data?
    A. 8   B. 9   C. 8.5   D. 8 and 9   11. **D**

12. What is the median of the data?
    A. 8   B. 9   C. 8.5   D. 8 and 9   12. **C**

13. What is the mean of the data?
    A. 3   B. 8   C. 8.5   D. 10   13. **C**

14. What is the standard deviation?
    A. 0   B. 0.957   C. 0.917   D. 1.417   14. **B**

15. Which number could, without being an outlier, be the tenth member of a set of data that includes 72, 63, 71, 67, 59, 75, 76, 60, and 70?
    A. 41   B. 43   C. 95   D. 96   15. **B**

16. A set of data has a mean of 6, a median of 7, a range of 8, an interquartile range of 5, and an upper quartile of 9. Find a possible box-and-whisker plot.
    A.   B.   C.   D.   16. **B**

17. A set of data has a lower quartile of 6, a median of 7, a mean of 9, and an interquartile range of 8. Find the greatest number that could be in the set and not be an outlier.
    A. 19   B. 21   C. 26   D. 28   17. **C**

For 2000 patients, blood-clotting times were normally distributed, with the mean time = 8 seconds, standard deviation = 3 seconds.

18. What percentage had a blood-clotting time between 8 and 14 seconds?
    A. 68%   B. 34%   C. 49.5%   D. 47.5%   18. **D**

19. How many patients had a blood-clotting times between 5 and 11 seconds?
    A. 68   B. 34   C. 1360   D. 680   19. **C**

20. How likely was a patient to have a clotting time over 11 seconds?
    A. 0.025   B. 0.16   C. 0.34   D. 0.135   20. **B**

Bonus
For a set of nine different positive numbers, what must be true?
    A. The range is greater than the mean.
    B. An outlier is greater than the upper quartile.
    C. All outliers are greater than the mode.
    D. The median is between the upper and lower quartiles.   Bonus **D**

A **Test and Review Generator** is provided in Apple, IBM, and Macintosh versions. You may use this software to create your own tests or worksheets, based on the needs of your students.

The **Performance Assessment Booklet** provides an alternate assessment for evaluating student progress. An assessment for this chapter can be found on pages 27–28.

The questions on these pages involve comparing two quantities, one in Column A and one in Column B. In certain questions, information related to one or both quantities is centered above them. All variables used stand for real numbers.

Directions:

Write A if the quantity in Column A is greater.

Write B if the quantity in Column B is greater.

Write C if the quantities are equal.

Write D if there is not enough information to determine the relationship.

Column A	Column B
1. B 0.4	$\sqrt{0.4}$

2. D

$$0 < x < 7$$
$$0 < y < 9$$

y	x

3. B

$$n < 0$$
$$b < 0$$

$n + b$	$n - b$

4. C one tenth of the product of the first positive ten integers | the product of the first positive nine integers

5. B 12% of 1600	16.5% of 1200

6. D $y \neq 0$

$\dfrac{y}{3}$	$\dfrac{3}{y}$

Column A	Column B

7. A $\dfrac{2}{\dfrac{3}{\dfrac{5}{7}}}$ | $\dfrac{6}{17}$

8. C   Let $*y$ denote the least integer equal to or greater than y.

$*0.4$	$*1.0$

9. A $b = d + 1$

the average of a, b, and c	the average of a, c, and d

10. D c and d are integers greater than 1.

$[1 + (-c)]^d$	$(-c)^d$

11. C $b < 0$

$\dfrac{b^9}{b^4}$	$\dfrac{b^{10}}{b^5}$

12. A $\dfrac{5}{b} = 2; \ 5 = \dfrac{2}{c}$

$c + \dfrac{1}{3}$	$b + \dfrac{11}{6}$

13. A $\dfrac{4}{k} < 0$

$\dfrac{-1}{k}$	$4k$

14. A $\dfrac{1}{k} < 0$

$\dfrac{-1}{k}$	k

Column A	Column B

15. **C** $\dfrac{3^4 + 3^5}{3^4}$ | $\dfrac{3^2 + 3^3}{3^2}$

16. **A**

$$n! = n(n-1)(n-2) \ldots (2)1$$

| $\dfrac{8!}{2!6!}$ | $4!$ |

17. **B**

$$2 + (-4) + 8 + \ldots$$

| sum of the first 6 terms | sum of the first 7 terms |

18. **D** y if $y = 3^x$ | y if $y = 3^{-x}$

19. **C**

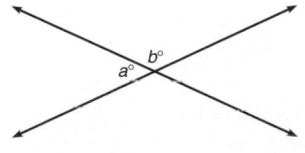

| a | $180 - b$ |

20. **A** $\sqrt{0.2}$ | $(0.2)^2$

21. **A** $\quad a > b > c > d > 0$
| $a - d$ | $b - c$ |

22. **B**

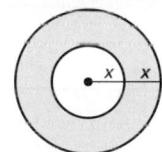

| the area of the the inner circle | the area of the shaded region |

23. **B** the number of points needed to divide a segment into five parts | 5 points

Column A	Column B

24. **C**

R   A   B   S

A is the midpoint of $\overline{RB}$.
B is the midpoint of $\overline{AS}$.

| RA | SB |

15

Probability

PREVIEWING THE CHAPTER

The chapter begins with students using the Basic Counting Principle to solve problems with independent and dependent events. Next, linear and circular permutations and combinations are examined and formulas derived to solve problems. Then students find the probability that an event will occur, the probability that events A *and* B will occur when the events are independent and when they are dependent, and the probability that events A *or* B will occur with mutually exclusive events. The chapter concludes with a lesson involving students in simulations and binomial experiments.

Problem-Solving Strategy Students combine the strategies of *act it out* and *use a model* to help them recognize relationships among the given data to solve problems.

Lesson Objective Chart

Lesson (Pages)	Lesson Objectives	State/Local Objectives
15-1 (682-683)	**15-1:** Solve problems by using models.	
15-2 (684-688)	**15-2:** Solve problems using the Basic Counting Principle.	
15-3 (689-693)	**15-3:** Solve problems involving permutations.	
15-4 (694-698)	**15-4:** Solve problems involving circular permutations.	
15-5 (699-704)	**15-5:** Solve problems involving combinations.	
15-6 (705-709)	**15-6:** Find the probability of an event and determine the odds of success or failure.	
15-7 (710-714)	**15-7:** Find the probability of two or more independent or dependent events.	
15-8 (715-719)	**15-8:** Find the probability of mutually exclusive events or inclusive events.	
15-9 (720-724)	**15-9A:** Use simulation to solve various probability problems.	
	15-9B: Use binomial experiments to find probabilities.	

ORGANIZING THE CHAPTER

You may want to refer to the **Course Planning Calendar** on page T44.

Lesson (Pages)	Pacing Chart (days) Course I	II	III	Reteaching	Practice	Enrichment	Evaluation	Technology	Lab Manual	Mixed Problem Solving	Applications	Cooperative Learning Activity	Multicultural	Transparencies
15-1 (682-683)	–	1	0.5		p. 110									15-1
15-2 (684-688)	–	1	1	p. 96	p. 111	p. 96	Quiz A, p. 205							15-2
15-3 (689-693)	–	1	1	p. 97	p. 112	p. 97		p. 15						15-3
15-4 (694-698)	–	1	1	p. 98	p. 113	p. 98	Quiz B, p. 205 Mid-Chapter Test, p. 209							15-4
15-5 (699-704)	–	2	1.5	p. 99	p. 114	p. 99		p. 32		p. 15				15-5
15-6 (705-709)	–	1	1	p. 100	p. 115	p. 100								15-6
15-7 (710-714)	–	1	1	p. 101	p. 116	p. 101	Quiz C, p. 206		pp. 45 46					15-7
15-8 (715-719)	–	1	1	p. 102	p. 117	p. 102					p. 33			15-8
15-9 (720-724)	–	1	1	p. 103	p. 118	p. 103	Quiz D, p. 206					p. 51	p. 15	15-9
Review (726-728)	–	1	1	Multiple Choice Tests, Forms 1A and 1B, pp. 197-200 Free Response Tests, Forms 2A and 2B, pp. 201-204										
Test (729)	–	1	1	Cumulative Review, pp. 207-208 Standardized Test Practice Questions, p. 210										

Course I: Chapters 1-13; Course II: Chapters 1-15; Course III: Chapters 1-17

Other Chapter Resources

Student Edition
Chapter Opener, pp. 680-681
Journal Entries, pp. 683, 688
Cooperative Learning Activity, p. 683
History Connection, p. 688
Mid-Chapter Review, p. 704
Portfolio Suggestion, p. 719
Technology, p. 725
Extended Project 4, pp. A14-A16

Teacher's Classroom Resources
Transparency 15-0
Real-World Applications Transparencies, 31, 32
Performance Assessment Booklet, pp. 29-30
Problem-of-the-Week Activity Cards, 30, 31
Tech Prep Applications Booklet, pp. 29-30
Lesson Plans, pp. 110-118

Other Supplements
Glencoe Mathematics Professional Series

Software
Test and Review Generator Software (Apple, IBM, and Macintosh)
Interactive Software (Macintosh)
Teacher's Guide for Software Resources

ENHANCING THE CHAPTER

Cooperative Learning

Intervening to Teach Cooperative-Learning Skills

In many of their other activities, both inside and outside of school, students are required to compete more often than to cooperate. Therefore, it may require some time and attention for students to develop positive group skills. Experienced researchers recommend that only a few of these skills be taught each semester. Each new skill should be clearly defined before the session begins and skills that were introduced earlier reviewed. Then, after the session begins, the teacher should monitor the groups and intervene when appropriate. Remember to intervene only when necessary and then in a positive manner. Once students recognize the need for the skill, they only need help with developing it. This involves the teacher including examples of expected behavior when the skill is first defined and then offering appropriate guidance and feedback as students practice the skill during their cooperative-learning sessions. After each session, you also should provide time for the students to discuss and assess their behaviors. To motivate the discussion, you can simply ask each group to list the two things they did better this time than the last time and the one thing they plan to do better the next time.

Technology

The BASIC program in the Technology Feature of this chapter enables students to simulate an event using the computer to do the randomizing of outcomes. Have students make conjectures about what other events could be randomized using this same program.

Critical Thinking

Critical thinking often involves looking for the less obvious. For example, suppose each time a person tosses a coin, the result is heads at least 75% of the time. Why? To say that the coin is not perfectly balanced is an obvious answer. Suppose that when anyone else tosses the same coin, the results are always close to 50% heads. Now, what is a possible explanation? When brainstorming with the goal of finding less obvious but reasonable explanations, students are exercising their higher-level thinking skills. You might want to have students look for new articles where the implied conclusion is not the only conclusion that could be supported by the data offered and present a report for a class discussion.

Cooperative Learning, p. 51

CHAPTER 15 NAME _____ DATE _____
Cooperative Learning Activity (Use after Lesson 15-9)

Probability

Complete the laboratory activity below.

Materials: 5 coins, 2 dice, deck of 52 cards, "bag" of 6 red chips, 2 white chips, and 1 blue chip for each student or team of students.

Make predictions using probability for the outcomes of the situations below. Then actually simulate the situation through experimentation, filling in the chart. Compare both your results and the class average to your prediction.
See students' work.

Probability Prediction		Experimentation		Comparison (+, −)	
Situation	Your Prediction	Number of Favorable Outcomes	Class Average	Your Number to Prediction	Class Average to Prediction
Example: How often will only 3 heads show when 5 coins are tossed together 16 times?	10	7	9	−3	−1
1. How often will the sum of 2 dice be 7 when they are tossed together 18 times?					
2. One card is selected from a deck of 52. If 13 cards are drawn how often will the card be a red card or an 8?					

3. Write a conclusion for each experiment based on your own results, the class average, and the predicted probability.

a. Situation 1: _____

b. Situation 2: _____

Technology, p. 15

CHAPTER 15 NAME _____ DATE _____
Scientific Calculator (Use after Lesson 15-3)

Evaluating Factorial Expressions

You can use a scientific calculator to evaluate factorial expressions.

Example 1: Evaluate $\frac{15!}{11!3!}$.

ENTER: 15 [x!] [÷] 11 [x!] [×] 3 [x!] [)] [=] 5460

Example 2: Evaluate $\frac{P(9, 3)}{P(6, 4)}$.

First, evaluate $P(6, 4)$ and store the result in memory.

$P(6, 4) = \frac{6!}{(6 - 4)!}$

ENTER 6 [x!] [÷] [(] 6 [−] 4 [)] [x!] [=] 360 [STO]

Then evaluate $P(9, 3)$ and divide the result by the number stored in memory.

$P(9, 3) = \frac{9!}{(9 - 3)!}$

ENTER 9 [x!] [÷] [(] 9 [−] 3 [)] [x!] [=] 504 [÷] [RCL] [=] 1.4

Use a calculator to evaluate each expression.

1. $\frac{10!}{3!2!}$
0.00126263

2. $\frac{16!}{10!4!}$
240,240

3. $\frac{17!}{5!2!}$
6188

4. $\frac{18!}{9!10!2!}$
2431

5. $\frac{13!}{4!5!10!}$
0.5958333333

6. $\frac{21!}{17!3!4!}$
49.875

7. $\frac{P(10, 3)}{P(12, 9)}$
9.018759019 E −6

8. $\frac{P(9, 4)}{P(11, 7)}$
0.0018181818

9. $\frac{P(15, 5)}{P(9, 4)}$
119.1666667

10. $\frac{P(16, 8)}{P(17, 11)}$
0.0010504202

11. $\frac{P(20, 12)}{P(17, 15)}$
0.3392857143

12. $\frac{P(16, 12)}{P(13, 7)}$
100,800

Problem of the Week Activity

The card shown below is one of two available for this chapter. It can be used as a class or small group activity.

Activity Card

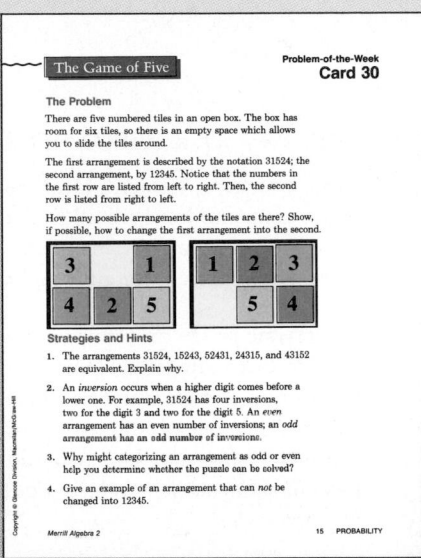

The Game of Five

Problem-of-the-Week
Card 30

The Problem

There are five numbered tiles in an open box. The box has room for six tiles, so there is an empty space which allows you to slide the tiles around.

The first arrangement is described by the notation 31524; the second arrangement, by 12345. Notice that the numbers in the first row are listed from left to right. Then, the second row is listed from right to left.

How many possible arrangements of the tiles are there? Show, if possible, how to change the first arrangement into the second.

Strategies and Hints

1. The arrangements 31524, 15243, 52431, 24315, and 43152 are equivalent. Explain why.
2. An *inversion* occurs when a higher digit comes before a lower one. For example, 31524 has four inversions, two for the digit 3 and two for the digit 5. An *even* arrangement has an even number of inversions; an *odd* arrangement has an odd number of inversions.
3. Why might categorizing an arrangement as odd or even help you determine whether the puzzle can be solved?
4. Give an example of an arrangement that can *not* be changed into 12345.

Merrill Algebra 2 15 PROBABILITY

Manipulatives and Models

The following materials may be used as models or manipulatives in Chapter 15.

- scientific calculator (Lesson 15-2)
- magazines, newspapers, and books (Lesson 15-4)
- coins, cards, or golf tees (Lessons 15-5, 15-6, 15-8, and 15-9)
- marbles (Lesson 15-6)
- box (Lesson 15-6)
- spinner (Lesson 15-8)

Outside Resources

Books/Periodicals

Kotz, Samuel and Donna F. Stroup. *Educational Guessing - How to Cope in an Uncertain World.* Marcel Dekker, Inc.

McGervey, John D.. *Probabilities in Everyday Life.* Nelson-Hall.

Films/Videotapes/Videodiscs

Probabilities, Parts 1 and 2, part of the Mainly Math Series, Great Plains National Instructional TV Library (GPN), P.O. Box 80669, Lincoln, NE 68501

Probability, from the Math Wise Series, Agency for Instructional Technology, 1111 W. 17th St., Bloomington, IN 47404

Software

Electronic Blackboard: Functions, COMPress, 338 Commerce Dr., Fairfield, CT 06430-5540

A Chance Look, WINGS for Learning/Sunburst Communications, 1600 Green Hills Rd., P.O. Box 660002, Scotts Valley, CA 95067-0002

Multicultural

Multicultural Activity, p. 15

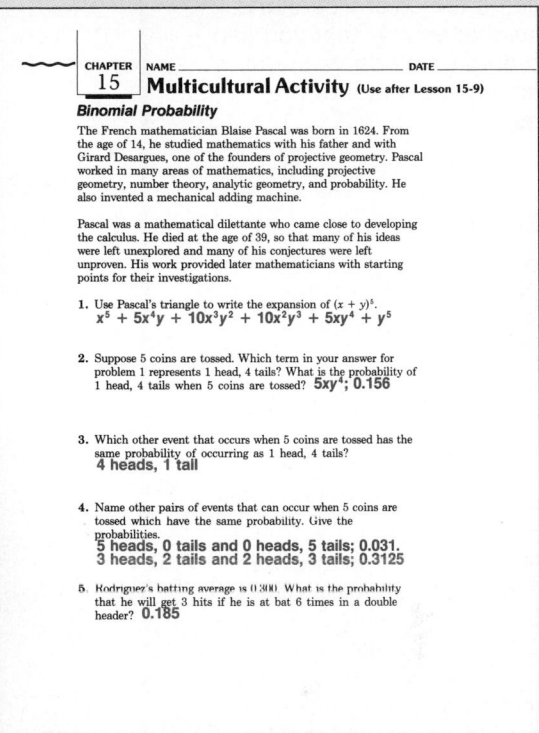

CHAPTER 15 NAME ______ DATE ______

Multicultural Activity (Use after Lesson 15-9)

Binomial Probability

The French mathematician Blaise Pascal was born in 1624. From the age of 14, he studied mathematics with his father and with Girard Desargues, one of the founders of projective geometry. Pascal worked in many areas of mathematics, including projective geometry, number theory, analytic geometry, and probability. He also invented a mechanical adding machine.

Pascal was a mathematical dilettante who came close to developing the calculus. He died at the age of 39, so that many of his ideas were left unexplored and many of his conjectures were left unproven. His work provided later mathematicians with starting points for their investigations.

1. Use Pascal's triangle to write the expansion of $(x + y)^5$.
   $x^5 + 5x^4y + 10x^3y^2 + 10x^2y^3 + 5xy^4 + y^5$
2. Suppose 5 coins are tossed. Which term in your answer for problem 1 represents 1 head, 4 tails? What is the probability of 1 head, 4 tails when 5 coins are tossed? $5xy^4$; 0.156
3. Which other event that occurs when 5 coins are tossed has the same probability of occurring as 1 head, 4 tails?
   4 heads, 1 tail
4. Name other pairs of events that can occur when 5 coins are tossed which have the same probability. Give the probabilities.
   5 heads, 0 tails and 0 heads, 5 tails; 0.031.
   3 heads, 2 tails and 2 heads, 3 tails; 0.3125
5. Rodriguez's batting average is 0.300. What is the probability that he will get 3 hits if he is at bat 6 times in a double header? 0.185

Lab Manual

Lab Activity, pp. 45-46

Name ______ **Activity 15 Worksheet**

Probability

1. Toss two coins 25 times. Tally each result as Heads-Heads (HH) or not Heads-Heads in the chart below.

Result	Tally
Heads-Heads	
not Head-Heads	

$\frac{\text{Number of HH}}{\text{Total Tosses}} =$ ______% win

2. A sample of 200 customers in a store gave the following results.

		SEX		
		Male	Female	Total
AGE	Under 30	60	50	110
	30 & Over	80	10	90
	Total	140	60	200

a. What is the probability a customer is under 30 and female? ______

b. What is the probability a customer is 30 or over? ______

c. If you were the manager of this store, what population would you target with your merchandise? ______

3. Public reactions to a new school tax levy are recorded below.

		For	Against	Did Not Vote	Total
AGE	Under 20	240	40	40	320
	20–40	100	120	60	280
	Over 40	100	80	20	200
	Total	440	240	120	800

a. What is the probability a person under 20 will vote for the levy? ______

b. What is the probability a person over 40 will vote at all? ______

c. How can the results of the poll be used by political parties to encourage more people to vote for or against the school tax levy? ______

Using the Chapter Opener

Transparency 15–0 is available in the Transparency Package. It provides a full-color visual and motivational activity that you can use to engage students in the mathematical content of the chapter.

Background Information

Environmentalists plan, develop, and carry out programs that study the relationship between the activities of man and the environment. They conduct and apply research and communicate their findings in scientific journals, impact analyses, reports, and other documents. Environmentalists employ sophisticated testing and measuring equipment, use laboratory equipment, and analyze volumes of data using computers. As a result of continuing efforts to preserve the environment, employment of environmentalists is expected to grow 14% to 24% through the 1990s.

CHAPTER OBJECTIVES

In this chapter you will:
- Find ways of grouping objects by combinations and permutations.
- Find the probability of an event.
- Predict events based on probability.

Explain why you think the world's population has grown more since 1990 than it did in the previous century.

Timing of Each Additional Billion of World Population

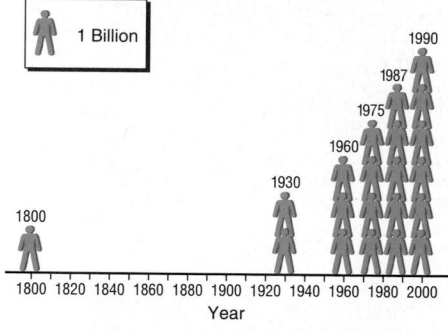

680

CAREERS IN ENVIRONMENTALISM

It's obvious: If we don't clean up after ourselves, our grandchildren will all live in one big toxic landfill. There won't be many plants or animals there, either (except for gulls and rats).

Everyone pretty much agrees about that. But it's another thing altogether to accept the responsibility to clean up a river, replant a forest, or detoxify a swamp. Each person thinks, *"It's too late to save this area. What can one person do? I'm only a student—the adults ought to do it. That's what they pay taxes for."*

No one can tell another person how much time and energy to give to the environmental movement. But if you want to make your living helping Earth recover from years of abuse, consider becoming an environmentalist.

Do you wonder about your drinking water, your air, your garden soil? Do you worry about oil spills and hazardous wastes? Does your street need more shade trees? Is your city's air full of smog? You may ask, *"What can I do about it?"*

Here are only some of the specializations available: agricultural engineer, biologist, communicator, consultant, ecologist, educator, environmental health scientist, environmental engineer, fisheries conservationist, forester, health physicist, industrial hygienist, landuse planner, public health doctor, range manager, recreationist, social scientist, soil conservationist, wildlife conservationist. Take your pick.

Chapter Project

Materials: paper, pencil, graph paper, library resources

Organize students into cooperative groups of environmentalists. Have each group prepare a "State of the Environment" report. That is, have each group adopt a specific area of environmental science. Then instruct each group to conduct research on the current status of efforts in its adopted area, to include and reflect international, national, state, and local efforts. Further instruct each group

to identify and contact at least one local organization to find how it is contributing either negatively or positively towards the local environment. Inform students that reports are to include data, charts, and graphs showing past, present, and expected future impact of environmental efforts. The following

is a partial list of research areas of environmental science.
- the ozone layer
- the greenhouse effect
- air/water pollution
- waste management
- endangered species
- resource management

Lesson	Connections (C) and Applications (A)	Examples	Exercises
15-2	A: Dining		28
	Transportation		29
15-3	A: Photography	1	
	Gemology		42
	Communication		44
	Travel		48
	C: Statistics		43
15-4	A: Construction		23
	Design		24
	Electricity		25
	Environmentalism		26
15-5	C: Geometry	3	24-29, 33
	Statistics		52
	A: Botany	2	
	Sports		51
	Science Fiction		53
	Business Finance		56
15-6	A: Finance		43
	Sports		44
15-7	C: Geometry		35
	A: Entertainment	2	
	Sports		31
15-8	A: Sports		32
	Business		33
15-9	C: Number Theory		37
	A: Traffic Control		31
	Baseball		32
	Trapshooting		33
	Physics		35

MORE ABOUT ENVIRONMENTALISM

Degree Required:

- Bachelor's Degree in Biology, Chemistry, or Environmental Science

Some environmentalists like:

- traveling around the world
- satisfaction that their work is helping to improve the quality of life and preserve the planet
- good salaries

Related Math Subjects:

- Advanced Algebra
- Trigonometry
- Probability/Statistics

Some environmentalists dislike:

- working with dangerous organisms and toxic substances
- working irregular hours
- pressure from political groups and industry

For more information on the various careers available in the field of Environmentalism, write to:

Institute of Environmental Sciences
940 East Northwest Highway
Mount Prospect, IL 60056

681

Lesson Resources

Practice Master 15-1

Transparency 15-1 contains the 5-Minute Check and a teaching aid for this lesson.

INTRODUCING THE LESSON

🕐 5-Minute Check

(over Chapter 14)

Given the set of data {12, 5, 8, 3, 9, 13, 6, 20, 5}, find the following.

1. median, mean, and mode
   8; 9; 5
2. upper quartile and lower quartile **12.5; 5**
3. range and interquartile range **17; 7.5**
4. any outliers **none**
5. standard deviation **≈5**

Motivating the Lesson

Bring a menu to class (you may want to make a transparency of the menu). Tell students that you want to order a sandwich, a beverage, and one side order. Using the menu, have students give several possible orders. Ask students how they would know what orders are possible.

TEACHING THE LESSON

Chalkboard Example

For the Example

For dinner, you have 5 choices for the main dish, 2 choices for vegetable, and 3 for beverage. How many different dinner choices are possible? **30**

15-1 Problem-Solving Strategy: Using Models

Objective 15-1

After studying this lesson, you should be able to:
- solve problems by using models.

Sometimes a problem is easier to solve if you act out the situation instead of trying to figure out which mathematical equation or formula to use. When you act things out, you can use models to represent different aspects of the problem you are solving.

Example

Suppose Grisky's Ice Cream Shoppe has 4 flavors of ice cream, 3 sauces, and 3 additional toppings. You are assigned the task of making every kind of sundae possible. Each sundae must have 2 scoops of 1 flavor of ice cream, 1 sauce, and 1 additional topping. How many different sundaes would you make?

One way to model this problem would be to use cutouts of circles to represent ice cream, squares to represent sauces, and triangles to represent the toppings. Use the initials of the items to label each figure.

Now use the items to physically build each sundae. Have your partner record each different type you create. When all possibilities are exhausted, count your results. You should have 36 different sundaes.

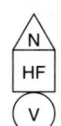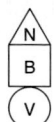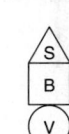

CHECKING FOR UNDERSTANDING

Communicating Mathematics

Read and study the lesson to answer each question.

1. Describe another way besides using models to determine the number of different sundaes that could be made. **lists, tree diagrams**
2. Discuss disadvantages of using models to solve problems. **The numbers may be too great to physically assemble each situation.**

RETEACHING THE LESSON

Using models, have students solve the following problem. Jane has 5 dresses, 3 pairs of shoes, and 3 jackets suitable for wear at her work. How many choices of outfits with these items are possible? **45**

3. Find the most likely sum you will roll each time two dice are thrown.

   a. Let *x* be the number on the first die and *y* be the number on the second die. What are all the possibilities for (*x*, *y*)? **See margin.**

   b. What is the smallest sum possible on each roll? **2**

   c. What is the greatest sum possible on each roll? **12**

   d. What is the most likely sum rolled? Why? **7, because more combinations for 7 exist than for any other number between 2 and 12.**

EXERCISES

Strategies

Look for a pattern.
Solve a simpler problem.
Act it out.
Guess and check.
Draw a diagram.
Make a chart.
Work backwards.

Solve. Use any strategy.

4. Three cruise ships leave New York for France on the same day. The round trip takes the first ship 12 days, the second ship 16 days, and the third ship 20 days. How many days will elapse before all three ships will leave New York again on the same day if none of the ships sits idle? **240**

5. In the land of Id, there are 3 coins. Each has a different value (17¢, 36¢, or 55¢), a different color (black, silver, or gold), and a different size (small, medium, or large). A randomly selected coin is either a black coin, small, or worth 17¢. Another coin is either gold, large, or worth 36¢. The large coin is worth more than the silver coin. What color, size, and value are each of the coins? **17¢ gold medium, 36¢ silver small, 55¢ black large**

6. The box at the right is made of 64 cubes. Two striped paths are painted on it to look like a ribbon. How many small cubes have no paint on them? **24**

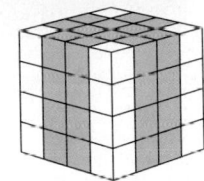

7. Determine the maximum and minimum perimeter of a figure made up of 12 square tiles. **minimum: 14 units, maximum: 26 units**

8. George can walk around a circular nature trail in 40 minutes. Amanda walks on the same trail starting at the same time but goes in the opposite direction. She meets George every 15 minutes. How long does it take Amanda to walk around the trail? **24 minutes**

Journal

Describe other topics in this book where making a model helps to solve the problem.

COOPERATIVE LEARNING ACTIVITY

Work in groups. Each person in the group must understand the solution and be able to explain it to any person in class.

There are 3 different geometry books and 3 different algebra books to be arranged in a row on a shelf. How many different ways can the six books be arranged if no two algebra books can be side by side? **72 ways**

EXTENDING THE LESSON

Math Power: Problem Solving

Have students model the lesson example if the ice cream may be served plain, with a sauce only, with a topping only, or with both a sauce and a topping. **There are 64 different sundaes.**

Additional Answer

3a. (1, 1), (1, 2), (1, 3), (1, 4), (1, 5), (1, 6), (2, 1), (2, 2), (2, 3), (2, 4), (2, 5), (2, 6), (3, 1), (3, 2), (3, 3), (3, 4), (3, 5), (3, 6), (4, 1), (4, 2), (4, 3), (4, 4), (4, 5), (4, 6), (5, 1), (5, 2), (5, 3), (5, 4), (5, 5), (5, 6), (6, 1), (6, 2), (6, 3), (6, 4), (6, 5), (6, 6)

EVALUATING THE LESSON

Checking for Understanding
Exercises 1–3 are designed to help you assess understanding through reading, writing, and speaking. You should work through Exercises 1–2 with your students, and then monitor their work on Exercise 3.

Closing the Lesson
Modeling Activity Have students use a model to find the number of outfits possible if someone takes 2 pairs of slacks, 3 shirts, and 4 pairs of shoes on a trip. **24**

APPLYING THE LESSON

Homework Exercises

Assignment Guide

Basic: 4 8
Average: 4–8
Enriched: 4–8

Practice Masters Booklet, p. 110

Lesson Resources

Reteaching Master 15-2
Practice Master 15-2
Enrichment Master 15-2

 Transparency 15-2 contains the 5-Minute Check and a teaching aid for this lesson.

INTRODUCING THE LESSON

⏱ 5-Minute Check

(over Lesson 15-1)

1. At the Burger Shack, you can order a burger rare, medium, or well done. It can be plain, or have one of these toppings: onions, relish, mayonnaise, cheese, ketchup, or tomato. How many different kinds of burgers can you order? **21**

Motivating the Lesson

Use the menu from Motivating the Lesson in Lesson 15-1. If the order is again a sandwich, a beverage, and a side order, have students figure out how many different orders there could be.

TEACHING THE LESSON

Teaching Tip ❶ Make sure students know how to read a tree diagram so they can identify the possibilities.

Objective 15-2

After studying this lesson, you should be able to:
- solve problems using the Basic Counting Principle.

Application

Jolie Martis is going to buy a new automobile. She has already chosen the make and model of the car but she still has three more decisions to make.

1. Does she want standard or automatic transmission?
2. Does she want to have a cassette player or does she want a compact disc player?
3. Does she want a silver, red, or white exterior?

These three decisions are called **independent events** since one decision does not affect the others. The **tree diagram** shown below illustrates all the different choices Jolie has in making her final three decisions. **Teaching Tip ❶**

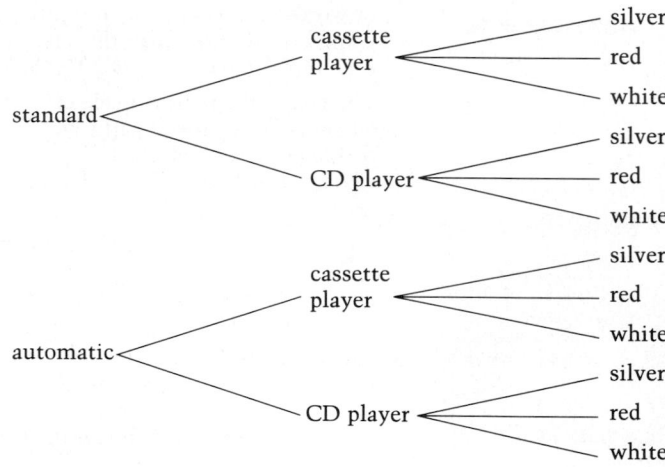

One of Jolie's choices is a red car with standard transmission and cassette player. There are 11 other choices, making a total of 12.

Remember that each decision is an independent event.

You can find the total number of choices that Jolie has without drawing a diagram.

Choices:	standard/automatic	cassette/CD player	silver/white/red
Number of choices:	2	2	3

The total number of choices can be found by multiplying the number of choices for each decision. Thus, the total number of choices is $2 \cdot 2 \cdot 3$ or 12. This application is an example of the **Basic Counting Principle.**

ALTERNATE TEACHING STRATEGIES

Using Calculators

Use the Basic Counting Principle and a calculator to solve several problems that are difficult to solve by modeling because the numbers are too large. For example, there are 20 students in a class. How many different ways might they be seated? A store has 30 different blouses and 25 different skirts. How many outfits are possible?

Basic Counting Principle	Suppose an event can occur in p different ways. Another event can occur in q different ways. There are $p \cdot q$ ways both events can occur.

This principle can be extended to any number of events.

Example 1

How many different 3-letter patterns can be formed using the letters x, y, and z, if a letter can be used more than once?

Since each choice of letter is not affected by the previous choice, these are *independent events*.

Letter:	1st	2nd	3rd
Number of choices:	3	3	3

There are $3 \cdot 3 \cdot 3$ or 27 possible patterns.

Some applications involve **dependent events.** That is, the number of choices for one event *does affect* other events.

Example 2

How many different 3-letter patterns can be formed using the letters x, y, and z, if each letter is used exactly once? **Teaching Tip ❷**

After the first letter is chosen, it cannot be chosen again. So there are only two choices for the second letter. Likewise, after the second choice is made, there is only one choice for the third letter. These are *dependent events*.

Letter:	1st	2nd	3rd
Number of choices:	3	2	1

There are $3 \cdot 2 \cdot 1$ or 6 patterns. Note that $3 \cdot 2 \cdot 1 = 3!$.

Example 3

How many 7-digit phone numbers can begin with the prefix 890?

Since each digit can be used any number of times, there are 10 choices for each of the last four digits of the phone number. These are independent events.

Digit in phone number:	4th	5th	6th	7th
Number of choices:	10	10	10	10

There are $10 \cdot 10 \cdot 10 \cdot 10 = 10^4$ or 10,000 phone numbers.

LESSON 15-2 THE COUNTING PRINCIPLE **685**

Example 4

Suppose five points in a plane represent towns that are connected by roads. Starting at any one town, how many different routes are there so that you visit each town exactly once?

Let's name the points A, B, C, D, and E. Since each town you visit limits the number of towns left to visit, these are dependent events.

Points:	1st	2nd	3rd	4th	5th
Number of choices:	5	4	3	2	1

$5 \cdot 4 \cdot 3 \cdot 2 \cdot 1 = 5!$

There are $5 \cdot 4 \cdot 3 \cdot 2 \cdot 1$ or 120 routes you could take.

CHECKING FOR UNDERSTANDING

Communicating Mathematics

Read and study the lesson to answer each question. **1–3. See margin.**

1. Describe the difference between independent and dependent events.

2. Give two examples of independent events.

3. Give two examples of dependent events.

4. Are the results of tossing a coin several times independent events or dependent events? **independent**

Guided Practice

5c. dependent or independent, based upon the availability of each color for a particular model

5. Tell whether the events are independent or dependent. **independent**
   a. selecting a mystery book and a history book at the library
   b. drawing cards from a deck to form a 5-card hand **dependent**
   c. selecting the color and model of a new automobile

6. How many different batting orders does a baseball team of nine players have if the pitcher bats last? **8! or 40,320 orders**

7. At Columbus High School, Darrin is taking six different classes. Assuming that each of these classes is offered each period, how many different schedules might he have? **6! or 720 schedules**

EXERCISES

Practice

A

9. dependent, if a person can only hold one office

Tell whether the events are independent or dependent.

8. choosing the color and size of a pair of pants **independent**

9. choosing a president, secretary, and treasurer for the Pep Club

10. choosing five numbers in a bingo game **dependent**

11. choosing the winner and loser of a chess game **dependent**

12. Each of five people guess the total number of runs in a baseball game. They write down the guess without telling what it is. **independent**

13. The numerals 0 through 9 are written on pieces of paper and placed in a jar. Three of them are selected one after the other without replacing any of the pieces of paper. **dependent**

Solve each problem.

14. The letters g, h, j, k, and l are to be used to form 5-letter passwords for an office security system. How many passwords can be formed if the letters can be used more than once in any password? **3125**

15. A store has 15 sofas, 12 lamps, and 10 tables at half price. How many different combinations of a sofa, a lamp, and a table can be sold at half price? **1800**

 Draw a tree diagram to illustrate all the possibilities. **See margin.**

16. the possibilities for boys and girls in a family with two children

17. the possibilities for boys and girls in a family with three children

Solve each problem.

18. A license plate must have two letters (not I or O) followed by three digits. The last digit cannot be zero. How many possible plates are there? **518,400**

19. There are five roads from Albany to Briscoe, six from Briscoe to Chadwick, and three from Chadwick to Dover. How many different routes are there from Albany to Dover via Briscoe and Chadwick? **90**

20. For a particular model of car, a car dealer offers 6 versions of that model, 18 body colors, and 7 upholstery colors. How many different possibilities are available for that model? **756**

21. How many ways can six different books be arranged on a shelf? **720**

22. Three different colored dice are tossed. How many distinct outcomes can occur? **216**

Teaching Tip ❸

23. How many ways can six books be arranged on a shelf if one of the books is a dictionary and it must be on an end? **240**

24. Using the letters from the word *equation*, how many 5-letter patterns can be formed in which q is followed immediately by u? **480**

25. Consider the letters a, e, i, o, r, s, and t.

   a. How many different 4-letter patterns can be formed from these letters if no letter occurs more than once? **840**

   b. How many of these patterns begin with a vowel and end with a consonant? **240**

26. How many 5-digit numbers exist between 65,000 and 69,999 if no digit is to be repeated in each number? **1344**

APPLYING THE LESSON

Homework Exercises

Assignment Guide

Basic: 8–22, 27–28, 30–34
Average: 12–24, 27–34
Enriched: 16–34

Chapter 15, Quiz A, (Lessons 15-1 through 15-2), is available in the Evaluation Masters Booklet, p. 205.

Teaching Tip ❸   For Exercises 23–26, have students draw a sketch or list some of the possibilities to check their understanding of each problem.

Practice Masters Booklet, p. 111

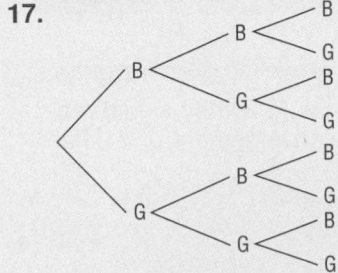

15-2 **Practice Worksheet**

NAME _____   DATE _____

The Counting Principle

Solve each problem.

1. A briefcase lock has 3 rotating cylinders, each containing 10 digits. How many numerical codes are possible? **1000**

2. A golf club manufacturer makes irons with 7 different shaft lengths, 3 different grips, 5 different lies, and 2 different club head materials. How many different combinations are offered? **210**

3. There are five different routes that a commuter can take from her home to the office. In how many ways can she make a round trip if she uses a different route coming than going? **20**

4. In how many ways can the 4 call letters of a radio station be arranged if the first letter must be W or K and no letters repeat? **27,600**

5. How many 7-digit phone numbers can be formed if the first digit cannot be 0 or 1? **8,000,000**

6. How many 7-digit phone numbers can be formed if the first digit cannot be 0 or 1 and if no digit can be repeated? **483,840**

Additional Answers

3. **Answers will vary. Sample answers are selecting members of a team from a group and the lottery.**

16.
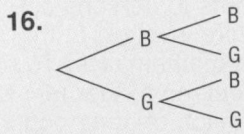

17.

33.

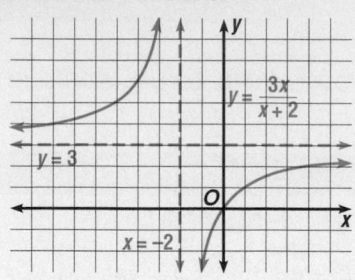

$y = \dfrac{3x}{x+2}$

$y = 3$

$x = -2$

Critical Thinking

In this text, when referring to a deck of cards, we mean a standard deck of 52 cards.

27. Suppose five cards are drawn from a deck of cards. Three were red and two were black.

   a. How many possibilities are there for this hand? **10,140,000**

   b. Suppose exactly one of the black cards is a face card. Now how many possibilities are there? *A face card is a jack, queen, or king.* **1,872,000**

Applications

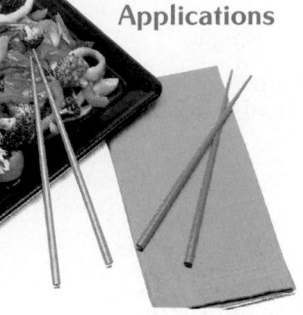

28. **Dining**   A Chinese restaurant offers a special price for customers who dine before 6:30 P.M. This offer includes an appetizer, a soup, and an entree all for $6.95. There are 4 choices of appetizers, 3 soups, and 5 entrees. How many different meals are available under this offer? **60 meals**

29. **Transportation**   Four ferry boats run round trips between Harrod and Lafayette.

   a. How many different ways can a traveler make a round trip? **16 ways**

   b. How many different ways can a traveler make a round trip, by riding a different ferry on the return trip? **12 ways**

30. **6 × 7 or 42, since 7 is the most probable total each time the dice are rolled.**

Mixed Review

30. Suppose you roll 2 dice six times. What is the most probable total of all six rolls? Why?   **(Lesson 15-1)**

31. Find the 27th term of $3 + 6 + 12 + 24 \ldots$. Express using exponents. **(Lesson 13-5)** $3(2)^{26}$

32. A piece of farm equipment valued at $60,000 depreciates 10% per year by the fixed rate method. After how many years will the value have depreciated to $45,000?   **(Lesson 11-7)** **2.73 years**

33. Graph $y = \dfrac{3x}{x+2}$.   **(Lesson 9-5)** **See margin.**

34. Find $[-6.2] + [4.3] + [-2.87] + [0.5]$.   **(Lesson 2-7)** **-6**

Journal

Suppose you forgot how the counting principle works. How could you figure out a problem without it?

HISTORY CONNECTION

Your skill at winning many kinds of games often relies on your ability to count the possible outcomes given certain choices. This skill of gaming can be traced to the early history of mankind.

An early form of our six-faced die has been found in Assyrian and Sumerian archaeological sites. It is made from the astragalus, which is the bone above the heel bone in sheep and deer. Babylonian and early Egyptian sites (about 3600 B.C.) have contained polished astragali and other colored markers used in game playing. However, these astragali are not uniform in shape and weight. So, a likelihood of a given roll was unpredictable. Perhaps this is one reason that there was not development of probability theory (unlike other fields of mathematics) in the early civilizations.

EXTENDING THE LESSON

Math Power: Reasoning

Ask students how they would represent the arrangement of x different items.
$x(x - 1)(x - 2) \ldots (1)$ or $x!$

History Connection

The History Connection features introduce students to persons or cultures who were involved in the development of mathematics. You may want students to further research the invention of other popular games.

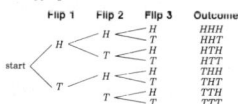

NAME _____ DATE _____

15-2   Enrichment Worksheet

Tree Diagrams and the Power Rule

If you flip a coin once, there are two possible outcomes: heads showing (*H*) or tails showing (*T*). The tree diagram to the right shows the four (2²) possible outcomes if you flip a coin twice.

Example 1: Draw a tree diagram to show all the possible outcomes for flipping a coin three times. List the outcomes.

There are eight (2³) possible outcomes. With each extra flip, the number of outcomes doubles. With 4 flips, there would be sixteen (2⁴) outcomes.

Example 2: In a cup there are a red, a blue, and a yellow marble. How many possible outcomes are there if you draw one marble at random, replace it, and then draw another?

There are nine (3²) possible outcomes.
The Power Rule for the number of outcomes states that if an experiment is repeated *n* times, and if there are *b* possible outcomes each time, there are *bⁿ* total possible outcomes.

Find the total number of possible outcomes for each experiment. Use tree diagrams to help you.

1. flipping a coin 5 times 2^5

2. doing the marble experiment 6 times 3^6

3. flipping a coin 8 times 2^8

4. rolling a 6-sided die 2 times 6^2

5. rolling a 6-sided die 3 times 6^3

6. rolling a 4-sided die 2 times 4^2

7. rolling a 4-sided die 3 times 4^3

8. rolling a 12-sided die 2 times 12^2

15-3 Linear Permutations

Objective
15-3
After studying this lesson, you should be able to:
- solve problems involving permutations.

Application

Before the beginning of the game, the girls basketball team waits for the introduction of the starters. The five starters sit in a row of 12 chairs while their teammates stand around them. How many different ways, or arrangements, are there for the five starters to sit in the 12 chairs?

After the first starting player chooses one of the 12 chairs, the second starter only has 11 choices left, and so on, until the fifth starter is seated. The number of choices for each player is affected by the choice of the previous player, so these are dependent events.

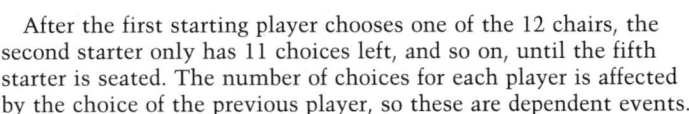

Player:	1st	2nd	3rd	4th	5th
Number of choices:	12	11	10	9	8

There are $12 \cdot 11 \cdot 10 \cdot 9 \cdot 8$ or 95,040 seating arrangements possible.
Teaching Tip ❶

The five starters were seated in a certain order. When a group of people or objects are arranged in a certain order, the arrangement is called a **permutation.** In a permutation, the *order* of the objects is very important. The arrangement of objects in a line is called a **linear permutation.**

Notice that $12 \cdot 11 \cdot 10 \cdot 9 \cdot 8$ is part of 12!. We can write an equivalent expression in terms of 12!.

$$12 \cdot 11 \cdot 10 \cdot 9 \cdot 8 = 12 \cdot 11 \cdot 10 \cdot 9 \cdot 8 \cdot \frac{7 \cdot 6 \cdot 5 \cdot 4 \cdot 3 \cdot 2 \cdot 1}{7 \cdot 6 \cdot 5 \cdot 4 \cdot 3 \cdot 2 \cdot 1}$$

$$= \frac{12 \cdot 11 \cdot 10 \cdot 9 \cdot 8 \cdot 7 \cdot 6 \cdot 5 \cdot 4 \cdot 3 \cdot 2 \cdot 1}{7 \cdot 6 \cdot 5 \cdot 4 \cdot 3 \cdot 2 \cdot 1} \text{ or } \frac{12!}{7!}$$

In P(12, 5), n = 12 and r = 5. Also,
$P(12, 5) = \frac{12!}{(12 - 5)!}$

Note that the denominator of $\frac{12!}{7!}$ is the same as $(12 - 5)!$.

P(n, r) can also be written $_nP_r$.

The number of ways to arrange 12 things taken 5 at a time is written as $P(12, 5)$. Thus, $P(n, r)$ is read "*n* objects taken *r* at a time" and is defined in the following manner.

Definition of
P(n, r)

The number of permutations of *n* objects taken *r* at a time is defined as follows.

$$P(n, r) = \frac{n!}{(n - r)!}$$

LESSON 15-3 LINEAR PERMUTATIONS **689**

ALTERNATE TEACHING STRATEGIES

Using Discussion

Using a list of possible subjects offered at your school, have students determine the number of different schedules possible. Assume no prerequisites or other class restrictions. Elicit student responses as to why, in this case, this is not a meaningful number. **Classes may have prerequisites, some classes are required and some are not, and so on.**

For Example 1
Solve each problem.

a. How many ways can 9 members of a family be seated in a theatre if the mother is seated on the aisle? **40,320**
b. How many ways can 3 books be placed on a shelf if chosen from a selection of 8 different books? **336**

For Example 2
How many ways can 2 geometry, 4 geography, 5 history, and 3 physics books be arranged on a shelf by subject? **829,440**

Teaching Tip ❷ This problem assumes that different linear arrangements of the same three cheerleaders are different groups.

Teaching Tip ❸ Example 2 assumes that each of the various types of books is different.

Example 1

APPLICATION

Photography

The eight high school cheerleaders are to have their pictures taken for the *Eagle*, their yearbook. How many different ways can three cheerleaders be chosen and lined up for each action shot? **Teaching Tip ❷**

Find the number of permutations of 8 people, taken 3 at a time.

$$P(n, r) = \frac{n!}{(n - r)!}$$

$$P(8, 3) = \frac{8!}{(8 - 3)!} \qquad n = 8, r = 3$$

$$= \frac{8 \cdot 7 \cdot 6 \cdot \cancel{5} \cdot \cancel{4} \cdot \cancel{3} \cdot \cancel{2} \cdot \cancel{1}}{\cancel{5} \cdot \cancel{4} \cdot \cancel{3} \cdot \cancel{2} \cdot \cancel{1}} \text{ or } 336$$

There are 336 possible ways three cheerleaders can be lined up for an action shot.

In Example 1, you may have observed that the factors of $(n - r)!$ are contained in $n!$. Instead of writing all the factors of each term, you could also have evaluated the expression in the following way.

$$\frac{8!}{(8 - 3)!} = \frac{8 \cdot 7 \cdot 6 \cdot \cancel{5}!}{\cancel{5}!} \qquad \frac{5!}{5!} = 1 \qquad \textit{Remember, by}$$
$$\textit{definition, } 0! = 1.$$
$$= 8 \cdot 7 \cdot 6 \text{ or } 336$$

Example 2

Teaching Tip ❸
How many ways can 4 algebra books, 3 chemistry books, and 5 history books be arranged on a shelf if the books are ordered according to subject?

First consider how many different ways the books in each subject can be arranged.

The algebra books can be arranged in $P(4, 4)$ or $4!$ different ways.
The chemistry books can be arranged in $P(3, 3)$ or $3!$ different ways.
The history books can be arranged in $P(5, 5)$ or $5!$ different ways.

Now consider how many ways the 3 subjects can be arranged. There are 3 subjects, so $P(3, 3) = 3!$ ways.

The total number of ways the books can be arranged is the product of these four permutations.

A	C	H
4!	3!	5!

3!

$$4! \cdot 3! \cdot 5! \cdot 3! \text{ or } 103,680 \text{ ways}$$

How many different arrangements can be made from the letters of the word *free*? The four letters can be arranged in $P(4, 4)$ or $4!$ ways. However, some of these 24 arrangements look the same. If we labeled the e's as e_1 and e_2, then e_1fre_2 is different from e_2fre_1. However, if you drop the subscripts, the two arrangements are indistinguishable. That is, they look the same. Whenever you have items that cannot be distinguished from one another, you must account for this in your final count of possible permutations.

The two e's can be arranged in $P(2, 2)$ or $2!$ ways. To find the number of different arrangements divide $P(4, 4)$ by $2!$.

$$\frac{P(4, 4)}{P(2, 2)} = \frac{4!}{2!}$$

$$= \frac{4 \cdot 3 \cdot 2!}{2!} \text{ or } 12 \qquad \text{There are 12 ways to arrange the letters.}$$

When some objects are alike, use the following rule to find the number of permutations of those objects.

Permutations with Repetitions	The number of permutations of n objects of which p are alike and q are alike is $$\frac{n!}{p!q!}$$

This rule can be extended for any number of objects that are repeated.

Example 3

How many 7-letter patterns can be formed from the letters of *benzene*?

Find the number of permutations of 7 letters of which 3 are e's and 2 are n's. You must divide $7!$ by both $3!$ and $2!$.

$$\frac{7!}{3!2!} = \frac{7 \cdot 6 \cdot 5 \cdot 4 \cdot 3!}{3! \cdot 2 \cdot 1} \text{ or } 420$$

There are 420 7-letter patterns.

CHECKING FOR UNDERSTANDING

Communicating Mathematics

Read and study the lesson to answer each question.

1. What is a permutation? **an arrangement in which order is important**

2. What is the value of $P(5, 5)$? **120**

3. Write an expression for the number of ways 7 books can be arranged in a row taken 3 books at a time. **$P(7, 3)$, or 210**

RETEACHING THE LESSON

Have students make up problems using permutations and if their problem is appropriate, have them work it.
Example: How many different arrangements can be made of 10 pieces of flatware laid in a row if three are spoons, four are forks, and three are knives? **4200**

692 Chapter 15

Closing the Lesson

Writing Activity Have each student find the number of different ways the letters of his or her first name can be arranged.

APPLYING THE LESSON

Homework Exercises

Assignment Guide

Basic: 11–32, 41–42, 45–50
Average: 17–36, 41–50
Enriched: 23–50

Teaching Tip A calculator is helpful for performing the calculations needed to complete the exercises.

Practice Masters Booklet, p. 112

Guided Practice Determine whether each statement is *true* or *false*.

4. $5! - 3! = 2!$ **false**   5. $6 \cdot 5! = 6!$ **true**

6. $\frac{6!}{3!} = 2!$ **false**   7. $(6 - 3)! = 6! - 3!$ **false**

How many different ways can the letters of each word be arranged?

Teaching Tip   8. FLOWER **720**   9. STUDY **120**   10. POP **3**

EXERCISES

Practice Determine whether each statement is *true* or *false*.

A 11. $\frac{6!}{8!} \cdot \frac{8!}{6!} = 1$ **true**   12. $3! + 4! = 5 \cdot 3!$ **true**   13. $\frac{6!}{30} = 4!$ **true**

14. $\frac{P(9, 9)}{9!} = 1$ **true**   15. $\frac{3!}{3} = \frac{2!}{2}$ **false**   16. $1!2!3!2! = 4!$ **true**

How many different ways can the letters of each word be arranged?

17. SEE **3**   18. PEGGY **60**   19. LEVEL **30**

20. MISSISSIPPI **34,650**   21. ALASKA **120**   22. ALGEBRA **2520**

B 23. PARALLEL **3360**   24. ESSENTIAL **90,720**   25. PERPENDICULAR
                                                  778,377,600

Evaluate each expression.

26. $\frac{P(10, 3)}{P(5, 3)}$ **12**   27. $\frac{P(6, 4)}{P(5, 3)}$ **6**   28. $\frac{P(5, 3)}{P(8, 5)P(5, 5)}$ **$\frac{1}{13,440}$**   29. $\frac{P(6, 3)P(4, 2)}{P(5, 2)}$ **72**

Solve each problem.

30. Don has 5 pennies, 3 nickels, and 4 dimes. The coins of each denomination are indistinguishable. How many ways can he arrange the coins in a row? **27,720**

                                                180

31. How many 6-digit numbers can be made using the digits from 833,284?

32. Five algebra and four geometry books are to be arranged on a shelf. How many ways can they be arranged if all the algebra books must be together? **14,400**

C 33. How many ways can 4 nickels and 5 dimes be distributed among 9 children if each is to receive one coin? **126**

34. There are 4 green boxes, 1 red box, and 1 blue box to be stacked one on top of the other. How many ways can they be stacked if the red box and the blue box are to be separated? **480**

15-3 NAME _____ DATE _____

Practice Worksheet

Linear Permutations

Evaluate each expression.

1. $\frac{8!}{6!}$ **56**   2. $P(8, 6)$ **20,160**

3. $\frac{P(7, 5)}{P(4, 3)}$ **105**   4. $\frac{P(6, 5)P(4, 4)}{P(5, 1)P(9, 2)}$ **48**

How many different ways can the letters of each word be arranged?

5. CANADA **120**   6. ILLINI **60**

7. ANNUALLY **5040**   8. MEMBERS **1260**

Solve each problem.

9. A photographer is taking a picture of a bride and groom together with 6 attendants. How many ways can he arrange the 8 people in a line if the bride and groom stand in the middle? **1440**

10. A person playing a word game has the following letters on her tray: QUOUNNTAGGRA. How many 12-letter arrangements could she make to see if a single word could be formed from all the letters? **29,937,600**

11. How many ways can 3 identical pen sets and 5 identical watches be given to 8 graduates if each receives one item? **56**

12. Three different hardcover books and five different paperbacks are placed on a shelf. How many ways can they be arranged if all the hardcover books are together? **4320**

Find *n* in each equation.

35. $P(n, 4) = 3[P(n, 3)]$ **6**

36. $n[P(5, 3)] = P(7, 5)$ **42**

37. $7[P(n, 5)] = P(n, 3) \cdot P(9, 3)$ **12**

38. $P(n, 4) = 40[P(n - 1, 2)]$ **8**

39. $208P(n, 2) = P(16, 4)$ **15**

40. $9P(n, 5) = P(n, 3) \cdot P(9, 3)$ **11**

Critical Thinking

41. In the junior class at Grenada Hills High School, the following statistics are true.

115 students take algebra 2 and 99 students take chemistry.
49 students take Spanish.
15 students take algebra 2 and chemistry.
20 students take algebra 2 and Spanish.
22 students take chemistry and Spanish.
12 students take algebra 2, chemistry, and Spanish.
31 students are not taking any of these three courses.

How many students are in the junior class? **249 students**

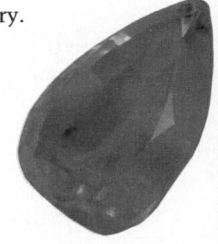

Applications

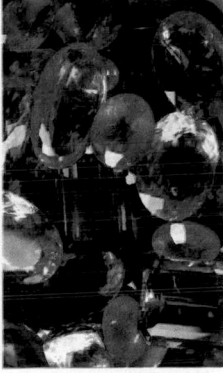

42. **Gemology** Madame Estelle designs jewelry. She is designing a bracelet that will contain a gem in each link of the bracelet. She has 8 emeralds, 5 rubies, and 3 diamonds. The gems in each type of stone are indistinguishable from one another. How many different bracelet designs are possible? **720,720 designs**

43. **Statistics** Nine scores received on a test were 82, 91, 75, 83, 64, 83, 77, 91, and 75.

a. In how many different orders might the scores be recorded? **45,360**

b. What is the average of these test scores? **about 80.1**

44. **Communication** There are 3 identical red flags and 5 identical white flags that are used to send signals. All 8 flags are arranged in a row. How many signals can be given? **56**

Mixed Review

46. **2, 3, 4, 5, 6, 7, 8**

45. How many ways can you have 50¢ using at least 1 quarter? (**Lesson 15-2**) **13 ways**

46. State the stems that would be used to make a stem-and-leaf plot for {63, 57, 49, 52, 64, 31, 27, 82, 47, 61}. (**Lesson 14-2**)

47. Solve $\log_3(x + 6) = 2 \log_3 x$. (**Lesson 12-3**) **3**

48. **Travel** A plane flies from Baltimore to Omaha with a tailwind of 120 km/h in 2.5 hours. On the return trip flying into the same wind takes 3.75 hours. In still air, the plane would have the same speed both ways. Find the distance from Baltimore to Omaha. (**Lesson 11-7**) **1800 km**

49. Solve the system $\begin{cases} x + 2y = 11 \\ x - 4y = 2 \end{cases}$. (**Lesson 3-2**) $\left(8, \frac{3}{2}\right)$

50. If $a = 2$, $b = -6$, and $c = 3$, find the value of d if $a^3b^2 + 4ac + 2d \geq 6c^2 - 4ab$. (**Lesson 1-7**) $d \geq -105$

EXTENDING THE LESSON

Math Power: Communication

Have students verbalize a solution process for the following problem then solve it. The reserve tennis team has four fewer players than does the varsity team. Two players from each team are chosen, in order, to play a match. The number of arrangements of varsity players is three times the number of arrangements of reserve play-ers. How many are on each team? $P(n, 2) = 3[P(n - 4, 2)]$; **10 varsity, 6 reserve players**

Enrichment Masters Booklet, p. 97

INTRODUCING THE LESSON

 5-Minute Check

(over Lesson 15-3)

1. *True* or *False*: $5! + 4! = 6 \cdot 4!$
   true
2. *True* or *False*: $\frac{8!}{8} = \frac{5!}{5}$ **false**
3. How many different ways can the letters of the word PEOPLE be arranged? $\frac{6!}{2!2!} = 180$
4. Evaluate $\frac{P(9, 5) \cdot P(6, 3)}{P(4, 4)}$.
   75,600
5. How many ways can 8 books be arranged on a shelf?
   40,320

Motivating the Lesson

Show students a circle graph. Discuss why the parts are arranged as they are. Have students name different arrangements of the parts of the graph.

Objective
15-4

After studying this lesson, you should be able to:
- solve problems involving circular permutations.

Application

Lee's Catering offers party trays that are made up of six items. Mrs. Sitkowski orders a tray with cheese, pickles, ham, salami, turkey, and roast beef. How many different ways can these items be arranged on the tray if each item must fit in its own section?

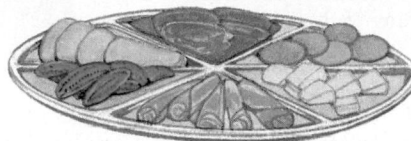

Let these letters represent the items.

c = cheese	p = pickles
h = ham	s = salami
t = turkey	r = roast beef

Think of each tray as a circle. Three possible arrangements of the various items are shown below.

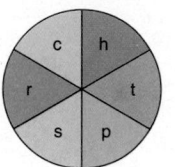 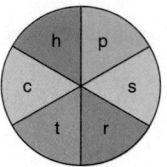 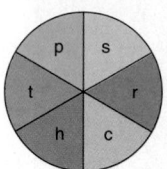

How does the arrangement change as the first tray is turned? Which arrangement is *really* different from the other two?

When 6 different objects are placed in a line, there are 6! or 720 arrangements of the 6 objects taken 6 at a time. However, when the 6 objects are arranged in a circle, some of the arrangements are alike. These arrangements fall into groups of 6. Once an arrangement is determined, the other five members of the group are formed by rotating the circle. Then you can rearrange the items and another group of 6 is formed. Thus, the total number of *really* different arrangements of 6 objects around a circle is $\frac{1}{6}$ of the total number of arrangements in a line.

$$\begin{aligned}
\frac{1}{6} \cdot 6! &= \frac{6 \cdot 5 \cdot 4 \cdot 3 \cdot 2 \cdot 1}{6} \\
&= 5 \cdot 4 \cdot 3 \cdot 2 \cdot 1 \\
&= 5! \text{ or } 120 \quad \textit{Note that } 5! = (6 - 1)!.
\end{aligned}$$

There are $(6 - 1)!$ arrangements of 6 objects in a circle. This is known as a **circular permutation.**

ALTERNATE TEACHING STRATEGIES

Using Connections

Using magazines, newspapers, and books, have students find several circle graphs. Have students find the number of different arrangements possible for each. For each graph, also find the number of different arrangements possible if the arrangements are in relation to the largest part of the graph.

Circular Permutations	If *n* distinct objects are arranged in a circle, then there are $\frac{n!}{n}$ or $(n - 1)!$ permutations of the objects around the circle.

Example 1

Five students are assigned to each project group. One group goes to the library to begin their research. If they sit at a round table, how many different seating arrangements are possible?

Since there are 5 people, there will be $(5 - 1)!$ or $4!$ arrangements.

$(5 - 1)! = 4!$
$\qquad = 4 \cdot 3 \cdot 2 \cdot 1$ or 24

There are 24 seating arrangements possible for the group.

Teaching Tips ❶ , ❷

Suppose *n* objects are in a circular arrangement, but the position of the objects is related to a fixed point. Rotating the circle will relate a different object to the fixed point and will make a new arrangement of the objects. Because of this fixed point, the permutations are now considered linear. The number of permutations for a circular permutation with a fixed point is *n!*. Consider the following contrasting situations.

I. Let each circle represent a table and the labeled points be the people at that table. Let the arrow represent the seat next to the door. How many arrangements are possible?

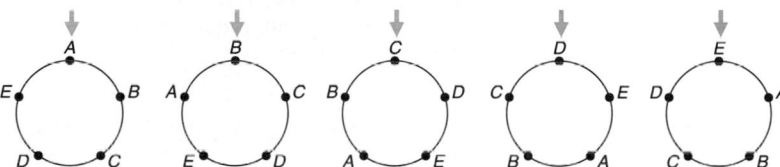

These arrangements can be considered different because in each one, a different person sits next to the door. Thus, there are $P(5, 5)$ or $5!$ arrangements relative to a fixed point.

$5! = 5 \cdot 4 \cdot 3 \cdot 2 \cdot 1$ or 120

II. Suppose three keys are placed on a key ring. How many different arrangements are possible?

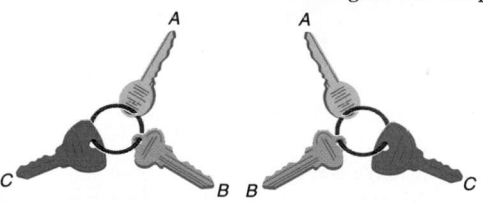

It appears that there are at most $(3 - 1)!$ or 2 different arrangements of keys on the ring.

But what happens if the first key ring arrangement is turned over?

LESSON 15-4   CIRCULAR PERMUTATIONS   695

Teaching Tip ❸ Remind students that circular arrangements are reflections only when the objects can actually be turned over. Therefore, the arrangement described in Example 1 could not be a reflection.

Teaching Tip ❸ When the key ring is turned over, the first arrangement becomes the second arrangement. Then there is really only one arrangement of the three keys. These two arrangements are **reflections** of each other. As a result, there are only half as many arrangements when reflections are possible.

$$\frac{(3 - 1)!}{2} = \frac{2 \cdot 1}{2} \text{ or } 1$$

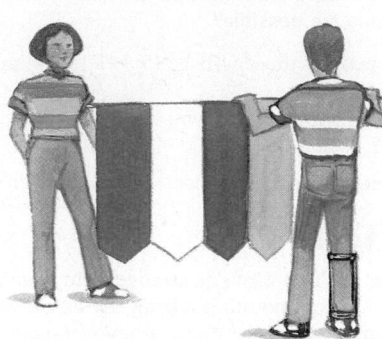

Reflections also occur in linear arrangements. Suppose Lyle holds a multicolored flag up for Rosa to see. From his perspective the flag is red, white, blue, and yellow, in order from left to right. However, from Rosa's view, it is yellow, blue, white, and red, from left to right.

If you were asked how many possible arrangements of these colors there were for the flag, your answer would be half of 4! or 12 arrangements.

Example 2

Six charms are to be placed on a bracelet.

a. **How many different ways can they be placed if the bracelet has no clasp?**

a. Since there is no fixed starting point for the arrangements, this is a circular permutation. However, since the bracelet can be turned over, it is also a reflection. So, the number of arrangements will be half that of a circular permutation.

$$\frac{(6 - 1)!}{2} = \frac{5!}{2}$$
$$= \frac{5 \cdot 4 \cdot 3 \cdot 2 \cdot 1}{2} \text{ or } 60$$

There are 60 different ways to arrange the charms.

b. **How many different ways can they be placed if the bracelet has a clasp?**

b. Since there is a clasp, this is treated as a linear permutation. However, it is still reflective.

$$\frac{6!}{2} = \frac{6 \cdot 5 \cdot 4 \cdot 3 \cdot 2 \cdot 1}{2} \text{ or } 360$$

There are 360 different ways to arrange the charms.

RETEACHING THE LESSON

Divide the class into groups. Give each group an expression used to find a permutation. First, have them make up their own word problem that would use that expression to find the answer. Then have them solve it and see if it makes sense. Example: $\frac{(5 - 1)!}{2}$

They would describe a circular permutation that is also a reflection. **12**

CHECKING FOR UNDERSTANDING

Communicating Mathematics

Read and study the lesson to answer each question. **See margin.**

1. How does a circular permutation differ from a linear permutation?
2. Explain how a reflection affects arrangements. **See margin.**
3. Under what condition is a circular arrangement treated as a linear permutation? **when there is a fixed reference point**

Guided Practice

Determine whether each arrangement is linear or circular. Then determine if it is also a reflection. Then find the number of arrangements.

4. 8 charms on a bracelet that has no clasp **circular, reflection, 2520**
5. a football huddle of 11 players **circular, not reflection, 3,628,800**
6. placing 6 coins in a circle on a table **circular, not reflection, 120**
7. 10 beads on a necklace with a clasp **linear, reflection, 1,814,400**

EXERCISES

Practice

Determine whether each arrangement is linear or circular. Then determine if it is also a reflection.

8. a pearl necklace that is open **linear, reflection**

9. circular, not reflection
10. linear, not reflection

9. four people seated around a square table relative to each other
10. people seated around a square table relative to one chair
11. a baseball team's batting order **linear, not reflection**

Evaluate each expression.

12. $\dfrac{P(6, 4) \cdot P(5, 2)}{5!}$ **60**
13. $\dfrac{P(8, 3) \cdot P(5, 4)}{P(6, 6)}$ **66**
14. $\dfrac{P(12, 6)}{P(12, 3) \cdot P(8, 2)}$ **9**

CONNECTION

Geometry

Solve each problem.

15. How many ways can 6 keys be arranged on a key ring? **60**
16. How many ways can 6 campers be arranged around a campfire? **120**
17. How many ways can 8 charms be arranged on a bracelet that has no clasp? **2520**
18. How many ways can 4 councilmen and 4 councilwomen be seated alternately at a round table? **72**
19. How many ways can 5 hors d'oeuvres be arranged around a plate? **24**
20. How many ways can 6 points be labeled A through F on the circle at the right, relative to its x-intercept? **720**

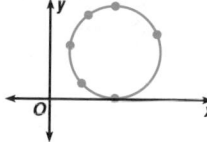

LESSON 15-4   CIRCULAR PERMUTATIONS   697

Additional Answers

1. In a circular permutation, there is no reference point for the exact beginning of the arrangement.
2. It reduces the number by half as many.

15-4 **Practice Worksheet**
NAME _____ DATE _____

Circular Permutations

Evaluate each expression.

1. $\dfrac{5!}{5}$ **24**
2. $\dfrac{7!}{2 \cdot 5!}$ **21**
3. $\dfrac{P(8, 3)}{7!}$ **$\dfrac{1}{15}$**

4. $\dfrac{P(6, 3) \cdot P(4, 2)}{4!}$ **60**
5. $\dfrac{P(7, 4) \cdot P(5, 3)}{P(6, 5)}$ **70**
6. $\dfrac{P(8, 5)}{P(9, 2) \cdot P(7, 3)}$ **$\dfrac{4}{9}$**

Solve each problem.

7. How many ways can 4 charms be arranged on a bracelet that has no clasp? **3**
8. How many ways can 4 charms be arranged on a bracelet that has a clasp? **12**

9. How many ways can 8 charms be arranged on a bracelet that has a clasp? **20,160**
10. How many ways can 8 charms be arranged on a bracelet that has no clasp? **2520**

11. How many ways can 5 men and 5 women be seated alternately at a round table? **1440**
12. How many ways can 6 red beads and 6 white beads be placed alternately on a necklace with no clasp? **21,600**

13. How many ways can 6 red beads and 6 white beads be placed alternately on a necklace that has a clasp? **129,600**
14. How many ways can Laura and her 6 friends be seated around a table if Laura sits at the head of the table? **720**

21. How many ways can 5 dinner guests be seated around a circular table if the only two married guests are seated next to each other? **12**

22. A necklace has 20 links and no clasp. How many ways can 6 different colored beads be added to the necklace if each bead requires one link? **19,380**

Critical Thinking

23. **Construction** On a square city block, there are 8 lots on each side of the street between cross-streets. If a builder is to build any one of five basic designed homes on each lot on the block, how many different arrangements could exist? Write your answer in exponential form. 5^{28}

Applications

24. **Design** Forty pearls are strung in a circle. Twenty-eight are white and 12 are black. How many ways can the pearls be strung if a clasp is used? **2,793,426,740**

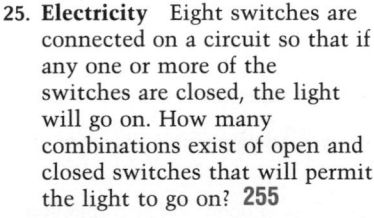

25. **Electricity** Eight switches are connected on a circuit so that if any one or more of the switches are closed, the light will go on. How many combinations exist of open and closed switches that will permit the light to go on? **255**

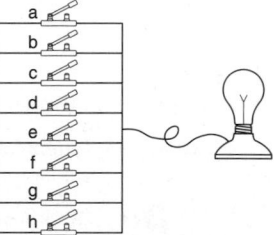

26. **Environmentalism** Sam Marshall is a world environmentalist who keeps video tapes of his research in different countries. On one circular carousel he has six tapes of South America, four tapes of Africa, and two tapes of Australia. How many different ways can he arrange those tapes on the carousel? **39,916,800**

Mixed Review

28. $\displaystyle\sum_{n=1}^{20} \frac{n+1}{2n+1}$

29. **3 positive real roots, or 1 positive real root and 2 imaginary roots**

31. $x^2 - 3x - 10$

27. How many ways can 5 books be placed on a shelf? **(Lesson 15-3)** **120**

28. Write $\frac{2}{3} + \frac{3}{5} + \frac{4}{7} + \frac{5}{9} + \cdots + \frac{21}{41}$ using sigma notation. **(Lesson 13-3)**

29. Tell the nature of the roots of $0 = x^3 - x^2 + 2x - 3$. **(Lesson 10-4)**

30. Solve $35 = 3b^2 - 8b$. Then use the sum and product of the roots to check your solution. **(Lesson 7-5)** $5, -\frac{7}{3}$

31. Use synthetic division to find $\dfrac{x^3 - 4x^2 - 7x + 10}{x - 1}$. **(Lesson 5-7)**

32. Discuss the relationships of the slopes of parallel lines compared with the slopes of perpendicular lines. **(Lesson 2-4)** **Parallel lines have equal slopes, whereas the slopes of perpendicular lines are negative reciprocals of each other.**

15-4 NAME _____ DATE _____

Enrichment Worksheet

Menu Choices for the Space Shuttle

The food list for the Space Shuttle contains 10 items classified as main dishes (M), 13 vegetable dishes (V), 8 desserts (D), and 3 appetizers (A). A typical meal might consist of the following:

Shrimp cocktail	1 appetizer (every other day, beginning on day 1)
Beef steak	1 main dish
Rice pilaf	
Green Beans	2 vegetables
Butterscotch pudding	1 dessert

1. Complete the chart to find the number of different menu combinations possible in the first six days of flight. Assume no dish is repeated.

Day	A	M	V_1	V_2	D	Number per Day
1	3	10	13	12	8	37,440
2	—	9	11	10	7	6,930
3	2	8	9	8	6	6,912
4	—	7	7	6	5	1,470
5	1	6	5	4	4	480
6	—	5	3	2	3	90
					Total:	53,322

2. How could you change the original conditions of the problem so that no meals would be repeated in seven days rather than six days? **Answers may vary. A sample answer is to increase both the appetizers and vegetables by 1.**
3. Use the results of Exercise 2. Find the new number of combinations. **For 4 appetizers and 14 vegetables, the number is 83,112.**

EXTENDING THE LESSON

Math Power: Problem Solving

Ask students how many links are on a bracelet with no clasp if 2 charms can be arranged 14 ways and each charm requires one link.

$$\frac{n!}{(n-2)!2 \cdot 2} = 14; \text{ 8 links}$$

15-5 Combinations

Objective
15-5

After studying this lesson, you should be able to:
■ solve problems involving combinations.

Application

Suppose six girls from a group of nine are chosen to start the championship volleyball game. In this case, the order in which the girls are chosen is not important. Such a selection is called a **combination.**

The combination of nine objects or people taken six at a time is written as $C(9, 6)$. You know that six objects can be arranged in 6! ways. These arrangements are eliminated with finding the number of combinations because order does not matter.

$$C(9, 6) = \frac{P(9, 6)}{6!}$$

$$= \frac{9!}{(9 - 6)! \cdot 6!} \qquad P(9, 6) = \frac{9!}{(9 - 6)!}$$

$$= \frac{9!}{3! \cdot 6!} \text{ or } 84$$

The six starters can be chosen from the nine team members in 84 ways.

In the solution above, notice that 3! and $(9 - 6)!$ are equivalent. This suggests the following definition.

Definition of $C(n, r)$

Teaching Tip ❶

> The number of combinations of *n* distinct objects taken *r* at a time is defined as follows.
>
> $$C(n, r) = \frac{n!}{(n - r)! r!}$$

$C(n, r)$ can also be written $_nC_r$.

The basic difference between a permutation and a combination is whether order is considered (as in permutation) or not (as in a combination).

Example 1

> The U.S. history class is preparing for its final exam. From a class of 18 males and 12 females, how many study groups of 2 males and 3 females can be formed?

Order is not considered. There are two questions to be considered.
• How many ways can 2 males be chosen from 18?
• How many ways can 3 females be chosen from 12?

The answer is the product of these two combinations, $C(18, 2)$ and $C(12, 3)$.

LESSON 15-5 COMBINATIONS 699

ALTERNATE TEACHING STRATEGIES

Mini-Math Lab

Divide the class into cooperative groups. Set up math stations, each with a different set of manipulatives, such as different coins, a deck of cards, golf tees, or cutouts of different colors. For each station, have each group write a verbal problem involving combinations, then solve the problem. Have each group share its problems with the class.

Lesson Resources

Reteaching Master 15-5
Practice Master 15-5
Enrichment Master 15-5
Technology Master, p. 32
Activity Master, p. 15

 Transparency 15-5 contains the 5-Minute Check and a teaching aid for this lesson.

INTRODUCING THE LESSON

🕐 5-Minute Check

(over Lesson 15-4)

1. How many ways can 6 people be seated relative to each other at a round table? **120**
2. How many ways can 6 people be arranged around a circular table if 2 people must be seated next to each other? **48**

Other Prerequisite Skills

Evaluate each expression.

3. $P(10, 4)$ **5040**
4. $3!P(6, 5) \cdot P(9, 2)$ **311,040**
5. $\dfrac{P(12, 6)}{P(12, 3) \cdot P(8, 2)}$ **9**

Motivating the Lesson

Ask one student to choose three other students from the class to be on a relay team with him or her. Ask the same student to select three other students from the class to work with him or her on a class project. Elicit student responses as to why order could be important in the first choice and is not important in the second choice.

TEACHING THE LESSON

Teaching Tip ❶ Emphasize that dividing by $r!$ in solving for $C(n, r)$ eliminates order being important. Otherwise, the formula would be the same as that for linear permutations.

Teaching Tip ❷   Point out that $\frac{8!}{(6!2!)} = \frac{(8 \cdot 7)}{2}$ and $\frac{4!}{(2!2!)} = \frac{(4 \cdot 3)}{2}$. Then ask students to identify a pattern.

You can use your calculator to evaluate this expression.

$$C(18, 2) \cdot C(12, 3) = \frac{18!}{(18-2)!2!} \cdot \frac{12!}{(12-3)!3!} \text{ or } \frac{18! \, 12!}{16! \, 2! \, 9! \, 3!}$$

ENTER: 18 $\boxed{x!}$ $\boxed{\times}$ 12 $\boxed{x!}$ $\boxed{\div}$ $\boxed{(}$ 16 $\boxed{x!}$ $\boxed{\times}$ 2 $\boxed{x!}$ $\boxed{\times}$

9 $\boxed{x!}$ $\boxed{\times}$ 3 $\boxed{x!}$ $\boxed{)}$ $\boxed{=}$ 33660

There are 33,660 possible combinations of 2 males and 3 females in a group.

Example 2

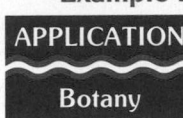
APPLICATION
Botany

A bucket at Fireside Florists contains 8 red carnations, 5 white daisies, and 4 blue carnations. How many bouquets can be chosen so that each bouquet has 2 red carnations, 1 white daisy, and 2 blue carnations? **Teaching Tip ❷**

This involves the product of three combinations—one for each type of flower.

$C(8, 2)$ Select 2 of the 8 red carnations.
$C(5, 1)$ Select 1 of the 5 white daisies.
$C(4, 2)$ Select 2 of the 4 blue carnations.

$$C(8, 2) \cdot C(5, 1) \cdot C(4, 2) = \frac{8!}{6!2!} \cdot \frac{5!}{4!1!} \cdot \frac{4!}{2!2!}$$

$$= \frac{8 \cdot 7 \cdot 6!}{6! \cdot 2} \cdot \frac{5 \cdot 4!}{4!} \cdot \frac{4 \cdot 3 \cdot 2!}{2 \cdot 2!}$$

$$= 28 \cdot 5 \cdot 6 \text{ or } 840$$

There are 840 bouquets that could be made.

An important skill in problem solving is being able to distinguish between permutations and combinations.

Example 3

CONNECTION
Geometry

A decagon is a polygon with 10 vertices and 10 sides. A diagonal is a segment that connects any two nonconsecutive vertices of a polygon.

Find the total number of diagonals that can be drawn in a decagon.

Each diagonal has two endpoints. Suppose one has endpoints A and E. Then segments AE and EA are the same. Thus, order is not important. The combination of 10 points taken two at a time gives the total number of segments connecting those 10 points.

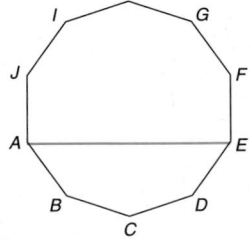

$$C(10, 2) = \frac{10!}{8!2!} \text{ or } 45$$

However, 45 is not our answer. Since 10 of the segments connecting the points are sides of the decagon, you must subtract 10 from 45, the number of combinations.

The total number of diagonals in a decagon is $45 - 10$ or 35.

Some applications can involve *both* permutations and combinations.

Example 4

From a deck of 52 cards, how many ways can 5 cards be drawn so that 3 are of one suit and 2 are of another? **Teaching Tip ③**

First consider how many ways 2 suits can be chosen from 4. Since a different number of cards is being selected from each suit, order is important. Then consider the combinations possible with each suit.

$P(4, 2)$ Select 2 suits from 4 suits.
$C(13, 3)$ Select 3 cards from 13 cards in one suit.
$C(13, 2)$ Select 2 cards from 13 cards in the other suit.

$$P(4, 2) \cdot C(13, 3) \cdot C(13, 2) = \frac{4!}{2!} \cdot \frac{13!}{10!3!} \cdot \frac{13!}{11!2!}$$
$$= 12 \cdot 286 \cdot 78 \text{ or } 267{,}696$$

There are 267,696 ways to draw the cards.

Teaching Tip ③   In Example 4, combinations may be used to select the suits rather than use $P(4, 2)$. There are $C(4, 1)$, or 4 ways, to first choose the suit that will have 3 cards. Then there are $C(3, 1)$, or 3 ways, to choose the suit that will have 2 cards. So $4 \cdot 3 = 12$, which equals $P(4, 2)$.

CHECKING FOR UNDERSTANDING

EVALUATING THE LESSON

Communicating Mathematics

Read and study the lesson to answer each question.

1. Describe the difference between a permutation and a combination.

2. A starting baseball team is formed from a group of 12 players. Explain why this might be considered a permutation.

3. A student approaches you and asks you for the permutation to your permutation lock. You look at them with confusion and then say, "You mean what's the combination to my combination lock!" The student insists upon using the word permutation instead of combination. Who is correct mathematically?
the student, because the order is important

1. **Permutation is an arrangement in which the order is important. Combination is an arrangement where order is not important.**
2. **The team bats in a certain order.**

Checking for Understanding

Exercises 1–11 are designed to help you assess understanding through reading, writing, and speaking. You should work through Exercises 1–3 with your students, and then monitor their work on Exercises 4–11.

Error Analysis

Have students simplify factorials in steps in order to understand the properties of factorials.

Guided Practice

Determine whether each situation involves a permutation or a combination.

4. 5 books on a shelf **permutation**
5. a rummy hand of 7 cards **combination**
6. a seating chart in a classroom **permutation**
7. finding the diagonals of a polygon **combination**

Evaluate each expression.

8. $C(5, 3)$ **10**
9. $C(12, 5)$ **792**
10. $C(3, 2) \cdot C(8, 3)$ **168**
11. $\dfrac{C(10, 3)}{C(5, 2)}$ **12**

LESSON 15-5 COMBINATIONS 701

Speaking Activity Have students compare and contrast linear permutations and combinations.

APPLYING THE LESSON

Homework Exercises

Assignment Guide

Basic: 12–39, 50–51, 54–60
Average: 21–44, 50–60
Enriched: 24–60
All: Mid-Chapter Review, 1–6

Reteaching Masters Booklet, p. 99

15-5 **Reteaching Worksheet**

Combinations

A **combination** is a selection of objects where the order is not important. (Remember that order is important in a permutation.) The number of combinations of n objects taken r at a time is denoted by the symbol $C(n, r)$. To find $C(n, r)$, use the following formula:

$C(n, r) = \frac{n!}{(n-r)!r!}$

Example: From a group of 8 men and 6 women, how many committees of 4 men and 3 women can be formed? Order is not considered.

$C(8, 4) \cdot C(6, 3) = \frac{8!}{(8-4)!4!} \cdot \frac{6!}{(6-3)!3!}$

$= \frac{8 \cdot 7 \cdot 6 \cdot 5 \cdot \cancel{4} \cdot \cancel{3} \cdot \cancel{2} \cdot \cancel{1}}{4 \cdot 3 \cdot 2 \cdot 1 \cdot \cancel{4} \cdot \cancel{3} \cdot \cancel{2} \cdot \cancel{1}} \cdot \frac{6 \cdot 5 \cdot 4 \cdot \cancel{3} \cdot \cancel{2} \cdot \cancel{1}}{3 \cdot 2 \cdot 1 \cdot \cancel{3} \cdot \cancel{2} \cdot \cancel{1}}$

$= 70 \cdot 20$ or 1400

Determine whether each situation involves permutations or combinations.

1. arrangement of 10 books on a shelf **permutation**
2. selection of a committee of 3 from 10 people **combination**
3. a hand of 6 cards from a deck of 52 cards **combination**
4. arrangement of 8 people around a circular table **permutation**
5. a subset of 12 elements contained in a set of 26 **combination**
6. a guest list of 3 friends that your family has said you can invite to dinner **combination**

Solve each problem.

7. There are 15 different books. How many groups of 6 books can be selected? **455**
8. From a group of 10 men and 12 women, how many committees of 5 men and 6 women can be formed? **232,848**
9. How many tennis teams of 6 players can be formed from 14 players without regard to position played? **3003**
10. From a standard deck of 52 cards, how many ways can 5 cards be drawn? **2,598,960**

EXERCISES

Practice Determine whether each situation involves a permutation or a combination.

12. 3-letter patterns, chosen from the letters in the word *algebra*

12. permutation

13. a hand of 5 cards from a deck of cards **combination**
14. a team of 5 people chosen from a group of 12 people **combination**

Determine whether each situation involves a permutation or a combination.

15. the answers on a true/false test **permutation**
16. the batting order of the Los Angeles Dodgers **permutation**
17. putting students in assigned seats **permutation**
18. 8 guests seated around a table for dinner **permutation**
19. a 2-man, 2-woman subcommittee of the Campaign Funds committee that has 8 men and 7 women **combination**

Evaluate each expression.

20. $C(7, 2)$ **21**
21. $C(8, 3)$ **56**
22. $C(8, 5) \cdot C(7, 3)$ **1960**
23. $C(24, 21)$ **2024**

CONNECTION
Geometry

On a circle are nine points randomly placed. In how many different ways can you form each polygon?

24. triangle **84**
25. quadrilateral **126**
26. pentagon **126**
27. hexagon **84**
28. octagon **9**
29. decagon **none**

B

Solve each problem.

30. You are required to read 5 books from a list of 12 great American novels. How many different groups can be selected? **792**
31. There are 85 telephones in the editorial department of 'TEEN magazine. How many 2-way connections can be made among the office phones? **3570**
32. How many starting baseball teams of 9 members can be formed from a bench of 14 multitalented players? **2002**
33. There are 27 people in an algebra class, but only 25 computers in the computer lab, so each student must take turns going to the lab. How many different groups of 25 can the teacher send to the lab? **351**

CONNECTION
Geometry

34. Suppose there are 8 points in a plane such that no three points are collinear. How many distinct triangles could be formed with 3 of these points as vertices? **56**

35. Consider a deck of cards.
    a. How many different 5-card hands can have 5 cards of the same suit? **5148**
    b. How many different 4-card hands can have each card from a different suit? **28,561**

702 CHAPTER 15 PROBABILITY

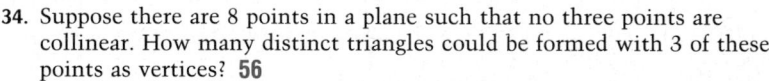

RETEACHING THE LESSON

Orally give students problems involving combinations or permutations. Have students write down the expression that would be used to solve that problem and then discuss why it is one or the other. Discuss ways to distinguish between the two types of problems.

Find the value of n.

36. $C(n, 8) = C(n, 3)$ **11**

37. $C(n, 12) = C(30, 18)$ **30**

38. $C(n, 5) = C(n, 7)$ **12**

39. $C(14, 3) = C(n, 11)$ **14**

 A bag contains 9 blue, 4 red, and 6 white chips. How many ways can 5 chips be selected to meet each condition?

40. all white **6**

41. all blue **126**

42. 2 red, 2 white, 1 blue **810**

43. all red **0**

44. 2 are blue **4320**

45. 2 one color, 3 another color **2808**

From a group of 8 juniors and 10 seniors, a committee of 5 is to be formed to discuss plans for the spring dance. How many committees can be formed given each condition?

46. all juniors **56**

47. 3 juniors, 2 seniors **2520**

48. 1 junior, 4 seniors **1680**

49. all seniors **252**

Critical Thinking   **50.** Prove $P(n, r) = r! \cdot C(n, r)$. **See margin.**

Applications   **51. Sports** How many different baseball teams of nine players can Gardena High School put on the field if they have four players that can only pitch and the remaining twelve players can play any of the other eight positions? **1980 teams**

52. Statistics The California state lottery is called "6/53," meaning a winner must select six different correct numbers from the numbers 1 through 53.

a. How many different ways can six numbers be selected? **22,957,480**

b. Suppose you had to select the numbers in a specific order. What would be the number of possibilities? **16,529,385,600**

c. Refer to your answers in parts **a** and **b**. Describe each situation as a permutation or a combination. Explain.
a. combination   b. permutation, because of order

53. Science Fiction The planets Laffaglonia and Madaglonia have been at war for centuries. At the Laffaglonia spy-training school, 10 agents are being trained for a secret mission. What the Laffaglonians don't know is that 2 of the 10 are actually Madaglonian counterspies. If 5 of the agents are chosen at random for a secret mission, how many groups will have at least one Madaglonian counterspy? **196**

Additional Answer

50. $P(n, r) = \dfrac{n!}{(n-r)!}$. **Multiply**

by $\dfrac{r!}{r!}$.

$P(n, r) = \dfrac{n!r!}{(n-r)!r!}$

However, $C(n, r) = \dfrac{n!}{(n-r)!r!}$.

By substitution,
$P(n, r) = r! \cdot C(n, r)$.

NAME _____   DATE _____

15-5 **Practice Worksheet**

Combinations

Evaluate each expression.

1. $C(8, 2)$ **28**

2. $C(11, 3)$ **165**

3. $C(20, 18)$ **190**

4. $C(9, 3) \cdot C(6, 2)$ **1260**

Find the value of x.

5. $C(x, 7) = C(x, 2)$ **9**

6. $C(11, 2) = C(x, 9)$ **11**

Solve each problem.

7. How many 4-person bobsled teams can be chosen from a group of 9 athletes? **126**

8. From a dessert cart in a fine restaurant, customers are allowed to pick 3 desserts from the 10 that are displayed. How many combinations are possible? **120**

9. How many diagonals does a polygon with 12 sides have? **54**

10. How many 5-sided polygons can be formed by joining any 5 of 11 points located on a circle? **462**

An urn contains 8 white, 6 blue, and 9 red balls. How many ways can 6 balls be selected to meet each condition?

11. All balls are red. **84**

12. Three are blue, 2 are white, and 1 is red. **5040**

13. Two are blue, and 4 are red. **1890**

14. Exactly 4 balls are white. **7350**

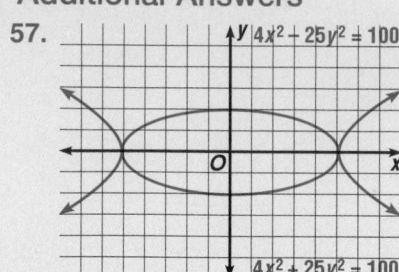
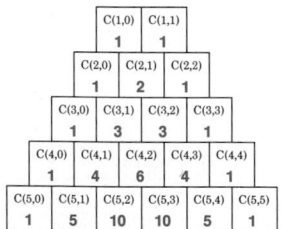
Mixed Review

54. How many ways can five people be seated around a circular table relative to each other? **(Lesson 15-4) 24 ways**

55. **Business** A piece of machinery valued at $75,000 depreciates at a steady rate of 8% yearly. When will the value be $15,000? Use $V_n = P(1 + r)^n$. **(Lesson 13-7) 19.3 years**

56. **Finance** If $200 is invested at 8% interest compounded continuously, when will the investment double? Use $A = Pe^{rt}$. **(Lesson 12-7) about 8.7 years**

57. For graphs see margin.

57. Graph $4x^2 + 25y^2 = 100$ and $4x^2 − 25y^2 = 100$. What kind of graph does each equation have? **(Lesson 9-7) ellipse, hyperbola**

58. Solve $\begin{cases} 2x − y − 5z = 3 \\ x + 4y − 2z = 3 \\ 5x + 3y + 2z = 1 \end{cases}$ using matrices. **(Lesson 4-7)** $\left(\frac{1}{5}, \frac{2}{5}, -\frac{3}{5}\right)$

59. Find the next three terms in this pattern.
$a, a^2, a^2b, a^2b^2, a^2b^2c, \underline{\ ?\ }, \underline{\ ?\ }, \underline{\ ?\ }$ **(Lesson 2-3)**
$a^2b^2c^2, a^2b^2c^2d, a^2b^2c^2d^2$

60. Find all integral ordered pairs (x, y) such that $xy = 64$. **(Lesson 1-5) See margin.**

≈≈≈ MID-CHAPTER REVIEW ≈≈≈

1. Six books are to be arranged on a shelf in your classroom. **(Lesson 15-1)**
   a. Name some models you could use to represent these books and how to arrange them. **See margin.**
   b. How many ways can the books be arranged if the first and last must always be the same two books? **24**

2. At the Burger Bungalow, you can order your hamburger with or without cheese, with or without onions or pickles, and either rare, medium, or well-done. **(Lesson 15-2)**
   a. What type of pictorial representation could you use to calculate the number of choices? **tree diagram**
   b. How many different hamburgers are possible? **24**

3. **Government** How many ways can the 100 United States senators seat themselves in a 100-seat auditorium if there are no restrictions? *Write your answer in factorial form.* **(Lesson 15-3) 100!**

4. In Kentucky, license plate numbers are composed of three letters followed by a dash and three numbers. The letters I and O are never used. How many license plates are possible? **(Lesson 15-3) 13,824,000**

5. Find the number of ways Sam, Renee, Julie, Henri, and Denzel can sit around a table if Denzel and Julie insist upon sitting together. **(Lesson 15-4) 3!2! or 12 ways**

6. In bridge, all 52 cards in a deck are dealt among four players. How many different hands are possible? *Write your answer in factorial form.* **(Lesson 15-5)** $\frac{52!}{13!39!}$

EXTENDING THE LESSON

Math Power: Reasoning

Find the value of n in each problem.
$C(3, 0) + C(3, 1) = C(n, 1)$ **4**
$C(5, 1) + C(5, 2) = C(n, 2)$ **6**
$C(4, 3) + C(4, 4) = C(n, 4)$ **5**
$C(6, 2) + C(6, 3) = C(n, 3)$ **7**
Then write a formula for the general relationship shown in the problems. $C(n, r) + C(n, r + 1) = C(n + 1, r + 1)$

Mid-Chapter Review

The Mid-Chapter Review provides students with a brief review of the concepts and skills in Lessons 15-1 through 15-5. Lesson numbers are given at the end of problems or instruction lines so students may review concepts not yet mastered.

Objective
15-6

After studying this lesson, you should be able to:
- find the probability of an event and determine the odds of success or failure.

Teaching Tip ❶

When a coin is tossed, only two outcomes are possible—*heads* or *tails*. The desired outcome is called a **success**. Any other outcome is referred to as a **failure**. The likelihood of a success or of a failure is called the **probability** of the event.

Probability of Success and of Failure	If an event can succeed in s ways and fail in f ways, then the probabilities of success, $P(s)$, and of failure, $P(f)$, are as follows. $$P(s) = \frac{s}{s+f} \qquad P(f) = \frac{f}{s+f}$$

What does the sum of s and f represent?

If the event cannot succeed, $P(s) = 0$ and $P(f) = 1$. If the event cannot fail, $P(s) = 1$ and $P(f) = 0$. Thus, $P(s)$ and $P(f)$ are always between 0 and 1, inclusive. In fact, the sum of $P(s)$ and $P(f)$ is always 1. Thus, they are called *complements*. So, if $P(s) = \frac{1}{3}$, then $P(f) = 1 - \frac{1}{3}$ or $\frac{2}{3}$.

Example 1

A box contains 5 blue pencils and 4 white pencils. If one pencil is chosen at random, what is the probability that it is blue?

The term at random means that an outcome is chosen without any preference.

The probability of selecting a blue pencil is written $P(blue\ pencil)$.

There are 5 ways to select a blue pencil from the box and 4 ways not to select a blue pencil from the box. The total number of possible selections is $5 + 4$, or 9.

$$P(blue\ pencil) = \frac{s}{s+f} \qquad \textit{Replace } s \textit{ with 5 and } f \textit{ with 4.}$$
$$= \frac{5}{5+4} \text{ or } \frac{5}{9}$$

The probability of selecting a blue pencil is $\frac{5}{9}$ or about 0.556.

ALTERNATE TEACHING STRATEGIES

Using Manipulatives

Give students a box containing 6 blue and 4 white marbles and tell them you will ask them to choose one. In reference to this event, have students write what probabilities are equal to $0, \frac{3}{5}, \frac{2}{5}$, and 1. Expand the lesson to include drawing more than one marble at a time and writing the accompanying probabilities.

Lesson Resources

Reteaching Master 15-6
Practice Master 15-6
Enrichment Master 15-6

 Transparency 15-6 contains the 5-Minute Check and a teaching aid for this lesson.

INTRODUCING THE LESSON

 ### 5-Minute Check

(over Lesson 15-5)
Determine whether each situation is a permutation or a combination.

1. a batting order in baseball **permutation**
2. a committee of 4 men and 5 women, chosen from 8 men and 7 women   **combination**
3. Evaluate $C(6, 2) \cdot C(4, 3)$.   **60**
4. How many committees of 4 men and 3 women can be formed from a group of 7 men and 8 women?   **$35 \cdot 56 = 1960$**
5. How many diagonals does a convex octagon have?   **20**

Motivating the Lesson

Toss a coin. Without revealing the result, ask students how likely the result is to be a head. Have students explain their reasoning.

TEACHING THE LESSON

Teaching Tip ❶   Emphasize that the terms *success* and *failure* refer only to whether an outcome happens or not and have no further meaning in this context. The terms can be confusing when a success refers to what normally may be considered failure, such as a team losing a ball game.

The counting methods you have studied for permutations and combinations are often used in determining probability.

Example 2

There are 6 men and 3 women on city council. A committee of 2 is to be selected at random to study the city's plans for park expansion. What is the probability that the 2 selected are women?

Since a committee is being formed, order is not important. So find the probability using combinations.

Teaching Tip ❷

There are $C(3, 2)$ ways to choose 2 women from 3 women. So, $C(3, 2) = s$. There are $C(9, 2)$ ways to form a committee of 2 from a group of 9 people. So, $s + f = C(9, 2)$.

$$P(two\ women) = \frac{C(3, 2)}{C(9, 2)} \qquad P(s) = \frac{s}{s + f}$$

$$= \frac{\frac{3!}{1!2!}}{\frac{9!}{7!2!}} \qquad C(n, r) = \frac{n!}{(n - r)!r!}$$

$$= \frac{3}{36} \text{ or } \frac{1}{12}$$

The probability of selecting 2 women for the committee is $\frac{1}{12}$ or about 0.083.   *0.083 = 8.3%*

You may have heard someone say, "The odds of that happening are 50/50." **Odds** is the term for the ratio of successes to failures.

Definition of Odds

Teaching Tip ❸

The odds of the successful outcome of an event is expressed as the ratio of the number of ways it can succeed to the number of ways it can fail.

Odds = number of successes:number of failures or $\frac{s}{f}$

Example 3

What are the odds of rolling a die and getting a 3?

Remember that when rolling a die there are 6 possible outcomes. The number 3 is only on one face of the die. Each of the other five faces have a number other than 3.

Odds of rolling a 3 $= \frac{1}{5}$ *1 outcome (3) is a success.*
5 outcomes (1, 2, 4, 5, 6) are failures.

The odds of rolling a 3 are 1 to 5.

Sometimes when figuring the odds, you must first find out the total number of possible outcomes. This can involve finding permutations and combinations.

Example 4

Suppose Amar draws 5 cards from a deck of 52 cards. What are the odds that the first 4 cards drawn will be of one suit and the 5th card will be of another suit?

First, find how many 5-card hands meet these conditions.

$P(4, 2)$ Select 2 suits among 4. Order is important since different numbers of cards are to come from each suit.

$C(13, 4)$ Select 4 cards from a suit containing 13 cards.

$C(13, 1)$ Select 1 card from the other suit.

Now use the counting principle.

$$P(4, 2) \cdot C(13, 4) \cdot C(13, 1) = \frac{4!}{2!} \cdot \frac{13!}{9!4!} \cdot \frac{13!}{12!1!} \text{ or } 111{,}540$$

So, the number of successes is 111,540.

Now find the total number of possible 5-card hands.

$$C(52, 5) = \frac{52!}{47!5!} \text{ or } 2{,}598{,}960$$

The number of 5-card hands that do not meet the conditions is $2{,}598{,}960 - 111{,}540$ or $2{,}487{,}420$. So, the number of failures is $2{,}487{,}420$.

The odds of a 5-card hand with the first 4 cards of one suit and the 5th card of another suit are $\frac{111{,}540}{2{,}487{,}420}$ or $\frac{143}{3189}$. This is about $\frac{1}{22}$ or 0.045.

CHECKING FOR UNDERSTANDING

Communicating Mathematics

Read and study the lesson to answer each question.

1. What is meant by $P(s)$? **the probability of success**

2. What is the value of $P(s) + P(f)$? Justify your result.
                                        1, $s + f$ = all possibilities

3. If $P(f) = \frac{4}{5}$, what is $P(s)$? $\frac{1}{5}$

4. Can $P(s) = \frac{3}{2}$? Explain your answer. **No, $0 \le P(s) \le 1$.**

5. Can the odds of an event occurring be $\frac{3}{2}$? Explain your answer. **yes**

Guided Practice

State the odds of an event occurring given the probability of the event.

6. $\frac{2}{3}$ $\frac{2}{1}$ 7. $\frac{5}{9}$ $\frac{5}{4}$ 8. $\frac{1}{2}$ $\frac{1}{1}$ 9. $\frac{3}{7}$ $\frac{3}{4}$

LESSON 15-6   PROBABILITY   707

RETEACHING THE LESSON

An alternate solution to finding $P(s)$ involves finding $P(f)$ and then subtracting the result from 1.

Error Analysis

Since odds $= \frac{s}{f}$, $P(s) = \frac{s}{(s+f)}$, and $P(f) = \frac{f}{(s+f)}$. So when converting odds to probability, one must add the numerator and denominator together to get the new denominator. When converting from probability to odds, one must subtract the numerator from the denominator to get either the new numerator or denominator, whichever the case may be.

Closing the Lesson

Modeling Activity Have students use models to show that $P(s) + P(f) = 1$.

APPLYING THE LESSON

Homework Exercises

Assignment Guide

Basic: 14–39, 42–43, 45–51
Average: 18–40, 42–51
Enriched: 19–51

Practice Masters Booklet, p. 115

State the probability of an event occurring given the odds of the event.

10. $\frac{3}{5}$ $\frac{3}{8}$ 11. $\frac{4}{3}$ $\frac{4}{7}$ 12. $\frac{8}{1}$ $\frac{8}{9}$ 13. $\frac{1}{5}$ $\frac{1}{6}$

EXERCISES

Practice   State the odds of an event occurring given the probability of the event.

14. $\frac{3}{4}$ $\frac{3}{1}$ 15. $\frac{1}{7}$ $\frac{1}{6}$ 16. $\frac{5}{8}$ $\frac{5}{3}$ 17. $\frac{7}{15}$ $\frac{7}{8}$

State the probability of an event occurring given the odds of the event.

18. $\frac{3}{7}$ $\frac{3}{10}$ 19. $\frac{5}{1}$ $\frac{5}{6}$ 20. $\frac{6}{5}$ $\frac{6}{11}$ 21. $\frac{1}{1}$ $\frac{1}{2}$

Solve each problem.

22. The odds are 6-to-1 that the crosstown rivals will win in the championship football game on Friday night. What is the probability that they will win? $\frac{6}{7}$

23. The probability of Kellyn getting an A on her final exam is $\frac{3}{4}$. What are the odds that she will *not* get an A? $\frac{1}{3}$

   A canister contains 20 pieces of candy: 5 strawberry flavored, 9 watermelon flavored, and 6 mint flavored. Two are selected at random. Find each probability.

24. P(2 strawberry) $\frac{1}{19} \approx 0.053$ 25. P(2 watermelon) $\frac{18}{95} \approx 0.189$

26. P(2 mint) $\frac{3}{38} \approx 0.079$ 27. P(1 strawberry and 1 mint) $\frac{3}{19} \approx 0.158$

There are 5 frozen juice bars and 8 frozen yogurt bars in the freezer. Dana reaches in the freezer and grabs 2 without looking. Find the probability of each selection. Then find the odds of that selection.

28. P(2 juice bars) $\frac{5}{39} \approx 0.128, \frac{5}{34}$ 29. P(2 yogurt bars) $\frac{14}{39} \approx 0.359, \frac{14}{25}$ 30. P(1 of each kind of bar) $\frac{20}{39} \approx 0.513, \frac{20}{19}$

Tommie's bank contains 7 pennies, 4 nickels, and 5 dimes. His parents tell him that he can spend the first three coins that he can shake out of the bank. Find each probability.

31. P(all pennies) $\frac{1}{16} \approx 0.063$ 32. P(all nickels) $\frac{1}{140} \approx 0.007$

33. P(1 dime, 2 nickels) $\frac{3}{56} \approx 0.054$ 34. P(2 pennies, 1 dime) $\frac{3}{16} \approx 0.188$

35. P(1 dime, 1 nickel, 1 penny) $\frac{1}{4} = 0.25$ 36. P(2 dimes, 1 quarter) **0**

Suppose you select 2 letters at random from the word *algebra*. Find each probability.

37. $\frac{2}{7} \approx 0.286$

37. *P*(selecting 2 consonants)

38. *P*(selecting 2 vowels) $\frac{1}{7} \approx 0.143$

39. *P*(selecting 1 vowel and 1 consonant) $\frac{4}{7} \approx 0.571$

C From a deck of 52 playing cards, 5 cards are dealt.

40. What are the odds of each event occurring?

    a. all aces **0**   **b.** all face cards $\frac{33}{108,257}$ **c.** all from one suit $\frac{33}{16,627}$

41a. 66,607:33
  b. 108,257:33
  c. 16,627:33

41. What are the odds against each event occurring?

    a. all hearts   **b.** all face cards   **c.** all from one suit

    d. the first 3 from one suit and the last 2 from another **3736:429**

Critical Thinking

42. A red die and a green die are tossed. What is the probability that the number showing on the green die is greater than the number showing on the red die? $\frac{5}{12}$

Applications

43. **Finance** The state of Ohio has a Super Lotto drawing twice a week in which 6 numbers out of 46 are drawn at random. The proceeds from the lottery help to finance education in the state. What is the probability of winning the Super Lotto? $\frac{1}{9,366,819}$

44. **Sports** A dart board is designed as shown at the right. A dart is thrown and hits the board. Find each probability. *Hint: What is the area of each ring?*

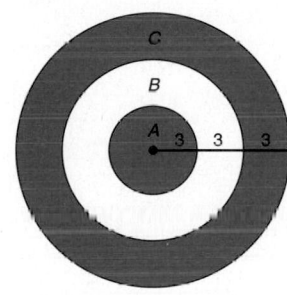

    a. *P*(landing in the A ring) $\frac{1}{9}$

    b. *P*(landing in the B ring) $\frac{1}{3}$

    c. *P*(landing in the C ring) $\frac{5}{9}$

Mixed Review

45. The Groveport Community Children's Chorus now has six altos and eight sopranos. For the songs they are performing at the spring concert, they need two alto soloists and two soprano soloists. How many ways can these four soloists be selected at random? **(Lesson 15-5) 420**

46. Expand $(4r + s)^5$. **(Lesson 13-7) See margin.**

47. Solve $\log_7 y = 4$. **(Lesson 12-3) 2401**

48. If $f(x) = 2x + 3$ and $g(x) = x^2 + 1$, find $f[g(x)]$. **(Lesson 10-7)** $2x^2 + 5$

49. Graph $2x^2 - x - 6 < y$. **(Lesson 8-6) See margin.**

50. Solve $6x^2 + 7x - 3 = 0$ by completing the square. **(Lesson 7-3)** $-\frac{3}{2}, \frac{1}{3}$

51. Simplify $\left(-\frac{1}{2} + \frac{i\sqrt{3}}{2}\right)^3$. **(Lesson 6-10) 1**

EXTENDING THE LESSON

**Math Power:
Problem Solving**

If 2 of the following statements are selected at random, what is *P*(both true)? **0**

- $P(5, 2) + P(5, 3) = P(6, 3)$
  false
- $C(5, 2) + C(5, 3) = C(6, 3)$
  true
- The letters from the word *odds* can form 24 4-letter patterns.
  false

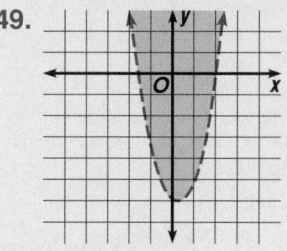

Lesson Resources

Reteaching Master 15-7
Practice Master 15-7
Enrichment Master 15-7
Lab Manual, pp. 45–46

 Transparency 15-7 contains the 5-Minute Check and a teaching aid for this lesson.

INTRODUCING THE LESSON

 5-Minute Check

(over Lesson 15-6)

1. State the odds of an event given the probability is $\frac{8}{9}$.

   8 to 1

2. State the probability of an event given the odds are 5 to 11. $\frac{5}{16}$

3. Two differently colored dice are tossed. How many distinct outcomes are possible? **36**

4. Two dice are tossed. What is the probability of a sum greater than 8? $\frac{5}{18}$

5. What are the odds of getting a seven when tossing two dice?

   $\frac{1}{5}$

Motivating the Lesson

Choose a topic and have students generate a list of independent events and a list of dependent events related to the topic. For example, if the topic is a basketball game, independent events might be making a foul shot and fouling another player. Dependent events might be the number of rebounds made and the number of baskets made.

15-7 Multiplying Probabilities

Objective
15-7

After studying this lesson, you should be able to:
- find the probability of two or more independent or dependent events.

Suppose you toss a red die and a blue die. The probability that the red die shows a 2 is $\frac{1}{6}$. The probability that the blue die shows a 2 is $\frac{1}{6}$. By using the Counting Principle, the probability that both dice show 2s is $\frac{1}{6} \cdot \frac{1}{6}$ or $\frac{1}{36}$. Since the outcome of tossing the red die does not affect the outcome of tossing the blue die, the events are independent.

Probability of Two Independent Events	If two events, **A** and **B**, are independent, then the probability of both events occurring is found as follows. $P(A \text{ and } B) = P(A) \cdot P(B)$

Example 1

Suppose you spin the spinner three times. Find the probability of each outcome.

a. *A*, then *A*, then *A*   **b.** *A*, then *B*, then *C*   **c.** *B*, then *C*, then *C*

Each of these outcomes is independent since what you spin on one turn does not affect the results of other turns.

a. $P(A,A,A) = P(A) \cdot P(A) \cdot P(A)$

$= \frac{3}{6} \cdot \frac{3}{6} \cdot \frac{3}{6}$

$= \frac{1}{2} \cdot \frac{1}{2} \cdot \frac{1}{2}$ or $\frac{1}{8}$

b. $P(A,B,C) = P(A) \cdot P(B) \cdot P(C)$

$= \frac{3}{6} \cdot \frac{2}{6} \cdot \frac{1}{6}$

$= \frac{1}{2} \cdot \frac{1}{3} \cdot \frac{1}{6}$ or $\frac{1}{36}$

c. $P(B,C,C) = P(B) \cdot P(C) \cdot P(C)$

$= \frac{2}{6} \cdot \frac{1}{6} \cdot \frac{1}{6}$

$= \frac{1}{3} \cdot \frac{1}{6} \cdot \frac{1}{6}$ or $\frac{1}{108}$

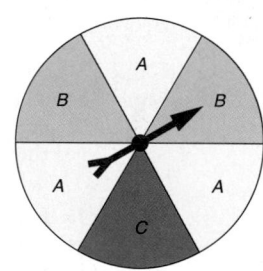

ALTERNATE TEACHING STRATEGIES

Using Critical Thinking

Present students with several different types of manipulatives. Have students list them according to whether they are suitable for determining probability of dependent events only (none listed), independent events only (spinners, die), or both independent and dependent events (anything that has items that can either be replaced or not).

Example 2

APPLICATION

Entertainment

The high school chorus often sings selections from a songbook called *Great American Tunes*. Even though they contain the same songs, 5 of the songbooks have red covers and 4 have blue. One student selects a songbook at random from the shelf, looks up a composer, and places the book back on the shelf. A second student does the same thing. What is the probability that both students looked at songbooks with red covers?

The events are independent since the first book is placed back on the shelf. The outcome of the second selection is not affected by the results of the first selection.

$P(\text{both red}) = P(\text{red}) \cdot P(\text{red})$

$= \dfrac{5}{9} \cdot \dfrac{5}{9} \text{ or } \dfrac{25}{81}$ $\dfrac{25}{81} \approx 0.309$, *which is a little less than* $\dfrac{1}{3}$.

Teaching Tip ❶

In the example above, what is the probability of selecting 2 red songbooks if the first selection is *not* put back on the shelf? These events are *dependent* because the outcome of the first selection does affect the outcome of the second selection. Suppose the first selection is red.

first selection   second selection   *Notice that when the red book is removed, there is not only one less red book but one less book on the shelf.*

$P(\text{red}) = \dfrac{5}{9}$ $P(\text{red}) = \dfrac{4}{8}$

$P(\text{both red}) = P(\text{red}) \cdot P(\text{red following red})$

$= \dfrac{5}{9} \cdot \dfrac{4}{8} \text{ or } \dfrac{5}{18}$

The probability of selecting 2 red songbooks is $\dfrac{5}{18}$ or about 0.278. This is an application of the probability of two dependent events.

Probability of Two Dependent Events	If two events, *A* and *B*, are dependent, then the probability of both events occurring is found as follows. $P(A \text{ and } B) = P(A) \cdot P(B \text{ following } A)$

Teaching Tip ❷

Example 3

There are 9 pennies, 7 dimes, and 5 nickels in an antique coin collection. Suppose two coins are to be selected at random from the collection without replacing the first one. Find the probability of each event.

Because the coins are not replaced, these events are dependent. Thus, $P(A \text{ and } B) = P(A) \cdot P(B \text{ following } A)$. Let p = penny, d = dime, and n = nickel.

a. a penny, then a dime
$P(p, \text{then } d) = P(p) \cdot P(d \text{ following } p)$
$P(p, \text{then } d) = \dfrac{9}{21} \cdot \dfrac{7}{20} \text{ or } \dfrac{3}{20}$
The probability is $\dfrac{3}{20}$ or 0.15.

b. two nickels
$P(n, \text{then } n) = P(n) \cdot P(n \text{ following } n)$
$P(n, \text{then } n) = \dfrac{5}{21} \cdot \dfrac{4}{20} \text{ or } \dfrac{1}{21}$
The probability is $\dfrac{1}{21}$ or about 0.048.

LESSON 15-7 MULTIPLYING PROBABILITIES   711

Chalkboard Examples

For Example 1
Suppose you spin the spinner four times. Find the probability that you get *B*, then *C*, then *B*, then *A*. $\dfrac{1}{108}$

For Example 2
A bag contains 6 orange, 8 blue, and 4 yellow marbles. What is the probability of selecting 2 blue marbles in succession providing the marble drawn first is then replaced before the second is drawn? $\dfrac{16}{81} \approx 0.198$

For Example 3
There are 3 quarters, 4 dimes, and 5 nickels in a purse. Suppose 3 coins are to be selected without replacement. Find the following probabilities.

a. selecting 3 quarters $\dfrac{1}{220} \approx 0.005$

b. selecting a quarter, then a dime, then a nickel
$\dfrac{1}{22} \approx 0.045$

Teaching Tip ❶   Emphasize that "replacement" is associated with independent events and "without replacement" is associated with dependent events.

Teaching Tip ❷   Be sure the students understand that the difference in determining probability for dependent and independent events is that the second event has one less possibility for dependent events.

EVALUATING THE LESSON

Checking for Understanding

Exercises 1–5 are designed to help you assess understanding through reading, writing, and speaking. You should work through Exercises 1–3 with your students, and then monitor their work on Exercises 4–5.

Teaching Tip ❸ You may want to work this exercise with replacement also and show how the answers are examples of the principles developed in Exercises 2 and 3.

Reteaching Masters Booklet, p. 101

Example 4 From a deck of 52 cards, an 8, a 9, and then another 8 are selected in that order.

a. First find the probability of this event occurring if the cards are replaced after each selection.

When the cards are replaced, the events are independent.

$P(8, 9, 8) = P(8) \cdot P(9) \cdot P(8)$

$P(8, 9, 8) = \frac{4}{52} \cdot \frac{4}{52} \cdot \frac{4}{52}$ or $\frac{1}{2197}$

The probability is $\frac{1}{2197}$ or about 0.0005.

b. Find the probability of the event occurring if the cards are not replaced.

When the cards are not replaced, the events are dependent.

$P(8, 9, 8) = P(8) \cdot P(9 \text{ following } 8) \cdot P(8 \text{ following } 9 \text{ following } 8)$

$P(8, 9, 8) = \frac{4}{52} \cdot \frac{4}{51} \cdot \frac{3}{50}$ or $\frac{2}{5525}$

The probability is $\frac{2}{5525}$ or about 0.0004.

CHECKING FOR UNDERSTANDING

Communicating Mathematics

1. Dependent events are affected by previous choices, independent are not.

Read and study the lesson to answer each question.

1. What is the difference between independent events and dependent events?

2. What effect does replacing the item before the second choice have on finding the probability of the event? **It makes the probability greater.**

3. In a given situation of selecting items, is the probability greater or less if replacement does not occur? **less Teaching Tip ❸**

Guided Practice

Determine if each event is independent or dependent. Then find the probability.

4. A bag contains 5 red, 3 green, and 8 blue marbles. Three are selected in sequence without replacement. What is the probability of selecting a red, a green, and a blue in that order? **dependent, $\frac{1}{28}$**

5. There are 4 glasses of iced tea and 3 glasses of lemonade on the counter. Bill drinks two of them at random. What is the probability that he drank 2 glasses of iced tea? **dependent, $\frac{2}{7}$**

RETEACHING THE LESSON

Give students a problem in which to find the probability of the event occuring with replacement and then find the probability of the event occuring without replacement. Have them discuss the results and determine when the probability will be greater and when it will be less.

EXERCISES

Practice

Determine if each event is independent or dependent. Then find the probability.

6. Monique came home from school to find a bowl of 5 apricots and 4 plums on the table. She decides to have a snack. First she selects one and then puts it back. She then selects another. What is the probability both selections were apricots? **independent, $\frac{25}{81}$**

7. When Josh plays Sven on his video game, the odds are 3 to 2 that he will win. What is the probability that he will win the next four games?
   independent, $\frac{81}{625}$

The Scrabble® tiles *A, B, E, I, J, K,* and *M* are placed face down in the lid of the game and mixed up. Two tiles are chosen at random. Find each probability.

8. *P(selecting 2 vowels)*, if no replacement occurs $\frac{1}{7} \approx 0.143$

9. *P(selecting 2 vowels)*, if replacement occurs $\frac{9}{49} \approx 0.184$

10. *P(selecting the same letter twice)*, if no replacement occurs **0**

Christine helps her dad do the dishes. There are 5 bowls, 5 glasses, and 6 plates sitting ready to be washed. She accidentally knocks two items off the counter and breaks them. Find each probability.

11. *P(breaking 2 plates)* $\frac{1}{8} \approx 0.125$

12. *P(breaking 2 bowls)* $\frac{1}{12} \approx 0.083$

13. *P(breaking a bowl, then a glass)*
    $\frac{5}{48} \approx 0.104$

14. *P(breaking a bowl and a glass)*
    $\frac{5}{24} \approx 0.208$

Two dice are tossed. Find each probability.

15. *P(two 3s)* $\frac{1}{36} \approx 0.028$

16. *P(no 3s)* $\frac{25}{36} \approx 0.694$

17. *P(3 and 4)* $\frac{1}{36} \approx 0.028$

18. *P(3 and any other number)*

19. *P(2 numbers alike)* $\frac{1}{6} \approx 0.167$

20. *P(2 different numbers)* $\frac{5}{6} \approx 0.833$

21. A jar contains 5 peanut butter cookies, 3 caramel delights, and 7 lemon cookies. If 3 cookies are selected in succession, find the probability of selecting one of each if:

    a. no cookies are replaced.   b. each cookie is replaced.

22. A box contains 8 blue markers, 7 black markers, and 3 red markers. Three are chosen one after the other. Find the probability that each is a different color if:

    a. no replacement occurs.   b. replacement occurs each time.

18. $\frac{5}{30} \approx 0.139$

21.a. $\frac{1}{26} \approx 0.038$

 b. $\frac{7}{225} \approx 0.031$

22.a. $\frac{7}{204} \approx 0.034$

 b. $\frac{21}{729} \approx 0.029$

C ▷ Ping-Pong™ balls numbered consecutively 1 to 100 are placed in a large hopper. Five balls are drawn at random. Find each probability.

26. $\dfrac{1}{635,013,559,600}$
$\approx 1.57 \times 10^{-12}$

27. $\dfrac{4}{635,013,559,600}$
$\approx 6.3 \times 10^{-12}$

28. $\dfrac{19}{1,160,054}$
$\approx 1.64 \times 10^{-5}$

23. $P(selecting\ all\ odd\ numbers)$, if replacement occurs $\dfrac{1}{32} \approx 0.031$

24. $P(selecting\ all\ odd\ numbers)$, if no replacement occurs $\dfrac{1081}{38,412} \approx 0.028$

25. $P(selecting\ 5\ consecutive\ numbers)$, if no replacement occurs $\dfrac{1}{94,109,400}$
$\approx 1.06 \times 10^{-8}$

Find each probability if 13 cards are drawn from a deck of 52 playing cards, and no replacement occurs.

26. $P(all\ diamonds)$
27. $P(all\ one\ suit)$
28. $P(all\ red\ cards)$
29. $P(all\ face\ cards)$ **0**

Critical Thinking

30. A bent coin has $P(heads) = \dfrac{1}{3}$ and $P(tails) = \dfrac{2}{3}$. What type of game rules could you devise so that the probability of success and the probability of failure are equal? **Answers will vary. Sample: When the coins are tossed give double credit for tossing heads.**

Applications

31. **Sports** Three darts are thrown at the dart board shown at the right.

a. Find the probability of all three darts landing in the center ring. $\dfrac{1}{729}$

b. Find the probability that each dart lands in a different ring. $\dfrac{5}{243}$

c. Find the probability that one dart is in the second ring and two are in the outer ring. $\dfrac{25}{243}$

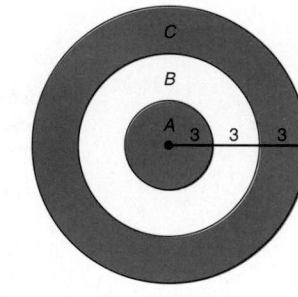

32. **School** Students in geometry class are practicing constructions. The classroom tool box contains 20 compasses. 12 of them have red pencils, 5 have blue pencils, and 3 have yellow pencils. Find the probability of picking two compasses, one with a yellow pencil and one with a red pencil. None of the compasses are put back in the box. $\dfrac{9}{95}$

Mixed Review

33. One die is blue and the other is white. If the dice are rolled, find the probability that the blue die shows an odd number and the white die shows an even number. **(Lesson 15-6)** $\dfrac{1}{4}$

34. Simplify $\dfrac{2z^2}{z^2 - 2z - 35} - \dfrac{z + 7}{z + 5}$. **(Lesson 11-4)** $\dfrac{z^2 + 49}{(z + 5)(z - 7)}$

36. $\begin{bmatrix} 1 & 0 \\ 0 & 1 \end{bmatrix}$

35. **Geometry** Find the midpoints of the sides of a triangle with vertices $R(0, 4)$, $S(2, 6)$, and $T(4, -2)$. **(Lesson 9-1)** **(1, 5), (2, 1), (3, 2)**

36. Write the matrix $I_{2\times2}$. **(Lesson 4-4)**

714 CHAPTER 15 PROBABILITY

EXTENDING THE LESSON

Math Power: Communication

Have students verbalize the solution process for the following problem, then solve the problem. How many people, selected at random, would have to be asked their birthdays in order for the probability of any two of them having the same birthday to be greater than $\dfrac{1}{2}$? Assume 366 different birthdays are possible. **23**

Enrichment Masters Booklet, p. 101

15-8 Adding Probabilities

Objective
15-8

After studying this lesson, you should be able to:
- find the probability of mutually exclusive events or inclusive events.

Teaching Tip

Suppose a card is drawn from a standard deck of 52 cards. What is the probability of drawing an ace or a king? Since no card is both an ace and a king, the events are said to be **mutually exclusive.** That is, the two events cannot occur at the same time. The probability of two mutually exclusive events can be found by adding their individual probabilities.

$$P(ace\ or\ king) = P(ace) + P(king)$$
$$= \frac{4}{52} + \frac{4}{52}$$
$$= \frac{8}{52} \text{ or } \frac{2}{13}$$

The probability of drawing an ace or a king is $\frac{2}{13}$ or about 0.154.

Probability of Mutually Exclusive Events	**The probability of one or the other of two mutually exclusive events, A and B, occurring is the sum of their probabilities.** $$P(A \text{ or } B) = P(A) + P(B)$$

Remember some of the special cases you had to account for when dealing with permutations. When some of the permutations were the same as a previous permutation, you had to adjust the formula to account for that duplication.

When two events are **inclusive events,** they can occur at the same time. The formula for the probability of inclusive events is an adjustment to the formula for mutually exclusive events. What is the probability of drawing an ace or a red card from a deck of cards?

$P(ace)$	$P(red\ card)$	$P(red\ ace)$
$\frac{4}{52}$	$\frac{26}{52}$	$\frac{2}{52}$
1 ace in each suit	*hearts and diamonds*	*ace of hearts and ace of diamonds*

The probability of drawing a red ace is counted twice, one for an ace and once for a red card. To find the correct probability you must subtract $P(red\ ace)$ from the sum of $P(aces)$ and $P(red\ cards)$.

$$P(ace \text{ or red card}) = \frac{4}{52} + \frac{26}{52} - \frac{2}{52} \text{ or } \frac{7}{13}$$

The probability of drawing an ace or a red card is $\frac{7}{13}$, or about 0.538.

LESSON 15-8 ADDING PROBABILITIES 715

ALTERNATE TEACHING STRATEGIES

Using Manipulatives
Students may work independently or with a partner. Have students use a spinner with 4 different colors and 6 different numbers to write several

verbal problems involving mutually exclusive and inclusive events. Have students exchange problems and solve.

Lesson Resources
Reteaching Master 15-8
Practice Master 15-8
Enrichment Master 15-8
Activity Master, p. 33

 Transparency 15-8 contains the 5-Minute Check and a teaching aid for this lesson.

INTRODUCING THE LESSON

🕐 5-Minute Check
(over Lesson 15-7)

1. In a bag are 5 red and 3 blue marbles. Two marbles are selected without replacement. What is the probability of drawing a red and a blue marble in that order? $\frac{15}{56}$

2. Two books are selected from a group of 5 algebra and 3 geometry books. What is the probability that both of them are geometry books? $\frac{3}{28}$

3. A bag contains 3 black marbles and 6 white marbles. A marble is drawn and then replaced. A second drawing is made. What is the probability that a black marble will be drawn both times? $\frac{1}{9}$

Motivating the Lesson
Ask students what is wrong with the statement, "Pedro made an A and a B on the test". Use student responses to develop an informal definition of mutually exclusive events.

TEACHING THE LESSON

Teaching Tip ❶ Emphasize that mutually exclusive events cannot occur simultaneously. Another example would be the toss of a coin. A coin can't show both heads and tails on the same toss.

Chalkboard Examples

For Example 1

A marble is selected from a bag containing 5 blue, 2 red, and 3 white marbles. What is the probability that it is a blue or a white marble? $\frac{4}{5}$ or 0.8

For Example 2

A letter is picked at random from the alphabet. What is the probability the letter is contained in the word *glass* or in the word *slower*? $\frac{4}{13} \approx 0.308$

For Example 3

A bag contains 7 red and 4 white marbles. Three marbles are selected. What is the probability that at least one is white?

$\frac{26}{33} \approx 0.788$

Probability of Inclusive Events

> The probability of one or the other of two inclusive events, *A* and *B*, occurring is the sum of the individual probabilities decreased by the probability of both occurring.
> $$P(A \text{ or } B) = P(A) + P(B) - P(A \text{ and } B)$$

Example 1

Leroy has 6 nickels, 4 pennies, and 3 dimes in his pocket. He takes one coin from his pocket at random. What is the probability it is a penny or a nickel?

These are mutually exclusive events since a coin cannot be a penny *and* a nickel. Find the sum of the individual probabilities.

$P(penny \text{ or } nickel) = P(penny) + P(nickel)$

$P(penny \text{ or } nickel) = \dfrac{4}{13} + \dfrac{6}{13}$ or $\dfrac{10}{13}$

The probability of selecting a penny or a nickel is $\dfrac{10}{13}$ or about 0.769.

Example 2

A card is selected from a deck of 52 cards. What is the probability it is a red card or a face card?

Since some red cards are also face cards, these events are inclusive.

$P(red \text{ or } face\ card) = P(red) + P(face\ card) - P(red\ face\ cards)$

$P(red \text{ or } face\ card) = \dfrac{26}{52} + \dfrac{12}{52} - \dfrac{6}{52}$ or $\dfrac{8}{13}$

The probability of selecting a red card or a face card is $\dfrac{8}{13}$ or about 0.615.

Example 3

There are 6 women and 7 men on the committee for city park enhancement. A subcommittee of 5 members is being selected at random to study the feasibility of redoing the landscaping in one of the parks. What is the probability that the committee will have at least 3 women?

At least 3 women means that the committee may have 3, 4, or 5 women. It is not possible to select a group of 3, a group of 4, and a group of 5 all in the same 5-member committee. The events are mutually exclusive.

$P(at\ least\ 3\ women) = P(3\ women) + P(4\ women) + P(5\ women)$

 *3 women, 2 men* *4 women, 1 man* *P(5 women, 0 men)*

$= \dfrac{C(6, 3) \cdot C(7, 2)}{C(13, 5)} + \dfrac{C(6, 4) \cdot C(7, 1)}{C(13, 5)} + \dfrac{C(6, 5) \cdot C(7, 0)}{C(13, 5)}$

$= \dfrac{140}{429} + \dfrac{35}{429} + \dfrac{2}{429}$ or $\dfrac{59}{143}$

The probability of at least 3 women on the committee is $\dfrac{59}{143}$ or about 0.413.

RETEACHING THE LESSON

Have students give examples of mutually exclusive events and also of inclusive events. Discuss why each example is one or the other.

CHECKING FOR UNDERSTANDING

Communicating Mathematics

Read and study the lesson to answer each question. **1–4. See margin.**

1. Give two examples of mutually exclusive events.

2. Give two examples of inclusive events.

3. Suppose you wanted to select a number at random from the numbers 1 to 100. What events must you consider in calculating the probability that the number is even or a multiple of 7?

4. Draw a Venn diagram to illustrate the events in Example 2.

Guided Practice

Determine if each event is inclusive or mutually exclusive. Then find the probability.

5. inclusive, $\frac{1}{4} = 0.25$

6. exclusive, $\frac{2}{221} \approx 0.009$

5. A hopper contains balls numbered consecutively from 1 to 10. A ball is chosen at random and a die is rolled. What is the probability of getting a 2 on only one of them?

6. Two cards are drawn from a standard deck of cards. What is the probability that the two cards are both kings or are both queens?

EXERCISES   Teaching Tip ❶

Practice

Determine if each event is inclusive or mutually exclusive. Then find the probability.

7. exclusive, $\frac{9}{91} \approx 0.099$

8. exclusive, $\frac{1}{2} = 0.5$

9. inclusive, $\frac{175}{221} \approx 0.79$

7. Mrs. Martell has 15 photos of relatives in her wallet. Five are pictures of her children, 3 are pictures of her sisters, and 7 are pictures of her grandchildren. She selects three photos at random. What is the probability that she has selected 3 photos of her children or 3 photos of her grandchildren?

8. Five coins are dropped onto the floor. What is the probability that at least three of them land heads-up?

9. Two cards are drawn from a deck of cards. What is the probability of having drawn a black card or an ace?

10. In homeroom, 3 of the 16 girls have red hair and 2 of the 15 boys have red hair. What is the probability of selecting a boy or a red-haired person as homeroom representative to student council? inclusive, $\frac{18}{31} \approx 0.581$

Additional Answers

1. rolling two dice, spinning a spinner twice

2. picking a face card or a black card; buying a 1993 model car or a blue car

3. How many even numbers are there, how many multiples of 7 are there, and how many even numbers are also multiples of 7?

4.
```
Deck of Cards
  Red     Face
```

EVALUATING THE LESSON

Checking for Understanding
Exercises 1–6 are designed to help you assess understanding through reading, writing, and speaking. You should work through Exercises 1–4 with your students, and then monitor their work on Exercises 5–6.

Closing the Lesson
Speaking Activity   Have students explain the difference in finding $P(A \text{ and } B)$ and $P(A \text{ or } B)$.

APPLYING THE LESSON

Homework Exercises

Assignment Guide
Basic: 7–26, 31–32, 35–39
Average: 11–28, 31–39
Enriched: 13–39

Teaching Tip ❷   A calculator is helpful for performing the calculations needed to complete the exercises.

Reteaching Masters Booklet, p. 102

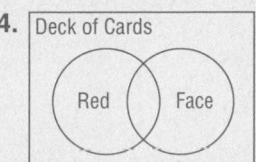

11. $\frac{2}{11} \approx 0.181$

12. $\frac{4}{11} \approx 0.363$

13. $\frac{14}{33} \approx 0.424$

14. $\frac{19}{33} \approx 0.576$

Ken has 11 coasters in a kitchen drawer. Six are cork and 5 are plastic. He selects three at random to use in the family room. Find each probability.

11. $P(all\ 3\ cork\ or\ all\ 3\ plastic)$ 12. $P(exactly\ 2\ plastic)$

13. $P(at\ least\ 2\ plastic)$ 14. $P(at\ least\ 2\ cork)$

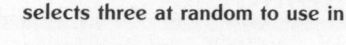

B Two cards are drawn from a deck of cards. Find each probability.

15. $P(both\ black\ or\ both\ face\ cards)$ 16. $P(both\ aces\ or\ both\ face\ cards)$

17. $P(both\ aces\ or\ both\ red)$ 18. $P(both\ either\ red\ or\ an\ ace)$

15. $\frac{188}{663} \approx 0.284$ 16. $\frac{12}{221} \approx 0.054$ 17. $\frac{55}{221} \approx 0.249$ 18. $\frac{71}{221} \approx 0.321$

The lunchroom workers are counting the money in the cash registers after lunch on Tuesday. Seven coins fall from the counter to the floor. Find each probability.   19. $\frac{7}{16} \approx 0.438$ 20. $\frac{29}{128} \approx 0.227$

19. $P(landing\ 3\ heads\ or\ 2\ tails)$ 20. $P(landing\ at\ least\ 5\ heads)$

21. $P(landing\ 3\ heads\ or\ 3\ tails)$ 22. $P(landing\ all\ heads\ or\ all\ tails)$

$\frac{35}{64} \approx 0.547$ $\frac{1}{64} \approx 0.016$

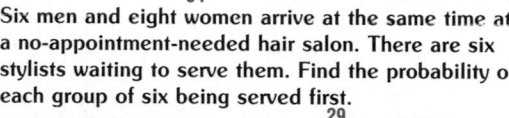

Six men and eight women arrive at the same time at a no-appointment-needed hair salon. There are six stylists waiting to serve them. Find the probability of each group of six being served first.

23. $P(all\ men\ or\ all\ women)$ $\frac{29}{3003} \approx 0.010$

24. $P(5\ men\ or\ 5\ women)$ $\frac{128}{1001} \approx 0.128$

25. $P(4\ men\ or\ 4\ women)$ $\frac{70}{143} \approx 0.490$

26. $P(at\ least\ 3\ men)$ $\frac{1589}{3003} \approx 0.529$

C The numbers 1 through 25 are written on Ping-Pong™ balls and placed in one hopper. The numbers 20 through 40 are also written on Ping-Pong™ balls and placed in a different hopper. One ball is chosen at random from each spinning hopper. Find each probability.

27. $P(each\ is\ a\ 20)$ $\frac{1}{525} \approx 0.002$ 28. $P(neither\ is\ a\ 20)$ $\frac{32}{35} \approx 0.914$

29. $P(at\ least\ one\ is\ a\ 22)$ $\frac{3}{35} \approx 0.086$ 30. $P(each\ is\ greater\ than\ 10)$ $\frac{3}{5} = 0.6$

Critical Thinking

31. Three urns sit on a table. In the gold urn are 2 red, 3 white, and 1 blue marble. In the silver urn are 5 red, 2 white, and 7 blue marbles. In the ceramic urn are 6 red and 4 white marbles. After an urn is chosen at random, one marble is selected. Suppose it is blue.

   a. What is the probability that it came from the ceramic urn? **0**

   b. What is the probability that it came from the gold urn? *Hint: Think of the probability of blue from the gold urn in relation to the probability of blue from gold, or silver, or ceramic.* $\frac{1}{4}$

Applications

32. **Sports** The Baltimore Oriole pitching staff has 4 left-handers and 7 right-handers. If 2 are selected at random to warm up, what is the probability that at least one of them is a left-hander? $\frac{34}{55} \approx 0.618$

Practice Masters Booklet, p. 117

33. Business At an income-tax information center, there are 8 phone operators on duty during the first shift from 7:00 A.M.–3:00 P.M., 12 operators on duty during the second shift from 3:00 P.M.–11:00 P.M., and 3 operators on duty during the third shift from 11:00 P.M.–7:00 A.M. Three operators are selected at random to be on a committee to revise procedures. What is the probability that all work the first shift or all work the third shift? $\frac{57}{1771} \approx 0.032$

Computer

34. The BASIC program below can be used to find probabilities of choosing a sample from each of two populations without replacement. Such probabilities are also called *hypergeometric*.

```
10 INPUT "ENTER THE NUMBER          120 PRINT "THE PROBABILITY
   IN GROUP A, ";A                       OF ";X; "FROM GROUP A
20 INPUT "ENTER THE NUMBER              AND ";Y; "FROM GROUP B
   IN GROUP B, ";B                       IS ";P;"."
30 INPUT "ENTER THE NUMBER          130 END
   CHOSEN FROM GROUP A, ";X         200 LET F1=1: F2=1: F3=1
40 INPUT "ENTER THE NUMBER          210 FOR I=1 TO C1
   CHOSEN FROM GROUP B, ";Y         220 LET F1=F1*I
50 LET C1=A: C2=X: C3=A-X           230 NEXT I
60 GOSUB 200: LET Y1=C              240 FOR I=1 TO C2
70 LET C1=B: C2=Y: C3=B-Y           250 LET F2=F2*I
80 GOSUB 200: LET Y2=C              260 NEXT I
90 LET C1=A+B: C2=X+Y: C3=A         270 FOR I=1 TO C3
   +B-C2                            280 LET F3=F3*I
100 GOSUB 200: LET Y3=C             290 NEXT I
110 LET P = Y1*Y2/Y3                300 LET C=F1/(F2*F3)
                                    310 RETURN
```

Use this program to find each probability. **a.** 0.317460, 0.039683, 0.007937

a. A bag contains 4 blue and 5 red marbles. Five marbles are drawn at random. Find P(3 *blue*, 2 *red*), P(4 *blue*, 1 *red*), and P(all *red*).

b. The math club has 6 boys and 12 girls. Three were selected at random to enter a contest. Find P(2 *boys*, 1 *girl*) and P(1 *boy*, 2 *girls*). **See below**

c. For every 11 computer disks, one is defective. If 10 disks are chosen at random, find P(1 *defective disk*) and P(no *defective disks*).
0.909090, 0.090909

34b. 0.220588, 0.485294

Mixed Review

35. $\frac{1}{20}$

35. Mr. Sunami has a corporate board meeting to attend. He has 4 suits and 5 shirts. He selects one suit and one shirt at random to wear to the meeting. What is the probability of each random outfit? **(Lesson 15-7)**

36. From a group of 8 men and 7 women, how many different committees of 3 men and 4 women can be formed? **(Lesson 15-1)** 1960

37. Find the missing geometric means in the sequence 6, __?__, __?__, 93.75. **(Lesson 13-4)** 15, 37.5

38. Solve $\log_6 (x + 5) + \log_6 (x - 4) = 2$. **(Lesson 12-3)** 7

39. If $p = 0.5ans$, find p if $a = 10.4$, $n = 6$, and $s = 12$. **(Lesson 1-1)** 374.4

EXTENDING THE LESSON

Math Power:
Problem Solving

One card is drawn from a standard deck of cards. What is the probability that it is a red card, a card from 2 through 6, or a card from 6 through 8? Encourage students to use a Venn diagram. $\frac{10}{13}$

Teaching Tip ❸ Point out to students that the subroutine in lines 200–310 computes combinations. In line 110, the combinations are used to compute the hypergeometric probability. The program does not check for nonsense questions such as the probability of choosing six elements from a population of fewer than six elements. Challenge students to modify the program so that inputs are limited to appropriate whole numbers.

Enrichment Masters Booklet, p. 102

INTRODUCING THE LESSON

 5-Minute Check

(over Lesson 15-8)

1. A bag contains 6 red and 5 white marbles. Three are selected. What is the probability that exactly 2 white marbles are drawn?
   $\frac{4}{11} \approx 0.363$

2. Find the probability of selecting 2 kings or 2 red cards from a deck of 52 cards.
   $\frac{55}{221} \approx 0.249$

3. There are 8 red, 3 blue, and 12 black marbles in a bag. If 3 are selected, what is the probability that all are red or all are blue? $\frac{57}{1771} \approx 0.032$

Motivating the Lesson

Toss 10 coins on a desk. Ask students how many coins they expect to land heads and how many to land tails. Look at the coins. If there are not 5 heads and 5 tails, ask students if they think there is a way to find the probability of getting the existing results. If there are 5 heads and 5 tails, repeat the toss.

15-9 Simulation and Binomial Experiments

Objectives

After studying this lesson, you should be able to:

15-9A ▪ use simulation to solve various probability problems, and
15-9B ▪ use binomial experiments to find probabilities.

Application

Brett normally makes 2 out of every 3 free throws she attempts in a basketball game. In other words, the probability that Brett will make a free throw is $\frac{2}{3}$. Suppose Brett attempts 4 free throws during Friday night's game. What is the probability that she will make 3 free throws and miss only one?

Let S stand for scoring when she attempts a free throw. Let M stand for missing when she attempts a free throw.

The possible ways of scoring on 3 free throws and missing 1 free throw are shown at the right. This shows the combination of 4 things (free throws) taken three at a time (scores), or $C(4, 3)$.

M	S	S	S
S	M	S	S
S	S	M	S
S	S	S	M

The terms of the binomial expansion of $(S + M)^4$ can be used to find the probabilities of each combination of scores and misses. **Teaching Tip ❶**
$$(S + M)^4 = S^4 + 4S^3M + 6S^2M^2 + 4SM^3 + M^4$$

term	meaning	coefficient of term
S^4	1 way to score all 4 times	$C(4, 4) = 1$
$4S^3M$	4 ways to score 3 times and miss 1 time	$C(4, 3) = 4$
$6S^2M^2$	6 ways to score 2 times and miss 1 time	$C(4, 2) = 6$
$4SM^3$	4 ways to score 1 time and miss 3 times	$C(4, 1) = 4$
M^4	1 way to miss all 4 times	$C(4, 0) = 1$

The probability that Brett scores on a free throw is $\frac{2}{3}$. So, the probability that she misses is $\frac{1}{3}$. To find the probability of scoring 3 out of 4 free throws, substitute $\frac{2}{3}$ for S and $\frac{1}{3}$ for M in the term $4S^3M$.

$4S^3M = 4\left(\frac{2}{3}\right)^3\left(\frac{1}{3}\right)$ or $\frac{32}{81}$, which is about 0.395. **Teaching Tip ❷**

Problems that can be solved using binomial expansion are called **binomial experiments**.

ALTERNATE TEACHING STRATEGIES

Using Computers

The following BASIC program simulates 100 rolls of a die.

```
10 FOR R = 1 TO 100
20 LET D = INT(6*RND(X) + 1)
30 PRINT D
40 NEXT R
50 END
```

Have students rewrite the program to simulate 150 spins of an 8-section spinner and run both programs.

Conditions of a Binomial Experiment	A binomial experiment exists *if and only if* these conditions occur. ■ There are exactly two possible outcomes for any trial. ■ There is a fixed number of trials. ■ The trials are independent. ■ The probability of each trial is the same.

Example 1

When Marty came home from school, he emptied his pockets onto his desk. There were 5 coins in his pocket. What is the probability that 3 coins landed heads and 2 coins landed tails?

There are only two possible outcomes, heads (H) or tails (T). The tossing of 5 coins are independent events. For each toss of a coin the probability is the same, and 5 coins are involved. This is a binomial experiment.

When $(H + T)^5$ is expanded, the term H^3T^2 represents 3 heads and 2 tails. The coefficient of H^3T^2 is $C(5, 3)$.

$P(3 \text{ heads, } 2 \text{ tails}) = C(5, 3)H^3T^2$ *Replace H with P(H) and T with P(T). Both P(H) and P(T) equal $\frac{1}{2}$.*

$$= \frac{5 \cdot 4}{2 \cdot 1}\left(\frac{1}{2}\right)^3\left(\frac{1}{2}\right)^2 \text{ or } \frac{5}{16}$$

The probability of 3 heads and 2 tails is $\frac{5}{16}$ or about 0.313.

Example 2

To practice for a jigsaw puzzle competition, Chad and Rashad put together 7 jigsaw puzzles. The probability that Chad puts in the last piece of a puzzle is $\frac{1}{5}$. The probability that Rashad puts in the last piece is $\frac{4}{5}$. What is the probability that Chad will put in the last piece of at least 3 puzzles?

There are only two possible outcomes for whoever puts in the last piece: Chad (C) or Rashad (R). Look at the binomial expansion of $(C + R)^7$.

$(C + R)^7 = C^7 + 7C^6R + 21C^5R^2 + 35C^4R^3 + 35C^3R^4 + 21C^2R^5 + 7CR^6 + R^7$

The probability of Chad putting in the last piece of at least 3 puzzles equals the sum of the probabilities of putting in the last piece of 3, 4, 5, 6, or all 7 puzzles.

$P(\text{Chad putting in the last piece of at least 3 puzzles})$
$= C^7 + 7C^6R + 21C^5R^2 + 35C^4R^3 + 35C^3R^4$

$$= \left(\frac{1}{5}\right)^7 + 7\left(\frac{1}{5}\right)^6\left(\frac{4}{5}\right) + 21\left(\frac{1}{5}\right)^5\left(\frac{4}{5}\right)^2 + 35\left(\frac{1}{5}\right)^4\left(\frac{4}{5}\right)^3 + 35\left(\frac{1}{5}\right)^3\left(\frac{4}{5}\right)^4$$

$$= \frac{1}{78,125} + \frac{28}{78,125} + \frac{336}{78,125} + \frac{2240}{78,125} + \frac{8960}{78,125} \text{ or } \frac{2313}{15,625}$$

The probability of Chad putting in the last piece of at least 3 puzzles is $\frac{2313}{15,625}$, or about 0.148.

TEACHING THE LESSON

Teaching Tip 1 The binomial expansion may be incorporated with combination notation. Thus, $(S + M)^4$ can be expanded as $C(4, 4)S^4 + C(4, 3)S^3M + C(4, 2)S^2M^2 + C(4, 1)SM^3 + C(4, 0)M^4$.

Teaching Tip 2 You may want to give students another example, such as the probability of scoring twice and missing twice, to be sure they understand how to use the binomial expansion.

Chalkboard Examples

For Example 1
A die is tossed 6 times. Find the probability that only one toss shows a 3. $\frac{3125}{7776} \approx 0.402$

For Example 2
Peggy guesses on all 10 questions of a true-false test. Find the probability that she gets exactly 8 correct. $\frac{45}{1024} \approx 0.044$

Example 3

A new family is moving in next door. We know that there are three children in the family, but have not seen any of them. What is the probability that there is at least one girl in the family?

$P(boy) = \frac{1}{2}$ and $P(girl) = \frac{1}{2}$. When tossing a coin, $P(H) = \frac{1}{2}$ and $P(T) = \frac{1}{2}$, so we could use coins to simulate the three children in the family.

Let H be boys and T be girls. Now toss 3 coins and record your results. Twenty tosses of the coins reveal these results.

TTH	HHH	HTT	TTT	THT	*The trials in blue are the ones that represent at least one girl.*
TTH	HHT	HTH	THH	HTT	
THH	TTH	HHH	HHH	HTT	
HHH	THH	HHT	HTT	TTT	

In our simulation, 16 of 20 trials yielded at least one T, or at least one girl. Therefore, based on this simulation, the probability of at least one girl in the family is $\frac{16}{20}$ or about 0.8.
The theoretical probability is 0.875.

CHECKING FOR UNDERSTANDING

Communicating Mathematics

Read and study the lesson to answer each question.

1. Can a binomial experiment represent dependent events? **no**

2. Name the conditions that must be satisfied for a problem to be classified as a binomial experiment. **See margin.**

3. In a binomial experiment, if $P(s) = n$, what is $P(f)$? **$1 - n$**

4. Name some objects that could be used to simulate a given situation. **coins, dice, spinners, random draws from a bag**

Guided Practice

5. binomial, $\frac{3}{8}$

6a. binomial, $\frac{1}{28,561}$

6b. not binomial

7a. binomial, $\frac{16}{81}$

7b. binomial, $\frac{4}{81}$

7c. binomial, $\frac{1}{9}$

Determine if each situation represents a binomial experiment or not. Solve those that represent a binomial experiment.

5. What is the probability of 2 heads and 1 tail if Angie tosses a coin 3 times?

6. What is the probability of Sergio drawing 4 aces from a deck of cards for each condition?

    a. He replaces the card each time.   **b.** He does not replace the card.

7. Eight red sour balls, 4 green sour balls, and 6 purple sour balls are placed in a paper bag. Two are selected with replacement after the first selection. Find each probability.

    a. both red   **b.** both green   **c.** both purple

    d. 1 red, 1 green   **e.** 1 red, 1 purple   **f.** 1 green, 1 purple
    not binomial   **not binomial**   **not binomial**

9. $\frac{3}{8} = 0.375$ **10.** $\frac{5}{16} \approx 0.313$ **11.** $\frac{3125}{7776} \approx 0.402$ **12.** $\frac{23}{648} \approx 0.035$ **13.** $\frac{625}{648} \approx 0.965$

EXERCISES

Practice

A

Find each probability if a coin is tossed four times.

8. $P(no\ heads)$ $\frac{1}{16} \approx 0.063$ **9.** $P(2\ heads,\ 2\ tails)$ **10.** $P(3\ or\ more\ heads)$

Find each probability if a die is tossed five times.

11. $P(only\ one\ 4)$ **12.** $P(at\ least\ three\ 4s)$ **13.** $P(no\ more\ than\ two\ 4s)$

B

Sandra Wilder carries tubes of lipstick in a bag in her purse. The probability of pulling out the color she wants is $\frac{1}{3}$. If she uses her lipstick 4 times in a day, find each probability.

14. $P(never\ the\ correct\ lipstick)$ **14.** $\frac{16}{81} \approx 0.198$

15. $P(at\ least\ 3\ times\ correct)$ **15.** $\frac{1}{9} \approx 0.111$

16. $P(no\ more\ than\ 3\ times\ correct)$ **16.** $\frac{80}{81} \approx 0.988$

Mark Clingan guesses at all 10 true/false questions on his sociology test. Find each probability. **17.** $\frac{15}{128} \approx 0.117$ **18.** $\frac{193}{512} \approx 0.377$ **19.** $\frac{1}{1024} \approx 0.001$

17. $P(7\ correct)$ **18.** $P(at\ least\ 6\ correct)$ **19.** $P(all\ wrong)$

20. $\frac{32}{625} \approx 0.051$

21. $\frac{21}{3125} \approx 0.007$

22. $\frac{821}{3125} \approx 0.263$

Jojo MacMahon plays for the Pickerington Badgers baseball team. He is now batting 0.200 (meaning 200 hits in 1000 times at bat). Find each probability for the next 5 times at bat.

20. $P(exactly\ 3\ hits)$ **21.** $P(at\ least\ 4\ hits)$ **22.** $P(at\ least\ 2\ hits)$

C

Find each probability if three coins are tossed.

23. $P(3\ tails)$ $\frac{1}{8} = 0.125$ **24.** $P(3\ heads)$ $\frac{1}{8} = 0.125$

25. $P(at\ least\ 2\ tails)$ $\frac{1}{2} = 0.5$ **26.** $P(exactly\ 2\ heads)$ $\frac{3}{8} = 0.375$

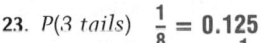

If a thumbtack is dropped, the probability of its landing point up is 0.4. Mrs. Wilson drops 10 tacks while putting up the lunch menus for the next week on the bulletin board. Find each probability.

27. *P(all point up)*
0.0001049

28. *P(exactly 3 point up)*
0.2149908

29. *P(at least 6 point up*
0.1662386

Critical Thinking

30. Mikel Fatur is a quarterback on the junior varsity squad at Monroe High School. In his freshman season, he has completed $\frac{2}{3}$ of his passes. Assume he will do the same in his sophomore year. Use simulation to find the probability of completing at least 6 of 10 passes for the entire game if he has already completed 4 of 5 passes in the first half.

31. $\frac{4536}{15,625} \approx 0.290$ **32.** $\frac{3840}{16,807} \approx 22.8\%$ $\frac{232}{243}$ or about 0.95

Applications

31. Traffic Control The probability that a signal at Darby Avenue is green is $\frac{3}{5}$. What is the probability that exactly 3 of the next seven cars will have to stop?

32. Baseball Four of every 7 pitches thrown by Elias Ramos are strikes. What is the probability that 4 of the next 5 pitches will be strikes? Write your answer as a percent.

33. Skeet Shooting Skeet shooting, also called trapshooting, involves a person shooting at clay discs, called clay pigeons, propelled into the air by a machine. Harold usually hits 9 out of 10 clay pigeons. If he shoots 12 times, find each probability.

    a. *P(all misses)* $\left(\frac{1}{10}\right)^{12} = 1.0 \times 10^{-12}$

    b. *P(exactly 7 hits)* **0.0037881**

    c. *P(all hits)* $\left(\frac{9}{10}\right)^{12} \approx 0.2824295$

    d. *P(at least 10 hits)* **0.8891300**

Mixed Review

34. There are 8 girls and 8 boys on the faculty advisory committee. Three are juniors. Find the probability of selecting a boy or a girl from the committee who is not a junior. **(Lesson 15-8)** $\frac{13}{16}$

35. Physics A ball dropped 120 feet bounces $\frac{2}{3}$ of the height from which it fell on each bounce. How far will it travel before coming to rest? **(Lesson 13-6) 600 ft**

36. Solve $9^{3y} = 27^{y-1}$. **(Lesson 12-7) –1**

37. Number Theory A fraction has a value of $\frac{6}{7}$. If 1 is added to its numerator, its value is $\frac{7}{8}$. Find the original fraction. **(Lesson 11-7)** $\frac{48}{56}$

EXTENDING THE LESSON

Math Power: Problem Solving

A student is guessing the answers on a true-false test of 9 questions. He will pass the test if he answers 5 questions correctly. The teacher has graded 8 questions and notices that he must answer the last question correctly in order to pass. What is the probability that he will pass? $\frac{35}{256} \approx 0.137$

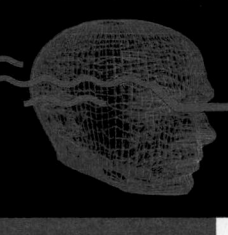

Technology

Coin Toss Simulation

```
10 LET T2 = 0: LET T3 = 0
20 LET H2 = 0: LET H3 = 0
30 FOR I = 1 TO 100
40 LET T = 0: LET H = 0
50 FOR N = 1 TO 3
60 LET R = RND (1)
70 IF R < 0.5 THEN 110
80 PRINT "TAIL";
90 LET T = T + 1
100 GOTO 130
110 PRINT "HEAD";
120 LET H = H + 1
130 NEXT N
134 PRINT
140 IF H = 3 THEN 180
150 IF T = 3 THEN 200
160 IF H = 2 AND T = 1 THEN 220
170 IF H = 1 AND T = 2 THEN 240
180 LET H3 = H3 + 1
190 GOTO 250
200 LET T3 = T3 + 1
210 GOTO 250
220 LET H2 = H2 + 1
230 GOTO 250
240 LET T2 = T2 + 1
250 NEXT I
254 PRINT
260 PRINT "HHH: ";H3
270 PRINT "TTT: ";T3
280 PRINT "HHT: ";H2
290 PRINT "HTT: ";T2
300 END
```

Probability is used to predict the outcome in games of chance involving tossing coins, rolling dice, selecting cards, or winning sweepstakes. A computer program can be used to do the actual counting in simulated situations where large samples are needed.

The BASIC program at the left simulates tossing three coins, prints the outcomes, and keeps totals of the possible outcomes of the 100 samples. Each time the program is run, the totals may be different due to the random selection of values in line 60.

The random numbers selected by the computer lie between 0 and 1. The program defines heads as numbers less than 0.5 and tails as numbers greater than or equal to 0.5.

The output shows each toss of the coin and lists the totals for the four possible combinations: 3 heads; 3 tails; 2 heads and 1 tail; or 1 head and 2 tails.

Example:	HHH:	11
	TTT:	19
	HHT:	38
	HTT:	32

Enter the program and run it several times. Notice the change in the totals. When you use the program for the exercises below, it may take the computer several minutes to complete the large samples.

EXERCISES

1. Run the program once. Write the actual percentage for each combination. **See students' work.**

2. $P(HHH) = \frac{1}{8}$,
   $P(TTT) = \frac{1}{8}$,
   $P(HHT) = \frac{1}{8}$,
   $P(HTT) = \frac{1}{8}$

2. Calculate the expected probability for each combination.

3. Change the program to increase the sample size to 1000. Delete lines 80 and 110. Then run the program. Find the probability for each combination. Compare these to your results in Exercise 2. **See students' work.**

4. Make a conjecture about the reliability of your probabilities in relation to the size of the sample. **The greater the sample, the more likely the probability is closer to theoretical probability.**

TECHNOLOGY   725

Using Technology

Objective This optional page shows how the BASIC programming language can be used to perform mathematical computations and to enhance and extend mathematical concepts.

Teaching Suggestions

Here is another example of a games program. This program simulates rolling two dice a specified number of times. Then it shows the number of times a number was rolled, the percentage of total rolls, and the expected percentage. You might have your students try to write other programs involving probability.

```
5 DIM A(12)
10 INPUT "ENTER NUMBER
   OF ROLLS DESIRED: ";R
20 FOR N = 2 TO 12
30 LET A(N) = 0
40 NEXT N
45 PRINT: PRINT
50 FOR I = 1 TO R
60 LET D1 = INT(6*RND
   (1) + 1)
70 LET D2 = INT(6*RND
   (1) + 1)
80 LET T = D1 + D2
90 PRINT T;" ";
100 LET C = 2
110 IF T = C THEN GOTO 140
120 LET C = C + 1
130 GOTO 110
140 LET A(C) = A(C) + 1
150 NEXT I
155 PRINT: PRINT
160 FOR M = 2 TO 12
170 LET P = INT(((A(M) / R)
    * 1000) + .5) / 10
175 LET E = INT((250 *
    (6 - ABS(7 - M)) / 9) +
    .5) / 10
180 PRINT "#";M;" TIMES
    ROLLED: ";A(M);"
    OR ";P;"% OF TOTAL."
185 PRINT "EXPEXTED
    PERCENTAGE:
    ";E;"%": PRINT
190 NEXT M
200 END
```

CHAPTER **15** # SUMMARY AND REVIEW

VOCABULARY

Upon completing this chapter you should be familiar with the following terms:

Basic Counting Principle	684	689	linear permutation
binomial experiment	720	715	mutually exclusive events
circular permutation	694	706	odds
combination	699	689	permutation
dependent events	685	705	probability
failure	705	722	simulation
inclusive events	715	705	success
independent events	684	684	tree diagram

SKILLS AND CONCEPTS

OBJECTIVES AND EXAMPLES	REVIEW EXERCISES

Upon completing this chapter, you should be able to:

■ solve problems using the Basic Counting Principle **(Lesson 15-2)**

How many 3-letter patterns are there if

a. repetition is allowed?

$26 \cdot 26 \cdot 26 = 17{,}576$ patterns

b. repetition is not allowed?

$26 \cdot 25 \cdot 24 = 15{,}600$ patterns

Use these exercises to review and prepare for the chapter test.

1. Using the digits 0, 1, 2, 3, and 4, how many 3-digit patterns can be formed if the numbers can be used more than once? **125 patterns**

2. Using the digits 5, 6, 7, 8, and 9, how many 3-digit patterns can be formed if each number can only be used once? **60 patterns**

■ solve problems involving permutations **(Lesson 15-3)**

Find the number of permutations of

a. 9 things taken 3 at a time.

$$P(9, 3) = \frac{9!}{(9 - 3)!} = \frac{9!}{6!} \text{ or } 504$$

b. the letters in MISSOURI.
There are 2 Is and 2 Ss in 8 letters.

$$\frac{n!}{p!q!} = \frac{8!}{2!2!} = 10{,}080$$

Evaluate each expression.

3. $\frac{P(7, 3)}{P(5, 2)}$ **10.5**   4. $\frac{P(8, 5)}{P(5, 3)}$ **112**

On a shelf are 8 mystery and 7 romance novels. How many ways can they be arranged for each situation?

5. all mysteries together. **1,625,702,400**

6. all mysteries together, all romances together. **406,425,600**

OBJECTIVES AND EXAMPLES	REVIEW EXERCISES

■ solve problems involving circular permutations   (Lesson 15-4)

Find the number of ways to arrange 5 fruits around a plate.
$(n-1)! = (5-1)! = 4!$ or 24 ways

Find the number of ways to arrange 6 large wooden beads on an elastic cord tied into a circle. (a reflection)

$\dfrac{(n-1)!}{2} = \dfrac{(6-1)!}{2}$ or 60 ways

7. How many ways can 8 people be seated at a round table? **5040**

8. How many ways can 10 charms be placed on a bracelet that has a clasp? **1,814,400**

9. Art is to make a flag with 5 differently colored rectangles arranged side by side. How many different ways could these rectangles be arranged? **60 ways**

■ solve problems involving combinations (Lesson 15-5)

Seven cards are drawn from a deck of 52 cards. In how many ways can 4 of one suit and 3 of another suit be drawn?

$P(4, 2) \cdot C(13, 4) \cdot C(13, 3)$

$= \dfrac{4!}{2!} \cdot \dfrac{13!}{4!9!} \cdot \dfrac{13!}{2!10!}$ or 2,453,880

There are 2,453,880 such hands.

10. How many baseball teams can be formed from 15 players if only 3 pitch while the others play the remaining 8 positions? **1485**

11. From a deck of 52 cards, how many different 4-card hands exist? **270,725**

■ find the probability and odds of an event (Lesson 15-6)

Find the probability of selecting a green marble if a bag holds 14 marbles, 6 of which are green.

$P(green) = \dfrac{6}{14} = \dfrac{3}{7} \approx 0.429$

odds $= \dfrac{6}{8}$ or $\dfrac{3}{4}$

12. A card is selected from a deck of 52 cards. What is the probability that it is a queen? What are the odds?
$\dfrac{1}{13} \approx 0.077;\ \dfrac{1}{12}$

13. A bag contains 6 red and 2 white marbles. If two marbles are selected, what is the probability that one is red and the other is white?
$\dfrac{3}{7} \approx 0.429$

■ find the probability of independent or dependent events   (Lesson 15-7)

Four green marbles and six red marbles are in a bag. Find the probability of drawing a green marble and then a red marble, if the marbles are not replaced.

$P(1g, 1r) = P(g) \cdot P(r\ following\ g)$

$= \dfrac{4}{10} \cdot \dfrac{6}{9}$ or $\dfrac{4}{15}$

14. In his pocket, Jose has 5 dimes, 7 nickels, and 4 pennies. He selects 4 coins. What is the probability that he has 2 dimes and 2 pennies?
$\dfrac{3}{91} \approx 0.033$

15. Ben has 6 blue socks and 4 black socks in a drawer. One dark morning he pulls out 2 socks. What is the probability that he has 2 black socks? $\dfrac{2}{15} \approx 0.133$

The Cumulative Review shown below can be used to review skills and concepts presented thus far in the text. Standardized Test Practice Questions are also provided in the Evaluation Masters booklet.

Evaluation Masters Booklet, pp. 207–208

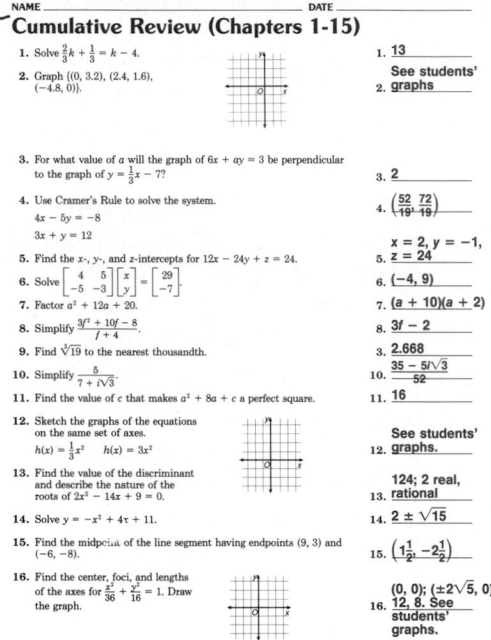

NAME _____ DATE _____

Cumulative Review (Chapters 1-15)

1. Solve $\frac{2}{3}k + \frac{1}{3} = k - 4$.   1. **13**
2. Graph {(0, 3.2), (2.4, 1.6), (−4.8, 0)}.   2. **See students' graphs**
3. For what value of a will the graph of $6x + ay = 3$ be perpendicular to the graph of $y = \frac{1}{3}x - 7$?   3. **2**
4. Use Cramer's Rule to solve the system.
   $4x - 5y = -8$
   $3x + y = 12$ 4. $\left(\frac{52}{19}, \frac{72}{19}\right)$
5. Find the x-, y-, and z-intercepts for $12x - 24y + z = 24$.   5. $x = 2, y = -1, z = 24$
6. Solve $\begin{bmatrix} 4 & 5 \\ -5 & -3 \end{bmatrix}\begin{bmatrix} x \\ y \end{bmatrix} = \begin{bmatrix} 29 \\ -7 \end{bmatrix}$.   6. **(−4, 9)**
7. Factor $a^2 + 12a + 20$.   7. **(a + 10)(a + 2)**
8. Simplify $\frac{3f^2 + 10f - 8}{f + 4}$.   8. **3f − 2**
9. Find $\sqrt[3]{19}$ to the nearest thousandth.   9. **2.668**
10. Simplify $\frac{5}{7 + i\sqrt{3}}$.   10. $\frac{35 - 5i\sqrt{3}}{52}$
11. Find the value of c that makes $a^2 + 8a + c$ a perfect square.   11. **16**
12. Sketch the graphs of the equations on the same set of axes.
    $h(x) = \frac{1}{3}x^2$ $h(x) = 3x^2$ 12. **See students' graphs.**
13. Find the value of the discriminant and describe the nature of the roots of $2x^2 - 14x + 9 = 0$.   13. **124; 2 real, rational**
14. Solve $y = -x^2 + 4x + 11$.   14. $2 \pm \sqrt{15}$
15. Find the midpoint of the line segment having endpoints (9, 3) and (−6, −8).   15. $\left(1\frac{1}{2}, -2\frac{1}{2}\right)$
16. Find the center, foci, and lengths of the axes for $\frac{x^2}{36} + \frac{y^2}{16} = 1$. Draw the graph.   16. **(0, 0); (±2√5, 0); 12, 8. See students' graphs.**

NAME _____ DATE _____

Cumulative Review (Chapters 1-15) continued

17. Graph the system and state the number of solutions.
    $x^2 + y^2 = 16$ $y = 6$ 17. **See students' graphs; none**
18. Find $(2x^3 + 3x^2 + x + 2) \div (x + 2)$.   18. $2x^2 - x + 3 - \frac{4}{x + 2}$
19. Find all rational zeros of $f(x) = (x + 1)(x - 3)(2x - 5)$.   19. **−1, 3, $\frac{5}{2}$**
20. Find $[g \circ f](-1)$ if $f(x) = 2x + 3$ and $g(x) = x - 1$.   20. **0**
21. Simplify $\frac{24x^3}{7} + \frac{-12x}{3y}$.   21. $\frac{6xy}{7}$
22. Solve $\frac{4}{y-1} = \frac{5y}{1-y}$.   22. $-\frac{4}{5}$
23. Sketch the graph of $y = \frac{1}{(x-1)(x-3)}$.   23. **See students' graphs.**
24. Solve $4^{2x} = 2^{2x+8}$.   24. **4**
25. Find antilog 4.4232.   25. **26,497.2**
26. Solve $\log_b(4x - 4) = \log_b 100$.   26. **26**
27. Find the first four terms of the geometric sequence for which $a_1 = 5$ and $r = 2$.   27. **5, 10, 20, 40**
28. Find the sum of the infinite geometric series with $a_1 = 125$ and $r = \frac{1}{5}$.   28. $\frac{625}{4}$
29. Find the next three terms of the sequence 85, 84, 82, 79, 75, ____, ____, ____.   29. **70, 64, 57**
30. Find the fifth term in the expansion of $\left(\frac{1}{5}x + y\right)$.   30. $\frac{7}{25}x^3y$
31. In a normal distribution, what percent of the items are within two standard deviations from the mean?   31. **95%**
32. Evaluate $\frac{P(8, 3) \cdot P(5, 4)}{P(6, 6)}$.   32. **56**
33. There are 7 pennies, 4 nickels, and 5 dimes in a bag. Three coins are selected. Find the probability of choosing 2 nickels and 1 penny.   33. $\frac{3}{40}$

OBJECTIVES AND EXAMPLES

■ find the probability of mutually exclusive events   **(Lesson 15-8)**

What is the probability of drawing a heart or a club from a deck of cards?

$P(heart\ or\ club) = P(heart) + P(club)$
$$= \frac{13}{52} + \frac{13}{52} \text{ or } \frac{1}{2}$$

■ find the probability of inclusive events **(Lesson 15-8)**

What is the probability of drawing a red card or a queen from a deck of cards?

$P(R\ or\ Q) = P(R) + P(Q) - P(RQ)$
$$= \frac{26}{52} + \frac{4}{52} - \frac{2}{52} \text{ or } \frac{7}{13}$$

■ solve a problem by simulation or binomial experiments   **(Lesson 15-1, Lesson 15-9)**

Six coins are tossed. Find $P(4H, 2T)$.

$(H + T)^6 = H^6 + 6H^5T + 15H^4T^2 + 20H^3T^3 + 15H^2T^4 + 6HT^5 + T^6$

$15H^4T^2 = 15\left(\frac{1}{2}\right)^4\left(\frac{1}{2}\right)^2 = \frac{15}{64}$

REVIEW EXERCISES

16. From a deck of 52 cards, one card is selected. What is the probability that it is an ace or a face card?
$\frac{4}{13} \approx$ **0.308**

17. In the numbers 1 through 20, what is the probability of selecting a number at random that is a multiple of 5 or a multiple of 7? $\frac{3}{10} =$ **0.3**

18. If a letter is selected at random from the alphabet, what is the probability that it is a letter from the words CAT or SKATE?
$\frac{3}{13} \approx$ **0.231**

19. If a card is selected from a deck of cards, find the probability that it is not red or not a face card. $\frac{23}{26} \approx$ **0.885**

20. Four coins are tossed. What is the probability that they show 3 heads and 1 tail?
$\frac{1}{4} =$ **0.250**

21. A die is tossed 5 times. What is the probability of at least two 3s?
$\frac{763}{3888} \approx$ **0.196**

APPLICATIONS AND CONCEPTS

22. **Geometry** Find the number of diagonals in a polygon that has 20 sides.   **(Lesson 15-1) 170**

23. **Tourism** A taxi in The Netherlands can hold 4 passengers safely. A party of 6 people wish to travel by taxi to the Hague. How many different groups can occupy the first taxi if it will be full? **(Lesson 15-5) 15 ways**

Evaluate each expression.

1. $P(6, 4)$ **360**
2. $P(8, 3)$ **336**
3. $C(8, 3)$ **56**
4. $C(6, 4)$ **15**

Solve each problem.

5. In a row are 8 chairs. How many ways can 5 people be seated? **6720**

6. From 8 shirts, 6 pairs of slacks, and 4 jackets, how many different outfits can be made? **192**

7. How many ways can the letters from the word *television* be arranged? **907,200**

8. How many different basketball teams could be formed from a group of 12 girls? **792**

9. How many ways can 11 books be arranged on a shelf? **39,916,800**

10. How many ways can 6 keys be placed on a key ring? **60**

11. Nine points are placed on a circle. How many triangles can be formed using these points, three at a time, as vertices? **84**

12. From a group of 4 men and 5 women, a committee of 3 is to be formed. What is the probability that it will have 2 men and 1 woman? $\frac{5}{14} \approx$ **0.357**

13. A red die and a green die are tossed. What is the probability that the red will show even and the green will show a number greater than four? $\frac{1}{6} \approx$ **0.167**

14. From a deck of cards, what is the probability of selecting a 4 followed by a 7 if no replacement occurs? $\frac{4}{663} \approx$ **0.006**

15. A letter is drawn at random from the letters A, B, C, D, E, and F. What is the probability the letter is a vowel? $\frac{1}{3}$

16. A state is chosen at random from the United States. What is the probability that the state is one of the five smallest states in population? $\frac{1}{10}$

17. **Geometry** There are 9 points in a plane such that no three of the points lie on the same line. How many different segments connect the points? **36**

18. **Transportation** A fleet of limousines is composed of 6 white limousines and 4 black limousines. A company wishes to rent 5 of them. How many ways can 2 white and 3 black limousines be selected? **60**

19. Five bent coins are tossed. The probability of heads is $\frac{2}{3}$ for each of them. What is the probability that no more than 2 will show heads? $\frac{17}{81} \approx$ **0.210**

20. While shooting arrows, William Tell can hit an apple 9 out of 10 times. What is the probability that he will hit it exactly 4 out of the next 7 times? $\frac{45,927}{2,000,000} \approx$ **0.023**

Bonus Determine all real values of w for which the statement $C(w + 1, 2) = 9 \cdot C(w, 1)$ is true. **17**

Using the Chapter Test

This page may be used as a test or as a review. In addition, two multiple-choice tests and two free-response tests are provided in the Evaluation Masters Booklet. Chapter 15 Test, Form 1A is shown below.

Evaluation Masters Booklet, pp. 197–198

NAME _____ DATE _____

Chapter 15 Test, Form 1A

Write the letter for the correct answer in the blank at the right of each problem.

1. An ice cream store has 42 flavors of ice cream and 8 toppings. For sundaes, the customer specifies the kind of ice cream and topping and whether it is with or without whipped cream. How many different ice cream sundaes can be ordered?
   A. 672   B. 336   C. 168   D. 1008   1. **A**

2. A license plate must have one letter (not I or O) followed by four digits followed by a different letter (not I or O). How many possible license plates are there?
   A. 2,782,080   B. 5,520,000   C. 5,760,000   D. 5,600,000   2. **B**

3. What is the value of $P(9, 5)$?
   A. 3024   B. 15,120   C. 126   D. 59,049   3. **B**

4. A clown has 8 balloons, each a different color. There are 6 children. How many ways can the clown give each child a balloon?
   A. 56   B. 720   C. 262,144   D. 20,160   4. **D**

5. On a shelf are 4 novels, 4 science books, and 3 history books, all different. How many ways can the books be arranged if all the novels are together?
   A. 120,960   B. 967,680   C. 40,320   D. 6912   5. **B**

6. How many ways can the letters in "bookkeeper" be arranged?
   A. 151,200   B. 3,628,800   C. 302,400   D. 907,200   6. **A**

7. How many ways can 8 people be seated at a round table?
   A. 20,160   B. 40,320   C. 5040   D. 2520   7. **C**

8. How many ways can 10 people be seated around a doctor's waiting room relative to the reception window?
   A. 362,880   B. 3,628,800   C. 181,440   D. 1,814,400   8. **B**

9. How many ways can 7 keys be placed on a key ring?
   A. 2520   B. 5040   C. 720   D. 360   9. **D**

10. How many ways can 9 charms be placed on a bracelet with a clasp?
    A. 181,440   B. 362,880   C. 40,320   D. 20,160   10. **A**

11. What is the value of $C(12, 8)$?
    A. 19,958,400   B. 11,880   C. 495   D. 96   11. **C**

12. A group has 6 men and 5 women. How many ways can a committee of 2 men and 4 women be formed?
    A. 48   B. 75   C. 3000   D. 150   12. **B**

NAME _____ DATE _____

Chapter 15 Test, Form 1A (continued)

13. From a standard deck of 52 cards, 4 cards are dealt. What is the probability that 3 cards are of one suit and one is of another?
    A. $\frac{4}{169}$ B. $\frac{3}{169}$ C. $\frac{11,154}{270,725}$ D. $\frac{44,616}{270,725}$ 13. **D**

14. In a bag are 4 green, 8 blue, and 5 red marbles. Two are selected at random without replacement. What are the odds that both are red?
    A. 5 to 63   B. 5 to 68   C. 63 to 5   D. 68 to 5   14. **A**

15. A red die and a blue die are tossed. What is the probability that the red die shows a three and the blue die shows a number greater than three?
    A. $\frac{1}{36}$ B. $\frac{1}{18}$ C. $\frac{1}{12}$ D. $\frac{2}{3}$ 15. **C**

16. Fifty tickets are numbered 1 to 50 and placed in a box. Three tickets are drawn at random without replacement. What is the probability that their numbers are all greater than 32?
    A. $\frac{57}{980}$ B. $\frac{51}{1225}$ C. $\frac{9}{1470}$ D. $\frac{87}{245}$ 16. **B**

17. In a bag are 4 yellow and 9 blue marbles. Three are selected at random without replacement. What is the probability that all three are yellow or all three are blue?
    A. $\frac{4}{143}$ B. $\frac{44}{143}$ C. $\frac{42}{143}$ D. $\frac{84}{143}$ 17. **B**

18. From a standard deck of 52 cards, three cards are dealt. What is the probability that all three cards are face cards or all cards are red?
    A. $\frac{110}{221}$ B. $\frac{117}{442}$ C. $\frac{331}{1326}$ D. $\frac{28}{221}$ 18. **D**

19. The probability that a loaded die will show six is $\frac{1}{3}$. What is the probability that 4 out of 10 tosses will show six?
    A. $\frac{16}{59,049}$ B. $\frac{64}{59,049}$ C. $\frac{4480}{19,683}$ D. $\frac{1130}{19,683}$ 19. **C**

20. A batter is now batting 0.300. (The probability of getting a hit is $\frac{3}{10}$.) In the next 4 at-bats, what is the probability of getting at least 3 hits?
    A. $\frac{81}{10,000}$ B. $\frac{270}{10,000}$ C. $\frac{756}{10,000}$ D. $\frac{837}{10,000}$ 20. **D**

Bonus

Simplify the expression $\frac{n \cdot (n + 1)! - 2(n!)}{(n + 1)! + n!}$

A. $n - 1$ B. $n - 2$ C. n D. $(n + 2)!$ Bonus **A**

16 Trigonometric Functions

PREVIEWING THE CHAPTER

This chapter on trigonometry begins with a lesson on angles placed in standard position on the coordinate plane. Students study coterminal angles and equivalent radian and degree measures. Students find the values of the six trigonometric functions and of expressions involving the functions, both with and without a calculator. Students then solve problems involving right triangles using right-triangle trigonometry. The chapter concludes with lessons on solving triangles and problems using the Law of Sines and the Law of Cosines.

Problem-Solving Strategy Students learn to *determine from a given set of information the number of possible solutions* and solve the triangle if solutions do exist.

Lesson Objective Chart

Lesson (Pages)	Lesson Objectives	State/Local Objectives
16-1 (732-736)	**16-1A:** Change radian measure to degree measure and vice versa.	
	16-1B: Identify coterminal angles.	
16-2 (737-741)	**16-2A:** Find the least possible angle that is coterminal to a given angle.	
	16-2B: Find the values of expressions involving sine and cosine.	
16-3 (742-745)	**16-3:** Find the values of other trigonometric functions.	
16-4 (746-750)	**16-4:** Find the values of expressions involving trigonometric functions.	
16-5 (751-755)	**16-5:** Use a calculator to find values of trigonometric functions.	
16-6 (756-760)	**16-6A:** Use right triangles to find trigonometric values.	
	16-6B: Solve problems involving right triangles using right triangle trigonometry.	
16-7 (762-766)	**16-7:** Solve word problems using right triangle trigonometry.	
16-8 (767-770)	**16-8:** Solve triangles and problems using the Law of Sines.	
16-9 (771-774)	**16-9:** Determine, from a given set of information, the number of possible solutions and solve the triangle if solutions do exist.	
16-10 (775-779)	**16-10:** Solve triangles and problems using the Law of Cosines.	

ORGANIZING THE CHAPTER

You may want to refer to the **Course Planning Calendar** on page T44.

Lesson (Pages)	Pacing Chart (days) Course			Reteaching	Practice	Enrichment	Evaluation	Technology	Lab Manual	Mixed Problem Solving	Applications	Cooperative Learning Activity	Multicultural	Transparencies
	I	II	III											
16-1 (732-736)	–	–	1	p. 104	p. 119	p. 104								16-1
16-2 (737-741)	–	–	1	p. 105	p. 120	p. 105	Quiz A, p. 219							16-2
16-3 (742-745)	–	–	1	p. 106	p. 121	p. 106		p. 33		p. 16				16-3
16-4 (746-750)	–	–	1	p. 107	p. 122	p. 107	Quiz B, p. 219							16-4
16-5 (751-755)	–	–	1	p. 108	p. 123	p. 108	Mid-Chapter Test, p. 223					p. 52		16-5
16-6 (756-760)	–	–	1	p. 109	p. 124	p. 109								16-6
16-7 (762-766)	–	–	1	p. 110	p. 125	p. 110	Quiz C, p. 220		pp. 47-48					16-7
16-8 (767-770)	–	–	1	p. 111	p. 126	p. 111		p. 16					p. 16	16-8
16-9 (771-774)	–	–	1		p. 127									16-9
16-10 (775-779)	–	–	1	p. 112	p. 128	p. 112	Quiz D, p. 220				p. 34			16-10
Review (780-782)	–	–	1	Multiple Choice Tests, Forms 1A and 1B, pp. 211-214 Free Response Tests, Forms 2A and 2B, pp. 215-218										
Test (783)	–	–	1	Cumulative Review, pp. 221-222 Standardized Test Practice Questions, p. 224										

Course I: Chapters 1-13; Course II: Chapters 1-15; Course III: Chapters 1-17

Other Chapter Resources

Student Edition

Chapter Opener, pp. 730-731
Challenge, p. 736
Applications in Music, p. 741
Applications in Optics, p. 745
Journal Entries, pp. 755, 766
Mid-Chapter Review, p. 755
Technology, p. 761
Cooperative Learning Activity, p. 774
Portfolio Suggestion, p. 779
College Entrance Exam Preview pp. 784-785
Extended Project 4, pp. A14-A16

Teacher's Classroom Resources

Transparency 16-0
Real-World Applications Transparencies, 33, 34
Performance Assessment Booklet, pp. 31-32
Problem-of-the-Week Activity Cards, 32, 33, 34
Tech Prep Applications Booklet, pp. 31-32
Lesson Plans, pp. 119-128

Other Supplements

Glencoe Mathematics Professional Series

Software

Test and Review Generator Software (Apple, IBM, and Macintosh)
Interactive Software (Macintosh)
Teacher's Guide for Software Resources

ENHANCING THE CHAPTER

Cooperative Learning

Providing Closure to the Lesson

After each session, ample time should be provided for students to summarize what they have learned. To reinforce their understanding of the academic content acquired during the session, groups should review the major points covered and discuss any additional questions that they may have about the content. Class discussions can be a proper forum for this review. For example, select a member of one group to discuss with the class what his or her group concluded and how they reached these conclusions. Encourage the reporter to be thorough by asking for specific examples or additional details about various points. Do not immediately accept or reject the report, but involve the rest of the class by asking members of other groups if they agree or disagree with the conclusions reached by the reporter's group and if any group used different procedures to arrive at the same conclusions. You can also ask groups to relate this content to content learned earlier and to provide examples of different settings or applications where the content could be utilized. Such sharing of ideas and methods will ensure a greater retention of the academic content learned during the group activities.

Technology

The BASIC program in the Technology Feature of this chapter enables students to determine the number of solutions in solving a given triangle. Another program for solving the triangle is given in the margin notes for the feature.

Critical Thinking

Frequent use of the term "higher" to describe the levels of analysis, synthesis, and evaluation in Bloom's taxonomy can lead one to make the false assumption that students must master content at the levels of knowledge, comprehension, and application before they can move on to these higher levels. Students who may have difficulty memorizing certain facts often exhibit, in a proper environment, the creative ability to analyze and identify patterns in these facts or find parallel models and new applications. The higher levels of Bloom's taxonomy should provide guideposts for planning interesting and challenging activities in mathematics that engage in the intellect of *all* students, not just those identified as having special talents.

Cooperative Learning, p. 52

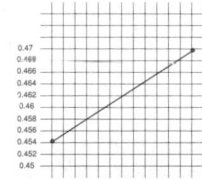

CHAPTER 16 — Cooperative Learning Activity (Use after Lesson 16-5)

Linear Interpolation by Graphing

The graph of the function $y = \sin x$ is a smooth curve as you have observed. When you use the process of interpolation to find a value that is not on your table, you are actually finding a value on the straight line connecting the known values from the table.

Suppose your table represented $\sin x$ for only whole number angles. You could create a graph to "interpolate" to find values for each 10 minutes.

"Interpolate" between $\sin 27°$ (0.4540) and $\sin 28°$ (0.4695), by following the procedure below. **For exercises 1-3, see students' graphs.**

1. On the grid below, mark the x-axis with values 27°, 27°10′, 27°20′, . . . , 28°.

2. On the y-axis, mark values between 0.4500 and 0.4700 (suggested scale 0.0020).

3. Plot $\sin 27°$ at 0.4540 and $\sin 28°$ at 0.4695. Connect with a line segment.

4. Read values for the following from your graph. Check against calculator values or values from a table.
   - a. $\sin 27°10′$
   - b. $\sin 27°20′$
   - c. $\sin 27°30′$
   - d. $\sin 27°40′$
   - e. $\sin 27°50′$

   Possible answers are as follows: a. 0.457 b. 0.459 c. 0.462 d. 0.464 e. 0.467. You may wish students to check their answers with those they would get by using a calculator.

Technology, p. 33

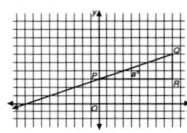

CHAPTER 16 — Graphing Calculators (Use after Lesson 16-3)

Tangents

Tangents of angles are closely related to slopes of lines. Consider the graph of $\overrightarrow{PQ}$ below.

At P an angle of $a°$ is formed by the portion of the line to the right of the y-axis and a horizontal ray, $\overrightarrow{PR}$, that points in the same direction as the positive x-axis. The slope of $\overrightarrow{PQ}$ can be determined by calculating $\tan a°$ in $\triangle PQR$.

$$\text{slope of } \overrightarrow{PQ} = \tan a° = \frac{3}{9}$$

If you know the measure of the angle that a line in the plane forms with a horizontal and the coordinates of a point on the line, you can write a reasonably correct equation for the line.

For each exercise, information about a line is given. Use a graphing calculator to find the tangent of the given angle and write an equation of the line. (Round slopes to the nearest tenth.) Check your answer by graphing on a calculator.

1. y-intercept 2; forms a 20° angle with a horizontal line $y = 0.4x + 2$

2. y-intercept −3; forms a 45° angle with a horizontal line $y = x - 3$

3. y-intercept 6; forms a 30° angle with a horizontal line $y = 0.6x + 6$

4. forms a 55° angle with a horizontal line; passes through the point (4, 1) $y - 1 = 1.4(x - 4)$

5. forms a 30° angle with a horizontal line; passes through the point (−2, 0) $y = 0.6(x + 2)$

6. One line has y-intercept − 1 and forms a 70° angle with a horizontal line. Another line has y-intercept 5 and forms a 10° angle with a horizontal line. Graph both lines and find approximate coordinates of the point of intersection. (2.3, 5.4)

Problem of the Week Activity

The card shown below is one of three available for this chapter. It can be used as a class or small group activity.

Activity Card

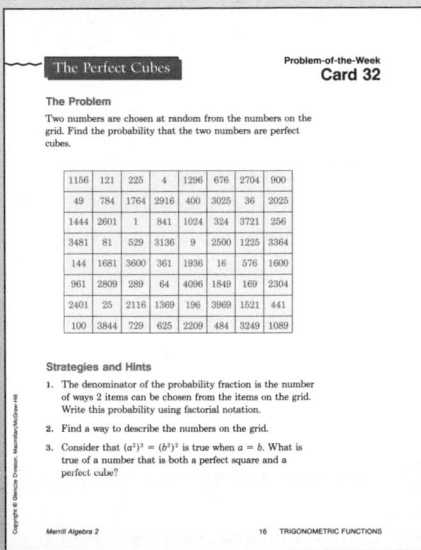

Manipulatives and Models

The following materials may be used as models or manipulatives in Chapter 16.

scientific calculator (all Lessons)
graph paper (Lessons 16-1 and 16-2)
corrugated cardboard (Lesson 16-2)
thumbtacks (Lesson 16-2 and 16-8)
string (Lesson 16-2)
compass (Lesson 16-2)
protractor (Lessons 16-2 and 16-8)
meterstick (Lessons 16-5 and 16-8)
construction paper (Lesson 16-6)
blueprints (Lesson 16-7)
drinking straws (Lesson 16-9)

Outside Resources

Books/Periodicals

Burn, R.P. *Groups, A Path to Geometry.* Cambridge University Press.

Thompson, J.E. *Trigonometry for the Practical Worker.* Van Nostrand.

Films/Videotapes/Videodiscs

Trigonometry, Educational Solutions, Inc., 95 University Pl. #4, New York, NY 10003

Zooms on Self-Similar Figures, International Film Bureau, Inc., 332 So. Michigan Ave., Chicago, IL 60604

The Story of Pi, part of the Project Mathematics Series, and *The Theorem of Pythagoras,* The National Council of Teachers of Mathematics (NCTM), 1096 Association Dr., Reston, VA 22091-1593

Software

Electronic Blackboard: Trigonometry, COMPress, 338 Commerce Dr., Fairfield, CT 06430-5540

Multicultural

Multicultural Activity, p. 16

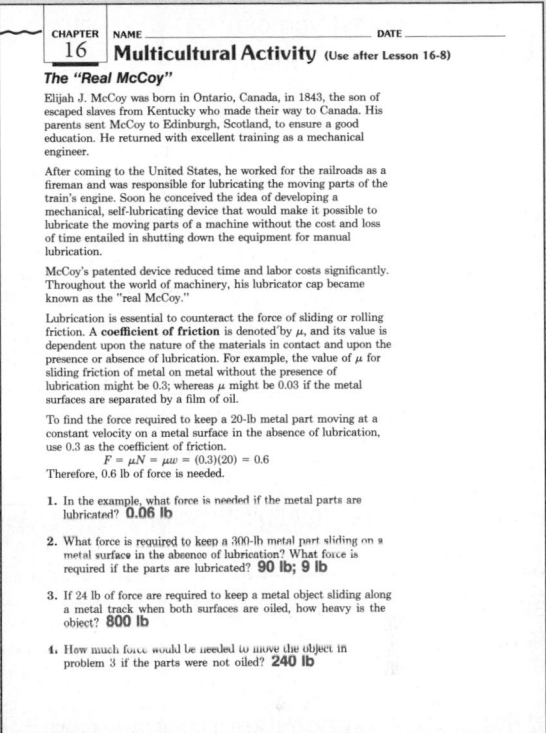

Lab Manual

Lab Activity, pp. 47-48

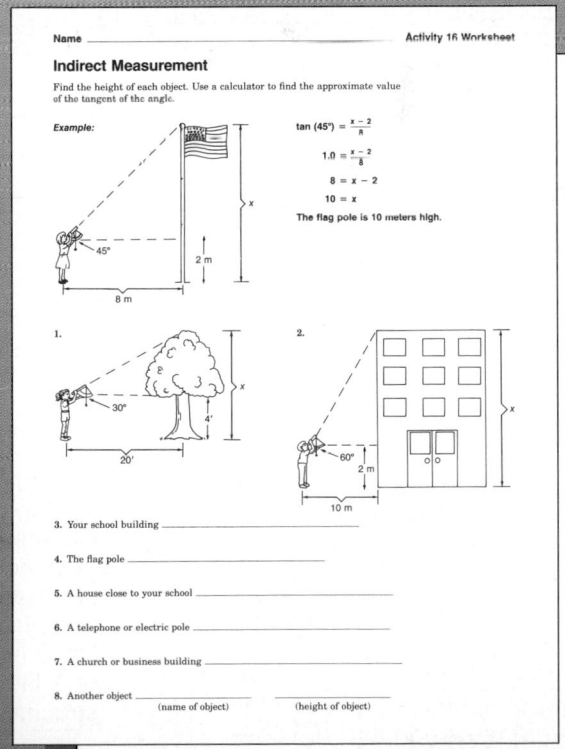

Using the Chapter Opener

Transparency 16–0 is available in the Transparency Package. It provides a full-color visual and motivational activity that you can use to engage students in the mathematical content of the chapter.

Background Information

Architects use knowledge of construction materials and methods, engineering practices, and architectural techniques to design and oversee the construction of safe, functional, and attractive buildings. Architects discuss the purpose, requirements, and cost with the client and then prepare drawings. Computer-aided design (CAD) systems are used to produce and modify designs. If an architect's plans are accepted, a final design is produced, plus a working design for use by contractors. Employment of architects is expected to rise 25% to 34% through the 1990s.

Trigonometric Functions

CHAPTER OBJECTIVES

In this chapter, you will:
- Find the values of trigonometric functions.
- Solve problems involving right triangles using right triangle trigonometry.
- Solve triangles using the law of sines and the law of cosines.

The blueprint of a unit in a multi-family complex is shown below with its scale. Find the approximate size of each room.

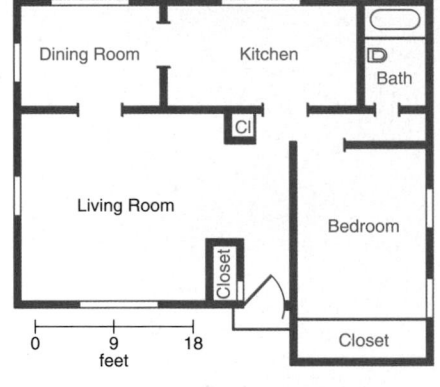

730

CAREERS IN ARCHITECTURE

If you could design your idea of the perfect house, what would it look like? How about designing the perfect office building, apartment building, school, hospital, factory, or airport terminal?

Think about the task of drawing up the plans for any of those buildings. You'd be relating its complex functions to space, color, texture, warmth, and light. It's not a career for everyone. Architecture requires a mind where art and science can meet to create a constructed human environment.

Of course, an architect usually isn't working for himself or herself. There is a client who must be satisfied and whose budget must be met. And don't forget to follow local building codes, zoning laws, fire regulations, handicapped-access ordinances, and all other applicable laws. They mostly deal with the functional aspects of the building: that includes heating, air-conditioning, ventilation, electricity, plumbing, and security. But there's more—Will there be a centralized intercom system? How about centralized vacuum cleaning? And what about outdoors—Will the architect also create the landscaping plan? How about outdoor lights? Will there be fences or walls? Is there ample parking?

Architecture is a rewarding career. It is art that can be lived in and used every day. And some of it will last for centuries to come.

Chapter Project

Materials: paper, pencil, ruler, compass, protractor, model-building materials

Organize students into cooperative groups of prospective architects. Assign each the task of designing and constructing a simple building or structure. Groups may choose to re-design and re-construct an existing building or structure, such as a home or the school. This approach may provide a sense of dimension for students not familiar with structural

measurements. Instruct groups to apply the following steps.
1. Have each group produce a set of sketches of its building or structure from all four geographical directions.
2. Have each group produce a set of "blueprints", showing all structural dimensions, to in-

clude east, west, north, and south exposures; floor plans; interior walls; and roof.
3. Have each group construct a scale model of its building or structure from its own blueprints.
4. Finally, have each group display and describe its model.

MORE ABOUT ARCHITECTURE

Degree Required:

Bachelor's Degree in architecture plus three years experience or a masters degree in architecture plus two years experience

Some architects like:

- working with people
- solving problems
- the opportunity to be creative
- creating something that will last

Related Math Subjects:

- Advanced Algebra
- Geometry
- Trigonometry
- Calculus
- Statistics/Probability

Some architects dislike:

- working long hours
- having to redo plans to please a client
- working with difficult or unpleasant people
- meeting deadlines

For more information on the various careers available in the field of Architecture, write to:

American Institute of Architects
1735 New York Avenue
Washington, D.C. 20006

731

Lesson	Connections (C) and Applications (A)	Examples	Exercises
16-1	C: Geometry	3	
	Probability		50
	A: Sports		42
16-2	C: Statistics		46
	A: Sports		44
	Construction		45
16-3	C: Geometry		47
	A: Surveying	3	
	Navigation		41
	Sports		42
16-4	C: Statistics		43
	A: Architecture	1	
	Navigation		41
	Travel		42, 46
	Biology		45
	Health		47
16-5	C: Statistics		43
	A: Navigation	4	
	Physics		39
	Electronics		40
	Optics		41
	Sports		42
16-6	A: Physics	3	
	Civil		40
	Engineer-		
	ing		
	Travel		41
	Finance		44
	Chemistry		45
16-7	C: Geometry		18, 23
	A: Forestry	1	
	Navigation	2	
	Astronomy	3	
	Broadcasting	4	26
	Transporta-		25
	tion		
	Travel		27
16-8	C: Statistics		36
	Geometry		28, 40
	A: Navigation	3	
	Surveying		34
	Aviation		35
	Biology		38
16-9	A: Engineering	3	
16-10	C: Geometry		28
	Statistics		37
	A: Aviation	2	35
	Navigation		33, 36
	Broadcasting		34

Lesson Resources

Reteaching Master 16-1
Practice Master 16-1
Enrichment Master 16-1

 Transparency 16-1 contains the 5-Minute Check and a teaching aid for this lesson.

INTRODUCING THE LESSON

 5-Minute Check

(over Chapter 15)

1. How many ways can 4 books be placed on a shelf from a selection of 10 books? **5040**
2. How many ways can 9 people be seated around a campfire? **40,320**
3. From a list of 18 books, how many groups of 6 can be selected? **18,564**
4. Four coins are tossed. What is the probability that they show 3 heads and 1 tail? $\frac{1}{4} = 0.25$
5. What is the probability of drawing a face card or a red card from a deck of 52 cards? $\frac{8}{13} \approx 0.615$

Motivating the Lesson

Have students play "Treasure Hunt" with a partner. Have each student draw a circle with a radius of 10 units on graph paper. On the circumference of that circle, locate 3 treasures. Guess the locations of the other student's treasures by using ordered pairs of whole numbers. A guess is a "find" if both coordinates are within 1 unit of the location.

TEACHING THE LESSON

Teaching Tip 1 You may want to mention that if the terminal side lies on one of the coordinate axes, the angle is called a *quadrantal angle*. For example, 270° and −180° are quadrantal angles.

Objectives

16-1A
16-1B

After studying this lesson, you should be able to:
- change radian measure to degree measure and vice versa, and
- identify coterminal angles.

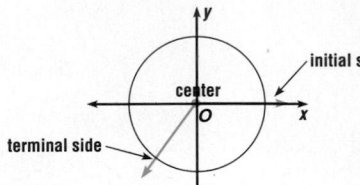

In the coordinate plane at the left, a circle is centered at the origin and two rays extend from the center. These rays form an angle. One ray, called the **initial side** of the angle, is fixed along the positive x-axis. The other ray, called the **terminal side** of the angle, can rotate about the center. An angle positioned like this, with its initial side along the x-axis and its vertex at the origin, is said to be in **standard position.**

The measures of angles in standard position whose terminal sides rotate counterclockwise are positive. **Teaching Tip 1**

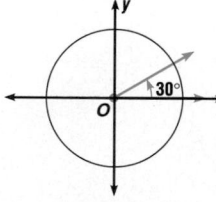 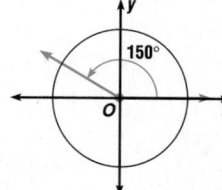 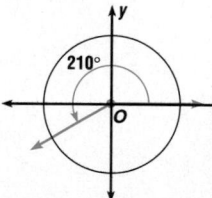

The measures of angles in standard position whose terminal sides rotate clockwise are negative.

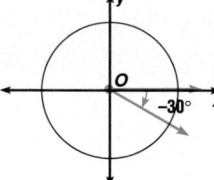 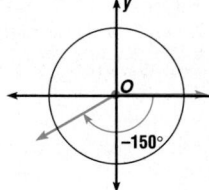 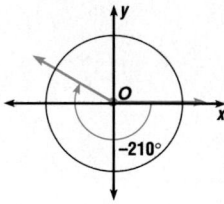

> *FYI . . .*
>
> The word *trigonometry* comes from the Greek *trigōnonmetria* meaning *angle measure*. The Greeks developed trigonometric ratios in an attempt to track the planets and stars.

When terminal sides rotate, they may sometimes make one or more complete revolutions about the center of the circle. An angle whose terminal side has made exactly one revolution about the center has a measure of 360°.

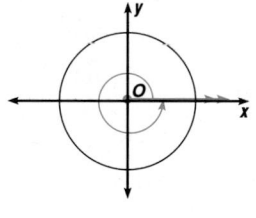

one revolution
360°

two revolutions
360° • 2 or 720°

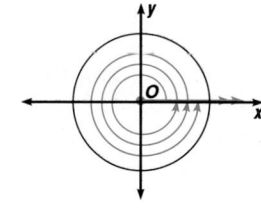

three revolutions
360° • 3 or 1,080°

732 CHAPTER 16 TRIGONOMETRIC FUNCTIONS

ALTERNATE TEACHING STRATEGIES

Using Cooperative Groups

Play another game of "Treasure Hunt" as described in Motivating the Lesson. Instead of two players, use two groups of two students each. Guess angle measures instead of coordinates, allowing use of calculators and protractors. A guess is correct if it is within 5° or 0.1 radian. Be sure students realize that there is more than one correct measure of an angle.

Teaching Tip ❷

Angles in standard position that have the same terminal side are called **coterminal angles.** For instance, 30°, 390°, and 750° are coterminal angles. The measures of coterminal angles always differ by an integral multiple of 360°.   *Why?*

Teaching Tip ❸

A **unit circle** is a circle centered at the origin whose radius is 1 unit long. Form an angle in standard position so that the rays of the angle intercept an arc 1 unit long. The measure of this angle is defined to be 1 **radian.** While degrees are the most common unit of angle measure, radians can also be used to describe the measure of an angle.

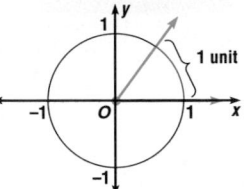

The circumference of any circle is $2\pi r$ where r is the radius measure. So the circumference of a unit circle is $2\pi(1)$ or 2π units. An angle representing one complete revolution of the circle measures 2π radians. Since we know that one complete revolution is 360°, the following proportion illustrates the relationship between radians and degrees.

$$\frac{\text{degree measure}}{360} = \frac{\text{radian measure}}{2\pi}$$

If you know the degree measure of an angle and you need to find the radian measure, multiply the number of degrees by $\frac{\pi}{180}$. $\frac{2\pi}{360} = \frac{\pi}{180}$

Example 1

Change each degree measure to radian measure.

a. 60°

$60 \cdot \frac{\pi}{180} = \frac{60\pi}{180}$ or $\frac{\pi}{3}$

b. 270°

$270 \cdot \frac{\pi}{180} = \frac{270\pi}{180}$ or $\frac{3\pi}{2}$

c. −45°

$-45 \cdot \frac{\pi}{180} = -\frac{45\pi}{180}$ or $-\frac{\pi}{4}$

If you know the radian measure of an angle and you need to find the degree measure, multiply the number of radians by $\frac{180}{\pi}$.

Example 2

Change each radian measure to degree measure.

a. $\frac{\pi}{12}$

$\frac{\pi}{12} \cdot \frac{180}{\pi} = \left(\frac{180\pi}{12\pi}\right)^\circ$
$= 15°$

b. $-\pi$

$-\pi \cdot \frac{180}{\pi} = \left(-\frac{180\pi}{\pi}\right)^\circ$
$= -180°$

c. 1

$1 \cdot \frac{180}{\pi} = \left(\frac{180}{\pi}\right)^\circ$
$\approx 57.30°$

Teaching Tip ❷   Note that the sum of the absolute values of the clockwise and counterclockwise measures of an angle totals 360°, assuming there have been no complete rotations in either direction.

Teaching Tip ❸   You may want to review the terms *intercept* and *arc.*

Chalkboard Examples

For Example 1
Change each degree measure to radian measure.

a. 80° $\frac{4\pi}{9}$

b. 415° $\frac{83\pi}{36}$

c. −160° $\frac{-8\pi}{9}$

For Example 2
Change each radian measure to degree measure.

a. $\frac{9\pi}{5}$ **324°**

b. $\frac{-3\pi}{2}$ **−270°**

c. $1\frac{1}{4}$ $\frac{-225°}{\pi} \approx$ **−71.6°**

EVALUATING THE LESSON

Checking for Understanding
Exercises 1–16 are designed to help you assess understanding through reading, writing, and speaking. You should work through Exercises 1–4 with your students, and then monitor their work on Exercises 5–16.

Closing the Lesson
Modeling Activity Have students use diagrams to model examples of the terms arc, standard position, radian, and coterminal angles.

Reteaching Masters Booklet, p. 104

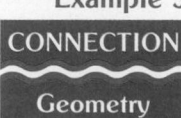

Example 3
CONNECTION
Geometry

The numbers on the face of a clock divide the circular face into twelve congruent sectors. Find the degree measure and the radian measure of the angle between any two consecutive numbers on a clock.

Since the face is divided into twelve congruent pieces, each angle must measure $\frac{1}{12}$ of the total measure of the circle. Since a clock face represents one complete revolution, the total measure is 360° or 2π radians.

degrees
$$\frac{\text{total measure}}{12} = \frac{360°}{12}$$
$$= 30°$$

radians
$$\frac{\text{total measure}}{12} = \frac{2\pi}{12}$$
$$= \frac{\pi}{6} \text{ radians}$$

The measure of the angle between any two consecutive numbers on a clock face is 30° or $\frac{\pi}{6}$ radians.

Convert 30° to radians to check that these measures are equivalent.

CHECKING FOR UNDERSTANDING

Communicating Mathematics

Read and study the lesson to answer these questions.

1. An angle with its vertex at the origin and its initial side along the positive x-axis is said to be in __?__. **standard position**

2. Describe coterminal angles and give an example of two angles that are coterminal. **in standard position with same terminal side; Answers vary.**

3. Define unit circle. **A circle centered at the origin with a radius 1 unit long.**

4. Find the degree measure and the radian measure of the angle formed by the hands of a clock when it is exactly 5 o'clock. **150° or $\frac{5\pi}{6}$ radians**

Guided Practice
Teaching Tip ④

Suppose angles with the following measures are in standard position. For each angle, name the quadrant that contains the terminal side.

5. $\frac{4\pi}{7}$ **II**
6. $\frac{5\pi}{3}$ **IV**
7. $-\frac{12\pi}{5}$ **IV**
8. $97°$ **II**
9. $-330°$ **I**
10. $-115°$ **III**

Teaching Tip ⑤

Determine whether each pair of angles is coterminal.

11. $\frac{\pi}{2}, \frac{3\pi}{2}$ **no**
12. $0, 8\pi$ **yes**
13. $\frac{2\pi}{5}, \frac{4\pi}{5}$ **no**
14. $75°, 435°$ **yes**
15. $20°, 2000°$ **no**
16. $-24°, 384°$ **no**

EXERCISES

Practice
A

Determine whether each pair of angles is coterminal.

17. $\frac{11\pi}{3}, \frac{16\pi}{3}$ **no**
18. $\frac{\pi}{8}, \frac{33\pi}{8}$ **yes**
19. $-\frac{5\pi}{9}, \frac{5\pi}{9}$ **no**
20. $440°, 80°$ **yes**
21. $-11°, -371°$ **yes**
22. $-39°, 681°$ **yes**

RETEACHING THE LESSON

Divide the class into groups. Have each group come up with five degree measures and five radian measures in which some are equal and some are not. Have groups exchange papers and decide which pairs are equal and which are not. Return to original groups to check and discuss.

Change each degree measure to radian measure.

B

23. $180°$ π

24. $-90°$ $-\dfrac{\pi}{2}$

25. $45°$ $\dfrac{\pi}{4}$

26. $540°$ 3π

27. $-225°$ $-\dfrac{5\pi}{4}$

28. $315°$ $\dfrac{7\pi}{4}$

29. $135°$ $\dfrac{3\pi}{4}$

30. $-210°$ $-\dfrac{7\pi}{6}$

31. $-120°$ $-\dfrac{2\pi}{3}$

Change each radian measure to degree measure.

C

32. $\dfrac{2\pi}{3}$ $120°$

33. π $180°$

34. $\dfrac{5\pi}{6}$ $150°$

35. $-\dfrac{7\pi}{4}$ $-315°$

36. $-\dfrac{8\pi}{3}$ $-480°$

37. $\dfrac{9\pi}{4}$ $405°$

38. 5 $\dfrac{900°}{\pi} \approx 286.48°$

39. $-2\dfrac{1}{3}$ $\dfrac{-420°}{\pi} \approx -133.69°$

40. $-6\dfrac{1}{2}$

$\dfrac{-1170°}{\pi} \approx -372.42°$

Critical Thinking

41. Explain why the measure of coterminal angles differ by a multiple of 360°. How would the radian measure of coterminal angles differ?
See margin.

Application

42. **Sports** A scuba diver uses a compass to navigate a straight line. The compass is aligned to the diver and a point toward which the diver wishes to travel. The ring on the compass, called a bezel, is turned so that the index needle is aligned over the compass needle. Now as long as the diver swims so that the compass needle aligns with the index needle, she will be swimming in a straight line to the desired location. If she wants to return to her starting point, she simply swims in the direction that is 180° from her original direction. This direction is called the reciprocal heading.

a. Carita has been swimming so that her compass points toward 18°. Where should the needle point when she swims back to the dock where she started? **198°**

b. On a certain dive, Carita found a formation that she wished to show her friend Dan on their next dive. When she saw the formation, she was swimming back to the dock so that her compass pointed to 234°. When she and Dan return to the formation, what should the heading on the compass be? **54°**

Additional Answer

41. **Coterminal angles have the same terminal side, so they differ only by the number of complete revolutions made. Since a complete revolution measures 360°, the measures must differ by an integral multiple of 360°. Radian measures of coterminal angles will differ by an integral multiple of 2π.**

APPLYING THE LESSON

Homework Exercises

Assignment Guide

Basic: 17–31, 41–48, 50–54
Average: 20–35, 41–54
Enriched: 23–54

Teaching Tip ❹   You may want to review the location of each quadrant.

Teaching Tip ❺   Encourage the use of diagrams and calculators where they would be helpful in solving the exercises.

Practice Masters Booklet, p. 119

16-1 | **Practice Worksheet**

NAME _____ DATE _____

Angles and the Unit Circle

Change each degree measure to radian measure.

1. $18°$ $\dfrac{\pi}{10}$

2. $-72°$ $-\dfrac{2\pi}{5}$

3. $-820°$ $-\dfrac{41\pi}{9}$

4. $6°$ $\dfrac{\pi}{30}$

5. $-250°$ $-\dfrac{25\pi}{18}$

6. $870°$ $\dfrac{29\pi}{6}$

7. $347°$ $\dfrac{347\pi}{180}$

8. $-165°$ $-\dfrac{11\pi}{12}$

9. $2\pi°$ $\dfrac{\pi^2}{90}$

10. $-\dfrac{4}{3}\pi°$ $-\dfrac{\pi^2}{135}$

Change each radian measure to degree measure.

11. 4π $720°$

12. $\dfrac{5}{2}\pi$ $450°$

13. $\dfrac{-7}{9}\pi$ $-140°$

14. $2\dfrac{3}{5}\pi$ $468°$

15. $\dfrac{13}{30}\pi$ $78°$

16. $-\dfrac{4}{7}\pi$ $-102\dfrac{6}{7}°$

17. 4 $\dfrac{720°}{\pi}$

18. $-\dfrac{5}{2}$ $-\dfrac{450°}{\pi}$

19. $\dfrac{5\pi}{4}$ $225°$

20. $\dfrac{3\pi}{16}$ $33\dfrac{3}{4}°$

Additional Answers

49. 30 IF $A < 2 * 3.1415927$
   THEN 70
   40 LET $A = A - 2 *$
   3.1415927
   70 LET $A = A + 2 *$
   3.1415927

52. $\log_3 27 + \log_3 3 \overset{?}{=} \log_3 81$
   $3 + 1 = 4$ ✔

53.

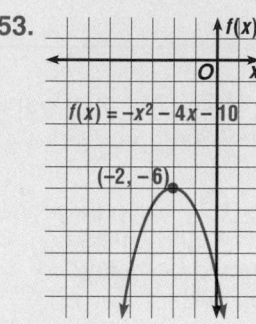

$f(x) = -x^2 - 4x - 10$

$(-2, -6)$

Teaching Tip ➏ The measures of the angles returned by the program will be A such that $0° \leq A < 360°$. Thus, if $A = n \cdot 360°$, the coterminal angle will be 0°.

Have students enter the degree measures 2594°, 1154°, -646°, and -2446°. The coterminal angle measures 74° for all of these angles. Students should realize that there are an infinite number of angles that have the same coterminal angle.

Enrichment Masters Booklet, p. 104

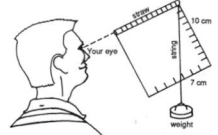
Computer
Teaching Tip ➏ Coterminal angles are those angles whose measures differ by a multiple of 360°. If the degree measure of an angle is entered into this program, the coterminal angle between 0° and 360° will be printed. The BASIC program below uses loops to add or subtract 360° until the angle is between 0° and 360°.

```
10   PRINT "ENTER A DEGREE MEASURE."
20   INPUT A
30   IF A < 360 THEN 60
40   LET A = A - 360
50   GOTO 30
60   IF A > = 0 THEN 90
70   LET A = A + 360
80   GOTO 60
90   PRINT "ITS COTERMINAL ANGLE
     MEASURES "; A; " DEGREES."
100  END
```

Find the coterminal angle between 0° and 360° for each of the following.

43. 720° **0°**   **44.** 1373.56° **293.56°**   **45.** -981° **99°**

State whether each pair of angles are coterminal.

46. -59°, 661° **yes**   **47.** 29°, 9361° **no**   **48.** 49°, 1129° **yes**

49. How should lines 30, 40, and 70 be modified if the angle measure is given in radians? **See margin.**

Mixed Review

50. Probability Chris guessed on all 10 questions on a true-false test. What is the probability that all of the guesses were correct? **(Lesson 15-9)** $\frac{1}{1024} \approx 0.001$

51. Find the sum of the geometric series for which $a_1 = 5$, $r = 4$, and $n = 8$. **(Lesson 13-5) 109,225**

52. Show that $\log_3 27 + \log_3 3 = \log_3 81$. **(Lesson 12-2) See margin.**

53. Graph the equation $f(x) = -x^2 - 4x - 10$. **(Lesson 8-3) See margin.**

54. Simplify $5^{-3}b^3x^4y^{-1}$. **(Lesson 5-2)** $\frac{b^3x^4}{5^3y}$

CHALLENGE

If (a, b) is on the unit circle, prove that each of the following points is also on the unit circle. **See Solutions Manual.**

    a. $(a, -b)$ **b.** (b, a) **c.** $(b, -a)$

EXTENDING THE LESSON

Math Power: Connections

Have students research the different phases of the moon. For each phase, have them draw a diagram, labeling the measure of the angle formed. In each diagram, Earth is at the origin, the ray from Earth to the sun forms the initial side of an angle, and the ray from Earth to the moon forms the terminal side of the angle.

Challenge

The challenge extends students' understanding of a unit circle. If needed, suggest that students recall the general equation of a circle.

16-2 Sine and Cosine Functions

Objectives

16-2A
16-2B

After studying this lesson, you should be able to:
- find the least possible angle that is coterminal to a given angle, and
- find the values of expressions involving sine and cosine.

Application

The waves shown at the right represent the fluctuations in energy produced by musical tones. An instrument called an oscilloscope converted the sound waves to electrical impulses and displayed the curves on the screen. A pure musical tone produces a curve that is the graph of the **sine function.** The sine function is one of the functions that can be defined in terms of the unit circle.

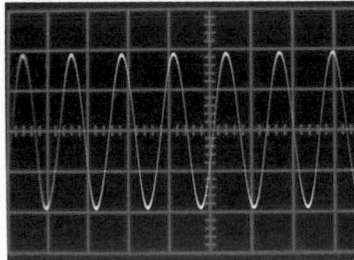

Consider an angle in standard position. Let the Greek letter θ (theta) stand for the measurement of the angle. The terminal side of this angle intersects the unit circle at a particular point. The x-coordinate of this point is called **cosine θ.** The y-coordinate of this point is called **sine θ.** Sine is abbreviated sin and cosine is abbreviated cos.

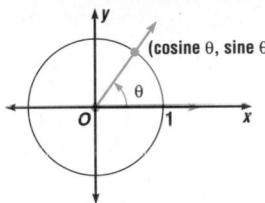

Definition of Sine and Cosine	Let θ stand for the measurement of an angle in standard position. Let (x, y) represent the coordinates of the point where the terminal side intersects the unit circle. Then $$\cos \theta = x \quad \text{and} \quad \sin \theta = y.$$

Example 1

Find sin 45°. **Teaching Tip ❶**

Consider the right triangle formed by two sides and a diagonal of a square. One side of this triangle is part of the initial side of a 45° angle, and the hypotenuse is along the terminal side.

$$\sqrt{s^2 + s^2} = 1 \qquad \text{Pythagorean Theorem}$$
$$\sqrt{2s^2} = 1 \qquad c = 1, a = s, b = s$$
$$s\sqrt{2} = 1$$
$$s = \frac{1}{\sqrt{2}} \text{ or } \frac{\sqrt{2}}{2} \qquad \textit{The length of each side is } \frac{\sqrt{2}}{2} \textit{ or about 0.707 units.}$$

The coordinates of the point labeled (x, y) are $\left(\frac{\sqrt{2}}{2}, \frac{\sqrt{2}}{2}\right)$. So, sin 45° $- \frac{\sqrt{2}}{2}$.

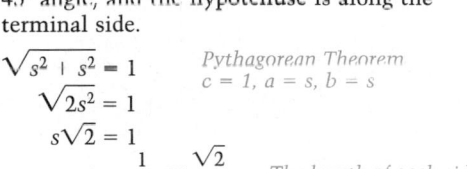

The triangle formed is an isosceles triangle.

LESSON 16-2 SINE AND COSINE FUNCTIONS 737

ALTERNATE TEACHING STRATEGIES

Mini-Math Lab

Provide students with a piece of graph paper fastened on a piece of corrugated cardboard, two thumbtacks, string, a compass, and a protractor. Using the definition of sine and cosine, have students confirm the values for

sine and cosine listed in the first table on page 738. Allow the use of calculators to simplify sine and cosine values in the table for ease of comparison.

Lesson Resources

Reteaching Master 16-2
Practice Master 16-2
Enrichment Master 16-2

Transparency 16-2 contains the 5-Minute Check and a teaching aid for this lesson.

INTRODUCING THE LESSON

🕐 5-Minute Check

(over Lesson 16-1)
Change each degree measure to radian measure.

1. 280° $\frac{14\pi}{9}$

2. −225° $\frac{-5\pi}{4}$

Change each radian measure to degree measure.

3. $\frac{11\pi}{4}$ **495°**

4. 3 $\frac{540°}{\pi} \approx 171.9°$

5. Are angles of 53° and −307° coterminal? **yes**

Motivating the Lesson

Ask students how many of them have ever ridden a Ferris wheel. Ask them if they know how their location on a Ferris wheel relates to trigonometry.

TEACHING THE LESSON

Teaching Tip ❶ These examples provide the background for the tables of sine and cosine values as given on page 738. You may want to use diagrams to have students recall the 30°−60° and 45°−45° right triangle relationships from geometry.

Example 2

Find sin 210°.

Study the graph at the right. The dashed line cuts the *x*-axis and the terminal side of the angle to form a 30°–60° right triangle. In a 30°–60°-right triangle, the side opposite the 30° angle is half the length of the hypotenuse. The length of the radius of the circle is 1 unit. Thus, *s* = 1 unit and $\dfrac{s}{2} = \dfrac{1}{2}$ unit.

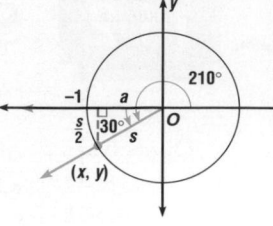

The *y*-coordinate of the point (*x*, *y*) is $-\dfrac{1}{2}$. So, sin 210° = $-\dfrac{1}{2}$. *Use the Pythagorean Theorem to check this result.*

The table at the right lists the signs of the sine and cosine functions for angles in standard position with terminal sides in each of the four quadrants. Recall that the coordinates of the point where the terminal side intersects the unit circle are (cos θ, sin θ).

Quadrant II	Quadrant I
cos θ −	cos θ +
sin θ +	sin θ +

Quadrant III	Quadrant IV
cos θ −	cos θ +
sin θ −	sin θ −

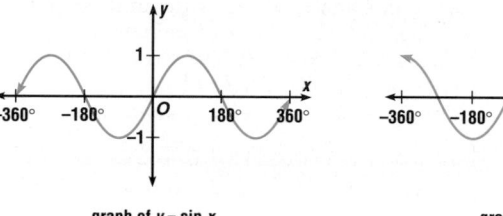

graph of y = sin x   graph of y = cos x

You could use the technique used in the examples to complete the following tables. *You should memorize the frequently-used values listed in these tables.* **Teaching Tip ❷**

degrees	0	30	45	60	90	120	135	150	180	210	225	240	270	300	315	330	360
radians	0	$\dfrac{\pi}{6}$	$\dfrac{\pi}{4}$	$\dfrac{\pi}{3}$	$\dfrac{\pi}{2}$	$\dfrac{2\pi}{3}$	$\dfrac{3\pi}{4}$	$\dfrac{5\pi}{6}$	π	$\dfrac{7\pi}{6}$	$\dfrac{5\pi}{4}$	$\dfrac{4\pi}{3}$	$\dfrac{3\pi}{2}$	$\dfrac{5\pi}{3}$	$\dfrac{7\pi}{4}$	$\dfrac{11\pi}{6}$	2π
sin θ	0	$\dfrac{1}{2}$	$\dfrac{\sqrt{2}}{2}$	$\dfrac{\sqrt{3}}{2}$	1	$\dfrac{\sqrt{3}}{2}$	$\dfrac{\sqrt{2}}{2}$	$\dfrac{1}{2}$	0	$-\dfrac{1}{2}$	$-\dfrac{\sqrt{2}}{2}$	$-\dfrac{\sqrt{3}}{2}$	−1	$-\dfrac{\sqrt{3}}{2}$	$-\dfrac{\sqrt{2}}{2}$	$-\dfrac{1}{2}$	0
cos θ	1	$\dfrac{\sqrt{3}}{2}$	$\dfrac{\sqrt{2}}{2}$	$\dfrac{1}{2}$	0	$-\dfrac{1}{2}$	$-\dfrac{\sqrt{2}}{2}$	$-\dfrac{\sqrt{3}}{2}$	−1	$-\dfrac{\sqrt{3}}{2}$	$-\dfrac{\sqrt{2}}{2}$	$-\dfrac{1}{2}$	0	$\dfrac{1}{2}$	$\dfrac{\sqrt{2}}{2}$	$\dfrac{\sqrt{3}}{2}$	1

The next chart contains the same information for angles from 360° to 720°. Compare the information in the two charts. As you can see, the values of sin θ and cos θ are the same for two angles that are coterminal.

738   CHAPTER 16   TRIGONOMETRIC FUNCTIONS

degrees	360	390	405	420	450	480	495	510	540	570	585	600	630	660	675	690	720
radians	2π	$\frac{13\pi}{6}$	$\frac{9\pi}{4}$	$\frac{7\pi}{3}$	$\frac{5\pi}{2}$	$\frac{8\pi}{3}$	$\frac{11\pi}{4}$	$\frac{17\pi}{6}$	3π	$\frac{19\pi}{6}$	$\frac{13\pi}{4}$	$\frac{10\pi}{3}$	$\frac{7\pi}{2}$	$\frac{11\pi}{3}$	$\frac{15\pi}{4}$	$\frac{23\pi}{6}$	4π
$\sin\theta$	0	$\frac{1}{2}$	$\frac{\sqrt{2}}{2}$	$\frac{\sqrt{3}}{2}$	1	$\frac{\sqrt{3}}{2}$	$\frac{\sqrt{2}}{2}$	$\frac{1}{2}$	0	$-\frac{1}{2}$	$-\frac{\sqrt{2}}{2}$	$-\frac{\sqrt{3}}{2}$	-1	$-\frac{\sqrt{3}}{2}$	$-\frac{\sqrt{2}}{2}$	$-\frac{1}{2}$	0
$\cos\theta$	1	$\frac{\sqrt{3}}{2}$	$\frac{\sqrt{2}}{2}$	$\frac{1}{2}$	0	$-\frac{1}{2}$	$-\frac{\sqrt{2}}{2}$	$-\frac{\sqrt{3}}{2}$	-1	$-\frac{\sqrt{3}}{2}$	$-\frac{\sqrt{2}}{2}$	$-\frac{1}{2}$	0	$\frac{1}{2}$	$\frac{\sqrt{2}}{2}$	$\frac{\sqrt{3}}{2}$	1

Every 360°, or 2π radians, represents one complete revolution of the terminal side. As you can see by comparing the table above with the one on page 738, for every 360° or 2π radians, the sine and cosine functions repeat their values. So, we can say that the sine and cosine functions are **periodic**. Each has a **period** of 360° or 2π radians.

Definition of Periodic Function	A function is called periodic if there is a number a such that $f(x) = f(x + a)$ for all x in the domain of the function. The least positive value of a for which $f(x) = f(x + a)$ is called the period of the function.

For the sine and cosine functions, $\cos(x + 360°) = \cos x$ and $\sin(x + 2\pi) = \sin x$. What are the values of $\cos(x + 2\pi)$ and $\sin(x + 360°)$? How can a negative angle be written as a positive angle?

Example 3

Find the value of each function.

a. $\sin 420°$
$\sin 420° = \sin(60 + 360)°$
$= \sin 60°$
$= \frac{\sqrt{3}}{2}$

b. $\cos\left(-\frac{3\pi}{4}\right)$
$\cos\left(-\frac{3\pi}{4}\right) = \cos\left(-\frac{3\pi}{4} + 2\pi\right)$
$= \cos\left(\frac{5\pi}{4}\right)$ or $\cos 225°$
$= -\frac{\sqrt{2}}{2}$

CHECKING FOR UNDERSTANDING

Communicating Mathematics

Read and study the lesson to answer these questions.

1. The terminal side of an angle with measure θ intersects the unit circle at a particular point.
   a. What is the x-coordinate of the point called? **cosine θ**
   b. What is the y-coordinate called? **sine θ**

2. What are the signs of the sine and cosine values for an angle whose terminal side lies in the third quadrant? **Sine and cosine are both negative.**

3. How are angles with measures of $-45°$ and $315°$ related? **They are coterminal angles.**

LESSON 16-2   SINE AND COSINE FUNCTIONS   739

RETEACHING THE LESSON

Give students an angle measure from each of the four quadrants that can be used in a 30°–60° or 45°–45° right triangle. Have them construct their own unit circle and diagram to find the sine and cosine value of that angle measure. Check these diagrams.

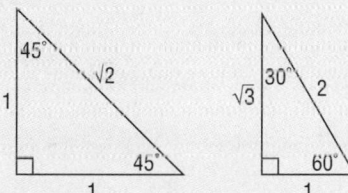
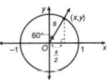

Closing the Lesson

Speaking Activity To emphasize the general meaning of the term *periodic,* have students list several events in nature that are periodic. Examples might be changes in moon phases, seasons, or tides.

Homework Exercises

Assignment Guide

Basic: 16–36, 43–44, 46–51
Average: 21–39, 43–51
Enriched: 25–51

Teaching Tip ❸ The purpose of Exercises 10–15 and 25–42 is to reinforce and apply previously developed relationships. Do not allow the use of calculators for these exercises.

Practice Masters Booklet, p. 120

Guided Practice

State whether the value of each function is positive or negative.

4. $\sin 200°$ **–**
5. $\cos 320°$ **+**
6. $\sin(-135°)$ **–**
7. $\cos 405°$ **+**
8. $\cos(-225°)$ **–**
9. $\sin 445°$ **+**

Teaching Tip ❸

Find each value. Use the tables on pages 738 and 739 or the properties of unit circles, and 30°–60° right triangles and 45°–45° right triangles.

10. $\sin\frac{4\pi}{3}$ **$-\frac{\sqrt{3}}{2}$**
11. $\cos\left(-\frac{7\pi}{3}\right)$ **$\frac{1}{2}$**
12. $\sin\left(-\frac{\pi}{6}\right)$ **$-\frac{1}{2}$**
13. $\cos\left(-\frac{3}{4}\pi\right)$ **$-\frac{\sqrt{2}}{2}$**
14. $\sin(-240°)$ **$\frac{\sqrt{3}}{2}$**
15. $\sin 660°$ **$-\frac{\sqrt{3}}{2}$**

EXERCISES

Practice

For each of the following, find the least positive angle measurement that is coterminal.

16. $680°$ **320°**
17. $-70°$ **290°**
18. $1020°$ **300°**
19. $-450°$ **270°**
20. 3π **π**
21. $\frac{9\pi}{2}$ **$\frac{\pi}{2}$**
22. $-\frac{\pi}{4}$ **$\frac{7\pi}{4}$**
23. $\frac{27\pi}{4}$ **$\frac{3\pi}{4}$**
24. $-760°$ **320°**

Find each value.

25. $\sin 45°$ **$\frac{\sqrt{2}}{2}$**
26. $\cos 150°$ **$-\frac{\sqrt{3}}{2}$**
27. $\cos\frac{11}{3}\pi$ **$\frac{1}{2}$**
28. $\sin\left(-\frac{5}{3}\pi\right)$ **$\frac{\sqrt{3}}{2}$**
29. $\sin\frac{3\pi}{2}$ **-1**
30. $\cos\frac{7}{4}\pi$ **$\frac{\sqrt{2}}{2}$**
31. $\sin(-180°)$ **0**
32. $\cos\left(-\frac{7}{4}\pi\right)$ **$\frac{\sqrt{2}}{2}$**
33. $\cos(-60°)$ **$\frac{1}{2}$**
34. $\sin 300°$ **$-\frac{\sqrt{3}}{2}$**
35. $\sin\left(-\frac{\pi}{6}\right)$ **$-\frac{1}{2}$**
36. $\sin\frac{4}{3}\pi$ **$-\frac{\sqrt{3}}{2}$**
37. $4(\sin 30°)(\cos 60°)$ **1**
38. $\frac{\sin 30° + \cos 60°}{2}$ **$\frac{1}{2}$**
39. $\frac{4\sin 300° + 2\cos 30°}{3}$ **$-\frac{\sqrt{3}}{3}$**
40. $\sin 30° + \sin 60°$ **$\frac{(1+\sqrt{3})}{2}$**
41. $(\sin 60°)^2 + (\cos 60°)^2$ **1**
42. $8(\sin 120°)(\cos 120°)$ **$-2\sqrt{3}$**

Critical Thinking

43. Use the method shown in Example 2 to prove that $\sin 60° = \frac{\sqrt{3}}{2}$. **See Solutions Manual.**

Applications

44. **Sports** Reba and Kyle are flying a kite. The kite string forms a 45° angle with the ground and the kite is 50 meters above the ground.
   a. Draw a diagram of the triangle formed by the kite string and the ground. **See students' work.**
   b. Find the approximate length of the kite string. **approximately 70.7 m**

45. Construction A support for the roof of a house is shown at the right. The center piece is 3 feet long and forms 60° angles with each of the braces. If each of the braces are 6 feet long, find the cosine of 60°. $\frac{1}{2}$

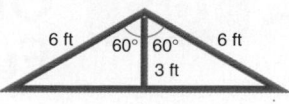
6 ft 60° 60° 6 ft
3 ft

Mixed Review

46. 19; 16; 18.5

46. Statistics During a cold spell lasting 43 days, the following high temperatures (in degrees Fahrenheit) were recorded in Chicago.

26	17	12	5	4	25	17	23	13	6	25	19	27	22	26
20	31	24	12	27	16	27	16	30	7	31	16	5	29	18
16	22	29	8	31	13	24	5	-7	20	29	18	12

Find the median, mode, and mean of the temperatures. **(Lesson 14-3)**

47. Jane and Pedro are stacking cans of mixed fruit in a display at the end of the grocery aisle. The top layer of the stack of cans has 1 can, the second layer has 4 cans, the third layer has 9 cans, and so on. How many cans are in the stack if it has 12 layers? **(Lesson 13-1)** **650 cans**

48. Simplify $\dfrac{\frac{3x}{4x-1}}{1+\frac{3x}{x-1}}$. **(Lesson 11-4)** $\dfrac{3x(x-1)}{(4x-1)^2}$

49. Find all zeros for the function $f(x) = x^3 - 2x^2 - 13x - 10$. **(Lesson 10-4)** **-1, -2, 5**

50. Simplify $(9 + 6i) - (3 + 2i)$. **(Lesson 6-9)** **6 + 4i**

51. Graph $4y - x \le 6$. **(Lesson 2-8)** **See margin.**

APPLICATIONS IN MUSIC

As you know, periodic functions are those functions whose values repeat after a certain period. The graphs of these functions are repetitive. Music is also periodic in nature. As you saw on the oscillogram on page 737, the graph produced by a musical tone closely resembles a sine curve. Hence, the sine curve is called pure or simple by musicians.

Graphs of musical tones have the same general shape, but different **frequencies.** The frequency of a curve is the number of cycles, or repetitions, in a given interval. The musical notes with higher frequencies are the higher pitched notes.

The vibrations of the string at the right show how musical notes are produced. The lowest frequency is called a fundamental and its multiples are called harmonics. Doubling the frequency raises the pitch one octave. So, the second harmonic is one octave above the fundamental. The fourth harmonic is one octave above the second harmonic and two octaves above the fundamental.

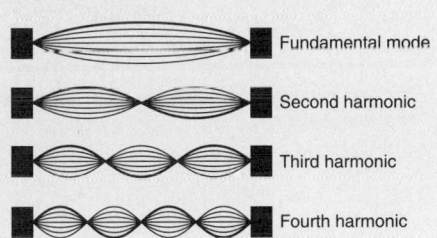
Fundamental mode
Second harmonic
Third harmonic
Fourth harmonic

LESSON 16-2 SINE AND COSINE FUNCTIONS 741

EXTENDING THE LESSON

Math Power: Communication

Have students write short paragraphs relating how each of the following topics might be represented by a sine function.

1. a water wheel
2. an animal population
3. a spring with a weight attached

Applications in Music

This feature explains some of the physics involved with sound. You may wish to involve the music and science departments in expanding the study of this concept.

Chapter 16, Quiz A, (Lessons 16–1 through 16–2), is available in the Evaluation Masters Booklet, p. 219.

Additional Answer

51.

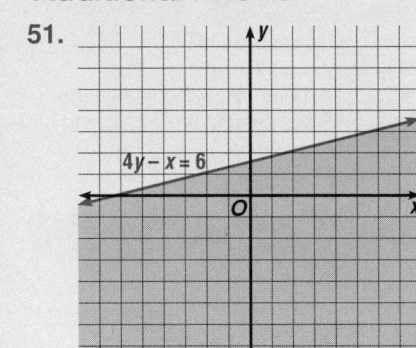
$4y - x = 6$

Enrichment Masters Booklet, p. 105

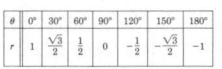
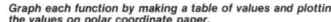

NAME _____ DATE _____

16-2 Enrichment Worksheet

Polar Coordinates

Consider an angle in standard position with its vertex at a point O called the *pole*. Its initial side is on a coordinatized axis called the *polar axis*. A point P on the terminal side of the angle is named by the *polar coordinates* (r, θ) where r is the directed distance of the point from O and θ is the measure of the angle. Graphs in this system may be drawn on polar coordinate paper such as the kind shown at the right.

The polar coordinates of a point are not unique. For example, $(3, 30°)$ names point P as well as $(3, 390°)$. Another name for P is $(-3, 210°)$. Can you see why? The coordinates of the pole are $(0, \theta)$ where θ may be any angle.

Example Draw the graph of the function $r = \cos \theta$.
Make a table of convenient values for θ and r. Then plot the points.

θ	0°	30°	60°	90°	120°	150°	180°
r	1	$\frac{\sqrt{3}}{2}$	$\frac{1}{2}$	0	$-\frac{1}{2}$	$-\frac{\sqrt{3}}{2}$	-1

Since the period of the cosine function is 180°, values of r for $\theta > 180°$ are repeated.

Graph each function by making a table of values and plotting the values on polar coordinate paper.

1. $r = 4$
$r = 4$ for all values of θ. Graph should be a circle with radius 4 and center at the pole.

2. $r = 3 \sin \theta$
Graph is circle of radius $\frac{3}{2}$ with center at $(\frac{3}{2}, 90°)$.

3. $r = 3 \cos 2\theta$
Graph looks like flower with 4 petals, points of petals are at $(3, 0°)$, $(3, 90°)$, $(3, 180°)$, $(3, 270°)$. All petals meet at pole.

4. $r = 2(1 + \cos \theta)$
Graph is heart-shaped curve, symmetric with respect to polar axis.

Lesson Resources

Reteaching Master 16-3
Practice Master 16-3
Enrichment Master 16-3
Technology Master, p. 33
Activity Master, p. 16

 Transparency 16-3 contains the 5-Minute Check and a teaching aid for this lesson.

INTRODUCING THE LESSON

 5-Minute Check

(over Lesson 16-2)
Find each value.

1. $\cos 30°$ $\dfrac{\sqrt{3}}{2}$

2. $\sin\left(\dfrac{-5\pi}{3}\right)$ $\dfrac{\sqrt{3}}{2}$

3. $\cos 900°$ -1

4. Is the value of $\cos \dfrac{5\pi}{3}$ positive or negative?   **positive**

Motivating the Lesson

Show students an empty box and tell them the area of its base, its width, and its height. Ask students to name what other information they can know about the box just by using the given information. Answers might include the volume of the box, its length, and its surface area. Emphasize that useful information can often be derived from other information.

TEACHING THE LESSON

Teaching Tip ❶   Remind students that the restrictions upon $\cos \theta$ and $\sin \theta$ are made so that the denominator is not zero. Thus the tan, sec, cot, and csc are not defined at those points.

16-3   Other Trigonometric Functions

Objective
16-3

After studying this lesson, you should be able to:
- find the values of other trigonometric functions.

Other trigonometric functions are defined using sine and cosine.

Definition of Tangent (tan), Cotangent (cot), Secant (sec), and Cosecant (csc)

Teaching Tip ❶

> Let θ stand for the measurement of an angle in standard position on the unit circle. Then the following equations hold true.
>
> If $\cos \theta \neq 0$, $\tan \theta = \dfrac{\sin \theta}{\cos \theta}$ and $\sec \theta = \dfrac{1}{\cos \theta}$.
>
> If $\sin \theta \neq 0$, $\cot \theta = \dfrac{\cos \theta}{\sin \theta}$ and $\csc \theta = \dfrac{1}{\sin \theta}$.

Example 1

The tables on pages 738 and 739 give values for $\sin \theta$ and $\cos \theta$.

Find each of the following.

a. $\tan 135°$

$\tan 135° = \dfrac{\sin 135°}{\cos 135°}$ *Definition of tangent*

$= \dfrac{\dfrac{\sqrt{2}}{2}}{-\dfrac{\sqrt{2}}{2}}$

$= -1$

b. $\sec 3.5\pi$

$\sec 3.5\pi = \dfrac{1}{\cos 3.5\pi}$ *Definition of secant*

$= \dfrac{1}{0}$

$\sec 3.5\pi$ is undefined.

Division by zero is undefined.

c. $\cot \dfrac{5\pi}{2}$

$\cot \dfrac{5\pi}{2} = \dfrac{\cos \dfrac{5\pi}{2}}{\sin \dfrac{5\pi}{2}}$ *Definition of cotangent*

$= \dfrac{0}{1}$

$= 0$

d. $\csc (-150°)$

$\csc (-150°) = \dfrac{1}{\sin (-150°)}$ *Definition of cosecant*

$= \dfrac{1}{\sin (210°)}$

$= \dfrac{1}{-\dfrac{1}{2}}$

$= -\dfrac{2}{1}$ or -2

ALTERNATE TEACHING STRATEGIES

Using Charts

Have students add values for tan, cot, sec, and csc to the table on page 738 that lists sin and cos. If the value is undefined, have students write "U" in the correct place on the chart.

Example 2

APPLICATION

Surveying

A surveyor finds that the angle between two merging roads is 120°. Find the value of each of the trigonometric functions for this angle.

$$\sin 120° = \frac{\sqrt{3}}{2}$$

$$\cos 120° = -\frac{1}{2}$$

$$\tan 120° = \frac{\sin 120°}{\cos 120°}$$
$$= \frac{\frac{\sqrt{3}}{2}}{-\frac{1}{2}}$$
$$= -\sqrt{3}$$

$$\csc 120° = \frac{1}{\sin 120°}$$
$$= \frac{1}{\frac{\sqrt{3}}{2}}$$
$$= \frac{2}{\sqrt{3}} \text{ or } \frac{2\sqrt{3}}{3}$$

$$\sec 120° = \frac{1}{\cos 120°}$$
$$= \frac{1}{-\frac{1}{2}}$$
$$= -\frac{2}{1} \text{ or } -2$$

$$\cot 120° = \frac{\cos 120°}{\sin 120°}$$
$$= \frac{-\frac{1}{2}}{\frac{\sqrt{3}}{2}}$$
$$= -\frac{1}{\sqrt{3}} \text{ or } -\frac{\sqrt{3}}{3}$$

CHECKING FOR UNDERSTANDING

Communicating Mathematics

1. $\tan \theta = \frac{3}{4}$;

   $\sec \theta = \frac{5}{4}$;

   $\cot \theta = \frac{4}{3}$;

   $\csc \theta = \frac{5}{3}$

Read and study the lesson to answer these questions.

1. If $\sin \theta = \frac{3}{5}$ and $\cos \theta = \frac{4}{5}$, find the other trigonometric functions for θ.

2. For any angle θ, $-1 \le \sin \theta \le 1$. What can you say about the range for csc θ? **csc θ ≤ -1 or csc θ ≥ 1**

3. Two functions are called reciprocal functions if their product is 1. For example, $y = \sin x$ and $y = \csc x$ are reciprocal functions since $\csc x = \frac{1}{\sin x}$ and $(\sin x)\left(\frac{1}{\sin x}\right) = 1$. What are the reciprocal functions for $y = \cos x$ and for $y = \tan x$? **$y = \sec x$; $y = \cot x$**

Guided Practice

10. $\sin 60° = \frac{\sqrt{3}}{2}$;

    $\cos 60° = \frac{1}{2}$;

    $\tan 60° = \sqrt{3}$;

    $\sec 60° = 2$;

    $\cot 60° = \frac{\sqrt{3}}{3}$; $\csc 60° = \frac{2\sqrt{3}}{3}$

State the values of 0° < θ < 360° for which each expression is not defined.

4. sin θ **none**
5. tan θ **90°, 270°**
6. cos θ **none**
7. cot θ **0°, 180°, 360°**
8. csc θ **0°, 180°, 360°**
9. sec θ **90°, 270°**

Find the value of each of the trigonometric functions for each angle measure. 11–12. See margin.

10. 60°
11. −225°
12. $\frac{3\pi}{2}$

RETEACHING THE LESSON

Have one student say a trigonometric function aloud and then point to another student to give the definition of that function. Continue this around the room until everyone has had a chance. Example: "csc 45°" Student points to another student who should say, "$\frac{1}{\sin 45°}$".

Additional Answers

11. $\sin -225° = \frac{\sqrt{2}}{2}$; $\cos -225° = -\frac{\sqrt{2}}{2}$; $\tan -225° = -1$; $\sec -225° = -\sqrt{2}$; $\cot -225° = -1$; $\csc -225° = \sqrt{2}$

12. $\sin \frac{3\pi}{2} = -1$; $\cos \frac{3\pi}{2} = 0$; $\tan \frac{3\pi}{2} =$ undefined; $\sec \frac{3\pi}{2} =$ undefined; $\cot \frac{3\pi}{2} = 0$; $\csc \frac{3\pi}{2} = -1$

Error Analysis

Have students especially watch the use of positive and negative signs. Have them draw a picture in order to determine the quadrant in which they are working.

Closing the Lesson

Writing Activity Have students make a quadrant table such as that following Example 2 on page 738. In addition to the sign information about sin and cos, have students include the sign of tan, cot, sec, and csc for each quadrant.

Practice Masters Booklet, p. 121

EXERCISES

Practice   **Find each value.**

A
13. cot 135° **−1**
14. csc 45° **$\sqrt{2}$**
15. sec 300° **2**

16. tan $\left(-\dfrac{\pi}{3}\right)$ **$-\sqrt{3}$**
17. csc (−210°) **2**
18. tan $\dfrac{7\pi}{6}$ **$\dfrac{\sqrt{3}}{3}$**

19. cot (−60°) **$-\dfrac{\sqrt{3}}{3}$**
20. sec 240° **−2**
21. cot $\left(-\dfrac{\pi}{6}\right)$ **$-\sqrt{3}$**

22. csc $\left(-\dfrac{\pi}{6}\right)$ **−2**
23. sec (−120°) **−2**
24. cot 210° **$\sqrt{3}$**

B
25. csc $\dfrac{\pi}{2}$ **1**
26. tan $\dfrac{9}{4}\pi$ **1**
27. tan $\left(-\dfrac{5}{6}\pi\right)$ **$\dfrac{\sqrt{3}}{3}$**

28. cot $\dfrac{7\pi}{4}$ **−1**
29. tan (−300°) **$\sqrt{3}$**
30. cot 540° **undefined**

31. sec (−30°) **$\dfrac{2\sqrt{3}}{3}$**
32. tan 405° **1**
33. csc 180° **undefined**

C
34. sec 390° **$\dfrac{2\sqrt{3}}{3}$**
35. cot (−600°) **$-\dfrac{\sqrt{3}}{3}$**
36. csc $\left(-\dfrac{7}{6}\pi\right)$ **2**

37. $\dfrac{\tan 300°}{\csc 540°}$ **undefined**
38. tan $\dfrac{13\pi}{4}$ − sec π **2**
39. csc $\left(-\dfrac{5}{2}\pi\right)$ sec $\left(-\dfrac{11}{6}\pi\right)$

$-\dfrac{2\sqrt{3}}{3}$

Critical Thinking
40. Angles with measures whose sum is 90° are called complementary angles. Explain how the values of the trigonometric functions for complementary angles are related.   *Hint: Find the values of the trigonometric functions for angles of 30° and 60° and compare.* **See margin.**

Applications
41. **Navigation** A ship's instruments indicate that it is headed on a course that forms an angle of 12.7° with the equator. After the ship has traveled 205 miles, it will still be just 45 miles from the equator. Assuming that sin 12.7° = $\dfrac{9}{41}$ and cos 12.7° = $\dfrac{40}{41}$, find the values of the other trigonometric functions of an angle with degree measure 12.7°. **See margin.**

42. **Sports** The sail at the right is in the shape of a right triangle. The bottom edge of the sail, called the foot, is 60 inches long. The edge of the sail that attaches to the mast, called the luff, is 144 inches long. The angle at the bottom of the sail measures approximately 67.4°. Find the value of each of the trigonometric functions for this angle. **See margin.**

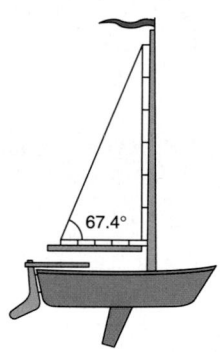

744   CHAPTER 16   TRIGONOMETRIC FUNCTIONS

Additional Answers

40. If x° + y° = 90° then:
sin x° = cos y°
tan x° = cot y°
sec x° = csc y°
cos x° = sin y°
cot x° = tan y°
csc x° = sec y°

41. tan 12.7° = $\dfrac{9}{40}$; sec 12.7° = $\dfrac{41}{40}$; cot 12.7° = $\dfrac{40}{9}$; csc 12.7° = $\dfrac{41}{9}$

42. sin 67.4° = $\dfrac{12}{13}$; cos 67.4° = $\dfrac{5}{13}$; tan 67.4° = $\dfrac{12}{5}$; sec 67.4° = $\dfrac{13}{5}$; cot 67.4° = $\dfrac{5}{12}$; csc 67.4° = $\dfrac{13}{12}$

16-3 Practice Worksheet

NAME _____ DATE _____

Other Trigonometric Functions

Find each value.

1. tan 135° **−1**
2. sec $\dfrac{\pi}{6}$ **$\dfrac{2\sqrt{3}}{3}$**

3. csc $-\dfrac{\pi}{6}$ **−2**
4. cot 210° **$-\sqrt{3}$**

5. sec 210° **$-\dfrac{2\sqrt{3}}{3}$**
6. csc $\left(-\dfrac{3}{4}\pi\right)$ **$-\sqrt{2}$**

7. tan $\dfrac{5}{3}\pi$ **$-\sqrt{3}$**
8. cot(−405°) **−1**

9. csc(−390°) **−2**
10. sec 270° **undefined**

11. cot(−87π) **undefined**
12. tan $\dfrac{13}{6}\pi$ **$\dfrac{\sqrt{3}}{3}$**

13. sec(−225°) **$-\sqrt{2}$**
14. csc $4\dfrac{2}{3}\pi$ **$\dfrac{2\sqrt{3}}{3}$**

15. tan(−720°) **0**
16. cot(−90°) **0**

17. sec 330° **$\dfrac{2\sqrt{3}}{3}$**
18. csc $-\dfrac{11\pi}{6}$ **2**

19. cot $\dfrac{9\pi}{4}$ **1**
20. tan $-\dfrac{3\pi}{4}$ **1**

744   Chapter 16

43. Shelby has 7 pennies, 4 dimes, 2 quarters, and 1 nickel in her wallet. She chooses one at random. What is the probability that it is a penny or a nickel?   **(Lesson 15-8)**

44. State the first term, the common ratio, the last term, and the number of terms for the geometric series described by $a_1 = 12$, $a_4 = \frac{3}{2}$, $n = 6$.
(Lesson 13-5)

45. Find the solution of the following system of equations. $4x^2 + 9y^2 = 36$
(Lesson 9-9) (±3, 0) $\qquad 4x^2 - 9y^2 = 36$

46. Solve $\sqrt[3]{3y - 1} - 2 = 0$.   **(Lesson 6-7) 3**

47. **Geometry**   The perimeter of a triangle is 56 feet. The length of the longest side is three times the difference between the lengths of the other two sides. The longest side is also twice as long as the shortest side. Find the lengths of the three sides.   **(Lesson 3-9) 24 ft, 20 ft, 12 ft**

48. Determine the slope of a line that passes through the points (6, 8) and (10, 22).   **(Lesson 2-4)** $\frac{7}{2}$

~~~~~ APPLICATIONS IN OPTICS ~~~~~

Scientists use refractometers to measure the change in direction, or bending, of light as it moves from one medium to another. The measurement is called the *index of refraction*. Refractometers are used in gemology to help identify different stones. Chemists use refractometers to determine the composition of unknown solutions or substances.

A refractometer uses the basic principles of **Snell's Law**. If n represents the index of refraction, I represents the angle of incidence, and r represents the angle of refraction, then the equation below states their relationship as light passes from a vacuum into another medium.

$n = \dfrac{\sin I}{\sin r}$ $0° < I \leq 90°,\ 0° < r \leq 90°$

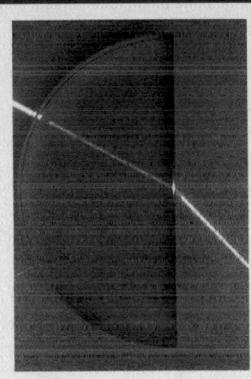

EXAMPLE   A beam of light moves from a vacuum to glass. If the angle of refraction is 30° and the index of refraction is $\sqrt{2}$, what is the angle of incidence?

$n = \dfrac{\sin I}{\sin r}$

$\sqrt{2} = \dfrac{\sin I}{\sin 30°}$ *Substitute $\sqrt{2}$ for n and 30° for r.*

$\sqrt{2} = \dfrac{\sin I}{\frac{1}{2}}$ $\sin 30° = \frac{1}{2}$

$\dfrac{\sqrt{2}}{2} = \sin I$

$45° = I$ The angle of incidence is 45°.

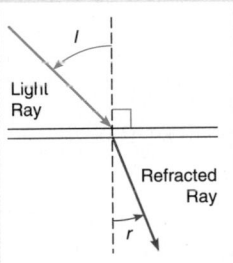

Light Ray

Refracted Ray

EXTENDING THE LESSON

Math Power: Reasoning

Two angles with measures whose sum is 180° are called *supplementary angles*. Make a general statement about each of the following for a pair of supplementary angles.   **All equal 0.**

1. difference of the sines
2. sum of the cosines
3. sum of the tangents
4. sum of the secants

Applications in Optics

This feature explains some of the physics involved with optics. You may ask students to list some situations where the image or light is "bent" by the medium through which it passes.

Enrichment Masters Booklet, p. 106

16-3   **Enrichment Worksheet**   NAME _____   DATE _____

Areas of Polygons and Circles

A regular polygon has sides of equal length and angles of equal measure. A regular polygon can be inscribed in or circumscribed about a circle. For n-sided regular polygons, the following area formulas can be used.

Area of circle $A_C = \pi r^2$

Area of inscribed polygon $A_I = \dfrac{nr^2}{2} \times \sin \dfrac{360°}{n}$

Area of circumscribed polygon $A_C = nr^2 \times \tan \dfrac{180°}{n}$

Use a calculator to complete the chart below for a unit circle (a circle of radius 1).

	Number of Sides	Area of Inscribed Polygon	Area Circle minus Area of Polygon	Area of Circumscribed Polygon	Area of Polygon minus Area of Circle
	3	1.2990381	1.8425545	5.1961524	2.054597
1.	4	2	1.1415927	4	0.8584073
2.	8	2.8284271	0.3131655	3.3137085	0.1721158
3.	12	3	0.1415926	3.2153903	0.0737977
4.	20	3.0901699	0.0514227	3.1676888	0.0260961
5.	24	3.1058285	0.0357641	3.1596599	0.0180672
6.	28	3.1152931	0.0262996	3.1548423	0.0132496
7.	32	3.1214452	0.0201475	3.1517249	0.0101322
8.	1000	3.1415720	0.0000206	3.1416030	0.0000103

9. What number do the areas of the circumscribed and inscribed polygons seem to be approaching? π

Lesson Resources
Reteaching Master 16-4
Practice Master 16-4
Enrichment Master 16-4

Transparency 16-4 contains the 5-Minute Check and a teaching aid for this lesson.

INTRODUCING THE LESSON

5-Minute Check

(over Lesson 16-3)
Find each value.

1. sec 240°   **−2**
2. tan (−300°)   **√3**
3. csc $\frac{4\pi}{3}$ **$-\frac{2\sqrt{3}}{3}$**

Other Prerequisite Skills

4. In what quandrant(s) is the sine an increasing function? **I, IV**
5. Find $6\left(\cos \frac{3\pi}{4}\right)\left(\sin \frac{\pi}{4}\right)$.   **−3**

Motivating the Lesson

Give students several answers, such as 1776, Abraham Lincoln, and 6 points, and ask them to verbalize appropriate questions for each. Emphasize that sometimes it is necessary to work backwards from what is normally considered an answer to find relevant information.

TEACHING THE LESSON

Teaching Tip ❶ You can have students apply the vertical line test to visually see that for each value of *x* there is more than one *y*-value associated with it. Thus, the domain must be restricted in order to have an inverse that is also a function.

16-4 Inverse Trigonometric Functions

Objective
16-4

After studying this lesson, you should be able to:
- find the values of expressions involving trigonometric functions.

Application

Phyllis Washington is an architect working on the design for a new home. She knows that the support for the roof will be shaped like two right triangles. Each right triangle will have one leg 8 feet long and a hypotenuse 16 feet long.

Teaching Tip ❶

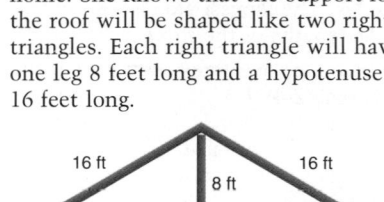

The sine of angle θ will be $\frac{1}{2}$. What will the measure of angle θ be? *You will solve this problem in Example 1.*

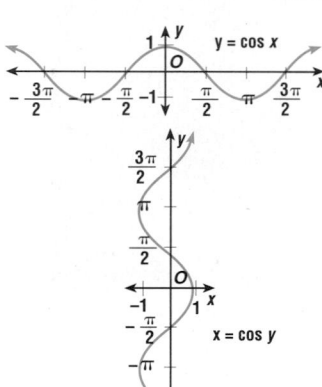

Sometimes you know the value of some trigonometric function for an angle and need to find the measure of the angle. The concept of inverse functions can be applied to find the inverse of trigonometric functions.

In Lesson 10-8, you learned that the inverse of a function is the relation in which all of the values of *x* and *y* are reversed. The graphs of the *y* = cos *x* function and its inverse, *x* = cos *y*, are shown at the left. Notice that the inverse is not a function, since it fails the vertical line test. None of the inverses of the trigonometric functions are functions.

We must restrict the domain of the trigonometric functions so that the inverses are functions. The values in these restricted domains are called **principal values.** Capital letters are used to distinguish trigonometric functions with restricted domains from the usual trigonometric functions. **Teaching Tip ❷**

Definitions of the Cosine, Sine, and Tangent Functions	$y = \text{Cos } x$ if and only if $y = \cos x$ and $0 \le x \le \pi$. $y = \text{Sin } x$ if and only if $y = \sin x$ and $-\frac{\pi}{2} \le x \le \frac{\pi}{2}$. $y = \text{Tan } x$ if and only if $y = \tan x$ and $-\frac{\pi}{2} \le x \le \frac{\pi}{2}$.

Teaching Tip ❸ The inverse of the Cosine function is called the **Arccosine function.** It is symbolized by **Cos⁻¹** or **Arccos.**

ALTERNATE TEACHING STRATEGIES

Using Cooperative Groups

Within cooperative groups of four students each, have one student give an Arccos or Arcsin value. Have another student sketch a diagram illustrating the problem. Have a third student find the corresponding sin or cos, and a final student determine the tangent. See Example 3 for a sample problem.

Definition of Inverse Cosine	Given $y = \text{Cos } x$, the inverse Cosine function is defined by the following equation. $y = \text{Cos}^{-1} x$ or $y = \text{Arccos } x$

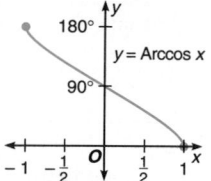

The Arccosine function has the following characteristics.

- Its domain is the set of real numbers from -1 to 1.
- Its range is the set of angle measurements from 0 to π.
- $\text{Cos } x = y$ if and only if $\text{Cos}^{-1} y = x$.
- $(\text{Cos}^{-1} \circ \text{Cos})(x) = (\text{Cos} \circ \text{Cos}^{-1})(x) = x$ *Recall function composition from Lesson 10-7.*

The definitions of the Arcsine and Arctangent functions are similar to the definition of the Arccosine function.

Definition of Inverse Sine and Inverse Tangent	Given $y = \text{Sin } x$, the inverse Sine function is defined by the following equation. $$y = \text{Sin}^{-1} x \text{ or } y = \text{Arcsin } x$$ Given $y = \text{Tan } x$, the inverse Tangent function is defined by the following equation. $$y = \text{Tan}^{-1} x \text{ or } y = \text{Arctan } x$$

The expressions in each row are equivalent.

$y = \text{Sin } x$	$x = \text{Sin}^{-1} y$ or $x = \text{Arcsin } y$
$y = \text{Cos } x$	$x = \text{Cos}^{-1} y$ or $x = \text{Arccos } y$
$y = \text{Tan } x$	$x = \text{Tan}^{-1} y$ or $x = \text{Arctan } y$

Now, use the definitions of the inverse functions to solve the application presented on page 746.

Example 1

APPLICATION

Architecture

The support for a roof is shaped like two right triangles each with one leg 8 feet long and the hypotenuse 16 feet long. The sine of angle θ will be $\frac{1}{2}$. What will θ be?

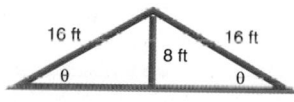

We know the sine of the angle and need to find the measurement of the angle. Use the Arcsine function to find the angle whose sine is $\frac{1}{2}$.

$$\text{Sin } \theta = \frac{1}{2}$$
$$\theta = \text{Arcsin } \frac{1}{2}$$
$$\theta = \frac{\pi}{6} \quad \theta \text{ is } \frac{\pi}{6} \text{ since it must be that } -\frac{\pi}{2} \leq \theta \leq \frac{\pi}{2}.$$

So the angle at the edge of the roof is $\frac{\pi}{6}$ radians or $30°$.

LESSON 16-4   INVERSE TRIGONOMETRIC FUNCTIONS   747

Teaching Tip ❷   You may want to review the terms *domain* and *range*.

Teaching Tip ❸   Be sure students realize that these terms are synonymous and may be used interchangeably. This is also true for equivalent terms for other trigonometric functions.

Chalkboard Example

For Example 1
Find each value.

a. $\text{Arcsin}\left(-\frac{\sqrt{2}}{2}\right)$ $-45°$ or $-\frac{\pi}{4}$

b. $\text{Arctan}\left(-\frac{\sqrt{3}}{3}\right)$ $-30°$ or $-\frac{\pi}{6}$

c. $\text{Arccos } 1$ $0°$

Example 2   Find $\cos\left(\text{Arcsin } \frac{\sqrt{2}}{2}\right)$.   **Teaching Tip ④**

$\text{Arcsin } \frac{\sqrt{2}}{2}$ is the angle whose sine is $\frac{\sqrt{2}}{2}$, so let $\theta = \text{Arcsin } \frac{\sqrt{2}}{2}$. Then $\text{Sin } \theta = \frac{\sqrt{2}}{2}$ and $\theta = \frac{\pi}{4}$. Therefore, $\text{Arcsin } \frac{\sqrt{2}}{2} = \frac{\pi}{4}$.   *Why is θ not $\frac{3\pi}{4}$?*

$$\cos\left(\text{Arcsin } \frac{2\sqrt{2}}{2}\right) = \cos \frac{\pi}{4} \qquad \textit{Substitute } \frac{\pi}{4} \textit{ for Arcsin } \frac{\sqrt{2}}{2}.$$
$$= \frac{\sqrt{2}}{2}$$

In the examples so far, the principal value of each inverse trigonometric function was known to be the value of a trigonometric function for some angle. Sometimes it is *not* known to which angle the principal value corresponds. In such a case, a diagram is almost a necessity.

Example 3   Find $\tan\left(\text{Sin}^{-1}\left(\frac{5}{13}\right)\right)$.

Let $\theta = \text{Sin}^{-1}\left(\frac{5}{13}\right)$.

Draw a diagram using the unit circle with angle θ so that its sine is $\frac{5}{13}$.

Substitute θ for $\text{Sin}^{-1}\left(\frac{5}{13}\right)$ in the original expression to obtain tan θ. So, now we need to find tan θ. To do this we need to find cos θ.

From the diagram and the Pythagorean Theorem, we see that $(\cos \theta)^2 + \left(\frac{5}{13}\right)^2 = 1$.

$$(\cos \theta)^2 + \left(\frac{5}{13}\right)^2 = 1 \qquad \textit{Solve for cos θ.}$$
$$\cos^2 \theta = 1 - \frac{25}{169}$$
$$\cos^2 \theta = \frac{144}{169}$$
$$\cos \theta = \frac{12}{13} \qquad \textit{Take the square root of each side.}$$

Now find tan θ.

$$\tan \theta = \frac{\sin \theta}{\cos \theta} \qquad \textit{Definition of tangent.}$$
$$= \frac{\frac{5}{13}}{\frac{12}{13}} \text{ or } \frac{5}{12} \qquad \text{Therefore, } \tan\left(\text{Sin}^{-1}\left(\frac{5}{13}\right)\right) = \frac{5}{12}.$$

RETEACHING THE LESSON

Have students graph the following functions on three graphs.

1. $y = \sin x$ $-\frac{\pi}{2} \le x \le \frac{\pi}{2}$

   $y = \text{Arcsin } x$

2. $y = \cos x$ $0 \le x \le \pi$

   $y = \text{Arccos } x$

3. $y = \tan x$ $-\frac{\pi}{2} \le x \le \frac{\pi}{2}$

   $y = \text{Arctan } x$

Also, have them graph the function $y = x$ on each of the three graphs. Discuss the relationships for each set of graphs.

CHECKING FOR UNDERSTANDING

Communicating Mathematics

Read and study the lesson to answer these questions.

1. How are $y = \text{Sin } x$ and $y = \text{Arcsin } x$ related? **See margin.**

2. Why must we restrict the domains of the trigonometric functions before finding the inverse functions? **See margin.**

3. How do you know when the domain of a trigonometric function is restricted? **Restricted domains are denoted with a capital letter.**

Guided Practice

Write each of the following in the form of an inverse function. **4–9. See margin.**

4. $a = \cos b$

5. $\sin y = x$

6. $\tan \alpha = \beta$

7. $\sin 30° = \dfrac{1}{2}$

8. $2 \cos 45° = y$

9. $-\dfrac{4}{3} = \tan x$

Find each value.

10. $\sin\left(\text{Cos}^{-1}\left(\dfrac{2}{3}\right)\right)$ $\dfrac{\sqrt{5}}{3}$

11. $\cos\left(\text{Cos}^{-1}\dfrac{4}{5}\right)$ $\dfrac{4}{5}$

12. $\cos\left(\text{Cos}^{-1}\dfrac{1}{2}\right)$ $\dfrac{1}{2}$

EXERCISES

Practice

Find each value.

13. $\text{Cos}^{-1}\left(-\dfrac{1}{2}\right)$ **120°**

14. $\sin\left(\text{Sin}^{-1}\dfrac{1}{2}\right)$ $\dfrac{1}{2}$

15. $\text{Sin}^{-1}\left(\cos\dfrac{\pi}{2}\right)$ **0°**

16. $\text{Tan}^{-1}(-1)$ **−45°**

17. $\text{Sin}\dfrac{\pi}{6}$ $\dfrac{1}{2}$

18. $\text{Sin}^{-1} 1$ **90°**

19. $\tan\left(\text{Cos}^{-1}\dfrac{6}{7}\right)$ $\dfrac{\sqrt{13}}{6}$

20. $\cot\left(\text{Sin}^{-1}\dfrac{5}{6}\right)$ $\dfrac{\sqrt{11}}{5}$

21. $\cot\left(\text{Sin}^{-1}\dfrac{7}{9}\right)$ $\dfrac{4\sqrt{2}}{7}$

22. $\sin\left(\text{Arctan}\dfrac{\sqrt{3}}{3}\right)$ $\dfrac{1}{2}$

23. $\cos\left(\text{Arcsin}\dfrac{3}{5}\right)$ $\dfrac{4}{5}$

24. $\tan(\text{Arctan } 3)$ **3**

25. $\text{Sin}^{-1}\left(\tan\dfrac{\pi}{4}\right)$ $\dfrac{\pi}{2}$ **or 90°**

26. $\text{Arctan }\sqrt{3}$ **60°**

27. $\text{Arccos}\dfrac{\sqrt{3}}{2}$ **30°**

28. $\cos(\text{Tan}^{-1}\sqrt{3})$ $\dfrac{1}{2}$

29. $\cos\left[\text{Arcsin}\left(-\dfrac{1}{2}\right)\right]$ $\dfrac{\sqrt{3}}{2}$

30. $\cos(\text{Tan}^{-1} 1)$ $\dfrac{\sqrt{2}}{2}$

31. $\dfrac{\sqrt{2}}{2}$

31. $\cos\left[\text{Cos}^{-1}\left(-\dfrac{\sqrt{2}}{2}\right) - \dfrac{\pi}{2}\right]$

32. $\sin\left(2 \text{ Sin}^{-1}\dfrac{1}{2}\right)$ $\dfrac{\sqrt{3}}{2}$

33. $\sin\left(2 \text{ Cos}^{-1}\dfrac{3}{5}\right)$ $\dfrac{24}{25}$

34. $\tan\left[\text{Cos}^{-1}\left(-\dfrac{3}{5}\right)\right]$ $-\dfrac{4}{3}$

35. $\sin\left(\text{Sin}^{-1}\dfrac{\sqrt{3}}{2}\right)$ $\dfrac{\sqrt{3}}{2}$

36. $\sin[\text{Arctan}(-\sqrt{3})]$

36. $-\dfrac{\sqrt{3}}{2}$

37. $\text{Cos}^{-1}\left(\sin\dfrac{3\pi}{2}\right)$

38. $\text{Tan}^{-1}\left(\cos\dfrac{3\pi}{2}\right)$ **0°**

39. $\text{Sin}^{-1}\left(\cos\dfrac{\pi}{6}\right)$

π **or 180°**

$\dfrac{\pi}{3}$ **or 60°**

Critical Thinking

40. Prove that $(\text{Cos}^{-1} \circ \text{Cos})(x) = (\text{Cos} \circ \text{Cos}^{-1})(x) = x$. **See students' work.**

LESSON 16-4 INVERSE TRIGONOMETRIC FUNCTIONS 749

Additional Answers

1. They are inverses of each other.
2. The trigonometric functions are not one-to-one functions.
4. $b = \text{Cos}^{-1} a$
5. $y = \text{Sin}^{-1} x$
6. $\alpha = \text{Tan}^{-1} \beta$

7. $30° = \text{Sin}^{-1}\dfrac{1}{2}$

8. $45° = \text{Cos}^{-1}\dfrac{y}{2}$

9. $x = \text{Tan}^{-1}\left(-\dfrac{4}{3}\right)$

16-4 Practice Worksheet

NAME _____ DATE _____

Inverse Trigonometric Functions

Find each value.

1. $\text{Cos}^{-1}\left(-\dfrac{\sqrt{3}}{2}\right)$ **150°**

2. $\text{Sin}^{-1}\left(-\dfrac{\sqrt{2}}{2}\right)$ **−45°**

3. $\text{Arctan}\left(-\dfrac{\sqrt{3}}{3}\right)$ **−30°**

4. $\text{Arccos } 1$ **0°**

5. $\sin\left(\text{Sin}^{-1}\dfrac{3}{8}\right)$ $\dfrac{3}{8}$

6. $\cos\left(\text{Sin}^{-1}-\dfrac{3}{5}\right)$ $\dfrac{4}{5}$

7. $\tan\left(\text{Cos}^{-1}-\dfrac{\sqrt{3}}{2}\right)$ $-\dfrac{\sqrt{3}}{3}$

8. $\sec\left(\text{Cos}^{-1}\dfrac{2}{9}\right)$ $\dfrac{9}{2}$

9. $\csc(\text{Arctan} -1)$ $-\sqrt{2}$

10. $\cot\left(\text{Arcsin}\dfrac{12}{13}\right)$ $\dfrac{5}{12}$

11. $\text{Sin}^{-1}\left(\cos\dfrac{\pi}{3}\right)$ **30°**

12. $\text{Cos}^{-1}\left(\tan\dfrac{3}{4}\pi\right)$ **180°**

13. $\sin\left(2 \text{ Cos}^{-1}\dfrac{15}{17}\right)$ $\dfrac{240}{289}$

14. $\cos\left(2 \text{ Sin}^{-1}\dfrac{\sqrt{3}}{2}\right)$ $-\dfrac{1}{2}$

15. $\sin\left(\text{Arctan}\dfrac{\sqrt{3}}{3}\right)$ $\dfrac{1}{2}$

16. $\text{Sin}^{-1}(\tan 45°)$ $\dfrac{\pi}{2}$

17. $\text{Cos}^{-1}\left(\text{Sin}\dfrac{\pi}{6}\right)$ $\dfrac{\pi}{3}$

18. $\sec\left(\text{Cos}^{-1}\dfrac{4}{5}\right)$ $\dfrac{5}{4}$

19. $\csc\left(\text{Sin}^{-1}\dfrac{9}{10}\right)$ $\dfrac{10}{9}$

20. $\cot(\text{Sin}^{-1} 0)$ **undefined**

Chapter 16, Quiz B, (Lessons 16–3 through 16–4), is available in the Evaluation Masters Booklet, p. 219.

Applications

41. Navigation The Western Princess sailed due east 24 miles before turning north. When the Princess became disabled and radioed for help, the rescue boat needed to know the fastest route to her. The navigator of the Princess found that the fastest route for the rescue boat would be 48 miles. The cosine of the angle at which the rescue boat should sail is $\frac{1}{2}$.

   a. Draw a diagram that represents the situation. **See students' work.**

   b. Find the angle at which the rescue boat should travel to aid the Western Princess. **60° north of east**

42. Travel Michelle and her family took a vacation to Oregon. As Michelle observed Mount Hood from a distance, the sine of the angle at which she looked up was $\frac{40}{41}$. Find the tangent of this angle. $\frac{40}{9}$

Mixed Review

43. Statistics The stem-and-leaf plot at the right represents the number of passengers served by certain airports in 1988. Find the range, quartiles, and interquartile range for the data. Then find any outliers. **(Lesson 14-4) 37,000,000; 18,000,000, 22,000,000, 31,000,000; 13,000,000; 53,000,000**

Stem	Leaf
1	6 6 7 7 8 8 8 9
2	0 0 2 2 2 7 7 9 9
3	1 5
4	0 1 5
5	3

3 | 1 = 31,000,000

44. Write the expression $\sum_{k=1}^{10} (2 + k)$ in expanded form and find the sum. **(Lesson 13-3)**
$$3 + 4 + 5 + 6 + 7 + 8 + 9 + 10 + 11 + 12; 75$$

45. Biology Bacteria of a certain strain can grow from 80 to 164 bacteria in 3 hours. Find k for the growth formula for this strain. **(Lesson 12-8)** *Hint: The exponential growth formula is $y = ne^{kt}$.* **0.2392**

46. Travel The time it takes to drive a certain distance varies inversely as to the rate of speed. Golda and John drove at 55 miles per hour for 4 hours to visit some friends in another city. Because of bad weather, they can only drive 45 miles per hour on the way home. How long will it take them to get home? **(Lesson 11-2)** $4\frac{8}{9}$ **hours**

47. Health Ty's heart rate is usually 120 beats per minute when he runs. If he runs for 2 hours every day, about how many beats will his heart make during two weeks worth of exercise sessions? Express the answer in both decimal and scientific notation. **(Lesson 5-1)** **201,600; 2.016 × 10⁵**

48. Find AA if $A = \begin{bmatrix} 2 & 7 \\ 0 & -1 \end{bmatrix}$. Write "not defined" if the product does not exist. **(Lesson 4-4)** $\begin{bmatrix} 4 & 7 \\ 0 & 1 \end{bmatrix}$

EXTENDING THE LESSON

Math Power: Problem Solving

Find $\cos\left[\text{Cos}^{-1}\left(\frac{\sqrt{3}}{2} \right) \right] + \sin 2[\text{Tan}^{-1} \sqrt{3} + \text{Tan}^{-1} (-1)]$.

$\frac{(1 + \sqrt{3})}{2}$

Enrichment Masters Booklet, p. 107

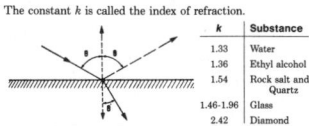

NAME _____ DATE _____

16-4 Enrichment Worksheet

Snell's Law

Snell's Law describes what happens to a ray of light that passes from air into water or some other substance. In the figure, the ray starts at the left and makes an angle of incidence θ with the surface.

Part of the ray is reflected, creating an angle of reflection θ. The rest of the ray is bent, or refracted, as it passes through the other medium. This creates angle θ'.

The angle of incidence equals the angle of reflection.

The angles of incidence and refraction are related by Snell's Law:

sin θ = k sin θ'

The constant k is called the index of refraction.

k	Substance
1.33	Water
1.36	Ethyl alcohol
1.54	Rock salt and Quartz
1.46-1.96	Glass
2.42	Diamond

Use Snell's Law to solve the following. Round angle measures to the nearest tenth of a degree.

1. If the angle of incidence at which a ray of light strikes the surface of a window is 45° and k = 1.6, what is the measure of the angle of refraction? **26.2°**

2. If the angle of incidence of a ray of light that strikes the surface of water is 50°, what is the angle of refraction? **35.2°**

3. If the angle of refraction of a ray of light striking a quartz crystal is 24°, what is the angle of incidence? **38.8°**

4. The angles of incidence and refraction for rays of light were measured five times for a certain substance. The measurements (one of which was in error) are shown in the table. Was the substance glass, quartz, or diamond? **glass**

θ	15°	30°	40°	60°	80°
θ'	9.7°	16.1°	21.2°	28.6°	33.2°

5. If the angle of incidence at which a ray of light strikes the surface of ethyl alcohol is 60°, what is the angle of refraction? **39.6°**

Objective

After studying this lesson, you should be able to:
- use a calculator to find values of trigonometric functions.

Application

Ships and airplanes measure distance in nautical miles. A nautical mile is equal to one **minute,** or $\frac{1}{60}$ of a degree of arc length on a meridian. The actual length varies slightly since Earth is not a perfect sphere. The formula 1 nautical mile equals $(6077 - 31 \cos 2\theta)$ feet, where θ is the latitude in degrees will give the approximate length of a nautical mile in a certain latitude. You will find the length of a nautical mile along the 30th parallel in Example 4.

Example 1

Find sin 67° using your calculator.   *Set your calculator in degree mode.*

ENTER: 67 [SIN] `0.9205048535`

The sine of 67° is approximately 0.9205.

Example 2

Find x in each of the following using your calculator.

a. **If sin x = 0.7590, find x.**

ENTER: 0.7590 [SIN⁻¹] `49.37611923`

The [SIN⁻¹] key may be a second function key on your calculator.

Therefore, *x* is approximatley 49.3761°.   *Round to four decimal places.*

b. **Suppose csc x = 4.2024. Find the value of x to the nearest minute.**

First use the second function and sin keys to find the decimal value of *x*.

$$\csc x = \frac{1}{\sin x}, \ \sin x = \frac{1}{4.2024}$$

ENTER: 4.2024 [¹/ₓ] [SIN⁻¹] `13.76612556`

Now subtract the whole number part and multiply the decimal portion by 60 to find the minutes.

ENTER: [−] 13 [=] [×] 60 [=] `45.96753346`

Therefore, *x* is approximately 13°46'.

LESSON 16-5   FINDING VALUES FOR TRIGONOMETRIC FUNCTIONS   751

ALTERNATE TEACHING STRATEGIES

Using Calculators

If a calculator designed to be used on an overhead projector is available, use it to demonstrate solving the example problems. Students can also be placed in cooperative groups based on similarities of calculators. Students can work together in these groups to solve the example problems.

Lesson Resources

Reteaching Master 16-5
Practice Master 16-5
Enrichment Master 16-5
Activity Master, p. 52

 Transparency 16-5 contains the 5-Minute Check and a teaching aid for this lesson.

INTRODUCING THE LESSON

🕐 5-Minute Check

(over Lesson 16-4)
Find each value.

1. tan⁻¹ 0   **0°**
2. sin⁻¹ $\frac{1}{2}$ **30° or $\frac{\pi}{6}$**
3. tan (Arctan 5)   **5**
4. sin (Arctan $-\sqrt{3}$)   **$\frac{\sqrt{3}}{2}$**
5. cos $\left(\text{Arcsin } \frac{3}{5}\right)$ **$\frac{4}{5}$**

Motivating the Lesson

Use a meterstick to measure several items that have a length of about one meter or a multiple of a meter. Introduce several items that cannot be measured in multiples of meters. Point out that, while it is easy to measure in whole units, it is not realistic in many situations, and that angles, also, may not be limited to those in the chart on page 738.

TEACHING THE LESSON

Teaching Tip ❶   Point out to students that many calculators differ. If the key sequence in the text does not work for a student's calculator, check the owner's manual.

Chalkboard Examples

For Example 1
Find each value.

a. sec 38° ≈ **1.2690**

b. cot $\left(\frac{4\pi}{3}\right)$ ≈ **13.6540**

For Example 2

a. If cos x = 0.7274, find x.
   x ≈ 43.3311°
b. If cot x = 1.2461, find the value of x to the nearest minute.   **x ≈ 38°45′**

For Example 3
Find each value.

a. cos $\left(\frac{\pi}{7}\right)$ ≈ **0.9010**

b. cot 55°24′ ≈ **0.6899**

For Example 4
Use the formula to find the length of a nautical mile on the 60th parallel.   **6092.5 feet or 1.15 miles**

For Example 5
Find 2 cot $\left(\text{Arcsin } \frac{1}{2}\right)$. ≈ **3.4641**

Example 3

Find each of the following.

a. cot $\left(\frac{\pi}{12}\right)$ *Set your calculator in radian mode.*

$$\cot x = \frac{1}{\tan x}$$

ENTER: [π] [÷] 12 [=] [TAN] [¹/ₓ] `3.732050808`

cot $\left(\frac{\pi}{12}\right)$ is approximately 3.7321.   *Round to four decimal places.*

b. tan 67°38′   *Make sure your calculator is in degree mode.*

Minutes must be changed to decimal form before you can use the calculator to find the trigonometric value. This is done by dividing the minutes by 60.

ENTER: 67 [+] 38 [÷] 60 [=] [TAN] `2.430193842`

So, tan 67°38′ is approximately 2.4302.

Now solve the application presented on page 751.

Example 4

APPLICATION

Navigation

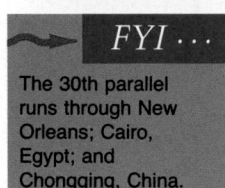

FYI …

The 30th parallel runs through New Orleans; Cairo, Egypt; and Chongqing, China.

Use the formula 1 nautical mile = (6077 − 31 cos 2θ), where θ is the latitude in degrees to find the length of a nautical mile on the 30th parallel.

1 nautical mile = 6077 − 31 cos 2θ   *Formula for the length of a nautical mile.*
= 6077 − 31 cos 2(30)   *Substitute 30 for θ.*
= 6077 − 31 cos 60

Use your calculator to find the value of the expression.

ENTER: 6077 [−] 60 [COS] [×] 31 [=] `6061.5`

Therefore, one nautical mile is about 6061.5 feet on the 30th parallel. This is $\frac{6061.5}{5280}$ or about 1.15 miles.

Your calculator can perform multiple functions with trigonometric values.

Example 5

Find tan $\left(\text{Cos}^{-1}\left(\frac{\sqrt{2}}{2}\right)\right)$.

ENTER: 2 [√] [÷] 2 [=] [COS⁻¹] [TAN] `1`

Therefore, tan $\left(\text{Cos}^{-1}\left(\frac{\sqrt{2}}{2}\right)\right)$ is 1.   *Check this result by drawing a diagram.*

CHECKING FOR UNDERSTANDING

Communicating Mathematics

1. Convert the minutes to a decimal first.

Read and study the lesson to answer these questions.

1. How can you use a calculator to find the trigonometric value of a measurement that is given in degrees and minutes?

2. Write the key sequence you would use to find the value of cot 48° on your calculator. Find the value of cot 48°. **See students' work; 0.9004**

3. How can you find the minutes of a degree measurement found on a calculator? **Multiply the decimal portion by 60.**

Guided Practice

Use a calculator to find each value. Round your answers to four decimal places.

4. sin 42° **0.6691**
5. cos 81° **0.1564**
6. tan 5° **0.0875**
7. cos 42°20′ **0.7392**
8. sin 3°10′ **0.0552**
9. tan 89°50′ **343.8**

Use a calculator to find the value of x, in degrees, for each trigonometric function. Round your answers to four decimal places. **10–15. See margin.**

10. sin x = 0.7364
11. cos x = 0.9912
12. tan x = 0.5923
13. sec x = 2.7504
14. csc x = 1.9735
15. cot x = 3.1376

EXERCISES

Practice

Use a calculator to find each value. Round your answers to four decimal places.

A
16. csc 75° **1.0353**
17. sin 730° **0.1736**
18. tan −90° **undefined**
19. cos 5π **−1**
20. cot $\frac{-3\pi}{5}$ **0.3249**
21. sin $\frac{7\pi}{3}$ **0.8660**

B
22. tan $\frac{11\pi}{8}$ **−2.4142**
23. sec $\frac{8\pi}{5}$ **3.2361**
24. cot 250° **0.3640**
25. sec 600° **−2**
26. sec 540° **−1**
27. csc 7π **undefined**

28. csc (−890°) **−5.7588**
29. (sin 95°)(tan 37°) **0.7507**
30. $\left(\sin\frac{\pi}{3}\right)\left(\cos\frac{\pi}{8}\right)$ **0.8001**
31. $\frac{3(\sin 50°) + 9(\cos 10°)}{\tan 290°}$ **−4.0624**
32. $\text{Sin}^{-1}\frac{15}{16}$ **69.6359°**
33. $\text{Cos}^{-1} 0.89$ **27.1268°**

C
34. $\text{Tan}^{-1}\frac{3}{2}$ **56.3099°**
35. $\frac{3\tan\frac{\pi}{6}}{2\sin\frac{\pi}{3} - \sec 3\pi}$ **0.6340**

36. $\tan\left(\text{Cos}^{-1}\frac{\sqrt{3}}{3}\right)$ **1.4142**
37. sin $[\text{Tan}^{-1}(-\sqrt{6})]$ **−0.9258**

LESSON 16-5   FINDING VALUES FOR TRIGONOMETRIC FUNCTIONS   753

Additional Answers
10. **47.4256**
11. **7.6067**
12. **30.6383**
13. **68.6796**
14. **30.4452**
15. **17.6779**

Closing the Lesson

Writing Activity Have students summarize the advantages of working with calculators when finding values involving trigonometric functions.

APPLYING THE LESSON

Homework Exercises

See assignment guide on page 753.

Practice Masters Booklet, p. 123

NAME _____ DATE _____

| 16-5 | **Practice Worksheet** |

Finding Values for Trigonometric Functions

Use a calculator to find each value. Round your answers to four decimal places.

1. $\sin 347°$ **−0.2250**

2. $\cos \frac{13}{5}\pi$ **−0.3090**

3. $\cot \frac{5}{8}\pi$ **−0.4142**

4. $\sec (−84°)$ **9.5668**

5. $\csc −\frac{10}{7}\pi$ **1.0257**

6. $\tan(−27452°)$ **28.6363**

7. $(\sec 18°)(\tan −67°)$ **−2.4771**

8. $\left(\csc \frac{\pi}{8}\right)\left(\cot \frac{13}{8}\pi\right)$ **−1.0824**

9. $\frac{3\cos 65° − \tan 11°}{\cot 5°}$ **0.0939**

10. $\frac{\sec \frac{3}{5}\pi}{\sin \frac{4}{5}\pi + \cot \frac{1}{5}\pi}$ **−1.6476**

11. $\cos^{-1} 0.9347$ **20.8203°**

12. $\tan^{-1} 12$ **85.2364°**

13. $\csc(\sin^{-1} 0.8)$ **1.2500**

14. $\cot(\text{Arccos } 0.321)$ **0.3389**

15. $\cos 28°$ **0.8829**

16. $\sin 18°30'$ **0.3173**

17. $\tan 72°$ **3.0777**

18. $\sec 12°12'$ **1.0231**

Use a calculator to find the value of x, in degrees, for each trigonometric function. Round your answers to four decimal places.

19. $\sin x = 0.4899$ **29.3340°**

20. $\cos x = 0.8258$ **34.3303°**

21. $\cos x = 0.5240$ **58.3991°**

22. $\tan x = 0.2074$ **11.7170°**

Critical Thinking

38. Some calculators allow you to work in a unit of angle measure called **gradians** or grads. There are 400 gradians in a circle. **See margin.**

   a. Find the trigonometric values for an angle that measures 100 grads.

   b. What is the measure of this angle in degrees and in radians?

Applications

39. **Physics** The maximum height that a projected object reaches is given by the formula $H = \dfrac{V_o^2 \sin^2 \theta}{2g}$, where V_o represents the initial velocity, θ represents the degree measure of the angle which the path of the object makes with the ground, and g represents the acceleration due to gravity. An arrow is released at an angle of 65° to the ground and with an initial velocity of 100 feet per second. If the acceleration due to gravity is 32 feet per second, what is the maximum height reached by the arrow?
   128.3 feet

40. **Electronics** The power P in watts absorbed by an AC circuit is given by the formula $P = IV \cos \theta$, where I is the current in amps, V is the voltage, and θ is the measure of the phase angle. Find the power absorbed by a circuit if its current is 2 amps, its voltage is 120 volts, and its phase angle is 70°. **82.1 watts**

41. **Optics** Rainbows that result from light passing through a prism are caused by the refraction of light. When the light passes from one medium, the air, into the other, glass, the light ray is bent and the rainbow results. According to Snell's Law, the angle at which the light ray approaches the prism, called the angle of incidence, and the angle at which the angle is bent, called the angle of refraction, are related by the formula $2 \sin I = 3 \sin r$. I is the measure of the angle of incidence and r is the measure of the angle of refraction. Find the angle of refraction for this prism in degrees and minutes if the angle of incidence is 60°. **35°16'**

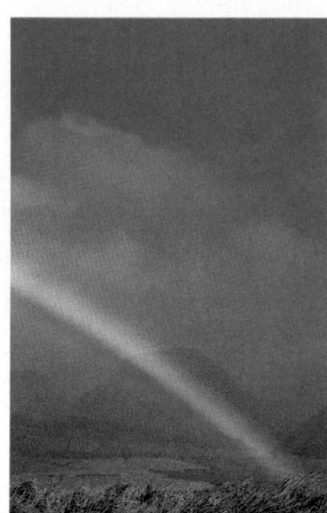

42. $\dfrac{3489}{6561}$ or $\dfrac{1163}{2187}$; approximately 0.532

Mixed Review

42. **Sports** Suppose Lynn and Maria swim 8 one-lap races. The probability that Lynn wins a race is $\dfrac{2}{3}$ and that Maria wins is $\dfrac{1}{3}$. What is the probability that Maria will win at least 3 of the races? **(Lesson 15-9)**

43. **Statistics** The points scored by the winning team in each National Football League game over a three-day period were 17, 24, 23, 30, 21, 30, 24, 20, 34, 24, 23, 30, 40, and 31. Find the median, mode, mean, and standard deviation of the scores. **(Lesson 14-6) 24; 24 and 30; 26.5; approximately 6 points**

Additional Answer

38a. sin 100 grads = 1;
   cos 100 grads = 0;
   tan 100 grads = undefined;
   sec 100 grads = undefined;
   csc 100 grads = 1;
   cot 100 grads = 0

38b. 100 grads = 90°

   $= \dfrac{\pi}{2}$ radians

44. Express $\log_3 35$ in terms of common logarithms. Then use a calculator to find its value. (**Lesson 12-7**) $\log_3 35 = \frac{\log 35}{\log 3}$; **approximately 3.2362**

45. Simplify the expression $\dfrac{\dfrac{x}{x^2 - 16}}{\dfrac{4x - 4}{x^2 - 2x - 8}}$. (**Lesson 11-3**) $\dfrac{x(x + 2)}{4(x - 1)(x + 4)}$

46. Solve $\frac{1}{3}|6x + 5| = 7$. (**Lesson 1-6**) $-\frac{13}{3}, \frac{8}{3}$

~ MID-CHAPTER REVIEW ~

Change each degree measure to radian measure. (**Lesson 16-1**)

1. $90°$ **$\frac{\pi}{2}$**
2. $150°$ **$\frac{5\pi}{6}$**
3. $-135°$ **$-\frac{3\pi}{4}$**

Change each radian measure to degree measure. (**Lesson 16-1**)

4. $\frac{3\pi}{2}$ **270°**
5. $-\frac{7\pi}{4}$ **-315°**
6. 2 **$\frac{360°}{\pi} \approx 114.59°$**

For each of the following, find the least positive angle measurement that is coterminal. (**Lesson 16-2**)

7. $420°$ **60°**
8. $1400°$ **320°**
9. $-\frac{8\pi}{9}$ **$\frac{10\pi}{9}$**

Find each value. (**Lesson 16-3**)

10. $\cos 150°$ **$-\frac{\sqrt{3}}{2}$**
11. $\tan 900°$ **0**
12. $\csc \frac{4}{3}\pi$ **$-\frac{2\sqrt{3}}{3}$**
13. $\sec \frac{9}{4}\pi$ **$\sqrt{2}$**
14. $\dfrac{\tan(-135°)}{\sec 270°}$ **undefined**
15. $\left(\cot\left(-\frac{3\pi}{4}\right)\right)\left(\sec\left(-\frac{\pi}{4}\right)\right)$ **$\sqrt{2}$**

Find each of the following. (**Lesson 16-4**)

16. $\text{Arctan } 1$ **45°**
17. $\text{Sin}^{-1}(-1)$ **-90°**
18. $\text{Cos } 45°$ **$\frac{\sqrt{2}}{2}$**
19. $\text{Sin}^{-1}\left(-\frac{1}{2}\right)$ **-30°**
20. $\text{Tan}^{-1}\frac{\sqrt{3}}{3}$ **30°**
21. $\text{Tan}\left(-\frac{\pi}{4}\right)$ **-1**

Use a calculator to find each value. Round your answers to four decimal places. (**Lesson 16-5**)

22. $\csc 85°$ **1.0038**
23. $\sin -530°$ **-0.1736**
24. $\dfrac{2(\sin 75°) + 6(\tan 12°)}{\cos(-25°)}$ **3.5387**

25. **Physics** The formula $R = \dfrac{V_o{}^2 \sin 2\theta}{g}$ gives the range of an object shot at an initial velocity of V_o feet per second at an angle of $\theta°$ to the ground. g represents the acceleration due to gravity, which is 32 feet per second. Find the angle at which a projectile was shot if its initial velocity was 128 feet per second and its range was 512 feet. (**Lesson 16-5**) **45°**

LESSON 16-5   FINDING VALUES FOR TRIGONOMETRIC FUNCTIONS   755

EXTENDING THE LESSON

Math Power: Problem Solving

Have students use calculators to solve the following problem.

$$\dfrac{\dfrac{2\sin 41.42° + 8\cos 724°}{\tan 815°}}{\dfrac{(\sec 91°)(\csc 89°)}{\tan 359°}}$$

-3283.9537

Mid-Chapter Review

The Mid-Chapter Review provides students with a brief review of the concepts and skills in Lessons 16-1 through 16-5. Lesson numbers are given at the end of problems or instruction lines so students may review concepts not yet mastered.

Enrichment Masters Booklet, p. 108

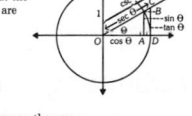

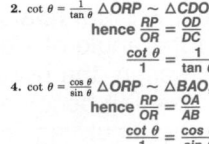

Lesson Resources

Reteaching Master 16-6
Practice Master 16-6
Enrichment Master 16-6

 Transparency 16-6 contains the 5-Minute Check and a teaching aid for this lesson.

INTRODUCING THE LESSON

 5-Minute Check

(over Lesson 16-5)

1. If sin x = 0.7169, find x.
   $x \approx$ **45.7991°**

Find each value using a calculator.

2. $\cos\left[\sin^{-1}\left(\frac{1}{5}\right)\right]$ **0.98**

3. cot 378° **3.08**

Other Prerequisite Skills

Use the Pythagorean Theorem to find the value of x in each triangle.

4.

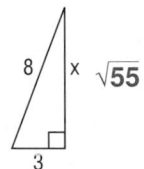

8 x $\sqrt{55}$

3

5.

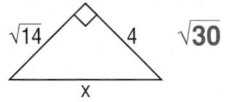

$\sqrt{14}$ 4 $\sqrt{30}$

x

Motivating the Lesson

Using a stack of books and a notebook, model a ramp. By changing the angle of elevation, show students how all parts of a triangle are related. For example, if the angle of elevation is increased, the hypoteneuse and the other leg become shorter and the other acute angle smaller if the notebook must rest on the books.

16-6 Solving Right Triangles

Objectives

After studying this lesson, you should be able to:

16-6A ■ use right triangles to find trigonometric values, and

16-6B ■ solve problems involving right triangles using right triangle trigonometry.

Application

A car is traveling 500 meters along a raised exit ramp, which makes a 3° angle with the ground. How far did the car rise on the 500-meter ramp?

Trigonometry can be used to solve problems like this where you need to find a missing measure of a triangle. *You will solve this problem in Example 3.*

Consider the right triangle below.

The **hypotenuse** of the triangle is side $\overline{AB}$. Its length is c units. **Teaching Tip ❶**

The side **opposite** angle A is side $\overline{BC}$. Its length is a units.

The side **adjacent** to angle A is side $\overline{AC}$. Its length is b units.

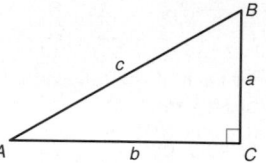

For convenience of notation, we refer to the angle with vertex at A as angle A and use A to stand for its measurement. Similarly, we refer to angle B and its measurement as B, and angle C and its measurement as C.

Suppose a unit circle is drawn with its center at vertex A as shown below.

The triangle in the interior of the unit circle is similar to triangle ABC. So, the measures of the corresponding sides of the triangle are proportional. That is,

$$\frac{1}{c} = \frac{x}{b} = \frac{y}{a}.$$

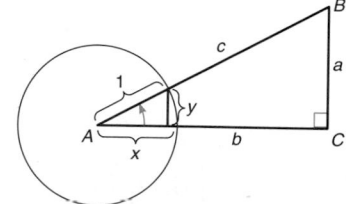

SOH-CAH-TOA is a helpful mnemonic device for remembering the first three equations.

$sin = \dfrac{opposite}{hypotenuse}$

$cos = \dfrac{adjacent}{hypotenuse}$

$tan = \dfrac{opposite}{adjacent}$

In this figure, sin $A = y$. Since the two triangles are similar, $\frac{y}{a} = \frac{1}{c}$. So, $y = \frac{a}{c}$ and, by substitution, sin $A = \frac{a}{c}$. Using this figure, we can define the trigonometric values in the following way.

$\sin A = \dfrac{a}{c}$ $\cos A = \dfrac{b}{c}$ $\tan A = \dfrac{a}{b}$

$\csc A = \dfrac{c}{a}$ $\sec A = \dfrac{c}{b}$ $\cot A = \dfrac{b}{a}$

756   CHAPTER 16   TRIGONOMETRIC FUNCTIONS

ALTERNATE TEACHING STRATEGIES

Using Manipulatives

Students may work independently or in cooperative groups. Have students cut several different right triangles from construction paper. Using a metric ruler and protractor, have them measure a side and an acute angle or two sides. Then have them solve the triangle. Confirm solutions by measuring.

Example 1

Find the sine, cosine, tangent, cosecant, secant, and cotangent of angle A. Round each value to four decimal places.

$\sin A = \dfrac{9}{15}$ or 0.6000 $\csc A = \dfrac{15}{9}$ or 1.6667

$\cos A = \dfrac{12}{15}$ or 0.8000 $\sec A = \dfrac{15}{12}$ or 1.2500

$\tan A = \dfrac{9}{12}$ or 0.7500 $\cot A = \dfrac{12}{9}$ or 1.3333

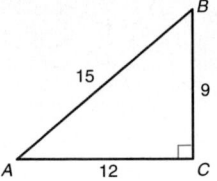

Example 2

Find $\sin A$. Round your answer to four decimal places.

$a^2 + 5^2 = 14^2$ *Use the Pythagorean Theorem to find the value of a.*
$\quad a^2 = 171$
$\quad\ a = \sqrt{171}$

$\sin A = \dfrac{opposite}{hypotenuse}$

$\quad\quad = \dfrac{\sqrt{171}}{14}$

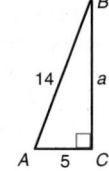

Now use a calculator to find the decimal value.

ENTER: 171 $\sqrt{\ }$ $\div$ 14 $=$ 0.9340497736

$\sin A$ is approximately 0.9340.

Consider two special right triangles. Triangle ABC is an isosceles right triangle. Assume that the congruent sides are each 1 unit long. This is a 45°-45°-right triangle. Find the length of the hypotenuse.

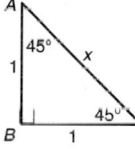

$1^2 + 1^2 = x^2$ *Use the Pythagorean Theorem.*
$\quad\ \ 2 = x^2$
$\quad \sqrt{2} = x$ The hypotenuse is $\sqrt{2}$ units long.

Now, write the trigonometric values.

$\sin 45° = \dfrac{1}{\sqrt{2}}$ or $\dfrac{\sqrt{2}}{2}$ $\cos 45° = \dfrac{1}{\sqrt{2}}$ or $\dfrac{\sqrt{2}}{2}$ $\tan 45° = \dfrac{1}{1}$ or 1

$\csc 45° = \dfrac{\sqrt{2}}{1}$ or $\sqrt{2}$ $\sec 45° = \dfrac{\sqrt{2}}{1}$ or $\sqrt{2}$ $\cot 45° = \dfrac{1}{1}$ or 1

Triangle DEG is an equilateral triangle. Assume that each side is 2 units long. The altitude $\overline{EF}$ forms a 30°-60°-right triangle. Since altitude $\overline{EF}$ is the perpendicular bisector of side $\overline{DG}$, the length of side $\overline{DF}$ is 1. Find the length of altitude $\overline{EF}$.

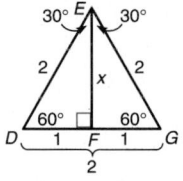

$x^2 + 1^2 = 2^2$ *Pythagorean Theorem*
$\quad\quad x^2 = 3$ *Subtract 1 from each side.*
$\quad\quad\ x = \sqrt{3}$ *Altitude $\overline{EF}$ is $\sqrt{3}$ units long.*

LESSON 16-6 SOLVING RIGHT TRIANGLES   757

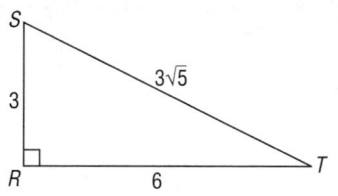
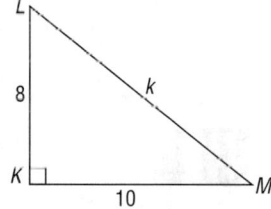

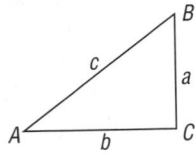
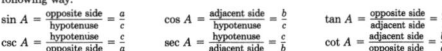

Now write the trigonometric values.

$\sin 30° = \frac{1}{2}$ $\cos 30° = \frac{\sqrt{3}}{2}$ $\tan 30° = \frac{1}{\sqrt{3}}$ or $\frac{\sqrt{3}}{3}$

$\csc 30° = \frac{2}{1}$ or 2 $\sec 30° = \frac{2}{\sqrt{3}}$ or $\frac{2\sqrt{3}}{3}$ $\cot 30° = \frac{\sqrt{3}}{1}$ or $\sqrt{3}$

$\sin 60° = \frac{\sqrt{3}}{2}$ $\cos 60° = \frac{1}{2}$ $\tan 60° = \frac{\sqrt{3}}{1}$ or $\sqrt{3}$

$\csc 60° = \frac{2}{\sqrt{3}}$ or $\frac{2\sqrt{3}}{3}$ $\sec 60° = \frac{2}{1}$ or 2 $\cot 60° = \frac{1}{\sqrt{3}}$ or $\frac{\sqrt{3}}{3}$

Trigonometric functions can be used to solve problems involving right triangles. Example 3 illustrates the solution to the application presented on page 756.

Example 3

APPLICATION

Physics

A car is traveling **500 meters along a raised exit ramp, whose angle to the ground has a measurement of 3°. How far did it rise during this distance? Round the answer to the nearest tenth of a meter.**

Draw a triangle to represent the situation.

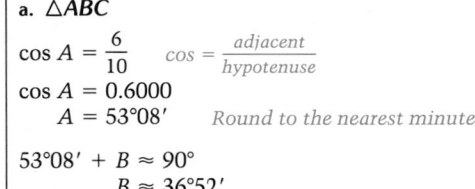
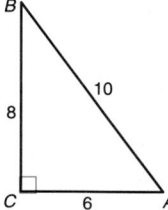

$\sin 3° = \frac{x}{500}$ $\sin = \frac{opposite}{hypotenuse}$

$0.0523 \approx \frac{x}{500}$

$26.2 \approx x$

The car will rise about 26.2 meters as it travels 500 meters on the exit ramp.

Finding all of the measures of the sides and the angles in a right triangle is called *solving the triangle*.

Teaching Tip ❷

Example 4

Solve each right triangle. Round measures of sides to the nearest tenth and measures of angles to the nearest minute.

a. $\triangle ABC$

$\cos A = \frac{6}{10}$ $\cos = \frac{adjacent}{hypotenuse}$

$\cos A = 0.6000$

$A = 53°08'$ *Round to the nearest minute.*

$53°08' + B \approx 90°$
$\qquad B \approx 36°52'$

Therefore, $A \approx 53°08'$ and $B \approx 36°52'$.

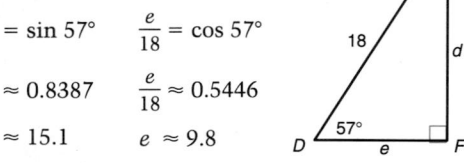

b. $\triangle DEF$

$\frac{d}{18} = \sin 57°$ $\frac{e}{18} = \cos 57°$

$\frac{d}{18} \approx 0.8387$ $\frac{e}{18} \approx 0.5446$

$d \approx 15.1$ $e \approx 9.8$

758   CHAPTER 16   TRIGONOMETRIC FUNCTIONS

RETEACHING THE LESSON

Orally have students suggest various methods to find the length of $\overline{AB}$. Have them see that there are various ways to solve this problem. $AB = 3\sqrt{6}$

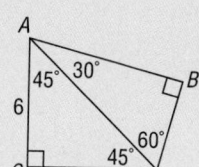

$57° + E = 90°$ *Angles D and E are complementary.*
$E = 41°$
Therefore, $d \approx 15.1$, $e \approx 9.8$, and $E = 41°$.

c. $\triangle ABC$

$4^2 + b^2 = 9^2$ *Since $\triangle ABC$ is a right triangle,*
$16 + b^2 = 81$ *use the Pythagorean Theorem.*
$b^2 = 65$
$b \approx 8.1$ *Round to the nearest tenth.*

$\sin A = \frac{4}{9} \approx 0.4444$ $\cos B = \frac{4}{9} \approx 0.4444$ Therefore, $b \approx 8.1$,
$A \approx 26°23'$ $B \approx 63°37'$ $A \approx 26°23'$, and $B \approx 63°37'$.

CHECKING FOR UNDERSTANDING

Communicating Mathematics
1. Find the measures of all angles and sides.
2. Answers may vary. One answer is that their sum is 90°.

Guided Practice
4. $\sin 15° = \frac{a}{37}$, 9.6
5. $\tan 76° = \frac{13}{b}$, 3.2
6. $\sin 49°13' = \frac{10}{c}$, 13.2
7. $\tan 71°13' = \frac{21.2}{b}$, 7.2.

Read and study the lesson to answer these questions.

1. What does it mean to solve a triangle?

2. If C is the right angle in right triangle ABC, what can we say about the measures of angles A and B?

3. If angles A and B are complementary angles, what can we say about $\sin A$ and $\cos B$? **They are equal.**

Use the triangle below to state equations that would enable you to solve each problem. Then solve. Round measures of sides to the nearest tenth and measures of angles to the nearest minute.

4. If $A = 15°$ and $c = 37$, find a.
5. If $A = 76°$ and $a = 13$, find b.
6. If $A = 49°13'$ and $a = 10$, find c.
7. If $a = 21.2$ and $A = 71°13'$, find b.
8. If $a = 13$ and $B = 16°$, find c.
9. If $A = 19°07'$ and $b = 11$, find c.

8. $\cos 16° = \frac{13}{c}$, 13.5   9. $\cos 19°7' = \frac{11}{c}$, 11.6

10. $b = 6$, $A = 53°8'$, $B = 36°52'$ 11. $b = 5$, $A = 67°23'$, $B = 22°37'$

EXERCISES

Practice
12. $c = 7.28$, $B = 74°3'$, $A = 15°57'$
13. $a = 10.82$, $A = 31°$, $B = 59°$

Solve each triangle described. Round measures of sides to the nearest hundredth and measures of angles to the nearest minute. 14–36. See margin.

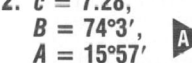
10. $c = 10$, $a = 8$
11. $c = 13$, $a = 12$
12. $a = 2$, $b = 7$
13. $c = 21$, $b = 18$
14. $a = 11$, $b = 21$
15. $b = 6$, $c = 13$
16. $A = 63°$, $a = 9.7$
17. $A = 16°$, $c = 14$
18. $A = 37°15'$, $b = 11$
19. $B = 42°10'$, $a = 9$
20. $B = 64°$, $c = 19.2$
21. $B = 83°$, $b = \sqrt{31}$

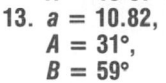
22. $a = 33$, $B = 33°$
23. $c = 6$, $B = 13°$
24. $b = 42$, $A = 77°$
25. $a = 9$, $B = 49°$
26. $b = 22$, $A = 22°22'$
27. $a = 44$, $B = 44°44'$

LESSON 16-6 SOLVING RIGHT TRIANGLES 759

Additional Answers
14. $c = 23.71$, $A = 27°39'$, $B = 62°21'$
15. $a = 11.53$, $A = 62°31'$, $B = 27°29'$
16. $B = 27°$, $c = 10.89$, $b = 4.94$
17. $a = 3.86$, $b = 13.46$, $B = 74°$
18. $B = 52°45'$, $c = 13.82$, $a = 8.36$
19. $A = 47°50'$, $c = 12.14$, $b = 8.15$
20. $A = 26°$, $a = 8.42$, $b = 17.26$
21. $A = 7°$, $a = 0.68$, $c = 5.61$
22. $A = 57°$, $c = 39.35$, $b = 21.43$

23. $A = 77°$, $a = 5.85$, $b = 1.35$
24. $B = 13°$, $a = 181.92$, $c = 186.71$
25. $A = 41°$, $b = 10.35$, $c = 13.72$
26. $B = 67°38'$, $a = 9.05$, $c = 23.79$
27. $A = 45°16'$, $c = 61.94$, $b = 43.59$

EVALUATING THE LESSON

Checking for Understanding
Exercises 1–9 are designed to help you assess understanding through reading, writing, and speaking. You should work through Exercises 1–3 with your students, and then monitor their work on Exercises 4–9.

Error Analysis
Have students first check their diagrams before setting up an equation to solve. Incorrect labeling such as using the c value for a leg and not the hypotenuse is a common mistake. Review labeling a right triangle.

Assignment Guide
Basic: 10–36, 39–40, 42–47
Average: 13–47
Enriched: 15–47

Practice Masters Booklet, p. 124

NAME _____ DATE _____
16-6 **Practice Worksheet**
Solving Right Triangles
Use the triangle below to state equations that would enable you to solve each problem. Then solve. Round measures of sides to the nearest tenth.

1. If $A = 20°$ and $c = 32$, find a.
10.9
2. If $A = 49°$ and $a = 17$, find b.
14.8
3. If $A = 27°18'$ and $a = 7$, find c.
15.3
4. If $a = 19.2$ and $A = 63°20'$, find b.
9.6
5. If $a = 28$ and $B = 41°$, find c.
37.1
6. If $A = 58°12'$ and $b = 34$, find c.
64.5

Solve each triangle described. Round measures of sides to the nearest hundredth and measures of angles to the nearest minute.

7. $a = 12$, $A = 35°$
$B = 55°$, $b = 17.13$, $c = 20.92$
8. $b = 25$, $B = 71°$
$A = 19°$, $a = 8.6$, $c = 26.44$
9. $a = 4$, $b = 7$
$A = 29°45'$, $B = 60°15'$, $c = 8.06$
10. $b = 52$, $c = 95$
$a = 79.50$, $A = 56°49'$, $B = 33°11'$
11. $A = 25°$, $c = 100$
$a = 42.26$, $b = 90.63$, $B = 65°$
12. $a = 7$, $c = 9$
$A = 51°3'$, $B = 38°57'$, $b = 5.66$

Closing the Lesson

Speaking Activity Explain what is meant by "solving the triangle".

APPLYING THE LESSON

Homework Exercises

See assignment guide on page 759.

Additional Answers

28. $A = 72°$, $c = 4.07$, $b = 1.26$
29. $B = 34°5'$, $a = 13.25$, $b = 8.97$
30. $B = 45°$, $b = 7$, $a = 7$
31. $B = 75°$, $a = 6.47$, $b = 24.15$
32. $A = 60°$, $c = 22$, $a = 19.05$
33. $A = 41°11'$, $B = 48°49'$, $b = 8$, $c = 10.63$
34. $B = 63°$, $c = 15.42$, $b = 13.74$
35. $B = 53°8'$, $A = 36°52'$, $a = 6$, $c = 10$
36. $A = 19°28'$, $B = 70°32'$, $c = 15$, $b = 14.14$

Enrichment Masters Booklet, p. 109

---

28. $B = 18°$, $a = \sqrt{15}$ 29. $A = 55°55'$, $c = 16$ 30. $A = 45°$, $c = 7\sqrt{2}$
31. $c = 25$, $A = 15°$ 32. $B = 30°$, $b = 11$ 33. $\tan A = \frac{7}{8}$, $a = 7$
34. $a = 7$, $A = 27°$ 35. $\tan B = \frac{8}{6}$, $b = 8$ 36. $\sin A = \frac{1}{3}$, $a = 5$

37. Solve the isosceles right triangle shown below. $CA = CB$.

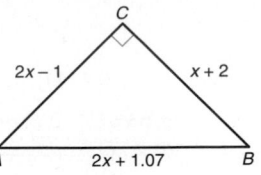

$x = 3$, $a = b = 5$, $c = 7.07$, $A = B = 45°$

38. Solve the equilateral triangle shown below.

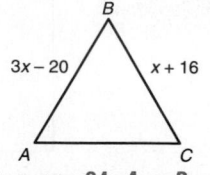

$x = 18$, $a = b = c = 34$, $A = B = C = 60°$

Critical Thinking

39. Can you solve a right triangle if you are given only the length of one side and the measure of one of the acute angles? Justify your answer. **yes; Justifications may vary.**

Applications

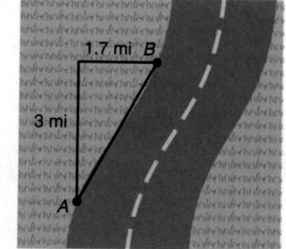

40. **Civil Engineering** The bearing of a road between two points, A and B, is the measure of the positive angle with vertex at point A that is measured clockwise from point B. Find the bearing of a road that runs directly from A to B if B is 3 miles north and 1.7 miles east of point A. **29°32'**

41. **Travel** Tom visited the Washington Monument on his summer vacation. He stood 1200 feet away from the base of the monument to take a picture and had to look up at an angle of 24°49' to see the top. Approximately how tall is the Washington Monument? **555 feet**

Mixed Review

42. How many different outfits can be made from 7 pairs of pants, 3 shirts, and 4 pairs of shoes? **(Lesson 15-1) 84**

43. Write $\sum_{n=1}^{5} 3^{n-1}$ in expanded form and find the sum. **(Lesson 13-5)**
43. $1 + 3 + 9 + 27 + 81$; 121

44. **Finance** Luis' grandfather invested $150 at 5% interest compounded quarterly. When the account was recently given to Luis, it contained $6230. How long ago did Luis' grandfather invest the $150? **(Lesson 12-7) 75 years ago**

45. **Chemistry** How much of a 35% salt solution must be added to a 10% salt solution to get 250 milliliters of a 20% solution? **(Lesson 11-7)** **100 mL**

46. Find the value of the discriminant for the quadratic equation $y^2 - 8y + 12 = 0$. Describe the nature of the roots. If the roots are real, tell whether they are rational or irrational. Then solve the equation. **(Lesson 7-4) 16; 2 real-rational; 6, 2**

47. Margaret mixed r cups of cashews with s cups of peanuts. This gave her 12 cups of nuts with one part cashews to three parts peanuts. Find r and s. **(Lesson 3-2) $r = 3$, $s = 9$**

EXTENDING THE LESSON

Math Power: Connections

Have students interview an architect, building contractor, or surveyor and write a report on how solving right triangles is used in his or her job.

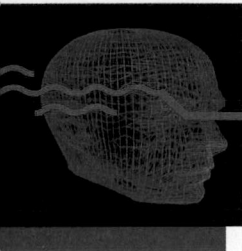

Technology
Solving Triangles

▶ BASIC
Spreadsheets
Software

Objective This optional page shows how the BASIC programming language can be used to perform mathematical computations and to enhance and extend mathematical concepts.

Teaching Suggestions

This program can be modified to find the solutions for a triangle, if they exist. The following is an example of this program.

The BASIC program below determines the number of solutions of a triangle given the lengths of two sides and the degree measure of the angle opposite one of them.

```
10      INPUT A,A1,B1
20      LET B = B1*SIN (A*3.1415927 / 180)
30      PRINT "B SIN A=";B
40      IF A > = 90 THEN 110
50      IF A1 < B THEN 120
60      IF A1 = B THEN 130
70      IF A1 < B1 THEN 100
80      IF A1 > B1 THEN 130
100     PRINT "TWO SOLUTIONS EXIST." : GOTO 140
110     IF A1 > B1 THEN 130
120     PRINT "NO SOLUTION EXISTS.": GOTO 140
130     PRINT "ONE SOLUTION EXISTS."
140     END
```

In the program, A represents the degree measure of the angle, $A1$ represents the measure of one side of the triangle, and $B1$ represents the measure of the other side.

It is important that you enter the data correctly when prompted.

- First enter the degree measure of the angle.
- Next enter the measure of the side opposite that angle.
- Then enter the measure of the other side.

The data must be entered in this order to obtain a correct output.

For a triangle in which $A = 26°$, $a = 3$, and $b = 7$, there is no solution, as shown by the output at the right.

```
] RUN
?26,3,7
B SIN A-3.06858807
NO SOLUTION EXISTS.
```

```
10      REM THIS PROGRAM
        SOLVES A TRIANGLE
        USING THE LAW OF
        SINES.
15      REM LINE 110-115 IN-
        CLUDE DATA FOR SIX
        TRIANGLES.
20      PRINT
25      REM AA -> ANGLE A
30      REM AB -> ANGLE B
35      REM AC -> ANGLE C
40      REM SA -> SIDE A
45      REM SB -> SIDE B
50      REM SC -> SIDE C
100     READ AA,AB,SA
110     DATA 30,60,12
111     DATA 34,67,34
112     DATA 23,56,78
113     DATA 12,13,23
114     DATA 56,123,45
115     DATA 123,124,23
116     DATA 0,0,0
120     IF AA = 0 THEN 220
125     LET AC = 180 - AA - AB
130     IF AC < 0 THEN 200
140     LET SB = SA*SIN
        (AB*3.14159 / 180) /
        SIN(AA*3.14159 / 180)
150     LET SC = SA*SIN
        (AC*3.14159 / 180) /
        SIN (AA*3.14159 / 180)
155     PRINT "ANGLE A =";AA
156     PRINT "ANGLE B =";AB
157     PRINT "SIDE A =";SA
158     PRINT "_____"
160     PRINT "ANGLE C =";AC
170     PRINT "SIDE B =";
        INT (100*SB + .5) / 100
180     PRINT "SIDE C =";
        INT (100*SC + .5) / 100
185     PRINT:PRINT
190     GOTO 100
200     PRINT "ANGLE A =";AA
201     PRINT "ANGLE B =";AB
202     PRINT "SIDE A =";SA
203     PRINT "_____"
205     PRINT "NO TRIANGLE
        EXISTS."
210     GOTO 100
220     END
```

EXERCISES

Use the program to determine the number of solutions. Also state the value of $b \sin A$ rounded to four decimal places.

one; 0.1743

1. $A = 103°$, $a = 5$, $b = 2$ **one; 1.9487**   2. $A = 175°$, $a = 19$, $b = 2$

4. none; 7.6604
5. two; 9.9864
6. two; 0.3653
7. one; 4.8127
8. two; 1.0333

3. $A = 77°$, $a = 1$, $b = 5$ **none; 4.8719**   4. $A = 130°$, $a = 8$, $b = 10$

5. $A = 38.62°$, $a = 15$, $b = 16$ 6. $A = 10.524°$, $a = 1$, $b = 2$

7. $A = 53°20'$, $a = 9$, $b = 6$ 8. $A = 9°55'$, $a = 3$, $b = 6$

TECHNOLOGY 761

Lesson Resources

Reteaching Master 16-7
Practice Master 16-7
Enrichment Master 16-7
Lab Manual, pp. 47–48

 Transparency 16-7 contains the 5-Minute Check and a teaching aid for this lesson.

INTRODUCING THE LESSON

 5-Minute Check

(over Lesson 16-6)

Solve each right triangle described. Round lengths to the nearest hundredth.

1. $A = 50°$, $a = 11$ $B = 40°$, $b = 9.23$, $c = 14.36$
2. $a = 15$, $c = 20$
   $A = 48°35'$, $B = 41°25'$, $b = 13.23$
3. $B = 31°$, $c = 12$ $A = 59°$, $a = 10.29$, $b = 6.18$

Motivating the Lesson

Show students a set of complete blueprints for a building. Have them list places where knowing angle measurements or side lengths of right triangles is important.

TEACHING THE LESSON

Teaching Tip ❶ Make sure students understand the terminology used. You may want to review the concepts of alternate interior angles and congruent angles.

Teaching Tip ❷ Point out to students that this is a method of indirect measurement and is frequently used to measure items or distances too difficult to measure directly.

Objective 16-7

After studying this lesson, you should be able to:
- solve word problems using right triangle trigonometry.

Application
Teaching Tip ❶

Terry Jacobs is standing on the deck of an aircraft carrier observing the approach of an airplane. The angle formed by her line of sight to the airplane and a horizontal is called the **angle of elevation.** The angle formed by the line of sight from the airplane pilot to Ms. Jacobs and a horizontal is called the **angle of depression.** The angles of elevation and depression are alternate interior angles, and since the lines of sight are parallel, they have equal measures.

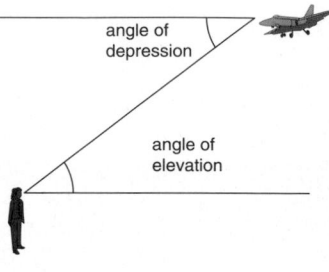

There are many applications of angles of depression and angles of elevation. The following examples illustrate some of these applications.

Example 1

Forestry
Teaching Tip ❷

Tami is standing 30 feet from the base of a tree. She measured the angle to the top of the tree with an astrolabe, which is a sighting device used to measure angles. As Tami looks to the top of the tree, the measurement of the angle of elevation is 65°. Find the height of the tree to the nearest tenth of a foot.

Let h represent the height of the tree.

$$\frac{h}{30} = \tan 65°$$
$$\frac{h}{30} \approx 2.1445$$
$$h \approx 64.335$$

The tree is about 64.3 feet tall.

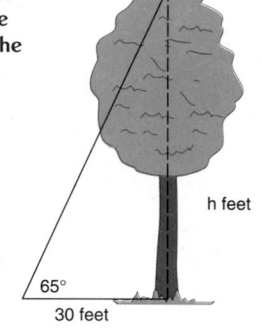

h feet

65°
30 feet

762   CHAPTER 16   TRIGONOMETRIC FUNCTIONS

ALTERNATE TEACHING STRATEGIES

Mini-Math Lab

Have students use an astrolabe or some other method to measure the angle of elevation for a tall object on the school grounds, such as a flagpole, tree, or building. Measure the distance from the astrolabe to the base of the object and determine the height of the object. Don't forget to include the distance of the astrolabe off the ground.

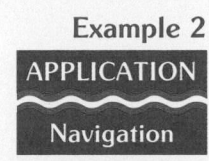

Example 2

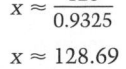

APPLICATION

Navigation

The top of a lighthouse is 120 meters above sea level. From the top of the lighthouse, the measurement of the angle of depression to a boat on the ocean is 43°. How far is the boat from the foot of the lighthouse?

Let x represent the distance from the lighthouse.

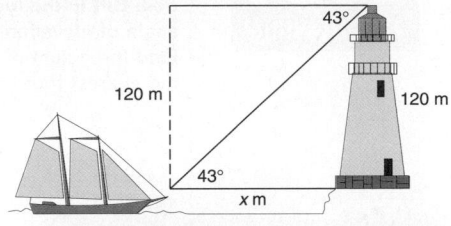

$$\tan 43° = \frac{120}{x} \qquad tan = \frac{opposite}{adjacent}$$

$$x = \frac{120}{\tan 43°}$$

$$x \approx \frac{120}{0.9325}$$

$$x \approx 128.69$$

The boat is about 129 meters from the lighthouse.

Example 3

APPLICATION

Astronomy

Eratosthenes, an astronomer who lived in Greece in the third century B.C., is credited with providing the first accurate measure of Earth's circumference. He found that at noon on the day of the summer solstice, the sun was directly over the city of Syene. At the same time, in Alexandria, which is north of Syene, the sun was 7°12′ south of being directly overhead. If the distance between the two cities was 5000 stadia, find Eratosthenes' measure of the circumference of Earth.

Draw a diagram.

Since there are 360° in a full rotation around Earth, the following proportion can be written.

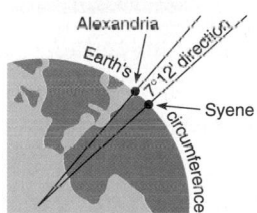

$$\frac{360°}{7°12′} = \frac{c}{5000}$$

$$(7°12′)c = (360°)5000$$

$$c = \frac{(360°)5000}{7°12′}$$

$$c = \frac{(360°)5000}{7.2°} \qquad 7°12′ = 7\frac{12°}{60} \text{ or } 7.2°$$

$$c = 250,000$$

Eratosthenes' measure of Earth's circumference was 250,000 stadia or 24,661 miles. This is only 158 miles less than the currently accepted value. *The stadium (singular form of stadia) is an ancient unit of measurement equal to about 0.098 mile.*

Chalkboard Examples

For Example 1

A boat is 70 m from a lighthouse. The measurement of the angle of elevation from the boat to the top of the lighthouse is 52°. Find the height of the lighthouse. **about 89.6 m**

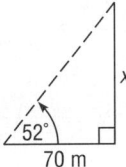

For Example 2

Trevor is standing on top of a cliff 200 feet above a lake. The measurement of the angle of depression to a boat on the lake is 21°. How far is the boat from the base of the cliff to the nearest foot? **x ≈ 521 feet**

For Example 3

On the planet Flippo, they have the celebration of the pink moon. In Zorbo, a city on Flippo, the pink moon has risen to directly overhead and the festival begins. In Tango, a city 100 bleeps away, the moon is still 8°15′ from being directly overhead, so their celebration has not begun. Find an approximation (to the nearest bleep) for the circumference of Flippo. **c ≈ 4364 bleeps**

LESSON 16-7 APPLICATIONS OF RIGHT TRIANGLES   763

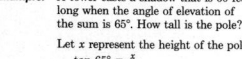
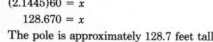
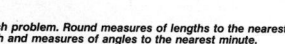
Example 4

APPLICATION

Broadcasting

Vonda and Bill are standing 100 feet apart and in a straight line with the WWV television tower. The angle of elevation from Bill to the tower is 30° and the angle of elevation from Vonda is 20°. Find the height of the television tower to the nearest foot.

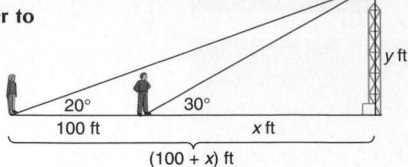

$\tan 30° = \frac{y}{x}$

$x \tan 30° = y$ *Solve for y.*

$x(0.5774) = y$ *$\tan 30° = 0.5774$*

$\tan 20° = \frac{y}{x + 100}$ *Solve for y.*

$(\tan 20°)(x + 100) = y$

$0.3640(x + 100) = y$ *$\tan 20° = 0.3640$*

$0.3640x + 36.40 = y$

$0.5774x = 0.3640x + 36.40$

$0.2134x = 36.40$

$x \approx 170.6$ *Round to the nearest tenth.*

$\frac{y}{170.6} \approx \tan 30°$ *$\tan 30° = \frac{y}{x}$*

$y \approx 98.5$ *Round to the nearest tenth.*

The antenna is about 99 feet tall.

CHECKING FOR UNDERSTANDING

Communicating Mathematics

Read and study the lesson to answer these questions. **1–2. See margin.**

1. What is the angle of elevation?

2. How is the angle of depression related to the angle of elevation?

Guided Practice

3. $7^2 + b^2 = 16^2$; 14.4
4. $a^2 + 10^2 = 20^2$; 17.3
5. $\tan A = \frac{7}{12}$; 30°15′

Use the triangle to state the equation that would enable you to solve each problem. Then solve.

3. If $c = 16$ and $a = 7$, find b.

4. If $b = 10$ and $c = 20$, find a.

5. If $a = 7$ and $b = 12$, find A.

6. If $a = b$ and $c = 12$, find B.
$a^2 + b^2 = c^2$, $a^2 + a^2 = 12^2$, $\cos B = \frac{a}{12}$; 45°

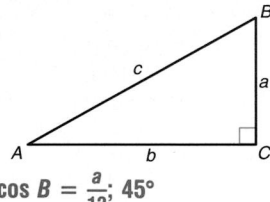

EXERCISES

Practice   For each triangle, find sin A, cos A, and tan A. Round your answers to four decimal places.

7.
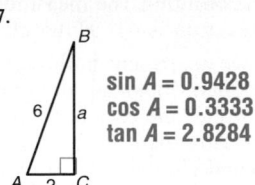
sin A = 0.9428
cos A = 0.3333
tan A = 2.8284

8.
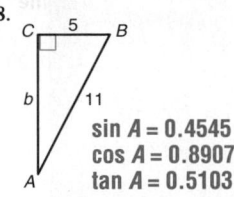
sin A = 0.4545
cos A = 0.8907
tan A = 0.5103

9.
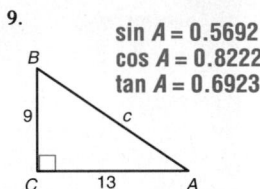
sin A = 0.5692
cos A = 0.8222
tan A = 0.6923

B Solve each problem. Round measures of lengths to the nearest hundredth and measures of angles to the nearest minute.

10. The flagpole in front of Stevenson High School casts a shadow 40 feet long when the measurement of the angle of elevation to the sun is 31°20′. How tall is the flagpole? **24.35 ft**

11. Aaron is standing 300 meters from the base of a radio tower. According to his astrolabe, the measurement of the angle of elevation to the top of the tower is 40°. How high is the tower? **251.73 m**

12. According to the pilot's instruments, the measurement of the angle of depression of an aircraft carrier from a plane 1000 feet above the water is 63°18′. How far is the plane from the carrier? **1119.36 ft**

13. Dana is flying a kite to which the angle of elevation is 70°. The string on the kite is 65 meters long. How far is the kite above the ground? **61.08 m**

14. A tree was broken in a recent storm. The top of the tree touches the ground 13 meters from the base. The top of the tree makes an angle of 29° with the ground. How tall was the tree before it was broken? **22.07 m**

15. Naren Thomas is an architect designing a new parking garage for the city. The floors of the garage are to be 20 feet apart. The exit ramps between each pair of floors are to be 120 feet long. What is the measurement of the angle of elevation of each ramp? **9°36′**

16. A railroad track rises 10 feet for every 400 feet along the track. What is the measurement of the angle the track forms with the horizontal? **1°26′**

17. Curtis and Cindy are observing the Washington Monument from $\frac{1}{4}$ mile away. The monument is 555 feet tall. What is the angle of elevation from Curtis and Cindy to the top of the monument? (1 mile = 5280 feet) **22°48′**

C
CONNECTION
Geometry

18. The diagram at the right shows square *ABCD*. The midpoint of side $\overline{AD}$ is *E*. Find the values of *x*, *y*, and *z* to the nearest minute.
$x = 63°26′; y = 26°34′; z = 63°26′$

19. Tabina and Russ are standing in a straight line with the base of a building. The measurement of the angle of elevation to the top of the building from the point where Tabina is standing is 38°20′. From the point where Russ is standing, 50 feet closer to the building, the measurement of the angle of elevation is 45°. How tall is the building? **188.89 ft**

20. Two apartment buildings are separated by an alley. As Beth looks out of her window 60 feet above the ground, she uses her astrolabe to find that the measurement of the angle of depression of the second building is 50°. She also finds that the angle of elevation to the top of the second building is 40°. About how tall is the second building? **102.25 ft**

21. A pendulum 50 centimeters long is moved 40° from the vertical. How far did the tip of the pendulum rise? **11.7 cm**

22. Olivia and Jason are standing 200 feet apart and in line with the base of a flagpole. The measurement of the angle of elevation of the top of the pole from Olivia is 30° and from Jason is 60°. How far is the flagpole from each of them? **100 ft from Jason, 300 ft from Olivia**

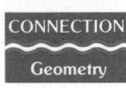
CONNECTION
Geometry

23. The isosceles triangle *RST* at the right has base $\overline{TS}$ measuring 10 centimeters and base angles each measuring 39°. Find the length of the altitude $\overline{QR}$. **4.05 cm**

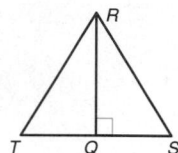

Critical Thinking

24. Prove that the angle of elevation is congruent to its corresponding angle of depression. **See students' work.**

Applications

25. **Transportation** A train travels 5000 meters along a track whose angle of elevation has a measurement of 2°. How much did it rise during this distance? **174.50 m**

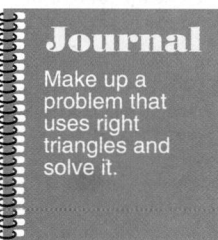
Journal
Make up a problem that uses right triangles and solve it.

26. **Broadcasting** A television antenna sits atop a building. From a point 200 feet from the base of the building, the measurement of the angle of elevation of the top of the antenna is 80°. The measurement of the angle of elevation of the bottom of the antenna from the same point is 75°. How tall is the antenna? **387.85 ft**

27. **Travel** A ship sails due north from its home port for 90 kilometers. It then turns east and sails for 40 kilometers before turning north again to sail for 70 kilometers. How far is the ship from its port? **164.92 km**

Mixed Review

28. Find the value of *n* if $C(n, 5) = C(n, 15)$. **(Lesson 15-4) 20**

29. Solve $3^5 = 3^{2n-1}$ for *n*. **(Lesson 12-1) 3**

30. Find all zeros of the function $g(x) = 24x^4 - 94x^3 + 61x^2 + 21x - 18$. **(Lesson 10-4)** $3, \dfrac{2}{3}, \dfrac{3}{4}, -\dfrac{1}{2}$

766 CHAPTER 16 TRIGONOMETRIC FUNCTIONS

EXTENDING THE LESSON

Math Power: Connections

The Great Pyramid of Cheops in Egypt has a square base. This base is 230 meters on a side. The faces of the pyramid make an angle of 51°50′ with the horizontal. How tall is the pyramid?
about 146 meters

16-8   Law of Sines

Objective
16-8

After studying this lesson, you should be able to:
- solve triangles and problems using the Law of Sines.

Application

A ship is sighted at sea from two observation points on the coastline which are 30 miles apart. The angle between the coastline and the line between the ship and the first observation point measures 34°. The angle between the coastline and the line between the ship and the second observation point measures 45°34'. How far is the ship from the second observation point?

You can use trigonometric functions to solve problems like this one which involve triangles that are *not* right triangles.
You will solve this problem in Example 3.

Consider $\triangle ABC$ with height h units and sides with lengths a units, b units, and c units. The area of this triangle is given by the equation area $= \frac{1}{2}bh$. Also, $\sin A = \frac{h}{c}$ or $h = c \sin A$. By combining these equations, we can find a new formula for the area of the triangle.

$$\text{area} = \frac{1}{2}bh = \frac{1}{2}b(c \sin A) \qquad h = c \sin A$$

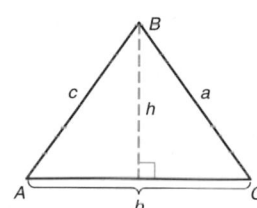

You can find two other formulas for the area of the triangle in a similar way.

$$\text{area} = \frac{1}{2}ac \sin B \qquad \text{area} = \frac{1}{2}ab \sin C$$

All of these formulas represent the area of the same triangle. So, the following must be true.

$$\frac{1}{2}bc \sin A = \frac{1}{2}ac \sin B = \frac{1}{2}ab \sin C$$

The **Law of Sines** is obtained by dividing each of expression above by $\frac{1}{2}abc$.

$$\frac{\sin A}{a} = \frac{\sin B}{b} = \frac{\sin C}{c}$$

Law of Sines

Let $\triangle ABC$ be any triangle with a, b, and c representing the measures of sides opposite angles with measurements A, B, and C respectively. Then,
$$\frac{\sin A}{a} = \frac{\sin B}{b} = \frac{\sin C}{c}.$$

LESSON 16-8   LAW OF SINES   767

ALTERNATE TEACHING STRATEGIES

Using Manipulatives

Have students use corrugated cardboard, string, and 3 thumbtacks to model a triangle. Using a protrator and a metric ruler, have them measure two sides and a nonincluded angle. Then have them solve the triangle and find its area. Confirm the solution by measurement. Repeat the activity for another triangle, this time measuring two angles and one nonincluded side.

Lesson Resources

Reteaching Master 16-8
Practice Master 16-8
Enrichment Master 16-8
Technology Master, p. 16
Multicultural Activity Master, p. 16

Transparency 16-8 contains the 5-Minute Check and a teaching aid for this lesson.

INTRODUCING THE LESSON

5-Minute Check
(over Lesson 16-7)

1. Two hikers are 300 meters from the base of a radio tower. The measurement of the angle of elevation to the top of the tower is 40°. How high is the tower to the nearest meter? **252 meters**

2. The top of a staircase is 3.5 m higher than the bottom. Viewed from the side, the horizontal length is 4.75 m. Find the angle of depression from the top of the stairway to the bottom.   **36°23'**

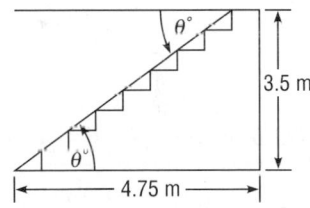

Motivating the Lesson

Show students a picture of a building built at a right angle with the ground. Ask how the height can be found. Show students a picture of the Leaning Tower of Pisa. Ask students why the previous method of finding height could not be used for this building. Emphasize that not all useful triangles are right triangles.

Example 1

Find the area of $\triangle ABC$ if $a = 11$, $b = 13$, and $C = 31°10'$.

$$\text{area} = \frac{1}{2}ab \sin C$$

$$\approx \frac{1}{2}(11)(13) \sin 31°10' \qquad \text{sin } 31°10' \approx 0.5175$$

$$\approx 37.001$$

To the nearest whole unit, the area is 37 square units.

Example 2

Use the Law of Sines to solve the triangle. Round when needed.

$$\frac{\sin B}{b} = \frac{\sin A}{a} \qquad \textit{Law of Sines}$$

$$\frac{\sin B}{79} = \frac{\sin 45°}{83}$$

$$\sin B = \frac{79 \sin 45°}{83} \approx 0.6730$$

$$B \approx 42°18' \qquad \textit{Round to the nearest minute.}$$

$$45° + 42°18' + C \approx 180° \qquad \textit{The sum of the angle}$$
$$C \approx 92°42' \qquad \textit{measures in a triangle is 180°.}$$

$$\frac{\sin 92°42'}{c} = \frac{\sin 45°}{83}$$

$$c = \frac{83 \sin 92°42'}{\sin 45°}$$

$$c \approx 117.3 \qquad \textit{Round to the nearest tenth.}$$

Therefore, $B \approx 42°18'$, $C \approx 92°42'$, and $c \approx 117.25$.

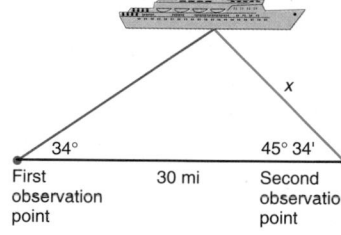

Example 3 is the solution to the application on page 767.

Example 3

A ship is sighted at sea from two observation points on the coastline which are 30 miles apart. The angle between the coastline and the line between the ship and the first observation point measures 34°. The angle between the coastline and the line between the ship and the second observation point measures 45°34'. How far is the ship from the second observation point?

Draw a diagram.

First, find the measure of the third angle.

$$34° + 45°34' + C = 180°$$
$$C = 100°26'$$

Now, use the Law of Sines to find x.

$$\frac{\sin 100°26'}{30} = \frac{\sin 34°}{x}$$

$$x = \frac{30 \sin 34°}{\sin 100°26'}$$

$$x = 17.06$$

The ship is approximately 17 miles from the second observation point.

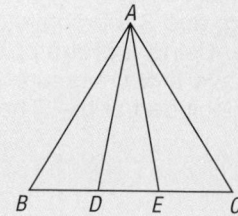

34°		45° 34'
First observation point	30 mi	Second observation point

RETEACHING THE LESSON

Work through the following problem as a class and discuss the various ways to solve it. Triangle *ABC* is an equilateral triangle whose sides are 18 cm long. Lines *AD* and *AE* are drawn trisecting angle *A* and intersecting side $\overline{BC}$ in points *D* and *E*. Find the lengths of segments *BD*, *DE*, and *EC* to two decimal places.   **BD = 6.25 cm, DE = 5.50 cm, EC = 6.25 cm**

CHECKING FOR UNDERSTANDING

Communicating Mathematics

Read and study the lesson to answer these questions.

1. One formula for the area of a triangle is $A = \frac{1}{2}bh$. State another formula for the area of a triangle.

2. For what kind of triangles does the Law of Sines hold true? **any triangle**

3. How far is the ship described in Example 3 from the first observation point? **approximately 21.8 miles**

1. area $= \frac{1}{2}bc \sin A$, or area $= \frac{1}{2}ac \sin B$, or area $= \frac{1}{2}ab \sin C$

Guided Practice

State an equation that would enable you to find the area of each triangle. Then find the area to the nearest tenth. **4–7. See margin.**

4. $a = 15$, $b = 20$, $C = 63°$

5. $b = 10$, $c = 17$, $A = 46°$

6. $a = 6$, $c = 4$, $B = 52°$

7. $a = 15$, $b = 30$, $C = 90°$

For each triangle ABC described, state an equation that would enable you to find each value. Then find the value.

8. If $a = 20$, $A = 40°$, and $B = 60°$, find b.

9. If $b = 10$, $a = 14$, and $A = 50°$, find B.

10. If $b = 2.8$, $A = 53°$, and $B = 61°$, find a.

11. If $c = 12$, $b = 16$, and $B = 42°$, find C.

8. $\dfrac{\sin 40°}{20} = \dfrac{\sin 60°}{b}$; **26.9**

9. $\dfrac{\sin 50°}{14} = \dfrac{\sin B°}{10}$; **33°10′**

10. $\dfrac{\sin 53°}{a} = \dfrac{\sin 61°}{2.8}$; **2.6**

11. $\dfrac{\sin 42°}{16} = \dfrac{\sin C}{12}$; **30°7′**

EXERCISES

Practice

Find the area of each triangle described below.

12. $a = 15$, $b = 22$, $C = 90°$ **165**

13. $a = 12$, $b = 12$, $C = 50°$ **55.155**

14. $a = 11.5$, $c = 14$, $B = 20°$ **27.533**

15. $a = 11$, $c = 5$, $B = 50°6′$ **21.097**

16. $b = 4$, $c = 19$, $A = 73°24′$ **36.4162**

17. $a = 9.4$, $c = 13.5$, $B = 95°$ **63.2086**

Solve each triangle described below. **23–25. See margin.**

18. $A = 40°$, $B = 60°$, $c = 20$

19. $a = 8$, $A = 49°$, $B = 57°$

20. $a = 80$, $b = 70$, $A = 83°10′$

21. $B = 70°$, $C = 58°$, $a = 84$

22. $A = 30°$, $C = 70°$, $c = 8$

23. $c = 17$, $b = 15$, $C = 64°40′$

24. $a = 14$, $b = 7.5$, $A = 103°$

25. $a = 23$, $A = 73°25′$, $C = 24°30′$

26. $b = 8$, $B = 36°36′$, $C = 119°$
$A = 24°24′$, $a = 5.54$, $c = 11.74$

27. $A = 105°$, $a = 18$, $b = 14$
$B = 48°42′$, $C = 26°18′$, $c = 8.3$

28. An isosceles triangle has a base of 22 centimeters and exactly one angle measuring 36°. Find its perimeter. *Hint: The two angles opposite the congruent sides of an isosceles triangle are congruent.* **93.19 cm**

Additional Answers

4. area $= \frac{1}{2}(15)(20) \sin 63°$; **133.7**

5. area $= \frac{1}{2}(10)(17) \sin 46°$; **61.1**

6. area $= \frac{1}{2}(6)(4) \sin 52°$; **9.5**

7. area $= \frac{1}{2}(15)(30) \sin 90°$; **225**

23. $B = 52°53′$, $A = 62°27′$, $a = 16.68$

24. $B = 31°28′$, $C = 45°32′$, $c = 10.25$

25. $B = 82°5′$, $b = 23.77$, $c = 9.95$

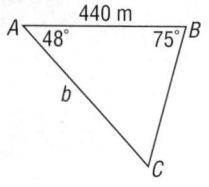

Error Analysis

So that incorrect assumptions are not made about a problem, have students draw a triangle from the given data and draw it in approximate proportion.

Closing the Lesson

Modeling Activity Have students use a model to explain the Law of Sines.

APPLYING THE LESSON

Homework Exercises

See assignment guide on page 769.

Enrichment Masters Booklet, p. 111

29. The longest side of a triangle is 34 yards. Two angles of the triangle are 40° and 65°. Find the length of the other two sides. **31.9 yd and 22.6 yd**

C ▸ **30.** A triangular lot faces two streets that meet at an angle measuring 85°. The sides of the lot facing the streets are each 160 feet in length. Find the perimeter of the lot. **536.19 ft**

31. Points X and Y are on opposite sides of a valley. Point C is 60 kilometers from point X. Angle YXC is 108° and angle YCX is 35°. Find the width of the valley. **57.2 km**

32. A flower bed is in the shape of an obtuse triangle. One angle is 45° and the opposite side is 28 feet long. The longest side is 36 feet long. Find the measures of the remaining angles and side. **115°, 20°, and 13.5 ft**

Critical Thinking

33. Prove that the Law of Sines holds true for right triangles. **See students' work.**

Applications

34. **Surveying** A building 60 feet tall is on the top of a hill. A surveyor stands at a point on the hill and finds that the angle of elevation to the top of the building has measurement 42° and to the bottom of the building has measurement 18°.

    a. Draw a diagram to represent this situation. **See students' work.**

    b. How far is the surveyor from the base of the building? **109.63 ft**

35. **Aviation** Two planes left John F. Kennedy Airport at the same time. Each plane is flying at a speed of 110 miles per hour. One plane flew in the direction 60° east of north and the other flew in the direction of 40° east of south.

    a. Draw a diagram to represent this situation. **See students' work.**

    b. How far apart are the planes after three hours? **424.24 miles**

Mixed Review

36. **Statistics** The number of years of life expected at birth for women in certain countries is given below. Make a box-and-whisker plot of the data, labeling any outliers. **(Lesson 14-5) See margin.**

    77.2 76.8 76.0 74.3 77.5 78.8 78.4 75.4 77.5
    76.0 73.7 75.6 77.2 79.5 79.5 75.0 72.9 76.2
    79.9 79.6 74.0 77.6 75.6 75.9 73.2

37. Expand the binomial $(x + 4)^6$. **(Lesson 13-7) See margin.**

38. **Biology** For a certain strain of bacteria, k in the exponential growth formula is 0.782 when t is measured in hours. How long will it take 10 bacteria to increase to 500 bacteria? *Hint: The exponential growth formula is $y = ne^{kt}$.* **(Lesson 12-8) 5.003 hours**

39. If $f(x) = x + 1$ and $g(x) = x^2$, find $f[g(x)]$ and $g[f(x)]$. **(Lesson 10-7)**

40. **Geometry** The formula for the area of a trapezoid is $A = \frac{h}{2}(b_1 + b_2)$, where A represents the measure of the area, h represents the measure of the altitude, and b_1 and b_2 represent the measures of the bases. Find the measure of the area of the trapezoid whose height is 8 cm and whose bases measure 12 cm and 20 cm. **(Lesson 1-1) 128 square cm**

770   CHAPTER 16   TRIGONOMETRIC FUNCTIONS

    39. $x^2 + 1$; $x^2 + 2x + 1$

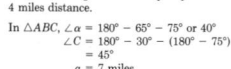
NAME _____ **DATE** _____

16-8 Enrichment Worksheet

Navigation

The bearing of a boat is an angle showing the direction the boat is heading. Often, the angle is measured from north, but it can be measured from any of the four compass directions. At the right, the bearing of the boat is 155°. Or, it can be described as 25° east of south (S25°E).

Example: A boat A sights the lighthouse B in the direction N65°E and the spire of a church C in the direction S75°E. According to the map, B is 7 miles from C in the direction N30°W. In order for A to avoid running aground, find the bearing it should keep to pass B at 4 miles distance.

In $\triangle ABC$, $\angle \alpha = 180° - 65° - 75°$ or 40°
$\angle C = 180° - 30° - (180° - 75°)$
$\quad = 45°$
$a = 7$ miles

With the Law of Sines,
$AB = \frac{a \sin C}{\sin \alpha} = \frac{7(\sin 45°)}{\sin 40°} = 7.7$ mi.

The ray for the correct bearing for A must be tangent at X to circle B with radius $BX = 4$. Thus $\triangle ABX$ is a right triangle.

Then $\sin \theta = \frac{BX}{AB} = \frac{4}{7.7} \approx 0.519$. Therefore, $\angle \theta = 31°18'$.

The bearing of A should be $65° - 31°18' = 33°42'$.

Solve the following.

1. Suppose the lighthouse B in the example is sighted at S30°W by a ship P due north of the church C. Find the bearing P should keep to pass B at 4 miles distance. **S64°51'W**

2. In the fog, the lighthouse keeper determines by radar that a boat 18 miles away is heading to the shore. The direction of the boat from the lighthouse is S80°E. What bearing should the lighthouse keeper radio the boat to take to come ashore 4 miles south of the lighthouse? **S87.2°E**

3. To avoid a rocky area along a shoreline, a ship at A travels 7 km to B, bearing 22°15', then 8 km to C, bearing 68°30', then 6 km to D, bearing 109°15'. Find the distance from A to D. **17.4 km**

EXTENDING THE LESSON

Math Power: Problem Solving

Two buildings are 25 miles apart with building B due east of building A. A shopping mall is under construction at N30°E of building A and N50°W of building B. Find the perpendicular distance from the mall to line AB. **about 10 miles**

Additional Answers

36.

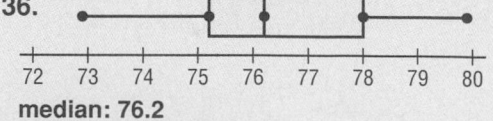

median: 76.2
lower quartile: 75.2
upper quartile: 78
interquartile range: 2.8
outliers: none
greatest value: 79.9
least value: 72.9

37. $x^6 + 24x^5 + 240x^4 + 1280x^3 + 3840x^2 + 6144x + 4096$

16-9 Problem-Solving Strategy: Examine the Solution

Objective
16-9

After studying this lesson, you should be able to:

■ determine, from a given set of information, the number of possible solutions and solve the triangle if solutions do exist.

When solving a triangle, you must analyze the data you are given in order to determine whether there is a solution or not.

When the lengths of two sides of a triangle and the measurement of the angle opposite one of them are given, a single solution does not always exist. In such a case, one of the following will be true.

1. No triangle exists.
2. Exactly one triangle exists.
3. Two triangles exist.

In other words, there may be no solutions, one solution, or two solutions.

Suppose you are given a, b, and A. First consider the case where $A < 90°$.

Teaching Tip ❶

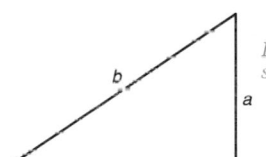
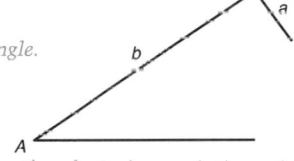

If $a = b \sin A$, the solution is a right triangle.

If $a = b \sin A$, one solution exists.

If $a < b \sin A$, no solution exists.

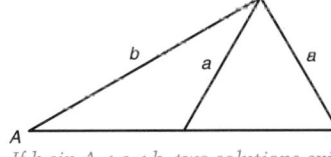

If $b \sin A < a < b$, two solutions exist.

If $a > b$, one solution exists.

Consider the case where $A \geq 90°$.

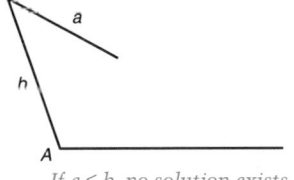
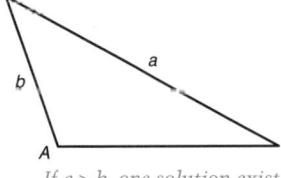

If $a \leq b$, no solution exists.

If $a > b$, one solution exists.

LESSON 16-9 PROBLEM-SOLVING STRATEGY: EXAMINE THE SOLUTION 771

Lesson Resources

Practice Master 16-9

Transparency 16-9 contains the 5-Minute Check and a teaching aid for this lesson.

INTRODUCING THE LESSON

🕐 5-Minute Check

(over Lesson 16-8)

1. Solve the triangle with $b = 3$, $c = 5$, and $B = 36°52'$ using the Law of Sines. $a = 4$, $A = 53°08'$, $C = 90°$

Other Prerequisite Skills

State whether the measurements given are possible.

2. $\triangle ABC$ with $AB = 6$, $BC = 2$, and $AC = 12$. **no**
3. $\triangle ABC$ with $\angle A = 30°$, $\angle B = 56°$, and $\angle C = 84°$. **no**
4. $\triangle ABC$ with $\angle C = 90°$, $\angle A = 60°$, $AB = 6$, and $BC = 3\sqrt{3}$. **yes**

Motivating the Lesson

Tell students that it is always a good idea to estimate how much you have spent while shopping before checking out. Show students a short receipt with the total removed and read the purchase amounts to them. Ask them which total is most reasonable, (0.1 the total), (actual total), or (10 times the total). Point out that the solution must realistically fit the data.

ALTERNATE TEACHING STRATEGIES

Using Models

Have students draw a base line on a piece of paper and mark a point on it, which will be the vertex of angle A. Give students two pieces of drinking straw of different lengths. These will be a and b. For those two pieces, have students complete an activity similar to that above, determining the solution set for the triangle, depending on the value of A.

TEACHING THE LESSON

Teaching Tip ❶ You may want to mention that this case is also called the *ambiguous case* since two solutions exist.

Chalkboard Examples

For Example 1

Solve each triangle described below.

a. $A = 50°$, $b = 10$, $a = 2$
Since $50° < 90°$ and $2 < 7.66$, **no solution exists.**

b. $A = 70°$, $a = 6$, $b = 11$
Since $70° < 90°$ and $6 < 10.34$, **no solution exists.**

For Example 2

Solve the triangle where $A = 32°$, $a = 7$, $b = 11$. **Solution I: $B = 123°37'$, $C = 24°23'$, $c = 5.5$; Solution II: $B = 56°23'$, $C = 91°37'$, $c = 13.2$**

Example 1

Solve the triangle where $A = 40°$, $b = 12$, and $a = 5$.

$$b \sin A = 12 \sin 40°$$
$$\approx 12(0.6428)$$
$$\approx 7.7136$$

Since $40° < 90°$ and $5 < 7.7136$, no solution exists.
Check this solution by trying to draw this triangle.

Example 2

Solve the triangle where $A = 58°$, $a = 26$, and $b = 29$.

$$b \sin A = 29 \sin 58°$$
$$\approx 29(0.8480)$$
$$\approx 24.5920$$

Since $58° < 90°$ and $24.5920 < 26 < 29$, there are two solutions.

$$\frac{\sin 58°}{26} = \frac{\sin B}{29} \qquad \text{Use the Law of Sines.}$$
$$\sin B = \frac{29 \sin 58°}{26} \qquad \sin 58° \approx 0.8480$$
$$\approx 0.9458$$

$B \approx 71°3'$ or $108°57'$ *Round to the nearest minute.*

Solution I: $m\angle B \approx 71°3'$ Solution II: $m\angle B \approx 108°57'$

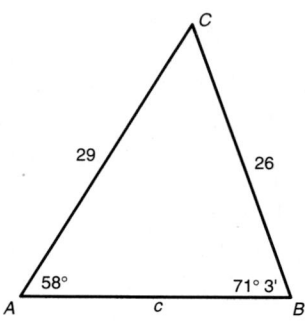
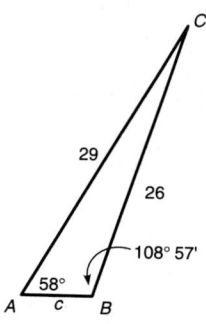

$$58° + 71°3' + C \approx 180°$$
$$C \approx 50°57'$$

$$c \approx \frac{26 \sin 50°57'}{\sin 58°} \quad \sin 50°57' \approx 0.7875$$
$$\approx 24.1 \quad \text{Round to the nearest tenth.}$$

One solution is $B \approx 71°3'$, $C \approx 50°57'$, and $c \approx 24.1$.

$$58° + 108°57' + C \approx 180°$$
$$C \approx 13°3'$$

$$c \approx \frac{26 \sin 13°3'}{\sin 58°} \quad \sin 13°3' \approx 0.2258$$
$$\approx 7.0 \quad \text{Round to the nearest tenth.}$$

Another solution is $B \approx 108°57'$, $C \approx 13°3'$, and $c \approx 7.0$.

RETEACHING THE LESSON

Working in groups, have each group work a problem to determine the number of solutions, and if a solution exists, to solve the triangle. Have one person from each group explain their answer to the class. No one in the group should know who is going to explain, so that all the members make sure they understand the group's solution.

Example 3

APPLICATION

Engineering

Kira was given an assignment to draw and then construct a triangular model of three steel girders for her engineering class. Two of the girders measured 7 cm and 6 cm, and the angle opposite the 7 cm girder had to be 30°. Could she construct the triangle? If so, how long did the third girder have to be?

$a = 7$, $b = 6$, and $A = 30°$.

Since $30° < 90°$ and $7 > 6$, one solution exists. There is one way that Kira can construct the triangle.

$\dfrac{\sin 30°}{7} = \dfrac{\sin B}{6}$ *Use the Law of Sines.*

$\sin B = \dfrac{6 \sin 30°}{7}$ *$\sin 30° = 0.5000$.*

$\sin B \approx 0.4286$

$B \approx 25°23'$ *Round to the nearest minute.*

$30° + 25°23' + C \approx 180°$
$C \approx 124°37'$

$\dfrac{\sin 30°}{7} = \dfrac{\sin 124°37'}{c}$ *$\sin 124°37' \approx 0.8230$*

$c = \dfrac{7 \sin 124°37'}{\sin 30°} \approx 11.5$ *Round to the nearest tenth.*

Kira should make a triangle with $B \approx 25°23'$, $C \approx 124°37'$, and $c \approx 11.5$.

CHECKING FOR UNDERSTANDING

Communicating Mathematics

Read and study the lesson to answer these questions.

1. When you are given the lengths of two sides of a triangle and the measurement of the angle opposite one of them, how many possible solutions to the triangle are there? **none, one, or two**

2. If you are given a, b, and A for a triangle and $A > 90°$, how many solutions are possible for this triangle? **none or one**

3. You are given a, b, and A for a triangle. $a \le b$ and $A < 90°$. What can you say about this triangle? **No solution exists.**

Guided Practice
Teaching Tip ❷

Determine the number of possible solutions for each triangle ABC described. If a solution exists, solve the triangle. **4–13. See margin.**

4. $a = 6$, $b = 8$, $A = 150°$

5. $a = 6$, $b = 8$, $A = 36°52'$

6. $a = 64$, $c = 90$, $C = 98°$

7. $a = 12$, $b = 19$, $A = 57°$

8. $a = 9$, $b = 20$, $A = 31°$

9. $a = 12$, $b = 14$, $A = 90°$

10. $a = 125$, $b = 150$, $A = 25°$

11. $A = 40°$, $b = 16$, $a = 10$

12. $a = 18$, $b = 20$, $A = 120°$

13. $A = 40°$, $b = 10$, $a = 8$

LESSON 16-9   PROBLEM-SOLVING STRATEGY: EXAMINE THE SOLUTION   773

Additional Answers

4. none

5. 2; $B = 53°7'$, $C = 90°1'$, $c = 10$; $B = 126°53'$, $C = 16°15'$, $c = 2.8$

6. 1; $A = 44°46'$, $B = 37°14'$, $b = 54.99$

7. none

8. none

9. none

10. 2; $B = 30°28'$, $C = 124°32'$, $c = 243.66$; $B = 149°32'$, $C = 5°28'$, $c = 28.18$

11. none

12. none

13. 2; $B = 53°28'$, $C = 86°32'$, $c = 12.4$; $B = 126°32'$, $C = 13°28'$, $c = 2.9$

Chalkboard Example

For Example 3
Solve the triangle where $A = 50°$, $b = 8$, $a = 12$. $B = 30°43'$, $C = 99°17'$, $c = 15.5$.

EVALUATING THE LESSON

Checking for Understanding

Exercises 1–13 are designed to help you assess understanding through reading, writing, and speaking. You should work through Exercises 1–3 with your students, and then monitor their work on Exercises 4–13.

Teaching Tip ❷   Encourage the use of diagrams and calculators where needed to solve the problems.

Closing the Lesson

Speaking Activity   Have students tell in their own words how to determine the number of solutions if given the measurements of two sides of a triangle and an angle opposite one of the given sides.

EXERCISES

Solve. Use any method.

14. Kirby needed to draw a triangle for his geometry class. He made one side 40 mm long. Another side was 32 mm long with the angle opposite measuring 48°19′. What was the length of the third side?

15. Simplify $\left[\left(\frac{1}{2}\right)^{-1} + \left(\frac{1}{3}\right)^{-1} + \left(\frac{1}{4}\right)^{-1} + \left(\frac{1}{5}\right)^{-1}\right]^{-1} \cdot \frac{1}{14}$

16. Donna changed the three on a die to a five. On another die, she changed the one to a three. What is the probability of rolling a sum of 6 with these two dice? $\frac{1}{12}$ **or approximately 0.0833**

17. The Cox family is making a triangular deck in their backyard. Two of the pieces of lumber they have to make the deck are 20 feet and 15 feet. If the angle opposite the 15-foot piece is to be 61°, can they construct the deck? If so, how long must the third piece of lumber be? **no solution**

18. Paul, Eric, and Garnet are playing a card game. They have a rule that when a player loses a hand, he must subtract enough points from his score to double each of the other player's scores. First Paul loses a hand, then Eric, and then Garnet. Each player now has 8 points. Who lost the most points? **Paul**

19. Sarah rolls two dice and finds the product of the numbers on the faces. What is the most likely product? **6 or 12**

20. The shapes below can be folded to make dice. Show how to fill in the missing numbers so that the numbers on opposite faces have a sum of 7.

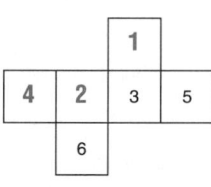 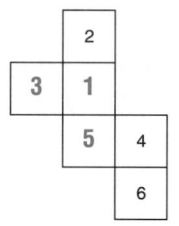 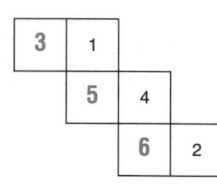

21. Insert operational symbols, +, −, ×, or ÷, and parentheses if necessary to make a true equation from 6 3 6 2 4 = 5. **Answers may vary. A sample answer is 6 + 3 − 6 − 2 + 4 = 5.**

COOPERATIVE LEARNING ACTIVITY

Work in groups. Each person in the group must understand the solution and be able to explain it to any person in class.

Construct a triangle with three altitudes of length 3 cm, 5 cm, and 6 cm. Can you construct a triangle whose altitudes are 2 cm, 6 cm, and 9 cm? Explain your answer. **For first triangle, see students' work. The second triangle is impossible. See Solutions Manual for explanation.**

774 CHAPTER 16 TRIGONOMETRIC FUNCTIONS

EXTENDING THE LESSON

Math Power: Communication

Have students verbalize how to solve the following problem and then solve it. The shorter side of a parallelogram is 4.4 cm, and the shorter diagonal is 6.2 cm. If the greatest angle of the parallelogram is 124°, find the perimeter. **Explanations will vary. about 23.8 cm**

Cooperative Learning Activity

This activity provides students with an opportunity to *learn* things together, not just do things together. You may wish to refer to pages T22–T23 and page 730c for the various elements of cooperative groups and specific goals and strategies for using them.

16-10 Law of Cosines

Objective
16-10

After studying this lesson, you should be able to:
- solve triangles and problems using the Law of Cosines.

Application

A pilot is flying from Chicago, Illinois to Columbus, Ohio, a distance of 300 miles. She starts her flight 15° off course and flies on this course for 75 miles. How far is she from Columbus?

Problems like this, where two sides of a triangle and an included angle are given, cannot be solved using the Law of Sines. You will use another formula, the **Law of Cosines** to solve this problem in Example 2.

Consider $\triangle ABC$ with height h units and sides with lengths a units, b units, and c units. Suppose segment AD is x units long. Then segment DC is $(b - x)$ units long.

Teaching Tip ❶

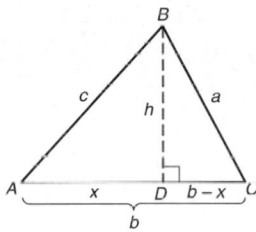

How are A, a, b, and c related?

$$
\begin{aligned}
a^2 &= (b - x)^2 + h^2 && \textit{Use the Pythagorean Theorem for } \triangle BDC. \\
&= b^2 - 2bx + x^2 + h^2 && \textit{Expand } (b - x)^2. \\
&= b^2 - 2bx + c^2 && \textit{In } \triangle ADB, c^2 = x^2 + h^2. \\
&= b^2 - 2b(c \cos A) + c^2 && \cos A = \frac{x}{c}, \textit{ so } x = c \cos A. \\
&= b^2 + c^2 - 2bc \cos A
\end{aligned}
$$

You can find two other formulas relating the lengths of sides to the cosine of B and C in a similar way. All three formulas, can be summarized as follows.

Law of Cosines

Let $\triangle ABC$ be any triangle with a, b, and c representing the measures of sides opposite angles with measurement A, B, and C respectively. Then, the following equations hold true.

$$a^2 = b^2 + c^2 - 2bc \cos A$$
$$b^2 = a^2 + c^2 - 2ac \cos B$$
$$c^2 = a^2 + b^2 - 2ab \cos C$$

LESSON 16-10   LAW OF COSINES   775

ALTERNATE TEACHING STRATEGIES

Using Discussion

Have initial classroom discussion concentrate primarily on development and use of the Law of Cosines. As you proceed through the examples, informally review the concepts learned in previous lessons in the chapter. Emphasize an integrated approach to problem solving that incorporates all skills in an approach that is both appropriate and efficient.

Lesson Resources

Reteaching Master 16-10
Practice Master 16-10
Enrichment Master 16-10
Activity Master, p. 34

 Transparency 16-10 contains the 5-Minute Check and a teaching aid for this lesson.

INTRODUCING THE LESSON

⏱ 5-Minute Check

(over Lesson 16-9)
Determine the number of possible solutions. If a solution exists, solve the triangle.

1. $a = 7$, $b = 6$, $A = 30°$
   1; $B = 25°22'$, $C = 124°38'$, $c = 11.52$
2. $b = 40$, $a = 32$, $A = 125°20'$
   No solutions exist.
3. $a = 26$, $b = 29$, $A = 58°$
   2; $B = 71°04'$, $C = 50°56'$, $c = 23.8$; $B = 108°56'$, $C = 13°04'$, $c = 6.93$

Motivating the Lesson

Tell students that a boy has built a two-sided ramp, with different slopes on each side. The top angle and the length of each side are known. Ask students to explain why the Law of Sines could not be used to solve this problem.

TEACHING THE LESSON

Teaching Tip ❶   Point out that this is another use of the Pythagorean Theorem.

Teaching Tip ❷ Point out that each form of the Law of Cosines uses four different variables. If any three of these are known, the fourth can be found.

Chalkboard Example

For Example 1
Solve each triangle.

a. $A = 38°$, $b = 6$, $c = 10$
   $a = 6.4$, $B = 35°15'$,
   $C = 106°45'$

b. $a = 15$, $b = 16$, $C = 23°$
   $c = 6.3$, $A = 68°29'$,
   $B = 88°31'$

Teaching Tip ❸ Point out how both laws may be used together to solve a triangle.

Teaching Tip ❷ You can use the Law of Cosines to solve a triangle in the following cases.

1. To find the length of the third side of any triangle if the lengths of two sides and the measurement of the included angle are given.

2. To find the measurement of an angle of a triangle if the lengths of the three sides are given.

Example 1

Solve each triangle. Round lengths to the nearest hundredth and angle measures to the nearest minute. Teaching Tip ❸

a. $A = 51°$, $b = 40$, $c = 45$

First, determine a using the Law of Cosines.

$a^2 = b^2 + c^2 - 2bc \cos A$ *Use the Law of Cosines.*
$a^2 = 40^2 + 45^2 - 2(40)(45) \cos 51°$ *$A = 51°$, $b = 40$, $c = 45$*
$a^2 = 1359.45$
$a \approx 36.87$

Next, use the Law of Sines to determine the measure of a second angle.

$\dfrac{\sin A}{a} = \dfrac{\sin B}{b}$ *Use the Law of Sines.*

$\dfrac{\sin 51°}{36.87} \approx \dfrac{\sin B}{40}$ *$a \approx 36.87$, $A = 51°$, $b = 40$*

$\sin B \approx \dfrac{40 \sin 51°}{36.87}$ *$\sin 51° \approx 0.7771$*

$\sin B \approx 0.8431$
$B \approx 57°28'$ *Round to the nearest minute.*

Finally, determine the measure of the third angle.

$51° + 57°28' + C \approx 180°$
$C \approx 71°32'$

Therefore, $a \approx 36.87$, $B \approx 57°28'$, and $C \approx 71°32'$.

b. $a = 5$, $b = 6$, and $c = 7$

First, use the Law of Cosines to find the measure of an angle.

$a^2 = b^2 + c^2 - 2bc \cos A$ *Use the Law of Cosines.*
$5^2 = 6^2 + 7^2 - 2(6)(7) \cos A$ *$a = 5$, $b = 6$, $c = 7$*
$2(6)(7) \cos A = 6^2 + 7^2 - 5^2$
$\cos A = \dfrac{6^2 + 7^2 - 5^2}{2(6)(7)}$
$\cos A \approx 0.7143$
$A \approx 44°25'$ *Round to the nearest minute.*

Next, use the Law of Sines to determine the measure of another angle.

$$\frac{\sin A}{a} = \frac{\sin B}{b} \qquad \textit{Use the Law of Sines.}$$

$$\frac{\sin 44°25'}{5} \approx \frac{\sin B}{6} \qquad a = 5,\, b = 6,\, A \approx 44°25'$$

$$\sin B \approx \frac{6 \sin 44°25'}{5}$$

$$\sin B \approx 0.8398$$

$$B \approx 57°7' \qquad \textit{Round to the nearest minute.}$$

Finally, determine the measure of the third angle.

$$44°25' + 57°7' + C \approx 180°$$

$$C \approx 78°28'$$

Therefore, $A \approx 44°25'$, $B \approx 57°7'$, and $C \approx 78°28'$.

Example 2

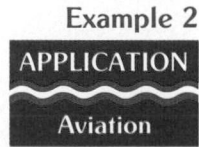

APPLICATION

Aviation

A pilot is flying from Chicago to Columbus, a distance of 300 miles. She starts her flight 15° off course and flies on this course for 75 miles. How far is she from Columbus? *This is the application presented on page 775.*

First, draw a diagram that represents the situation.

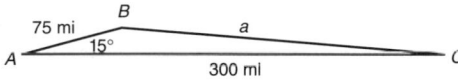

Since you know the measure of two sides and the included angle, use the Law of Cosines.

$A = 15°$, $b = 300$ miles, and $c = 75$ miles.

$$a^2 = b^2 + c^2 - 2bc \cos A$$

$$a^2 = 300^2 + 75^2 - 2(300)(75) \cos 15° \qquad \textit{Use the Law of Cosines.}$$

$$a^2 \approx 52{,}158.34$$

$$a \approx 228.38 \qquad \text{The pilot is about 228 miles from Columbus.}$$

CHECKING FOR UNDERSTANDING

Communicating Mathematics

Read and study the lesson to answer these questions. **length of third side**

1. What measures can you find using the Law of Cosines in a triangle if the lengths of two sides and the measurement of the included angle are given?

2. What measures can you find using the Law of Cosines in a triangle if the lengths of all three sides are given? **any of the angles**

3. How do you know when to use the Law of Cosines and when to use the Law of Sines to solve a triangle? **See margin.**

4. By what angle will the pilot in Example 2 have to correct her path to reach Columbus? **19°53'**

LESSON 16-10 LAW OF COSINES 777

RETEACHING THE LESSON

Have students work the following problem: The distance between three cities, A, B, and C are $AB = 120$ km, $AC = 50$ km, and $BC = 150$ km. C is due west of A. In what direction is B from A if B is north of the line through A and C? Have students find the other angle measures too, in order to verify their answer, remembering that the sum of the angles of a triangle is 180°. **N28°E**

Chalkboard Example

For Example 2
The sides of a triangle measure 16 cm, 20 cm, and 32 cm. Find the measure of the largest angle. **125°06'**

EVALUATING THE LESSON

Checking for Understanding
Exercises 1–12 are designed to help you assess understanding through reading, writing, and speaking. You should work through Exercises 1–4 with your students, and then monitor their work on Exercises 5–12.

Additional Answer
3. **Law of Cosines: given all three sides or two sides and the included angle; Law of Sines: given two sides and a non-included angle or two angles and a side**

Reteaching Masters Booklet, p. 112

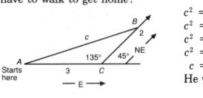

16-10 **Reteaching Worksheet**
NAME _____ DATE _____
Law of Cosines

The Law of Cosines

Let $\triangle ABC$ be any triangle with a, b, and c representing the measures of sides opposite angles with measurements A, B, and C, respectively. Then, the following equations are true.
$$a^2 = b^2 + c^2 - 2bc \cos A$$
$$b^2 = a^2 + c^2 - 2ac \cos B$$
$$c^2 = a^2 + b^2 - 2ab \cos C$$

Use the law of cosines to solve a triangle in the following cases.
1. To find the length of the third side of any triangle if the lengths of two sides and the measurement of the included angle are given.
2. To find the measurement of an angle of a triangle if the lengths of three sides are given.

Example: A hiker walks 3 miles due east from his house. He then turns 45° and walks 2 miles northeast. How far will he have to walk to get home?

$$c^2 = a^2 + b^2 - 2ab \cos C$$
$$c^2 = 2^2 + 3^2 - 2(2)(3) \cos 135°$$
$$c^2 = 4 + 9 - 12(-0.7071)$$
$$c^2 = 21.4852$$
$$c = 4.64$$
He will have to walk 4.64 miles.

Solve each triangle described below.
1. $a = 14$, $c = 20$, $B = 38°$
   $b = 12.44$, $A = 43°52'$,
   $C = 98°8'$
2. $A = 60°$, $c = 17$, $b = 12$
   $a = 15.13$, $B = 43°23'$,
   $C = 76°37'$
3. $a = 4$, $b = 6$, $c = 3$
   $A = 36°20'$, $B = 117°17'$,
   $C = 26°23'$
4. $A = 20°$, $b = 100$, $c = 84$
   $a = 35.63$, $B = 73°43'$,
   $C = 86°17'$
5. A diver leaps 2.5 feet off the board and jackknifes 10 feet into the water at an angle of 20°. How far from the edge of the board does she enter the water?
   7.70 feet
6. Some children set up a tepee in the woods. The poles are 7 feet long, and the children want the distance between adjacent poles to be 4 feet at the base. How wide must the angle be between the poles?
   33°12'

Chapter 16 777

Closing the Lesson

Writing Activity Have students write a short paragraph explaining how they would know whether to use the Law of Sines or the Law of Cosines to solve a problem.

APPLYING THE LESSON

Homework Exercises

Assignment Guide

Basic: 13–28, 32–34, 37–40
Average: 15–29, 32–40
Enriched: 17–40

Chapter 16, Quiz D, (Lessons 16-8 through 16-10), is available in the Evaluation Masters Booklet, p. 220.

Practice Masters Booklet, p. 128

Guided Practice

5. sines; $b = 14.7$, $B = 109°3'$, $C = 30°57'$
6. cosines; $a = 4.5$, $B = 58°59'$, $C = 81°1'$
7. cosines; $b = 18.5$, $A = 40°57'$, $C = 79°3'$
8. cosines; $A = 53°35'$, $B = 59°33'$, $C = 65°52'$
9. sines; $a = 9.6$, $b = 14$, $B = 70°$
10. cosines; $c = 6.5$, $A = 76°5'$, $B = 68°55'$
11. sines; $c = 23.3$, $A = 26°10'$, $C = 110°52'$
12. sines; $a = 26.4$, $b = 31.2$, $B = 101°26'$

Determine whether the Law of Sines or the Law of Cosines should be used first to solve each triangle described below. Then solve each triangle.

5. $a = 10, A = 40°, c = 8$
6. $A = 40°, b = 6, c = 7$
7. $a = 14, c = 21, B = 60°$
8. $a = 14, b = 15, c = 16$
9. $A = 40°, C = 70°, c = 14$
10. $a = 11, b = 10.5, C = 35°$
11. $a = 11, b = 17, B = 42°58'$
12. $A = 56°, C = 22°34', c = 12.2$

EXERCISES

Practice

Solve each triangle described below. **13–26. See margin.**

13. $A = 35°, b = 16, c = 19$
14. $a = 140, b = 185, c = 166$
15. $a = 5, b = 12, c = 13$
16. $a = 20, c = 24, B = 47°$

17. $a = 21.5, b = 13, C = 38°20'$
18. $A = 40°, B = 59°, c = 14$
19. $a = 51, c = 61, B = 19°$
20. $a = 13.7, A = 25°26', B = 78°$
21. $a = 11, b = 13, c = 15$
22. $a = 345, b = 648, c = 442$
23. $c = 10.3, a = 21.5, b = 16.71$
24. $A = 28°50', b = 5, c = 4.9$
25. $A = 29°, b = 7.6, c = 14.1$
26. $a = 8, b = 24, c = 18$

27. Two sides of a triangular plot of land have lengths of 400 feet and 600 feet. The measurement of the angle between those sides is 46°20'. Find the perimeter and the area of the plot. **1434.26 ft; 86,804.28 ft²**

CONNECTION
Geometry

28. The sides of a triangle are 6.8 cm, 8.4 cm, and 4.9 cm. Find the measure of the smallest angle. **35°41'**

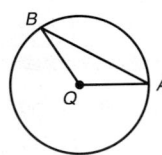

29. The sides of a parallelogram are 55 cm and 71 cm. Find the length of each diagonal if the larger angle measures 106°. **76.90 cm, 101.09 cm**

30. Circle Q has a radius of 15 cm. Two radii, $\overline{QA}$ and $\overline{QB}$, form an angle of 123°. Find the length of chord $\overline{AB}$. **26.4 cm**

31. The sides of a triangular lot are 50 meters, 70 meters, and 85 meters. Find the measure of the angle opposite the shortest side. **36°1'**

Critical Thinking

32. A triangle has angles that measure 48°, 79°, and 53°. Can you find the measures of the sides? If not, why not? **no; multiple solutions, you can however, determine the ratio of the three sides**

Additional Answers

13. $a = 10.91, B = 57°16',$ $C = 87°44'$
14. $A = 46°37', B = 73°50',$ $C = 59°33'$
15. $A = 22°37', B = 67°23',$ $C = 90°$
16. $b = 17.92, A = 54°42',$ $C = 78°18'$
17. $c = 13.88, A = 106°9',$ $B = 35°31'$
18. $C = 81°, a = 9.11, b = 12.15$
19. $b = 20.95, A = 52°25',$ $C = 108°35'$
20. $b = 31.20, C = 76°34',$ $c = 31.03$
21. $A = 45°34', B = 57°34',$ $C = 76°52'$
22. $A = 29°58', B = 110°15',$ $C = 39°47'$

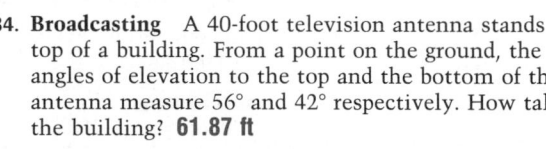

Applications 33. **Navigation** Two ships, the *Indiana* and the *Hoggett Bay*, left San Francisco at noon. The *Indiana* traveled 40° north of west at a speed of 20 knots. The *Hoggett Bay* traveled 10° west of south at a speed of 15 knots. How far apart will they be at 11:00 P.M.? (1 knot = 1 nautical mile per hour) **334.6 nautical miles**

34. **Broadcasting** A 40-foot television antenna stands on top of a building. From a point on the ground, the angles of elevation to the top and the bottom of the antenna measure 56° and 42° respectively. How tall is the building? **61.87 ft**

35. **Aviation** Ed Gallagher flew his plane 1200 kilometers north before turning 15° clockwise. He flew 850 kilometers in that direction and then landed. How far is Mr. Gallagher from his starting point? **2033 km**

36. **Navigation** A ship at sea is 70 miles from one radio transmitter and 130 miles from another. The measurement of the angle between the signals is 130°. How far apart are the transmitters? **183.03 miles**

Mixed Review 37. **Statistics** The estimated populations for 1990 of selected metropolitan areas in the U.S. are listed in the table below. Make a back-to-back stem-and-leaf plot of the rounded and truncated values of the data. (Lesson 14-2) **See margin.**

Capital City	Pop. (thousands)	Capital City	Pop. (thousands)
Albany, NY	874	Honolulu, HI	836
Austin, TX	782	Jackson, MS	395
Baton Rouge, LA	528	Little Rock, AR	513
Boulder, CO	225	Madison, WI	367
Charleston, WV	250	Montgomery, AL	293
Des Moines, IA	393	Oklahoma City, OK	959
Harrisburg, PA	588	Salem, OR	278
Hartford, CT	768	Sarasota, FL	278

Portfolio
Select some of your work from this chapter that shows how you used a calculator or computer. Place it in your portfolio.

38. Solve $\log_x \sqrt{5} = \frac{1}{4}$. (Lesson 12-2) **25**

39. Simplify $\dfrac{x^2 + 49}{x^2 - 49} + \dfrac{x}{7 - x} + \dfrac{7}{x + 7}$. (Lesson 11-4) **0**

40. Find the inverse of the function $g(x) = (x - 4)^2$. (Lesson 10-8)
$y = \pm\sqrt{x} + 4$

LESSON 16-10 LAW OF COSINES 779

EXTENDING THE LESSON

Math Power:
Problem Solving

Find the area of a regular octagon inscribed in a circle whose radius measures 6 mm. **about 101.8 mm²**

SUMMARY AND REVIEW

VOCABULARY

Upon completing this chapter, you should be familiar with the following terms:

adjacent side	756	767	Law of Sines
angle of depression	762	751	minutes
angle of elevation	762	756	opposite side
Arccosine	747	739	period
Arcsine	747	739	periodic function
Arctangent	747	746	principal value
cosecant	742	733	radian
cosine	736	742	secant
cotangent	742	736	sine
coterminal	733	732	standard position
gradian	754	742	tangent
hypotenuse	756	732	terminal side
initial side	732	733	unit circle
Law of Cosines	775		

SKILLS AND CONCEPTS

OBJECTIVES AND EXAMPLES	REVIEW EXERCISES

Upon completing this chapter, you should be able to:

Use these exercises to review and prepare for the chapter test.

- change radian measure to degree measure and vice versa. **(Lesson 16-1)**

Change the degree measure 240° to radians.

$$240 \cdot \frac{\pi}{180} = \frac{240\pi}{180} \text{ or } \frac{4\pi}{3}$$

Change the radian measure $-\frac{4\pi}{3}$ to degrees.

$$-\frac{4\pi}{3} \cdot \frac{180}{\pi} = \left(-\frac{720\pi}{3\pi}\right)^{\circ} \text{ or } -240°$$

Change each degree measure to radians.

1. 255° $\frac{17\pi}{12}$ 2. −315° $-\frac{7\pi}{4}$

3. 270° $\frac{3\pi}{2}$ 4. 120° $\frac{2\pi}{3}$

Change each radian measure to degrees.

5. $\frac{\pi}{3}$ 60°   6. $\frac{7\pi}{4}$ 315°

7. $-\frac{5\pi}{12}$ −75°   8. $\frac{4}{3}$ $\frac{240°}{\pi}$

OBJECTIVES AND EXAMPLES	REVIEW EXERCISES

- evaluate expressions involving sine and cosine. **(Lesson 16-2)**

Find sin 570°.

$$\sin 570° = \sin(210 + 360)°$$
$$= \sin 210°$$
$$= -\frac{1}{2}$$

Find each value.

9. $\cos 210°$ $-\frac{\sqrt{3}}{2}$ 10. $\cos 3\pi$ -1

11. $\sin(-150°)$ $-\frac{1}{2}$ 12. $\sin\frac{5}{4}\pi$ $-\frac{\sqrt{2}}{2}$

13. $\cos(-135°)$ $-\frac{\sqrt{2}}{2}$ 14. $\cos 300°$ $\frac{1}{2}$

15. $(\sin 30°)^2 + (\cos 30°)^2$ 1

16. $(\sin 45°)(\sin 225°)$ $-\frac{1}{2}$

- find the values of other trigonometric functions. **(Lesson 16-3)**

Find tan 150°.

$$\tan 150° = \frac{\sin 150°}{\cos 150°}$$
$$= \frac{\frac{1}{2}}{\frac{\sqrt{3}}{2}}$$
$$= -\frac{1}{\sqrt{3}} \text{ or } -\frac{\sqrt{3}}{3}$$

Find each value.

17. $\csc 135°$ $\sqrt{2}$ 18. $\csc \pi$ **undefined**

19. $\sec(-30°)$ $\frac{2\sqrt{3}}{3}$ 20. $\cot\frac{7}{6}\pi$ $\sqrt{3}$

21. $\tan 120°$ $-\sqrt{3}$ 22. $\sec(-60°)$ 2

- find the value of expressions involving trigonometric functions. **(Lesson 16-4)**

Find $\cos^{-1}\left(-\frac{\sqrt{3}}{2}\right)$.

$$\theta = \cos^{-1}\left(-\frac{\sqrt{3}}{2}\right)$$
$$\cos\theta = -\frac{\sqrt{3}}{2}$$
$$\theta = \frac{5\pi}{6}$$

Find each value. 28. $\frac{\sqrt{3}}{2}$

23. $\sin^{-1}(-1)$ $-90°$ 24. $\cos^{-1}\left(\frac{\sqrt{3}}{2}\right)$ $30°$

25. $\tan^{-1}\sqrt{3}$ $60°$ 26. $\sin^{-1}\left(\tan\frac{\pi}{4}\right)$ $90°$

27. $\cos(\sin^{-1}1)$ 0 28. $\sin\left(2\sin^{-1}\frac{1}{2}\right)$

- use a calculator to find values of trigonometric functions. **(Lesson 16-5)**

If sin x = 0.5346, find x.

ENTER:

0.5346 $\boxed{\text{SIN}^{-1}}$ 32.3167847

Therefore, x is approximately 32.3167°.

Use a calculator to find each value. Round your answers to four decimal places.

29. $\cos x = 0.7924$ 30. $\csc x = 1.3729$
   37.5896°   **46.7512°**

31. $\left(\cos\frac{2\pi}{3}\right)\left(\sin\frac{\pi}{4}\right)$ -0.3536

32. $\tan[\cos^{-1}0.8 + \sin^{-1}(-0.4)]$ 0.2362

The Cumulative Review shown below can be used to review skills and concepts presented thus far in the text. Standardized Test Practice Questions are also provided in the Evaluation Masters Booklet.

Evaluation Masters Booklet, pp. 221–222

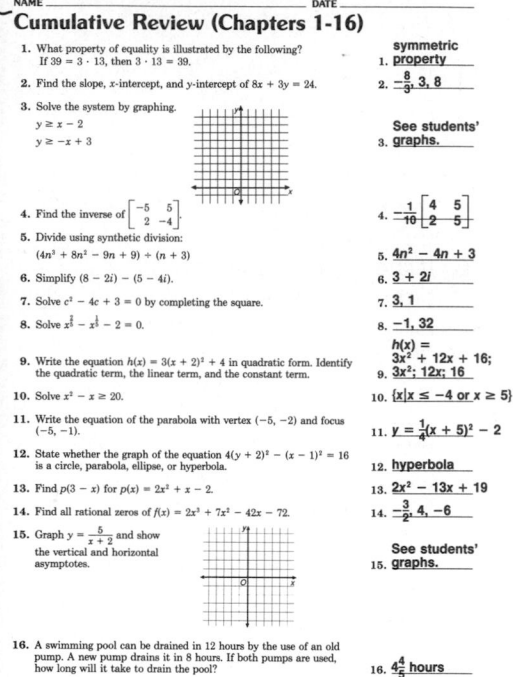
- solve problems involving right triangles using right triangle trigonometry. (Lesson 16-6)

Solve the right triangle.

$\frac{a}{14} = \sin 42°$ \qquad $\frac{b}{14} = \cos 42°$

$a \approx 9.4$ \qquad\qquad $b \approx 10.4$

$B = 90° - 42°$ or $48°$

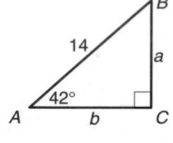

- solve triangles using the Law of Sines. (Lesson 16-8)

According to the Law of Sines,

$$\frac{\sin A}{a} = \frac{\sin B}{b} = \frac{\sin C}{c}.$$

- solve triangles using the Law of Cosines. (Lesson 16-10)

According to the Law of Cosines,
$a^2 = b^2 + c^2 - 2bc \cos A$
$b^2 = a^2 + c^2 - 2ac \cos B$
$c^2 = a^2 + b^2 - 2ab \cos C$

Solve $\triangle ABC$ (with right angle C). Round lengths to the nearest tenth and angle measures to the nearest minute.

33. If $c = 16$ and $a = 7$, find b.   **14.4**
34. If $a = 7$ and $b = 12$, find A.   **30°15'**
35. If $b = 10$ and $c = 20$, find a.   **17.3**
36. If $a = b$ and $c = 12$, find B.   **45°**
37. If $A = 25°$ and $c = 6$, find b.   **5.4**
38. If $a = 1$ and $b = 3$, find A.   **18°26'**

Use the Law of Sines to solve each triangle described below. 39–42. See margin.

39. $A = 83°10'$, $a = 80$, $b = 10$
40. $A = 50°$, $b = 12$, $a = 10$
41. $B = 46°$, $C = 83°$, $b = 65$
42. $A = 45°$, $B = 30°$, $b = 20$

Use the Law of Cosines to solve each triangle described below. 43–46. See margin.

43. $C = 65°$, $a = 4$, $b = 7$
44. $b = 2$, $c = 5$, $A = 60°$
45. $a = 6$, $b = 7$, $C = 40°$
46. $B = 24°$, $a = 42$, $c = 6.5$

APPLICATIONS AND CONNECTIONS

47. **Aviation** A pilot 3000 feet above the ocean notes the measurement of the angle of depression to a ship is 42°. How far is the plane from the ship? (Lesson 16-7)   **4483.48 ft**

48. **Geometry** When Tracy stands 50 meters from the school's flagpole, the angle of elevation to the top measures 48°. How tall is the pole? (Lesson 16-7)   **55.53 m**

49. **Firefighting** A firefighter needs to use a 14-meter ladder to enter a window which is 13.5 meters above the ground. How far from the base of the building should the ladder be placed? (Lesson 16-7)   **3.7 m**

50. **Engineering** An engineering student is assigned to construct a triangular model of three steel girders. Two of the girders measured 20 cm and 15 cm, and the angle opposite the 15 cm girder had to be 61°. Could the model be made? If so, how long is the third girder? (Lesson 16-9)   **50. No solution exists.**

Additional Answers

39. $B = 7°8'$, $C = 89°42'$, $c = 80.57$
40. $c = 11.65$, $C = 63°11'$, $B = 66°49'$, $c = 3.78$, $C = 16°49'$, $B = 113°11'$
41. $A = 51°$, $a = 70.22$, $c = 89.69$
42. $C = 105°$, $a = 28.28$, $c = 38.64$
43. $c = 6.43$, $A = 34°19'$, $B = 80°41'$

44. $a = 4.36$, $B = 23°24'$, $C = 96°36'$
45. $c = 4.54$, $A = 58°4'$, $B = 81°56'$
46. $b = 36.16$, $A = 151°47'$, $C = 4°13'$

Change each degree measure to radians.

1. $-45°$ $-\dfrac{\pi}{4}$
2. $275°$ $\dfrac{55\pi}{36}$
3. $330°$ $\dfrac{11\pi}{6}$
4. $-600°$ $-\dfrac{10\pi}{3}$

Change each radian measure to degrees.

5. $-\dfrac{\pi}{6}$ $-30°$
6. $\dfrac{11}{2}\pi$ $990°$
7. $-\dfrac{7\pi}{4}$ $-315°$
8. $-2\dfrac{1}{3}$ $\dfrac{-420°}{\pi} \approx -133.69°$

Find each value.

9. $\cos(-120°)$ $-\dfrac{1}{2}$
10. $\sin\dfrac{7}{4}\pi$ $-\dfrac{\sqrt{2}}{2}$
11. $\cos\dfrac{3\pi}{4}$ $-\dfrac{\sqrt{2}}{2}$
12. $\sin 390°$ $\dfrac{1}{2}$

13. $\tan 135°$ -1
14. $\cot 300°$ $-\dfrac{\sqrt{3}}{3}$
15. $\sec\left(-\dfrac{7}{6}\pi\right)$ $-\dfrac{2\sqrt{3}}{3}$
16. $\csc\dfrac{5\pi}{6}$ 2

17. $\sin^{-1}\left(-\dfrac{\sqrt{3}}{2}\right)$ $-60°$
18. $\operatorname{Arctan} 1$ $45°$
19. $\operatorname{Cos}^{-1}(\sin -60°)$ $150°$
20. $\sin 2\left(\operatorname{Arccos}\dfrac{1}{2}\right)$ $\dfrac{\sqrt{3}}{2}$

Find the value of x to the nearest minute.

21. $\sin x = 0.6712$ $42°10'$
22. $\cos x = 0.1389$ $82°1'$
23. $\csc x = 1.2955$ $50°32'$
24. $\tan x = 0.8999$ $41°59'$

Solve each right triangle. Round lengths to the nearest tenth and angle measures to the nearest minute. 25–28. See margin.

25. $a = 7, A = 49°$
26. $a = 7, c = 16$
27. $B = 75°, b = 6$
28. $A = 22°, c = 8$

29. **Determine the number of possible solutions for a triangle where $A = 40°$, $b = 10$ and $a = 14$. If a solution exists, solve the triangle. 1; $B = 27°20'$, $C = 112°40'$, $c = 20.1$**

30. **Firefighting** A firefighter leaned a 32-foot ladder against a building. The top of the ladder touches the building 26 feet above the ground. What is the measurement of the angle formed between the ladder and the ground? **54°20'**

31. **Aviation** A plane flew 1000 kilometers north. Then it changed direction by turning 20° clockwise and flew for another 700 kilometers. How far was the plane from its starting point? **1675 km**

32. **Geology** From the top of a cliff, a geologist spots a dried river bed. The measurement of the angle of depression to the river bed is 70°. The cliff is 50 meters high. How far is the river bed from the base of the cliff? **18.2 m**

33. **Geometry** The longest side of a triangle is 23 yards. Two of the angles are 23° and 49°. Find the measures of the other two sides and the remaining angle. **9.45 yd, 18.25 yd, 108°**

Bonus Suppose $\sin x = 0.5660$ and the terminal side of angle x is in the second quadrant. Find the value of x to the nearest minute. **145°32'**

Using the Chapter Test

This page may be used as a test or as a review. In addition, two multiple-choice tests and two free-response tests are provided in the Evaluation Masters Booklet. Chapter 16 Test, Form 1A is shown below.

Evaluation Masters Booklet, pp. 211–212

NAME _____ DATE _____

Chapter 16 Test, Form 1A

Write the letter for the correct answer in the blank at the right of each problem.

1. What is 100° expressed in radians?
   A. $\dfrac{5}{9}$ B. $\dfrac{5\pi}{9}$ C. $\dfrac{10}{9}$ D. $\dfrac{10\pi}{9}$ 1. **B**

2. What is $\dfrac{5\pi}{4}$ radians expressed in degrees?
   A. $\dfrac{225}{\pi}$ B. $225°$ C. $\dfrac{112.5}{\pi}$ D. $112.5°$ 2. **B**

3. What is 4 radians expressed in degrees?
   A. $\dfrac{1}{45}°$ B. $\dfrac{\pi°}{45}$ C. $720°$ D. $\dfrac{720°}{\pi}$ 3. **D**

4. What is the least positive angle measure that is coterminal with $-400°$?
   A. $40°$ B. $80°$ C. $320°$ D. $400°$ 4. **C**

5. What is the value of $\cos\left(\dfrac{\pi}{4}\right)$?
   A. $\dfrac{\sqrt{2}}{2}$ B. $-\dfrac{\sqrt{2}}{2}$ C. $\dfrac{\sqrt{3}}{2}$ D. $-\dfrac{\sqrt{3}}{2}$ 5. **A**

6. What is the value of $\sec(-300°)$?
   A. $\dfrac{2\sqrt{3}}{3}$ B. 2 C. $-\dfrac{2\sqrt{3}}{3}$ D. -2 6. **B**

7. What is the value of $3\sin 120° \cos 120°$?
   A. $-\dfrac{3}{4}$ B. $-\dfrac{3\sqrt{3}}{4}$ C. $\dfrac{3}{4}$ D. $\dfrac{3\sqrt{3}}{4}$ 7. **B**

8. What is the value of $\cot 450°$?
   A. 0 B. undefined C. -1 D. 1 8. **A**

9. What is the value of $\operatorname{Tan}^{-1}(-1)$?
   A. $45°$ B. $-45°$ C. $135°$ and $315°$ D. $90°$ 9. **B**

10. What is the value of $2\csc(\operatorname{Cot}^{-1}\sqrt{3})$?
    A. 1 B. $\dfrac{1}{2}$ C. 2 D. 4 10. **D**

11. Use a calculator to find the value of $\cos 253°$. Round your answer to the nearest ten-thousandth.
    A. 0.9563 B. -0.7314 C. -0.0051 D. undefined   11. **B**

12. Use a calculator to find the value of x measured in degrees if $\csc x = 3.4892$. Round your answer to the nearest minute.
    A. $16°39'$ B. $73°21'$ C. $74°1'$ D. undefined   12. **A**

NAME _____ DATE _____

Chapter 16, Test Form 1A (continued)

For questions 13 and 14, refer to the diagram at the right.

13. What is the value of $\csc A$ to the nearest ten-thousandth?
    A. 2.1250 B. 1.1333 C. 1.8750 D. 0.5333 13. **B**

14. What is the value of $\cot B$ to the nearest ten-thousandth?
    A. 2.1250 B. 1.1333 C. 1.8750 D. 0.5333 14. **C**

15. Find the measure of $\angle A$ to the nearest degree in the triangle at the right.
    A. $49°$ B. $37°$ C. $41°$ D. $53°$ 15. **C**

16. Suppose that a and b are the lengths of two sides of a triangle and A is the measure of the angle opposite the side with measure a. Which of the following sets of conditions is it impossible to satisfy?
    A. $A < 90°, a > b\sin A$ B. $A < 90°, b\sin A < a < b$
    C. $A \geq 90°, a \leq b$ D. $A \geq 90°, a > b$ 16. **C**

17. Find the length of the longest side of a triangle with $A = 40°$, $B = 60°$, and $a = 5$.
    A. 6.43 B. 5 C. 6.74 D. 7.66 17. **D**

18. Find the measure of $\angle B$ in a triangle where $C = 30°$, $c = 22$, and $b = 42$.
    A. $72°40'$ B. $77°20'$ C. $72°40'$ and $107°20'$ D. no triangle possible   18. **C**

19. Which of the following could be the measure of $\angle C$ in a triangle with $A = 73°$, $a = 3$, and $c = 10$?
    A. $90°$ B. $77°$ C. $103°$ D. no triangle possible   19. **D**

20. An observer on Earth notes that the angle formed by her lines of sight to star A and star B is $40°$. It is known that star A is 15 light years from Earth. The distance from Earth to star B is 6 light years. What is the distance between the stars to the nearest light year?
    A. 11 B. 14 C. 9 D. 16 20. **A**

Bonus

Two cities are 10 miles apart. An object is seen hovering in the sky above the line joining the two cities. The angles of elevation of the object are 24° and 40°. What is the height of the object above the ground to the nearest tenth of a mile?
    A. 2.9 mi B. 4.5 mi C. 7.2 mi D. 9.5 mi   Bonus **A**

A **Test and Review Generator** is provided in Apple, IBM, and Macintosh versions. You may use this software to create your own tests or worksheets, based on the needs of your students.

The **Performance Assessment Booklet** provides an alternate assessment for evaluating student progress. An assessment for this chapter can be found on pages 31–32.

Additional Answers

25. $b = 6.1, c = 9.3, B = 41°$
26. $b = 14.4, A = 25°57'$, $B = 64°3'$
27. $c = 6.2, a = 1.6, A = 15°$
28. $a = 3.0, b = 7.4, B = 68°$

The test questions on these pages deal with a variety of concepts from arithmetic, algebra, and geometry.

Directions: Choose the one best answer. Write A, B, C, or D.

1. The length of a rectangle is 1 unit and
B the width is w. If the width is increased by 3 units, by how many units will the perimeter be increased?

   (A) 4   (B) 6

   (C) $2w + 3$ (D) $2w + 6$

2. O is the center of the circle below. $\overline{MO}$
A is perpendicular to $\overline{NO}$ and the area of triangle MON is 40. What is the area of circle O?

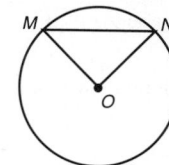

   (A) 80π (B) 40π (C) 20π (D) 160π

3. The distance between point $X(4, 0)$ and Y
D is 8. The coordinates of point Y could be any of the following except

   (A) $(-4, 0)$ (B) $(0, 4\sqrt{3})$

   (C) $(4, 8)$ (D) $(8, 0)$

4. $x^2 + y^2 = 16$
A $\quad\quad xy = 8$
   $(x + y)^2 = ?$

   (A) 32   (B) 22   (C) 16   (D) 24

5. If $x = -6$ and $\frac{1}{2y} = -12$, what is the
D value of y in terms of x?

   (A) $x - 6$ (B) $2x - 6$

   (C) $\frac{1}{2x}$ (D) $\frac{1}{4x}$

6. 5% of what number is 81?

B (A) 405   (B) 1620

   (C) 16,200   (D) 0.405

7. The area of triangle ABC is 16 square
B units. Angle C is 45°. What is AC?

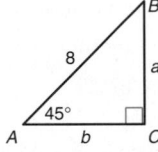

   (A) $16\sqrt{2}$ (B) $4\sqrt{2}$

   (C) $8\sqrt{2}$ (D) $24\sqrt{2}$

8. A person travels five miles north,
D fifteen miles west, and fifteen miles north. How far (to the nearest mile) is he from the starting point?

   (A) 35   (B) 30   (C) 30   (D) 25

9. If $n^2 - 4 = -3n$, what is the value of
B $\left(n + \frac{3}{2}\right)^2$?

   (A) 5   (B) $6\frac{1}{4}$ (C) 11

   (D) cannot be determined

10. If $x^2 = 25$, then 2^{x-1} could equal

D (A) 2   (B) 4   (C) 8   (D) 16

11. If $\frac{x}{6} > x$, which could be a value for x?

A

(A) -6 (B) 0

(C) 5 (D) 6

12. If $0 < n < 1$, which of the following
A increases as n increases?

  I. $1 - n^2$
  II. $n - 1$
  III. $\frac{1}{n^2}$

(A) II only

(B) III only

(C) I and III only

(D) II and III only

13. If $-a < 0 < -b$, which of the following
C is true?

(A) $0 < b < 0$

(B) $a < 0 < b$

(C) $b < 0 < a$

(D) $0 < b < a$

14. If b is an odd integer greater than one,
D which of the following must be an odd
integer?

(A) $b^3 - 1$

(B) $b^3 - b^2$

(C) $1 + b^3$

(D) $\frac{3b - 3}{b - 1}$

15. If k is any odd integer and $x = 6k$, then
A $\frac{x}{2}$ will always be

(A) odd (B) even

(C) positive (D) negative

16. If $a + b = 8$ and $3b - 4 = -13a$, then
C what is the value of a?

(A) $\frac{-13}{3}$ (B) -3

(C) -2 (D) 10

TEST TAKING TIP

You can prepare for taking a college entrance exam by working through practice tests such as this. The more you work with the material in a format similar to the actual test, the better you become in the art of test taking. Do not wait until the night before taking a college entrance exam to review. Allow yourself plenty of time in the weeks before taking a test to review the basic skills and formulas which are tested. Find your weaknesses so that you can seek help.

When taking a college entrance exam work quickly through the problems, skipping those problems which take more than the average amount of time allotted for doing a problem. Mark these in the test booklet and come back to them after you have completed the problems which you could easily do. Take time out after several problems to freshen your mind.

17. If $x > y$ and $z < 0$, which of the
C following are true?

  I. $xz < yz$
  II. $x + z > y + z$
  III. $x - z < y - z$

(A) I only

(B) II only

(C) I and II only

(D) I, II, and III

Trigonometric Identities and Equations

PREVIEWING THE CHAPTER

The chapter begins with a lesson where students draw graphs of the trigonometric functions. Then students start with the equation for the unit circle and derive the basic trigonometric identities and use them to simplify and evaluate expressions. Students learn to verify trigonometric identities using various methods, including the sum and difference formulas and the half- and double-angle formulas. Students then solve a variety of trigonometric equations. The chapter concludes with a lesson on complex numbers in polar form and the application of DeMoivre's Theorem.

Problem-Solving Strategy   Students learn to use the strategy *working backwards* when it is faster to determine how the problem ends and work backward rather than start from the beginning to find a solution.

Lesson Objective Chart

Lesson (Pages)	Lesson Objectives	State/Local Objectives
17-1 (790-796)	**17-1A:** Graph trigonometric functions.	
	17-1B: Find the amplitude and period for variations of the sine and cosine functions.	
17-2 (797-800)	**17-2:** Use trigonometric identities to simplify and/or evaluate expressions.	
17-3 (803-806)	**17-3:** Verify trigonometric identities using various methods.	
17-4 (807-809)	**17-4:** Solve problems using the strategy of working backwards.	
17-5 (810-814)	**17-5A:** Find values of sine and cosine involving sum and difference formulas.	
	17-5B: Verify identities using the sum and difference formulas.	
17-6 (815-819)	**17-6A:** Find values of sine and cosine involving half- and double-angles.	
	17-6B: Verify identities using half- and double-angle formulas.	
17-7 (822-827)	**17-7:** Solve trigonometric equations.	
17-8 (829-833)	**17-8A:** Convert numbers in the rectangular form to polar form and vice versa.	
	17-8B: Multiply complex numbers in polar form.	
	17-8C: Apply DeMoivre's Theorem.	

ORGANIZING THE CHAPTER

You may want to refer to the **Course Planning Calendar** on page T44.

Lesson (Pages)	Pacing Chart (days) Course I	II	III	Reteaching	Practice	Enrichment	Evaluation	Technology	Lab Manual	Mixed Problem Solving	Applications	Cooperative Learning Activity	Multicultural	Transparencies
17-1 (790-796)	–	–	1.5	p. 113	p. 129	p. 113		p. 34			p. 35		p. 17	17-1
17-2 (797-800)	–	–	1	p. 114	p. 130	p. 114	Quiz A, p. 233							17-2
17-3 (803-806)	–	–	1	p. 115	p. 131	p. 115		p. 17						17-3
17-4 (807-809)	–	–	0.5		p. 132		Quiz B, p. 233 Mid-Chapter Test, p. 237			p. 17				17-4
17-5 (810-814)	–	–	1	p. 116	p. 133	p. 116								17-5
17-6 (815-819)	–	–	1	p. 117	p. 134	p. 117	Quiz C, p. 234							17-6
17-7 (822-827)	–	–	1	p. 118	p. 135	p. 118						p. 53		17-7
17-8 (829-833)	–	–	1	p. 119	p. 136	p. 119	Quiz D, p. 234							17-8
Review (834-836)	–	–	1	Multiple Choice Tests, Forms 1A and 1B, pp. 225-228 Free Response Tests, Forms 2A and 2B, pp. 229-232 Cumulative Review, pp. 235-236 Standardized Test Practice Questions, p. 238										
Test (837)	–	–	1											

Course I: Chapters 1-13; Course II: Chapters 1-15; Course III: Chapters 1-17

Other Chapter Resources

Student Edition

Chapter Opener, pp. 786-787
Graphing Calculator Exploration, pp. 788-789
Graphing Calculator Exploration, pp. 801-802
Cooperative Learning Activity, p. 809
Mid-Chapter Review, p. 814
Journal Entries, pp. 819, 827
Graphing Calculator Exploration, pp. 820-821
Technology, p. 828
Portfolio Suggestion, p. 833
Extended Project 4, pp. A14-A16

Teacher's Classroom Resources

Transparency 17-0
Real-World Applications Transparencies, 35, 36
Performance Assessment Booklet, pp. 33-34
Problem-of-the-Week Activity Cards, 35, 36
Tech Prep Applications Booklet, pp. 33-34
Lesson Plans, pp. 129-136

Other Supplements

Glencoe Mathematics Professional Series

Software

Test and Review Generator Software (Apple, IBM, and Macintosh)
Interactive Software (Macintosh)
Teacher's Guide for Software Resources

ENHANCING THE CHAPTER

Cooperative Learning

Assessing How Well the Group Functioned

To ensure improved performance in cooperative-learning sessions, it is important to process what students have learned about group skills after each session. Whole-class discussions can be a valuable way to do this since groups can learn from the experiences of other groups. Such discussions should concentrate on how well the groups functioned during the session, what things were done well, and what things could be improved. To begin the processing, select one member from a group to discuss with the class one or two things that they did well during the session. Encourage the reporter to provide details and examples. Ask about specific actions taken by group members that helped, such as encouraging each other to participate, keeping one another focused on the task, paraphrasing or expanding on contributions, and so on. If you wish, you can also ask a reporter to discuss something that the group could have done better or would like to work harder on. The reporter need not use names but should be as specific as possible. The emphasis should be on improving the effectiveness of students in cooperating with and assisting other members of their group. This sharing of ideas and experiences will promote improved group behavior in future sessions.

Technology

The Technology Feature after Lesson 17-7 shows how to use the *Mathematical Exploration Toolkit* to solve equations involving trigonometric functions. The CALC command SOLVEFOR will automatically solve some trigonometric equations, but others must first be simplified. Students will need to choose operations to change the form of the equations. CALC can be set to degree or radian mode. The graphing capabilities of MET can be used to estimate solutions to equations involving mixtures of algebraic and transcendental expressions. If each side of the equation is graphed as a separate function, the intersections represent the solutions of the equation.

Critical Thinking

Opportunities should be provided for *all* students to develop their critical-thinking skills. Having them work with partners or in small, heterogeneous groups provides a support system as they endeavor to seek alternatives, move away from the obvious, produce a large number of ideas, take different approaches, embellish ideas, take a guess, build mental images, and develop the courage to expose oneself to failure and defend one's own ideas. Ample research shows that inspiring all students to think at a higher level gives dignity to their efforts in mathematics, leads them to remember concepts longer, and inspires them to develop a lifelong enthusiasm for learning.

Cooperative Learning, p. 53

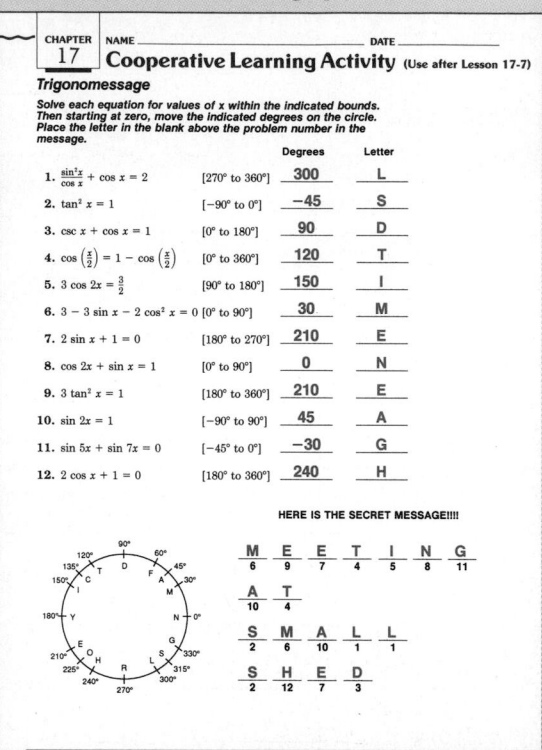

Technology, p. 17

Problem of the Week Activity

The card shown below is one of two available for this chapter. It can be used as a class or small group activity.

Activity Card

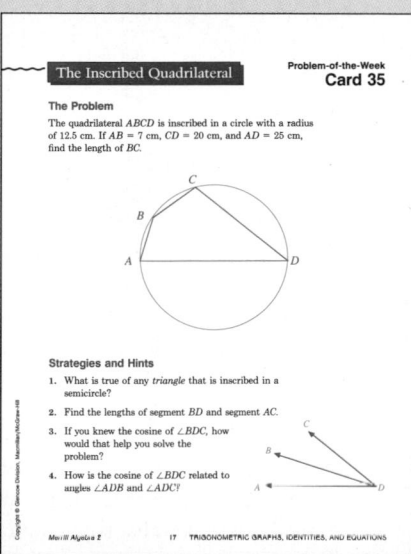

Manipulatives and Models

The following materials may be used as models or manipulatives in Chapter 17.

- wave simulator or picture of ocean waves (Lesson 17-1).
- ball (Lesson 17-6)
- clear tumbler (Lesson 17-7)
- polar graph paper (Lesson 17-8)
- polar projection map (Lesson 17-8)

Outside Resources

Books/Periodicals

Smale, Steve. *The Mathematics of Time.* Springer-Verlag.

Woodcock, Alexander and Monte Davis. *Catastrophe Theory.* E. P. Dutton.

Films/Videotapes/Videodiscs

Modeling the Universe, Pyramid Films and Video Inc., P.O. Box 1048, Santa Monica, CA 90406

Adventures in Perceptions, Journal Films, Inc., 930 Pitner Ave., Evanston, IL 60202

Software

Mathematics Exploration Toolkit, IBM, 4111 Northside Pkwy. NW, P.O. Box 2150, Atlanta, GA 30327-3015

Microsoft Mu-Math, Microsoft Corporation, 16011 NE 36th Way, Box 97017, Redmond, WA 98073-9717

Pre-Calculus, True BASIC, Inc., 12 Commerce Ave., West Lebanon, NH 03766

Supplementary MathTools, William K. Bradford Publishing Company, 310 School St., Acton, MA 01720

Multicultural

Multicultural Activity, p. 17

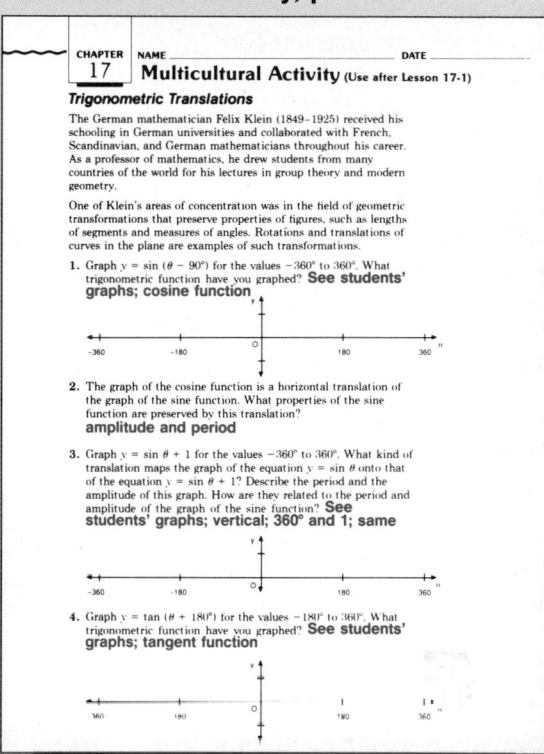

Application

Application, p. 35

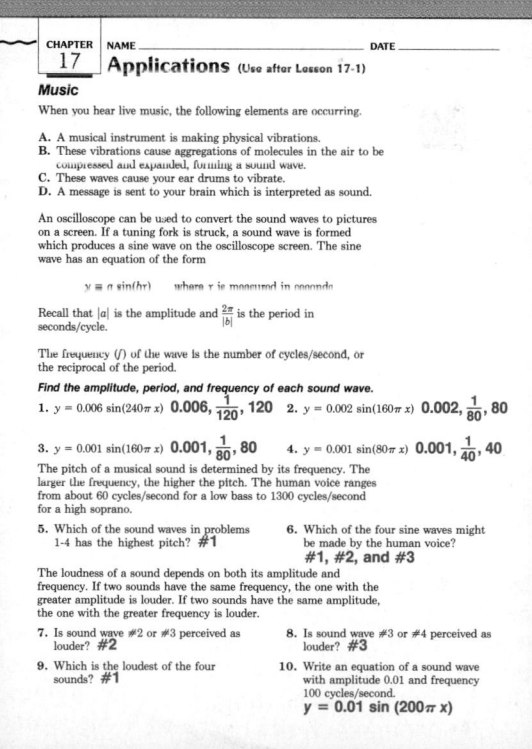

Background Information

In addition to studying surface rocks, geologists study data collected by satellites, conduct geological surveys, construct maps, and measure Earth's gravity and magnetic field. They analyze data collected through seismic prospecting, or bouncing sound waves off deeply buried rock layers. Geologists also test chemical and physical properties in laboratories. They use microscopes, gravity meters, cameras, compasses, seismographs, x-ray diffractometers, and computer-based equipment. Exploration and the need for geologists is expected to grow 5% to 13% in the 1990s.

CHAPTER OBJECTIVES

In this chapter, you will:
- Draw graphs of trigonometric functions.
- Use trigonometric identities.
- Solve trigonometric equations.
- Work with complex numbers in polar form.

Water flows down into deep water tables like (a). But when the water table is high as in (b) the water flows toward bodies of water. What might affect the level of the water table?

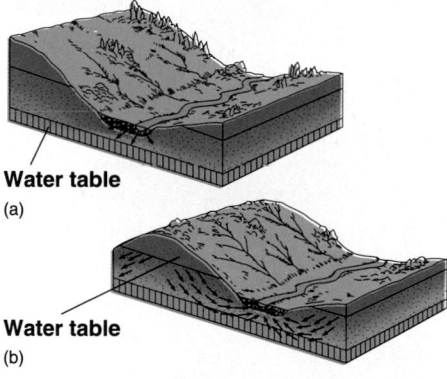

Water table
(a)

Water table
(b)

786

CAREERS IN GEOLOGY

Would you like a career that required you to travel to far-away sites by helicopter or jeep? Would you enjoy covering large areas on foot with a backpack full of rock samples? Or would you like to work overseas or even at sea?

The career: geologist. The goal: Earth. Geologists study it at close range by studying bits of it—rocks—in their labs. They study Earth at long range with satellites, seismographs, sonar, and other instruments.

A geologist might work in the petroleum industry exploring for oil and natural gas. He or she might advise engineers who construct dams, tunnels, and highways. Another field is environmental protection. Geologists can monitor groundwater quality, manage and clean up toxic wastes. Or they can research how human activities affect Earth's atmosphere, oceans, rivers, and land.

A geologist can spend a lifetime studying time. How old is the moon? When did certain creatures live and die to become the fossils we see today? When did certain mountain ranges rise and fall, drying up some seas and creating others? One of the latest techniques for dating objects uses the isotope chlorine-36. Another uses Earth's axis of rotation, which has changed its orientation several times since Earth was formed.

Chapter Project

Materials: paper, pencil, graph paper, library resources

Organize students into cooperative groups of prospective geologists. Assign each group the task of conducting research in at least one of the following specific areas of the geological makeup of your local area.
- minerals and rocks
- rock formations
- fossil history
- geologic history
- mountain formations
- glacial history
- ocean formation
- mining
- petroleum resources
- earthquake potential

Have each group prepare a report on its selected research to include maps, charts, tables, timelines, and so on. In addition, instruct each group to construct a model of your area, highlighting those aspects of the geological makeup that are related to its area of research. Finally, have each group display its model and present its report to the class.

MORE ABOUT GEOLOGY

Degree Required:
- Bachelor's Degree in geology or geophysics

Some geologists like:
- solving problems
- the variety of their work
- traveling
- working with others
- good salaries

Related Math Subjects:
- Advanced Algebra
- Geometry
- Trigonometry
- Calculus
- Statistics/Probability

Some geologists dislike:
- the possibility of injury while on the job
- being far away from home and family for long periods of time
- the primitive living conditions in the field
- the physically demanding nature of the work while at a site under investigation

For more information on the various careers available in Geology, write to:

American Institute of Professional Geologists
7828 Vance Drive
Arvada, CO 80003

787

Lesson	Connections (C) and Applications (A)	Examples	Exercises
17-1	A: Physics	3	
	Zoology		62
	Business		69
	C: Statistics		64
17-2	A: Surveying		50
	Entertain-ment		51
	Horticulture		54
17-3	C: Probability		31
	Statistics		32
	A: Physics	2	
	Optics		30
17-4	A: Fire Fighting	2	
17-5	A: Geology	5	37
17-6	C: Statistics		37
	A: Physics	2	
	Sports		35
17-7	C: Statistics		54
	A: Optics	6	50
	Physics		49
17-8	C: Probability		41
	Statistics		43
	A: Biology		38
	Entertain-ment		39
	Sports		40
	Demograph-ics		44

Objective: Graph trigonometric functions on a graphing calculator.

Motivating the Lesson
Have students graph $y = \sin x$ on their graphing calculators. Explain the definition of period to them. Ask them what they think would happen to the graph if you multiplied the function by 2, or if you multiplied it by $\frac{1}{2}$. Make a chart tallying what your students think will happen to the graph.

TEACHING THE LESSON

Teaching Tip ❶ On the Casio, press MODE 4 EXE On the TI-81, press MODE ▼ ▼ ▶ ENTER .

Teaching Tip ❷ Trigonometric functions are periodic functions because they repeat.

More Examples
Graph $y = \cos x$.

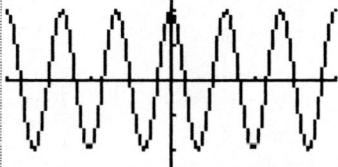

Graphing Calculator Exploration: Graphing Trigonometric Functions

Graphing calculators are capable of graphing trigonometric functions in both degrees and radians. In this lesson, we will use degrees.

Example 1

Graph the function $y = \sin x$.

The Casio fx-7000G has the sine function as a built-in function. It will automatically set the viewing window for viewing a complete graph of the function. *Make sure your calculator is in degree mode.* **Teaching Tip ❶**

Casio

ENTER: GRAPH SIN EXE

For the TI-81, the viewing window must be set. Use the window [-360, 360] by [-1.6, 1.6] with a scale factor of 180 for the x-axis and 0.5 for the y-axis.

TI-81

ENTER: Y= SIN X|T GRAPH

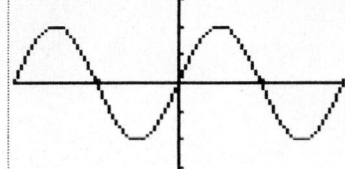

Notice that the y-values of the graph are between -1 and 1. The **amplitude** of the graph of a periodic function is half the absolute value of the difference between its maximum and minimum values. So the amplitude of this graph is 1. The period of this function is 360°. *How could you graph this function in radians?* **Teaching Tip ❷**

Example 2

Graph $y = 2 \cos 3x$. Use the viewing window [-360, 360] by [-2.6, 2.6] with a scale factor of 180 for the x-axis and 1 for the y-axis. State the amplitude and period of the graph.

Casio

ENTER: GRAPH 2 COS (3 ALPHA X
) EXE

TI-81

ENTER: Y= 2 COS (3 X|T) GRAPH

The amplitude of this graph is 2. The period is 120°. *Zoom-in to check this result.*

As Example 2 demonstrates, the amplitude of the function $y = a \sin bx$ or $y = a \cos bx$ is $|a|$ and the period is $\frac{360°}{|b|}$.

788 CHAPTER 17 TRIGONOMETRIC GRAPHS, IDENTITIES, AND EQUATIONS

If students are having difficulty with the meaning of the terminology in this section, graph the base function along with a function that alters it. This way they can see how the graph changed.

Example 3

Graph $y = \sin(x + 90°)$. Use the viewing window [−360, 360] by [−1.6, 1.6] with a scale factor of 180 for the x-axis and 0.5 for the y-axis. How does this graph compare to the graph of $y = \sin x$?

Casio

ENTER:

90 <button>)</button> <button>EXE</button>

TI-81

ENTER:

<button>GRAPH</button>

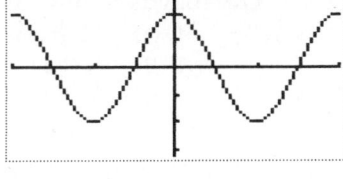

This graph is shaped the same as the graph of $y = \sin x$, except it is shifted to the left by 90°. This is called a 90° **phase shift**.

You can also graph the other trigonometric functions on the graphing calculator.

Example 4

Graph $y = \csc x$. Use the viewing window [−360, 360] by [−5, 5] with a scale factor of 180 on the x-axis and 1 on the y-axis. State the period of the graph.

$\csc x = \dfrac{1}{\sin x}$ **Teaching Tip ❸**
Teaching Tip ❹

Casio

ENTER: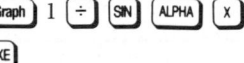

<button>EXE</button>

TI-81 **Teaching Tip ❺**

ENTER: <button>Y=</button> 1 <button>÷</button> <button>SIN</button> <button>XIT</button> <button>GRAPH</button>

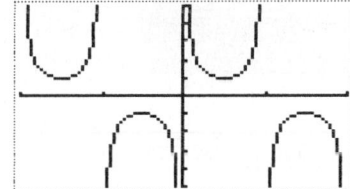

The vertical asymptotes may appear on the viewing screen.

The period of this graph is 360°. This graph has no amplitude, since there are no maximum or minimum values for the function.

EXERCISES

Graph each equation on your graphing calculator so the complete graph is shown. Then sketch each graph. **See students' graphs.**

1. $y = \cos x$
2. $y = \tan(-x)$
3. $y = -2 \sin 3x$
4. $y = \csc x$
5. $y = \cot x$
6. $y = \tan(x - 180°)$
7. $y = 2 \cos \frac{1}{2}x$
8. $y = 3 \sin \frac{2}{3}x$
9. $y = 5 \csc(-2x)$
10. $y = 3 \tan(30x)$
11. $y = 9 \cot 3.5x$
12. $y = 15 \cos 15x$
13. $y = 12 \cos(x + 45°)$
14. $y = 4 \tan(90° - x)$
15. $y = 0.5 \csc(2x - 90°)$
16. $y = 0.2 \sec(360° - 3x)$

GRAPHING CALCULATOR EXPLORATION: GRAPHING TRIGONOMETRIC FUNCTIONS **789**

EXTENDING THE LESSON

Math Power: Reasoning

Graph the functions $y = \cos x$ and $y = \sec x$ in the same viewing window of [−360, 360] by [−5, 5]. Have students compare the two graphs. For example, they have the same period, they intersect whenever $y = 1$, and so on. Also have them notice that when y is zero for the $\cos x$, there is no value for $\sec x$. Ask them why. **Because the denominator of**

$\sec x = \dfrac{1}{\cos x}$ **would be zero and the function is undefined there.** Also compare $\sin x$ with $\csc x$ and $\tan x$ with $\cot x$.

Teaching Tip ❸ The graphs of $\sec x$ and $\cot x$ can also be graphed this way.

Teaching Tip ❹ This is *not* the inverse of the function $y = \cos x$.

Teaching Tip ❺ The TI-81 will draw what appears to be the asymptotes for this function. Explain that it is merely making an attempt to connect points of the graph and here again you need to understand the mathematical concepts.

More Examples

Graph $y = -3 \sin \left(\frac{1}{2}\right)x$. Use the viewing window [−720, 720] by [−5, 5] with scale factors of 180 for the x-axis and 1 for the y-axis. State the amplitude and period of the graph.
amplitude = −3
period = 720°

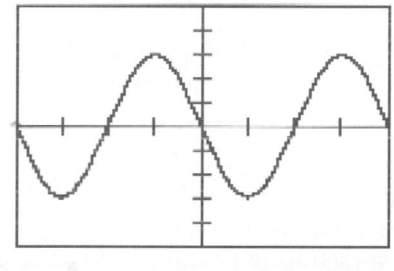

EVALUATING THE LESSON

Closing the Lesson

Writing Activity Graph ten trigonometric functions on a demonstration computer or on an overhead graphing calculator. Then have students write an equation for each function based on the graph.

APPLYING THE LESSON

Homework Exercises

Assignment Guide

All: 1−16

Lesson Resources

Reteaching Master 17-1
Practice Master 17-1
Enrichment Master 17-1
Technology Master, p. 34
Activity Master, p. 35
Multicultural Activity Master, p. 17

 Transparency 17-1 contains the 5-Minute Check and a teaching aid for this lesson.

INTRODUCING THE LESSON

 **5-Minute Check**

(over Chapter 16)

1. Find sin 570°. $-\dfrac{1}{2}$
2. Find the value of
   (sin 45°)(sin 225°). $-\dfrac{1}{2}$
3. Find tan (−120°). $\sqrt{3}$
4. Find $\text{Sin}^{-1}\left(\tan \dfrac{\pi}{4}\right)$.   90°
5. Use the calculator to find x if tan x = 0.4286.   23°

Motivating the Lesson

Show students a wave simulator or a picture of ocean waves. Ask students what the waves have in common. Use student responses to develop informal definitions of period and amplitude.

TEACHING THE LESSON

Teaching Tip ❶ Remind students of common radian measure equivalents, $90° = \dfrac{\pi}{2}$, $180° = \pi$, and so on.

Teaching Tip ❷ Be careful that students do not confuse the use of y on these graphs with its use in Lesson 16−2, where (x, y) is represented by $(\cos x, \sin x)$.

Objectives

17-1A
17-1B

After studying this lesson, you should be able to:
- graph trigonometric functions, and
- find the amplitude and period for variations of the sine and cosine functions.

Application

FYI...

The force that a spring exerts increases linearly with the amount it is stretched or compressed. This relationship, which shows that such a spring oscillates in harmonic motion, is called Hooke's Law.

If a weight is attached to a spring and the weight is pushed up, or pulled down, and released, it tends to rise and fall alternately. The weight is said to be oscillating in harmonic motion. If the position of the weight, y, is graphed over time, t, the result is the graph of a sine or cosine curve.

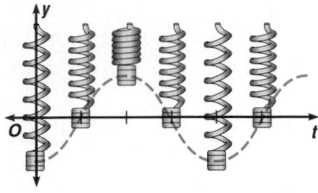

To graph the sine or cosine function, use the horizontal axis for the values of θ expressed in either degrees or radians. Use the vertical axis for values of sin θ or cos θ. Ordered pairs for these points are of the form $(\theta, \sin \theta)$ and $(\theta, \cos \theta)$. **Teaching Tip ❶**

θ	0	30	45	60	90	120	135	150	180	210	225	240	270	300	315	330	360
sin θ	0	$\frac{1}{2}$	$\frac{\sqrt{2}}{2}$	$\frac{\sqrt{3}}{2}$	1	$\frac{\sqrt{3}}{2}$	$\frac{\sqrt{2}}{2}$	$\frac{1}{2}$	0	$-\frac{1}{2}$	$-\frac{\sqrt{2}}{2}$	$-\frac{\sqrt{3}}{2}$	−1	$-\frac{\sqrt{3}}{2}$	$-\frac{\sqrt{2}}{2}$	$-\frac{1}{2}$	0
nearest tenth	0	0.5	0.7	0.9	1	0.9	0.7	0.5	0	−0.5	−0.7	−0.9	−1	−0.9	−0.7	−0.5	0
cos θ	1	$\frac{\sqrt{3}}{2}$	$\frac{\sqrt{2}}{2}$	$\frac{1}{2}$	0	$-\frac{1}{2}$	$-\frac{\sqrt{2}}{2}$	$-\frac{\sqrt{3}}{2}$	−1	$-\frac{\sqrt{3}}{2}$	$-\frac{\sqrt{2}}{2}$	$-\frac{1}{2}$	0	$\frac{1}{2}$	$\frac{\sqrt{2}}{2}$	$\frac{\sqrt{3}}{2}$	1
nearest tenth	1	0.9	0.7	0.5	0	−0.5	−0.7	−0.9	−1	−0.9	−0.7	−0.5	0	0.5	0.7	0.9	1

After plotting several points, complete the graphs of $y = \sin \theta$ and $y = \cos \theta$ by connecting the points with a smooth, continuous curve.

Teaching Tip ❷
Negative values of θ would be represented to the left of zero.

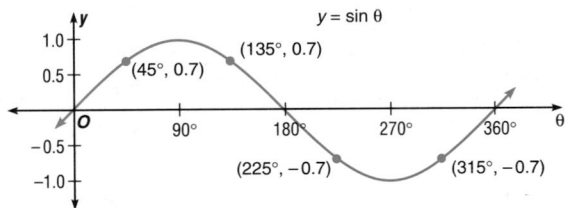

ALTERNATE TEACHING STRATEGIES

Using Connections

There are many applications of graphs of trigonometric functions. For example, some animal populations vary periodically. If a fox population is at a minimum of 200 foxes 2.7 years after starting a study and reaches a maximum of 700 foxes 2.4 years later, have students sketch the graph and predict the population 7 years after the study started.   **about 250 foxes**

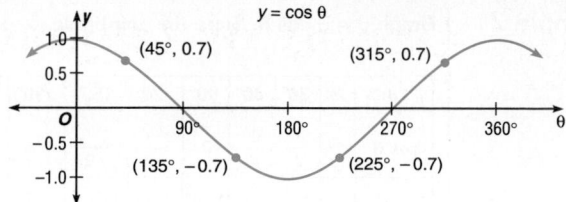

$y = \cos\theta$

(45°, 0.7) (315°, 0.7)

(135°, −0.7) (225°, −0.7)

As you recall from your studies of the sine and cosine functions in Chapter 16, both of these functions have a **period** of 360° or 2π radians. That is, the graph of both functions repeat themselves every 360° or 2π radians. The following example is a variation of the sine function that has a period less than 360°.

Example 1

Graph $y = \sin 2\theta$. State the period.

First, complete a table of values.

θ	0°	15°	30°	45°	60°	75°	90°	105°	120°	135°	150°	165°	180°
2θ	0°	30°	60°	90°	120°	150°	180°	210°	240°	270°	300°	330°	360°
$\sin 2\theta$	0	$\frac{1}{2}$	$\frac{\sqrt{3}}{2}$	1	$\frac{\sqrt{3}}{2}$	$\frac{1}{2}$	0	$-\frac{1}{2}$	$-\frac{\sqrt{3}}{2}$	−1	$-\frac{\sqrt{3}}{2}$	$-\frac{1}{2}$	0

Then plot the points given by the ordered pairs of the form (θ, y), and connect to form a curve.

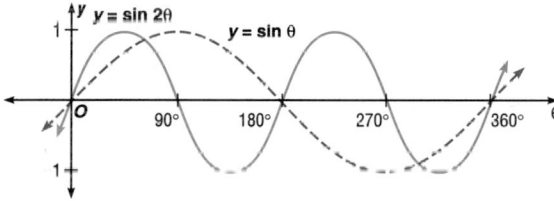

Teaching Tip ❸

The graph of $y = \sin 2\theta$ repeats every 180° or π radians. Therefore, the period of $y = \sin 2\theta$ is 180° or π radians. *Notice that the period is $\frac{360°}{2}$ or $\frac{2\pi}{2}$.*

Teaching Tip ❹

The trigonometric function you graphed in Example 1 has a maximum value of 1 and a minimum value of −1. The **amplitude** of the graph of a periodic function is the absolute value of half the difference between its maximum value and its minimum value. So in Example 1, the amplitude of the graph is $\left|\frac{1 - (-1)}{2}\right|$ or 1. The graphs in the following examples have amplitudes other than 1.

LESSON 17-1 GRAPHS OF TRIGONOMETRIC FUNCTIONS 791

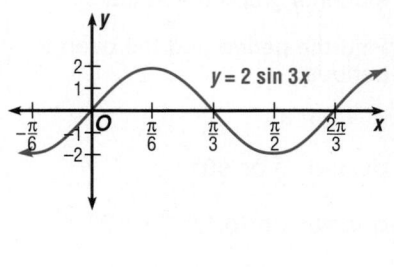
Example 2 | Graph $y = \frac{1}{2} \cos \theta$. State the amplitude.

θ	0°	30°	60°	90°	120°	150°	180°	210°	240°	270°	300°	330°	360°
$\cos \theta$	1	$\frac{\sqrt{3}}{2}$	$\frac{1}{2}$	0	$-\frac{1}{2}$	$-\frac{\sqrt{3}}{2}$	-1	$-\frac{\sqrt{3}}{2}$	$-\frac{1}{2}$	0	$\frac{1}{2}$	$\frac{\sqrt{3}}{2}$	1
$\frac{1}{2}\cos \theta$	$\frac{1}{2}$	$\frac{\sqrt{3}}{4}$	$\frac{1}{4}$	0	$-\frac{1}{4}$	$\frac{\sqrt{3}}{4}$	$-\frac{1}{2}$	$-\frac{\sqrt{3}}{4}$	$-\frac{1}{4}$	0	$\frac{1}{4}$	$\frac{\sqrt{3}}{4}$	$\frac{1}{2}$

The amplitude of $y = \frac{1}{2} \cos \theta$ is $\frac{1}{2}$.   *Notice that the amplitude is $\left|\frac{1}{2}\right|$ or $\frac{1}{2}$.*

There are many applications of trigonometry in the real world. The motion of a weight on a spring is one such application.

Example 3

APPLICATION

Physics

The motion of a weight on a certain kind of spring can be described by the equation $y = 3 \cos 2\pi t$, where y is the number of inches the weight is from its equilibrium position, when $y = 0$, after t seconds.

a. Graph the function and state the amplitude and the period.

t seconds	0	$\frac{1}{12}$	$\frac{1}{6}$	$\frac{1}{4}$	$\frac{1}{3}$	$\frac{5}{12}$	$\frac{1}{2}$	$\frac{7}{12}$	$\frac{2}{3}$	$\frac{3}{4}$	$\frac{5}{6}$	$\frac{11}{12}$	1
$2\pi t$ radians	0	$\frac{\pi}{6}$	$\frac{\pi}{3}$	$\frac{\pi}{2}$	$\frac{2\pi}{3}$	$\frac{5\pi}{6}$	π	$\frac{7\pi}{6}$	$\frac{4\pi}{3}$	$\frac{3\pi}{2}$	$\frac{5\pi}{3}$	$\frac{11\pi}{6}$	2π
$\cos 2\pi t$	1	$\frac{\sqrt{3}}{2}$	$\frac{1}{2}$	0	$-\frac{1}{2}$	$-\frac{\sqrt{3}}{2}$	-1	$-\frac{\sqrt{3}}{2}$	$-\frac{1}{2}$	0	$\frac{1}{2}$	$\frac{\sqrt{3}}{2}$	1
$3 \cos 2\pi t$	3	$\frac{3\sqrt{3}}{2}$	$\frac{3}{2}$	0	$-\frac{3}{2}$	$-\frac{3\sqrt{3}}{2}$	-3	$-\frac{3\sqrt{3}}{2}$	$-\frac{3}{2}$	0	$\frac{3}{2}$	$\frac{3\sqrt{3}}{2}$	3

Notice that the amplitude is $|3|$ or 3 and the period is $\frac{2\pi}{|2\pi|}$ or 1.

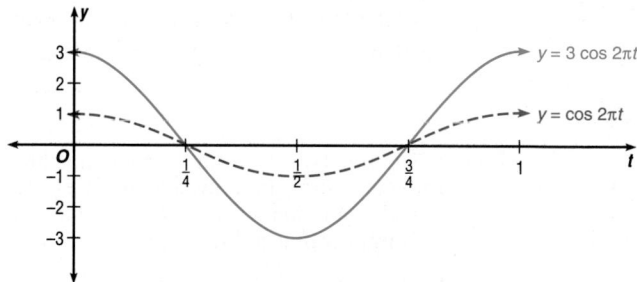

The amplitude of the graph of $y = 3 \cos 2\pi t$ is 3 and the period is 1.

b. Find the position of the weight after 6 seconds.

Find y when $t = 6$.

$$y = 3 \cos 2\pi t$$
$$= 3 \cos 2\pi(6) \qquad \textit{Substitute 6 for t.}$$
$$= 3 \cos 12\pi = 3(1) \text{ or } 3 \qquad \cos 12\pi = 1$$

After 6 seconds, the weight will be 3 in. above the equilibrium position.

From these examples, we can make the following generalizations.

Amplitudes and Periods	For functions of the form $y = a \sin b\theta$ and $y = a \cos b\theta$ the amplitude is $|a|$ and the period is $\dfrac{360°}{|b|}$ or $\dfrac{2\pi}{|b|}$.

Example 4

State the amplitude and period of $y = \dfrac{3}{2} \cos \dfrac{1}{2}\theta$. Then draw the graph.

The amplitude is $\left|\dfrac{3}{2}\right|$ or $\dfrac{3}{2}$. The period is $\dfrac{360°}{\left|\dfrac{1}{2}\right|}$ or $720°$. $\qquad 720° = 4\pi \ radians$

The graph has a shape like $y = \cos \theta$.

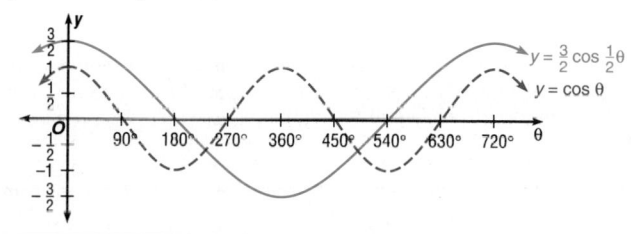

The other trigonometric functions can be graphed as well. Make a table of values and graph $y = \tan \theta$. $\qquad$ *nd = not defined*

θ	0°	30°	45°	60°	90°	120°	135°	150°	180°	210°	225°	240°	270°	300°	315°	330°	360°
$\tan \theta$	0	$\dfrac{\sqrt{3}}{3}$	1	$\sqrt{3}$	nd	$-\sqrt{3}$	-1	$-\dfrac{\sqrt{3}}{3}$	0	$\dfrac{\sqrt{3}}{3}$	1	$\sqrt{3}$	nd	$-\sqrt{3}$	-1	$\dfrac{\sqrt{3}}{3}$	0

The tangent function, $y = \tan \theta$, is not defined for 90°, 270°, and so on. We say that it is not defined for $90° + k \cdot 180°$, where k is an integer. The graph is separated by vertical asymptotes, indicated by dashed lines.

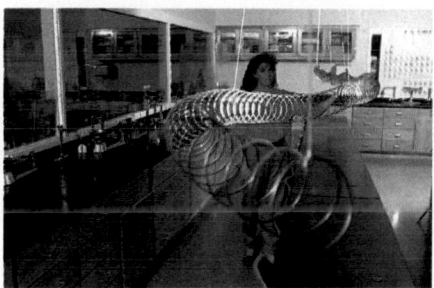

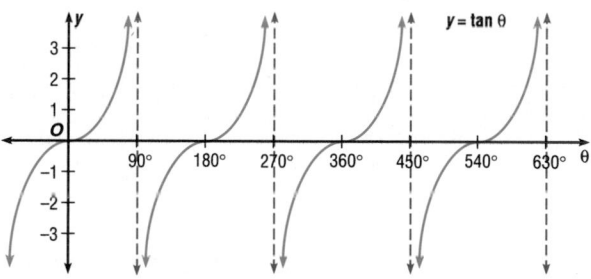

LESSON 17-1 GRAPHS OF TRIGONOMETRIC FUNCTIONS 793

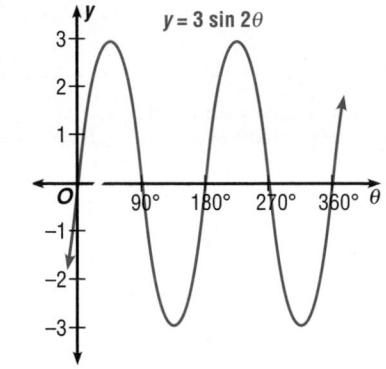

Chalkboard Example

For Example 5

Graph $y = \frac{1}{2} \cot \frac{1}{2}\theta$. The period is 360°.

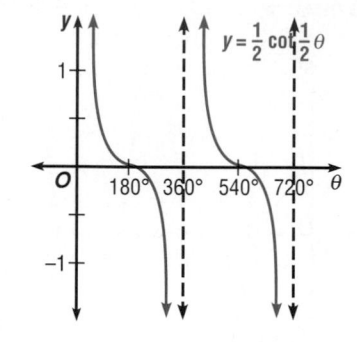

EVALUATING THE LESSON

Checking for Understanding

Exercises 1–27 are designed to help you assess understanding through reading, writing, and speaking. You should work through Exercises 1–3 with your students, and then monitor their work on Exercises 4–27.

Reteaching Masters Booklet, p. 113

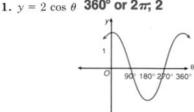
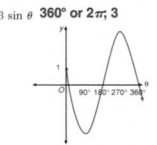
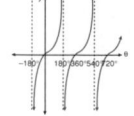 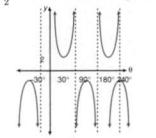

The period of the tangent function is 180° or π radians. Since the tangent function is not defined for $90° + k \cdot 180°$, it has no amplitude.

The graphs of the secant, cosecant, and cotangent functions are shown below. Compare them to the graphs of the cosine, sine, and tangent functions, which are shown in red.

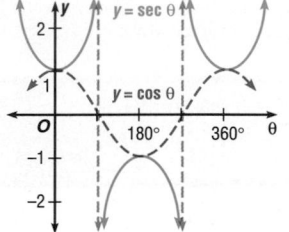 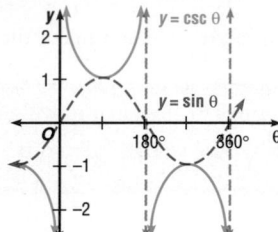 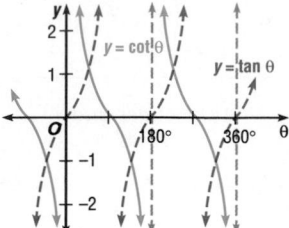

Notice that the periods of the secant and cosecant functions are 360° or 2π radians. The period of the cotangent function is 180° or π radians. What are the amplitudes of the secant, cosecant, and cotangent functions?

Example 5

Graph $y = -\frac{1}{2} \csc 2\theta$.

nd = not defined

θ	0°	15°	30°	45°	60°	75°	90°	105°	120°	135°	150°	165°	180°
2θ	0°	30°	60°	90°	120°	150°	180°	210°	240°	270°	300°	330°	360°
$-\frac{1}{2}\csc 2\theta$	nd	-1	$-\frac{\sqrt{3}}{3}$	$-\frac{1}{2}$	$\frac{\sqrt{3}}{3}$	-1	nd	1	$\frac{\sqrt{3}}{3}$	$\frac{1}{2}$	$\frac{\sqrt{3}}{3}$	1	nd

The period is $\frac{360°}{|2|}$ or 180°. This function is not defined for 0°, 90°, 180°, and so on. Thus, it has no amplitude.

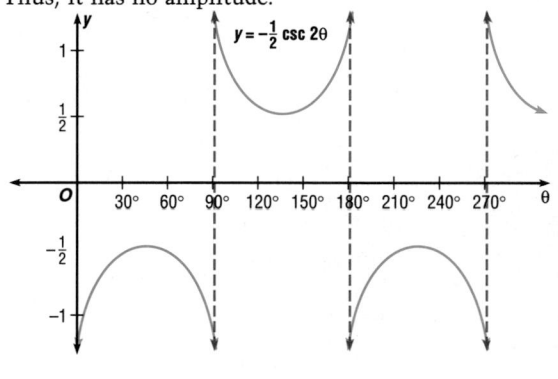

RETEACHING THE LESSON

Demonstrate the effects of a, b, and c in $y = a \cdot \sin(bx + c)$ and $y = a \cdot \cos(bx + c)$ using an overhead projection of the screen of a computer or graphing calculator.

CHECKING FOR UNDERSTANDING

Communicating Mathematics
1. The values of the function repeat in 180° intervals.
2. See students' work.

Read and study the lesson to answer these questions.

1. What does it mean to say that the period of a function is 180°?
2. In your own words, explain what the amplitude of a function is.
3. Judging from the results of Example 5, how can you find the amplitude and the period of $y = a \csc b\theta$? **no amplitude; period $= \frac{360°}{|b|}$ or $\frac{2\pi}{|b|}$**

Guided Practice

State the amplitude and period of each function.

4. $y = \sin \theta$ **1, 2π**
5. $y = 3 \sin \theta$ **3, 2π**
6. $y = \frac{1}{2} \cos \theta$ **$\frac{1}{2}$, 2π**

7. $y = 3 \cos \frac{1}{2}\theta$ **3, 4π**
8. $y = \frac{2}{3} \cos \theta$ **$\frac{2}{3}$, 2π**
9. $y = 6 \sin \frac{2}{3}\theta$ **6, 3π**

10. $y = -2 \sin \theta$ **2, 2π**
11. $y = -3 \sin \frac{2}{3}\theta$ **3, 3π**
12. $y = 4 \sin \frac{1}{2}\theta$ **4, 4π**

13. $y = -\frac{1}{2} \cos \frac{3}{4}\theta$ **$\frac{1}{2}$, $\frac{8\pi}{3}$**
14. $3y = 2 \sin \frac{1}{2}\theta$ **$\frac{2}{3}$, 4π**
15. $y = -6 \sin 2\theta$ **6, π**

State the period of each function.

16. $y = \sec 3\theta$ **$\frac{2\pi}{3}$**
17. $y = 4 \sec \theta$ **2π**
18. $y = 3 \tan \theta$ **π**

19. $y = \cot 5\theta$ **$\frac{\pi}{5}$**
20. $y = \cot \frac{1}{3}\theta$ **3π**
21. $y = \tan 3\theta$ **$\frac{\pi}{3}$**

22. $y = \tan \frac{1}{2}\theta$ **2π**
23. $y = \csc 2\theta$ **π**
24. $y = \csc \frac{3}{4}\theta$ **$\frac{8\pi}{3}$**

25. $y = \frac{1}{2} \sec \frac{1}{2}\theta$ **4π**
26. $y = 6 \cot 2\theta$ **$\frac{\pi}{2}$**
27. $y = \frac{3}{4} \csc \frac{2}{3}\theta$ **3π**

EXERCISES

Practice

Graph each function. 28-60. See Solutions Manual.

28. $y = \sin \theta$
29. $y = 3 \sin \theta$
30. $y = \frac{1}{2} \cos \theta$

31. $y = \frac{2}{3} \cos \theta$
32. $y = \cos 3\theta$
33. $y = \sin 4\theta$

34. $y = 5 \sin \theta$
35. $y = \cos 2\theta$
36. $y = -2 \sin \theta$

37. $y = \cot \theta$
38. $y = 3 \sec \theta$
39. $y = \sec 3\theta$

40. $y = \csc \frac{1}{3}\theta$
41. $y = 2 \sec \theta$
42. $y = \frac{1}{3} \sec \theta$

43. $y = 2 \tan \theta$
44. $y = \csc 2\theta$
45. $y = 4 \sin \frac{1}{2}\theta$

46. $y = 6 \sin \frac{2}{3}\theta$
47. $y = 3 \cos \frac{1}{2}\theta$
48. $y = 4 \cos \frac{3}{4}\theta$

49. $y = -3 \sin \frac{2}{3}\theta$
50. $y = -6 \sin 2\theta$
51. $y = 2 \sin \frac{1}{5}\theta$

52. $y = -\cot \theta$
53. $y = 3 \csc \frac{1}{2}\theta$
54. $y = -\frac{1}{2} \cot 2\theta$

55. $y = \frac{1}{2} \tan \theta$
56. $3y = 2 \sin \frac{1}{2}\theta$
57. $\frac{3}{4}y = \frac{2}{3} \sin \frac{3}{5}\theta$

58. $\frac{1}{2}y = 3 \sin 2\theta$
59. $y = -\frac{1}{2} \cos \frac{3}{4}\theta$
60. $\frac{1}{2}y = 5 \csc 3\theta$

LESSON 17-1 GRAPHS OF TRIGONOMETRIC FUNCTIONS 795

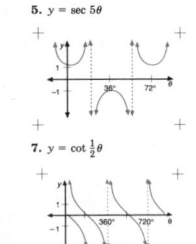
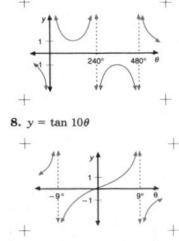
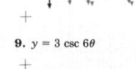
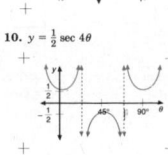
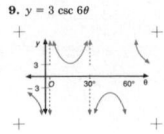

61. Graph and state the equation involving sine that has an amplitude of 3 and a period of 540°. **See Solutions Manual for graph;** $y = 3 \sin \frac{2}{3}\theta$

Application

62. Zoology In predator-prey systems, the number of predators and the number of prey tend to vary periodically. In a certain region with coyotes as predators and rabbits as prey, the rabbit population R varied according to the equation $R = 1000 + 250 \sin \frac{\pi t}{2}$, with the time, t, in years since January 1, 1960. **See Solutions Manual.**

a. Graph the function for the number of rabbits.

b. What was the population of rabbits on January 1, 1960? **1000**

c. What is the maximum rabbit population? On what date was the maximum population of rabbits first reached? **1250; January 1, 1961**

d. What is the minimum rabbit population? On what date was the minimum population of rabbits first reached? **750; January 1, 1963**

Mixed Review

63. Determine whether the pair of angles whose measurements are 434° and 794° are coterminal. **(Lesson 16-1) yes**

64. Statistics Find the median, mode, and mean of {90, 89, 83, 95, 99, 100, 82, 81, 87, 94, 97, 98}. **(Lesson 14-3) 92; no mode; 91.25**

65. Use sigma notation to express $6 + 9 + 12 + 15 + 18 + 21$. **(Lesson 13-2)** **Answers may vary. Sample answer:** $\sum\limits_{n=1}^{6} (3 + 3n)$

66. Simplify $(4^{\sqrt{3}})^{\sqrt{2}}$. **(Lesson 12-1)** $4^{\sqrt{6}}$

67. Find all zeros of the function $f(x) = 4x^4 - 35x^3 + 78x^2 + 28x - 165$. **(Lesson 10-4)** $3, -\frac{5}{4}, \frac{7 \pm \sqrt{5}}{2}$

68. Simplify $(6 + i)(6 - i)$. **(Lesson 6-9) 37**

69. Business The Bright Idea Company makes floor lamps and table lamps, each of which must be assembled and packed. The time an employee takes to assemble a floor lamp is 18 minutes and to assemble a table lamp is 12 minutes. It takes 1 minute to package a floor lamp and 2 minutes to package a table lamp. Each employee can spend 240 hours assembling lamps and 20 hours packing lamps.

69.a. 600 floor lamps, 300 table lamps

a. If a floor lamp sells for $85 and a table lamp sells for $75, how many of each should the company make to maximize their revenue?

b. What is the maximum weekly revenue? **(Lesson 3-7) $73,500**

EXTENDING THE LESSON

Math Power: Communication

Have students research and write a short report on operation and uses of oscilloscopes.

Enrichment Masters Booklet, p. 113

NAME _____ DATE _____

17-1 Enrichment Worksheet

Blueprints

Interpreting blueprints requires the ability to select and use trigonometric functions and geometric properties. The figure below represents a plan for an improvement to a roof. The metal fitting shown makes a 30° angle with the horizontal. The vertices of the geometric shapes are *not* labeled in these plans. Relevant information must be selected and the appropriate function used to find the unknown measures.

Example: Find the unknown measures in the figure at the right.

The measures x and y are the legs of a right triangle. The measure of the hypotenuse is $\frac{15}{16}'' + \frac{5}{16}''$ or $\frac{20}{16}''$.

$\frac{y}{\frac{20}{16}} = \cos 30°$

$\frac{x}{\frac{20}{16}} = \sin 30°$

$y = 1.08''$ $x = 0.63''$

Find the unknown measures of each of the following.

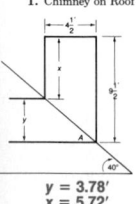

1. Chimney on Roof

$y = 3.78'$
$x = 5.72'$
$\angle A = 40°$

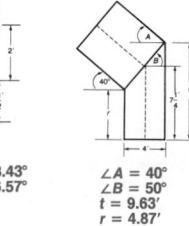

2. Air Vent

$\angle C = 63.43°$
$\angle D = 26.57°$

3. Elbow Joint

$\angle A = 40°$
$\angle B = 50°$
$t = 9.63'$
$r = 4.87'$

Objective
17-2

After studying this lesson, you should be able to:
- use trigonometric identities to simplify and/or evaluate expressions.

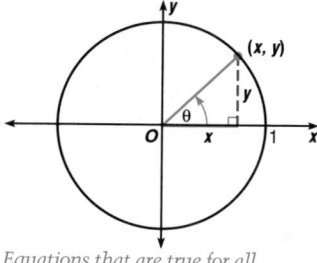

Equations that are true for all values of the variables for which they are defined are called identities.

Let θ be the measurement of an angle in standard position. Let (x, y) be the coordinates of the point of intersection of the terminal side of the angle and the unit circle. Then, as you know, $\cos \theta = x$ and $\sin \theta = y$.

The equation for the unit circle is $x^2 + y^2 = 1$. By substituting $\cos \theta$ for x and $\sin \theta$ for y, we have the following equation.

$$(\cos \theta)^2 + (\sin \theta)^2 = 1$$

This equation is usually written as follows.

$$\cos^2 \theta + \sin^2 \theta = 1$$

An equation like $\cos^2 \theta + \sin^2 \theta = 1$ is called an **identity** because it is true for all values of θ. Some other trigonometric identities are given below.

Basic Trigonometric Identities	**The following trigonometric identities hold true for all values of θ except those for which either side of the equation is undefined.** $$\cos^2 \theta + \sin^2 \theta = 1$$ **The following two identities result when each side of the equation $\cos^2 \theta + \sin^2 \theta = 1$ is divided by $\sin^2 \theta$ or by $\cos^2 \theta$.** $$\tan^2 \theta + 1 = \sec^2 \theta$$ $$\cot^2 \theta + 1 = \csc^2 \theta$$

The steps in the following example show the development of a basic trigonometric identity. The expression on one side of the equation is transformed into the exact form of the expression on the other side.

Example 1

Show that $1 + \tan^2 \theta = \sec^2 \theta$.

$$1 + \tan^2 \theta = 1 + \left(\frac{\sin \theta}{\cos \theta}\right)^2 \quad \textit{Definition of } \tan \theta$$

$$= 1 + \frac{\sin^2 \theta}{\cos^2 \theta}$$

$$= \frac{\cos^2 \theta}{\cos^2 \theta} + \frac{\sin^2 \theta}{\cos^2 \theta} \quad 1 = \frac{\cos^2 \theta}{\cos^2 \theta}$$

$$= \frac{\cos^2 \theta + \sin^2 \theta}{\cos^2 \theta}$$

$$= \frac{1}{\cos^2 \theta} \text{ or } \sec^2 \theta \quad \text{Therefore, } 1 + \tan^2 \theta = \sec^2 \theta.$$

ALTERNATE TEACHING STRATEGIES

Using Questioning
While solving Example 1, have students name each step and its justification. Then ask students to show step-by-step that $\cot^2 \theta + 1 = \csc^2 \theta$. When simplifying expressions that contain trigonometric functions, question students to develop criteria for determining that an expression is simplified.

17-2 Lesson Notes

Lesson Resources
Reteaching Master 17-2
Practice Master 17-2
Enrichment Master 17-2

 Transparency 17-2 contains the 5-Minute Check and a teaching aid for this lesson.

INTRODUCING THE LESSON

5-Minute Check

(over Lesson 17-1)

State the amplitude and period of each function.

1. $y = 4 \cos \frac{3\theta}{4}$ $4, \frac{8\pi}{3}$

2. $y = \sin 4\theta$ $1, \frac{\pi}{2}$

3. State the period of $\cot \frac{\theta}{3}$. 3π

4. In which quadrants is the secant an increasing function? **I and II**

5. Graph the function $y = \sin 2\theta$.

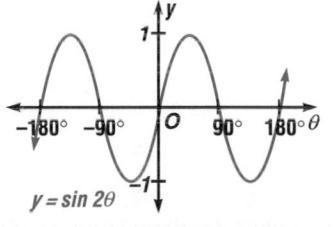

Motivating the Lesson
Ask students what the difference is between identical and fraternal twins. From student responses, develop the concept that the term *identical*, and thus *identity*, means that any characteristic named is true for all individuals classified as identical.

TEACHING THE LESSON

Chalkboard Examples

For Example 1
Show that
$\cot \theta + \tan \theta = \csc \theta \sec \theta$.

$$\cot \theta + \tan \theta = \frac{\cos \theta}{\sin \theta} + \frac{\sin \theta}{\cos \theta}$$
$$= \frac{\cos^2 \theta + \sin^2 \theta}{\sin \theta \cos \theta}$$
$$= \frac{1}{\sin \theta \cos \theta}$$
$$= \csc \theta \sec \theta$$

For Example 2
Find $\cos \theta$ if $\sin \theta = \frac{2}{3}$ and
$0° \le \theta \le 90°$. $\frac{\sqrt{5}}{3}$

For Example 3
The sine of angle A is $\frac{1}{2}$. Find
$\tan A$. Assume that angle A is
obtuse. $-\frac{\sqrt{3}}{3}$

For Example 4
Simplify
$\left(\frac{\cos^3 \beta}{\sin \beta}\right) \tan \beta + \left(\frac{\sin^3 \beta}{\cos \beta}\right) \cot \beta$.   **1**

Reteaching Masters Booklet, p. 114

Example 2

Find $\csc \beta$ if $\cot \beta = \frac{3}{5}$ and $180° \le \beta \le 270°$.

$$\csc^2 \beta = 1 + \cot^2 \beta \qquad \textit{Trigonometric identity: } 1 + \cot^2 \theta = \csc^2 \theta$$
$$= 1 + \left(\frac{3}{5}\right)^2 \qquad \textit{Substitute } \frac{3}{5} \textit{ for } \cot \beta.$$
$$= \frac{34}{25} \qquad \textit{Take the square root of each side.}$$
$$\csc \beta = -\sqrt{\frac{34}{25}} \qquad \textit{csc } \beta \textit{ is negative for values of } \beta \textit{ between } 180° \textit{ and } 270°.$$
$$= -\frac{\sqrt{34}}{5}$$

Example 3

If $\tan A = 4$, find $\cos A$. Assume that angle A is acute.

$$\sec^2 A = 1 + \tan^2 A \qquad \textit{Trigonometric identity}$$
$$= 1 + (4)^2$$
$$= 17$$
$$\left(\frac{1}{\cos^2 A}\right) = 17 \qquad \textit{sec } A = \frac{1}{\cos A}$$
$$\cos^2 A = \frac{1}{17}$$
$$\cos A = \sqrt{\frac{1}{17}} \qquad \textit{cos } A \textit{ is positive for acute angles.}$$
$$= \frac{\sqrt{17}}{17}$$

Trigonometric identities can also be used to simplify expressions containing trigonometric functions. Simplifying an expression that contains trigonometric functions means that the expression is written as a numerical value or in terms of a single trigonometric function, if possible.

Example 4

Simplify $\frac{1}{1 + \sin x} + \frac{1}{1 - \sin x}$.

$$\frac{1}{1 + \sin x} + \frac{1}{1 - \sin x} = \frac{(1 - \sin x) + (1 + \sin x)}{(1 + \sin x)(1 - \sin x)}$$
$$= \frac{2}{1 - \sin^2 x}$$
$$= \frac{2}{\cos^2 x} \qquad \sin^2 x + \cos^2 x = 1$$
$$= 2\sec^2 x \qquad \sec x = \frac{1}{\cos x}$$

798   CHAPTER 17   TRIGONOMETRIC GRAPHS, IDENTITIES, AND EQUATIONS

RETEACHING THE LESSON

See Examples 2 and 3. If $\cot B$ is given as $\frac{3}{5}$, then a first quadrant reference triangle can be drawn. So $c = \sqrt{34}$.
Consideration of the sign of a given trigonometric function and the interval for B allows for all other trigonometric functions to be found.

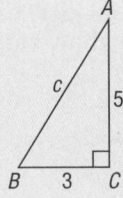

CHECKING FOR UNDERSTANDING

Communicating Mathematics

Read and study the lesson to answer these questions.

1. What do the coordinates (x, y) represent on the unit circle? **See margin.**

2. What does it mean to simplify an expression containing trigonometric functions? **See margin.**

3. When $\sin \theta < 0$ and $\cos \theta < 0$, in which quadrant does the terminal side of θ lie? **III**

4. In which quadrants might the angle whose measurement is β terminate if $\tan \beta = -\frac{4}{3}$? **II or IV**

Guided Practice

Simplify each expression.

5. $\tan \theta \cos^2 \theta$ **$\sin \theta \cos \theta$**
6. $\dfrac{\sin^2 \theta + \cos^2 \theta}{\sin^2 \theta}$ **$\csc^2 \theta$**
7. $\csc^2 \theta - \cot^2 \theta$ **1**

8. $\csc^2 \gamma - \cot^2 \gamma$ **1**
9. $\cos \alpha \csc \alpha$ **$\cot \alpha$**
10. $\tan x \csc x$ **$\sec x$**

11. $\dfrac{\cos x \csc x}{\tan x}$ **$\cot^2 x$**
12. $\dfrac{\tan x}{\sin x}$ **$\sec x$**
13. $\sin \theta \cot \theta$ **$\cos \theta$**

14. $\dfrac{1 - \sin^2 \alpha}{\sin^2 \alpha}$ **$\cot^2 \alpha$**
15. $\dfrac{1 + \tan^2 x}{1 + \cot^2 x}$ **$\tan^2 x$**
16. $\dfrac{\tan \beta}{\cot \beta}$ **$\tan^2 \beta$**

Solve for values of θ between $0°$ and $90°$.

17. If $\cot \theta = 2$, find $\tan \theta$. **$\dfrac{1}{2}$**
18. If $\sin \theta = \dfrac{4}{5}$, find $\cos \theta$. **$\dfrac{3}{5}$**

19. If $\cos \theta = \dfrac{2}{3}$, find $\sin \theta$. **$\dfrac{\sqrt{5}}{3}$**
20. If $\cos \theta = \dfrac{2}{3}$, find $\csc \theta$. **$\dfrac{3\sqrt{5}}{5}$**

EXERCISES

Practice

 Solve for values of θ between $0°$ and $90°$.

21. If $\cos \theta = \dfrac{4}{5}$, find $\tan \theta$. **$\dfrac{3}{4}$**
22. If $\sin \theta = \dfrac{1}{2}$, find $\cos \theta$. **$\dfrac{\sqrt{3}}{2}$**

23. If $\sin \theta = \dfrac{3}{4}$, find $\sec \theta$. **$\dfrac{4\sqrt{7}}{7}$**
24. If $\tan \theta = 4$, find $\sin \theta$. **$\dfrac{4\sqrt{17}}{17}$**

Solve for values of θ between $90°$ and $180°$.

25. If $\sin \theta = \dfrac{1}{2}$, find $\tan \theta$. **$-\dfrac{\sqrt{3}}{3}$**
26. If $\cos \theta = -\dfrac{3}{5}$, find $\csc \theta$. **$\dfrac{5}{4}$**

27. If $\tan \theta = -2$, find $\sec \theta$. **$-\sqrt{5}$**
28. If $\sin \theta = \dfrac{3}{5}$, find $\cos \theta$. **$-\dfrac{4}{5}$**

 Solve for values of θ between $180°$ and $270°$.

29. If $\sec \theta = -3$, find $\tan \theta$. **$2\sqrt{2}$**
30. If $\cos \theta = -\dfrac{3}{5}$, find $\csc \theta$. **$-\dfrac{5}{4}$**

31. If $\sin \theta = -\dfrac{1}{2}$, find $\cos \theta$. **$-\dfrac{\sqrt{3}}{2}$**
32. If $\cot \theta = \dfrac{1}{4}$, find $\csc \theta$. **$-\dfrac{\sqrt{17}}{4}$**

Additional Answers

1. **Given an angle in standard position whose measurement is θ and which intersects the unit circle at point (x, y), $x = \cos \theta$ and $y = \sin \theta$.**

2. **Write the expression as a numerical value or in terms of a single trigonometric function.**

17-2 Practice Worksheet

NAME _____ DATE _____

Trigonometric Identities

Solve for values of θ between $0°$ and $90°$.

1. If $\cos \theta = \dfrac{5}{13}$, find $\sin \theta$. $\dfrac{12}{13}$
2. If $\sec \theta = 2$, find $\tan \theta$. $\sqrt{3}$

3. If $\cot \theta = \dfrac{1}{2}$, find $\sin \theta$. $\dfrac{2\sqrt{5}}{5}$
4. If $\tan \theta = \dfrac{2}{5}$, find $\cot \theta$. $\dfrac{5}{2}$

Solve for values of θ between $180°$ and $270°$.

5. If $\sin \theta = -\dfrac{15}{17}$, find $\sec \theta$. $-\dfrac{17}{8}$
6. If $\tan \theta = 4$, find $\sec \theta$. $-\sqrt{17}$

7. If $\csc \theta = -\dfrac{3}{2}$, find $\cot \theta$. $\dfrac{\sqrt{5}}{2}$
8. If $\sin \theta = -\dfrac{2}{9}$, find $\csc \theta$. $-\dfrac{9}{2}$

Solve for values of θ between $270°$ and $360°$.

9. If $\cos \theta = \dfrac{3}{10}$, find $\cot \theta$. $-\dfrac{3\sqrt{91}}{91}$
10. If $\tan \theta = -\dfrac{1}{2}$, find $\sin \theta$. $-\dfrac{\sqrt{5}}{5}$

11. If $\csc \theta = -8$, find $\sec \theta$. $\dfrac{8\sqrt{7}}{21}$
12. If $\sec \theta = 3$, find $\cot \theta$. $-\dfrac{\sqrt{2}}{4}$

Speaking Activity Have students explain how trigonometric identities can be used to simplify an expression that contains trigonometric functions.

APPLYING THE LESSON

Homework Exercises

See assignment guide on page 799.

Chapter 17, Quiz A, (Lessons 17-1 through 17-2), is available in the Evaluation Masters Booklet, p. 233.

Teaching Tip ❶ Point out that students must be able to justify each step in the development of the identity.

Enrichment Masters Booklet, p. 114

```
~  17-2   NAME _____  DATE _____
         Enrichment Worksheet

Heron's Formula

Heron's formula can be used to find the area of a triangle if you
know the lengths of the three sides. Consider any triangle ABC. Let
K represent the area of △ABC. Then
```

$K = \frac{1}{2} bc \sin A$

$K^2 = \frac{b^2 c^2 \sin^2 A}{4}$ *Square both sides.*

$= \frac{b^2 c^2 (1 - \cos^2 A)}{4}$

$= \frac{b^2 c^2 (1 + \cos A)(1 - \cos A)}{4}$

$= \frac{b^2 c^2}{4}\left(1 + \frac{b^2 + c^2 - a^2}{2bc}\right)\left(1 - \frac{b^2 + c^2 - a^2}{2bc}\right)$ *Use the law of cosines.*

$= \frac{b + c + a}{2} \cdot \frac{b + c - a}{2} \cdot \frac{a + b - c}{2} \cdot \frac{a - b + c}{2}$ *Simplify.*

Let $s = \frac{a + b + c}{2}$. Then $s - a = \frac{b + c - a}{2}, s - b = \frac{a + c - b}{2}, s - c = \frac{a + b - c}{2}$.

$K^2 = s(s - a)(s - b)(s - c)$ *Substitute.*

$K = \sqrt{s(s - a)(s - b)(s - c)}$

Heron's Formula | The area of △ABC is $\sqrt{s(s - a)(s - b)(s - c)}$, where $s = \frac{a + b + c}{2}$.

Use Heron's formula to find the area of △ABC.

1. $a = 3, b = 4.4, c = 7$ **4.1**   2. $a = 8.2, b = 10.3, c = 9.5$ **36.8**

3. $a = 31.3, b = 92.0, c = 67.9$ **782.9**   4. $a = 0.54, b = 1.32, c = 0.78$ **no such triangle**

5. $a = 321, b = 178, c = 298$ **26160.9**   6. $a = 0.05, b = 0.08, c = 0.04$ **0.00082**

7. $a = 21.5, b = 33.0, c = 41.7$ **351.6**   8. $a = 2.08, b = 9.13, c = 8.99$ **9.3**

Solve for values of θ between 270° and 360°.

33. If $\tan \theta = -1$, find $\sec \theta$. $\sqrt{2}$ 34. If $\cos \theta = \frac{5}{13}$, find $\sin \theta$. $-\frac{12}{13}$

35. If $\csc \theta = -\frac{5}{3}$, find $\cos \theta$. $\frac{4}{5}$ 36. If $\sec \theta = \frac{5}{3}$, find $\cos \theta$. $\frac{3}{5}$

Simplify each expression.

37. $\sec^2 \theta - 1$ **$\tan^2 \theta$**   38. $\csc \alpha \cos \alpha \tan \alpha$ **1**

39. $\tan \beta \cot \beta$ **1**   40. $\sin x + \cos x \tan x$ **$2 \sin x$**

41. $\frac{1}{\sin^2 \theta} - \frac{\cos^2 \theta}{\sin^2 \theta}$ **1**   42. $\sin \beta(1 + \cot^2 \beta)$ **$\csc \beta$**

43. $2(\csc^2 \theta - \cot^2 \theta)$ **2**   44. $\frac{\tan^2 \theta - \sin^2 \theta}{\tan^2 \theta \sin^2 \theta}$ **1**

▶ **Show that each equation is an identity. 45–48. See Solutions Manual.**

Teaching Tip ❶

45. $1 + \cot^2 \theta = \csc^2 \theta$ 46. $\sin x \sec x = \tan x$

47. $\frac{\sec \theta}{\csc \theta} = \tan \theta$ 48. $\sec \alpha - \cos \alpha = \sin \alpha \tan \alpha$

Critical Thinking   49. If $\tan \beta = \frac{3}{4}$, find $\frac{\sin \beta \sec \beta}{\cot \beta}$. $\frac{9}{16}$

Applications   50. **Surveying** A surveyor found that the angle between the line from his position to a building and the line from his position to a road had a sine value of $\frac{5}{9}$.

    a. Find the value of the cosine of this angle. Assume that the angle is acute.

    b. Find the value of the cotangent of this angle. Assume that the angle is obtuse.

    c. Find the value of the secant of this angle. Assume that the angle is obtuse.

    50. a. $\frac{\sqrt{56}}{9}$ **b.** $-\frac{\sqrt{56}}{5}$ **c.** $\frac{9\sqrt{56}}{56}$

Mixed Review   51. **Entertainment** Jeanine is writing a word puzzle for the school newspaper. She is scrambling words for the readers to unscramble to find the answer to the riddle. How many different ways could Jeanine scramble the word HOMECOMING? **(Lesson 15-2) 907,200**

52. State the excluded values of x if $\frac{2x + 1}{3x} - \frac{x - 1}{x} = \frac{1}{2x + 3}$. Then solve and check. **(Lesson 11-5)** $0, -\frac{3}{2}; -2, 3$

53. Write an equation for the circle whose center is $(6, 0)$ and whose radius is 6 inches. **(Lesson 9-3)** $(x - 6)^2 + y^2 = 36$

    $y = 200x - 2x^2$

54. **Horticulture** Bill Taylor's garden has a fence along one side. He wishes to fence in the other three sides with 200 feet of fencing. Write a quadratic function to describe the area of the garden. **(Lesson 8-1)**

55. Simplify $(8b^2 - 4b + 1) \div (2b - 1)$. **(Lesson 5-7)** $4b + \frac{1}{2b - 1}$

56. State the domain and range of the relation $\{(0, 4), (8, -8), (8, 3), (0, -12), (0, 0)\}$. Then state if the relation is a function. **(Lesson 2-1)** **domain:** $\{0, 8\}$; **range:** $\{-12, -8, 0, 3, 4\}$; **no**

EXTENDING THE LESSON

Math Power: Problem Solving

If $\cot \theta = \frac{4}{5}$ and θ is in the third quadrant, find

$$\frac{\cos \theta \csc \theta}{\tan \theta} \cdot \frac{(\csc \theta + 1)(\csc \theta - 1)}{\dfrac{1 - \cos^2 \theta}{1 - \sin^2 \theta}}.$$

$\dfrac{4096}{15,625}$

Graphing Calculator Exploration: Verifying Trigonometric Identities

You can use your graphing calculator to determine whether an equation is a trigonometric identity. Recall that equations that are *true* for all values of the variable for which they are defined are called *identities*.

The expressions on each side of the equals sign can be graphed as two different functions to verify identities. For example, if you were trying to verify that $\sec^2 x + \csc^2 x = \sec^2 x \csc^2 x$ is an identity, you would graph $y = \sec^2 x + \csc^2 x$ and $y = \sec^2 x \csc^2 x$. If the graphs of the two functions don't match, then the equation is not an identity. If the graphs do coincide, then the equation *may* be an identity. The equation must be verified algebraically to be sure that it is an identity.

Example 1

Use your graphing calculator to determine whether $\sec^2 x + \csc^2 x = \sec^2 x \csc^2 x$ may be an identity. **Teaching Tip ❶**

Graph the equations $y = \sec^2 x + \csc^2 x$ and $y = \sec^2 x \csc^2 x$. Use the viewing window $[-360, 360]$ by $[-10, 10]$ with a scale factor of 180 for the x-axis and 1 for the y-axis.

Recall that $\sec x = \dfrac{1}{\cos x}$ and $\csc x = \dfrac{1}{\sin x}$. **Teaching Tip ❷**

Casio

ENTER:
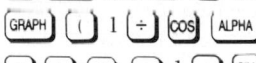
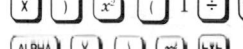

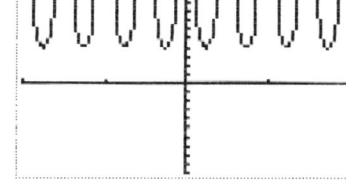

TI-81

ENTER: [Y=] [(] 1 [÷] [COS] [X|T] [)] [x²] [+] [(] 1 [÷] [SIN] [X|T]
[)] [x²] [ENTER] [(] 1 [÷] [COS] [X|T] [)] [x²] [(] 1 [÷] [SIN]
[X|T] [)] [x²] [GRAPH]

Since the graphs of the two functions coincide, the equation *may* be an identity. *Graph the functions again in the opposite order to be sure that the graphs match.*

GRAPHING CALCULATOR EXPLORATION: VERIFYING TRIGONOMETRIC IDENTITIES 801

Graphing Calculator Exploration

INTRODUCING THE LESSON

Objective: Graph trigonometric identities on a graphing calculator to verify whether they are true.

Motivating the Lesson

Put the trigonometric identity $\cos^2 x + \sin^2 x = 1$ on the chalkboard or overhead. Ask students if this is a true statement. Then ask them how they can show whether it is true. Show students that you can graph both sides on a graphing calculator to verify identities.

TEACHING THE LESSON

Teaching Tip ❶ Graphing two functions on a graphing calculator does not prove that they are identities because the two may be off by a very small fraction and you may not be able to tell this on your calculator.

Teaching Tip ❷ Entering $x²$ before x will result in a calculator error. On the graphing calculator, you need to enter the function and then square it. You will also need to use parentheses around the function or else the calculator will read it as, for example, $\cos(x^2)$ instead of $\cos^2 x$.

RETEACHING THE LESSON

If students are having problems with entering the functions correctly into the calculator, write the keystrokes on the chalkboard or overhead for a few identities. This may help them to see where parentheses are needed.

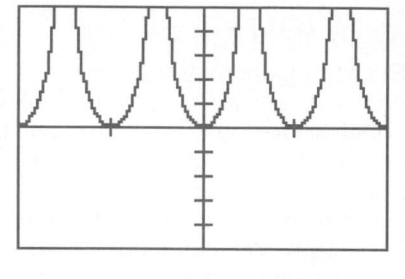

EVALUATING THE LESSON

APPLYING THE LESSON

Example 2 Use a graphing calculator to determine whether $\tan \dfrac{x}{2} = \dfrac{2 \sin x}{1 + 2 \cos x}$ may be an identity.

Graph the equations $y = \tan \dfrac{x}{2}$ and $y = \dfrac{2 \sin x}{1 + 2 \cos x}$. Use the viewing window $[-180, 540]$ by $[-6, 6]$ with a scale factor of 180 for the x-axis and 2 for the y-axis.

Casio

ENTER: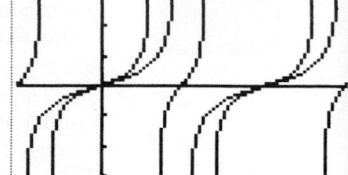

TI-81

ENTER: [Y=] [TAN] [(] [X|T] [÷] [2] [)]
[ENTER] [(] [2] [SIN] [X|T] [)] [÷]
[(] [1] [+] [2] [COS] [X|T] [)]
[GRAPH]

Vertical asymptotes may appear on the viewing screen.

The graphs of the functions do not match, so the equation is not an identity.

EXERCISES

Use your graphing calculator to determine whether each equation *may* be an identity. Write *yes* or *no*.

1. $\dfrac{1 + \sin x}{\cos x} = \dfrac{\cos x}{1 - \sin x}$ **yes**

2. $\cot x + \tan x = \csc x \cot x$ **no**

3. $\tan x (\cot x + \tan x) = \sec^2 x$ **yes**

4. $\cos^2 x + \tan^2 x \cos^2 x = 1$ **yes**

5. $\sin(90° - x) = \cos x$ **yes**

6. $\cot^2 x \sec^2 x = 1 + \cot^2 x$ **yes**

7. $\sin x + \cos x \tan x = 2 \sin x$ **yes**

8. $\cos x \sin x \tan x = 1$ **no**

9. $\csc x - \cos x = \sin x \tan x$ **no**

10. $\dfrac{1}{\sec x} + \dfrac{1}{\csc x} = 1$ **no**

11. $\sin(x - 90°) = \cos x$ **no**

12. $\dfrac{1}{\sin^2 x} + \dfrac{1}{\cos^2 x} = 1$ **no**

13. $\dfrac{1 + \tan x}{1 + \cot x} = \dfrac{\sin x}{\cos x}$ **no**

14. $\dfrac{\sec x}{\sin x} - \dfrac{\sin x}{\cos x} = \cot x$ **yes**

15. $\dfrac{\cos x}{\sec x - 1} + \dfrac{\cos x}{\sec x + 1} = 2 \cot^2 x$ **yes**

16. $\dfrac{\sin x}{1 + \cos x} = \dfrac{1 - \cos x}{\sin x}$ **yes**

17. $\dfrac{\csc^2 x}{\csc x - 1} = \dfrac{1 + \sin x}{\sin x}$ **no**

18. $\dfrac{\tan x}{1 + \tan x} = \dfrac{\sin x}{\sin x + \cos x}$ **yes**

19. $\cos 3x + 1 = 2 \cos^2 x$ **yes**

20. $\cos 2x + 2 \sin^2 x = 1$ **yes**

EXTENDING THE LESSON

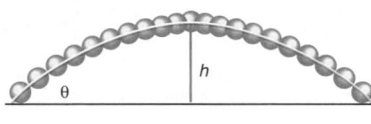

17-3 Verifying Trigonometric Identities

Objective 17-3

After studying this lesson, you should be able to:

■ verify trigonometric identities using various methods.

Application

The formula for the height of a projected object is $h = \dfrac{v_o^2 \sin^2 \theta}{2g}$, where θ is the measure of the angle of the elevation of the path of the object, v_o is the initial velocity of the

object, and g is the acceleration due to gravity. Is $h = \dfrac{v_o^2 \tan^2 \theta}{2g \sec^2 \theta}$ an equivalent

form for the height of the object? *You will solve this problem in Example 2.*

You can use the basic trigonometric identities and the definitions of the trigonometric functions to verify other identities. For example, suppose you wish to know if $\tan \theta(\cot \theta + \tan \theta) = \sec^2 \theta$ is an identity. It is not sufficient to try some value of θ and conclude that the statement is true for all values of θ if it is true for that one. To verify that an equation is an identity, the general case must be considered. **Teaching Tip ❶**

Verifying an identity is like checking the solution to an equation. You do not know if the expressions on each side of the equation are equal. That is what you are trying to verify. So, you must simplify one or both sides of the sentence *separately* until they are the same. Often, it is easier to work with only one side of the sentence. You may choose either side.

$$\tan \theta(\cot \theta + \tan \theta) \stackrel{?}{=} \sec^2 \theta \qquad \textit{Simplify the left side only.}$$
$$\tan \theta \left(\frac{1}{\tan \theta} + \tan \theta\right) \stackrel{?}{=} \sec^2 \theta \qquad \cot \theta = \frac{1}{\tan \theta}$$
$$1 + \tan^2 \theta \stackrel{?}{=} \sec^2 \theta \qquad \textit{Distributive property}$$
$$\sec^2 \theta = \sec^2 \theta \qquad 1 + \tan^2 \theta = \sec^2 \theta$$

Teaching Tip ❷

Thus, $\tan \theta(\cot \theta + \tan \theta) = \sec^2 \theta$ is an identity.

ALTERNATE TEACHING STRATEGIES

Using Models

To help students learn the basic trigonometric identities, have them write each side of the identity on separate cards. Have students match the cards that go together.

17-3 Lesson Notes

Lesson Resources

Reteaching Master 17-3
Practice Master 17-3
Enrichment Master 17-3
Technology Master, p. 17

Transparency 17-3 contains the 5-Minute Check and a teaching aid for this lesson.

INTRODUCING THE LESSON

⏱ 5-Minute Check

(over Lesson 17-2)

Simplify.

1. $\cos^2 \alpha + \tan^2 \alpha \cdot \cos^2 \alpha$ 1

2. $\dfrac{\cos \theta \cdot \csc \theta}{\tan \theta}$ $\cot^2 \theta$

3. Find $\cos \beta$ if $\tan \beta = -\dfrac{3}{5}$ and $90° \le \beta \le 180°$. $\dfrac{-5\sqrt{34}}{34}$

4. Find $\sin \theta$ if $\tan \theta = \sqrt{7}$ and $180° \le \theta \le 270°$. $\dfrac{-\sqrt{14}}{4}$

5. In which quadrants is cosecant a decreasing function?   I and IV

Motivating the Lesson

Ask students how many of them have ever used the phrase, "In other words, ...". Ask them what it means. Point out that there is more than one way to say the same thing.

TEACHING THE LESSON

Teaching Tip ❶   Caution students that identities hold for all values of the variable except those for which either side of the equation is undefined.

Teaching Tip ❷   Emphasize that students should look for relationships among the given expressions to determine the best expression to use when substituting.

Example 1

Verify $\dfrac{\cos^2 x}{1 - \sin x} = 1 + \sin x$.

Notice that if the denominator, $1 - \sin x$, is multiplied by $1 + \sin x$, the result is $1 - \sin^2 x$, which equals $\cos^2 x$.

$$\frac{\cos^2 x}{1 - \sin x} \stackrel{?}{=} 1 + \sin x$$

$$\frac{\cos^2 x}{1 - \sin x} \cdot \frac{1 + \sin x}{1 + \sin x} \stackrel{?}{=} 1 + \sin x \qquad \text{\textit{Multiply the numerator and denominator by } } 1 + \sin x.$$

$$\frac{\cos^2 x(1 + \sin x)}{1 - \sin^2 x} \stackrel{?}{=} 1 + \sin x \qquad \text{\textit{Simplify.}}$$

$$\frac{\cos^2 x(1 + \sin x)}{\cos^2 x} \stackrel{?}{=} 1 + \sin x \qquad \cos^2 x = 1 - \sin^2 x$$

$$1 + \sin x = 1 + \sin x$$

The identity could also be verified by working from the right side. The first step would be to multiply $1 + \sin x$ by $\dfrac{1 - \sin x}{1 - \sin x}$.

Example 2

APPLICATION

Physics

The formula for the height of a projected object is $h = \dfrac{v_o^2 \sin^2 \theta}{2g}$.

Is $h = \dfrac{v_o^2 \tan^2 \theta}{2g \sec^2 \theta}$ an equivalent formula for the height of the object?

$$\frac{v_o^2 \sin^2 \theta}{2g} \stackrel{?}{=} \frac{v_o^2 \tan^2 \theta}{2g \sec^2 \theta} \qquad \text{\textit{Simplify the right side.}}$$

$$\frac{v_o^2 \sin^2 \theta}{2g} \stackrel{?}{=} \frac{v_o^2 \left(\dfrac{\sin^2 \theta}{\cos^2 \theta}\right)}{2g\left(\dfrac{1}{\cos^2 \theta}\right)} \qquad \tan^2 \theta = \frac{\sin^2 \theta}{\cos^2 \theta}, \ \sec^2 \theta = \frac{1}{\cos^2 \theta}$$

$$\frac{v_o^2 \sin^2 \theta}{2g} \stackrel{?}{=} \frac{\dfrac{v_o^2 \sin^2 \theta}{\cos^2 \theta}}{\dfrac{2g}{\cos^2 \theta}} \qquad \text{\textit{Simplify.}}$$

$$\frac{v_o^2 \sin^2 \theta}{2g} = \frac{v_o^2 \sin^2 \theta}{2g} \qquad \text{\textit{Multiply the numerator and denominator of the right side by } } \cos^2 \theta.$$

So, the formulas are equivalent.

The following suggestions may be helpful as you verify trigonometric identities. Study the examples to see how these suggestions can be used to verify an identity.

■ Start with the more complicated side of the equation. Transform the expression into the form of the simpler side.

or

Work with each side of the equation at the same time. Transform each expression separately into the same form.

RETEACHING THE LESSON

Have students verify some trigonometric identities by numerical substitution. For each value that the students pick for the angle, have them compute the values of both sides of the identity. To avoid roundoff errors, round results to 2 fewer places than used in the calculations. Stress that this only verifies the identity for the value chosen.

- Substitute one or more basic trigonometric identities to simplify the expression.
- Try factoring or multiplying to simplify the expression.
- Multiply both the numerator and the denominator by the same trigonometric expression.

Example 3

Verify that $1 - \cot^4 \beta = 2 \csc^2 \beta - \csc^4 \beta$.

$$1 - \cot^4 \beta \stackrel{?}{=} 2 \csc^2 \beta - \csc^4 \beta$$
$$(1 - \cot^2 \beta)(1 + \cot^2 \beta) \stackrel{?}{=} \csc^2 \beta \,(2 - \csc^2 \beta) \qquad \textit{Factor each side.}$$
$$[1 - (\csc^2 \beta - 1)][\csc^2 \beta] \stackrel{?}{=} (2 - \csc^2 \beta)(\csc^2 \beta) \qquad \textit{1 + cot}^2 \beta = csc^2 \beta$$
$$(2 - \csc^2 \beta)(\csc^2 \beta) = (2 - \csc^2 \beta)(\csc^2 \beta) \qquad \textit{Simplify.}$$

Thus, the identity is verified.

Chalkboard Example

For Example 3

Verify $\csc x + 1 = \dfrac{\cot^2 x}{\csc x - 1}$.

$$\csc x + 1 \stackrel{?}{=} \frac{\cot^2 x(\csc x + 1)}{(\csc x - 1)(\csc x + 1)}$$
$$\csc x + 1 \stackrel{?}{=} \frac{\cot^2 x(\csc x + 1)}{\csc^2 x - 1}$$
$$\csc x + 1 \stackrel{?}{=} \frac{\cot^2 x(\csc x + 1)}{\cot^2 x}$$
$$\csc x + 1 = \csc x + 1$$

CHECKING FOR UNDERSTANDING

Communicating Mathematics

Read and study the lesson to answer these questions.

1. Describe the different methods you can use to verify trigonometric identities. **See students' work.**

2. Verify the identity in Example 2 by simplifying each side separately into the same form. **See students' work.**

Guided Practice

Verify that each of the following is an identity. **3–6. See Solutions Manual.**

3. $\sin \theta \sec \theta \cot \theta = 1$

4. $\tan^2 x \cos^2 x = 1 - \cos^2 x$

5. $\csc y \sec y = \cot y + \tan y$

6. $\tan \alpha \sin \alpha \cos \alpha \csc^2 \alpha = 1$

EVALUATING THE LESSON

Checking for Understanding

Exercises 1–6 are designed to help you assess understanding through reading, writing, and speaking. You should work through Exercises 1–2 with your students, and then monitor their work on Exercises 3–6.

Assignment Guide

Basic: 7–22, 29–35
Average: 10–25, 29–35
Enriched: 13–35

EXERCISES

Practice

Verify that each of the following is an identity. **7–20. See Solutions Manual.**

 A

7. $\sec^2 x - \tan^2 x = \tan x \cot x$

8. $\dfrac{1}{\sec^2 \theta} + \dfrac{1}{\csc^2 \theta} = 1$

9. $\dfrac{\sec \alpha}{\sin \alpha} - \dfrac{\sin \alpha}{\cos \alpha} = \cot \alpha$

10. $\tan^2 \theta - \sin^2 \theta = \tan^2 \theta \sin^2 \theta$

11. $\dfrac{\sin \alpha}{1 - \cos \alpha} + \dfrac{1 - \cos \alpha}{\sin \alpha} = 2 \csc \alpha$

12. $\dfrac{\sec \beta + \csc \beta}{1 + \tan \beta} = \csc \beta$

B
13. $\dfrac{1 - \cos x}{\sin x} = \dfrac{\sin x}{1 + \cos x}$

14. $\dfrac{\sin \theta}{\sec \theta} = \dfrac{1}{\tan \theta + \cot \theta}$

15. $\dfrac{1 - \cos x}{1 + \cos x} = (\csc x - \cot x)^2$

16. $\dfrac{\sec \theta + 1}{\tan \theta} = \dfrac{\tan \theta}{\sec \theta - 1}$

17. $\dfrac{\cot \theta + \csc \theta}{\sin \theta + \tan \theta} = \cot \theta \csc \theta$

18. $\cos^2 x + \tan^2 x \cos^2 x = 1$

19. $\dfrac{1 - 2 \cos^2 \beta}{\sin \beta \cos \beta} = \tan \beta - \cot \beta$

20. $\dfrac{1 + \tan^2 \theta}{\csc^2 \theta} = \tan^2 \theta$

LESSON 17-3 VERIFYING TRIGONOMETRIC IDENTITIES 805

Practice Masters Booklet, p. 131

17-3 NAME _____ DATE _____
Practice Worksheet
Verifying Trigonometric Identities
Verify that each of the following is an identity.

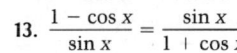
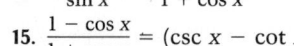

1. $(1 + \sin \theta)(1 - \sin \theta) = \frac{1}{\sec^2 \theta}$
$(1 + \sin \theta)(1 - \sin \theta) \stackrel{?}{=} \frac{1}{\sec^2 \theta}$
$1 - \sin^2 \theta \stackrel{?}{=} \cos^2 \theta$
$\cos^2 \theta = \cos^2 \theta$

2. $\cos^2 x \cot^2 x = \cot^2 x - \cos^2 x$
$\cos^2 x \cot^2 x \stackrel{?}{=} \cot^2 x - \cos^2 x$
$\cos^2 x \cdot \frac{\cos^2 x}{\sin^2 x} \stackrel{?}{=} \frac{\cos^2 x}{\sin^2 x} - \frac{\cos^2 x \sin^2 x}{\sin^2 x}$
$\frac{\cos^4 x}{\sin^2 x} \stackrel{?}{=} \frac{\cos^2 x(1 - \sin^2 x)}{\sin^2 x}$
$\frac{\cos^4 x}{\sin^2 x} = \frac{\cos^4 x}{\sin^2 x}$

3. $\tan^4 w + 2 \tan^2 w + 1 = \sec^4 w$
$\tan^4 w + 2 \tan^2 w + 1 \stackrel{?}{=} \sec^4 w$
$(\tan^2 w + 1)^2 \stackrel{?}{=} \sec^4 w$
$(\sec^2 w)^2 \stackrel{?}{=} \sec^4 w$
$\sec^4 w = \sec^4 w$

4. $\sin^2 x(\csc^2 x + \sec^2 x) = \sec^2 x$
$\sin^2 x(\csc^2 x + \sec^2 x) \stackrel{?}{=} \sec^2 x$
$1 + \frac{\sin^2 x}{\cos^2 x} \stackrel{?}{=} \sec^2 x$
$1 + \tan^2 x \stackrel{?}{=} \sec^2 x$
$\sec^2 x = \sec^2 x$

5. $\frac{\sin x + \cos x}{1 - \sin x} = \frac{1 + \cot x}{\csc x - 1}$
$\frac{\sin x + \cos x}{1 - \sin x} \stackrel{?}{=} \frac{1 + \cot x}{\csc x - 1}$
$\frac{\frac{\sin x}{\sin x} + \frac{\cos x}{\sin x}}{\frac{1}{\sin x} - \frac{\sin x}{\sin x}} \stackrel{?}{=} \frac{1 + \cot x}{\csc x}$
$\frac{1 + \cot x}{\csc x - 1} = \frac{1 + \cot x}{\csc x - 1}$

6. $\frac{1 - \tan x}{1 + \tan x} = \frac{\cot x - 1}{\cot x + 1}$
$\frac{1 - \tan x}{1 + \tan x} \stackrel{?}{=} \frac{\cot x - 1}{\cot x + 1}$
$\frac{\frac{1}{\tan x} - \frac{\tan x}{\tan x}}{\frac{1}{\tan x} + \frac{\tan x}{\tan x}} \stackrel{?}{=} \frac{\cot x - 1}{\cot x + 1}$
$\frac{\cot x - 1}{\cot x + 1} = \frac{\cot x - 1}{\cot x + 1}$

Error Analysis

It is important that students do not assume nor use properties of equality when trying to establish an identity.
For example prove $x = x + 2$.

Multiply by 2.	$2x = 2x + 4$
Add 4.	$2x + 4 = 2x + 8$
Divide by 2.	$x + 2 = x + 4$
Subtract 2.	$x = x + 2$

Equality is *not* a given.

Closing the Lesson

Speaking Activity Have students explain what is meant by verifying a trigonometric identity.

APPLYING THE LESSON

Homework Exercises

See assignment guide on page 805.

Enrichment Masters Booklet, p. 115

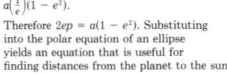

Verify that each of the following is an identity. 21–28. See Solutions Manual.

21. $\dfrac{\cos y}{1 + \sin y} + \dfrac{\cos y}{1 - \sin y} = 2 \sec y$

22. $\dfrac{1 + \sin x}{\sin x} = \dfrac{\cot^2 x}{\csc x - 1}$

23. $\cot x(\cot x + \tan x) = \csc^2 x$

24. $\cos^4 \theta - \sin^4 \theta = \cos^2 \theta - \sin^2 \theta$

25. $\dfrac{1 + \tan \gamma}{1 + \cot \gamma} = \dfrac{\sin \gamma}{\cos \gamma}$

26. $\dfrac{\tan^2 x}{\sec x - 1} = 1 + \dfrac{1}{\cos x}$

27. $1 + \sec^2 x \sin^2 x = \sec^2 x$

28. $\sin \theta + \cos \theta = \dfrac{1 + \tan \theta}{\sec \theta}$

Critical Thinking

29. Create a trigonometric identity. Explain the method you used to do this. Then trade with another student and verify each other's identities. **See students' work.**

Applications

30. **Optics** The illumination, E, in footcandles on a surface that is R feet from a source of light with intensity I candelas is $E = \dfrac{I \cos \theta}{R^2}$, where θ is the measure of the angle between the direction of the light and a line perpendicular to the surface being illuminated.

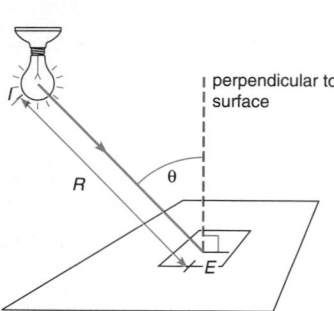

perpendicular to surface

a. Show that the formula $E = \dfrac{I \cot \theta}{R^2 \csc \theta}$ is equivalent to the one given above. **See students' work.**

b. Find the illumination on a surface that is 10 feet from a source of light that emits 12 candelas. Angle θ measures 0°. **0.12 footcandles**

c. An illumination of about 20 footcandles is recommended for reading. How far away should a 75-watt light of intensity 90 candelas be placed if angle θ measures 30°? **1.97 feet**

31. $\dfrac{2187}{16384}$ or about 0.133

Mixed Review

31. **Probability** Leshia wins 3 out of every 4 games of chess that she plays. If she played 7 games with Edward, what is the probability that Leshia won all of the games? **(Lesson 15-9)**

32. **Statistics** The cost per cup of several different types of juices are given below. Make a stem-and-leaf plot of the costs. **(Lesson 14-2) See margin.**

11¢ 9¢ 6¢ 9¢ 12¢ 4¢ 4¢ 8¢ 6¢ 4¢ 16¢
12¢ 11¢ 19¢ 7¢ 19¢ 7¢ 19¢ 4¢ 6¢ 5¢ 6¢

33. Write an expression for $\log_5 82$ in terms of common logarithms. Then approximate the logarithm to three decimal places. **(Lesson 12-7)** $\dfrac{\log 82}{\log 5}$; **2.738**

34. Find the sum and the product of the roots of the quadratic equation $2x^2 + 10x + 8 = 0$. Then solve the equation. **(Lesson 7-5) −5, 4; −1, −4**

35. Find the transpose and the inverse of $\begin{bmatrix} -10 & 3 \\ 0 & -2 \end{bmatrix}$. **(Lesson 4-4) See margin.**

Enrichment Worksheet

NAME _____ DATE _____

17-3 Enrichment Worksheet

Planetary Orbits

The orbit of a planet around the sun is an ellipse with the sun at one focus. Let the pole of a polar coordinate system be that focus and the polar axis be toward the other focus. The polar equation of an ellipse is $r = \dfrac{2\,ep}{1 - e \cos \theta}$. Since $2p = \dfrac{b^2}{c}$ and $b^2 = a^2 - c^2$, $2p = \dfrac{a^2 - c^2}{c} = \dfrac{a^2}{c}\left(1 - \dfrac{c^2}{a^2}\right)$.

Because $e = \dfrac{c}{a}$, $2p = a\!\left(\dfrac{a}{c}\right)\!(1 - (\tfrac{c}{a})^2) = a\!\left(\dfrac{1}{e}\right)(1 - e^2)$.

Therefore $2ep = a(1 - e^2)$. Substituting into the polar equation of an ellipse yields an equation that is useful for finding distances from the planet to the sun.

$$r = \dfrac{a(1 - e^2)}{1 - e \cos \theta}$$

Note that e is the eccentricity of the orbit and a is the length of the semi-major axis of the ellipse. Also, a is the mean distance of the planet from the sun.

Example: The mean distance of Venus from the sun is 67.24×10^6 miles and the eccentricity of its orbit is 0.006788. Find the minimum and maximum distances of Venus from the sun.
The minimum distance occurs when $\theta = \pi$.
$r = \dfrac{67.24 \times 10^6(1 - 0.006788^2)}{1 - 0.006788 \cos \pi} = 66.78 \times 10^6$ miles
The maximum distance occurs when $\theta = 0$.
$r = \dfrac{67.24 \times 10^6(1 - 0.006788^2)}{1 - 0.006788 \cos 0} = 67.70 \times 10^6$ miles

Complete each of the following.

1. The mean distance of Mars from the sun is 141.64×10^6 miles and the eccentricity of its orbit is 0.093382. Find the minimum and maximum distances of Mars from the sun.
max. dist. = 15.49×10^7 mi   **min. dist. = 12.84×10^7 mi**

2. The minimum distance of Earth from the sun is 91.445×10^6 miles and the eccentricity of its orbit is 0.016734. Find the mean and maximum distances of Earth from the sun.
max. dist. = 93.00×10^6 mi   **mean dist. = 91.47×10^6 mi**

EXTENDING THE LESSON

Math Power: Problem Solving

Verify the following identity.

$$\dfrac{\sec x - \tan x}{\dfrac{\cos x}{1 + \sin x}} = 1$$

Additional Answer

32.
Stem	Leaf
0	4 4 4 4
●	5 6 6 6 6 7 7 8 9 9
1	1 1 2 2
●	6 9 9 9

1 | 1 represents 11¢

35. $\begin{bmatrix} -10 & 0 \\ 3 & -2 \end{bmatrix}$; $\begin{bmatrix} -\dfrac{1}{10} & -\dfrac{3}{20} \\ 0 & -\dfrac{1}{2} \end{bmatrix}$

17-4 Problem-Solving Strategy: Working Backwards

Objective
17-4

After studying this lesson, you should be able to:
- solve problems using the strategy of working backwards.

Most problems are given to you with a set of conditions. Then you must find a solution. However, in some cases, like verifying a trigonometric identity, it is faster to determine how the problem ends and then work backwards rather than start from the beginning to find the solution.

Example 1

Find the sum of the reciprocals of two numbers whose sum is 2 and whose product is 3.

Let x and y be the numbers.
We could set up these equations.

$$x + y = 2$$
$$xy = 3$$

But, solving the system of equations is complicated. Rather than using this approach, work backwards. The desired outcome is $\frac{1}{x} + \frac{1}{y}$.

$$\frac{1}{x} + \frac{1}{y} = \frac{y}{xy} + \frac{x}{xy} \qquad \textit{The LCD is xy.}$$
$$= \frac{x + y}{xy}$$

Looking back to our two original equations, we can see that $x + y = 2$ and $xy = 3$. So, $\frac{x + y}{xy} = \frac{2}{3}$.

The sum of the reciprocals is $\frac{2}{3}$.

Example 2

APPLICATION

Fire Fighting

A fire fighter spraying water on a fire stood on the middle rung of a ladder. The smoke lessened, so she moved up 3 rungs. It got too hot, so she backed down 5 rungs. Later, she went up 7 rungs and stayed until the fire was out. Then, she climbed the remaining 4 rungs and went into the building. How many rungs does the ladder have? Teaching Tip **1**

We know that the fire fighter was on the middle rung in the beginning.

She climbed up 3, backed up 5, went up 7, then up 4 more. So she went up $3 + (-5) + 7 + 4$ or 9 rungs.

Since she had to climb 9 rungs to enter the building and she was on the middle rung, there are 19 rungs on the ladder.

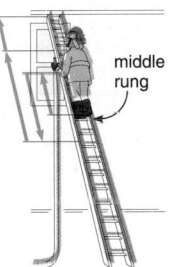

middle rung

LESSON 17-4 PROBLEM-SOLVING STRATEGY: WORKING BACKWARDS 807

ALTERNATE TEACHING STRATEGIES

Using Cooperative Groups

Working in cooperative groups, have students write several verbal problems that can be solved by working backwards. Have groups exchange problems then solve them.

Lesson Resources

Practice Master 17-4
Activity Master, p. 17

 Transparency 17-4 contains the 5-Minute Check and a teaching aid for this lesson.

INTRODUCING THE LESSON

 5-Minute Check

(over Lesson 17-3)
True or *False:*

1. $\sin \theta \cdot \cot \theta = \cos \theta$ **true**
2. $1 + \tan^2 \theta = \cot^2 \theta$ **false**

Verify each identity.

3. $\tan^2 \beta - \sin^2 \beta = \tan^2 \beta$
   $\quad \sin^2 \beta$
   $\frac{\sin^2 \beta}{\cos^2 \beta} - \sin^2 \beta = \tan^2 \beta$
   $\quad \sin^2 \beta$
   $\sin^2 \beta \left(\frac{1}{\cos^2 \beta} - 1 \right) = \tan^2 \beta$
   $\quad \sin^2 \beta$
   $\sin^2 \beta (\sec^2 \beta - 1) =$
   $\quad \tan^2 \beta \sin^2 \beta$
   $\sin^2 \beta \cdot \tan^2 \beta = \tan^2 \beta$
   $\quad \sin^2 \beta$

4. $\cot^2 \alpha - \cot^2 \alpha \cdot \sec^2 \alpha = -1$
   $\cot^2 \alpha (1 - \sec^2 \alpha) = -1$
   $\cot^2 \alpha (-\tan^2 \alpha) = -1$
   $\cot^2 \alpha - \left(\frac{1}{\cot^2 \alpha} \right) = -1$
   $-1 = -1$

Motivating the Lesson

Show students a receipt that has been handwritten and totaled. Ask them if they thought the total were too much, what they would do to check it. Elicit student responses regarding working backwards from the total.

TEACHING THE LESSON

Teaching Tip **1** Encourage use of diagrams where needed to help solve the problems.

CHECKING FOR UNDERSTANDING

Communicating Mathematics

1. when it is faster to start from the end than from the beginning

Read and study the lesson to answer these questions.

1. When can you use the strategy of working backwards?

2. How many rungs would the ladder used by the fire fighter in Example 2 have had if she had been standing three-fourths of the way up the ladder? **36**

3. Explain how the strategy of working backwards can be used when you are verifying a trigonometric identity. **See students' work.**

Guided Practice

Solve each problem by working backwards.

4. If the sum of two numbers is 4 and the product of the numbers is 7, find the sum of the squares of the reciprocals of these numbers. $\frac{2}{49}$

5. A pirate found a treasure chest containing silver coins. He buried half of them and gave half of the remaining coins to his mother. If he was left with 4550 coins, how many were in the chest when he found it? **18,200**

6. After cashing her paycheck, Caroline paid her father back the $15 she had borrowed. She then spent half of the remaining money on clothes, and then spent half of what remained on a concert ticket. She bought a cassette tape for $7.45 and had $10.25 left. What was the amount of Caroline's paycheck? **$85.80**

Exercises Use any strategy. **Teaching Tip ②**

Strategies

Look for a pattern.
Solve a simpler problem.
Act it out.
Guess and check.
Draw a diagram.
Make a chart.
Work backwards.

7. Juana collects postcards from the places that she has visited. If she counts the postcards by twos, threes, fours, fives, or sixes, there is always one left over. If she counts the postcards by sevens, none remain. What is the fewest number of postcards Juana could have? **301**

8. Find the value of $\sqrt{11 + \sqrt{72}} + \sqrt{11 - \sqrt{72}}$. **6**

9. Kevin and Madeline are starting to play a game. They each roll one die to determine who will go first. What is the most likely product of the numbers on the dice? Justify your answer. **6 or 12**

10. How many positive integers less than 500 have an odd number of positive integral factors? **22**

11. If the sum of two numbers is 2 and the product of the same two numbers is 3, find the sum of the squares of the reciprocals of these numbers. $-\frac{2}{9}$

808 CHAPTER 17 TRIGONOMETRIC GRAPHS, IDENTITIES, AND EQUATIONS

RETEACHING THE LESSON

Ann gives Pat and Sue as much money as each of them already has. Then Pat gives Ann and Sue as much money as each of them has. Finally, Sue gives Ann and Pat as much money as each of them has. Each girl ends up with $8. How much did each begin with?
Ann: $13, Pat: $7, Sue: $4

13. Answers may vary. A sample answer is
$5[5(5 + 5) - (5 + 5)]$.

15. 24, 25, 32, 43, 49, 51, 57, 68, 75, 76, 93, or 99

12. A customer bought a magazine from a bookstore for $3.50 and paid the cashier with a $10 bill. Since the cash register did not contain enough small bills to give the customer change, the bookstore manager went next door to the record store to get change. After the customer left, the record store manager came in to say that the $10 bill is counterfeit. The bookstore manager apologized and exchanged the counterfeit bill for a good one. How much money did the bookstore lose? **$10**

13. Mathematically combine six 5s so that 200 results.

14. Solve for x if $(\log x)^2 = \log (x^2)$. **1 or 100**

15. The fifth power of a two-digit number, x, ends in x. Find x.

16. What fraction of the area of rectangle $WXYZ$ is shaded? $\frac{2}{3}$

17. Tim used to collect model cars. He decides to give them away. First, he gave half of them plus half a car to his younger brother, Brad. Then he gives half of what is left plus half a car more to his friend Tammy. Tim has one car left, which he gives to Aaron. How many cars did Tim start with? (Assume that no car is cut in half.) **7**

COOPERATIVE LEARNING ACTIVITY

Work in groups. Each person in the group must understand the solution and be able to explain it to any person in class.

Arrange the numbers 1, 2, 2, 3, 4, 6, 6, and 12 in place of the letters a, b, c, d, e, f, g, and h so that $abc - cde - efg - gha$.
See margin.

a	b	c
h		d
g	f	e

EXTENDING THE LESSON

Math Power: Connections

Marta was balancing her checkbook. She had written checks for $13.85, $19.72, and $59.66. She had made one deposit of $97.92. Her bank statement stated that she had a final balance of $164.30. What was her starting balance? **$159.61**

Cooperative Learning Activity

This activity provides students with an opportunity to *learn* things together, not just do things together. You may wish to refer to pages T6–T8 and page 6C for the various elements of cooperative groups and specific goals and strategies for using them.

Chapter 17, Quiz B, (Lessons 17–3 through 17–4), is available in the Evaluation Masters Booklet, p. 233.

Teaching Tip ❷ Point out that, in solving the problems, there may be more than one correct strategy or a combination of strategies.

Answer for Cooperative Learning Activity

Sample answers are

2	3	4
6		6
2	12	1

3	4	6
2		2
12	1	6

Practice Masters Booklet, p. 132

Lesson Resources
Reteaching Master 17-5
Practice Master 17-5
Enrichment Master 17-5

 Transparency 17-5 contains the 5-Minute Check and a teaching aid for this lesson.

INTRODUCING THE LESSON

⏱ 5-Minute Check
(over Lesson 17-4)

1. If the sum of two numbers is 2 and the product is 3, find the sum of the squares of the reciprocals of these numbers.

$-\dfrac{2}{9}$

Other Prerequisite Skills

2. Find $\tan \theta$ if $\sin \theta = \dfrac{5}{13}$ and

$0° \le \theta \le 90°$. $\dfrac{5}{12}$

3. Verify $\csc \theta - \sin \theta = \cos \theta \cot \theta$.

$\dfrac{1}{\sin \theta} - \sin \theta = \cos \theta \cot \theta$

$\dfrac{1}{\sin \theta}(1 - \sin^2 \theta) = \cos \theta \cot \theta$

$\dfrac{1}{\sin \theta}(\cos^2 \theta) = \cos \theta \cot \theta$

$\dfrac{\cos \theta}{\sin \theta} \cos \theta = \cos \theta \cot \theta$

$\cos \theta \cot \theta = \cos \theta \cot \theta$

Motivating the Lesson
On a transparency, show a pizza drawn as a unit circle cut into 6 equal pieces. Ask students what must be done if seven students show up to eat the pizza and each student must have an equal share.

TEACHING THE LESSON

Teaching Tip ❶ Students will find it helpful to memorize values of the sine and cosine function for 0°, 30°, 45°, 60°, 90°, 120°, 135°, 150°, and 180°.

17-5 Sum and Difference of Angles Formulas

Objective
After studying this lesson, you should be able to:
17-5A ▪ find values of sine and cosine involving sum and difference formulas, and
17-5B ▪ verify identities using the sum and difference formulas.

Application

A geologist surveys a rectangular piece of land to determine whether it is suitable for development. He stands at one corner of the piece of property and measures the angle between one side of the lot and the line from his position to the opposite corner of the lot as 30°. He then measures the angle between that line and the line to the point in the property where a river crosses the property line as 45°. If the geologist stands 100 yards from the opposite corner of the property, how far is he from the point where the river crosses the property line? *You will solve this problem in Example 5.*

It is often helpful to use formulas for the trigonometric values of the difference or sum of two angles. For example, you could find sin 15° by evaluating sin (45 − 30)°. **Teaching Tip ❶**

The figure at the right shows two angles, α and β, in standard position on the unit circle.

Use the distance formula to find d, where $(x_1, y_1) = (\cos \alpha, \sin \alpha)$ and $(x_2, y_2) = (\cos \beta, \sin \beta)$.

$d = \sqrt{(\cos \alpha - \cos \beta)^2 + (\sin \alpha - \sin \beta)^2}$

$d^2 = (\cos \alpha - \cos \beta)^2 + (\sin \alpha - \sin \beta)^2$

$d^2 = (\cos^2 \alpha - 2 \cos \alpha \cos \beta + \cos^2 \beta) + (\sin^2 \alpha - 2 \sin \alpha \sin \beta + \sin^2 \beta)$

$d^2 = \cos^2 \alpha + \sin^2 \alpha + \cos^2 \beta + \sin^2 \beta - 2 \cos \alpha \cos \beta - 2 \sin \alpha \sin \beta$

$d^2 = 1 + 1 - 2 \cos \alpha \cos \beta - 2 \sin \alpha \sin \beta$ *$\sin^2 \alpha + \cos^2 \alpha = 1$ and $\sin^2 \beta + \cos^2 \beta = 1$*

$d^2 = 2 - 2 \cos \alpha \cos \beta - 2 \sin \alpha \sin \beta$

810 CHAPTER 17 TRIGONOMETRIC GRAPHS, IDENTITIES, AND EQUATIONS

ALTERNATE TEACHING STRATEGIES

Using Discussion
Discuss with students the development of the sum and difference of angle formulas for cos $(a \pm b)$ and sin $(a - b)$ as they are illustrated on page 811. Have students work with a partner to develop the formula for sin $(a + b)$, discussing and justifying each step.

Now find the value of d^2 when the angle having measure $\alpha - \beta$ is in standard position on the unit circle, as shown in the figure below.

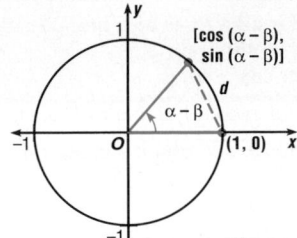

$[\cos(\alpha - \beta),$
$\sin(\alpha - \beta)]$

$$d = \sqrt{[\cos(\alpha - \beta) - 1]^2 + [\sin(\alpha - \beta) - 0]^2}$$
$$d^2 = [\cos(\alpha - \beta) - 1]^2 + [\sin(\alpha - \beta) - 0]^2$$
$$= [\cos^2(\alpha - \beta) - 2\cos(\alpha - \beta) + 1] + \sin^2(\alpha - \beta)$$
$$= \cos^2(\alpha - \beta) + \sin^2(\alpha - \beta) - 2\cos(\alpha - \beta) + 1$$
$$= \qquad\qquad 1 \qquad\qquad - 2\cos(\alpha - \beta) + 1$$
$$= 2 - 2\cos(\alpha - \beta)$$

By equating the two expressions for d^2, it is possible to find a formula for $\cos(\alpha - \beta)$.

$$d^2 = d^2$$
$$2 - 2\cos(\alpha - \beta) = 2 - 2\cos\alpha\cos\beta - 2\sin\alpha\sin\beta$$
$$-1 + \cos(\alpha - \beta) = -1 + \cos\alpha\cos\beta + \sin\alpha\sin\beta \qquad \textit{Divide each side by } -2.$$
$$\cos(\alpha - \beta) = \cos\alpha\cos\beta + \sin\alpha\sin\beta \qquad \textit{Add 1 to each side.}$$

Use the formula for $\cos(\alpha - \beta)$ to find a formula for $\cos(\alpha + \beta)$.

$$\cos(\alpha + \beta) = \cos[\alpha - (-\beta)] \qquad\qquad \textbf{Teaching Tip ❷}$$
$$= \cos\alpha\cos(-\beta) + \sin\alpha\sin(-\beta)$$
$$= \cos\alpha\cos\beta - \sin\alpha\sin\beta \qquad \cos(-\beta) = \cos\beta; \sin(-\beta) = -\sin\beta$$

Example 1

Use the formula for $\cos(\alpha - \beta)$ to find $\cos(90° - \theta)$.

$$\cos(90° - \theta) = \cos 90° \cos\theta + \sin 90° \sin\theta$$
$$= 0 \cdot \cos\theta + 1 \cdot \sin\theta$$
$$= \sin\theta$$

Example 2

Use the formula for $\cos(90° - \theta)$ from Example 1 to find $\sin(90° - \gamma)$.

$$\sin(90° - \gamma) = \cos[90° - (90° - \gamma)] \qquad \textit{Substitute } (90° - \gamma) \textit{ for } \theta$$
$$= \cos(90° - 90° + \gamma) \qquad\quad \textit{in } \sin\theta = \cos(90° - \theta).$$
$$= \cos\gamma$$

Example 3

Use the formulas for $\cos(90° - \theta)$ and $\sin(90° - \theta)$ from Examples 1 and 2 and the formula for $\cos(\alpha - \beta)$ to find $\sin(\alpha - \beta)$.

$$\sin(\alpha - \beta) = \cos[90° - (\alpha - \beta)] \quad \textit{Substitute } (\alpha - \beta) \textit{ for } \theta \textit{ in } \sin\theta = \cos(90° - \theta).$$
$$= \cos[(90° - \alpha) + \beta)] \quad \textit{Distributive and associative properties}$$
$$= \cos(90° - \alpha)\cos\beta - \sin(90° - \alpha)\sin\beta$$
$$= \sin\alpha\cos\beta - \cos\alpha\sin\beta$$

LESSON 17-5   SUM AND DIFFERENCE OF ANGLES FORMULAS   811

Teaching Tip ❷ You may want to use the symmetry of the unit circle to illustrate these relationships.

Chalkboard Examples

For Example 1

Use the formula for $\cos(\alpha + \beta)$ to find $\cos(270° + \theta)$.   **$\sin\theta$**

For Example 2

Use the formula for $\cos(270° + \theta)$ found in Chalkboard Example 1 to find $\sin(270° + \theta)$.   **$-\cos\theta$**

For Example 3

Use the formulas for $\cos(270° + \theta)$ and $\sin(270° + \theta)$ found in Chalkboard Examples 1 and 2 and the formula for $\cos(\alpha + \beta)$ to find $\sin(\alpha + \beta)$.
$\sin\alpha\cos\beta + \cos\alpha\sin\beta$

Teaching Tip ③   Be sure students understand the symbolism used in these formulas.

Teaching Tip ④   Point out that any sum or difference equal to 105° can be used, such as 135° − 30°, but for convenience, choices should be made that use known sines and cosines.

We can state the sum and difference identities as follows.
Teaching Tip ③

Sum and Difference of Angles Formulas	The following identities hold true for all values of α and β. cos (α ± β) = cos α cos β ∓ sin α sin β sin (α ± β) = sin α cos β ± cos α sin β

The following examples show how to evaluate expressions using the sum and difference formulas.

Example 4

Evaluate cos 105°.   **Teaching Tip ④**

cos 105° = cos (60° + 45°)
  = cos 60° cos 45° − sin 60° sin 45°   cos (α + β) =
  = $\frac{1}{2} \cdot \frac{\sqrt{2}}{2} - \frac{\sqrt{3}}{2} \cdot \frac{\sqrt{2}}{2}$ or $\frac{\sqrt{2} - \sqrt{6}}{4}$ cos α cos β − sin α sin β

$\dfrac{\sqrt{2} - \sqrt{6}}{4} \approx -0.2588$

Example 5

APPLICATION

Geology

As shown in the diagram below, a geologist measures the angle between one side of a rectangular lot and the line from his position to the opposite corner of the lot as 30°. He then measures the angle between that line and the line to the point in the property where a river crosses the property line as 45°. If the geologist stands 100 yards from the opposite corner of the property, how far is he from the point where the river crosses the property line?

First find x.

$\sin 30° = \dfrac{x}{100}$

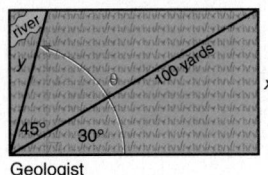

$100\left(\dfrac{1}{2}\right) = x$

50 = x

Geologist

Now, find sin θ expressed as sin (30° + 45°).

sin (30° + 45°) = sin 30° cos 45° + cos 30° sin 45°
  = $\frac{1}{2} \cdot \frac{\sqrt{2}}{2} + \frac{\sqrt{3}}{2} \cdot \frac{\sqrt{2}}{2}$ or $\frac{\sqrt{2} + \sqrt{6}}{4}$

$\sin \theta = \dfrac{50}{y}$

$y = \dfrac{50}{\dfrac{\sqrt{2} + \sqrt{6}}{4}}$ *Substitute* $\dfrac{\sqrt{2} + \sqrt{6}}{4}$ *for* sin θ.

$y = \dfrac{50}{\dfrac{\sqrt{2} + \sqrt{6}}{4}} \cdot \dfrac{\sqrt{2} - \sqrt{6}}{\sqrt{2} - \sqrt{6}}$

$y = \dfrac{50 (\sqrt{2} - \sqrt{6})}{\dfrac{2 - 6}{4}} = 50\sqrt{6} - 50\sqrt{2}$ or about 51.76

The geologist stands approximately 51.76 yards from the point where the river crosses the property line.

RETEACHING THE LESSON

Using cos (A − B) = cos A · cos B + sin A · sin B derived by analytic geometry, tell how to derive these other identities.

to find	substitute	in
cos (A + B)	−B for B	cos (A − B)
cos (90 − x)	90 for A	cos (A − B)
sin (90 − x)	90 − x = x	cos (90 − x)
sin (A − B)	A − B for x	cos (90 − x)
sin (A + B)	−B for B	sin (A − B)

CHECKING FOR UNDERSTANDING

Communicating Mathematics

Read and study the lesson to answer these questions. *See margin.*

1. Is it true that $\sin(x + y) = \sin x + \sin y$? Justify your answer.
2. Describe a method to find the exact value for cos 15°. Then find the value. **See students' work.;** $\dfrac{\sqrt{6} + \sqrt{2}}{4}$

Guided Practice

Express each angle measurement in terms of sums or differences of 30°, 45°, 60°, and 90° or their multiples.

3. $-15°$ **30° − 45°**   4. $165°$ **135° + 30°**   5. $75°$ **30° + 45°**

6. $285°$ **225° + 60°**   7. $255°$ **225° + 30°**   8. $345°$ **300° + 45°**

EXERCISES

Practice

9. $\dfrac{\sqrt{6} + \sqrt{2}}{4}$

10. $\dfrac{-\sqrt{2} - \sqrt{6}}{4}$

11. $\dfrac{\sqrt{6} - \sqrt{2}}{4}$

12. $\dfrac{\sqrt{6} - \sqrt{2}}{4}$

13. $\dfrac{-\sqrt{6} - \sqrt{2}}{4}$

14. $\dfrac{\sqrt{6} + \sqrt{2}}{4}$

15. $\dfrac{\sqrt{2} - \sqrt{6}}{4}$

16. $\dfrac{\sqrt{2} + \sqrt{6}}{4}$

17. $\dfrac{-\sqrt{6} - \sqrt{2}}{4}$

18. $\dfrac{\sqrt{3}}{2}$

19. $\dfrac{1}{2}$

20. $\dfrac{\sqrt{3}}{2}$

21. $\dfrac{1}{2}$

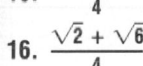 **A** Evaluate each expression.

9. $\sin 75°$ 10. $\sin 285°$ 11. $\cos 75°$

12. $\sin 165°$ 13. $\cos 195°$ 14. $\sin 105°$

15. $\cos 255°$ 16. $\cos 345°$ 17. $\cos 165°$

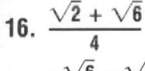 **B**
18. $\sin 40° \cos 20° + \cos 40° \sin 20°$ 19. $\sin 65° \cos 35° - \cos 65° \sin 35°$

20. $\cos 25° \cos 5° - \sin 25° \sin 5°$ 21. $\cos 80° \cos 20° + \sin 80° \sin 20°$

Verify that each of the following is an identity. **22–31. See Solutions Manual.**

22. $\cos(270° - \theta) = -\sin\theta$ 23. $\sin(270° - \theta) = -\cos\theta$

24. $\sin(180° + \theta) = -\sin\theta$ 25. $\sin(90° + \theta) = \cos\theta$

26. $\cos(180° + \theta) = -\cos\theta$ 27. $\cos(90° + \theta) = -\sin\theta$

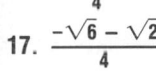 **C**
28. $\sin\left(\theta + \dfrac{\pi}{3}\right) - \cos\left(\theta + \dfrac{\pi}{6}\right) = \sin\theta$

29. $\sin(x + y)\sin(x - y) = \sin^2 x - \sin^2 y$

30. $\sin(60° + \theta) + \sin(60° - \theta) = \sqrt{3}\cos\theta$

31. $\sin(x + 30°) + \cos(x + 60°) = \cos x$

Use the identity $\tan(\alpha - \beta) = \dfrac{\tan\alpha - \tan\beta}{1 + \tan\alpha\tan\beta}$ to evaluate each expression.

32. $\tan(315° - 120°)$ **2 − √3**   33. $\tan(225° - 120°)$ **−2 − √3**

34. $\tan(30° + 30°)$ **√3**   35. $\tan 195°$ **2 − √3**

Critical Thinking

36. Use the formulas for $\sin(\alpha + \beta)$ and $\cos(\alpha + \beta)$ to derive the formula for $\tan(\alpha + \beta)$. *Hint: Divide all terms of the expression by cos α cos β.* **See Solutions Manual.**

LESSON 17-5 SUM AND DIFFERENCE OF ANGLES FORMULAS 813

Additional Answer

1. **no; A counter example is:**
$$\sin(30° + 45°)$$
$$= \sin 30° + \sin 45°$$
$$= \frac{1}{2} + \frac{\sqrt{2}}{2}$$
$$= \frac{1 + \sqrt{2}}{2}$$
$$\approx 1.2071$$
Since a sine value cannot be greater than 1, this statement must be false.

NAME _____   **DATE** _____

17-5 Practice Worksheet

Sum and Difference of Angles Formulas

Evaluate each expression.

1. $\cos 75°$ $\dfrac{\sqrt{6} - \sqrt{2}}{4}$ 2. $\cos 375°$ $\dfrac{\sqrt{6} + \sqrt{2}}{4}$

3. $\sin(-165°)$ $\dfrac{\sqrt{2} - \sqrt{6}}{4}$ 4. $\sin(-105°)$ $\dfrac{-\sqrt{2} - \sqrt{6}}{4}$

5. $\sin 95° \cos 55° + \cos 95° \sin 55°$ $\dfrac{1}{2}$ 6. $\cos 160° \cos 40° + \sin 160° \sin 40°$ $-\dfrac{1}{2}$

7. $\tan(135° + 120°)$ $2 + \sqrt{3}$ 8. $\tan(315° - \theta)$ $\dfrac{\tan\theta + 1}{\tan\theta - 1}$

Verify that each of the following is an identity.

9. $\cos(180° - \theta) = -\cos\theta$

$\cos(180° - \theta)$
$= \cos 180° \cos\theta + \sin 180° \sin\theta$
$= (-1)\cos\theta + 0 \cdot \sin\theta$
$= -\cos\theta$

10. $\sin(360° + \theta) = \sin\theta$

$\sin(360° + \theta)$
$= \sin 360° \cos\theta + \cos 360° \sin\theta$
$= 0 \cdot \cos\theta + 1 \cdot \sin\theta$
$= \sin\theta$

11. $\sin(45° + \theta) - \sin(45° - \theta) = \sqrt{2}\sin\theta$

$\sin(45° + \theta) - \sin(45° - \theta)$
$= \sin 45° \cos\theta + \cos 45° \sin\theta -$
$\quad (\sin 45° \cos\theta - \cos 45° \sin\theta)$
$= 2 \cdot \cos 45° \sin\theta$
$= \sqrt{2}\sin\theta$

12. $\cos\left(x - \dfrac{\pi}{6}\right) + \sin\left(x - \dfrac{\pi}{3}\right) = \sin x$

$\cos\left(x - \dfrac{\pi}{6}\right) + \sin\left(x - \dfrac{\pi}{3}\right)$
$= \cos x \cos\dfrac{\pi}{6} + \sin x \sin\dfrac{\pi}{6} +$
$\quad \sin x \cos\dfrac{\pi}{3} - \cos x \sin\dfrac{\pi}{3}$
$= \dfrac{\sqrt{3}}{2}\cos x + \dfrac{1}{2}\sin x + \dfrac{1}{2}\sin x - \dfrac{\sqrt{3}}{2}\cos x$
$= \sin x$

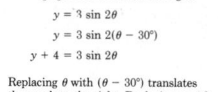
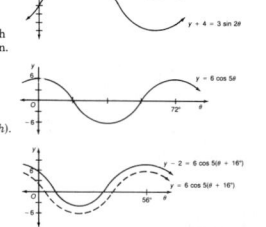
Application   **37. Geology**   A geologist stands on a ledge and finds that the angle of depression to a river's surface is 12°. The angle of depression to the river bed below the surface is 13°. The geologist is 1500 feet from the river's surface.

  a. Write an expression for the sine of the angle between the line from the geologist to the river's surface and the line from the geologist to the river bed. $\sin 1° = \sin 13° \cos 12° - \cos 13° \sin 12°$

  b. How far above the river bed is the surface of the water?   **27.5 feet**

Mixed Review

38. Find the least positive angle measurement that is coterminal to $-120°$. (Lesson 16-1)   **240°**

39. Find the sum of the geometric series described by $a_1 = 2$, $a_9 = 512$, $n = 10$.   (Lesson 13-5)   **2046**

40. Find $\dfrac{2x^6y^3}{a^3b^7} \div \dfrac{4x^2y}{ab^3}$.   (Lesson 11-1) $\dfrac{x^4y^2}{2a^2b^4}$

41. If $f(x) = x^2 + 8$ and $g(x) = x - 3$, find $[f \circ g](3)$ and $[g \circ f](3)$. (Lesson 10-7)   **8, 14**

42. Write the equation of a parabola with position 3 units to the right of the parabola with equation $f(x) = x^2$.   (Lesson 8-3) $f(x) = (x - 3)^2$

43. State the property shown by the statement "If $7 = n$, then $n = 7$." (Lesson 1-3)   **symmetric property of equality**

∼∼∼∼∼∼ MID-CHAPTER REVIEW ∼∼∼∼∼∼

State the amplitude and period of each function.   (Lesson 17-1)

1. $y = \sin 4\theta$ $1, \dfrac{\pi}{2}$ **or 90°**   **2.** $y = 5 \cos \theta$ **5, 2π or 360°**   **3.** $y = 4 \cos \dfrac{3}{4}\theta$ **4, $\dfrac{8\pi}{3}$ or 480°**

State the period of each function.   (Lesson 17-1)

4. $y = \csc 4\theta$ $\dfrac{\pi}{2}$ **or 90°**   **5.** $y = 4 \tan \theta$ **π or 180°**   **6.** $y = \cot \dfrac{1}{5}\theta$ **5π or 900°**

Solve for values between 90° and 180°.   (Lesson 17-2)

7. If $\cot \theta = -\dfrac{3}{5}$, find $\csc \theta$. $\dfrac{\sqrt{34}}{5}$ **8.** If $\tan \alpha = -\dfrac{3}{5}$, find $\cos \alpha$. $-\dfrac{5\sqrt{34}}{34}$

Verify that each of the following is an identity.   (Lesson 17-3)   **9–10. See margin.**

9. $\cot \beta = \cos \beta \csc \beta$ **10.** $1 = \dfrac{1}{\sec^2 \alpha - \sec^2 \alpha \sin^2 \alpha}$

11. Finance   Martin is selling tickets to a fundraiser. He sold 4 to family members, then gave half of what he had left to his sister for her to sell. He sold twelve more to coworkers and had 15 tickets left to sell. How many tickets did Martin have in all?   (Lesson 17-4)   **58**

Evaluate each expression.   (Lesson 17-5)

12. $\sin 195°$ $\dfrac{\sqrt{2} - \sqrt{6}}{4}$ **13.** $\cos 285°$ $\dfrac{\sqrt{6} - \sqrt{2}}{4}$ **14.** $\sin -75°$ $\dfrac{-\sqrt{6} - \sqrt{2}}{4}$

EXTENDING THE LESSON

Math Power: Communication

Have students verbalize to a partner the steps in solving the following problem, writing them if necessary, then solve the problem. Use the identity $\tan (a - b) =$

$\dfrac{\tan a - \tan b}{1 + \tan a \tan b}$ to find $\cot (a - b)$.

$\cot (a - b) = \dfrac{1 + \cot a \cot b}{\cot b - \cot a}$

Mid-Chapter Review

The Mid-Chapter Review provides students with a brief review of the concepts and skills in Lessons 17–1 through 17–5. Lesson numbers are given at the end of problems or instruction lines so students may review concepts not yet mastered.

Objectives
17-6A
17-6B

After studying this lesson, you should be able to:
- find values of sine and cosine involving half and double angles, and
- verify identities using half and double angle formulas.

You can use the formula for sin $(\alpha + \beta)$ to find the sine of twice an angle θ and the formula for cos $(\alpha + \beta)$ to find the cosine of twice an angle θ. Let θ represent the measure of the angle.

$$\sin 2\theta = \sin (\theta + \theta) \qquad\qquad \cos 2\theta = \cos (\theta + \theta)$$
$$= \sin \theta \cos \theta + \cos \theta \sin \theta \qquad = \cos \theta \cos \theta - \sin \theta \sin \theta$$
$$= 2 \sin \theta \cos \theta \qquad\qquad = \cos^2 \theta - \sin^2 \theta$$

You can find alternate forms for cos 2θ by making substitutions into the expression $\cos^2 \theta - \sin^2 \theta$.

$$\cos^2 \theta - \sin^2 \theta = (1 - \sin^2 \theta) - \sin^2 \theta$$
$$= 1 - 2 \sin^2 \theta \qquad \textit{Substitute } 1 - \sin^2 \theta \textit{ for } \cos^2 \theta.$$
$$\cos^2 \theta - \sin^2 \theta = \cos^2 \theta - (1 - \cos^2 \theta)$$
$$= 2 \cos^2 \theta - 1 \qquad \textit{Substitute } 1 - \cos^2 \theta \textit{ for } \sin^2 \theta.$$

These formulas are called the **double-angle formulas.**
Teaching Tip

*Double-Angle
Formulas*

> **The following identities hold true for all values of θ.**
> $\sin 2\theta = 2 \sin \theta \cos \theta \qquad \cos 2\theta = \cos^2 \theta - \sin^2 \theta$
> $\qquad\qquad\qquad\qquad\quad \cos 2\theta = 1 - 2 \sin^2 \theta$
> $\qquad\qquad\qquad\qquad\quad \cos 2\theta = 2 \cos^2 \theta - 1$

Example 1

Suppose x is between $90°$ and $180°$ and sin $x = \frac{1}{2}$. Find cos $2x$.

Use the identity cos $2x = 1 - 2 \sin^2 x$.

$$\cos 2x = 1 - 2 \sin^2 x$$
$$= 1 - 2\left(\frac{1}{2}\right)^2 \qquad \textit{Substitute } \frac{1}{2} \textit{ for sin } x.$$
$$= \frac{1}{2}$$

The value of cos $2x$ is $\frac{1}{2}$.

ALTERNATE TEACHING STRATEGIES

Using Critical Thinking
Have students use a double angle formula to find cos 60°. Then have them also use a half angle formula to find cos 60°. Compare results.

Lesson Resources
Reteaching Master 17-6
Practice Master 17-6
Enrichment Master 17-6

Transparency 17-6 contains the 5-Minute Check and a teaching aid for this lesson.

INTRODUCING THE LESSON

5-Minute Check

(over Lesson 17-5)
Write each angle in terms of sums or differences of 30°, 45°, 60°, and 90° or their multiples.

1. −165°   −135° − 30°
2. 105°   45° + 60°
3. Evaluate sin 195°. $\frac{\sqrt{2} - \sqrt{6}}{4}$
4. Evaluate cos 285°. $\frac{\sqrt{6} - \sqrt{2}}{4}$
5. Verify the identity
   cos (270° − θ) = −sin θ.
   $\cos (270° - \theta) \overset{?}{=} -\sin \theta$
   $\cos 270° \cdot \cos \theta +$
   $\sin 270° \cdot \sin \theta \overset{?}{=} -\sin \theta$
   $0 - 1 \cdot \sin \theta \overset{?}{=} -\sin \theta$
   $-\sin \theta = -\sin \theta$

Motivating the Lesson
Toss a ball to a student in the class. Tell students that the distance the ball travels can be related to a trigonometric function.

TEACHING THE LESSON

Teaching Tip ❶ Point out that the formula used to find cos 2θ depends on what information is given in the problem.

Example 2

APPLICATION

Physics

The range of a projected object is the distance that it travels from the point where it is released. In the absence of air resistance, a projectile released at an angle of elevation, θ, with an initial velocity of v_o has a range of $R = \dfrac{v_o^2}{g} \sin 2\theta$, where g is the acceleration due to gravity. Find the range of a projectile with an initial velocity of 88 feet per second if $\sin \theta = \frac{3}{5}$ and $\cos \theta = \frac{4}{5}$. The acceleration due to gravity is 32 feet per second squared.

Use the double-angle formula to find sin 2θ.

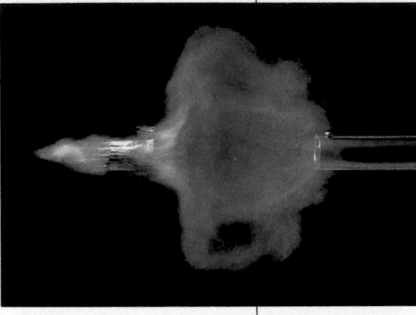

$$\sin 2\theta = 2 \sin \theta \cos \theta \qquad \text{\textit{Double-angle formula}}$$
$$= 2\left(\frac{3}{5}\right)\left(\frac{4}{5}\right) \qquad \textit{Substitute } \tfrac{3}{5} \textit{ for sin } \theta \textit{ and } \tfrac{4}{5} \textit{ for cos } \theta.$$
$$= \frac{24}{25}$$

Now find the range.

$$R = \frac{v_o^2}{g} \sin 2\theta \qquad \textit{Use the formula for range.}$$
$$= \frac{(88)^2}{32}\left(\frac{24}{25}\right) \qquad \textit{Substitute 88 for } v_o, \textit{ 32 for } g, \textit{ and } \tfrac{24}{25} \textit{ for sin } 2\theta.$$
$$= 232.32$$

The range of this projectile is 232.32 feet.

You can also derive formulas to find the cosine and sine of half a given angle. Let α represent the measure of this angle.

Find $\cos \frac{\alpha}{2}$.	Find $\sin \frac{\alpha}{2}$.	
$2 \cos^2 \theta - 1 = \cos 2\theta$	$1 - 2 \sin^2 \theta = \cos 2\theta$	*Use double-angle formulas.*
$2 \cos^2 \frac{\alpha}{2} - 1 = \cos \alpha$	$1 - 2 \sin^2 \frac{\alpha}{2} = \cos \alpha$	*Substitute α for 2θ and $\frac{\alpha}{2}$ for θ.*
$\cos^2 \frac{\alpha}{2} = \frac{1 + \cos \alpha}{2}$	$\sin^2 \frac{\alpha}{2} = \frac{1 - \cos \alpha}{2}$	*Solve for the squared term.*
$\cos \frac{\alpha}{2} = \pm\sqrt{\frac{1 + \cos \alpha}{2}}$	$\sin \frac{\alpha}{2} = \pm\sqrt{\frac{1 - \cos \alpha}{2}}$	*Take the square root of each side.*

These are called the **half-angle** formulas.

Half-Angle Formulas	The following identities hold true for all values of α. $$\cos \frac{\alpha}{2} = \pm\sqrt{\frac{1 + \cos \alpha}{2}} \qquad \sin \frac{\alpha}{2} = \pm\sqrt{\frac{1 - \cos \alpha}{2}}$$

Example 3

Suppose $\sin x = -\dfrac{9}{41}$ and x is in the fourth quadrant. Find $\cos \dfrac{x}{2}$.

Since $\cos \dfrac{x}{2} = \pm\sqrt{\dfrac{1 + \cos x}{2}}$, we must find $\cos x$ first.

Use $\cos^2 x + \sin^2 x = 1$.

$$\cos^2 x + \sin^2 x = 1$$

$$\cos^2 x + \left(-\frac{9}{41}\right)^2 = 1 \qquad \textit{Substitute } -\frac{9}{41} \textit{ for } \sin x.$$

$$\cos^2 x = 1 - \frac{81}{1681}$$

$$\cos^2 x = \frac{1600}{1681}$$

$$\cos x = \pm\frac{40}{41}$$

Since x is in the fourth quadrant, $\cos x = \dfrac{40}{41}$.

$$\cos \frac{x}{2} = \pm\sqrt{\frac{1 + \cos x}{2}} \qquad \textit{Half-angle formula}$$

$$= \pm\sqrt{\frac{1 + \dfrac{40}{41}}{2}} \qquad \textit{Substitute } \frac{40}{41} \textit{ for } \cos x.$$

$$= \pm\sqrt{\frac{81}{82}} \text{ or } \pm\frac{9\sqrt{82}}{82}$$

Since x is in the fourth quadrant, x is between 270° and 360°. Thus, $\dfrac{x}{2}$ is

between 135° and 180°, and $\cos \dfrac{x}{2}$ is negative. The solution is $-\sqrt{\dfrac{81}{82}}$ or

$-\dfrac{9\sqrt{82}}{82}$ or about −0.9939.

CHECKING FOR UNDERSTANDING

Communicating Mathematics

Read and study the lesson to answer these questions.

1. Use the information from Example 1 to find the value of $\sin 2x$ if x is between 90° and 180° and $\sin x = \dfrac{1}{2}$. $-\dfrac{\sqrt{3}}{2}$

2. Explain how to find $\sin x$ if $2x$ is in the third quadrant. **See students' work.**

3. Use the information from Example 3 to find $\sin \dfrac{x}{2}$ if $\sin x = -\dfrac{9}{41}$ and x is in the fourth quadrant. $\dfrac{\sqrt{82}}{82}$

LESSON 17-6   DOUBLE-ANGLE AND HALF-ANGLE FORMULAS   817

RETEACHING THE LESSON

To convince students of the validity of the formulas, have them find the value of sin 30° using the half-angle formulas. Then have them find the value using a calculator or a table. You may wish to do the same for the double-angle formulas.

Teaching Tip ❷   Regarding the half-angle formulas, remind students that the sign of the solution is determined by the quadrant of the angle.

EVALUATING THE LESSON

Checking for Understanding

Exercises 1−11 are designed to help you **assess** understanding through reading, writing, and speaking. You should work through Exercises 1−3 with your students, and then monitor their work on Exercises 4−11.

Reteaching Masters Booklet, p. 117

17-6	NAME _____ DATE _____
	Reteaching Worksheet

Double-Angle and Half-Angle Formulas

Sometimes you want to find the cosine or sine of double an angle or half an angle. To do this you can use the following formulas.

Double-Angle Formulas
$\sin 2\theta = 2\sin\theta\cos\theta$
$\cos 2\theta = \cos^2\theta - \sin^2\theta$
$\cos 2\theta = 1 - 2\sin^2\theta$
$\cos 2\theta = 2\cos^2\theta - 1$

Half-Angle Formulas
$\cos \dfrac{a}{2} = \pm\sqrt{\dfrac{1 + \cos a}{2}}$
$\sin \dfrac{a}{2} = \pm\sqrt{\dfrac{1 - \cos a}{2}}$

Example: Suppose x is between 90° and 180° and $\cos x = -\dfrac{3}{5}$. Find $\cos \dfrac{x}{2}$.

Since x is in the second quadrant, $\dfrac{x}{2}$ is in the first quadrant and $\cos \dfrac{x}{2} > 0$.

$$\cos \frac{x}{2} = \sqrt{\frac{1 + \cos x}{2}}$$

$$= \sqrt{\frac{1 + \left(-\frac{3}{5}\right)}{2}}$$

$$= \sqrt{\frac{1}{5}} \text{ or } \frac{\sqrt{5}}{5}$$

Find $\sin 2x$, $\cos 2x$, $\sin \dfrac{x}{2}$, and $\cos \dfrac{x}{2}$ for each of the following.

1. $\sin x = \dfrac{1}{4}$, x is in the first quadrant.
$\sin 2x = \dfrac{\sqrt{15}}{8}$, $\cos 2x = \dfrac{7}{8}$
$\sin \dfrac{x}{2} = \dfrac{\sqrt{8 - 2\sqrt{15}}}{4}$,
$\cos \dfrac{x}{2} = \dfrac{\sqrt{8 + 2\sqrt{15}}}{4}$

2. $\sin x = -\dfrac{1}{8}$, x is in the fourth quadrant.
$\sin 2x = -\dfrac{\sqrt{63}}{32}$, $\cos 2x = \dfrac{31}{32}$,
$\sin \dfrac{x}{2} = \dfrac{1}{4}\sqrt{8 - \sqrt{63}}$,
$\cos \dfrac{x}{2} = \dfrac{1}{4}\sqrt{8 + \sqrt{63}}$

3. $\cos x = -\dfrac{3}{5}$, x is in the third quadrant.
$\sin 2x = \dfrac{24}{25}$, $\cos 2x = -\dfrac{7}{25}$,
$\sin \dfrac{x}{2} = \dfrac{2}{5}\sqrt{5}$, $\cos \dfrac{x}{2} = -\dfrac{\sqrt{5}}{5}$

4. $\cos x = -\dfrac{4}{5}$, x is in the second quadrant.
$\sin 2x = -\dfrac{24}{25}$, $\cos 2x = \dfrac{7}{25}$,
$\sin \dfrac{x}{2} = \dfrac{3\sqrt{90}}{10}$, $\cos \dfrac{x}{2} = \dfrac{\sqrt{10}}{10}$

5. $\sin x = -\dfrac{3}{5}$, x is in the fourth quadrant.
$\sin 2x = -\dfrac{24}{25}$, $\cos 2x = \dfrac{7}{25}$,
$\sin \dfrac{x}{2} = \dfrac{\sqrt{10}}{10}$, $\cos \dfrac{x}{2} = -\dfrac{3\sqrt{10}}{10}$

6. $\cos x = -\dfrac{2}{3}$, x is in the second quadrant.
$\sin 2x = -\dfrac{4\sqrt{5}}{9}$, $\cos 2x = -\dfrac{1}{9}$,
$\sin \dfrac{x}{2} = \dfrac{\sqrt{30}}{6}$, $\cos \dfrac{x}{2} = \dfrac{\sqrt{6}}{6}$

Closing the Lesson

Modeling Activity   Have students use a diagram of a unit circle to model how to determine the quadrant of $2x$ or $\frac{x}{2}$ if the quadrant of x is known.

APPLYING THE LESSON

Homework Exercises

Assignment Guide

Basic: 12–25, 34–40
Average: 14–29, 34–40
Enriched: 16–40

Chapter 17, Quiz C, (Lessons 17–5 through 17–6), is available in the Evaluation Masters Booklet, p. 234.

Practice Masters Booklet, p. 134

---

818   Chapter 17

Guided Practice

Teaching Tip ❸

4. If x is in the first quadrant, in which quadrant does the terminal side for $2x$ lie? **I or II**

5. x is a second quadrant angle. In which quadrant does the terminal side for $2x$ lie? **III or IV**

6. If x is a fourth quadrant angle, in which quadrant does the terminal side for $2x$ lie? **III or IV**

7. x is a third quadrant angle. In which quadrant does the terminal side for $2x$ lie? **I or II**

8. x is a first quadrant angle. In which quadrant does the terminal side for $\frac{x}{2}$ lie? **I**

9. If x is an angle whose terminal side lies in the second quadrant, in which quadrant does the terminal side for $\frac{x}{2}$ lie? **I**

Find sin $2x$, cos $2x$, sin $\frac{x}{2}$, and cos $\frac{x}{2}$ for each of the following.

10. sin $x = \frac{5}{13}$, x is in the second quadrant $-\frac{120}{169}, \frac{119}{169}, \frac{\sqrt{26}}{26}, \frac{5\sqrt{26}}{26}$

11. cos $x = \frac{1}{5}$, x is in the fourth quadrant $-\frac{4\sqrt{6}}{25}, \frac{23}{25}, \frac{\sqrt{10}}{5}, -\frac{\sqrt{15}}{5}$

EXERCISES

Practice

Find sin $2x$, cos $2x$, sin $\frac{x}{2}$, and cos $\frac{x}{2}$ for each of the following, given the quadrant in which the terminal side of x lies.   **See margin.**

 A

12. cos $x = \frac{3}{5}$, first quadrant

13. sin $x = \frac{4}{5}$, second quadrant

14. cos $x = -\frac{2}{3}$, third quadrant

15. cos $x = -\frac{1}{3}$, third quadrant

B

16. sin $x = -\frac{3}{4}$, fourth quadrant

17. sin $x = -\frac{3}{5}$, third quadrant

18. sin $x = -\frac{1}{4}$, third quadrant

19. cos $x = -\frac{1}{3}$, second quadrant

Evaluate each expression using the half-angle formulas.

20. sin 105° $\frac{\sqrt{2+\sqrt{3}}}{2}$

21. cos $\frac{\pi}{8}$ $\frac{\sqrt{2+\sqrt{2}}}{2}$

22. sin $22\frac{1}{2}°$ $\frac{\sqrt{2-\sqrt{2}}}{2}$

23. sin 195° $-\frac{\sqrt{2-\sqrt{3}}}{2}$

24. cos $\frac{19\pi}{12}$ $\frac{\sqrt{2-\sqrt{3}}}{2}$

25. sin $\frac{7\pi}{8}$ $\frac{\sqrt{2-\sqrt{2}}}{2}$

C

Verify that each of the following is an identity. **26–33. See Solutions Manual.**

26. $(\sin x + \cos x)^2 = 1 + \sin 2x$

27. $\cos^2 2x + 4 \sin^2 x \cos^2 x = 1$

28. $\sin 2x = 2 \cot x \sin^2 x$

29. $\sin^2 \theta = \frac{1}{2}(1 - \cos 2\theta)$

Additional Answers

12. $\frac{24}{25}, -\frac{7}{25}, \frac{\sqrt{5}}{5}, \frac{2\sqrt{5}}{5}$

13. $-\frac{24}{25}, -\frac{7}{25}, \frac{2\sqrt{5}}{5}, \frac{\sqrt{5}}{5}$

14. $\frac{4\sqrt{5}}{9}, -\frac{1}{9}, \frac{\sqrt{30}}{6}, -\frac{\sqrt{6}}{6}$

15. $\frac{4\sqrt{2}}{9}, -\frac{7}{9}, \frac{\sqrt{6}}{3}, -\frac{\sqrt{3}}{3}$

16. $-\frac{3\sqrt{7}}{8}, -\frac{1}{8}, \frac{\sqrt{8-2\sqrt{7}}}{4}, -\frac{\sqrt{8+2\sqrt{7}}}{4}$

17. $\frac{24}{25}, \frac{7}{25}, \frac{3\sqrt{10}}{10}, -\frac{\sqrt{10}}{10}$

18. $\frac{\sqrt{15}}{8}, \frac{7}{8}, \frac{\sqrt{8+2\sqrt{15}}}{4}, -\frac{\sqrt{8-2\sqrt{15}}}{4}$

19. $-\frac{4\sqrt{2}}{9}, -\frac{7}{9}, \frac{\sqrt{6}}{3}, \frac{\sqrt{3}}{3}$

30. $\dfrac{1}{\sin x \cos x} - \dfrac{\cos x}{\sin x} = \tan x$

31. $\sin^4 x - \cos^4 x = 2 \sin^2 x - 1$

32. $\tan^2 \dfrac{x}{2} = \dfrac{1 - \cos x}{1 + \cos x}$

33. $2 \cos^2 \dfrac{x}{2} = 1 + \cos x$

Teaching Tip ③ Encourage students to use diagrams to help solve Exercises 4–9. In determining the quadrant for $\dfrac{x}{2}$ or $2x$, remind students to consider both maximum and minimum possible values of x.

Critical Thinking

34. Explain the method you would use to find $\sin x$ if $\sin 4x = \dfrac{2}{3}$ and the terminal side of $4x$ lies in the second quadrant. Then find $\sin x$.

See students' work.; $\dfrac{\sqrt{18 - 3\sqrt{18 - 6\sqrt{5}}}}{6}$

Applications

35. Sports A golf ball leaves the club with an initial velocity of 100 feet per second. The distance the ball travels is found by the formula

$$d = \dfrac{v_o^2}{g} \sin 2\theta,$$

where v_o is the initial velocity, g is the acceleration due to gravity and θ is the measurement of the angle that the path of the ball makes with the ground. The acceleration due to gravity is 32 feet per second squared.

a. Find the distance the ball travels if the angle between the path of the ball and the ground measures 60°.
270.6 feet

b. Find the distance the ball travels if the angle between the path of the ball and the ground measures 30°.
270.6 feet

c. At what angle should the ball leave the head of the golf club for it to travel the maximum distance? Explain your answer. **45°; The greatest value of the sine function is 1 and $\sin 2\theta = 1$ when $\theta = 45°$.**

Mixed Review

36. Find $\text{Sin}^{-1} 1$. **(Lesson 16-4) 90°**

37. Statistics The prices of several different brands of running shoes are listed below. Make a stem-and-leaf plot of the prices. **(Lesson 14-3)**
$59 $46 $70 $76 $55 $65 $70 $60 $78 $55 $69
$58 $59 $60 $65 $69 $58 $60 $46 $62 $52 $55 **See margin.**

38. Find the four arithmetic means between 6 and 26.
Use $a_n = a_1 + (n - 1)d$. **(Lesson 13-2) 10, 14, 18, 22**

39. Evaluate the expression $9^{\log_9 5}$. **(Lesson 12-2) 5**

40. State whether the equation $y = \dfrac{10}{x}$ represents a direct or inverse variation. Then state the constant of variation. **(Lesson 11-2) inverse; 10**

LESSON 17-6 DOUBLE-ANGLE AND HALF-ANGLE FORMULAS 819

EXTENDING THE LESSON

Math Power:
Problem Solving

Have students find the exact value of tan 15° using the half-angle formulas. $2 - \sqrt{3}$ or $\sqrt{7 - 4\sqrt{3}}$

Additional Answer

37. Stem | Leaf

Stem	Leaf
4 ●	6 6
5	2
●	5 5 5 8 8 9 9
6	0 0 0 2
●	5 5 9 9
7	0 0
●	6 8

6 | 0 represents $60.

Objective: Graph trigonometric equations on a graphing calculator and find the roots of the equation.

Motivating the Lesson

Write the equation $3x^2 + 2x + 4 = 0$ on the chalkboard or overhead. Then substitute sin x for x to obtain the equation $3 \sin^2 x + 2 \sin x + 4 = 0$. Ask students if it is still a function. **yes** Can it be solved? **yes** If so, can it be solved by graphing? **yes** How?

TEACHING THE LESSON

Teaching Tip ❶ This is similar to solving linear equations and solving exponential functions.

Teaching Tip ❷ This viewing window will show all of the values of x that the problem asked for, plus give an idea of what is happening around the endpoints of the section of graph that we want to look at.

Teaching Tip ❸ Parentheses are only needed around a trigonometric function if you are raising it to a power. If you are multiplying the function, you do not need parentheses.

Teaching Tip ❹ You may find it easier to redraw the graph in the original viewing window before zooming in to find the second zero.

Graphing Calculator Exploration: Solving Trigonometric Equations

The coordinates of the points that make up the graph of a trigonometric function represent all of the values that satisfy the function. When we solve a trigonometric equation, we are interested in finding the values of x that satisfy the equation, or make its value 0. So, we can solve trigonometric equations by graphing the related trigonometric function and finding the x-intercepts. This approach for solving a trigonometric equation is the same method we used to solve exponential equations in the Graphing Calculator Exploration on pages 551–552. **Teaching Tip ❶**

Example 1

Solve $2 \sin^2 x - 5 \sin x - 2 = 0$ if $0° \le x < 360°$.

The solutions or roots of the equation $2 \sin^2 x - 5 \sin x - 2 = 0$ are also zeros of the function $f(x) = 2 \sin^2 x - 5 \sin x - 2$.

Teaching Tip ❷

Choose a viewing window to roughly approximate the location of the zeros of the function $f(x) = 2 \sin^2 x - 5 \sin x - 2$. One possible window is $[-10, 370]$ by $[-5, 5]$ with a scale factor of 30 on the x-axis and 0.5 on the y-axis.

Now graph. *Make sure your calculator is in degree mode.*

Casio

ENTER: [GRAPH] 2 [(] [SIN] [ALPHA] [X]

[)] [x^2] [−] 5 [SIN] [ALPHA] [X]

[−] 2 [EXE]

TI-81 **Teaching Tip ❸**

ENTER: [Y=] 2 [(] [SIN] [X|T] [)] [x^2]

[−] 5 [SIN] [X|T] [−] 2 [GRAPH]

Based on this graph, there are solutions between 180° and 210° and between 330° and 360°. Zoom in on each solution to determine the zeros more accurately. **Teaching Tip ❹**

The zoom-in process reveals that the solutions to the equation are approximately 200.5° and 339.5°.

820   CHAPTER 17   TRIGONOMETRIC GRAPHS, IDENTITIES, AND EQUATIONS

Solve the examples in this section by graphing two separate equations and then finding the intersection points. You should get the same answer as when you graphed the entire equation and looked for zeros.

Example 2

Solve $2 \sin x - 3 = 0$ if $0° \le x < 360°$.

Use the viewing window $[-90, 450]$ by $[-6, 2]$ with a scale factor of 90 on the x-axis and 1 on the y-axis.

Casio

ENTER:  $-$ 3 EXE

TI-81

ENTER: Y= 2 SIN X|T $-$ 3 GRAPH

The graph doesn't intersect the x-axis, so there are no solutions.

Example 3

Solve $\sin 2x + \cos x + 1 = 0$ if $-360 \le x < 360$.

Use the viewing window $[-370, 370]$ by $[-3, 3]$ with a scale factor of 90 on the x-axis and 1 on the y-axis.

Casio

ENTER: GRAPH SIN (2 ALPHA X

) + COS ALPHA X +

1 EXE

TI-81

ENTER: Y= SIN (2 X|T) + COS X|T + 1 GRAPH

Based on this graph, there are solutions near $-270°$, $-180°$, $90°$, and $180°$. Use the zoom-in process to determine the solutions more accurately.

The zoom-in process reveals that the solutions to the equation are approximately $-249.7°$, $-180°$, $110.3°$, and $180°$.

EXERCISES

Solve each equation for the indicated values of x.

1. $\tan x = \sin x$, $0° \le x < 360°$ **0°, 180°**
2. $\cos 2x = \cos x$, $0° \le x < 360°$ **0°, 120°, 240°**
3. $\sin 2x = \sin x$, $-360° \le x < 360°$ **See margin.**
4. $\tan 2x = \cos 3x$, $-360° \le x < 360°$ **See margin.**
5. $2 \cos^2 x - \sin x = 1$, $0° \le x < 360°$ **30°, 150°, 270°**
6. $3 \sin 2x - 5 \sin x = 1$, $-360° \le x < 360°$ **-342.8°, -197.2°, 17.2°, 162.8°**
7. $3 \cos x = 2 \cos 2x$, $-360° \le x < 360°$ **-244.8°, -115.2°, 115.2°, 244.8°**
8. $\sin x + \cos 2x + 1 = 0$, $0° \le x < 360°$ **281.3°, 308.7°**

GRAPHING CALCULATOR EXPLORATION: SOLVING TRIGONOMETRIC EQUATIONS   821

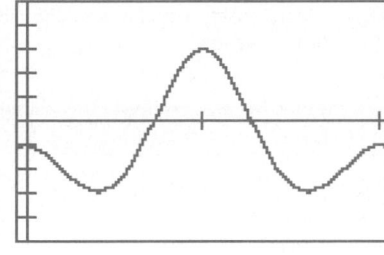
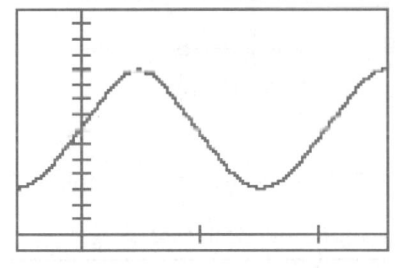

Lesson Resources

Reteaching Master 17-7
Practice Master 17-7
Enrichment Master 17-7
Activity Master, p. 53

 Transparency 17-7 contains the 5-Minute Check and a teaching aid for this lesson.

INTRODUCING THE LESSON

 5-Minute Check

(over Lesson 17-6)

1. x is a third quadrant angle. In which quadrant does the terminal side for $\frac{x}{2}$ lie? **II**

2. If $\sin x = \frac{4}{5}$ and x is in the second quadrant, find $\cos 2x$.
   $-\frac{7}{25}$

3. If $\sin x = -\frac{3}{4}$ and x is in the third quadrant, find $\sin \frac{x}{2}$.
   $\frac{-\sqrt{8 + 2\sqrt{7}}}{4}$

4. Find $\cos 165°$ using the half-angle formulas.
   $\frac{-\sqrt{2 + \sqrt{3}}}{2}$

Motivating the Lesson

Have students look at a page of a book through a clear tumbler with about an inch of water in it. Raise and lower the tumbler and observe the appearance of the printed material on the page. Ask if the material looks any different than it would without the water and tumbler. Ask if students can explain the difference.

TEACHING THE LESSON

Teaching Tip ❶ Be sure students understand that x is limited because this problem deals with periodic functions and, if x were not limited, there would be an infinite number of solutions.

17-7 Solving Trigonometric Equations

Objective
17-7

After studying this lesson, you should be able to:
- solve trigonometric equations.

Application

When you look at an object that is under water, it appears to be closer to the surface than it really is. Light travels faster in air than it does in water so it bends when it enters the water, causing the things in the water to appear closer than they are. According to Snell's Law, the angle at which the light enters the water, I, is related to the angle at which the light travels in the water, r, by the equation $\dfrac{\sin I}{\text{speed of light in air}} = \dfrac{\sin r}{\text{speed of light in water}}$. Is there any angle at which you could direct a beam of light at the surface of a pool so that the light is not bent? *You will solve this problem in Example 6.*

Trigonometric identities are true for *all* values of the variable for which the equation is defined. Most **trigonometric equations**, like most algebraic equations, are true for *some* but not *all* values of the variable.

Example 1

Solve $\sin^2 x + \cos 2x - \cos x = 0$ if $0° \le x < 360°$.   **Teaching Tip ❶**

$$\sin^2 x + \cos 2x - \cos x = 0$$
$$\sin^2 x + (1 - 2\sin^2 x) - \cos x = 0 \qquad \textit{cos 2x = 1 − 2 sin}^2\textit{ x}$$
$$1 - \sin^2 x - \cos x = 0$$
$$\cos^2 x - \cos x = 0 \qquad \textit{cos}^2\textit{ x = 1 − sin}^2\textit{ x}$$
$$\cos x\,(\cos x - 1) = 0 \qquad \textit{Factor out cos x.}$$

Now use the zero product property.
$$\cos x = 0 \qquad \text{or} \qquad \cos x - 1 = 0$$
$$x = 90° \text{ or } 270° \qquad\qquad \cos x = 1$$
$$x = 0°$$

The solutions are 0°, 90°, and 270°.

822 CHAPTER 17 TRIGONOMETRIC GRAPHS, IDENTITIES, AND EQUATIONS

ALTERNATE TEACHING STRATEGIES

Using Models

Working independently or in cooperative groups, have students work through Examples 1–6, simplifying until each problem is in terms of one trigonometric function in as simple a form as possible. Then have students use a graph of the function or a unit circle to model the solution to the problem.

Trigonometric equations are usually solved for values of the variable between 0° and 360° or 0 radians and 2π radians. There are solutions outside that interval. These other solutions differ by integral multiples of the period of the function.

Example 2

Solve $\cos\theta + 1 = 0$ for all values of θ if θ is measured in radians.

$$\cos\theta + 1 = 0$$
$$\cos\theta = -1$$

Look at the graph of $y = \cos\theta$ to find solutions to $\cos\theta = -1$.

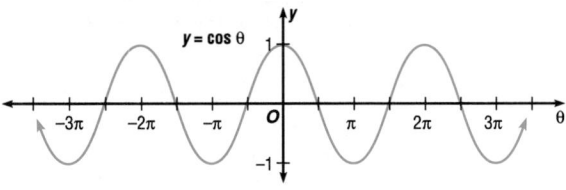

The solutions are π, 3π, 5π, and so on, and $-\pi$, -3π, -5π, and so on. The only solution in the interval 0 radians to 2π radians is π. The period of the cosine function is 2π radians. So the solutions can be written as $\pi + 2n\pi$, where n is any integer.

If an equation cannot be solved easily by factoring, try writing the expression in terms of only one trigonometric function.

Example 3

Solve $\cos^2 x - 1 = \sin^2 x$.

$$\cos^2 x - 1 = \sin^2 x$$
$$\cos^2 x - 1 = 1 - \cos^2 x \qquad sin^2 x = 1 - \cos^2 x$$
$$2\cos^2 x = 2$$
$$\cos^2 x = 1 \qquad \text{Divide each side by 2.}$$
$$\cos x = \pm 1 \qquad \text{Take the square root of each side.}$$
$$x = 0° + n \cdot 360° \text{ or } 180° + n \cdot 360°$$

The solutions are $0° + n \cdot 360°$ and $180° + n \cdot 360°$ where n is any integer.

Some trigonometric equations have *no solution*. In other words, there is no replacement for the variable that will make the sentence true. For example, the equation $\sin x = -3$ has no solution, since all values of $\sin x$ are between -1 and 1, inclusive. Thus, the solution set for $\sin x = -3$ is $\varnothing$.

LESSON 17-7   SOLVING TRIGONOMETRIC EQUATIONS   823

Chalkboard Examples

For Example 4

Find all solutions if $0 \le \theta < 2\pi$.
$2 \sin^2 \theta + 3 \sin \theta - 2 = 0$

$\dfrac{\pi}{6}, \dfrac{5\pi}{6}$

For Example 5

Solve $\cos \theta = 1 + \sin \theta$ if $0° \le \theta < 360°$.   **$0°, 270°$**

Example 4 | Solve $2 \cos^2 \theta - 3 \cos \theta - 2 = 0$ if $0 \le \theta < 2\pi$.

$$2 \cos^2 \theta - 3 \cos \theta - 2 = 0$$
$$(\cos \theta - 2)(2 \cos \theta + 1) = 0 \qquad \textit{Factor.}$$

$\cos \theta - 2 = 0$ or $2 \cos \theta + 1 = 0$ *Zero product property*

$\cos \theta = 2$ $2 \cos \theta = -1$

There is no solution to $\cos \theta = 2$ since all values of $\cos \theta$ are between -1 and 1, inclusive.

                                    $\cos \theta = -\dfrac{1}{2}$

                                    $\theta = \dfrac{2\pi}{3}$ or $\dfrac{4\pi}{3}$

The solutions are $\dfrac{2\pi}{3}$ and $\dfrac{4\pi}{3}$.

Some algebraic operations, such as squaring, may result in answers that are *not* solutions of the original equation. So, it is necessary to check your solutions to trigonometric equations.

Example 5 | Solve $\cos x = 1 + \sin x$ if $0° \le x < 360°$.

$$\cos x = 1 + \sin x$$
$$\cos^2 x = (1 + \sin x)^2 \qquad \textit{Square each side of the equation.}$$
$$1 - \sin^2 x = 1 + 2 \sin x + \sin^2 x \qquad \textit{cos}^2 \textit{ x} = 1 - \textit{sin}^2 \textit{ x}$$
$$0 = 2 \sin x + 2 \sin^2 x$$
$$0 = 2 \sin x \,(1 + \sin x) \qquad \textit{Factor.}$$

$2 \sin x = 0$ or $1 + \sin x = 0$ *Zero product property*

$\sin x = 0$ $\sin x = -1$

$x = 0°$ or $180°$ $x = 270°$

Check:

$\cos x = 1 + \sin x$	$\cos x = 1 + \sin x$	$\cos x = 1 + \sin x$
$\cos 0° \overset{?}{=} 1 + \sin 0°$	$\cos 180° \overset{?}{=} 1 + \sin 180°$	$\cos 270° \overset{?}{=} 1 + \sin 270°$
$1 \overset{?}{=} 1 + 0$	$-1 \overset{?}{=} 1 + 0$	$0 \overset{?}{=} 1 + (-1)$
$1 = 1 \;\checkmark$	$-1 \ne 1$	$0 = 0 \;\checkmark$

The solutions are $0°$ and $270°$.

Now solve the application presented on page 822.

RETEACHING THE LESSON

A general approach to solving, or at least approximating a solution to an equation is to "graph and squeeze." Graphing utilities and simple computer programs can reduce the tedium of repeated long calculations and precision graphing. The function must be continuous near its zeros.

Example 6

Example 6

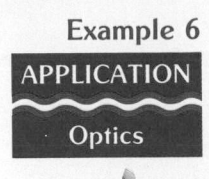

According to Snell's Law, the angle at which the light enters water, *I*, is related to the angle at which the light travels in the water, *r*, by the equation $\dfrac{\sin I}{\text{speed of light in air}} = \dfrac{\sin r}{\text{speed of light in water}}$. Is there any angle at which you could direct a beam of light at the surface of a pool so that the light is not bent? The speed of light in air is approximately 3.00×10^8 meters per second, and the speed of light in water is approximately 2.00×10^8 meters per second.

If the light is not bent, the angle at which it strikes the water is the same as the angle at which it travels in the water. Then *I* = *r*.

Teaching Tip ❷

$$\frac{\sin I}{\text{speed of light in air}} = \frac{\sin r}{\text{speed of light in water}}$$

$$\frac{\sin I}{3.00 \times 10^8} = \frac{\sin I}{2.00 \times 10^8} \quad \textit{Substitute I for r.}$$

$(2.00 \times 10^8) \sin I = (3.00 \times 10^8) \sin I \qquad \textit{Subtract } (2.00 \times 10^8) \sin I \textit{ from each side.}$

$$0 = (1.00 \times 10^8) \sin I$$

$$0 = \sin I$$

$$0° = I$$

The light will not bend if you hold it so it strikes the water at an angle of $0°$. This is directing the light at an angle perpendicular to the surface of the water.

CHECKING FOR UNDERSTANDING

Communicating Mathematics

Read and study the lesson to answer these questions.

1. How many solutions are there to the equation $\sin x = -\dfrac{1}{2}$? **infinitely many**

2. How many solutions for $\cos 2x = \dfrac{1}{2}$ are in the interval $0° \le x < 360°$? State the solutions. **4; 30°, 150°, 210°, 330°**

3. How many solutions exist for the equation $\cos x = -2$? **none**

Guided Practice

How many solutions does each equation have if $0° \le \theta < 360°$? Find all solutions. **See margin.**

4. $\sin \theta = \dfrac{1}{2}$

5. $\cos \theta = -\dfrac{\sqrt{3}}{2}$

6. $\tan \theta = 1$

7. $\cos^2 \theta = 1$

8. $\sin^2 \theta = 3$

9. $\tan \theta = -3$

10. $\sin 2\theta = \dfrac{1}{2}$

11. $\sin \dfrac{1}{2}\theta = -\dfrac{\sqrt{3}}{2}$

12. $\sin^2 2\theta = \dfrac{1}{2}$

13. $\sin 3\theta = -2$

14. $\sin 2\theta = -\dfrac{\sqrt{3}}{2}$

15. $\cos 8\theta = 1$

LESSON 17-7 SOLVING TRIGONOMETRIC EQUATIONS 825

Additional Answers

4. 2; 30°, 150°
5. 2; 150°, 210°
6. 2; 45°, 225°
7. 2; 0°, 180°
8. 0
9. 2; about 108°26′, about 288°26′
10. 4; 15°, 75°, 195°, 255°
11. 0

12. 8; 22°30′, 67°30′, 112°30′, 157°30′, 202°30′, 247°30′, 292°30′, 337°30′
13. 0
14. 4; 120°, 150°, 300°, 330°
15. 8; 0°, 45°, 90°, 135°, 180°, 225°, 270°, 315°

Closing the Lesson

Writing Activity Have students write a short paragraph explaining why it is necessary to check solutions to trigonometric equations.

APPLYING THE LESSON

Homework Exercises

Additional Answers

16. 45°, 135°, 225°, 315°
17. 60°, 120°, 240°, 300°
18. 30°, 150°, 270°
19. 90°, 270°
20. 30°, 90°, 150°, 270°
21. 30°, 150°
22. $\dfrac{\pi}{3}, \dfrac{5\pi}{3}$
23. $\dfrac{7\pi}{6}, \dfrac{11\pi}{6}$
24. $\dfrac{\pi}{6}, \dfrac{5\pi}{6}, \dfrac{7\pi}{6}, \dfrac{11\pi}{6}$
25. $\dfrac{4\pi}{3}, \dfrac{5\pi}{3}$

Practice Masters Booklet, p. 135

NAME _____ **DATE** _____

17-7 Practice Worksheet

Solving Trigonometric Equations

Find all solutions if 0° ≤ x < 360°.

1. $\sin 2x - \sqrt{3}\sin x = 0$
   0°, 180°,
   30°, 330°

2. $\sqrt{2}\cos x = \sin 2x$
   90°, 270°,
   45°, 135°

Find all solutions if 0 ≤ x < 2π.

3. $\cos x + \cos(90 - x) = 0$
   $\frac{3}{4}\pi, \frac{7}{4}\pi$

4. $\tan^2 x + \sec x = 1$
   $0, \frac{2}{3}\pi, \frac{4}{3}\pi$

Solve each equation for all values of x if x is measured in degrees.

5. $\sin^2 x \cos x = \cos x$
   90° + 180n°

6. $\csc^2 x - 3\csc x + 2 = 0$
   30° + 360n°, 90° + 360n°,
   150° + 360n°

7. $\frac{3}{1+\cos x} = 4(1 - \cos x)$
   60° + 180n°, 120° + 180n°

8. $\sqrt{2}\cos^3 x = \cos^2 x$
   90° + 180n°, ± 45° + 360n°

Solve each equation for all values of θ if θ is measured in radians.

9. $\cos^2\theta = \sin^2\theta$
   $\frac{\pi}{4} + \frac{\pi n}{2}$

10. $\cot\theta = \cot^3\theta$
    $\frac{\pi}{2} + n\pi, \frac{\pi}{4} + \frac{\pi n}{2}$

11. $\sqrt{2}\sin^3\theta = \sin^2\theta$
    $\frac{\pi}{4} + 2\pi n, \frac{3\pi}{4} + 2\pi n$

12. $\cos^2\theta\sin\theta = \sin\theta$
    $0 + n\pi$

EXERCISES

Practice Find all solutions if 0° ≤ x < 360°. **See margin.**

16. $2\sin^2 x - 1 = 0$
17. $4\cos^2 x = 1$
18. $2\cos^2 x = \sin x + 1$
19. $\sin 2x = 2\cos x$
20. $\sin 2x = \cos x$
21. $4\sin^2 x - 4\sin x + 1 = 0$

Find all solutions if 0 ≤ θ < 2π. **See margin.**

22. $2\cos\theta - 1 = 0$
23. $2\sin\theta = -1$
24. $4\sin^2\theta = 1$
25. $2\sin\theta = -\sqrt{3}$
26. $2\sin^2\theta = -\sin\theta$
27. $2\sin^2\theta - \sin\theta = 1$

Solve each equation for all values of x if x is measured in degrees. **See margin.**

28. $\sin^2 x - 2\sin x - 3 = 0$
29. $\sin x = \cos x$
30. $\tan x = \sin x$
31. $\cos 2x = \cos x$
32. $3\cos 2x - 5\cos x = 1$
33. $\sin x = 1 + \cos x$
34. $\tan^2 x - \sqrt{3}\tan x = 0$
35. $\cos 2x + \cos x + 1 = 0$
36. $\cos x \tan x - \sin^2 x = 0$
37. $\sin^2 x - \sin x = 0$

Solve each equation for all values of θ if θ is measured in radians. **See margin.**

38. $\cos 2\theta + 3\cos\theta - 1 = 0$
39. $2\sin^2\theta - 3\sin\theta - 2 = 0$
40. $2\sin^2\theta - \cos\theta - 1 = 0$
41. $3\sin^2\theta - \cos^2\theta = 0$
42. $\cos^2\theta - \dfrac{7}{2}\cos\theta - 2 = 0$
43. $\cos^2\theta - \dfrac{5}{2}\cos\theta - \dfrac{3}{2} = 0$
44. $2\cos^2\theta + 3\sin\theta - 3 = 0$
45. $4\cos^2\theta - 4\cos\theta + 1 = 0$
46. $\cos\theta = 3\cos\theta - 2$
47. $\cos 2\theta = 1 - \sin\theta$

Critical Thinking

48. Solve $\dfrac{\tan x - \sin x}{\tan x + \sin x} = \dfrac{\sec x - 1}{\sec x + 1}$ for all values of x if x is measured in radians. **all reals except $0 + \dfrac{n\pi}{2}$ where n is any integer**

Applications

49. **Physics** The motion of a weight on a spring can be described by the equation $y = 2\sin\left(\pi t - \dfrac{\pi}{2}\right)$, where y is the distance in feet from the equilibrium point and t is the time in seconds.
   a. What is the position of the weight after 2 seconds? **−2 feet from equilibrium point**
   b. When is the weight at the equilibrium point? **0.5 + n seconds, where n is any integer**
   c. What is the period of this function? **2 seconds**

50. **Optics** A beam of light moves from a vacuum to water. If the angle of incidence is 60° and the angle of refraction is 30°, use the formula $n = \dfrac{\sin I}{\sin r}$, where I is the measure of the angle of incidence and r is the measure of the angle of refraction, to find the index of refraction, n. **$\sqrt{3}$ or about 1.732**

Additional Answers

26. $0, \pi, \dfrac{7\pi}{6}, \dfrac{11\pi}{6}$
27. $\dfrac{\pi}{2}, \dfrac{7\pi}{6}, \dfrac{11\pi}{6}$
28. 270° + n · 360°
29. 45° + n · 180°
30. 0° + n · 180°
31. 0° + n · 120°
32. 120° + n · 360°, 240° + n · 360°
33. 90° + n · 360°, 180° + n · 360°
34. 0° + n · 180°, 60° + n · 180°
35. 90° + n · 180°, 120° + n · 360°, 240° + n · 360°
36. 0° + n · 180°, 90° + n · 360°

51. The BASIC program below finds solutions to $2\cos^2 x + 3\cos x - 2 = 0$ within a given interval. The interval is entered in degrees. By modifying lines 20 and 120, you can solve other trigonometric equations.

```
10  PRINT "FIND THE          100  PRINT "NO SOLUTIONS
    SOLUTIONS OF"                  BETWEEN";X1; "AND";
20  PRINT "2*COS(X)^2 +            X2;"DEGREES."
    3*COS(X) - 2 = 0"; PRINT  110  GOTO 180
30  INPUT "ENTER THE LEAST    120  LET F = 2*COS(Y)^2 +
    VALUE TO BE TESTED.";X1        3*COS(Y) - 2
40  INPUT "ENTER THE          130  IF ABS(F) > 0.0000001
    GREATEST VALUE TO BE           THEN 160
    TESTED."; X2             140  LET X = 1
50  PRINT                    150  PRINT "ONE SOLUTION
60  FOR J = X1 TO X2              IS"; J; "DEGREES."
70  LET Y = J/57.2957795;    160  RETURN
    GOSUB 120               170  PRINT "THESE ARE THE
80  NEXT J                        SOLUTIONS BETWEEN";
90  IF X = 1 THEN 180             X1; "AND"; X2
                            180  END
```

Make the necessary changes in the program to solve each equation for values of x within the given interval.

a. $2\cos^2 x + 3\cos x - 2 = 0$ between 0° and 180° **60°**

b. $2\cos x - \sin 2x = 0$ between 0° and 360° **90°, 270°**

c. $2\sin^2 x + \sin x - 1 = 0$ between 180° and 240° **no solution**

d. $\sin x + \cos x \tan^2 x = 0$ between -360° and 0° **-360°, -225°, -180°, -45°, 0°**

e. $\cos 2x + \sin x = 1$ between 0° and 720° **0°, 30°, 150°, 180°, 360°, 390°, 510°, 540°, 720°**

Mixed Review

52. Find the value of cos 300°. (**Lesson 16-2**) $\frac{1}{2}$

53. Vanessa has 5 quarters and 7 dimes in her change purse. She selects a coin and replaces it in the bag. She then selects a second coin. What is the probability that Vanessa draws a quarter both times? (**Lesson 15-7**) $\frac{25}{144} \approx 0.174$

54. **Statistics** Find the median, mode, and mean of {0, 0, 0, 4, 5, 8, 10, 12, 15, 20}. (**Lesson 14-3**) **6.5; 0; 7.4**

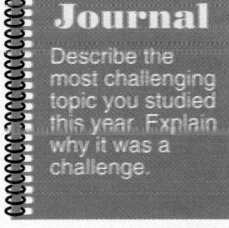
Journal
Describe the most challenging topic you studied this year. Explain why it was a challenge.

55. Find the sum of the positive integers less than 100 that are divisible by 5. (**Lesson 13-3**) **950**

56. Show that $\log_3 27 + \log_3 3 = \log_3 81$. (**Lesson 12-2**) **See margin.**

57. Find the inverse of the function $f(x) = 0$. (**Lesson 10-8**) $x = 0$

EXTENDING THE LESSON

Math Power: Connections

Have students further research the field of optics and write a short report relating trigonometric functions to use of refracted light in astronomy, gemology, or other areas.

Teaching Tip ❸ Since computers calculate values of trigonometric functions for angles measured in radians, line 70 converts radians to degrees. This program finds integral solutions within the specified interval. Change the increment of the loop which begins at line 60 to find nonintegral solutions.

Additional Answers

37. $0° + n \cdot 180°, 90° + n \cdot 360°$

38. $\frac{\pi}{3} + 2n\pi, \frac{5\pi}{3} + 2n\pi$

39. $\frac{7\pi}{6} + 2n\pi, \frac{11\pi}{6} + 2n\pi$

40. $\pi + 2n\pi, \frac{\pi}{3} + 2n\pi, \frac{5\pi}{3} + 2n\pi$

41. $\frac{\pi}{6} + n\pi, \frac{5\pi}{6} + n\pi$

42. $\frac{2\pi}{3} + 2n\pi, \frac{4\pi}{3} + 2n\pi$

43. $\frac{2\pi}{3} + 2n\pi, \frac{4\pi}{3} + 2n\pi$

44. $\frac{\pi}{6} + 2n\pi, \frac{5\pi}{6} + 2n\pi, \frac{\pi}{2} + 2n\pi$

45. $\frac{\pi}{3} + 2n\pi, \frac{5\pi}{3} + 2n\pi$

46. $0 + 2n\pi$

47. $0 + n\pi, \frac{\pi}{6} + 2n\pi, \frac{5\pi}{6} + 2n\pi$

56. $\log_3 27 + \log_3 3 \overset{?}{=} \log_3 81$
$3 + 1 = 4$

Enrichment Masters Booklet, p. 118

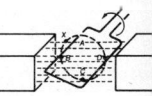

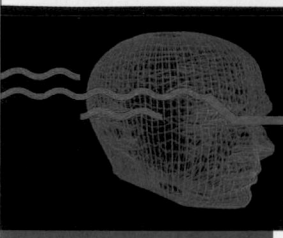

Technology

BASIC
Spreadsheets
▶ Software

Trigonometric Equations

The *Mathematical Exploration Toolkit (MET)* can be used to solve equations involving trigonometric functions. Some equations can be solved automatically with the SOLVEFOR command. Other equations require choosing the appropriate step to simplify the equation before the computer can solve it. Since SIMPLIFY and SOLVEFOR do not obtain numerical solutions, you must use the VALUE command. Other CALC commands (and their shortened forms) are listed below.

ADD (add)	SUBTRACT (sub)	MULTIPLY (mul)
DIVIDE (div)	DEGREES (deg)	FACTOR (fac)
GETRIGHT (getr)	RADIANS (rad)	SIMPLIFY (simp)
SOLVEFOR (sol)	SUBSTITUTE (subst)	VALUE (val)

 # is used to enter π.

Example   Solve $\tan^2 x - \tan x - 2 = 0$, for $-900° \le x \le 900°$.

ENTER: deg
       tan^2(x)−tan(x)−2=0
       subst z tan(x)
       sol z

       subst tan(x) z
       sol x
       getr
       val
       tan(x)=−1
       sol x
       getr
       val

```
sets degree mode
tan^2(x) - tan(x) - 2 = 0
z^2 - z - 2 = 0
z = -1
z = 2
tan(x) = 2
x = arctan(2)
arctan(2)
63.4349
tan(x) = -1
x = arctan(-1)
arctan(-1)
-45
```

The solutions of $\tan^2 x - \tan x - 2 = 0$ are $x = -45°$ or $63.4349°$.

EXERCISES

Use CALC to solve each equation for the principle solution in degrees.

1. $\sec x + 3 = 5$ **60°**
2. $\tan 2x - 1 = 0$ **22.5°**
3. $4\cot^2 x - 4\cot x + 1 = 0$ **63.4349°**
4. $3\sin^2 2x = 2\sin 2x$ **0°, 20.9052°**
5. $3\csc x - 5 = \csc x + 2$ **16.6015°**
6. $\sin^2 x - \cos 2x = 1$ **−54.7356°, 54.7356°**

17-8 Trigonometric Notation for Complex Numbers

Objectives

After studying this lesson, you should be able to:

17-8A ▪ convert numbers in rectangular form to polar form and vice versa,

17-8B ▪ multiply complex numbers in polar form, and

17-8C ▪ apply DeMoivre's Theorem.

As you learned in Chapter 6, complex numbers of the form $a + bi$, called **rectangular form,** can be graphed on a complex plane. In this plane, the x-axis represents the real part of the complex number and the y-axis represents the imaginary part. The number $a + bi$ is graphed at (a, b) on the complex plane. Study how some complex numbers have been graphed on the coordinate plane at the right.

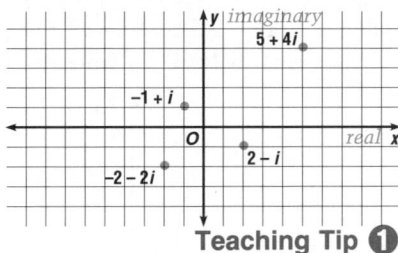

Teaching Tip ❶

Another way to express complex numbers is to use **polar coordinates.** A polar coordinate system is composed of a series of concentric circles with a center called the **pole.** A point in the plane is described by its distance from the pole, r, and the angle θ formed by the positive x-axis and the ray from the pole through the point. Study the graph at the right. Notice that $\cos \theta = \frac{x}{r}$ and $\sin \theta = \frac{y}{r}$. So, $x = r \cos \theta$ and $y = r \sin \theta$. These values can be substituted for x and y in the rectangular form, $x + yi$, to obtain the **polar** or **trigonometric form** of a complex number.

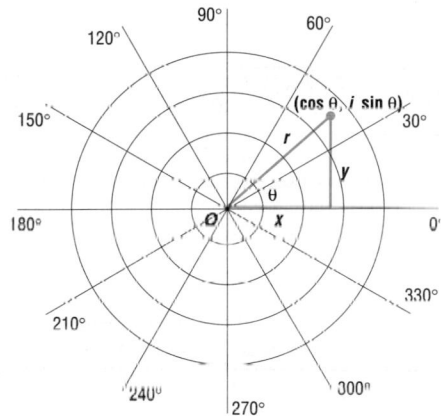

Polar form of $x + yi$	$x + yi = r \cos \theta + (r \sin \theta)i$ $= r(\cos \theta + i \sin \theta)$

$r(\cos \theta + i \sin \theta)$ *is abbreviated* r cis θ.

Values for r and θ can be obtained from rectangular coordinates of the form $x + yi$ by using the following expressions for r and θ.

$r = \sqrt{x^2 + y^2}$ *Pythagorean theorem:* $r^2 = x^2 + y^2$

$\theta = \text{Arctan} \frac{y}{x}$ when $x > 0$ **Teaching Tip ❷**

$\theta = \text{Arctan} \frac{y}{x} + \pi$ when $x < 0$

LESSON 17-8 TRIGONOMETRIC NOTATION FOR COMPLEX NUMBERS 829

ALTERNATE TEACHING STRATEGIES

Mini-Math Lab

At each of several stations, post a graph showing representation of a complex number by use of polar coordinates. For each, have students write the $x + yi$ form of the number and also the polar form.

Lesson Resources

Reteaching Master 17-8
Practice Master 17-8
Enrichment Master 17-8

  Transparency 17-8 contains the 5-Minute Check and a teaching aid for this lesson.

INTRODUCING THE LESSON

🕐 5-Minute Check

(over Lesson 17-7)

How many solutions does each equation have if $0° \leq \theta \leq 360°$?

1. $\cos 2\theta = \frac{3}{2}$ **0**

2. $\tan^2 \theta = 1$ **4**

3. Solve $\sin^2 \theta = \cos^2 \theta - 1$ if $0° \leq \theta \leq 2\pi$.   **0, π**

4. Solve $\cos \theta + \sin \theta = 1$ for all values of θ if θ is measured in radians.   **$0 + 2n\pi, \frac{\pi}{2} + 2n\pi$**

   for any integer n

5. Solve $\cos x = \cos 2x$ for all values of θ if θ is measured in degrees.   **$0° + n \cdot 120°$**

Motivating the Lesson

Ask students what is meant by the term *polar.* Show them a piece of polar graph paper and a polar projection map of either the north or south pole. Have them compare and contrast these grids.

TEACHING THE LESSON

Teaching Tip ❶ Point out that this expression for $\cos \theta$ and $\sin \theta$ does not differ from that in Lesson 16-2. $\cos \theta = x$ and $\sin \theta = y$ are $\cos \theta = \frac{x}{r}$ and $\sin \theta = \frac{y}{r}$ for a unit circle, where $r = 1$.

Teaching Tip ❷ Note that $\text{Arctan} \frac{y}{x}$ is undefined when $x = 0$.

For Example 1
Write in polar form.

a. $-1 - i$

$\sqrt{2}\left(\cos \frac{5\pi}{4} + i \sin \frac{5\pi}{4}\right)$

b. $\sqrt{3} + i$ $\quad 2\left(\cos \frac{\pi}{6} + i \sin \frac{\pi}{6}\right)$

For Example 2
Write in rectangular form.

a. $10 (\cos 30° + i \sin 30°)$
   $5\sqrt{3} + 5i$
b. $2 (\cos 150° + i \sin 150°)$
   $-\sqrt{3} + i$

For Example 3
Find each product.

a. $2 (\cos 10° + i \sin 10°) \cdot$
   $3 (\cos 5° + i \sin 5°)$.
   $6 (\cos 15° + i \sin 15°)$
b. $2 (\cos 45° + i \sin 45°) \cdot$
   $5 (\cos 45° + i \sin 45°)$.
   $10 (\cos 90° + i \sin 90°)$

Example 1

Write $-1 + i$ in polar form.   Teaching Tip ❸

$-1 + i$ is in rectangular form, $x + yi$. So, $x = -1$ and $y = 1$.

$r = \sqrt{x^2 + y^2}$ $\qquad \theta = \text{Arctan} \frac{y}{x} + \pi$ *Notice that $x < 0$.*

$= \sqrt{(-1)^2 + (1)^2}$ $\qquad = \text{Arctan} \frac{1}{-1} + \pi$

$= \sqrt{2}$ $\qquad\qquad = -\frac{\pi}{4} + \pi$ or $\frac{3\pi}{4}$

Therefore, $-1 + i = \sqrt{2}\left(\cos \frac{3\pi}{4} + i \sin \frac{3\pi}{4}\right)$.

Example 2

Write $7(\cos 210° + i \sin 210°)$ in rectangular form.

$7(\cos 210° + i \sin 210°)$ is in polar form, $r(\cos \theta + i \sin \theta)$. So, $r = 7$ and $\theta = 210°$.

$x = r \cos \theta$ $\qquad\qquad y = r \sin \theta$

$= 7 \cos 210°$ $\qquad\qquad = 7 \sin 210°$

$= 7\left(-\frac{\sqrt{3}}{2}\right)$ $\qquad\quad = 7\left(-\frac{1}{2}\right)$

$= -\frac{7\sqrt{3}}{2}$ $\qquad\qquad = -\frac{7}{2}$

Therefore, $7(\cos 210° + i \sin 210°) = -\frac{7\sqrt{3}}{2} + -\frac{7}{2}i$.

You can find the product of two complex numbers in polar form. Let $r_1(\cos \alpha + i \sin \alpha)$ and $r_2(\cos \beta + i \sin \beta)$ represent two complex numbers. Find the product.

$r_1(\cos \alpha + i \sin \alpha)r_2(\cos \beta + i \sin \beta)$

$= r_1 r_2(\cos \alpha \cos \beta + \cos \alpha\, i \sin \beta + i \sin \alpha \cos \beta + i^2 \sin \alpha \sin \beta)$

$= r_1 r_2[(\cos \alpha \cos \beta - \sin \alpha \sin \beta) + i(\sin \alpha \cos \beta + \cos \alpha \sin \beta)]$

$= r_1 r_2[\cos (\alpha + \beta) + i \sin (\alpha + \beta)]$

Product of Complex Numbers in Polar Form	The product of two complex numbers $r_1(\cos \alpha + i \sin \alpha)$ and $r_2(\cos \beta + i \sin \beta)$ can be found by using the following formula. $r_1(\cos \alpha + i \sin \alpha)r_2(\cos \beta + i \sin \beta) = r_1 r_2[\cos (\alpha + \beta) + i \sin (\alpha + \beta)]$

Example 3

Find the product of $4 (\cos 57° + i \sin 57°)$ and $3 (\cos 41° + i \sin 41°)$.

$4 (\cos 57° + i \sin 57°) \cdot 3 (\cos 41° + i \sin 41°)$

$= 4 \cdot 3 [\cos (57° + 41°) + i \sin (57° + 41°)]$

$= 12 (\cos 98° + i \sin 98°)$

The product is $12 (\cos 98° + i \sin 98°)$.

The formula for the product of complex numbers can be used to find the square of a complex number.

$$[r(\cos\theta + i\sin\theta)]^2 = [r(\cos\theta + i\sin\theta)] \cdot [r(\cos\theta + i\sin\theta)]$$
$$= r^2[\cos(\theta + \theta) + i\sin(\theta + \theta)]$$
$$= r^2(\cos 2\theta + i\sin 2\theta)$$

The formula for the product of complex numbers can be used to find any power of complex numbers. This is known as DeMoivre's Theorem.

DeMoivre is pronounced D'Mwov.

DeMoivre's Theorem	$[r(\cos\theta + i\sin\theta)]^n = r^n(\cos n\theta + i\sin n\theta)$

Example 4

Find $(2\sqrt{3} + 2i)^4$ using polar coordinates.

First write $2\sqrt{3} + 2i$ in polar form. Let $x = 2\sqrt{3}$ and $y = 2$.

$$r = \sqrt{(2\sqrt{3})^2 + (2)^2} \qquad \theta = \text{Arctan}\,\frac{2}{2\sqrt{3}} \qquad \textit{Notice } x > 0.$$

$$= \sqrt{16} \text{ or } 4 \qquad\qquad = \text{Arctan}\,\frac{\sqrt{3}}{3}$$

$$\qquad\qquad\qquad = \frac{\pi}{6}$$

Since $r = 4$ and $\theta = \frac{\pi}{6}$, $2\sqrt{3} + 2i = 4\left(\cos\frac{\pi}{6} + i\sin\frac{\pi}{6}\right)$.

Next, use DeMoivre's Theorem to find the fourth power of the complex number in polar form.

$$(2\sqrt{3} + 2i)^4 = \left[4\left(\cos\frac{\pi}{6} + i\sin\frac{\pi}{6}\right)\right]^4$$

$$= (4)^4\left(\cos\frac{4\pi}{6} + i\sin\frac{4\pi}{6}\right)$$

$$= 256\left(\cos\frac{2\pi}{3} + i\sin\frac{2\pi}{3}\right)$$

Finally, write the result in rectangular form.

$$256\left(\cos\frac{2\pi}{3} + i\sin\frac{2\pi}{3}\right) = 256\left(-\frac{1}{2} + i\frac{\sqrt{3}}{2}\right)$$

$$= -128 + 128i\sqrt{3}$$

So, $(2\sqrt{3} + 2i)^4 = -128 + 128i\sqrt{3}$.

Teaching Tip ④

RETEACHING THE LESSON

Have students use expansion to check answers for finding small powers of complex numbers using DeMoivre's Theorem. To check Example 4, expand $(2\sqrt{3} + 2i)^4$.

$$[(2\sqrt{3} + 2i)(2\sqrt{3} + 2i)]^2 = [8 + 8\sqrt{3} \cdot i]^2$$
$$= [8(1 + \sqrt{3} \cdot i)]^2$$
$$= 64(1 + 2\sqrt{3} \cdot i + 3i^2)$$
$$= 64(-2 + 2\sqrt{3} \cdot i)$$
$$= -128 + 128\sqrt{3} \cdot i$$

Chalkboard Example

For Example 4

a. Find $(1 - i)^{10}$.

$$= 32\left(\cos\frac{3\pi}{2} + i\sin\frac{3\pi}{2}\right)$$
$$= -32i$$

b. Find $(\sqrt{3} + i)^4$.

$$= 16\left(\cos\frac{2\pi}{3} + i\sin\frac{2\pi}{3}\right)$$
$$= -8 + 8i\sqrt{3}$$

Teaching Tip ④ You may want to have students use binomial expansion and a calculator to check the results.

Reteaching Masters Booklet, p. 119

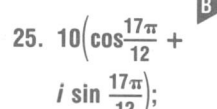
CHECKING FOR UNDERSTANDING

Communicating Mathematics

2. $\sqrt{2}\left(\cos\frac{7\pi}{4} + i\sin\frac{7\pi}{4}\right)$

3. $12\left(\cos\frac{5\pi}{6} + i\sin\frac{5\pi}{6}\right)$

Read and study the lesson to answer these questions.

1. Describe how you can convert $a + bi$ to polar form. **See margin.**
2. Write $1 - i$ in polar form.
3. Find the product of $6\left(\cos\frac{\pi}{6} + i\sin\frac{\pi}{6}\right)$ and $2\left(\cos\frac{2\pi}{3} + i\sin\frac{2\pi}{3}\right)$.

Guided Practice

Write each number in polar form. **4–6. See margin.**

4. $1 - i$ 5. $7i$ 6. $-2 + 2i$

Write each number in rectangular form.

7. $2(\cos 0 + i\sin 0)$ **2**   8. $3(\cos\pi + i\sin\pi)$ **−3**   9. $\cos\frac{\pi}{2} + i\sin\frac{\pi}{2}$ **i**

State the polar coordinates of each point.

10.
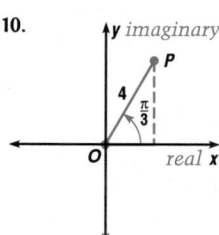

11.
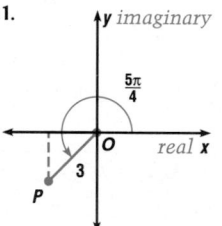

12.
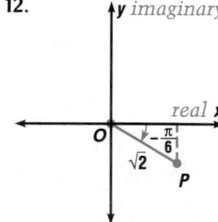

$4\left(\cos\frac{\pi}{3} + i\sin\frac{\pi}{3}\right)$ $3\left(\cos\frac{5\pi}{4} + i\sin\frac{5\pi}{4}\right)$ $\sqrt{2}\left(\cos\left(-\frac{\pi}{6}\right) + i\sin\left(-\frac{\pi}{6}\right)\right)$

EXERCISES

Practice

Write each number in polar form. **13–18. See margin.**

13. $1 + i$ 14. $-3 - 3i$ 15. $3i$
16. $-5 - i$ 17. $-2 + 5i$ 18. $2\sqrt{3} - 3i$

24. $18\left(\cos\frac{4\pi}{3} + i\sin\frac{4\pi}{3}\right);$
    $-9 - 9i\sqrt{3}$

25. $10\left(\cos\frac{17\pi}{12} + i\sin\frac{17\pi}{12}\right);$
    $-2.59 - 9.66i$

26. $\sqrt{3}\left(\cos\frac{5\pi}{8} + i\sin\frac{5\pi}{8}\right);$
    $-0.66 + 1.6i$

Write each number in rectangular form.

19. $\sqrt{2}\left(\cos\frac{5\pi}{4} + i\sin\frac{5\pi}{4}\right)$ **−1 − i**   20. $6\left(\cos\frac{3\pi}{2} + i\sin\frac{3\pi}{2}\right)$ **−6i**

21. $12\left(\cos\frac{5\pi}{3} + i\sin\frac{5\pi}{3}\right)$ **6 − 6i√3**   22. $2(\cos 3 + i\sin 3)$ **−1.98 + 0.28i**

Find each product. Then express the result in rectangular form.

23. $8\left(\cos\frac{3\pi}{4} + i\sin\frac{3\pi}{4}\right) \cdot 2\left(\cos\frac{5\pi}{4} + i\sin\frac{5\pi}{4}\right)$ **16(cos 2π + i sin 2π); 16**

24. $3\left(\cos\frac{7\pi}{6} + i\sin\frac{7\pi}{6}\right) \cdot 6\left(\cos\frac{\pi}{6} + i\sin\frac{\pi}{6}\right)$

25. $5\left(\cos\frac{3}{4}\pi + i\sin\frac{3}{4}\pi\right) \cdot 2\left(\cos\frac{2}{3}\pi + i\sin\frac{2}{3}\pi\right)$

26. $\frac{1}{3}\left(\cos\frac{7\pi}{8} + i\sin\frac{7\pi}{8}\right) \cdot 3\sqrt{3}\left(\cos\left(-\frac{\pi}{4}\right) + i\sin\left(-\frac{\pi}{4}\right)\right)$

27. $(1 + i)(-1 - i)$ **−2i**   28. $(\sqrt{3} + i)(-2 + 2i)$ **−5.46 + 1.46i**

29. $(2 - 2i)(1 - i)$ **−4i**   30. $(8 - 2i)(3 + 5i)$ **34 + 34i**

832 CHAPTER 17 TRIGONOMETRIC GRAPHS, IDENTITIES, AND EQUATIONS

Additional Answers

1. $r = \sqrt{a^2 + b^2}$; $\theta = \text{Arctan}\frac{b}{a}$
   if $a > 0$ and $\theta = \text{Arctan}\frac{b}{a} + \pi$ if $a < 0$

4. $\sqrt{2}\left(\cos\left(-\frac{\pi}{4}\right) + i\sin\left(-\frac{\pi}{4}\right)\right)$

5. $7\left(\cos\frac{\pi}{2} + i\sin\frac{\pi}{2}\right)$

6. $2\sqrt{2}\left(\cos\frac{3\pi}{4} + i\sin\frac{3\pi}{4}\right)$

13. $\sqrt{2}\left(\cos\frac{\pi}{4} + i\sin\frac{\pi}{4}\right)$

14. $3\sqrt{2}\left(\cos\frac{5\pi}{4} + i\sin\frac{5\pi}{4}\right)$

15. $3\left(\cos\frac{\pi}{2} + i\sin\frac{\pi}{2}\right)$

16. $\sqrt{26}(\cos 3.34 + i\sin 3.34)$

17. $\sqrt{29}(\cos 1.95 + i\sin 1.95)$

18. $\sqrt{21}(\cos(-0.71) + i\sin(-0.71))$

Find each power. Express the result in rectangular form.

31. $[3(\cos \pi + i \sin \pi)]^3$ **−27**

32. $\left[2\left(\cos \dfrac{\pi}{2} + i \sin \dfrac{\pi}{2}\right)\right]^5$ **32i**

33. **−16√2 −16i√2** $\left[2\left(\cos \dfrac{\pi}{4} + i \sin \dfrac{\pi}{4}\right)\right]^5$

34. $\left(\cos \dfrac{7\pi}{6} + i \sin \dfrac{7\pi}{6}\right)^3$ **−i**

35. $(-3 + 3i)^3$ **54 + 54i**

36. $(3 + 4i)^4$ **−527 −336i**

Critical Thinking

37. Use DeMoivre's Theorem to find the square root of i.

$\left(\cos \dfrac{\pi}{4} + i \sin \dfrac{\pi}{4}\right)$ or $\dfrac{\sqrt{2}}{2} + \dfrac{i\sqrt{2}}{2}$

Applications

38. Biology The spiral of a chambered nautilus is a logarithmic spiral. You can graph the shape of a nautilus on a polar coordinate system. For integral values of n, plot the points $(1 + 0.1n, 10n°)$ on polar graph paper. Connect the points with a smooth curve. **See Solutions Manual.**

39. Entertainment The groove in a record is a spiral like the chambered nautilus. Look at the graph you drew for Exercise 38. The loops of the spiral become shorter as they approach the center. Does the needle on the record player travel along the groove faster or slower as it approaches the center of the record? *Hint: The turntable makes the same number of revolutions per minute every minute that the record plays.* **The needle travels slower as it approaches the center of the record.**

Mixed Review

40. 18.09 feet or 18 feet 1 inch

40. Sports Patty is practicing her free throws. She knows that the rim of the basket is 10 feet above the floor. From the spot on the floor where she is standing, the angle of elevation to the rim is 33°33′. Find the distance from Patty's feet to the rim. **(Lesson 16-6)**

41. Probability What is the probability that you can toss a fair coin five times and get five heads? **(Lesson 15-9)** $\dfrac{1}{32}$ or **0.03125**

42. A local business would like to find a word to represent the last four digits in their telephone number. Each of the digits in their number has three corresponding letters on the telephone dial. How many letter combinations can they make? **(Lesson 15-1) 81**

43. Statistics Two dice were thrown 18 times with the following sums. Find the median, mode, and mean of the sums. **(Lesson 14-3) 8; 8; 6.94**
8 11 10 8 8 7 10 3 5 9 10 8 2 9 5 2 3 7

44. Demographics The population of Grove City increases by approximately 3% each year. If its population is now 15,000, approximately what will its population be in ten years? **(Lesson 13-5) 20,159 people**

45. Write an expression for $\log_{12} 50$ in terms of common logarithms. Then find the value of the expression. **(Lesson 12-4)** $\dfrac{\log 50}{\log 12}$; **1.5743**

46. Find the vertices and foci of the hyperbola whose equation is $25x^2 - 4y^2 = 100$. **(Lesson 9-5)** $(\pm2, 0); (\pm\sqrt{29}, 0)$

EXTENDING THE LESSON

Math Power: Problem Solving

Working in cooperative groups, have students generate problems illustrating DeMoivre's Theorem. Exchange problems with another group then solve the problems.

Chapter 17, Quiz D, (Lessons 17–7 through 17–8), is available in the Evaluation Masters Booklet, p. 234.

Enrichment Masters Booklet, p. 119

NAME _____ DATE _____

17-8 Enrichment Worksheet

DeMoivre's Theorem and Roots of Complex Numbers

DeMoivre's Theorem can be used in reverse to find nth roots of complex numbers.

> The nth roots of $r(\cos \theta + i \sin \theta)$, where $r > 1$,
> are given by the formula
> $$\sqrt[n]{r}\left(\cos \frac{\theta + 2\pi k}{n} + i \sin \frac{\theta + 2\pi k}{n}\right)$$
> where k has the values $0, 1, \ldots,$ and $n - 1$.

Example: Find the cube roots of -1.

First, put -1 into polar form. $-1 = (\cos \pi + i \sin \pi)$

In the formula, use $n = 3$ and $k = 0, 1,$ and 2.

For $k = 0$: $\sqrt[3]{-1} = \sqrt[3]{1}\left(\cos \frac{\pi}{3} + i \sin \frac{\pi}{3}\right) = \frac{1}{2} + \frac{i\sqrt{3}}{2}$

For $k = 1$: $\sqrt[3]{-1} = \sqrt[3]{1}\left(\cos \frac{\pi + 2\pi}{3} + i \sin \frac{\pi + 2\pi}{3}\right) = -1$

For $k = 2$: $\sqrt[3]{-1} = \sqrt[3]{1}\left(\cos \frac{\pi + 4\pi}{3} + i \sin \frac{\pi + 4\pi}{3}\right) = \frac{1}{2} - \frac{i\sqrt{3}}{2}$

Solve each problem.

1. Find the cube roots of 1.
   $1, -\frac{1}{2} + \frac{i\sqrt{3}}{2}, -\frac{1}{2} - \frac{i\sqrt{3}}{2}$

2. Find the cube roots of i.
   $-i, \frac{\sqrt{3}}{2} + \frac{1}{2}i, -\frac{\sqrt{3}}{2} + \frac{1}{2}i$

3. Find the sixth roots of 1. Then draw a unit circle and graph your results.
   $1, -1, \frac{1}{2} + \frac{i\sqrt{3}}{2}, \frac{1}{2} - \frac{i\sqrt{3}}{2},$
   $-\frac{1}{2} + \frac{i\sqrt{3}}{2}, -\frac{1}{2} - \frac{i\sqrt{3}}{2}$

VOCABULARY

Upon completing this chapter you should be familiar with the following terms:

amplitude	791	829	polar form
DeMoivre's Theorem	831	829	pole
identity	797	829	rectangular form
period	791	822	trigonometric equations
polar coordinates	829	829	trigonometric form

SKILLS AND CONCEPTS

OBJECTIVES AND EXAMPLES	REVIEW EXERCISES

Upon completing this chapter, you should be able to:

■ find the amplitude and period for variations of the sine and cosine functions, and graph them. **(Lesson 17-1)**

State the amplitude and the period of the function $y = 2 \cos \theta$. Then graph.

For $y = a \sin b\theta$ or $y = a \cos b\theta$,

amplitude $= |a| = |2|$ or 2, and

period $= \dfrac{360°}{|b|} = \dfrac{360°}{|1|}$ or 360°.

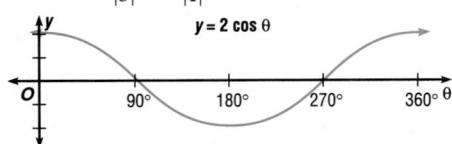

Use these exercises to prepare for the chapter test.
See Solutions Manual for graphs.
State the period and amplitude for each function. Then graph the function.

1. $y = \sin x$ **1, 2π**   2. $y = -\dfrac{1}{2} \cos \theta$ **$\dfrac{1}{2}$, 2π**

3. $y = 4 \sin 2\theta$ **4, π**   4. $y = \sin \dfrac{1}{2}\theta$ **1, 4π**

State the period of each function. Then graph. See Solutions Manual for graphs.

5. $y = 5 \sec x$ **2π**   6. $y = \tan 4\theta$ **$\dfrac{\pi}{4}$**

7. $y = 2 \cot 6\theta$ **$\dfrac{\pi}{6}$**   8. $y = \dfrac{1}{2} \csc \dfrac{2}{3}\theta$ **3π**

■ use trigonometric identities to simplify and/or evaluate expressions.
(Lesson 17-2)

Basic Trigonometric Identities

$\sin^2 \theta + \cos^2 \theta = 1$
$1 + \tan^2 \theta = \sec^2 \theta$
$1 + \cot^2 \theta = \csc^2 \theta$

Solve for values of θ between 90° and 180°.

9. If $\sin \theta = \dfrac{1}{2}$, find $\cos \theta$. **$-\dfrac{\sqrt{3}}{2}$**   10. If $\cot \theta = -\dfrac{1}{4}$, find $\csc \theta$. **$\dfrac{\sqrt{17}}{4}$**

Solve for values of θ between 270° and 360°.

11. If $\csc \theta = -\dfrac{5}{3}$, find $\cot \theta$. **$-\dfrac{4}{3}$**   12. If $\sin \theta = -\dfrac{1}{2}$, find $\sec \theta$. **$\dfrac{2\sqrt{3}}{3}$**

The Chapter Summary and Review begins with an alphabetical listing of the new terms that were presented in the chapter. Have students define each term and provide an example of it, if appropriate.

The Skills and Concepts presented in the chapter are reviewed using a side-by-side format. Encourage students to refer to the Objectives and Examples on the left as they complete the Review Exercises on the right.

The Chapter Summary and Review ends with exercises that review Applications and Connections.

- verify trigonometric identities.
  (Lesson 17-3)

  Verify $\tan x + \cot x = \sec x \csc x$.

  $\tan x + \cot x \overset{?}{=} \sec x \csc x$

  $\dfrac{\sin x}{\cos x} + \dfrac{\cos x}{\sin x} \overset{?}{=} \sec x \csc x$

  $\dfrac{\sin^2 x + \cos^2 x}{\cos x \sin x} \overset{?}{=} \sec x \csc x$

  $\dfrac{1}{\cos x \sin x} \overset{?}{=} \sec x \csc x$

  $\sec x \csc x = \sec x \csc x$

Verify that each of the following is an identity. See Solutions Manual.

13. $\sin^4 x - \cos^4 x = \sin^2 x - \cos^2 x$

14. $\dfrac{\sin \theta}{\tan \theta} + \dfrac{\cos \theta}{\cot \theta} = \cos \theta + \sin \theta$

15. $\dfrac{\sin \theta}{1 - \cos \theta} = \csc \theta + \cot \theta$

16. $\cot^2 \theta \sec^2 \theta = 1 + \cot^2 \theta$

17. $\sec x(\sec x - \cos x) = \tan^2 x$

18. $\dfrac{\cos x}{\csc x} - \dfrac{\sin x}{\cos x} = -\sin^2 x \tan x$

19. $\dfrac{\csc \theta + 1}{\cot \theta} = \dfrac{\cot \theta}{\csc \theta - 1}$

- evaluate expressions and verify trigonometric identities using the sum and difference formulas. (Lesson 17-5)

  Sum and Difference Formulas

  $\cos (\alpha \pm \beta) = \cos \alpha \cos \beta \mp \sin \alpha \sin \beta$
  $\sin (\alpha \pm \beta) = \sin \alpha \cos \beta \pm \cos \alpha \sin \beta$

Evaluate each expression.

20. $\sin 105°$ $\dfrac{\sqrt{2} + \sqrt{6}}{4}$ 21. $\cos 15°$ $\dfrac{\sqrt{6} + \sqrt{2}}{4}$

22. $\cos 285°$ $\dfrac{\sqrt{6} - \sqrt{2}}{4}$ 23. $\sin 195°$ $\dfrac{\sqrt{2} - \sqrt{6}}{4}$

Verify that each of the following is an identity. See Solutions Manual.

24. $\cos (90° - \theta) = \sin \theta$

25. $\cos (x + y) + \cos (x - y) = 2 \cos x \cos y$

26. $\cos (60° + \theta) + \cos (60° - \theta) = \cos \theta$

- evaluate expressions and verify trigonometric identities using the half- and double-angle formulas.
  (Lesson 17-6)

  Double-Angle Formulas

  $\sin 2\theta = 2 \sin \theta \cos \theta$
  $\cos 2\theta = \cos^2 \theta - \sin^2 \theta$
  $\cos 2\theta = 1 - 2 \sin^2 \theta$
  $\cos 2\theta = 2 \cos^2 \theta - 1$

  Half-Angle Formulas

  $\cos \dfrac{\alpha}{2} = \pm \sqrt{\dfrac{1 + \cos \alpha}{2}}$

  $\sin \dfrac{\alpha}{2} = \pm \sqrt{\dfrac{1 - \cos \alpha}{2}}$

27. If $\sin x = -\dfrac{3}{5}$ and x is in the third quadrant, find $\sin 2x$. $\dfrac{24}{25}$

28. If $\sin x = \dfrac{1}{4}$ and x is in the first quadrant, find $\cos 2x$. $\dfrac{7}{8}$

29. If $\cos x = \dfrac{2}{5}$ and $\cos 2x = -\dfrac{17}{25}$, find $\sin x$. $\dfrac{\sqrt{21}}{5}$

30. If $\cos x = \dfrac{1}{6}$ and x is in the first quadrant, find $\sin \dfrac{x}{2}$. $\dfrac{\sqrt{15}}{6}$

31. Verify $(\sin x - \cos x)^2 = 1 - \sin 2x$.
    See Solutions Manual.

CHAPTER 17 835

The Cumulative Review shown below can be used to review skills and concepts presented thus far in the text. Standardized Test Practice Questions are also provided in the Evaluation Masters Booklet.

Evaluation Masters Booklet, pp. 235–236

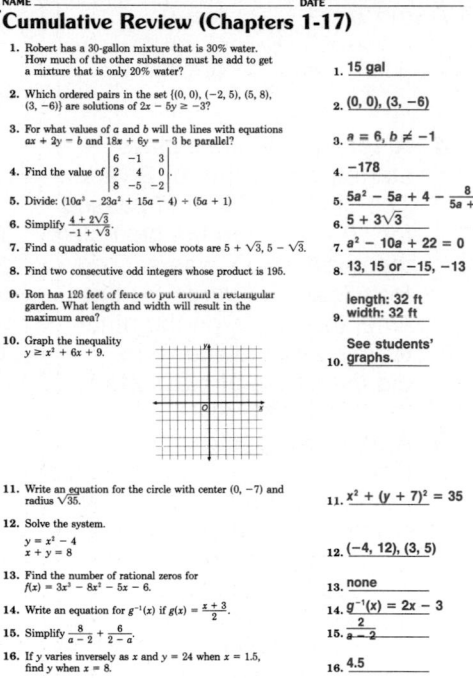

Cumulative Review (Chapters 1-17)

1. Robert has a 30-gallon mixture that is 30% water. How much of the other substance must he add to get a mixture that is only 20% water?
   1. **15 gal**

2. Which ordered pairs in the set $\{(0, 0), (-2, 5), (5, 8), (3, -6)\}$ are solutions of $2x - 5y \geq -3$?
   2. **(0, 0), (3, -6)**

3. For what values of a and b will the lines with equations $ax + 2y = b$ and $18x + 6y = -3$ be parallel?
   3. **$a = 6, b \neq -1$**

4. Find the value of $\begin{vmatrix} 6 & -1 & 3 \\ 2 & 4 & 0 \\ 8 & -5 & -2 \end{vmatrix}$.
   4. **-178**

5. Divide: $(10a^3 - 23a^2 + 15a - 4) \div (5a + 1)$
   5. **$2a^2 - 5a + 4 - \frac{8}{5a+1}$**

6. Simplify $\frac{4 + 2\sqrt{3}}{-1 + \sqrt{3}}$.
   6. **$5 + 3\sqrt{3}$**

7. Find a quadratic equation whose roots are $5 + \sqrt{3}, 5 - \sqrt{3}$.
   7. **$a^2 - 10a + 22 = 0$**

8. Find two consecutive odd integers whose product is 195.
   8. **13, 15 or -15, -13**

9. Ron has 128 feet of fence to put around a rectangular garden. What length and width will result in the maximum area?
   9. **length: 32 ft width: 32 ft**

10. Graph the inequality $y \geq x^2 + 6x + 9$.
    10. **See students' graphs.**

11. Write an equation for the circle with center $(0, -7)$ and radius $\sqrt{35}$.
    11. **$x^2 + (y + 7)^2 = 35$**

12. Solve the system.
    $y = x^2 - 4$
    $x + y = 8$
    12. **(-4, 12), (3, 5)**

13. Find the number of rational zeros for $f(x) = 3x^3 - 8x^2 - 5x - 6$.
    13. **none**

14. Write an equation for $g^{-1}(x)$ if $g(x) = \frac{x+3}{2}$.
    14. **$g^{-1}(x) = 2x - 3$**

15. Simplify $\frac{8}{a-2} + \frac{6}{2-a}$.
    15. **$\frac{2}{a-2}$**

16. If y varies inversely as x and $y = 24$ when $x = 1.5$, find y when $x = 8$.
    16. **4.5**

Cumulative Review (Chapters 1-17)—continued

17. Write $7^{-2} = \frac{1}{49}$ in logarithmic form.
    17. **$\log_7 \frac{1}{49} = -2$**

18. Find antilog $0.5688 - 4$.
    18. **0.0003705**

19. Find the 12th term in the arithmetic sequence $-17, -13, -9, \ldots$.
    19. **27**

20. Find the first four terms of the sequence in which $a_1 = 2$ and $a_{n+1} = 2a_n + 1$.
    20. **2, 5, 11, 23**

21. Evaluate $\frac{7!}{4!}$.
    21. **210**

22. Find n if $C(n, 5) = C(n, 7)$.
    22. **12**

23. Seven coins are tossed. What is the probability that 2 tails or 3 heads occur?
    23. **$\frac{7}{16}$**

For questions 24 through 26, use the table of Susan's scores in the archery contest.

7	9	5	1	5	3
5	3	7	9	7	3
1	7	5	5	9	5

24. Make a frequency distribution chart for the data.
    24. **See students' work.**

25. Find the median, mode, and mean for the data.
    25. **5; 5; $5\frac{1}{3}$**

26. Find the standard deviation for the data.
    26. **~2.4**

27. Show that $\frac{\tan^2 \theta - \sin^2 \theta}{\tan^2 \theta \sin^2 \theta} = 1$.
    27. **See students' work.**

28. Solve $\sin 2x = \cos x$ if $0° \leq x < 360°$.
    28. **30°, 90°, 150°, 270°**

29. Find $\cos \left(\sin^{-1} \frac{\sqrt{3}}{2} \right)$.
    29. **$\frac{1}{2}$**

30. Find the value of $\sec 60° + \cot 30°$.
    30. **$2 + \sqrt{3}$**

31. Graph $y = -2 \sin \theta$.
    31. **See students' graphs.**

32. Find $\sin 2x$, $\cos 2x$, $\sin \frac{x}{2}$, and $\cos \frac{x}{2}$ if $\cos x = \frac{1}{6}$ and x is in the first quadrant.
    32. **$\frac{\sqrt{35}}{18}, -\frac{17}{18}; \frac{\sqrt{15}}{6}, \frac{\sqrt{21}}{6}$**

33. Find $(-2 + 2i\sqrt{3})^5$.
    33. **$-512 + 256i\sqrt{3}$**

■ solve trigonometric equations. (Lesson 17-7)

Solve $\sin 2\theta + \sin \theta = 0$ if $0° \leq \theta < 360°$.

$$\sin 2\theta + \sin \theta = 0$$
$$2 \sin \theta \cos \theta + \sin \theta = 0$$
$$\sin \theta (2 \cos \theta + 1) = 0$$

$\sin \theta = 0$ or $2 \cos \theta + 1 = 0$
$\theta = 0°$ or $180°$ $\cos \theta = -\frac{1}{2}$
         $\theta = 120°$ or $240°$

35. $\frac{7\pi}{6} + 2n\pi, \frac{11\pi}{6} + 2n\pi$

■ work with complex numbers in rectangular and polar form. (Lesson 17-8)

Find $(2 + 2i)^4$ using polar coordinates.

$r = \sqrt{(2)^2 + (2)^2}$ $\theta = \text{Arctan} \frac{2}{2}$
$= 2\sqrt{2}$ $= \frac{\pi}{4}$

$(2 + 2i)^4 = \left[2\sqrt{2} \left(\cos \frac{\pi}{4} + i \sin \frac{\pi}{4} \right) \right]^4$

$= (2\sqrt{2})^4 \left(\cos \frac{4\pi}{4} + i \sin \frac{4\pi}{4} \right)$

$= 64(\cos \pi + i \sin \pi)$

$= 64(-1 + 0i)$

$= -64$

Find all solutions if $0° \leq \theta < 360°$.

32. $2 \cos^2 x + \sin^2 x = 2 \cos x$ **0°**

33. $\cos x = 1 - \sin x$ **0°, 90°**

34. $2 \sin 2x = 1$ **15°, 75°, 195°, 255°**

Solve each equation for all values of θ if θ is measured in radians.

35. $6 \sin^2 \theta - 5 \sin \theta - 4 = 0$

36. $\cos 2\theta \sin \theta = 1$ **$\frac{3\pi}{2} + 2n\pi$**

37. $\sin \frac{\theta}{2} + \cos \frac{\theta}{2} = \sqrt{2}$ **$\frac{\pi}{2} + 2n\pi$**

Express each complex number in polar form.

38. $-6i$ 39. $-2 + 2i\sqrt{3}$

$6 \left(\cos \frac{3\pi}{2} + i \sin \frac{3\pi}{2} \right)$ $4 \left(\cos \frac{2\pi}{3} + i \sin \frac{2\pi}{3} \right)$

Express each complex number in rectangular form.

40. $4 \left(\cos \frac{5\pi}{6} + i \sin \frac{5\pi}{6} \right)$ **$-2\sqrt{3} + 2i$**

41. $8 \left(\cos \frac{7\pi}{4} + i \sin \frac{7\pi}{4} \right)$ **$4\sqrt{2} - 4i\sqrt{2}$**

Find each product. Express the result in rectangular form.   **$-4 + 4i\sqrt{3}$**

42. $2 \left(\cos \frac{\pi}{3} + i \sin \frac{\pi}{3} \right) \cdot 4 \left(\cos \frac{\pi}{3} + i \sin \frac{\pi}{3} \right)$

43. $(2 + 2i)^8$ **4096**   44. $(-2 - 2i\sqrt{3})^3$ **64**

APPLICATIONS AND CONNECTIONS

45. **Surveying** A surveyor found that the angle between the line from her position to a building site and the line from her position to a road has a sine value of $\frac{4}{5}$. Find the cosine and the cotangent of this angle. (Lesson 17-2)
    $\frac{3}{5}, \frac{3}{4}$

46. **Finance** Tim received his paycheck Tuesday morning. He put half of the money in his savings account. He then gave $10 to a local charity. He spent one-fourth of his remaining pay on pizza with friends and $12 was left. How much was Tim's paycheck? (Lesson 17-4) **$52**

State the amplitude and period of each function. Then graph. **See Solutions Manual for graphs.**

1. $y = 2 \sin 2x$ **2, π**

2. $y = 2 \cos \frac{1}{5}\theta$ **2, 10π**

3. $y = \frac{3}{4} \cos \frac{2}{3}x$ **$\frac{3}{4}$, 3π**

State the period of each function. Then graph. **See Solutions Manual for graphs.**

4. $y = \csc 6\theta$ **$\frac{\pi}{3}$**

5. $y = 3 \tan \frac{1}{3}\theta$ **3π**

6. $y = \frac{4}{3} \cot \frac{1}{2}\theta$ **2π**

Solve each of the following for values of θ between 180° and 270°.

7. If $\sin \theta = -\frac{1}{2}$, find $\tan \theta$. **$\frac{\sqrt{3}}{3}$**

8. If $\cot \theta = \frac{3}{4}$, find $\sec \theta$. **$-\frac{5}{3}$**

Verify that each of the following is an identity. **See Solutions Manual.**

9. $\frac{\cos x}{1 - \sin^2 x} = \sec x$

10. $\frac{\sec x}{\sin x} - \frac{\sin x}{\cos x} = \cot x$

11. $\frac{1 + \tan^2 \theta}{\cos^2 \theta} = \sec^4 \theta$

12. **Entertainment** On a game show, all the contestants start with the same number of points and they are awarded points for questions answered correctly and lose points for questions answered incorrectly. Kim answered four 20-point questions correctly, then two 50-point questions incorrectly. In her final round question, Kim doubled her score and won the game with 460 points. How many points does each player have at the start of the game? **250**

Evaluate each expression.

13. $\cos 165°$ **$\frac{-\sqrt{2} - \sqrt{6}}{4}$**

14. $\sin 255°$ **$\frac{-\sqrt{2} - \sqrt{6}}{4}$**

15. $2 \sin 75° \cos 75°$ **$\frac{1}{2}$**

16. If x is in the first quadrant and $\cos x = \frac{3}{4}$, find $\sin \frac{x}{2}$. **$\frac{\sqrt{2}}{4}$**

17. If $\cos 2x = \frac{7}{9}$ and $\sin x = \frac{1}{3}$, find $\cos x$. **$\frac{2\sqrt{2}}{3}$**

Find all solutions if $0° \le x < 360°$.

18. $\sec x = 1 + \tan x$ **0°**

19. $\cos 2x + \sin x = 1$ **0°, 30°, 150°, 180°**

20. $2 \sin x \cos x - \sin x = 0$ **0°, 60°, 180°, 300°**

Solve each equation for all values of θ if θ is measured in radians.

21. $\sin \frac{\theta}{2} + \cos \theta - 1$ **$0 + 2n\pi, \frac{\pi}{3} + 2n\pi, \frac{5\pi}{3} + 2n\pi$**

22. $3 \tan^2 \theta - \sqrt{3} \tan \theta = 0$ **$0 + n\pi, \frac{\pi}{6} + n\pi$**

23. Express $-4 + 4i$ in polar form. **$4\sqrt{2}\left(\cos \frac{3\pi}{4} + i \sin \frac{3\pi}{4}\right)$**

24. Express $2\left(\cos \frac{\pi}{3} + i \sin \frac{\pi}{3}\right)$ in rectangular form. **$1 + i\sqrt{3}$**

25. Find the product $4\left(\cos \frac{3\pi}{2} + i \sin \frac{3\pi}{2}\right) \cdot 3\left(\cos \frac{\pi}{4} + i \sin \frac{\pi}{4}\right)$. Express the answer in rectangular form. **$6\sqrt{2} - 6i\sqrt{2}$**

Bonus Find $(1 - i)^8$ by DeMoivre's Theorem. **16**

Using the Chapter Test

This page may be used as a test or as a review. In addition, two multiple-choice tests and two free-response tests are provided in the Evaluation Masters Booklet. Chapter 17 Test, Form 1A is shown below.

Evaluation Masters Booklet, pp. 225–226

NAME _____ DATE _____

Chapter 17 Test, Form 1A

Write the letter for the correct answer in the blank at the right of each problem.

1. What is the amplitude of $y = -8 \cos 2\theta$?
   A. 2   B. -2   C. 8   D. -8   1. __C__

2. What is the period of $y = -3 \sin 4\theta$?
   A. -3   B. 4   C. 4π D. $\frac{\pi}{2}$ 2. __D__

3. Which equation is graphed at the right?
   A. $y = -2 \cos \frac{1}{3}x$ B. $y = 2 \cos(-3x)$
   C. $y = -\frac{2}{3} \cos \frac{1}{3}x$ D. $y = \frac{2}{3} \cos\left(-\frac{1}{3}x\right)$ 3. __C__

4. What is the period of $y = \tan 3\theta$?
   A. $\frac{2\pi}{3}$ B. $\frac{\pi}{3}$ C. 3π D. 6π 4. __B__

5. Which equation is graphed at the right?
   A. $y = 4 \sec \frac{3}{2}x$ B. $y = 4 \csc \frac{3}{2}x$
   C. $y = 4 \sec \frac{2}{3}x$ D. $y = 4 \csc \frac{2}{3}x$ 5. __D__

6. If $\cos \theta = -\frac{2}{3}$ and θ is between 90° and 180°, what is the value of $\sin \theta$?
   A. $-\frac{\sqrt{5}}{3}$ B. $\frac{\sqrt{5}}{3}$ C. $\frac{\sqrt{13}}{3}$ D. $\frac{\sqrt{13}}{3}$ 6. __B__

7. If $\tan \theta = \frac{1}{4}$ and θ is between 180° and 270°, what is the value of $\sec \theta$?
   A. $\frac{\sqrt{15}}{4}$ B. $\frac{-\sqrt{15}}{4}$ C. $\frac{\sqrt{17}}{4}$ D. $-\frac{\sqrt{17}}{4}$ 7. __D__

8. What is the simplest form of $\frac{\sin^2 \theta + \cos^2 \theta}{\tan^2 \theta}$?
   A. $\cot^2 \theta$ B. $\sin^4 \theta + \sin^2 \theta$
   C. $\cos^2 \theta + \cos^4 \theta$ D. $\csc^2 \theta$ 8. __A__

9. A television set was placed on sale at $600 off. The sale price was then reduced by 35%. The television set was finally sold at half the last marked price. If the price paid when the set was sold was $117.00 [...], what [...]?
   A. $385   B. $515   C. $721   D. $827   9. __A__

10. What is the value of $\cos 75° \cos 45° - \sin 75° \sin 45°$?
    A. $\frac{1}{2}$ B. $\frac{\sqrt{3}}{2}$ C. $\frac{\sqrt{2}}{2}$ D. undefined   10. __A__

NAME _____ DATE _____

Chapter 17, Test Form 1A (continued)

11. What is the value of $\sin(-15°)$?
    A. $\frac{\sqrt{6} - \sqrt{2}}{4}$ B. $\frac{\sqrt{6} + \sqrt{2}}{4}$ C. $\frac{-\sqrt{6} + \sqrt{2}}{4}$ D. $\frac{-\sqrt{6} - \sqrt{2}}{4}$ 11. __C__

12. Find the value of $\sin 2x$ if $\sin x = -\frac{2}{3}$ and x is in the third quadrant.
    A. $-\frac{1}{9}$ B. $-\frac{4\sqrt{5}}{9}$ C. $\frac{1}{9}$ D. $\frac{4\sqrt{5}}{9}$ 12. __D__

13. Find the value of $\sin \frac{x}{2}$ if $\cos x = \frac{2}{3}$ and x is in the fourth quadrant.
    A. $\frac{1}{3}$ B. $-\frac{1}{3}$ C. $\frac{\sqrt{6}}{6}$ D. $-\frac{\sqrt{6}}{6}$ 13. __C__

14. Which expression is not equal to 1? Assume no expressions are undefined.
    A. $\sin^2 x + \cot^2 x \sin^2 x$ B. $\frac{\sin^2 x}{1 - \cos x} - \cos x$
    C. $\csc^2 x + \cot^2 x$ D. none of these   14. __C__

15. If $0° \le x < 360°$, what are the solutions of $3 \sin x = 2 \cos^2 x$?
    A. 30°, 150°   B. 30°, 120°
    C. 30°, 330°   D. 150°, 330°   15. __A__

16. What are all the solutions of $\cos 2x + \cos x - 2 = 0$?
    A. 0°, 360°   B. 0° + 360°n
    C. 0°, 180°, 360°   D. 0° + 180°n 16. __B__

17. Which of the following is not a solution of $\sin 2x = \cos x$?
    A. 0°   B. 90°   C. 330°   D. 750°   17. __C__

18. What is $-5i$ written in polar form?
    A. $-5\left(\cos \frac{\pi}{2} + i \sin \frac{\pi}{2}\right)$ B. $5\left(\cos \frac{\pi}{2} + i \sin \frac{\pi}{2}\right)$
    C. $-5\left(\cos \frac{3\pi}{2} + i \sin \frac{3\pi}{2}\right)$ D. $5\left(\cos \frac{3\pi}{2} + i \sin \frac{3\pi}{2}\right)$ 18. __D__

19. What is the product of $3\left(\cos \frac{\pi}{3} + i \sin \frac{\pi}{3}\right)$ and $4\left(\cos \frac{\pi}{6} + i \sin \frac{\pi}{6}\right)$ expressed in rectangular form?
    A. 12   B. $12i$ C. $12 - 12i$ D. $12 + 12i$ 19. __B__

20. What is $\left(\cos \frac{5\pi}{6} + i \sin \frac{5\pi}{6}\right)^4$ written in simplest rectangular form?
    A. $\frac{1 + i\sqrt{3}}{2}$ B. $\frac{1 - i\sqrt{3}}{2}$
    C. $\frac{-1 + i\sqrt{3}}{2}$ D. $\frac{-1 - i\sqrt{3}}{2}$ 20. __D__

Bonus
If $y = \frac{1}{2} \cos 4x$, find all values of x so that y is a maximum.
A. $45n°$ B. $90n°$ C. $180n°$ D. $1440n°$ Bonus __B__

A **Test and Review Generator** is provided in Apple, IBM, and Macintosh versions. You may use this software to create your own tests or worksheets, based on the needs of your students.

The **Performance Assessment Booklet** provides an alternate asssessment for evaluating student progress. An assessment for this chapter can be found on pages 33–34.

APPENDIX: USING TABLES

Tables of common logarithms and values of trigonometric functions are provided for use in case a scientific calculator is not available. This guide will show you how to use these tables to find common logarithms, antilogarithms, and values of trigonometric functions and inverse trigonometric functions.

How To Use Logarithmic Tables

You can use the logarithmic tables to find the common logarithm of any number. The values in the table have been rounded to the nearest ten-thousandth.

To find the logarithm of a number greater than or equal to 1 but less than 10, read across the row that contains the first two digits of the number and down the column that contains the third digit. For example, if you need to find the logarithm of 1.23 read across the row labeled 12 and down the column labeled 3. The common logarithm of 1.23 is 0.0899.

Common Logarithms of Numbers

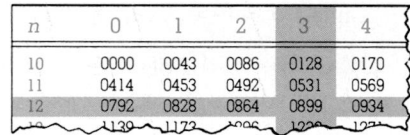

n	0	1	2	3	4
10	0000	0043	0086	0128	0170
11	0414	0453	0492	0531	0569
12	0792	0828	0864	0899	0934
13	1139	1173		1239	12

$$\log 1.23 = 0.0899$$

To find the logarithm of a number that is not between 1 and 10, use the table to find the mantissa and use scientific notation to supply the characteristic.

Example 1

Find log 395.

First, write the number in scientific notation.

$$395 = 3.95 \times 10^2$$

The characteristic is the power of 10. In this case, the characteristic is 2. Now use the table to find the logarithm of the 3.95, this is the mantissa.

$$\log 3.95 = 0.5966 \qquad \textit{The mantissa is 0.5966.}$$

The logarithm of 395 is 2.5966.

You can also use the table of logarithms to find antilogarithms of numbers by simply reversing the process for finding a logarithm.

Example 2

Find antilog 3.5821.

Begin by separating the logarithm into the characteristic and the mantissa.

characteristic = 3   mantissa = 0.5821

Then use the table to find the number for which 0.5821 is the logarithm. It is located in the row labeled 38 and the column labeled 2.

antilog 3.5821 = (antilog 0.5821) × 10³
     = 38.2 × 10³
     = 3820

n	0	1	2	3	4
10	0000	0043	0086	0128	0170
37	5682	5694	5705	5717	5729
38	5798	5809	5821	5832	5843
39	5911	5922	5933	5944	5955

log 3.82 = 0.5821

The antilog of 3.5821 is 3820.

The table of logarithms includes mantissas of numbers with three significant digits. Sometimes you may need to find logarithms more of numbers with more digits. You will need to use **interpolation** to use the table to find these logarithms.

Example 3

Approximate the value of log 1.327.

The logarithm of 1.327 is between the logarithms of 1.32 and 1.33. Find these values in the table and write a proportion to find log 1.327.

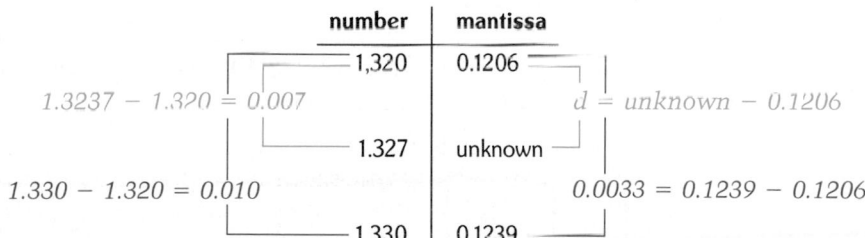

	number	mantissa
	1,320	0.1206
	1.327	unknown
	1.330	0.1239

$1.3237 - 1.320 = 0.007$

$1.330 - 1.320 = 0.010$

$d = unknown - 0.1206$

$0.0033 = 0.1239 - 0.1206$

$$\frac{0.007}{0.010} = \frac{d}{0.0033}$$

$0.00231 = d$

$0.0023 = d$ *Round to the nearest ten-thousandth, like the values in the table.*

Since the values in the table are increasing, add d to the mantissa of 1.320.

log 1.327 = log 1.320 + d
     = 0.1206 + 0.0023
     = 0.1229   The logarithm of 1.327 is approximately 0.1229.

You can use the method of interpolation to find an antilogarithm that cannot be obtained directly from the table as well.

How To Use Trigonometric Tables

You can use the trigonometric tables to find decimal approximations for the values of trigonometric functions. Values are listed for angle measurements between 0° and 90° in intervals of ten minutes.

Angle measurements from 0°00′ to 45°00′ are listed on the left-hand side of the tables. When finding a value for an angle in this range, use the column titles at the top of the table. Angle measurements from 45°00′ to 90°00′ are listed on the right-hand side of the tables. When finding a value for an angle in this range, use the column titles at the bottom on the table.

Example 1

Find cos 27°10′.

Read across the row labeled 27°10′ and down the column labeled Cos. *Remember to use the column titles at the top of the table for an angle between 0° and 45°.*

Values of Trigonometric Functions

Angle	Sin	Cos	Tan	Cot	Sec	Csc	
27°00′	0.4540	0.8910	0.5095	1.963	1.122	2.203	63°00′
10′	0.4566	0.8897	0.5132	1.949	1.124	2.190	50′
20′	0.4592	0.8884	0.5169	1.935	1.126	2.178	40′
30′	0.4617	0.8870	0.5206	1.921	1.127	2.166	30′
40′	0.4643	0.8857	0.5243	1.907	1.129	2.154	20′
50′	0.4669	0.8843	0.5280	1.894	1.131	2.142	10′
28°00′	0.4695	0.8829					

The value of cos 27°10′ is 0.8897

Example 2

Find tan 54°30′.

Read across the row labeled 54°30′ and up the column labeled Tan. *Remember to use the column titles at the bottom of the table for an angle between 45° and 90°.*

						1.736	50′
20′	0.5783	0.8158	0.7089	1.411	1.226	1.729	40′
30′	0.5807	0.8141	0.7133	1.402	1.228	1.722	30′
40′	0.5831	0.8124	0.7177	1.393	1.231	1.715	20′
50′	0.5854	0.8107	0.7221	1.385	1.233	1.708	10′
36°00′	0.5878	0.8090	0.7265	1.376	1.236	1.701	54°00′
	Cos	Sin	Cot	Tan	Csc	Sec	Angle

The value of tan 54°30′ is 1.402.

You can use the sum and difference formulas and the half- and double-angle formulas for sine and cosine to find the trigonometric values of angles whose measurements are not listed in the table. For example, you can find sin 153° by using the difference formula for and sin (180° − 27°).

You can also use interpolation to find approximations of trigonometric values for angle measurements that are not listed in the tables.

COMMON LOGARITHMS OF NUMBERS

n	0	1	2	3	4	5	6	7	8	9
10	0000	0043	0086	0128	0170	0212	0253	0294	0334	0374
11	0414	0453	0492	0531	0569	0607	0645	0682	0719	0755
12	0792	0828	0864	0899	0934	0969	1004	1038	1072	1106
13	1139	1173	1206	1239	1271	1303	1335	1367	1399	1430
14	1461	1492	1523	1553	1584	1614	1644	1673	1703	1732
15	1761	1790	1818	1847	1875	1903	1931	1959	1987	2014
16	2041	2068	2095	2122	2148	2175	2201	2227	2253	2279
17	2304	2330	2355	2380	2405	2430	2455	2480	2504	2529
18	2553	2577	2601	2625	2648	2672	2695	2718	2742	2765
19	2788	2810	2833	2856	2878	2900	2923	2945	2967	2989
20	3010	3032	3054	3075	3096	3118	3139	3160	3181	3201
21	3222	3243	3263	3284	3304	3324	3345	3365	3385	3404
22	3424	3444	3464	3483	3502	3522	3541	3560	3579	3598
23	3617	3636	3655	3674	3692	3711	3729	3747	3766	3784
24	3802	3820	3838	3856	3874	3892	3909	3927	3945	3962
25	3979	3997	4014	4031	4048	4065	4082	4099	4116	4133
26	4150	4166	4183	4200	4216	4232	4249	4265	4281	4298
27	4314	4330	4346	4362	4378	4393	4409	4425	4440	4456
28	4472	4487	4502	4518	4533	4548	4564	4579	4594	4609
29	4624	4639	4654	4669	4683	4698	4713	4728	4742	4757
30	4771	4786	4800	4814	4829	4843	4857	4871	4886	4900
31	4914	4928	4942	4955	4969	4983	4997	5011	5024	5038
32	5051	5065	5079	5092	5105	5119	5132	5145	5159	5172
33	5185	5198	5211	5224	5237	5250	5263	5276	5289	5302
34	5315	5328	5340	5353	5366	5378	5391	5403	5416	5428
35	5441	5453	5465	5478	5490	5502	5514	5527	5539	5551
36	5563	5575	5587	5599	5611	5623	5635	5647	5658	5670
37	5682	5694	5705	5717	5729	5740	5752	5763	5775	5786
38	5798	5809	5821	5832	5843	5855	5866	5877	5888	5899
39	5911	5922	5933	5944	5955	5966	5977	5988	5999	6010
40	6021	6031	6042	6053	6064	6075	6085	6096	6107	6117
41	6128	6138	6149	6160	6170	6180	6191	6201	6212	6222
42	6232	6243	6253	6263	6274	6284	6294	6304	6314	6325
43	6335	6345	6355	6365	6375	6385	6395	6405	6415	6425
44	6435	6444	6454	6464	6474	6484	6493	6503	6513	6522
45	6532	6542	6551	6561	6571	6580	6590	6599	6609	6618
46	6628	6637	6646	6656	6665	6675	6684	6693	6702	6712
47	6721	6730	6739	6749	6758	6767	6776	6785	6794	6803
48	6812	6821	6830	6839	6848	6857	6866	6875	6884	6893
49	6902	6911	6920	6928	6937	6946	6955	6964	6972	6981
50	6990	6998	7007	7016	7024	7033	7042	7050	7059	7067
51	7076	7084	7093	7101	7110	7118	7126	7135	7143	7152
52	7160	7168	7177	7185	7193	7202	7210	7218	7226	7235
53	7243	7251	7259	7267	7275	7284	7292	7300	7308	7316
54	7324	7332	7340	7348	7356	7364	7372	7380	7388	7396

The values given are mantissas correct to four decimal places. For example, log 5.42 = 0.7340

n	0	1	2	3	4	5	6	7	8	9
55	7404	7412	7419	7427	7435	7443	7451	7459	7466	7474
56	7482	7490	7497	7505	7513	7520	7528	7536	7543	7551
57	7559	7566	7574	7582	7589	7597	7604	7612	7619	7627
58	7634	7642	7649	7657	7664	7672	7679	7686	7694	7701
59	7709	7716	7723	7731	7738	7745	7752	7760	7767	7774
60	7782	7789	7796	7803	7810	7818	7825	7832	7839	7846
61	7853	7860	7868	7875	7882	7889	7896	7903	7910	7917
62	7924	7931	7938	7945	7952	7959	7966	7973	7980	7987
63	7993	8000	8007	8014	8021	8028	8035	8041	8048	8055
64	8062	8069	8075	8082	8089	8096	8102	8109	8116	8122
65	8129	8136	8142	8149	8156	8162	8169	8176	8182	8189
66	8195	8202	8209	8215	8222	8228	8235	8241	8248	8254
67	8261	8267	8274	8280	8287	8293	8299	8306	8312	8319
68	8325	8331	8338	8344	8351	8357	8363	8370	8376	8382
69	8388	8395	8401	8407	8414	8420	8426	8432	8439	8445
70	8451	8457	8463	8470	8476	8482	8488	8494	8500	8506
71	8513	8519	8525	8531	8537	8543	8549	8555	8561	8567
72	8573	8579	8585	8591	8597	8603	8609	8615	8621	8627
73	8633	8639	8645	8651	8657	8663	8669	8675	8681	8686
74	8692	8698	8704	8710	8716	8722	8727	8733	8739	8745
75	8751	8756	8762	8768	8774	8779	8785	8791	8797	8802
76	8808	8814	8820	8825	8831	8837	8842	8848	8854	8859
77	8865	8871	8876	8882	8887	8893	8899	8904	8910	8915
78	8921	8927	8932	8938	8943	8949	8954	8960	8965	8971
79	8976	8982	8987	8993	8998	9004	9009	9015	9020	9025
80	9031	9036	9042	9047	9053	9058	9063	9069	9074	9079
81	9085	9090	9096	9101	9106	9112	9117	9122	9128	9133
82	9138	9143	9149	9154	9159	9165	9170	9175	9180	9186
83	9191	9196	9201	9206	9212	9217	9222	9227	9232	9238
84	9243	9248	9253	9258	9263	9269	9274	9279	9284	9289
85	9294	9299	9304	9309	9315	9320	9325	9330	9335	9340
86	9345	9350	9355	9360	9365	9370	9375	9380	9385	9390
87	9395	9400	9405	9410	9415	9420	9425	9430	9435	9440
88	9445	9450	9455	9460	9465	9469	9474	9479	9484	9489
89	9494	9499	9504	9509	9513	9518	9523	9528	9533	9538
90	9542	9547	9552	9557	9562	9566	9571	9576	9581	9586
91	9590	9595	9600	9605	9609	9614	9619	9624	9628	9633
92	9638	9643	9647	9652	9657	9661	9666	9671	9675	9680
93	9685	9689	9694	9699	9703	9708	9713	9717	9722	9727
94	9731	9736	9741	9745	9750	9754	9759	9763	9768	9773
95	9777	9782	9786	9791	9795	9800	9805	9809	9814	9818
96	9823	9827	9832	9836	9841	9845	9850	9854	9859	9863
97	9868	9872	9877	9881	9886	9890	9894	9899	9903	9908
98	9912	9917	9921	9926	9930	9934	9939	9943	9948	9952
99	9956	9961	9965	9969	9974	9978	9983	9987	9991	9996

VALUES OF TRIGONOMETRIC FUNCTIONS

Angle	Sin	Cos	Tan	Cot	Sec	Csc	
0°00′	0.0000	1.0000	0.0000	—	1.000	—	90°00′
10′	0.0029	1.0000	0.0029	343.8	1.000	343.8	50′
20′	0.0058	1.0000	0.0058	171.9	1.000	171.9	40′
30′	0.0087	1.0000	0.0087	114.6	1.000	114.6	30′
40′	0.0116	0.9999	0.0116	85.94	1.000	85.95	20′
50′	0.0145	0.9999	0.0145	68.75	1.000	68.76	10′
1°00′	0.0175	0.9998	0.0175	57.29	1.000	57.30	89°00′
10′	0.0204	0.9998	0.0204	49.10	1.000	49.11	50′
20′	0.0233	0.9997	0.0233	42.96	1.000	42.98	40′
30′	0.0262	0.9997	0.0262	38.19	1.000	38.20	30′
40′	0.0291	0.9996	0.0291	34.37	1.000	34.38	20′
50′	0.0320	0.9995	0.0320	31.24	1.001	31.26	10′
2°00′	0.0349	0.9994	0.0349	28.64	1.001	28.65	88°00′
10′	0.0378	0.9993	0.0378	26.43	1.001	26.45	50′
20′	0.0407	0.9992	0.0407	24.54	1.001	24.56	40′
30′	0.0436	0.9990	0.0437	22.90	1.001	22.93	30′
40′	0.0465	0.9989	0.0466	21.47	1.001	21.49	20′
50′	0.0494	0.9988	0.0495	20.21	1.001	20.23	10′
3°00′	0.0523	0.9986	0.0524	19.08	1.001	19.11	87°00′
10′	0.0552	0.9985	0.0553	18.07	1.002	18.10	50′
20′	0.0581	0.9983	0.0582	17.17	1.002	17.20	40′
30′	0.0610	0.9981	0.0612	16.35	1.002	16.38	30′
40′	0.0640	0.9980	0.0641	15.60	1.002	15.64	20′
50′	0.0669	0.9978	0.0670	14.92	1.002	14.96	10′
4°00′	0.0698	0.9976	0.0699	14.30	1.002	14.34	86°00′
10′	0.0727	0.9974	0.0729	13.73	1.003	13.76	50′
20′	0.0756	0.9971	0.0758	13.20	1.003	13.23	40′
30′	0.0785	0.9969	0.0787	12.71	1.003	12.75	30′
40′	0.0814	0.9967	0.0816	12.25	1.003	12.29	20′
50′	0.0843	0.9964	0.0846	11.83	1.004	11.87	10′
5°00′	0.0872	0.9962	0.0875	11.43	1.004	11.47	85°00′
10′	0.0901	0.9959	0.0904	11.06	1.004	11.10	50′
20′	0.0929	0.9957	0.0934	10.71	1.004	10.76	40′
30′	0.0958	0.9954	0.0963	10.39	1.005	10.43	30′
40′	0.0987	0.9951	0.0992	10.08	1.005	10.13	20′
50′	0.1016	0.9948	0.1022	9.788	1.005	9.839	10′
6°00′	0.1045	0.9945	0.1051	9.514	1.006	9.567	84°00′
10′	0.1074	0.9942	0.1080	9.255	1.006	9.309	50′
20′	0.1103	0.9939	0.1110	9.010	1.006	9.065	40′
30′	0.1132	0.9936	0.1139	8.777	1.006	8.834	30′
40′	0.1161	0.9932	0.1169	8.556	1.007	8.614	20′
50′	0.1190	0.9929	0.1198	8.345	1.007	8.405	10′
7°00′	0.1219	0.9925	0.1228	8.144	1.008	8.206	83°00′
10′	0.1248	0.9922	0.1257	7.953	1.008	8.016	50′
20′	0.1276	0.9918	0.1287	7.770	1.008	7.834	40′
30′	0.1305	0.9914	0.1317	7.596	1.009	7.661	30′
40′	0.1334	0.9911	0.1346	7.429	1.009	7.496	20′
50′	0.1363	0.9907	0.1376	7.269	1.009	7.337	10′
8°00′	0.1392	0.9903	0.1405	7.115	1.010	7.185	82°00′
10′	0.1421	0.9899	0.1435	6.968	1.010	7.040	50′
20′	0.1449	0.9894	0.1465	6.827	1.011	6.900	40′
30′	0.1478	0.9890	0.1495	6.691	1.011	6.765	30′
40′	0.1507	0.9886	0.1524	6.561	1.012	6.636	20′
50′	0.1536	0.9881	0.1554	6.435	1.012	6.512	10′
9°00′	0.1564	0.9877	0.1584	6.314	1.012	6.392	81°00′
	Cos	Sin	Cot	Tan	Csc	Sec	Angle

For the values of cos, sin, tan, and so on for angles greater than 45°, use the angle measures listed on the right and the functions on the bottom. For example, cos 81° = 0.1564.

VALUES OF TRIGONOMETRIC FUNCTIONS

Angle	Sin	Cos	Tan	Cot	Sec	Csc	
9°00′	0.1564	0.9877	0.1584	6.314	1.012	6.392	81°00′
10′	0.1593	0.9872	0.1614	6.197	1.013	6.277	50′
20′	0.1622	0.9868	0.1644	6.084	1.013	6.166	40′
30′	0.1650	0.9863	0.1673	5.976	1.014	6.059	30′
40′	0.1679	0.9858	0.1703	5.871	1.014	5.955	20′
50′	0.1708	0.9853	0.1733	5.769	1.015	5.855	10′
10°00′	0.1736	0.9848	0.1763	5.671	1.015	5.759	80°00′
10′	0.1765	0.9843	0.1793	5.576	1.016	5.665	50′
20′	0.1794	0.9838	0.1823	5.485	1.016	5.575	40′
30′	0.1822	0.9833	0.1853	5.396	1.017	5.487	30′
40′	0.1851	0.9827	0.1883	5.309	1.018	5.403	20′
50′	0.1880	0.9822	0.1914	5.226	1.018	5.320	10′
11°00′	0.1908	0.9816	0.1944	5.145	1.019	5.241	79°00′
10′	0.1937	0.9811	0.1974	5.066	1.019	5.164	50′
20′	0.1965	0.9805	0.2004	4.989	1.020	5.089	40′
30′	0.1994	0.9799	0.2035	4.915	1.020	5.016	30′
40′	0.2022	0.9793	0.2065	4.843	1.021	4.945	20′
50′	0.2051	0.9787	0.2095	4.773	1.022	4.876	10′
12°00′	0.2079	0.9781	0.2126	4.705	1.022	4.810	78°00′
10′	0.2108	0.9775	0.2156	4.638	1.023	4.745	50′
20′	0.2136	0.9769	0.2186	4.574	1.024	4.682	40′
30′	0.2164	0.9763	0.2217	4.511	1.024	4.620	30′
40′	0.2193	0.9757	0.2247	4.449	1.025	4.560	20′
50′	0.2221	0.9750	0.2278	4.390	1.026	4.502	10′
13°00′	0.2250	0.9744	0.2309	4.331	1.026	4.445	77°00′
10′	0.2278	0.9737	0.2339	4.275	1.027	4.390	50′
20′	0.2306	0.9730	0.2370	4.219	1.028	4.336	40′
30′	0.2334	0.9724	0.2401	4.165	1.028	4.284	30′
40′	0.2363	0.9717	0.2432	4.113	1.029	4.232	20′
50′	0.2391	0.9710	0.2462	4.061	1.030	4.182	10′
14°00′	0.2419	0.9703	0.2493	4.011	1.031	4.134	76°00′
10′	0.2447	0.9696	0.2524	3.962	1.031	4.086	50′
20′	0.2476	0.9689	0.2555	3.914	1.032	4.039	40′
30′	0.2504	0.9681	0.2586	3.867	1.033	3.994	30′
40′	0.2532	0.9674	0.2617	3.821	1.034	3.950	20′
50′	0.2560	0.9667	0.2648	3.776	1.034	3.906	10′
15°00′	0.2588	0.9659	0.2679	3.732	1.035	3.864	75°00′
10′	0.2616	0.9652	0.2711	3.689	1.036	3.822	50′
20′	0.2644	0.9644	0.2742	3.647	1.037	3.782	40′
30′	0.2672	0.9636	0.2773	3.606	1.038	3.742	30′
40′	0.2700	0.9628	0.2805	3.566	1.039	3.703	20′
50′	0.2728	0.9621	0.2836	3.526	1.039	3.665	10′
16°00′	0.2756	0.9613	0.2867	3.487	1.040	3.628	74°00′
10′	0.2784	0.9605	0.2899	3.450	1.041	3.592	50′
20′	0.2812	0.9596	0.2931	3.412	1.042	3.556	40′
30′	0.2840	0.9588	0.2962	3.376	1.043	3.521	30′
40′	0.2868	0.9580	0.2994	3.340	1.044	3.487	20′
50′	0.2896	0.9572	0.3026	3.305	1.045	3.453	10′
17°00′	0.2924	0.9563	0.3057	3.271	1.046	3.420	73°00′
10′	0.2952	0.9555	0.3089	3.237	1.047	3.388	50′
20′	0.2979	0.9546	0.3121	3.204	1.048	3.356	40′
30′	0.3007	0.9537	0.3153	3.172	1.049	3.326	30′
40′	0.3035	0.9528	0.3185	3.140	1.049	3.295	20′
50′	0.3062	0.9520	0.3217	3.108	1.050	3.265	10′
18°00′	0.3090	0.9511	0.3249	3.078	1.051	3.236	72°00′
	Cos	Sin	Cot	Tan	Csc	Sec	Angle

VALUES OF TRIGONOMETRIC FUNCTIONS

Angle	Sin	Cos	Tan	Cot	Sec	Csc	
18°00′	0.3090	0.9511	0.3249	3.078	1.051	3.236	72°00′
10′	0.3118	0.9502	0.3281	3.047	1.052	3.207	50′
20′	0.3145	0.9492	0.3314	3.018	1.053	3.179	40′
30′	0.3173	0.9483	0.3346	2.989	1.054	3.152	30′
40′	0.3201	0.9474	0.3378	2.960	1.056	3.124	20′
50′	0.3228	0.9465	0.3411	2.932	1.057	3.098	10′
19°00′	0.3256	0.9455	0.3443	2.904	1.058	3.072	71°00′
10′	0.3283	0.9446	0.3476	2.877	1.059	3.046	50′
20′	0.3311	0.9436	0.3508	2.850	1.060	3.021	40′
30′	0.3338	0.9426	0.3541	2.824	1.061	2.996	30′
40′	0.3365	0.9417	0.3574	2.798	1.062	2.971	20′
50′	0.3393	0.9407	0.3607	2.773	1.063	2.947	10′
20°00′	0.3420	0.9397	0.3640	2.747	1.064	2.924	70°00′
10′	0.3448	0.9387	0.3673	2.723	1.065	2.901	50′
20′	0.3475	0.9377	0.3706	2.699	1.066	2.878	40′
30′	0.3502	0.9367	0.3739	2.675	1.068	2.855	30′
40′	0.3529	0.9356	0.3772	2.651	1.069	2.833	20′
50′	0.3557	0.9346	0.3805	2.628	1.070	2.812	10′
21°00′	0.3584	0.9336	0.3839	2.605	1.071	2.790	69°00′
10′	0.3611	0.9325	0.3872	2.583	1.072	2.769	50′
20′	0.3638	0.9315	0.3906	2.560	1.074	2.749	40′
30′	0.3665	0.9304	0.3939	2.539	1.075	2.729	30′
40′	0.3692	0.9293	0.3973	2.517	1.076	2.709	20′
50′	0.3719	0.9283	0.4006	2.496	1.077	2.689	10′
22°00′	0.3746	0.9272	0.4040	2.475	1.079	2.669	68°00′
10′	0.3773	0.9261	0.4074	2.455	1.080	2.650	50′
20′	0.3800	0.9250	0.4108	2.434	1.081	2.632	40′
30′	0.3827	0.9239	0.4142	2.414	1.082	2.613	30′
40′	0.3854	0.9228	0.4176	2.394	1.084	2.595	20′
50′	0.3881	0.9216	0.4210	2.375	1.085	2.577	10′
23°00′	0.3907	0.9205	0.4245	2.356	1.086	2.559	67°00′
10′	0.3934	0.9194	0.4279	2.337	1.088	2.542	50′
20′	0.3961	0.9182	0.4314	2.318	1.089	2.525	40′
30′	0.3987	0.9171	0.4348	2.300	1.090	2.508	30′
40′	0.4014	0.9159	0.4383	2.282	1.092	2.491	20′
50′	0.4041	0.9147	0.4417	2.264	1.093	2.475	10′
24°00′	0.4067	0.9135	0.4452	2.246	1.095	2.459	66°00′
10′	0.4094	0.9124	0.4487	2.229	1.096	2.443	50′
20′	0.4120	0.9112	0.4522	2.211	1.097	2.427	40′
30′	0.4147	0.9100	0.4557	2.194	1.099	2.411	30′
40′	0.4173	0.9088	0.4592	2.177	1.100	2.396	20′
50′	0.4200	0.9075	0.4628	2.161	1.102	2.381	10′
25°00′	0.4226	0.9063	0.4663	2.145	1.103	2.366	65°00′
10′	0.4253	0.9051	0.4699	2.128	1.105	2.352	50′
20′	0.4279	0.9038	0.4734	2.112	1.106	2.337	40′
30′	0.4305	0.9026	0.4770	2.097	1.108	2.323	30′
40′	0.4331	0.9013	0.4806	2.081	1.109	2.309	20′
50′	0.4358	0.9001	0.4841	2.066	1.111	2.295	10′
26°00′	0.4384	0.8988	0.4877	2.050	1.113	2.281	64°00′
10′	0.4410	0.8975	0.4913	2.035	1.114	2.268	50′
20′	0.4436	0.8962	0.4950	2.020	1.116	2.254	40′
30′	0.4462	0.8949	0.4986	2.006	1.117	2.241	30′
40′	0.4488	0.8936	0.5022	1.991	1.119	2.228	20′
50′	0.4514	0.8923	0.5059	1.977	1.121	2.215	10′
27°00′	0.4540	0.8910	0.5095	1.963	1.122	2.203	63°00′
	Cos	Sin	Cot	Tan	Csc	Sec	Angle

VALUES OF TRIGONOMETRIC FUNCTIONS

Angle	Sin	Cos	Tan	Cot	Sec	Csc	
27°00′	0.4540	0.8910	0.5095	1.963	1.122	2.203	63°00′
10′	0.4566	0.8897	0.5132	1.949	1.124	2.190	50′
20′	0.4592	0.8884	0.5169	1.935	1.126	2.178	40′
30′	0.4617	0.8870	0.5206	1.921	1.127	2.166	30′
40′	0.4643	0.8857	0.5243	1.907	1.129	2.154	20′
50′	0.4669	0.8843	0.5280	1.894	1.131	2.142	10′
28°00′	0.4695	0.8829	0.5317	1.881	1.133	2.130	62°00′
10′	0.4720	0.8816	0.5354	1.868	1.134	2.118	50′
20′	0.4746	0.8802	0.5392	1.855	1.136	2.107	40′
30′	0.4772	0.8788	0.5430	1.842	1.138	2.096	30′
40′	0.4797	0.8774	0.5467	1.829	1.140	2.085	20′
50′	0.4823	0.8760	0.5505	1.816	1.142	2.074	10′
29°00′	0.4848	0.8746	0.5543	1.804	1.143	2.063	61°00′
10′	0.4874	0.8732	0.5581	1.792	1.145	2.052	50′
20′	0.4899	0.8718	0.5619	1.780	1.147	2.041	40′
30′	0.4924	0.8704	0.5658	1.767	1.149	2.031	30′
40′	0.4950	0.8689	0.5696	1.756	1.151	2.020	20′
50′	0.4975	0.8675	0.5735	1.744	1.153	2.010	10′
30°00′	0.5000	0.8660	0.5774	1.732	1.155	2.000	60°00′
10′	0.5025	0.8646	0.5812	1.720	1.157	1.990	50′
20′	0.5050	0.8631	0.5851	1.709	1.159	1.980	40′
30′	0.5075	0.8616	0.5890	1.698	1.161	1.970	30′
40′	0.5100	0.8601	0.5930	1.686	1.163	1.961	20′
50′	0.5125	0.8587	0.5969	1.675	1.165	1.951	10′
31°00′	0.5150	0.8572	0.6009	1.664	1.167	1.942	59°00′
10′	0.5175	0.8557	0.6048	1.653	1.169	1.932	50′
20′	0.5200	0.8542	0.6088	1.643	1.171	1.923	40′
30′	0.5225	0.8526	0.6128	1.632	1.173	1.914	30′
40′	0.5250	0.8511	0.6168	1.621	1.175	1.905	20′
50′	0.5275	0.8496	0.6208	1.611	1.177	1.896	10′
32°00′	0.5299	0.8480	0.6249	1.600	1.179	1.887	58°00′
10′	0.5324	0.8465	0.6289	1.590	1.181	1.878	50′
20′	0.5348	0.8450	0.6330	1.580	1.184	1.870	40′
30′	0.5373	0.8434	0.6371	1.570	1.186	1.861	30′
40′	0.5398	0.8418	0.6412	1.560	1.188	1.853	20′
50′	0.5422	0.8403	0.6453	1.550	1.190	1.844	10′
33°00′	0.5446	0.8387	0.6494	1.540	1.192	1.836	57°00′
10′	0.5471	0.8371	0.6536	1.530	1.195	1.828	50′
20′	0.5495	0.8355	0.6577	1.520	1.197	1.820	40′
30′	0.5519	0.8339	0.6619	1.511	1.199	1.812	30′
40′	0.5544	0.8323	0.6661	1.501	1.202	1.804	20′
50′	0.5568	0.8307	0.6703	1.492	1.204	1.796	10′
34°00′	0.5592	0.8290	0.6745	1.483	1.206	1.788	56°00′
10′	0.5616	0.8274	0.6787	1.473	1.209	1.781	50′
20′	0.5640	0.8258	0.6830	1.464	1.211	1.773	40′
30′	0.5664	0.8241	0.6873	1.455	1.213	1.766	30′
40′	0.5688	0.8225	0.6916	1.446	1.216	1.758	20′
50′	0.5712	0.8208	0.6959	1.437	1.218	1.751	10′
35°00′	0.5736	0.8192	0.7002	1.428	1.221	1.743	55°00′
10′	0.5760	0.8175	0.7046	1.419	1.223	1.736	50′
20′	0.5783	0.8158	0.7089	1.411	1.226	1.729	40′
30′	0.5807	0.8141	0.7133	1.402	1.228	1.722	30′
40′	0.5831	0.8124	0.7177	1.393	1.231	1.715	20′
50′	0.5854	0.8107	0.7221	1.385	1.233	1.708	10′
36°00′	0.5878	0.8090	0.7265	1.376	1.236	1.701	54°00′
	Cos	Sin	Cot	Tan	Csc	Sec	Angle

VALUES OF TRIGONOMETRIC FUNCTIONS

Angle	Sin	Cos	Tan	Cot	Sec	Csc	
36°00′	0.5878	0.8090	0.7265	1.376	1.236	1.701	54°00′
10′	0.5901	0.8073	0.7310	1.368	1.239	1.695	50′
20′	0.5925	0.8056	0.7355	1.360	1.241	1.688	40′
30′	0.5948	0.8039	0.7400	1.351	1.244	1.681	30′
40′	0.5972	0.8021	0.7445	1.343	1.247	1.675	20′
50′	0.5995	0.8004	0.7490	1.335	1.249	1.668	10′
37°00′	0.6018	0.7986	0.7536	1.327	1.252	1.662	53°00′
10′	0.6041	0.7969	0.7581	1.319	1.255	1.655	50′
20′	0.6065	0.7951	0.7627	1.311	1.258	1.649	40′
30′	0.6088	0.7934	0.7673	1.303	1.260	1.643	30′
40′	0.6111	0.7916	0.7720	1.295	1.263	1.636	20′
50′	0.6134	0.7898	0.7766	1.288	1.266	1.630	10′
38°00′	0.6157	0.7880	0.7813	1.280	1.269	1.624	52°00′
10′	0.6180	0.7862	0.7860	1.272	1.272	1.618	50′
20′	0.6202	0.7844	0.7907	1.265	1.275	1.612	40′
30′	0.6225	0.7826	0.7954	1.257	1.278	1.606	30′
40′	0.6248	0.7808	0.8002	1.250	1.281	1.601	20′
50′	0.6271	0.7790	0.8050	1.242	1.284	1.595	10′
39°00′	0.6293	0.7771	0.8098	1.235	1.287	1.589	51°00′
10′	0.6316	0.7753	0.8146	1.228	1.290	1.583	50′
20′	0.6338	0.7735	0.8195	1.220	1.293	1.578	40′
30′	0.6361	0.7716	0.8243	1.213	1.296	1.572	30′
40′	0.6383	0.7698	0.8292	1.206	1.299	1.567	20′
50′	0.6406	0.7679	0.8342	1.199	1.302	1.561	10′
40°00′	0.6428	0.7660	0.8391	1.192	1.305	1.556	50°00′
10′	0.6450	0.7642	0.8441	1.185	1.309	1.550	50′
20′	0.6472	0.7623	0.8491	1.178	1.312	1.545	40′
30′	0.6494	0.7604	0.8541	1.171	1.315	1.540	30′
40′	0.6517	0.7585	0.8591	1.164	1.318	1.535	20′
50′	0.6539	0.7566	0.8642	1.157	1.322	1.529	10′
41°00′	0.6561	0.7547	0.8693	1.150	1.325	1.524	49°00′
10′	0.6583	0.7528	0.8744	1.144	1.328	1.519	50′
20′	0.6604	0.7509	0.8796	1.137	1.332	1.514	40′
30′	0.6626	0.7490	0.8847	1.130	1.335	1.509	30′
40′	0.6648	0.7470	0.8899	1.124	1.339	1.504	20′
50′	0.6670	0.7451	0.8952	1.117	1.342	1.499	10′
42°00′	0.6691	0.7431	0.9004	1.111	1.346	1.494	48°00′
10′	0.6713	0.7412	0.9057	1.104	1.349	1.490	50′
20′	0.6734	0.7392	0.9110	1.098	1.353	1.485	40′
30′	0.6756	0.7373	0.9163	1.091	1.356	1.480	30′
40′	0.6777	0.7353	0.9217	1.085	1.360	1.476	20′
50′	0.6799	0.7333	0.9271	1.079	1.364	1.471	10′
43°00′	0.6820	0.7314	0.9325	1.072	1.367	1.466	47°00′
10′	0.6841	0.7294	0.9380	1.066	1.371	1.462	50′
20′	0.6862	0.7274	0.9435	1.060	1.375	1.457	40′
30′	0.6884	0.7254	0.9490	1.054	1.379	1.453	30′
40′	0.6905	0.7234	0.9545	1.048	1.382	1.448	20′
50′	0.6926	0.7214	0.9601	1.042	1.386	1.444	10′
44°00′	0.6947	0.7193	0.9657	1.036	1.390	1.440	46°00′
10′	0.6967	0.7173	0.9713	1.030	1.394	1.435	50′
20′	0.6988	0.7153	0.9770	1.024	1.398	1.431	40′
30′	0.7009	0.7133	0.9827	1.018	1.402	1.427	30′
40′	0.7030	0.7112	0.9884	1.012	1.406	1.423	20′
50′	0.7050	0.7092	0.9942	1.006	1.410	1.418	10′
45°00′	0.7071	0.7071	1.000	1.000	1.414	1.414	45°00′
	Cos	Sin	Cot	Tan	Csc	Sec	Angle

GLOSSARY

absolute value The absolute value of a number is the number of units that it is from zero on the number line. (31)

additive identity Zero is the additive identity. The sum of any number and zero is identical to the original number. (14)

additive inverse If the sum of two numbers is zero, they are called additive inverses or opposites of each other. (14)

amplitude For functions of the form $y = a \sin b\theta$ and $y = a \cos b\theta$, the amplitude is $|a|$. (793)

angle of depression An angle of depression is the angle formed by a horizontal line and the line of sight to an object at a lower level. (762)

angle of elevation The angle of elevation is the angle formed by a horizontal line, and the line of sight to an object at a higher level. (762)

antilogarithm If $\log x = a$, then $x = $ antilog a. (564)

Arccosine Given $y = \text{Cos } x$, the inverse cosine function is defined by $y = \text{Cos}^{-1} x$ or $y = \text{Arccos } x$. (746)

Arcsine Given $y = \text{Sin } x$, the inverse sine function is defined by $y = \text{Sin}^{-1} x$ or $y = \text{Arc sin } x$. (747)

Arctangent Given $y = \text{Tan } x$, the inverse tangent function is defined by $y = \text{Tan}^{-1} x$ or $y = \text{Arctan } x$. (747)

arithmetic means The terms between any two nonconsecutive terms of an arithmetic sequence are called arithmetic means. (598)

arithmetic sequence An arithmetic sequence is a sequence in which the difference between any two consecutive terms is the same. (596)

arithmetic series The indicated sum of the terms of an arithmetic sequence is called an arithmetic series. (602)

associativity The way you group, or associate, three or more numbers does not change their sum or their product. (14)

asymptote Asymptotes are lines that a curve approaches. (417)

augmented matrix An augmented matrix is a matrix representation of a system of equations. Each row of the matrix corresponds to an equation in the system. Each column corresponds to the coefficients of a given variable or the constant term. (195)

axis of symmetry An axis of symmetry is the line about which a figure is symmetric. (360)

bar graph A bar graph shows how specific quantities compare to one another. (639)

binomial A polynomial with two unlike terms is a binomial. (223)

boundary A boundary is a line or curve that separates a graph into two parts. (379)

box and whisker plot In a box and whisker plot, the quartiles and extreme values of a set of data are displayed using a number line. (658)

characteristic The characteristic is the power of 10 by which that number is multiplied when the number is expressed in scientific notation. (563)

circle A circle is a set of points in a plane each of which is the same distance from a given point. The given distance is the radius of the circle and the given point is the center of the circle. (405)

circle graph A circle graph shows how parts are related to the whole. (639)

circular permutations If n objects are arranged in a circle, then there are $\frac{n!}{n}$ or $(n-1)!$ permutations of the n objects around the circle. (695)

coefficient The numerical factor of a monomial is the coefficient. (210)

coefficient matrix A coefficient matrix is a matrix representation of the coefficients of the variables in a system of equations. Each row of the matrix corresponds to an equation in the system. Each column corresponds to the coefficients of a given variable. (183)

combination The number of combinations of n objects, taken r at a time, is defined as

$$C(n,r) = \frac{n!}{(n-r)!r!} \quad (699)$$

common difference The common difference of an arithmetic sequence is the constant that is the difference between successive terms. (596)

common logarithms Common logarithms are logarithms to base 10. (563)

common ratio The common ratio of a geometric sequence is the constant that is the ratio of successive terms. (608)

commutativity The order in which two numbers are added or multiplied does not change their sum or product. That is, for all numbers a and b, $a + b = b + a$ and $a \cdot b = b \cdot a$. (14)

complex fraction A complex rational expression, also called a complex fraction, is an expression whose numerator or denominator, or both, contain rational expressions. (519)

complex number A complex number is any number that can be written in the form $a + bi$ where a and b are real numbers and i is the imaginary unit. a is the real part and bi is the imaginary part. (292)

composition of functions Given functions f and g, the composite function $f \circ g$ can be described by $[f \circ g](x) = f[g(x)]$. (487)

conic section A conic section is a curve formed by slicing a hollow double cone with a plane. The equation of a conic section can be written in the form $Ax^2 + Bxy + Cy^2 + Dx + Ey + F = 0$ where A, B, and C are not all zero. (427)

conjugate axis The conjugate axis of a hyperbola is the segment perpendicular to the transverse axis at its center. (417)

conjugates 1. Binomials of the form $a + b\sqrt{c}$ and $a - b\sqrt{c}$ are conjugates of each other. (266) **2.** Complex conjugates are complex numbers of the form $a + bi$ and $a - bi$. (297)

consistent and dependent system A system of equations where the graphs of the equations are the same line is called a consistent and dependent system. There is an infinite number of solutions to this system of equations. (109)

consistent and independent system A system of equations that has one ordered pair as its solution is a consistent and independent system. (109)

constant A monomial that contains no variable is a constant. (210)

constant function A constant function is a function of the form $f(x) = b$ where the slope is zero. (62)

constant of variation The constant k in either of the equations $y = kx$ or $y = \dfrac{k}{x}$ is called the constant of variation. (510)

coordinate matrix A matrix containing coordinates of a geometric figure is called a coordinate matrix. (161)

coordinate plane The plane determined by the perpendicular axes is called the coordinate plane. (52)

coordinates Each point in the coordinate plane corresponds to an ordered pair of numbers called its coordinates. (52)

cosecant Let θ stand for the measurement of an angle in standard position on the unit circle. Then the following equation holds true: $\csc \theta = \dfrac{1}{\sin \theta}$ (742)

cosine Let θ stand for the measurement of an angle in standard position on the unit circle. Let (x, y) represent the point where the terminal side intersects the unit circle. Then the following equation holds: $\cos \theta = x$ (737)

cotangent Let θ stand for the measurement of an angle in standard position on the unit circle. Then the following equation holds true: $\cot \theta = \dfrac{\cos \theta}{\sin \theta}$ (742)

coterminal angles Angles in standard position that have the same terminal side are called coterminal angles. (733)

cubic expression A cubic expression is a polynomial in one variable of degree 3. (451)

D

degree of monomial The degree of a monomial is the sum of the exponents of its variables. (210)

degree of polynomial The degree of a polynomial is the degree of the monomial of greatest degree. (223)

dependent events Two events are dependent when the outcome of the first event affects the outcome of the second event. (685)

depressed polynomial A polynomial whose degree is less than the original polynomial is called a depressed polynomial. It is the result of factoring out a factor of the original polynomial. (461)

determinant A determinant is a square array of numbers having a numerical value. (118)

dilation A dilation is a transformation in which size is altered. (162)

dimension In a matrix consisting of n rows and m columns, the matrix is said to have dimension $n \times m$ (read "n by m"). (161)

directrix See parabola (400)

direct variation A direct variation is a linear function described by $y = mx$ or $f(x) = mx$ where $m \neq 0$. (87)

discriminant In the quadratic formula, the expression under the radical sign, $b^2 - 4ac$, is called the discriminant. (329)

distributive property For all numbers a, b, and c,
$a(b + c) = ab + ac$ and
$(b + c)a = ba + ca$. (15)

domain The domain is the set of all first coordinates of the ordered pairs of a relation (53)

E

element An element of a matrix is any value in the array of values. (161)

ellipse An ellipse is the set of all points in a plane such that the sum of the distances from two given points in the plane, called the foci, is constant. (409)

equation A statement of equality between two mathematical expressions is called an equation. (18)

expansion by minors Expansion by minors is a method that can be used to find the value of any third or higher order determinant. (167)

exponential equation An equation in which the variables appear as exponents is called an exponential equation. (575)

exponential function An equation in the form $y = a^x$, where $a > 0$ and $a \neq 1$, is called an exponential function. (548)

F

factorial If n is a positive integer, the expression $n!$ (n factorial) is defined as $n! = n(n - 1)(n - 2) \cdots (1)$ (627)

Fibonacci sequence A Fibonacci sequence is a special sequence often found in nature. It is named after its discoverer, Leonardo Fibonacci. (594)

focus (foci) See parabola (400), ellipse (409), or hyperbola. (416)

frequency distribution A frequency distribution shows how data are spread out. (668)

function A function is a relation in which each element of the domain is paired with exactly one element of the range. (53)

G

geometric means The terms between any two nonconsecutive terms of a geometric sequence are called geometric means. (610)

geometric sequence A geometric sequence is a sequence in which each term after the first is the product of the preceding term and the common ratio. (608)

geometric series The indicated sum of the terms of a geometric sequence is called a geometric series. (615)

greatest integer The greatest integer of x is written $[x]$ and means the greatest integer *not* greater than x. (88)

H

half-plane A half-plane is the region of a graph on one side of a boundary. (379)

histogram A histogram is a bar graph that shows a frequency distribution. (668)

hyperbola A hyperbola is the set of all points in a plane such that the absolute value of the difference of the distances from any point on the hyperbola to two given points in the plane, called the foci, is constant. (416)

hypotenuse The hypotenuse is the side opposite the right angle in a right triangle. (756)

I

identity An identity is an equation that is true for all values of the variable for which both sides of the equation are defined. (797)

identity function An identity function is a linear function described by $y = x$ or $f(x) = x$. (87)

identity matrix for multiplication The identity matrix, I, for multiplication is a square matrix with a 1 for every element of the principal diagonal and a 0 in all other positions. (179)

imaginary number An imaginary number is a complex number of the form $a + bi$, where $b \neq 0$. The imaginary unit i is defined by $i^2 = -1$. (288)

inclusive events Two events are inclusive if the outcomes of the events may be the same. (715)

inconsistent system An inconsistent system is a system of equations where the graph of the equations is parallel lines. There is no solution to this system of equations. (109)

independent events Two events are independent if the outcome of one event does not affect the outcome of the other event. (684)

index of summation An index of summation is a variable used with the summation symbol (Σ). (605)

infinite geometric series An infinite geometric series is the indicated sum of the terms of an infinite geometric sequence. (620)

integers (Z) The set of numbers {. . ., -3, -2, -1, 0, 1, 2, 3, . . .}. (13)

interquartile range The interquartile range of a set of data is the difference between the upper and lower quartiles of the set. (654)

inverse functions Two polynomial functions f and g are inverse functions if and only if both their compositions are the identity function. (491)

inverse matrix For a matrix A, with a nonzero determinant, the inverse matrix, A^{-1}, of A is that matrix with the property $A \cdot A^{-1} = A^{-1} \cdot A = I$ (179)

inverse relations Two relations are inverse relations if and only if whenever one relation contains the element (a, b), the other relation contains the element (b, a). (493)

inverse variation A rational equation in two variables of the form $xy = k$, where k is a constant, is called an inverse variation. The constant k is called the constant of variation, and y is said to vary inversely as x. (511)

irrational numbers (I) Irrational numbers are real numbers that cannot be written as terminating or repeating decimals. (13)

J

joint variation If $y = kxy$ where k is a constant, $x \neq 0$, and $y \neq 0$, y is said to vary jointly as x and z. (512)

L

latus rectum A latus rectum is the line segment through the focus of a parabola perpendicular to its axis of symmetry with endpoints on the parabola. (401)

like terms Two monomials that are the same or differ only by their coefficients are called like terms. (210)

linear equation A linear equation is an equation whose graph is a straight line. (60)

linear expression A linear expression is a polynomial in one variable of degree 1. (451)

linear function A linear function can be defined by $f(x) = mx + b$ where m and b are real numbers. Any function whose ordered pairs satisfy a linear equation in two variables is a linear function. (62)

linear permutation The arrangement of n objects in a certain linear order is called a linear permutation. The number of linear permutations of n objects, taken r at a time, is defined as $P(n, r) = \dfrac{n!}{(n-r)!}$. (689)

linear programming Linear programming is a method for finding the maximum or the minimum value of a function in two variables subject to given constraints on the variables. (130)

line graph A line graph shows trends or changes. (639)

line plot In a line plot, data are recorded and displayed using a number line (642)

logarithm Suppose $b > 0$ and $b \neq 1$. Then for $n > 0$, there is a number p such that $\log_b n = p$ if and only if $b^p = n$. (553)

logarithmic function An equation of the form $y = \log_b x$ where $b > 0$ and $b \neq 1$ is called a logarithmic function. (555)

lower quartile The quartile that is less than the median is called the lower quartile. (654)

major axis The major axis is the longer of the two line segments that form the axes of symmetry for an ellipse. (410)

mantissa The mantissa is the logarithm of a number between 1 and 10. (563)

mapping A mapping illustrates how each element in the domain of a relation is paired with an element in the range. (53)

matrix A matrix is a rectangular arrangement of terms in rows and columns enclosed in brackets or large parentheses. (161)

matrix equation The matrix equation form of a system of equations is an equation of the form $AX = C$. A is the coefficient matrix for the system. X is the column matrix consisting of the variables of the system. C is the column matrix consisting of the constant terms of the system. (184)

mean The mean of a set of data is the sum of all the values divided by the number of values. (648)

median The median of a set of data is the middle value. If there are two middle values, it is the value halfway between. (648)

minor A minor is the determinant formed when the row and column containing the element are deleted. (167)

minor axes The minor axis is the shorter of the two line segments that form the axes of symmetry for an ellipse. (410)

minute A minute is a unit of angle measure that is $\dfrac{1}{60}$ of a degree. (751)

mode The mode of a set of data is the most frequent value. (648)

monomial A monomial is an expression that is a number, a variable, or the product of a number and one or more variables. (210)

multiplicative identity One is the multiplicative identity. The product of any number and one is identical to the original number. (14)

multiplicative inverses If the product of two numbers is one, they are called multiplicative inverses or reciprocals of each other. (14)

mutually exclusive events Two events are mutually exclusive if their outcomes can never be the same. (715)

natural logarithms Natural logarithms are logarithms to the base e. (568)

natural numbers (N) The set of numbers $\{1, 2, 3, 4 \ldots\}$ (13)

normal distribution Normal distributions have bell-shaped, symmetric graphs. About 68% of the items are within one standard deviation from the mean. About 95% of the items are within two standard deviations from the mean. About 99% of the items are within three standard deviations from the mean. (668)

nth root For any numbers a and b, and any positive integer n, if $a^n = b$, then a is an nth root of b. (252)

nth term The nth term of an arithmetic sequence with the first term a_1 and common difference d is given by the following equation.
$$a_n = a_1 + (n - 1)d \quad (597)$$
The nth term of a geometric sequence with first term a, and common ratio r is given by the following equation.
$$a_n = a_1 r^{n-1} \quad (608)$$

octant Three mutually perpendicular planes separate space into eight regions, each called an octant. (139)

odds The odds of the successful outcome of an event is expressed as the ratio of the number of ways it can succeed to the number of ways it can fail.

Odds – the ratio of s to f or $\frac{s}{f}$ (706)

open sentence Sentences with variables to be replaced are called open sentences. (18)

ordered pair Points in a plane can be located by using ordered pairs of real numbers. The ordered pair are the coordinates of the point. (52)

ordered triple **1.** The solution to an equation in three variables is called an ordered triple. (139) **2.** Each point in space corresponds to three numbers called an ordered triple. (139)

origin The origin is the point on the coordinate plane whose coordinates are (0, 0). (52)

outlier An outlier is any value in a set of data that is at least 1.5 interquartile ranges beyond the upper or lower quartile. (654)

parabola **1.** The general shape of the graph of a quadratic function is called a parabola. (317) **2.** A parabola is the set of all points that are the same distance from a given point and a given line. The point is called the focus. The line is called the directrix. (400)

parallel lines In a plane, lines with the same slope are called parallel lines. Also, vertical lines are parallel. (68)

Pascal's triangle Pascal's triangle is the pyramid formation of the coefficients of binomial expansions. (625)

period For a function f, the least positive value of a for which $f(x) = f(x + a)$ is the period of the function. (739)

periodic function A function f is called periodic if there is a number a such that $f(x) = f(x + a)$. (739)

permutation A permutation is the arrangement of things in a certain order. (689)

perpendicular lines Two nonvertical lines are perpendicular if and only if the product of their slopes is -1. Any vertical line is perpendicular to any horizontal line. (69)

polar coordinates The polar coordinates of a point P are written in the form (r, θ), where r is the distance from the pole to point P and θ is the measure of an angle which has the polar axis as its initial side and $\overrightarrow{OP}$ as its terminal side. (829)

polar form The polar form of the complex number $x + yi$ is $r(\cos \theta + i \sin \theta)$. (829)

polynomial A polynomial is a monomial or a sum of monomials. (223)

polynomial function A polynomial equation in the form $p(x) = a_n x^n + a_{n-1}x^{n-1} + \cdots + a_1 x + a_0$ is a polynomial function. The coefficients $a_0, a_1, a_2, \ldots, a_{n-1}, a_n$ are real numbers, a_0 is not zero, and n is a nonnegative integer. (451)

polynomial in one variable A polynomial in one variable, x, is an expression of the form $a_0 x^n + a_1 x^{n-1} + \cdots + a_{n-2}x^2 + a_{n-1}x + a_n$. The coefficients a_0, a_1, a_2 are real numbers, a_0 is not zero, and n represents a nonnegative integer. (450)

prediction equation The equation of the line suggested by the dots on a scatter plot is a prediction equation. (80)

principal root The principal root is the nonnegative root. If there is no nonnegative root, the principal root is negative. (253)

principal values The values in the domain of the functions like Cosine, Sine, and Tangent are the principal values. (746)

probability If an event can succeed in s ways and fail in f ways, then the probabilities of success $P(s)$ and of failure $P(f)$ are
$$P(s) = \frac{s}{s+f} \text{ and } P(f) = \frac{f}{s+f} \quad (705)$$

pure imaginary number For any positive real number, b, $\sqrt{-(b^2)} = \sqrt{b^2}\sqrt{-1}$ or bi where i is a number whose square is -1. bi is called a pure imaginary number. (288)

Q

quadrants Two perpendicular number lines separate the plane into four parts called quadrants. (52)

quadratic equation Any equation that can be written in the form $ax^2 + bx + c = 0$, where a, b, and c are real numbers and $a \neq 0$, is a quadratic equation. (316)

quadratic expression A quadratic expression is a polynomial in one variable of degree 2. (451)

quadratic form For any numbers a, b, and c, except $a = 0$, an equation that may be written as $a[f(x)]^2 + b[f(x)] + c = 0$, where $f(x)$ is some expression in x, is in quadratic form. (340)

quadratic formula The solutions of a quadratic equation of the form $ax^2 + bx + c = 0$ with $a \neq 0$ are given by the quadratic formula.
$$x = \frac{-b \pm \sqrt{b^2-4ac}}{2a} \quad (327)$$

quadratic function A quadratic function is a function described by an equation of the form $f(x) = ax^2 + bx + c$ where $a \neq 0$. (353)

quartiles In a set of data, quartiles are the values that separate the data into four equal parts. (654)

R

radian A radian is an angle that intercepts an arc whose length is 1 unit. (733)

radical equations Radical equations are equations containing variables in the radicands. (282)

radius The radius of a circle is the distance from the center to any point on the circle. (405)

range **1.** The range is a set of all second coordinates of the ordered pairs of a relation. (53) **2.** The range of a set of data is the difference between the greatest and least values in the set. (653)

rational equation A rational equation is an equation that contains one or more rational expressions. (527)

rational exponents For any nonzero number b, and any integers m and n, $n > 1$
$$b^{\frac{m}{n}} = \sqrt[n]{b^m} = (\sqrt[n]{b})^m$$
except when $\sqrt[n]{b}$ does not represent a real number. (270)

rational function A rational function is an equation of the form $f(x) = \frac{p(x)}{q(x)}$ where $p(x)$ and $q(x)$ are polynomial functions and $q(x) \neq 0$. (506)

rational numbers (**Q**) Rational numbers are numbers that can be expressed in the form $\frac{m}{n}$ where m and n are integers and n is not zero. (13)

real numbers (**R**) Irrational numbers together with rational numbers form the set of real numbers. (13)

reciprocal The reciprocal of a number is its multiplicative inverse. (14)

rectangular form The rectangular form of a complex number is $a + bi$. (829)

relation A relation is a set of ordered pairs. (53)

root A root is a solution of an equation. (316)

rotation A rotation is a transformation in which the plane containing the image is rotated around a fixed point. (174)

scalar multiplication In scalar multiplication of a matrix, each element of the matrix is multiplied by a constant to form a new matrix. (162)

scatter plot A scatter plot shows visually the nature of a relationship, both shape and closeness. (80)

scientific notation A number is expressed in scientific notation when it is in the form $a \times 10^n$ where $1 \le a < 10$ and n is an integer. (212)

secant Let θ stand for the measurement of an angle in standard position on the unit circle. Then the following equation holds true: $\sec \theta = \dfrac{1}{\cos \theta}$ (742)

sequence A sequence is a set of numbers in a specific order. (596)

series The indicated sum of the terms of a sequence is a series. (602)

sigma notation The Σ symbol is used to indicate a sum of a series. (605)

sine Let θ stand for the measurement of an angle in standard position on the unit circle. Let (x, y) represent the point where the terminal side intersects the unit circle. Then the following equation holds. $\sin \theta = y$ (737)

slope The slope of a line described by $f(x) = mx + b$ is m. Slope is also given by $m = \dfrac{y_2 - y_1}{x_2 - x_1}$ (66)

solution set A solution set is the set of all replacements for variables that make an open sentence true. (32)

square matrix A matrix that has the same number of rows as columns is called a square matrix. (161)

square root For any numbers a and b, if $a^2 = b$, then a is a square root of b. (252)

standard deviation From a set of data with n values, if x_i represents a value such that $1 \le i \le n$, and $\overline{x}$ represents the mean, then the standard deviation is $\sqrt{\dfrac{\displaystyle\sum_{i=1}^{n}(x_i - \overline{x})^2}{n}}$. (664)

standard form The standard form of a linear equation is $Ax + By = C$ where A, B, and C are real numbers and A and B are not both zero. (60)

standard position An angle with its vertex at the origin and its initial side along the positive x-axis is said to be in standard position. (732)

stem and leaf plot In a stem and leaf plot, each piece of data is separated into two numbers that are used to form the stem and leaf. The data are organized into two columns. The column on the left is the stem and the column on the right is the leaf. (642)

sum of a geometric series The sum, S_n, of the first n terms of a geometric series is given by the following formula.
$$S_n = \frac{a_1 - a_1 r^n}{1 - r} \text{ or } S_n = \frac{a_1(1 - r^n)}{1 - r} \text{ where}$$
$r \ne 1$ (615)

sum of an arithmetic series The sum, S_n, of the first n terms of an arithmetic series is given by the following formula.
$$S_n = \frac{n}{2}(a_1 + a_n) \text{ or}$$
$$S_n = \frac{n}{2}[2a_1 + (n - 1)d] \quad (603)$$

sum of an infinite geometric series The sum of an infinite geometric series is given by the formula
$$S = \frac{a_1}{1 - r} \text{ where } -1 < r < 1. \quad (620)$$

synthetic division A shortcut method used to divide polynomials by binomials is called synthetic division. (241)

synthetic substitution Synthetic substitution is the process of using the Remainder Theorem and synthetic division to find the value of a function. (460)

system of equations A set of equations with the same variables is a system of equations. (108)

system of inequalities A set of inequalities with the same variables is a system of inequalities. (122)

tangent   Let θ stand for the measurement of an angle in standard position on the unit circle. Then the following equation holds true: $\tan \theta = \frac{\sin \theta}{\cos \theta}$ (742)

term   **1.** Each monomial in a polynomial is called a term. (223) **2.** A term is each number in a sequence.   (596)

trace   A trace is the line formed by the intersection of a plane with one of the three coordinate planes.   (141)

translation   A translation is a transformation in which a figure is moved from one location to another without changing its orientation, size, or shape.   (163)

transverse axis   The line segment of a hyperbola of length $2a$ that has its endpoints at the vertices is called the transverse axis.   (417)

tree diagram   A tree diagram is a diagram used to show the total number of possible outcomes.   (684)

trichotomy property   For any two numbers a and b, one of the following statements is true.

$$a < b, a = b, a > b \quad (36)$$

trigonometric equation   A trigonometric equation is an equation involving one or more trigonometric functions which is true for some, but not all, values of the variable.   (822)

trigonometric form   The trigonometric form of the complex number $x + yi$ is $r(\cos\theta + i \sin\theta)$.   (829)

trinomial   A polynomial with three unlike terms is called a trinomial.   (223)

unit circle   A unit circle has a radius of 1 unit.   (733)

upper quartile   The quartile that is greater than the median is called the upper quartile.   (654)

variable   A variable is a symbol that represents an unknown quantity.   (18)

vertex of hyperbola   The point on each branch of the hyperbola nearest the center is called a vertex of the hyperbola.   (417)

vertex of parabola   The point of intersection of the parabola and its axis of symmetry is called the vertex of the parabola. (360)

vertical line test   If any vertical line drawn on the graph of a relation passes through no more than one point of that graph, then the relation is a function.   (54)

whole numbers (W)   The set of numbers {0, 1, 2, 3, . . .}.   (13)

x-intercept   An x-intercept is the value of x when the value of the function or y is zero.   (69)

y-intercept   A y-intercept is the value of a function when x is 0.   (69)

Z

zero exponent   For any number a, except $a = 0$, $a^0 = 1$.   (215)

zero of function   For any polynomial function $f(x)$, if $f(a) = 0$, then a is a zero of the function.   (317)

zero product property   For any real numbers a and b, if $ab = 0$ then $a = 0$ or $b = 0$.   (317)

SELECTED ANSWERS

CHAPTER 1   EQUATIONS AND INEQUALITIES

Pages 10–12   Lesson 1-1

5. -3 **7.** 54 **9.** 2 **11.** -8 **13.** 37
15. $A = (y + 5)(y - 5)$ cm^2 **17.** 21 **19.** 41 **21.** 4
23. 10 **25.** 11 **27.** 26 **29.** 0.09 **31.** -63
33. 272.16 **35.** 0 **37.** 0.75 **39.** \$737
41. \$39,548.57 **43.** 93.6 **45.** $53\frac{1}{4}$ **49.** 754 gallons
51. a. 24.85 ft^2 **b.** 2614.68 ft^2

Pages 16–17   Lesson 1-2

7. Q, R **9.** I, R **11.** N, W, Z, Q, R **13.** Q, R
15. Z, Q, R **17.** N, W, Z, Q, R **19.** commutative $\times$
21. commutative $+$ **23.** 1; N, W, Z, Q, R **25.** -9;
Z, Q, R **27.** -24; Z, Q, R **29.** $\frac{3}{2}$, 1.5; Q, R
31. true **33.** false; $\frac{3}{2}$, 1.5 **35.** true **37.** true
39. additive inverse **41.** commutative $+$
43. multiplicative inverse **45.** additive identity
47. $10a + 2b$ **49.** $12 + 20a$ **51.** $\frac{2}{3}a + \frac{5}{2}b$
53. $4.4m - 2.9n$ **57a.** no **57b.** yes **57c.** The
difference of two such numbers is always divisible by
9 **58.** 0 **59.** -2 **60.** 94 **61.** \$17,400

Page 21   Lesson 1-3

5. Reflexive property of equality **7.** Addition
property of equality **9.** Multiplication property of
equality **11.** 3 **13.** $\frac{5}{4}$ **15.** 4 **17.** $-\frac{21}{8}$, -2.625
19. 2 **21.** $\frac{7}{4}$, 1.75 **23.** $-\frac{2}{3}$, -0.667 **25.** -6
27. all reals **29.** 1 **33.** $t = \frac{A - p}{pr}$ **35.** $\sqrt{3}$; I, R
36. commutative $+$ **37.** 44.4

Pages 26–28   Lesson 1-4

5. $5x - 4$ **7.** $3 - 2n$ **9.** $6x^2$ **11.** $4(8 + x)$
13. $8 + 4n$ **15.** \$7 **17.** 118 **19.** 18 years old
21. Mrs. Gampp, 43; Brittany, 19 **23.** \$428 **25.** 4
adults, 20 students **27.** 3 hours **31.** add 6 inches to
the length and 3 inches to the width **32.** Reflexive
property of equality **33.** Substitution property
34. $4x + 8$ **35.** -3.5

Page 28   Mid-Chapter Review

1. 39 **2.** 83 **3.** -5 **4.** -79 **5.** \$97.71 **6.** I, R
7. Q, R **8.** N, W, Z, Q, R **9.** distributive
10. associative **11.** 25.75 **12.** no solution
13. $3n + 9$ **14.** $(n + 2)^2$ **15.** 168 **16.** 13

Page 30   Lesson 1-5

5. WWWWLL, WWWLLW, WLWLWW, WWWLWL,
WWLWLW, LWWLWW, WWLWWL, WLWWLW,
WLLWWW, WLWWWL, LWWWLW, LWLWWW,
LWWWWL, WWLLWW, LLWWWW **7.** Assume
that your monthly salary is \$1000 to start with and
the first cut or raise will occur in January. Your final
salary will be \$990 a month with either option.
However, if you take the cut first, your salary for
January will be \$900. If you take the raise first, you
salary for January will be \$1100. So, if you take the
cut first, your total income for the year will be \$900
+ 11(\$990) or \$11,790. If you take the raise first, your
total income for the year will be \$1100 + 11(\$990) or
\$11,990. Taking the raise first gives you more total
income for the year. **9.** 36 students

Pages 34–35   Lesson 1-6

5. 16 **7.** -16 **9.** 5 **11.** 2, -2 **13.** -2, -1, 0
15. no solution **17.** 13, 25 **19.** 15, -7
21. 6, -18 **23.** 5, -13 **25.** 10.5, -19.5 **27.** $-\frac{7}{2}$
29. 5, $-\frac{19}{3}$ **31.** 3.5, 10.5 **33.** 0, $-\frac{10}{3}$ **35.** 1
37. 1, -9 **39.** no solution **43.** 1.05 and 0.95 pounds
45. 139, 193, 319, 391, 913, 931 **46.** E, A, AH; E,
AH, A; A, E, AH; A, AH, E; AH, E, A; AH, A, E
47. $x + x^2$ **48.** 7; N, W, Z, Q, R

Pages 39–40   Lesson 1-7

5.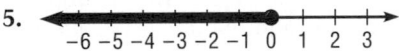

7.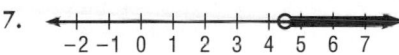

9.

11. $\{x | x \geq 5\}$ **13.** $\{s | s < 6\}$ **15.** $\{t | t \leq -8\}$
17. $\{y | y > 17.6\}$ **19.** $\{x | x < 0\}$ **21.** $\{z | z \leq 5\}$
23. $\{x | x > 2.25\}$ **25.** $\{x | x \leq 3.5\}$ **27.** $\{m | m \geq 1\}$
29. $\{y | y < -1\}$ **31.** $\{x | x \geq 423\}$ **33.** $\{x | x \leq 1.6\overline{}\}$
35. $\{x | x \leq -1.425\}$ **37.** no solution **39.** \$60.37
41. 20 games **43.** 81 **45.** \$75,000; \$56,250
47. $9.999 \leq d \leq 10.001$ **49.** 11 **50.** no solution
51. $-\frac{15}{2}$ **52.** $2x + 17y$ **53.** $\frac{3}{2}$

Pages 44–45 Lesson 1-8

5. $|x| < 7$ **7.** $|x| > 11$

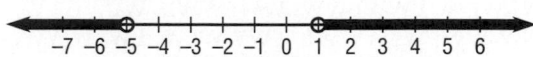

9. $|x| < 6$ **11.** $|x| \leq 9$ **13.** $|x| \leq 6$

15. $\{x | x < -5 \text{ or } x > 1\}$

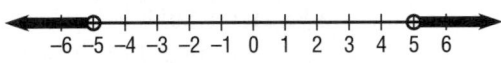

19. $\{x | -3 < x < 3\}$

23. $\{x | x < -5 \text{ or } x > 5\}$

27. $\varnothing$

31. $\{x | -30 < x < 60\}$

35. $\{x | -1 < x < 4\}$

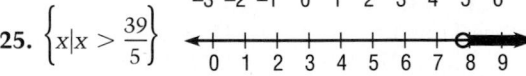

39. $\{x | -2 \leq x \leq 7\}$

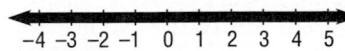

43. $\{x | x \geq 0\}$

49a. maximum = 7.322 cm; minimum = 7.318 cm
49b. Tolerance = 0.03 cm   **50.** My best friend is taller than I am; My best friend and I are the same height; My best friend is shorter than I am.
51. 21.25   **52.** 3264   **53.** passenger train, 89 mph; express train, 99 mph   **54.** additive identity   **55.** 8%

Pages 46–48 Chapter 1 Summary and Review

1. 92   **3.** $\dfrac{13}{12}$ **5.** 6,400 feet   **7.** Q, R   **9.** I, R
11. additive identity   **13.** $2a - 4b$ **15.** $-\dfrac{33}{13}$ **17.** 8
19. length 21 ft, width 11 ft   **21.** no solution

23. $\{x | x < 6\}$

25. $\left\{x \middle| x > \dfrac{39}{5}\right\}$

27. $\{x | x < 0 \text{ or } x \geq 1\}$

29. all reals

31. 64   **33.** from 5.25 to 6 gallons

**CHAPTER 2 LINEAR RELATIONS
AND FUNCTIONS**

Pages 55–57 Lesson 2-1

7. quadrant III   **9.** no quadrant, y-axis   **11.** relation
13. D = $\{4, 8, -10\}$, R = $\{3, 4, 8, -2\}$; no

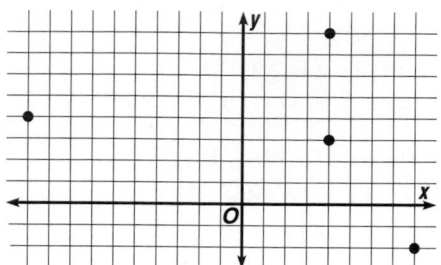

17. 4   **21.** $\dfrac{7}{10}$ **23.** -1 **25.** undefined   **27.** not a function
29. not a function   **31.** function   **33.** 2423
35. 41.3776   **37.** $(-3, -3)$ **39.** -12 **41.** $\dfrac{a^2 + 3a - 10}{a + 2}$
43. no

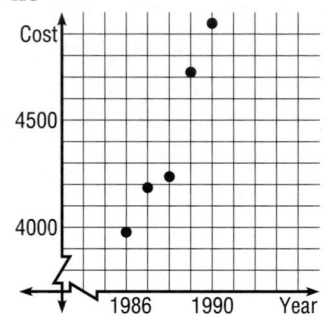

45. $\{x | x < -3 \text{ or } x > 9\}$ **46.** $\{y | -8 < y < 6\}$ **47.** 11 posters   **48.** N, W, Z, Q, R   **49.** -84.96 **50.** -9800

Pages 62–63 Lesson 2-2

5. no; it contains an exponent greater than 1.   **7.** yes
9. yes   **11.** $3x - y = 2$ **13.** $x = 10$
15. $3x - y = -12$ **17.** $y = 4.5 - 2x$

19.

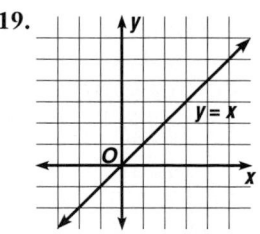

21. $m = \dfrac{n + 3}{-5}$ **23.** $r = \dfrac{144 - 9t}{8}$

25.

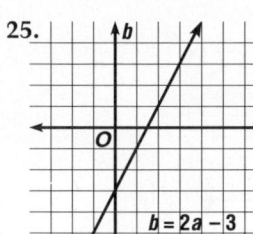

b = 2a - 3

29.

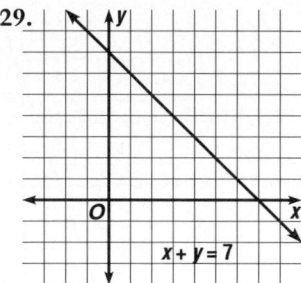

x + y = 7

33.

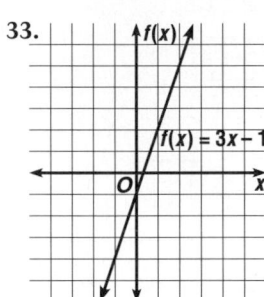

f(x) = 3x - 1

39. $102   **41.** It is not a function because one of the x-values is paired with two different y-values.

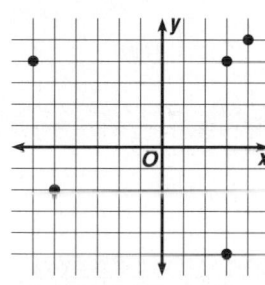

42. 9   **43.** 24 ways   **44.** 10.5 inches   **45.** $p + 5$

Page 65   Lesson 2-3

5. 36   **7.** 30   **9.** $686

Pages 70–73   Lesson 2-4

9. 2, -2, 1   **11.** 2, none, 0   **13.** 2, 3, $-\frac{2}{3}$ **15.** $-\frac{5}{2}$
17. $\frac{3}{5}$ **19.** 8   **21.** falls   **23.** rises   **25.** rises
27. y: 9, x: $-\frac{3}{2}$ **29.** y: -2, x: none   **31.** y: -6, x: $\frac{6}{5}$
33. y: -2, x: 2   **35.** y: 5, x: 3

37.

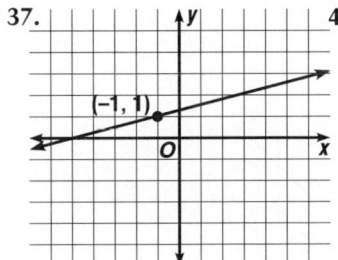

(-1, 1)

41.

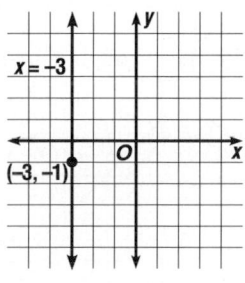

x = -3

(-3, -1)

47. 65 mph   **48.** 50   **49.** 5   **50.** $\frac{1}{2}$ **51.** distributive property

Page 72   Mid-Chapter Review

1a. D = {0, 5, 10, 15, 20, 25, 30, 35, 40},
R = {30, 27, 16, 9, 4, 1, -2, -4, -5}

1b. yes

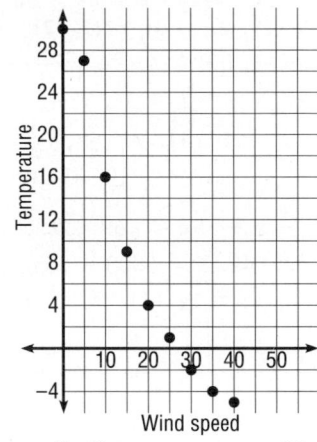

2. 19   **3.** $y = \dfrac{7 - 2x}{4}$ **4.** $s = 21 - \dfrac{21}{8}t$
5. $c = \dfrac{3}{4}a + \dfrac{1}{2}b - 6$ **6.** no

7.

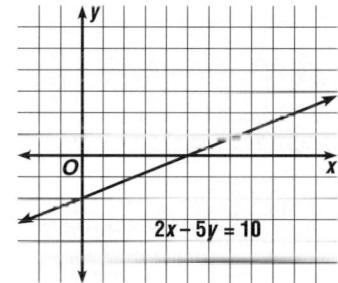

2x - 5y = 10

8. 135

9. $m = \dfrac{2}{3}$, x: 3, y: -2

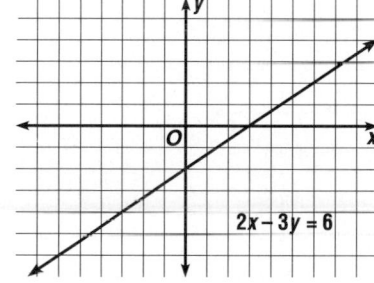

2x - 3y = 6

10. $m = -\dfrac{2}{3}$, x: 4.5, y: 3

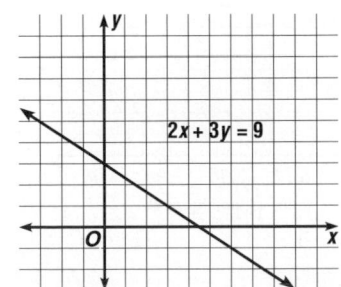

2x + 3y = 9

Pages 76–79 Lesson 2-5

7. $3x + y = -4$ **9.** $y = 2.5x$ **11.** $y = 0$
13. $m = -\frac{3}{4}$, y: -3 **15.** $m = -0.2$, y: -6
17. $m = -\frac{3}{5}$, y: 6 **19.** $2x + 3y = 12$ **21.** $y = 3x - 6$
23. no slope-intercept form **25.** $y = -\frac{4}{5}x - \frac{7}{5}$,
$4x + 5y = -7$ **27.** $y = -\frac{5}{2}x + 16$, $5x + 2y = 32$
29. $y = \frac{3}{2}x$, $3x - 2y = 0$ **31.** $y = \frac{3}{4}x - \frac{1}{4}$,
$3x - 4y = 1$ **33.** $y = -1$, $y = -1$ **35.** $y = \frac{1}{3}x + \frac{2}{3}$
37. $y = -\frac{1}{15}x - \frac{23}{5}$, $x + 15y = -69$ **39.** 3 **41.** $\frac{5}{7}$
43. 15,963.5 lb/in^2 **45.** $d = 6000 - 75x$
47a. $m = -2$, y: 2; $y = -2x + 2$ **47b.** $m = \frac{4}{3}$, y: $5\frac{2}{3}$,
$y = \frac{4}{3}x + 5\frac{2}{3}$ **47c.** $m = \frac{4}{3}$, y: $-\frac{2}{3}$; $y = \frac{4}{3}x - \frac{2}{3}$
47d. $m = \frac{1}{2}$, y: $-3\frac{1}{2}$, $y = \frac{1}{2}x - 3\frac{1}{2}$ **48.** $\frac{2}{3}$ **49.** x: 4,
y: -6 **50.** 0 **51.** $\{x|x > -7\}$ **52.** 24 ways

Pages 83–84 Lesson 2-6

5. 3.0 cm **7a.** 400 **7b.** 2,000,000 **7c.** $S = 400A + 2,000,000$ **7d.** $6,000,000 **7e.** $35,000

9a.

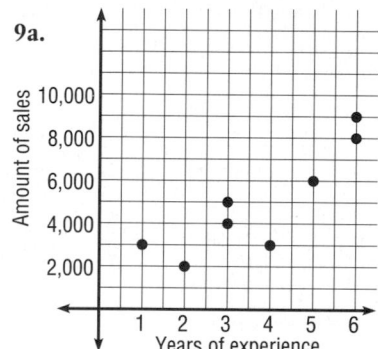

9b. $y = 1333x$
9c. $10,666
9d. $0
9e. about 5.5 years

13a. $y = -50x + 226.5$ **13b.** 31,500 bushels
13c. $4.02

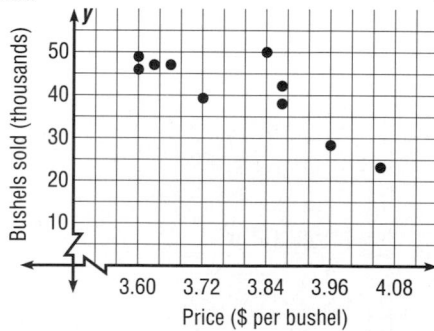

15. $y + x = 6$ **16.** -2

17.

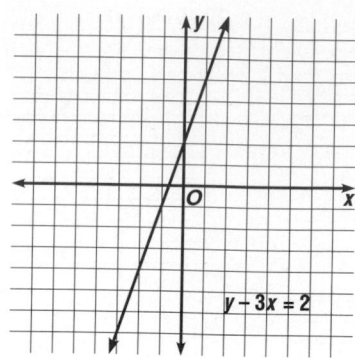

18. 152 **19.** $-9x + 14y$

Pages 89–90 Lesson 2-7

7. G **9.** A **11.** D **13.** identity **15.** greatest integer function **17.** -5 **19.** 2

21.

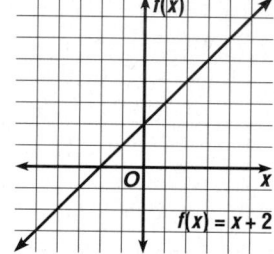

25.

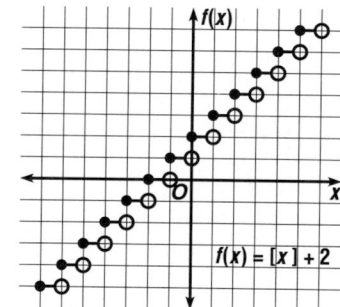

29. same graph translated 1 unit down

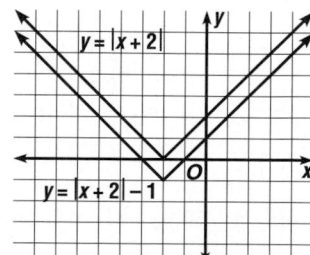

33. same shape graph reflected over x-axis

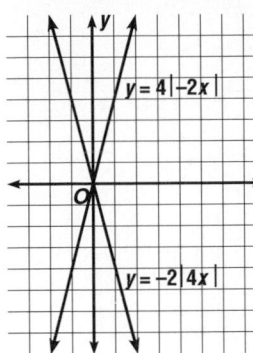

35. If $a > 0$, the two graphs are the same. If $a < 0$, the graphs are reflected images over the x-axis.

11.

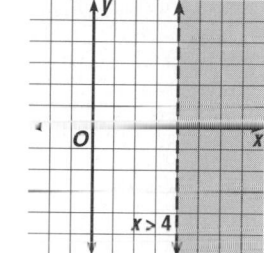

37.

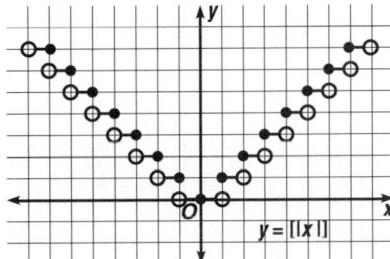

15.

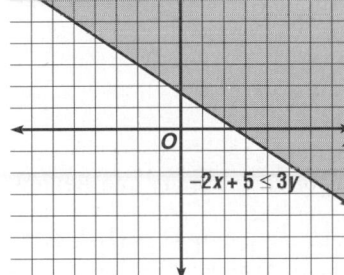

39.

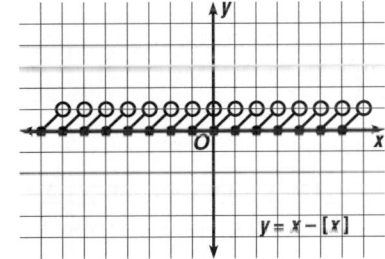

19.

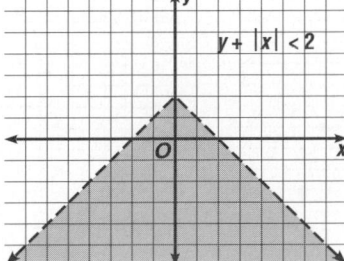

43. step function

44a. $1200y = -x + 40.3$

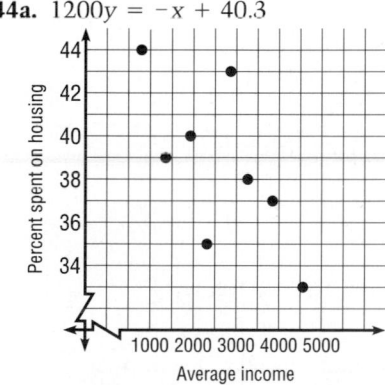

23.

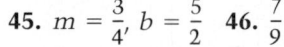

27.

44b. about 37.8%   **44c.** about $1725

45. $m = \dfrac{3}{4}$, $b = \dfrac{5}{2}$ **46.** $\dfrac{7}{9}$

Pages 94–95   Lesson 2-8

7. $(0, 0)$, $(2, -3)$ **9.** $(-1, 2)$

31.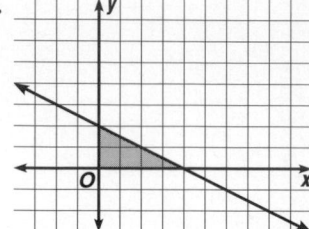

35.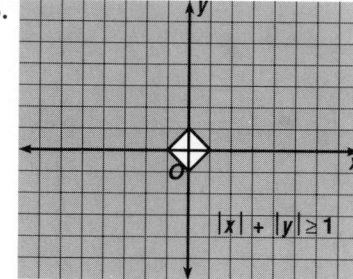

40.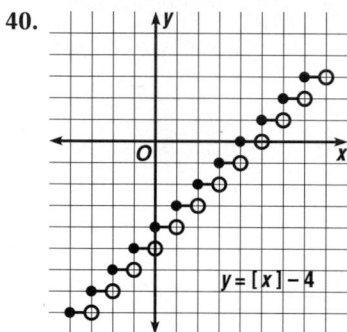

41. $a^2 - 6a + 14$

42. all reals

43. 1000

7. yes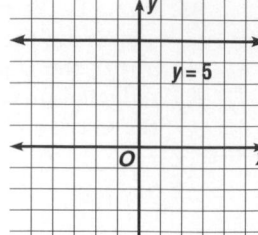

9. yes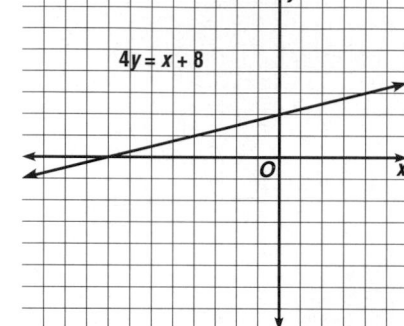

11. $-\dfrac{3}{8}$

13. perpendicular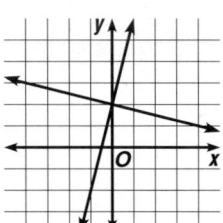

15. parallel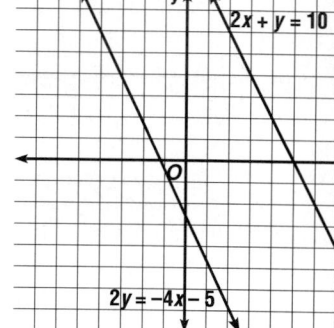

17. $y = -3x - 1$; $3x + y = -1$ **19.** $y = \dfrac{5}{2}x + 5$; $5x - 2y = -10$ **21.** $y = \dfrac{2}{3}x - \dfrac{1}{3}$; $2x - 3y = 1$

23. 70.3 kg

Pages 96–98 Chapter 2 Summary and Review

1. D = {-3, 3, 4, 6}, R = {-6, -3, -2, 2}; yes

3. D = {1, 2, 3, -3.5}, R = {-4.5, 4, 4.5}; yes

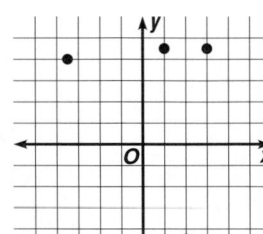

5. $12a^2 - 4a - 1$

25. 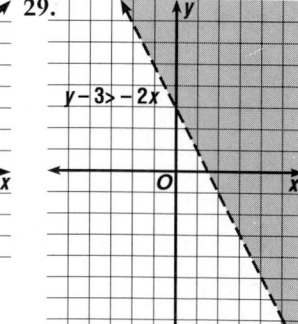 **29.**

33. $c = 10 + 0.15x$; yes **35.** $s = 5.5h - 10$, \$166

CHAPTER 3 SYSTEMS OF EQUATIONS AND INEQUALITIES

5. consistent and independent, $\left(\frac{11}{7}, \frac{1}{7}\right)$

7. no solutions: inconsistent

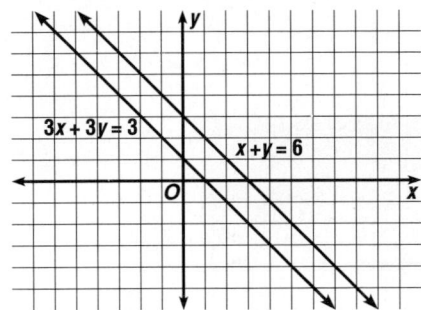

11. $(2, -6)$; consistent and independent

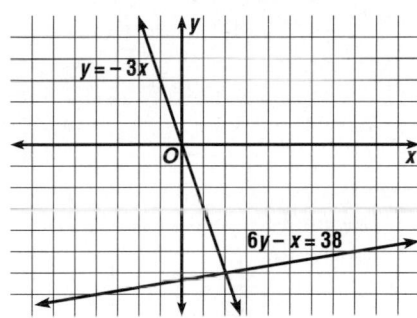

15. no solutions; inconsistent

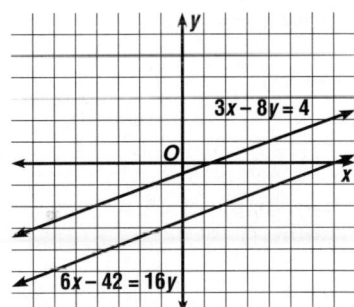

19. $(5, 3)$; consistent and independent

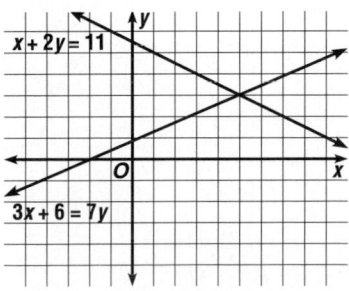

23. no solutions; inconsistent

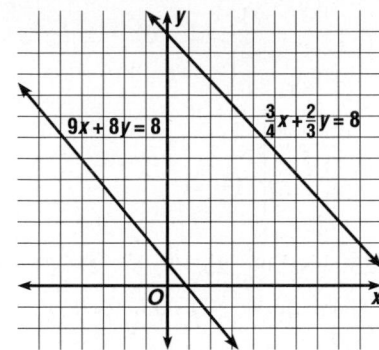

25. $a = 3, b = 8$ **27.** $a = -4, b = 5$ **29.** 2 of the $30 drums and 5 of the $20 drums **31.** $(0, 0)$, $(-1, -3)$

32.

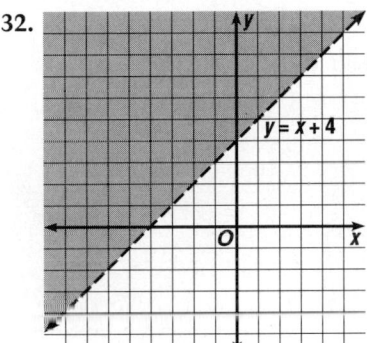

33. -1 **34.** $D = \{9, 2, 1\}$, $R = \{3, -7, 1\}$; yes
35. $\{x|x > 12\}$

5. x: first by 3 and second by -2; y: first by 4 and second by 3; $(2, 1)$ **7.** x: first by -2 and second by 3; y: first by -5 and second by 4; $(-2, 3)$ **9.** x: first by -3; y: first by 7 and second by 8; $(4, 1)$ **11.** $\left(\frac{4}{3}, \frac{2}{3}\right)$
13. $(3, -5)$ **15.** $(4, -1)$ **17.** $(-9, -7)$ **19.** $(-5, 6)$
21. $\left(\frac{1}{4}, \frac{2}{3}\right)$ **23.** $(5.25, 0.75)$ **25.** $(3, 3)$ **27.** $\left(-1, \frac{2}{3}\right)$
29. $\left(\frac{21}{4}, -\frac{27}{4}\right)$ **31.** $\left(\frac{10}{3}, \frac{8}{3}\right)$ **33.** $(10, 25)$
35. $(-5, -2)$, $(4, 4)$, $(-2, -8)$, $(1, 10)$ **37.** 15 inches by 28 inches **39a.** 11 years ago; 1 and 5 **39b.** 2 and 20; 7 years ago **39c.** 28 and 56; 11 years from now
40. $(-2, -4)$ **41.** $(0, 2)$ **42.** $y = -2x + 7$ **43.** 3

5. 0 **7.** 1 **9.** 20 **11.** -13

13. $x = \dfrac{\begin{vmatrix} 3 & -1 \\ 5 & 2 \end{vmatrix}}{\begin{vmatrix} 4 & -1 \\ 3 & 2 \end{vmatrix}}, \; y = \dfrac{\begin{vmatrix} 4 & 3 \\ 3 & 5 \end{vmatrix}}{\begin{vmatrix} 4 & -1 \\ 3 & 2 \end{vmatrix}}; \; (1, 1)$

15. $x = \dfrac{\begin{vmatrix} 8 & -2 \\ 21 & -5 \end{vmatrix}}{\begin{vmatrix} 1 & -2 \\ 3 & -5 \end{vmatrix}}$, $y = \dfrac{\begin{vmatrix} 1 & 8 \\ 3 & 21 \end{vmatrix}}{\begin{vmatrix} 1 & -2 \\ 3 & -5 \end{vmatrix}}$; $(2, -3)$

17. $s = \dfrac{\begin{vmatrix} 6 & 1 \\ 2 & -1 \end{vmatrix}}{\begin{vmatrix} 1 & 1 \\ 1 & -1 \end{vmatrix}}$, $t = \dfrac{\begin{vmatrix} 1 & 6 \\ 1 & 2 \end{vmatrix}}{\begin{vmatrix} 1 & 1 \\ 1 & -1 \end{vmatrix}}$; $(4, 2)$

19. -18 **21.** 17 **23.** -31.38 **25.** $(5, 1)$ **27.** $(3, -1)$
29. $\left(2, \dfrac{13}{8}\right)$ **31.** $(-3, 1)$ **33.** $\left(\dfrac{2}{3}, 0\right)$ **35.** $(0.75, 0.5)$
37. $(6, 9)$ **39.** $\left(\dfrac{9}{64}, \dfrac{49}{16}\right)$ **41.** half inch, 4¢; quarter
inch, 3¢ **43.** $(-1, 2)$ **44.** $(-4, -4)$ **45.** -4
46. $D = \{-11, 0, 1, 3, 9, 12\}$, $R = \{-6, -4, -3, 0, 1, 7, 8\}$;
no **47.** $17, -1$

Pages 124–125   Lesson 3-4

5. no **7.** no **9.** $(3, 1), (-3, -1), (2, 1), (1, 2), (-1, -2)$
11. $(3, 1), (2, 1), (1, 2)$ **13.** $(2, 1), (1, 2), (-1, -2)$

15. 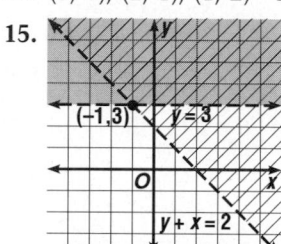 **19.**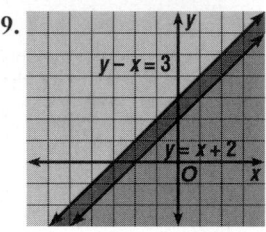

23. 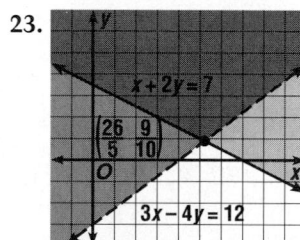 **27.**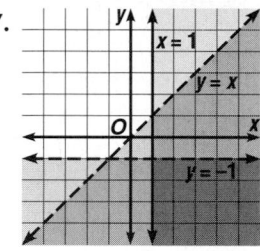

31.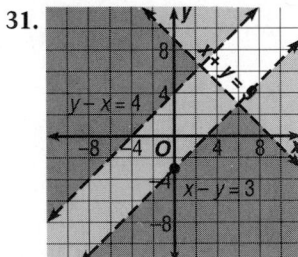

35. $y < 0$ or $x < 0$ **36.** $(7, -2)$ **37.** $(4.27, -5.11)$
38. 83 **39.** $x + 3y = -54$ **40.** $p \le 400$

Page 125   Mid-Chapter Review
1. $(2, 1)$ **2.** $(1, 3)$ **3.** $\left(\dfrac{10}{3}, \dfrac{1}{6}\right)$ **4.** $(3, 3)$ **5.** $\left(\dfrac{13}{5}, -\dfrac{22}{5}\right)$
6. 34 **7.** $(3, 1)$ **8.** $\left(-\dfrac{1}{7}, -\dfrac{17}{7}\right)$

9.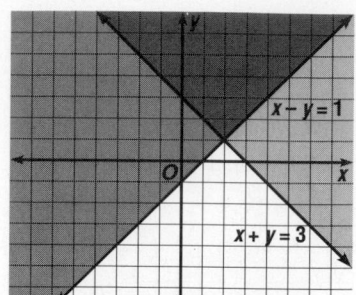

10.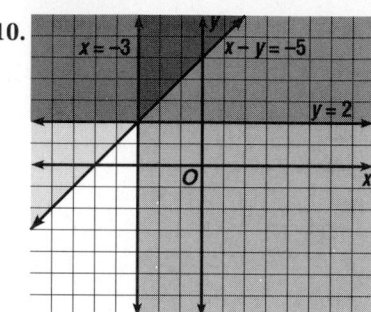

Pages 127–128   Lesson 3-5
5. 34th **7.** 1027 pages **9.**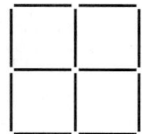
11. 0 **13.** no; 3

Pages 132–133   Lesson 3-6
5. 14 **7.** -4 **9.** max: $f(0, 8) = 24$; min: $f(0, 0) = 0$
11. max: $f(4, 0) = 2$; min: $f(0, 8) = -12$ **13.** 18
15. 17 **17.** 1
19. vertices: $(1, 2), (1, 4), (5, 8), (5, 2)$;
   max: $f(5, 2) = 11$; min: $(1, 4) = -5$

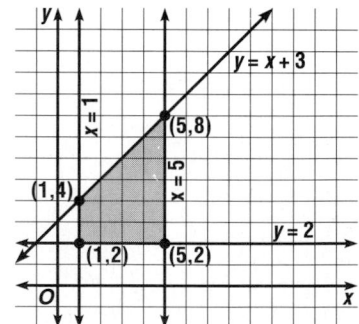

23. vertices: $(0, 1), (1, 3), (6, 3), (10, 1)$;
   max: $f(1, 3) = 8$; min: $f(10, 1), = -7$

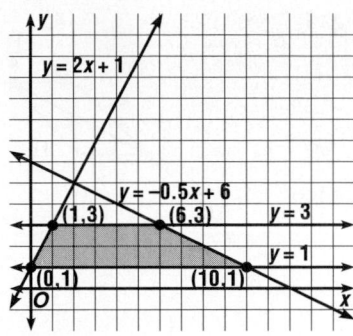

27. vertices: $(-4.08, -2)$, $(-1.58, 1)$, $(-0.4, 1)$, $(-0.4, -2)$; max: $f(-0.4, 1) = 0.4$; min: $f(-4.08, -2) = -20.32$ 29. vertices : $(1, 0)$, $(0, 1)$, $(0, 5)$, $(3, 0)$, $(3, 5)$; max: $f(3, 5) = 56$; min: $f(1, 0) = 12$ 31. 100 acres of corn, 150 acres of soybeans

33.

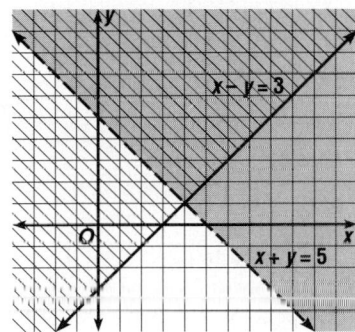

35.

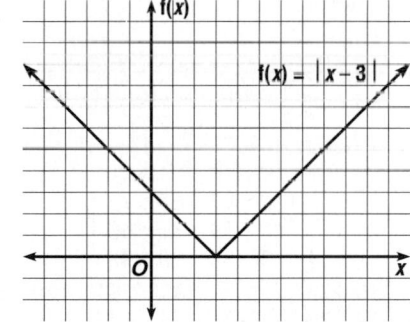

36. $(8, 0)$ and $(0, -2)$ 37. 90

Pages 136–138   Lesson 3-7

5. $0 \le a \le 9$; $b \ge 18$

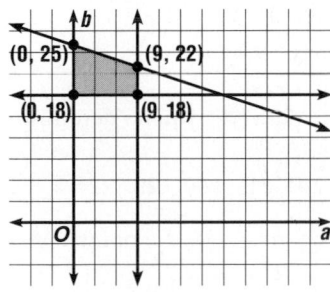

9. $P(0, 18) = 360$, $P(0, 25) = 500$, $P(9, 22) = 530$, $P(9, 18) = 450$ 11. 530 pounds   13. 30 footballs, 0 basketballs   15a. $a \ge 0$, $b \ge 0$, $4a + b \le 32$, $a + 6b \le 54$ 15b. 14 gallons $(6A, 8B)$ 17a. 30 jean jackets, 10 leather jackets   17b. 10 jean jackets, 20 leather jackets
20. vertices: $(0, 3)$, $(0, 6)$, $(2, 5)$, $(1, 3)$;
     max: $f(1, 3) = -3$; min: $f(0, 6) = -12$

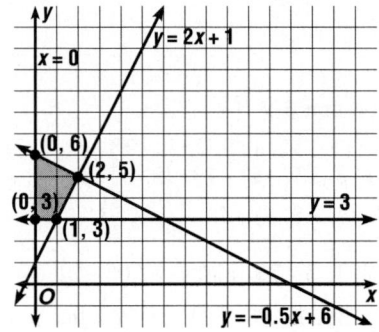

21. vertices: $(0, 60)$, $(0, 70)$, $(10, 70)$, $(50, 30)$, $(50, 10)$;
     max: $f(50, 30) = 290$; min: $f(0, 60) = 180$

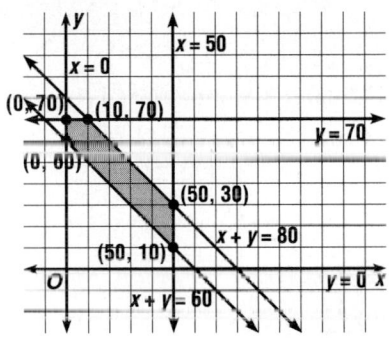

22. no   23. no solution   24. Reflexive property of equality

Pages 142–143   Lesson 3-8

5. 4   7. 2   9. x: 1, y: -5, z: 2   11. x: 10, y: 6, z: 15
13. 4   15. 7   17. 3
19. x: $\frac{5}{2}$, y: -10, z: 5;

$4x - y = 10$,
$2x + z = 5$,
$-y + 2z = 10$

23. x: $-\frac{12}{5}$, y: $\frac{3}{2}$, z: none

$5x = -12$,
$2y = 3$,
$5x - 8y = -12$

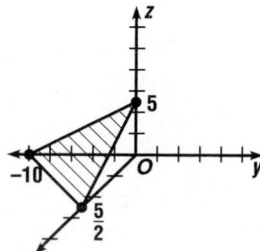

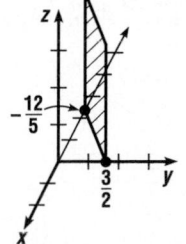

25. $12x + 2y - 3z = 6$ **27.** $2x - 8y - z = 2$
29. $5x - 2z = -10$ **31a.** 1200 cubic inches
31b. 680 square inches **31c.** It is eight times greater.
33a. $c \geq 0, r \geq 0, c + r \leq 275, \frac{c}{9} + \frac{c}{12} \leq 25$

33b. 225 acres of cotton and 0 acres of corn, for a
profit of \$5625 **34.** $(0, 0), (1, -2)$, and $(-3, 1)$
35. $\frac{32}{7}$ **36.** all reals

27. x: 4, y: 4, z: -2;
$x + y = 4$;
$x - 2z = 4$;
$y - 2z = 4$

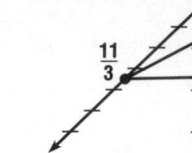

29. $(-4, 2, 1)$ **31.** 99

33. 24 multiple-choice
and 6 essay

Pages 147–149 Lesson 3-9

5. yes **7.** no **9.** yes **11.** $(-9, 2, 4)$ **13.** $(0, 1, 2)$
15. $(5, 3, 7)$ **17.** $(-8, 13, -5)$ **19.** $(0, 2, -1)$
21. $(-2, 1, 3)$ **23.** $(4, -8, 3)$ **25.** $\left(\frac{2}{3}, 1, \frac{3}{2}\right)$
27. $\left(\frac{1}{2}, \frac{1}{3}, \frac{1}{4}\right)$ **29.** 2, 1, 3 **33.** pizza–\$1.05, salad–
\$1.75, soda–\$0.50 **35.** x: -8, y: 4, z: -6 **36.** x: 4,
y: 6, z: -12 **37.** $(1, -2)$ **38.** $c = 25(t - 0.5) + 35$
39. $y = -\frac{3}{2}x - \frac{1}{2}$

Pages 150–152 Chapter 3 Summary and Review

1. infinite; consistent
and dependent

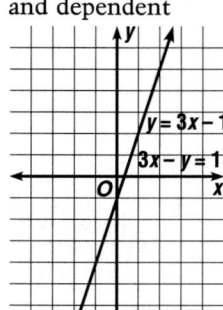

5. $(6.25, 1.75)$
7. $\left(\frac{14}{5}, \frac{4}{5}\right)$
9. -2
11. $(7, 2)$

13.

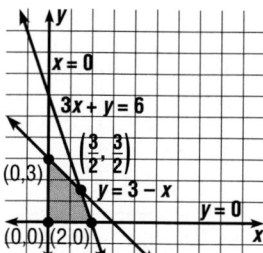

17. vertices: $(0, 0), (0, 3)$,
$(2, 0), \left(\frac{3}{2}, \frac{3}{2}\right)$;
max: $f(0, 3) = 12$;
min: $f(0, 0) = 0$

19. 2 **21.** none
23. 1 **25.** 3

CHAPTER 4 MATRICES

Pages 157–158 Lesson 4-1

3. Carol is a teacher and does sculpture. Dena is a
lawyer and fixes cars. Rae is a doctor and likes
gardening. **5.** 16: A, B, C, D, E, H, I, K, M, O, T, U,
V, W, X, Y **7a.** yes **7b.** yes **7c.** no **7d.** yes
9. rabbit, duck

Pages 164–166 Lesson 4-2

7. $V_{1 \times 3}$; $[14 \quad -10 \quad -52]$ **9.** $x = 2\frac{1}{2}, y = 1, z = 3$
11. $A_{3 \times 2} = \begin{bmatrix} 8 & -12 \\ 16 & 4 \\ 0 & 12 \end{bmatrix}$ **13.** $C_{1 \times 3} = [10 \quad -4 \quad 5]$
15. $x = 1, y = 2$ **17.** $x = 5, y = 3, z = 2$ **19.** $x = 2$,
$y = -5$ **21.** $\begin{bmatrix} 7 & 0 & 23 \\ 10 & 15 & -15 \end{bmatrix}$ **23.** $\begin{bmatrix} 28 \\ -16 \\ 3 \end{bmatrix}$
25a. $\begin{bmatrix} 4 & 4 & 4 & 4 \\ -2 & -2 & -2 & -2 \end{bmatrix}$ **25b.** $B'(10, -1), T'(1, -7)$,
$U'(7, 3)$ **27.** $x = 2, y = 7, z = -2$ **29.** $x = 3, y = 5$,
$m = 10, r = 2$ **31.** $M(0, 0); N(-3, 10); P(-8, 6)$;
$Q(-10, 4)$ **33a.** $M = \begin{bmatrix} 120 & 97 & 64 & 75 \\ 80 & 59 & 36 & 60 \\ 72 & 84 & 29 & 48 \end{bmatrix}$,
$T = \begin{bmatrix} 112 & 87 & 56 & 74 \\ 84 & 65 & 39 & 70 \\ 88 & 98 & 43 & 60 \end{bmatrix}, S = \begin{bmatrix} 232 & 184 & 120 & 149 \\ 164 & 124 & 75 & 130 \\ 160 & 182 & 72 & 108 \end{bmatrix}$
33b. 106.25 pounds **34.** $2x - 7y = -16$ **35.** $1\frac{2}{9}$
36. $\left\{a | a \geq \frac{4}{3}\right\}$ **37.** -139

Pages 170–172 Lesson 4-3

5. 31 **7.** no determinant **9.** $x = \pm 7$
11. $A = \frac{1}{2}\begin{vmatrix} 4 & -5 & 1 \\ 3 & 8 & 1 \\ -2 & 3 & 1 \end{vmatrix}$ **13.** 87 **15.** no determinant
17. $x = -\frac{14}{3}$ or 2 **19.** 24 **21.** -60 **23.** $x = 4, -1$
25. $x = \frac{5}{3}, -4$ **27.** If the area $= 0$, the points are
collinear. **31.** 5 **32.** $\begin{bmatrix} -2 & 9 & 22 \\ 20 & 12 & -1 \end{bmatrix}$

33. $\begin{bmatrix} -28 & 20 & -44 \\ 8 & -16 & 36 \end{bmatrix}$ **34.**

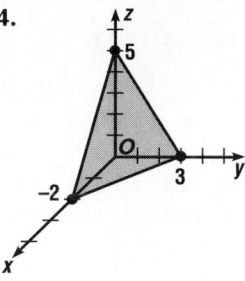

35. 15, 9   **36.** $5x - 6y = 30$

Pages 175–178   Lesson 4-4

7. 4×2 **9.** not defined   **11.** $\begin{bmatrix} 5 & -2 \\ 1 & 2 \end{bmatrix}$ **13.** 1×2

15. not defined   **17.** $\begin{bmatrix} 15 & -8 & -10 \\ -7 & 23 & 16 \end{bmatrix}$ **19.** $[-1, 33]$

21. $[-18]$ **23.** not possible to evaluate
25. $D'(1, -1)$, $E'(1, -4)$, $F'(3, -4)$, $G'(3, -1)$ **27.** not

defined   **29.** $\begin{bmatrix} -39 & 9 \\ 5 & 16 \end{bmatrix}$ **31.** $(-5, 3)$, $(7, 2)$, $(4, -1)$

33. $w = 1$, $y = 0$, $x = 0$, $z = 1$; the same matrix you
began with
35. nickels $243.20
    dimes $199.80
    quarters $521.95
         $964.95

39.

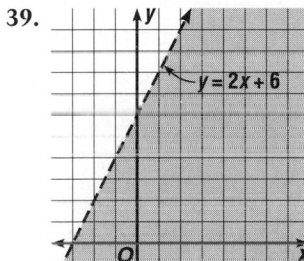

40.

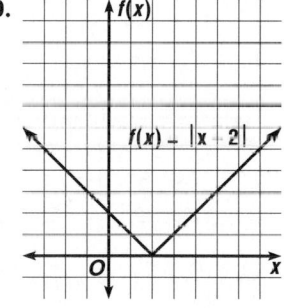

41. $164, $123

Pages 182–183   Lesson 4-5

5. yes   **7.** no, det $= 0$ **9.** $-\dfrac{1}{3}\begin{bmatrix} 1 & -2 \\ -2 & 1 \end{bmatrix}$

11. $\dfrac{1}{32}\begin{bmatrix} 1 & 5 \\ -6 & 2 \end{bmatrix}$ **13.** $\dfrac{1}{7}\begin{bmatrix} 1 & -1 \\ 4 & 3 \end{bmatrix}$ **15.** no inverse

exists   **17.** true   **19.** false

23. $\begin{bmatrix} -5 & -2 & 15 & -15 \\ 21 & -6 & -63 & 27 \\ -11 & 18 & 33 & 23 \end{bmatrix}$

24.

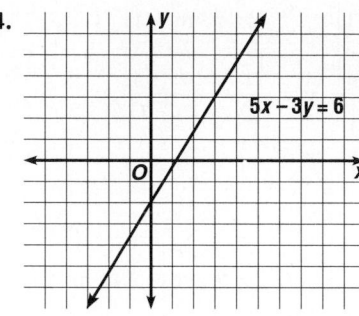

25. $\dfrac{9}{2}, \dfrac{4}{9}, -2$ **26.** 18 arrangements

Page 183   Mid-Chapter Review

1. Sue/Lou, Liz/Matt, Jane/Bob   **2.** $M'(-1, 8)$,
$A'(-2, -3)$, $T'(-7, 2)$, $H'(-11, 8)$ **3.** $\begin{bmatrix} 4 & -0.5 \\ 0 & -1.5 \end{bmatrix}$

4. $\begin{bmatrix} 4 & 1 \\ 0 & -8 \\ -2 & -16 \end{bmatrix}$ **5.** -119 **6.** 30 square units

7. $\begin{bmatrix} -15 & 6 \\ 19 & 43 \\ -6 & -24 \end{bmatrix}$ **8.** cannot be evaluated

9. $-\dfrac{1}{17}\begin{bmatrix} 1 & -5 \\ -3 & -2 \end{bmatrix}$

Pages 188–189   Lesson 4-6

3. $\begin{bmatrix} 5 & 2 \\ 2 & 9 \end{bmatrix} \cdot \begin{bmatrix} a \\ b \end{bmatrix} = \begin{bmatrix} -49 \\ 5 \end{bmatrix}$ **5.** $5x + y = 26$
                          $2x - 3y = 41$

7. $\left(\dfrac{1}{3}, -\dfrac{2}{3}\right)$ **9.** $3x + y = 13$ **11.** $x - 2y = -8$
                  $4x - 2y = 24$ $3x + y + 2z = 9$
                                $4x - 3y + 3z = 1$

13. $\begin{bmatrix} 2 & 5 \\ 3 & 4 \end{bmatrix} \cdot \begin{bmatrix} x \\ y \end{bmatrix} = \begin{bmatrix} 1 \\ 12 \end{bmatrix}$ **15.** $\left(\dfrac{3}{4}, \dfrac{1}{2}\right)$

17. $\left(\dfrac{2}{3}, 1, -\dfrac{4}{3}\right)$ **19.** $\left(\dfrac{3}{4}, \dfrac{2}{3}\right)$ **21.** 7 trips for the 10-ton
truck and 13 for the 12-ton truck

23. $\dfrac{1}{18}\begin{bmatrix} 6 & 2 \\ 3 & 4 \end{bmatrix}$ **24.** $\begin{bmatrix} 1 & 0 & 0 \\ 0 & 1 & 0 \\ 0 & 0 & 1 \end{bmatrix}$ **25.** $(1, -3)$, $(-1, 3)$,

$(5, 6)$, $(5, 1)$; 17; -13 **26.** $-\dfrac{11}{6}$ **27.** $3x + 7y = 5$

28. $\{x | 7 < x < 10\}$ **29.** $\left\{t \Big| t < \dfrac{4}{3} \text{ or } t > \dfrac{14}{3}\right\}$

Pages 192–193   Lesson 4-7

5. $\begin{vmatrix} 6 & 1 \\ 5 & -8 \end{vmatrix}$

7. $x = \dfrac{\begin{vmatrix} -6 & 4 & -1 \\ 2 & -2 & 3 \\ -10 & 2 & -4 \end{vmatrix}}{\begin{vmatrix} 2 & 4 & -1 \\ 1 & -2 & 3 \\ 1 & 2 & -4 \end{vmatrix}}$, $y = \dfrac{\begin{vmatrix} 2 & -6 & -1 \\ 1 & 2 & 3 \\ 1 & -10 & -4 \end{vmatrix}}{\begin{vmatrix} 2 & 4 & -1 \\ 1 & -2 & 3 \\ 1 & 2 & -4 \end{vmatrix}}$,

$z = \dfrac{\begin{vmatrix} 2 & 4 & -6 \\ 1 & -2 & 2 \\ 1 & 2 & -10 \end{vmatrix}}{\begin{vmatrix} 2 & 4 & -1 \\ 1 & -2 & 3 \\ 1 & 2 & -4 \end{vmatrix}}$; $\left(-3, \dfrac{1}{2}, 2\right)$ **9.** yes   **11.** no

13. no unique solution   **15.** $\left(-\dfrac{1}{3}, 2, 7\right)$ **17.** $\left(6, -\dfrac{1}{2}, 2\right)$

19. $\begin{aligned} 2c + 3f &= 3.65 \\ c + 2m &= 2.47 \\ c + 2f + m &= 3.01 \end{aligned}$

23. 17 small, 24 medium, and 11 large   **24.** a matrix with 2 rows and 4 columns

25. 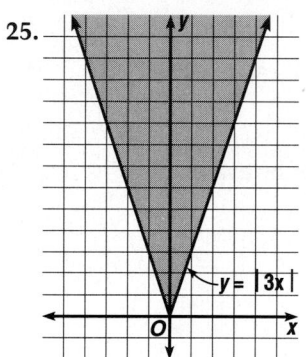   **26.**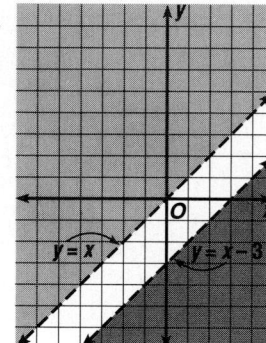

27. $12.02

Pages 199–200   Lesson 4-8

5. $\begin{aligned} x + 3z &= -2 \\ 3x + 9y - 2z &= -5 \\ -4x + y - 7z &= 3 \end{aligned}$ **7.** $\begin{bmatrix} 5 & -3 & 7 \\ 3 & 9 & 3 \end{bmatrix}$; $\left(1, -\dfrac{2}{3}\right)$

11. $\begin{bmatrix} 7 & -3 & 41 \\ 2 & 5 & 0 \end{bmatrix}$; $(5, -2)$ **13.** unique   **15.** an equation in two variables   **17.** $(-1, 2, -3)$ **19.** 48°, 24°, 108°   **23.** chicken, $0.95 per piece; salad, $1.05; roll, $0.35   **24.** $\begin{bmatrix} 1 & 5 & 2 \\ 3 & -3 & 2 \\ 2 & 4 & -1 \end{bmatrix} \cdot \begin{bmatrix} x \\ y \\ z \end{bmatrix} = \begin{bmatrix} 10 \\ 2 \\ -15 \end{bmatrix}$

25. 34   **26.** $\left(\dfrac{2}{3}, 5\right)$ **27.** $(4, 2)$ **28.** Distributive property

Pages 202–204   Chapter 4 Summary and Review

1. $P_{2 \times 3}$ **3.** $\begin{bmatrix} 24 & -9 & 6 \\ 12 & 3 & 21 \end{bmatrix}$ **5.** $(3, 8)$ **7.** -36

9. $[30 \quad 31]$ **11.** $\begin{bmatrix} 1 & 0 & 0 & 0 \\ 0 & 1 & 0 & 0 \\ 0 & 0 & 1 & 0 \\ 0 & 0 & 0 & 1 \end{bmatrix}$ **13.** $\dfrac{1}{2}\begin{bmatrix} 7 & -6 \\ -9 & 8 \end{bmatrix}$

15. $(5, -3)$ **17.** $\left(-\dfrac{1}{2}, 1, 6\right)$ **19.** $(6, -1)$ **21.** Alan: soup, Bill: salad, Cathy: sandwich   **23.** $A'(9, -3)$, $B'(1, 3)$, $C'(2, -4)$ **25.** $M'(0, 5)$, $P'(-6, -2)$, $Q'(4, 3)$

CHAPTER 5   POLYNOMIALS

Pages 213–214   Lesson 5-1

5. yes, 1, 2   **7.** yes, -5, 2   **9.** no   **11.** yes, 0, none   **13.** 8.104×10^2 **15.** 9×10^9 **17.** 7.21×10^7 **19.** 42,000   **21.** 57   **23.** 3,210,000   **25.** x **27.** ab^2 **29.** y^{12} **31.** 8^{14} **33.** $81a^4$ **35.** $\dfrac{1}{2}x^5y^{10}$ **37.** $7a^6$ **39.** $114a^4b^4$ **41.** 9.025×10^7; 90,250,000   **43.** 3.15×10^6; 3,150,000   **45.** 1.904×10^2; 190.4   **47.** 2.475×10^8; 247,500,000   **49.** 1.2×10^5; 120,000   **53.** 3.75×10^5 kilometers   **55.** $(2, 1, -1)$ **56.** $(2, 5, 4)$ **57.** 27, 15   **58.** $y = 4 - \dfrac{3}{4}x$ **59.** $\{x | 4 \le x \le 2\}$ **60.** yes; 1

Pages 218–219   Lesson 5-2

5. x^2 **7.** r^3 **9.** $\dfrac{5}{y^3}$ **11.** $\dfrac{1}{3}$ **13.** 1   **15.** 10,000   **17.** t^2 **19.** $3x^5$ **21.** $-12s^3$ **23.** $\dfrac{y^7}{x^3}$ **25.** $\dfrac{1}{7z^2}$ **27.** $\dfrac{1}{5b^2}$ **29.** $4b^2c^3$ **31.** $\dfrac{1}{2}$ **33.** $-3s^6$ **35.** $-\dfrac{cd^4}{12}$ **37.** a^4b^2 **39.** 243   **41.** $\dfrac{1}{25}$ **43.** $3ab^3$ **45.** $\dfrac{1}{ab}$ **47.** 29   **49.** $4t^{14}$ **51.** $\dfrac{4}{9y^4}$ **53.** 5×10^0; 5   **55.** 6×10^0; 6   **57.** $3.\overline{27} \times 10^{-4}$; $0.0003\overline{27}$ **59.** 2.1×10^6; 2,100,000   **63.** 1.2×10^{-4} or 0.00012 seconds   **64.** 4.5×10^9; 4,500,000,000   **65.** 5.0625×10^{12}; 5,062,500,000,000   **66.** $\begin{bmatrix} -14 & -15 \\ 4 & 20 \end{bmatrix}$ **67.** 2   **68.** one answer is x: first by 4, second by -3; y: first by 3, second by 4.   **69.** $x - 8y = -4$ **70.** 21

Pages 221–222   Lesson 5-3

5. 4 inches   **7.** 10   **9.**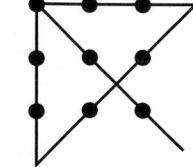
11. Any line in the plane of the square that passes through the point of intersection of the diagonals of the square separates it into two congruent parts, so there are infinitely many ways.   **13.** $10^2 - 2^2$, $11^2 - 5^2$, $14^2 - 10^2$, $25^2 - 23^2$ **15.** ≈ 1473 square feet

Pages 225–228 Lesson 5-4

5. 2 **7.** 6 **9.** 3 **11.** 9 **13.** $2x - 2y$
15. $3p^3 - 6p^2 + 9p$ **17.** $10y^2 + 6y$ **19.** $-9a + 13b$

21. $4a^2 - 10d + 20$ **23.** $r^2 - r + 6$ **25.** $-19y$
27. $4gf^2 - 4fbh$ **29.** $\dfrac{1}{x^2} + \dfrac{1}{x^3} - \dfrac{3}{x^4}$ **31.** $12a^2 +$

$4ab + \dfrac{b}{4}$ **33.** $x^2 + 9x + 14$ **35.** $s^4 + s^2 - 20$
37. $6x^2 + 31x + 35$ **39.** $2w^4 - 7w^2 - 15$
41. $42p^2 - 89p + 45$ **43.** $a^2 - 2ab + b^2$ **45.** $d^2 +$
$6d + 9$ **47.** $y^2 - 4y + 4$ **49.** $4p^2 + 4pq^3 + q^6$
51. $16m^2 - 24mn + 9n^2$ **53.** $1 + 8r + 16r^2$
55. $3x^2 + 9xy + 6y^2$ **57.** $64x^2 - 4y^2$ **59.** $2x^3 -$
$9x^2 - 7x + 24$ **61.** $3m^3 - 7m^2 - 24m + 16$
63. $b^3 + 2b^2 - 5b - 6$ **65.** $2a^3 - 7a^2 + 4a + 4$
67. $2k^3 - 11k^2 + 21k + 63$ **71.** $19.95 +$
$0.25\,(m - 50)$ **72.** $16 - 4\pi$ or about 3.4 square

inches **73.** 64 square meters **74.** $\begin{bmatrix} \frac{1}{3} & 0 \\ \frac{1}{15} & \frac{1}{5} \end{bmatrix}$

75. $\left(\dfrac{3}{4}, \dfrac{1}{2}\right)$ **76.** The graph of $y = 3[x]$ jumps by threes
at intervals of one unit. The graph of $y = [3x]$ jumps
by ones at intervals of $\frac{1}{3}$ unit. **77.** 449

Page 228 Mid-Chapter Review

1. $8d^2 - 5c^2$ **2.** 0 **3.** $48x^6y^3$ **4.** $\dfrac{4}{243}x^8y^5$
5. 1.536×10^{12}; 1,536,000,000,000 **6.** $3b^2$
7. $2m^4n^2$ **8.** $4y$ **9.** $-\dfrac{1}{8w^3t}$ **10.** 3×10^7; 30,000,000
11. 1.42083×10^3, $1420.8\overline{3}$ **12.** 640 acres
13. $-x - 9y$ **14.** $2d^2 + 5d + 6$
15. $6y^2 + 11y - 72$ **16.** $x^2 + 4x - 21$
17. $m^2 + 4m + 4$ **18.** $4x^2 - 12x + 9$
19. $x^3 - 4x^2 - 3x + 18$ **20.** $2y^3 - 22y + 28$

Pages 233–234 Lesson 5-5

5. $3(s + t)$ **7.** $a(b + c)$ **9.** $(r + 3)(r - 3)$
11. $(10 + m)(10 - m)$ **13.** $(3y - 2)(y + 4k)$
15. $3p(3p - q)$ **17.** $-5x(3x + 1)$
19. $2(c - d)(ab + 5d)$ **21.** $(y + 3)^2$ **23.** $(r + 8)^2$
25. $3(a^2 + 2a + 3y)$ **27.** $5xy(x - 2y)$
29. $(x + 2)(x^2 - 2x + 4)$ **31.** $(f - 9)^2$ **33.** $(s + 6)^2$
35. $(2x - 3)(2x + 3)$ **37.** $(2s - 7)(2s - 3)$
39. $x(x + 7)(x - 5)$ **41.** $(p - 2b)^2$
43. $(f - 1)(f^2 + f + 1)$ **45.** $\left(x + y - \dfrac{1}{2}\right)\left(x + y + \dfrac{1}{2}\right)$
47. $(m - k + 3)(m + k - 3)$
49. $(a + b)(1 + 3a - 3b)$
51. $(1 - 2m^2)(1 + 2m^2 + 4m^4)$
57. $(3x - 5)(x + 1)$;

$x + 1$ ▭
$3x - 5$

58. $s^2 + 6s + 9$ **59.** $14x^2 + 26x - 4$ **60.** $3x = 12$;
$x - 2y = 8$ **61.** $M_{3 \times 5}$ **62.** $f(0.1, -0.3) = 0.36$
63. no **64.** $t = 12$

Pages 238–240 Lesson 5-6

5. $5b - 4 + 7a$ **7.** $2rs + s - 3r$ **9.** $\dfrac{1}{4(y^2 - 5)^2}$

11. $c + 5$ **13.** $-\dfrac{w^2}{w + 1}$ **15.** $4q^2 + 3pq - 5p$
17. $2k^2 - 3py + 4p^2y$ **19.** $a - 12$ **21.** $n - 15$
23. $2x + 7 + \dfrac{5}{x - 3}$ **25.** $-s - 10 + \dfrac{44}{6 - s}$
27. $2y^2 + 5y + 2$ **29.** $3x^2 - 2x + 3$
31. $r^2 - 6r + 9 - \dfrac{1}{r - 3}$ **33.** $2x^2 - 3x - 2$

35. $2t^2 + 2t - \dfrac{3}{t - 1}$ **37.** $s^2 + 2s + 4$
39. $x^2 - 2x + 3$ **41.** $a + 1,\ a - 1$
43. -48 **47.** $\dfrac{1}{8}$ inch **48.** $4(a - 2)(a + 2)$

49. $(d - 13)(d + 2)$ **50.** $\dfrac{1}{3}$ **51.** 7 chairs, 4 tables
52. $-2, -1, 0$ **53.** I, R

Pages 244–245 Lesson 5-7

5. no **7.** no **9.** no **11.** $2b^2 - b - 1 + \dfrac{4}{b + 1}$
13. $3x^2 + x + 3 + \dfrac{2}{x - 1}$ **15.** $4x^3 - 9x^2 + 7x - 6$ **17.**
$2b^2 - 5b - 3$ **19.** $x^2 + 4x + 3$
21. $n^3 - 3n^2 - 15n - 21$
23. $z^4 + 2z^3 - 2z^2 - \dfrac{3}{z - 2}$

25. $2s^3 + s^2 - 2s + \dfrac{3}{2s - 1}$

27. $2x^3 + 3x^2 + 2x - 1 - \dfrac{13}{2x - 3}$
29. $y^4 + 2y^3 + 4y^2 + 5y + 10$ **31.** Both are 0
33. $2w - 4$ inches **35.** $x^3 + 5x^2 + 8x + 26 + \dfrac{70}{x - 3}$

37. $2x^4 + x^3 - 7x^2 + 13x - 21 + \dfrac{24}{x + 1}$

39. $x^4 - 3x^3 - 6x^2 + 8x + 36 - \dfrac{36}{x + 3}$ **40.** $x - 6$

41. $a^2 + 3a - 2 - \dfrac{1}{a + 4}$ **42.** 9×1 **43.** 3
44. $11x + y = 2$

Pages 246–247 Chapter 5 Summary and Review

1. m **3.** y^{13} **5.** $144\,x^4y^6$ **7.** 1.344×10^{15};
1,344,000,000,000,000 **9.** a^2 **11.** $\dfrac{1}{64}$ **13.** $\dfrac{1}{a^6b^4}$
15. 2×10^7; 20,000,000 **17.** $2x + 5y$
19. $m^2 + 3m - 10$ **21.** $n^3 - n^2 - 5n + 2$
23. $5(a + b)$ **25.** $(s + 1)(s + 6)$ **27.** $(b - 4)$
$(b^2 + 4b + 16)$ **29.** $(x + 3)^2$ **31.** $2y(y - 7)(y + 7)$
33. $6y + 4$ **35.** $4s - 2$ **37.** $x^2 + 3 + \dfrac{5}{x - 4}$

39. $3y^2 + y - 1 + \dfrac{2}{2y+3}$ **41.** 5.865696×10^{12} or 5,865,696,000,000 miles **43.** one-half **45.** $(0.9)^3 p$ or 0.729 p

CHAPTER 6   IRRATIONAL AND COMPLEX NUMBERS

Pages 255–257   Lesson 6-1
7. -11 **9.** y **11.** $-|x|$ **13.** -5 **15.** $4|a|b^2$
17. $|x+3|$ **19.** 7.416 **21.** -3.609 **23.** 8.000
25. -9.950 **27.** 2.844 **29.** 3.448 **31.** 14 **33.** 3
35. -6 **37.** -10 **39.** 0.5 **41.** $5|y^3|$ **43.** ± 24
45. $9|a|b^2$ **47.** $-2bc$ **49.** $4a^2b$ **51.** $|3x + y|$
53. $s + t$ **55.** $|r + s|$ **57.** $|x + 5|$ **59.** $|3a + 1|$
61. $|s - t|$ **65.** about 4.2 rotations per minute
66. $t^2 - 2t + 1$ **67.** $x^2 - x + 7 + \dfrac{3}{5x - 3}$
68. 1.4985×10^7; 14,985,000 **69.** $(-1, 0, 1)$
70. 2×3, no determinant **71.** 4 **72.** a step function

Pages 262–263   Lesson 6-2
5. $3\sqrt{3}$ **7.** $7y^2\sqrt{2}$ **9.** $2\sqrt[3]{2}$ **11.** $y\sqrt{y}$ **13.** $t\sqrt[4]{t}$
15. $\dfrac{\sqrt{3}}{\sqrt{3}}; \dfrac{\sqrt{3}}{3}$ **17.** $\dfrac{\sqrt{b}}{\sqrt{b}}; \dfrac{3\sqrt{b}}{b}$ **19.** $\dfrac{\sqrt[3]{3}}{\sqrt[3]{3}}; \dfrac{7\sqrt[3]{3}}{3}$
21. $12\sqrt{6}$ **23.** $2\sqrt[3]{7}$ **25.** $15\sqrt{3}$ **27.** $4xy\sqrt{x}$
29. $\sqrt{2}$ **31.** $\sqrt[4]{11}$ **33.** $36\sqrt{6}$ **35.** $2\sqrt[4]{7}$ **37.** $48\sqrt{7}$
39. $3\sqrt{2} - 2\sqrt{3}$ **41.** $3a^2b\sqrt[4]{b}$ **43.** $\sqrt[3]{9}$ **45.** $\dfrac{\sqrt{15a}}{6a}$
47. $\sqrt{ab} + a\sqrt{b}$ **49.** $\dfrac{3\sqrt[3]{2}}{5}$ **51.** $\dfrac{\sqrt{10x}}{8x}$ **53.** 7 inches
55. 9.73 inches **57.** $25b^2$ **58.** $-11|bc^3|$
59. 3.8×10^{-6}; 0.0000038 **60.** No, only square matrices have inverses. **61.** $x = 8, y = 4, z = -3$
62. -8

Pages 266–268   Lesson 6-3
5. $5 + \sqrt{7}$ **7.** $\sqrt{3} - \sqrt{10}$ **9.** $2 + 2\sqrt{3}$ **11.** $\sqrt{3}$
13. $11\sqrt[3]{6}$ **15.** $4\sqrt{2}$ **17.** $5\sqrt{5} - 10\sqrt{2}$ **19.** $-7\sqrt{3}$
21. $17 + 7\sqrt{5}$ **23.** $9x^2 - 5y$ **25.** $19 + 8\sqrt{3}$
27. $4\sqrt{5} + 23\sqrt{6}$ **29.** $-\sqrt[3]{2}$ **31.** $\sqrt[3]{6}$
33. $15\sqrt[3]{5} - 6\sqrt[3]{3}$ **35.** $25 - 5\sqrt{2} + 5\sqrt{6} - 2\sqrt{3}$
37. $49 - 11y$ **39.** $\dfrac{3 - \sqrt{5}}{4}$ **41.** $14\sqrt{6} + 2\sqrt[3]{3}$
43. $15\sqrt[4]{2}$ **45.** $|y| + y^2 + y^4$ **47.** $m^3 + 4$
49. $\dfrac{\sqrt{x^2 - 1}}{x - 1}$ **51.** $\dfrac{16\sqrt{10}}{5}$ **55.** $2\sqrt{7}$ or 5.3 seconds
56. $15\sqrt{6}$ **57.** $5mn^2\sqrt[4]{m}$
58. $(1 - 2a)(1 + 2a + 4a^2)$ **59.** c^9 **60.** 3×3; -68
61. maximum: 6 at (6, 0); minimum: -5 at (0, 5)

Pages 272–274   Lesson 6-4
5. 4 **7.** 8 **9.** $\dfrac{1}{9}$ **11.** 49 **13.** 81 **15.** 6 **17.** $\sqrt{6}$
19. $\sqrt{2}$ **21.** $\sqrt[3]{4}$ **23.** $17^{\frac{1}{3}}$ **25.** $y^{\frac{1}{4}}$ **27.** $5a^{\frac{3}{2}}b^2$
29. $27^{\frac{1}{4}}$ **31.** $n^{\frac{2}{3}}$ **33.** $16^{\frac{1}{3}}a^{\frac{5}{3}}b^{\frac{7}{3}}$ **35.** $\sqrt{6}$ **37.** $\sqrt[4]{n^3}$
39. $2a^2\sqrt[3]{4a}$ **41.** $p^2\sqrt[4]{p^2q^3}$ **43.** $\sqrt[5]{9r^2s^3}$
45. $\sqrt[3]{5s^2t}$ **47.** $\dfrac{1}{2}$ **49.** 4 **51.** 81 **53.** 3 **55.** 0.2
57. 36 **59.** $\sqrt[6]{x^2y^3}$ **61.** $\sqrt{2}$ **63.** $yz^2\sqrt[6]{x^5y^3z^2}$
65. $3\sqrt[6]{3}$ **69.** \$1797.27 **71.** $5 - 3\sqrt{3}$ **72.** $5\sqrt{3}$
73. $a - 2b$ **74.** $\dfrac{1}{14}\begin{bmatrix} 4 & 1 \\ 2 & -3 \end{bmatrix}$ **75.** 70¢
76. $29x - 10y$

Page 274   Mid-Chapter Review
1. $-9|x|$ **2.** $|a + 7|$ **3.** $-4x^3$ **4.** $4|m|n\sqrt{3n}$
5. $3\sqrt{2} + 10\sqrt{3}$ **6.** $\dfrac{\sqrt{5}}{3}$ **7.** $\dfrac{6\sqrt[3]{2x^2}}{x}$ **8.** $3b^2r^2\sqrt[4]{3r}$
9. 3.53 seconds **10.** $-8\sqrt{2}$ **11.** $29 - 3\sqrt{3}$ **12.** 114
13. $\dfrac{11 + 7\sqrt{3}}{13}$ **14.** 12 **15.** $\sqrt[12]{5^8x^6y^9}$ **16.** $3^{\frac{1}{2}}a^{\frac{1}{2}}b^{\frac{2}{3}}|c|$

Page 276   Lesson 6-5
5. 6 **7.** 48 **9.** 16 cm by 16 cm

Pages 279–280   Lesson 6-6
5. $\dfrac{4^{\frac{1}{2}}}{4^{\frac{1}{2}}}, 2$ **7.** $\dfrac{a^{\frac{2}{3}}}{a^{\frac{2}{3}}}, \dfrac{a^{\frac{2}{3}}}{a}$ **9.** $\dfrac{t^{\frac{1}{2}} - 1}{t^{\frac{1}{2}} - 1}, \dfrac{t^{\frac{1}{2}} - 1}{t - 1}$ **11.** $\dfrac{q^{\frac{1}{2}} + r^{\frac{1}{2}}}{q^{\frac{1}{2}} + r^{\frac{1}{2}}},$

$\dfrac{q^{\frac{3}{2}} + qr^{\frac{1}{2}}}{q - r}$ **13.** $\dfrac{t^{\frac{3}{2}} - s^{\frac{3}{2}}}{t^{\frac{3}{2}} - s^{\frac{1}{2}}}, \dfrac{2t^{\frac{3}{2}} - 2s^{\frac{1}{2}}}{t^3 - s}$ **15.** $\dfrac{w + w^{\frac{1}{2}}}{w + w^{\frac{1}{2}}},$

$\dfrac{w^2 + w^{\frac{3}{2}} + w + w^{\frac{1}{2}}}{w^2 - w}$ **17.** $\dfrac{s^{\frac{5}{5}}}{s}$ **19.** $\dfrac{t^{\frac{1}{6}}}{t}$ **21.** $\dfrac{x^{\frac{1}{2}} - 1}{x - 1}$

23. $\dfrac{t^{\frac{1}{2}}}{t(t + 1)}$ **25.** $4 \cdot 6^{\frac{1}{3}}$ **27.** $\dfrac{ab^{\frac{1}{2}}c^{\frac{1}{2}}}{c^2}$ **29.** $\dfrac{n^2 + 3}{n}$

31. $3x^{\frac{5}{3}} + 4x^{\frac{8}{3}}$ **33.** $\dfrac{3xy^{\frac{3}{2}}z^{\frac{2}{3}}}{z}$ **35.** $\dfrac{r^2 - 2r^{\frac{3}{2}}}{r - 4}$ **37.** $\dfrac{1}{b - 1}$

39. $3xy^3$ **41.** $\dfrac{b^2}{a}$ **45.** $\dfrac{20}{3^t}$ units **46.** $\dfrac{1}{2}$ **47.** $5^{\frac{3}{7}}$
48. $2x^2 - 4x + 4$ **49.** They are the same line.
50. 1

Pages 284–286   Lesson 6-7
5. 25 **7.** 16 **9.** 14 **11.** 3 **13.** $-\dfrac{\sqrt{2}}{2}$ **15.** $-\sqrt{3}$
17. $\dfrac{12 - 4\sqrt{2}}{7}$ **19.** $\dfrac{1 + \sqrt{5}}{-2}$ **21.** 13 **23.** 7 **25.** $5\frac{1}{3}$

27. 23 **29.** -1 **31.** 3 **33.** 21 **35.** 8 **37.** 4
39. no solution **41.** 5.41 **43.** 7.41 **45.** 4
47. $r = \pm\sqrt{y^2 - s^2}$ **49.** $c = \dfrac{2mM}{r^3}$ **53.** $10\sqrt{15}$ or
about 38.73 centimeters on each side
55. $\dfrac{r^{\frac{1}{2}}s}{1 + r}$ **56.** $\dfrac{25a^{21}}{b^8}$ **57.** 8 **58.** yes **59.** 100 adults
and 50 students **60.** Yes, each member of the domain
is paired with exactly one member of the range.

Pages 290–291 Lesson 6-8
5. $6i$ **7.** -2 **9.** -3 **11.** $20i$ **13.** $13i$ **15.** $5i\sqrt{2}$
17. $\dfrac{2}{3}i$ **19.** $\dfrac{i\sqrt{5}}{5}$ **21.** i **23.** $-i$ **25.** -4 **27.** $-7\sqrt{2}$
29. -12 **31.** $-8i$ **33.** $9i$ **35.** $4i\sqrt{3}$ **37.** 24
39. $-20i$ **41.** $\pm4i$ **43.** $\pm11i$ **45.** $\pm3i$ **47.** $\pm2i\sqrt{3}$
49. $\pm i\dfrac{\sqrt{5}}{2}$ **53a.** i **53b.** -1 **53c.** $-i$ **53d.** 1

53e. $-i$ **53f.** 1 **53g.** i **53h.** -1 **54.** $\dfrac{7\sqrt{2} - 14}{2}$
55. $\dfrac{6(11 + 2\sqrt{3})}{109}$ **56.** $|x - 2|$ **57.** $(a + 1)(a^2 - a + 1)$
58. 65¢, 30¢, 15¢ **59.** 153 **60.** 120

Pages 294–296 Lesson 6-9
5. $7 + 2i$ **7.** 3 **9.** 10 **11.** $20 + 12i$ **13.** $-10 + 10i$
15. 17 **17.** $x = 2, y = -3$ **19.** $x = 3, y = 0$
21. $x = 7, y = 2$ **23.** $5 + 5i$ **25.** $7 + 3i$ **27.** $3 - 8i$
29. $2 + i$ **31.** $5 - 3i\sqrt{3}$ **33.** $-9i$ **35.** $33 + 13i$
37. $32 - 24i$ **39.** $22 - 29i$ **41.** $-7 + 24i$ **43.** 3
45. 13

47. $2 + 5i$
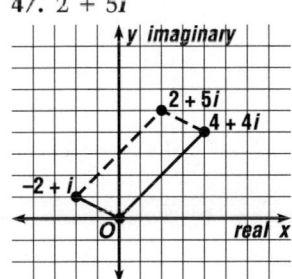

49. $3 - 5i$
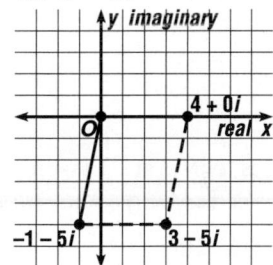

51. $x = 6, y = \dfrac{7}{2}$ **53.** $x = -1, y = -3$ **55.** $x = 3,$
$y = 1$ **57.** $20 + 15i$ **59.** $148 - 222i$
61. $130 + 110i$ **63.** $-a - bi$ **65.** $(a + bi) \cdot$
$1 = (a \cdot 1) + (bi \cdot 1) = a + bi$ **67.** $(1 + i, -1 + 2i),$
$(-1 + 2i, -4 - 4i), (-4 - 4i, -1 + 32i),$
$(-1, + 32i, -1024 - 64i)$ **69.** $\dfrac{i\sqrt{3}}{3}$ **70.** $\pm2i\sqrt{2}$

71. $5\sqrt[4]{5}$ **72.** $y^3 + 3y^2 - 16y + 55 - \dfrac{166}{y + 3}$
73. approximately 4.4×10^{46} times **74.** $\begin{bmatrix} 1 & 7 \\ 1 & 2 \\ 8 & 13 \end{bmatrix}$
75.
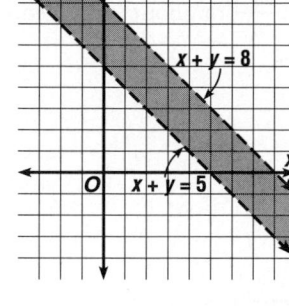
76. no solution, inconsistent
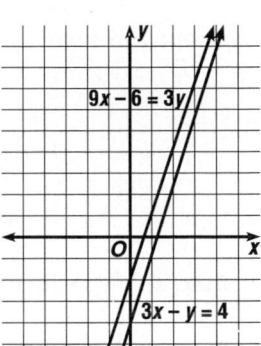

77. no

Pages 299-301 Lesson 6-10
5. $4 - i$ **7.** $5 + 4i$ **9.** $-5i$ **11.** $10i$ **13.** $12 + i$
15. $5 - 4i \cdot \dfrac{5 + 4i}{41} = \dfrac{25 - 16i^2}{41} = \dfrac{25 + 16}{41} = 1$
17. 68 **19.** 29 **21.** 2 **23.** 81 **25.** 100 **27.** $\dfrac{5 + i}{2}$
29. $\dfrac{21 + 13i}{5}$ **31.** $\dfrac{9 + i}{41}$ **33.** $\dfrac{1 - 2i}{5}$ **35.** $2 - i$
37. $\dfrac{12 - 10i}{61}$ **39.** $\dfrac{4\sqrt{3} - 8i}{7}$ **41.** $\dfrac{3 + i\sqrt{3}}{4}$ **43.** $\dfrac{2 - 3i\sqrt{5}}{7}$
45. $\dfrac{3 + 4i}{25}$ **47.** $\dfrac{3 - 7i}{58}$ **49.** $\dfrac{5 + 6i}{122}$ **51.** $\dfrac{1 - 3i}{4}$
53. $-2 - 8i$ **55.** $\dfrac{a - bi}{a^2 + b^2}$ **57.** $\dfrac{3 - 4i\sqrt{7}}{11}$ **59.** 9
61. $\dfrac{-1}{2} \ i$ **65.** $7 + 7i$ **66.** $148 - 64i$ **67.** 2n
68. 1.9663×10^6 **69.** yes, $(-2, 4, 3)$ **70.** 465

71.
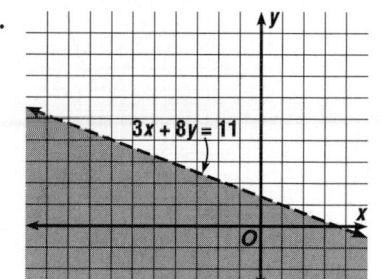
72. 13, -31

Pages 302-304 Chapter 6 Summary and Review
1. $7|x|$ **3.** $|3p - 5q|$ **5.** $4\sqrt{6}$ **7.** $3|a|\sqrt{2b}$ **9.** $\dfrac{3\sqrt{5}}{2}$
11. $10\sqrt{2} + 3\sqrt{10}$ **13.** $14 - \sqrt{6}$ **15.** $17\sqrt[3]{3x^2}$

17. 47   **19.** $r^{\frac{3}{4}}$ **21.** $\sqrt[3]{5}$ **23.** 5   **25.** 32   **27.** $\frac{5^{\frac{2}{3}}}{5}$

29. $\frac{a^{\frac{1}{4}}}{a}$ **31.** $3 + 3\sqrt{2}$ **33.** 7   **35.** 6   **37.** $11i$

39. -15 **41.** $21 + 5i$ **43.** $46 + 3i$ **45.** $8 + 13i$

47. $\frac{8 - 11i}{2}$ **49.** $\frac{8 + i}{65}$ **51.** $\frac{5\sqrt{2}}{2}$ or about 3.54 seconds

53. about 23.94 cm

CHAPTER 7   QUADRATIC EQUATIONS

Page 311   Lesson 7-1

5. $A = 2, B = 1, C = 9, D = 7, E = 8$

7.

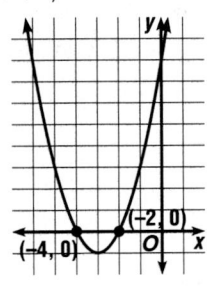

Pages 319–321   Lesson 7-2

7. no   **9.** no   **11.** $-2, 1$ **13.** $0, 16$ **15.** $-6, -2$

17. $-\frac{7}{3}, -5$

19. $-4, -2$ **23.** $-1.5, 3$

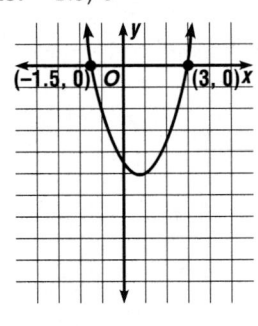

25. $4, -3$ **27.** 6   **29.** $4, -1$ **31.** $\frac{3}{2}, -7$ **33.** $\frac{5}{3}, -3$

35. $\frac{1}{3}, -\frac{3}{2}$ **37.** 4 seconds, 48 ft, 48 ft   **39.** $5, -8$

41. $-\frac{5}{6}, 1$ **43.** $0, 9, -9$ **45.** $0, 1, \frac{8}{9}$

49. 20 m × 50 m   **50.** 56, 25   **51.** $75a^3b$

52. $5m^3n^2\sqrt{3m}$ **53.** $\left(\frac{1}{4}, 6, -\frac{1}{6}\right)$ **54.** deluxe, 35¢;

glazed, 30¢; cake, 20¢   **55.** 0.6 amperes

Pages 324–326   Lesson 7-3

5. no   **7.** no   **9.** 400   **11.** $\frac{81}{4}$ **13.** $\frac{225}{4}$ **15.** $-11, 8$

17. $-15, 12$ **19.** $\frac{7 \pm \sqrt{29}}{2}$ **21.** $\frac{-3 \pm \sqrt{41}}{2}$ **23.** $\frac{1}{2}, \frac{1}{4}$

25. $2 \pm \frac{2\sqrt{6}}{3}$ **27.** $\pm \frac{i\sqrt{ac}}{a}$ **29.** $\frac{-b \pm \sqrt{b^2 - 4ac}}{2a}$

31. 21×15 in.   **33.** 20 seconds   **35.** 15, 5   **36.** 22

37.

$$
\begin{array}{r}
a^2 - 6 \\
a - 5 \overline{\smash{)}\, a^3 - 5a^2 - 6a + 30} \\
\underline{a^3 - 5a^2} \quad\quad\quad\quad \\
-6a + 30 \\
\underline{-6a + 30} \\
0
\end{array}
$$

38. 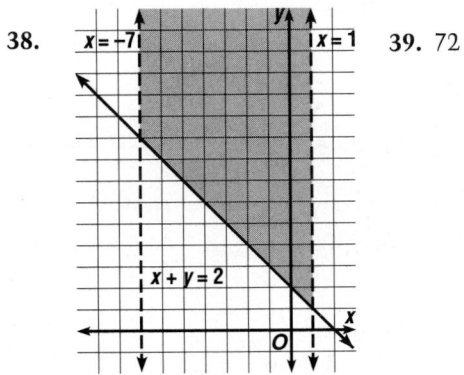   **39.** 72

Page 326   Mid-Chapter Review

1. 853   **2.** $7, -5$ **3.** $-9, 3$ **4.** $-\frac{3}{4}, 4$ **5.** $\pm\frac{5}{2}$

6. $0, \pm 9$ **7.** $\frac{1}{4}, -5$ **8.** $-6 \pm 4\sqrt{2}$ **9.** 0.52 in.

Pages 330–331   Lesson 7-4

7. $a = 1, b = 0, c = -16; 64; \pm 4$ **9.** $a = 6, b = 2,$

$c = 1; -20; \frac{-1 \pm i\sqrt{5}}{6}$ **11.** $a = 3, b = -1, c = 3; -35;$

$\frac{1 \pm i\sqrt{35}}{6}$ **13.** $0; 1$ R, Q; 2   **15.** $144; 2$ R, Q; $7, -5$

17. $16; 2$ R, Q; $-\frac{3}{2}, -\frac{1}{2}$ **19.** $16; 2$ R, Q; $-\frac{3}{2}, -\frac{5}{2}$

21. $-16; 2$ Im; $3 \pm 2i$ **23.** $36; 2$ R, Q; $0, 6$

25. $-144; 2$ Im; $\frac{2 \pm 3i}{2}$ **27.** $-100; 2$ Im $-2 \pm 5i$

29. $21; 2$ R, I; $\frac{-1 \pm \sqrt{21}}{2}$; $1.79, -2.79$ **31.** $41; 2$ R, I;

$\frac{-3 \pm \sqrt{41}}{8}$; $0.43, -1.18$ **33.** $97; 2$ R, I; $\frac{-5 \pm \sqrt{97}}{4}$; $1.21,$

-3.71 **37.** 18.2 m × 23.5 m   **39.** $-7 \pm \sqrt{61}$

40. 8, −3

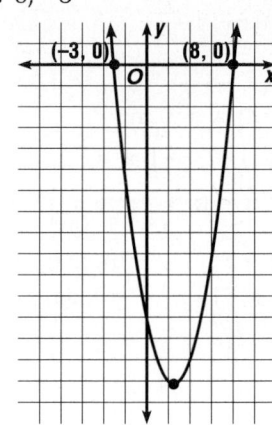

41. $12a^2 - 15a - 63$

42. $\begin{bmatrix} 1 & 1 & 1 & 10 \\ 1 & 0 & -1 & 1 \\ 1 & -1 & -1 & 0 \end{bmatrix}$

43. 11

Pages 336−338   Lesson 7-5

7. $-\frac{3}{4}, -3$ **9.** $0, -\frac{3}{5}$ **11.** $\frac{1}{15}, -\frac{4}{15}$ **13.** −3, −2

15. 5, 4 **17.** $3, -\frac{1}{2}$ **19.** $\frac{5 \pm \sqrt{17}}{4}$ **21.** $\frac{3}{4}, -6$

23. $x^2 - 6x - 16 = 0$ **25.** $2x^2 - 7x + 3 = 0$

27. $25x^2 - 4 = 0$ **29.** $x^2 - (3\sqrt{3})x + 6 = 0$ **31.** ±4 **33.** $\frac{4}{5}, -\frac{2}{3}$ **35.** $-\frac{1}{4}, -\frac{4}{3}$ **37.** $x^2 + 36 = 0$

39. $2x^2 - 2x - 3 = 0$ **41.** 4 **43.** −5 **45.** 240 ft/s

47. 64 ft/s, 48 ft **48.** $\frac{5 + i\sqrt{7}}{4}$ **49.** 13

50. $-3 + 3\sqrt{2} - \sqrt{5} + \sqrt{10}$ **51.** $(b + 7)(a + 4)$

52. $\begin{bmatrix} 1 & 0 & 0 \\ 0 & 1 & 0 \\ 0 & 0 & 1 \end{bmatrix}$ **53.** 2 hours **54.** 1 cm, 2 cm, 3 cm, 4 cm, 5 cm, 6 cm, 7 cm

Pages 342−343   Lesson 7-6

7. yes **9.** yes **11.** yes **13.** yes **15.** yes **17.** 8

19. 4 **21.** $(x^{\frac{1}{2}})^2 - 10(x^{\frac{1}{2}}) + 25 = 0$

23. $z^2(z^2 + 6z + 8) = 0$ **25.** $(r^{\frac{1}{3}})^2 - 5(r^{\frac{1}{3}}) + 6 = 0$

27. $(x^{\frac{1}{4}})^2 + 7(x^{\frac{1}{4}}) + 12 = 0$ **29.** 0, −3, −2 **31.** $0, \pm\frac{1}{4}$

33. $-1 \pm i\sqrt{3}, 2$ **35.** ±2, ±1 **37.** $5, \frac{-5 \pm 5i\sqrt{3}}{2}$

39. $w = 4$ in., $l = 7$ in., $h = 8$ in., $V = 224$ in.³

41. 27, 125 **43.** 4 **45.** $\frac{4}{9}$ **47.** 3.5 m

49. $\frac{3 \pm \sqrt{5}}{2}$ **50.** $10\sqrt{6}$ **51.**
$\begin{array}{r|rrrr} -3 & 2 & 15 & 22 & -15 \\ & & -6 & -27 & 15 \\ \hline & 2 & 9 & -5 & 0 \end{array}$

52. $(3a - 7)(2a + 5)$ **53.** A matrix I such that $A \cdot I = A$. $I_{3 \times 3} = \begin{bmatrix} 1 & 0 & 0 \\ 0 & 1 & 0 \\ 0 & 0 & 1 \end{bmatrix}$

54.

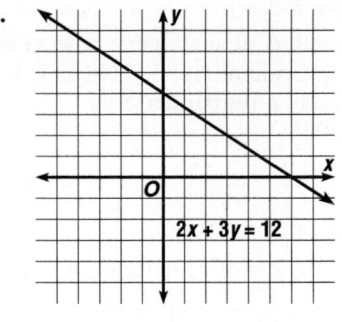

$2x + 3y = 12$

Pages 344−346   Chapter 7 Summary and Review

1. 41312432 **3.** $-7, \frac{5}{2}$

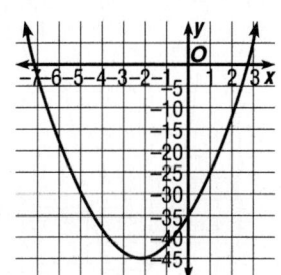

5. $\frac{3}{2}$ **7.** $\frac{1}{4}, -\frac{3}{2}$ **9.** −3, 8 **11.** −12, 8 **13.** $\frac{5 \pm i\sqrt{7}}{4}$

15. −3, 0 **17.** 16, 2 real roots; rational; $\frac{4}{7}, 0$

19. −3, 15; 12, −45 **21.** $\frac{\pm\sqrt{33}}{3}; 0, -\frac{11}{3}$

23. $x^2 + 2x - 24 = 0$ **25.** $x^2 - 10x + 34 = 0$

27. $\frac{5}{3}, -3, 0$ **29.** $4, -2 \pm 2i\sqrt{3}$ **31.** 2, −2

33. 3 feet **35.** 60.3 seconds

CHAPTER 8   QUADRATIC RELATIONS AND FUNCTIONS

Pages 354−355   Lesson 8-1

5. yes **7.** yes **9.** no **11.** no **13.** $5x^2; -7x; 2$

15. $\frac{1}{3}n^2; 0, 4$ **17.** $z^2; 3z; 0$ **19.** $9t^2; 6t; -7$

21. $f(x) = x^2 - 6x + 9$ **23.** $h(x) = 9x^2 + 12x + 4$

25. $f(x) = -16x^2 + 64x - 64$ **27.** $f(x) = 4x^2 + 8x + 14$ **29.** $g(x) = 6x^2 + 24x + 29$ **31.** $r =$ the radius; area $= \pi r^2$ **33.** $s =$ the measure of the length of a leg; area $= \frac{1}{2}s^2$ **35.** $x =$ one of the numbers; sum $= 2x^2 - 20x + 100$ **37.** $w =$ the width of the kennel; area $= 50w - w^2$

41. $I(p) = 800 + 10p - 2.5p^2$ **42.** $1(x^3)^2 + 3(x^3) - 10 = 0$ **43.** 1 or 9 **44.** 85 **45.** 0.2 **46.** $x^2 - 0.4x + 0.16 - \frac{2.864}{x + 0.4}$ **47.** 2.592×10^{10} km/day **48.** (−2, 3)

Pages 357–358 Lesson 8-2

5. 15 **7.** 0 **9.** Remainders of successive powers of 5 divided by 7 repeat in a cycle of six: 5, 4, 6, 2, 3, 1, . . . So $5^{100} \div 7$ will have a remainder of 2. **11.** 0 **13.** 420 **15.** 4 **17.** 2025

Pages 363–364 Lesson 8-3

7. $(4, 0)$, $x = 4$ **9.** $(0, 3)$, $x = 0$ **11.** $(6, 4)$, $x = 6$ **13.** $\left(\frac{1}{5}, 1\right)$, $x = \frac{1}{5}$ **15.** $y = [x - (-2)]^2 + 0$
17. $y = (x - 2)^2 + 2$ **19.** $f(x) = (x - 2)^2$, $(2, 0)$, $x = 2$ **21.** $f(x) = (x - 0)^2 + 9$, $(0, 9)$, $x = 0$
23. $f(x) = [x - (-5)]^2 - 25$, $(-5, -25)$, $x = -5$
25. $f(x) = [x - (-4)]^2 + 4$, $(-4, 4)$, $x = -4$

27.

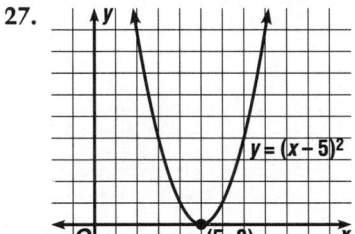

31.

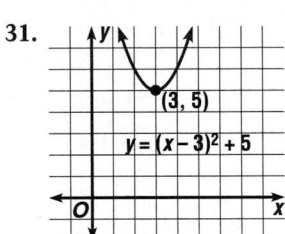

35.

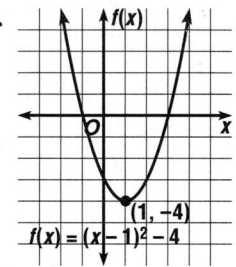

39.

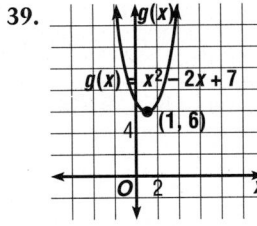

43. $(0, -5)$; $y = x^2 - 5$ **45.** $(-3, 2)$; $y = (x + 3)^2 + 2$

47a.

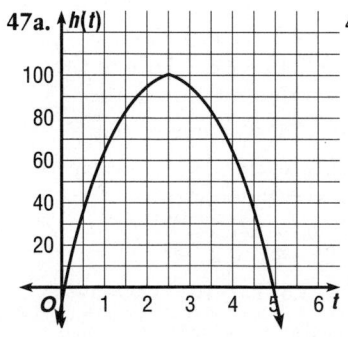

47b. 2.5 seconds; 100 feet

49. $4x^2$; $-8x$; -2 **50.** $x^2 - x - 56 = 0$ **51.** 14
52. 6 **53.** $-\frac{1}{2}$

Pages 370–372 Lesson 8-4

5. $(9, 0)$, $x = 9$, up **7.** $(0, -6)$, $x = 0$, up
9. $(-3, -1)$, $x = -3$, up **11.** $\left(-2, -\frac{4}{3}\right)$, $x = -2$, up
13. $f(x) = -2x^2 + 4$ **15.** $f(x) = (x - 2)^2 + 1$; $(2, 1)$; $x = 2$; up **17.** $f(x) = -3(x - 2)^2 + 12$; $(2, 12)$; $x = 2$; down **19.** $f(x) = 3(x - 3)^2 - 16$; $(3, -16)$; $x = 3$; up
21. $f(x) = -\frac{1}{2}(x - 5)^2 - 1$; $(5, -1)$; $x = 5$; down
23. $y = 3(x - 1)^2$ **25.** $y = -\frac{1}{2}(x + 2)^2 - 3$
27. $y = -\frac{3}{4}(x - 4)^2 + 1$ **29.** $y = 2x^2 - x$
31. $y = \frac{1}{2}x^2 - 2x - 1$

33.

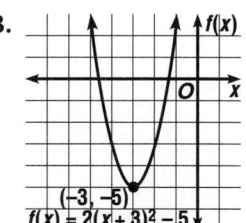

37.

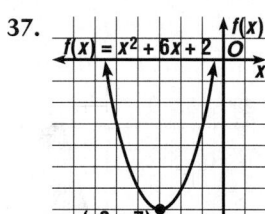

41.

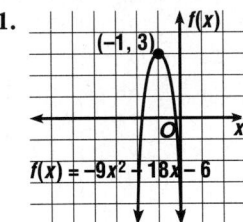

45. $(-2, 0)$, $x = -2$ **46.** $(3, -11)$, $x = 3$ **47.** 5, -5
48. $4 - 2\sqrt{3}$ **49.** $2x^2z + 3x + 5xyz$ **50.** no

51. yes **52.**

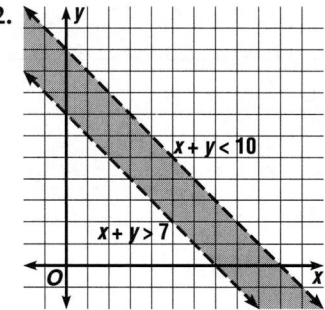

Page 372 Mid-Chapter Review

1. $g(x) = x^2 + 4x + 4$ **2.** $f(x) = 3x^2 - 30x + 79$
3. Let $n =$ one of the numbers; product $= 50n - n^2$
4. Let $l =$ the length; area $= 21l - l^2$ **5.** 9 in. × 9 in. **6.** They have the same shape, but the graph of $y = (x - 7)^2$ is shifted 7 units to the right.
7. $(2, -4)$, $x = 2$ **8.** $(-4, 0)$, $x = -4$ **9.** $(-2, 6)$, $x = -2$ **10.** $(0, 0)$, $x = 0$ **11.** $y = x^2 + 3$
12. $f(x) = (x + 3)^2 - 6$, $(-3, -6)$, $x = -3$, up
13. $f(x) = -9(x + 1)^2 - 1$, $(-1, -1)$, $x = -1$, down

Pages 375–378 Lesson 8-5

5a. $x + 20$ **5b.** $x(x + 20)$ or $x^2 + 20x$

5c.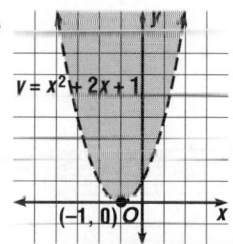

5d. -10 and 10 **7.** $18, 18$ **9.** $\dfrac{37}{2}, \dfrac{37}{2}$ **11.** $-8, -8$
13. 6 in. by 6 in.; 36 sq. in. **15.** 60 ft $\times$ 30 ft
17. \$350 **19.** \$3.50 **21.** 12.5 cm by 12.5 cm by
5 cm **23.** 16 inches **25.** 60 ft; 64 ft; 4 seconds
29a. 78 feet **29b.** between 5 and 6 seconds
29c. about 3 seconds **29d.** 126 feet **30.** 1
31. $f(x) = (x - 3)^2$ **32.** 16 **33.** $14 + 5i$
34. $(3x - 2)^2$

Pages 381–382 Lesson 8-6

5. yes **7.** yes **9.** yes **11.** no

13. 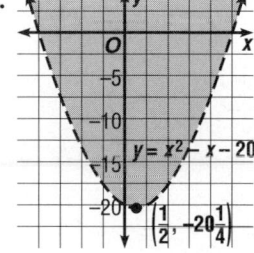   **17.**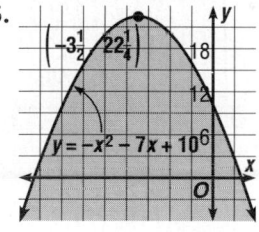

21.   **25.**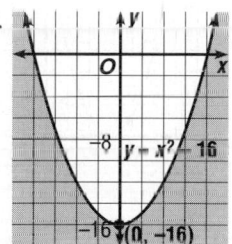

31. Substitute values for x and $f(x)$. $30 \neq -90.3$. The
ball hits the ground about 337 ft from the plate.
32. 175 **33.** $-20, 20$ **34.** $8 \pm 3\sqrt{6}$ **35.** $\dfrac{2\sqrt{2}}{3}$
36. 1.32×10^9 kilometers

Pages 386–387 Lesson 8-7

5. both > 0 or both < 0 **7.** one ≥ 0 and one ≤ 0
9. both > 0 or both < 0 **11.** one ≥ 0 and one ≤ 0
13. one ≥ 0 and one ≤ 0 **15.** $\{x \mid x \leq 3 \text{ or } x \geq 6\}$

17. $\{x \mid x > -2 \text{ or } x < -9\}$ **19.** $\{n \mid n \geq 2.5 \text{ or } n \leq -3.8\}$
21. $\{q \mid q \geq 4 \text{ or } q \leq -6\}$ **23.** $\left\{b \mid -\dfrac{3}{2} < b < 2\right\}$
25. $\{p \mid -1 \leq p \leq 5\}$ **27.** $\{w \mid w \leq 0 \text{ or } w \geq 2\}$
29. $\{d \mid d \leq -4 \text{ or } d \geq 7\}$
31. $\left\{x \mid x > \dfrac{5\sqrt{2}}{2} \text{ or } x < \dfrac{-5\sqrt{2}}{2}\right\}$ **33.** $\varnothing$ **35.** {all reals}
37. $\left\{x \mid x > \dfrac{1}{3} \text{ or } x < -2\right\}$
39. $\left\{t \mid \dfrac{-1 - \sqrt{10}}{2} < t < \dfrac{-1 + \sqrt{10}}{2}\right\}$ **47.** no
49. Let n = number of decreases; $-17 \leq n \leq 2$

50. yes **51.**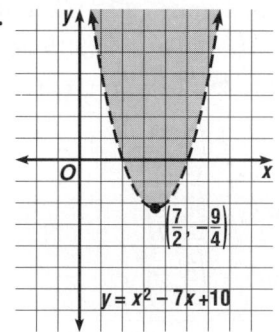

52. $x^2; 3x; -2$ **53.** 64 **54.** $3a\sqrt{5} - 3\sqrt{ab} +$
$\sqrt{30ab} - b\sqrt{6}$ **55.** $(a - b + 4)(a + b - 4)$
56. 823

Pages 388–390 Chapter 8 Summary and Review

1. $f(x) = x^2 + 4x + 4$ **3.** $3x^2; 2x; -1$
5. $y = (x - 7)^2$ **7.**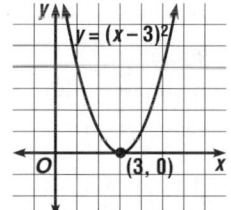

9. $f(x) = (x - 1)^2$, $(1, 0)$, $x = 1$
11. $f(x) = (x - 1)^2 + 3$, $(1, 3)$, $x = 1$, up
13. $f(x) = -2(x + 10)^2 + 210$, $(-10, 210)$, $x = -10$,
down **15.** $\dfrac{5}{2}, -\dfrac{5}{2}$

17. 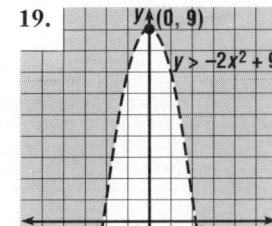   **19.**

21. $\{x | -1 < x < 10\}$ **23.** $\left\{a | a \geq \dfrac{3}{4} \text{ or } a \leq -2\right\}$ **25.** 1
27. \$13.75   **29.** 10 seconds

CHAPTER 9   THE DISTANCE AND MIDPOINT FORMULAS

Pages 398–399   Lesson 9-1
5. 3 units   **7.** 8.9 units   **9.** $16\dfrac{19}{24}$ units   **11.** 13 units
13. 4 units   **15.** $\sqrt{58}$ units   **17.** $\sqrt{2}$ units
19. $\sqrt{4.58}$ units   **21.** 16 units   **23.** 5 or -1 **25.** 7.1 or 13.1   **27.** (12, 5)   **29.** $\left(\dfrac{9}{16}, \dfrac{5}{4}\right)$ **31.** (10, -7)

33. midpoint of $\overline{MN} = \left(\dfrac{1}{2}, \dfrac{13}{2}\right)$

midpoint of $\overline{MO} = \left(5, \dfrac{1}{2}\right)$

midpoint of $\overline{NO} = \left(\dfrac{5}{2}, 2\right)$

35. $AB = \sqrt{(-3 - (-1))^2 + (0 - 4)^2}$
$= \sqrt{(-2)^2 + (-4)^2}$
$= \sqrt{4 + 16}$
$= \sqrt{20}$
$AC = \sqrt{(-3 - 1)^2 + (0 - (-2))^2}$
$= \sqrt{(-4)^2 + 2^2}$
$= \sqrt{16 + 4}$
$= \sqrt{20}$

39. $5\dfrac{7}{8}$ inches   **40.** $\{x | x > -3 \text{ or } x < -7\}$
41. $\{a | a \geq 1.5 \text{ or } a \leq -2.5\}$ **42.** $\pm i\sqrt{5}, \pm\sqrt{6}$
43. $x = 2, y = 3$ **44.** $3(m + 2p)(m^2 - 2mp + 4p^2)$
45. $4x - y = 11; 5y = 25$

Pages 403–404   Lesson 9-2
5. 4   **7.** 25   **9.** $\dfrac{49}{4}$ **11.** $y = -\dfrac{1}{4}x^2$
13. $y = (x + 2)^2 - 3$
15. $(-2, 3)$; $x = -2$; $\left(-2, 3\dfrac{1}{4}\right)$; $y = 2\dfrac{3}{4}$; up; 1

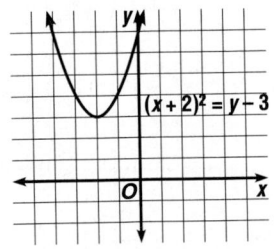

19. (4, 2); $x = 4$; (4, 3); $y = 1$; up; 4

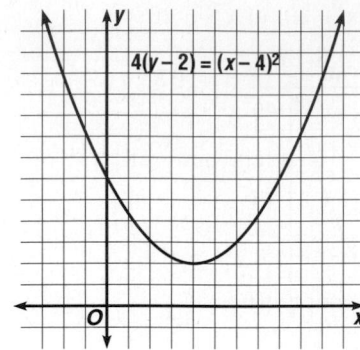

23. (4, 8); $y = 8$; (3, 8); $x = 5$, left; 4

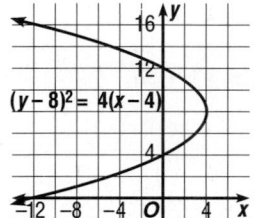

27. (3, 5); $x = 3$; $\left(3, 5\dfrac{1}{2}\right)$; $y = 4\dfrac{1}{2}$; up; 2

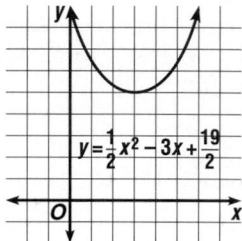

31. (4, 2); $x = 4$; $\left(4, 2\dfrac{1}{12}\right)$; $y = 1\dfrac{11}{12}$; up; $\dfrac{1}{3}$

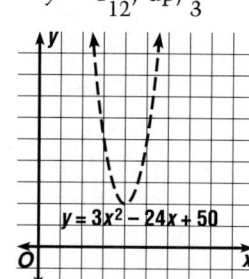

35. $x = \dfrac{1}{4}(y - 2)^2 + 5$

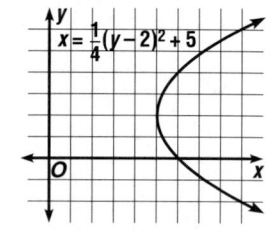

39. $x = \dfrac{1}{10}(y + 3)^2 + 7\dfrac{1}{2}$

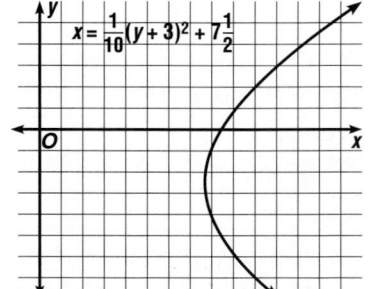

43. $x = \frac{1}{4}(y - 3)^2 + 4$ **47.** $y = \frac{1}{6}(x + 1)^2 + \frac{1}{2}$

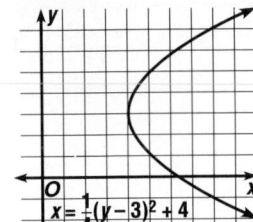

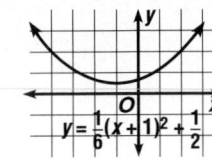

49. $\left(0, 2\frac{1}{2}\right)$ **51.** $\sqrt{37}$ units   **52.** $\left(\frac{3}{2}, -\frac{5}{2}\right)$ **53.** 18 cm

54. 88 and 89 or −88 and −89   **55.** $\frac{3x^{\frac{1}{5}}}{x}$

56. $a^3 - 6a^2 - 7a + 60$ **57.** yes, −24, 5

Pages 406–408   Lesson 9-3

7. parabola   **9.** circle   **11.** parabola   **13.** (0, 3), 6

15. $\left(-2, \frac{2}{3}\right)$, $2\sqrt{2}$ **17.** (0, −5), $\frac{9}{8}$

19. (−5, 0), 8

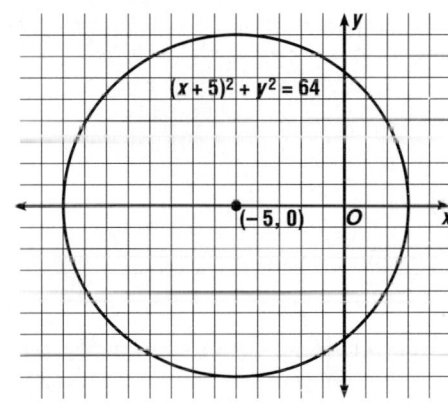

23. (0, −2), 2   **27.** (−2, 1), 9

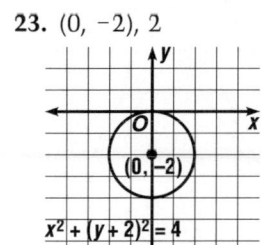   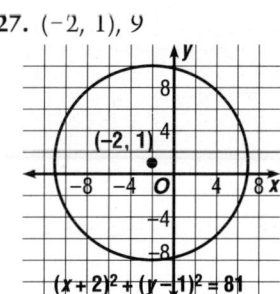

31. (9, 9), $\sqrt{109}$

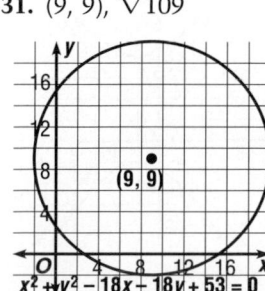

35. (2, 0), $\sqrt{13}$

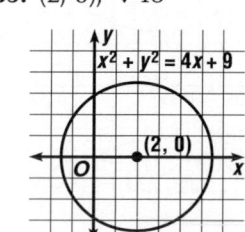

39. $\left(0, -\frac{9}{2}\right)$, $\sqrt{19}$ **43.** (−1, 0), $\sqrt{11}$

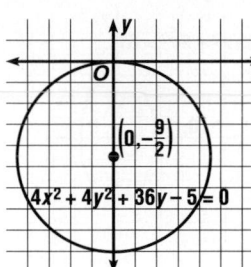

45. $x^2 + (y - 3)^2 = 49$ **47.** $(x + 1)^2 + (y + 5)^2 = 4$
49. $(x + 3)^2 + (y + 9)^2 = \frac{25}{36}$ **51.** $(x - 3)^2 +$
$(y - 3)^2 = 18$ **53.** $(x + 1)^2 + (y - 6)^2 = 45$
55. $(x - 4)^2 + (y + 3)^2 = 16$ **57.** $(x - 4)^2 +$
$(y - 16)^2 = 169$ **59.** no   **60.** $x = \frac{1}{6}y^2$

61. $y = -\frac{1}{4}(x - 2)^2 + 5$ **62.** yes

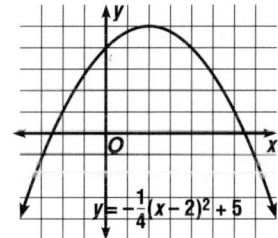

63. $1(y^{-3})^2 + 4(y^{-3}) - 32 = 0$ **64.** $\frac{-2\sqrt{3}}{9}$

65. $2(2k + 3)(k + 5)$ **66.** $\begin{bmatrix} \frac{1}{8} & 0 \\ -\frac{1}{32} & -\frac{1}{4} \end{bmatrix}$

Pages 413–415   Lesson 9-4

5. (0, 0), V   **7.** (11, −8), V   **9.** $\frac{x^2}{12} + \frac{y^2}{28} = 1$

11. $\frac{(x + 3)^2}{9} + \frac{(y - 5)^2}{4} = 1$ **13.** $\frac{(x - 3)^2}{16} + \frac{(y + 2)^2}{9} = 1$

15. (0, 0); $(\pm 2\sqrt{5}, 0)$;   **17.** (0, 0); $(0, \pm\sqrt{7})$;
12, 8   8, 6

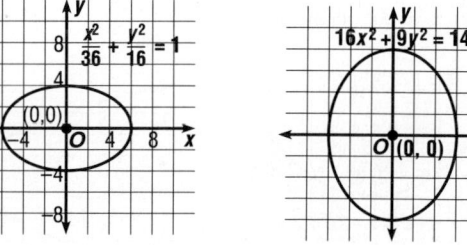

19. $\frac{x^2}{36} + \frac{y^2}{20} = 1$

21. $(0, 0)$; $(\pm 4, 0)$; 10, 6   **25.** $(0, 0)$; $(0, \pm\sqrt{6})$; 6, $2\sqrt{3}$

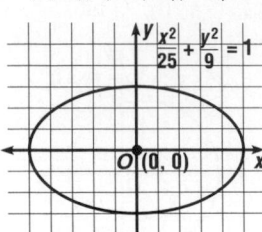

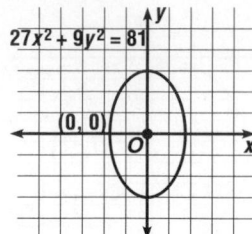

29. $(-8, 7)$; $(-8 \pm\sqrt{57}, 7)$; 22, 16

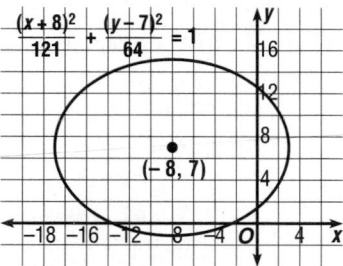

33. $(2, 2)$; $(2, 4)$, $(2, 0)$; $2\sqrt{7}$, $2\sqrt{3}$

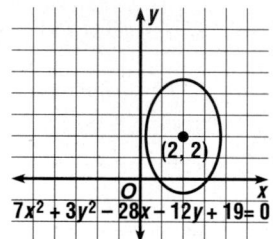

35. $\dfrac{x^2}{36} + \dfrac{y^2}{100} = 1$ **37.** $\dfrac{(x-5)^2}{64} + \dfrac{4(y-4)^2}{81} = 1$

39. $\dfrac{(x+2)^2}{16} + \dfrac{(y-3)^2}{36} = 1$ **43.** $(x-6)^2 + (y-2)^2 = 25$ **44.** $(x-1)^2 + (x-5)^2 = 26$

45. $f(x) = (x+1)^2 - 3$; $(-1, -3)$; $x = -1$; up   **46.** no

47. 98   **48.** 19, 27, 35, 43, 51

Page 415   Mid-Chapter Review

1. 10 units   **2.** $2\sqrt{10}$ units   **3.** $(4, -4)$ **4.** $\left(\dfrac{3}{2}, 6\right)$

5. $(0, 0)$; $x = 0$; $(0, -3)$; $y = 3$; down; 12   **6.** $(3, -2)$; $y = -2$, $(5, -2)$; $x = 1$; right; 8

7. $y = \dfrac{1}{8}(x-3)^2 + 3$ **8.** $x = -\dfrac{1}{2}(y-4)^2 + \dfrac{1}{2}$

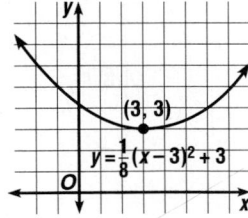

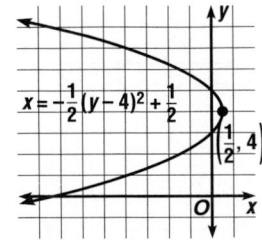

9. parabola   **10.** circle   **11.** $(0, 0)$, $3\sqrt{3}$ units

12. $(-3, 1)$, 9 units   **13.** $\dfrac{x^2}{14} + \dfrac{y^2}{28} = 1$

14. $\dfrac{(x-1)^2}{5} + \dfrac{(y-2.5)^2}{10} = 1$ **15.** $\dfrac{(x-3)^2}{32} + \dfrac{(y-1)^2}{81} = 1$

Pages 420–422   Lesson 9-5

5. ellipse   **7.** hyperbola   **9.** hyperbola

11. $\dfrac{x^2}{5} - \dfrac{y^2}{10} = 1$ **13.** $\dfrac{(y-1)^2}{168} - \dfrac{(x-2)^2}{42} = 1$

15. $(\pm 4, 0)$; $(\pm 2\sqrt{5}, 0)$; $\pm\dfrac{1}{2}$ **17.** $(\pm 3, 0)$; $(\pm\sqrt{13}, 0)$; $\pm\dfrac{2}{3}$

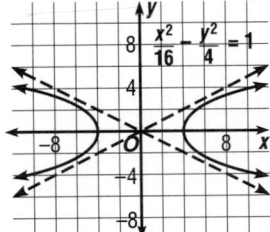

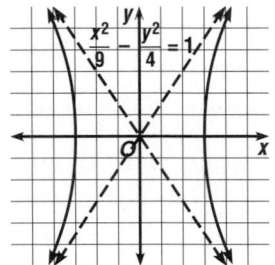

19. $\dfrac{x^2}{4} - \dfrac{y^2}{12} = 1$ **21.** $\dfrac{(x-3)^2}{4} - \dfrac{(y+5)^2}{9} = 1$

23. $\dfrac{y^2}{4} - \dfrac{x^2}{21} = 1$

25. $(\pm 6, 0)$; $(\pm\sqrt{37}, 0)$; $\pm\dfrac{1}{6}$ **29.** $(\pm 2, 0)$; $(\pm\sqrt{13}, 0)$; $\pm\dfrac{3}{2}$

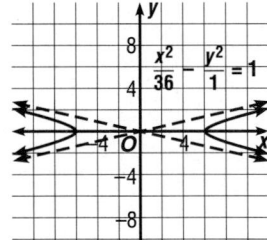

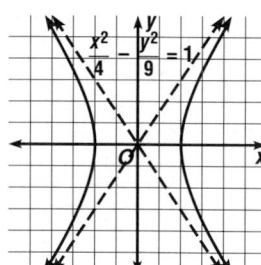

33. $(0, \pm 10)$; $(0, \pm 2\sqrt{61})$; $\pm\dfrac{5}{6}$ **37.** $(2, -2)$, $(2, 8)$; $(2, 3 \pm\sqrt{41})$; $\pm\dfrac{5}{4}$

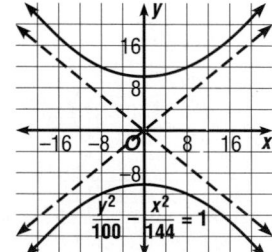

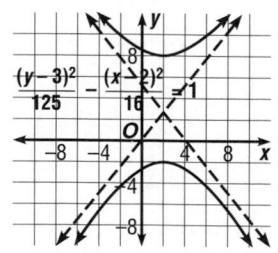

41. $(4 \pm 2\sqrt{5}, -2)$; $(4 \pm 3\sqrt{5}, -2)$; $\pm\dfrac{\sqrt{5}}{2}$

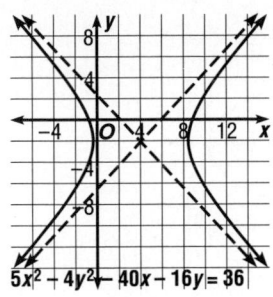

$5x^2 - 4y^2 - 40x - 16y = 36$

45. $\dfrac{(y-4)^2}{4} - \dfrac{(x-5)^2}{36} = 1$

47.

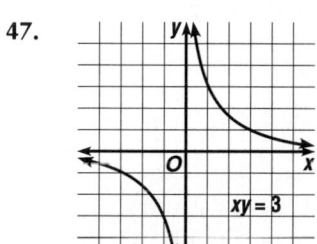

$xy = 3$

51.

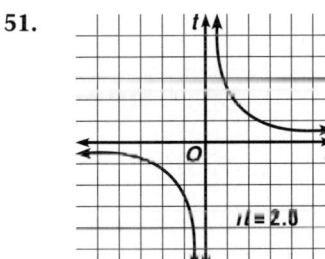

$H = 2.0$

52. $(0, 0)$, $(0, \pm\sqrt{21})$;
10 units, 4 units

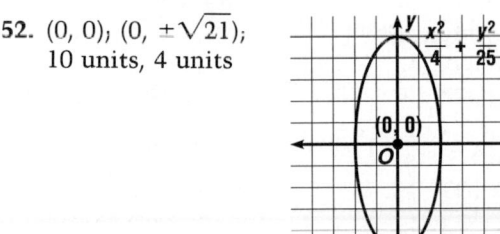

$\dfrac{x^2}{4} + \dfrac{y^2}{25} = 1$

$(0, 0)$

53. $\dfrac{(x-1)^2}{25} + \dfrac{(y-4)^2}{9} = 1$ **54.** $\{x \mid -\sqrt{6} \le x \le \sqrt{6}\}$

55. $-2, -3$ **56.** $\dfrac{5^{\frac{1}{3}}}{5^{\frac{1}{3}}}$

Page 424 Lesson 9-6

5. 20 **7.** 239

Pages 429–431 Lesson 9-7

5. parabola **7.** hyperbola **9.** hyperbola **11.** ellipse

13. $y = \dfrac{1}{8}x^2$; parabola

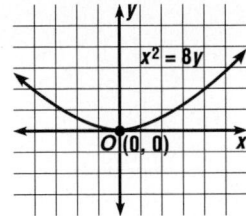

$x^2 = 8y$

$O (0, 0)$

17. $\dfrac{y^2}{16} - \dfrac{x^2}{8} = 1$;
hyperbola

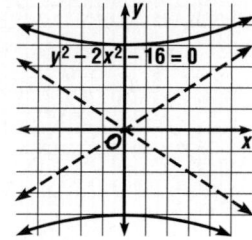

$y^2 - 2x^2 - 16 = 0$

21. $\dfrac{(y-5)^2}{16} - \dfrac{(x+1)^2}{4} = 1$; hyperbola

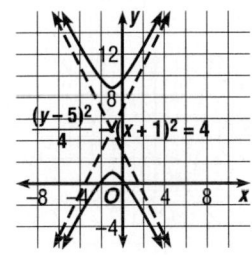

$\dfrac{(y-5)^2}{4} - (x+1)^2 = 4$

25. $\dfrac{(x-3)^2}{25} + \dfrac{(y-1)^2}{9} = 1$; ellipse

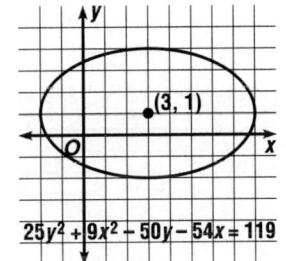

$(3, 1)$

$25y^2 + 9x^2 - 50y - 54x = 119$

29. isolated point

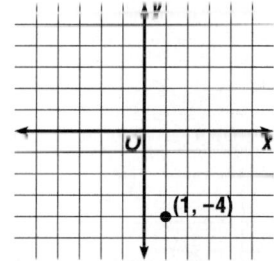

$(1, -4)$

33a. ellipse **33b.** hyperbola **33c.** circle
33d. ellipse **33e.** parabola **33f.** degenerated case
35. $\dfrac{(y-2)^2}{36} - \dfrac{(x+2)^2}{64} = 1$

36.

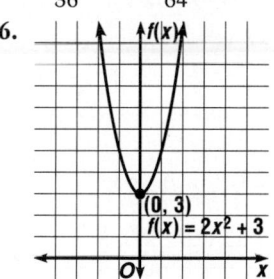

$(0, 3)$

$f(x) = 2x^2 + 3$

37. $3, -\dfrac{1}{3}$ **38.** $-3rs$

Pages 434–436   Lesson 9-8

5.

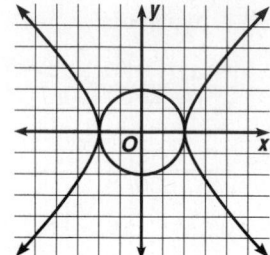

9. $(\pm 2\sqrt{3}, 2)$

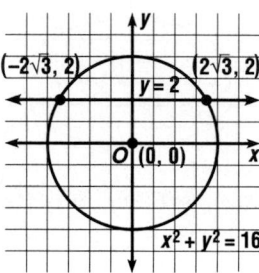

13. $(-1, 1)$, $(2, 4)$

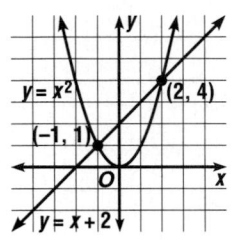

17. $(\pm 5.2, 6)$

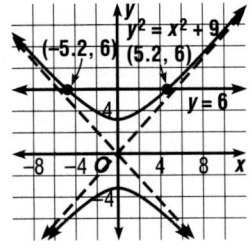

21. $(4, -1.5)$, $(-3, 2)$

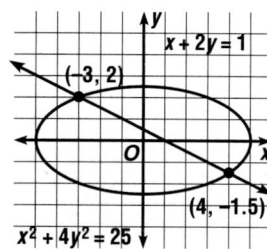

25. no solution

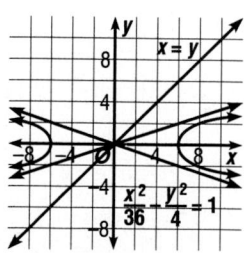

29. $(3, 0)$, $(-3, -6)$

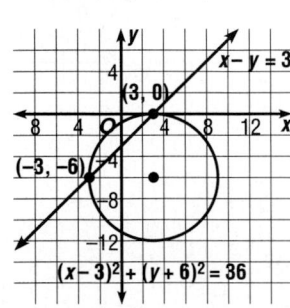

33. (0.3) $(\pm 2.4, -2.8)$

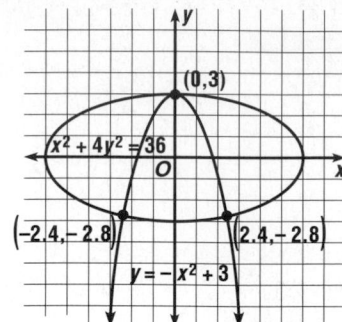

37. no solution

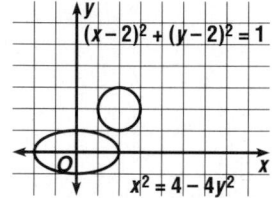

43. approximately $(13.6, 21)$ or $(13.6, -21)$: that is 13.6 miles east and 21 miles north or south

44. hyperbola

45. $\dfrac{x^2}{4} + \dfrac{y^2}{1} = 1$; ellipse

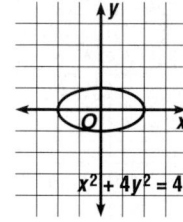

46. yes   **47.** $-7, 2$ **48.** $p^2 + 5p - 7 + \dfrac{8}{2p - 3}$

Pages 441–443   Lesson 9-9

5. elimination; $(2, \pm\sqrt{3})$, $(-2, \pm\sqrt{3})$

7. substitution; no solutions   **9.** substitution; $(0, 9)$, $(0, -9)$, $\left(-\dfrac{1}{2}, \pm\dfrac{\sqrt{323}}{2}\right)$ **11.** $x^2 + y^2 \geq 25$, $x^2 + y^2 \leq 100$ **13.** $(2, 4)$, $(-1, 1)$ **15.** $(3, 0)$, $(-5, -4)$ **17.** $(-4, -3)$, $(-3, -4)$ **19.** $(\pm 3\sqrt{3}, 6)$

21. no solutions   **23.** no solutions   **25.** $\left(4, -\dfrac{3}{2}\right)$, $(-3, 2)$ **27.** $(-1, -1)$, $(2, -4)$ **29.** $(1, \pm 5)$, $(-1, \pm 5)$ **31.** $(3, 7)$, $(8, 4)$

33.

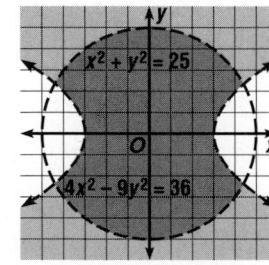

37.

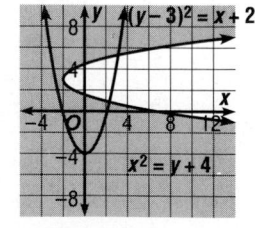

41.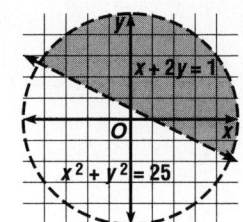

45.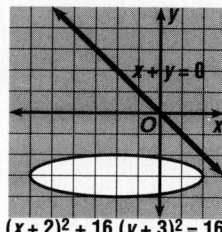

51. 20 ft by 24 ft **53.** no solution **54.** (8, 0); $x = 8$;
up **55.** 36 miles **56.** $-7, -\frac{1}{2}$
57. $-5 - 2\sqrt{6}$ **58.** $32x^3y^6$

Pages 444–446 Chapter 9 Summary and Review

1. $6\sqrt{2}$ **3.** $\sqrt{16.85}$ **5.** $\left(2, -\frac{7}{2}\right)$ **7.** $\left(1, \frac{3}{2}\right)$

9. (0, 0); $y = 0$; (−2, 0); **13.** (0, 0); ($\pm\sqrt{7}$, 0); 8, 6
$x = 2$; left; 8

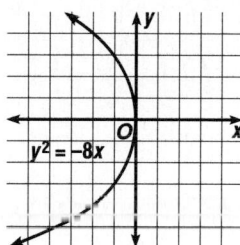 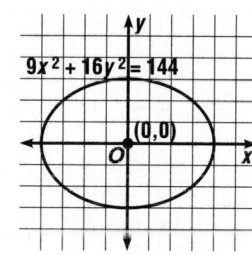

17. parabola **19.** circle

21. (−2, 0), (2, 4) **23.** (1.6, 2.4),
(−2.6, 6.6)

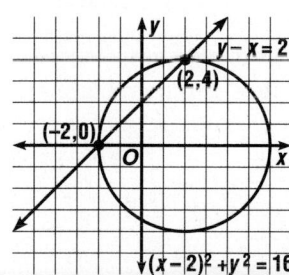

25.

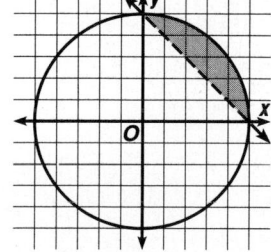

27. $(x - 12)^2 + (y - 25)^2 = 2304$ **29.** a hyperbola
with foci ($\pm\sqrt{13}$, 0), vertices (±3, 0), and asymptotes
$y = \pm\frac{3}{2}$

Pages 454–456 Lesson 10-1

5. yes, 5 **7.** yes, 0 **9.** no **11.** no **13.** yes, 3
15. 10 **17.** 25 **19.** even, 4 **21.** odd, 2 **23.** −47
25. −52 **27.** −21 **29.** 36 **31.** 575 **33.** $\frac{305}{6}$
35. $2x + 2h - 3$ **37.** $x^2 + 2xh + h^2 - 2x - 2h + 5$
39. $x^3 + 3hx^2 + 3h^2x + h^3 + 4x + 4h$
41. $2x^3 + 6hx^2 + 6h^2x + 2h^3 - x^2 - 2hx - h^2 + 4$
43. $4x^2 + 20$ **45.** $x^3 + \frac{x^2}{4} - 8$ **47.** even, 0
49. $6x + 34$ **51.** $2x^2 + 24x + 18$ **53.** $-5x - 8$
55. $-x^3 - 9x^2 - 9x - 4$ **59.** $65,892
60. (1, −2), (−1, −2)
61. 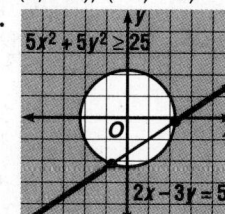 **62.** $f(x) = x^2 - 2x + 7$ (1,6)

63. no **64.** $x = 3, y = 0; x = 0, y = -\frac{3}{2}i$ **65.** 45 fish

Pages 462–464 Lesson 10-2

7. 5, 4 **9.** 6, 5 **11.** 12 **13.** 0
15. $(x^3 - 8x^2 + 2x - 1) - (x^2 - 9x + 11)(x + 1) - 12$; no
17. $(x^4 - 16) = (x^3 + 2x^2 + 4x + 8)(x - 2) + 0$; yes
19. $(6x^3 + 9x^2 - 6x + 2) = (6x^2 - 3x)(x + 2) + 2$; no
21. $(4x^4 - 2x^2 + x + 1) = (4x^3 + 4x^2 + 2x + 3)(x - 1) + 4$; no **23.** 11, 5
25. −23, −2 **27.** 31, 1 **29.** $x - 3, x - 1$ **31.** $x - 1,$
$x + 2$ **33.** $x - 2, x^2 + 2x + 4$ **35.** $2x - 3, 2x + 3,$
$4x^2 + 9$ **37.** $(x + 1)^2(x - 1)(x^2 + 1)$ **39.** 3 **41.** 1, 4
43a. $A = 1000(1 + r)^6 + 1000(1 + r)^5 + 1000(1 + r)^4$
$+ 1200(1 + r)^3 + 1200(1 + r)^2 + 2000(1 + r)$
43b. $8916.76 **45.** −22 **46.** $3x^2 - 6x - 9$
47. (−4, 0); 7 **48.** $\{y|5 \le y \le 12\}$
49. $\frac{13}{3}, -\frac{13}{3}$ **50.** 34 **51.** $\begin{bmatrix} 28 & 0 \\ 21 & -7 \end{bmatrix}$

Pages 466–467 Lesson 10-3

5. 70 **7.** Darcy - English, Janna - sociology,
Ray - Math **9a.** a square **9b.** $\frac{x}{5}$ square units
11. one-fourth **13.** cube 1: 0, 1, 2, 6, 7, 8; cube 2:
1, 2, 0, 3, 4, 5. Nine can be formed by an
upside-down 6.

Pages 473–474 Lesson 10-4

5. $f(-x) = -3x^5 + 7x^2 + 8x + 1$
7. $f(-x) = 4x^4 + 3x^3 + 2x^2 + x + 1$ **9.** 0; 3 or 1;
0 or 2 **11.** 1; 3 or 1; 0 or 2 **13.** 2 or 0; 2 or 0; 0, 2,
or 4 **15.** 0; 1; 2 **17.** 5, 3, or 1; 5, 3, or 1; 0, 2, 4, 6,

19. $4, 1 + i, 1 - i$ **21.** $-\dfrac{3}{2}, 1 + 4i, 1 - 4i$

23. $2i, -2i, \dfrac{i}{2}, -\dfrac{i}{2}$ **25.** $2 + 3i, 2 - 3i, -1$ **27.** $3 - 2i,$
$3 + 2i, -1, 1$ **29.** $f(x) = x^3 - 3x^2 + 4x - 12$
31. $f(x) = x^4 + 2x^3 + 7x^2 + 30x + 50$ **33.** $f(x) =$
$x^6 - 2x^5 + 15x^4 - 26x^3 + 62x^2 - 72x + 72$
35. 5 cm by 12 cm by 2 cm   **37.** 0, 30   **38.** $y = -\dfrac{x^2}{16}$
39. $f(x) = x^2 + 6; (0, 6), x = 0$ **40.** 681,177,600 or
6.811776×10^8

Pages 474   Mid-Chapter Review

1. -210 **2.** $6a^6 - 3a^4 + 4a^2 - 9$ **3.** $6x^3 + 15x^2 +$
$16x - 2$ **4.** $x - 3, x - 2$ **5.** $2x + 7, x + 5$ **6.** 24,
32, 68, 76   **7.** 2 or 0; 1; 0 or 2   **8.** 1; 1; 2   **9.** $f(x) =$
$x^3 - 3x^2 + 4x - 2$ **10.** $f(x) = x^4 + 7x^3 + 13x^2 -$
$23x - 78$

Pages 478–480   Lesson 10-5

5. $\pm1, \pm2$ **7.** $\pm1, \pm2, \pm3, \pm6$ **9.** $\pm1, \pm2, \pm5, \pm10$
11. $\pm1, \pm2, \pm4, \pm\dfrac{1}{3}, \pm\dfrac{2}{3}, \pm\dfrac{4}{3}$ **13.** $\pm1, \pm5$ **15.** $\pm1,$

$\pm2, \pm3, \pm6, \pm9, \pm18$ **17.** $\pm1, \pm2, \pm\dfrac{1}{2}, \pm\dfrac{1}{3}, \pm\dfrac{1}{6}, \pm\dfrac{2}{3}$
19. $\pm1, \pm\dfrac{1}{2}, \pm\dfrac{1}{4}, \pm2, \pm3, \pm\dfrac{3}{2}, \pm\dfrac{3}{4}, \pm6$ **21.** $-5, -6, 10$
23. $-1, -1, 2$ **25.** 0, 9   **27.** $\dfrac{1}{2}, -\dfrac{1}{3}, -2$ **29.** 1, -1

31. $2, -3, -3$ **33.** -6 **35.** $0, 2, -2$ **37.** 6 units by 8

units by 3 units   **39.** $\dfrac{2}{3}, \dfrac{-3 \pm \sqrt{17}}{4}$ **41.** $-2, \dfrac{4}{3}, \dfrac{-3 \pm i}{2}$

43. $3, \dfrac{2}{3}, -\dfrac{2}{3}, \dfrac{-3 \pm \sqrt{13}}{2}$
47. radius = 1 in. and height = 5 in.   **48.** 2 or 0; 1; 2
or 4   **49.** $f(x) = x^3 - 2x^2 + 5x + 26$
50. $(\pm3, 0)$ **51.** yes

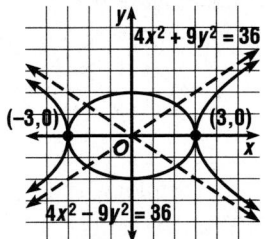

Pages 484–485   Lesson 10-6

5a. $f(-4) = 138, f(-3) = 19, f(-2) = -6, f(-1) = 3,$
$f(0) = 10, f(1) = 3, f(2) = -6, f(3) = 19, f(4) = 138$
5b. -3 and $-2, -2$ and $-1, 1$ and $2, 2$ and $3; -2.6,$
$-1.2, 1.2, 2.6$ **5c.** negative between -2.5 and -1.2
and between 1.2 and 2.5; positive between -1.2 and
1.2, less than -2.5 and greater than 2.5
5d. minimums at 2 and -2, maximum at 0

5e.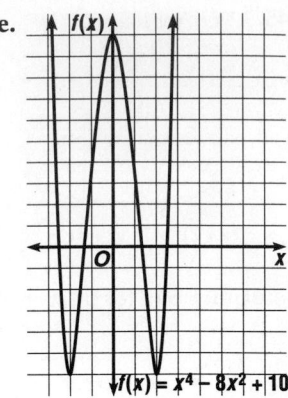

7. 0.6   **9.** 1.6, $-1.3, -2.4$ **11.** -1 **13.** no real zeros

15. 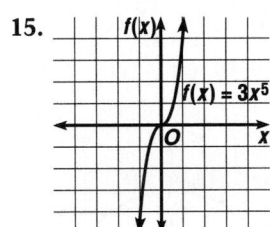   **19.**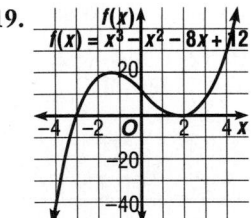

23.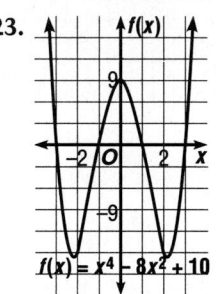

27. $-3.6, -1.6, -0.7, 0.6, 1.3$

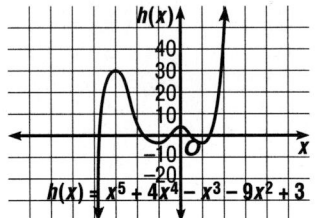

31. -2.0

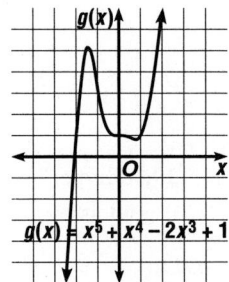

33b. 0 **33c.** There are none. **33d.** The ends of an even degree graph both point up or down and the ends of an odd degree function point in opposite directions. **35.** 0.56 centimeters **36.** CDT - compact disks; CD - tapes; T - compact disks and tapes **37.** 30 and 30 **38.** $x^2(y + 5)(y - 5)$ **39.** no

Pages 489–490   Lesson 10-7

5. 9, 6, 12 **7.** 20, 2, 0 **9.** −234, 0, 2 **11.** 10, 6
13. 64, 64 **15.** −7, 11 **17.** 10x, 10x **19.** x, x
21. $|x - 3|, |x| - 3$ **23.** 4 **25.** 12 **27.** 16 **29.** $9x^2$
31. $g \circ f = \{(1, 0), (0, 1)\}$ **35.** $140

36.
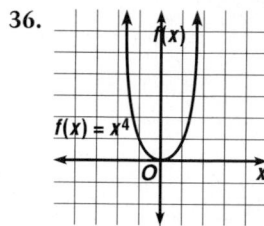

37. 1, −1, 1.7, −1.7 **38.** $(x - 6)^2 + (y - 1)^2 = 20$
39. 190

Pages 494–495   Lesson 10-8

5. {(−2, −1), (−2, 3), (4, 1), (6, 0)}, no
7. {(4, 2), (1, −3), (8, 2)}, yes
9. {(11, 6), (7, −2), (3, 0), (3, −5)}, no
11. $f^{-1}(x) = x + 5$ **13.** $x = 8$ **15.** $f^{-1}(x) = 2x - 4$
17. $y = \pm\sqrt{x + 9}$

19.
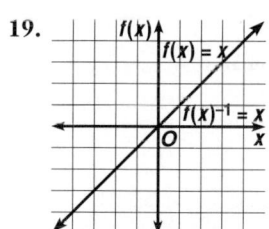
23.
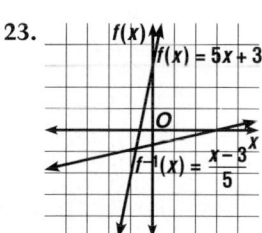

27.
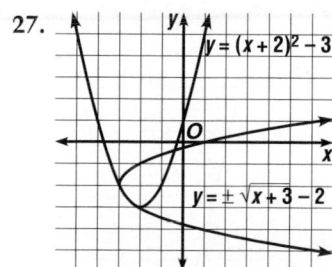

29. yes **31.** yes **33.** no **35.** yes **37.** no
39. $I(m) = 280 + 0.03m$; $4000 **41a.** yes
41b. yes **41c.** no **42.** $3x - 3$
43. $g \circ f = \{(2, 5), (3, -7), (6, -3)\}$; $f \circ g$ does not exist
44. no, because of the variable in the denominator

45. $\dfrac{x^{\frac{2}{3}}}{x - 1}$ **46.** $a^3 - a^2 + 2a - 2$

Pages 496–498   Chapter 10 Summary and Review

1. $6x - 9$ **3.** $x^2 + 2xh + h^2 - x - h$ **5.** $x + 2$,
$x + 2$ **7.** 3 or 1; 1; 2 or 0
9. 0; 0 or 2; 4 or 2 **11.** $-\dfrac{1}{2}$,
3, 4 **13.** −3, 2, 4

15. 0.8 See graph
at right.
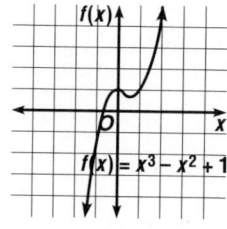

17. $[f \circ g](x) = 6x + 7$, $[g \circ f](x) = 6x + 1$ **19.** $f \circ g$
does not exist, $g \circ f = \{(2, 5), (-1, -1), (3, 2)\}$ **21.** yes
23. Craig: Julliard; Vanessa: DeVry; Devin: Case
Western Reserve; Anita: Judson **25.** 9 by 11 by 25
units

CHAPTER 11   RATIONAL POLYNOMIAL EXPRESSIONS

Pages 508–509   Lesson 11-1

5. $x = 3, y = 0$ **7.** $x = 1, x = -5, y = 0$

9.
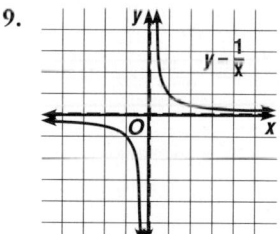
13.
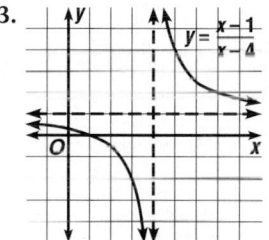

17.
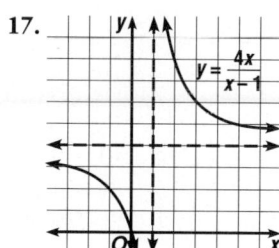
21.
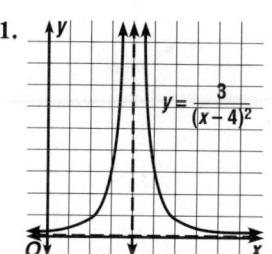

25.
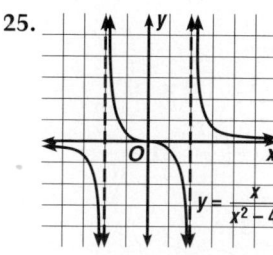

29a.

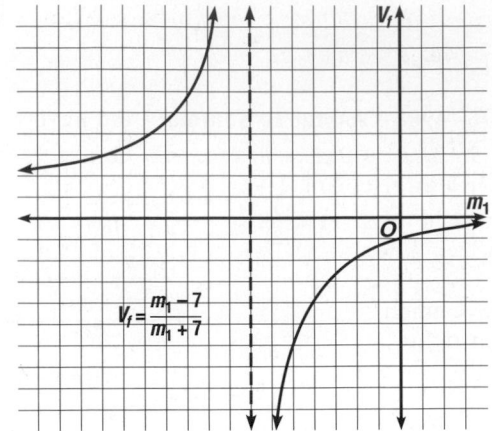

$$V_f = \frac{m_1 - 7}{m_1 + 7}$$

29b. $V_f \approx -0.83$ m/s   **30.** $f^{-1}(x) = \dfrac{2x - 2}{5}$ **31.** (0, 0), 5

32. -3 **33.** $1 \pm \dfrac{\sqrt{11}}{2}$ **34.** $(x + 3y)(x - 1)$

Pages 513–515   Lesson 11-2

5. direct, $-\dfrac{1}{6}$ **7.** direct, $\dfrac{1}{2}$ **9.** direct, 4   **11.** joint, k

13. $y = 112$ **15.** $y = 120$ **17.** $y = 36$ **19.** $r = \dfrac{84}{11}$

21. 118.5 km   **23.** 1.125   **25.** $y = 48$ **27.** $x = \dfrac{100}{7}$

29. Heavenly Hog   **31.** $g = 15$ **33.** $y = 32$

37a. $I = \dfrac{6}{R}$ **37b.** 6   **39.** 44 mph

40.

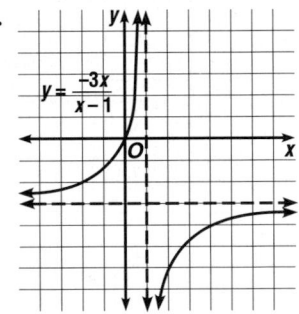

$$y = \frac{-3x}{x - 1}$$

41. -1, 3, -4 **42.** $(-3, -1)$, $(5, 7)$

43. $f(x) = x(55 - x)$ **44.** $25\sqrt{2}$ **45.** $\begin{bmatrix} -4 & 0 & 9 \\ 16 & -4 & 14 \\ 7 & -1 & 19 \end{bmatrix}$

46. Gladys 30, Maria 10

Pages 520–521   Lesson 11-3

7. $3x^2y^2$, $-\dfrac{y^3}{6x}$ **9.** $4x^5y$, $-2xy^2$ **11.** $(m + 5)$, $\dfrac{1}{2}$

13. x, $\dfrac{4}{x - 1}$ **15.** y **17.** $\dfrac{3a^2}{2bc}$ **19.** $-\dfrac{ad^2}{2}$ **21.** $\dfrac{5x^3}{3y^2}$

23. $\dfrac{ac^4d}{b}$ **25.** a **27.** 1   **29.** -1 **31.** $-\dfrac{y}{w^2 - y^2}$

33. $\dfrac{y - 2}{x - 4}$ **35.** $\dfrac{x - 2}{x + 2}$ **37.** $\dfrac{w - 3}{w - 4}$ **39.** 5, 12, 13 inches

41. $\dfrac{a(a + 2)}{a + 1}$ **43.** -1 **45.** 1; An equal number of men and women favor the tax.   **47.** $x = 4$ **48.** \$11,680
49. hyperbola   **50.** $11 - i$, $1 + 3i$, $32 - 7i$
51. Complex, Real, Rational, Integer, Whole, Natural

Page 521   Mid-Chapter Review

1.

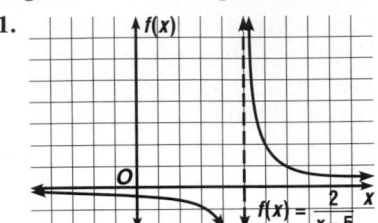

$$f(x) = \frac{2}{x - 5}$$

3.

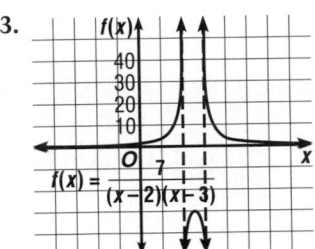

$$f(x) = \frac{7}{(x - 2)(x - 3)}$$

4. $x = 24$ **5.** $m = 22$ **6.** $\dfrac{22a^3}{5bc}$ **7.** $\dfrac{7}{2}$ **8.** $(m + 4)(3m + 4)$

Pages 525–526   Lesson 11-4

5. 78   **7.** 2000   **9.** $x(x - 2)(x + 2)$

11. $3(x + 5)(x - 3)$ **13.** $\dfrac{7 + 9a}{ab}$ **15.** $\dfrac{3t^2 - 19t + 36}{t - 5}$

17. $\dfrac{-12x + 21xy - 4y}{6x^2y}$ **19.** $\dfrac{13}{y - 8}$ **21.** $\dfrac{y^2 - 2y + 2}{y - 1}$

23. $\dfrac{x(x - 9)}{(x + 3)(x - 3)}$ **25.** $\dfrac{5x + 16}{(x + 2)^2}$ **27.** $\dfrac{2(a - 2)}{3(a + 1)}$

29. $\dfrac{-4x^2 - 5x - 2}{(x + 1)^2}$ **31.** 0   **33.** $\dfrac{x^3 + 4x^2 + 7x + 17}{x^2 - 4}$

35. $\dfrac{2x^2 + x - 4}{(x - 1)(x - 2)}$ **37.** $\dfrac{2}{2x - 5}$

41. $\dfrac{-3x - 26}{(x + 2)(x - 3)}$ mph

43. $\dfrac{x^2 + 10x - 8}{x(x - 2)}$ **44.** $\dfrac{1 - 2x}{3x + 1}$

45. 27

46. $\{x \mid x \le 1 \text{ or } x \ge 7\}$ **47.** 4

48. See graph at right.

49. about 28 in.

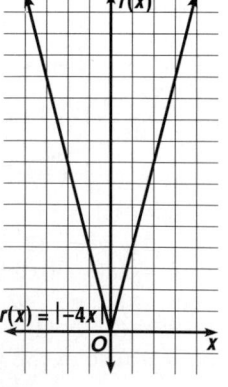

$$r(x) = |-4x|$$

Pages 529–530   Lesson 11-5

5. $2x, 0$ **7.** $7(2 + m), -2$ **9.** $x^2, 0$ **11.** $-3, \frac{1}{6}$ **13.** 2

15. 5 **17.** $-6, 1$ **19.** $2, 6$ **21.** $-6, \frac{3}{2}$ **23.** $\frac{-3 + 3\sqrt{2}}{2}$

25. 14 **27.** $-6, -2$ **29.** $\varnothing$ **31.** $0, -4$ **35a.** 5

35b. 6.15 **36.** $\frac{11x}{13y^2}$ **37.** $\frac{3 + 4x}{x}$ **38.** $\frac{45b - 28a}{20ab}$

39. $x = 1, x = 4, y = 0$ **40.** $(2, \pm\sqrt{21})$

41. $(0, 1), \left(-\frac{5}{2}, \frac{9}{4}\right)$ **42.** $\left(\frac{5 + \sqrt{5}}{2}, \frac{5 + \sqrt{5}}{2}\right)$

43.

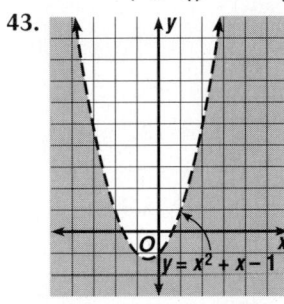

44. $42 - 6\sqrt{2} + 7\sqrt{3} - \sqrt{6}$
45a. Sample: $d = 25f$ **45b.** about 11 gallons

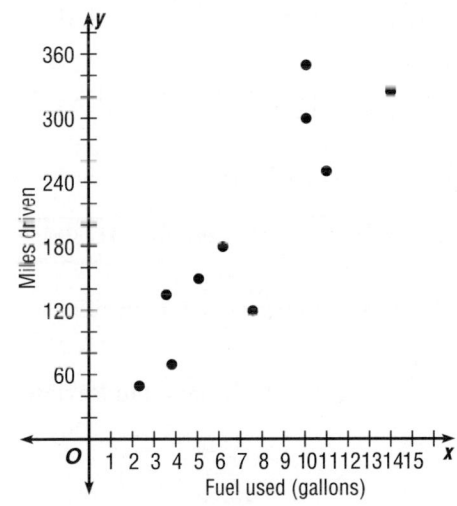

Page 534   Lesson 11-6

5.

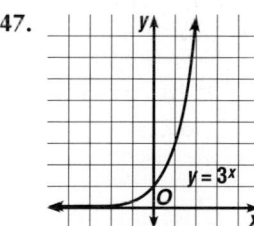

7. $\frac{1}{10}$ **9.** 5 cows, 1 pig, 94 geese

Pages 537–539   Lesson 11-7

5. $\frac{x}{6} - \frac{x}{18} = 1$ **7.** $r = \frac{524}{9}$ **9.** 20 h   **11.** 19

13. 550 mph   **15.** 5 tons   **17.** $\frac{7}{13}$ **19a.** \$550

19b. \$44   **23.** 1 **24.** $\frac{13}{30a}$ **25.** $\frac{7y^2}{8}$ **26.** $f(x) = x^3 -$
$6x^2 + 9x + 50$ **27.** $2\sqrt{53}$ **28.** $5s^2 - 9s - 2$

Pages 540–542   Chapter 11 Summary and Review

1.

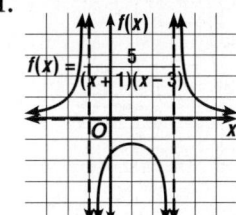

5.

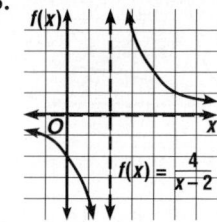

7. $y = -37.5$ **9.** $x = 8$ **11.** $x = 0.192$

13. $\frac{ay - 2a - 3y + 6}{a - x}$ **15.** $6b(a - b)$ **17.** $\frac{2}{n - 3}$

19. $\frac{28a - 27b}{12ab}$ **21.** $\frac{7}{5(x + 1)}$ **23.** $\frac{18}{y - 2}$ **25.** $\frac{25b + 16}{24b}$

27. $\frac{10}{9}$ **29.** 3 **31.** $\frac{3}{2}$ **33.** $6\sqrt{2}$ meters   **35.** 8, 10

CHAPTER 12   EXPONENTIAL AND LOGARITHMIC FUNCTIONS

Pages 549–550   Lesson 12-1

5. 1.6 **7.** 2.1 **9.** 18.9 **11.** 2^3 **13.** -3 **15.** -2 **17.**
$-\frac{3}{2}$ **19.** 0.5 **21.** 3.0 **23.** 2.4 **25.** 81 **27.** $2^{5\sqrt{7}}$

29. x^4 **31.** $-\frac{1}{2}$ **33.** -2 **35.** $-\frac{1}{3}$ **37.** 2 **39.** 3

41. -22 **43.** 2 **45.** $1, -3$

47.

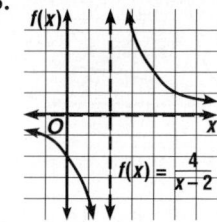

51a. $y = 100 \times (1.08)^x$ **51b.** \$342.59   **52.** 360 mL
53. $52, -23$ **54.** yes; $0 \le 4^2 - 7$ **55.** 41 by 43 units

56. $\frac{3x^{\frac{1}{3}}y - 2x}{xy}$ **57.** $(b - 1)(3b - 2y)$

Pages 556–557   Lesson 12-2

7. $\log_{10} 1000 = 3$ **9.** $2^6 = 64$ **11.** $9^{\frac{3}{2}} = 27$ **13.** 3

15. 2 **17.** 256 **19.** 2 **21.** -2 **23.** $\frac{1}{2}$ **25.** 6 **27.** 9

29. 18 **31.** $\frac{1}{25}$ **33.** 5 **35.** 4 **37.** no solution

39. ± 8

41.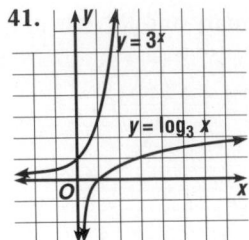

43.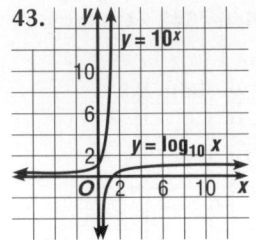

45. $\log_4 4 + \log_4 16 \stackrel{?}{=} \log_4 64$ **47.** $\log_2 8 \cdot \log_8 2 \stackrel{?}{=} 1$
$1 + 2 = 3$ $3 \cdot \frac{1}{3} = 1$
51. 12 hours **52.** $11^{4\sqrt5}$ **53.** $x + 5; \frac{1}{3}$ **54.** 3 or 1; 0;
0 or 2 **55.** $(0, \pm9); (0, \pm3\sqrt{13}; \pm\frac{3}{2}$ **56.** 18, -120
57. 58 **58.** 679

Pages 561–562   Lesson 12-3

5. $2\log_5 x + 2\log_5 y$ **7.** $\log_2 r + \frac{1}{2}\log_2 t$ **9.** 16
11. 2 **13.** 5.614 **15.** 1.222 **17.** -0.415 **19.** 6.755
21. -1.193 **23.** 7 **25.** 6 **27.** 44 **29.** 3 **31.** 10
33. 2 **35.** 5 **37.** $\frac{1}{3}$ **39.** $\frac{x^4}{2}$ **41.** $\frac{1}{2}[n + 1]$
43a. $\text{pH} = 6.1 + \log_{10} B - \log_{10} C$ **43b.** a very
weak base **43c.** 7.197 **44.** 1 **45.** neither exist
46. $4 \pm i\sqrt6$ **47.** $(q + s)(3p + q - s)$
48. $\{x|x > 4 \text{ or } x < -4\}$

Pages 565–566   Lesson 12-4

5. 0.7582 **7.** 2.3 **9.** 2.9032; 2 **11.** $-1.2441; -2$
13. $-0.5302; -1$ **15.** 167.8 **17.** 0.5513 **19.** 0.0107
21. 0.1851 **23.** 1.9925, 1, 0.9925 **25.** 2.9156, 2,
0.9156 **27.** 0.7345, 0, 0.7345 **29.** $-2.3010, -3$,
0.6990 **31.** 3, 3, 0 **33a.** $10^{5.3}$ or about 199,526
times more intense **33b.** $10^{6.9-4.3} = 10^{2.6}$ or about
398 times stronger **34.** 72 **35.** $-\frac{2}{3}$ **36.** 3, -5, $-\frac{5}{2}$
37. $2 \times 2; -20$

Page 566   Mid-Chapter Review

1. 2 **2.** -7 **3.** 3, -1 **4.** 2 **5.** $\frac{1}{2}$ **6.** -3 **7.** 24
8. 8 **9.** 3 **10.** 2.3598 **11.** 0.8033 **12.** 0.0062
13. $10^{8.3-6.9} = 10^{1.4}$ or about 25 times more intense

Pages 569–570   Lesson 12-5

5. 1.454 **7.** 1.530 **9.** 0.4549 **11.** 1.976 **13.** 1.598
15. 9.290 **17.** -0.6106 **19.** 1 **21.** 1.682
23. 0.1866 **25.** 133.1 **27.** 41.32 **29.** 42.92
33a. -0.000385 **33b.** approximately 0.0213 grams
34. 2.5440; 2; 0.5440 **35.** $\frac{5x - 13}{(x - 2)(x - 3)}$
36. $(2, \pm\sqrt3), (-2, \pm\sqrt3)$ **37.** $\{x|-6 \le x \le 6\}$
38. sofa–$700, love seat–$350, coffee table–$180

Pages 572–573   Lesson 12-6

5a. 5 rolls **5b.** 4.48 rolls **5c.** Yes, since she can't
buy 4.48 rolls, she must buy 5. **7.** grandfather,
father, and son each receive $7 **9.** 7, 6, 3, 2, 0
(alphabetical order)
11. sample answers are:

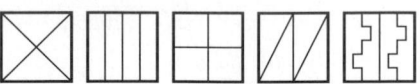

Pages 576–578   Lesson 12-7

5. $\frac{\log 100}{\log 8}$; 2.2146 **7.** $\frac{\log 169}{\log 4}$; 3.7004
9. $\frac{\log 34}{2 \log 3}$; 1.6049 **11.** $\frac{-\log 22}{\log 3}$; -2.8136 **13.** 1.683
15. 2.064 **17.** 1.090 **19.** 0.594 **21.** 1.937
23. 4.7549 **25.** 3.8394 **27.** 2.8446 **29.** 2.3059
31. ±2.0397 **33.** ±2.2325 **35.** 3.2838 **37.** -2.1507
39. 1.1201 **41.** 2.9172 **43.** 0.3011 **45.** 2.3475
47. 5 years, 5 months **49a.** $485.95
49b. $14,996.47 **50.** 11.26 **51.** $f(x) = (x + 8)^2 + 3$;
$(-8, 3); x = -8$ **52.** $\frac{1}{5}, -\frac{3}{5}$ **53.** 2.72 seconds
54. $\frac{wt^3}{9}$ **55.** domain: $\{-8, 0, 1, 9\}$; range: $\{-3, 0, 3\}$;
yes **56.** 21 games

Pages 583–585   Lesson 12-8

5. 7.27 **7.** 11.1 **9.** about 11 years, 6 months
11. 1.3863 **13.** 15.28 years **15a.** 28.78 years
15b. 57.56 years **17.** 20.56% **19.** 59 weeks
23. -0.000385 **25.** 11 **27.** 48 **29.** 81 **31.** 28
33. 1.277 **34.** $\pm1, \pm2, \pm4, \pm\frac{1}{3}, \pm\frac{2}{3}, \pm\frac{4}{3}$ **35.** x^2,
$18x$, 81 **36.** 10 in. by 12 in. **37.** 15.4 cm
38. $\{x|x < 2\}$

Pages 586–588   Chapter 12 Summary and Review

1. $3^{2\sqrt2}$ **3.** $7^{2\sqrt2-2\sqrt3}$ **5.** -1 **7.** $-\frac{7}{4}$ **9.** $\log_7 343 = 3$
11. $\log_4 1 = 0$ **13.** $4^3 = 64$ **15.** $6^{-2} = \frac{1}{36}$ **17.** 7
19. 3 **21.** 3 **23.** $\frac{1}{4}$ **25.** 3 **27.** $-4, 3$ **29.** 1.5165
31. 2.2618 **33.** 48 **35.** 14 **37.** 1 **39.** -3
41. -2.5029 **43.** 0.0003609 **45.** 0.8329 **47.** 7.21
49. 5.7286 **51.** ±2.2452 **53.** -4.8188 **55.** 0.5416
57. 13.30 years **59.** 6.76 years

CHAPTER 13   SEQUENCES AND SERIES

Page 595   Lesson 13-1

5. 1, 1, 2, 3, 5, 8, 13, 21, 34, 55, 89, 144, 233, 377,
610, 987, 1597, 2584, 4181, 6765 **7.** 12 **9.** $299.18
11. 110 cm²

Pages 599–601   Lesson 13-2

5. 4, 7, 10, 13, 16   **7.** 16, 14, 12, 10, 8   **9.** $\frac{3}{4}, \frac{1}{2}, \frac{1}{4},$

$0, -\frac{1}{4}$ **11.** 17, 21, 25, 29   **13.** −13, −18, −23, −28

15. $\frac{7}{2}, \frac{9}{2}, \frac{11}{2}, \frac{13}{2}$ **17.** −241   **19.** 46   **21.** $\frac{11}{2}$ **23.** 416
25. 19   **27.** 8   **29.** 30, the midpoint   **31.** −50
33. −37
35. $-\frac{13}{3}, -\frac{2}{3}$

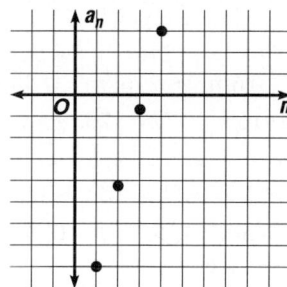

39. 56, 42, 35

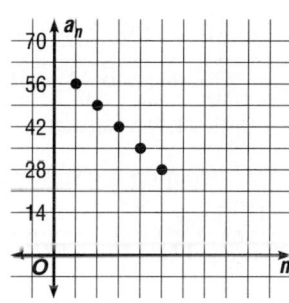

41. 19, 16.5, 14, 11.5   **43.** 2, 9, 16   **47.** 780 ft
48. aceg, acegi, acegik   **49.** 5
50. $\frac{(3x-2)(x+1)(2x-3)}{(x+2)(x-3)(2x+1)}$ **51.** −3388

52.

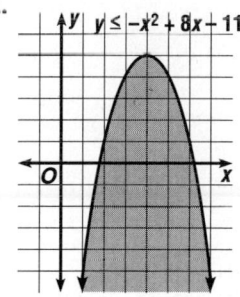

53a. 900 W, 1400 G   **53b.** $1060

Pages 605–607   Lesson 13-3

5. 120   **7.** 10,500   **9.** 240   **11.** 240   **13.** 10,100
15. 1155   **17.** 856   **19.** 104   **21.** 162   **23.** −220
25. 26   **27.** 5555   **29.** −45   **31.** 552   **33.** $\frac{45}{2}$
35. 1, 5, 9   **37.** 6, 36, 66   **41.** No, because the
auditorium only has 1065 seats.   **42.** 510
43. $x = -1, 8$ **44.** 77   **45.** (3, 1, 6)   **46.** 37, 37, 14

Page 607   Mid-Chapter Review

1. 3   **2.** 1, 3, 4, 7, 11, 18, 29, 47   **3.** 9   **4.** 416
5. 552   **6.** −420   **7.** $491,700

Pages 612–614   Lesson 13-4

5. yes, 5   **7.** yes, $\frac{3}{2}$ **9.** no   **11.** 3, −6, 12, −24
13. 54, 162   **15.** 27, 9   **17.** 2, −4   **19.** 27, −9, 3, −1

21.

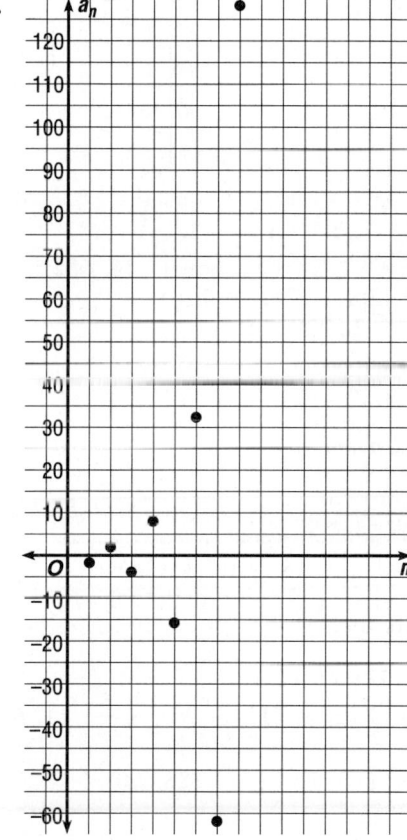

23. 32   **25.** 3   **27.** 1

29. 2, 4

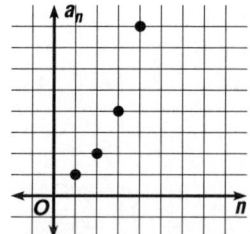

33. 14, 28, 56 or −14, 28, −56

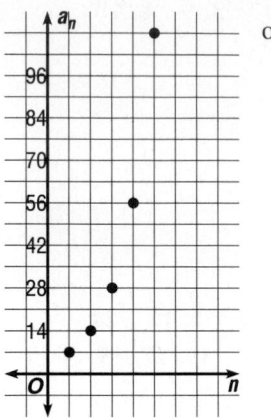 or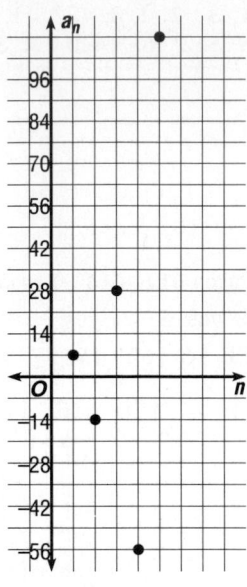

37. $a_n = 36\left(\dfrac{1}{3}\right)^{n-1}$ **41.** 34.9% **43.** $\dfrac{1}{1024}$ or approximately 0.098% of the original **44.** 632.5 **45.** −3, 2, 5 **46.** $2m^3 + 7m^2 + 4m - 4$ **47.** $(a^2 + 4b^4)(a - 2b^2)(a + 2b^2)$

48.

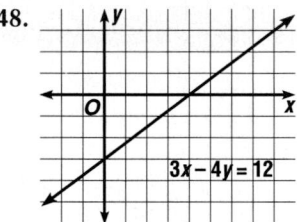

49. 186.84 square inches

Pages 618–619 Lesson 13-5

5. 9; −2; −72; 4 **7.** 2; 4; 512; 5 **9.** $-\dfrac{1}{4}, \dfrac{5}{64}$ **11.** 63

13. 189 **15.** $\dfrac{61}{9}$ **17.** 176 **19.** 1,328,600

21. 114,681 **23.** 10.66 **25.** $\dfrac{11}{16}$ **27.** 300 **29.** $\dfrac{781}{5}$

31. 5.99 **33.** $\dfrac{4095}{256}$ **35.** $\displaystyle\sum_{n=1}^{6} 2(-3)^{n-1}$ **37.** 4 **39.** 4

41. 8 **45.** 127 **47.** $\dfrac{1}{3}$, 1 **48.** 0.2392 **49.** 3 hours 7 minutes **50.** $n = m$ **51.** (2, 1)

Pages 623–624 Lesson 13-6

5. 12, $\dfrac{1}{4}$, 16 **7.** 1, $-\dfrac{1}{3}, \dfrac{3}{4}$ **9.** 48, $\dfrac{1}{3}$, 72 **11.** $\dfrac{7}{9}$ **13.** $\dfrac{152}{999}$

15. 4 **17.** 14 **19.** 27 **21.** $\dfrac{9}{4}$ **23.** 9 **25.** 8

27. does not exist **29.** $\dfrac{100}{11}$ **31.** $\dfrac{31}{99}$ **33.** $\dfrac{41}{90}$

35. $4 + 3 + \dfrac{9}{4}$ **37.** $9 - 3 + 1$ **39.** 800 feet
41. −7.5 **42.** ±6, 12, ±24 **43.** 52 **44.** 22 **45.** all reals

Pages 629–630 Lesson 13-7

5. 362, 880 **7.** 90 **9.** 120 **11.** 5, 108a **13.** 6, $-10b^2z^3$ **15.** $y^7 + 7y^6p + 21y^5p^2 + 35y^4p^3 + 35y^3p^4 + 21y^2p^5 + 7yp^6 + p^7$ **17.** $r^6 - 6r^5m + 15r^4m^2 - 20r^3m^3 + 15r^2m^4 - 6rm^5 + m^6$
19. $81r^4 + 108r^3y + 54r^2y^2 + 12ry^3 + y^4$
21. $16x^4 + 96x^3y + 216x^2y^2 + 216xy^3 + 81y^4$
23. $64m^6 - 576m^5 + 2160m^4 - 4320m^3 + 4860m^2 - 2916m + 729$ **25.** $\dfrac{1}{729}y^6 + \dfrac{2}{27}y^5 + \dfrac{5}{3}y^4 + 20y^3 + 135y^2 + 486y + 729$ **27.** $35x^3y^4$
29. $-2,088,281,250a^4b^7$ **31.** $k + 3$ **33.** $(k + 2)!$
35. $26\dfrac{1}{3}\%$ **37a.** 1, 4, 6, 4, 1 **37b.** 1, 12, 66, 220, 495, 792, 924, 792, 495, 220, 66, 12, 1 **37c.** 1, −6, 15, −20, 15, −6, 1 **37d.** 1, −10, 45, −120, 210, −252, 210, −120, 45, −10, 1 **38.** $\dfrac{4}{3}$ **39.** about 300 years
40. $\dfrac{x + 1}{(2x - 3)(3x - 2)}$ **41.** 2 or 0 positive real; 3 or 1 negative real; 0, 2, or 4 imaginary **42.** 24 hours

Pages 632–634 Chapter 13 Summary and Review

1. 38 **3.** −11 **5.** 12 **7.** 10 **9.** −3, 1, 5 **11.** 2322
13. 1330 **15.** $\dfrac{64}{3}$ **17.** −108, 324 **19.** 1452 **21.** $\dfrac{21}{8}$

23. −6 **25.** $-\dfrac{16}{13}$ **27.** $\dfrac{3}{4}$ **29.** $a^3 + 3a^2b + 3ab^2 + b^3$
31. $243r^5 + 405r^4s + 270r^3s^2 + 90r^2s^3 + 15rs^4 + s^5$
33. $-13,107,200x^9$ **35.** 220 feet **37.** $284,766

CHAPTER 14 STATISTICS

Pages 640–641 Lesson 14-1

5a. 3,400,000 **5b.** 90%

5c.

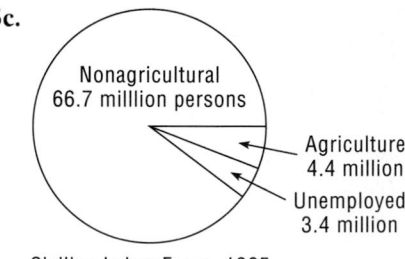

Civilian Labor Force, 1965

7. $\dfrac{8}{9}$ **9.** 6, −2 **11.** 24 times **13.** 11, 101, 131, 151, 181, 191, 313, 353, 373, 383, 727, 757, 787, 797, 919, and 929

Pages 645–647 Lesson 14-2

5a. 299 **5b.** 277 **5c.** 11 **5d.** 280, 290

7a.

Stem	Leaf
6	8
7	0 3
●	5 6 8 9
8	0 0 1 1 1 2 2 2
●	

7 | 3 represents 73 games.

7b. Ewing, Pippen, and Lewis
7c. Robinson **7d.** 14 **7e.** 81 or 82 **7f.** 6

9g.

Stem	Leaf
16	1
17	3 6
18	2 3
19	
20	3 4 9
21	0 2 8 8
22	5
23	3
24	
25	
26	3

16 | 1 represents 1610 points.

9h. Jordan **9i.** Tripucka **9j.** 1027 **9k.** 5
9l.

Stem	Leaf
2	3 3 3 3 3
●	5 6 6 6 7 7 7 8 9
3	3

2 | 3 represents 23 points.
9m. Jordan **9n.** Johnson and McHale **9o.** 10
9p. 22.5 and 26.5 **9q.** 9

11.

Stem	Leaf
4	2 3
●	6 6 7 8 9 9
5	0 0 1 1 1 1 2 2 4 4 4 4
●	5 5 5 5 6 6 6 7 7 7 7 8
6	0 1 1 1 2 4 4
●	5 8 9

4 | 2 represents 42 years old.
Most of the presidents were 50–59.

12.

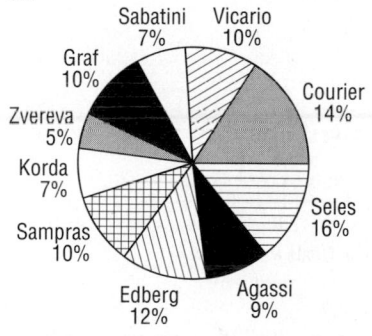

13. 10, 12.2, 14.4, 16.6, 18.8 **14.** 2 **15.** 121, 11
16. $f(x) = 45x^2 - 60x + 24$ **17.** 36 and 16

Pages 651–652   Lesson 14-3

5. 4; 4; 3 **7.** 9; 9; 9 **9.** 43; no mode; 30.6
11. 3.45; 2.1; 3.6 **13.** 12; 12 and 13; about 12.3

15. 99; no mode; 91 **17.** 4; 6; about 3.7 **19.** $5.00;
$5.00; $5.42 **21a.** mean; It is higher. **21b.** mode; It
is lower and is what most employees make. It reflects
the most representative worker. **25.** 205 miles

26. $y = \dfrac{1}{8}x^2 + 1$ **27.** $\begin{bmatrix} 30 & 36 \\ 0 & -12 \end{bmatrix}$ **28.** $-\dfrac{11}{3}, \dfrac{25}{3}$

Pages 655–657   Lesson 14-4

5. 150 **7.** 79 **9.** 16 **11.** 37, 39, 47; 10 **13.** 50.5,
59, 68.5; 18 **15.** 19; 2, 5, 7; 5 **17.** 170; 1025, 1075,
1125; 100 **19.** 480; 160, 265, 345; 185 **21.** 20
23. none **25.** none **27.** $370; $177.50, $237, $294;
$116.50; $500 **29.** 102; 21, 34, 60; 39; 121 **31.** 49;
40; 50.3 **32.** 2; 3; 162; 5 **33.** $f^{-1}(x) = \dfrac{x + 4}{3}$

34. $\dfrac{3\sqrt{5} - 3}{4}$ **35.** $-6a^4b^4 + 12a^5b^3 - 21a^4b^2$

36. $c = 10\left(t - \dfrac{1}{2}\right) + 35$

Page 657   Mid-Chapter Review

1.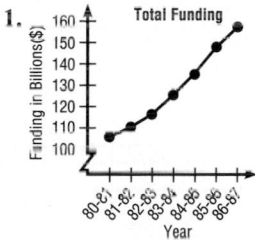

3.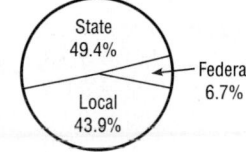

Sources of Funding for 1985-1986

4.

rounded	stem	truncated
6	4	5 9
7 3 0	5	2 7
5 1	6	1 5 9
0	7	

Using rounded data,
1|6| represents
$60,500,000,000 to
$61,499,999,000.

Using truncated data,
|6|1 represents
$61,000,000,000 to
$61,999,999,000.

5.

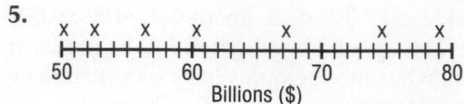

6. $9,105,569,000; no mode; $9,154,106,000
7. $52,878,386,000; $110,191,257,000,
$126,055,419,000; $149,004,882,000; $38,813,625,000;
none

21. $(-8, 3); 5$

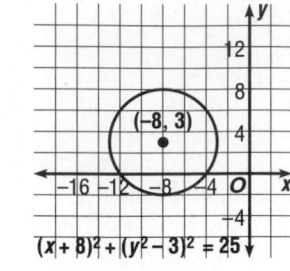

$(x + 8)^2 + (y^2 - 3)^2 = 25$

Pages 660–662   Lesson 14-5

5a. 20   **5b.** 26   **5c.** 25%   **5d.** 21 and 28   **7a.** 210
7b. 670, 700   **7c.** 50%   **7d.** 75%

9.

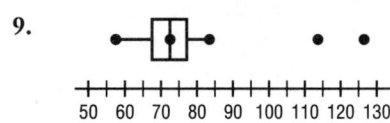

LV = 57.7, LQ = 63.05, M = 72.35,
UQ = 77.55, GV = 83.3,
outliers: 113.3, 126.7

11.

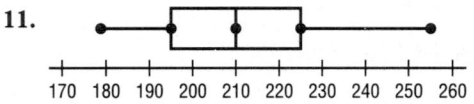

LV = 178, LQ = 195, M = 210, UQ = 225
GV = 83.3, outliers: none

13a.

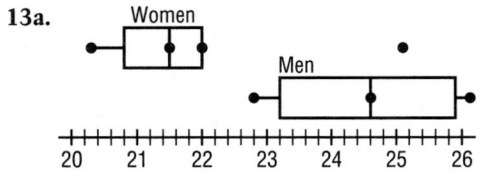

Men: LV = 22.8   Women: LV = 20.3
      LQ = 23.2   LQ = 20.8
      M = 24.6   M = 21.5
      UQ = 25.9   UQ = 22.0
      GV = 26.2   GV = 22.0
      outliers: none   outliers: 25.1

13b. Men marry at a later age than women.

15.

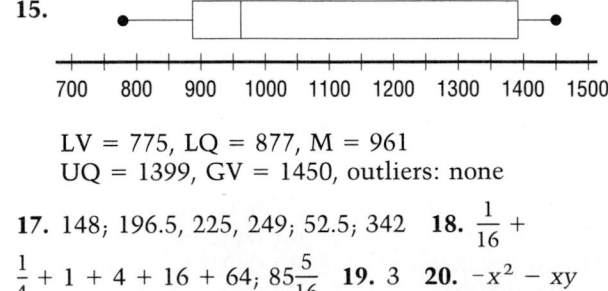

LV = 775, LQ = 877, M = 961
UQ = 1399, GV = 1450, outliers: none

17. 148; 196.5, 225, 249; 52.5; 342   **18.** $\frac{1}{16} +$
$\frac{1}{4} + 1 + 4 + 16 + 64; 85\frac{5}{16}$ **19.** 3   **20.** $-x^2 - xy$

Pages 666–667   Lesson 14-6

5. 5; 3.6   **7.** 250; 50   **9.** 82.2; 7.1   **11.** 97.9
13. 10.6   **15a.** 8.8   **15b.** 5.9   **15c.** 6.7
15d. Selby Sales   **19.** 11.09°; 0.097°   **20.** 3.9839
21. 7, −1   **22.** $\{x|-1 \le x \le 8\}$ **23.** 9 by 13 units

Pages 670–673   Lesson 14-7

7a. 68%   **7b.** 34%   **7c.** 97.5%   **7d.** 97   **9a.** 50%
9b. 15.5%   **9c.** 95%   **13a.** rejected
13b. X1 = 10 * 0.3 = 3
       X2 = 10 * 0.7 = 7
       Since X1 is less than 5, the procedure is stopped.
13c. yes   **14.** 17, 19, 21   **15.** 5   **16.** $\frac{3}{2(a - 1)}$

17. $\frac{(x + 1)^2}{5} + \frac{(y - 2.5)^2}{10} = 1$; ellipse

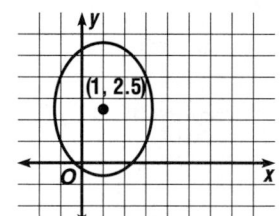

Pages 674–676   Chapter 14 Summary and Review

1.

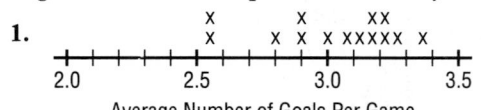

Average Number of Goals Per Game

3. 7.1; none; about 6.7   **5.** 20,735.5; none; 21,479.7
7. 15; 84, 87, 90; 6; no outliers   **9.** 106; 94.5, 100,
105; 10.5; 19, 125   **11.** 47; 23.5, 35.5, 41.5; 18; no
outliers   **13.** 1.3   **15.** 784.6   **17.** 1500   **19.** 2.5%
21a. 6,021,362; no mode; 6,706,047.4
21b. 6,872,285; 5,448,988.5, 6,021,362, 7,464,143.5;
2,015,155; 11,781,270   **23a.** 1600   **23b.** 250
23c. 97%   **23d.** 97.5%

CHAPTER 15 PROBABILITY

Page 683 Lesson 15-1

3a. (1, 1), (1, 2), (1, 3), (1, 4), (1, 5), (1, 6), (2, 1), (2, 2), (2, 3), (2, 4), (2, 5), (2, 6), (3, 1), (3, 2), (3, 3), (3, 4), (3, 5), (3, 6), (4, 1), (4, 2), (4, 3), (4, 4), (4, 5), (4, 6), (5, 1), (5, 2), (5, 3), (5, 4), (5, 5), (5, 6), (6, 1), (6, 2), (6, 3), (6, 4), (6, 5), (6, 6) **3b.** 2 **3c.** 12
3d. 7, because more combinations for 7 exist than for any other number between 2 and 12. **5.** 17¢ gold medium, 36¢ silver small, 55¢ black large
7. minimum: 14 units, maximum: 26 units

Pages 686–688 Lesson 15-2

5a. independent **5b.** dependent **5c.** dependent or independent, based upon the availability of each color for a particular model **7.** 6! or 720 schedules
9. dependent, if a person can only hold one office
11. dependent **13.** dependent **15.** 1800 combinations

17.

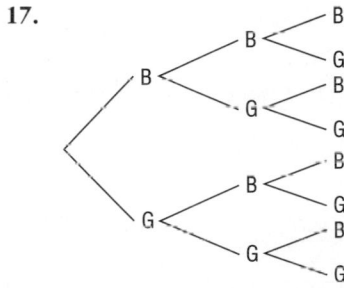

19. 90 routes **21.** 720 ways **23.** 240 ways
25a. 840 patterns **25b.** 240 patterns
27a. 10,140,000 **27b.** 1,872,000 **29a.** 16 ways
29b. 12 ways **30.** 6×7 or 42, since 7 is the most probable total each time the dice are rolled
31. $3(2)^{26}$ **32.** 2.73 years

33.

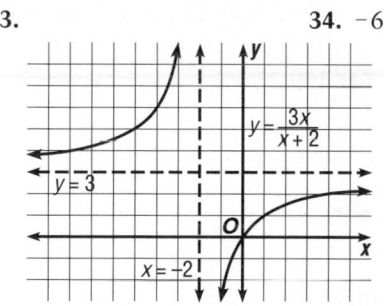

34. -6

Pages 692–693 Lesson 15-3

5. true **7.** false **9.** 120 **11.** true **13.** true
15. false **17.** 3 **19.** 30 **21.** 120 **23.** 3360
25. 778,377,600 **27.** 6 **29.** 72 **31.** 180 **33.** 126
35. 6 **37.** 12 **39.** 15 **43a.** 45,360

43b. about 80.1 **45.** 13 ways **46.** 2, 3, 4, 5, 6, 7, 8
47. 3 **48.** 1800 km **49.** $\left(8, \dfrac{3}{2}\right)$ **50.** $d \geq -105$

Pages 697–698 Lesson 15-4

5. circular, not reflection, 3,628,800 **7.** linear, reflection, 1,814,400 **9.** circular, not reflection
11. linear, not reflection **13.** 56 **15.** 60 **17.** 2520
19. 24 **21.** 12 **23.** 5^{28} **25.** 255 ways **27.** 120

28. $\displaystyle\sum_{n=1}^{20} \dfrac{n+1}{2n+1}$ **29.** 3 positive real roots, or 1

positive real root and 2 imaginary roots **30.** 5, $-\dfrac{7}{3}$

31. $x^2 - 3x - 10$ **32.** Parallel lines have equal slopes, whereas the slopes of perpendicular lines are negative reciprocals of each other.

Pages 701–704 Lesson 15-5

5. combination **7.** combination **9.** 792 **11.** 12
13. combination **15.** permutation **17.** permutation
19. combination **21.** 56 **23.** 2024 **25.** 126
27. 84 **29.** none **31.** 3570 **33.** 351 **35a.** 5148
35b. 28,561 **37.** 30 **39.** 14 **41.** 126 **43.** 0
45. 2808 **47.** 2520 **49.** 252 **51.** 1980 teams
53. 196 **54.** 24 ways **55.** 19.3 years **56.** about 8.7 years

57. ellipse, hyperbola

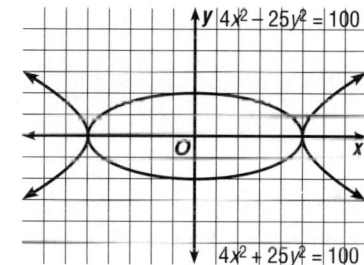

58. $\left(\dfrac{1}{5}, \dfrac{2}{5}, -\dfrac{3}{5}\right)$ **59.** $a^2b^2c^2$, $a^2b^2c^2d$, $a^2b^2c^2d^2$
60. (1, 64), (2, 32), (4, 16), (8, 8), (16, 4), (32, 2), (64, 1), (−1, −64), (−2, −32), (−4, −16), (−8, −8), (−16, −4), (−32, −2), (−64, −1)

Page 704 Mid-Chapter Review

1a. squares, pencils, buttons—arranged in a straight line **1b.** 24 **2a.** tree diagram **2b.** 24 **3.** 100!
4. 13,824,000 **5.** 3!2! or 12 ways **6.** $\dfrac{52!}{13!39!}$

Pages 707–709 Lesson 15-6

7. $\dfrac{5}{4}$ **9.** $\dfrac{3}{4}$ **11.** $\dfrac{4}{7}$ **13.** $\dfrac{1}{6}$ **15.** $\dfrac{1}{6}$ **17.** $\dfrac{7}{8}$ **19.** $\dfrac{5}{6}$ **21.** $\dfrac{1}{2}$

23. $\dfrac{1}{3}$ **25.** $\dfrac{18}{95} \approx 0.189$ **27.** $\dfrac{3}{19} \approx 0.158$

29. $\dfrac{14}{39} \approx 0.359$, $\dfrac{14}{25}$ **31.** $\dfrac{1}{16} \approx 0.063$ **33.** $\dfrac{3}{56} \approx 0.054$

35. $\frac{1}{4} = 0.25$ **37.** $\frac{2}{7} \approx 0.286$ **39.** $\frac{4}{7} \approx 0.571$
41a. 66,607:33 **41b.** 108,257:33 **41c.** 16,627:33
43. $\frac{1}{9,366,819}$ **45.** 420 **46.** $1024r^5 + 1280r^4s + 640r^3s^2 + 160r^2s^3 + 20rs^4 + s^5$ **47.** 2401
48. $2x^2 + 5$

49.

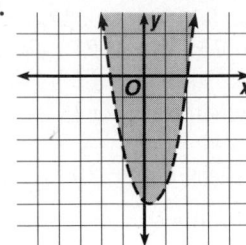

50. $-\frac{3}{2}, \frac{1}{3}$ **51.** 1

Pages 712–714   Lesson 15-7
5. dependent, $\frac{2}{7}$ **7.** independent, $\frac{81}{625}$ **9.** $\frac{9}{49} \approx 0.184$

11. $\frac{1}{8} = 0.125$ **13.** $\frac{5}{48} \approx 0.104$ **15.** $\frac{1}{36} \approx 0.028$

17. $\frac{1}{36} \approx 0.028$ **19.** $\frac{1}{6} \approx 0.167$ **21a.** $\frac{1}{26} \approx 0.038$

21b. $\frac{7}{225} \approx 0.031$ **23.** $\frac{1}{32} \approx 0.031$ **25.** $\frac{1}{94,109,400} \approx$

1.06×10^{-8} **27.** $\frac{4}{635,013,559,600} \approx 6.3 \times 10^{-12}$

29. 0 **31a.** $\frac{1}{729}$ **31b.** $\frac{5}{243}$ **31c.** $\frac{25}{243}$ **33.** $\frac{1}{4}$

34. $\frac{z^2 + 49}{(z + 5)(z - 7)}$ **35.** (1, 5), (2, 1), (3, 2)

36. $\begin{bmatrix} 1 & 0 \\ 0 & 1 \end{bmatrix}$

Pages 717–719   Lesson 15-8
5. inclusive, $\frac{7}{30} \approx 0.233$ **7.** exclusive, $\frac{9}{91} \approx 0.099$

9. inclusive, $\frac{175}{221} \approx 0.79$ **11.** $\frac{2}{11} \approx 0.181$

13. $\frac{14}{33} \approx 0.424$ **15.** $\frac{188}{663} \approx 0.284$ **17.** $\frac{55}{221} \approx 0.249$

19. $\frac{7}{16} \approx 0.438$ **21.** $\frac{35}{64} \approx 0.547$ **23.** $\frac{29}{3003} \approx 0.010$

25. $\frac{70}{143} \approx 0.490$ **27.** $\frac{1}{525} \approx 0.002$ **29.** $\frac{46}{525} \approx 0.088$

33. $\frac{57}{1771} \approx 0.032$ **35.** $\frac{1}{20}$ **36.** 1960 **37.** 15, 37.5
38. 7 **39.** 374.4

Pages 723–724   Lesson 15-9
5. binomial, $\frac{3}{8}$ **7a.** binomial, $\frac{16}{81}$ **7b.** binomial, $\frac{4}{81}$

7c. binomial, $\frac{1}{9}$ **7d.** not binomial **7e.** not binomial

7f. not binomial **9.** $\frac{3}{8} = 0.375$ **11.** $\frac{3125}{7776} \approx 0.402$

13. $\frac{625}{648} \approx 0.965$ **15.** $\frac{1}{9} \approx 0.111$ **17.** $\frac{15}{128} \approx 0.117$

19. $\frac{1}{1024} \approx 0.001$ **21.** $\frac{21}{3125} \approx 0.007$ **23.** $\frac{1}{8} = 0.125$

25. $\frac{1}{2} = 0.5$ **27.** 0.0001049 **29.** 0.1662386

31. $\frac{4536}{15,625} \approx 0.290$ **33a.** $\left(\frac{1}{10}\right)^{12} = 1.0 \times 10^{-12}$

33b. 0.0037881 **33c.** $\left(\frac{9}{10}\right)^{12} \approx 0.2824295$

33d. 0.8891300 **34.** $\frac{13}{16}$ **35.** 600 ft **36.** -1 **37.** $\frac{48}{56}$

Pages 726–728   Chapter 15 Summary and Review
1. 125 patterns **3.** 10.5 **5.** 1,625,702,400 **7.** 5040
9. 60 ways **11.** 270,725 **13.** $\frac{3}{7} \approx 0.429$

15. $\frac{2}{15} \approx 0.133$ **17.** $\frac{3}{10} = 0.3$ **19.** $\frac{23}{26} \approx 0.885$

21. $\frac{763}{3888} \approx 0.196$ **23.** 15 ways

CHAPTER 16   TRIGONOMETRIC FUNCTIONS

Pages 734–736   Lesson 16-1
5. II **7.** IV **9.** I **11.** no **13.** no **15.** no **17.** no
19. no **21.** yes **23.** π **25.** $\frac{\pi}{4}$ **27.** $-\frac{5\pi}{4}$ **29.** $\frac{3\pi}{4}$

31. $-\frac{2\pi}{3}$ **33.** 180° **35.** $-315°$ **37.** 405°

39. $\frac{-420°}{\pi} \approx -133.69°$ **43.** 0° **45.** 99° **47.** no
49. 30 IF A < 2 * 3.1415927 THEN 70; 40 LET A = A − 2 * 3.1415927; 70 LET A = A + 2 × 3.1415927
50. $\frac{1}{1024} \approx 0.001$ **51.** 109,225
52. $\log_3 27 + \log_3 3 \overset{?}{=} \log_3 81$
  $\quad 3 \; + \; 1 \; = 4 \checkmark$

53.

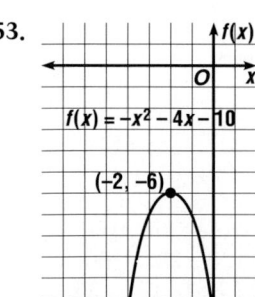

54. $\frac{b^3x^4}{5^3y}$

Pages 740–741 Lesson 16-2

5. + **7.** + **9.** + **11.** $\frac{1}{2}$ **13.** $-\frac{\sqrt{2}}{2}$ **15.** $-\frac{\sqrt{3}}{2}$

17. 290° **19.** 270° **21.** $\frac{\pi}{2}$ **23.** $\frac{3\pi}{4}$ **25.** $\frac{\sqrt{2}}{2}$ **27.** $\frac{1}{2}$

29. -1 **31.** 0 **33.** $\frac{1}{2}$ **35.** $-\frac{1}{2}$ **37.** 1 **39.** $-\frac{\sqrt{3}}{3}$

41. 1 **45.** $\frac{1}{2}$ **46.** 19; 16; 18.5 **47.** 650 cans

48. $\frac{3x(x-1)}{(4x-1)^2}$ **49.** $-1, -2, 5$ **50.** $6 + 4i$

51.

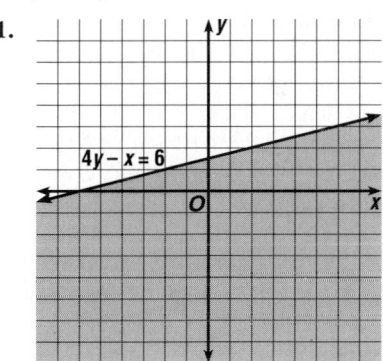

$4y - x = 6$

Pages 743–745 Lesson 16-3

5. 90°, 270° **7.** 0°, 180°, 360° **9.** 90°, 270° **11.** sin $-225° = \frac{\sqrt{2}}{2}$; cos $-225° = -\frac{\sqrt{2}}{2}$; tan $-225° = -1$; sec $-225° = -\sqrt{2}$; cot $-225° = -1$; csc $-225° = \sqrt{2}$

13. -1 **15.** 2 **17.** 2 **19.** $-\frac{\sqrt{3}}{3}$ **21.** $-\sqrt{3}$ **23.** -2

25. 1 **27.** $\frac{\sqrt{3}}{3}$ **29.** $\sqrt{3}$ **31.** $\frac{2\sqrt{3}}{3}$ **33.** undefined

35. $-\frac{\sqrt{3}}{3}$ **37.** undefined **39.** $-\frac{2\sqrt{3}}{3}$ **41.** tan $12.7° = \frac{9}{40}$; sec $12.7° = \frac{41}{40}$; cot $12.7° = \frac{40}{9}$; csc $12.7° = \frac{41}{9}$

43. $\frac{4}{7}$ **44.** $12; \frac{1}{2}; \frac{3}{8}; 6$ **45.** $(\pm 3, 0)$ **46.** 3 **47.** 24 ft, 20 ft, 12 ft **48.** $\frac{7}{2}$

Pages 749–750 Lesson 16-4

5. $y = \text{Sin}^{-1} x$ **7.** $30° = \text{Sin}^{-1} \frac{1}{2}$ **9.** $x = \text{Tan}^{-1}\left(-\frac{4}{3}\right)$

11. $\frac{4}{5}$ **13.** 120° **15.** 0° **17.** $\frac{1}{2}$ **19.** $\frac{\sqrt{13}}{6}$ **21.** $\frac{4\sqrt{2}}{7}$

23. $\frac{4}{5}$ **25.** $\frac{\pi}{2}$ or 90° **27.** 30° **29.** $\frac{\sqrt{3}}{2}$ **31.** $\frac{\sqrt{2}}{2}$

33. $\frac{24}{25}$ **35.** $\frac{\sqrt{3}}{2}$ **37.** π or 180° **39.** $\frac{\pi}{3}$ or 60°

41a.

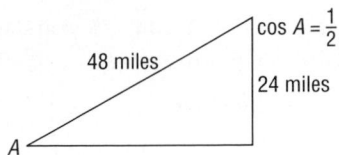

48 miles
24 miles
$\cos A = \frac{1}{2}$
A

41b. 60° north of east **43.** 37,000,000; 18,000,000, 22,000,000, 31,000,000; 13,000,000; 53,000,000
44. $3 + 4 + 5 + 6 + 7 + 8 + 9 + 10 + 11 + 12$; 75
45. 0.2392 **46.** $4\frac{8}{9}$ hours **47.** 201,600; 2.016×10^5

48. $\begin{bmatrix} 4 & 7 \\ 0 & 1 \end{bmatrix}$

Pages 753–755 Lesson 16-5

5. 0.1564 **7.** 07392 **9.** 343.8 **11.** 7.6067
13. 68.6796 **15.** 17.6779 **17.** 0.1736 **19.** -1
21. 0.8660 **23.** 3.2361 **25.** -2 **27.** undefined
29. 0.7507 **31.** -4.0624 **33.** 27.1268° **35.** 0.6340
37. -0.9258 **39.** 128.3 feet **41.** 35°16' **42.** $\frac{3489}{6561}$ or $\frac{1163}{2187}$; approximately 0.532 **43.** 24; 24 and 30; 26.5; approximately 6 points **44.** $\log_3 35 = \frac{\log 35}{\log 3}$; approximately 3.2362 **45.** $\frac{u(u+1)}{4(x-1)(x+4)}$ **46.** $\frac{13}{3}, \frac{8}{3}$

Page 755 Mid-Chapter Review

1. $\frac{\pi}{2}$ **2.** $\frac{5\pi}{6}$ **3.** $-\frac{3\pi}{4}$ **4.** 270° **5.** $-315°$

6. $\frac{360°}{\pi} \approx 114.59°$ **7.** 60° **8.** 320° **9.** $\frac{10\pi}{9}$ **10.** $-\frac{\sqrt{3}}{2}$

11. 0 **12.** $-\frac{2\sqrt{3}}{3}$ **13.** $\sqrt{2}$ **14.** undefined **15.** $\sqrt{2}$

16. 45° **17.** $-90°$ **18.** $\frac{\sqrt{2}}{2}$ **19.** $-30°$ **20.** 30°
21. -1 **22.** 1.0038 **23.** -0.1736 **24.** 3.5387
25. 45°

Pages 759–760 Lesson 16-6

5. $\tan 76° = \frac{13}{b}$; 3.2 **7.** $\tan 71°13' = \frac{21.2}{b}$; 7.2

9. $\cos 19°07' = \frac{11}{c}$; 11.6 **11.** $b = 5, A = 67°23'$, $B = 22°37'$ **13.** $a = 10.82, A = 31°, B = 59°$
15. $a = 11.53, A = 62°31', B = 27°29'$ **17.** $a = 3.86$, $b = 13.46, B = 74°$ **19.** $A = 47°50', c = 12.14$, $b = 8.15$ **21.** $A = 7°, a = 0.68, c = 5.61$
23. $A = 77°, a = 5.85, b = 1.35$ **25.** $A = 41°$, $b = 10.35, c = 13.72$ **27.** $A = 45°16', c = 61.94$, $b = 43.59$ **29.** $B = 34°5', a = 13.25, b = 8.97$
31. $B = 75°, a = 6.47, b = 24.15$ **33.** $A = 41°11'$, $B = 48°49', b = 8, c = 10.63$ **35.** $B = 53°8'$, $A = 36°52', a = 6, c = 10$ **37.** $x = 3, a = b = 5$, $c = 7.07, A = B = 45°$ **41.** 555 feet **42.** 84

43. $1 + 3 + 9 + 27 + 81$; 121   **44.** 75 years ago
45. 100 ml   **46.** 16; 2 real-rational; 6, 2   **47.** $r = 3$, $s = 9$

Pages 764–766   Lesson 16-7
3. $7^2 + b^2 = 16^2$; 14.4   **5.** $\tan A = \dfrac{7}{12}$; 30°15′
7. $\sin A = 0.9428$, $\cos A = 0.3333$, $\tan A = 2.8284$
9. $\sin A = 0.5692$, $\cos A = 0.8222$, $\tan A = 0.6923$
11. 251.73 m   **13.** 61.08 m   **15.** 9°36′   **17.** 22°48′
19. 188.89 ft   **21.** 11.7 m   **23.** 4.05 cm
25. 174.50 m   **27.** 164.92 km   **28.** 20   **29.** 3   **30.** 3, $\dfrac{2}{3}, \dfrac{3}{4}, -\dfrac{1}{2}$

Pages 769–770   Lesson 16-8
5. area $= \dfrac{1}{2}(10)(17) \sin 46°$; 61.1   **7.** area $= \dfrac{1}{2}(15)(30)$ $\sin 90°$; 225   **9.** $\dfrac{\sin 50°}{14} = \dfrac{\sin B}{10}$; 33°10′
11. $\dfrac{\sin 42°}{16} = \dfrac{\sin C}{12}$; 30°7′   **13.** 55.155   **15.** 21.097
17. 63.2086   **19.** $C = 74°$, $b = 8.89$, $c = 10.19$
21. $A = 52°$, $b = 100.17$, $c = 90.40$ **23.** $B = 52°53′$, $A = 62°27′$, $a = 16.68$ **25.** $B = 82°5′$, $b = 23.77$, $c = 9.95$ **27.** $B = 48°42′$, $C = 26°18′$, $c = 8.3$
29. 31.9 yd and 22.6 yd   **31.** 57.2 km

35a. 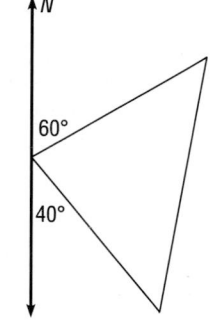   **35b.** 424.24 miles

60°
40°

36.

median: 76.2   outliers: none
lower quartile: 75.2   greatest value: 79.9
upper quartile: 78   least value: 72.9
interquartile range: 2.8

37. $x^6 + 24x^5 + 240x^4 + 1280x^3 + 3840x^2 + 6144x + 4096$ **38.** 5.003 hours   **39.** $x^2 + 1$; $x^2 + 2x + 1$ **40.** 128 square cm

Pages 773–774   Lesson 16-9
5. 2; $B = 53°7′$, $C = 90°1′$, $c = 10$; $B = 126°53′$, $C = 16°15′$, $c = 2.8$ **7.** None   **9.** None   **11.** None
13. 2; $B = 53°28′$, $C = 86°32′$, $c = 12.4$; $B = 126°32′$, $C = 13°28′$, $c = 2.9$ **15.** $\dfrac{1}{14}$ **17.** no solution   **19.** 6 or 12
21. A sample answer is $6 + 3 - 6 - 2 + 4 = 5$.

Pages 778–779   Lesson 16-10
5. law of sines; $b = 14.7$, $B = 109°3′$, $C = 30°57′$
7. law of cosines; $b = 18.5$, $A = 40°57′$, $C = 79°3′$
9. law of sines; $a = 9.6$, $b = 14$, $B = 70°$ **11.** law of sines; $c = 23.3$, $A = 26°10′$, $C = 110°52′$ **13.** $a = 10.91$, $B = 57°16′$, $C = 87°44′$ **15.** $A = 22°37′$, $B = 67°23′$, $C = 90°$ **17.** Two solutions: $C = 13.88$, $A = 73°54′$, $B = 67°46′$; $C = 13.88$, $A = 106°6′$, $B = 35°31′$
19. $b = 20.95$, $A = 52°25′$, $C = 108°35′$
21. $A = 45°34′$, $B = 57°34′$, $C = 76°52′$
23. $A = 102°55′$, $B = 49°15′$, $C = 27°50′$
25. $a = 8.31$, $B = 26°19′$, $C = 124°41′$ **27.** 1434.26 ft; 86,804.28 ft^2 **29.** 76.90 cm, 101.09 cm   **31.** 36°1′
33. 334.6 nautical miles   **35.** 2033 km

37.

			Rounded	Stem	Truncated			
9	8	8	5 3	2	2 5 7 7 9			
			9 7	3	6 9 9			
			0	4				
		9	3 1	5	1 2 8			
				6				
			8 7	7	6 8			
			7 4	8	3 7			
			6	9	5			

Using rounded data, 7 |3| represents 365,000 to 374,000 people.

Using truncated data, |3| 6 represents 360,000 to 369,000 people.

38. 25   **39.** 0   **40.** $y = \pm\sqrt{x} + 4$

Pages 780–782   Chapter 16 Summary and Review
1. $\dfrac{17\pi}{12}$ **3.** $\dfrac{3\pi}{2}$ **5.** 60°   **7.** −75°   **9.** $-\dfrac{\sqrt{3}}{2}$ **11.** $-\dfrac{1}{2}$
13. $-\dfrac{\sqrt{2}}{2}$ **15.** 1   **17.** $\sqrt{2}$ **19.** $\dfrac{2\sqrt{3}}{3}$ **21.** $-\sqrt{3}$
23. −90°   **25.** 60°   **27.** 0   **29.** 37.5896°   **31.** −0.3536
33. 14.4   **35.** 17.3   **37.** 5.4   **39.** $B = 7°8′$, $C = 89°42′$, $c = 80.6$ **41.** $A = 51°$, $a = 70.22$, $c = 89.69$
43. $c = 6.43$, $A = 34°19′$, $B = 80°41′$ **45.** $c = 4.54$, $A = 58°9′$, $B = 81°51′$ **47.** 4483.48 ft   **49.** 3.7 m

Pages 795–796   Lesson 17-1

5. 3, 2π **7.** 3, 4π **9.** 6, 3π **11.** 3, 3π **13.** $\frac{1}{2}$, $\frac{8\pi}{3}$

15. 6, π **17.** 2π **19.** $\frac{\pi}{5}$ **21.** $\frac{\pi}{3}$ **23.** π **25.** 4π

27. 3π

29. 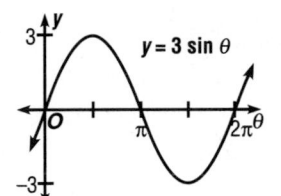   **33.**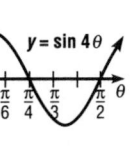

37.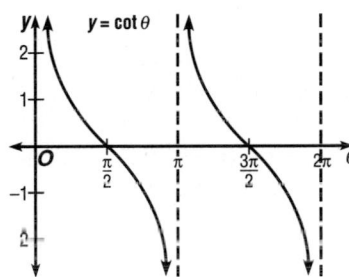

41.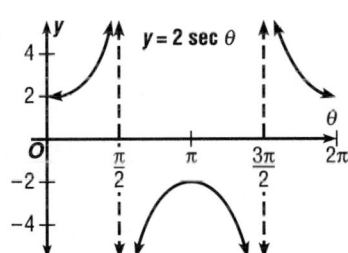

45.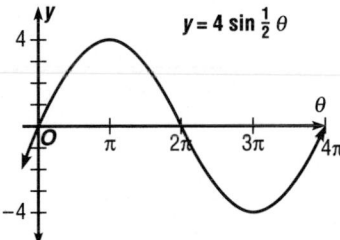

49.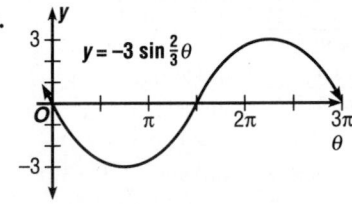

53.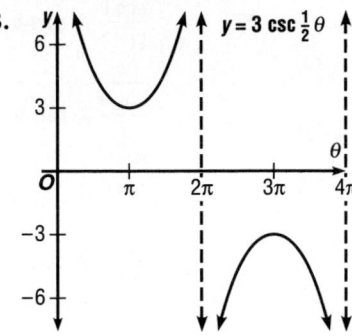

57.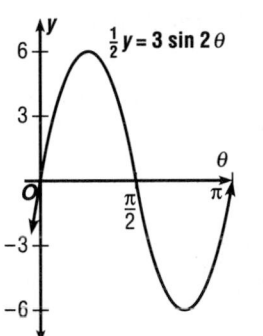

61a.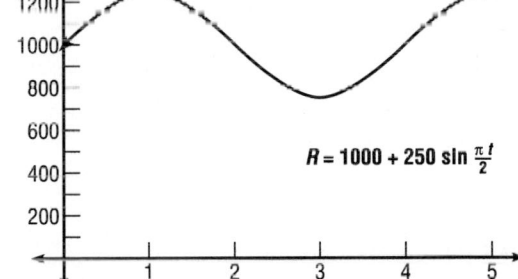

63. yes   **64.** 92; no mode; 91.25

65. A sample answer is $\sum_{n=1}^{6} 3 + 3n$.   **66.** $4^{\sqrt{6}}$

67. 3, $-\frac{5}{4}$, $\frac{7 \pm \sqrt{5}}{2}$ **68.** 37   **69a.** 600 floor lamps, 300 table lamps   **69b.** $73,500

Pages 799–800   Lesson 17-2

5. $\sin \theta \cos \theta$ **7.** 1   **9.** $\cot \alpha$ **11.** $\cot^2 x$ **13.** $\cos \theta$

15. $\tan^2 x$ **17.** $\frac{1}{2}$ **19.** $\frac{\sqrt{5}}{3}$ **21.** $\frac{3}{4}$ **23.** $\frac{4\sqrt{7}}{7}$

25. $-\frac{\sqrt{3}}{3}$ **27.** $-\sqrt{5}$ **29.** $2\sqrt{2}$ **31.** $-\frac{\sqrt{3}}{2}$ **33.** $\sqrt{2}$

35. $\frac{4}{5}$ **37.** $\tan^2 \theta$ **39.** 1   **41.** 1   **43.** 2

45. $1 + \cot^2 \theta \overset{?}{=} \csc^2 \theta$

$\dfrac{\sin^2 \theta + \cos^2 \theta}{\sin^2 \theta} \overset{?}{=} \csc^2 \theta$

$\dfrac{1}{\sin^2 \theta} \overset{?}{=} \csc^2 \theta$

$\csc^2 \theta = \csc^2 \theta$

47. $\dfrac{\sec \theta}{\csc \theta} \overset{?}{=} \tan \theta$

$\dfrac{\dfrac{1}{\cos \theta}}{\dfrac{1}{\sin \theta}} \overset{?}{=} \tan \theta$

$\dfrac{1}{\cos \theta} \cdot \dfrac{\sin \theta}{1} \overset{?}{=} \tan \theta$

$\dfrac{\sin \theta}{\cos \theta} \overset{?}{=} \tan \theta$

$\tan \theta = \tan \theta$

51. 907,200 **52.** $0, -\dfrac{3}{2}, -2, 3$ **53.** $(x - 6)^2 +$

$y^2 = 36$ **54.** $200x - 2x^2$ **55.** $4b + \dfrac{1}{2b - 1}$

56. domain: $\{0, 8\}$; range: $\{-12, -8, 0, 3, 4\}$; no

Pages 805–806 Lesson 17-3

3. $\sin \theta \sec \theta \cot \theta \overset{?}{=} 1$

$\sin \theta \cdot \dfrac{1}{\cos \theta} \cdot \dfrac{1}{\tan \theta} \overset{?}{=} 1$

$\dfrac{\sin \theta}{\cos \theta} \cdot \dfrac{1}{\tan \theta} \overset{?}{=} 1$

$\tan \theta \cdot \dfrac{1}{\tan \theta} \overset{?}{=} 1$

$1 = 1$

5. $\csc y \sec y \overset{?}{=} \cot y + \tan y$

$\dfrac{1}{\sin y} \cdot \dfrac{1}{\cos y} \overset{?}{=} \dfrac{\cos y}{\sin y} + \dfrac{\sin y}{\cos y}$

$\dfrac{1}{\sin y} \cdot \dfrac{1}{\cos y} \overset{?}{=} \dfrac{\cos^2 y + \sin^2 y}{\sin y \cos y}$

$\dfrac{1}{\sin y \cos y} = \dfrac{1}{\sin y \cos y}$

7. $\sec^2 x - \tan^2 x \overset{?}{=} \tan x \cot x$

$1 \overset{?}{=} \tan x \cdot \dfrac{1}{\tan x}$

$1 \overset{?}{=} \dfrac{\tan x}{\tan x}$

$1 = 1$

9. $\dfrac{\sec \alpha}{\sin \alpha} - \dfrac{\sin \alpha}{\cos \alpha} \overset{?}{=} \cot \alpha$

$\dfrac{1}{\cos \alpha \sin \alpha} - \dfrac{\sin \alpha}{\cos \alpha} \overset{?}{=} \cot \alpha$

$\dfrac{1 - \sin^2 \alpha}{\cos \alpha \sin \alpha} \overset{?}{=} \cot \alpha$

$\dfrac{\cos^2 \alpha}{\cos \alpha \sin \alpha} \overset{?}{=} \cot \alpha$

$\dfrac{\cos \alpha}{\sin \alpha} \overset{?}{=} \cot \alpha$

$\cot \alpha = \cot \alpha$

11. $\dfrac{\sin \alpha}{1 - \cos \alpha} + \dfrac{1 - \cos \alpha}{\sin \alpha} \overset{?}{=} 2 \csc \alpha$

$\dfrac{\sin^2 \alpha + (1 - \cos \alpha)^2}{(1 - \cos \alpha)(\sin \alpha)} \overset{?}{=} \dfrac{2}{\sin \alpha}$

$\dfrac{\sin^2 \alpha + 1 - 2\cos \alpha + \cos^2 \alpha}{(1 - \cos \alpha)\sin \alpha} \overset{?}{=} \dfrac{2}{\sin \alpha}$

$\dfrac{2 - 2\cos \alpha}{(1 - \cos \alpha)\sin \alpha} \overset{?}{=} \dfrac{2}{\sin \alpha}$

$\dfrac{2(1 - \cos \alpha)}{(1 - \cos \alpha)\sin \alpha} \overset{?}{=} \dfrac{2}{\sin \alpha}$

$\dfrac{2}{\sin \alpha} = \dfrac{2}{\sin \alpha}$

13. $\dfrac{1 - \cos x}{\sin x} \overset{?}{=} \dfrac{\sin x}{1 + \cos x}$

$\dfrac{1 - \cos x}{\sin x} \overset{?}{=} \dfrac{\sin x(1 - \cos x)}{(1 + \cos x)(1 - \cos x)}$

$\dfrac{1 - \cos x}{\sin x} \overset{?}{=} \dfrac{\sin x(1 - \cos x)}{1 - \cos^2 x}$

$\dfrac{1 - \cos x}{\sin x} \overset{?}{=} \dfrac{\sin x(1 - \cos x)}{\sin^2 x}$

$\dfrac{1 - \cos x}{\sin x} = \dfrac{1 - \cos x}{\sin x}$

15. $\dfrac{1 - \cos x}{1 + \cos x} \overset{?}{=} (\csc x - \cot x)^2$

$\dfrac{1 - \cos x}{1 + \cos x} \overset{?}{=} \left(\dfrac{1}{\sin x} - \dfrac{\cos x}{\sin x}\right)^2$

$\dfrac{1 - \cos x}{1 + \cos x} \overset{?}{=} \left(\dfrac{1 - \cos x}{\sin x}\right)^2$

$\dfrac{1 - \cos x}{1 + \cos x} \overset{?}{=} \dfrac{(1 - \cos x)^2}{\sin^2 x}$

$\dfrac{1 - \cos x}{1 + \cos x} \overset{?}{=} \dfrac{(1 - \cos x)^2}{1 - \cos^2 x}$

$\dfrac{1 - \cos x}{1 + \cos x} \overset{?}{=} \dfrac{(1 - \cos x)(1 - \cos x)}{(1 - \cos x)(1 + \cos x)}$

$\dfrac{1 - \cos x}{1 + \cos x} = \dfrac{1 - \cos x}{1 + \cos x}$

17. $\dfrac{\cot \theta + \csc \theta}{\sin \theta + \tan \theta} \overset{?}{=} \cot \theta \csc \theta$

$\dfrac{\dfrac{\cos \theta}{\sin \theta} + \dfrac{1}{\sin \theta}}{\sin \theta + \dfrac{\sin \theta}{\cos \theta}} \overset{?}{=} \dfrac{\cos \theta}{\sin \theta} \cdot \dfrac{1}{\sin \theta}$

$\dfrac{\dfrac{\cos \theta + 1}{\sin \theta}}{\dfrac{\sin \theta \cos \theta + \sin \theta}{\cos \theta}} \overset{?}{=} \dfrac{\cos \theta}{\sin \theta} \cdot \dfrac{1}{\sin \theta}$

$\dfrac{\dfrac{\cos \theta + 1}{\sin \theta}}{\dfrac{\sin \theta(\cos \theta + 1)}{\cos \theta}} \overset{?}{=} \dfrac{\cos \theta}{\sin \theta} \cdot \dfrac{1}{\sin \theta}$

$\dfrac{\cos \theta + 1}{\sin \theta} \cdot \dfrac{\cos \theta}{\sin \theta(\cos \theta + 1)} \overset{?}{=} \dfrac{\cos \theta}{\sin^2 \theta}$

$\dfrac{\cos \theta}{\sin^2 \theta} = \dfrac{\cos \theta}{\sin^2 \theta}$

19. $\dfrac{1 - 2\cos^2 \beta}{\sin \beta \cos \beta} \overset{?}{=} \tan \beta - \cot \beta$

$\dfrac{1 - 2\cos^2 \beta}{\sin \beta \cos \beta} \overset{?}{=} \dfrac{\sin \beta}{\cos \beta} - \dfrac{\cos \beta}{\sin \beta}$

$\dfrac{1 - 2\cos^2 \beta}{\sin \beta \cos \beta} \overset{?}{=} \dfrac{\sin^2 \beta - \cos^2 \beta}{\cos \beta \sin \beta}$

$\dfrac{1 - 2\cos^2 \beta}{\sin \beta \cos \beta} \overset{?}{=} \dfrac{1 - \cos^2 \beta - \cos^2 \beta}{\cos \beta \sin \beta}$

$\dfrac{1 - 2\cos^2 \beta}{\sin \beta \cos \beta} = \dfrac{1 - 2\cos^2 \beta}{\sin \beta \cos \beta}$

21.
$\dfrac{\cos y}{1 + \sin y} + \dfrac{\cos y}{1 - \sin y} \overset{?}{=} 2 \sec y$

$\dfrac{\cos y (1 - \sin y) + \cos y(1 + \sin y)}{(1 + \sin y)(1 - \sin y)} \overset{?}{=} \dfrac{2}{\cos y}$

$\dfrac{\cos y - \cos y \sin y + \cos y + \cos y \sin y}{1 - \sin^2 y} \overset{?}{=} \dfrac{2}{\cos y}$

$\dfrac{2\cos y}{\cos^2 y} \overset{?}{=} \dfrac{2}{\cos y}$

$\dfrac{2}{\cos y} = \dfrac{2}{\cos y}$

23. $\cot x(\cot x + \tan x) \overset{?}{=} \csc^2 x$

$\cot^2 x + \tan x \cot x \overset{?}{=} \csc^2 x$

$\cot^2 x + \tan x \cdot \dfrac{1}{\tan x} \overset{?}{=} \csc^2 x$

$\cot^2 x + 1 \overset{?}{=} \csc^2 x$

$\csc^2 x = \csc^2 x$

25.
$\dfrac{1 + \tan \gamma}{1 + \cot \gamma} \overset{?}{=} \dfrac{\sin \gamma}{\cos \gamma}$

$\dfrac{1 + \dfrac{\sin \gamma}{\cos \gamma}}{1 + \dfrac{\cos \gamma}{\sin \gamma}} \overset{?}{=} \dfrac{\sin \gamma}{\cos \gamma}$

$\dfrac{\dfrac{\cos \gamma + \sin \gamma}{\cos \gamma}}{\dfrac{\sin \gamma + \cos \gamma}{\sin \gamma}} \overset{?}{=} \dfrac{\sin \gamma}{\cos \gamma}$

$\dfrac{\cos \gamma + \sin \gamma}{\cos \gamma} \cdot \dfrac{\sin \gamma}{\cos \gamma + \sin \gamma} \overset{?}{=} \dfrac{\sin \gamma}{\cos \gamma}$

$\dfrac{\sin \gamma}{\cos \gamma} = \dfrac{\sin \gamma}{\cos \gamma}$

27. $1 + \sec^2 x \sin^2 x \overset{?}{=} \sec^2 x$

$1 + \dfrac{1}{\cos^2 x} \cdot \dfrac{\sin^2 x}{1} \overset{?}{=} \sec^2 x$

$1 + \dfrac{\sin^2 x}{\cos^2 x} \overset{?}{=} \sec^2 x$

$1 + \tan^2 x \overset{?}{=} \sec^2 x$

$\sec^2 x = \sec^2 x$

31. $\dfrac{2187}{16,384}$ or about 0.133

32.

Stem	Leaf										
0	4	4	4	4							
●	5	6	6	6	6	7	7	8	9	9	
1	1	1	2	2							
●	6	9	9	9							

1 | 1 represents 11¢.

33. $\dfrac{\log 82}{\log 5}$; 2.738 **34.** $-5, 4;\ -1, -4$

35. $\begin{bmatrix} -10 & 0 \\ 3 & -2 \end{bmatrix};\ \begin{bmatrix} -\dfrac{1}{10} & -\dfrac{3}{20} \\ 0 & -\dfrac{1}{2} \end{bmatrix}$

Pages 808–809 Lesson 17-4
5. 18,200 **7.** 301 **9.** 6 or 12 **11.** $-\dfrac{2}{9}$ **13.** A
sample answer is $5[5(5 + 5) - (5 + 5)]$. **15.** 24, 25,
32, 43, 49, 51, 57, 68, 75, 76, 93, or 99 **17.** 7

Pages 813–814 Lesson 17-5
3. $30° - 45°$ **5.** $30° + 45°$ **7.** $225° + 30°$
9. $\dfrac{\sqrt{6} + \sqrt{2}}{4}$ **11.** $\dfrac{\sqrt{6} - \sqrt{2}}{4}$ **13.** $\dfrac{-\sqrt{6} - \sqrt{2}}{4}$
15. $\dfrac{\sqrt{2} - \sqrt{6}}{4}$ **17.** $\dfrac{-\sqrt{6} - \sqrt{2}}{4}$ **19.** $\dfrac{1}{2}$ **21.** $\dfrac{1}{2}$

23.
$\sin (270° - \theta) \overset{?}{=} -\cos \theta$
$\sin 270° \cos \theta - \cos 270° \sin \theta \overset{?}{=} -\cos \theta$
$-1 \cdot \cos \theta - 0 \cdot \sin \theta \overset{?}{=} -\cos \theta$
$-\cos \theta = -\cos \theta$

25.
$\sin (90° + \theta) \overset{?}{=} \cos \theta$
$\sin 90° \cos \theta + \cos 90° \sin \theta \overset{?}{=} \cos \theta$
$1 \cdot \cos \theta + 0 \cdot \sin \theta \overset{?}{=} \cos \theta$
$\cos \theta = \cos \theta$

27.
$\cos (90° + \theta) \overset{?}{=} -\sin \theta$
$\cos 90° \cos \theta - \sin 90° \sin \theta \overset{?}{=} -\sin \theta$
$0 \cdot \cos \theta - 1 \cdot \sin \theta \overset{?}{=} -\sin \theta$
$-\sin \theta = -\sin \theta$

33. $-2 - \sqrt{3}$ **35.** $2 - \sqrt{3}$ **37a.** $\sin 1° =$
$\sin 13° \cos 12° - \cos 13° \sin 12°$ **37b.** 27.5 feet
38. 240° **39.** 2046 **40.** $\dfrac{x^4 y^2}{2a^2 b^4}$ **41.** 8, 14
42. $f(x) = (x - 3)^7$ **43.** symmetric property of equality

Page 814 Mid-Chapter Review
1. $1, \dfrac{\pi}{2}$ or 90° **2.** $5, 2\pi$ or 360° **3.** $4, \dfrac{8\pi}{3}$ or 480°
4. $\dfrac{\pi}{2}$ or 90° **5.** π or 180° **6.** 5π or 900° **7.** $\dfrac{\sqrt{34}}{5}$
8. $-\dfrac{5\sqrt{34}}{34}$

9.
$\cot \beta \overset{?}{=} \cos \beta \csc \beta$
$\cot \beta \overset{?}{=} \cos \beta \left(\dfrac{1}{\sin \beta}\right)$
$\cot \beta \overset{?}{=} \dfrac{\cos \beta}{\sin \beta}$
$\cot \beta = \cot \beta$

10. $1 \overset{?}{=} \dfrac{1}{\sec^2 \alpha - \sec^2 \alpha \sin^2 \alpha}$ $1 \overset{?}{=} \dfrac{1}{1}$

$1 \overset{?}{=} \dfrac{1}{\sec^2 \alpha (1 - \sin^2 \alpha)}$ $1 = 1$

$1 \overset{?}{=} \dfrac{1}{\dfrac{1}{\cos^2 \alpha} (\cos^2 \alpha)}$

11. 58   **12.** $\dfrac{\sqrt{2}-\sqrt{6}}{4}$ **13.** $\dfrac{\sqrt{6}-\sqrt{2}}{4}$ **14.** $\dfrac{-\sqrt{6}-\sqrt{2}}{4}$

Pages 818–819   Lesson 17-6

5. III or IV   **7.** I or II   **9.** I   **11.** $-\dfrac{4\sqrt{6}}{25}, -\dfrac{23}{25}, \dfrac{\sqrt{10}}{5},$

$-\dfrac{\sqrt{15}}{5}$ **13.** $-\dfrac{24}{25}, -\dfrac{7}{25}, \dfrac{2\sqrt{5}}{5}, \dfrac{\sqrt{5}}{5}$ **15.** $\dfrac{4\sqrt{2}}{9}, -\dfrac{7}{9}, \dfrac{\sqrt{6}}{3},$

$-\dfrac{\sqrt{3}}{3}$ **17.** $\dfrac{24}{25}, \dfrac{7}{25}, \dfrac{3\sqrt{10}}{10}, -\dfrac{\sqrt{10}}{10}$ **19.** $-\dfrac{4\sqrt{2}}{9}, -\dfrac{7}{9}, \dfrac{\sqrt{6}}{3}, \dfrac{\sqrt{3}}{3}$

21. $\dfrac{\sqrt{2+\sqrt{2}}}{2}$ **23.** $-\dfrac{\sqrt{2-\sqrt{3}}}{2}$ **25.** $\dfrac{\sqrt{2-\sqrt{2}}}{2}$

27. $\cos^2 2x + 4\sin^2 x\cos^2 x \overset{?}{=} 1$
$\qquad \cos^2 2x + \sin^2 2x \overset{?}{=} 1$
$\qquad\qquad\qquad\quad 1 = 1$

29. $\sin^2 \theta \overset{?}{=} \dfrac{1}{2}(1 - \cos 2\theta)$

$\quad \sin^2 \theta \overset{?}{=} \dfrac{1}{2}[1 - (1 - 2\sin^2 \theta)]$

$\quad \sin^2 \theta \overset{?}{=} \dfrac{1}{2}(2\sin^2 \theta)$

$\quad \sin^2 \theta = \sin^2 \theta$

31.
$$\sin^4 x - \cos^4 x \overset{?}{=} 2\sin^2 x - 1$$
$$(\sin^2 x - \cos^2 x)(\sin^2 x + \cos^2 x) \overset{?}{=} 2\sin^2 x - 1$$
$$(\sin^2 x - \cos^2 x)\cdot 1 \overset{?}{=} 2\sin^2 x - 1$$
$$[\sin^2 x - (1 - \sin^2 x)] \overset{?}{=} 2\sin^2 x - 1$$
$$\sin^2 x - 1 + \sin^2 x \overset{?}{=} 2\sin^2 x - 1$$
$$2\sin^2 x - 1 = 2\sin^2 x - 1$$

33. $\qquad 2\cos^2 \dfrac{x}{2} \overset{?}{=} 1 + \cos x$ **35a.** 270.6 feet

$2\left(\pm\sqrt{\dfrac{1 + \cos x}{2}}\right)^2 \overset{?}{=} 1 + \cos x$

$\qquad 2\left(\dfrac{1 + \cos x}{2}\right) \overset{?}{=} 1 + \cos x$

$\qquad\qquad 1 + \cos x = 1 + \cos x$

35b. 270.6 feet   **35c.** 45°; The greatest value of the sine function is 1 and $\sin 2\theta = 1$ when $\theta = 45°$.
36. 90°

37.

Stem	Leaf						
4							
●	6	6					
5	2						
●	5	5	5	8	8	9	9
6	0	0	0	2			
●	5	5	9	9			
7	0	0					
●	6	8					

6 | 0 represents $60.
38. 10, 14, 18, 22   **39.** 5   **40.** inverse; 10

Pages 825–827   Lesson 17-7

5. 2; 150°, 210°   **7.** 2; 0°, 180°   **9.** 2; about 108°26′, about 288°26′   **11.** 0   **13.** 0   **15.** 8; 0°, 45°, 90°, 135°, 180°, 225°, 270°, 315°   **17.** 60°, 120°, 240°, 300°   **19.** 90°, 270°   **21.** 30°, 150°   **23.** $\dfrac{7\pi}{6}, \dfrac{11\pi}{6}$ **25.** $\dfrac{4\pi}{3}, \dfrac{5\pi}{3}$

27. $\dfrac{\pi}{2}, \dfrac{7\pi}{6}, \dfrac{11\pi}{6}$ **29.** $45° + n\cdot 180°$ **31.** $0° + n\cdot 120°$ **33.** $90° + n\cdot 360°, 180° + n\cdot 360°$ **35.** $90° + n\cdot 180°, 120° + n\cdot 360°, 240° + n\cdot 360°$ **37.** $0° + n\cdot 180°, 90° + n\cdot 360°$ **39.** $\dfrac{7\pi}{6} + 2n\pi, \dfrac{11\pi}{6} + 2n\pi$

41. $\dfrac{\pi}{6} + n\pi, \dfrac{5\pi}{6} + n\pi$ **43.** $\dfrac{2\pi}{3} + 2n\pi, \dfrac{4\pi}{3} + 2n\pi$

45. $\dfrac{\pi}{3} + 2n\pi, \dfrac{5\pi}{3} + 2n\pi$ **47.** $0 + n\pi, \dfrac{\pi}{6} + 2n\pi,$

$\dfrac{5\pi}{6} + 2n\pi$ **49a.** −2 feet from the equilibrium point
49b. $0.5 + n$ seconds, where n is any integer   **49c.** 2 seconds   **51a.** 60°   **51b.** 90°, 270°   **51c.** no solution   **51d.** −360°, −225°, −180°, −45°, 0°   **51e.** 0°, 30°, 150°, 180°, 360°, 390°, 510°, 540°, 720°   **52.** $\dfrac{1}{2}$

53. $\dfrac{25}{144} \approx 0.174$ **54.** 6.5; 0; 7.4   **55.** 950
56. $\log_3 27 + \log_3 3 \overset{?}{=} \log_3 81$ **57.** $x = 0$
$\qquad\quad 3 \ + \ 1 \ = 4$

Pages 832–833   Lesson 17-8

5. $7\left(\cos \dfrac{\pi}{2} + i\sin \dfrac{\pi}{2}\right)$ **7.** 2   **9.** i

11. $3\left(\cos \dfrac{5\pi}{4} + i\sin \dfrac{5\pi}{4}\right)$ **13.** $\sqrt{2}\left(\cos \dfrac{\pi}{4} + i\sin \dfrac{\pi}{4}\right)$

15. $3\left(\cos \dfrac{\pi}{2} + i\sin \dfrac{\pi}{2}\right)$

17. $\sqrt{29}(\cos 1.95 + i\sin 1.95)$ **19.** $-1 - i$
21. $6 - 6i\sqrt{3}$ **23.** $16(\cos 2\pi + i\sin 2\pi)$; 16
25. $10\left(\cos \dfrac{17\pi}{12} + i\sin \dfrac{17\pi}{12}\right)$; $-2.59 - 9.66i$ **27.** $-2i$
29. $-4i$ **31.** -27 **33.** $-16\sqrt{2} - 16i\sqrt{2}$
35. $54 + 54i$ **39.** The needle travels slower as it approaches the center of the record.   **40.** 18.09 feet or 18 feet 1 inch   **41.** $\dfrac{1}{32}$ or 0.03125   **42.** 81   **43.** 8;

8; 6.94   **44.** 20,159 people   **45.** $\dfrac{\log 50}{\log 12}$; 1.5743

46. $(\pm 2, 0)$; $(\pm\sqrt{29}, 0)$

Pages 834–836   Chapter 17 Summary and Review

1. 1, 2π

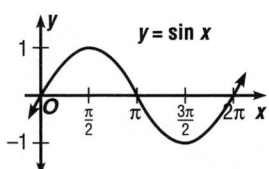

$y = \sin x$

5. 2π

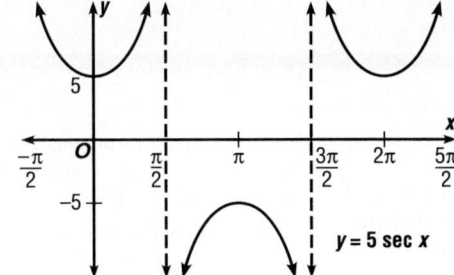

$y = 5 \sec x$

9. $-\dfrac{\sqrt{3}}{2}$ **11.** $-\dfrac{4}{3}$

13.
$$\sin^4 x - \cos^4 x \stackrel{?}{=} \sin^2 x - \cos^2 x$$
$$(\sin^2 x - \cos^2 x)(\sin^2 x + \cos^2 x) \stackrel{?}{=} \sin^2 x - \cos^2 x$$
$$(\sin^2 x - \cos^2 x) \cdot 1 \stackrel{?}{=} \sin^2 x - \cos^2 x$$
$$\sin^2 x - \cos^2 x = \sin^2 x - \cos^2 x$$

15.
$$\frac{\sin \theta}{1 - \cos \theta} \stackrel{?}{=} \csc \theta + \cot \theta$$
$$\frac{\sin \theta}{1 - \cos \theta} \stackrel{?}{=} \frac{1}{\sin \theta} + \frac{\cos \theta}{\sin \theta}$$
$$\frac{\sin \theta}{1 - \cos \theta} \stackrel{?}{=} \frac{1 + \cos \theta}{\sin \theta}$$
$$\frac{\sin \theta}{1 - \cos \theta} \stackrel{?}{=} \frac{(1 + \cos \theta)(1 - \cos \theta)}{\sin \theta(1 - \cos \theta)}$$
$$\frac{\sin \theta}{1 - \cos \theta} \stackrel{?}{=} \frac{1 - \cos^2 \theta}{\sin \theta(1 - \cos \theta)}$$
$$\frac{\sin \theta}{1 - \cos \theta} \stackrel{?}{=} \frac{\sin^2 \theta}{\sin \theta(1 - \cos \theta)}$$
$$\frac{\sin \theta}{1 - \cos \theta} = \frac{\sin \theta}{1 - \cos \theta}$$

17.
$$\sec x (\sec x - \cos x) \stackrel{?}{=} \tan^2 x$$
$$\sec^2 x - 1 \stackrel{?}{=} \tan^2 x$$
$$\tan^2 x = \tan^2 x$$

19.
$$\frac{\csc \theta + 1}{\cot \theta} \stackrel{?}{=} \frac{\cot \theta}{\csc \theta - 1}$$
$$\frac{(\csc \theta + 1)(\csc \theta - 1)}{\cot \theta (\csc \theta - 1)} \stackrel{?}{=} \frac{\cot \theta}{\csc \theta - 1}$$
$$\frac{\csc^2 \theta - 1}{\cot \theta (\csc \theta - 1)} \stackrel{?}{=} \frac{\cot \theta}{\csc \theta - 1}$$
$$\frac{\cot^2 \theta}{\cot \theta (\csc \theta - 1)} \stackrel{?}{=} \frac{\cot \theta}{\csc \theta - 1}$$
$$\frac{\cot \theta}{\csc \theta - 1} = \frac{\cot \theta}{\csc \theta - 1}$$

21. $\dfrac{\sqrt{6} + \sqrt{2}}{4}$ **23.** $\dfrac{\sqrt{2} - \sqrt{6}}{4}$ **25.** $2 \cos x \cos y$

27. $\dfrac{24}{25}$ **29.** $\dfrac{\sqrt{21}}{5}$

31.
$$(\sin x - \cos x)^2 \stackrel{?}{=} 1 - \sin 2x$$
$$\sin^2 x - 2 \sin x \cos x + \cos^2 x \stackrel{?}{=} 1 - \sin 2x$$
$$1 - 2 \sin x \cos x \stackrel{?}{=} 1 - \sin 2x$$
$$1 - \sin 2x = 1 - \sin 2x$$

33. $0°, 90°$ **35.** $\dfrac{7\pi}{6} + 2n\pi, \dfrac{11\pi}{6} + 2n\pi$ **37.** $\dfrac{\pi}{2} + 2n\pi$

39. $4\left(\cos \dfrac{2\pi}{3} + i \sin \dfrac{2\pi}{3}\right)$ **41.** $4\sqrt{2} - 4i\sqrt{2}$

43. 4096

INDEX

Absolute values, 31-35, 43-45, 351
  equations, 32-35, 47, 87-90
  functions, 87-90
  inequalities, 43-45, 48, 93, 95,
    123-125

Adams, Ansel, 522

Addition
  associate property of, 14-17
  commutative property of, 14-17,
    20
  of complex numbers, 293-295,
    304
  of fractions, 522
  identity property, 14-15
  inverse property of, 14-17
  of matrices, 160, 163-166
  of polynomials, 210, 213, 223,
    225-226, 247, 264
  property for inequalities, 36
  property of equality, 19
  of radical expressions, 264-265,
    267
  of rational expressions, 522-526,
    541
  of zero, 14-15

Additive identity, 14-15

Additive inverses, 14-17

Amortizations, 631

Amplitudes, 788-789, 791-795, 834

Angles, 732-740, 756
  complementary, 744, 759
  coterminal, 733-736
  of depression, 762-766
  of elevation, 762, 764-766
  of incidence, 754
  initial sides, 732
  inscribed, 227
  measures of, 733-735, 754, 780
  of refraction, 754
  of regular polygons, 49
  in standard position, 732-734
  terminal sides, 732-739
  of triangles, 199
  vertices, of, 732

Antilogarithms,
  common, 564-566, 588
  natural, 567, 569

Arccosine, 746-753, 781

Arcsine, 747-749, 751, 781

Arctangent, 747, 749, 753

Area
  of circles, 285
  of parallelograms, 12, 514, 518
  of rectangles, 229, 237, 310, 316,
    354-355, 362, 376, 380-381,
    518
  of squares, 223, 225, 572-573
  of trapezoids, 12, 514
  of triangles, 12, 169, 171-172,
    512, 767-769

Arithmetic means, 598-600, 610,
  632

Arithmetic sequences, 596-601,
  610, 632
  common difference, 596-600,
    632
  nth term of, 597-600, 632
  recursive formulas for, 597-599,
    632

Arithmetic series, 602-607, 633

Associative properties
  of addition, 14-17
  of multiplication, 14-15, 288

Asymptotes, 417-421, 445, 505-
  509, 540, 551, 793-794

Augmented matrices, 194-195,
  201, 204

Averages
  medians, 648-652, 654-655, 658-
    660, 674-675
  means, 15, 648-652, 664-671,
    674-675
  modes, 648-652, 674

Axes
  conjugate, 417
  major, 410-415
  minor, 410-414
  transverse, 417-419, 421

Axis of symmetry, 360
  for ellipses, 410
  for hyperbolas, 417
  for parabolas, 360-364, 367-370,
    383, 388-389, 400-404, 445

Bar graphs, 639-641
  histograms, 663, 668, 672

BASIC programs, 35, 79, 116, 117,
  143, 177, 178, 194, 291, 332,
  365, 378, 430, 486, 495, 579,
  631, 672, 673, 719, 725, 736,
  761, 827

Basic Counting Principle, 684-685,
  726

Bellaschi, Pietro, 422

Bell curves, 668-669, 676

Bernoulli, Jacob, 263

Best-fit lines, 80

Binomial experiments, 720-728

Binomials, 223-224
  difference of cubes, 231-233
  differences of squares, 230-231,
    233, 247
  dividing by, 459-463
  factoring, 230-233, 247, 319-320
  multiplying, 224-227, 247
  powers of, 625-630, 634, 721,
    728
  sums of cubes, 232-233

Binomial Theorem, 625-630, 634

Boundaries, 92-94, 98, 379-381,
  389

Box-and-whisker plots, 658-663,
  675

Boyle's Law, 421, 432

Briggs, Henry, 570

Calculators, 16, 55-56, 75, 131-132,
  168, 180, 242, 281, 322, 328,
  470, 483, 507-508, 512, 533, 547,
  571, 598
  antilogarithms, 565, 567, 569,
    588
  common logarithms, 564, 565,
    588
  factorial keys, 627
  graphing, 22-23, 58-59, 76, 85-86,
    104-107, 159-160, 201, 312-
    315, 350-352, 359, 425-426,
    437-438, 457-458, 504-505,
    551-552, 788-789, 801-802,
    820-821
  inverse keys, 254-255
  memory keys, 328
  natural logarithms, 567, 569, 588
  power keys, 254-256, 271
  root keys, 254
  statistical mode, 85-86, 665
  for trigonometric functions, 751-
    753, 781

Cardano, Gerolamo, 288

Careers
in air traffic control, 250-251
in anesthesiology, 636-637
in architecture, 730-731
in city planning, 308-309
in construction management, 502-503
in energy engineering, 6-8
in environmentalism, 680-681
in financial planning, 448-449
in forensic sciences, 348-349, 381
in genetic engineering, 208-209
in geology, 786-787
in industrial design, 154-155
in market research, 102-103
in medical technology, 394-395
in oceanography, 50-51
in pharmacology, 592-593
in systems analysis, 544-545

Cartesian coordinate planes, 52-55
quadrants of, 52

Center
of circle, 398-399, 405-407, 445, 829
of ellipse, 410-414
of hyperbola, 417-419, 421
poles, 829

Challenges, 172, 736

Change of base formula, 575-576

Characteristic, 563-565, 570, 587

Circle graphs, 533, 639-641

Circles
area of, 285
center of, 398-399, 405-407, 445
circumference of, 733, 763
concentric, 382, 406
diameters of, 398-399
graphs of, 405-407, 425-431, 433-443, 445
radii, 405-407, 445, 733
unit, 733-734, 736-737, 756, 797, 799

Circular cones, 20-21

Circular permutations, 694-698
reflexive, 696-698

Circumference, 733, 763

Coefficient matrices, 184-188, 203

Coefficients
of binomial expansions, 625-630, 721
of monomials, 210, 213

College Entrance Exam Preview, 100-101, 206-207, 306-307, 392-393, 500-501, 590-591, 678-679, 784-785

Combinations, 699-703, 706-707

Common difference, 596-600, 632

Common logarithms, 563-566, 574-577, 582, 587-588
antilogarithms, 564-566, 588
characteristic, 563-565, 570
mantissa, 563-565, 570, 587

Common ratios, 608-614, 633

Commutative properties
of addition, 14-17, 20
of multiplication, 14-17, 259, 288

Complementary angles, 744, 759

Completing the square, 322-327, 345, 366-368, 373

Complex Conjugates Theorem, 471

Complex fractions, 519

Complex numbers, 292-301
adding, 293-295, 304
conjugates, 297-300, 471
dividing, 297-301, 304
equal, 292, 294-295
graphing, 293, 295
multiplicative inverses of, 299-300, 304
multiplying, 293-297, 830-833
polar form, 829-833, 836
powers of, 831, 833, 836
rationalizing the denominators, 298
rectangular form, 829-833, 836
simplifying, 293-301, 304
subtracting, 293-294, 304

Complex rational expressions, 519-520, 524-526, 541

Composition of functions, 487-494, 497-498

Compound interest, 269, 567-569, 574-575, 579, 583-584

Compound sentences, 42-45, 48

Computers
BASIC, 35, 79, 116, 117, 143, 177, 178, 194, 291, 332, 365, 378, 430, 486, 495, 579, 631, 672, 673, 719, 725, 736, 761, 827
Data Insights, 91, 663
Mathematical Exploration Toolkit, 41, 235, 287, 431, 531, 828
spreadsheets, 486, 579, 631
statistical graphs, 663

Cones, 20-21

Conics, 400-422, 425-447
circles, 405-407, 425-431, 433-443, 445
degenerated cases, 429
ellipses, 408-415, 417, 425-436, 438, 440, 445
hyperbolas, 416-422, 425-438, 440, 445

parabolas, 54, 317-321, 323, 329, 335, 344, 360-373, 379-381, 383, 388-389, 400-404, 422, 425-438, 445, 451-453, 459

Conjugate axes, 417

Conjugates, 266-267, 278, 471
complex, 297-300

Connections
biology, 234, 263, 452, 547, 578
fine arts, 515
geometry, 9, 12, 20, 26-27, 57, 64, 69, 71, 78, 114-115, 120, 131, 163-166, 169, 171, 175-177, 182, 199, 221, 225-228, 237, 293, 295, 339, 343, 354-355, 362, 380-381, 397-399, 484, 494, 512, 518, 520, 600, 686, 697, 700, 734
history, 35, 79, 149, 178, 286, 338, 382, 408, 570, 688
language, 257, 480
physics, 321, 384
probability, 628
statistics, 15

Consistent systems of equations, 109-111

Constant functions, 62, 87, 89, 451

Constants, 210, 451
of variation, 510-514

Constant terms, 353-354, 388

Constraints, 129-132, 151

Cooperative Learning Activities, 30, 65, 128, 158, 222, 276, 311, 358, 424, 467, 534, 573, 595, 641, 683, 774, 809

Coordinate matrices, 161, 163-166

Coordinates, 52, 86, 105, 737
polar, 829

Cosecant, 742-744, 751, 753, 756-758, 797-800, 805-806, 834-835
graphs of, 789, 794-795

Cosine, 737-743, 746-751, 753-759, 781-782, 797-800, 804-806, 810-836
graph of, 738, 746, 788-795, 823, 834
inverse of, 746-747, 749, 751-753, 781
law of, 775-778, 782
principal values of, 746

Cotangent, 742-744, 752-753, 756-758, 797-800, 803, 805-806, 834-845
graph of, 794-795

Coterminal angles, 733-736

Counting principle, 684-685, 726

Cramer's Rule, 118-121, 149, 151, 190-194, 204
and BASIC, 194

Critical points, 385

Cross multiplication, 511

Cube roots, 252-255

Cubes
  difference of, 231-233
  perfect, 260
  sum of, 232-233

Cubic expressions, 451

Cubic functions, 451-452, 484

Cylinders, 482, 486

D

Data Insights, 91, 663

Decimals
  to fractions, 621, 623
  repeating, 13, 621, 623
  terminating, 13

Degenerated case, 429

Degree
  angle measure, 733-735
  of equations, 316
  even, 452-455
  of monomials, 210, 213, 223
  odd, 452-455, 483
  of polynomial functions, 452-455
  of polynomials, 223, 225, 451, 454
  to radians, 733, 735, 780
  radians to, 733, 735, 780

De Moivre's Theorem, 831, 833

Denominators, 516-519, 522-525
  least common, 522-529, 535-536
  rationalizing the, 260-262, 266, 271, 278-279, 298

Dependent events, 685-689
  probability of, 711-714

Dependent systems of equations, 109-111, 198

Depressed polynomials, 461-462, 468, 478

Descartes, René, 79, 288, 471

Descartes' rule of signs, 471-477

Determinants, 118-121, 159-160, 167-172, 181, 190-192, 194
  expansion by minors, 167-168
  second-order, 118-121
  third-order, 167-171, 190-191

Diagonals, 64-65, 702

Diameters, 398-399

Dickison, Randal, 265

Difference
  of angles formula, 810-813, 835
  common, 596-600, 632
  of cubes, 231-233
  of squares, 230-231, 233, 247

Dilation, 162-165

Dimensions of matrices, 161-164

Diophantus, 382

Directrix, 400-404, 445

Direct variations, 87, 89, 510-515, 540

Discriminants, 329-332, 345

Distance formula, 396-400, 405, 409, 416, 444, 810

Distributive property, 15-17, 20, 224-225, 229, 231, 275, 535, 575, 803

Division
  of complex numbers, 297-301, 304
  of fractions, 517
  long, 459-460
  of monomials, 215-219, 236, 246
  of polynomials, 236-248, 459-463
  of powers, 215-219, 246, 559
  properties for inequalities, 37
  property of equality, 19-20
  of radical expressions, 260-262, 266-267, 302, 517-521, 541
  synthetic, 241-245, 248, 459-463, 468, 470, 478-479

Dogon of Mali, 408

Domains, 53-58, 488-489

Double-angle formula, 815-819, 835

E

e, 567-570

Einstein, Albert, 35

Einstein, Mileva Maric, 35

Elements of matrices, 161-163, 200

Elimination method, 112-115, 119, 144, 146, 150, 369, 440-441

Ellipses, 408-415, 417, 425-436, 440, 445
  axis of symmetry, 410
  centers of, 410-414
  foci of, 409-415, 445
  major axes, 410-415
  minor axes, 410-414

Empty set, 32, 122, 823

Equations, 18-21
  absolute value, 32-35, 47, 87-90
  of asymptotes, 417-421, 505
  of axis of symmetry, 360-364, 367-370, 388-389
  checking solutions, 32-33, 282-285, 318, 334, 337, 340-341, 528-530, 536-537, 824
  of circles, 405-407, 427-430, 445

of conic sections, 427-429, 445
  degrees of, 316
  of ellipses, 409-415, 427-430, 445
  exponential, 548-588
  of hyperbolas, 416-421, 427-430
  linear, 58-87, 91-98, 108-121
  logarithmic, 553-564, 586-587
  matrix, 184-189
  of parabolas, 400-404, 427-430, 445
  of planes, 139-142
  polynomial, 339-343, 451-499
  prediction, 80-84, 91, 98
  quadratic, 313-345, 373-378, 389, 451
  quadratic form, 340-346
  radical, 281-287, 303
  rational, 527-530, 535-539, 542
  of regression lines, 86
  roots of, 461, 469, 471, 481
  systems of, 162, 184-204, 369, 432-443, 446
  in three variables, 139-149, 152
  trigonometric, 820-828, 836
  writing, 73-84

Eratosthenes, 763

Estimations
  extrapolations, 578
  interpolations, 578
  prediction equations, 80-84
  using, 571-573

Euler, 570

Even degree functions, 452-455

Even numbers, 254, 258, 270, 272

Events
  dependent, 685-689, 711-714
  inclusive, 715-718, 728
  independent, 684-688, 710-714
  mutually exclusive, 715-718, 728

Expansion by minors, 167-168

Exponential equations, 548-554

Exponential functions, 546-550
  definition of, 548
  graphs of, 546-548, 550, 554
  Property of equality of, 548-549, 554

Exponents
  irrational numbers as, 546, 549
  negative, 216-219, 246
  rational, 269-274, 277-280, 303
  real numbers, 547-548
  of zero, 215-216, 246

Expressions, 8-11
  algebraic, 9-11, 24
  cubic, 451
  evaluating, 8-11, 22-23, 46
  linear, 451
  quadratic, 451
  rational, 516-527, 531, 541

simplifying, 15, 17, 47, 516-520, 531
verbal, 24
Extraneous solutions, 282, 284-285
Extrapolation, 578

Factorials, 627-630, 634
Factors
greatest common, 229-232, 516, 519-520
of polynomials, 229-233, 235, 238, 247, 317-320, 323-324, 339, 344, 461-463, 468-469, 471-472, 480
prime, 523
quadratic, 339, 342, 346
Factor Theorem, 461, 478, 496
Failures, 705-707
Families of equations, 68
Feasible regions, 129-130
Ferguson, Helaman R. P., 515
Fibonacci, Leonardo, 594
Fibonacci sequence, 594-595
Foci
of ellipses, 409-415, 445
of hyperbolas, 416-421, 445
of parabolas, 400-404, 445
FOIL method, 224-225, 265, 293, 297, 316
Fractals, 292, 295-296
Fractions
adding, 522
complex, 519
decimals to, 621, 623
dividing, 517
multiplying, 517
reciprocals, 517-519
in simplest form, 516
Franklin, Benjamin, 18
Frequencies, 741
Frequency distributions, 668-673
normal, 664, 668-672, 676
skewed, 670
Functions, 53-63, 66-79, 96-98
absolute value, 87-90
Arccosine, 746-747, 749, 751-753, 781
Arcsine, 747-749, 751, 781
Arctangent, 747, 749, 753
composition of, 487-498
constant, 62, 87, 89, 451
cosecant, 742-744, 751, 753, 756-758, 794-795, 797-800, 805-806, 834-835

cosine, 737-743, 746-751, 753-759, 775-779, 781-782, 790-795, 797-800, 804-806, 810-836
cotangent, 742-744, 752-753, 756-758, 794-795, 797-800, 803, 805-806, 834-835
cubic, 451-452, 484
direct variation, 87, 89
even degree, 452-455
exponential, 546-552
greatest integer, 88-90
identity, 87, 492-493, 498, 555
inverse, 491-495, 498, 551, 555, 557, 746-753
linear, 62-63, 66-87, 91-94, 96-98, 108-121, 451-452
logarithmic, 551-552, 554-557, 581-584, 587
mappings, 488-489
odd degrees, 452-455, 483
periodic, 739, 741
polynomial, 451-464, 468-499, 506
quadratic, 317-319, 353-355, 360-378, 388-389, 451-452
rational, 504-509, 540
secant, 742-744, 753, 756-758, 794-795, 797-800, 803-805, 834-835
sine, 737-743, 746-751, 753-759, 767-770, 772-773, 776-778, 781-782, 790-791, 793-800, 803-805, 810-836
step, 88-90
tangent, 742-744, 746-749, 752-758, 762-764, 781, 793-795, 797-800, 803-805, 813-814, 834-835
vertical line test for, 54, 56
zeros of, 317, 453-455, 461, 469-486, 497
Fundamental Theorem of Algebra, 458, 469-470, 477

General formula for growth and decay, 581
Geometric means, 610-611, 614
Geometric sequences, 608-614, 633
common ratios, 608-614, 633
geometric means, 610-611, 614
recursive formulas for, 609, 611, 633
Geometric series, 615-624, 633
infinite, 620-624, 633
Geometry
angles, 49, 199, 227, 732-740, 756

area, 12, 169, 171-172, 223, 225-226, 228-229, 237, 285, 310, 316, 354-355, 362, 376, 380-381, 512, 514, 518, 572-573, 767-769
circles, 285, 382, 398-399, 405-407, 733-734
cones, 20-21
convex polygons, 64, 128
cubes, 252, 255
cylinders, 482
decagons, 700
diagonals, 64-65, 700
hyperbolic paraboloids, 422
midpoints, 397-399, 444
parallel lines, 68, 75-77, 97, 382
parallelograms, 12, 78, 281, 514, 518
perimeters, 24, 26, 63, 112, 148, 220, 281, 310, 376
perpendicular lines, 68-70, 76-77, 97
prisms, 343, 468, 478
pyramids, 476
Pythagorean Theorem, 263-264, 281, 396-397, 410, 737-738, 748, 757, 775, 829
rectangles, 57, 69, 71, 112, 229, 237, 310, 316, 354-355, 362, 376, 380-381
spheres, 9
squares, 223, 225, 572-573
trapezoids, 12, 514
triangles, 12, 26, 148, 169, 171-172, 199, 512, 737-738, 756, 756-779, 782
volume, 9, 20-21, 252, 255, 343, 468, 476, 478, 482, 484, 486
Goddard, Robert, 319
Gradians, 754
Graphing Calculator Explorations
conic sections, 425-426
evaluating expressions, 22-23
families of parabolas, 350-352
graphing exponential and logarithmic functions, 551-552
graphing linear equations, 58-59
graphing polynomial equations and approximating real zeros, 457-458
graphing rational functions, 504-505
graphing systems of equations, 104-107
lines of regression, 85-86
locating the vertex of a parabola, 359
matrices, 159-160
matrix row operations, 201
quadratic equations, 312-315
solving quadratic systems, 437-438

verifying trigonometric identities, 801-802

Graphs, coordinate
asymptotes, 505-509, 540, 551, 793-794
boundaries, 92-94, 98, 379-381, 389
linear programming, 129-139, 151
midpoints, 397-399, 444
number lines, 13, 31, 37-39, 43-44, 48, 385
of absolute value functions, 87-90
of circles, 405-407, 425-431, 433-443, 445
of complex numbers, 293, 295, 829
of constant functions, 87
of cosecants, 789, 794-795
of cosine, 738, 746, 788-795, 823, 834
of cotangent, 794-795
of ellipses, 408-415, 417, 425-436, 438, 440, 445
of exponential functions, 546-548, 550-552, 554
of hyperbolas, 416-422, 425-438, 440, 445
of identity functions, 87
of inequalities, 37-39, 43-44, 48, 122-125, 129-138, 151
of inverse functions, 492-494
of linear inequalities, 92-95
of lines, 58-73, 80-87, 91-94, 104-114, 120, 140-142, 150, 152, 451-452
of logarithmic functions, 551-552, 554
of ordered pairs, 52-54, 56-57
of parabolas, 54, 312-323, 329, 335, 344, 350-352, 359-373, 379-389, 400-404, 422, 425-438, 445, 451-453, 459
of polynomial functions, 451-463, 469-470, 482-485, 488, 504
of quadratic inequalities, 379-383, 385-386, 389, 441-443
of rational functions, 504-509
of secant, 794-795
of sine, 737-738, 788-796, 834
of step functions, 88-90
of systems of equations, 104-112, 114, 150, 432-441
of systems of inequalities, 105-107, 122-125, 129-138, 151, 440-443
of tangent, 793-795
slopes of, 66-83, 97, 108-110
three-dimensional, 139-143, 151-152

Graphs, statistical
bar, 639-641, 668
box-and-whisker plots, 658-663, 675
circle, 533, 639-641
histograms, 663, 668, 672
line, 639-641
line plots, 642, 645, 663, 674
lines of regression, 85-86
pictographs, 680
scatter plots, 80-86, 91, 98

Greatest common factors (GCF), 229-232, 516, 519-520

Greatest integer function, 88-90

Grouping symbols, 8-12

Guess and check, 310-311, 318, 344

Half-angle formulas, 816-819, 835

Half-planes, 379

Harmonic means, 530

Histograms, 663, 668, 672

Horizontal lines, 67

Hypatia, 382

Hyperbolas, 416-436, 440, 445
asymptotes, 417-421, 445
axes of symmetry, 417
centers of, 417-419, 421
conjugate axes, 417
foci of, 416-421, 445
transverse axes, 417-419, 421
vertices of, 417-421, 445

Hyperbolic paraboloids, 422

Hypergeometric probabilities, 719

Hypotenuse, 756

Identities
additive, 14-15
matrix, 179-181, 203
multiplicative, 14-15, 178-181, 203
trigonometric, 797-807, 811-835

Identity function, 87, 492-493, 498, 555

Imaginary numbers, 288-301, 469-474
conjugates, 297-300, 471
multiplying, 288-290
powers of, 289-291, 304
pure, 288-292, 304
as roots, 329-331, 341, 345

Imaginary unit, 288

Inclusive events, 715-718, 728

Inconsistent systems of equations, 198

Independent events, 684-688
probability of, 710-714

Independent systems of equations, 109-111

Index
even, 270, 272
of roots, 253, 270, 272
of summation, 605, 622

Inequalities, 36-40
absolute values, 43-45, 48, 93, 95, 123-125
addition property for, 36
compound sentences, 42-45, 48
constraints, 129-132, 151
division properties for, 37
graphing, 37-39, 43-44, 48, 92-95, 98, 122-125, 129-138, 151, 379-383, 385-386, 389
linear, 92-95
multiplication properties for, 37
quadratic, 379-387, 389-390
solving, 36-45, 48, 383-386, 390
systems of, 105-107, 122-125, 129-138, 151, 441-443, 446

Infinite geometric series, 620-624

Inscribed angles, 227

Integers, 13-14, 16, 292

Integral Zero Theorem, 475-476

Interest
compound, 269, 567-569, 574-575, 579, 583-584
simple, 10-12, 571

Interpolation, 578

Interquartile ranges, 654-659, 675

Inverse keys, 254-255

Inverses
additive, 14-17
of complex numbers, 299-304
of functions, 491-495, 498, 551, 555, 557, 746-753
of matrices, 159-160, 179-189, 203
multiplicative, 14-15, 179-189, 203, 299-300, 304, 517-519
of relations, 493

Inverse variations, 511-515, 540

Irrational numbers, 13-14, 16, 47, 254, 292
decimal approximations of, 254-256, 322, 328
exponents as, 546, 549

Isosceles triangles, 26, 737, 757, 769

Joffe, Abram, 35
Joint variations, 512-515, 540

Kepler, Johann, 286
Khufu, 476

Latus rectum, 401-404, 445
Law of Cosines, 775-778, 782
Law of Sines, 767-777, 782
Lee, John, 422
Like radical expressions, 264
Like terms, 15, 55, 210, 224, 524, 535
Linear equations, 60-63, 96
  direct variations, 87, 89
  graphing, 58-63, 66, 68-69, 108-114, 120, 140-142, 150, 152
  slope-intercept form, 73-83, 97, 108-109
  standard form of, 60-62, 73-77, 97, 184
  in three variables, 139-149, 152
  writing, 73-84
Linear expressions, 451
Linear functions, 62-63, 96, 451-452
  constant function, 62
  zero function, 62
Linear inequalities, 92-95
Linear permutations, 689-697, 726
  reflexive, 696-698
Linear programming, 129-139, 151
  constraints, 129-132, 151
  feasible regions, 129-130
Linear terms, 353-354, 388
Line graphs, 639-641
Line plots, 642, 645, 663, 674
Lines
  best-fit, 80, 85
  boundaries, 92-94, 98
  graphs of, see Linear Equations
  median fit, 91
  number, 13, 31-39, 43-44, 48, 385
  parallel, 68, 75-77, 97, 382
  perpendicular, 68-70, 76-77, 97

of regression, 85-86
slopes of, 66-83, 97
Line segment
  midpoints of, 397-399, 444
Location principle, 482-486, 497
Logarithmic functions, 554-557, 581-584, 587
  definition of, 555
  graphs of, 551-552, 554
  Property of equality for, 555, 558-560, 574-575
Logarithmic scales, 553, 558, 567
Logarithm keys, 564, 566, 568, 588
Logarithms, 553-570, 574-589
  antilogarithms, 564-569, 588
  applications of, 580-584
  change of base formula, 575-576
  characteristic, 563-565, 570, 587
  common, 563-566, 574-578, 582, 587-588
  mantissa, 563-565, 570, 587
  natural, 567-570, 580-583, 588
  power property of, 560-561, 574-575, 580, 587
  product property of, 558, 587
  quotient property of, 559-560, 587
Long division, 459-460
Lower quartile, 654-659, 675

Major axes, 410-415
Mantissa, 563-564, 565, 570, 587
Mappings, 53, 55
  of compositions, 488-489
Mathematical Exploration Toolkit, 41, 235, 287, 431, 531, 828
Matrices, 156-205, 515
  adding, 160, 163-166
  augmented, 194-201, 204
  coefficient, 184-188, 203
  column, 161
  coordinate, 161, 163-166
  determinants of, 159-160, 167-172, 181, 190-192, 194, 203
  dimensions of, 159, 161, 164
  elements of, 161-163, 200
  equal, 161-162, 164-166
  equations, 184-189
  identity, 179-181, 203
  inverses of, 159-160, 179-189, 203
  multiplying, 160, 173-189, 203
  reduced, 196, 204
  rotation, 174-175, 182
  row, 161
  row operations, 195-201

scalar multiplication of, 162-166
square, 161, 167-168
translation, 164
transposing, 159
Matrix logic, 156-158
Maximum values, 312, 359, 373-378, 389, 788-789
  relative, 457, 483-484
Means
  arithmetic, 598-600, 610, 632
  averages, 15, 648-652, 664-675
  geometric, 610-611
  harmonic, 530
Medians, 648-660, 674-675
Memory keys, 328
Mendelbroit, Benoit, 296
Michelangelo, 422
Midpoints, 397-399, 444
Minimum values, 312, 359, 373-377, 389, 788-789
  relative, 457, 483-484
Minor axes, 410-414
Minors, 167-168, 170
Mixed numbers, 522
Modes, 648-652, 674
Monomials, 210-219, 223
  adding, 210, 213, 264
  coefficients, 210, 213
  constants, 210
  degrees of, 210, 213, 223
  dividing, 215-219, 236, 246
  like terms, 210
  multiplying, 211, 213, 246
  subtracting, 210, 213
Multiplication
  associative property of, 14-15, 288
  commutative property of, 14-17, 259, 288
  of complex numbers, 293-295, 297, 304, 830-833
  cross, 511
  FOIL method, 224-225, 265, 293, 297, 316
  of fractions, 517
  identity matrices for, 179-181
  identity property of, 14-15
  of imaginary numbers, 288-290
  inverse matrices for, 179-189
  inverse property of, 14-15
  of matrices, 160, 173-178, 179-189, 203
  of monomials, 211, 213, 246
  by one, 14-15
  of polynomials, 224-227, 247
  of powers, 211-214, 246, 548, 558, 586
  of probabilities, 710-714, 727
  properties for inequalities, 37

property of equality, 19
  of radical expressions, 259, 262, 265-267, 302
  of rational expressions, 517-520, 541
  scalar, 162-163, 165-166, 202
  zero product property, 317-318, 339, 341, 461, 469, 822, 824
Mutually exclusive events, 715-718, 728

Napier, John, 570
Natural logarithms, 567-570, 581-583, 588
Natural numbers, 13-14, 16, 292
Nervi, Pier, 422
Normal distribution, 664, 668-676
Null hypothesis, 672-673
Number lines, 13
  graphing inequalities on, 31-39, 43-44, 48, 385
  line plots, 642, 645, 663, 674
Numerators, 516-519, 522-524

Octants, 139, 142, 151
Odd degree functions, 452-455, 483
Odd numbers, 254, 257-258
Odds, 706-709
Ohm's law, 506
Open sentences, 18
Opposites, 14
Order of operations, 8-10, 22, 46
Ordered pairs, 52-57, 61, 117
  of inverse functions, 492-494
Ordered triples, 139-143
Origin, 52, 732-733
Outliers, 654-657, 659-660, 675

Palindromes, 641
Parabolas, 54, 312-315, 317-321, 323, 329, 335, 344, 360-373, 379-383, 388-389, 400-404, 422, 425-438, 445, 451-453, 459
  axis of symmetry, 360-365, 367-370, 383, 388-389, 400-404, 422, 445

directions of openings, 350-351, 359, 365-370, 373, 379-380, 383, 389, 401-403, 445
  directrix, 400-404, 445
  families of, 350-352
  focus of, 400-404, 445
  latus rectum, 401-404, 445
  maximum points, 312, 359
  minimum points, 312, 359
  vertices of, 350-351, 359-370, 373, 379-380, 383, 388-389, 400-404, 445
Parallel lines, 68, 75-76, 97, 382
Parallelograms, 78
  area of, 12, 514, 518
  perimeters of, 281
Pascal's triangles, 625-626, 629
Patterns
  Binomial Theorems, 625-630, 634
  looking for, 64-66, 594-595
  sequences, 594-602, 608-614, 632-633
Perfect cubes, 260
Perfect numbers, 311
Perfect squares, 260, 322-327
  trinomials, 323-327
Perimeters, 24
  of parallelograms, 281
  of rectangles, 112, 310, 376
  of squares, 63
  of triangles, 26, 148, 220
Periodic functions, 739
  also see cosecant, cosine, cotangent, secant, sine, and tangent
Periods, 739, 788-789, 791-795, 834
Permutations
  circular, 694-698, 727
  linear, 689-693, 695-697, 726
  with repetitions, 691-693, 726
Perpendicular lines, 68-70, 76, 97
Phase shifts, 789
Pictographs, 680
Planes
  equations of, 139-142
  half, 379
Points
  breakeven, 103
  critical, 385
  discontinuity, 504-505
  graphing, 52-57
  midpoints, 397-399, 444
Polar coordinates, 829
Polar form, 829-833
Poles, 829
Polygons
  convex, 64, 128
  diagonals of, 64, 700, 702
  regular, 49

Polynomial equations, 451-469
Polynomial functions
  composition of, 487-498
  constant, 451
  cubic, 451-452
  even degree, 452-455
  graphs of, 451-459, 461, 463, 469-470, 482-485, 488, 504
  identity, 492-493, 498
  inverse, 491-495, 498
  odd degree, 452-455, 482
  quadratic, 451-452
  linear, 451-452
  relative maximum, 483-484
  relative minimum, 483-484
  zeros of, 453-455, 461, 469-486, 497
Polynomials, 223-249, 480
  adding, 210, 213, 223-226, 247
  binomials, 223-224
  constants, 451
  cubic expressions, 451
  degrees of, 223, 225, 451, 454
  depressed, 461-462, 468, 478
  descending order of, 223, 241, 471
  dividing, 215-219, 236-248, 459-463
  factoring, 235, 317-320, 323-324, 339, 344, 461-463, 468-469, 471-472, 480
  linear expressions, 451
  monomials, 210-219, 223, 246
  multiplying, 211, 213, 224-227, 246-247
  in one variable, 450-451, 454
  quadratic expressions, 451
  subtracting, 210, 213, 224-226, 247
  trinomials, 223
Power keys, 254-256, 271
Powers
  of binomials, 625-634, 721, 728
  of complex numbers, 831, 833, 836
  dividing, 215-219, 246, 559
  of imaginary numbers, 289-291, 304
  multiplying, 211-214, 246, 548, 558, 586
  of products, 211, 213-214, 246
  property of logarithms, 560-561, 574-575, 580, 587
  of quotients, 217-218, 236
  raising to powers, 211, 213, 217, 246, 548, 560, 586
Prediction equations, 80-84, 91, 98
Prime factors, 523
Prime numbers, 310
Principle roots, 253-255
Principal values, 746

Prisms
  volume of, 343, 468, 478
Probability, 684-729
  adding, 715-719, 728
  Basic Counting Principle, 684-
    685, 726
  binomial expansions, 628-630
  binomial experiments, 720-724,
    728
  combinations, 699-707, 716, 727
  dependent events, 685-689, 711-
    714
  of failure, 705, 707
  hypergeometric, 719
  inclusive events, 715-718, 728
  independent events, 684-688,
    710-714
  multiplying, 710-714
  mutually exclusive events, 715-
    718, 728
  odds, 706-709
  permutations, 689-707, 726-727
  Punnett squares, 209, 234
  simulations, 423-424, 722-725
  of success, 705-725, 727-728
  tree diagrams, 684, 687
Problem-solving strategies
  combining strategies, 465-467
  draw a diagram, 220-222
  examine the solution, 771-774
  guess and check, 310-311
  identify subgoals, 275-276
  list the possibilities, 29-30
  look for a pattern, 64-65, 594-
    595
  make a graph, 638-641
  make a table, 356-358
  organizing data, 532-534
  solve a simpler problem, 126-128
  use a model, 423-424
  use matrix logic, 156-158
  using estimation, 571-573
  using models, 682-683
  working backwards, 807-809
Products
  of one, 14-15
  of logarithms, 558, 587
  of powers, 211-214, 246, 548,
    558, 586
  of radicals, 258-259, 261
  of roots, 333-337, 345
Projects, Extended, 913-928
Properties
  addition, 14-17, 19, 36
  associative, 14-17, 288
  commutative, 14-17, 20, 259, 288
  distributive, 15-17, 20, 224-225,
    229, 231, 275, 535, 575, 803
  division, 19-20
  of equality, 18-21
  of equality of exponential func-
    tions, 548-549, 554

of equality of logarithmic functions, 555, 558-560, 574-575
identity, 14-15
for inequalities, 36-37
inverse, 14-17
of inverse functions, 492
of logarithms, 558-561, 587
multiplication, 19, 37
of multiplication, 14-17
of radicals, 258-261
of real numbers, 14-19, 47
reflexive, 18
subtraction, 19-21, 36
symmetric, 18
transitive, 18-21
trichotomy, 36
zero product, 317-318, 339, 341,
  461, 469, 822, 824
Proportions, 510-512, 578
  inverse, 511-515
Pure imaginary numbers, 288-292
Pyramids, 475, 483
Pythagorean Theorem, 263-264,
  281, 396-397, 410, 737-738, 748,
  757, 775, 829

Quadrants, 52, 129, 738-739, 817-
  819
Quadratic equations, 313-337
  applications of, 373-378, 389
  completing the square, 322-327
  degrees of, 316, 451
  factoring, 313-315, 317-320
  quadratic formula, 313-314, 327-
    334, 341, 345, 469, 478
  standard form of, 326, 332
  sum and product of roots, 333-
    337, 345
Quadratic expressions, 451
Quadratic factors, 339, 342, 346
Quadratic form, 340-343, 346
Quadratic formula, 313-314, 327-
  331, 333-334, 341, 345, 469, 478
  discriminants, 329-332, 345
Quadratic functions, 317-319, 353-
  355, 451-452
  applications of, 373-378, 389
  graphing, 312-323, 329, 335, 344,
    360-373, 388-389
  maximum values, 373-378, 389
  minimum values, 373-377, 389
  zeros of, 317
Quadratic inequalities, 379-390
  critical points, 385
  graphing, 379-383, 385-386, 389
  solving, 383-386, 390

Quadratic terms, 353-354, 388
Quartiles
  lower, 654-655, 658-659, 675
  upper, 654-655, 658-659, 675
Quotient properties
  of logarithms, 559-560, 587
  of powers, 215-219, 246, 559
  of radicals, 259-260

Radians, 733-735, 739, 780
Radicals, 252-274, 277-305
  adding, 264-265, 267
  conjugates, 266-267, 297-300
  decimal approximations, 254-256
  dividing, 260-262, 266-267, 302
  equations containing, 281-287,
    303
  imaginary numbers, 288-303
  like, 264
  multiplying, 259, 262, 265-267,
    302
  product property of, 258-261
  quotient property, 259-260
  rational exponents, 269-274,
    277-280, 303
  rationalizing the denominator,
    260-266, 271, 278-279, 298
  simplifying, 253-256, 258-274,
    277-280, 302-303
  subtraction, 264, 267
Radical signs, 253
Radicand, 253
Radii, 405-407, 445, 733
Raleigh, Sir Walter, 25
Ranges
  of data, 653-657
  interquartile, 654-657, 659, 675
  of relations, 53-56, 58-59, 85,
    105, 313, 488-489
Rational equations, 527-530, 542
  applications of 535-539
Rational exponents, 269-277, 303
Rational expressions, 516-527
  adding, 522-526, 541
  complex, 519-520, 524-526, 541
  dividing, 517-521, 541
  multiplying, 517-520, 541
  in simplest form, 516-520, 531
  subtracting, 524-526
Rational functions
  asymptotes, 506-509, 540
  definition, 506
  graphing, 504-509, 540
Rationalizing the denominators,
  260-262, 266, 271, 278-279, 298

Rational numbers, 13-16, 292
  as exponents, 269-280, 303
Rational Zero Theorem, 475, 478, 497
Ratios, 521
  common, 608-614, 633
Real numbers, 13-19, 292, 469-473
  as exponents, 547-548
  properties of, 14-19, 47
  roots of, 252-257
Reciprocals, 14, 19, 517-519, 807
  functions, 743
  negative, 68-70
Rectangles, 69, 71
  area of, 229, 237, 310, 316, 354-355, 362, 376, 380-381, 518
  perimeter of, 112, 220, 310, 376
  vertices of, 57
Rectangular form, 829-833, 836
Rectangular prisms, 343, 468, 477
Recursive formulas, 597-599, 609, 611, 632-633
Reduced matrices, 196, 204
Reflections, 493, 552, 696
Reflexive property of equality, 18
Regression lines, 85-86
Relations, 53-63, 66-100
  domain of, 53-56, 58
  functions, 53-63, 66-79, 96-98
  inverse, 493
  mappings of, 53, 55
  range of, 53-56, 58-59, 85, 105, 313, 488-489
Relative maximum, 457, 483-484
Relative minimum, 457, 483-484
Remainder Theorem, 459-461
Repeating decimals, 13
  to fractions, 621, 623
Right triangles, 737-738, 756-766
  applications of, 762-766
  hypotenuse, 756
  Pythagorean Theorem, 263-264, 281, 396-397, 410, 737-738, 748, 775, 829
  solving, 758-760, 782
Root keys, 254
Roots, 252-257, 314, 316
  cube, 252-256
  of equations, 461, 469, 471, 480
  even, 258
  imaginary, 329-331, 341, 345
  nature of, 329-332, 345
  odd, 258
  principle, 253-255
  square, 252-256
  sum and product of, 333-347
Rotation matrices, 174-175, 182

Rudolff, Christoff, 253
Ryan, Paul, 422

Scalar multiplication
  dilations, 162-165
  of matrices, 160, 162-166, 202
Scatter plots, 80-86, 91, 98
Scientific notation, 212-217, 246, 563
Secant, 742-744, 753, 756-758, 797-800, 803-805, 834-835
  graphs of, 794-795
Second-order determinants, 118-121, 151, 167-168, 181
Segments
  midpoints of, 397-399, 444
Seki Kowa, 149
Sequences
  arithmetic, 596-602, 610, 632
  common difference, 596-600, 632
  common ratio, 608-614, 633
  Fibonacci, 594-595
  geometric, 608-614, 633
  recursive formulas for, 597-599, 609, 611, 632-633
  terms of, 596-602, 608-614, 632-633
Series, 570, 602-607
  arithmetic, 602-607, 633
  geometric, 615-624, 633
  infinite, 620-624, 633
Sets
  empty, 32, 122, 823
  solution, 32
Sigma notation, 605-606, 617, 619, 622, 627-628, 634
Simple interest, 10-12, 571
Simplest form, 516-520
Simulations, 423-424, 722-723
  coin toss, 725
Sine, 737-743, 745-759, 781-782, 793-800, 803-805, 810-836
  graphs of, 737-738, 788-791, 793-796, 834
  inverse of, 747-749, 751, 781
  law of, 767-770, 772-773, 776-777, 782
  principal values of, 746
Slope-intercept form, 73-83, 97, 108-109
Slopes, 66-83, 97, 108-110
  of asymptotes, 418-421, 445
  of parallel lines, 68, 75-76, 97

of perpendicular lines, 68-70, 76, 97
Snell's Law, 745, 754, 822, 825
Solutions
  checking, 32-33, 113, 145, 185-186, 282-285, 318, 334, 337, 340-341, 528-530, 536-537, 824
  extraneous, 282, 284-285
  imaginary, 329-331, 341, 345
  roots, 316, 329-338, 480
  sets, 32
  of systems of equations, 108-121, 150-151
  test for unique, 190-192
Sostratus of Chidus, 763
Spheres, 9, 486
Spreadsheets, 486, 579, 631
Square roots, 252-256
Squares
  area of, 223, 225, 572-573
  completing the, 322-327, 345, 366-368, 373
  difference of, 230-231, 233, 247
  perfect, 231-233, 260, 322-327
  perimeters of, 63
  Punnett, 209, 234
Standard deviations, 664-671, 675
Standard form
  of equations of conic sections, 401, 405-406, 410-412, 417-418, 427-429
  of linear equations, 60-62, 73-77, 97, 184
  of quadratic equations, 326, 332
Standard position, 732-734
Statistics, 638-677
  bar graphs, 639-641, 668
  bell curves, 668-669, 676
  box-and-whisker plots, 658-663, 675
  circle graphs, 533, 639-641
  dispersion, 653
  frequency distribution, 668-673
  harmonic means, 530
  histograms, 663, 668, 672
  interquartile ranges, 654-657, 659, 675
  line graphs, 639-641
  line plots, 642, 645, 663, 674
  means, 15, 648-652, 664-671, 674-675
  medians, 648-652, 654-655, 658-660, 674-675
  modes, 648-652, 674
  normal distribution, 664, 668-672, 676
  null hypothesis, 672-673
  outliers, 654-657, 659-660, 675
  pictographs, 680
  prediction equations, 80-84, 91, 98

quartiles, 654-659
ranges, 653-657
samples, 638
scatter plots, 80-86, 91, 98
standard deviations, 664-667,
    669-671, 675
stem-and-leaf plots, 642-647,
    651-656, 663, 666, 674
Step functions, 88-90
Stradia, 763
Substitution
    method, 112-116, 145, 409, 441
    synthetic, 460, 462-464, 476
Subtraction
    of complex numbers, 293-294,
        304
    of monomials, 210, 213
    of polynomials, 224-226, 247
    property for inequalities, 36
    property of equality, 19-21
    of radical expressions, 264, 267
    of rational expressions, 524-526
Successes, 705-707
Sums
    of angles, 810-815, 835
    of arithmetic series, 603-607,
        633
    of cubes, 232-233
    of geometric series, 615-624, 633
    of infinite geometric series, 620-
        624, 633
    of roots, 333-337, 345
    of zero, 14-15
Symmetric property of equality, 18
Symmetry, 360, 551
Synthetic division, 241-245, 248,
    459-463, 468, 470, 478-479
Synthetic substitution, 460, 462-
    464, 476
Systems of equations, 108-121, 369
    augmented matrices, 195-204
    consistent, 109-111
    Cramer's Rule, 118-121, 149,
        151, 190-194, 204
    dependent, 109-111, 198
    elimination method, 112-119,
        144, 146, 150, 369, 440-441
    graphing, 104-105, 107-112, 114,
        150, 432-441
    inconsistent, 198
    independent, 109-111
    matrix equations for, 184-189
    quadratic, 432-443, 446
    solving, 104-105, 107-121, 150-
        152, 162, 184-204
    substitution method, 112, 114-
        116, 145, 439, 441
Systems of inequalities, 122-125
    graphs of, 105-107, 122-125, 129-
        138, 151, 441-443, 446

linear programming, 129-138,
    151

Tangent, 742-749, 752-758, 762-
    764, 781, 797-805, 834-835
    graph of, 793-795
    inverse of, 747, 749, 753
    principal values of, 746
Technology features
    amortization, 631
    coin toss simulation, 727
    compound interest, 579
    conic sections, 431
    Cramer's Rule, 194
    discriminants and roots, 332
    factoring, 235
    median-fit lines, 91
    quadratic functions, 365
    rational expressions, 531
    solving equations and inequali-
        ties, 41
    solving radical equations, 287
    solving systems of equations,
        117
    solving triangles, 761
    statistical graphs, 663
    trigonometric equations, 828
    zeros of polynomial functions,
        486
Terminal sides, 732-733, 737-739
Terminating decimals, 13
Terms
    constant, 353-354, 388
    like, 15, 55, 210, 224, 524, 535
    linear, 353-354, 388
    nth, 597-600, 609-613, 632-633
    quadratic, 353-354, 388
    of sequences, 596-614, 632-633
    of series, 602-606, 615-622, 633
Third-order determinants, 167-171,
    190-191, 203
Topology, 183
Traces, 141-142, 152
Transformations
    dilations, 162-165
    rotations, 174-177, 182
    translations, 163-165, 350-351
Transitive property of equality,
    18-21
Translations, 163-165, 350-351
    matrices, 164
Transverse axes, 417-419, 421
Trapezoids, 12, 514
Tree diagrams, 684, 687

Triangles
    area of, 12, 169, 171-172, 512,
        767, 769
    isosceles, 26, 737, 757, 769
    Pascal's, 625-626, 629
    perimeter of, 26, 148
    Pythagorean Theorem, 263-264,
        281, 396-397, 410, 737-738,
        748, 757, 775, 829
    right, 737-738, 756-766, 782
    solving, 758-761, 768-773, 782
    sums of angles, 199
Trichotomy property, 36
Trigonometry, 732-807, 810-837
    arccosine, 746-753, 781
    arcsine, 747-749, 751, 781
    arctangent, 747, 749, 753
    cosecant, 742-744, 751-758, 794-
        806, 834-835
    cosine, 737-743, 746-759, 775-
        782, 790-800, 804-806, 810-836
    cotangent, 742-744, 752-758,
        794-800, 803-806, 834-835
    difference of angles formulas,
        810-813, 835
    double-angle formulas, 815-819,
        835
    equations, 820-828, 836
    graphs, 737-738, 746, 790-796,
        823, 834
    identities, 797-800, 801-807,
        811-819, 822-824, 835
    law of cosines, 775-778, 782
    law of sines, 767-770, 772-773,
        776-777, 782
    notation for complex numbers,
        829-833, 836
    secant, 742-744, 753-758, 794-
        805, 834-835
    sine, 737-759, 767-778, 781-782,
        790-805, 810-836
    solving triangles, 758-761, 768-
        769, 771-773, 782
    sums of angles formulas, 810-
        815, 835
    tangent, 742-758, 762-764, 781,
        793-805, 813-814, 834-835
Trinomials, 223
    factoring, 229-233, 247, 317-318,
        320, 323-324, 339, 344
    perfect square, 231-233, 323-327
Truncated values, 643-644

Unit circles, 733-734, 736-737,
    756, 797, 799
Upper quartiles, 654-655, 658-659,
    675

V

Variations, 510-515
  constants of, 510-514
  direct, 87, 89, 510-515, 540
  inverse, 511-515, 540
  joint, 512-515, 540
Venn diagrams, 13
Vertical lines, 67
Vertical line test, 54, 56
Vertices, 114-115, 120
  of angles, 732
  of hyperbolas, 417-421, 445
  of parabolas, 350-351, 359-370,
    373, 379-380, 383, 388-389,
    400-404, 445
  of rectangles, 57
Volume
  of cones, 20-21
  of cubes, 252, 255
  of cylinders, 482, 486
  of prisms, 343, 468, 477
  of pyramids, 475, 483
  of spheres, 9, 486

W

Whole numbers, 13-14, 16, 292

X

x-axis, 52, 85, 139-140, 318, 340,
  457, 732, 788-789, 821
x-coordinates, 52, 86, 105, 737
x-intercepts, 59, 69-72, 93, 141-
  142, 152, 312, 314, 318, 340,
  457, 483, 820

Y

y-axis, 52, 85, 139-140, 457, 788-
  789, 821
y-coordinates, 52, 86, 105, 737
y-intercepts, 59, 69-83, 93, 97, 109-
  110, 141-142, 152, 457

Z

z-axis, 139-140
Zero function, 62
Zero Product Property, 317-318,
  339, 341, 461, 469, 822, 824
Zeros
  adding, 14-15
  approximating 457, 481-482,
    484-486, 497
  Descartes' rule of signs, 471-473,
    476-477, 481-482
  as exponents, 215-216, 246
  of functions, 317, 453-455, 457-
    458, 461, 469-486, 497
  Integral Zero Theorem, 475-476
  location principle, 482, 484, 486,
    497
  Rational Zero Theorem, 475,
    478, 497
z-intercepts, 141-142, 152

PHOTO CREDITS

Cover, G. R. Beechler

v(t), Michael A. Kellar/The Stock Market, **(b),** C. Garoutte/Tom Stack & Assoc; **vi,** Aaron Haupt; **vii(t),** Randy Duchaine/The Stock Market, **(b),** Erik Simonsen/The Image Bank; **viii(t),** Michel Tcherevkoff/The Image Bank, **(b),** Hartman-Dewitt/Comstock; **ix(t),** Rob Atkins/The Image Bank, **(b),** Larry Hamill; **x,** Aaron Haupt; **xi(t),** Will McIntyre/Photo Researchers, **(b),** Kunio Owaki/The Stock Market; **xii(t),** Thomas Kitchin/Tom Stack & Assoc, **(b),** Hank Morgan/Rainbow; **xiii(t),** Charles West/The Stock Market, **(b),** Robert J. Herke/The Image Bank; **xiv,** Aaron Haupt; **xv(t),** Galen Rowell/Mountain Light, **(b),** Grant V. Faint/The Image Bank; **xvi,** Galen Rowell/Mountain Light; **6,** Doug Martin; **7,** Michael A. Kellar/The Stock Market; **8,** Skip Comer; **10,** Ted Rice; **12,** Ralph Cowan/Tony Stone Images; **14,** Doug Martin; **17,** Skip Comer; **18,** Elaine Shay; **21,** Monica V. Brown; **22,** Elaine Shay; **24,** Skip Comer; **27,** Elaine Shay; **28,** Skip Comer; **29,** Tony Stone Images; **30,** Skip Comer; **34,** Doug Martin; **35,** Bettmann Archive; **36,** C. J. Zimmerman/FPG; **38,** Skip Comer; **40,** John Biever/Sports Illustrated © TIME, Inc; **45,** Gary Guisinger/Photo Researchers; **50,** Marty Snyderman; **51,** C. Garoutte/Tom Stack & Assoc; **52,** H. P. Merton/The Stock Market; **53,** Skip Comer; **57,** Mike Surowiak/Tony Stone Images; **61,** Four By Five/Superstock; **63,** Larry Hamill; **65,** Elaine Shay; **75,** Stephen Frink/The Stock Market; **78(t),** Skip Comer, **(b),** David Dennis; **79,** The Bettmann Archive; **81,82,** Skip Comer; **84,** Andy Sacks/Tony Stone Images; **87,** The Telegraph Color Library/FPG; **90,** Ronald C. Modra/Sports Illustrated; **92,** David Sailors/The Stock Market; **94,** Skip Comer; **95,** Andrew Sacks/Tony Stone Images; **102,** Doug Martin; **103,** R. Duchain/The Stock Market; **109,112,** Skip Comer; **116,** Doug Martin; **122,** SuperStock; **125,** Skip Comer; **126,** Doug Martin; **129,** The Telegraph Colour Library/FPG; **131,133,** Skip Comer; **137(t),** Lewis Portnoy/The Stock Market, **(b),** Skip Comer; **139,** Seth Goltzer/The Stock Market; **143,** Frank Cezus/Tony Stone Images; **149,** Skip Comer; **154,** John Madera/The Stock Market; **155,** Erik Simonsen/The Image Bank; **156,** Chris Jones/The Stock Market; **157,** Elaine Shay; **166,** Skip Comer; **167,** Jeff Zaruba/The Stock Market; **172,** Connie Geocaris/Tony Stone Images; **173,** Skip Comer; **174,** David L. Perry; **187,191,** Skip Comer; **193,** George Anderson; **200,** Skip Comer; **204,** Elaine Shay; **208,** Matt Meadows/Peter Arnold, Inc; **209,** Michel Tcherevkoff/Image Bank; **210,** D. Stoecklein/The Stock Market; **212,** California Institute of Technology; **214,** Daniele Pellegrini/Photo Researchers; **215,** NASA; **216,** Paul Silverman/Fundamental Photographs; **219,** Bob Thomason/Tony Stone Images; **221,** Elaine Shay; **223,236,** Doug Martin; **240,243,** Skip Comer; **248,** Lee Foster/FPG; **250,** Doug Martin; **251,** Hartman-Dewitt/Comstock; **255(l),** Doug Martin, **(r),** Ken Frick; **256,** Allen B. Smith/Tom Stack & Assoc; **258,** George H. Matchneer; **261,** Stock Concepts; **263,** file photo; **265,** Roy Morsch/The Stock Market; **268,** Hank Morgan/Science Source/Photo Researchers; **276,** file photo; **277,** NASA; **280,** Elaine Shay; **281,275,** Doug Martin; **286,** NASA; **291,** Al Satterwhite/The Image Bank; **292,** Digital Art/Westlight; **295,** Michael Melford/Image Bank; **296(t),** Hansen Planetarium, **(b),** Courtesy IBM; **298,** Michael Melford/Image Bank; **301,** Dale O'Dell/Comstock; **308,** Doug Martin; **309,** Rob Atkins/The Image Bank; **310,** Denver Bryan/Comstock; **311,** Johnny Johnson; **316,** Hank Morgan/Rainbow; **320,** Tim Courlas; **321,** Henri Georgi/Comstock; **323,** Skip Comer; **325,** Steven E. Sutton/DUOMO; **328,** Skip Comer; **331,** NASA; **337,** Doug Martin; **338,** Yale Babylonian Collection; **343,346,** NASA; **348,** Doug Martin; **349,** Larry Hamill; **353,** Doug Martin; **355,** Hank Morgan/Science Scource/Photo Researchers; **358,** Elaine Shay; **364,** Skip Comer; **366,** Tim Courlas; **371,** Hartman-Dewitt/Comstock; **373,** A. Schmidecker/FPG; **376,** Matt Bradley/Tom Stack & Assoc; **379(t),** Skip Comer, **(b),** Gary Gladstone/The Image Bank; **381,** Doug Martin; **382,** Harvey Lloyd/Stock Market; **383,** Doug Martin; **387,** Gary Bumgarner/Tony Stone Images; **390,** Alan Carey; **394,** Doug Martin; **395,** Will & Deni McIntyre/Photo Researchers; **400,** Nadia MacKenzie/Tony Stone Images; **402,** David M. Dennis; **405,** John Turner/FPG; **408,** Russ Kinne/Comstock; **410,** Don Carrol/The Image Bank; **414,** Jack Zehrt/FPG; **418,** K. Iwasaki/The Stock Market; **421,** Richard Dole/DUOMO; **422,** Gerald L. French/The Photo File; **424,** Doug Martin; **428,** Charles Palek/Tom Stack & Assoc; **432,** Doug Martin; **434,** Brian Parker/Tom Stack & Assoc; **436(l),** Paul J. Sutton/DUOMO, **(r),** David Madison/DUOMO; **440,** Jim Brown/The Stock Market; **443,** Ted Mahieu/The Stock Market; **448,** Doug Martin; **449,** Kunio Owaki/The Stock Market; **452,** E. R. Degginger; **454(t),** Robert & Linda Mitchell, **(b),** Robert & Linda Mitchell; **456,** Elaine Shay; **459(t),** Bryan Yablonski/DUOMO, **(b),** file photo; **462,** Al Tielemans/DUOMO; **464,** Doug Martin; **465,** Elaine Shay; **467(t),** Richard Steedman/The Stock Market, **(b),** Luis Villota/The Stock Market; **468,** Doug Martin; **469,** Elaine Shay; **474,** Howard Sochurek/The Stock Market; **476(t),** Smithsonian Institution, **(b),** Paul Steel/The Stock Market; **479,** S. Barry O'Rourke/The Stock Market; **481,** Andy Canfield/The Image Bank; **485(t),** Hartman-Dewitt/Comstock, **(b),** Tim Courlas; **487,489,** Tim Courlas; **490,** Doug Martin; **491,495,** Tim Courlas; **498,** Skip Comer; **502,** Larry Hamill; **503,** Thomas Kitchin/Tom Stack & Assoc; **506,** Skip Comer; **509,** National Highway Traffic Safety Administration; **510,** NASA; **512,** Skip Comer; **514,** Elaine Shay; **515(t),** Ray Mathis/The Stock Market, **(b),** UMBILLIC TORUS NC by Sculptor/Mathematician Helaman Ferguson, photo credit: Terry Clough; **518,** Geoffrey Gove/The Image Bank; **521,** John Kelly/The Image Bank; **522,** Ansel Adams/Ansel Adams Publication Rights Trust/Mount Williamson/Sierra Nevada; **526,** Franco Fontana/The Image Bank; **530,** Joanna McCarthy/The Image Bank; **532,534,** Skip Comer; **536,** Don Landwehrle/The Image Bank; **537,** Jany Sauvanet/Photo Researchers; **538,** Walter Bibikow/The Image Bank; **542,** Tim Courlas; **544(t),** Doug Martin, **(b),** Antonio Luiz Hamdan/The Image Bank; **545,** Hank

Morgan/Rainbow; **546,** Tom Broker/Rainbow; **550,** Courtesy of AT&T; **553,** Ted Mahien/The Stock Market; **557,** Skip Comer; **559,** Peter Miller/Photo Researchers; **562,** Steve Dunwell/The Image Bank; **564,** Lou Jawitz/The Image Bank; **566,** Bettmann Archive; **567,** Tim Courlas; **568(tl),** Janet Adams, **(bl),** George Matchneer; **(br),** Frank Cezus; **570,** Culver Pictures, Inc; **572,** Skip Comer; **573(t),** Johnny Johnson, **(b),** Frans Lanting/Minden Pictures; **574,** Doug Martin; **577,** Tim Courlas; **578,** Skip Comer; **580,** CNRI Science Photo Library/Photo Researchers; **581(l),** Murray Alcosser/The Image Bank, **(r),** Gregory Heisler/The Image Bank; **583,585,** Skip Comer; **592,** Doug Martin; **593,** Charles West/The Stock Market; **595(t),** Pete Turner/The Image Bank, **(b),** Elaine Shay; **596(t),** Richard Dole/DUOMO, **(b),** Steven E. Sutton/DUOMO; **598,** Steve Lissau; **601,** Lou Jones/Image Bank; **602,** Tom Sanders/The Stock Market; **603,** Val D'Isere, France/DUOMO; **607,** Doug Martin; **608,** Custom Medical Stock Photo; **610,** Comstock; **614,** Tim Courlas; **615,** Comstock; **616,** Atomic Energy Commission; **619,** Gerald L. French/The Photo File; **620,** Tom Pantages; **622,** Doug Martin; **624(l),** DUOMO, **(r),** Elaine Shay; **628,** Doug Martin; **630,** Devik Murray/The Image Bank; **636,** SIU/Peter Arnold; **637,** Robert J. Henke/The Image Bank; **638,** Cliff Fuelner/The Image Bank; **639,** David Madison/DUOMO; **640,** Alan Goldsmith/The Stock Market; **644,** Dan Helms/DUOMO; **645,** Tim Courlas; **646,** Al Tielemans/ DUOMO; **647,** Paul J. Sutton/DUOMO; **648,** Lynn Goldsmith/LGI; **650,** Skip Comer; **651,** Galen Rowell; **652(t),** Ira Block/The Image Bank, **(b),** Steve Niedorf/The Image Bank; **653,** Grant V. Faint/The Image Bank; **654(t),** Harald Sund/The Image Bank, **(b),** C. David Hiser/The Image Bank; **656(t),** Ken Frick, **(b),** Richard Hansen/Photo Researchers; **658,** Larry Hamill; **659,** Tim Courlas; **661,** Steven E. Sutton/DUOMO; **662,** David Madison/DUOMO; **664,** Ernst Brown/Comstock; **665,** Ben Glass/Movie Still Archives; **667,** Hans Wendler/ The Image Bank; **669,** Doug Martin; **670,** Michel Tcherevkopf/The Image Bank; **671,** Garry Gay/The Image Bank; **680,** Frans Lanting/Minden Pictures; **681,** Galen Rowell/Mountain Light; **682,** J. Barry O'Rourke/The Stock Market; **684,** Aaron Haupt; **685,** Skip Comer; **687,688,** Elaine Shay; **689,** Al Tielemans/DUOMO; **690,** Steven Sutton/DUOMO; **691,692,** Skip Comer; **693,** Malcolm S. Kirk/Peter Arnold; **697,** William Roy/The Stock Market; **698,** David L. Perry; **699,** Joe Dimaggio/The Stock Market; **701(t),** Elaine Shay, **(b),** Skip Comer; **702,** Doug Martin; **703,** The Washnik Studio/The Stock Market; **705,708,** Elaine Shay; **709,** Doug Martin; **711,** Sheila Goode-Green; **712,** Alford W. Cooper/Photo Researchers; **714,** Skip Comer; **716,** Steven Burr Williams/The Image Bank; **717,** Doug Martin; **718(t),** Ben Simmons/The Stock Market, **(b),** Uwe Omner/The Image Bank; **719,** Smithsonian Institution; **721,** Skip Comer; **722,** Doug Martin; **723,** Elaine Shay; **724,** Hickson & Associates; **728,** Paul Trummer/The Image Bank; **730,** Doug Martin; **731,** Grant V. Faint/The Image Bank; **733,** Doug Martin; **735(t),** Doug Martin, **(b),** Elaine Shay; **737(l),** Skip Comer, **(r),** Kodansha; **740,** Dave Davidson/The Stock Market; **741,** Xenophon A. Beake/The Stock Market; **743(l),** Michael R. Schneps/The Image Bank, **(r),** National Maritime Museum; **744(t),** Charles C. Place/The Image Bank, **(b),** Art Resource; **745,** Kodansha; **746,** Doug Martin; **750,** William McKinney/Photo Researchers; **751,** Russ Kinne/Comstock; **754,** Stuart Cohen/Comstock; **756,** Jim Olive/Peter Arnold; **760,** Aaron Haupt; **762,** Tony Stone Images; **763,** F. Stuart Westmoreland/Tom Stack & Associates; **764,** Greg Heisler/The Image Bank; **765,** Joe Brilla, Jr; **766,** Comstock; **767,** Diana Calder/The Stock Market; **768,** Pat & Tom Leeson/Photo Researchers; **770,** David Cavagnaro; **771,** Aaron Haupt; **773,** Ben Simmons/The Stock Market; **774,** Gerald L. French/The Photo File; **775,** Lindsay Gerard; **777,** Randall Schieber; **779,** Carl Purcell/Photo Researchers; **786,** Doug Martin; **787,** Galen Rowell; **793,** Doug Martin; **796(t),** Lynn Stone, **(b),** Larry Brock/Tom Stack & Assoc; **803,** Ben Rose/The Image Bank; **806,** Elaine Shay; **807,** Ken Frick; **808,** Comstock; **809,810,** Doug Martin; **812,** Michael Collier; **814,** Steven M. Krasemann/Photo Researchers; **816,** Stephn Dalton/Photo Researchers; **819(t),** Michel Hans/Photo Researchers, **(b),** Skip Comer; **825,** Skip Comer; **826,** Tom Tracy/The Stock Market; **833(t),** Dan McCoy/Rainbow, **(b),** J. H. Carmichael/The Image Bank; **A1,** James Blinn/JPL; **A2,** file photo; **A3(tl),** Jack Zehrt/FPG, **(bl),** Ruth Bogart, **(r),** Courtesy Tiara Observatory; **A4,** First Image; **A5,** Tom Tracy/FPG; **A6,** Mak-1; **A7(t),** Tom Tracy/The Stock Market, **(b),** Mak-1; **A8, A9,** Mak-1; **A10(tl),** Ken Frick, **(bl),** First Image, **(r),** Larry Hamill; **A11(t),** FPG/Sandak/National Gallery of Art, **(b),** Skip Comer; **A12,** Larry Hamill; **A13,** Tim Courlas; **A14,** Kenji Kerins; **A15,** Doug Martin; **A16,** Courtesy JPL.

GLENCOE

EXTENDED PROJECTS

for Merrill Algebra 2 with Trigonometry

PROJECTS

1 Predicting the
   Future A2

2 Waste Not, Want
   Not A6

3 The Million-Dollar
   Challenge A10

4 Creating Order
   From Chaos A14

Project 1 Notes

Objectives

- Search for relationships between sets of data representing natural phenomena and possible predictors of those phenomena.
- Use mathematical methods such as scatter plots and prediction equations to analyze potential relationships between sets of data.
- Identify when relationships between events are causal and when they are coincidental.

Overview

In this project, students choose a phenomenon that is not understood completely and attempt to find a predictor that can be used to predict the future behavior of the phenomenon. The predictor may have a suspected causal link with the phenomenon or it may be only statistically linked with it. In either case, students will illustrate the link using mathematical methods from Chapters 1-4 and possible additional methods of their own creation. Students will test their predictor by making a prediction and checking it against the actual behavior of the phenomenon they are studying.

Mathematical Content

Students should incorporate ideas from Chapters 1-4 in their analysis, possibly including but not limited to functions and variables, scatter plots, lines of regression, median-fit lines, and graphing. You may wish to ask students to use graphing calculators in their work.

PROJECT 1

Predicting the Future

The better we understand nature, the more accurately we are able to predict its behavior. Ancient peoples had no understanding of the movements of the sun and the moon, so predicting such events with accuracy was impossible. As a result, they believed that eclipses occurred when their gods were angry. When astronomers discovered the causes of eclipses and calculated the orbits of the sun and the moon, they were able to predict the timing of eclipses with pinpoint accuracy.

Human nature, too, is better understood today than ever before. Corporations routinely take the findings of sociologists and psychologists and use them in advertising campaigns to persuade people to purchase their products.

Despite great advances in science, however, much of nature remains a mystery. Making accurate predictions about these areas is as chancy as predicting eclipses was for ancient peoples. Will there be a hurricane? What parts of the world will be affected? How will people vote in the presidential election? Will the stock market go up or down?

In an effort to make predictions about natural occurrences that are not fully understood, some people search for *predictors*, events or facts which, for no obvious reason, seem to correlate with the occurrences. For example, geologist Ruth Simon has discovered that cockroaches become more active during the hours leading up to a major earthquake. Political analysts have noted that the candidate with the longer name has won nearly 75% of the presidential elections in American history.

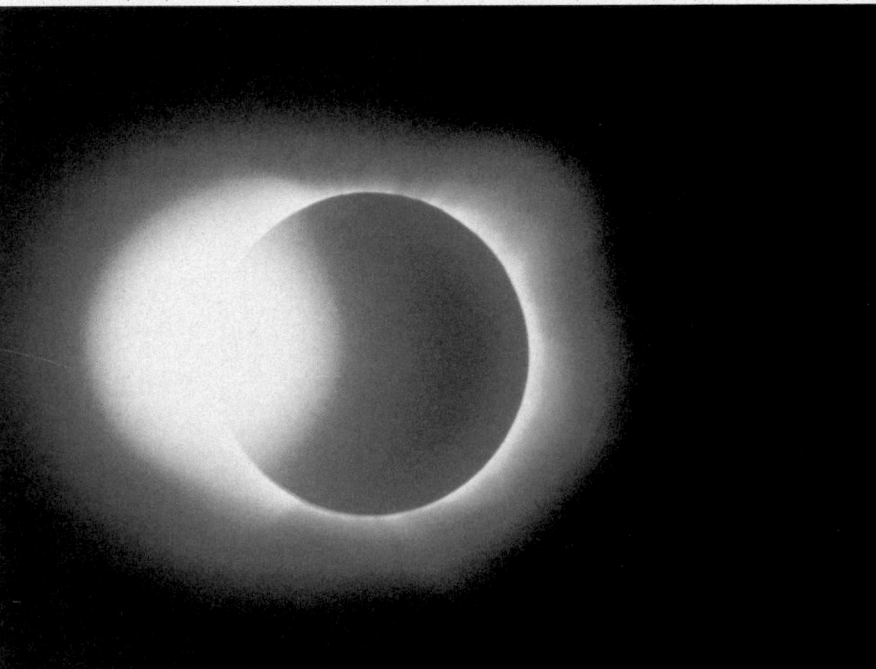

A2

Find a Predictor

In this project, you will attempt to find a predictor that can be used to predict the behavior of some natural phenomenon. You will analyze several possible predictors to find the one with the best promise. Then you will use the one you chose to make a prediction about the future.

Project Description

After agreeing on a phenomenon to study, group members collect data and search for patterns in the data relating the phenomenon to other possible causal factors. Through brainstorming they identify several possible predictors. They collect data on the predictors, then analyze the data to find the predictor with the best chance of predicting the future behavior of the phenomenon. Finally, they test their results by making a prediction using their chosen predictor and observing an actual outcome or several actual outcomes.

Group Size

Students should work in groups of three to five.

Time

Students will need four to six weeks to complete the project.

Materials Needed

Students will need research materials such as almanacs and encyclopedias to find data for their analyses. Depending on how they choose to approach their analyses, they may need graphing calculators, graph paper, calculators, and/or computers.

Resources

Students may wish to consult a statistics text to learn more about correlation, regression, lines of best fit, and other topics that may help them in their analyses of data in this project.

A3

Tips for Groups

Groups should choose a phenomenon to study that is of interest to all members of the group. If groups have difficulty agreeing, suggest new areas of interest they may not have considered.

Examples

Sports: One sports analyst has pointed out that the Notre Dame football team usually wins home games that it plays the week after it loses on the road.

Popular music: Recordings by groups with at least one million-seller under their belts appear to be far more likely to sell a million records than do recordings by other groups.

Assessment

In assessing reports, look for clear, cogent explanations, strong arguments, creative efforts to find correlations among variables, and thinking that indicates that students understand how sets of data can relate to one another. While identification of an accurate predictor should be praised, it is the critical and creative analysis of data and search for correlations that are most important in this project.

Getting Started

Follow these steps to carry out your project.

- Choose a phenomenon that interests you whose behavior cannot be predicted with total accuracy. It could be something that occurs in the natural world (for example, weather patterns, changes in sizes of wildlife populations, or appearances of comets). Or it could involve human nature (for example, voting patterns, success of relief pitchers in baseball, or consumer preferences in fashions, films, or music). Be sure that there is plenty of data available on the phenomenon you choose and that the phenomenon is not completely arbitrary in its behavior.

- Collect data on the phenomenon. Study it, searching for patterns, and discuss your findings with your group.

- Brainstorm with your group to identify at least four possible predictors of the phenomenon. Spend a good deal of time searching for promising predictors. Those you settle on may have a seemingly close connection with the phenomenon or, like the "last name" predictor for presidents, may seem unrelated to it.

- Collect data on your predictors.

- Analyze your predictors. Your analysis should include some of the methods discussed in Chapters 1-4. You may wish to draw scatter plots and find prediction equations. You can use a graphing calculator to draw lines of regression or a computer to draw median-fit lines. After you complete your analysis, choose the predictor you judge to have the most promise.

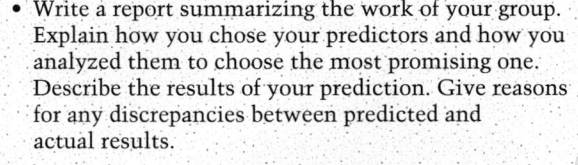

- Use your predictor to predict the future behavior of the phenomenon you have studied.

- Write a report summarizing the work of your group. Explain how you chose your predictors and how you analyzed them to choose the most promising one. Describe the results of your prediction. Give reasons for any discrepancies between predicted and actual results.

A4

Extensions

1. Find and express in algebraic language a function relating your predictor and the phenomenon you studied in this project.
2. Describe possible connections between your predictor and the phenomenon that may explain the success of your predictor.
3. Find examples in history where deepening understanding of nature allowed people to predict the behavior of phenomenon previously believed to be arbitrary and unpredictable.

Culminating Activities

Show what you have learned in this project by completing one of the following activities.

1. Make an oral presentation to the class describing your results in this project.
2. Conduct a classroom debate on this topic: "Mathematics Can Be Used to Illuminate All of the Phenomena of Nature."
3. Outline a method for finding predictors of little understood phenomena.

Additional Notes

Be sure groups work on their projects at a regular pace throughout the project period, rather than attempt to complete them at a mad pace as the deadline approaches. You may wish to provide regular times in class for groups to work on their projects.

After students have completed their projects, set aside some class time for discussion. You may wish to ask these questions.

- What was the most difficult problem you had to solve?
- If you repeated the project, what would you do differently this time?
- How does mathematics deepen your understanding of the world?
- What did you learn by working on this project?

Scoring Rubric

Top Level: Complete work. Clear, coherent, unambiguous explanation. Effective communication. Strong arguments. Understanding of math ideas and processes. Goes beyond requirements of problem.

Second Level: Solid work but less complete and less elegant than above. Does not go beyond requirements of problem.

Third Level: Complete response but muddled explanation. Incomplete arguments. Some understanding of math but vague or unclear responses.

Fourth Level: Omits significant parts. Major errors.

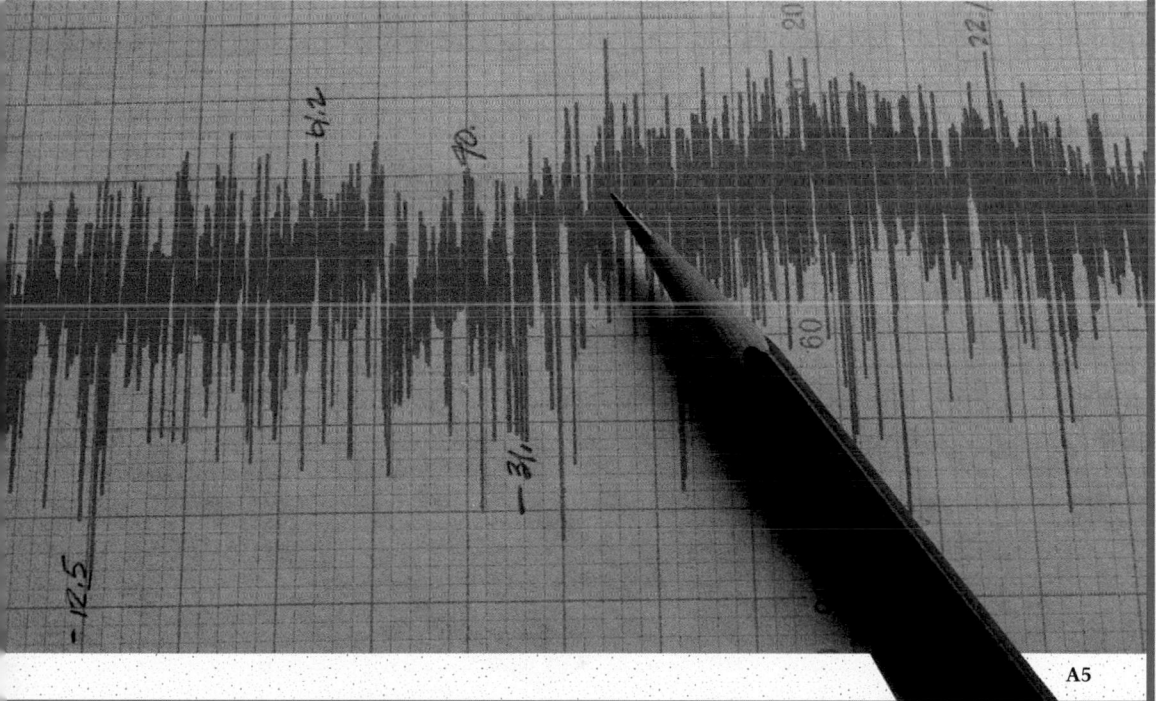

A5

Project 2 Notes

Objectives

- Investigate relationships between the volume and surface area of a rectangular prism.
- Discover how a rectangular prism can be constructed with maximum volume or with a specified volume.

Overview

Physical objects are endowed with certain characteristics. Changes in one will affect some characteristics but will have no effect at all on others. For example, a change in the weight of the objects in a box will alter the box's density but not its dimensions.

In this project, students investigate relationships between two closely-related physical characteristics, volume and surface area. They do this in a real-world context by looking at questions an engineer or designer might face: How can I maximize the volume of a product cut from a pattern of specified area? How can I use that pattern to create a product of specified volume while using the least material?

Mathematical Content

Students should incorporate ideas from Chapters 5-8 in their projects, possibly including but not limited to quadratic equations, the quadratic formula, quadratic functions, and analyzing graphs of quadratic functions.

Waste Not, Want Not

A manufacturer uses rectangular pieces of sheet metal with squares removed from the corners as patterns for open-topped wastebaskets.

The sides are folded up to produce the rectangular-prism-shaped wastebaskets.

The volume and surface area of a wastebasket depend on the size of the corners that are removed. Suppose a design engineer begins with a 12-by-20 inch rectangle. Removal of 3-inch squares results in a 14-by-6-by-3 inch wastebasket. This wastebasket would have a volume of 252 cubic inches and a surface area of 288 square inches.

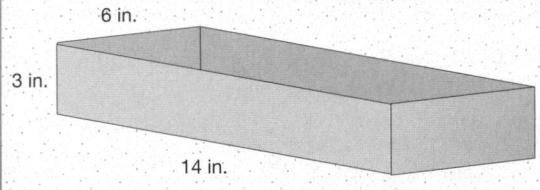

Removal of 4-inch squares results in a 12-by-4-by-4 inch wastebasket with a volume of 192 cubic inches and a surface area of 224 square inches.

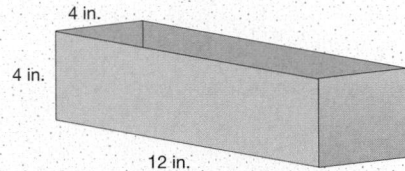

Two important constraints have been placed on the design engineer: wastebaskets should have a large volume to attract customers, but as small a surface area as possible, to cut down on the cost of material.

A6

Design a Wastebasket

A design engineer has been asked to answer the following questions. Given a rectangular piece of sheet metal measuring m inches by n inches:

1. How can it be cut to obtain a wastebasket with the maximum volume? What is the surface area of the wastebasket?

2. How can it be cut to obtain a particular desired volume? If there are several ways to cut it, which one uses the least material?

3. What are the relationships between the volume and surface area of a wastebasket as the size of the corner changes?

In this project, you will attempt to answer these questions.

Project Description
Students use rectangular patterns with congruent squares cut from the corners to make open-topped rectangular prisms. By noting patterns in their results they infer relationships between the volume and surface area of rectangular prisms. They attempt to use these to work out methods for maximizing the volume of a prism constructed from a pattern of specified dimensions and for cutting such a pattern to obtain a prism of specified volume.

Group Size
Students should work in groups of three to five.

Time
Students will need four to six weeks to complete the project.

Materials Needed
paper or posterboard, tape, glue, scissors, calculators, graphing calculators

Resources
All major manufacturers employ engineers or designers whose job it is to design packaging. Students may wish to contact engineers to discuss the problems raised in this project. Motivated students can research calculus texts to find how the derivative can be used to find maxima and minima of functions.

Tips for Groups

Encourage groups to plan their research carefully, working out sensible divisions of labor in designing and constructing prisms. After they have tentative answers to the questions posed in the project, encourage them to test their hypotheses on a new set of models they have yet to investigate.

Assessment

In assessing projects, look for thorough research, thoughtful analyses of data, complete and clearly communicated answers to questions, and creative relationships between volume and surface area, carefully explained.

Getting Started

Follow these steps to carry out your project.

- Design wastebaskets on paper and make models of your designs. Find the volumes and surface areas of your models. Keep accurate records of your results.

- Study the models looking for relationships among corner-square sizes, volumes, and surface areas. Discuss your preliminary findings with your group.

- Work out a plan for investigating the three design questions posed on the previous page. Among the tools you may decide to use are graphs, formulas, diagrams, tables, calculators, graphing calculators, and computers.

- Answer the questions posed on page A7.

- Actually build the preferred wastebasket using available materials like cardboard, plywood, or metal.

A8

Extensions

1. As you learned in Chapter 8, the graphs of quadratic functions are parabolas. The vertex of a parabola is the maximum or minimum point on the parabola. Suppose that the volume, V, of a wastebasket is given by the expression $V = Ax^2 + Bx + C$, where x is the length of a side of the corner square. Find a formula for the value of x that will produce the maximum volume.

2. Draw a pattern for a large piece of material that would be cut into smaller pieces to form wastebaskets that meet the criteria. Be sure to account for overlap when the wastebaskets are assembled. Also, try to minimize the amount that cannot be used.

3. Contact an engineer who designs packages for a manufacturer. Find out the kinds of problems the engineer is asked to solve. How does the engineer minimize manufacturing costs without sacrificing the attractiveness of the package?

4. Choose a consumer product sold in a package familiar to most people. Redesign the package in a way you think would attract more customers. Explain why you think your package is better than the one currently in use.

5. Investigate other shapes that are commonly used for wastebaskets. For example, consider wastebaskets shaped like cylinders and wastebaskets shaped like upside down pyramids with the vertex removed. How do the volumes and surface areas of these wastebaskets compare?

Culminating Activities

Show what you have learned in this project by completing one of the following activities.

1. Imagine that you are a design engineer working for the wastebasket manufacturer. Write a report for your employer in which you answer the three questions posed under the problem "Design a Wastebasket."

2. Give an oral presentation to your class in which you outline the relationships between surface area and volume that you discovered in this project.

3. A wastebasket manufacturer plans to make open-topped wastebaskets from rectangular patterns measuring 32-by-40 inches. Write a report for the manufacturer recommending the best design to use and outlining the reasons behind your recommendation.

A9

Additional Notes

Be sure groups work on their projects at a regular pace throughout the project period, rather than attempt to complete them at a mad pace as the deadline approaches. You may wish to provide regular times in class for groups to work on their projects.

Answer

Given a wastebasket of volume $V = Ax^2 + Bx + C$, where x is the length of a side of the corner square, the maximum volume is obtained when $x = -\dfrac{B}{2A}$.

Scoring Rubric

Top Level: Complete work. Clear, coherent, unambiguous explanation. Effective communication. Strong arguments. Understanding of math ideas and processes. Goes beyond requirements of problem.

Second Level: Solid work but less complete and less elegant than above. Does not go beyond requirements of problem.

Third Level: Complete response but muddled explanation. Incomplete arguments. Some understanding of math but vague or unclear responses.

Fourth Level: Omits significant parts. Major errors.

The Million-Dollar Challenge

Objectives

- Use logarithms to analyze appreciations in values of collectibles.
- Select, from many choices, investments that appear likely to increase in value.

Overview

Practically everyone has had the experience of throwing something away that later proves to have completely unexpected value. Unrecognized rarity, unappreciated beauty, unanticipated public demand can all combine to create treasure from something as mundane as a set of old comic books or baseball cards. The successful investor is the person who can recognize the rarity, appreciate the beauty, and anticipate future public demand before discarding the seemingly mundane. In this project, students will attempt to do just that by analyzing promising investments in collectibles to see which have the best chance of becoming treasures.

Mathematical Content

Students should incorporate ideas from Chapters 9-13 in their analysis, possibly including but not limited to logarithms, exponential equations, graphing, use of a graphing calculator, and organizing data.

In 1856, the country of British Guiana issued a one-cent black-on-magenta postage stamp. On April 4, 1856, a letter bearing one of those stamps was posted. Today the stamp on that letter is the only surviving specimen of the 1856 British Guiana issue. Per pound, it may be the most valuable item on Earth. In 1980, an anonymous buyer purchased the stamp for $850,000. Using the formula $V_n = P(1 + r)^n$, we can determine that the stamp appreciated at an annual rate of about 16% during the 124 years that elapsed between 1856 and 1980. At $850,000 per $\frac{1}{20,000}$-lb weight for a typical stamp, the one-cent black-on-magenta stamp is worth about $17 billion per pound today.

The investor who bought the British Guiana stamp in 1873 for 84¢ made a very good investment. But not all stamps are good investments. Today's postage stamps, issued by the millions, will never become rare enough to appreciate significantly. Most will probably decrease in value year after year.

People with money to spend are always on the lookout for investments that will appreciate steadily and reliably over the years. Real estate is almost always a dependable investment. But what about purchases like stamps, coins, gold, paintings, antiques, baseball cards, cars—things you can keep in your home to enjoy while they appreciate? If you had a million dollars to invest in such items, which ones would you buy?

A10

Choose an Investment

An investor has turned over a million dollars to you. Your job is to choose three areas of investments and then to purchase items from those areas that can be kept in the investor's home. The investor is not interested in stocks, bonds, real estate, or other "paper" investments. Purchases must be items like those listed above—stamps, gold, and so on—that the investor can enjoy at home while they appreciate. In return for your recommendation, the investor will pay you one-half the amount the $1 million investment appreciates each year. There is an added incentive for you to choose the three areas wisely: should any of the items lose value, you will be required to pay back one-half the amount of yearly depreciation to the investor.

A11

Project Description

Students choose areas with promise as good investments in collectibles. They gather and analyze data on past performance of each potential investment. After discussion, they decide on the three areas with the best chance for future growth. They assemble materials to support their choices. Then they decide how best to apply $1 million to the purchase of items from each of the three areas.

Group Size

Students should work in groups of three to five.

Time

Students will need four to six weeks to complete the project.

Materials Needed

graphing paper, calculators, and art supplies for student investment reports

Resources

Students will need research materials carrying past and current prices of items they choose to investigate. Every potential collectible is thoroughly documented in this fashion. Students should contact local retailers in the areas they choose to investigate for titles and information about availability of price guides.

Students may also wish to contact an investment advisor for ideas on how to analyze their data and anticipate future demand.

Tips for Groups

Students may be overly enthusiastic about choosing their own areas of special interest for investment. Caution them to look at these areas with cold and calculating eyes. Such personal bias, if looked at uncritically, can lead to costly mistakes.

Assessment

In assessing projects, look for careful, thorough, creative analysis of data, and strong, clearly stated, amply documented supporting arguments and materials. Reward groups that discover and make strong cases for promising but previously unrecognized areas for investment.

Additional Notes

Be sure groups work on their projects at a regular pace throughout the project period, rather than attempt to complete them at a mad pace as the deadline approaches. You may wish to provide regular times in class for groups to work on their projects.

After students have completed their projects, set aside some class time for discussion. You may wish to ask these questions.

- Would you characterize collectibles as a safe, somewhat risky, or very risky investment? Explain.
- What factors influence the value of a collectible? How can a collector exploit these factors to gain an advantage over other investors?
- What did you learn by working on this project?

Getting Started

Follow these steps to carry out your project.

- Brainstorm with your group. Choose at least six areas where you think good investments might be found.
- Collect data from recent years on prices of items in the areas you have chosen.
- Analyze the data. Use logarithms, formulas, graphs, calculators, or any other methods you choose to answer questions like the following.
  1. At what annual rate has the item appreciated in the past year? 2 years? 5 years? 10 years?
  2. Has the rate of appreciation been constant? If not, how can you predict future appreciation rates?
  3. What other factors besides past performance might affect future prices of the item?
- Choose the three areas where you will invest the million dollars.
- Create graphs, displays, tables, or any other materials that you can use to convince the investor that you have done your homework well.
- Decide exactly how you will spend the money.

A12

Extensions

1. The British Guiana stamp has appreciated at about 16% annually. Suppose a Roman coin that once belonged to the emperor Julius Caesar and was worth a penny at the time it was minted has appreciated at a modest 5% per year. First, guess which of the following choices is closest to the current value of the coin. Then calculate the value. **c**
   a. about $20   b. about $2,000   c. about $2,000,000
   d. about $200,000,000,000,000,000,000,000,000,000,000,000,000.

2. Research and report on appreciation in the value of paintings by the Dutch artist Vincent van Gogh.

3. Research supply and demand. Write a paper explaining how the price of a commodity is affected by supply and demand.

Culminating Activities

Show what you have learned in this project by completing one of the following activities.

1. Prepare a report for the investor. Outline and justify your recommendations on how the million dollars should be spent. Include any supplementary material such as graphs or charts that might support your conclusions. Develop a 10-year forecast on the growth potential for the investments you have recommended.

2. Write an article entitled "Investing in Collectibles" for a financial newspaper or magazine.

A13

Scoring Rubric

Top Level: Complete work. Clear, coherent, unambiguous explanation. Effective communication. Strong arguments. Understanding of math ideas and processes. Goes beyond requirements of problem.

Second Level: Solid work but less complete and less elegant than above. Does not go beyond requirements of problem.

Third Level: Complete response but muddled explanation. Incomplete arguments. Some understanding of math but vague or unclear responses.

Fourth Level: Omits significant parts. Major errors.

Objectives

- Create a classification system for a chosen area of interest.
- Analyze data to determine the proportions of a total population falling under given categories.

Overview

We sort and classify objects in countless ways, from the simple or mundane (the lights in a room are on or off) to the interesting or useful (a baseball player is a right-handed pitcher) to the precise and critically important (a hurricane is Force 17 on the Beaufort scale). Classifications can be refined by increasing the number of categories or dimensions they address. Classifying a baseball player by left- or right-handedness, position, height, weight, and age, for example, will create a huge number of 5-dimension categories and could be usefully employed by a manager to analyze team needs. In this project, students will create a classification system that could be used by people working in an area of student interest.

Mathematical Content

Students should incorporate ideas from Chapters 14-17 in their projects, possibly including but not limited to data gathering, measures of central tendency, variation, standard deviation, and probability.

Creating Order From Chaos

The inclination to sort and classify is probably as old as human nature itself. Archeologists have discovered fuel logs and animal bones neatly stacked by prehistoric peoples according to size. Today we arrange compact discs alphabetically and classify mountains by height.

Behind the tendency of prehistoric and contemporary people alike is the human need to make sense of and gain some control over an apparently disorderly world.

Classifications can be harmful, as when people categorize or stereotype each other by race or religion. Other classifications of individuals can be sources of great insight. Some psychologists use a 4-dimensional system to classify people according to whether they are extroverted or introverted (E or I), sensing or intuitive (S or N), feeling or thinking (F or T), and judging or perceiving (J or P). Sixteen classifications result. Research suggests that about 13% of the population are type ESTJ and about 1% are type INFP. Knowledge of one's type can be a source of self-understanding and an incentive for personal growth.

Every branch of science has numerous classification systems. Astronomers classify stars by their surface temperatures. Geologists classify rocks by their crystal form, hardness, specific gravity, and several other categories. The mineral galena, for example, is cubical, 2.5 in hardness, and 7.5 in specific gravity. In a 3-dimensional [crystal form, hardness, specific gravity] classification system, galena could be classified as a [Cu, H2.5, SG7.5] mineral. The three dimensions in the classification distinguish galena from nearly every other mineral.

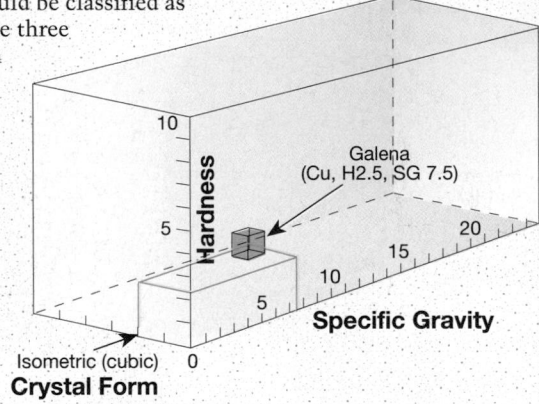

3-Dimensional Classification System

Create a Classification System

In this project, you will collect and analyze data in an area of interest to you. Then you will create a classification system that could be of use to people doing research in the area you have chosen. You will analyze your data to determine the frequency of each of the categories in your system and any other statistics you feel would be of value to people using your system.

Getting Started

Follow these steps to carry out your project.

- Brainstorm with your group to choose an area of mutual interest for which you will create your classification system. The area can be from science, social studies, language arts, art, sports, or another topic you prefer. Be sure that a classification system is not already in use in the area you choose.

- Choose a number of important and distinguishing categories that you can use to classify items in your area. Examples of categories are specific gravity (rocks) and surface temperature (stars). You should choose an ample number of categories, since after collecting data you may find that one or more categories are not as distinguishing as you had anticipated. These can always be dropped.

- Collect data on your categories.

- Define your classification system. With the perfect system, an item's classification should place it together with other items that are similar to it in important and useful ways. Your system should have at least three distinguishing dimensions or categories.

- Calculate the portion of the entire population that is represented by each classification in your system. For example, in the psychology classification system discussed above, 13% of the population is classified ESTJ. Compile any other statistics that might help you demonstrate the importance and usefulness of your system.

Project Description

Students choose an area of interest for which they feel a classification system would be useful. They choose several distinguishing categories within the area and collect data on each. After analyzing the data, they define their classification system. Using their data, they calculate the relative frequencies of each category in the system and calculate any additional statistics they feel are important.

Group Size

Students should work in groups of three to five.

Time

Students will need four to six weeks to complete the project.

Materials Needed

research materials, possibly including basic texts in chosen areas of study, calculators, art materials

Resources

To obtain the data they will need, students may need to contact experts working in the areas they choose. An effort to classify trees, for example, may not be productive until students obtain figures on relative numbers of hardwoods and softwoods, heights of trees, and so on. A phone call to the local university botany department might yield the name of a botanist specializing in trees and a list of relevant reference books.

A15

Tips for Groups

Caution groups not to rush to choose their area of interest. They will need to choose an area with an abundance of useful available data and could waste a good deal of time by selecting one that is short on data.

Assessment

In assessing projects, look for careful collection and analysis of data, creative choices of classification systems, and strong, clearly stated explanations of the value of classification systems. Reward groups that create statistics that are especially helpful in illuminating the usefulness of their systems.

Additional Notes

Be sure groups work on their projects at a regular pace throughout the project period, rather than attempt to complete them at a mad pace as the deadline approaches. You may wish to provide regular times in class for groups to work on their projects.

Scoring Rubric

Top Level: Complete work. Clear, coherent, unambiguous explanation. Effective communication. Strong arguments. Understanding of math ideas and processes. Goes beyond requirements of problem.

Second Level: Solid work but less complete and less elegant than above. Does not go beyond requirements of problem.

Third Level: Complete response but muddled explanation. Incomplete arguments. Some understanding of math but vague or unclear responses.

Fourth Level: Omits significant parts. Major errors.

Extensions

1. Research and report on the taxonomic system for classifying plants and animals.

2. An N-dimensional classification system has a classifications in the first dimension, b in the second, c in the third, and so on, through z in the Nth. How many distinct N-dimensional classifications can be delineated using the system? $a \times b \times c \times ... \times z$ **classifications**

3. The Richter scale is a 1-dimensional classification system that classifies earthquakes according to their energy. Choose a familiar 1-dimensional system and propose a second dimension that could be used to classify objects of study more precisely.

Culminating Activities

Show what you have learned in this project by completing one of the following activities.

1. Write a report describing your work on this project. Explain the importance of your classification system. Describe the system and tell how you collected your data and compiled your statistics. Give examples of how your system can be used.

2. Make an oral report to the class describing your classification system. Bring several examples of items in your area of study and demonstrate how each can be classified using your system.

A16